CONDENSED INSTRUCTIONS ON THE USE OF VOLUME 2*

EXAMPLE

I am interested in seeing what information on the intermetallic compound $NpCo_2$ exists.

STEP 1

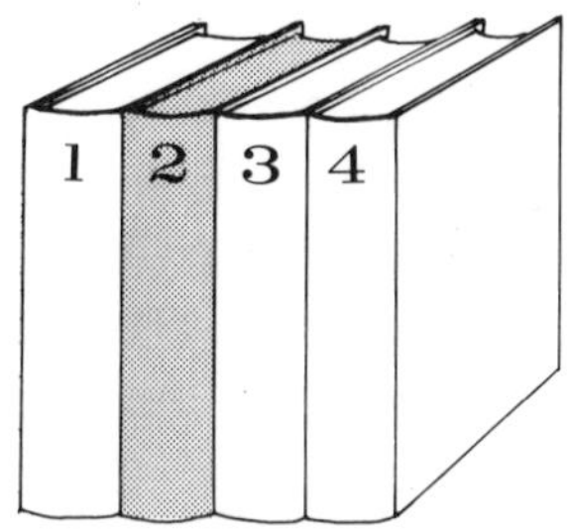

a. **Select** the volume which contains the material of interest.

b. Look at the *Table of Contents* and also note that **instructions** on the use of each part of the volume are given at the beginning of that part. (*Note* especially item V of the instructions for Part A of each volume.)

a. Intermetallic compounds are in Volume 2.

b. I look at the introduction to the *Materials Directory* (Part A) and see in item V that neptunium is more metallic than cobalt. Therefore, I should look for neptunium cobalt in Part A.

STEP 2

a. Look for the **material name** in Part A, the *Materials Directory.*

b. Note the seven-digit **substance number** and **properties** covered in the retrieval guide.

a. I look for neptunium cobalt in the *Materials Directory* (Part A) and find on page A28:

Substance Name		Property	Number
Neptunium tri-Chloride	Np Cl_3	q	106-8095
Neptunium-Cobalt	Np Co_2	q	106-8663
Neptunium tri-Iodide	Np I_3	q	114-8025

b. "106-8663" represents $NpCo_2$, and property "q" represents magnetic susceptibility.

STEP 3

a. Look in the **property chapter** of interest in Part B, *Search Parameters,* for the seven-digit **substance number** obtained from Part A, the *Materials Directory.*

b. Use the five **search parameters** (physical state, subject, language, temperature, and year) to locate **EPIC numbers** of interest.

a. I look in Chapter 17 (magnetic susceptibility) of Part B *(Search Parameters)* for 106-8663, and see on page B131:

Substance Number	Phys. State	Subject	Language	Temperature	Year	EPIC Number
106-8663	S	D	E	L	1975	63278
8663	S	D	E	N	1975	63278

b. Using the code keys in the footnote, I see that there is only one English language document for data on a solid in both the low and normal temperature ranges. I write down EPIC number 63278.

STEP 4

a. Look up **EPIC numbers** in Part C, the *Bibliography,* to obtain complete **bibliographic citation** information for documents covering the properties of a given material of interest.

a. I look for bibliographic citation information in Part C. For EPIC number 63278, I see on page C181:

63278 **MAGNETIC PROPERTIES OF NEPTUNIUM LAVES PHASES: NEPTUNIUM MANGANESE, NEPTUNIUM IRON, NEPTUNIUM COBALT, AND NEPTUNIUM NICKEL**
ALDRED, A. T. DUNLAP, B. D. LAM, D. J.
LANDER, G. H. MUELLER, M. H. NOWIK, I.
PHYS. REV.
11 B (1), 530–44, 1975.

NOTE

a. Look up an author's name in Part D, the *Author Index,* to see all documents written by this author and reported in this volume.

a. I look up Aldred, A. T. in the *Author Index* (Part D) and see on page D2:

ALDRED A T 49502 54963 58053
63278 63305

A total of five documents by the same author are reported in this volume, with complete bibliographic citation information available in Part C.

*For additional details on the use of this volume, see the introductory remarks for Parts A, B, C, and D, scan the *Table of Contents,* and also note the *Condensed Materials Index* on the opposite page.

electronic properties research literature retrieval guide

1972-1976

volume 2
inorganic and intermetallic compounds

Editors

J. F. CHANEY

T. M. PUTNAM

electronic properties research literature retrieval guide

1972–1976

A Comprehensive Compilation of Scientific and Technical Literature by the Center for Information and Numerical Data Analysis and Synthesis (CINDAS), Purdue University

Volume 1. Elements

Volume 2. Inorganic and Intermetallic Compounds

Volume 3. Alloys and Cermets

Volume 4. Mixtures, Rocks and Minerals, Composites and Systems, Polymers

See inside front and back covers for CONDENSED MATERIALS INDEX to the FOUR-VOLUME RETRIEVAL GUIDE

New literature on electronic properties is being constantly accumulated at CINDAS. Contact CINDAS and use its interim updating search services for the most current scientific information

electronic properties research literature retrieval guide

1972-1976

volume 2
inorganic and intermetallic compounds

Editors

J. F. CHANEY

T. M. PUTNAM

PART A. MATERIALS DIRECTORY
PART B. SEARCH PARAMETERS
PART C. BIBLIOGRAPHY
PART D. AUTHOR INDEX

IFI/PLENUM · NEW YORK · WASHINGTON · LONDON

Library of Congress Cataloging in Publication Data

Purdue University, Lafayette, Ind. Center for Information and Numerical Data Analysis and Synthesis.
Electronic properties research literature retrieval guide, 1972–1976.

Includes indexes.
1. Materials–Bibliography. 2. Electronic structure–Bibliography. I. Chaney, James F. II. Putnam, Thomas Milton, 1945- III. Title.
Z5853.M38P82 1979 [TA403] 016.6201'1297 79-16082
ISBN 0-306-68010-6

IFI/Plenum Data Company
A Division of Plenum Publishing Corporation
227 West 17th Street, New York, N.Y. 10011

Printed in the United States of America

CONTENTS OF VOLUME 2

PREFACE

The phenomenal growth of science and technology has brought about a universal appreciation of the fact that present limitations in many technical developments are often a direct result of the paucity of knowledge on material properties. Engineering developments in the years ahead will be closely linked to the research that is done today to contribute to a better understanding of the properties of matter, of which electronic, electrical, magnetic, and optical properties constitute a major segment.

While research on the properties of materials continues, adequate steps are not being taken to ensure that this invaluable body of information is coordinated, synthesized, organized, and disseminated to the ultimate user, namely, the individual scientist and engineer.

It is generally agreed that the present level of research support on physical properties of matter falls short of existing needs and anticipated future demands; but what is even more disturbing is the fact that engineering groups across the nation are using no more than a fraction of the information already available, either because it is in a form not directly useful to them or, often, because its existence is not generally known. As a result, such information remains buried in the world's scientific literature. The repercussions of this latter condition are indeed serious since it leads to unintentional duplication of research effort with the resultant waste of time and scientific manpower.

In conjunction with its research activities, CINDAS screens the world's literature and collects published information on a wide range of materials in the field of electronic properties. This information concerns data, theoretical estimation methods and experimental measurement techniques. Technical papers come from journals, abstracting services, reports, doctoral dissertations, masters theses, and many other sources. Full evaluation and analysis of the collected raw data are needed before publications on recommended values can be prepared. Such an effort is obviously time consuming and expensive, and therefore this critical evaluation is currently performed at a rather modest funding level. The end result is that much of the available world literature is not being processed and distilled.

When the Electronic Properties Information Center (EPIC), formerly operated by the Hughes Aircraft Co., was merged with CINDAS in 1972, the basic activities of EPIC were continued, however, in a much restructured form, closely paralleling procedures and concepts used in the area of thermophysical properties. Hence, as a complementary effort to its data evaluation activities, the present companion set of four volumes entitled "Electronic Properties Research Literature Retrieval Guide" is published for the first time by CINDAS. Somewhat similar in intent, but much less structured in presentation, three volumes (each in two parts) were published earlier by EPIC in 1965, 1967, and 1971, entitled "Electronic Properties of Materials—A Guide to the Literature."

The present work significantly differs from its predecessor sets both in comprehensiveness of coverage and ease of specific retrieval. This four-volume work reports 19,104 references on 15 electronic, electrical, magnetic, and optical properties and seven property groups, namely, electron emission, luminescence, magnetoelectric, magnetomechanical, photoelectronic, piezoelectronic, and thermoelectric properties. These properties are reported for some 9634 materials, and an additional 2124 synonyms and trade names are incorporated to assist the user in identifying the material of interest.

It is sincerely hoped that the "Electronic Properties Research Literature Retrieval Guide" will constitute a permanent and valuable contribution to science and technology as well as to scientific documentation. These volumes, and those to follow, should prove to be an invaluable source of information to every scientist and engineer, with a scope of knowledge humanly impossible to master for any one individual or any group of individuals. Perhaps even more important, it is hoped that a wealth of information, heretofore unknown, will have been made available to many, including the specialist. The CINDAS staff is most anxious to receive comments, suggestions, and criticism from all users of these volumes. All communications will be gratefully appreciated. Specific information concerning CINDAS' operations, services, publications, and research activities can be obtained by communicating with the Director.

The preparation of these volumes was made possible through the collective financial support received from a large number of governmental, industrial, and nonprofit research organizations. Their interest and support are gratefully acknowledged. I wish to specifically acknowledge the major support received from the Department of Defense in connection with the operation of the Thermophysical and Electronic Properties Information Analysis Center (TEPIAC), which has made this work possible.

In closing, I wish to acknowledge the individual and collective accomplishments of CINDAS' Scientific Documentation Division: Mr. H. K. Koutoujian and Miss M. A. Carlson, Technical Coding; Mrs. M. R. Troyer, Documentalist; Mrs. F. L. Frist, Mrs. C. Greene, and Mrs. G. M. Halstead, Computer Operations; Mr. C. C. Hsiao, Computer Programmer; Mrs. S. J. Creamer and Mrs. J. A. Brittingham, Library. Special thanks are extended to the staff of R. R. Donnelley and Sons, Chicago, Illinois, for their cooperation and the computer-assisted phototypesetting of this new Retrieval Guide.

Y. S. Touloukian

Director, Center for Information and
Numerical Data Analysis and Synthesis
Distinguished Atkins Professor
of Engineering

Part A
MATERIALS DIRECTORY

PART A

USE OF MATERIALS DIRECTORY

I. ORGANIZATION AND GENERAL CONSIDERATIONS

The organization of Electronic Properties Information Center (EPIC) files at CINDAS is by material. A *Condensed Materials Index* to the four-volume Electronic Properties Retrieval Guide is located on the inside front and back covers of this volume.

In order to index the world literature, the classification system must be general and systematic, and yet flexible. Therefore, CINDAS has adopted a highly structured classification scheme which arranges materials into logical groups that have closely related chemical composition. However, certain materials may fit into more than one group. When this occurs, CINDAS will put the material in the most specific group.

Within this system of classification by material name, there exists a class of pertinent information for which no specific material name would be appropriate, e.g., "Theory of the Electrical Conductivity of Solids" or "New Technique for the Magnetic Susceptibility Measurement of Liquids." Literature covering this class of publications is not reported in this volume but is available at CINDAS, and a special computer search and retrieval can be made upon request.

The index to materials is given alphabetically by name within group in the main body of Part A (see *Table of Contents*). The substance names were alphabetized by a computer and as a result of constraints present at the time, alphabetization may at times depart from conventional practice. Specifically, numerical prefixes and blank spaces are disregarded. Similarly, punctuation and special characters do influence alphabetization in certain instances.

Because of these peculiarities it is recommended that the user of the *Materials Directory* be alert and browse carefully in the general region where the material is likely to be found. It will be noted that more than 3500 synonyms, equivalents, and cross references have been incorporated in the *Materials Directories* of the four volumes of this set. A cross reference is preceded by the words "see also" and a synonym or equivalent is followed by the word "see." To assure complete coverage it would be advisable to look up all "see" and "see also" entries in order to capture maximum information. Read items V and VI of these instructions in each volume for more detailed guidance concerning that specific volume.

It may be of interest to point out at this juncture that the user of this index should not be concerned with the structure of the seven-digit EPIC substance number associated with each substance. These numbers serve to uniquely identify a substance, and their structure is only of internal significance to CINDAS.

II. DEFINITIONS AND LIMITATIONS USED IN MATERIAL CLASSIFICATION

For the effective use of the materials index of this volume certain definitions and limitations of terms as accepted by CINDAS should be understood. These are briefly listed below:

1. *Impurities*—For the purposes of Classification, CINDAS defines the "impurity" limits as follows:
   Elements (Volume 1). Total of impurities must be <0.5 percent and individual impurity <0.2 percent by weight. A metallic element having impurities in excess of these limits is considered an alloy (Volume 3), whereas a nonmetallic element having impurities in excess of these limits is considered a mixture (Volume 4).
   Compounds (Volume 2). Total of impurities must be <5.0 percent and individual impurity <2.0 percent by weight. A compound with impurities in excess of these limits is considered a mixture (Volume 4) or possibly a cermet (Volume 3, see also 9 below).
2. *Doping*—Doped materials are identified by physical state code D in Part B (Search Parameters). Further breakdown into 10 groups of dopants based on chemical table groups are available at CINDAS, and a special computer search and retrieval can be made upon request.
3. *Isotopes*—Isotopes are listed under the corresponding elements as a single entry. Exceptions are the isotopes of hydrogen and helium, which are designated separately as deuterium, tritium, helium-3, and helium-4.
4. *Ions*—Ions are not listed separately but are identified by physical state code I in Part B (Search Parameters) (i.e., argon ion is listed under argon).
5. *Intercalates*—An intercalated substance is listed separately as "substance name, intercalated."
6. *Intermetallic Compounds* (Volume 2)—These metal–metal compounds are treated the same as inorganic compounds.

7. *Ferrous Alloys* (Volume 3)—A ferrous alloy is one in which iron, Fe, is the principal constituent by weight (Fe ≧ any other single element). All ferrous and nonferrous alloys are governed by the criteria of "impurity" defined above.

   One class is assigned to each major element that is alloyed with Fe. The ordering within each class is alphabetical for commercial designations and experimental alloys. The individual experimental alloy entries are in descending weight percent order of element names. For groups of alloys having a range in composition, consideration is given to the upper and lower limits of composition in class selection and the alloys are accordingly listed in one or more classes. For example, a 0 to 100 percent range of Si alloyed with Fe would be listed in the Iron–Silicon Class (Volume 3), the Nonmetallic Element Mixture Class (Volume 4), and also as the pure elements Si and Fe (Volume 1).
8. *Nonferrous Alloys* (Volume 3)—A nonferrous alloy is one in which an element other than iron is the principal constituent. All general considerations discussed above for the case of ferrous alloys also pertain to nonferrous alloys.
9. *Cermets* (Volume 3)—Cermets include combinations of metals with ceramics. Entries are listed in descending weight percent order.
10. *Systems* (Volume 4)—Includes composites, laminates, and other layered structures (see item III below). Components of layered structures are listed in the order in which they occur. Components of composites are listed in alphabetical order.

III. SPECIAL CONSIDERATIONS FOR CERTAIN PHYSICAL PROPERTIES

Thermoelectric properties (t) of two materials in contact are coded separately under each of the materials and not for the system consisting of the two materials.

Similarly, *electron emission properties* (i) and *work function* (u) of a solid material A covered with a thin layer of another material B is coded under material A for physical state solid (S) and under material B for physical state thin film (T) and not for the system consisting of the two materials.

Magnetic susceptibility (q) includes Curie and Néel temperatures.

Electrical resistivity (j) includes the superconductive transition temperature, which is clearly identified by physical state superconductive (C).

IV. EXCLUSIONS TO MATERIAL AND PROPERTY COVERAGE

While CINDAS attempts to cover the world research literature on all matter for the twenty-two electronic properties it monitors, for reasons of scientific and technical rationale and practical expediency it has become necessary to put a number of constraints on material coverage.

1. Data on all organic (defined as consisting of carbon and any hydrogen isotope simultaneously) compounds are generally excluded except for polymeric materials.
2. Data on aqueous or organic solutions or mixtures are excluded.
3. Data on electronic devices are excluded.
4. Data reported under unsteady-state and nonequilibrium conditions are excluded.
5. Patents and patent applications are excluded.
6. Unidentifiable product catalogs and promotional literature are excluded.

V. SPECIAL CONSIDERATIONS FOR THIS VOLUME

Naming of compounds generally follows the IUPAC Nomenclature of Inorganic Chemistry, American Version. However, to aid consistent computerized alphabetization, all numerical prefixes are ignored during alphabetization (i.e., sorted as if numerical prefixes did not exist). In case of any difficulty in locating a specific compound, one should order the elements from the most metallic to the most nonmetallic (see listing below) and look up that name. This is especially useful for intermetallic and complex compounds. This order is (for the metals) Fr, Cs, Rb, K, Na, Li, Ra, Ba, Sr, Ca, Mg, Be, Lw, No, Md, Fm, Es, Cs, Cf, Bk, Cm, Am, Pu, Np, U, Pa, Th, Ac, Lu, Yb, Tm, Er, Ho, Dy, Tb, Gd, Eu, Sm, Pm, Nd, Pr, Ce, La, Y, Sc, Hf, Zr, Ti, Ta, Nb, V, W, Mo, Cr, Re, Tc, Mn, Pt, Ir, Os, Pd, Rh, Ru, Ni, Co, Fe, Au, Ag, Cu, Hg, Cd, Zn, Tl, In, Ga, Al, Pb, Sn, Ge, Bi, Sb, Po; (for the nonmetals) B, Si, C, As, P, N, H, Te, Se, S, At, I, Br, Cl, O, F.

VI. USEFUL REFERENCES FOR MATERIALS IDENTIFICATION FOR THIS VOLUME

The latest editions of the following selected references were found useful by CINDAS in the classification and identification of materials:

1. *Chemical Synonyms and Trade Names,* W. Gardner and E. I. Cooke, CRC Press, Cleveland, Ohio.
2. *The Condensed Chemical Dictionary,* G. G. Hanley, Van Nostrand Reinhold Co., New York, New York.
3. *Handbook of Chemistry and Physics,* The Chemical Rubber Co., Cleveland, Ohio.
4. *Handbook of Material Trade Names,* O. T. Zimmerman and I. Lavine, Industrial Research Service, Inc., Dover, New Hampshire.
5. *Nomenclature of Inorganic Chemistry,* American Version; International Union of Pure and Applied Chemistry.
6. *Webster's New International Unabridged Dictionary,* G & C Merriam Co., Springfield, Massachusetts.

VOLUME 2. INORGANIC AND INTERMETALLIC COMPOUNDS

Substance Name	*Property*	*Number*
NONSPECIFIC ENTRIES	**CLASS 100**	
Alkali Tungstate		
see Compound, Alkali Tungstate	j	100-8022
Alloy, Heusler (Ternary Intermetallic)	q	100-8064
see also Compound, Intermetallic		100-8017
Antimony Chalcogenide		
see Compound, Antimony Chalcogenide	t	100-8023
Bismuth Chalcogenide		
see Compound, Bismuth Chalcogenide	t	100-8024
Compound; (General)	a–oqrstuv	100-0045
Compound; $I + III + VI_2$	dfjm	100-8071
Compound; $I + VII$	afs	100-8074
Compound; $II + IV$	d	100-8034
Compound; $II + IV + V_2$	bfhjs	100-8031
Compound; $II + VI$	abdefhijmoqrstuv	100-8007
Compound; $III + V$	abdefhijkoqstuv	100-8008
Compound; $IV + VI$	bdefijoqstuv	100-8038
Compound; $I_3 + V$	i	100-8063
Compound; $V + VI$	q	100-8039
Compound, A-15	j	100-8061
Compound, Alkali Halide	a–fhijkmoprsuv	100-8003
Compound, Alkaline Earth Halide	aj	100-8050
Compound, Alkali Tungstate	j	100-8022
Compound, Antimony Chalcogenide	t	100-8023
Compound, Barium Halide	j	100-8056
see also Compound, Halide		100-8059
Compound, Bismuth Chalcogenide	t	100-8024
Compound, Boride	jt	100-8035
Compound, Calcium Halide	j	100-8055
see also Compound, Halide		100-8059
Compound, Carbide	jl	100-8068
Compound, Cerium	jq	100-8076
Compound, Chalcogenide	abdfrst	100-8021
see also Compound, Antimony Chalcogenide		100-8023
see also Compound, Transition Metal Chalcogenide		100-8043
see also Compound, Bismuth Chalcogenide		100-8024
see also Glass, Chalcogenide		100-8016
Compound, Diamond Type	dh	100-8047
Compound, Ferrite	bnpqs	100-8058
Compound, Ferrous	q	100-8004
Compound, Fluoride	h	100-0003
Compound, Garnet		
see Garnet; (General)	p	100-8060
Compound, Halide	abdfhjsu	100-8059
see also Compound, Alkali Halide		100-8003
see also Compound, Alkaline Earth Halide		100-8050
see also Compound, Barium Halide		100-8056
see also Compound, Calcium Halide		100-8055
see also Compound, Lithium Halide		100-8052
see also Compound, Magnesium Halide		100-8054
see also Compound, Silver Halide		100-8019
see also Compound, Sodium Halide		100-8053
Compound, Intercalated	jq	100-8067
Compound, Intermetallic	hjnq	100-8017
see also Alloy, Heusler (Ternary Intermetallic)		100-8064
see also Compound, Praseodymium – Transition Metal Intermetallic		100-8045
Compound, Lithium Halide	j	100-8052
see also Compound, Halide		100-8059
Compound, Magnesium Halide	j	100-8054
see also Compound, Halide		100-8059
Compound, Metallic	dfs	100-8006
Compound, Niobium	jqt	100-8069
Compound, Nitrate	jo	100-8044
Compound, Oxide	fij	100-8029
see also Compound, Transition Metal Oxide		100-8040

Substance Name	*Property*	*Number*
Compound, Perovskite	m	100-8033
Compound, Pnictide	bfoq	100-8041
see also Rare Earth Pnictide		100-8042
Compound, Praseodymium – Transition Metal Intermetallic	q	100-8045
Compound, Rare Earth Molybdate		
see Rare Earth Molybdate	g	100-8028
Compound, Rare Earth Pnictide		
see Rare Earth Pnictide	q	100-8042
Compound, Refractory	jl	100-8027
Compound, Refractory Oxide	bjq	100-8072
Compound, Silicide	jqt	100-8036
see also Compound, Transition Metal Silicide		100-8030
see also Rare Earth Silicide		100-8057
Compound, Silver Halide	r	100-8019
Compound, Sodium Halide	j	100-8053
see also Compound, Halide		100-8059
Compound, Sulfide	fj	100-8026
Compound, Telluride	qr	100-8037
Compound, Transition Metal	dfrt	100-8025
Compound, Transition Metal Chalcogenide	adfhjloqrt	100-8043
Compound, Transition Metal Hydride	jq	100-8048
Compound, Transition Metal Oxide	fjlqt	100-8040
Compound, Transition Metal Silicide	j	100-8030
Compound, Tungstate	hj	100-8011
see also Compound, Alkali Tungstate		100-8022
Compound, Uranium	jq	100-8075
Compound, Zinc Blend		
see Compound; $II + VI$	abdefhijmoqrstuv	100-8007
Compound, Zinc Blend		
see Compound; $III + V$	abdefhijkoqstuv	100-8008
Ferrite		
see Compound, Ferrite	bnpqs	100-8058
Fluoride		
see Compound, Fluoride	h	100-0003
Freon; (General)	h	100-8062
Garnet; (General)	p	100-8060
Garnet, Rare Earth Ferrate		
see Rare Earth Garnet	ajnpqs	100-8010
Garnet, Rare Earth Ferrate		
see Rare Earth Ferrite (Ortho)	ajnpqs	100-8015
Garnet, Yttrium Iron (Mixed)		
see Yttrium Iron Garnet, Mixed (General)	fjkloqt	100-8013
Glass, Chalcogenide	abdfhjorst	100-8016
see also Compound, Chalcogenide		100-8021
Metal, A-15		
see Compound, A-15	j	100-8061
Optical Waveguide	s	100-8065
Rare Earth Chalcogenide	djlnqrt	100-8005
Rare Earth - Cobalt $RECo_{17}$	np	100-8051
Rare Earth - Cobalt $RECo_5$	np	100-8049
Rare Earth Compound	adjnpqt	100-8009
Rare Earth Ferrite (Ortho)	ajnpqs	100-8015
Rare Earth Garnet	ajnpqs	100-8010
Rare Earth Halide	j	100-8070
Rare Earth Molybdate	g	100-8028
Rare Earth Pnictide	q	100-8042
Rare Earth Silicide	jlt	100-8057
see also Compound, Silicide		100-8036
Semiconductor	a–oqrstuv	100-0055
Semiconductor, Zinc Blend		
see Compound; $II + VI$	abdefhijmoqrstuv	100-8007
Semiconductor, Zinc Blend		
see Compound; $III + V$	abdefhijkoqstuv	100-8008

Property: **a.** Absorption coefficient; **b.** Dielectric constant; **c.** Dielectric strength; **d.** Energy band structure; **e.** Effective mass; **f.** Energy gap; **g.** Electric hysteresis; **h.** Energy level; **i.** Electron emission properties; **j.** Electrical resistivity; **k.** Magnetoelectric properties; **l.** Hall coefficient; **m.** Luminescence properties; **n.** Magnetic hysteresis; **o.** Mobility; **p.** Magnetomechanical properties; **q.** Magnetic susceptibility; **r.** Photoelectronic properties; **s.** Refractive index; **t.** Thermoelectric properties; **u.** Work function; **v.** Piezoelectric properties.

Substance Name	Property	Number
Transition Metal Compound		
see Compound, Transition Metal	dfrt	100-8025
Yttrium Iron Garnet, Mixed (General)	fjkloqt	100-8013

INORGANIC AND INTERMETALLIC COMPOUNDS CLASSES 102 TO 133

Substance Name	Property	Number
A B-1 MgF_2		
see Irtran 1 (Kodak) MgF_2	abs	110-8118
A D 995 (Coors Ceramics Co) Al_2O_3	bj	102-8432
see also Aluminum sesqui- Oxide Al_2O_3		102-0002
A D A $NH_4H_2AsO_4$		
see Ammonium di- Hydrogen Arsenate $NH_4H_2AsO_4$	bgjsv	102-8027
A D D P $ND_4D_2PO_4$		
see Ammonium di- Hydrogen Phosphate, Deuterated $ND_4D_2PO_4$	bgsv	108-0114
A D P $NH_4H_2PO_4$		
see Ammonium di- Hydrogen Phosphate $NH_4H_2PO_4$	abgjsv	112-0038
Alsimag 196 (American Lava Corp)	j	102-8422
see also Steatite, Grade L 4		102-8423
Alumin $NaAlO_2$		
see Sodium Aluminate $NaAlO_2$	bj	102-0018
Aluminum Ammonium Sulfate $AlNH_4(SO_4)_2$		
see Ammonium Aluminum Sulfate $NH_4Al(SO_4)_2$	h	102-8448
Aluminum Antimonide $AlSb$	abdefh–moqrstuv	102-8001
Aluminum Arsenide $AlAs$	abdefhjmorsv	102-8132
Aluminum dodeca- Boride AlB_{12}	fjlt	102-8012
Aluminum Bromide $AlBr_3$	b	102-0034
Aluminum Carbide Chloride AlC_9Cl_{3-x}	a	102-8471
Aluminum Chloride $AlCl_3$	h	102-0033
Aluminum Ferrate $Al_xFe_{3-x}O_4$	p	102-8408
Aluminum Fluoride AlF_3	i	102-0015
see also Fluellite AlF_3		521-8066
Aluminum Fluorosilicate $(AlF)_2SiO_4$		
see Fluoroaluminum Silicate $(AlF)_2SiO_4$	b	102-8135
Aluminum Iodide AlI_3	j	102-0035
Aluminum Nitride AlN	abcdfhjmorsv	102-0105
Aluminum Nitrogen Hydrogen Sulfate $AlNH_4(SO_4)_2$		
see Ammonium Aluminum Sulfate $NH_4Al(SO_4)_2$	h	102-8448
Aluminum Orthovanadate $AlVO_4$		
see Aluminum Vanadate (V) $AlVO_4$	a	102-8481
Aluminum Oxide AlO	ai	102-8199
di- Aluminum Oxide Al_2O	a	102-8201
Aluminum sesqui- Oxide Al_2O_3	abcdfghijkmoqstu	102-0002
see also A D 995 (Coors Ceramics Co) Al_2O_3		102-8432
see also Corundum Al_2O_3		521-0077
see also Lucalox (General Electric) Al_2O_3		102-8281
see also Ruby Al_2O_3		521-0191
see also Sapphire Al_2O_3		521-0064
Aluminum Phosphate $AlPO_4$	b	102-0210
tetra- Aluminum di- Phosphate $Al_4P_2O_{11}$	s	102-8299
Aluminum octa- Phosphate $Al_{10}P_8O_{25}$	s	102-8300
Aluminum Phosphide AlP	abdfhijmosv	102-0248
Aluminum Pyrovanadate $Al_4V_6O_{21}$		
see tetra- Aluminum hexa- Vanadate (V) $Al_4V_6O_{21}$	a	102-8482
Aluminum Selenide Al_2Se_3	t	102-8015
Aluminum Silicate Al_2SiO_5	a	102-8400
see also Montmorillonite Al_2SiO_5		521-0764
see also Sillimanite Al_2SiO_5		521-0034
hexa- Aluminum di- Silicate $Al_6Si_2O_{13}$		
see Mullite $3Al_2O_3.2SiO_2$	bfj	102-8359
Aluminum Silicon Oxide Fluoride $(AlF)_2SiO_4$		
see Fluoroaluminum Silicate $(AlF)_2SiO_4$	b	102-8135
Aluminum Sulfate $Al_2(SO_4)_3$	bs	102-0027
tetra- Aluminum Sulfate Al_4SO_4	s	102-8301
Aluminum Sulfide Al_2S_3	a	102-8016
Aluminum Vanadate (V) $AlVO_4$	a	102-8481
Aluminum Vanadate $Al_xV_{2-x}O_4$	q	102-8365
tetra- Aluminum hexa- Vanadate (V) $Al_4V_6O_{21}$	a	102-8482

Substance Name	Property	Number
hexa- Amminechromium penta- Chlorocadmate $(Cr(NH_3)_6)(CdCl_5)$	q	106-8124
tri- Amminecobalt (I I I) Chloride $(Co(NH_3)_3)Cl_3$	h	106-8445
hexa- Amminecobalt (I I I) Chloride $(Co(NH_3)_6)Cl_3$	h	106-8446
hexa- Amminerhodium (3+) Ion $Rh(NH_3)_6$	m	112-8028
Ammonia NH_3	abhijlmqst	112-0010
Ammonium Alum $NH_4Al(SO_4)_2$	b	102-8023
Ammonium Aluminum Sulfate $NH_4Al(SO_4)_2$	h	102-8448
Ammonium Beryllium tetra- Fluoride $(NH_4)_2BeF_4$		
see Ammonium tetra- Fluoroberyllate $(NH_4)_2BeF_4$	bgnv	104-8169
Ammonium Beryllium tetra- Fluoride, Deuterated $(ND_4)_2BeF_4$		
see Ammonium tetra- Fluoroberyllate, Deuterated $(ND_4)_2BeF_4$	b	104-8168
Ammonium Bromide NH_4Br	abhjm	104-0146
Ammonium Cadmium Sulfate $(NH_4)_2Cd_2(SO_4)_3$	b	106-8248
Ammonium Cesium Chloride NH_4CsCl_6		
see Ammonium hexa- Chlorocesate NH_4CsCl_6	u	106-8355
Ammonium Chlorate NH_4ClO_4		
see Ammonium Perchlorate NH_4ClO_4	bjt	106-8033
Ammonium Chloride NH_4Cl	abhjs	106-0045
Ammonium hexa- Chlorocesate NH_4CsCl_6	u	106-8355
Ammonium hexa- Chloroiridate (I V) $(NH_4)_2IrCl_6$	q	106-8483
Ammonium Chromium di- Sulfate $NH_4Cr(SO_4)_2$	b	106-0116
di- Ammonium Cobalt di- Sulfate $(NH_4)_2Co(SO_4)_2$	aq	106-0114
di- Ammonium Copper Sulfate $(NH_4)_2Cu(SO_4)_2$	q	106-8569
Ammonium tetra- Fluoroberyllate $(NH_4)_2BeF_4$	bgnv	104-8169
Ammonium tetra- Fluoroberyllate, Deuterated $(ND_4)_2BeF_4$	b	104-8168
di- Ammonium hepta- Fluorodiphosphate $(NH_4)_2P_2F_7$	g	110-8252
Ammonium di- Hydrogen Arsenate $NH_4H_2AsO_4$	bgjsv	102-8027
Ammonium mono- Hydrogen Arsenate $(NH_4)_2HAsO_4$	bjsv	102-8028
Ammonium di- Hydrogen Arsenate, Deuterated $ND_4D_2AsO_4$	g	102-8412
di- Ammonium tri- Hydrogen Iodate $(NH_4)_2H_3IO_6$	g	112-8082
di- Ammonium tri- Hydrogen Iodate, Deuterated $(ND_4)_2D_3IO_6$	g	108-8056
Ammonium di- Hydrogen Phosphate $NH_4H_2PO_4$	abgjsv	112-0038
Ammonium mono- Hydrogen Phosphate $(NH_4)_2HPO_4$	s	112-0036
Ammonium di- Hydrogen Phosphate, Deuterated $ND_4D_2PO_4$	bgsv	108-0114
Ammonium Hydrogen Sulfate NH_4HSO_4	bfgj	112-0033
tri- Ammonium Hydrogen di- Sulfate $(NH_4)_3H(SO_4)_2$	g	112-8081
Ammonium Iodide NH_4I	bg	112-0275
Ammonium Iridium Chloride $(NH_4)_2IrCl_6$		
see Ammonium hexa- Chloroiridate (I V) $(NH_4)_2IrCl_6$	q	106-8483
Ammonium Iron di- Sulfate $NH_4Fe(SO_4)_2$	f	110-0034
di- Ammonium Iron Sulfate $(NH_4)_2FeSO_4$	q	110-8122
Ammonium Lithium Sulfate NH_4LiSO_4	g	112-8080
Ammonium Nitrate NH_4NO_3	bj	112-0008
Ammonium Perchlorate NH_4ClO_4	bjt	106-8033
di- Ammonium di- Phosphide hepta- Fluoride $(NH_4)_2P_2F_7$		
see di- Ammonium hepta- Fluorodiphosphate $(NH_4)_2P_2F_7$	g	110-8252
Ammonium Sulfate $(NH_4)_2SO_4$	abfgjqsv	112-0035
Ammonium Sulfate, Deuterated $(ND_4)_2SO_4$	b	108-8017
di- Ammonium Uranyl tetra- Chloride $(NH_4)_2UO_2Cl_4$	m	106-8745

Property: a. Absorption coefficient; **b.** Dielectric constant; **c.** Dielectric strength; **d.** Energy band structure; **e.** Effective mass; **f.** Energy gap; **g.** Electric hysteresis; **h.** Energy level; **i.** Electron emission properties; **j.** Electrical resistivity; **k.** Magnetoelectric properties; **l.** Hall coefficient; **m.** Luminescence properties; **n.** Magnetic hysteresis; **o.** Mobility; **p.** Magnetomechanical properties; **q.** Magnetic susceptibility; **r.** Photoelectronic properties; **s.** Refractive index; **t.** Thermoelectric properties; **u.** Work function; **v.** Piezoelectric properties.

Substance Name	*Property*	*Number*
Antimony Arsenic Selenide $Sb_xAs_{2-x}Se_3$	abcdfjors	102-8171
see also Antimony Sesquiselenide ≥ Arsenic Sesquiselenide		508-0086
see also Arsenic Sesquiselenide ≥ Antimony Sesquiselenide		508-0085
Antimony sesqui-Boride Sb_2B_3	f	104-8405
Antimony tri-Bromide $SbBr_3$	hr	104-0094
Antimony Bromosulfide $SbSBr$	af	104-8195
Antimony tri-Chloride $SbCl_3$	bhr	106-0296
Antimony penta-Fluoride SbF_5	j	110-0125
Antimony tri-Iodide SbI_3	hjr	114-0059
Antimony Iodobromosulfide $SbSI_xBr_{1-x}$	gr	104-8175
Antimony Iodosulfide $SbSI$	abdfghijqruv	114-0060
Antimony tri-Oxide SbO_3	jr	122-8026
Antimony sesqui-Oxide Sb_2O_3	abcjrs	122-0019
Antimony Selenide $SbSe_{1-x}$	bdfjrt	126-8046
Antimony sesqui-Selenide Sb_2Se_3	abdfhijlorst	126-8030
Antimony Selenide Iodide $SbSeI$	jru	114-8051
Antimony sesqui-Sulfide Sb_2S_3	abcfjorsv	126-0014
Antimony Sulfide Bromide $SbSBr$		
see Antimony Bromosulfide $SbSBr$	af	104-8195
Antimony Sulfide Iodide $SbSI$		
see Antimony Iodosulfide $SbSI$	abdfghijqruv	114-0060
Antimony Sulfide Iodide Bromide		
$SbSI_xBr_{1-x}$		
see Antimony Iodobromosulfide $SbSI_xBr_{1-x}$	gr	104-8175
Antimony tri-Telluride $SbTe_3$	j	126-8086
Antimony sesqui-Telluride Sb_2Te_3	abdefhjloqrst	126-8032
Antimony Telluride Sb_2Te_{3-x}	jt	126-8095
Antimony Telluride Selenide $Sb_2Te_xSe_{3-x}$	jlt	126-8075
see also Antimony Sesquitelluride ≥ Antimony Sesquiselenide		508-0104
Arcton 0 CF_4	c	106-8689
see also Carbon tetra-Fluoride CF_4		106-0231
see also Freon 14 CF_4		106-8477
Arcton 3 $CClF_3$	c	106-8690
see also Chlorotrifluoromethane $CClF_3$		106-0021
see also Freon 13 $CClF_3$		106-8476
Arcton 9 CCl_3F	c	106-8692
see also Freon 11 CCl_3F		106-8517
see also tri-Chlorofluoromethane CCl_3F		106-0147
Arsenic tri-Bromide $AsBr_3$	hr	102-0119
Arsenic tri-Chloride $AsCl_3$	bhr	102-0038
Arsenic mono-Fluoride AsF	hu	102-0317
Arsenic tri-Fluoride AsF_3	b	102-0032
Arsenic tri-Iodide AsI_3	hr	102-0182
Arsenic sesqui-Oxide As_2O_3	i	102-0011
Arsenic mono-Selenide $AsSe$	afs	102-8371
Arsenic sesqui-Selenide As_2Se_3	abcdfhijmoqrst	102-8031
tetra-Arsenic tetra-Selenide As_4Se_4	hi	102-8392
Arsenic Selenide Iodide $AsSeI$	j	102-8164
Arsenic Selenide Iodide $AsSeI_{1-x}$	j	102-8165
Arsenic Selenide Oxide $AsSeO$	r	102-8182
Arsenic Selenide Sulfide $As_2Se_xS_{3-x}$	ar	102-8183
see also Arsenic Sesquiselenide ≥ Arsenic Sesquisulfide		508-0444
see also Arsenic Sesquisulfide ≥ Arsenic Sesquiselenide		508-0443
Arsenic sesqui-Sulfide As_2S_3	abdfjmopqrst	102-0086
see also Orpiment As_2S_3		521-0757
see also Servofrax Arsenic Sesquisulfide Glass		102-8387
tetra-Arsenic tetra-Sulfide As_4S_4	dhijm	102-8070
Arsenic Telluride $AsTe_{1-x}$	fjlot	102-8383
Arsenic sesqui-Telluride As_2Te_3	adefjklorst	102-8133
Arsenic Telluride di-Selenide As_2TeSe_2	afjr	102-8163
Arsenic Telluride Selenide $As_2Te_xSe_{3-x}$	abcdfhjklmoqrt	102-8106
see also Arsenic Sesquiselenide ≥ Arsenic Sesquitelluride		508-0018
see also Arsenic Sesquitelluride ≥ Arsenic Sesquiselenide		508-0019
Arsenic di-Telluride Selenide As_2Te_2Se	afhjo	102-8396
tri-Arsenic di-Telluride Selenide As_3Te_2Se	f	102-8395
Barium Aluminate $BaAl_{12}O_{19}$	m	102-8154
Barium Aluminum Ferrate $BaAl_xFe_{12-x}O_{19}$	q	102-8366
Barium di-Aluminum tetra-Sulfide		
$BaAl_2S_4$		
see Barium tetra-Thiodialuminate $BaAl_2S_4$	jm	102-8503
tri-Barium Bismuth (III) Molybdate (VI)		
$Ba_3Bi_2MoO_9$	g	104-8364

Substance Name	*Property*	*Number*
Barium di-Bismuth (III) di-Niobate (V)		
$BaBi_2Nb_2O_9$	b	104-8186
di-Barium Bismuth (III) Vanadate (V)		
Ba_2BiVO_6	g	104-8365
Barium hexa-Boride BaB_6	j	104-8031
Barium Bromide $BaBr_2$	jm	104-0186
di-Barium Cadmium Tungstate (VI) Ba_2CdWO_6	f	104-8233
Barium Calcium Cerium Titanate		
$Ba_xCa_yCe_{1-x-y}TiO_3$	j	104-8381
Barium Calcium Titanate $Ba_xCa_{1-x}TiO_3$	j	104-8382
Barium Calcium Tungstate (VI) $Ba_xCa_{3-x}WO_6$	iju	104-8303
di-Barium Calcium Tungstate (VI) Ba_2CaWO_6	f	104-8234
Barium Carbonate $BaCO_3$	b	104-0233
Barium Cerium Lead Titanate		
$Ba_xCe_yPb_{1-x-y}TiO_3$	j	104-8379
Barium Cerium Titanate $Ba_xCe_{1-x}TiO_3$	j	104-8378
Barium Cerium Titanate Silicate		
$Ba_xCe_{1-x}Ti_ySi_{1-y}O_3$	j	104-8372
Barium Cerium Titanate Stannate		
$Ba_xCe_{1-x}Ti_ySn_{1-y}O_3$	j	104-8373
Barium Cerium Zirconate Titanate		
$Ba_xCe_{1-x}Zr_yTi_{1-y}O_3$	j	104-8388
Barium Chlorate $Ba(ClO_3)_2$	bf	104-0294
Barium Chloride $BaCl_2$	abfij	104-0055
Barium Chloride Fluoride $BaClF$		
see Barium Fluorochloride $BaClF$	ah	104-8259
Barium Chromate $BaCrO_4$	i	104-0485
Barium Cobaltate (IV) $BaCoO_3$	q	104-8200
di-Barium Cobaltate (IV) Ba_2CoO_4	q	104-8203
Barium Cobalt Carbonate $Ba_3Co_2CO_9$	q	104-8201
Barium Cobalt Ferrate $BaCo_2Fe_{16}O_{27}$	p	104-8240
di-Barium Cobalt (II) Tungstate (VI)		
Ba_2CoWO_6	q	104-8124
Barium tetra-Cyanoplatinate $Ba(Pt(CN)_4)$	jm	104-8117
di-Barium Dysprosium Molybdate (V) Ba_2DyMoO_6	fjq	104-8450
di-Barium Dysprosium Tungstate (V) Ba_2DyWO_6	fjq	104-8452
di-Barium Erbium Molybdate (V) Ba_2ErMoO_6	fjq	104-8451
di-Barium Erbium Tungstate (V) Ba_2ErWO_6	fjq	104-8453
Barium di-Europium (III) di-Ferrate (III)		
$BaEu_2Fe_2O_7$	q	104-8300
Barium Ferrate (IV) $BaFeO_3$	q	104-8461
Barium Ferrate $BaFeO_{3-x}$	q	104-8173
Barium Ferrate $BaFe_{12}O_{19}$	ajnpqt	104-8106
Barium Fluoride BaF_2	abdfhjmstv	104-0104
see also Optovac (BaF_2)		104-8432
Barium Fluorochloride $BaClF$	ah	104-8259
Barium octa-Fluorodiyttrate BaY_2F_8	ahi	104-8251
Barium tetra-Fluoroferrate $BaFeF_4$	q	104-8313
Barium tetra-Fluoromagnesate $BaMgF_4$	bsv	104-8421
Barium tetra-Fluoromanganate $BaMnF_4$	k	104-8317
Barium tetra-Fluorozincate $BaZnF_4$	s	104-8422
di-Barium Gadolinium Molybdate (V) Ba_2GdMoO_6	fjq	104-8449
di-Barium Gadolinium Tungstate (V) Ba_2GdWO_6	fjq	104-8454
Barium di-Gallium tetra-Selenide		
$BaGa_2Se_4$		
see Barium tetra-Selenodigallate $BaGa_2Se_4$	j	104-8456
Barium di-Gallium tetra-Sulfide		
$BaGa_2S_4$		
see Barium tetra-Thiodigallate $BaGa_2S_4$	jm	104-8116
Barium Germanate $BaGeO_3$	bj	104-8354
di-Barium di-Germanium Titanate (IV)		
$Ba_2Ge_2TiO_8$	v	104-8285
Barium-Gold $BaAu_5$	u	102-8170
Barium Hydride BaH_2	fjt	104-0471
Barium Indium Ferrate $BaIn_xFe_{12-x}O_{19}$	q	104-8314
Barium di-Indium tetra-Selenide		
$BaIn_2Se_4$		
see Barium tetra-Selenodiindate $BaIn_2Se_4$	j	104-8458
Barium di-Indium tetra-Sulfide		
$BaIn_2S_4$		
see Barium tetra-Thiodiindate $BaIn_2S_4$	jm	104-8457
Barium Iodide BaI_2	j	104-0187

Property: a. Absorption coefficient; **b.** Dielectric constant; **c.** Dielectric strength; **d.** Energy band structure; **e.** Effective mass; **f.** Energy gap; **g.** Electric hysteresis; **h.** Energy level; **i.** Electron emission properties; **j.** Electrical resistivity; **k.** Magnetoelectric properties; **l.** Hall coefficient; **m.** Luminescence properties; **n.** Magnetic hysteresis; **o.** Mobility; **p.** Magnetomechanical properties; **q.** Magnetic susceptibility; **r.** Photoelectronic properties; **s.** Refractive index; **t.** Thermoelectric properties; **u.** Work function; **v.** Piezoelectric properties.

Substance Name	Property	Number
Barium Iron Aluminum Oxide		
$BaFe_{12-x}Al_xO_{19}$		
see Barium Aluminum Ferrate $BaAl_xFe_{12-x}O_{19}$	q	102-8366
Barium Iron tetra- Fluoride $BaFeF_4$		
see Barium tetra- Fluoroferrate $BaFeF_4$	q	104-8313
Barium Lanthanum Aluminate $Ba_xLa_{1-x}AlO_{3-y}$	j	102-8493
Barium Lanthanum Manganese Ferrate		
$Ba_xLa_{1-x}Mn_yFe_{1-y}O_3$	q	104-8351
Barium Lanthanum Titanate $Ba_xLa_{1-x}TiO_3$	j	104-8380
Barium Lead Germanate $Ba_xPb_{5-x}Ge_3O_{11}$	g	104-8188
Barium Lead Niobate $Ba_xPb_{1-x}Nb_2O_6$	bgv	104-8161
Barium Lead Titanate $Ba_xPb_{1-x}TiO_3$	gj	104-8237
Barium Magnesium Cerium Titanate		
$Ba_xMg_yCe_{1-x-y}TiO_3$	j	104-8385
Barium Magnesium tetra- Fluoride $BaMgF_4$		
see Barium tetra- Fluoromagnesate $BaMgF_4$	bsv	104-8421
Barium Magnesium Titanate $Ba_xMg_{1-x}TiO_3$	j	104-8386
di- Barium Magnesium Tungstate (V I) Ba_2MgWO_6	fm	104-8196
Barium Manganese tetra- Fluoride $BaMnF_4$		
see Barium tetra- Fluoromanganate $BaMnF_4$	k	104-8317
tri- Barium Molybdenum (V I) Bismuthate		
(I I I) $Ba_3MoBe_2O_9$		
see tri- Barium Bismuth (I I I) Molybdate (V I)		
$Ba_3Bi_2MoO_9$	g	104-8364
Barium Molydate (V I) $BaMoO_4$	hm	104-8228
Barium Nickelate (I V) $BaNiO_3$	q	104-8460
Barium Niobate (V) $BaNb_2O_6$	bgv	104-8160
Barium Niobium Bismuth Oxide		
$BaNb_2Bi_2O_9$		
see Barium di- Bismuth (I I I) di- Niobate (V)		
$BaBi_2Nb_2O_9$	b	104-8186
Barium Niobium Lead Oxide		
$Ba_{1-x}Nb_2Pb_xO_6$		
see Barium Lead Niobate $Ba_xPb_{1-x}Nb_2O_6$	bgv	104-8161
Barium Nitrate $Ba(NO_3)_2$	bjs	104-0038
Barium Nitrite $Ba(NO_2)_2$	j	104-0435
Barium Oxide BaO	bdefhijloqstu	104-0049
Barium Peroxide BaO_2	bh	104-0039
Barium Phophate $Ba(PO_3)_2$	m	104-8444
Barium Platinum Carbide Nitride		
$Ba(Pt(CN)_4)$		
see Barium tetra- Cyanoplatinate $Ba(Pt(CN)_4)$	jm	104-8117
di- Barium Rhenium Cobaltate Ba_2ReCoO_6	q	104-8152
Barium Scandium Aluminum Ferrate		
$BaSc_xAl_yFe_{12-x-y}O_{19}$	npq	104-8308
Barium Scandium Ferrate $BaSc_xFe_{12-x}O_{19}$	npq	104-8307
Barium Scandium Gallium Ferrate		
$BaSc_xGa_yFe_{12-x-y}O_{19}$	npq	104-8309
Barium Selenide $BaSe$	dfijsu	104-8032
Barium tetra- Selenodigallate $BaGa_2Se_4$	j	104-8456
Barium tetra- Selenodiindate $BaIn_2Se_4$	j	104-8458
Barium tri- Selenotantalate $BaTaSe_3$	q	104-8440
Barium Selenotantalate $BaTa_{1-x}Se_3$	fjq	104-8441
Barium Silicate $BaSiO_3$	s	104-0027
di- Barium Silicon Tungsten hexa- Oxide		
Ba_2SiWO_6		
see di- Barium Tungsten Silicate Ba_2WSiO_6	f	104-8235
Barium Stannate $BaSnO_3$	b	104-8163
Barium Strontium Calcium Cerium Titanate		
$Ba_xSr_yCa_zCe_{1-x-y-z}TiO_3$	j	104-8383
Barium Strontium Calcium Oxide $Ba_xSr_yCa_{1-x-y}O$	iu	104-8271
Barium Strontium Calcium Titanate		
$Ba_xSr_yCa_{1-x-y}TiO_3$	j	104-8384
Barium Strontium Cerium Titanate		
$Ba_xSr_yCe_{1-x-y}TiO_3$	j	104-8387
Barium Strontium Cerium Titanate Stannate		
$Ba_xSr_yCe_{1-x-y}Ti_zSn_{1-z}O_3$	j	104-8374
Barium Strontium Niobate $Ba_{1-x}Sr_xNb_2O_6$	abfgnqrsv	104-8171
Barium Strontium Oxide $Ba_xSr_{1-x}O$	iju	104-8270
Barium Strontium Tellurate $Ba_{1-x}Sr_xTeO_3$	b	104-8216
Barium Strontium Titanate $Ba_{1-x}Sr_xTiO_3$	bghjq	104-0386
Barium Strontium Titanate Stannate		
$Ba_xSr_{1-x}Ti_ySn_{1-y}O_3$	j	104-8377

Substance Name	Property	Number
Barium Strontium Zinc Ferrate		
$Ba_xSr_{2-x}Zn_2Fe_{12}O_{22}$	q	104-8246
Barium Sulfate $BaSO_4$	abim	104-0025
see also Barite $BaSO_4$		521-0223
Barium mono- Sulfide BaS	abdfijmstu	104-0196
Barium Tantalum tri- Selenide $BaTaSe_3$		
see Barium tri- Selenotantalate $BaTaSe_3$	q	104-8440
Barium Tantalum tri- Sulfide $BaTaS_3$		
see Barium tri- Thiotantalate $BaTaS_3$	fjq	104-8438
Barium Telluride $BaTe$	dfijsu	104-8033
Barium tetra- Thiodialuminate $BaAl_2S_4$	jm	102-8503
Barium tetra- Thiodigallate $BaGa_2S_4$	jm	104-8116
Barium tetra- Thiodiindate $BaIn_2S_4$	jm	104-8457
Barium tri- Thiotantalate $BaTaS_3$	fjq	104-8438
Barium Thiotantalate $BaTa_{1-x}S_3$	fjq	104-8439
Barium Titanate (I V) $BaTiO_3$	abcdf-jmnoqrstv	104-0013
Barium di- Titanate (I V) $BaTi_2O_5$	b	104-8321
Barium tri- Titanate (I V) $BaTi_3O_7$	b	104-8322
Barium Titanate $BaTi_{1-x}O_{3-x}$	b	104-8312
Barium Titanate Silicate $BaTi_xSi_{1-x}O_3$	j	104-8375
Barium Titanate Stannate $BaTi_xSn_{1-x}O_3$	j	104-8376
Barium Titanium Germanium Oxide		
$Ba_2TiGe_2O_8$		
see di- Barium di- Germanium Titanate (I V)		
$Ba_2Ge_2TiO_8$	v	104-8285
Barium Titanium Manganese Zinc Ferrate		
$BaTi_xMn_yZn_zFe_{12-x-y-z}O_{19}$	q	104-8151
Barium Titanium Niobate $Ba_6Ti_2Nb_8O_{30}$	abfs	104-8164
Barium Tungstate (V I) $BaWO_4$	bhm	104-0384
tri- Barium Tungstate (V I) Ba_3WO_6	f	104-8236
di- Barium Tungsten Cadmium hexa- Oxide		
Ba_2WCdO_6		
see di- Barium Cadmium Tungstate (V I) Ba_2CdWO_6	f	104-8233
di- Barium Tungsten Cobalt hexa- Oxide		
Ba_2WCoO_6		
see di- Barium Cobalt (I I) Tungstate (V I)		
Ba_2CoWO_6	q	104-8124
di- Barium Tungsten Silicate Ba_2WSiO_6	f	104-8235
di- Barium Tungsten Zinc hexa- Oxide		
Ba_2WZnO_6		
see di- Barium Zinc Tungstate Ba_2ZnWO_6	f	104-8232
di- Barium Uranium (V I) Cobaltate (I I)		
Ba_2UCoO_6	q	104-8324
di- Barium Uranium (V I) Manganate (I I)		
Ba_2UMnO_6	q	104-8325
di- Barium Uranium (V I) Nickelate (I I)		
Ba_2UNiO_6	q	104-8326
Barium Vanadate (V) $Ba(VO_3)_2$	s	104-8298
Barium Vanadate (I I) BaV_2O_3	m	104-8178
Barium dodeca- Vanadate $BaV_{12}O_{30}$	q	104-8436
tri- Barium Vanadate (V) $Ba_3V_2O_8$	m	104-8352
di- Barium Vandadium (V) Bismuthate (I I I)		
Ba_2VBiO_6		
see di- Barium Bismuth (I I I) Vanadate (V)		
Ba_2BiVO_6	g	104-8365
Barium di- Yttrium octa- Fluoride		
BaY_2F_8		
see Barium octa- Fluorodiyttrate BaY_2F_8	ahi	104-8251
di- Barium Yttrium Molybdate (V) Ba_2YMoO_6	fjq	104-8448
di- Barium Yttrium Tungstate (V) Ba_2YWO_6	fjq	104-8455
Barium Zinc Ferrate $BaZn_2Fe_{16}O_{27}$	p	104-8241
Barium Zinc tetra- Fluoride $BaZnF_4$		
see Barium tetra- Fluorozincate $BaZnF_4$	s	104-8422
di- Barium Zinc tri- Sulfide Ba_2ZnS_3	m	104-8348
di- Barium Zinc Tungstate Ba_2ZnWO_6	f	104-8232
Barium Zirconate $BaZrO_3$	bj	104-0188
Barium Zirconium Silicate $BaZrSiO_5$	adi	104-8257
di- Barium di- Zirconium Silicate		
$Ba_2Zr_2Si_3O_{12}$	di	104-8258
Barium Zirconium Titanium tri- Oxide		
$BaZr_xTi_{1-x}O_3$	j	104-8204
Beryllia		
see Beryllium Oxide BeO	abcdfghijmqsuv	104-0002

Property: **a.** Absorption coefficient; **b.** Dielectric constant; **c.** Dielectric strength; **d.** Energy band structure; **e.** Effective mass; **f.** Energy gap; **g.** Electric hysteresis; **h.** Energy level; **i.** Electron emission properties; **j.** Electrical resistivity; **k.** Magnetoelectric properties; **l.** Hall coefficient; **m.** Luminescence properties; **n.** Magnetic hysteresis; **o.** Mobility; **p.** Magnetomechanical properties; **q.** Magnetic susceptibility; **r.** Photoelectronic properties; **s.** Refractive index; **t.** Thermoelectric properties; **u.** Work function; **v.** Piezoelectric properties.

Substance Name	*Property*	*Number*
Beryllium Aluminum Silicate $Be_3Al_2Si_6O_{18}$	b	102-0389
see also Beryl $Be_3Al_2(SiO_3)_6$		521-0130
Beryllium di-Boride BeB_2	dfi	104-8447
Beryllium di-Boride di-Carbide BeB_2C_2	jlt	104-0572
Beryllium dodeca-Boride di-Carbide $BeB_{12}C_2$	jlt	104-0573
di-Beryllium Carbide Be_2C	j	104-8398
Beryllium Carbonate $BeCO_3$	b	104-8165
13-Beryllium Ceride $Be_{13}Ce$	qt	104-8315
Beryllium Chloride $BeCl$	j	104-0110
dodeca-Beryllium Chromide $Be_{12}Cr$	n	104-8319
Beryllium - Chromium - Manganese $Be_2Cr_xMn_{1-x}$	j	104-8290
Beryllium - Cobalt $BeCo$	d	104-8426
Beryllium - Copper $BeCu$	di	104-8296
Beryllium - Dysprosium $Be_{13}Dy$	nq	104-8335
Beryllium - Erbium $Be_{13}Er$	nq	104-8337
Beryllium - Europium $Be_{13}Eu$	q	104-8332
Beryllium Fluoride BeF_2	jm	104-0118
Beryllium - Gadolinium $Be_{13}Gd$	nq	104-8333
Beryllium - Holmium $Be_{13}Ho$	nq	104-8336
Beryllium Lanthanate $Be_2La_2O_5$	ahm	104-8133
Beryllium - Lanthanum $Be_{13}La$	q	104-8328
Beryllium - Lutetium $Be_{13}Lu$	q	104-8340
Beryllium - Molybdenum Be_2Mo	j	104-8205
Beryllium - Molybdenum $Be_{12}Mo$	j	104-8209
Beryllium - Molybdenum $Be_{22}Mo$	j	104-8211
Beryllium - Neodymium $Be_{13}Nd$	q	104-8330
Beryllium - Niobium $Be_{12}Nb$	j	104-8207
Beryllium Oxide BeO	abcdfghijmqsuv	104-0002
see also Thermalox 995 BeO		104-8349
Beryllium - Praseodymium $Be_{13}Pr$	q	104-8329
Beryllium - Rhenium $Be_{22}Re$	j	104-8253
di-Beryllium Rhodide Be_2Rh	j	104-8206
Beryllium - Samarium $Be_{13}Sm$	q	104-8331
Beryllium Sulfide BeS	s	104-8036
dodeca-Beryllium Tantalide $Be_{12}Ta$	j	104-8208
Beryllium - Terbium $Be_{13}Tb$	nq	104-8334
Beryllium - Thorium $Be_{13}Th$	q	104-8342
Beryllium - Thulium $Be_{13}Tm$	nq	104-8338
Beryllium - Thulium - Lanthanum $Be_{13}Tm_xLa_{1-x}$	q	104-8341
Beryllium - Tungsten $Be_{12}W$	j	104-8210
Beryllium - Tungsten $Be_{13}W$	j	104-8252
Beryllium - Tungsten $Be_{22}W$	j	104-8212
Beryllium - Uranium $Be_{13}U$	q	104-8343
Beryllium - Vanadium - Chromium $Be_2V_xCr_{1-x}$	j	104-8291
Beryllium - Ytterbium $Be_{13}Yb$	q	104-8339
Beryllium - Zirconium $Be_{13}Zr$	j	104-8306
octa-Beryllium di-Zirconium penta-Niobide $Be_8Zr_2Nb_5$	j	104-8371
Bis(penta-Fluoroethyl)trifluoromethylamine $CF_3N(C_2F_5)_2$		
see Bis-(penta-Fluoroethyl)trifluoromethylamine $CF_3N(C_2F_5)_2$	c	106-8579
Bismuth Antimonide Bi_xSb_{1-x}	efhjklo	104-8224
Bismuth Antimony Selenide Iodide $Bi_xSb_{1-x}SeI$	jr	104-8294
see also Antimony Selenide Iodide ≥ Bismuth Selenide Iodide		508-0537
see also Bismuth Selenide Iodide ≥ Antimony Selenide Iodide		508-0536
Bismuth Antimony Sulfide $Bi_xSb_{2-x}S_3$	r	104-8190
Bismuth Antimony tri-Telluride $BiSbTe_3$	j	104-8395
Bismuth Antimony Telluride $Bi_xSb_{2-x}Te_3$	defjklot	104-8109
see also Antimony Sesquitelluride ≥ Bismuth Sesquitelluride		508-0096
see also Bismuth Sesquitelluride ≥ Antimony Sesquitelluride		508-0095
Bismuth Antimony Telluride Selenide $Bi_xSb_{1-x}Te_ySe_{3-y}$	efjot	104-8194
see also Antimony Sesquitelluride ≥ Antimony Sesquiselenide ≥ Bismuth Sesquitelluride		508-0108
see also Bismuth Sesquiselenide ≥ Antimony Sesquitelluride		508-0117
see also Bismuth Sesquitelluride ≥ Antimony Sesquiselenide ≥ Antimony Sesquitelluride		508-0107

Substance Name	*Property*	*Number*
Bismuth Antimony Telluride Sulfide $Bi_xSb_{2-x}Te_yS_{3-y}$	f	104-8428
see also Antimony Sesquisulfide ≥ Bismuth Sesquitelluride		508-0169
see also Bismuth Sesquitelluride ≥ Antimony Sesquisulfide		508-0109
Bismuth mono-Bromide $BiBr$	m	104-8274
Bismuth tri-Bromide $BiBr_3$	j	104-0149
Bismuth mono-Chloride $BiCl$	m	104-8275
Bismuth tri-Chloride $BiCl_3$	j	104-0081
Bismuth Chloride Oxide $BiClO$	mr	104-8134
Bismuth (III) Ferrate (III) $BiFeO_3$	bnq	104-0529
di-Bismuth tetra-Ferrate $Bi_2Fe_4O_9$	q	104-8292
Bismuth Germanate $BiGe_3O_{12}$	bs	104-8166
tetra-Bismuth (III) tri-Germanate $Bi_2Ge_3O_{12}$	ams	104-8180
dodeca-Bismuth (III) Germanate $Bi_{12}GeO_{20}$	abfhjmqsv	104-0533
Bismuth tri-Iodide BiI_3	adefhjmr	104-0331
Bismuth Iodide Oxide $BiIO$	af	104-8121
see also Bismuth Triodide ≥ Bismuth Sesquioxide		508-0050
Bismuth Iodosulfide $BiSI$	b	104-8356
Bismuth Iron Titanium Oxide $Bi_9Fe_5Ti_3O_9$		
see Titanium Bismuth Ferrate $Ti_3Bi_9Fe_5O_9$	q	104-8122
di-Bismuth (III) Molybdate (VI) Bi_2MoO_6	u	104-8346
di-Bismuth (III) di-Molybdate (VI) $Bi_2Mo_2O_9$	u	104-8347
di-Bismuth (III) tri-Molybdate (VI) $Bi_2Mo_3O_{12}$	su	104-8302
hexa-Bismuth (III) di-Molybdate (VI) $Bi_6Mo_2O_{15}$	su	104-8301
Bismuth Neodymium Ferrate $Bi_{1-x}Nd_xFeO_3$	nq	104-8154
Bismuth sesqui-Oxide Bi_2O_3	abfjrstu	104-0021
Bismuth Oxide Bi_2O_{3-x}	as	104-8423
Bismuth mono-Selenide $BiSe$	l	104-8369
Bismuth sesqui-Selenide Bi_2Se_3	defhjkloqtv	104-8042
Bismuth Selenide Iodide $BiSeI$	jq	104-8214
see also Bismuth Sesquiselenide ≥ Bismuth Triodide		508-0049
tetra-Bismuth (III) tri-Silicate $Bi_4Si_3O_{12}$	s	104-8295
dodeca-Bismuth Silicate $Bi_{12}SiO_{20}$	aefhirs	104-8231
Bismuth mono-Sulfide BiS	loq	104-8043
Bismuth sesqui-Sulfide Bi_2S_3	jr	104-8044
Bismuth Sulfide Iodide $BiSI$		
see Bismuth Iodosulfide $BiSI$	b	104-8356
Bismuth mono-Telluride $BiTe$	jqt	104-8272
Bismuth sesqui-Telluride Bi_2Te_3	abdefh–loqrstuv	104-8045
Bismuth Telluride Bromide $BiTeBr$	adf	104-0431
Bismuth di-Telluride Selenide $BiTe_2Se$	f	104-8255
di-Bismuth Telluride Selenide Bi_2TeSe	f	104-8427
Bismuth Telluride Selenide $Bi_2Te_xSe_{3-x}$	defhjlotu	104-8108
see also Bismuth Sesquiselenide ≥ Bismuth Sesquitelluride		508-0098
see also Bismuth Sesquitelluride ≥ Bismuth Sesquiselenide		508-0097
di-Bismuth di-Telluride Selenide Bi_2Te_2Se	j	104-8396
Bismuth Telluride Selenide Sulfide $Bi_2Te_xSe_yS_{3-x-y}$	f	104-8429
di-Bismuth di-Telluride Sulfide Bi_2Te_2S		
see di-Bismuth Thioditellurate Bi_2Te_2S	j	104-8389
octa-Bismuth hepta-Telluride penta-Sulfide $Bi_8Te_7S_5$	hj	104-8199
di-Bismuth Thioditellurate Bi_2Te_2S	j	104-8389
tetra-Bismuth (III) tri-Titanate (IV) $Bi_4Ti_3O_{12}$	bgjnoq	104-0337
dodeca-Bismuth (III) Titanate (IV) $Bi_{12}TiO_{20}$	fhs	104-8123
hexa-Bismuth (III) Tungstate (VI) Bi_6WO_{12}	j	104-8172
Bismuth Vanadate $BiVO_4$	b	104-8443
di-Borane B_2H_6	ah	104-0016
penta-Borane B_5H_9	i	104-0086
Borate (1-) Ion BO_2	h	104-8126
Boron Arsenide BAs	ef	102-8379
Boron mono-Carbide BC	efjot	104-0249
tetra-Boron Carbide B_4C	fj	104-0109
Boron tri-Chloride BCl_3	ad	104-0051
Boron Fluoride BF_3	ahj	104-0050

Property: a. Absorption coefficient; **b.** Dielectric constant; **c.** Dielectric strength; **d.** Energy band structure; **e.** Effective mass; **f.** Energy gap; **g.** Electric hysteresis; **h.** Energy level; **i.** Electron emission properties; **j.** Electrical resistivity; **k.** Magnetoelectric properties; **l.** Hall coefficient; **m.** Luminescence properties; **n.** Magnetic hysteresis; **o.** Mobility; **p.** Magnetomechanical properties; **q.** Magnetic susceptibility; **r.** Photoelectronic properties; **s.** Refractive index; **t.** Thermoelectric properties; **u.** Work function; **v.** Piezoelectric properties.

Substance Name	Property	Number
Boron Hydride B_5H_9		
see penta-Borane B_5H_9	i	104-0086
Boron Nitride BN	abcdfhijmpqrstuv	104-0007
tri-Boron tetra-Nitride B_3N_4	j	104-8430
Boron Oxide B_2O_3	abfjrs	104-0015
Boron Phosphide BP	abdfhjostv	104-0295
hexa-Boron Phosphide B_6P	fjost	104-8366
13-Boron di-Phosphide $B_{13}P_2$	j	104-8297
Bromine mono-Chloride $BrCl$	a	104-8266
Bromine mono-Fluoride BrF	i	104-8267
Bromine penta-Fluoride BrF_5	s	104-8400
Bromine tri-Fluride BrF_3	s	104-8399
Bromopentamminerhodium (2+) Ion $Rh(NH_3)_5Br$	m	104-8131
Bromotrifluoromethane $CBrF_3$	bcs	104-0008
Brush Thermalox 995 BeO		
see Thermalox 995 BeO	i	104-8349
BSN		
see Barium Strontium Niobate $Ba_{1-x}Sr_xNb_2O_6$	abfgnqrsv	104-8171
Cadmium Antimonide $CdSb$	adefhjlorst	106-8001
Cadmium Antimony Arsenide $CdSb_{1-x}As_2$	afjqt	102-8466
Cadmium di-Arsenide $CdAs_2$	fjnqst	102-8188
tri-Cadmium di-Arsenide Cd_3As_2	abdefhjklost	102-8035
Cadmium Arsenide Phosphide $Cd_3As_xP_{2-x}$	abefhos	102-8232
see also tri-Cadmium Diarsenide ≥ tri-Cadmium Diphosphide		508-0342
see also tri-Cadmium Diphosphide ≥ tri-Cadmium Diarsenide		508-0343
Cadmium di-Arsenidogermanate $CdGeAs_2$	abdefhjlnoqrst	102-8069
Cadmium di-Arsenidosilicate $CdSiAs_2$	efjorst	102-8083
Cadmium di-Arsenidostannate $CdSnAs_2$	defhijlost	102-8096
Cadmium di-Arsenidothallate $CdTlAs_2$	q	102-8469
Cadmium Azide $Cd(N_3)_2$	bfrs	106-8135
Cadmium Bromide $CdBr_2$	abjmr	104-0052
Cadmium Chloride $CdCl_2$	ajm	106-0126
Cadmium Chromium Selenide $CdCr_2Se_{4-x}$		
see Cadmium Selenochromate $CdCr_2Se_{4-x}$	dfjnoq	106-8438
Cadmium Cobalt Thiochromate $Cd_xCo_{1-x}Cr_2S_4$	ahnqs	106-8227
Cadmium Copper Chromium Sulfide $Cd_xCu_{1-x}Cr_2S_4$		
see Cadmium Copper Thiochromate $Cd_xCu_{1-x}Cr_2S_4$	nq	106-8435
Cadmium Copper Thiochromate $Cd_xCu_{1-x}Cr_2S_4$	nq	106-8435
Cadmium Ferrite $Cd_xFe_{3-x}O_4$	j	106-8150
Cadmium Fluoride CdF_2	abdefhjlmors	106-0385
Cadmium di-Gallium tetra-Selenide $CdGa_2Se_4$		
see Cadmium tetra-Selenodigallate $CdGa_2Se_4$	bdfjmors	106-8154
Cadmium Gallium Selenochromate $Cd_xGa_{1-x}Cr_2Se_4$	jr	106-8823
Cadmium di-Gallium tetra-Sulfide $CdGa_2S_4$		
see Cadmium tetra-Thiodigallate $CdGa_2S_4$	adfhm	106-8155
Cadmium Germanium Antimony Arsenide $CdGeSb_xAs_{2-x}$	jr	102-8435
Cadmium Germanium di-Arsenide $CdGeAs_2$		
see Cadmium di-Arsenidogermanate $CdGeAs_2$	abdefhjlnoqrst	102-8069
Cadmium Germanium Arsenide $CdGe_{1-x}As_2$	fjqr	102-8467
Cadmium Germanium Arsenide Phosphide $CdGeAs_xP_{2-x}$	fj	102-8436
see also Cadmium Germanium Diarsenide ≥ Cadmium Germanium Diphosphide		508-0159
see also Cadmium Germanium Diphosphide ≥ Cadmium Germaniu Diarsenide		508-0160
Cadmium Germanium di-Phosphide $CdGeP_2$	adefhjlnoqst	106-0941
Cadmium Germanium Silicon Arsenide $CdGe_xSi_{1-x}As_2$	fr	102-8455
Cadmium Indium Germanium tetra-Sulfide $CdInGeS_4$		
see Cadmium Indium tetra-Thiogermanate $CdInGeS_4$	fhjmor	106-8528
Cadmium di-Indium tetra-Selenide $CdIn_2Se_4$		
see Cadmium tetra-Selenoindate $CdIn_2Se_4$	af	106-8796
Cadmium di-Indium tetra-Sulfide $CdIn_2S_4$		
see Cadmium tetra-Thiodiindate $CdIn_2S_4$	abdefhjmoqrs	106-1256
Cadmium di-Indium tetra-Telluride $CdIn_2Te_4$		
see Cadmium tetra-Telluroindate $CdIn_2Te_4$	fjt	106-8589
Cadmium di-Indium Telluride tri-Selenide $CdIn_2TeSe_3$		
see Cadmium Tellurotriselenoindate $CdIn_2TeSe_3$	a	106-8797
Cadmium Indium Telluride Selenide $CdIn_2Te_xSe_{4-x}$		
see Cadmium Telluroselenoindate $CdIn_2Te_xSe_{4-x}$	af	106-8795
Cadmium Indium tetra-Thiogermanate $CdInGeS_4$	fhjmor	106-8528
Cadmium Iodide CdI_2	dhj	106-0047
Cadmium Iron Oxide $Cd_xFe_{3-x}O_4$		
see Cadmium Ferrite $Cd_xFe_{3-x}O_4$	j	106-8150
Cadmium Lead Telluride $Cd_xPb_{1-x}Te$	lot	106-8295
Cadmium Molybdate (V I) $CdMoO_4$	hm	106-8427
di-Cadmium Niobate (V) $Cd_2Nb_2O_7$	bq	106-8242
Cadmium Oxide CdO	abdefhijkloqstu	106-0057
Cadmium di-Phosphide CdP_2	adfjm	106-8200
Cadmium tetra-Phosphide CdP_4	adfjlt	106-8611
tri-Cadmium di-Phosphide Cd_3P_2	abdefhjlost	106-1085
Cadmium Pyroniobate $Cd_2Nb_2O_7$		
see di-Cadmium Niobate (V) $Cd_2Nb_2O_7$	bq	106-8242
Cadmium Selenide $CdSe$	abdefh-moqrstuv	106-8040
Cadmium Selenide Sulfide $CdSe_xS_{1-x}$	abdefhjmoqrsv	106-8132
Cadmium tetra-Selenochromate (I I I) $CdCr_2Se_4$	abdfjklnopqrst	106-8312
Cadmium Selenochromate $CdCr_2Se_{4-x}$	dfjnoq	106-8438
Cadmium tetra-Selenodigallate $CdGa_2Se_4$	bdfjmors	106-8154
Cadmium tetra-Selenoindate $CdIn_2Se_4$	af	106-8796
Cadmium Silicon di-Arsenide $CdSiAs_2$		
see Cadmium di-Arsenidosilicate $CdSiAs_2$	efjorst	102-8083
Cadmium Silicon di-Phosphide $CdSiP_2$	aefhjmors	106-8342
Cadmium Sulfate $CdSO_4$	m	106-0067
Cadmium Sulfide CdS	a-fh-mopqrstuv	106-0363
Cadmium Sulfide Oxide CdS_xO_{1-x}	r	106-8758
Cadmium Telluride $CdTe$	a-fhijklmoqrstuv	106-8041
see also Irtran 6 (Kodak) $CdTe$		106-8358
Cadmium Telluride Selenide $CdTe_xSe_{1-x}$	adfhjmort	106-8234
Cadmium Telluride Sulfide $CdTe_xS_{1-x}$	efhjs	106-8580
Cadmium tetra-Telluroindate $CdIn_2Te_4$	fjt	106-8589
Cadmium Telluroselenoindate $CdIn_2Te_xSe_{4-x}$	af	106-8795
Cadmium Tellurotriselenoindate $CdIn_2TeSe_3$	a	106-8797
Cadmium Thallium di-Arsenide $CdTlAs_2$		
see Cadmium di-Arsenidothallate $CdTlAs_2$	q	102-8469
Cadmium Thallium Arsenide $CdTl_{1-x}As_2$	fjqt	102-8468
Cadmium tetra-Thiochromate (I I I) $CdCr_2S_4$	amq	106-1299
Cadmium Thiochromateindate $CdCr_xIn_{2-x}S_4$	jq	106-8144
Cadmium tetra-Thiodigallate $CdGa_2S_4$	adfhm	106-8155
Cadmium tetra-Thiodiindate $CdIn_2S_4$	abdefhjmoqrs	106-1256
Cadmium Tin di-Arsenide $CdSnAs_2$		
see Cadmium di-Arsenidostannate $CdSnAs_2$	defhijlost	102-8096
Cadmium Tin Germanium di-Arsenide $CdSn_xGe_{1-x}As_2$	fjr	102-8434
Cadmium Tin di-Phosphide $CdSnP_2$	afjmors	106-1519
Cadmium Titanate (I V) $CdTiO_3$	bg	106-8293
Cadmium Tungstate (V I) $CdWO_4$	am	106-8430
Cadmium dodeca-Vanadate $CdV_{12}O_{30}$	q	106-8794
tri-Cadmium Vanadate (V) $Cd_3V_2O_8$	m	106-8676
Cadmium Zinc Antimonide $Cd_xZn_{1-x}Sb$	jklot	106-8467
Cadmium di-Zinc di-Antimonide $CdZn_2Sb_2$	lt	106-8125
di-Cadmium Zinc di-Antimonide Cd_2ZnSb_2	lt	106-8126
Cadmium Zinc Arsenide $Cd_xZn_{3-x}As_2$	fjl	102-8311
see also tri-Cadmium Diarsenide ≥ tri-Zinc Diarsenide		508-0523
see also tri-Zinc Diarsenide ≥ tri-Cadmium Diarsenide		508-0524
Cadmium Zinc Selenide $Cd_xZn_{1-x}Se$	fhjmq	106-8133
see also Cadmium Selenide ≥ Zinc Selenide		508-0237
see also Zinc Selenide ≥ Cadmium Selenide		508-0238
Cadmium Zinc Selenochromate $Cd_xZn_{1-x}Cr_2Se_4$	r	106-8822
Cadmium Zinc Sulfide $Cd_xZn_{1-x}S$	defhjmqrs	106-8134
Cadmium Zinc Sulfide $CdZnS$	m	106-8186
Cadmium Zinc Telluride $Cd_xZn_{1-x}Te$	adefhjlmort	106-8127
see also Cadmium Telluride ≥ Zinc Telluride		508-0001
see also Zinc Telluride ≥ Cadmium Telluride		508-0239
Calcia		
see Calcium Oxide CaO	abdefhijlmoqstu	106-0004

Property: **a.** Absorption coefficient; **b.** Dielectric constant; **c.** Dielectric strength; **d.** Energy band structure; **e.** Effective mass; **f.** Energy gap; **g.** Electric hysteresis; **h.** Energy level; **i.** Electron emission properties; **j.** Electrical resistivity; **k.** Magnetoelectric properties; **l.** Hall coefficient; **m.** Luminescence properties; **n.** Magnetic hysteresis; **o.** Mobility; **p.** Magnetomechanical properties; **q.** Magnetic susceptibility; **r.** Photoelectronic properties; **s.** Refractive index; **t.** Thermoelectric properties; **u.** Work function; **v.** Piezoelectric properties.

Substance Name	Property	Number
Calcium Aluminate $CaAl_2O_4$	s	102-0003
Calcium di-Ammonium tetra-Hydrogen Bis-(di-Phosphate) $Ca(NH_4)_2H_4(P_2O_7)_2$	s	106-8619
di-Calcium Ammonium tri-Hydrogen Bis-(di-Phosphate) $Ca_2NH_4H_3(P_2O_7)_2$	s	106-8618
Calcium tetra-Ammonium hexa-Hydrogen Tetrakis-(di-Phosphate) $Ca(NH_4)_4H_6(P_2O_7)_4$	s	106-8617
Calcium di-Ammonium di-Phosphate $Ca(NH_4)_2P_2O_7$	s	106-8616
Calcium Boride CaB_6	j	104-8049
Calcium Bromide $CaBr_2$	j	104-0185
Calcium Carbonate $CaCO_3$	abhms	106-0005
see also Aragonite $CaCO_3$		521-0105
see also Calcite $CaCO_3$		521-0075
see also Limestone $CaCO_3$		521-0085
Calcium Cerate (IV) $CaCeO_3$	b	106-8239
Calcium Cerium Fluoride $Ca_xCe_{1-x}F_{3-y}$	j	106-8828
Calcium-Cerium-Lanthanum-Silver $Ca_xCe_yLa_{1-x-y}Ag$	j	102-8456
Calcium Chloride $CaCl_2$	abfij	106-0204
Calcium Chromate (VI) $CaCrO_4$	i	106-8308
tri-Calcium di-Chromium (III) tri-Silicate $Ca_3Cr_2Si_3O_{12}$	adh	106-8751
Calcium tetra-Cyanonickelate $CaNi(CN)_4$	s	106-8830
di-Calcium Ferrate (III) $Ca_2Fe_2O_5$	anq	106-8557
Calcium Fluoride CaF_2	abdfhijmstv	106-0026
see also Fluorite CaF_2		521-0096
see also Irtran 3 (Kodak) CaF_2		106-8357
see also IRG 12 CaF_2		106-8695
see also Optovac (CaF_2)		106-8789
penta-Calcium Fluoride Phosphate $Ca_5F(PO_4)_3$	ahms	106-8432
Calcium di-Gallium tetra-Selenide $CaGa_2Se_4$ see Calcium tetra-Selenodigallate $CaGa_2Se_4$	jm	106-8831
Calcium di-Gallium tetra-Sulfide $CaGa_2S_4$ see Calcium tetra-Thiodigallate $CaGa_2S_4$	jm	106-8142
Calcium Germanate $CaGeO_3$	m	106-8464
di-Calcium Germanate Ca_2GeO_4	m	106-8463
tri-Calcium Germanate Ca_3GeO_5	m	106-8465
Calcium mono-Hydride CaH	adh	106-8671
Calcium di-Hydrogen di-Phosphate $CaH_2P_2O_7$	s	106-8614
tri-Calcium di-Hydrogen Bis-(di-Phosphate) $Ca_3H_2(P_2O_7)_2$	s	106-8615
Calcium Iodate $Ca(IO_3)_2$	s	106-1070
Calcium mono-Iodide CaI	i	106-8255
Calcium di-Iodide CaI_2	j	106-0507
di-Calcium di-Iron penta-Oxide $Ca_2Fe_2O_5$ see di-Calcium Ferrate (III) $Ca_2Fe_2O_5$	anq	106-8557
Calcium Lanthanum Aluminate $Ca_xLa_{1-x}AlO_{3-y}$	j	102-8492
Calcium Lanthanum Manganate $Ca_xLa_{1-x}MnO_3$	j	106-8699
Calcium Lanthanum Manganese Ferrate $Ca_xLa_{1-x}Mn_yFe_{1-y}O_3$	q	106-8672
Calcium-Lead Ca_2Pb see di-Calcium Plumbide Ca_2Pb	jt	106-8524
Calcium Lead Bismuth Vanadium Ferrate $Ca_xPb_yBi_{3-x-y}V_zFe_{5-z}O_{12}$	p	104-8350
Calcium Lead Zirconium Titanium Oxide $Ca_xPb_{1-x}Zr_yTi_{1-y}O_3$	bjv	106-8473
Calcium Magnesium Silicate $CaMgSi_2O_6$	s	106-0940
Calcium Magnesium Titanate $CaMg_xTi_{1-x}O_{3-y}$	j	106-8829
di-Calcium Magnesium Tungstate (VI) Ca_2MgWO_6	f	106-8433
Calcium di-Magnesium di-Yttrium tri-Germanium dodeca-Oxide $CaMg_2Y_2Ge_3O_{12}$	ahs	106-8540
Calcium Manganese Copper Ferrite $Ca_xMn_yCu_zFe_{3-x-y-z}O_4$	n	106-8554
Calcium Manganese Copper Zinc Ferrite $(Ca, Mn, Cu, Zn)_xFe_{3-x}O_4$	n	106-8556
tri-Calcium di-Manganese (III) tri-Germanate $Ca_3Mn_2Ge_3O_{12}$	q	106-8632

Substance Name	Property	Number
Calcium Manganese Iron Copper Oxide $Ca_xMn_yFe_zCu_{3-x-y-z}O_4$ see Calcium Manganese Copper Ferrite $Ca_xMn_yCu_zFe_{3-x-y-z}O_4$	n	106-8554
Calcium Manganese Iron Copper Zinc Oxide $(Ca, Mn, Fe, Cu)_xZn_{3-x}O_4$ see Calcium Manganese Copper Zinc Ferrite $(Ca, Mn, Cu, Zn)_xFe_{3-x}O_4$	n	106-8556
Calcium Molybdate (VI) $CaMoO_4$	bhjm	106-0768
Calcium Nickel Carbide Nitride $CaNi(CN)_4$ see Calcium tetra-Cyanonickelate $CaNi(CN)_4$	s	106-8830
Calcium Nickel Ferrite $Ca_xNi_{1-x}Fe_2O_4$	j	110-8040
Calcium Niobate (V) $CaNb_2O_6$	b	106-8240
di-Calcium Niobate (V) $Ca_2Nb_2O_7$	bsv	106-8241
Calcium Nitrate $Ca(NO_3)_2$	b	106-0135
Calcium Nitrite $Ca(NO_2)_2$	j	106-8238
Calcium Oxide CaO	abdefhijlmoqstu	106-0004
Calcium tri-Oxosilicate $CaSiO_3$	s	106-8046
see also Suolunite $CaSiO_3$		521-8065
see also Wollastonite $CaSiO_3$		521-8034
di-Calcium tetra-Oxosilicate Ca_2SiO_4	s	106-0092
di-Calcium octa-Oxosilicate $Ca_2Si_3O_8$	s	106-8613
tri-Calcium penta-Oxosilicate Ca_3SiO_5	ms	106-0093
Calcium Phosphate $Ca(PO_3)_2$	m	106-8636
di-Calcium di-Phosphate $Ca_2P_2O_7$	hms	106-8452
tri-Calcium Phosphate $Ca_3(PO_4)_2$	hm	106-0413
Calcium Phosphide Oxide Fluoride see penta-Calcium Fluoride Phosphate $Ca_5F(PO_4)_3$	ahms	106-8432
di-Calcium Plumbide Ca_2Pb	jt	106-8524
Calcium Pyroniobate $Ca_2Nb_2O_7$ see di-Calcium Niobate (V) $Ca_2Nb_2O_7$	bsv	106-8241
Calcium Pyrophosphate $Ca_2P_2O_7$ see di-Calcium di-Phosphate $Ca_2P_2O_7$	hms	106-8452
Calcium Selenide $CaSe$	dfijmsu	106-8045
Calcium tetra-Selenodigallate $CaGa_2Se_4$	jm	106-8831
Calcium Silicate $CaSiO_3$ see Calcium tri-Oxosilicate $CaSiO_3$	s	106-8046
Calcium Silicate Ca_2SiO_4 see di-Calcium tetra-Oxosilicate Ca_2SiO_4	s	106-0092
Calcium Silicate $Ca_2Si_3O_8$ see di-Calcium octa-Oxosilicate $Ca_2Si_3O_8$	s	106-8613
Calcium Silicate Ca_3SiO_5 see tri-Calcium penta-Oxosilicate Ca_3SiO_5	ms	106-0093
Calcium mono-Silicide $CaSi$	d	106-8756
Calcium di-Silicide $CaSi_2$	d	106-8047
di-Calcium Silicide Ca_2Si	d	106-8757
di-Calcium Stannide Ca_2Sn	jt	106-8523
Calcium Sulfate $CaSO_4$	bim	106-0051
see also Gypsum $CaSO_4$		521-0083
Calcium Sulfide CaS	bdfhijmqsu	106-0508
Calcium Telluride $CaTe$	dfijsu	106-8048
Calcium tetra-Thiodigallate $CaGa_2S_4$	jm	106-8142
Calcium-Tin Ca_2Sn see di-Calcium Stannide Ca_2Sn	jt	106-8523
Calcium Titanate (IV) $CaTiO_3$	bgjs	106-0218
Calcium Titanium Aluminate $CaTi_xAl_{1-x}O_{3-y}$	j	102-8495
Calcium Tungstate (VI) $CaWO_4$	abfhijms	106-0610
Calcium Tungstate Molybdate $CaW_xMo_{1-x}O_4$	j	106-8675
di-Calcium Tungsten Cobalt hexa-Oxide Ca_2WCoO_6	q	106-8160
Calcium Uranium Phosphide Oxide $Ca(UO_2PO_4)_2$ see Calcium Uranyl Phosphate $Ca((UO_2)PO_4)_2$	jmnq	106-8414
Calcium Uranyl Phosphate $Ca((UO_2)PO_4)_2$	jmnq	106-8414
Calcium Vanadate (V) $Ca(VO_3)_2$	js	106-8588
Calcium Vanadate (II) CaV_2O_3	m	106-8301
Calcium dodeca-Vanadate $CaV_{12}O_{30}$	q	106-8793
tri-Calcium Vanadate (V) $Ca_3V_2O_8$	hm	106-8679
Calcium Vanadium Bismuth Ferrate $Ca_xV_yBi_{3-x}Fe_{5-y}O_{12}$	npqs	104-8162

Property: a. Absorption coefficient; **b.** Dielectric constant; **c.** Dielectric strength; **d.** Energy band structure; **e.** Effective mass; **f.** Energy gap; **g.** Electric hysteresis; **h.** Energy level; **i.** Electron emission properties; **j.** Electrical resistivity; **k.** Magnetoelectric properties; **l.** Hall coefficient; **m.** Luminescence properties; **n.** Magnetic hysteresis; **o.** Mobility; **p.** Magnetomechanical properties; **q.** Magnetic susceptibility; **r.** Photoelectronic properties; **s.** Refractive index; **t.** Thermoelectric properties; **u.** Work function; **v.** Piezoelectric properties.

Substance Name	Property	Number
Calcium Vanadium Iron Bismuth Oxide		
$Ca_x V_y Fe_{5-y} Bi_{3-x} O_{12}$		
see Calcium Vanadium Bismuth Ferrate		
$Ca_x V_y Bi_{3-x} Fe_{5-y} O_{12}$	npqs	104-8162
Calcium Vanadium Iron Lead Bismuth Oxide		
$Ca_x V_z Fe_{5-z} Pb_y Bi_{3-x-y} O_{12}$		
see Calcium Lead Bismuth Vanadium Ferrate		
$Ca_x Pb_y Bi_{3-x-y} V_z Fe_{5-z} O_{12}$	p	104-8350
Calcium Yttrium Fluoride $Ca_x Y_{1-x} F_{2-y}$	jm	106-8767
see also Yttrium Trifluoride ≥ Calcium Fluoride		508-0217
di-Calcium penta-Yttrium 19-Fluoride		
$Ca_2 Y_5 O_{19}$	m	106-8520
Calcium Yttrium Iron Bismuth Oxide		
$Ca_x Y_{3-x-y} Fe_5 Bi_y O_{12}$		
see Yttrium Calcium Bismuth Ferrate		
$Y_{3-x-y} Ca_x Bi_y Fe_5 O_{12}$	q	104-8181
Calcium Yttrium Iron Germanium Oxide		
$Ca_x Y_{3-x} Fe_{5-y} Ge_y O_{12}$		
see Yttrium Calcium Germanium Ferrate		
$Y_{3-x} Ca_x Ge_y Fe_{5-y} O_{12}$	q	106-8321
Calcium Yttrium Iron Silicon Oxide		
$Ca_x Y_{3-x} Fe_{5-y} Si_y O_{12}$		
see Yttrium Calcium Silicon Ferrate		
$Y_{3-x} Ca_x Si_y Fe_{5-y} O_{12}$	q	106-8320
Calcium Yttrium Iron Tin Oxide		
$Ca_x Y_{3-x} Fe_{5-y} Sn_y O_{12}$		
see Yttrium Calcium Tin Ferrate		
$Y_{3-x} Ca_x Sn_y Fe_{5-y} O_{12}$	q	106-8319
Calcium Yttrium Zirconium Ferrate		
$Ca_x Y_{3-x} Zr_y Fe_{5-y} O_{12}$		
see Yttrium Calcium Zirconium Ferrate		
$Y_{3-x} Ca_x Zr_y Fe_{5-y} O_{12}$	q	106-8318
Calcium Yttrium Zirconium Iron Bismuth Oxide		
$Ca_x Y_{3-x-y} Zr_z Fe_{5-z} Bi_y O_{12}$		
see Yttrium Calcium Bismuth Zirconium Ferrate		
$Y_{3-x-y} Ca_x Bi_y Zr_z Fe_{5-z} O_{12}$	q	104-8182
Calcium Zirconate $Ca Zr O_3$	bj	106-8654
octa-Carbon Bromide $C_8 Br$	jqt	104-8254
Carbon Bromide tri-Fluoride $C Br F_3$		
see Bromotrifluoromethane $C Br F_3$	bcs	104-0008
Carbon tetra-Chloride $C Cl_4$	abcfjrs	106-0002
Carbon Chloride $C_6 Cl_6$		
see hexa-Chlorobenzene $C_6 Cl_6$	q	106-8638
Carbon Chloride tri-Fluoride $C Cl F_3$		
see Chlorotrifluoromethane $C Cl F_3$	abcs	106-0021
Carbon di-Chloride di-Fluoride $C Cl_2 F_2$		
see di-Chlorodifluoromethane $C Cl_2 F_2$	abcs	106-0001
Carbon tri-Chloride Fluoride $C Cl_3 F$		
see tri-Chlorofluoromethane $C Cl_3 F$	abc	106-0147
di-Carbon Chloride penta-Fluoride		
$C_2 Cl F_5$		
see Chloropentafluoroethane $C Cl F_2 C F_3$	bcs	106-0233
Carbon tetra-Fluoride $C F_4$	abchi	106-0231
see also Arcton 0 $C F_4$		106-8689
see also Freon 14 $C F_4$		106-8477
di-Carbon tetra-Fluoride $C_2 F_4$		
see tetra-Fluoroethylene $C_2 F_4$	i	106-0049
di-Carbon hexa-Fluoride $C_2 F_6$		
see hexa-Fluoroethane $C_2 F_6$	bcs	106-0066
tri-Carbon octa-Fluoride $C_3 F_8$		
see octa-Fluoropropane $C_3 F_8$	cs	106-0034
tetra-Carbon octa-Fluoride $C_4 F_8$		
see octa-Fluorocyclobutane $C_4 F_8$	bcs	106-0039
Carbon Iodide Chloride $C_8 I Cl$		
see Graphite Iodide Chloride $C_8 I Cl$	j	106-8541
tri-Carbon Iodide hepta-Fluoride		
$C_3 F_7 I$		
see hepta-Fluoroiodopropane $C_3 F_7 I$	s	106-8685
Carbon Nitrate $C_8 N O_3$		
see Graphite Nitrate $C_8 N O_3$	j	106-8494
Carbon Nitride $C N$	m	106-8188
Carbon Nitride Fluoride $C_4 N F_{11}$		
see penta-Fluoroethyl-bis-(Trifluoromethyl)amine		
$C_2 F_5 N (C F_3)_2$	c	106-8577
Carbon Nitride Fluoride $C_5 N F_{13}$		
see Bis-(penta-Fluoroethyl)trifluoromethylamine		
$C F_3 N (C_2 F_5)_2$	c	106-8579
Carbon Nitride Fluoride $C_6 N F_{15}$		
see Tris-(penta-Fluoroethyl)amine $N (C_2 F_5)_3$	c	106-8578
Carbon mono-Oxide $C O$	abhimru	106-0008
Carbon di-Oxide $C O_2$	abchijms	106-0003
di-Carbon tetra-Oxide $C_2 O_4$	m	106-8187
Carbon di-Selenide $C Se_2$	hi	106-8307
Carbon Selenide Sulfide $C S Se$		
see Thiocarbonyl Selenide $C S Se$	hi	106-8306
Carbon mono-Sulfide $C S$	pq	106-8426
Carbon di-Sulfide $C S_2$	abhms	106-0011
Carbonyl Fluoride $C O F_2$	aq	106-0052
Carbonyl Selenide $C O Se$	hi	106-8305
C D A $Cs_2 H_2 As O_4$		
see Cesium di-Hydrogen Arsenate $Cs H_2 As O_4$	bgqsv	102-8137
Cerium mono-Aluminide $Ce Al$	jq	102-8156
Cerium di-Aluminide $Ce Al_2$	jqt	102-8157
Cerium tri-Aluminide $Ce Al_3$	jq	102-8128
Cerium tetra-Aluminide $Ce Al_4$	jq	102-8158
Cerium Ammonium di-Sulfate $Ce N H_4 (S O_4)_2$	q	106-8621
Cerium Arsenide $Ce As$	f	102-8351
Cerium hexa-Boride $Ce B_6$	j	104-8052
Cerium tri-Chloride $Ce Cl_3$	j	106-0239
Cerium Chromium tri-Selenide $Ce Cr Se_3$	jloq	106-8364
Cerium-Cobalt $Ce Co_2$	d	106-8847
Cerium-Cobalt $Ce Co_5$	np	106-8221
Cerium-Cobalt-Germanium $Ce Co_2 Ge_2$	q	106-8168
Cerium-Cobalt-Iron-Copper		
$Ce_{1+x} Co_{5-y-z} Fe_y Cu_z$	np	106-8220
Cerium Cobalt Silicide $Ce Co_x Si_{2-x}$	q	106-8402
Cerium-Copper $Ce Cu_2$	t	106-8516
Cerium-Copper $Ce Cu_6$	q	106-8801
Cerium tri-Fluoride $Ce F_3$	as	106-0387
di-Cerium Germanium penta-Sulfide		
$Ce_2 Ge S_5$		
see di-Cerium penta-Thiogermanate $Ce_2 Ge S_5$	fj	106-8471
Cerium Hydride $Ce H_3$	jqt	106-8049
Cerium-Indium $Ce In_3$	jqt	106-8118
Cerium Indium tri-Selenide $Ce In Se_3$		
see Cerium tri-Selenoindate $Ce In Se_3$	q	106-8800
Cerium Indium tri-Sulfide $Ce In S_3$		
see Cerium tri-Thioindate $Ce In S_3$	f	106-1809
Cerium tri-Iodide $Ce I_3$	aj	106-8416
Cerium-Iridium $Ce Ir_2$	j	106-8838
Cerium-Iridium $Ce_7 Ir_3$	q	106-8380
Cerium-Iron $Ce Fe_2$	dpq	106-8403
Cerium-Lanthanum-Palladium $Ce_x La_{1-x} Pd_3$	j	106-8491
Cerium-Lead $Ce Pb_3$		
see Cerium tri-Plumbide $Ce Pb_3$	qt	106-8634
Cerium Magnesium penta-Nitrate $Ce Mg(N O_3)_5$	q	106-0112
Cerium di-Manganese di-Germanide $Ce Mn_2 Ge_2$	nq	106-8713
Cerium Metaphosphate $Ce (P O_3)_3$		
see Cerium (I I I) Phosphite $Ce (P O_3)_3$	q	106-8210
Cerium-Nickel $Ce Ni_2$	d	106-8848
Cerium-Nickel $Ce Ni_5$	j	106-8343
Cerium-Nickel $Ce_3 Ni$	t	106-8515
Cerium-Nickel $Ce_7 Ni_3$	q	106-8377
Cerium Nitride $Ce N$	df	106-0590
Cerium-Osmium $Ce Os_2$	j	106-8837
Cerium mono-Oxide $Ce O$	h	106-8513
Cerium di-Oxide $Ce O_2$	abfhjmqs	106-0192
Cerium Oxide $Ce O_{2-x}$	fjo	106-8356
Cerium sesqui-Oxide $Ce_2 O_3$	b	106-0326
Cerium-Palladium $Ce Pd_3$	jqt	106-8119
Cerium-Palladium $Ce_7 Pd_3$	q	106-8379
Cerium (I I I) Phosphite $Ce (P O_3)_3$	q	106-8210
Cerium-Platinum $Ce_7 Pt_3$	q	106-8381
Cerium tri-Plumbide $Ce Pb_3$	qt	106-8634
Cerium-Rhodium $Ce Rh_2$	j	106-8836
Cerium-Rhodium $Ce_7 Rh_3$	q	106-8378
Cerium-Ruthenium $Ce Ru_2$	j	106-8145
Cerium tri-Selenoindate $Ce In Se_3$	q	106-8800

Property: **a.** Absorption coefficient; **b.** Dielectric constant; **c.** Dielectric strength; **d.** Energy band structure; **e.** Effective mass; **f.** Energy gap; **g.** Electric hysteresis; **h.** Energy level; **i.** Electron emission properties; **j.** Electrical resistivity; **k.** Magnetoelectric properties; **l.** Hall coefficient; **m.** Luminescence properties; **n.** Magnetic hysteresis; **o.** Mobility; **p.** Magnetomechanical properties; **q.** Magnetic susceptibility; **r.** Photoelectronic properties; **s.** Refractive index; **t.** Thermoelectric properties; **u.** Work function; **v.** Piezoelectric properties.

Substance Name	*Property*	*Number*
di- Cerium nona- Selenotristannate $Ce_2 Sn_3 Se_9$	j	106-8612
penta- Cerium tri- Silicide $Ce_5 Si_3$	j	106-8792
Cerium - Silver $Ce Ag$	q	102-8216
Cerium tri- Stannide $Ce Sn_3$	jqt	106-8595
Cerium mono- Sulfide $Ce S$	j	106-8706
Cerium sesqui- Sulfide $Ce_2 S_3$	jqt	106-0523
tri- Cerium tetra- Sulfide $Ce_3 S_4$	jo	106-8522
Cerium Sulfide $Ce_3 S_{4-x}$	jo	106-8707
Cerium Telluride $Ce Te$	jt	106-8194
di- Cerium tri- Telluride $Ce_2 Te_3$	jt	106-8196
tri- Cerium tetra- Telluride $Ce_3 Te_4$	jt	106-8195
tetra- Cerium hepta- Telluride $Ce_4 Te_7$	jt	106-8197
Cerium - Thallium $Ce Tl$	j	106-8606
Cerium - Thallium $Ce Tl_3$	j	106-8607
Cerium - Thallium $Ce_3 Tl$	j	106-8608
Cerium - Thallium $Ce_5 Tl_3$	j	106-8609
di- Cerium penta- Thiogermanate $Ce_2 Ge S_5$	fj	106-8471
Cerium tri- Thioindate $Ce In S_3$	f	106-1809
Cerium - Tin $Ce Sn_3$		
see Cerium tri- Stannide $Ce Sn_3$	jqt	106-8595
di- Cerium tri- Tin nona- Selenide		
$Ce_2 Sn_3 Se_9$		
see di- Cerium nona- Selenotristannate $Ce_2 Sn_3 Se_9$	j	106-8612
Cerium Titanate $Ce Ti O_3$	i	106-8809
Cerium Titanium Niobate $Ce Ti Nb O_6$	fj	106-1804
Cerium Yttrium Aluminate		
$Ce_x Y_{3-x} Al_5 O_{12}$		
see Yttrium Cerium Aluminate $Y_{3-x} Ce_x Al_5 O_{12}$	m	102-8146
Cerium Yttrium Iron Oxide		
$Ce_x Y_{3-x} Fe_5 O_{12}$		
see Yttrium Cerium Ferrate $Y_{3-x} Ce_x Fe_5 O_{12}$	p	106-8162
Cerium - Yttrium - Ruthenium $Ce_{1-x} Y_x Ru_2$	j	106-8286
Cesium Alum $Cs Al (S O_4)_2$	b	102-8136
Cesium Aluminum Silicate $Cs Al Si O_4$	i	102-8457
tri- Cesium Antimonide $Cs_3 Sb$	adfiou	106-8008
Cesium Antimony di- Sulfide $Cs Sb S_2$		
see Cesium di- Thioantimonate $Cs Sb S_2$	fhjt	106-8658
Cesium Arsenide di- Selenide $Cs As Se_2$		
see Cesium di- Selenoarsenate $Cs As Se_2$	af	102-8152
Cesium Azide $Cs N_3$	afhm	106-8536
tri- Cesium Bismuthide $Cs_3 Bi$	ai	104-8007
Cesium Bismuthide Antimonide $Cs_3 Bi_x Sb_{1-x}$	iu	104-8401
Cesium Bromide $Cs Br$	abdhjmst	104-0106
Cesium tetra- Bromocobaltate (I I) $Cs_2 Co Br_4$	h	106-8443
Cesium tri- Bromomagnesate $Cs Mg Br_3$	bq	104-8223
Cesium tri- Bromomanganate $Cs Mn Br_3$	bdhq	104-8153
Cesium hexa- Bromozirconate $Cs_2 Zr Br_6$	mq	104-8107
Cesium octa- Carbide $Cs C_8$	ahj	106-8497
Cesium Carbide $Cs C_{1-x}$	a	106-8784
Cesium Carbonate $Cs_2 C O_3$	b	106-1419
Cesium Chloride $Cs Cl$	abdhijmstu	106-0203
Cesium tri- Chlorochromate $Cs Cr Cl_3$	h	106-8395
Cesium tetra- Chlorocobaltate (I I) $Cs_2 Co Cl_4$	h	106-8442
Cesium penta- Chlorocobaltate (I I) $Cs_3 Co Cl_5$	fq	106-8387
Cesium tri- Chloromanganate $Cs Mn Cl_3$	q	106-8131
di- Cesium tetra- Chloromanganate $Cs_2 Mn Cl_4$	q	106-8629
tri- Cesium penta- Chloromanganate $Cs_3 Mn Cl_5$	q	106-8630
di- Cesium hexa- Chloroneptunate $Cs_2 Np Cl_6$	hq	106-8576
Cesium tri- Chloronickelate $Cs Ni Cl_3$	q	106-8649
Cesium tri- Chloroplumbate $Cs Pb Cl_3$	b	106-8246
di- Cesium hexa- Chlorosodiumlutetate		
$Cs_2 Na Lu Cl_6$		
see di- Cesium Sodium hexa- Chlorolutetate		
$Cs_2 Na Lu Cl_6$	hq	106-8421
di- Cesium hexa- Chlorotantalate $Cs_2 Ta Cl_6$	j	106-8350
Cesium hexa- Chlorozirconate $Cs_2 Zr Cl_6$	h	106-8351
di- Cesium Chromate $Cs_2 Cr O_4$	ij	106-1430
Cesium di- Chromate $Cs_2 Cr_2 O_7$	i	106-8309
Cesium Chromium tri- Boride $Cs Cr B_3$	ah	104-8215
Cesium Chromium tri- Chloride $Cs Cr Cl_3$		
see Cesium tri- Chlorochromate $Cs Cr Cl_3$	h	106-8395
Cesium Chromium hexa- Fluoroferrate $Cs Cr Fe F_6$	q	106-8281
Cesium Chromium hexa- Fluoromanganate $Cs Cr Mn F_6$	q	106-8278

Substance Name	*Property*	*Number*
di- Cesium Cobalt tetra- Bromide		
$Cs_2(Co Br_4)$		
see Cesium tetra- Bromocobaltate (I I) $Cs_2 Co Br_4$	h	106-8443
Cesium Cobalt Carbide Nitride Sulfide		
$Cs_2(Co(S C N)_4)$		
see di- Cesium tetra- Thiocyanatocobaltate		
$Cs_2(Co(S C N)_4)$	h	106-8441
di- Cesium Cobalt tetra- Chloride		
$Cs_2(Co Cl_4)$		
see Cesium tetra- Chlorocobaltate (I I) $Cs_2 Co Cl_4$	h	106-8442
tri- Cesium Cobalt penta- Chloride		
$Cs_3 Co Cl_5$		
see Cesium penta- Chlorocobaltate (I I) $Cs_3 Co Cl_5$	fq	106-8387
di- Cesium Cobalt tetra- Iodide		
$Cs_2(Co I_4)$		
see Cesium tetra- Iodocobaltate (I I) $Cs_2 Co I_4$	h	106-8444
Cesium Cobalt Zinc Chloride $Cs_3 Co_x Zn_{1-x} Cl_5$	fq	106-8386
di- Cesium Copper Sulfate $Cs_2 Cu (S O_4)_2$	q	106-8570
Cesium Fluoride $Cs F$	abdfhijsu	106-0237
di- Cesium Fluoride Phosphate $Cs_2 F P O_3$	qs	106-8330
di- Cesium hexa- Fluorogermanate $Cs_2 Ge F_5$	hm	106-8304
Cesium tri- Fluoromanganate $Cs Mn F_3$	abqs	106-8300
Cesium hexa- Fluoromolybdate (V) $Cs Mo F_6$	q	106-8288
Cesium tri- Fluoronickelate $Cs Ni F_3$	nq	106-1522
Cesium hexa- Fluororhenate $Cs Re F_6$	q	106-8839
di- Cesium hexa- Fluorosodiumholmate		
$Cs_2 Na Ho F_6$		
see di- Cesium Sodium hexa- Fluoroholmate		
$Cs_2 Na Ho F_6$	hq	106-8539
Cesium hexa- Fluorotungstate $Cs W F_6$	q	106-8840
di- Cesium Germanium hexa- Fluoride		
$Cs_2 Ge F_5$		
see di- Cesium hexa- Fluorogermanate $Cs_2 Ge F_5$	hm	106-8304
Cesium - Gold $Cs Au$	abdfjs	102-8314
Cesium di- Hydrogen Arsenate $Cs H_2 As O_4$	bgqsv	102-8137
Cesium di- Hydrogen Arsenate, Deuterated		
$Cs D_2 As O_4$	bgsv	102-8166
Cesium Hydrogen Chloride Fluoride $Cs_2 H Cl_6 F$	m	106-8292
Cesium di- Hydrogen Phosphate $Cs H_2 P O_4$	b	106-8772
Cesium di- Hydrogen Phosphate, Deuterated		
$Cs D_2 P O_4$	bg	106-8773
Cesium tri- Hydrogen Selenite $Cs H_3(Se O_3)_2$	bg	106-8245
Cesium Iodide $Cs I$	abdhijms	106-0238
Cesium tetra- Iodocobaltate (I I) $Cs_2 Co I_4$	h	106-8444
Cesium Lead Chloride $Cs Pb Cl_3$		
see Cesium tri- Chloroplumbate $Cs Pb Cl_3$	b	106-8246
Cesium Magnesium tri- Bromide $Cs Mg Br_3$		
see Cesium tri- Bromomagnesate $Cs Mg Br_3$	bq	104-8223
Cesium Magnesium hexa- Fluoroferrate $Cs Mg Fe F_6$	q	106-8283
Cesium Manganese tri- Bromide $Cs Mn Br_3$		
see Cesium tri- Bromomanganate $Cs Mn Br_3$	bdhq	104-8153
Cesium Manganese tri- Chloride $Cs Mn Cl_3$		
see Cesium tri- Chloromanganate $Cs Mn Cl_3$	q	106-8131
di- Cesium Manganese tetra- Chloride		
$Cs_2 Mn Cl_4$		
see di- Cesium tetra- Chloromanganate $Cs_2 Mn Cl_4$	q	106-8629
tri- Cesium Manganese penta- Chloride		
$Cs_3 Mn Cl_5$		
see tri- Cesium penta- Chloromanganate $Cs_3 Mn Cl_5$	q	106-8630
Cesium Manganese tri- Fluoride $Cs Mn F_3$		
see Cesium tri- Fluoromanganate $Cs Mn F_3$	abqs	106-8300
Cesium Manganese hexa- Fluoroferrate $Cs Mn Fe F_6$	q	106-8285
Cesium Molybdenum hexa- Fluoride $Cs Mo F_6$		
see Cesium hexa- Fluoromolybdate (V) $Cs Mo F_6$	q	106-8288
Cesium di- Molybdenum tri- Nitrate		
$Cs Mo_2(N O_3)_3$	m	106-8434
di- Cesium Neptunium hexa- Chloride		
$Cs_2 Np Cl_6$		
see di- Cesium hexa- Chloroneptunate $Cs_2 Np Cl_6$	hq	106-8576
Cesium Nickelate (I I I) $Cs Ni O_2$	q	106-8620
Cesium Nickel tri- Chloride $Cs Ni Cl_3$		
see Cesium tri- Chloronickelate $Cs Ni Cl_3$	q	106-8649
Cesium Nickel tri- Fluoride $Cs Ni F_3$		
see Cesium tri- Fluoronickelate $Cs Ni F_3$	nq	106-1522

Property: a. Absorption coefficient; b. Dielectric constant; c. Dielectric strength; d. Energy band structure; e. Effective mass; f. Energy gap; g. Electric hysteresis; h. Energy level; i. Electron emission properties; j. Electrical resistivity; k. Magnetoelectric properties; l. Hall coefficient; m. Luminescence properties; n. Magnetic hysteresis; o. Mobility; p. Magnetomechanical properties; q. Magnetic susceptibility; r. Photoelectronic properties; s. Refractive index; t. Thermoelectric properties; u. Work function; v. Piezoelectric properties.

Substance Name	Property	Number
Cesium Nickel hexa-Fluoroferrate $CsNiFeF_6$	q	106-8282
Cesium Nitrate $CsNO_3$	bj	106-0384
Cesium Nitride CsN_3		
see Cesium Azide CsN_3	afhm	106-8536
Cesium Nitrite $CsNO_2$	j	106-0961
Cesium (I) Oxide Cs_2O	airsu	106-8050
Cesium di-Oxofluorosulfate $CsSO_2F$	q	106-8833
Cesium Phosphorus Oxide Fluoride		
Cs_2PO_3F		
see di-Cesium Fluoride Phosphate Cs_2FPO_3	qs	106-8330
Cesium Potassium Antimonide CsK_2Sb	adfiju	106-8388
di-Cesium Potassium hexa-Fluoropraseodymate		
Cs_2KPrF_6	hq	106-8538
Cesium Rhenium hexa-Fluoride $CsReF_6$		
see Cesium hexa-Fluororhenate $CsReF_6$	q	106-8839
Cesium di-Rubidium Antimonide $CsRb_2Sb$	u	106-8542
Cesium Rubidium Antimonide $Cs_xRb_{3-x}Sb$	ai	106-8736
Cesium di-Selenoarsenate $CsAsSe_2$	af	102-8152
di-Cesium Sodium Americium hexa-Chloride		
$Cs_2NaAmCl_6$		
see di-Cesium Sodium hexa-Chloroamericate		
$Cs_2NaAmCl_6$	hq	106-8420
di-Cesium Sodium Cerium hexa-Chloride		
$Cs_2NaCeCl_6$		
see di-Cesium Sodium hexa-Chlorocerate		
$Cs_2NaCeCl_6$	h	106-8405
di-Cesium Sodium hexa-Chloroamericate		
$Cs_2NaAmCl_6$	hq	106-8420
di-Cesium Sodium hexa-Chlorocerate		
$Cs_2NaCeCl_6$	h	106-8405
di-Cesium Sodium hexa-Chlorodysprosate		
$Cs_2NaDyCl_6$	hq	106-8410
di-Cesium Sodium hexa-Chloroerbate $Cs_2NaErCl_6$	hq	106-8412
di-Cesium Sodium hexa-Chlorogadolinate		
$Cs_2NaGdCl_6$	hq	106-8408
di-Cesium Sodium hexa-Chloroholmate $Cs_2NaHoCl_6$	hq	106-8411
di-Cesium Sodium hexa-Chlorolutetate		
$Cs_2NaLuCl_6$	hq	106-8421
di-Cesium Sodium hexa-Chloroneodymate		
$Cs_2NaNdCl_6$	ahmq	106-8407
di-Cesium Sodium hexa-Chloroneptunate		
$Cs_2NaNpCl_6$	hq	106-8418
di-Cesium Sodium hexa-Chloroplutomate		
$Cs_2NaPuCl_6$	hq	106-8419
di-Cesium Sodium hexa-Chloropraseodymate		
$Cs_2NaPrCl_6$	hq	106-8406
di-Cesium Sodium hexa-Chloroterbate $Cs_2NaTbCl_6$	hq	106-8409
di-Cesium Sodium hexa-Chlorothulate $Cs_2NaTmCl_6$	hq	106-8413
di-Cesium Sodium hexa-Chlorouranate Cs_2NaUCl_6	hq	106-8417
di-Cesium Sodium hexa-Chloroytterbate		
$Cs_2NaYbCl_6$	hq	106-8404
di-Cesium Sodium hexa-Chloroyttrate Cs_2NaYCl_6	ah	106-8225
di-Cesium Sodium Dysprosium hexa-Chloride		
$Cs_2NaDyCl_6$		
see di-Cesium Sodium hexa-Chlorodysprosate		
$Cs_2NaDyCl_6$	hq	106-8410
di-Cesium Sodium Erbium hexa-Chloride		
$Cs_2NaErCl_6$		
see di-Cesium Sodium hexa-Chloroerbate		
$Cs_2NaErCl_6$	hq	106-8412
di-Cesium Sodium hexa-Fluoroholmate Cs_2NaHoF_6	hq	106-8539
di-Cesium Sodium Gadolinium hexa-Chloride		
$Cs_2NaGdCl_6$		
see di-Cesium Sodium hexa-Chlorogadolinate		
$Cs_2NaGdCl_6$	hq	106-8408
di-Cesium Sodium Holmium hexa-Chloride		
$Cs_2NaHoCl_6$		
see di-Cesium Sodium hexa-Chloroholmate		
$Cs_2NaHoCl_6$	hq	106-8411
di-Cesium Sodium Holmium hexa-Fluoride		
Cs_2NaHoF_6		
see di-Cesium Sodium hexa-Fluoroholmate		
Cs_2NaHoF_6	hq	106-8539

Substance Name	Property	Number
di-Cesium Sodium Lutetium hexa-Chloride		
$Cs_2NaLuCl_6$		
see di-Cesium Sodium hexa-Chlorolutetate		
$Cs_2NaLuCl_6$	hq	106-8421
di-Cesium Sodium Neodymium hexa-Chloride		
$Cs_2NaNdCl_6$		
see di-Cesium Sodium hexa-Chloroneodymate		
$Cs_2NaNdCl_6$	ahmq	106-8407
di-Cesium Sodium Neptunium hexa-Chloride		
$Cs_2NaNpCl_6$		
see di-Cesium Sodium hexa-Chloroneptunate		
$Cs_2NaNpCl_6$	hq	106-8418
di-Cesium Sodium Plutonium hexa-Chloride		
$Cs_2NaPuCl_6$		
see di-Cesium Sodium hexa-Chloroplutomate		
$Cs_2NaPuCl_6$	hq	106-8419
di-Cesium Sodium Praseodymium hexa-Chloride		
$Cs_2NaPrCl_6$		
see di-Cesium Sodium hexa-Chloropraseodymate		
$Cs_2NaPrCl_6$	hq	106-8406
di-Cesium Sodium Terbium hexa-Chloride		
$Cs_2NaTbCl_6$		
see di-Cesium Sodium hexa-Chloroterbate		
$Cs_2NaTbCl_6$	hq	106-8409
di-Cesium Sodium Thulium hexa-Chloride		
$Cs_2NaTmCl_6$		
see di-Cesium Sodium hexa-Chlorothulate		
$Cs_2NaTmCl_6$	hq	106-8413
di-Cesium Sodium Uranium hexa-Chloride		
Cs_2NaUCl_6		
see di-Cesium Sodium hexa-Chlorouranate		
Cs_2NaUCl_6	hq	106-8417
di-Cesium Sodium Ytterbium hexa-Chloride		
$Cs_2NaYbCl_6$		
see di-Cesium Sodium hexa-Chloroytterbate		
$Cs_2NaYbCl_6$	hq	106-8404
di-Cesium Sodium Yttrium hexa-Chloride		
Cs_2NaYCl_6		
see di-Cesium Sodium hexa-Chloroyttrate		
Cs_2NaYCl_6	ah	106-8225
Cesium Sulfate Cs_2SO_4	fj	106-0956
Cesium Sulfide Oxide Fluoride $CsSO_2F$		
see Cesium di-Oxofluorosulfate $CsSO_2F$	q	106-8833
di-Cesium Tantalum hexa-Chloride		
Cs_2TaCl_6		
see di-Cesium hexa-Chlorotantalate Cs_2TaCl_6	j	106-8350
Cesium Telluride Cs_2Te	dfi	106-8290
Cesium di-Thioantimonate $CsSbS_2$	fhjt	106-8658
di-Cesium tetra-Thiocyanatocobaltate		
$Cs_2(Co(SCN)_4)$	h	106-8441
Cesium Tungsten hexa-Fluoride $CsWF_6$		
see Cesium hexa-Fluorotungstate $CsWF_6$	q	106-8840
Cesium Uranium Sulfide Oxide		
$Cs_2(UO_2)_2(SO_4)_3$		
see di-Cesium di-Uranyl Sulfate		
$Cs_2(UO_2)_2(SO_4)_3$	m	106-8429
di-Cesium Uranyl tetra-Chloride $Cs_2UO_2Cl_4$	m	106-8747
di-Cesium di-Uranyl Sulfate		
$Cs_2(UO_2)_2(SO_4)_3$	m	106-8429
Cesium Vanadium hexa-Fluoroferrate $CsVFeF_6$	q	106-8284
di-Cesium Zirconium hexa-Bromide		
Cs_2ZrBr_6		
see Cesium hexa-Bromozirconate Cs_2ZrBr_6	mq	104-8107
di-Cesium Zirconium hexa-Chloride		
Cs_2ZrCl_6		
see Cesium hexa-Chlorozirconate Cs_2ZrCl_6	h	106-8351
Chlorine mono-Fluoride ClF	hsu	106-8537
Chlorine tri-Fluoride ClF_3	bhijs	106-0129
Chlorine penta-Fluoride ClF_5	bj	106-1084
Chlorine di-Oxide ClO_2	m	106-8264
hexa-Chlorobenzene C_6Cl_6	q	106-8638
di-Chlorodifluoromethane CCl_2F_2	abcs	106-0001
see also Freon 12 CCl_2F_2		106-8475

Property: **a.** Absorption coefficient; **b.** Dielectric constant; **c.** Dielectric strength; **d.** Energy band structure; **e.** Effective mass; **f.** Energy gap; **g.** Electric hysteresis; **h.** Energy level; **i.** Electron emission properties; **j.** Electrical resistivity; **k.** Magnetoelectric properties; **l.** Hall coefficient; **m.** Luminescence properties; **n.** Magnetic hysteresis; **o.** Mobility; **p.** Magnetomechanical properties; **q.** Magnetic susceptibility; **r.** Photoelectronic properties; **s.** Refractive index; **t.** Thermoelectric properties; **u.** Work function; **v.** Piezoelectric properties.

Substance Name	Formula	Property	Number
tri- Chlorofluoromethane	CCl_3F	abc	106-0147
see also Arcton 9	CCl_3F		106-8692
see also Freon 11	CCl_3F		106-8517
Chloropentafluoroethane	$CClF_2CF_3$	bcs	106-0233
see also Freon 115	$CClF_2CF_3$		106-8478
Chloropentamminerhodium (2+) Ion	$Rh(NH_3)_5Cl$	m	106-8180
tetra- Chlorostannane	$SnCl_4$		
see Tin tetra- Chloride	$SnCl_4$	bjq	106-0152
Chlorosulfuric Acid	$ClSO_3H$	q	106-0225
di- Chlorotetrafluoroethane	$C_2Cl_2F_4$	c	106-0166
see also Freon 114	$C_2Cl_2F_4$		106-8691
hexa- Chlorotitanium (3-) Ion	$TiCl_6$	q	106-8215
Chlorotrifluoroethylene	$ClFCCF_2$	s	106-0128
Chlorotrifluoromethane	$CClF_3$	abcs	106-0021
see also Arcton 3	$CClF_3$		106-8690
see also Freon 13	$CClF_3$		106-8476
Chromium hepta- Aluminide	$CrAl_7$	j	102-8316
Chromium Aluminum penta- Fluoride	$CrAlF_5$		
see Chromium penta- Fluoroaluminate	$CrAlF_5$	q	102-8336
Chromium Ammonia Cadmium Chloride	$(Cr(NH_3)_6)(CdCl_5)$		
see hexa- Amminechromium penta- Chlorocadmate	$(Cr(NH_3)_6)(CdCl_5)$	q	106-8124
Chromium mono- Antimonide	$CrSb$	adfqst	106-8014
Chromium Antimony Telluride	$CrSb_xTe_{1-x}$	qr	106-8566
Chromium mono- Boride	CrB	ju	104-8053
Chromium di- Boride	CrB_2	dhjlqtu	104-8159
Chromium Boride	CrB_{1-x}	u	104-8435
di- Chromium Boride	Cr_2B	u	104-8283
tri- Chromium di- Boride	Cr_3B_2	j	104-8407
tri- Chromium tetra- Boride	Cr_3B_4	ju	104-8281
tetra- Chromium Boride	Cr_4B	j	104-8406
penta- Chromium tri- Boride	Cr_5B_3	u	104-8282
hepta- Chromium Boride tetra- Carbide	Cr_7BC_4	jlqt	104-0409
Chromium tri- Bromide	$CrBr_3$	nq	104-0347
Chromium Cadmium Gallium Selenide	$Cr_2Cd_xGa_{1-x}Se_4$		
see Cadmium Gallium Selenochromate	$Cd_xGa_{1-x}Cr_2Se_4$	jr	106-8823
Chromium Cadmium Indium Sulfide	$Cr_xCdIn_{2-x}S_4$		
see Cadmium Thiochromateindate	$CdCr_xIn_{2-x}S_4$	jq	106-8144
di- Chromium Cadmium tetra- Selenide	Cr_2CdSe_4		
see Cadmium tetra- Selenochromate (III)	$CdCr_2Se_4$	abdfjklnopqrst	106-8312
Chromium Cadmium Selenide	Cr_2CdSe_{4-x}		
see Cadmium Selenochromate	$CdCr_2Se_{4-x}$	dfjnoq	106-8438
di- Chromium Cadmium tetra- Sulfide	Cr_2CdS_4		
see Cadmium tetra- Thiochromate (III)	$CdCr_2S_4$	amq	106-1299
Chromium Cadmium Zinc Selenide	$Cr_2Cd_xZn_{1-x}Se_4$		
see Cadmium Zinc Selenochromate	$Cd_xZn_{1-x}Cr_2Se_4$	r	106-8822
tri- Chromium di- Carbide	Cr_3C_2	jt	106-0062
hepta- Chromium tri- Carbide	Cr_7C_3	qt	106-0138
23- Chromium hexa- Carbide	$Cr_{23}C_6$	t	106-0797
Chromium - Cobalt	$CrCo$		
see Chromium mono- Cobaltide	$CrCo$	n	106-8776
Chromium Cobalt Cadmium Sulfide	$Cr_2Co_xCd_{2-x}S_4$		
see Cadmium Cobalt Thiochromate	$Cd_xCo_{1-x}Cr_2S_4$	ahnqs	106-8227
Chromium Cobalt Ferrite	$Cr_xCoFe_{2-x}O_4$		
see Cobalt Chromium Ferrite	$CoCr_xFe_{2-x}O_4$	b	106-8235
Chromium mono- Cobaltide	$CrCo$	n	106-8776
di- Chromium Cobalt tetra- Sulfide	Cr_2CoS_4		
see Cobalt (II) tetra- Thiochromate (III)	$CoCr_2S_4$	abhq	106-8226
Chromium Complex Cation	$(Cr(NH_3)_6)(CdCl_5)$		
see hexa- Amminechromium penta- Chlorocadmate	$(Cr(NH_3)_6)(CdCl_5)$	q	106-8124
Chromium - Copper	$CrCu$	j	106-8660

Substance Name	Formula	Property	Number
Chromium Copper Cadmium Sulfide	$Cr_2Cu_xCd_{1-x}S_4$		
see Cadmium Copper Thiochromate	$Cd_xCu_{1-x}Cr_2S_4$	nq	106-8435
Chromium Copper di- Oxide	$CrCuO_2$		
see Copper Chromate	$CuCrO_2$	i	106-1058
di- Chromium Copper tetra- Oxide	Cr_2CuO_4		
see Copper (II) Chromate (III)	$CuCr_2O_4$	aq	106-8487
di- Chromium Copper tetra- Selenide	Cr_2CuSe_4		
see Copper (II) tetra- Selenochromate (III)	$CuCr_2Se_4$	afjnpqst	106-8549
Chromium Copper Selenide Bromide	Cr_2CuSe_3Br		
see Copper tri- Selenobromodichromate	$CuCr_2Se_3Br$	jlt	104-8176
di- Chromium Copper Selenide tri- Sulfide	Cr_2CuSeS_3		
see Copper (II) Selenotrithiochromate (III)	$CuCr_2SeS_3$	q	106-8592
Chromium Copper Selenide Sulfide	$Cr_2CuSe_xS_{4-x}$		
see Copper Selenothiochromate	$CuCr_2Se_xS_{4-x}$	q	106-8590
di- Chromium Copper di- Selenide di- Sulfide	$Cr_2CuSe_2S_2$		
see Copper (II) di- Selenodithiochromate (III)	$CuCr_2Se_2S_2$	q	106-8593
di- Chromium Copper tri- Selenide Sulfide	Cr_2CuSe_3S		
see Copper (II) tri- Selenothiochromate (III)	$CuCr_2Se_3S$	q	106-8594
di- Chromium Copper tetra- Sulfide	Cr_2CuS_4		
see Copper (II) tetra- Thiochromate (III)	$CuCr_2S_4$	aqs	106-8591
Chromium tri- Fluoride	CrF_3	h	106-8059
Chromium penta- Fluoroaluminate	$CrAlF_5$	q	102-8336
Chromium penta- Fluorotitanate	$CrTiF_5$	q	106-8572
Chromium penta- Fluorovanadate	$CrVF_5$	q	106-8573
Chromium mono- Germanide	$CrGe$	jlqt	106-8819
Chromium di- Germanide	$CrGe_2$	jlqt	106-8820
tri- Chromium Germanide	Cr_3Ge	jlqt	106-8669
penta- Chromium tri- Germanide	Cr_5Ge_3	jlqt	106-8642
undeca- Chromium octa- Germanide	$Cr_{11}Ge_8$	jlqt	106-8818
Chromium Germanium Silicide	$Cr_5Ge_xSi_{3-x}$	jlqt	106-8759
Chromium - Gold	$CrAu_4$	q	102-8362
Chromium (III) Iodate	$Cr(IO_3)_3$	q	106-8582
Chromium tri- Iodide	CrI_3	n	106-8061
Chromium Iron Copper Selenide Sulfide	$Cr_{3-x-y}Fe_xCu_ySe_zS_{4-z}$		
see Copper Chromium Selenothioferrate	$Cu_xCr_yFe_{3-x-y}Se_3S_{4-z}$	kq	106-8147
Chromium Iron Copper Sulfide	$Cr_{3-x-y}Fe_xCu_yS_4$		
see Copper Chromium Thioferrate	$Cu_xCr_yFe_{3-x-y}S_4$	kq	106-8148
Chromium Iron hexa- Fluorothallate	$CrFeTlF_6$	q	106-8280
Chromium di- Iron tetra- Selenide	$CrFe_2Se_4$		
see Chromium tetra- Selenodiferrate	$CrFe_2Se_4$	q	106-8265
di- Chromium Iron tetra- Selenide	Cr_2FeSe_4		
see di- Chromium tetra- Selenoferrate	Cr_2FeSe_4	efjloqt	106-8394
di- Chromium Iron tetra- Sulfide	Cr_2FeS_4		
see di- Chromium tetra- Thioferrate	Cr_2FeS_4	kq	106-8436
Chromium Iron Thallium hexa- Fluoride	$CrFeTlF_6$		
see Chromium Iron hexa- Fluorothallate	$CrFeTlF_6$	q	106-8280
Chromium Manganate	$CrMnO_3$	q	106-8212
Chromium Manganese Antimonide	$Cr_xMn_{1-x-y}Sb$	nq	106-8368
Chromium Manganese hexa- Fluorothallate	$CrMnTlF_6$	q	106-8277
Chromium - Manganese - Gold	$Cr_xMn_{1-x}Au_4$	q	102-8361

Property: **a.** Absorption coefficient; **b.** Dielectric constant; **c.** Dielectric strength; **d.** Energy band structure; **e.** Effective mass; **f.** Energy gap; **g.** Electric hysteresis; **h.** Energy level; **i.** Electron emission properties; **j.** Electrical resistivity; **k.** Magnetoelectric properties; **l.** Hall coefficient; **m.** Luminescence properties; **n.** Magnetic hysteresis; **o.** Mobility; **p.** Magnetomechanical properties; **q.** Magnetic susceptibility; **r.** Photoelectronic properties; **s.** Refractive index; **t.** Thermoelectric properties; **u.** Work function; **v.** Piezoelectric properties.

Substance Name	Property	Number
Chromium Manganese Selenide Sulfide		
$Cr_2MnSe_xS_{4-x}$		
see Chromium Selenothiomanganate $Cr_2MnSe_xS_{4-x}$	q	106-8116
di-Chromium Manganese tetra-Sulfide		
Cr_2MnS_4		
see di-Chromium tetra-Thiomanganate Cr_2MnS_4	q	106-8115
Chromium Manganese Thallium Fluoride		
$CrMnTlF_6$		
see Chromium Manganese hexa-Fluorothallate $CrMnTlF_6$	q	106-8277
di-Chromium Mercury tetra-Selenide		
Cr_2HgSe_4		
see Mercury tetra-Selenochromate $HgCr_2Se_4$	kq	106-8812
Chromium-Nickel $CrNi_3$	j	106-8512
di-Chromium (I I I) Nickelate (I I) Cr_2NiO_4	j	106-0575
Chromium Nickel Iron Oxide		
$Cr_xNiFe_{2-x}O_4$		
see Nickel Chromium Ferrite $NiCr_xFe_{2-x}O_4$	np	106-8161
di-Chromium Nickel tetra-Selenide		
Cr_2NiSe_4		
see di-Chromium tetra-Selenonickelate Cr_2NiSe_4	fjt	106-8392
Chromium mono-Nitride CrN	jlt	106-0452
Chromium Nitride CrN_{1-x}	j	106-8460
Chromium mono-Oxide CrO	iu	106-8063
Chromium di-Oxide CrO_2	abenqr	106-0327
Chromium tri-Oxide CrO_3	ij	106-0328
Chromium Oxide CrO_{2-x}	nq	106-8141
Chromium sesqui-Oxide Cr_2O_3	abdfijq	106-0031
Chromium mono-Phosphide CrP	j	106-8064
Chromium (I I) Selenide $CrSe$	j	106-8389
Chromium sesqui-Selenide Cr_2Se_3	ejloq	106-8391
Chromium Selenide Cr_2Se_{3-x}	j	106-8625
tri-Chromium tetra-Selenide Cr_3Se_4	jq	106-8584
Chromium Selenide Cr_3Se_{4-x}	q	106-8624
hepta-Chromium octa-Selenide Cr_7Se_8	j	106-8390
Chromium tetra-Selenodiferrate $CrFe_2Se_4$	q	106-8265
di-Chromium tetra-Selenoferrate Cr_2FeSe_4	efjloqt	106-8394
di-Chromium tetra-Selenomercurate		
Cr_2HgSe_4		
see Mercury tetra-Selenochromate $HgCr_2Se_4$	kq	106-8812
di-Chromium tetra-Selenonickelate Cr_2NiSe_4	fjt	106-8392
Chromium Selenothiomanganate $Cr_2MnSe_xS_{4-x}$	q	106-8116
Chromium mono-Silicide $CrSi$	djt	106-8521
Chromium di-Silicide $CrSi_2$	defjlot	106-8143
tri-Chromium Silicide Cr_3Si	djt	106-8545
tri-Chromium di-Silicide Cr_3Si_2	o	106-8065
penta-Chromium tri-Silicide Cr_5Si_3	djlqtu	106-8262
Chromium sesqui-Sulfide Cr_2S_3	fjlnoqt	106-1079
tri-Chromium tetra-Sulfide Cr_3S_4	j	106-8585
Chromium (I I I) Tantalate $CrTaO_4$	j	106-8674
Chromium mono-Telluride $CrTe$	jlpq	106-8157
Chromium Telluride $CrTe_{1-x}$	q	106-8267
Chromium sesqui-Telluride Cr_2Te_3	jq	106-8201
tri-Chromium tetra-Telluride Cr_3Te_4	j	106-8586
Chromium Telluride Selenide $Cr_2Te_2Se_{1-x}$	nq	106-8328
Chromium Telluride Selenide $Cr_3Te_xSe_{4-x}$	jnq	106-8587
di-Chromium Telluride Selenide Sulfide Cr_2TeSeS	nq	106-8753
di-Chromium Telluride di-Sulfide Cr_2TeS_2	nq	106-8761
Chromium Telluride Sulfide $Cr_2Te_2S_{1-x}$	nq	106-8329
Chromium Telluride Sulfide $Cr_2Te_{1-x}S_2$	nq	106-8760
di-Chromium tetra-Thioferrate Cr_2FeS_4	kq	106-8436
Chromium Thioferrate Cr_2FeS_{4-x}	q	106-8437
di-Chromium tetra-Thiomanganate Cr_2MnS_4	q	106-8115
Chromium Titanium penta-Fluoride $CrTiF_5$		
see Chromium penta-Fluorotitanate $CrTiF_5$	q	106-8572
Chromium Vanadium penta-Fluoride $CrVF_5$		
see Chromium penta-Fluorovanadate $CrVF_5$	q	106-8573
di-Chromium Zinc tetra-Selenide		
Cr_2ZnSe_4		
see Zinc tetra-Selenodichromate $ZnCr_2Se_4$	fjqt	106-8270
Cobalt mono-Aluminide $CoAl$	abdjlrt	102-8437
di-Cobalt nona-Aluminide Co_2Al_9	j	102-8317
Cobalt (I I) di-Antimonate (V) $CoSb_2O_6$	q	106-8639
Cobalt tri-Antimonide $CoSb_3$	jt	106-8018
Cobalt Borate Iodide $Co_3B_7O_{13}I$		
see Cobalt Iodoborate $Co_3B_7O_{13}I$	b	104-8355
Cobalt mono-Boride CoB	fjpq	104-8055
Cobalt di-Bromide $CoBr_2$	jq	104-0171
Cobalt Carbonate $CoCO_3$	nq	106-0622
Cobalt di-Chloride $CoCl_2$	ahq	106-0240
Cobalt Chromium Ferrite $CoCr_xFe_{2-x}O_4$	b	106-8235
Cobalt Complex Cation		
$(Co(NH_3)_3)Cl_3$		
see tri-Amminecobalt (I I I) Chloride		
$(Co(NH_3)_3)Cl_3$	h	106-8445
Cobalt Complex Cation		
$(Co(NH_3)_6)Cl_3$		
see hexa-Amminecobalt (I I I) Chloride		
$(Co(NH_3)_6)Cl_3$	h	106-8446
Cobalt Complex Cation		
$(CoNO_2(NH_3)_5)(NO_3)_2$		
see Nitropentaamminecobalt (I I I) Nitrate		
$(CoNO_2(NH_3)_5)(NO_3)_2$	h	106-8447
Cobalt Complex Cation		
$(Co(NO_2)_2(NH_3)_4)NO_3$		
see di-Nitrotetraamminecobalt (I I I) Nitrate		
$(Co(NO_2)_2(NH_3)_4)NO_3$	h	106-8448
Cobalt Complex Cation		
$Co(NO_2)_3(NH_3)_3$		
see tri-Nitrotriamminecobalt (I I I)		
$Co(NO_2)_3(NH_3)_3$	h	106-8449
Cobalt Copper Ferrite $Co_xCu_yFe_{3-x-y}O_4$	jp	106-8163
Cobalt (I I) Ferrite $CoFe_2O_4$	ajn	106-8596
Cobalt Ferrite $Co_xFe_{3-x}O_4$	fjnopt	106-8149
Cobalt di-Fluoride CoF_2	abhp	106-0058
Cobalt tri-Fluoride CoF_3	h	106-8070
Cobalt mono-Gallide $CoGa$	abr	106-8742
Cobalt (I I) Iodate $Co(IO_3)_2$	q	106-8583
Cobalt Iodide Boracite $Co_3B_7O_{13}I$		
see Cobalt Iodoborate $Co_3B_7O_{13}I$	b	104-8355
Cobalt Iodoborate $Co_3B_7O_{13}I$	b	104-8355
Cobalt-Iron $CoFe$	n	106-8508
Cobalt Iron Copper Oxide		
$Co_xFe_{3-x-y}Cu_yO_4$		
see Cobalt Copper Ferrite $Co_xCu_yFe_{3-x-y}O_4$	jp	106-8163
Cobalt Iron Oxide $Co_xFe_{3-x}O_4$		
see Cobalt Ferrite $Co_xFe_{3-x}O_4$	fjnopt	106-8149
Cobalt di-Iron tetra-Selenide		
$CoFe_2Se_4$		
see Cobalt tetra-Selenodiferrate $CoFe_2Se_4$	q	106-8266
Cobalt Iron Silicide $Co_xFe_{1-x}Si$	jt	106-8164
Cobalt Iron Sulfide $Co_xFe_{1-x}S_2$	jnq	106-8120
Cobalt Monophosphide CoP	n	106-8774
Cobalt (I I) Niobate (V) $CoNb_2O_6$	bj	106-8243
Cobalt di-Nitrate $Co(NO_3)_2$	q	106-0115
Cobalt Nitride Hydride Chloride		
$(Co(NH_3)_3)Cl_3$		
see tri-Amminecobalt (I I I) Chloride		
$(Co(NH_3)_3)Cl_3$	h	106-8445
Cobalt Nitride Hydride Chloride		
$(Co(NH_3)_6)Cl_3$		
see hexa-Amminecobalt (I I I) Chloride		
$(Co(NH_3)_6)Cl_3$	h	106-8446
Cobalt Nitride Hydride Oxide		
$(CoNO_2(NH_3)_5)(NO_3)_2$		
see Nitropentaamminecobalt (I I I) Nitrate		
$(CoNO_2(NH_3)_5)(NO_3)_2$	h	106-8447
Cobalt Nitride Hydride Oxide		
$(Co(NO_2)_2(NH_3)_4)NO_3$		
see di-Nitrotetraamminecobalt (I I I) Nitrate		
$(Co(NO_2)_2(NH_3)_4)NO_3$	h	106-8448
Cobalt Nitride Hydride Oxide		
$Co(NO_2)_3(NH_3)_3$		
see tri-Nitrotriamminecobalt (I I I)		
$Co(NO_2)_3(NH_3)_3$	h	106-8449
Cobalt mono-Oxide CoO	abdfhjlnopqtu	106-0081
tri-Cobalt tetra-Oxide Co_3O_4	dhju	106-0095
Cobalt Oxide $Co_{1-x}O$	t	106-8765

Property: a. Absorption coefficient; **b.** Dielectric constant; **c.** Dielectric strength; **d.** Energy band structure; **e.** Effective mass; **f.** Energy gap; **g.** Electric hysteresis; **h.** Energy level; **i.** Electron emission properties; **j.** Electrical resistivity; **k.** Magnetoelectric properties; **l.** Hall coefficient; **m.** Luminescence properties; **n.** Magnetic hysteresis; **o.** Mobility; **p.** Magnetomechanical properties; **q.** Magnetic susceptibility; **r.** Photoelectronic properties; **s.** Refractive index; **t.** Thermoelectric properties; **u.** Work function; **v.** Piezoelectric properties.

Substance Name	Property	Number
Cobalt Peroxytitanate		
see di-Cobalt (I I) Titanate (I V) Co_2TiO_4	nq	106-8551
di-Cobalt Phosphide Co_2P	d	106-8072
Cobalt (I I) Selenate $CoSeO_3$	q	106-8682
Cobalt di-Selenide $CoSe_2$	q	106-8543
Cobalt Selenide Sulfide $CoSe_xS_{2-x}$	q	106-8544
Cobalt tetra-Selenodiferrate $CoFe_2Se_4$	q	106-8266
Cobalt mono-Silicide $CoSi$	efjot	106-8074
Cobalt di-Silicide $CoSi_2$	ejlt	106-8075
di-Cobalt Silicide Co_2Si	j	106-8076
tri-Cobalt Silicide Co_3Si	n	106-8550
Cobalt (I I) Sulfate $CoSO_4$	n	106-8466
Cobalt mono-Sulfide CoS	aij	106-8485
Cobalt di-Sulfide CoS_2	jnq	106-0927
Cobalt (I I) tetra-Thiochromate (I I I)		
$CoCr_2S_4$	abhq	106-8226
di-Cobalt (I I) Titanate (I V) Co_2TiO_4	nq	106-8551
Cobalt (I I) Tungstate (V I) $CoWO_4$	abhq	106-8244
Cobalt (I I) Vanadate (I I I) CoV_2O_4	a	106-8768
Cobalt Vanadate $Co_xV_{3-x}O_4$	q	106-8741
Cobalt-Zinc $CoZn_{13}$	jkq	106-8363
Cobalt Zinc Tungstate $Co_xZn_{1-x}WO_4$	q	106-8657
Cobalt Zirconate $CoZr_3O$	q	106-8656
Commercial Fused Silica T08	b	122-8057
see also Silica, Fused		122-8045
Coors A D 995 Al_2O_3		
see A D 995 (Coors Ceramics Co) Al_2O_3	bj	102-8432
Copper Aluminide $CuAl$	q	102-8092
Copper di-Aluminide $CuAl_2$	jq	102-8117
di-Copper Aluminide Cu_2Al	jq	102-8093
tri-Copper Aluminide Cu_3Al	j	102-8472
Copper Aluminum Ferrite $CuAl_xFe_{2-x}O_4$	n	102-8462
Copper Aluminum di-Selenide $CuAlSe_2$		
see Copper di-Selenoaluminate $CuAlSe_2$	afs	102-8337
Copper Aluminum di-Sulfide $CuAlS_2$		
see Copper di-Thioaluminate $CuAlS_2$	af	102-0244
Copper Antimony di-Boride $CuSbB_2$	f	104-8403
Copper Antimony di-Selenide $CuSbSe_2$		
see Copper di-Selenoantimonate $CuSbSe_2$	jlt	106-8653
Copper Antimony Selenide Cu_3SbSe_4		
see tri-Copper tetra-Selenoantimonate Cu_3SbSe_4	afjlost	106-8344
Copper Antimony di-Sulfide $CuSbS_2$		
see Copper di-Thioantimonate $CuSbS_2$	jt	106-0505
Copper Antimony di-Telluride $CuSbTe_2$		
see Copper di-Telluroantimonate $CuSbTe_2$	jt	106-8650
di-Copper Arsenide Cu_2As	jq	102-8082
tri-Copper Arsenide Cu_3As	ij	102-8040
Copper Arsenide Cu_5As_{2-x}	jq	102-8080
Copper Arsenide $Cu_{3-x}As$	jq	102-8081
Copper Arsenide di-Selenide $CuAsSe_2$	dh	102-8243
tri-Copper Arsenide tetra-Selenide Cu_3AsSe_4	afhjost	102-8248
tri-Copper Arsenide tetra-Sulfide Cu_3AsS_4	fjst	102-8249
Copper Azide CuN_3	bfrs	106-1019
Copper Bismuth di-Selenide $CuBiSe_2$		
see Copper di-Selenobismuthate $CuBiSe_2$	jt	104-8323
Copper Bismuth di-Telluride $CuBiTe_2$		
see Copper di-Tellurobismuthate $CuBiTe_2$	jt	104-8320
Copper mono-Boride CuB	j	104-8424
Copper 24-Boride CuB_{24}	fjt	104-8446
di-Copper Boride Cu_2B	f	104-8404
Copper (I) Bromide $CuBr$	bdhijmqstv	104-0022
Copper Bromide Chloride $CuBr_xCl_{1-x}$	afm	104-8333
Copper-Cadmium Cu_2Cd_3	j	106-8787
Copper-Cadmium Cu_5Cd_8	j	106-8500
Copper (I) Chloride $CuCl$	abcdefhijmstv	106-0158
Copper (I I) Chloride $CuCl_2$	n	106-0113
Copper Chromate $CuCrO_2$	i	106-1058
Copper (I I) Chromate (I I I) $CuCr_2O_4$	aq	106-8487
Copper Chromium Selenothioferrate		
$Cu_xCr_yFe_{3-x-y}Se_3S_{4-z}$	kq	106-8147
Copper Chromium Thioferrate $Cu_xCr_yFe_{3-x-y}S_4$	kq	106-8148
Copper Complex Cation		
see Hydroxocopper Periodate $Cu_2(OH)H_2IO_6$	q	106-8189
Copper (I I) Ferrite $CuFe_2O_4$	fjklnpq	106-8439

Substance Name	Property	Number
Copper (I I) Fluoride CuF_2	j	106-0337
Copper Gallium di-Selenide $CuGaSe_2$		
see Copper di-Selenogallate $CuGaSe_2$	afjost	106-8457
Copper Gallium di-Sulfide $CuGaS_2$		
see Copper di-Thiogallate $CuGaS_2$	abdfhjmorv	106-8209
Copper Gallium di-Telluride $CuGaTe_2$		
see Copper di-Tellurogallate $CuGaTe_2$	fjost	106-8458
Copper di-Germanium tri-Phosphide		
$CuGe_2P_3$		
see Copper tri-Phosphidodigermanate $CuGe_2P_3$	fjost	106-8454
di-Copper Germanium tri-Selenide		
Cu_2GeSe_3		
see di-Copper tri-Selenogermanate Cu_2GeSe_3	afjlost	106-8338
Copper Germanium Selenide $Cu_2Ge_{1-x}Se_3$	jt	106-8641
di-Copper Germanium tri-Sulfide		
Cu_2GeS_3		
see di-Copper tri-Thiogermanate Cu_2GeS_3	fjlost	106-8456
octa-Copper Germanium hexa-Sulfide		
Cu_8GeS_6		
see octa-Copper hexa-Thiogermanate Cu_8GeS_6	jl	106-8686
di-Copper Germanium tri-Telluride		
Cu_2GeTe_3		
see di-Copper tri-Tellurogermanate Cu_2GeTe_3	lot	106-8339
di-Copper Germanium tetra-Thioferrate		
Cu_2GeFeS_4	q	106-8268
see also Briartite Cu_2GeFeS_4		521-8013
Copper (I) Hydride CuH	j	106-8385
Copper Hydroxide Hydrogen Iodide Oxide		
$Cu_2(OH)H_2IO_6$		
see Hydroxocopper Periodate $Cu_2(OH)H_2IO_6$	q	106-8189
Copper Indium Gallium Sulfide		
$CuIn_xGa_{1-x}S_2$		
see Copper Thioindategallate $CuIn_xGa_{1-x}S_2$	df	106-8129
Copper Indium di-Selenide $CuInSe_2$		
see Copper di-Selenoindate $CuInSe_2$	fjmoru	106-8271
Copper Indium di-Sulfide $CuInS_2$		
see Copper di-Thioindate $CuInS_2$	dfjlo	106-8299
Copper Indium Sulfide $CuInS_{1-x}$	fjlo	106-8766
Copper Indium di-Telluride $CuInTe_2$		
see Copper di-Telluroindate $CuInTe_2$	fjost	106-8455
Copper (I) Iodide CuI	adefhijmstv	106-0036
Copper Iodide CuI_{1-x}	jm	106-8146
Copper (I) tetra-Iodomercurate (I I) Cu_2HgI_4	j	106-8749
Copper di-Iron tetra-Oxide $CuFe_2O_4$		
see Copper (I I) Ferrite $CuFe_2O_4$	fjklnpq	106-8439
Copper Iron Zinc tetra-Oxide		
$Cu_xFe_2Zn_{1-x}O_4$		
see Copper Zinc Ferrite $Cu_xZn_{1-x}Fe_2O_4$	bj	106-8214
Copper Iron Zinc tetra-Oxide		
$Cu_xFe_{3-x-y}Zn_yO_4$		
see Copper Zinc Ferrite $Cu_xZn_yFe_{3-x-y}O_4$	j	106-8361
Copper Lead Antimonide tri-Sulfide		
$CuPbSbS_3$		
see Copper Lead tri-Thioantimonate $CuPbSbS_3$	frs	106-8581
Copper Lead tri-Thioantimonate $CuPbSbS_3$	frs	106-8581
di-Copper Mercury tetra-Iodide		
Cu_2HgI_4		
see Copper (I) tetra-Iodomercurate (I I)		
Cu_2HgI_4	j	106-8749
Copper di-Nitrate $Cu(NO_3)_2$	nq	106-0872
Copper Nitrogen Hydrogen Sulfate		
$(NH_4)_2Cu(SO_4)_2$		
see di-Ammonium Copper Sulfate		
$(NH_4)_2Cu(SO_4)_2$	q	106-8569
Copper (I I) Oxide CuO	abfijqt	106-0068
Copper Oxide CuO_{1-x}	ij	106-8711
Copper (I) Oxide Cu_2O	abdefhijlmortu	106-0127
see also Cuprite Cu_2O		521-0644
Copper di-phosphide CuP_2	d	106-8799
tri-Copper Phosphide Cu_3P	d	106-1204
Copper tri-Phosphidodigermanate $CuGe_2P_3$	fjost	106-8454
Copper (I I) Selenate $CuSeO_3$	q	106-8683
Copper (I) Selenide Cu_2Se	efjloqt	106-8081
Copper Selenide $Cu_{2-x}Se$	fjlort	106-8335

Property: **a.** Absorption coefficient; **b.** Dielectric constant; **c.** Dielectric strength; **d.** Energy band structure; **e.** Effective mass; **f.** Energy gap; **g.** Electric hysteresis; **h.** Energy level; **i.** Electron emission properties; **j.** Electrical resistivity; **k.** Magnetoelectric properties; **l.** Hall coefficient; **m.** Luminescence properties; **n.** Magnetic hysteresis; **o.** Mobility; **p.** Magnetomechanical properties; **q.** Magnetic susceptibility; **r.** Photoelectronic properties; **s.** Refractive index; **t.** Thermoelectric properties; **u.** Work function; **v.** Piezoelectric properties.

Substance Name	Property	Number
Copper di-Selenoaluminate $CuAlSe_2$	afs	102-8337
Copper di-Selenoantimonate $CuSbSe_2$	jlt	106-8653
tri-Copper tetra-Selenoantimonate Cu_3SbSe_4	afjlost	106-8344
Copper di-Selenobismuthate $CuBiSe_2$	jt	104-8323
Copper tri-Selenobromodichromate $CuCr_2Se_3Br$	jlt	104-8176
Copper (I I) tetra-Selenochromate (I I I) $CuCr_2Se_4$	afjnpqst	106-8549
Copper (I I) di-Selenodithiochromate (I I I) $CuCr_2Se_2S_2$	q	106-8593
Copper di-Selenogallate $CuGaSe_2$	afjost	106-8457
di-Copper tri-Selenogermanate Cu_2GeSe_3	afjlost	106-8338
Copper di-Selenoindate $CuInSe_2$	fjmoru	106-8271
Copper di-Selenoiridate $CuIrSe_2$	fjost	106-8459
di-Copper tri-Selenostannate Cu_2SnSe_3	afjlost	106-8340
Copper di-Selenothallate $CuTlSe_2$	jt	106-8652
Copper Selenothiochromate $CuCr_2Se_xS_{4-x}$	q	106-8590
Copper (I I) tri-Selenothiochromate (I I I) $CuCr_2Se_3S$	q	106-8594
Copper (I I) Selenotrithiochromate (I I I) $CuCr_2SeS_3$	q	106-8592
tri-Copper Silicide Cu_3Si	j	106-8498
tetra-Copper Silicide Cu_4Si	o	106-8082
Copper mono-Stannide $CuSn$	j	106-8024
tri-Copper Stannide Cu_3Sn	jq	106-8025
penta-Copper Stannide Cu_5Sn	j	106-8502
penta-Copper octa-Stannide Cu_5Sn_8	j	106-8503
31-Copper octa-Stannide $Cu_{31}Sn_8$	j	106-8501
Copper (I I) Sulfate $CuSO_4$	ab	106-0132
see also Chalcanthite $CuSO_4$		521-8082
Copper (I I) Sulfide CuS	aij	106-0023
Copper di-Sulfide CuS_2	j	106-1487
Copper (I) Sulfide Cu_2S	abdefhjlorstu	106-0104
Copper Sulfide $Cu_{2-x}S$	ajo	106-8694
Copper (I I) Telluride $CuTe$	jl	106-8156
Copper (I) Telluride Cu_2Te	efjlotu	106-8084
Copper Telluride $Cu_{2-x}Te$	jt	106-8646
di-Copper Telluride Sulfide $Cu_2Te_xS_{1-x}$	efjlot	106-8529
octa-Copper tri-Telluride Sulfide Cu_8Te_3S	t	106-8752
Copper di-Telluroantimonate $CuSbTe_2$	jt	106-8650
Copper di-Tellurobismuthate $CuBiTe_2$	jt	104-8320
Copper di-Tellurogallate $CuGaTe_2$	fjost	106-8458
di-Copper tri-Tellurogermanate Cu_2GeTe_3	lot	106-8339
Copper di-Telluroindate $CuInTe_2$	fjost	106-8455
di-Copper tri-Tellurostannate Cu_2SnTe_3	t	106-8341
Copper di-Tellurothallate $CuTlTe_2$	jt	106-8651
Copper Thallium di-Selenide $CuTlSe_2$		
see Copper di-Selenothallate $CuTlSe_2$	jt	106-8652
Copper Thallium di-Telluride $CuTlTe_2$		
see Copper di-Tellurothallate $CuTlTe_2$	jt	106-8651
Copper di-Thioaluminate $CuAlS_2$	af	102-0244
Copper di-Thioantimonate $CuSbS_2$	jt	106-0505
Copper (I I) tetra-Thiochromate (I I I) $CuCr_2S_4$	aqs	106-8591
Copper tri-Thiodiferrate $CuFe_2S_3$	q	106-8568
Copper di-Thioferrate $CuFeS_2$	a	106-0791
see also Copper Pyrite $CuFeS_2$		521-0099
Copper di-Thiogallate $CuGaS_2$	abdfhjmorv	106-8209
di-Copper tri-Thiogermanate Cu_2GeS_3	fjlost	106-8456
octa-Copper hexa-Thiogermanate Cu_8GeS_6	jl	106-8686
Copper di-Thioindate $CuInS_2$	dfjlo	106-8299
Copper Thioindategallate $CuIn_xGa_{1-x}S_2$	df	106-8129
di-Copper tri-Thiostannate Cu_2SnS_3	fjlost	106-8453
tetra-Copper tetra-Thiostannate Cu_4SnS_4	jl	106-8687
Copper-Tin $CuSn$		
see Copper mono-Stannide $CuSn$	j	106-8024
Copper-Tin Cu_3Sn		
see tri-Copper Stannide Cu_3Sn	jq	106-8025
Copper-Tin Cu_5Sn		
see penta-Copper Stannide Cu_5Sn	j	106-8502
Copper-Tin Cu_5Sn_8		
see penta-Copper octa-Stannide Cu_5Sn_8	j	106-8503
Copper-Tin $Cu_{31}Sn_8$		
see 31-Copper octa-Stannide $Cu_{31}Sn_8$	j	106-8501
di-Copper Tin tri-Selenide Cu_2SnSe_3		
see di-Copper tri-Selenostannate Cu_2SnSe_3	afjlost	106-8340
di-Copper Tin tri-Sulfide Cu_2SnS_3		
see di-Copper tri-Thiostannate Cu_2SnS_3	fjlost	106-8453
tetra-Copper Tin tetra-Sulfide Cu_4SnS_4		
see tetra-Copper tetra-Thiostannate Cu_4SnS_4	jl	106-8687
di-Copper Tin tri-Telluride Cu_2SnTe_3		
see di-Copper tri-Tellurostannate Cu_2SnTe_3	t	106-8341
Copper-Zinc $CuZn$	defhij	106-8289
Copper-Zinc Cu_2Zn_3	j	106-8786
Copper-Zinc Cu_5Zn_8	j	106-8499
Copper Zinc Ferrite $Cu_xZn_yFe_{3-x-y}O_4$	j	106-8361
Copper Zinc Ferrite $Cu_xZn_{1-x}Fe_2O_4$	bj	106-8214
Corning Glass Code 7905 (Vycor Fused Silica)	abs	122-8047
see also Silica, Fused		122-8045
Corning Glass Code 7940 (Fused Silica)	abcjms	122-8046
see also Silica, Fused		122-8045
Curium di-Boride CmB_2	j	104-8433
Deuterium Bromide DBr		
see Hydrogen Bromide, Deuterated DBr	bs	104-0056
Deuterium Fluoride DF		
see Hydrogen Fluoride, Deuterated DF	hi	108-0021
Deuterium Hydride DH		
see Hydrogen, Monodeuterated HD	hs	108-8026
Deuterium Hydrogen Sulfide		
see Hydrogen Sulfide, Monodeuterated HDS	h	108-8016
Deuterium Iodide DI		
see Hydrogen Iodide, Deuterated DI	b	108-8006
Deuterium Oxide D_2O		
see Water, Deuterated D_2O	abhqs	108-0005
Deuterium Tritide DT		
see Hydrogen, Monodeuterated, Monotritiated DT	b	108-8035
Diborane B_2H_6		
see di-Borane B_2H_6	ah	104-0016
Dynasil Fused Quartz	s	122-8125
see also Silica, Fused		122-8045
Dynasil Fused Quartz 4000	bs	122-8048
see also Silica, Fused		122-8045
Dysprosium Aluminate $DyAlO_3$	n	102-0298
Dysprosium di-Aluminide $DyAl_2$	jnq	102-8261
tri-Dysprosium di-Aluminide Dy_3Al_2	nq	102-8369
Dysprosium Antimonide $DySb$	jpq	108-8001
Dysprosium Arsenate $DyAsO_4$	hq	102-8127
Dysprosium Arsenide $DyAs$	f	102-8353
Dysprosium tetra-Boride DyB_4	q	104-8310
Dysprosium dodeca-Boride DyB_{12}	qu	104-8142
Dysprosium Chloride $DyCl_3$	jq	106-0621
Dysprosium Chromate (I I I) $DyCrO_3$	knq	106-1516
Dysprosium-Cobalt $DyCo_5$		
see Dysprosium penta-Cobaltide $DyCo_5$	jlnpt	106-8527
Dysprosium-Cobalt Dy_2Co_{17}		
see di-Dysprosium 17-Cobaltide Dy_2Co_{17}	np	106-8726
Dysprosium Cobalt Ferrate $DyCo_xFe_{1-x}O_3$	n	106-8798
Dysprosium Cobalt Ferride $DyCo_xFe_{3-x}$	q	106-8136
Dysprosium di-Cobalt di-Germanide $DyCo_2Ge_2$	q	106-8173
Dysprosium Cobalt Germanium Ferrate $Dy_3Co_xGe_yFe_{5-x-y}O_{12}$	npq	106-8372
Dysprosium penta-Cobaltide $DyCo_5$	jlnpt	106-8527
di-Dysprosium 17-Cobaltide Dy_2Co_{17}	np	106-8726
Dysprosium-Cobalt-Iron $DyCo_xFe_{3-x}$		
see Dysprosium Cobalt Ferride $DyCo_xFe_{3-x}$	q	106-8136
Dysprosium Deuteride DyD		
see Dysprosium Hydride, Deuterated DyD_{1-x}	j	108-8028
tri-Dysprosium penta-Ferrate (I I I) $Dy_3Fe_5O_{12}$	npqs	108-8007
Dysprosium di-Ferride $DyFe_2$	npq	108-8010
Dysprosium tri-Ferride $DyFe_3$	nq	108-8013
Dysprosium Ferrite $DyFeO_3$	knpq	108-0087
Dysprosium Gadolinium Nickelide $Dy_xGd_{1-x}Ni_2$	q	108-8038
Dysprosium Garnet $Dy_3Fe_5O_{1.}$		
see tri-Dysprosium penta-Ferrate (I I I) $Dy_3Fe_5O_{12}$	npqs	108-8007

Property: **a.** Absorption coefficient; **b.** Dielectric constant; **c.** Dielectric strength; **d.** Energy band structure; **e.** Effective mass; **f.** Energy gap; **g.** Electric hysteresis; **h.** Energy level; **i.** Electron emission properties; **j.** Electrical resistivity; **k.** Magnetoelectric properties; **l.** Hall coefficient; **m.** Luminescence properties; **n.** Magnetic hysteresis; **o.** Mobility; **p.** Magnetomechanical properties; **q.** Magnetic susceptibility; **r.** Photoelectronic properties; **s.** Refractive index; **t.** Thermoelectric properties; **u.** Work function; **v.** Piezoelectric properties.

Substance Name	Property	Number
di- Dysprosium Germanium penta- Sulfide		
Dy_2GeS_5		
see di- Dysprosium penta- Thiogermanate Dy_2GeS_5	fjo	108-8044
Dysprosium - Gold $DyAu_2$	jq	102-8109
Dysprosium Hydride, Deuterated DyD_{1-x}	j	108-8028
Dysprosium Hydride Oxide $DyOOH$		
see Dysprosium Hydroperoxide $DyOOH$	k	108-8046
Dysprosium Hydroperoxide $DyOOH$	k	108-8046
Dysprosium Hydroxide $Dy(OH)_3$	q	108-8008
Dysprosium Indate $DyInO_3$	hq	108-8029
tri- Dysprosium Indide Dy_3In	q	108-8042
Dysprosium - Iron $DyFe_2$		
see Dysprosium di- Ferride $DyFe_2$	npq	108-8010
Dysprosium - Iron $DyFe_3$		
see Dysprosium tri- Ferride $DyFe_3$	nq	108-8013
Dysprosium Iron Aluminide $DyFe_xAl_{2-x}$	n	102-8459
see also Dysprosium Dialuminide ≥ Dysprosium Diferride		508-0495
see also Dysprosium Diferride ≥ Dysprosium Dialuminide		508-0496
Dysprosium di- Iron di- Silicide $DyFe_2Si_2$	j	108-8043
Dysprosium Magneside $DyMg$	nq	108-8030
Dysprosium di- Manganese di- Germanide $DyMn_2Ge_2$	nq	108-8058
Dysprosium - Nickel $DyNi_2$		
see Dysprosium di- Nickelide $DyNi_2$	q	108-8037
Dysprosium - Nickel $DyNi_3$		
see Dysprosium tri- Nickelide $DyNi_3$	q	108-8049
Dysprosium Nickel Cobaltide $DyNi_xCo_{2-x}$	n	106-8668
Dysprosium Nickel di- Ferride $DyNiFe_2$	q	108-8050
Dysprosium Nickel Ferride $DyNi_xFe_{3-x}$	q	108-8052
Dysprosium di- Nickel Ferride $DyNi_2Fe$	q	108-8051
Dysprosium di- Nickelide $DyNi_2$	q	108-8037
Dysprosium tri- Nickelide $DyNi_3$	q	108-8049
Dysprosium Nitride DyN	df	108-8047
Dysprosium sesqui- Oxide Dy_2O_3	bjqs	108-0052
Dysprosium Oxide Carbonate $Dy_2O_2(CO_3)$	q	106-8257
Dysprosium Oxide Hydroxide $DyOOH$		
see Dysprosium Hydroperoxide $DyOOH$	k	108-8046
Dysprosium mono- Palladide $DyPd$	q	108-8022
Dysprosium di- Palladide $DyPd_2$	q	108-8019
Dysprosium tri- Palladide $DyPd_3$	q	108-8018
Dysprosium sesqui- Palladide Dy_2Pd_3	q	108-8020
tri- Dysprosium di- Palladide Dy_3Pd_2	q	108-8023
tetra- Dysprosium penta- Palladide Dy_4Pd_5	q	108-8021
penta- Dysprosium di- Palladide Dy_5Pd_2	q	108-8024
Dysprosium Phosphate $DyPO_4$	nqs	104-0095
Dysprosium Praseodymium Aluminide $Dy_xPr_{1-x}Al_2$	q	102-8267
Dysprosium Praseodymium Nickelide $Dy_xPr_{1-x}Ni_2$	q	108-8036
hepta- Dysprosium tri- Rhodide Dy_7Rh_3	q	108-8027
Dysprosium di- Silicide $DySi_2$	j	108-8057
Dysprosium - Silver $DyAg_2$	q	102-8368
Dysprosium Sulfide DyS	q	108-8048
Dysprosium Sulfide Dy_2S_3	ehjlot	108-0079
Dysprosium Terbium Ferride $Dy_xTb_{1-x}Fe_2$	p	108-8011
di- Dysprosium penta- Thiogermanate Dy_2GeS_5	fjo	108-8044
Dysprosium di- Titanate (I V) $Dy_2Ti_2O_7$	nq	108-8053
Dysprosium Vanadate (I I I) $DyVO_3$	q	108-8034
Dysprosium Vanadate (V) $DyVO_4$	hmq	108-8012
Dysprosium Yttrium Cobaltide $Dy_xY_{2-x}Co_{17}$	np	106-8727
Dysprosium mono- Zincide $DyZn$	p	108-8009
di- Dysprosium 17- Zincide Dy_2Zn_{17}	q	108-8041
Erbium Aluminide $ErAl_2$	q	102-8099
Erbium Antimonide $ErSb$	pq	109-8001
Erbium Arsenide $ErAs$	f	102-8355
Erbium tetra- Boride ErB_4	q	104-8311
Erbium dodeca- Boride ErB_{12}	qu	104-8144
Erbium Cerium Aluminide $Er_xCe_{1-x}Al_3$	q	102-8131
Erbium Chloride $ErCl_3$	jqs	106-0628
Erbium - Cobalt $ErCo_2$	nq	106-8130
Erbium - Cobalt Er_2Co_{17}	pq	106-8597
Erbium - Cobalt - Germanium $ErCo_2Ge_2$	q	106-8176
Erbium Dysprosium Ferrate $Er_xDy_{1-x}FeO_3$	n	108-8059
Erbium Europium Aluminum Ferrate		
$ErEu_2Al_xFe_{5-x}O_{12}$	bs	102-8488
Erbium Europium Gallium Aluminum Ferrate		
$Er_{3-x}Eu_xGa_yAl_zFe_{5-y-z}O_{12}$	n	102-8116
Erbium Europium Gallium Ferrate		
$ErEu_2Ga_xFe_{5-x}O_{12}$	bs	109-8099
Erbium Europium Gallium Ferrate		
$Er_{3-x}Eu_xGa_yFe_{5-y}O_{12}$	anps	109-8013
Erbium Europium Iron Aluminum Oxide		
$ErEu_2Fe_xAl_{5-x}O_{12}$		
see Erbium Europium Aluminum Ferrate		
$ErEu_2Al_xFe_{5-x}O_{12}$	bs	102-8488
Erbium Ferrate $Er_3Fe_5O_{12}$	ps	109-8011
Erbium Ferrite $ErFeO_3$	abjns	109-0029
Erbium Gadolinium Gallium Ferrate		
$Er_{3-x}Gd_xGa_yFe_{5-y}O_{12}$	ns	109-8014
Erbium Gallium Ferrate $Er_3Ga_xFe_{5-x}O_{12}$	n	109-8024
Erbium Germanate Er_2GeO_5	fj	109-0040
Erbium - Gold $ErAu_2$	q	102-8123
Erbium Hydride Oxide $ErOOH$		
see Erbium Hydroperoxide $ErOOH$	k	109-8076
Erbium Hydroperoxide $ErOOH$	k	109-8076
Erbium Hydroxide $Er(OH)_3$	h	109-8012
Erbium - Indium Er_3In	q	109-8067
Erbium - Iron $ErFe_2$	npq	109-8015
Erbium - Iron $ErFe_3$	nq	109-8016
Erbium - Iron Er_2Fe_{17}	nq	109-8072
Erbium - Iron Er_6Fe_{23}	q	109-8098
Erbium Iron Gallium Oxide		
$Er_3Fe_{5-x}Ga_xO_{12}$		
see Erbium Gallium Ferrate $Er_3Ga_xFe_{5-x}O_{12}$	n	109-8024
Erbium Lanthanum Fluoride $Er_xLa_{1-x}F_3$	am	109-8080
Erbium di- Manganese di- Germanide $ErMn_2Ge_2$	nq	109-8086
Erbium - Nickel Er_2Ni_{17}	nq	109-8073
Erbium Nitride ErN	df	109-8079
Erbium sesqui- Oxide Er_2O_3	bfjmrs	109-0001
Erbium Oxide Carbonate $Er_2O_2(CO_3)$	q	106-8273
Erbium Oxide Hydroxide $ErOOH$		
see Erbium Hydroperoxide $ErOOH$	k	109-8076
Erbium Phosphate $ErPO_4$	hq	109-8053
Erbium - Rhodium Er_7Rh_3	q	109-8036
Erbium - Ruthenium $ErRu_2$	j	109-8107
Erbium mono- Selenide $ErSe$	j	109-8083
Erbium sesqui- Selenide Er_2Se_3	j	109-8084
Erbium - Silver $ErAg$	q	102-8102
Erbium - Silver $ErAg_2$	q	102-8391
Erbium Sulfide ErS	q	109-8081
Erbium sesqui- Telluride Er_2Te_3	j	109-8085
Erbium Vanadate (I I I) $ErVO_3$	q	109-8050
Erbium Vanadate (V) $ErVO_4$	hmq	109-8054
Erbium - Zinc $ErZn$	p	109-8022
Erbium - Zinc $ErZn_{12}$	jq	109-8031
Erbium - Zinc Er_2Zn_{17}	q	109-8052
Europium Aluminate $EuAlO_3$	hm	102-8120
Europium di- Aluminum tetra- Sulfide		
$EuAl_2S_4$		
see Europium tetra- Thiodialuminate $EuAl_2S_4$	jm	102-8496
Europium hexa- Boride EuB_6	jqt	104-8136
Europium di- Chloride $EuCl_2$	u	106-8086
Europium tri- Chloride $EuCl_3$	msu	106-8087
Europium Chloride Fluoride $EuClF$	mq	106-8192
tri- Europium penta- Ferrate (I I I)		
$Eu_3Fe_5O_{12}$	nps	109-8065
Europium di- Fluoride EuF_2	b	109-0019
Europium Gallate $Eu_3Ga_5O_{12}$	am	109-8018
Europium Gallium Ferrate $Eu_3Ga_xFe_{5-x}O_{12}$	p	109-8077
Europium di- Gallium tetra- Selenide		
$EuGa_2Se_4$		
see Europium tetra- Selenodigallate $EuGa_2Se_4$	jm	109-8105
Europium di- Gallium tetra- Sulfide		
$EuGa_2S_4$		
see Europium tetra- Thiodigallate $EuGa_2S_4$	jm	109-8103
Europium di- Indium tetra- Selenide		
$EuIn_2Se_4$		
see Europium tetra- Selenodiindate $EuIn_2Se_4$	j	109-8106

Property: a. Absorption coefficient; **b.** Dielectric constant; **c.** Dielectric strength; **d.** Energy band structure; **e.** Effective mass; **f.** Energy gap; **g.** Electric hysteresis; **h.** Energy level; **i.** Electron emission properties; **j.** Electrical resistivity; **k.** Magnetoelectric properties; **l.** Hall coefficient; **m.** Luminescence properties; **n.** Magnetic hysteresis; **o.** Mobility; **p.** Magnetomechanical properties; **q.** Magnetic susceptibility; **r.** Photoelectronic properties; **s.** Refractive index; **t.** Thermoelectric properties; **u.** Work function; **v.** Piezoelectric properties.

Substance Name	Property	Number
Europium di- Indium tetra- Sulfide		
$Eu In_2 S_4$		
see Europium tetra- Thiodiindate $Eu In_2 S_4$	j	109-8104
Europium Iron Gallate		
$Eu_3 Fe_x Ga_{5-x} O_{12}$		
see Europium Gallium Ferrate $Eu_3 Ga_x Fe_{5-x} O_{12}$	p	109-8077
Europium di- Iron di- Silicide $Eu Fe_2 Si_2$	j	109-8068
Europium Lanthanum Sulfide $Eu_x La_{1-x} S$	q	109-8033
Europium - Lead $Eu Pb_3$		
see Europium tri- Plumbide $Eu Pb_3$	q	109-8095
Europium Molybdate $Eu_2(Mo O_4)_3$	b	109-8028
Europium tri- Nitrate $Eu(N O_3)_3$	am	109-8008
Europium Nitride $Eu N$	df	109-8078
Europium mono- Oxide $Eu O$	abdfhijklnopqru	109-0025
Europium Oxide $Eu O_{1-x}$	afjlo	109-8034
Europium sesqui- Oxide $Eu_2 O_3$	bs	109-0007
Europium - Palladium $Eu Pd_3$	h	109-8075
Europium penta- Phosphate $Eu P_5 O_{14}$	ahm	109-8066
Europium Phosphide $Eu P$	fq	109-8074
Europium di- Phosphide $Eu P_2$	joq	109-8087
di- Europium Phosphide $Eu_2 P$	q	109-8088
Europium sesqui- Phosphide $Eu_2 P_3$	q	109-8089
tri- Europium di- Phosphide $Eu_3 P_2$	q	109-8090
tri- Europium tetra- Phosphide $Eu_3 P_4$	q	109-8091
tetra- Europium tri- Phosphide $Eu_4 P_3$	q	109-8092
tetra- Europium undeca- Phosphide $Eu_4 P_{11}$	q	109-8093
penta- Europium nona- Phosphide $Eu_5 P_9$	q	109-8094
Europium tri- Plumbide $Eu Pb_3$	q	109-8095
Europium Samarium Sulfide $Eu_x Sm_{1-x} S$	afjqt	109-8064
Europium Scandium Vanadate $Eu_x Sc_{1-x} V O_4$	m	109-8101
Europium mono- Selenide $Eu Se$	abdefhjklmnopqt	109-8019
Europium Selenide $Eu Se_{1+x}$	fjqt	109-8042
Europium sesqui- Selenide $Eu_2 Se_3$	q	109-8047
tri- Europium tetra- Selenide $Eu_3 Se_4$	q	109-8048
tetra- Europium hepta- Selenide $Eu_4 Se_7$	q	109-8049
Europium tetra- Selenodigallate $Eu Ga_2 Se_4$	jm	109-8105
Europium tetra- Selenodiindate $Eu In_2 Se_4$	j	109-8106
Europium di- Silicide $Eu Si_2$	d	109-8096
Europium Silver Silicide $Eu Ag_x Si_{2-x}$	nq	102-8207
Europium tri- Stannide $Eu Sn_3$	jq	109-8029
Europium mono- Sulfide $Eu S$	abdfhijmnpqt	109-8020
Europium (I I I) Tantalate $Eu Ta O_4$	q	109-0036
Europium mono- Telluride $Eu Te$	adfhjmpqt	109-8021
Europium Telluride $Eu Te_{1+x}$	fjqt	109-8040
Europium Telluride $Eu Te_{2+x}$	fjqt	109-8041
Europium sesqui- Telluride $Eu_2 Te_3$	q	109-8045
tri- Europium tetra- Telluride $Eu_3 Te_4$	q	109-8046
tri- Europium hepta- Telluride $Eu_3 Te_7$	q	109-8043
tetra- Europium hepta- Telluride $Eu_4 Te_7$	q	109-8044
Europium tetra- Thiodialuminate $Eu Al_2 S_4$	jm	102-8496
Europium tetra- Thiodigallate $Eu Ga_2 S_4$	jm	109-8103
Europium tetra- Thiodiindate $Eu In_2 S_4$	j	109-8104
Europium - Tin $Eu Sn_3$		
see Europium tri- Stannide $Eu Sn_3$	jq	109-8029
Europium Titanate $Eu Ti O_3$	hnq	109-8058
di- Europium (I I) Titanate (I V) $Eu_2 Ti O_4$	hnq	109-8059
tri- Europium (I I) di- Titanate (I V)		
$Eu_3 Ti_2 O_7$	q	109-8060
Europium Titanium Niobate $Eu Ti Nb O_6$	fj	109-0060
Europium (I I I) Tungstate (V) $Eu W O_4$	bfjq	109-8071
Europium (I I I) Vanadate (I I I) $Eu V O_3$	nq	109-8039
Europium (I I I) Vanadate (V) $Eu V O_4$	m	109-8032
Europium Yttrium Iron Aluminum Oxide		
$Eu_x Y_{3-x} Fe_{5-y} Al_y O_{12}$		
see Yttrium Europium Aluminum Ferrate		
$Y_x Eu_{3-x} Al_y Fe_{5-y} O_{12}$	n	102-8101
Europium Yttrium Iron Gallium Oxide		
$Eu_x Y_{3-x} Fe_4 Ga O_{12}$		
see Yttrium Europium Gallium Ferrate		
$Y_x Eu_{3-x} Ga Fe_4 O_{12}$	s	109-8100
Europium Yttrium Iron Gallium Oxide		
$Eu_x Y_{3-x} Fe_{5-y} Ga_y O_{12}$		
see Yttrium Europium Gallium Ferrate		
$Y_x Eu_{3-x} Ga_y Fe_{5-y} O_{12}$	knpq	109-8017
Europium Yttrium Iron Oxide		
$Eu_x Y_{3-x} Fe_5 O_{12}$		
see Yttrium Europium Ferrate $Y_x Eu_{3-x} Fe_5 O_{12}$	p	109-8023
Europium Yttrium Sulfite $Eu_x Y_{2-x} S O_2$	m	109-8037
Europium Yttrium Vanadate $Eu_x Y_{1-x} V O_4$	m	109-8097
Ferrite 2 V T (Russian)	n	110-8229
Ferrite 50 V Ch Z (Russian)	bq	110-8188
Ferrite 1000 N M Z (Russian)	n	110-8227
Ferrite 1500 N M Z (Russian)	n	110-8228
Ferrite 2000 - N M 3 (Russian)	nq	110-8245
Ferrite N Z 4 (Japanese)	n	110-8212
Fluoroaluminum Silicate $(Al F)_2 Si O_4$	b	102-8135
see also Topaz $(Al F)_2 Si O_4$		521-0082
hexa- Fluorobenzene $C_6 F_6$	i	106-0762
octa- Fluorocyclobutane $C_4 F_8$	bcs	106-0039
see also Freon C318 $C_4 F_8$		106-8481
di- Fluorodisulfane $F S S F$		
see di- Sulfur di- Fluoride $S_2 F_2$	i	110-0288
hexa- Fluoroethane $C_2 F_6$	bcs	106-0066
see also Freon 116 $C_2 F_6$		106-8479
Tris- (penta- Fluoroethyl)amine $N (C_2 F_5)_3$	c	106-8578
penta- Fluoroethyl Bis(Trifluoromethyl)amine		
$C_2 F_5 N (C F_3)_2$		
see penta- Fluoroethyl-bis-(Trifluoromethyl)amine		
$C_2 F_5 N (C F_3)_2$	c	106-8577
tetra- Fluoroethylene $C_2 F_4$	i	106-0049
Bis- (penta- Fluoroethyl)trifluoromethylamine		
$C F_3 N (C_2 F_5)_2$	c	106-8579
penta- Fluoroethyl-bis-(Trifluoromethyl)amine		
$C_2 F_5 N (C F_3)_2$	c	106-8577
hepta- Fluoroiodopropane $C_3 F_7 I$	s	106-8685
octa- Fluoropropane $C_3 F_8$	cs	106-0034
Fluorosulfuric Acid $F S O_3 H$	q	110-8281
Freon 11 $C Cl_3 F$	abc	106-8517
see also Arcton 9 $C Cl_3 F$		106-8692
see also tri- Chlorofluoromethane $C Cl_3 F$		106-0147
Freon 12 $C Cl_2 F_2$	c	106-8475
see also di- Chlorodifluoromethane $C Cl_2 F_2$		106-0001
Freon 13 $C Cl F_3$	c	106-8476
see also Arcton 3 $C Cl F_3$		106-8690
see also Chlorotrifluoromethane $C Cl F_3$		106-0021
Freon 14 $C F_4$	c	106-8477
see also Arcton 0 $C F_4$		106-8689
see also Carbon tetra- Fluoride $C F_4$		106-0231
Freon 114 $C_2 Cl_2 F_4$	c	106-8691
see also di- Chlorotetrafluoroethane $C_2 Cl_2 F_4$		106-0166
Freon 115 $C Cl F_2 C F_3$	c	106-8478
see also Chloropentafluoroethane $C Cl F_2 C F_3$		106-0233
Freon 116 $C_2 F_6$	c	106-8479
see also hexa- Fluoroethane $C_2 F_6$		106-0066
Freon C318 $C_4 F_8$	c	106-8481
see also octa- Fluorocyclobutane $C_4 F_8$		106-0039
Fused Quartz		
see Silica, Fused	abdfjmoqs	122-8045
Gadolinium Aluminate $Gd Al O_3$	hm	102-0297
Gadolinium di- Aluminide $Gd Al_2$	jq	102-8168
Gadolinium Antimonide $Gd Sb$	jpq	111-8106
Gadolinium Antimony Arsenide $Gd Sb_x As_{1-x}$	fo	104-8202
Gadolinium Arsenide $Gd As$	f	102-8347
Gadolinium di- Arsenidogermanate $Gd Ge As_2$	q	102-8309
Gadolinium Bismuth Ferrate $Gd_{3-x} Bi_x Fe_5 O_{12}$	a	104-8125
Gadolinium hexa- Boride $Gd B_6$	j	104-8392
Gadolinium Bromide $Gd Br_3$	j	104-0309
tri- Gadolinium Carbide $Gd_3 C$	q	106-8470
Gadolinium Cerium Aluminide $Gd_x Ce_{1-x} Al_3$	q	102-8130
Gadolinium Cerium Yttrium Aluminate		
$Gd_x Ce_y Y_{3-x-y} Al_5 O_{12}$		
see Yttrium Gadolinium Cerium Aluminate		
$Y_{3-x-y} Gd_x Ce_y Al_5 O_{12}$	m	102-8145
Gadolinium - Cerium - Yttrium - Ruthenium		
$Gd_x Ce_{1-x-y} Y_y Ru_2$	jq	106-8287
Gadolinium tri- Chloride $Gd Cl_3$	jnq	106-0608

Property: **a.** Absorption coefficient; **b.** Dielectric constant; **c.** Dielectric strength; **d.** Energy band structure; **e.** Effective mass; **f.** Energy gap; **g.** Electric hysteresis; **h.** Energy level; **i.** Electron emission properties; **j.** Electrical resistivity; **k.** Magnetoelectric properties; **l.** Hall coefficient; **m.** Luminescence properties; **n.** Magnetic hysteresis; **o.** Mobility; **p.** Magnetomechanical properties; **q.** Magnetic susceptibility; **r.** Photoelectronic properties; **s.** Refractive index; **t.** Thermoelectric properties; **u.** Work function; **v.** Piezoelectric properties.

Substance Name	*Property*	*Number*
Gadolinium Chromate (I I I) $GdCrO_3$	kq	106-8323
Gadolinium - Cobalt $GdCo$	npqt	106-8510
Gadolinium - Cobalt $GdCo_2$	jq	106-8375
Gadolinium - Cobalt $GdCo_3$	q	106-8599
Gadolinium - Cobalt $GdCo_5$	nq	106-8223
Gadolinium - Cobalt $GdCo_{5-x}$	q	106-8781
Gadolinium - Cobalt Gd_xCo_{1-x}	npq	106-8486
Gadolinium - Cobalt Gd_2Co_7	nq	106-8224
Gadolinium - Cobalt Gd_2Co_{17}	q	106-8598
Gadolinium - Cobalt - Aluminum $GdCo_xAl_{2-x}$	q	102-8274
Gadolinium - Cobalt - Aluminum $GdCo_{5-x}Al_x$	n	102-8264
Gadolinium - Cobalt - Copper $GdCo_{5-x}Cu_x$	n	106-8490
Gadolinium - Cobalt - Germanium $GdCo_2Ge_2$	q	106-8175
Gadolinium Cobalt Germanium Ferrate $Gd_3Co_xGe_yFe_{5-x-y}O_{12}$	npq	106-8370
Gadolinium Cobalt Silicide $GdCo_xSi_{2-x}$	q	106-8396
Gadolinium - Copper $GdCu_6$	q	106-8804
Gadolinium Cuprate (I I) Gd_2CuO_4	jt	106-8644
Gadolinium Europium Oxide $Gd_xEu_{1-x}O$	bijoqt	109-8051
Gadolinium Europium Phosphate $Gd_xEu_yP_5O_{14}$	adfh	109-8082
Gadolinium Europium Selenide $Gd_xEu_{1-x}Se$	nq	109-8070
Gadolinium Europium Sulfide $Gd_xEu_{1-x}S$	n	109-8055
Gadolinium Europium Yttrium Iron Aluminum Oxide $Gd_xEu_yY_{3-x-y}Fe_{5-z}Al_zO_{12}$ see Yttrium Gadolinium Europium Aluminum Ferrate $Y_{3-x-y}Gd_xEu_yAl_zFe_{5-z}O_{12}$	n	102-8113
Gadolinium Ferrate $GdFeO_3$	q	110-8175
tri- Gadolinium penta- Ferrate (I I I) $Gd_3Fe_5O_{12}$	pqs	110-0199
Gadolinium di- Ferride $GdFe_2$	npq	110-8092
Gadolinium tri- Ferride $GdFe_3$	q	110-8278
di- Gadolinium 17- Ferride Gd_2Fe_{17}	nq	110-8268
Gadolinium tri- Fluoride GdF_3	m	110-0350
tri- Gadolinium penta- Gallate $Gd_3Ga_5O_{12}$	jnpqs	111-8020
Gadolinium - Gallium $GdGa_2$	q	111-8137
Gadolinium Gallium Garnet see tri- Gadolinium penta- Gallate $Gd_3Ga_5O_{12}$	jnpqs	111-8020
Gadolinium Gallium tri- Selenide $GdGaSe_3$ see Gadolinium tri- Selenogallate $GdGaSe_3$	fhjot	111-8153
Gadolinium Garnet $Gd_3Fe_5O_{1i}$ see tri- Gadolinium penta- Ferrate (I I I) $Gd_3Fe_5O_{12}$	pqs	110-0199
Gadolinium Germanate Gd_2GeO_5	fj	111-0104
Gadolinium Germanium di- Arsenide $GdGeAs_2$ see Gadolinium di- Arsenidogermanate $GdGeAs_2$	q	102-8309
Gadolinium Germanium Sulfide Gd_2GeS_5 see di- Gadolinium penta- Thiogermanate Gd_2GeS_5	fjo	111-8133
Gadolinium Germanium Telluride $Gd_xGe_{1-x}Te$	o	111-8122
see also Germanium Monotelluride ≥ Gadolinium Monotelluride		508-0176
Gadolinium - Gold $GdAu_2$	q	102-8111
Gadolinium di- Hydride GdH_2	j	111-8096
Gadolinium Hydride GdH_{1-x}	j	111-8095
Gadolinium Hydroxide $Gd(OH)_3$	npq	111-8138
Gadolinium Indate $GdInO_3$	hq	114-8057
Gadolinium - Indium Gd_3In	q	111-8130
Gadolinium - Iridium $GdIr_2$	jq	111-8062
Gadolinium - Iron $GdFe_2$ see Gadolinium di- Ferride $GdFe_2$	npq	110-8092
Gadolinium - Iron $GdFe_3$ see Gadolinium tri- Ferride $GdFe_3$	q	110-8278
Gadolinium - Iron Gd_2Fe_{17} see di- Gadolinium 17- Ferride Gd_2Fe_{17}	nq	110-8268
Gadolinium Iron Aluminide $GdFe_xAl_{2-x}$	q	102-8273
Gadolinium Iron Bismuth Oxide $Gd_{3-x}Fe_5Bi_xO_{12}$ see Gadolinium Bismuth Ferrate $Gd_{3-x}Bi_xFe_5O_{12}$	a	104-8125
Gadolinium Iron Silicide $GdFe_xSi_{2-x}$	q	110-8138
Gadolinium Lanthanum Aluminide $Gd_xLa_{1-x}Al_2$	jq	102-8257
Gadolinium - Lanthanum - Ruthenium $Gd_xLa_{1-x}Ru_2$	j	111-8103
Gadolinium Lanthanum Yttrium Iron Gallium Oxide $Gd_xLa_yY_{3-x-y}Fe_{5-z}Ga_zO_{12}$ see Yttrium Gadolinium Lanthanum Gallium Ferrate $Y_{3-x-y}Gd_xLa_yGa_zFe_{5-z}O_{12}$	n	110-8055
Gadolinium - Lead $GdPb_3$ see Gadolinium tri- Plumbide $GdPb_3$	q	111-8186
Gadolinium di- Manganese di- Germanide $GdMn_2Ge_2$	jnq	111-8181
Gadolinium - Manganese - Iron $Gd_6Mn_xFe_{23-x}$	nq	110-8220
Gadolinium Molybdate (I I I) $GdMoO_3$	a	111-8036
Gadolinium Molybdate (V I) $Gd_2(MoO_4)_3$	abgjnqsv	111-0046
Gadolinium Molybdenum Phoshide Oxide $GdPMo_{12}O_{40}$ see Gadolinium Phosphorus dodeca- Molybdate $GdPMo_{12}O_{40}$	q	111-8091
Gadolinium - Nickel $GdNi$	q	111-8085
Gadolinium - Nickel $GdNi_2$	jnqt	111-8044
Gadolinium - Nickel $GdNi_5$	jq	111-8076
Gadolinium - Nickel Gd_2Ni_7	q	111-8084
Gadolinium - Nickel Gd_2Ni_{17}	nq	111-8083
Gadolinium Nickel Ferride $Gd_2Ni_xFe_{17-x}$	nq	110-8269
Gadolinium mono- Nitride GdN	df	111-0052
Gadolinium Nitride Oxide GdN_xO_{1-x}	nq	111-8205
Gadolinium - Osmium $GdOs_2$	j	111-8211
Gadolinium sesqui- Oxide Gd_2O_3	bjmqs	111-0003
Gadolinium - Palladium $GdPd$	q	111-8048
Gadolinium - Palladium $GdPd_2$	q	111-8046
Gadolinium - Palladium $GdPd_3$	q	111-8045
Gadolinium - Palladium Gd_3Pd_2	q	111-8049
Gadolinium - Palladium Gd_4Pd_5	q	111-8047
Gadolinium - Palladium Gd_5Pd_2	q	111-8050
Gadolinium Phosphite GdP_3O_9	q	111-8159
Gadolinium Phosphorus dodeca- Molybdate $GdPMo_{12}O_{40}$	q	111-8091
Gadolinium - Platinum $GdPt_2$	jq	111-8064
Gadolinium tri- Plumbide $GdPb_3$	q	111-8186
Gadolinium - Rhodium $GdRh_2$	jq	111-8063
Gadolinium - Rhodium Gd_7Rh_3	q	111-8086
Gadolinium - Ruthenium $GdRu_2$	j	111-8024
Gadolinium Samarium Sulfide $Gd_xSm_{1-x}S$	hq	111-8206
Gadolinium Scandium Aluminate $Gd_3Sc_2Al_3O_{12}$	s	102-8489
Gadolinium Selenide $GdSe$	jq	111-8067
Gadolinium Selenide $GdSe_{1-x}$	jlq	111-8066
Gadolinium sesqui- Selenide Gd_2Se_3	ejot	111-8154
Gadolinium Selenide Gd_2Se_{3-x}	jt	111-8077
Gadolinium tri- Selenogallate $GdGaSe_3$	fhjot	111-8153
Gadolinium di- Silicide $GdSi_2$	j	111-8174
Gadolinium - Silver $GdAg_2$	q	102-8388
Gadolinium tri- Stannide $GdSn_3$	q	111-8185
Gadolinium sesqui- Sulfide Gd_2S_3	dehjloqt	111-8071
tri- Gadolinium tetra- Sulfide Gd_3S_4	jlt	111-8025
Gadolinium Sulfide $Gd_{3-x}S_4$	fjloqt	111-8065
Gadolinium Sulfide Oxide Gd_2SO_2 see Gadolinium Sulfoxylate Gd_2SO_2	hm	111-8051
Gadolinium Sulfoxylate Gd_2SO_2	hm	111-8051
di- Gadolinium Telluride Gd_2Te	j	111-8175
Gadolinium sesqui- Telluride Gd_2Te_3	j	111-8176
di- Gadolinium penta- Thiogermanate Gd_2GeS_5	fjo	111-8133
Gadolinium - Tin $GdSn_3$ see Gadolinium tri- Stannide $GdSn_3$	q	111-8185
Gadolinium Vanadate (I I I) $GdVO_3$	q	111-8105
Gadolinium Vanadate (V) $GdVO_4$	km	111-8035
Gadolinium - Yttrium - Cobalt $Gd_xY_{1-x}Co_2$	q	106-8374
Gadolinium Yttrium Ferrate $Gd_xY_{3-x}Fe_5O_{12}$ see Yttrium Gadolinium Ferrate $Y_xGd_{3-x}Fe_5O_{12}$	aqs	110-8222
Gadolinium Yttrium Iron Aluminum Oxide $Gd_{3-x}Y_xFe_{5-y}Al_yO_{12}$ see Yttrium Gadolinium Aluminum Ferrate $Y_xGd_{3-x}Al_yFe_{5-y}O_{12}$	b	102-8385
Gadolinium Yttrium Iron Gallium Lead Oxide $Gd_xY_{3-x-y}Fe_{5-z}Ga_zPb_yO_{12}$ see Yttrium Gadolinium Gallium Lead Ferrate $Y_{3-x-y}Gd_xGa_zPb_yFe_{5-z}O_{12}$	n	110-8056
Gadolinium Yttrium Iron Gallium Oxide $Gd_xY_{3-x}Fe_{5-y}Ga_yO_{12}$ see Yttrium Gadolinium Gallium Ferrate $Y_{3-x}Gd_xGa_yFe_{5-y}O_{12}$	npqt	110-8038
Gadolinium Yttrium Oxide $Gd_xY_{1-x}O_2$	jq	111-8193

Property: **a.** Absorption coefficient; **b.** Dielectric constant; **c.** Dielectric strength; **d.** Energy band structure; **e.** Effective mass; **f.** Energy gap; **g.** Electric hysteresis; **h.** Energy level; **i.** Electron emission properties; **j.** Electrical resistivity; **k.** Magnetoelectric properties; **l.** Hall coefficient; **m.** Luminescence properties; **n.** Magnetic hysteresis; **o.** Mobility; **p.** Magnetomechanical properties; **q.** Magnetic susceptibility; **r.** Photoelectronic properties; **s.** Refractive index; **t.** Thermoelectric properties; **u.** Work function; **v.** Piezoelectric properties.

Substance Name	Property	Number
Gadolinium - Zinc $Gd Zn_2$	hq	111-8094
Gadolinium - Zinc $Gd Zn_{12}$	jq	111-8043
Gadolinium - Zinc $Gd_2 Zn_{17}$	q	111-8120
Gadolinium di- Zirconate $Gd_2 Zr_2 O_7$	j	111-8152
Gallium Aluminum Antimonide $Ga_x Al_{1-x} Sb$	adfjlor	102-8333
Gallium Aluminum Arsenide $Ga_{1-x} Al_x As$	abdefhijlmors	102-8094
see also Gallium Arsenide ≥ Aluminum Arsenide		508-0136
Gallium Aluminum Nitride $Ga_x Al_{1-x} N$	m	102-8185
Gallium Aluminum Phosphide $Ga_{1-x} Al_x P$	afhm	102-8075
Gallium Antimonide $Ga Sb$	abdefh–v	111-8002
see also Gallium Antimonide, Natural $Ga Sb$		521-8008
Gallium Antimonide $Ga Sb_{1-x}$	abfjlors	111-8019
Gallium Antimonide Arsenide $Ga Sb_x As_{1-x}$	bdefijot	102-8420
Gallium Antimony Oxide $Ga_{1-x} Sb_{1-y} O_{1-x}$	cjs	111-8195
Gallium Arsenide $Ga As$	a–fh–oqrstuv	102-8041
Gallium Arsenide $Ga As_{1-x}$	aj	102-8186
Gallium Arsenide Phosphide $Ga As_{1-x} P_x$	abdefh–oqrst	102-8095
see also Gallium Arsenide ≥ Gallium Phosphide		508-0174
see also Gallium Phosphide ≥ Gallium Arsenide		508-0175
Gallium di- Chloride $Ga Cl_2$	u	106-8088
Gallium Ferrate $Ga_x Fe_{5-x} O_{12}$	s	110-8153
di- Gallium Germanium tri- Telluride $Ga_2 Ge Te_3$		
see di- Gallium tri- Tellurogermanate $Ga_2 Ge Te_3$	jqt	111-8016
Gallium di- Iodide $Ga I_2$	j	111-8177
Gallium tri- Iodide $Ga I_3$	u	111-8006
Gallium Lead Telluride $Ga_x Pb_{1-x} Te$	jnoqt	111-8117
see also Lead Monotelluride ≥ Gallium Monotelluride		508-0128
Gallium Nitride $Ga N$	abdefhjlmoqrsv	111-0021
Gallium sesqui- Oxide $Ga_2 O_3$	aijot	111-0001
Gallium Phosphide $Ga P$	a–fhijklmoqrstuv	111-0008
Gallium mono- Selenide $Ga Se$	abdefhijklmoqrst	111-8007
Gallium Selenide $Ga Se_{1-x}$	bfj	111-8128
see also Gallium ≥ Seleneium		425-8028
see also Selenium ≥ Gallium		510-0151
Gallium sesqui- Selenide $Ga_2 Se_3$	abfjqs	111-8008
Gallium Selenide Sulfide $Ga Se_x S_{1-x}$	fhm	111-8022
see also Gallium Monoselenide ≥ Gallium Monosulfide		508-0298
see also Gallium Monosulfide ≥ Gallium Monoselenide		508-0299
Gallium Selenide Sulfide $Ga_2 Se_x S_{3-x}$	m	111-8056
Gallium mono- Sulfide $Ga S$	afhjmort	111-0029
Gallium sesqui- Sulfide $Ga_2 S_3$	a	111-0101
Gallium mono- Telluride $Ga Te$	abefhjlrs	111-8009
di- Gallium Telluride $Ga_2 Te$	j	111-8112
Gallium sesqui- Telluride $Ga_2 Te_3$	afjmrt	111-8010
Gallium Telluride Selenide $Ga Te_x Se_{1-x}$	aj	111-8073
di- Gallium tri- Tellurogermanate $Ga_2 Ge Te_3$	jqt	111-8016
General Electric Fused Quartz	b	122-8129
see also Silica, Fused		122-8045
General Electric Fused Quartz 101	b	122-8095
see also Silica, Fused		122-8045
General Electric Fused Quartz 105	a	122-8094
see also Silica, Fused		122-8045
General Electric Fused Quartz 106	s	122-8132
see also Silica, Fused		122-8045
General Electric Fused Quartz 124	b	122-8096
see also Silica, Fused		122-8045
General Electric Fused Quartz 125	b	122-8097
see also Silica, Fused		122-8045
General Electric Fused Quartz 151	abs	122-8049
see also Silica, Fused		122-8045
di- Germanium Antimonate (I I I) $Ge_2 Sb_2 O_7$	s	111-8131
Germanium Antimony Selenide $Ge Sb_2 Se_4$		
see Germanium tetra- Selenoantimonate $Ge Sb_2 Se_4$	afs	111-8132
Germanium di- Antimony tetra- Telluride $Ge Sb_2 Te_4$		
see Germanium tetra- Tellurodiantimonate $Ge Sb_2 Te_4$	ehj	111-8157
Germanium tetra- Antimony tetra- Telluride $Ge Sb_4 Te_4$		
see Germanium tetra- Tellurotetraantimonate $Ge Sb_4 Te_4$	ehj	111-8158
Germanium Arsenide Selenide $Ge As Se$	f	102-8227
Germanium Arsenide Telluride $Ge As Te$	ft	102-8214
Germanium Bismuthide $Ge_x Bi_{1-x}$	afhr	104-8213
Germanium dodeca- Bismuth 20- Oxide $Ge Bi_{12} O_{20}$		
see dodeca- Bismuth (I I I) Germanate $Bi_{12} Ge O_{20}$	abfhjmqsv	104-0533
tri- Germanium Bismuth dodeca- Oxide $Ge_3 Bi O_{12}$		
see Bismuth Germanate $Bi Ge_3 O_{12}$	bs	104-8166
tri- Germanium tetra- Bismuth dodeca- Oxide $Ge_3 Bi_4 O_{12}$		
see tetra- Bismuth (I I I) tri- Germanate $Bi_2 Ge_3 O_{12}$	ams	104-8180
Germanium Bismuth Telluride $Ge_x Bi_{1-x} Te$	j	104-8397
see also Germanium Monotelluride ≥ Bismuth Monotelluride		508-0441
Germanium tri- Fluoride $Ge F_3$	h	110-8155
Germanium tetra- Fluoride $Ge F_4$	h	110-0041
Germanium mono- Oxide $Ge O$	ajsu	111-8014
Germanium di- Oxide $Ge O_2$	abdfhjqrs	111-0006
Germanium mono- Selenide $Ge Se$	afhjlost	111-8079
Germanium di- Selenide $Ge Se_2$	afhjst	111-8015
Germanium Selenide $Ge Se_{1-x}$	b	111-8129
see also Germanium ≥ Selenium		427-8020
see also Selenium ≥ Germanium		510-0023
Germanium sesqui- Selenide $Ge_2 Se_3$	ft	111-8114
Germanium tetra- Selenoantimonate $Ge Sb_2 Se_4$	afs	111-8132
Germanium Silicide $Ge Si$	dt	111-8151
Germanium mono- Sulfide $Ge S$	fjqst	111-0015
Germanium di- Sulfide $Ge S_2$	afq	111-0098
Germanium Sulfide $Ge S_{1-x}$	b	111-8194
Germanium sesqui- Sulfide $Ge_2 S_3$	js	111-8080
Germanium mono- Telluride $Ge Te$	abdefh–oqrstu	111-8021
Germanium di- Telluride $Ge Te_2$	adfhjrt	111-8075
Germanium Telluride $Ge Te_{1-x}$	afhjlort	111-8108
di- Germanium hepta- Telluride $Ge_2 Te_7$	f	111-8109
Germanium Telluride Selenide $Ge Te Se$	s	111-8113
Germanium Telluride Selenide $Ge Te_x Se_{1-x}$	befjost	111-8162
see also Germanium Monoselenide ≥ Germanium Monotelluride		508-0079
see also Germanium Monotelluride ≥ Germanium Monoselenide		508-0080
Germanium Telluride Selenide $Ge Te_x Se_{2-x}$	adfhjrst	111-8078
see also Germanium Diselenide ≥ Germanium Ditelluride		508-0077
see also Germanium Ditelluride ≥ Germanium Diselenide		508-0078
tri- Germanium tetra- Telluride di- Selenide $Ge_3 Te_4 Se_2$	f	111-8110
Germanium tetra- Tellurodiantimonate $Ge Sb_2 Te_4$	ehj	111-8157
Germanium tetra- Tellurotetraantimonate $Ge Sb_4 Te_4$	ehj	111-8158
Gold di- Aluminide $Au Al_2$	dhijm	102-8283
Gold di- Antimonide $Au Sb_2$	j	102-8002
Gold - Copper $Au Cu$	jt	102-8072
Gold - Copper $Au Cu_3$	adhjlnqt	102-8187
Gold - Copper $Au_2 Cu_3$	j	102-8244
Gold - Copper $Au_3 Cu$	hjlnqt	102-8223
Gold - Gallium $Au Ga$	k	102-8502
Gold - Gallium $Au Ga_2$	dijq	102-8255
Gold - Indium $Au In_2$	jq	102-8394
Gold - Lead $Au Pb_2$		
see Gold di- Plumbide $Au Pb_2$	jk	102-8197
Gold - Lead $Au Pb_3$		
see Gold tri- Plumbide $Au Pb_3$	fj	102-8196
Gold - Lead / $Au_2 Pb$		
see di- Gold Plumbide $Au_2 Pb$	jk	102-8198
Gold sesqui- Phosphide $Au_2 P_3$	f	102-8049
Gold di- Plumbide $Au Pb_2$	jk	102-8197
Gold tri- Plumbide $Au Pb_3$	fj	102-8196
di- Gold Plumbide $Au_2 Pb$	jk	102-8198
Gold - Silver $Au Ag$	h	102-8286
Gold - Silver $Au Ag_3$	djl	102-8287
Gold - Silver $Au_2 Ag_3$	jl	102-8330
Gold - Silver $Au_3 Ag$	hjl	102-8288
Gold mono- Stannide $Au Sn$	dfhj	102-8005
Gold di- Stannide $Au Sn_2$	j	102-8006
Gold tetra- Stannide $Au Sn_4$	j	102-8007
Gold - Tin $Au Sn$		
see Gold mono- Stannide $Au Sn$	dfhj	102-8005
Gold - Tin $Au Sn_2$		
see Gold di- Stannide $Au Sn_2$	j	102-8006

Property: a. Absorption coefficient; b. Dielectric constant; c. Dielectric strength; d. Energy band structure; e. Effective mass; f. Energy gap; g. Electric hysteresis; h. Energy level; i. Electron emission properties; j. Electrical resistivity; k. Magnetoelectric properties; l. Hall coefficient; m. Luminescence properties; n. Magnetic hysteresis; o. Mobility; p. Magnetomechanical properties; q. Magnetic susceptibility; r. Photoelectronic properties; s. Refractive index; t. Thermoelectric properties; u. Work function; v. Piezoelectric properties.

Substance Name	*Property*	*Number*
Gold - Tin $AuSn_4$		
see Gold tetra-Stannide $AuSn_4$	j	102-8007
Gold - Zinc $AuZn$	j	102-8282
Graphite Iodide Chloride C_8ICl	j	106-8541
Graphite Nitrate C_8NO_3	j	106-8494
Hafnium mono-Antimonide $HfSb$	j	112-8001
Hafnium di-Boride HfB_2	ejloqtu	104-8157
Hafnium Boron Deuteride $Hf(BD_4)_4$		
see Hafnium Hydroborate, Deuterated $Hf(BD_4)_4$	h	104-8130
Hafnium Boron Hydride $Hf(BH_4)_4$		
see Hafnium Hydroborate $Hf(BH_4)_4$	h	104-8129
Hafnium Bromide $HfBr$	m	104-8177
Hafnium Cadmate $HfCdO_3$	bnq	106-8750
Hafnium mono-Carbide HfC	hjltu	106-0639
Hafnium Carbide HfC_{1-x}	qu	106-8558
Hafnium tetra-Chloride $HfCl_4$	fj	106-0077
Hafnium di-Ferride $HfFe_2$	j	110-8263
Hafnium mono-Germanide $HfGe$	j	111-8173
Hafnium di-Germanide $HfGe_2$	jlqt	111-8143
penta-Hafnium tri-Germanide Hf_5Ge_3	jlqt	111-8144
Hafnium Hydroborate $Hf(BH_4)_4$	h	104-8129
Hafnium Hydroborate, Deuterated $Hf(BD_4)_4$	h	104-8130
Hafnium mono-Iodide HfI	dm	112-8044
Hafnium - Iron $HfFe_2$		
see Hafnium di-Ferride $HfFe_2$	j	110-8263
Hafnium Lead tri-Oxide $HfPbO_3$		
see Lead (I I) Hafnate $PbHfO_3$	bg	112-0604
Hafnium Nickel Oxide Hf_3NiO	q	112-8076
Hafnium mono-Nitride HfN	ijltu	112-0247
Hafnium di-Osmide $HfOs_2$	j	112-8101
Hafnium mono-Oxide HfO	ah	112-8049
Hafnium di-Oxide HfO_2	abhjoqs	112-0021
Hafnium di-Rhenide $HfRe_2$	j	112-8100
Hafnium mono-Selenide $HfSe$	j	112-8091
Hafnium di-Selenide $HfSe_2$	b	112-8069
Hafnium penta-Selenide $HfSe_5$	b	112-8070
Hafnium Silicate $HfSiO_4$	h	112-8061
Hafnium di-Silicide $HfSi_2$	d	112-8096
Hafnium di-Sulfide HfS_2	bdf	112-0569
Hafnium tri-Sulfide HfS_3	a	112-8095
Hafnium di-Sulfide, Intercalated HfS_2	hj	112-8065
Hafnium mono-Telluride $HfTe$	j	112-8092
Hafnium di-Telluride $HfTe_2$	b	112-8071
Hafnium - Vanadium HfV_2	jq	112-8055
Hafnium - Vanadium - Ruthenium HfV_xRu_{2-x}	q	112-8077
Hafnium - Zirconium - Vanadium $Hf_xZr_{1-x}V_2$	j	112-8056
Heavy Spar $BaSO_4$		
see Barium Sulfate $BaSO_4$	abim	104-0025
Heavy Water		
see Water, Deuterated D_2O	abhqs	108-0005
Holmium di-Aluminide $HoAl_2$	q	102-8266
Holmium Antimonide $HoSb$	jpq	112-8008
Holmium Arsenate $HoAsO_4$	q	102-8373
Holmium Arsenide $HoAs$	f	102-8354
Holmium dodeca-Boride HoB_{12}	qu	104-8143
Holmium tri-Chloride $HoCl_3$	ju	106-8089
Holmium - Cobalt $HoCo_5$	np	106-8525
Holmium Cobaltate $HoCoO_3$	jqt	106-8322
Holmium - Cobalt - Germanium $HoCo_2Ge_2$	q	106-8172
Holmium - Cobalt - Iron $HoCo_xFe_{3-x}$	q	106-8137
Holmium Ferrate (I I I) $HoFeO_3$	n	110-0375
tri-Holmium penta-Ferrate (I I I) $Ho_3Fe_5O_{12}$	pqs	110-8057
Holmium - Gadolinium - Nickel $Ho_xGd_{1-x}Ni_2$	q	111-8111
Holmium - Gold $HoAu_2$	q	102-8121
Holmium Hydroxide $Ho(OH)_3$	q	112-8030
Holmium - Iron $HoFe_2$	npq	110-8068
Holmium - Iron $HoFe_3$	nq	110-8060
Holmium Manganese Ferrate $HoMn_xFe_{1-x}O_3$	q	110-8049
Holmium di-Manganese di-Germanide $HoMn_2Ge_2$	nq	111-8183
Holmium - Nickel $HoNi_2$	q	112-8059
Holmium - Nickel Ho_2Ni_{17}	nq	112-8068
Holmium Nitride HoN	df	112-8075
Holmium sesqui-Oxide Ho_2O_3	bjst	112-0481

Substance Name	*Property*	*Number*
Holmium Oxide Carbonate $Ho_2O_2(CO_3)$	q	106-8274
Holmium - Palladium $HoPd$	q	112-8039
Holmium - Palladium $HoPd_2$	q	112-8036
Holmium - Palladium $HoPd_3$	q	112-8035
Holmium - Palladium Ho_2Pd_3	q	112-8037
Holmium - Palladium Ho_3Pd_2	q	112-8040
Holmium - Palladium Ho_4Pd_5	q	112-8038
Holmium - Palladium Ho_5Pd_2	q	112-8041
Holmium - Praseodymium - Aluminum $Ho_xPr_{1-x}Al_2$	q	102-8265
Holmium - Praseodymium - Nickel $Ho_xPr_{1-x}Ni_2$	q	112-8058
Holmium - Rhodium Ho_7Rh_3	q	112-8046
Holmium - Silver $HoAg$	q	102-8073
Holmium - Silver $HoAg_2$	q	102-8390
Holmium Terbium Ferride $Ho_xTb_{1-x}Fe_2$	np	110-8272
Holmium Vanadate (I I I) $HoVO_3$	q	112-8057
Holmium Vanadate (V) $HoVO_4$	m	112-8043
Holmium di-Yttrium penta-Ferrate (I I I) $HoY_2Fe_5O_{12}$	p	110-8273
Holmium - Zinc $HoZn$	n	112-8047
Holmium - Zinc $HoZn_2$	p	112-8031
Holmium - Zinc Ho_2Zn_{17}	q	112-8060
Homosil Fused Silica	b	122-8060
see also Silica, Fused		122-8045
Hydrobromic Acid HBr		
see Hydrogen Bromide HBr	bgjs	104-0040
Hydrochloric Acid HCl		
see Hydrogen Chloride HCl	abijms	106-0009
Hydrofluoric Acid HF		
see Hydrogen Fluoride HF	abdfhims	110-0269
Hydrogen, Monodeuterated HD	hs	108-8026
Hydrogen, Monodeuterated, Monotritiated DT	b	108-8035
Hydrogen Boride Sulfide HBS		
see Thioboric Acid HBS	pq	104-8225
Hydrogen Bromide HBr	bgjs	104-0040
Hydrogen Bromide, Deuterated DBr	bs	104-0056
Hydrogen Chlorate $HClO_4$		
see Perchloric Acid $HClO_4$	s	106-8733
Hydrogen Chloride HCl	abijms	106-0009
Hydrogen Chloride, Deuterated DCl	s	106-8732
Hydrogen Chloride Oxide H_3OClO_4		
see Oxonium Perchlorate H_3OClO_4	j	106-8263
Hydrogen Cyanide HCN	j	106-8730
Hydrogen Fluoride HF	abdfhims	110-0269
Hydrogen Fluoride, Deuterated DF	hi	108-0021
Hydrogen Iodide HI	bgj	112-0034
Hydrogen Iodide, Deuterated DI	b	108-8006
Hydrogen Oxide Fluoride HOF		
see Hypofluorous Acid HOF	hiq	110-0224
Hydrogen Peroxide H_2O_2	a	112-0007
Hydrogen Phosphide Oxide $H_{3+x}P_{1+x}O_{4+3x}$		
see Polyphosphoric Acid $H_{3+x}P_{1+x}O_{4+3x}$	q	112-8045
Hydrogen Sulfide H_2S	abhijs	112-0004
Hydrogen Sulfide, Monodeuterated HDS	h	108-8016
Hydrogen Sulfide Chloride Oxide HSO_3Cl		
see Chlorosulfuric Acid $ClSO_3H$	q	106-0225
Hydrogen Sulfide Oxide Fluoride HSO_3F		
see Fluorosulfuric Acid FSO_3H	q	110-8281
Hydroxocopper Periodate $Cu_2(OH)H_2IO_6$	q	106-8189
Hypofluorous Acid HOF	hiq	110-0224
Ice H_2O		
see Water H_2O	abcdfhijlmqrstu	112-0001
Indium Antimonide $InSb$	a–fh–oqrstuv	114-8001
Indium Antimonide $InSb_{1-x}$	f	114-8070
Indium Antimony Arsenide $InSb_xAs_{1-x}$	bdefhjort	102-8018
see also Indium Antimonide $\geq$ Indium Arsenide		508-0344
see also Indium Arsenide $\geq$ Indium Antimonide		508-0345
Indium Antimony Sulfide $In_{2-x}Sb_xS_3$	js	114-8048
Indium Arsenide $InAs$	a–fhijklmoqrstuv	102-8054
Indium Arsenide Phosphide $InAs_xP_{1-x}$	abdefhijkloqst	102-0041
see also Indium Arsenide $\geq$ Indium Phosphide		508-0225
see also Indium Phosphide $\geq$ Indium Arsenide		508-0226
Indium Arsenide Sulfide $In_{2-x}As_xS_3$	js	102-8144

Property: **a.** Absorption coefficient; **b.** Dielectric constant; **c.** Dielectric strength; **d.** Energy band structure; **e.** Effective mass; **f.** Energy gap; **g.** Electric hysteresis; **h.** Energy level; **i.** Electron emission properties; **j.** Electrical resistivity; **k.** Magnetoelectric properties; **l.** Hall coefficient; **m.** Luminescence properties; **n.** Magnetic hysteresis; **o.** Mobility; **p.** Magnetomechanical properties; **q.** Magnetic susceptibility; **r.** Photoelectronic properties; **s.** Refractive index; **t.** Thermoelectric properties; **u.** Work function; **v.** Piezoelectric properties.

Substance Name	Property	Number
Indium di-Arsenidogermanate $InGeAs_2$	jt	102-8335
Indium mono-Bismuthide $InBi$	fjloqt	104-8010
di-Indium Bismuthide In_2Bi	joqt	104-8011
penta-Indium tri-Bismuthide In_5Bi_3	j	104-8367
Indium Bismuth tri-Selenide $InBiSe_3$	j	104-8394
Indium Bismuth Selenide $In_xBi_{2-x}Se$	t	104-8370
Indium tri-Bromide $InBr_3$	j	104-8066
Indium mono-Chloride $InCl$	j	106-0252
Indium di-Chloride $InCl_2$	ju	106-8090
Indium tri-Chloride $InCl_3$	ju	106-8091
Indium Gallium Antimonide $In_xGa_{1-x}Sb$	abdefhjkloqtv	111-8031
see also Gallium Antimonide ≥ Indium Antimonide		508-0248
see also Indium Antimonide ≥ Gallium Antimonide		508-0490
Indium Gallium Arsenide $In_xGa_{1-x}As$	abdefijklmosu	102-8142
see also Gallium Arsenide ≥ Indium Arsenide		508-0084
see also Indium Arsenide ≥ Gallium Arsenide		508-0247
Indium Gallium Arsenide Phosphide		
$In_xGa_{1-x}As_yP_{1-y}$	dfim	102-8104
see also Gallium Phosphide ≥ Indium Arsenide		508-0506
Indium Gallium Phosphide $In_xGa_{1-x}P$	adfhijlmos	111-8026
see also Gallium Phosphide ≥ Indium Phosphide		508-0259
see also Indium Phosphide ≥ Gallium Phosphide		508-0258
Indium Gallium Sulfide $In_xGa_{2-x}S_3$	hrt	111-8192
Indium Germanium di-Arsenide $InGeAs_2$		
see Indium di-Arsenidogermanate $InGeAs_2$	jt	102-8335
di-Indium Germanium tri-Telluride		
In_2GeTe_3		
see di-Indium tri-Tellurogermanate In_2GeTe_3	jqt	111-8017
Indium tri-Iodide InI_3	j	114-8008
Indium Lead Telluride $In_xPb_{1-x}Te$	jot	114-8065
Indium mono-Nitride InN	fjoq	114-0078
Indium sesqui-Oxide In_2O_3	abefjos	114-0015
Indium Phosphide InP	abdefh-moqrstuv	114-0017
Indium Phosphide tetra-Sulfide $InPS_4$		
see Indium tetra-Thiophosphate $InPS_4$	s	114-8077
Indium mono-Selenide $InSe$	afjlt	114-8067
Indium Selenide $InSe_{1-x}$	bfjt	114-8069
see also Indium ≥ Selenium		431-8029
di-Indium Selenide In_2Se	dij	114-8041
Indium sesqui-Selenide In_2Se_3	adfjkt	114-8010
hexa-Indium hepta-Selenide In_6Se_7	jl	114-8049
Indium mono-Sulfide InS	j	114-0028
Indium sesqui-Sulfide In_2S_3	afjmst	114-0046
tetra-Indium penta-Sulfide In_4S_5	j	114-8089
Indium mono-Telluride $InTe$	fjloqrt	114-8011
di-Indium Telluride In_2Te	j	114-8063
Indium sesqui-Telluride In_2Te_3	aefjlorst	114-8012
Indium Telluride Selenide $In_2Te_xSe_{3-x}$	afj	114-8064
di-Indium tri-Tellurogermanate In_2GeTe_3	jqt	111-8017
Indium tetra-Thiophosphate $InPS_4$	s	114-8077
Indium Vanadate (V) $InVO_4$	hm	114-8096
Infrasil Fused Silica	s	122-8126
see also Silica, Fused		122-8045
Infrasil Fused Silica 1	ab	122-8062
see also Silica, Fused		122-8045
Infrasil Fused Silica 2	ab	122-8098
see also Silica, Fused		122-8045
Iodic Acid HIO_3	bs	112-0096
Iodine mono-Bromide IBr	ahu	104-8265
Iodine mono-Chloride ICl	ahjmu	106-0168
Iodine tri-Chloride ICl_3	j	106-1290
Iodine mono-Fluoride IF	i	110-8187
Iodoheptafluoropropane C_3F_7I		
see hepta-Fluoroiodopropane C_3F_7I	s	106-8685
Iodopentamminerhodium (2+) Ion $Rh(NH_3)_5I$	m	112-8029
IRG 12 CaF_2	s	106-8695
see also Calcium Fluoride CaF_2		106-0026
Iridium Bromide Carbonate $IrBrCO_3$	jo	104-8184
Iridium Cadmium hexa-Hydroxide $IrCd(OH)_6$	q	106-8810
Iridium Carbon Bromide Oxide $IrCO_3Br$		
see Iridium Bromide Carbonate $IrBrCO_3$	jo	104-8184
Iridium Copper di-Selenide $IrCuSe_2$		
see Copper di-Selenoiridate $CuIrSe_2$	fjost	106-8459
Iridium tri-Silicide $IrSi_3$	j	114-8086
Iridium Zinc hexa-Hydroxide $IrZn(OH)_6$	q	112-8098
Iron mono-Aluminide $FeAl$	ejlt	102-8438
Iron di-Aluminide $FeAl_2$	j	102-8444
Iron tri-Aluminide $FeAl_3$	j	102-8445
di-Iron penta-Aluminide Fe_2Al_5	j	102-8446
di-Iron hepta-Aluminide Fe_2Al_7	j	102-8447
tri-Iron Aluminide Fe_3Al	jq	102-8107
Iron Aluminide Silicide $Fe_3Al_xSi_{1-x}$	j	102-8405
Iron Aluminum Oxide $Fe_xAl_{3-x}O_4$		
see Aluminum Ferrate $Al_xFe_{3-x}O_4$	p	102-8408
Iron di-Arsenide $FeAs_2$	h	102-8056
Iron Arsenide Phosphide $Fe_2As_xP_{1-x}$	q	102-8124
tetra-Iron di-Bismuth Mona-Oxide		
$Fe_4Bi_2O_9$		
see di-Bismuth tetra-Ferrate $Bi_2Fe_4O_9$	q	104-8292
Iron Bismuth Oxide $FeBiO_3$		
see Bismuth (III) Ferrate (III) $BiFeO_3$	bnq	104-0529
Iron (III) Borate $FeBO_3$	anqrs	104-8198
Iron mono-Boride FeB	jnqt	104-8068
di-Iron Boride Fe_2B	jnt	104-8420
tri-Iron Carbide Fe_3C	nq	106-0210
Iron undeca-Carbide tri-Chloride $FeC_{11}Cl_3$	a	106-8785
Iron (II) Carbonate $FeCO_3$	hs	106-0498
Iron di-Chloride $FeCl_2$	abhnpq	106-0046
Iron tri-Chloride $FeCl_3$	aq	106-0090
Iron tri-Chloride, Intercalated $FeCl_3$	q	106-8655
Iron Chloride Oxide $FeOCl$		
see Iron Oxychloride $FeOCl$	f	106-8534
Iron Copper Aluminate $Fe_xCuAl_{2-x}O_4$		
see Copper Aluminum Ferrite $CuAl_xFe_{2-x}O_4$	n	102-8462
Iron di-Copper Germanium tetra-Sulfide		
$FeCu_2GeS_4$		
see di-Copper Germanium tetra-Thioferrate		
Cu_2GeFeS_4	q	106-8268
di-Iron Copper tetra-Oxide Fe_2CuO_4		
see Copper (II) Ferrite $CuFe_2O_4$	fjklnpq	106-8439
Iron Copper Selenide $FeCuSe$	j	106-8645
Iron Copper di-Sulfide $FeCuS_2$		
see Copper di-Thioferrate $CuFeS_2$	a	106-0791
di-Iron Copper tri-Sulfide Fe_2CuS_3		
see Copper tri-Thiodiferrate $CuFe_2S_3$	q	106-8568
Iron Copper Zinc Oxide		
$Fe_2Cu_xZn_{1-x}O_4$		
see Copper Zinc Ferrite $Cu_xZn_{1-x}Fe_2O_4$	bj	106-8214
Iron (II) hexa-Cyanoargentate $FeAg_4(CN)_6$	s	102-8451
Iron di-Fluoride FeF_2	bhi	110-0017
Iron tri-Fluoride FeF_3	ahq	110-0065
Iron Gallium Oxide $Fe_xGa_{5-x}O_{12}$		
see Gallium Ferrate $Ga_xFe_{5-x}O_{12}$	s	110-8153
Iron - Germanium $FeGe_2$	t	110-8181
Iron - Germanium Fe_3Ge	q	110-8200
Iron Hydride Oxide $FeOOH$		
see Iron Hydroperoxide $FeOOH$	q	110-8105
Iron Hydroperoxide $FeOOH$	q	110-8105
Iron (III) Hydroxide $Fe(OH)_3$	n	110-8213
Iron (III) Iodate $Fe(IO_3)_3$	q	110-8207
dodeca-Iron Lead 19-Oxide $Fe_{12}PbO_{19}$		
see Lead (II) dodeca-Ferrate (III)		
$PbFe_{12}O_{19}$	jqt	110-8036
di-Iron Nitride Fe_2N	q	110-8013
tri-Iron Nitride Fe_3N	q	110-8236
tetra-Iron Nitride Fe_4N	q	110-0173
Iron Nitride $Fe_{2-x}N$	nq	110-8235
Iron mono-Oxide FeO	bdfhjmqu	110-0030
see also Wustite FeO		521-8027
Iron Oxide FeO_{1-x}	afhijt	110-8135
Iron sesqui-Oxide Fe_2O_3	abcdfjnopqst	110-0011
see also Hematite Fe_2O_3		521-0104
tri-Iron tetra-Oxide Fe_3O_4	abdfhjkmnpqtu	110-0025
see also Magnetite Fe_3O_4		521-0067
Iron Oxide Hydroxide $FeOOH$		
see Iron Hydroperoxide $FeOOH$	q	110-8105
Iron Oxychloride $FeOCl$	f	106-8534
Iron Oxychloride, Intercalated $FeOCl$	fjt	106-8535

Property: **a.** Absorption coefficient; **b.** Dielectric constant; **c.** Dielectric strength; **d.** Energy band structure; **e.** Effective mass; **f.** Energy gap; **g.** Electric hysteresis; **h.** Energy level; **i.** Electron emission properties; **j.** Electrical resistivity; **k.** Magnetoelectric properties; **l.** Hall coefficient; **m.** Luminescence properties; **n.** Magnetic hysteresis; **o.** Mobility; **p.** Magnetomechanical properties; **q.** Magnetic susceptibility; **r.** Photoelectronic properties; **s.** Refractive index; **t.** Thermoelectric properties; **u.** Work function; **v.** Piezoelectric properties.

Substance Name	Property	Number
Iron Phosphate $FePO_4$	q	110-0193
di-Iron Phosphide Fe_2P	pq	110-8014
Iron Phosphide tri-Sulfide $FePS_3$	aq	110-8126
Iron Selenide $FeSe$	fjot	110-8203
Iron sesqui-Selenide Fe_2Se_3	fjot	110-8204
tri-Iron tetra-Selenide Fe_3Se_4	fjoqt	110-8082
hepta-Iron octa-Selenide Fe_7Se_8	fjoqt	110-8205
di-Iron tetra-Selenotitanate Fe_2TiSe_4	q	110-8081
Iron mono-Silicide $FeSi$	djnpt	110-8015
Iron di-Silicide $FeSi_2$	djt	110-8064
tri-Iron Silicide Fe_3Si	djnp	110-8063
penta-Iron tri-Silicide Fe_5Si_3	u	110-8199
Iron tetra-Silver hexa-Cyanide $FeAg_4(CN)_6$		
see Iron (II) hexa-Cyanoargentate $FeAg_4(CN)_6$	s	102-8451
Iron mono-Sulfide FeS	aijlqt	110-0007
Iron di-Sulfide FeS_2	dfhjt	110-0010
see also Marcasite FeS_2		521-8016
Iron (III) Tantalate $FeTaO_4$	j	110-8249
Iron Telluride $FeTe_{1-x}$	jq	110-8283
Iron di-Thiocuprate $FeCuS_2$		
see Copper di-Thioferrate $CuFeS_2$	a	106-0791
di-Iron tri-Thiocuprate Fe_2CuS_3		
see Copper tri-Thiodiferrate $CuFe_2S_3$	q	106-8568
Iron tetra-Thiodititanate $FeTi_2S_4$	q	110-8097
di-Iron tetra-Thiotitanate Fe_2TiS_4	n	110-8218
Iron Thiotitanate $Fe_{1-x}TiS_2$	nq	110-8050
Iron-Zinc $FeZn_{13}$	jkq	110-8124
Iron Zinc Oxide $Fe_{3-x}Zn_xO_4$		
see Zinc Ferrite $Zn_xFe_{3-x}O_4$	j	110-8048
Irtran 1 (Kodak) MgF_2	abs	110-8118
see also Magnesium Fluoride MgF_2		110-0023
Irtran 2 (Kodak) ZnS	abs	126-8073
see also Zinc Sulfide ZnS		126-0005
Irtran 3 (Kodak) CaF_2	as	106-8357
see also Calcium Fluoride CaF_2		106-0026
Irtran 4 (Kodak) $ZnSe$	abfos	126-8074
see also Zinc Selenide $ZnSe$		126-8052
Irtran 5 (Kodak) MgO	abs	119-8048
see also Magnesium Oxide MgO		119-0002
Irtran 6 (Kodak) $CdTe$	abfos	106-8358
see also Cadmium Telluride $CdTe$		106-8041
Irtran 51 (Kodak) MgF_2		
see Irtran 1 (Kodak) MgF_2	abs	110-8118
Irtran AB-1 MgF_2		
see Irtran 1 (Kodak) MgF_2	abs	110-8118
Irtran AB-2 (Kodak) ZnS		
see Irtran 2 (Kodak) ZnS	abs	126-8073
Jacinth		
see Zirconium Silicate $ZrSiO_4$	hjs	122-8070
Japanese Industries Fused Silica	b	122-8059
see also Silica, Fused		122-8045
Jargon		
see Zirconium Silicate $ZrSiO_4$	hjs	122-8070
KCP		
see Potassium tetra-Cyanobromoplatinate $K_2Pt(CN)_4Br_x$	abfjoqr	104-8183
KDA KH_2AsO_4		
see Potassium di-Hydrogen Arsenate KH_2AsO_4	bfgjnqsv	102-0054
KDDA KD_2AsO_4		
see Potassium di-Hydrogen Arsenate, Deuterated KD_2AsO_4	bfgjsv	102-0281
KDDP KD_2PO_4		
see Potassium di-Hydrogen Phosphate, Deuterated KD_2PO_4	bgijnqsv	108-0014
KDP K_2HPO_4		
see di-Potassium Hydrogen Phosphate K_2HPO_4	b	112-0637
K01 MgF_2		
see Irtran 1 (Kodak) MgF_2	abs	110-8118
K02 ZnS		
see Irtran 2 (Kodak) ZnS	abs	126-8073
K03 CaF_2		
see Irtran 3 (Kodak) CaF_2	as	106-8357
K04 $ZnSe$		
see Irtran 4 (Kodak) $ZnSe$	abfos	126-8074
K05 MgO		
see Irtran 5 (Kodak) MgO	abs	119-8048
K06 $CdTe$		
see Irtran 6 (Kodak) $CdTe$	abfos	106-8358
Kodak AB-1		
see Irtran 1 (Kodak) MgF_2	abs	110-8118
Kodak AB-2		
see Irtran 2 (Kodak) ZnS	abs	126-8073
Kodak Irtran 5 MgO		
see Irtran 5 (Kodak) MgO	abs	119-8048
KRS-5	abhs	104-8191
see also Thallium Iodide Bromide $Tl_5I_3Br_2$		104-0434
KRS-6	as	104-8192
KSN $K_xNa_{1-x}NbO_3$		
see Potassium Sodium Niobate $K_xNa_{1-x}NbO_3$	bjv	116-8025
KTN $KTaNbO_3$		
see Potassium Tantalum Niobate $KTaNbO_3$	b	116-8023
Lanthanum Aluminate $LaAlO_3$	hjmq	102-0191
Lanthanum di-Aluminide $LaAl_2$	ahjt	102-8189
Lanthanum tri-Aluminide $LaAl_3$	j	102-8129
Lanthanum mono-Antimonide $LaSb$	p	118-8001
Lanthanum Arsenide $LaAs$	f	102-8350
Lanthanum Bismuth Ferrate $La_{1-x}Bi_xFeO_3$	q	104-8150
Lanthanum hexa-Boride LaB_6	aijqsu	104-8069
Lanthanum Boride Carbide $LaBC$	jq	104-8437
Lanthanum di-Boride di-Carbide LaB_2C_2	jqt	104-0575
Lanthanum di-Boride tetra-Carbide LaB_2C_4	jqt	104-0574
Lanthanum tri-Bromide $LaBr_3$	bfhjm	104-0306
Lanthanum di-Carbide LaC_2	q	106-1343
Lanthanum Carbide LaC_{2-x}	j	106-8712
Lanthanum Carbon Chloride Oxide $La_3Cl(CO_3)_4$		
see Lanthanum Chloride Carbonate $La_3Cl(CO_3)_4$	sv	106-8254
Lanthanum Chlorate $LaClO$	m	106-8362
Lanthanum tri-Chloride $LaCl_3$	hjm	106-0259
Lanthanum Chloride Carbonate $La_3Cl(CO_3)_4$	sv	106-8254
Lanthanum Chromate (III) $LaCrO_3$	fijt	106-1083
Lanthanum Chromium tri-Selenide $LaCrSe_3$		
see Lanthanum tri-Selenochromate $LaCrSe_3$	jlq	106-8365
Lanthanum-Cobalt $LaCo$	j	106-8506
Lanthanum-Cobalt $LaCo_5$	nq	106-8222
Lanthanum Cobaltate (III) $LaCoO_3$	nq	106-8316
Lanthanum Cobaltate $LaCoO_{3-x}$	nq	106-8317
di-Lanthanum Cobaltate (II) La_2CoO_4	jq	106-8193
Lanthanum-Cobalt-Copper $LaCo_xCu_{5-x}$	q	106-8813
Lanthanum-Cobalt-Copper $LaCo_2Cu_3$	q	106-8814
Lanthanum-Cobalt-Copper $LaCo_3Cu_2$	nq	106-8815
Lanthanum-Cobalt-Copper $LaCo_4Cu$	q	106-8816
Lanthanum-Cobalt-Germanium $LaCo_2Ge_2$	q	106-8167
Lanthanum Cuprate $LaCuO_3$	q	106-8359
di-Lanthanum Cuprate (II) La_2CuO_4	jqt	106-8349
Lanthanum Ferrate (III) $LaFeO_3$	q	110-8173
Lanthanum dodeca-Ferrate $LaFe_{12}O_{19}$	q	110-8080
Lanthanum tri-Fluoride LaF_3	abhjms	110-0083
Lanthanum Gallate $LaGaO_3$	m	111-8081
Lanthanum Germanate La_2GeO_5	fj	111-0093
di-Lanthanum Germanium penta-Sulfide La_2GeS_5		
see di-Lanthanum penta-Thiogermanate La_2GeS_5	fj	111-8098
Lanthanum di-Hydride LaH_2	dj	112-0698
Lanthanum Hydride LaH_{3-x}	j	112-8088
Lanthanum-Indium La_3In	fjq	114-8044
Lanthanum-Indium / $LaIn_3$	dhjq	114-8054
Lanthanum Indium tri-Sulfide $LaInS_3$		
see Lanthanum tri-Thioindate $LaInS_3$	fq	114-0111
Lanthanum tri-Iodide LaI_3	j	114-0088
Lanthanum di-Iridide $LaIr_2$	j	114-8101

Property: a. Absorption coefficient; **b.** Dielectric constant; **c.** Dielectric strength; **d.** Energy band structure; **e.** Effective mass; **f.** Energy gap; **g.** Electric hysteresis; **h.** Energy level; **i.** Electron emission properties; **j.** Electrical resistivity; **k.** Magnetoelectric properties; **l.** Hall coefficient; **m.** Luminescence properties; **n.** Magnetic hysteresis; **o.** Mobility; **p.** Magnetomechanical properties; **q.** Magnetic susceptibility; **r.** Photoelectronic properties; **s.** Refractive index; **t.** Thermoelectric properties; **u.** Work function; **v.** Piezoelectric properties.

Substance Name	*Property*	*Number*
Lanthanum Iron Bismuth Oxide		
$La_{1-x}FeBi_xO_3$		
see Lanthanum Bismuth Ferrate $La_{1-x}Bi_xFeO_3$	q	104-8150
Lanthanum - Iron - Germanium $LaFe_xGe_{2-x}$	nq	110-8143
Lanthanum Iron Oxide $LaFe_{12}O_{19}$		
see Lanthanum dodeca- Ferrate $LaFe_{12}O_{19}$	q	110-8080
Lanthanum Iron Sulfide $La_2Fe_2S_5$		
see di- Lanthanum penta- Thiodiferrate $La_2Fe_2S_5$	q	110-8223
Lanthanum - Lead $LaPb_3$		
see Lanthanum tri- Plumbide $LaPb_3$	hjqt	118-8055
Lanthanum Lead Bismuth Zirconium Niobium Ferrate		
(La, Pb, Bi) (Zr, Nb, Fe) O_3	gj	104-8318
Lanthanum Lead Manganese Ferrate		
$La_xPb_{1-x}Mn_yFe_{1-y}O_3$	q	110-8248
Lanthanum Lead Stannide $LaPb_xSn_{3-x}$	jqt	118-8056
Lanthanum Manganate (I I I) $LaMnO_3$	jk	118-8065
Lanthanum di- Manganese di- Germanide $LaMn_2Ge_2$	nq	111-8178
Lanthanum Manganese Iron Lead Oxide		
$La_xMn_yFe_{1-y}Pb_{1-x}O_3$		
see Lanthanum Lead Manganese Ferrate		
$La_xPb_{1-x}Mn_yFe_{1-y}O_3$	q	110-8248
di- Lanthanum Nickelate (I I) La_2NiO_4	jqt	118-8026
Lanthanum - Nickel - Cobalt $LaNi_xCo_{5-x}$	q	106-8272
Lanthanum Niobate (V) $LaNbO_4$	hm	118-8043
Lanthanum mono- Nitride LaN	df	118-0008
Lanthanum - Osmium $LaOs_2$	j	118-8030
Lanthanum mono- Oxide LaO	h	118-8040
Lanthanum sesqui- Oxide La_2O_3	jmq	118-0003
di- Lanthanum di- Oxosulfate La_2SO_2	fhmq	118-8015
di- Lanthanum hexa- Oxosulfate La_2SO_6	m	118-8032
Lanthanum tri- Palladide $LaPd_3$	j	118-8052
Lanthanum Phosphate $LaPO_4$	hm	118-8021
Lanthanum penta- Phosphate LaP_5O_{14}	m	118-8101
Lanthanum di- Platinide $LaPt_2$	j	118-8104
Lanthanum tri- Plumbide $LaPb_3$	hjqt	118-8055
Lanthanum di- Rhodide $LaRh_2$	j	118-8103
Lanthanum di- Ruthenide $LaRu_2$	j	118-8047
Lanthanum Scandate $LaScO_3$	b	118-0070
Lanthanum mono- Selenide $LaSe$	j	118-8077
Lanthanum sesqui- Selenide La_2Se_3	j	118-8091
tri- Lanthanum tetra- Selenide La_3Se_4	j	118-8051
Lanthanum tri- Selenochromate $LaCrSe_3$	jlq	106-8365
Lanthanum mono- Silicide $LaSi$	dj	118-8097
Lanthanum di- Silicide $LaSi_2$	dj	118-8092
penta- Lanthanum tri- Silicide La_5Si_3	dj	118-8098
Lanthanum - Silver $LaAg$	j	102-8327
Lanthanum - Silver - Indium $LaAg_xIn_{1-x}$	hq	102-8162
Lanthanum tri- Stannide $LaSn_3$	dhjqt	118-8005
Lanthanum Sulfate La_2SO_2		
see di- Lanthanum di- Oxosulfate La_2SO_2	fhmq	118-8015
Lanthanum Sulfate La_2SO_6		
see di- Lanthanum hexa- Oxosulfate La_2SO_6	m	118-8032
Lanthanum mono- Sulfide LaS	j	118-0028
Lanthanum di- Sulfide LaS_2	j	118-8078
Lanthanum sesqui- Sulfide La_2S_3	bd	118-0026
tri- Lanthanum tetra- Sulfide La_3S_4	j	118-8079
Lanthanum Tantalate $LaTaO_4$	hm	118-8060
Lanthanum mono- Telluride $LaTe$	j	118-8080
Lanthanum sesqui- Telluride La_2Te_3	j	118-8093
tri- Lanthanum tetra- Telluride La_3Te_4	j	118-8081
Lanthanum - Thallium $LaTl_3$	jqt	118-8053
Lanthanum - Thallium - Tin $LaTl_{3-x}Sn_x$	jqt	118-8054
di- Lanthanum penta- Thiodiferrate $La_2Fe_2S_5$	q	110-8223
di- Lanthanum penta- Thiogermanate La_2GeS_5	fj	111-8098
Lanthanum tri- Thioindate $LaInS_3$	fq	114-0111
Lanthanum - Tin $LaSn_3$		
see Lanthanum tri- Stannide $LaSn_3$	dhjqt	118-8005
Lanthanum - Tin - Indium $LaSn_xIn_{2-x}$	jq	114-8055
Lanthanum di- Titanate (I V) $La_2Ti_2O_7$	g	118-8088
Lanthanum Titanium Aluminosilicate	b	102-8375
Lanthanum Titanium Lead Oxide		
$La_xTiPb_{1-x}O_3$		
see Lead Lanthanum Titanate $Pb_xLa_{1-x}TiO_3$	bv	118-8075

Substance Name	*Property*	*Number*
Lanthanum Titanium Lead Oxide		
$La_xTi_{1-y}Pb_{1-x}O_3$		
see Lead Lanthanum Titanate $Pb_xLa_{1-x}Ti_{1-y}O_3$	b	118-8038
Lanthanum Titanium Manganese Lead Oxide		
$La_xTi_yMn_{1-y}Pb_{1-x}O_3$		
see Lead Lanthanum Titanium Manganate		
$Pb_xLa_{1-x}Ti_yMn_{1-y}O_3$	bv	118-8076
Lanthanum Titanium Silicate (General)	b	118-8070
Lanthanum Vanadate (I I I) $LaVO_3$	fjq	118-8019
Lanthanum Vanadate (V) $LaVO_4$	m	118-8022
Lanthanum Yttrium Cobaltate $La_xY_{1-x}CoO_3$	jt	106-8564
Lanthanum Yttrium Selenide $La_xY_{3-x}Se_4$	j	118-8082
Lanthanum Yttrium Sulfide $La_xY_{3-x}S_4$	j	118-8083
Lanthanum Yttrium Telluride $La_xY_{3-x}Te_4$	j	118-8084
Lanthanum Zirconate La_2ZrO_5	b	118-8089
Lanthanum Zirconium Niobium Iron Lead Bismuthate		
$La_{1-x}(ZrNb)_yFe_{1-y}(PbBi)_xO_3$		
see Lanthanum Lead Bismuth Zirconium Niobium Ferrate		
(La, Pb, Bi) (Zr, Nb, Fe) O_3	gj	104-8318
Lanthanum Zirconium Titanium Lead Oxide		
$La_xZr_yTi_{1-y}Pb_{1-x}O_3$		
see Lead Lanthanum Zirconium Titanate		
$Pb_{1-x}La_xZr_yTi_{1-y}O_3$	abcgjqrsv	118-8018
Lead di- Antimony tetra- Sulfide $PbSb_2S_4$	fhjrt	123-8065
Lead Azide $Pb(N_3)_2$	abfrs	120-0233
Lead Bismuth Antimony Arsenide $PbBiSbAs$	j	102-8410
Lead tetra- Bismuth hepta- Telluride		
$PbBi_4Te_7$		
see Lead (I I) hepta- Tellurobismuthate (I I I)		
$PbBi_4Te_7$	ehj	104-8360
Lead (I I) tetra- Borate PbB_4O_7	bf	104-8118
di- Lead (I I) di- Borate $Pb_2B_2O_5$	bf	104-8120
penta- Lead (I I) octa- Borate $Pb_5B_8O_{17}$	bf	104-8119
Lead mono- Bromide $PbBr$	m	104-8273
Lead di- Bromide $PbBr_2$	abdfhjmot	104-0069
Lead Carbonate $PbCO_3$	b	106-0496
Lead mono- Chloride $PbCl$	m	106-8552
Lead di- Chloride $PbCl_2$	abdfhjmst	106-0060
Lead tetra- Chloride $PbCl_4$	q	106-8092
Lead Chloride Fluoride $PbClF$	j	106-0059
di- Lead (I I) Cobalt (I I) Tungstate (V I)		
Pb_2CoWO_6	b	106-8250
Lead (I I) dodeca- Ferrate (I I I) $PbFe_{12}O_{19}$	jqt	110-8036
Lead (I I) Fluoride PbF_2	abdfhjqs	110-0021
Lead (I I) Germanate $PbGeO_3$	b	111-8155
tri- Lead (I I) Germanate Pb_3GeO_5	b	111-8156
tri- Lead (I I) di- Germanate $Pb_3Ge_2O_7$	bgqv	111-8061
penta- Lead (I I) tri- Germanate $Pb_5Ge_3O_{11}$	bfgjr	111-8068
Lead Germanium Selenide $Pb_xGe_{1-x}Se$	f	111-8161
Lead Germanium Silicon Oxide $Pb_5Ge_{3-x}Si_xO_{11}$	g	111-8069
Lead Germanium Telluride $Pb_xGe_{1-x}Te$	afhjlot	111-8127
see also Lead Monotelluride $\geq$ Germanium Monotelluride		508-0489
Lead (I I) Hafnate $PbHfO_3$	bg	112-0604
Lead (I I) Hydroxoiodide $Pb(OH)I$	m	112-8027
Lead mono- Iodide PbI	efjr	114-8018
Lead di- Iodide PbI_2	abdfhmrt	114-0006
Lead Iron Oxide $PbFe_{12}O_{19}$		
see Lead (I I) dodeca- Ferrate (I I I)		
$PbFe_{12}O_{19}$	jqt	110-8036
Lead Lanthanum Titanate $Pb_xLa_{1-x}TiO_3$	bv	118-8075
Lead Lanthanum Titanate $Pb_xLa_{1-x}Ti_{1-y}O_3$	b	118-8038
Lead Lanthanum Titanium Manganate		
$Pb_xLa_{1-x}Ti_yMn_{1-y}O_3$	bv	118-8076
Lead Lanthanum Zirconium Titanate		
$Pb_{1-x}La_xZr_yTi_{1-y}O_3$	abcgjqrsv	118-8018
Lead (I I) Molybdate (V I) $PbMoO_4$	bhmqs	119-0073
Lead (I I) Niobate (V) $PbNb_2O_6$	bgv	120-0235
Lead (I I) tetra- Niobate (V) $PbNb_4O_{11}$	s	120-8109
di- Lead (I I) Niobate (V) $Pb_2Nb_2O_7$	bgn	120-8181
Lead Nitrate $Pb(NO_3)_2$	abs	120-0081
Lead Nitride $Pb(N_3)_2$		
see Lead Azide $Pb(N_3)_2$	abfrs	120-0233
Lead mono- Oxide PbO	abefhijoqrstu	122-0050
Lead di- Oxide PbO_2	fijst	122-0068

Property: a. Absorption coefficient; **b.** Dielectric constant; **c.** Dielectric strength; **d.** Energy band structure; **e.** Effective mass; **f.** Energy gap; **g.** Electric hysteresis; **h.** Energy level; **i.** Electron emission properties; **j.** Electrical resistivity; **k.** Magnetoelectric properties; **l.** Hall coefficient; **m.** Luminescence properties; **n.** Magnetic hysteresis; **o.** Mobility; **p.** Magnetomechanical properties; **q.** Magnetic susceptibility; **r.** Photoelectronic properties; **s.** Refractive index; **t.** Thermoelectric properties; **u.** Work function; **v.** Piezoelectric properties.

Substance Name	Property	Number
Lead sesqui-Oxide Pb_2O_3	bj	122-0051
tri-Lead tetra-Oxide Pb_3O_4	bijs	122-0067
dodeca-Lead 19-Oxide $Pb_{12}O_{19}$	js	122-8122
tri-Lead (I I) di-Phosphate $Pb_3P_2O_8$	b	122-0133
Lead mono-Selenide $PbSe$	abdefh-moqrstuv	123-8017
Lead Selenide Sulfide $PbSe_xS_{1-x}$	abfhims	123-8058
see also Lead Monosulfide ≥ Lead Monoselenide		508-0532
tetra-Lead (I I) Silicate Pb_4SiO_6	g	122-8123
Lead Sulfate $PbSO_4$	bmq	122-8036
Lead mono-Sulfide PbS	abdefh-moqrstuv	123-0003
see also Galena PbS		521-8025
Lead Sulfide Oxide PbS_xO_{1-x}	alor	122-8044
Lead (I I) Tantalate $PbTa_2O_6$	b	122-0414
Lead mono-Telluride $PbTe$	abd-mopqrstuv	123-8018
Lead Telluride Selenide $PbTe_xSe_{1-x}$	adfjot	123-8074
see also Lead Monotelluride ≥ Lead Monoselenide		508-0110
Lead Telluride Sulfide $PbTe_xS_{1-x}$	efjt	123-8094
see also Lead Monosulfide ≥ Lead Monotelluride		508-0533
see also Lead Monotelluride ≥ Lead Monosulfide		508-0334
Lead (I I) hepta-Tellurobismuthate (I I I) $PbBi_4Te_7$	ehj	104-8360
Lead Tin Selenide $Pb_xSn_{1-x}Se$	abdefhjklmoqrst	123-8039
Lead Tin Sulfide $Pb_xSn_{1-x}S$	f	123-8093
Lead Tin Telluride $Pb_{1-x}Sn_xTe$	abdefghjklmoqrst	123-8051
see also Lead Monotelluride ≥ Tin Monotelluride		508-0040
see also Tin Monotelluride ≥ Lead Monotelluride		508-0373
Lead Tin Telluride Selenide $Pb_{1-x}Sn_xTe_{1-y}Se_y$	afhjot	123-8050
see also Lead Monoselenide ≥ Tin Monotelluride		508-0170
see also Lead Monotelluride ≥ Tin Monoselenide		508-0388
see also Tin Monotelluride ≥ Lead Monoselenide		508-0171
Lead Tin Zirconium Titanate $PbSn_xZr_yTi_{1-x-y}O_3$	g	122-8042
Lead (I I) Titanate (I I) $PbTiO_2$	b	122-8116
Lead (I I) Titanate (I V) $PbTiO_3$	abfgjpqstv	122-0013
Lead Titanate $Pb_{1-x}TiO_{3-x}$	bg	122-8056
Lead (I I) Tungstate (V I) $PbWO_4$	bh	122-0054
Lead Tungsten Ferrate $PbW_xFe_{1-x}O_3$	q	110-8142
Lead Uranium Ferrate $PbU_xFe_{1-x}O_3$	nq	110-8139
Lead Uranium Tungsten Ferrate $PbU_xW_yFe_{1-x-y}O_3$	bq	110-8141
Lead Zinc Niobate $PbZn_xNb_{1-x}O_3$	bg	120-8039
tri-Lead (I I) Zinc di-Niobate (V) $Pb_3ZnNb_2O_9$	s	120-8043
Lead (I I) Zirconate $PbZrO_3$	bcgj	122-0292
Lead Zirconium Titanate $PbZr_xTi_{1-x}O_3$	bcgjnqrtv	122-0196
Lead Zirconium Titanium Niobate $Pb_xZr_yTi_zNb_{1-x-y-z}O_3$	qs	120-8126
Lithium penta-Aluminate $LiAl_5O_8$	jm	102-8105
Lithium Aluminum Ferrate $Li_xAl_yFe_{3-x-y}O_4$	jnp	102-8118
Lithium Aluminum tetra-Hydride $LiAlH_4$		
see Lithium tetra-Hydridoaluminate $LiAlH_4$	j	102-8262
Lithium Aluminum Silicate $LiAlSiO_4$	s	102-8304
Lithium Aluminum di-Silicate $LiAlSi_2O_6$	s	102-8305
Lithium Aluminum Silicate (General)	bc	102-8313
Lithium tetra-Ammine $Li(NH_3)_4$	jk	112-8067
Lithium Antimony Selenide $LiSbSe_2$		
see Lithium di-Selenoantimonate $LiSbSe_2$	fhjt	118-8073
Lithium Antimony Sulfide $LiSbS_2$		
see Lithium di-Thioantimonate $LiSbS_2$	fhjt	118-8072
Lithium Arsenide di-Selenide $LiAsSe_2$		
see Lithium di-Selenoarsenate $LiAsSe_2$	af	102-8148
Lithium Barium tri-Fluoride $LiBaF_3$		
see Lithium tri-Fluorobarate $LiBaF_3$	ahm	104-8238
Lithium Bismuthide $LiBi$	j	104-8013
Lithium tetra-Borate $Li_2B_4O_7$	m	104-8113
Lithium Boron tetra-Fluoride $LiBF_4$		
see Lithium tetra-Fluoroborate $LiBF_4$	j	104-8286
Lithium Bromide $LiBr$	abdfhjstu	104-0105
Lithium-Cadmium $LiCd$	j	106-8423
Lithium-Cadmium $LiCd_2$	j	106-8424
Lithium-Cadmium $LiCd_3$	j	106-8425
Lithium Carbonate Li_2CO_3	bj	106-0409
Lithium Chlorate $LiClO_3$	j	106-8710
Lithium Chloride $LiCl$	abdfhijmsu	106-0159

Substance Name	Property	Number
Lithium tri-Chlorocuprate $LiCuCl_3$	nq	106-8492
Lithium Chromate (I I I) $LiCrO_2$	iq	106-8229
di-Lithium Chromate Li_2CrO_4	ij	106-1418
Lithium Chromium Ferrate $LiCr_xFe_{5-x}O_8$	jq	106-8117
Lithium Chromium Nickelate $Li_xCr_yNi_{2-x-y}O_2$	q	106-8230
Lithium Cobaltate $Li_xCo_{1-x}O$	j	106-8700
Lithium-Copper-Aluminum $LiCuAl_2$	j	102-8294
Lithium Copper tri-Chloride $LiCuCl_3$		
see Lithium tri-Chlorocuprate $LiCuCl_3$	nq	106-8492
Lithium Cuprate $Li_xCu_{1-x}O$	j	106-8702
Lithium Europium tri-Hydride $LiEuH_3$		
see Lithium tri-Hydridoeuropate $LiEuH_3$	h	109-8057
Lithium Ferrate $LiFe_2O_4$	jp	110-8259
Lithium penta-Ferrate (I I I) $LiFe_5O_8$	bjn	110-0236
Lithium Ferrate $Li_xFe_{3-x}O_4$	abjlnopqt	110-8112
Lithium Ferrite $LiFeO_2$	np	110-0026
Lithium Fluoride LiF	abcdefhijmpsuv	110-0024
di-Lithium Fluoride Phosphate Li_2FPO_3	qs	110-8108
Lithium tri-Fluorobarate $LiBaF_3$	ahm	104-8238
Lithium tetra-Fluoroborate $LiBF_4$	j	104-8286
Lithium tetra-Fluoronickelate (I I) Li_2NiF_4	a	110-8157
Lithium tetra-Fluoroterbate $LiTbF_4$	ajnq	110-8234
Lithium tetra-Fluorothulate $LiTmF_4$	ahm	110-8169
Lithium tetra-Fluoroytterbate (I I I) $LiYbF_4$	ah	110-8170
Lithium tetra-Fluoroyttrate $LiYF_4$	afhms	110-0352
di-Lithium tetra-Gadolinium hepta-Molybdate (V I) $Li_2Gd_4(MoO_4)_7$	gq	111-8135
Lithium Gallate $LiGaO_2$	bv	111-8042
Lithium penta-Gallate $LiGa_5O_8$	h	111-8028
Lithium Germanate Li_2GeO_3	bsv	111-8125
Lithium Hydride LiH	abdfhijmr	112-0098
Lithium Hydride, Deuterated LiD	abfhij	108-0029
Lithium tetra-Hydridoaluminate $LiAlH_4$	j	102-8262
Lithium tri-Hydridoeuropate $LiEuH_3$	h	109-8057
Lithium tri-Hydrogen Selenite $LiH_3(SeO_3)_2$	b	112-0671
Lithium Hydroxide $LiOH$	afi	118-8048
Lithium Indate $LiInO_3$	b	114-0077
Lithium Indium di-Selenide $LiInSe_2$		
see Lithium di-Selenoindate $LiInSe_2$	v	114-8045
Lithium Indium di-Sulfide $LiInS_2$		
see Lithium di-Thioindate $LiInS_2$	v	114-8046
Lithium Iodide LiI	abdfhjms	114-0010
Lithium Iron Aluminum Oxide $Li_xFe_yAl_{3-x-y}O_4$		
see Lithium Aluminum Ferrate $Li_xAl_yFe_{3-x-y}O_4$	jnp	102-8118
Lithium Iron di-Oxide $LiFeO_2$		
see Lithium Ferrite $LiFeO_2$	np	110-0026
Lithium Iron Zinc Oxide $Li_xFe_{3-x-y}Zn_yO_4$		
see Lithium Zinc Ferrite $Li_xZn_yFe_{3-x-y}O_4$	jqt	110-8123
Lithium Lanthanum Molybdate (V I) $LiLa(MoO_4)_2$	hm	118-8016
Lithium Magnesium Chromium Manganese Copper Oxide $Li_xMg_yCr_zMn_{2-y-z}Cu_{1-x}O_4$	jq	106-8185
Lithium Manganate $Li_xMn_{1-x}O$	j	118-8090
Lithium Manganese Ferrite $Li_xMn_yFe_{3-x-y}O_4$	n	110-8113
Lithium Manganese Selenide $Li_xMn_{1-x}Se$	jqr	118-8017
Lithium Molybdate (V I) Li_2MoO_4	j	118-8094
Lithium Neodymium di-Molybdate (V I) $LiNd(MoO_4)_2$	q	118-8069
Lithium Neodymium tetra-Phosphate $LiNdP_4O_{12}$	ahms	118-8061
Lithium Nickel Cobaltate $Li_xNi_yCo_{1-x-y}O$	j	106-8701
di-Lithium Nickel tetra-Fluoride Li_2NiF_4		
see Lithium tetra-Fluoronickelate (I I) Li_2NiF_4	a	110-8157
Lithium Nickel Oxide $Li_xNi_{1-x}O$	j	118-8064
Lithium Niobate (I I I) $LiNbO_2$	gj	118-8059
Lithium Niobate (V) $LiNbO_3$	abcdfghijmnqrsv	118-0037
Lithium tri-Niobate (V) $LiNb_3O_8$	m	118-8068
Lithium Nitrate $LiNO_3$	fj	118-0004
Lithium Nitride Hydride $Li(NH_3)_4$		
see Lithium tetra-Ammine $Li(NH_3)_4$	jk	112-8067
Lithium Nitrite $LiNO_2$	j	118-0031

Property: **a.** Absorption coefficient; **b.** Dielectric constant; **c.** Dielectric strength; **d.** Energy band structure; **e.** Effective mass; **f.** Energy gap; **g.** Electric hysteresis; **h.** Energy level; **i.** Electron emission properties; **j.** Electrical resistivity; **k.** Magnetoelectric properties; **l.** Hall coefficient; **m.** Luminescence properties; **n.** Magnetic hysteresis; **o.** Mobility; **p.** Magnetomechanical properties; **q.** Magnetic susceptibility; **r.** Photoelectronic properties; **s.** Refractive index; **t.** Thermoelectric properties; **u.** Work function; **v.** Piezoelectric properties.

Substance Name	Property	Number
Lithium Nitrogen Hydrogen Sulfate		
NH_4LiSO_4		
see Ammonium Lithium Sulfate NH_4LiSO_4	g	112-8080
Lithium (I) Oxide Li_2O	ij	118-0002
Lithium Phosphate Li_3PO_4	hq	118-8027
di- Lithium Phosphorus Oxide Fluoride		
Li_2PO_3F		
see di- Lithium Fluoride Phosphate Li_2FPO_3	qs	110-8108
Lithium Scandium Manganese Ferrite		
$Li_xSc_yMn_zFe_{3-x-y-z}O_4$	n	110-8114
Lithium di- Selenoantimonate $LiSbSe_2$	fhjt	118-8073
Lithium di- Selenoarsenate $LiAsSe_2$	af	102-8148
Lithium di- Selenoindate $LiInSe_2$	v	114-8045
tetra- Lithium Silicate Li_4SiO_4	j	118-8066
Lithium Spinel $Li_2O.5Al_2O_3$		
see Lithium penta- Aluminate $LiAl_5O_8$	jm	102-8105
tetra- Lithium Stannide Li_4Sn	j	118-8099
Lithium Sulfate Li_2SO_4	bfjsv	118-0042
Lithium Tantalate (I I I) $LiTaO_2$	s	118-8050
Lithium Tantalate (V) $LiTaO_3$	abgqsv	118-0041
Lithium Terbium tetra- Fluoride $LiTbF_4$		
see Lithium tetra- Fluoroterbate $LiTbF_4$	ajnq	110-8234
Lithium di- Thioantimonate $LiSbS_2$	fhjt	118-8072
Lithium di- Thioindate $LiInS_2$	v	114-8046
Lithium Thulium tetra- Fluoride $LiTmF_4$		
see Lithium tetra- Fluorothulate $LiTmF_4$	ahm	110-8169
Lithium - Tin Li_4Sn		
see tetra- Lithium Stannide Li_4Sn	j	118-8099
Lithium di- Titanate $LiTi_2O_4$	j	118-8095
Lithium Titanium (I V) Ferrate (I I I)		
$LiTiFeO_4$	npq	110-8172
Lithium Titanium Ferrite $Li_xTi_yFe_{3-x-y}O_4$	npq	110-8171
Lithium Titanium Iron Zinc Oxide		
$Li_xTi_yFe_zZn_{3-x-y-z}O_4$		
see Lithium Titanium Zinc Ferrate		
$Li_xTi_yZn_zFe_{3-x-y-z}O_4$	n	110-8275
Lithium Titanium Sulfide $Li_xTi_{1+y}S_2$	j	118-8063
Lithium Titanium Zinc Ferrate		
$Li_xTi_yZn_zFe_{3-x-y-z}O_4$	n	110-8275
Lithium Tungstate Li_xWO_3	j	118-8062
Lithium Vanadate Bronze LiV_6O_{15}	jq	118-8087
Lithium Vanadium Zinc Oxide $LiVZnO_4$		
see Lithium Zinc Vanadate (V) $LiZnVO_4$	m	118-8067
Lithium Ytterbium tetra- Fluoride $LiYbF_4$		
see Lithium tetra- Fluoroytterbate (I I I) $LiYbF_4$	ah	110-8170
Lithium Yttrium tetra- Fluoride $LiYF_4$		
see Lithium tetra- Fluoroyttrate $LiYF_4$	afhms	110-0352
Lithium Zinc Ferrite $Li_xZn_yFe_{3-x-y}O_4$	jqt	110-8123
Lithium Zinc Iron Oxide		
$Li_xZn_yFe_{3-x-y}O_4$		
see Lithium Zinc Ferrite $Li_xZn_yFe_{3-x-y}O_4$	jqt	110-8123
Lithium Zinc Vanadate (V) $LiZnVO_4$	m	118-8067
Lucalox (General Electric) Al_2O_3	bs	102-8281
see also Aluminum sesqui- Oxide Al_2O_3		102-0002
Lutetium Aluminate $Lu_3Al_5O_{12}$	m	102-0303
Lutetium di- Aluminide $LuAl_2$	j	102-8326
Lutetium Arsenide $LuAs$	f	102-8358
Lutetium dodeca- Boride LuB_{12}	qu	104-8147
Lutetium - Cobalt - Germanium $LuCo_2Ge_2$	q	106-8179
Lutetium di- Cobaltide $LuCo_2$	q	106-8780
di- Lutetium 17- Cobaltide Lu_2Co_{17}	np	106-8724
Lutetium - Erbium $LuEr_3$	n	109-8063
Lutetium tri- Fluoride LuF_3	j	110-8017
Lutetium - Iron $LuFe_2$	npq	110-8133
Lutetium - Iron Lu_2Fe_{17}	q	110-8129
Lutetium - Iron Lu_2Fe_{23}	q	110-8131
Lutetium Manganate (I I I) $LuMnO_3$	q	118-8024
Lutetium Manganese Ferrate $LuMn_xFe_{1-x}O_3$	q	110-8107
Lutetium Niobate (V) $LuNbO_4$	h	118-8041
Lutetium Nitride LuN	df	118-8071
Lutetium - Osmium $LuOs_2$	j	118-8106
Lutetium sesqui- Oxide Lu_2O_3	bjs	118-0020
Lutetium Phosphate $LuPO_4$	hm	118-8045
Lutetium - Ruthenium $LuRu_2$	j	118-8105

Substance Name	Property	Number
Lutetium - Silver $LuAg$	j	102-8329
Lutetium Sulfate Lu_2SO_6	m	118-8033
Lutetium Sulfite Lu_2SO_2	hm	118-8096
Lutetium Tantalate $LuTaO_4$	h	118-8042
Lutetium Thulium Cobaltide $Lu_xTm_{2-x}Co_{17}$	np	106-8725
Lutetium Vanadate (I I I) $LuVO_3$	q	118-8049
Lutetium Vanadate (V) $LuVO_4$	m	118-8023
Lutetium - Zinc $LuZn_{12}$	jq	118-8057
Magnesium di- Aluminate $MgAl_2O_4$	ahjms	102-0013
see also Spinel $MgAl_2O_4$		521-8036
tri- Magnesium di- Aluminide Mg_3Al_2	j	102-8291
Magnesium Aluminum Ferrate $Mg_xAl_yFe_{3-x-y}O_4$	jq	102-8140
Magnesium Aluminum Ferrite $MgAl_xFe_{2-x}O_4$	nq	102-8465
di- Magnesium tetra- Aluminum penta- Silicate		
$Mg_2Al_4Si_5O_{18}$	j	102-8426
see also Cordierite $2MgO.2Al_2O_3.5SiO_2$		521-0443
Magnesium Antimonide Mg_3Sb_2	afjt	119-8001
Magnesium - Bismuth Mg_xBi_{1-x}	j	104-8256
Magnesium - Bismuth Mg_3Bi_2	afhjt	104-8015
Magnesium Borate $Mg_2B_2O_5$	m	104-8135
Magnesium Boron Chloride Oxide		
$Mg_3B_7O_{13}Cl$		
see Magnesium Chloroborate $Mg_3B_7O_{13}Cl$	b	104-8167
Magnesium Boron Ferrate (I I I) $MgBFeO_4$	q	104-8278
Magnesium Bromide $MgBr_2$	j	104-0077
Magnesium - Cadmium $MgCd$	j	106-8139
Magnesium - Cadmium $MgCd_3$	j	106-8138
Magnesium - Cadmium Mg_3Cd	j	106-8140
Magnesium Carbonate $MgCO_3$	b	106-0015
see also Magnesite $MgCO_3$		521-0006
Magnesium - Cerium $MgCe$	nq	106-8507
Magnesium Cerium (I I I) undeca- Aluminate		
$MgCeAl_{11}O_{19}$	m	102-8370
Magnesium Cerium Nitrate $Mg_3Ce_2(NO_3)_{12}$	q	106-8782
Magnesium Chloride $MgCl_2$	afij	106-0141
Magnesium Chloroborate $Mg_3B_7O_{13}Cl$	b	104-8167
Magnesium di- Chromate (I I I) $MgCr_2O_4$	j	106-8696
Magnesium octa- Chromate (I I I) $MgCr_8O_{13}$	j	106-8697
tetra- Magnesium di- Chromate (I I I)		
$Mg_4Cr_2O_7$	j	106-8698
Magnesium Chromium Manganese Copper Zinc Oxide		
$Mg_xCr_yMn_{2-x-y}Cu_{1-z}Zn_zO_4$	jq	106-8184
Magnesium Chromium Manganese Ferrite		
$Mg_xCr_yMn_zFe_{3-x-y-z}O_4$	n	106-8740
Magnesium Cobalt Aluminum Ferrite		
$Mg_xCo_{1-x}Al_yFe_{2-y}O_4$	n	102-8463
Magnesium - Copper - Aluminum $MgCuAl_2$	j	102-8295
Magnesium tetra- Cyanoplatinate (I I)		
$Mg(Pt(CN)_4)$	jm	106-8152
Magnesium Ferrite $MgFe_2O_4$	ajnp	110-8253
Magnesium Ferrite $Mg_xFe_{3-x}O_4$	anpq	110-8090
Magnesium Fluoride MgF_2	abdfhijmpst	110-0023
see also Irtran 1 (Kodak) MgF_2		110-8118
Magnesium - Gadolinium $MgGd$	q	111-8089
Magnesium Gallate $MgGa_2O_4$	m	111-8082
Magnesium - Germanium Mg_2Ge	dhij	111-8037
Magnesium Germanium di- Nitride $MgGeN_2$		
see Magnesium di- Nitridogermanate $MgGeN_2$	af	111-8116
Magnesium - Holmium $MgHo$	q	112-8048
Magnesium Hydroxide $Mg(OH)_2$	a	112-8078
Magnesium Hydroxide, Deuterated $Mg(OD)_2$	a	108-8054
Magnesium Iodide MgI_2	j	114-8020
Magnesium Iron Aluminum Oxide		
$MgFe_xAl_{2-x}O_4$		
see Magnesium Aluminum Ferrite $MgAl_xFe_{2-x}O_4$	nq	102-8465
Magnesium Iron Aluminum Oxide		
$Mg_xFe_yAl_{3-x-y}O_4$		
see Magnesium Aluminum Ferrate $Mg_xAl_yFe_{3-x-y}O_4$	jq	102-8140
Magnesium Iron Boron Oxide $MgFeBO_4$		
see Magnesium Boron Ferrate (I I I) $MgBFeO_4$	q	104-8278
Magnesium Iron hexa- Fluorothallate $MgFeTlF_6$	q	110-8086
Magnesium Iron Oxide $Mg_xFe_{3-x}O_4$		
see Magnesium Ferrite $Mg_xFe_{3-x}O_4$	anpq	110-8090

Property: **a.** Absorption coefficient; **b.** Dielectric constant; **c.** Dielectric strength; **d.** Energy band structure; **e.** Effective mass; **f.** Energy gap; **g.** Electric hysteresis; **h.** Energy level; **i.** Electron emission properties; **j.** Electrical resistivity; **k.** Magnetoelectric properties; **l.** Hall coefficient; **m.** Luminescence properties; **n.** Magnetic hysteresis; **o.** Mobility; **p.** Magnetomechanical properties; **q.** Magnetic susceptibility; **r.** Photoelectronic properties; **s.** Refractive index; **t.** Thermoelectric properties; **u.** Work function; **v.** Piezoelectric properties.

Substance Name	*Property*	*Number*
Magnesium mono-Lanthanide $MgLa$	q	118-8039
Magnesium-Lead Mg_2Pb		
see di-Magnesium Plumbide Mg_2Pb	dj	119-8057
Magnesium Lead Stannide $Mg_2Pb_xSn_{1-x}$	jlo	119-8109
Magnesium di-Lead (I I) Tungstate (V I)		
$MgPb_2WO_6$	bgh	119-8103
Magnesium Manganate (I I I) $MgMn_2O_4$	q	119-8030
hexa-Magnesium Manganate (I V) Mg_6MnO_8	q	119-8024
Magnesium Manganese Aluminum Ferrite		
$Mg_xMn_yAl_{1-x-y}Fe_2O_4$	jn	102-8341
Magnesium Manganese Cobalt Ferrite		
$Mg_xMn_{1-x-y}Co_yFe_2O_4$	np	106-8294
Magnesium Manganese Cuprate $Mg_xMn_{2-x}CuO_4$	jq	106-8183
Magnesium Manganese Ferrite $Mg_xMn_yFe_{3-x-y}O_4$	nr	110-8233
see also Ferrite 2 V T (Russian)		110-8229
Magnesium Manganese Ferrite $Mg_xMn_{1-x}Fe_2O_4$	bjklnop	110-8042
Magnesium Manganese Iron Oxide		
$Mg_xMn_{1-x}Fe_2O_4$		
see Magnesium Manganese Ferrite $Mg_xMn_{1-x}Fe_2O_4$	bjklnop	110-8042
Magnesium Manganese Iron Zinc Oxide		
$Mg_xMn_yZn_{1-x-y}Fe_2O_4$		
see Magnesium Manganese Zinc Ferrite		
$Mg_xMn_yZn_{1-x-y}Fe_2O_4$	n	110-8091
Magnesium Manganese Telluride $Mg_xMn_{1-x}Te_2$	fjn	119-8042
Magnesium Manganese Zinc Ferrite		
$Mg_xMn_yZn_{1-x-y}Fe_2O_4$	n	110-8091
Magnesium-Neodymium $MgNd$	nq	119-8060
Magnesium di-Nickel (I) Ferrate (I I)		
$MgNi_2FeO_3$	q	110-8198
Magnesium Niobate (V) $MgNb_2O_6$	b	119-0105
di-Magnesium Niobide Mg_2Nb	j	119-8104
Magnesium di-Niobium (V) tri-Plumbate (I I)		
$MgNb_2Pb_3O_9$	abfhqs	119-8035
Magnesium Niobium Plumbate $Mg_xNb_{1-x}PbO_3$	b	119-8115
Magnesium di-Nitridogermanate $MgGeN_2$	af	111-8116
Magnesium di-Nitridosilicate $MgSiN_2$	af	119-8081
Magnesium Oxide MgO	abcdefhijmoqrstu	119-0002
see also Irtran 5 (Kodak) MgO		119-8048
see also Magnorite (Norton Co) MgO		119-8089
see also Periclase MgO		521-0132
Magnesium Platinum Carbide Nitride		
$Mg(Pt(CN)_4)$		
see Magnesium tetra-Cyanoplatinate (I I)		
$Mg(Pt(CN)_4)$	jm	106-8152
di-Magnesium Plumbide Mg_2Pb	dj	119-8057
Magnesium-Praseodymium $MgPr$	nq	119-8059
Magnesium-Samarium $MgSm$	q	119-8061
Magnesium Scandium Chromium Manganese Ferrite		
$(Mg, Sc, Cr, Mn)_xFe_{3-x}O_4$	n	106-8737
Magnesium Scandium Ferrite $MgSc_xFe_{2-x}O_4$	n	110-8257
Magnesium Scandium Indium Manganese Ferrite		
$(Mg, Sc, In, Mn)_xFe_{3-x}O_4$	n	110-8256
Magnesium Scandium Manganese Ferrite		
$Mg_xSc_yMn_zFe_{3-x-y-z}O_4$	n	110-8255
Magnesium Selenide $MgSe$	dfiju	119-8008
Magnesium Silicate Mg_2SiO_4	ms	119-8028
see also Forsterite Mg_2SiO_4		521-8073
see also Olivine Mg_2SiO_4		521-8033
di-Magnesium Silicide Mg_2Si	bdfhijlo	119-8009
Magnesium Silicide di-Nitride $MgSiN_2$		
see Magnesium di-Nitridosilicate $MgSiN_2$	af	119-8081
Magnesium di-Stannide $MgSn_2$	j	119-8077
di-Magnesium Stannide Mg_2Sn	adefhijkloqrt	119-8002
Magnesium Stannide Germanide $Mg_2Sn_xGe_{1-x}$	j	119-8119
Magnesium Stannide Silicide $Mg_2Sn_xSi_{1-x}$	j	119-8107
Magnesium Sulfate $MgSO_4$	b	119-0003
Magnesium Sulfide MgS	dfijsu	119-0064
Magnesium Tantalum Plumbate $Mg_xTa_{1-x}PbO_3$	s	119-8088
Magnesium Telluride $MgTe$	bf	119-8010
Magnesium di-Telluride $MgTe_2$	fjn	119-8041
Magnesium-Terbium $MgTb$	nq	119-8063
Magnesium-Tin $MgSn_2$		
see Magnesium di-Stannide $MgSn_2$	j	119-8077

Substance Name	*Property*	*Number*
Magnesium-Tin Mg_2Sn		
see di-Magnesium Stannide Mg_2Sn	adefhijkloqrt	119-8002
Magnesium Titanate (I V) $MgTiO_3$	bj	119-0021
Magnesium di-Titanate (I V) $MgTi_2O_5$	j	119-8105
di-Magnesium Titanate (I V) Mg_2TiO_4	jm	119-8027
Magnesium Tungstate (V I) $MgWO_4$	ab	119-0049
Magnesium Tungsten Lead Oxide $MgWPb_2O_6$		
see Magnesium di-Lead (I I) Tungstate (V I)		
$MgPb_2WO_6$	bgh	119-8103
Magnesium Vanadate (V) $Mg(VO_3)_2$	s	119-8090
Magnesium Vanadate (I I) MgV_2O_3	m	119-8039
Magnesium Vanadate (I I I) MgV_2O_4	fjt	119-8093
Magnesium Vanadate $Mg_xV_{2-x}O_4$	fjt	119-8094
Magnesium Vanadium Cobalt Ferrite		
$Mg_xV_yCo_{1-x}Fe_{2-y}O_4$	fj	106-8260
Magnesium-Yttrium MgY	q	119-8062
Magnesium Yttrium Iron Silicon Oxide		
$Ma_xY_3Fe_{5-x-y}Si_yO_{12}$		
see Yttrium Magnesium Silicon Ferrate		
$Y_{3-x}Mg_xSi_yFe_{5-y}O_{12}$	q	110-8104
Magnesium-Zinc $MgZn$	j	119-8073
Magnesium-Zinc $MgZn_2$	j	119-8054
Magnesium-Zinc $MgZn_{13}$	j	119-8053
Magnesium-Zinc Mg_2Zn_3	j	119-8074
Magnesium-Zinc Mg_2Zn_{11}	j	119-8075
Magnesium-Zinc Mg_7Zn_3	j	119-8076
Magnorite (Norton Co) MgO	s	119-8089
see also Magnesium Oxide MgO		119-0002
Manganese hexa-Aluminide $MnAl_6$	j	102-8315
tetra-Manganese undeca-Aluminide Mn_4Al_{11}	jq	102-8477
Manganese-Aluminum-Germanium $MnAlGe$	anpqst	102-8098
Manganese mono-Antimonide $MnSb$	jlq	119-8003
di-Manganese Antimonide Mn_2Sb	nq	119-8004
Manganese Antimonide Arsenide $Mn_2Sb_xAs_{1-x}$	q	102-8487
see also di-Manganese Antimonide $\geq$ di-Manganese Arsenide		508-0561
see also di-Manganese Arsenide $\geq$ di-Manganese Antimonide		508-0562
Manganese mono-Arsenide $MnAs$	djpq	102-8058
di-Manganese Arsenide Mn_2As	q	102-8059
Manganese Arsenide Phosphide $MnAs_xP_{1-x}$	djq	102-8458
Manganese Arsenide Telluride $MnAs_xTe_{1-x}$	j	102-8430
Manganese Bismuthide $MnBi$	abnpqst	104-8016
Manganese (I I) tetra-Borate MnB_4O_7	npq	104-8227
Manganese mono-Boride MnB	n	104-8072
Manganese di-Boride MnB_2	q	104-8073
Manganese di-Bromide $MnBr_2$	bhq	104-0043
Manganese Carbonate $MnCO_3$	nq	106-0497
see also Rhodochrosite $MnCO_3$		521-0614
Manganese di-Chloride $MnCl_2$	abhjq	106-0018
Manganese-Cobalt $MnCo$	jq	106-8384
Manganese-Cobalt-Aluminum $MnCo_2Al$	q	102-8500
Manganese-Cobalt-Gallium $MnCo_2Ga$	q	106-8843
Manganese-Cobalt-Germanium $MnCo_2Ge$	q	106-8844
Manganese di-Cobalt Silicide $MnCo_2Si$	q	106-8845
Manganese-Cobalt-Tin $MnCo_2Sn$	q	106-8846
Manganese-Copper-Aluminum $MnCu_2Al$	q	102-8499
Manganese Copper Antimonide $MnCuSb$	q	106-8297
Manganese-Copper-Bismuth $Mn_3Cu_4Bi_4$	hnq	104-8250
Manganese Copper Ferrite $Mn_xCu_yFe_{3-x-y}O_4$	jnq	106-8553
Manganese-Copper-Indium $MnCu_2In$	q	106-8841
Manganese-Copper-Tin $MnCu_2Sn$	q	106-8842
Manganese Copper Tin Ferrite		
$Mn_xCu_ySn_3Fe_{3-x-y-z}O_4$	n	106-8739
Manganese Copper Zinc Ferrite		
$Mn_xCu_yZn_zFe_{3-x-y-z}O_4$	n	106-8555
Manganese Ferrate $Mn_xFe_{1-x}O$	nq	110-8265
Manganese Ferrate $Mn_xFe_{1-x}O_{1-x}$	aj	110-8136
Manganese Ferrite $MnFe_2O_4$	jklnot	110-8119
see also Jacobsite $MnFe_2O_4$		521-8028
Manganese Ferrite $Mn_xFe_{3-x}O_4$	jnpt	110-8047
Manganese di-Fluoride MnF_2	abhijmnq	110-0018
Manganese tri-Fluoride MnF_3	ahm	110-8018
Manganese-Gallium $MnGa$	nq	111-8039
Manganese-Gallium Mn_2Ga_5	q	111-8027
Manganese Gallium Germanide $MnGaGe$	anqst	111-8038

Property: a. Absorption coefficient; **b.** Dielectric constant; **c.** Dielectric strength; **d.** Energy band structure; **e.** Effective mass; **f.** Energy gap; **g.** Electric hysteresis; **h.** Energy level; **i.** Electron emission properties; **j.** Electrical resistivity; **k.** Magnetoelectric properties; **l.** Hall coefficient; **m.** Luminescence properties; **n.** Magnetic hysteresis; **o.** Mobility; **p.** Magnetomechanical properties; **q.** Magnetic susceptibility; **r.** Photoelectronic properties; **s.** Refractive index; **t.** Thermoelectric properties; **u.** Work function; **v.** Piezoelectric properties.

Substance Name	Property	Number
Manganese Germanium Telluride $Mn_x Ge_{1-x} Te$	jnq	111-8092
Manganese - Gold $Mn Au$	j	102-8219
Manganese - Gold $Mn Au_2$	jk	102-8220
Manganese - Gold $Mn Au_3$	jq	102-8221
Manganese - Gold $Mn Au_4$	q	102-8360
Manganese (I I) Iodate $Mn (I O_3)_2$	q	114-8073
Manganese di- Iodide $Mn I_2$	ahq	114-8021
Manganese - Iron $Mn Fe$	jq	110-8134
Manganese Iron Copper Oxide		
$Mn_x Fe_y Cu_{3-x-y} O_4$		
see Manganese Copper Ferrite $Mn_x Cu_y Fe_{3-x-y} O_4$	jnq	106-8553
Manganese Iron Copper Zinc Oxide		
$Mn_x Fe_y Cu_z Zn_{3-x-y-z} O_4$		
see Manganese Copper Zinc Ferrite		
$Mn_x Cu_y Zn_z Fe_{3-x-y-z} O_4$	n	106-8555
Manganese di- Iron tetra- Oxide $Mn Fe_2 O_4$		
see Manganese Ferrite $Mn Fe_2 O_4$	jklnot	110-8119
Manganese Iron Oxide $Mn_x Fe_{1-x} O_{1-x}$		
see Manganese Ferrate $Mn_x Fe_{1-x} O_{1-x}$	aj	110-8136
Manganese Iron Oxide $Mn_x Fe_{3-x} O_4$		
see Manganese Ferrite $Mn_x Fe_{3-x} O_4$	jnpt	110-8047
Manganese tetra- Iron tri- Silicide $Mn Fe_4 Si_3$	q	110-8147
Manganese Iron Silicide $Mn_x Fe_{5-x} Si_3$	q	110-8150
di- Manganese tri- Iron tri- Silicide $Mn_2 Fe_3 Si_3$	q	110-8146
tri- Manganese di- Iron tri- Silicide $Mn_3 Fe_2 Si_3$	q	110-8149
tetra- Manganese Iron tri- Silicide $Mn_4 Fe Si_3$	q	110-8148
Manganese Iron Zinc Oxide		
$Mn_x Fe_2 Zn_{1-x} O_4$		
see Manganese Zinc Ferrite $Mn_x Zn_{1-x} Fe_2 O_4$	j	110-8120
Manganese Iron Zinc Oxide		
$Mn_x Fe_{3-x-y} Zn_y O_4$		
see Manganese Zinc Ferrite $Mn_x Zn_y Fe_{3-x-y} O_4$	bjnpq	110-8073
Manganese Lead Selenide $Mn_x Pb_{1-x} Se$	a	119-8087
Manganese Mercury Telluride $Mn_x Hg_{1-x} Te$	kq	112-8042
Manganese - Nickel $Mn Ni_3$	jlnq	119-8047
Manganese Nickel Antimonide $Mn Ni Sb$	q	119-8038
Manganese di- Nickel Antimonide $Mn Ni_2 Sb$	q	119-8124
Manganese Nickelate $Mn_x Ni_{3-x} O_4$	j	119-8045
Manganese - Nickel - Bismuth $Mn_5 Ni_2 Bi_4$	hnq	104-8247
Manganese Nickel Cobalt Copper Ferrite		
$(Mn, Ni, Co, Cu)_x Fe_{3-x} O_4$	np	106-8684
Manganese Nickel Copper Antimonide $Mn Ni_x Cu_{1-x} Sb$	q	106-8256
Manganese - Nickel - Gallium $Mn Ni_2 Ga$	q	111-8212
Manganese - Nickel - Indium $Mn Ni_2 In$	q	114-8104
Manganese - Nickel - Tin $Mn Ni_2 Sn$	q	119-8125
Manganese (I I) Niobate (V) $Mn Nb_2 O_6$	bj	119-8033
Manganese mono- Oxide $Mn O$	abdfhijlnoqrt	119-0008
Manganese di- Oxide $Mn O_2$	bhijot	119-0010
Manganese Oxide $Mn O_{1-x}$	aj	119-8056
Manganese sesqui- Oxide $Mn_2 O_3$	bf	119-0007
tri- Manganese tetra- Oxide $Mn_3 O_4$	aj	119-0026
Manganese - Palladium - Aluminum $Mn Pd_2 Al$	q	102-8501
Manganese - Palladium - Bismuth $Mn_5 Pd_2 Bi_4$	hnq	104-8249
Manganese - Palladium - Gallium $Mn Pd_2 Ga$	q	111-8213
Manganese - Palladium - Germanium $Mn Pd Ge$	q	111-8032
Manganese - Palladium - Indium $Mn Pd_2 In$	q	114-8105
Manganese Palladium Telluride $Mn Pd Te$	q	119-8029
Manganese - Palladium - Tin $Mn Pd_2 Sn$	q	119-8126
Manganese Phosphide $Mn P$	dfjknpq	119-0041
Manganese Phosphide tri- Sulfide $Mn P S_3$		
see Manganese tri- Thiophosphate $Mn P S_3$	aq	119-8052
di- Manganese di- Phosphorus hepta- Oxide		
$Mn_2 P_2 O_7$		
see Manganese Pyrophosphate $Mn_2 P_2 O_7$	q	119-8046
Manganese - Platinum - Tin $Mn Pt Sn$	nq	119-8092
Manganese Pyrophosphate $Mn_2 P_2 O_7$	q	119-8046
Manganese - Rhodium - Bismuth $Mn_5 Rh_2 Bi_4$	hq	104-8248
Manganese - Rhodium - Germanium $Mn Rh Ge$	q	111-8033
Manganese (I I) Selenate $Mn Se O_3$	q	119-8100
Manganese Selenide $Mn Se$	q	119-8014
Manganese mono- Silicide $Mn Si$	djnqt	119-8015
Manganese di- Silicide $Mn Si_2$	dj	119-8016
Manganese Silicide $Mn Si_{2-x}$	efot	119-8026
tri- Manganese Silicide $Mn_3 Si$	j	119-8116
tri- Manganese penta- Silicide $Mn_3 Si_5$	d	119-8112
penta- Manganese tri- Silicide $Mn_5 Si_3$	djnqu	119-8058
hexa- Manganese Silicide $Mn_6 Si$	d	119-8113
Manganese mono- Sulfide $Mn S$	afiq	119-0043
see also Alabandin $Mn S$		521-8023
Manganese di- Sulfide $Mn S_2$	fhj	119-0051
see also Hauerite $Mn S_2$		521-8024
Manganese mono- Telluride $Mn Te$	djq	119-8091
Manganese di- Telluride $Mn Te_2$	fjnqt	119-8040
Manganese Telluride Selenide $Mn Te_x Se_{1-x}$	q	119-8025
Manganese tri- Thiophosphate $Mn P S_3$	aq	119-8052
Manganese Tin Telluride $Mn_x Sn_{1-x} Te$	jln	119-8037
Manganese (I I) Tungstate (V I) $Mn W O_4$	b	119-8034
Manganese - Zinc $Mn Zn_{13}$	jknq	119-8050
Manganese Zinc Ferrite $Mn_x Zn_y Fe_{3-x-y} O_4$	bjnpq	110-8073
see also Ferrite 1000 N M Z (Russian)		110-8227
see also Ferrite 1500 N M Z (Russian)		110-8228
see also Franklinite $Mn_x Zn_y Fe_{3-x-y} O_4$		521-1017
Manganese Zinc Ferrite $Mn_x Zn_{1-x} Fe_2 O_4$	j	110-8120
Mercury Azide $Hg_2(N_3)_2$	bfrs	112-8024
Mercury (I I) Bromide $Hg Br_2$	j	104-0093
Mercury Cadmium Selenide $Hg_x Cd_{1-x} Se$	aefhjkot	106-8531
Mercury Cadmium Telluride $Hg_x Cd_{1-x} Te$	abdefhjklmoqrst	106-8128
see also Cadmium Telluride $\geq$ Mercury (I I) Telluride		508-0041
see also Mercury (I I) Telluride $\geq$ Cadmium Telluride		508-0150
Mercury Cadmium Zinc Sulfide $Hg_x Cd_y Zn_{1-x-y} S$	bfjrs	106-8469
Mercury (I) Chloride $Hg Cl$	bj	106-0251
Mercury (I I) Chloride $Hg Cl_2$	abjs	106-0227
Mercury (I I) Fluoride $Hg F_2$	dh	110-8020
Mercury mono- Indide $Hg In$	fj	112-8094
Mercury (I I) Iodide $Hg I_2$	fjor	112-0040
Mercury (I I) Oxide $Hg O$	befoqsu	112-0011
Mercury (I I) Selenide $Hg Se$	abdefhijkopqt	112-8020
Mercury Selenide Sulfide $Hg Se_x S_{1-x}$	defjot	112-8032
Mercury tetra- Selenochromate $Hg Cr_2 Se_4$	kq	106-8812
Mercury (I I) Sulfide $Hg S$	abdefhijmoqrsuv	112-0402
see also Cinnabar $Hg S$		521-0749
Mercury (I I) Telluride $Hg Te$	abdefh-moqstuv	112-8025
Mercury Telluride Selenide $Hg Te_x Se_{1-x}$	efjot	112-8083
Mercury Telluride Sulfide $Hg Te_x S_{1-x}$	jot	112-8084
Mercury Zinc Selenide $Hg_x Zn_{1-x} Se$	fjo	112-8085
Mercury Zinc Sulfide $Hg_x Zn_{1-x} S$	f	112-8086
Mercury Zinc Telluride $Hg_x Zn_{1-x} Te$	efjot	112-8087
see also Zinc Telluride $\geq$ Mercury (I I) Telluride		508-0177
tri- Molybdenum Aluminide $Mo_3 Al$	j	102-8321
Molybdenum Aluminum Thiostannate $Mo_5 Al_{1-x} Sn S_6$	jq	102-8450
Molybdenum (V I) di- Bismuthate (I I I)		
$Mo Bi_2 O_6$		
see di- Bismuth (I I I) Molybdate (V I) $Bi_2 Mo O_6$	u	104-8346
di- Molybdenum (V I) di- Bismuthate (I I I)		
$Mo_2 Bi_2 O_9$		
see di- Bismuth (I I I) di- Molybdate (V I)		
$Bi_2 Mo_2 O_9$	u	104-8347
di- Molybdenum (V I) hexa- Bismuthate (I I I)		
$Mo_2 Bi_6 O_{15}$		
see hexa- Bismuth (I I I) di- Molybdate (V I)		
$Bi_6 Mo_2 O_{15}$	su	104-8301
tri- Molybdenum (V I) di- Bismuthate (I I I)		
$Mo_3 Bi_2 O_{12}$		
see di- Bismuth (I I I) tri- Molybdate (V I)		
$Bi_2 Mo_3 O_{12}$	su	104-8302
Molybdenum di- Boride $Mo B_2$	q	104-8075
di- Molybdenum Boride $Mo_2 B$	m	104-8076
Molybdenum penta- Boride $Mo_2 B_5$	jloqu	104-8114
Molybdenum di- Bromide tri- Fluoride		
$Mo Br_2 F_3$		
see Molybdenum (V) tri- Fluorobromate $Mo Br_2 F_3$	q	102-8077
Molybdenum Cadmium tetra- Oxide $Mo Cd O_4$		
see Cadmium Molybdate (V I) $Cd Mo O_4$	hm	106-8427
di- Molybdenum Carbide $Mo_2 C$	jt	106-0640
Molybdenum - Cobalt $Mo Co$		
see Molybdenum mono- Cobaltide $Mo Co$	n	106-8777
Molybdenum mono- Cobaltide $Mo Co$	n	106-8777

Property: **a.** Absorption coefficient; **b.** Dielectric constant; **c.** Dielectric strength; **d.** Energy band structure; **e.** Effective mass; **f.** Energy gap; **g.** Electric hysteresis; **h.** Energy level; **i.** Electron emission properties; **j.** Electrical resistivity; **k.** Magnetoelectric properties; **l.** Hall coefficient; **m.** Luminescence properties; **n.** Magnetic hysteresis; **o.** Mobility; **p.** Magnetomechanical properties; **q.** Magnetic susceptibility; **r.** Photoelectronic properties; **s.** Refractive index; **t.** Thermoelectric properties; **u.** Work function; **v.** Piezoelectric properties.

Substance Name	Property	Number
tri- Molybdenum Cobalt tetra- Sulfide		
$Mo_3 Co S_4$		
see tri- Molybdenum tetra- Thiocobaltate $Mo_3 Co S_4$	j	106-8336
tri- Molybdenum Copper tetra- Sulfide		
$Mo_3 Cu S_4$		
see tri- Molybdenum tetra- Thiocuprate $Mo_3 Cu S_4$	jq	106-8754
tetra- Molybdenum Copper penta- Sulfide		
$Mo_4 Cu S_5$		
see tetra- Molybdenum penta- Thiocuprate $Mo_4 Cu S_5$	j	106-8337
Molybdenum (V) tri- Fluorobromate $Mo Br_2 F_3$	q	102-8077
Molybdenum Gallium Selenide		
$Mo_2 Ga_{1-x} Se_4$		
see Molybdenum Selenogallate $Mo_2 Ga_{1-x} Se_4$	q	111-8052
Molybdenum Gallium Sulfide $Mo_2 Ga_{1-x} S_4$		
see Molybdenum Thiogallate $Mo_2 Ga_{1-x} S_4$	q	111-8053
Molybdenum Gallium Thiostannate $Mo_5 Ga_{1-x} Sn S_6$	jnq	111-8191
Molybdenum di- Germanide $Mo Ge_2$	j	111-8148
tri- Molybdenum Germanide $Mo_3 Ge$	jlqt	111-8126
penta- Molybdenum tri- Germanide $Mo_5 Ge_3$	jlqt	111-8149
13- Molybdenum 23- Germanide $Mo_{13} Ge_{23}$	jlqt	111-8150
Molybdenum - Iridium $Mo_3 Ir$	j	114-8068
tri- Molybdenum Iron tetra- Sulfide		
$Mo_3 Fe S_4$		
see tri- Molybdenum tetra- Thioferrate $Mo_3 Fe S_4$	j	110-8116
Molybdenum Lead Oxide $Mo Pb O_4$		
see Lead (I I) Molybdate (V I) $Pb Mo O_4$	bhmqs	119-0073
hexa- Molybdenum Lead hepta- Sulfide		
$Mo_6 Pb S_7$		
see hexa- Molybdenum hepta- Thioplumbate $Mo_6 Pb S_7$	jq	119-8111
Molybdenum Lead Sulfide $Mo_{4-2x} Pb_x S_4$	j	119-8110
tri- Molybdenum Manganese tetra- Sulfide		
$Mo_3 Mn S_4$		
see tri- Molybdenum tetra- Thiomanganate $Mo_3 Mn S_4$	j	119-8043
tri- Molybdenum Nickel tetra- Sulfide		
$Mo_3 Ni S_4$		
see tri- Molybdenum tetra- Thionickelate $Mo_3 Ni S_4$	j	119-8044
Molybdenum Nitride $Mo N$	j	119-8066
Molybdenum - Osmium $Mo_3 Os$	j	119-8083
Molybdenum di- Oxide $Mo O_2$	aberu	119-0005
Molybdenum tri- Oxide $Mo O_3$	abdgjsu	119-0015
Molybdenum penta- Oxide $Mo_2 O_5$	u	119-8018
Molybdenum mono- Phosphide $Mo P$	j	119-8106
tri- Molybdenum Rhenide $Mo_3 Re$	j	119-8102
Molybdenum - Rhodium $Mo Rh_2$	iu	119-8079
Molybdenum di- Selenide $Mo Se_2$	fhjlort	119-8084
tri- Molybdenum tetra- Selenide $Mo_3 Se_4$	j	119-8069
Molybdenum di- Selenide, Intercalated $Mo Se_2$	j	119-8086
Molybdenum Selenogallate $Mo_2 Ga_{1-x} Se_4$	q	111-8052
Molybdenum di- Silicide $Mo Si_2$	dijt	119-8019
tri- Molybdenum Silicide $Mo_3 Si$	dj	119-8082
penta- Molybdenum tri- Silicide $Mo_5 Si_3$	dij	119-8031
tetra- Molybdenum Silver penta- Sulfide		
$Mo_4 Ag S_5$		
see tetra- Molybdenum penta- Thioargentate $Mo_4 Ag S_5$	j	102-8174
Molybdenum di- Sulfide $Mo S_2$	abdefhjloqrtu	119-0001
see also Molybdenum di- Sulfide, Intercalated $Mo S_2$		119-8080
Molybdenum tri- Sulfide $Mo S_3$	hjq	119-8020
tri- Molybdenum tetra- Sulfide $Mo_3 S_4$	j	119-8071
Molybdenum di- Sulfide, Intercalated $Mo S_2$	adhjq	119-8080
Molybdenum di- Telluride $Mo Te_2$	fhjo	119-8101
tri- Molybdenum Telluride $Mo_3 Te$	j	119-8072
tetra- Molybdenum penta- Thioargentate $Mo_4 Ag S_5$	j	102-8174
tri- Molybdenum tetra- Thiocobaltate $Mo_3 Co S_4$	j	106-8336
tri- Molybdenum tetra- Thiocuprate $Mo_3 Cu S_4$	jq	106-8754
tetra- Molybdenum penta- Thiocuprate $Mo_4 Cu S_5$	j	106-8337
tri- Molybdenum tetra- Thioferrate $Mo_3 Fe S_4$	j	110-8116
Molybdenum Thiogallate $Mo_2 Ga_{1-x} S_4$	q	111-8053
tri- Molybdenum tetra- Thiomanganate $Mo_3 Mn S_4$	j	119-8043
tri- Molybdenum tetra- Thionickelate $Mo_3 Ni S_4$	j	119-8044
hexa- Molybdenum hepta- Thioplumbate $Mo_6 Pb S_7$	jq	119-8111
Molybdenum Thiostannate $Mo_3 Sn_{1-x} S_4$	j	119-8070
penta- Molybdenum hexa- Thiostannate $Mo_5 Sn S_6$	jq	106-8755
Molybdenum Tin Sulfide $Mo_3 Sn_{1-x} S_4$		
see Molybdenum Thiostannate $Mo_3 Sn_{1-x} S_4$	j	119-8070

Substance Name	Property	Number
penta- Molybdenum Tin hexa- Sulfide		
$Mo_5 Sn S_6$		
see penta- Molybdenum hexa- Thiostannate $Mo_5 Sn S_6$	jq	106-8755
Molybdouranic Acid $H_8(U Mo_{12} O_{42})$	q	112-8033
Mullite $3 Al_2 O_3 . 2 Si O_2$	bfj	102-8359
Neodymium Aluminate $Nd Al O_3$	b	102-0362
Neodymium Antimonide $Nd Sb$	jlqt	120-8001
Neodymium di- Antimonide $Nd Sb_2$	jlqt	120-8174
tetra- Neodymium tri- Antimonide $Nd_4 Sb_3$	jlqt	120-8175
penta- Neodymium tri- Antimonide $Nd_5 Sb_3$	jlqt	120-8176
Neodymium Arsenide $Nd As$	f	102-8345
Neodymium hexa- Boride $Nd B_6$	j	104-8391
Neodymium tri- Bromide $Nd Br_3$	j	104-8079
Neodymium Carbon Hydride Oxide		
$Nd(O H) C O_3$		
see Neodymium Hydroxide Carbonate $Nd(O H) C O_3$	sv	106-8253
Neodymium Cerium Aluminide $Nd_x Ce_{1-x} Al_2$	q	102-8275
Neodymium tri- Chloride $Nd Cl_3$	j	106-0268
Neodymium Chromate (I I I) $Nd Cr O_3$	fj	106-1485
Neodymium Chromium tri- Selenide $Nd Cr Se_3$		
see Neodymium tri- Selenochromate $Nd Cr Se_3$	q	106-8367
Neodymium - Cobalt $Nd Co_5$	npq	106-8218
Neodymium - Cobalt $Nd_2 Co_{17}$	q	106-8600
Neodymium Cobaltate (I I I) $Nd Co O_3$	j	106-1544
Neodymium - Cobalt - Germanium $Nd Co_2 Ge_2$	q	106-8169
Neodymium - Copper $Nd Cu_6$	q	106-8803
Neodymium (I I I) Cuprate (I I) $Nd_2 Cu O_4$	jt	106-8348
Neodymium Ferrate $Nd_3 Fe_5 O_{12}$	np	110-8240
Neodymium Fluoride $Nd F$	as	110-8214
Neodymium tri- Fluoride $Nd F_3$	as	110-0090
Neodymium Germanate $Nd_2 Ge O_5$	fj	111-0103
di- Neodymium Germanium penta- Sulfide		
$Nd_2 Ge S_5$		
see di- Neodymium penta- Thiogermanate $Nd_2 Ge S_5$	fj	111-8100
Neodymium Germanium Telluride $Nd_x Ge_{1-x} Te$	o	111-8121
see also Germanium Monotelluride ≥ Neodymium Monotelluride		508-0341
Neodymium Hydroxide Carbonate $Nd(O H) C O_3$	sv	106-8253
Neodymium - Indium $Nd_3 In$	q	114-8072
Neodymium Indium tri- Selenide $Nd In Se_3$		
see Neodymium tri- Selenoindate $Nd In Se_3$	q	114-8092
Neodymium Indium tri- Sulfide $Nd In S_3$		
see Neodymium tri- Thioindate $Nd In S_3$	fjqt	114-0112
Neodymium tri- Iodide $Nd I_3$	aj	114-8024
Neodymium - Iridium $Nd Ir_2$	j	114-8103
Neodymium - Iron $Nd_2 Fe_{17}$	q	110-8271
Neodymium Iron Bismuth Oxide		
$Nd_x Fe Bi_{1-x} O_3$		
see Bismuth Neodymium Ferrate $Bi_{1-x} Nd_x Fe O_3$	nq	104-8154
Neodymium - Iron - Germanium $Nd Fe_x Ge_{2-x}$	nq	110-8144
Neodymium di- Iron di- Silicide $Nd Fe_2 Si_2$	j	110-8211
Neodymium Lanthanum Phosphate $Nd_x La_{1-x} P_5 O_{14}$	m	118-8100
Neodymium di- Manganese di- Germanide $Nd Mn_2 Ge_2$	nq	111-8180
Neodymium - Nickel $Nd Ni_5$	j	120-8049
Neodymium - Nickel $Nd_7 Ni_3$	q	120-8060
Neodymium Nickelate (I I) $Nd_2 Ni O_4$	jt	120-8050
Neodymium Nickel Silicide $Nd Ni_x Si_{2-x}$	nq	120-8065
Neodymium Nitride $Nd N$	df	120-0211
Neodymium di- Osmide $Nd Os_2$	j	120-8187
Neodymium mono- Oxide $Nd O$	as	120-8107
Neodymium sesqui- Oxide $Nd_2 O_3$	abfjqsu	120-0010
Neodymium - Palladium $Nd_7 Pd_3$	q	120-8062
Neodymium penta- Phosphate $Nd P_5 O_{14}$	hm	120-8182
Neodymium - Platinum $Nd Pt_2$	j	120-8186
Neodymium - Platinum $Nd_7 Pt_3$	q	120-8063
Neodymium Praseodymium Ferrate $Nd_x Pr_{1-x} Fe O_3$	s	110-8161
Neodymium - Rhodium $Nd Rh_2$	j	120-8185
Neodymium - Rhodium $Nd_7 Rh_3$	q	120-8061
Neodymium - Ruthenium $Nd Ru_2$	j	120-8184
Neodymium Scandate $Nd Sc O_3$	b	120-8036
Neodymium Selenide $Nd_{3-x} Se_4$	joqt	120-8136
Neodymium tri- Selenochromate $Nd Cr Se_3$	q	106-8367
Neodymium tri- Selenoindate $Nd In Se_3$	q	114-8092
di- Neodymium nona- Selenotristannate $Nd_2 Sn_3 Se_9$	j	120-8108

Property: **a.** Absorption coefficient; **b.** Dielectric constant; **c.** Dielectric strength; **d.** Energy band structure; **e.** Effective mass; **f.** Energy gap; **g.** Electric hysteresis; **h.** Energy level; **i.** Electron emission properties; **j.** Electrical resistivity; **k.** Magnetoelectric properties; **l.** Hall coefficient; **m.** Luminescence properties; **n.** Magnetic hysteresis; **o.** Mobility; **p.** Magnetomechanical properties; **q.** Magnetic susceptibility; **r.** Photoelectronic properties; **s.** Refractive index; **t.** Thermoelectric properties; **u.** Work function; **v.** Piezoelectric properties.

Substance Name	Property	Number
Neodymium Silicate	s	120-8183
Neodymium di-Silicide $Nd Si_2$	j	120-8162
Neodymium Silver Silicide $Nd Ag Si$	nq	102-8206
Neodymium tri-Stannide $Nd Sn_3$	j	120-8106
Neodymium Sulfide $Nd S$	jq	120-8074
Neodymium di-Sulfide $Nd S_2$	q	120-8129
Neodymium sesqui-Sulfide $Nd_2 S_3$	ehjloqt	120-0106
tri-Neodymium tetra-Sulfide $Nd_3 S_4$	nq	120-8031
Neodymium Tantalate $Nd Ta O_4$	q	120-0214
di-Neodymium penta-Thiogermanate $Nd_2 Ge S_5$	fj	111-8100
Neodymium tri-Thioindate $Nd In S_3$	fjqt	114-0112
Neodymium-Tin $Nd Sn_3$		
see Neodymium tri-Stannide $Nd Sn_3$	j	120-8106
Neodymium Tin Selenide $Nd_2 Sn_3 Se_9$		
see di-Neodymium nona-Selenotristannate		
$Nd_2 Sn_3 Se_9$	j	120-8108
Neodymium Titanium Niobate $Nd Ti Nb O_6$	fj	120-0286
Neodymium Vanadate (I I I) $Nd V O_3$	nq	120-8076
Neodymium Yttrium Ferrate		
$Nd_x Y_{3-x} Fe_5 O_{12}$		
see Yttrium Neodymium Ferrate $Y_x Nd_{3-x} Fe_5 O_{12}$	np	110-8239
Neodymium-Zinc $Nd Zn_{13}$	j	120-8058
Neptunium di-Aluminide $Np Al_2$	nq	102-8258
Neptunium Antimonide $Np Sb$	q	120-8075
Neptunium Arsenide $Np As$	jnq	102-8225
Neptunium tri-Bromide $Np Br_3$	q	104-8080
Neptunium Carbide $Np C$	jq	106-8302
Neptunium Carbide $Np C_{1-x}$	eq	106-8228
Neptunium tri-Chloride $Np Cl_3$	q	106-8095
Neptunium-Cobalt $Np Co_2$	q	106-8663
Neptunium tri-Iodide $Np I_3$	q	114-8025
Neptunium-Iridium $Np Ir_2$	q	114-8061
Neptunium-Iron $Np Fe_2$	nq	110-8238
Neptunium-Manganese $Np Mn_2$	nq	119-8096
Neptunium-Nickel $Np Ni_2$	nq	120-8130
Neptunium Nitride $Np N$	jnq	120-8066
Neptunium-Osmium $Np Os_2$	jnq	120-8082
Neptunium-Osmium-Ruthenium $Np Os_x Ru_{1-x}$	jnq	120-8131
Neptunium di-Oxide $Np O_2$	h	120-0005
Neptunium-Palladium $Np Pd_3$	jnqr	120-8078
Neptunium mono-Phosphide $Np P$	hjnq	120-8021
Neptunium-Platinum $Np Pt$	q	120-8112
Neptunium-Rhodium $Np Rh_3$	jq	120-8034
Neptunium-Ruthenium $Np Ru_2$	jnq	120-8083
Nesa (Pittsburgh Plate Glass Co) (Tin Suboxide)	i	122-8138
Nickel Aluminide $Ni Al$	djklqt	102-8374
Nickel tri-Aluminide $Ni Al_3$	j	102-8319
tri-Nickel Aluminide $Ni_3 Al$	jkq	102-8195
Nickel Aluminum Ferrite $Ni Al_x Fe_{2-x} O_4$	n	102-8461
Nickel (I I) di-Antimonate (V) $Ni Sb_2 O_6$	q	120-8113
Nickel Borate Chloride $Ni_3 B_7 O_{13} Cl$		
see Nickel Chloroborate $Ni_3 B_7 O_{13} Cl$	nq	104-8359
Nickel Borate Iodide $Ni_3 B_7 O_{13} I$		
see Nickel Iodoborate $Ni_3 B_7 O_{13} I$	bnq	104-8170
Nickel Boride $Ni B$	jq	104-8081
Nickel Carbonate $Ni C O_3$	nq	106-0623
Nickel Carbon Oxide $Ni(C O)_4$		
see Nickel Carbonyl $Ni(C O)_4$	ajn	106-8532
Nickel Carbonyl $Ni(C O)_4$	ajn	106-8532
Nickel (I I) Chloride $Ni Cl_2$	afhiq	106-0033
Nickel Chlorine Boracite $Ni_3 B_7 O_{13} Cl$		
see Nickel Chloroborate $Ni_3 B_7 O_{13} Cl$	nq	104-8359
Nickel Chloroborate $Ni_3 B_7 O_{13} Cl$	nq	104-8359
Nickel hexa-Chlorostannate $Ni Sn Cl_6$	q	106-8332
Nickel Chromium Ferrite $Ni Cr_x Fe_{2-x} O_4$	np	106-8161
Nickel-Cobalt $Ni Co$		
see Nickel mono-Cobaltide $Ni Co$	n	106-8775
Nickel Cobalt Aluminum Ferrite		
$Ni_x Co_{1-x} Al_y Fe_{2-y} O_4$	n	102-8464
Nickel Cobalt Copper Ferrite		
$Ni_x Co_y Cu_z Fe_{3-x-y-z} O_4$	p	106-8198
Nickel Cobalt Ferrite $Ni_x Co_y Fe_{3-x-y} O_4$	np	106-8574
Nickel mono-Cobaltide $Ni Co$	n	106-8775
Nickel Cobalt Iron Aluminate		
$Ni_x Co_{1-x} Fe_y Al_{2-y} O_4$		
see Nickel Cobalt Aluminum Ferrite		
$Ni_x Co_{1-x} Al_y Fe_{2-y} O_4$	n	102-8464
Nickel Cobalt Iron Copper Oxide		
$Ni_x Co_y Fe_{3-x-y-z} Cu_z O_4$		
see Nickel Cobalt Copper Ferrite		
$Ni_x Co_y Cu_z Fe_{3-x-y-z} O_4$	p	106-8198
Nickel Cobalt Iron Vanadium Oxide		
$Ni_x Co_{1-x} Fe_{2-y} V_y O_4$		
see Nickel Cobalt Vanadium Ferrite		
$Ni_x Co_{1-x} V_y Fe_{2-y} O_4$	fj	106-8259
Nickel Cobalt Iron Zinc Oxide		
$Ni_x Co_y Fe_z Zn_{3-x-y-z} O_4$		
see Nickel Cobalt Zinc Ferrite		
$Ni_x Co_y Zn_z Fe_{3-x-y-z} O_4$	np	106-8640
Nickel Cobalt Phosphide $Ni Co P$	n	106-8038
Nickel Cobalt Silicide $Ni_x Co_{1-x} Si$	jt	106-8165
Nickel Cobalt Sulfide $Ni_x Co_{1-x} S_2$	jnq	106-8121
Nickel Cobalt Vanadium Ferrite		
$Ni_x Co_{1-x} V_y Fe_{2-y} O_4$	fj	106-8259
Nickel Cobalt Zinc Ferrite		
$Ni_x Co_y Zn_z Fe_{3-x-y-z} O_4$	np	106-8640
Nickel Copper Ferrite $Ni_x Cu_y Fe_{3-x-y} O_4$	p	106-8199
Nickel Copper Ferrite $Ni_x Cu_{1-x} Fe_2 O_4$	fjlnq	106-8565
Nickel Copper Sulfide $Ni_x Cu_{1-x} S_2$	jq	106-8122
Nickel Copper Zinc Ferrite		
$Ni_x Cu_y Zn_z Fe_{3-x-y-z} O_4$	q	106-8298
Nickel Copper Zinc Ferrite		
$Ni_x Cu_y Zn_{1-x-y} Fe_2 O_4$	jnq	106-8735
Nickel (I I) Ferrite $Ni Fe_2 O_4$	abjklnopqt	110-0028
Nickel Ferrite $Ni_x Fe_{3-x} O_4$	fjlnopqt	110-8046
Nickel di-Fluoride $Ni F_2$	abhiqs	110-0019
Nickel mono-Gallide $Ni Ga$	abjrt	111-8187
Nickel tri-Gallide $Ni Ga_3$	jt	111-8189
tri-Nickel Gallide $Ni_3 Ga$	jkqt	111-8041
tri-Nickel di-Gallide $Ni_3 Ga_2$	jt	111-8188
Nickel Indium Antimonide $Ni_x In_{1-x} Sb$	k	114-8062
Nickel (I I) Iodate $Ni(I O_3)_2$	q	114-8074
Nickel Iodine Boracite $Ni_3 B_7 O_{13} I$		
see Nickel Iodoborate $Ni_3 B_7 O_{13} I$	bnq	104-8170
Nickel Iodoborate $Ni_3 B_7 O_{13} I$	bnq	104-8170
Nickel-Iron $Ni Fe$	np	110-8101
Nickel-Iron $Ni_3 Fe$	jlnpq	110-8102
Nickel Iron Aluminate $Ni Fe_x Al_{2-x} O_4$		
see Nickel Aluminum Ferrite $Ni Al_x Fe_{2-x} O_4$	n	102-8461
Nickel Iron Copper Oxide		
$Ni_x Fe_2 Cu_{1-x} O_4$		
see Nickel Copper Ferrite $Ni_x Cu_{1-x} Fe_2 O_4$	fjlnq	106-8565
Nickel Iron Copper Oxide		
$Ni_x Fe_{3-x-y} Cu_y O_4$		
see Nickel Copper Ferrite $Ni_x Cu_y Fe_{3-x-y} O_4$	p	106-8199
Nickel Iron Copper Zinc Oxide		
$Ni_x Fe_{3-x-y-z} Cu_y Zn_z O_4$		
see Nickel Copper Zinc Ferrite		
$Ni_x Cu_y Zn_z Fe_{3-x-y-z} O_4$	q	106-8298
Nickel di-Iron tetra-Oxide $Ni Fe_2 O_4$		
see Nickel (I I) Ferrite $Ni Fe_2 O_4$	abjklnopqt	110-0028
Nickel Iron Oxide $Ni_x Fe_{3-x} O_4$		
see Nickel Ferrite $Ni_x Fe_{3-x} O_4$	fjlnopqt	110-8046
Nickel Iron Phosphide $Ni_x Fe_{2-x} P$	p	110-8232
Nickel di-Iron tetra-Selenide		
$Ni Fe_2 Se_4$		
see Nickel tetra-Selenodiferrate $Ni Fe_2 Se_4$	joqt	110-8083
Nickel Iron Zinc Oxide		
$Ni_x Fe_2 Zn_{1-x} O_4$		
see Nickel Zinc Ferrite $Ni_x Zn_{1-x} Fe_2 O_4$	jlnopqt	110-8121
Nickel Iron Zinc Oxide		
$Ni_x Fe_{3-x-y} Zn_y O_4$		
see Nickel Zinc Ferrite $Ni_x Zn_y Fe_{3-x-y} O_4$	bjnpq	110-8070
Nickel di-Neodymium tetra-Oxide		
$Ni Nd_2 O_4$		
see Neodymium Nickelate (I I) $Nd_2 Ni O_4$	jt	120-8050
Nickel (I I) Niobate (V) $Ni Nb_2 O_6$	bj	120-8037

Property: **a.** Absorption coefficient; **b.** Dielectric constant; **c.** Dielectric strength; **d.** Energy band structure; **e.** Effective mass; **f.** Energy gap; **g.** Electric hysteresis; **h.** Energy level; **i.** Electron emission properties; **j.** Electrical resistivity; **k.** Magnetoelectric properties; **l.** Hall coefficient; **m.** Luminescence properties; **n.** Magnetic hysteresis; **o.** Mobility; **p.** Magnetomechanical properties; **q.** Magnetic susceptibility; **r.** Photoelectronic properties; **s.** Refractive index; **t.** Thermoelectric properties; **u.** Work function; **v.** Piezoelectric properties.

Substance Name	Property	Number
Nickel mono- Oxide NiO	a–fhijlmopqrstu	120-0001
di- Nickel Phosphide Ni_2P	jlt	120-8013
tri- Nickel Phosphide Ni_3P	jlt	120-8132
dodeca- Nickel penta- Phosphide $Ni_{12}P_5$	jlt	120-8133
Nickel Phosphide tri- Sulfide $NiPS_3$		
see Nickel tri- Thiophosphite $NiPS_3$	aq	120-8052
Nickel (I I) Selenate $NiSeO_3$	q	120-8135
Nickel di- Selenide $NiSe_2$	jq	120-8064
Nickel Selenide Sulfide $NiSe_xS_{2-x}$	jn	120-8041
Nickel tetra- Selenodiferrate $NiFe_2Se_4$	joqt	110-8083
Nickel Silicide $NiSi$	t	120-8089
Nickel di- Silicide $NiSi_2$	t	120-8090
di- Nickel Silicide Ni_2Si	j	120-8017
Nickel Sulfate $NiSO_4$	ab	120-0043
Nickel mono- Sulfide NiS	abdfhijlq	120-0006
see also Millerite NiS		521-8020
Nickel di- Sulfide NiS_2	fq	120-0190
Nickel Sulfide NiS_{1-x}	jqt	120-8023
Nickel tri- Thiophosphite $NiPS_3$	aq	120-8052
Nickel Tin hexa- Chloride $NiSnCl_6$		
see Nickel hexa- Chlorostannate $NiSnCl_6$	q	106-8332
Nickel (I I) Titanate (I V) $NiTiO_3$	j	120-8161
Nickel (I I) Tungstate (V I) $NiWO_4$	abh	120-8038
Nickel Vanadium Ferrite $NiV_xFe_{2-x}O_4$	fj	110-8079
Nickel Yttrium Iron Germanium Oxide		
$Ni_xY_3Fe_{5-x-y}Ge_yO_{12}$		
see Yttrium Nickel Germanium Ferrate		
$Y_3Ni_xGe_yFe_{5-x-y}O_{12}$	npq	110-8127
Nickel Zinc Ferrite $Ni_xZn_yFe_{3-x-y}O_4$	bjnpq	110-8070
Nickel Zinc Ferrite $Ni_xZn_{1-x}Fe_2O_4$	jlnopqt	110-8121
Nickel mono- Zincide $NiZn$	d	120-8178
Niobium tri- Aluminide $NbAl_3$	j	102-8416
di- Niobium Aluminide Nb_2Al	j	102-8417
tri- Niobium Aluminide Nb_3Al	jnqt	102-8169
Niobium Aluminum Antimonide $Nb_3Al_xSb_{1-x}$	j	102-8421
Niobium Aluminum Germanide $Nb_xAl_yGe_{1-x-y}$	j	102-8398
Niobium Aluminum Germanide $Nb_3Al_xGe_{1-x}$	jq	102-8100
Niobium Aluminum Germanide $Nb_{3-y}Al_xGe_{1-x}$	jq	102-8485
Niobium Aluminum Germanide $Nb_{4-y}Al_xGe_{1-x}$	jq	102-8486
Niobium Aluminum Silicide $Nb_3Al_xSi_{1-x}$	j	102-8194
Niobium Aluminum Stannide $Nb_3Al_xSn_{1-x}$	j	102-8409
Niobium Antimonate $NbSbO_4$	fr	120-8180
Niobium di- Antimonide $NbSb_2$	q	120-8002
tri- Niobium Antimonide Nb_3Sb	jqt	120-8003
penta- Niobium tetra- Antimonide Nb_5Sb_4	q	120-8004
Niobium mono- Arsenide $NbAs$	q	102-8418
Niobium di- Arsenide $NbAs_2$	q	102-8419
tri- Niobium Bismuthide Nb_3Bi	j	104-8368
Niobium (I I I) Boride NbB	jpqu	104-8230
Niobium di- Boride NbB_2	jlqtu	104-8083
Niobium Boride NbB_{1-x}	u	104-8434
tri- Niobium di- Boride Nb_3B_2	u	104-8280
tri- Niobium tetra- Boride Nb_3B_4	ju	104-8344
penta- Niobium tetra- Boride Nb_5B_4	u	104-8279
Niobium tetra- Bromide $NbBr_4$	fj	104-8299
Niobium Cadmium Oxide $Nb_2Cd_2O_7$		
see di- Cadmium Niobate (V) $Cd_2Nb_2O_7$	bq	106-8242
Niobium mono- Carbide NbC	dfhijklnoqtu	106-0309
Niobium Carbide NbC_{1-x}	jqtu	106-1062
di- Niobium Carbide Nb_2C	ju	106-1001
Niobium Carbide Nitride NbC_xN_{1-x}	j	106-8504
see also Niobium Mononitride ≥ Niobium Monocarbide		508-0400
Niobium tetra- Chloride $NbCl_4$	fj	106-1025
Niobium Chromium di- Cadmium hexa- Oxide		
$NbCrCd_2O_6$	n	106-8826
Niobium - Cobalt $NbCo_3$	n	106-8662
Niobium Cobalt Oxide Nb_2CoO_6		
see Cobalt (I I) Niobate (V) $CoNb_2O_6$	bj	106-8243
Niobium Cobalt Plumbate $Nb_xCo_{1-x}PbO_3$	b	106-8764
Niobium (V) Cuprate (I I) Nb_2CuO_6	j	106-1796
Niobium (V) Ferrite (I I) Nb_2FeO_6	j	110-8267
Niobium Fluoropentaoxodivanadate NbV_2O_5F	q	110-8201
tri- Niobium Gallide Nb_3Ga	j	111-8118
penta- Niobium tri- Gallide Nb_5Ga_3	j	111-8198

Substance Name	Property	Number
Niobium Gallium Aluminide $Nb_3Ga_xAl_{1-x}$	j	102-8479
hexa- Niobium Gallium Antimonide Nb_6GaSb	j	111-8164
Niobium Gallium Germanide $Nb_3Ga_xGe_{1-x}$	j	111-8163
hexa- Niobium Gallium Phosphide Nb_6GaP	j	111-8165
Niobium Gallium Stannide $Nb_3Ga_xSn_{1-x}$	j	111-8160
Niobium di- Germanide $NbGe_2$	jlqt	111-8145
tri- Niobium Germanide Nb_3Ge	j	111-8102
penta- Niobium Germanide Nb_5Ge	q	111-8029
penta- Niobium tri- Germanide Nb_5Ge_3	jlqt	111-8107
Niobium Germanide $Nb_{5-x}Ge$	jq	111-8199
Niobium Germanium Silicide $NbGeSi$	j	111-8169
Niobium Germanium Silicide $NbGe_xSi_{2-x}$	jt	111-8168
Niobium - Gold Nb_3Au	jq	102-8415
Niobium Hydride NbH	jn	112-8022
hexa- Niobium Indium Antimonide Nb_6InSb	j	114-8080
hexa- Niobium Indium Arsenide Nb_6InAs	j	102-8442
Niobium Indium Stannide $Nb_3In_xSn_{1-x}$	j	114-8079
Niobium Indium Zirconide $Nb_3In_xZr_{1-x}$	j	114-8082
Niobium tetra- Iodide NbI_4	fj	114-8075
Niobium mono- Iridide $NbIr$	j	114-8091
Niobium tri- Iridide $NbIr_3$	j	114-8083
di- Niobium Iridide Nb_2Ir	j	114-8090
tri- Niobium Iridide Nb_3Ir	j	114-8084
tri- Niobium di- Iridide Nb_3Ir_2	j	114-8085
Niobium Lead Oxide Nb_2PbO_6		
see Lead (I I) Niobate (V) $PbNb_2O_6$	bgv	120-0235
Niobium Lead Oxide $Nb_2Pb_2O_7$		
see di- Lead (I I) Niobate (V) $Pb_2Nb_2O_7$	bgn	120-8181
Niobium Lead Oxide Nb_4PbO_{11}		
see Lead (I I) tetra- Niobate (V) $PbNb_4O_{11}$	s	120-8109
di- Niobium Manganese hexa- Oxide		
Nb_2MnO_6		
see Manganese (I I) Niobate (V) $MnNb_2O_6$	bj	119-8033
Niobium Molybdenum Selenide $Nb_xMo_{1-x}Se_2$	j	119-8118
di- Niobium Nickel hexa- Oxide Nb_2NiO_6		
see Nickel (I I) Niobate (V) $NiNb_2O_6$	bj	120-8037
Niobium Nickel Plumbate $Nb_xNi_{1-x}PbO_3$	b	120-8169
Niobium mono- Nitride NbN	dfhjklnqt	120-0045
Niobium Nitride NbN_{1-x}	fjklmt	120-0199
di- Niobium Nitride Nb_2N	j	120-8067
tetra- Niobium tri- Nitride Nb_4N_3	j	120-8068
tetra- Niobium penta- Nitride Nb_4N_5	j	120-8069
penta- Niobium hexa- Nitride Nb_5N_6	j	120-8070
Niobium Nitride Oxide $NbN_{1-x}O_{1-y}$	j	120-8172
tri- Niobium Osmide Nb_3Os	j	120-8159
Niobium mono- Oxide NbO	j	120-0044
Niobium di- Oxide NbO_2	hj	120-0042
Niobium sesqui- Oxide Nb_2O_3	j	120-8019
di- Niobium penta- Oxide Nb_2O_5	bcfjost	120-0004
Niobium Oxide Nb_2O_{5-x}	jot	120-8151
Niobium mono- Phosphide NbP	jq	120-8148
tri- Niobium Platinide Nb_3Pt	j	120-8160
Niobium tri- Rhenide $NbRe_3$	j	120-8166
Niobium tri- Rhodide $NbRh_3$	j	120-8157
tri- Niobium Rhodide Nb_3Rh	j	120-8093
Niobium mono- Selenide $NbSe$	jt	120-8156
Niobium di- Selenide $NbSe_2$	abdfjklnoqst	120-8042
Niobium Selenide $NbSe_{2-x}$	q	120-8096
Niobium di- Selenide, Intercalated $NbSe_2$	a	120-8097
Niobium Selenide Sulfide $NbSe_xS_{2-x}$	j	120-8177
Niobium di- Silicide $NbSi_2$	djlot	120-8147
tri- Niobium Silicide Nb_3Si	j	120-8081
penta- Niobium tri- Silicide Nb_5Si_3	dj	120-8167
Niobium di- Stannide $NbSn_2$	j	120-8005
tri- Niobium Stannide Nb_3Sn	dfjknq	120-8006
tri- Niobium di- Stannide Nb_3Sn_2	j	120-8145
tetra- Niobium Stannide Nb_4Sn	jq	120-8146
hexa- Niobium penta- Stannide Nb_6Sn_5	j	120-8007
Niobium Stannide Antimonide $Nb_3Sn_xSb_{1-x}$	j	120-8137
Niobium Stannide Bismuthide $Nb_3Sn_xBi_{1-x}$	j	104-8362
Niobium di- Sulfide NbS_2	dj	120-0172
Niobium sesqui- Sulfide Nb_2S_3	fjlot	120-0140
Niobium tri- Technetide $NbTc_3$	j	120-8150
Niobium mono- Telluride $NbTe$	jt	120-8158

Property: **a.** Absorption coefficient; **b.** Dielectric constant; **c.** Dielectric strength; **d.** Energy band structure; **e.** Effective mass; **f.** Energy gap; **g.** Electric hysteresis; **h.** Energy level; **i.** Electron emission properties; **j.** Electrical resistivity; **k.** Magnetoelectric properties; **l.** Hall coefficient; **m.** Luminescence properties; **n.** Magnetic hysteresis; **o.** Mobility; **p.** Magnetomechanical properties; **q.** Magnetic susceptibility; **r.** Photoelectronic properties; **s.** Refractive index; **t.** Thermoelectric properties; **u.** Work function; **v.** Piezoelectric properties.

Substance Name	Property	Number
Niobium di-Telluride $NbTe_2$	jqt	120-8149
Niobium tetra-Telluride $NbTe_4$	jqt	120-8153
tri-Niobium tetra-Telluride Nb_3Te_4	jqt	120-8154
penta-Niobium tetra-Telluride Nb_5Te_4	q	120-8155
Niobium-Tin $NbSn_2$		
see Niobium di-Stannide $NbSn_2$	j	120-8005
Niobium-Tin Nb_3Sn		
see tri-Niobium Stannide Nb_3Sn	dfjknq	120-8006
Niobium-Tin Nb_6Sn_5		
see hexa-Niobium penta-Stannide Nb_6Sn_5	j	120-8007
Niobium Tungsten Oxide $Nb_xW_{2-x}O_5$	jt	120-8152
Niobium Tungsten Selenide $Nb_xW_{1-x}Se_2$	efhjot	120-8079
Niobium Vanadium Oxide Fluoride NbV_2O_5F		
see Niobium Fluoropentaoxodivanadate NbV_2O_5F	q	110-8201
Niobium di-Vanadium Stannide NbV_2Sn	j	120-8143
di-Niobium Vanadium Stannide Nb_2VSn	j	120-8144
Niobium Zinc Germanide $Nb_xZn_{5-x}Ge_3$	j	111-8166
Niobium Zinc Lead Oxide $Nb_xZn_{1-x}PbO_3$		
see Lead Zinc Niobate $PbZn_xNb_{1-x}O_3$	bg	120-8039
Niobium Zinc Lead Oxide $Pb_3ZnNb_2O_9$		
see tri-Lead (I I) Zinc di-Niobate (V) $Pb_3ZnNb_2O_9$	s	120-8043
Nitric Acid HNO_3	a	112-8052
Nitrogen tri-Flouride NF_3	ah	110-0004
Nitrogen di-Fluoride NF_2	hi	110-0377
di-Nitrogen tetra-Fluoride N_2F_4	hi	110-0343
Nitrogen Hydride NH_3		
see Ammonia NH_3	abhijlmqst	112-0010
Nitrogen Hydride Oxide NHO_3		
see Nitric Acid HNO_3	a	112-8052
Nitrogen mono-Oxide NO	ahi	120-0002
Nitrogen di-Oxide NO_2	him	120-0014
Nitrogen tri-Oxide NO_3	m	120-8032
di-Nitrogen Oxide N_2O	abchim	120-0003
Nitropentaamminecobalt (I I I) Nitrate $(CoNO_2(NH_3)_5)(NO_3)_2$	h	106-8447
Nitrosyl Fluorocarbonate $NO(CF_3)_2$	h	106-8303
di-Nitrotetraamminecobalt (I I I) Nitrate $(Co(NO_2)_2(NH_3)_4)NO_3$	h	106-8448
tri-Nitrotriamminecobalt (I I I) $Co(NO_2)_3(NH_3)_3$	h	106-8449
2000-N M 3 (Russian)		
see Ferrite 2000-N M 3 (Russian)	nq	110-8245
Optosil Fused Silica	a	122-8130
see also Silica, Fused		122-8045
Optosil Fused Silica 1	ab	122-8058
see also Silica, Fused		122-8045
Optosil Fused Silica 2	b	122-8099
see also Silica, Fused		122-8045
Optosil Fused Silica 3	b	122-8100
see also Silica, Fused		122-8045
Optovac (BaF_2)	a	104-8432
see also Barium Fluoride BaF_2		104-0104
Optovac (CaF_2)	a	106-8789
see also Calcium Fluoride CaF_2		106-0026
Optovac (KBr)	ajo	104-8242
see also Potassium Bromide KBr		104-0006
Optovac (KCl)	ajo	106-8488
see also Potassium Chloride KCl		106-0006
Optovac (SrF_2)	a	110-8274
see also Strontium Fluoride SrF_2		110-0132
Osmium tetra-Oxide OsO_4	ahiu	122-8004
Oxonium Perchlorate H_3OClO_4	j	106-8263
Oxotetrachlorovanadate (4-) Ion $VOCl_4$	q	106-8216
Palladium-Bismuth $PdBi_2$	t	104-8411
Palladium-Bismuth $PdBi_3$	t	104-8412
Palladium-Bismuth $PdBi_4$	t	104-8413
Palladium-Bismuth $PdBi_5$	t	104-8414
Palladium-Bismuth $PdBi_8$	t	104-8415
Palladium-Bismuth $PdBi_{13}$	t	104-8416
Palladium di-Chloride $PdCl_2$	a	106-8101
Palladium-Copper $PdCu_3$	j	106-8519
Palladium mono-Deuteride PdD		
see Palladium mono-Hydride, Deuterated PdD	j	108-8060
Palladium-Gold-Gallium $Pd_xAu_{1-x}Ga_2$	jq	102-8256
Palladium Gold Telluride $Pd_xAu_{1-x}Te_2$	j	102-8397
Palladium mono-Hydride PdH	jq	112-8079
see also Palladium mono-Hydride, Deuterated PdD		108-8060
Palladium Hydride PdH_{1-x}	jq	112-0577
di-Palladium Hydride Pd_2H	jq	112-0240
tetra-Palladium Hydride Pd_4H	q	112-0662
Palladium mono-Hydride, Deuterated PdD	j	108-8060
Palladium-Iron $PdFe$	n	110-8250
Palladium Nickel Aluminide $Pd_xNi_{3-x}Al$	q	102-8407
17-Palladium 15-Selenide $Pd_{17}Se_{15}$	j	123-8040
tri-Palladium di-Silver Sulfide Pd_3Ag_2S		
see tri-Palladium Thiodiargentide Pd_3Ag_2S	jq	102-8088
tri-Palladium Thiodiargentide Pd_3Ag_2S	jq	102-8088
Pass And Seymour E 211 M	j	102-8425
see also Steatite, Grade L 5		102-8424
Pentaborane B_5H_9		
see penta-Borane B_5H_9	i	104-0086
Perchloric Acid $HClO_4$	s	106-8733
Perfluorodiethylmethylamine $CF_3N(C_2F_5)_2$		
see Bis-(penta-Fluoroethyl)trifluoromethylamine $CF_3N(C_2F_5)_2$	c	106-8579
Perfluorodimethylethylamine $C_2F_5N(CF_3)_2$		
see penta-Fluoroethyl-bis-(Trifluoromethyl)amine $C_2F_5N(CF_3)_2$	c	106-8577
Perfluoroethylamine $N(C_2F_5)_3$		
see Tris-(penta-Fluoroethyl)amine $N(C_2F_5)_3$	c	106-8578
Perfluoromethane		
see Carbon tetra-Fluoride CF_4	abchi	106-0231
Perfluoropropane C_3F_8		
see octa-Fluoropropane C_3F_8	cs	106-0034
Phosphorus tri-Chloride PCl_3	b	106-0182
Phosphorus Chloride Oxide $POCl_3$		
see Phosphoryl Chloride $POCl_3$	bjm	106-0183
Phosphorus tri-Chlorosulfite $PSCl_3$		
see Thiophosphoryl Chloride $PSCl_3$	hm	106-8431
Phosphorus penta-Fluoride PF_5	hi	110-0298
tri-Phosphorus penta-Nitride P_3N_5	j	120-8102
Phosphorus Nitride P_3N_{5-x}	j	120-8103
Phosphorus Nitride Oxide PNO		
see Phosphoryl Nitride PON	hj	120-8071
di-Phosphorus penta-Oxide P_2O_5	ab	122-0064
Phosphorus Oxychloride $POCl_3$		
see Phosphoryl Chloride $POCl_3$	bjm	106-0183
Phosphorus mono-Selenide PSe	afr	123-8099
Phosphorus sesqui-Selenide P_2Se_3	afr	123-8100
di-Phosphorus penta-Selenide P_2Se_5	afr	123-8025
tetra-Phosphorus tri-Sulfide P_4S_3	fj	123-0027
Phosphorus Sulfide Chloride $PSCl_3$		
see Thiophosphoryl Chloride $PSCl_3$	hm	106-8431
Phosphoryl Chloride $POCl_3$	bjm	106-0183
Phosphoryl Nitride PON	hj	120-8071
Platinum mono-Antimonide $PtSb$	ejklot	123-8004
Platinum di-Antimonide $PtSb_2$	jkl	123-8005
Platinum-Cobalt $PtCo$	t	106-8511
Platinum Germanide $PtGe$	q	111-8059
di-Platinum Germanide Pt_2Ge	q	111-8060
Platinum-Iron $PtFe$	jnq	110-8077
Platinum-Iron $PtFe_3$	jnq	110-8117
Platinum mono-Oxide PtO	as	122-8012
Platinum Oxide PtO_x	j	122-8087
Platinum di-Oxide PtO_2	h	122-8013
Platinum-Palladium-Iron $Pt_xPd_{3-x}Fe$	n	110-8065
penta-Platinum tetra-Selenide Pt_5Se_4	j	123-8041
Platinum Silicide $PtSi$	jq	123-8047
di-Platinum Silicide Pt_2Si	q	123-8048
Platinum mono-Stannide $PtSn$	q	123-8008
Platinum Telluride $PtTe$	j	123-8042

Property: a. Absorption coefficient; **b.** Dielectric constant; **c.** Dielectric strength; **d.** Energy band structure; **e.** Effective mass; **f.** Energy gap; **g.** Electric hysteresis; **h.** Energy level; **i.** Electron emission properties; **j.** Electrical resistivity; **k.** Magnetoelectric properties; **l.** Hall coefficient; **m.** Luminescence properties; **n.** Magnetic hysteresis; **o.** Mobility; **p.** Magnetomechanical properties; **q.** Magnetic susceptibility; **r.** Photoelectronic properties; **s.** Refractive index; **t.** Thermoelectric properties; **u.** Work function; **v.** Piezoelectric properties.

Substance Name	*Property*	*Number*
Platinum - Tin $PtSn$		
see Platinum mono- Stannide $PtSn$	q	123-8008
PLT		
see Lead Lanthanum Titanate $Pb_xLa_{1-x}TiO_3$	bv	118-8075
PLTM		
see Lead Lanthanum Titanium Manganate $Pb_xLa_{1-x}Ti_yMn_{1-y}O_3$	bv	118-8076
Plutonium di- Aluminide $PuAl_2$	jq	102-8160
Plutonium mono- Arsenide $PuAs$	q	102-8155
Plutonium tri- Bromide $PuBr_3$	q	104-8087
Plutonium mono- Carbide PuC	j	106-0750
Plutonium Carbide PuC_{1-x}	j	106-8703
Plutonium tri- Chloride $PuCl_3$	q	106-0286
Plutonium tri- Fluoride PuF_3	q	110-8029
Plutonium tri- Iodide PuI_3	nq	114-8033
Plutonium - Iridium $PuIr_2$	j	114-8059
Plutonium - Iron Pu_6Fe	j	110-8197
Plutonium mono- Oxide PuO	h	122-8074
Plutonium di- Oxide PuO_2	hj	122-0077
Plutonium Oxide PuO_{2-x}	j	122-0397
Plutonium - Palladium $PuPd_3$	jq	123-8059
Plutonium - Palladium Pu_3Pd_4	q	123-8063
Plutonium - Palladium Pu_5Pd_4	q	123-8064
Plutonium mono- Phosphide PuP	hq	123-0014
Plutonium - Rhodium $PuRh_2$	jq	123-8057
Plutonium - Rhodium $PuRh_3$	jq	123-8043
Plutonium - Ruthenium $PuRu_2$	j	123-8056
Plutonium Uranium Aluminide $Pu_xU_{1-x}Al_2$	jq	102-8161
Plutonium Uranium Carbide $Pu_xU_{1-x}C$	j	106-8704
Plutonium - Zinc $PuZn_2$	jq	123-8061
PLZT Ceramic		
see Lead Lanthanum Zirconium Titanate $Pb_{1-x}La_xZr_yTi_{1-y}O_3$	abcgjqrsv	118-8018
PNT (Na Doped Lead Titanate) $Pb_{1-x}Na_{2y}TiO_{3-x+y}$		
see Lead Titanate $Pb_{1-x}TiO_{3-x}$	bg	122-8056
Polyphosphoric Acid $H_{3+x}P_{1+x}O_{4+3x}$	q	112-8045
Polytran (Harshaw Chemical Co) (K Cl)	a	106-8790
see also Potassium Chloride KCl		106-0006
Polytran (Harshaw Chemical Co) (Na Cl)	a	106-8748
see also Sodium Chloride $NaCl$		106-0024
Potassium Alum $KAl(SO_4)_2$		
see Potassium Aluminum Sulfate $KAl(SO_4)_2$	bs	102-0024
Potassium undeca- Aluminate $KAl_{11}O_{17}$	j	102-8308
Potassium Aluminum Selenate $KAl(SeO_4)_2$	h	102-8449
Potassium Aluminum Sulfate $KAl(SO_4)_2$	bs	102-0024
Potassium Ammonium Chlorocuprate $K_x(NH_4)_{2-x}CuCl_4$	knq	106-8400
Potassium Ammonium Sulfate $K_x(NH_4)_{2-x}SO_4$	g	112-8097
see also Ammonium Sulfate ≥ Potassium Sulfate		508-0480
see also Potassium Sulfate ≥ Ammonium Sulfate		508-0494
tri- Potassium Antimonide K_3Sb	adf	116-8003
Potassium Antimonide Selenide $KSbSe_2$		
see Potassium di- Selenoantimonate $KSbSe_2$	fhjt	116-8038
Potassium Antimony Sulfide $KSbS_2$		
see Potassium di- Thioantimonate $KSbS_2$	fhjt	116-8037
Potassium Arsenide di- Selenide $KAsSe_2$		
see Potassium di- Selenoarsenate $KAsSe_2$	af	102-8150
Potassium Azide KN_3	afhm	116-0030
Potassium Boron tetra- Fluoride KBF_4		
see Potassium tetra- Fluoroborate KBF_4	j	104-8289
Potassium Bromate $KBrO_3$	b	104-0129
Potassium Bromide KBr	abcdefhijmnorst	104-0006
see also Optovac (K Br)		104-8242
Potassium Bromide Chloride KBr_xCl_{1-x}	abj	104-8189
see also Potassium Bromide ≥ Potassium Chloride		508-0067
see also Potassium Chloride ≥ Potassium Bromide		508-0066
Potassium Bromide Oxide $KBrO_3$		
see Potassium Bromate $KBrO_3$	b	104-0129
Potassium octa- Carbide KC_8	hj	106-8495
Potassium 16- Carbide KC_{16}	hj	106-8563
Potassium Carbide Nitride KCN		
see Potassium Cyanide KCN	b	106-0318
Potassium Carbide Nitride Sulfide $KSCN$		
see Potassium Thiocyanate $KSCN$	bj	106-0401
Potassium Carbonate K_2CO_3	bjs	106-0050
Potassium Chlorate $KClO_3$	b	106-0494
Potassium Chlorate $KClO_4$		
see Potassium Perchlorate $KClO_4$	b	106-0108
Potassium Chloride KCl	a-jmoprstuv	106-0006
see also Optovac (K Cl)		106-8488
see also Polytran (Harshaw Chemical Co) (K Cl)		106-8790
see also Sylvine KCl		521-8041
Potassium Chloride Oxide $KClO_3$		
see Potassium Chlorate $KClO_3$	b	106-0494
Potassium Chloride Oxide $KClO_4$		
see Potassium Perchlorate $KClO_4$	b	106-0108
di- Potassium tetra- Chlorochromate K_2CrCl_4	aq	106-8681
Potassium hexa- Chloroiridate (I V) K_2IrCl_6	q	106-8484
tetra- Potassium hexa- Chloromanganate K_4MnCl_6	q	106-8631
Potassium hexa- Chlororhenate (I V) K_2ReCl_6	h	106-0652
Potassium Chlorosulfonate KSO_3Cl	q	106-8835
Potassium hexa- Chlorotantalate (I V) K_2TaCl_6	j	106-8352
di- Potassium hexa- Chlorotechnetate K_2TcCl_6	h	106-8353
Potassium Chromate K_2CrO_4	bi	106-0063
Potassium di- Chromate $K_2Cr_2O_7$	ijs	106-0064
Potassium Chromium Alum $KCr(SO_4)_2$		
see Potassium Chromium Sulfate $KCr(SO_4)_2$	bq	106-0117
di- Potassium Chromium tetra- Chloride K_2CrCl_4		
see di- Potassium tetra- Chlorochromate K_2CrCl_4	aq	106-8681
tri- Potassium Chromium hexa- Fluoride K_3CrF_6		
see tri- Potassium hexa- Fluorochromate K_3CrF_6	m	106-8622
Potassium Chromium Sulfate $KCr(SO_4)_2$	bq	106-0117
Potassium Cobalt tri- Fluoride $KCoF_3$		
see Potassium tri- Fluorocobaltate $KCoF_3$	hq	106-8461
Potassium Cobalt Nitride Hydride Oxide $K(Co(NO_2)_4(NH_3)_2)$		
see Potassium tetra- Nitrodiamminecobaltate (I I I) $K(Co(NO_2)_4(NH_3)_2)$	h	106-8450
Potassium Cobalt Nitride Oxide $K_3(Co(NO_2)_6)$		
see Potassium hexa- Nitrocobaltate (I I I) $K_3(Co(NO_2)_6)$	h	106-8451
di- Potassium Cobalt Sulfate $K_2Co(SO_4)_2$	aq	106-8575
Potassium Copper tri- Fluoride $KCuF_3$		
see Potassium tri- Fluorocuprate (I I) $KCuF_3$	q	106-1103
di- Potassium Copper tetra- Fluoride K_2CuF_4		
see Potassium tetra- Fluorocuprate (I I) K_2CuF_4	q	106-8269
di- Potassium Copper Sulfate $K_2Cu(SO_4)_2$	q	106-8571
Potassium Cyanide KCN	b	106-0318
Potassium tetra- Cyanobromoplatinate $K_2Pt(CN)_4Br_x$	abfjoqr	104-8183
Potassium tetra- Cyanochloroplatinate $K_2Pt(CN)_4Cl_x$	jqt	106-8325
Potassium hexa- Cyanocobaltate (I I I) $K_3(Co(CN)_6)$	ahm	106-8383
Potassium hexa- Cyanoferrate (I I I) $K_3Fe(CN)_6$	q	106-8610
Potassium hexa- Cyanoferrate (I I) $K_4Fe(CN)_6$	abfs	106-8236
Potassium tetra- Cyanoplatinate (I I) $K_2Pt(CN)_4$	jm	106-8151
Potassium tetra- Cyanoplatinate Bromide $K_2Pt(CN)_4Br_x$		
see Potassium tetra- Cyanobromoplatinate $K_2Pt(CN)_4Br_x$	abfjoqr	104-8183
Potassium tetra- Cyanoplatinate Chloride $K_2Pt(CN)_4Cl_x$		
see Potassium tetra- Cyanochloroplatinate $K_2Pt(CN)_4Cl_x$	jqt	106-8325
Potassium Fluoride KF	abcdfhijsu	110-0037
di- Potassium Fluoride Phosphate K_2FPO_3	qs	110-8110
Potassium tetra- Fluoroborate KBF_4	j	104-8289
tri- Potassium hexa- Fluorochromate K_3CrF_6	m	106-8622
Potassium tri- Fluorocobaltate $KCoF_3$	hq	106-8461

Property: a. Absorption coefficient; **b.** Dielectric constant; **c.** Dielectric strength; **d.** Energy band structure; **e.** Effective mass; **f.** Energy gap; **g.** Electric hysteresis; **h.** Energy level; **i.** Electron emission properties; **j.** Electrical resistivity; **k.** Magnetoelectric properties; **l.** Hall coefficient; **m.** Luminescence properties; **n.** Magnetic hysteresis; **o.** Mobility; **p.** Magnetomechanical properties; **q.** Magnetic susceptibility; **r.** Photoelectronic properties; **s.** Refractive index; **t.** Thermoelectric properties; **u.** Work function; **v.** Piezoelectric properties.

Substance Name	Property	Number
Potassium tri- Fluorocuprate (I I) $KCuF_3$	q	106-1103
Potassium tetra- Fluorocuprate (I I) K_2CuF_4	q	106-8269
Potassium tri- Fluoroferrate $KFeF_3$	hq	110-8066
Potassium hexa- Fluorogermanate K_2GeF_6	hm	110-8095
Potassium di- Fluoroiodate KIO_2F_2		
see Potassium di- Oxodifluoroiodate KIO_2F_2	s	110-8154
Potassium tri- Fluoromagnesate $KMgF_3$	adhm	110-0279
Potassium tri- Fluoromanganate $KMnF_3$	abhqs	110-8039
di- Potassium tetra- Fluoromanganate K_2MnF_4	p	110-8224
Potassium Fluoromanganatecobaltate $KMn_xCo_{1-x}F_3$	aq	106-8468
Potassium hexa- Fluoromolybdate (V) $KMoF_6$	q	110-0395
Potassium tri- Fluoronickelate $KNiF_3$	dhiq	110-8041
Potassium tetra- Fluoronickelate (I I) K_2NiF_4	ap	110-8156
Potassium Fluoroniobate $KNbO_{3-x}F_x$	bq	110-8076
Potassium hexa- Fluororhenate $KReF_6$	q	110-8286
Potassium hexa- Fluorotungstate KWF_6	q	110-8287
Potassium tri- Fluorozincate $KZnF_3$	ahm	110-8137
di- Potassium Germanium hexa- Fluoride		
K_2GeF_6		
see Potassium hexa- Fluorogermanate K_2GeF_6	hm	110-8095
Potassium Hydride KH	hm	112-8050
Potassium di- Hydrogen Arsenate KH_2AsO_4	bfgjnqsv	102-0054
Potassium di- Hydrogen Arsenate, Deuterated		
KD_2AsO_4	bfgjsv	102-0281
Potassium di- Hydrogen Phosphate KH_2PO_4	abgjnqsv	112-0028
di- Potassium Hydrogen Phosphate K_2HPO_4	b	112-0637
Potassium di- Hydrogen Phosphate, Deuterated		
KD_2PO_4	bgijnqsv	108-0014
Potassium di- Hydrogen Phosphate, Partly Deuterated		
$KH_{2-x}D_xPO_4$	bcgjs	108-8025
Potassium tri- Hydrogen Selenate, Trideuterated		
$KD_3(SeO_3)_2$	b	108-8045
Potassium Hydrogen Sulfate $KHSO_4$	q	112-0406
Potassium Hydrogen Sulfide KHS	s	112-8072
Potassium Hydroxide KOH	j	112-8093
Potassium Iodate KIO_3	bg	114-0018
Potassium Iodide KI	abcdefhijmrsv	114-0001
Potassium Iodide di- Oxide di- Fluoride		
KIO_2F_2		
see Potassium di- Oxodifluoroiodate KIO_2F_2	s	110-8154
di- Potassium tri- Iodoargentate K_2AgI_3	amq	102-8260
Potassium Iodyldifluoride KIO_2F_2		
see Potassium di- Oxodifluoroiodate KIO_2F_2	s	110-8154
di- Potassium Iridium hexa- Chloride		
K_2IrCl_6		
see Potassium hexa- Chloroiridate (I V) K_2IrCl_6	q	106-8484
Potassium Iron Carbide Nitride		
$K_3Fe(CN)_6$		
see Potassium hexa- Cyanoferrate (I I I)		
$K_3Fe(CN)_6$	q	106-8610
Potassium Iron Carbide Nitride		
$K_4Fe(CN)_6$		
see Potassium hexa- Cyanoferrate (I I)		
$K_4Fe(CN)_6$	abfs	106-8236
Potassium Iron tri- Fluoride $KFeF_3$		
see Potassium tri- Fluoroferrate $KFeF_3$	hq	110-8066
Potassium di- Lead (I I) penta- Niobate (V)		
$KPb_2Nb_5O_{15}$	bgs	116-8044
Potassium Lead Zinc Niobate		
$K_{1-x}Pb_xZn_yNb_{1-y}O_3$	b	116-8024
Potassium Magnesium tri- Fluoride $KMgF_3$		
see Potassium tri- Fluoromagnesate $KMgF_3$	adhm	110-0279
tetra- Potassium Manganese hexa- Chloride		
K_4MnCl_6		
see tetra- Potassium hexa- Chloromanganate K_4MnCl_6	q	106-8631
Potassium Manganese Cobalt Fluoride		
$KMn_xCo_{1-x}F_3$		
see Potassium Fluoromanganatecobaltate		
$KMn_xCo_{1-x}F_3$	aq	106-8468
Potassium Manganese tri- Fluoride $KMnF_3$		
see Potassium tri- Fluoromanganate $KMnF_3$	abhqs	110-8039
di- Potassium Manganese tetra- Fluoride		
K_2MnF_4		
see di- Potassium tetra- Fluoromanganate K_2MnF_4	p	110-8224

Substance Name	Property	Number
Potassium Molybdate (V) $KMoO_3$	d	116-8016
Potassium Molybdate $K_{1-x}MoO_3$	jo	116-8028
Potassium Molybdenum hexa- Fluoride $KMoF_6$		
see Potassium hexa- Fluoromolybdate (V) $KMoF_6$	q	110-0395
Potassium Neodymium tetra- Phosphate $KNdP_4O_{12}$	m	116-8029
Potassium Nickelate (I I) K_2NiO_2	q	116-8034
Potassium Nickel tri- Fluoride $KNiF_3$		
see Potassium tri- Fluoronickelate $KNiF_3$	dhiq	110-8041
di- Potassium Nickel tetra- Fluoride		
K_2NiF_4		
see Potassium tetra- Fluoronickelate (I I) K_2NiF_4	ap	110-8156
di- Potassium Nickel tetra- Fluoride		
K_2NiF_4		
see Potassium tetra- Fluoronickelate (I I) K_2NiF_4	ap	110-8156
Potassium Niobate (V) $KNbO_3$	bgsv	116-0031
Potassium Niobate Fluoride $KNbO_{3-x}F_x$		
see Potassium Fluoroniobate $KNbO_{3-x}F_x$	bq	110-8076
Potassium penta- Niobium di- Lead 15- Oxide		
$KNb_5Pb_2O_{15}$		
see Potassium di- Lead (I I) penta- Niobate (V)		
$KPb_2Nb_5O_{15}$	bgs	116-8044
Potassium Niobium Zinc Lead Oxide		
$K_{1-x}Nb_{1-y}Zn_yPb_xO_3$		
see Potassium Lead Zinc Niobate		
$K_{1-x}Pb_xZn_yNb_{1-y}O_3$	b	116-8024
Potassium Nitrate KNO_3	bj	116-0001
Potassium tri- Nitride KN_3		
see Potassium Azide KN_3	afhm	116-0030
tri- Potassium Nitride K_3N	m	116-8042
Potassium Nitrite KNO_2	bj	116-0012
Potassium hexa- Nitrocobaltate (I I I)		
$K_3(Co(NO_2)_6)$	h	106-8451
Potassium tetra- Nitrodiamminecobaltate (I I I)		
$K(Co(NO_2)_4(NH_3)_2)$	h	106-8450
Potassium tri- Oxochlorosulfate KSO_3Cl		
see Potassium Chlorosulfonate KSO_3Cl	q	106-8835
Potassium di- Oxodifluoroiodate KIO_2F_2	s	110-8154
Potassium di- Oxofluorosulfate KSO_2F	q	110-8282
Potassium Perchlorate $KClO_4$	b	106-0108
Potassium Phosphate K_3PO_4	b	116-0043
Potassium Phosphorus Oxide Fluoride		
K_2PO_3F		
see di- Potassium Fluoride Phosphate K_2FPO_3	qs	110-8110
Potassium Platinum Carbide Nitride		
$K_2(Pt(CN)_4)$		
see Potassium tetra- Cyanoplatinate (I I)		
$K_2Pt(CN)_4$	jm	106-8151
Potassium Platinum Carbide Nitride Bromide		
$K_2Pt(CN)_4Br_x$		
see Potassium tetra- Cyanobromoplatinate		
$K_2Pt(CN)_4Br_x$	abfjoqr	104-8183
Potassium Platinum Carbide Nitride Chloride		
$K_2Pt(CN)_4Cl_x$		
see Potassium tetra- Cyanochloroplatinate		
$K_2Pt(CN)_4Cl_x$	jqt	106-8325
di- Potassium Rhenium hexa- Chloride		
K_2ReCl_6		
see Potassium hexa- Chlororhenate (I V) K_2ReCl_6	h	106-0652
Potassium Rhenium hexa- Fluoride $KReF_6$		
see Potassium hexa- Fluororhenate $KReF_6$	q	110-8286
Potassium Selenate K_2SeO_4	b	116-0024
di- Potassium Selenide K_2Se	j	116-8010
Potassium di- Selenoantimonate $KSbSe_2$	fhjt	116-8038
Potassium di- Selenoarsenate $KAsSe_2$	af	102-8150
di- Potassium tetra- Silicate $K_2Si_4O_9$	s	116-8033
di- Potassium Silver tri- Iodide K_2AgI_3		
see di- Potassium tri- Iodoargentate K_2AgI_3	amq	102-8260
Potassium di- Sodium Antimonide KNa_2Sb	adfij	116-8026
tri- Potassium Sodium tetra- Chloride K_3NaCl_4	s	106-8489
Potassium Sodium Niobate $K_xNa_{1-x}NbO_3$	bjv	116-8025
Potassium Sodium Tantalate $K_xNa_{1-x}TaO_3$	g	116-8040
Potassium Sodium Tungsten Bronze $K_xNa_yWO_3$	as	116-8030
Potassium di- Strontium Niobate (V)		
$KSr_2Nb_5O_{15}$	b	116-8022

Property: **a.** Absorption coefficient; **b.** Dielectric constant; **c.** Dielectric strength; **d.** Energy band structure; **e.** Effective mass; **f.** Energy gap; **g.** Electric hysteresis; **h.** Energy level; **i.** Electron emission properties; **j.** Electrical resistivity; **k.** Magnetoelectric properties; **l.** Hall coefficient; **m.** Luminescence properties; **n.** Magnetic hysteresis; **o.** Mobility; **p.** Magnetomechanical properties; **q.** Magnetic susceptibility; **r.** Photoelectronic properties; **s.** Refractive index; **t.** Thermoelectric properties; **u.** Work function; **v.** Piezoelectric properties.

Substance Name	*Property*	*Number*
Potassium Sulfate K_2SO_4	bfij	116-0005
di- Potassium Sulfide K_2S	s	116-0016
di- Potassium di- Sulfide K_2S_2	s	116-8011
di- Potassium tri- Sulfide K_2S_3	j	116-8012
di- Potassium tetra- Sulfide K_2S_4	j	116-8013
di- Potassium penta- Sulfide K_2S_5	j	116-8014
di- Potassium hexa- Sulfide K_2S_6	j	116-8031
Potassium Sulfide Chloride Oxide KSO_3Cl		
see Potassium Chlorosulfonate KSO_3Cl	q	106-8835
Potassium Sulfide Oxide $K_2S_2O_3$		
see Potassium di- Thionate $K_2S_2O_3$	s	116-8035
Potassium Sulfide Oxide $K_2S_3O_6$		
see Potassium tri- Thionate $K_2S_3O_6$	b	116-8018
Potassium Sulfide Oxide $K_2S_4O_6$		
see Potassium tetra- Thionate $K_2S_4O_6$	b	116-8019
Potassium Sulfide Oxide $K_2S_5O_6$		
see Potassium penta- Thionate $K_2S_5O_6$	b	116-8020
Potassium Sulfide Oxide $K_3S_6O_6$		
see Potassium hexa- Thionate $K_3S_6O_6$	b	116-8021
Potassium Sulfide Oxide Fluoride KSO_2F		
see Potassium di- Oxofluorosulfate KSO_2F	q	110-8282
Potassium Sulfite K_2SO_3	qs	116-8036
Potassium Tantalate $KTaO_3$	bdfghmnosv	116-0017
Potassium Tantalate $KTaO_{3-x}$	j	116-8027
di- Potassium Tantalum hexa- Chloride K_2TaCl_6		
see Potassium hexa- Chlorotantalate (I V) K_2TaCl_6	j	106-8352
Potassium Tantalum Niobate $KTaNbO_3$	b	116-8023
Potassium Tantalum Niobate $KTa_{1-x}Nb_xO_3$	abghjmnqrsv	116-8017
di- Potassium Technetium hexa- Chloride K_2TcCl_6		
see di- Potassium hexa- Chlorotechnetate K_2TcCl_6	h	106-8353
Potassium di- Thioantimonate $KSbS_2$	fhjt	116-8037
Potassium Thiocyanate $KSCN$	bj	106-0401
Potassium di- Thionate $K_2S_2O_3$	s	116-8035
Potassium tri- Thionate $K_2S_3O_6$	b	116-8018
Potassium tetra- Thionate $K_2S_4O_6$	b	116-8019
Potassium penta- Thionate $K_2S_5O_6$	b	116-8020
Potassium hexa- Thionate $K_3S_6O_6$	b	116-8021
Potassium Tungstate $K_{1-x}WO_3$	b	116-8043
Potassium Tungsten hexa- Fluoride KWF_6		
see Potassium hexa- Fluorotungstate KWF_6	q	110-8287
tri- Potassium Uranyl penta- Fluoride $K_3UO_2F_5$	m	110-8209
Potassium Vanadate Bronze KV_6O_{15}	jq	116-8039
Potassium Yttrium di- Molybdate (V I) $KY(MoO_4)_2$	q	116-8032
Potassium Zeolite	abfj	102-8191
Potassium Zinc tri- Fluoride $KZnF_3$		
see Potassium tri- Fluorozincate $KZnF_3$	ahm	110-8137
Praseodymium (I I I) Aluminate $PrAl_{o3}$	ahm	102-8393
Praseodymium di- Aluminide $PrAl_2$	q	102-8272
Praseodymium tri- Aluminide $PrAl_3$	hj	102-8259
Praseodymium Antimonide $PrSb$	fjopq	123-8013
Praseodymium Arsenide $PrAs$	f	102-8344
Praseodymium hexa- Boride PrB_6	jq	104-8239
Praseodymium tri- Bromide $PrBr_3$	j	104-8088
Praseodymium Cerium Aluminide $Pr_xCe_{1-x}Al_2$	q	102-8276
Praseodymium tri- Chloride $PrCl_3$	jm	106-0626
Praseodymium Chromium tri- Selenide $PrCrSe_3$		
see Praseodymium tri- Selenochromate $PrCrSe_3$	jloq	106-8366
Praseodymium - Cobalt $PrCo_3$	q	106-8601
Praseodymium - Cobalt $PrCo_5$	jnpq	106-8204
Praseodymium - Cobalt - Copper $PrCo_{5-x}Cu_x$	jnpq	106-8360
Praseodymium - Cobalt - Germanium $PrCo_2Ge_2$	q	106-8166
Praseodymium - Cobalt - Iron $Pr_2Co_{17-x}Fe_x$	np	106-8326
Praseodymium - Copper $PrCu_6$	q	106-8802
di- Praseodymium Cuprate Pr_2CuO_4	jt	106-8832
Praseodymium (I I I) Ferrate $PrFeO_3$	q	110-8174
Praseodymium tri- Fluoride PrF_3	as	110-0107
di- Praseodymium Germanium penta- Sulfide Pr_2GeS_5		
see di- Praseodymium penta- Thiogermanate Pr_2GeS_5	fj	111-8099
Praseodymium - Indium Pr_3In	q	114-8071

Substance Name	*Property*	*Number*
Praseodymium Indium tri- Selenide $PrInSe_3$		
see Praseodymium tri- Selenoindate $PrInSe_3$	q	114-8093
Praseodymium Indium tri- Sulfide $PrInS_3$		
see Praseodymium tri- Thioindate $PrInS_3$	fjqt	114-0113
Praseodymium tri- Iodide PrI_3	j	114-8034
Praseodymium - Iridium $PrIr_2$	j	114-8102
Praseodymium - Iridium Pr_7Ir_3	q	114-8056
Praseodymium - Iron Pr_2Fe_{17}	q	110-8270
Praseodymium Lanthanum Selenide $Pr_xLa_{1-x}Se_4$	j	118-8085
Praseodymium Lanthanum Sulfide $Pr_xLa_{1-x}S_4$	j	118-8086
Praseodymium Lanthanum Thallium $Pr_xLa_{1-x}Tl$	h	118-8044
Praseodymium di- Manganese di- Germanide $PrMn_2Ge_2$	nq	111-8179
Praseodymium - Nickel $PrNi_5$	jq	120-8028
Praseodymium - Nickel Pr_7Ni_3	q	120-8059
Praseodymium mono- Nitride PrN	dfh	120-0166
Praseodymium - Osmium $PrOs_2$	j	122-8142
Praseodymium sesqui- Oxide Pr_2O_3	abfs	122-0038
tetra- Praseodymium hepta- Oxide Pr_4O_7	fju	122-8041
hexa- Praseodymium undeca- Oxide Pr_6O_{11}	q	122-8106
Praseodymium - Palladium Pr_7Pd_3	q	123-8053
Praseodymium - Platinum $PrPt_2$	j	123-8109
Praseodymium - Platinum $PrPt_5$	q	123-8045
Praseodymium - Platinum Pr_7Pt_3	q	123-8054
Praseodymium - Rhodium $PrRh_2$	j	123-8108
Praseodymium - Rhodium Pr_7Rh_3	q	123-8052
Praseodymium - Ruthenium $PrRu_2$	j	123-8107
Praseodymium mono- Selenide $PrSe$	q	123-8078
Praseodymium di- Selenide $PrSe_2$	q	123-8079
Praseodymium sesqui- Selenide Pr_2Se_3	q	123-8080
tri- Praseodymium tetra- Selenide Pr_3Se_4	q	123-8081
tri- Praseodymium hepta- Selenide Pr_3Se_7	q	123-8082
tetra- Praseodymium hepta- Selenide Pr_4Se_7	q	123-8083
Praseodymium tri- Selenochromate $PrCrSe_3$	jloq	106-8366
Praseodymium tri- Selenoindate $PrInSe_3$	q	114-8093
penta- Praseodymium tri- Silicide Pr_5Si_3	j	123-8103
Praseodymium tri- Stannide $PrSn_3$	j	123-8014
Praseodymium mono- Sulfide PrS	q	123-0012
Praseodymium di- Sulfide PrS_2	q	123-8076
Praseodymium sesqui- Sulfide Pr_2S_3	q	123-0015
tri- Praseodymium tetra- Sulfide Pr_3S_4	jq	123-8075
penta- Praseodymium hexa- Sulfide Pr_5S_6	q	123-8077
Praseodymium mono- Telluride $PrTe$	q	123-8084
Praseodymium di- Telluride $PrTe_2$	q	123-8085
Praseodymium tri- Telluride $PrTe_3$	q	123-8086
Praseodymium sesqui- Telluride Pr_2Te_3	q	123-8087
di- Praseodymium penta- Telluride Pr_2Te_5	q	123-8088
tri- Praseodymium tetra- Telluride Pr_3Te_4	q	123-8089
tri- Praseodymium hepta- Telluride Pr_3Te_7	q	123-8090
tetra- Praseodymium hepta- Telluride Pr_4Te_7	q	123-8091
tetra- Praseodymium undeca- Telluride Pr_4Te_{11}	q	123-8092
Praseodymium - Thallium $PrTl_3$	q	123-8055
Praseodymium - Thallium Pr_3Tl	hq	123-8046
di- Praseodymium penta- Thiogermanate Pr_2GeS_5	fj	111-8099
Praseodymium tri- Thioindate $PrInS_3$	fjqt	114-0113
Praseodymium - Tin $PrSn_3$		
see Praseodymium tri- Stannide $PrSn_3$	j	123-8014
Praseodymium Titanium Niobate $PrTiNbO_6$	fj	120-0288
Praseodymium Vanadate (I I I) $PrVO_3$	q	122-8082
Praseodymium Vanadate (V) $PrVO_4$	m	122-8039
Praseodymium - Zinc $PrZn$	q	123-8105
P S N $K_xNa_{1-x}NbO_3$		
see Potassium Sodium Niobate $K_xNa_{1-x}NbO_3$	bjv	116-8025
P S Z T		
see Lead Tin Zirconium Titanate $PbSn_xZr_yTi_{1-x-y}O_3$	g	122-8042
P Y G		
see Yttrium Gallium Aluminate $Y_3Ga_xAl_{5-x}O_{12}$	ms	102-8200
P Z T		
see Lead Zirconium Titanate $PbZr_xTi_{1-x}O_3$	bcgjnqrtv	122-0196
P Z T 65/35		
see Lead Zirconium Titanate $PbZr_xTi_{1-x}O_3$	bcgjnqrtv	122-0196
P Z T N		
see Lead Zirconium Titanium Niobate $Pb_xZr_yTi_zNb_{1-x-y-z}O_3$	qs	120-8126

Property: **a.** Absorption coefficient; **b.** Dielectric constant; **c.** Dielectric strength; **d.** Energy band structure; **e.** Effective mass; **f.** Energy gap; **g.** Electric hysteresis; **h.** Energy level; **i.** Electron emission properties; **j.** Electrical resistivity; **k.** Magnetoelectric properties; **l.** Hall coefficient; **m.** Luminescence properties; **n.** Magnetic hysteresis; **o.** Mobility; **p.** Magnetomechanical properties; **q.** Magnetic susceptibility; **r.** Photoelectronic properties; **s.** Refractive index; **t.** Thermoelectric properties; **u.** Work function; **v.** Piezoelectric properties.

Property: **a.** Absorption coefficient; **b.** Dielectric constant; **c.** Dielectric strength; **d.** Energy band structure; **e.** Effective mass; **f.** Energy gap; **g.** Electric hysteresis; **h.** Energy level; **i.** Electron emission properties; **j.** Electrical resistivity; **k.** Magnetoelectric properties; **l.** Hall coefficient; **m.** Luminescence properties; **n.** Magnetic hysteresis; **o.** Mobility; **p.** Magnetomechanical properties; **q.** Magnetic susceptibility; **r.** Photoelectronic properties; **s.** Refractive index; **t.** Thermoelectric properties; **u.** Work function; **v.** Piezoelectric properties.

Substance Name	Property	Number
Rubidium Sodium Erbium Yttrium Fluoride $Rb_2 Na Er_x Y_{1-x} F_6$ see Rubidium Sodium Fluoroerbateyttrate $Rb_2 Na Er_x Y_{1-x} F_6$	hq	109-8062
di- Rubidium Sodium Europium hexa- Fluoride $Rb_2 Na Eu F_6$ see di- Rubidium Sodium hexa- Fluoroeuropate $Rb_2 Na Eu F_6$	hq	109-8056
di- Rubidium Sodium hexa- Fluoroerbate $Rb_2 Na Er F_6$	hq	109-8061
Rubidium Sodium Fluoroerbateyttrate $Rb_2 Na Er_x Y_{1-x} F_6$	hq	109-8062
di- Rubidium Sodium hexa- Fluoroeuropate $Rb_2 Na Eu F_6$	hq	109-8056
di- Rubidium Sodium hexa- Fluorogadolinate $Rb_2 Na Gd F_6$	hq	110-8192
di- Rubidium Sodium hexa- Fluoroholmate $Rb_2 Na Ho F_6$	hq	110-8193
di- Rubidium Sodium hexa- Fluoroterbate $Rb_2 Na Tb F_6$	hq	110-8194
di- Rubidium Sodium hexa- Fluorothulate $Rb_2 Na Tm F_6$	hq	110-8195
di- Rubidium Sodium hexa- Fluoroytterbate $Rb_2 Na Yb F_6$	hq	110-8196
di- Rubidium Sodium Gadolinium hexa- Fluoride $Rb_2 Na Gd F_6$ see di- Rubidium Sodium hexa- Fluorogadolinate $Rb_2 Na Gd F_6$	hq	110-8192
di- Rubidium Sodium Holmium hexa- Fluoride $Rb_2 Na Ho F_6$ see di- Rubidium Sodium hexa- Fluoroholmate $Rb_2 Na Ho F_6$	hq	110-8193
di- Rubidium Sodium Terbium hexa- Fluoride $Rb_2 Na Tb F_6$ see di- Rubidium Sodium hexa- Fluoroterbate $Rb_2 Na Tb F_6$	hq	110-8194
di- Rubidium Sodium Thulium hexa- Fluoride $Rb_2 Na Tm F_6$ see di- Rubidium Sodium hexa- Fluorothulate $Rb_2 Na Tm F_6$	hq	110-8195
di- Rubidium Sodium Ytterium hexa- Fluoride $Rb_2 Na Yb F_6$ see di- Rubidium Sodium hexa- Fluoroytterbate $Rb_2 Na Yb F_6$	hq	110-8196
Rubidium Sulfate $Rb_2 S O_4$	fj	122-0299
Rubidium di- Thioantimonate $Rb Sb S_2$	fhjt	125-8036
Rubidium Tungsten hexa- Fluoride $Rb W F_6$ see Rubidium hexa- Fluorotungstate $Rb W F_6$	q	110-8289
Rubidium Uranium Nitride Oxide $Rb U O_2(N O_3)_3$ see Rubidium Uranyl Nitrate $Rb U O_2(N O_3)_3$	am	120-8044
di- Rubidium Uranyl tetra- Chloride $Rb_2 U O_2 Cl_4$	m	106-8746
tri- Rubidium Uranyl penta- Fluoride $Rb_3 U O_2 F_5$	m	110-8210
Rubidium Uranyl Nitrate $Rb U O_2(N O_3)_3$	am	120-8044
Rubidium Vanadium hexa- Fluoroferrate $Rb V Fe F_6$	q	110-8087
Ruthenium di- Oxide $Ru O_2$	j	122-0089
Ruthenium tetra- Oxide $Ru O_4$	hi	122-8021
Samarium di- Aluminide $Sm Al_2$	q	102-8167
Samarium Antimonide $Sm Sb$	fpq	126-8001
Samarium Arsenide $Sm As$	fjo	102-8346
Samarium - Bismuth $Sm Bi$	fjo	104-8304
Samarium hexa- Boride $Sm B_6$	jlqt	104-8158
Samarium (I I I) Chromate (I I I) $Sm Cr O_3$	fj	106-1249
Samarium - Cobalt $Sm Co_5$	dhnpq	106-8123
Samarium - Cobalt $Sm_2 Co_7$	n	106-8219
Samarium - Cobalt $Sm_2 Co_{17}$	npq	106-8190
Samarium - Cobalt - Aluminum $Sm_2 Co_x Al_{17-x}$	npq	102-8334
Samarium - Cobalt - Copper $Sm Co_{5-x} Cu_x$	np	106-8233
Samarium - Cobalt - Germanium $Sm Co_2 Ge_2$	q	106-8170
Samarium - Cobalt - Iron - Copper $Sm Co_{5-x-y} Fe_x Cu_y$	np	106-8291
Samarium - Copper $Sm Cu_6$	q	106-8805
Samarium (I I I) Cuprate (I I) $Sm_2 Cu O_4$	jt	106-8347
Samarium Ferrate $Sm_3 Fe_5 O_{12}$	npqs	110-0245
Samarium Ferrite $Sm Fl O_3$	n	110-0368
di- Samarium Germanium penta- Sulfide $Sm_2 Ge S_5$ see di- Samarium penta- Thiogermanate $Sm_2 Ge S_5$	fj	111-8101
Samarium Indium tri- Selenide $Sm In Se_3$ see Samarium tri- Selenoindate $Sm In Se_3$	q	114-8094
Samarium Indium tri- Sulfide $Sm In S_3$ see Samarium tri- Thioindate $Sm In S_3$	fq	114-0114
Samarium di- Iridide $Sm Ir_2$	q	114-8052
Samarium - Iron $Sm Fe_2$	np	110-8163
Samarium Iron Silicide $Sm Fe_x Si_{2-x}$	q	110-8145
Samarium Lanthanum Sulfide $Sm_{1-x} La_x S$	hq	118-8025
Samarium Molybdate $Sm_2(Mo O_4)_3$	b	119-8036
Samarium - Neodymium - Cobalt $Sm_x Nd_{1-x} Co_5$	nq	106-8472
Samarium Neodymium Selenide $Sm_x Nd_{1-x} Se$	fj	120-8051
Samarium - Nickel $Sm Ni_2$	q	120-8046
Samarium Nitride $Sm N$	df	120-8116
Samarium - Osmium $Sm Os_2$	j	122-8145
Samarium sesqui- Oxide $Sm_2 O_3$	jq	122-0097
Samarium - Palladium $Sm Pd_3$	hq	123-8073
Samarium Phosphide $Sm P$	fjo	123-8070
Samarium di- Platinide $Sm Pt_2$	q	123-8049
Samarium - Praseodymium - Cobalt $Sm_{1-x} Pr_x Co_5$	n	106-8205
Samarium Praseodymium Ferrate $Sm_x Pr_{1-x} Fe O_3$	s	110-8162
Samarium - Rhodium $Sm Rh_2$	q	125-8026
Samarium - Rhodium $Sm_7 Rh_3$	q	125-8027
Samarium Selenide $Sm Se$	adfjmq	126-8070
Samarium Selenide $Sm_{3-x} Se_4$	joqt	126-8135
Samarium Selenide Sulfide $Sm Se_x S_{1-x}$	jlmo	126-8069
Samarium tri- Selenoindate $Sm In Se_3$	q	114-8094
di- Samarium nona- Selenotristannate $Sm_2 Sn_3 Se_9$	j	126-8118
Samarium di- Silicide $Sm Si_2$	d	126-8159
Samarium mono- Sulfide $Sm S$	dhjmq	126-0025
Samarium sesqui- Sulfide $Sm_2 S_3$	q	126-0039
tri- Samarium tetra- Sulfide $Sm_3 S_4$	jt	126-0059
Samarium Sulfide $Sm_3 S_{4-x}$	j	126-8139
tetra- Samarium tri- Sulfide $Sm_4 S_3$	j	126-8138
Samarium Tantalate $Sm Ta O_4$	q	122-0441
Samarium mono- Telluride $Sm Te$	adj	126-8110
di- Samarium penta- Thiogermanate $Sm_2 Ge S_5$	fj	111-8101
Samarium tri- Thioindate $Sm In S_3$	fq	114-0114
Samarium Tin Selenide $Sm_2 Sn_3 Se_9$ see di- Samarium nona- Selenotristannate $Sm_2 Sn_3 Se_9$	j	126-8118
Samarium Titanium Niobate $Sm Ti Nb O_6$	fj	120-0287
Samarium Vanadate (I I I) $Sm V O_3$	q	122-8081
Samarium Vanadate (V) $Sm V O_4$	m	122-8040
Samarium - Yttrium - Cobalt $Sm_x Y_{1-x} Co_5$	n	106-8667
Samarium Yttrium Iron Gallium Oxide $Sm_x Y_{3-x} Fe_{5-y} Ga_y O_{12}$ see Yttrium Samarium Gallium Ferrate $Y_{3-x} Sm_x Ga_y Fe_{5-y} O_{12}$	npq	110-8098
Samarium Yttrium Sulfide $Sm_x Y_{1-x} S$	hq	126-8156
Samarium - Zinc $Sm Zn_{12}$	jq	126-8058
Samarium (I I I) di- Zirconate $Sm_2 Zr_2 O_7$	j	122-8120
Sawyer Crystal Quartz	m	122-8050
see also Silica, Fused		122-8045
S B N see Barium Strontium Niobate $Ba_{1-x} Sr_x Nb_2 O_6$	abfgnqrsv	104-8171
Scandium di- Aluminide $Sc Al_2$	j	102-8324
Scandium tri- Aluminide $Sc Al_3$	j	102-8320
Scandium Arsenide $Sc As$	f	102-8348
Scandium tri- Chloride $Sc Cl_3$	j	106-0298
Scandium di- Ferride $Sc Fe_2$	j	110-8261
Scandium - Indium $Sc_3 In$	p	114-8078
Scandium di- Iridide $Sc Ir_2$	j	114-8099
Scandium - Iron $Sc Fe_2$ see Scandium di- Ferride $Sc Fe_2$	j	110-8261
Scandium Manganese Copper Ferrite $Sc_x Mn_y Cu_z Fe_{3-x-y-z} O_4$	jnq	106-8738
Scandium Manganese Ferrite $Sc_x Mn Fe_{2-x} O_4$	n	110-8258
Scandium mono- Nitride $Sc N$	df	120-0056
Scandium di- Osmide $Sc Os_2$	j	122-8143
Scandium sesqui- Oxide $Sc_2 O_3$	fjst	122-0093

Substance Name	Property	Number
Scandium Phosphide ScP	f	123-8069
Scandium di-Ruthenide $ScRu_2$	j	125-8044
Scandium mono-Silicide $ScSi$	d	126-8147
tri-Scandium penta-Silicide Sc_3Si_5	d	126-8148
penta-Scandium tri-Silicide Sc_5Si_3	d	126-8149
Scandium Titanium Oxide $Sc_xTi_{2-x}O_3$	fjt	120-8179
Scandium Vanadate (V) $ScVO_4$	hmp	122-8091
Scandium Vanadate $Sc_xV_{1-x}O_3$	fj	122-8134
Selenium di-Oxide SeO_2	a	122-0095
Servofrax Arsenic Sesquisulfide Glass	b	102-8387
see also Arsenic sesqui-Sulfide As_2S_3		102-0086
Silica, Fused	abdfjmoqs	122-8045
see also Commercial Fused Silica T08		122-8057
see also Corning Glass Code 7905 (Vycor Fused Silica)		122-8047
see also Corning Glass Code 7940 (Fused Silica)		122-8046
see also Dynasil Fused Quartz		122-8125
see also Dynasil Fused Quartz 4000		122-8048
see also General Electric Fused Quartz		122-8129
see also General Electric Fused Quartz 101		122-8095
see also General Electric Fused Quartz 105		122-8094
see also General Electric Fused Quartz 106		122-8132
see also General Electric Fused Quartz 124		122-8096
see also General Electric Fused Quartz 125		122-8097
see also General Electric Fused Quartz 151		122-8049
see also Homosil Fused Silica		122-8060
see also Infrasil Fused Silica		122-8126
see also Infrasil Fused Silica 1		122-8062
see also Infrasil Fused Silica 2		122-8098
see also Japanese Industries Fused Silica		122-8059
see also Optosil Fused Silica		122-8130
see also Optosil Fused Silica 1		122-8058
see also Optosil Fused Silica 2		122-8099
see also Optosil Fused Silica 3		122-8100
see also Sawyer Crystal Quartz		122-8050
see also Spectrosil Fused Silica A		122-8128
see also Spectrosil Fused Silica W F		122-8086
see also Suprasil Fused Quartz 1		122-8101
see also Suprasil Fused Quartz 2		122-8102
see also Suprasil Fused Quartz W		122-8131
see also Suprasil Fused Quartz W 1		122-8052
see also Suprasil Fused Quartz W 2		122-8103
see also Ultrasil Fused Silica		122-8061
Silica, Vitreous		
see Silica, Fused	abdfjmoqs	122-8045
Silica Glass		
see Silica, Fused	abdfjmoqs	122-8045
Silicon mono-Arsenide $SiAs$	afos	102-8331
Silicon Arsenide di-Telluride $SiAsTe_2$		
see Silicon di-Telluroarsenate $SiAsTe_2$	j	102-8293
Silicon Carbide SiC	abdefh-moqrstuv	106-0035
Silicon di-Carbide SiC_2	adh	106-8817
Silicon tetra-Chloride $SiCl_4$	b	106-0007
Silicon di-Fluoride SiF_2	ahim	110-0045
Silicon tetra-Fluoride SiF_4	ah	110-0012
Silicon tetra-Hydride SiH_4	s	112-0016
Silicon mono-Nitride SiN	js	120-0066
tri-Silicon tetra-Nitride Si_3N_4	abcdfhijmsu	120-8024
Silicon Nitride Oxide $SiNO$		
see Silicon Oxynitride $SiNO$	abcs	120-0221
Silicon mono-Oxide SiO	abcfhijnrsu	122-0096
Silicon di-Oxide SiO_2	abcdefghijmors	122-0009
see also Quartz SiO_2		521-8003
see also Silica, Fused		122-8045
Silicon Oxide SiO_{1-x}	js	122-8105
Silicon sesqui-Oxide Si_2O_3	as	122-8076
Silicon Oxynitride $SiNO$	abcs	120-0221
Silicon mono-Phosphide SiP	af	123-8068
Silicon mono-Telluride $SiTe$	fjt	126-8083
Silicon di-Telluride $SiTe_2$	af	126-8076
Silicon sesqui-Telluride Si_2Te_3	fjm	126-8072
Silicon di-Telluroarsenate $SiAsTe_2$	j	102-8293
Silver undeca-Aluminate $AgAl_{11}O_{17}$	j	102-8307
di-Silver Aluminide Ag_2Al	j	102-8240
tri-Silver Aluminide Ag_3Al	jlt	102-8241

Substance Name	Property	Number
tri-Silver di-Aluminide Ag_3Al_2	j	102-8239
Silver Aluminum di-Telluride $AgAlTe_2$		
see Silver di-Telluroaluminate $AgAlTe_2$	dfm	102-8399
tri-Silver Antimony tri-Sulfide		
Ag_3SbS_3		
see tri-Silver tri-Thioantimonate Ag_3SbS_3	bj	102-0296
Silver Antimony di-Telluride $AgSbTe_2$		
see Silver di-Telluroantimonate $AgSbTe_2$	fjrt	102-8141
Silver Arsenide di-Sulfide $AgAsS_2$		
see Silver di-Thioarsenate $AgAsS_2$	jr	102-8339
tri-Silver Arsenide tri-Sulfide		
Ag_3AsS_3		
see tri-Silver tri-Thioarsenate Ag_3AsS_3	abjsv	102-8134
Silver Azide AgN_3	abfrst	102-8078
Silver Bismuth di-Telluride $AgBiTe_2$		
see Silver di-Tellurobismuthate $AgBiTe_2$	jt	102-8380
Silver Bromide $AgBr$	abdefhijmorst	102-0009
Silver-Cadmium $AgCd$	j	102-8290
Silver-Cadmium Ag_5Cd_8	j	102-8280
Silver Carbide Nitride $AgCN$		
see Silver Cyanide $AgCN$	b	102-0183
Silver Chloride $AgCl$	abcdefhijmost	102-0010
Silver di-Chloromercurate $AgHgCl_2$	s	102-8452
Silver Copper Telluride $AgCuTe$	jlo	102-8454
Silver Copper Telluride $Ag_xCu_{2-x}Te$	jlo	102-8453
see also Copper (I) Telluride $\geq$ di-Silver Telluride		508-0487
see also di-Silver Telluride $\geq$ Copper (I) Telluride		508-0488
Silver Cyanide $AgCN$	b	102-0183
Silver Fluoride AgF	dfhj	102-8173
di-Silver Fluoride Ag_2F	j	102-0246
Silver Gallium di-Selenide $AgGaSe_2$		
see Silver di-Selenogallate $AgGaSe_2$	afjost	102-8228
Silver Gallium di-Sulfide $AgGaS_2$		
see Silver di-Thiogallate $AgGaS_2$	abfhijlmos	102-8139
Silver Gallium di-Telluride $AgGaTe_2$		
see Silver di-Tellurogallate $AgGaTe_2$	dfjost	102-8229
di-Silver Germanium tri-Selenide		
Ag_2GeSe_3		
see di-Silver tri-Selenogermanate Ag_2GeSe_3	t	102-8175
octa-Silver Germanium hexa-Sulfide		
Ag_8GeS_6		
see octa-Silver hexa-Thiogermanate Ag_8GeS_6	bjq	102-8085
di-Silver Germanium tri-Telluride		
Ag_2GeTe_3		
see di-Silver tri-Tellurogermanate Ag_2GeTe_3	t	102-8176
di-Silver tri-Hydrogen Iodate $Ag_2H_3IO_6$	g	102-8413
di-Silver tri-Hydrogen Iodate, Deuterated		
$Ag_2D_3IO_6$	g	102-8414
Silver-Indium Ag_2In	j	102-8377
Silver-Indium Ag_3In	j	102-8378
Silver Indium di-Selenide $AgInSe_2$		
see Silver di-Selenoindate $AgInSe_2$	fhjost	102-8230
Silver Indium di-Sulfide $AgInS_2$		
see Silver di-Thioindate $AgInS_2$	adfhmo	102-8235
Silver penta-Indium octa-Sulfide		
$AgIn_5S_8$		
see Silver octa-Thioindate $AgIn_5S_8$	m	102-8342
Silver Indium di-Telluride $AgInTe_2$		
see Silver di-Telluroindate $AgInTe_2$	dfjmost	102-8231
Silver Iodide AgI	adfhijmorstv	102-0005
Silver Iodide Bromide AgI_xBr_{1-x}	r	102-8079
hexa-Silver tetra-Iodide Tungstate $Ag_6I_4WO_4$	jt	102-8087
Silver tetra-Iodomercurate (I I) Ag_2HgI_4	j	102-8303
tri-Silver di-Lead octa-Thiotriantimonate		
$Ag_3Pb_2Sb_3S_8$	fjr	102-0382
see also Freieslebenite $Ag_3Pb_2Sb_3S_8$		521-8010
Silver Mercury di-Chloride $AgHgCl_2$		
see Silver di-Chloromercurate $AgHgCl_2$	s	102-8452
di-Silver Mercury tetra-Iodide		
Ag_2HgI_4		
see Silver tetra-Iodomercurate (I I) Ag_2HgI_4	j	102-8303

Property: **a.** Absorption coefficient; **b.** Dielectric constant; **c.** Dielectric strength; **d.** Energy band structure; **e.** Effective mass; **f.** Energy gap; **g.** Electric hysteresis; **h.** Energy level; **i.** Electron emission properties; **j.** Electrical resistivity; **k.** Magnetoelectric properties; **l.** Hall coefficient; **m.** Luminescence properties; **n.** Magnetic hysteresis; **o.** Mobility; **p.** Magnetomechanical properties; **q.** Magnetic susceptibility; **r.** Photoelectronic properties; **s.** Refractive index; **t.** Thermoelectric properties; **u.** Work function; **v.** Piezoelectric properties.

Substance Name	Property	Number
tetra- Silver Mercury di- Selenide di- Iodide		
$Ag_4 Hg Se_2 I_2$		
see tetra- Silver di- Selenodiiodomercurate		
$Ag_4 Hg Se_2 I_2$	j	102-8253
octa- Silver Mercury di- Sulfide hexa- Iodide		
$Ag_8 Hg S_2 I_6$		
see octa- Silver di- Thiohexaiodomercurate		
$Ag_8 Hg S_2 I_6$	j	102-8250
Silver Nitrate $Ag N O_3$	bj	102-0030
Silver tri- Nitride $Ag N_3$		
see Silver Azide $Ag N_3$	abfrst	102-8078
Silver Nitride Oxide $Ag_7 O_8 N O_3$		
see Silver Oxide Nitrate $Ag_7 O_8 N O_3$	j	102-8312
Silver Nitrite $Ag N O_2$	am	102-8224
Silver (I I) Oxide $Ag O$	j	102-8068
Silver (I) Oxide $Ag_2 O$	bjr	102-0031
Silver Oxide Nitrate $Ag_7 O_8 N O_3$	j	102-8312
Silver di- Phosphide $Ag P_2$	d	102-8483
di- Silver Selenide $Ag_2 Se$	aefjlot	102-8065
tetra- Silver di- Selenodiiodomercurate		
$Ag_4 Hg Se_2 I_2$	j	102-8253
Silver di- Selenogallate $Ag Ga Se_2$	afjost	102-8228
di- Silver tri- Selenogermanate $Ag_2 Ge Se_3$	t	102-8175
Silver di- Selenoindate $Ag In Se_2$	fhjost	102-8230
di- Silver tri- Selenostannate $Ag_2 Sn Se_3$	t	102-8177
Silver di- Selenothallate $Ag Tl Se_2$	jt	102-8382
Silver mono- Stannide $Ag Sn$	j	102-8289
tri- Silver Stannide $Ag_3 Sn$	j	102-8215
penta- Silver octa- Stannide $Ag_5 Sn_8$	j	102-8292
Silver Sulfate $Ag_2 S O_4$	j	102-0001
Silver Sulfide $Ag_2 S$	aefjlort	102-0120
tri- Silver Sulfide Iodide $Ag_o S I$	j	102-8480
Silver Telluride $Ag Te$	jl	102-8202
di- Silver Telluride $Ag_2 Te$	adefjklot	102-8066
Silver Telluride Sulfide $Ag_2 Te_{1-x} S_x$	ejlot	102-8108
Silver di- Telluroaluminate $Ag Al Te_2$	dfm	102-8399
Silver di- Telluroantimonate $Ag Sb Te_2$	fjrt	102-8141
Silver di- Tellurobismuthate $Ag Bi Te_2$	jt	102-8380
Silver di- Tellurogallate $Ag Ga Te_2$	dfjost	102-8229
di- Silver tri- Tellurogermanate $Ag_2 Ge Te_3$	t	102-8176
Silver di- Telluroindate $Ag In Te_2$	dfjmost	102-8231
di- Silver tri- Tellurostannate $Ag_2 Sn Te_3$	t	102-8178
Silver di- Tellurothallate $Ag Tl Te_2$	jt	102-8381
Silver Thallium di- Selenide $Ag Tl Se_2$		
see Silver di- Selenothallate $Ag Tl Se_2$	jt	102-8382
Silver Thallium di- Telluride $Ag Tl Te_2$		
see Silver di- Tellurothallate $Ag Tl Te_2$	jt	102-8381
tri- Silver tri- Thioantimonate $Ag_3 Sb S_3$	bj	102-0296
Silver di- Thioarsenate $Ag As S_2$	jr	102-8339
tri- Silver tri- Thioarsenate $Ag_3 As S_3$	abjsv	102-8134
see also Proustite $Ag_3 As S_3$		521-0755
Silver di- Thiogallate $Ag Ga S_2$	abfhijlmos	102-8139
octa- Silver hexa- Thiogermanate $Ag_8 Ge S_6$	bjq	102-8085
octa- Silver di- Thiohexaiodomercurate		
$Ag_8 Hg S_2 I_6$	j	102-8250
Silver di- Thioindate $Ag In S_2$	adfhmo	102-8235
Silver octa- Thioindate $Ag In_5 S_8$	m	102-8342
octa- Silver hexa- Thiostannate $Ag_8 Sn S_6$	bjq	102-8086
see also Canfieldite $Ag_8 Sn S_6$		521-8012
Silver - Tin $Ag Sn$		
see Silver mono- Stannide $Ag Sn$	j	102-8289
Silver - Tin $Ag_3 Sn$		
see tri- Silver Stannide $Ag_3 Sn$	j	102-8215
Silver - Tin $Ag_5 Sn_8$		
see penta- Silver octa- Stannide $Ag_5 Sn_8$	j	102-8292
di- Silver Tin tri- Selenide $Ag_2 Sn Se_3$		
see di- Silver tri- Selenostannate $Ag_2 Sn Se_3$	t	102-8177
octa- Silver Tin hexa- Sulfide $Ag_8 Sn S_6$		
see octa- Silver hexa- Thiostannate $Ag_8 Sn S_6$	bjq	102-8086
di- Silver Tin tri- Telluride $Ag_2 Sn Te_3$		
see di- Silver tri- Tellurostannate $Ag_2 Sn Te_3$	t	102-8178
Silver Tungsten Iodide Oxide $Ag I_4 W O_4$		
see hexa- Silver tetra- Iodide Tungstate		
$Ag_6 I_4 W O_4$	jt	102-8087
Silver - Zinc $Ag Zn$	dehj	102-8278
Silver - Zinc $Ag_5 Zn_8$	j	102-8279
Sodalite Hydroxide $Na_{3+x} Al_3 Si_3 O_{12}(O H)_x$	m	102-8103
Sodium β- Alumina		
see Sodium Aluminate $Na Al O_2$	bj	102-0018
Sodium Aluminate $Na Al O_2$	bj	102-0018
Sodium undeca- Aluminate $Na Al_{11} O_{17}$	fj	102-8306
tri- Sodium Aluminum tri- Fluoride		
$Na_3 Al F_3$		
see tri- Sodium tri- Fluoroaluminate $Na_3 Al F_3$	s	102-8153
tri- Sodium Aluminum hexa- Fluoride		
$Na_3 Al F_6$		
see tri- Sodium hexa- Fluoroaluminate $Na_3 Al F_6$	jms	102-0016
Sodium Aluminum Hydroxide Silicate		
$Na_{3+x} Al_3(O H)_x Si_3 O_{12}$		
see Sodalite Hydroxide		
$Na_{3+x} Al_3 Si_3 O_{12}(O H)_x$	m	102-8103
Sodium Ammonium Selenate $Na N H_4 Se O_4$	gs	112-8051
Sodium Ammonium Sulfate, Dideuterated		
$Na N H_2 D_2 S O_4$	s	108-8039
Sodium Ammonium Sulfate, Partly Deuterated		
$Na N H_x D_{4-x} S O_4$	s	108-8040
Sodium Antimony di- Selenide $Na Sb Se_2$		
see Sodium di- Selenoantimonate $Na Sb Se_2$	fhjt	120-8122
Sodium Antimony di- Sulfide $Na Sb S_2$		
see Sodium di- Thioantimonate $Na Sb S_2$	fhjt	120-8121
tri- Sodium Antimony nona- Sulfide		
$Na_3 Sb S_9$		
see tri- Sodium nona- Thioantimonate $Na_3 Sb S_9$	s	120-8030
Sodium Argentonitrite $Na Ag(N O_2)_2$		
see Sodium Silver Nitrite $Na Ag(N O_2)_2$	bghmv	102-0342
Sodium Arsenide di- Selenide $Na As Se_2$		
see Sodium di- Selenoarsenate $Na As Se_2$	af	102-8149
Sodium Azide $Na N_3$	afhmr	120-0032
Sodium di- Barium penta- Niobate (V)		
$Na Ba_2 Nb_5 O_{15}$	abgjmqsv	104-8110
Sodium di- Barium penta- Tantalate (V)		
$Na Ba_2 Ta_5 O_{15}$	bq	104-8112
Sodium Barium Tantalum Niobate		
$Na Ba_2 Ta_x Nb_{5-x} O_{15}$	bq	104-8111
Sodium Barium Vanadate (V) $Na Ba V O_4$	m	104-8353
Sodium Bismuthide $Na Bi$	j	104-8363
Sodium Bismuth Titanate $Na_x Bi_{1-x} Ti O_3$	g	104-8357
Sodium Boron tetra- Fluoride $Na B F_4$		
see Sodium tetra- Fluoroborate $Na B F_4$	j	104-8287
Sodium Bromate $Na Br O_3$	abhs	104-0302
Sodium Bromide $Na Br$	abcdfhijmstu	104-0053
Sodium Cadmium Vanadate (V) $Na Cd V O_4$	m	106-8678
Sodium di- Calcium di- Nickel (I I) tri- Vanadate (V)		
$Na Ca_2 Ni_2 V_3 O_{12}$	q	106-8546
Sodium Calcium Vanadate (V) $Na Ca V O_4$	m	106-8677
Sodium Calcium Vanadium Nickel Oxide		
$Na Ca_2 V_3 Ni_2 O_{12}$		
see Sodium		
di- Calcium di- Nickel (I I) tri- Vanadate (V)		
$Na Ca_2 Ni_2 V_3 O_{12}$	q	106-8546
Sodium Carbide Nitride $Na C N$		
see Sodium Cyanide $Na C N$	b	106-0317
Sodium Carbide Nitride Sulfide $Na S C N$		
see Sodium Thiocyanate $Na S C N$	j	106-8708
Sodium Carbonate $Na_2 C O_3$	bj	106-0061
Sodium - Cesium $Na_2 Cs$	u	106-8530
Sodium Chlorate $Na Cl O_3$	abfhjos	106-0156
Sodium Chlorate $Na Cl O_4$		
see Sodium Perchlorate $Na Cl O_4$	b	106-8213
Sodium Chloride $Na Cl$	abcdfhijmoqrstuv	106-0024
see also Polytran (Harshaw Chemical Co) (Na Cl)		106-8748
see also Rock Salt $Na Cl$		521-0007
Sodium Chlorosulfonate $Na S O_3 Cl$	q	106-8834
Sodium Chromate (I I I) $Na Cr O_2$	i	106-8310
di- Sodium Chromate $Na_2 Cr O_4$	i	106-1378
Sodium di- Chromate $Na_2 Cr_2 O_7$	i	106-0133

Property: **a.** Absorption coefficient; **b.** Dielectric constant; **c.** Dielectric strength; **d.** Energy band structure; **e.** Effective mass; **f.** Energy gap; **g.** Electric hysteresis; **h.** Energy level; **i.** Electron emission properties; **j.** Electrical resistivity; **k.** Magnetoelectric properties; **l.** Hall coefficient; **m.** Luminescence properties; **n.** Magnetic hysteresis; **o.** Mobility; **p.** Magnetomechanical properties; **q.** Magnetic susceptibility; **r.** Photoelectronic properties; **s.** Refractive index; **t.** Thermoelectric properties; **u.** Work function; **v.** Piezoelectric properties.

Property: a. Absorption coefficient; b. Dielectric constant; c. Dielectric strength; d. Energy band structure; e. Effective mass; f. Energy gap; g. Electric hysteresis; h. Energy level; i. Electron emission properties; j. Electrical resistivity; k. Magnetoelectric properties; l. Hall coefficient; m. Luminescence properties; n. Magnetic hysteresis; o. Mobility; p. Magnetomechanical properties; q. Magnetic susceptibility; r. Photoelectronic properties; s. Refractive index; t. Thermoelectric properties; u. Work function; v. Piezoelectric properties.

Substance Name	Property	Number
Sodium Ytterbium Yttrium Fluoride $Na Yb_x Y_{1-x} F_4$	m	110-8115
Sodium Yttrium tetra- Fluoride $Na Y F_4$		
see Sodium tetra- Fluoroyttrate $Na Y F_4$	m	110-8221
Sodium Zeolite	abfj	102-8190
di- Sodium Zinc Germanate $Na_2 Zn Ge O_4$	fghjmr	111-8119
di- Sodium Zirconium Silicate $Na_2 Zr Si O_5$	aim	120-8088
Spectrosil Fused Silica A	s	122-8128
see also Silica, Fused		122-8045
Spectrosil Fused Silica W F	a	122-8086
see also Silica, Fused		122-8045
Steatite, Grade L 4	j	102-8423
see also Alsimag 196 (American Lava Corp)		102-8422
Steatite, Grade L 5	j	102-8424
see also Pass And Seymour E 211 M		102-8425
Strontium tetra- Aluminate $Sr Al_4 O_7$	ms	102-8340
Strontium di- Aluminum tetra- Sulfide		
$Sr Al_2 S_4$		
see Strontium tetra- Thiodialuminate $Sr Al_2 S_4$	jm	102-8497
Strontium Antimonate (V) $Sr Sb_2 O_6$	m	122-8063
Strontium di- Bismuth (I I I) Tantalate		
$Sr Bi_2 Ta_2 O_9$	b	104-8187
Strontium Bromide $Sr Br$	j	104-0103
Strontium Calcium Fluoride $Sr_x Ca_{1-x} F_2$	hm	106-8428
Strontium Carbonate $Sr C O_3$	b	106-0758
Strontium Chloride $Sr Cl_2$	abfhijms	106-0234
Strontium Chromate $Sr Cr O_4$	i	106-1273
Strontium Cobalt (I I) Lanthanum Niobate (V)		
$Sr Co La Nb O_6$	q	106-8159
Strontium Cobalt (I I) Lanthanum Tantalate		
$Sr Co La Ta O_6$	q	106-8158
di- Strontium Dysprosium Molybdate (V)		
$Sr_2 Dy Mo O_6$	fjq	108-8061
di- Strontium Erbium Molybdate (V) $Sr_2 Er Mo O_6$	fjq	109-8102
Strontium Europium Ferrate $Sr Eu_2 Fe_2 O_7$	q	109-8069
Strontium dodeca- Ferrate (I I I) $Sr Fe_{12} O_{19}$	jt	110-8037
Strontium Fluoride $Sr F_2$	abdfhjmstv	110-0132
see also Optovac ($Sr F_2$)		110-8274
di- Strontium Fluorotrioxoferrate		
$Sr_2 Fe O_3 F$		
see di- Strontium tri- Oxofluoroferrate $Sr_2 Fe O_3 F$	q	110-8045
di- Strontium Gadolinium Molybdate (V)		
$Sr_2 Gd Mo O_6$	fjq	111-8207
Strontium Gallium Ferrate $Sr Ga_6 Fe_6 O_{12}$	a	110-8159
Strontium di- Gallium tetra- Selenide		
$Sr Ga_2 Se_4$		
see Strontium tetra- Selenodigallate $Sr Ga_2 Se_4$	j	111-8208
Strontium di- Gallium tetra- Sulfide		
$Sr Ga_2 S_4$		
see Strontium tetra- Thiodigallate $Sr Ga_2 S_4$	ajm	111-8023
Strontium di- Indium tetra- Selenide		
$Sr In_2 Se_4$		
see Strontium tetra- Selenodiindate $Sr In_2 Se_4$	j	114-8098
Strontium di- Indium tetra- Sulfide		
$Sr In_2 S_4$		
see Strontium tetra- Thiodiindate $Sr In_2 S_4$	jm	114-8097
Strontium Iodide $Sr I_2$	j	114-0011
Strontium hexa- Iron hexa- Gallium dodeca- Oxide		
$Sr Fe_6 Ga_6 O_{12}$		
see Strontium Gallium Ferrate $Sr Ga_6 Fe_6 O_{12}$	a	110-8159
Strontium Iron Oxide $Sr Fe_{12} O_{19}$		
see Strontium dodeca- Ferrate (I I I) $Sr Fe_{12} O_{19}$	jt	110-8037
di- Strontium Iron tri- Oxide Fluoride		
$Sr_2 Fe O_3 F$		
see di- Strontium tri- Oxofluoroferrate $Sr_2 Fe O_3 F$	q	110-8045
Strontium - Lanthanum $Sr La$	m	118-8035
Strontium - Lanthanum $Sr La_3$	m	118-8031
Strontium - Lanthanum $Sr_3 La$	m	118-8034
Strontium Lanthanum Cobaltate $Sr_x La_{1-x} Co O_6$	j	106-8806
Strontium Lanthanum Fluoride $Sr_x La_{1-x} F_{3-y}$	j	110-8280
Strontium Lanthanum Manganate $Sr_x La_{1-x} Mn O_3$	q	118-8102
Strontium Lanthanum Manganese Ferrate		
$Sr_x La_{1-x} Mn_y Fe_{1-y} O_3$	q	110-8247
Strontium Lanthanum Niobium Cobalt Oxide		
$Sr La Nb Co O_6$		
see Strontium Cobalt (I I) Lanthanum Niobate (V)		
$Sr Co La Nb O_6$	q	106-8159
Strontium Lanthanum Tantalum Cobalt Oxide		
$Sr La Ta Co O_6$		
see Strontium Cobalt (I I) Lanthanum Tantalate		
$Sr Co La Ta O_6$	q	106-8158
Strontium Lanthanum Vanadate $Sr_x La_{1-x} V O_3$	fjq	118-8028
Strontium Lead Germanate $Sr_x Pb_{5-x} Ge_3 O_{11}$	g	111-8070
Strontium Lead Titanate $Sr_x Pb_{1-x} Ti O_3$	gq	122-8043
Strontium Lead Zirconium Titanate		
$Sr_x Pb_{1-x} Zr_y Ti_{1-y} O_3$	bgq	122-8079
di- Strontium Magnesium Tungstate (V I)		
$Sr_2 Mg W O_6$	f	119-8067
Strontium Molybdate (V I) $Sr Mo O_4$	bhm	119-0050
Strontium Neodymium Cobaltate $Sr_x Nd_{1-x} Co O_6$	j	106-8807
Strontium Neodymium Cobaltate $Sr_x Nd_{1-x} Co O_{1-x}$	j	106-8808
Strontium Niobate (V) $Sr Nb_2 O_6$	b	120-8114
di- Strontium Niobate (V) $Sr_2 Nb_2 O_7$	b	120-8040
Strontium Nitrate $Sr(N O_3)_2$	bs	120-0080
Strontium Oxide $Sr O$	bdefhijloqstu	122-0031
di- Strontium tri- Oxofluoroferrate $Sr_2 Fe O_3 F$	q	110-8045
tri- Strontium Phosphate $Sr_3 P O_4$	m	122-8069
penta- Strontium di- Phosphate Silicate		
$Sr_5(P O_4)_2 Si O_4$	m	122-8066
di- Strontium Rhenium (V I) Ferrate (I I)		
$Sr_2 Re Fe O_6$	jq	110-8216
tri- Strontium Rhenium (V I) di- Ferrate (I I I)		
$Sr_3 Re Fe_2 O_9$	fjq	110-8217
Strontium Selenide $Sr Se$	dfijmsu	126-8079
Strontium tetra- Selenodigallate $Sr Ga_2 Se_4$	j	111-8208
Strontium tetra- Selenodiindate $Sr In_2 Se_4$	j	114-8098
di- Strontium Stannide $Sr_2 Sn$	jt	126-8099
Strontium Sulfate $Sr S O_4$	bim	122-0132
Strontium Sulfide $Sr S$	abdfhijmsu	126-0017
Strontium Tantalum Bismuth Oxide		
$Sr Ta_2 Bi_2 O_9$		
see Strontium di- Bismuth (I I I) Tantalate		
$Sr Bi_2 Ta_2 O_9$	b	104-8187
Strontium Tellurate $Sr Te O_3$	bgsv	122-8067
Strontium Telluride $Sr Te$	adfijsu	126-8080
Strontium tetra- Thiodialuminate $Sr Al_2 S_4$	jm	102-8497
Strontium tetra- Thiodigallate $Sr Ga_2 S_4$	ajm	111-8023
Strontium tetra- Thiodiindate $Sr In_2 S_4$	jm	114-8097
Strontium - Tin $Sr_2 Sn$		
see di- Strontium Stannide $Sr_2 Sn$	jt	126-8099
Strontium Titanate (I V) $Sr Ti O_3$	abcdfghj-oqrsv	122-0030
Strontium Titanium Aluminate $Sr Ti_x Al_{1-x} O_{3-y}$	j	102-8494
Strontium Titanium Lead Oxide		
$Sr_{1-x} Ti Pb_x O_3$		
see Strontium Lead Titanate $Sr_x Pb_{1-x} Ti O_3$	gq	122-8043
Strontium Titanium Vanadate $Sr Ti_x V_{1-x} O_3$	b	122-8141
Strontium Tungstate (V I) $Sr W O_4$	bhm	122-0198
Strontium Uranium Ferrate $Sr U_x Fe_{1-x} O_3$	bnq	110-8140
Strontium Uranium Iron Oxide		
$Sr U_x Fe_{1-x} O_3$		
see Strontium Uranium Ferrate $Sr U_x Fe_{1-x} O_3$	bnq	110-8140
Strontium Vanadate (V) $Sr (V O_3)_2$	s	122-8107
Strontium di- Vanadate (I I) $Sr V_2 O_3$	mq	122-8037
Strontium dodeca- Vanadate $Sr V_{12} O_{30}$	q	122-8137
tri- Strontium Vanadate (V) $Sr_3 (V O_4)_2$	m	122-8119
di- Strontium Yttrium Molybdate (V) $Sr_2 Y Mo O_6$	fjq	119-8120
Strontium Zirconate $Sr Zr O_3$	bj	122-8115
Strontium Zirconium Titanium Lead Oxide		
$Sr_x Zr_y Ti_{1-y} Pb_{1-x} O_3$		
see Strontium Lead Zirconium Titanate		
$Sr_x Pb_{1-x} Zr_y Ti_{1-y} O_3$	bgq	122-8079
di- Sulfur di- Chloride $S_2 Cl_2$	b	106-0184
Sulfur Chloride Oxide $S O_2 Cl_2$		
see Sulfuryl Chloride $S O_2 Cl_2$	bj	106-8731
Sulfur tetra- Fluoride $S F_4$	hi	110-0219
Sulfur hexa- Fluoride $S F_6$	abchjs	110-0040
di- Sulfur di- Fluoride $S_2 F_2$	i	110-0288

Property: a. Absorption coefficient; **b.** Dielectric constant; **c.** Dielectric strength; **d.** Energy band structure; **e.** Effective mass; **f.** Energy gap; **g.** Electric hysteresis; **h.** Energy level; **i.** Electron emission properties; **j.** Electrical resistivity; **k.** Magnetoelectric properties; **l.** Hall coefficient; **m.** Luminescence properties; **n.** Magnetic hysteresis; **o.** Mobility; **p.** Magnetomechanical properties; **q.** Magnetic susceptibility; **r.** Photoelectronic properties; **s.** Refractive index; **t.** Thermoelectric properties; **u.** Work function; **v.** Piezoelectric properties.

Substance Name	Property	Number
Sulfur di-Oxide SO_2	abhim	122-0010
Sulfur tri-Oxide SO_3	bi	122-0011
Sulfur Oxychloride SO_2Cl_2		
see Sulfuryl Chloride SO_2Cl_2	bj	106-8731
Sulfuryl Chloride SO_2Cl_2	bj	106-8731
Suprasil Fused Quartz 1	ab	122-8101
see also Silica, Fused		122-8045
Suprasil Fused Quartz 2	ab	122-8102
see also Silica, Fused		122-8045
Suprasil Fused Quartz W	a	122-8131
see also Silica, Fused		122-8045
Suprasil Fused Quartz W 1	abs	122-8052
see also Silica, Fused		122-8045
Suprasil Fused Quartz W 2	bs	122-8103
see also Silica, Fused		122-8045
di-Tantalum Aluminide Ta_2Al	j	102-8478
Tantalum mono-Antimonide $TaSb$	j	126-8140
di-Tantalum tri-Arsenide Ta_2As_3	j	102-8427
Tantalum Borate $TaBO_4$	m	104-8179
Tantalum di-Boride TaB_2	jqu	104-8090
Tantalum mono-Carbide TaC	hjlqtu	106-0205
Tantalum Carbide TaC_{1-x}	jklqu	106-8559
di-Tantalum Carbide Ta_2C	j	106-0673
Tantalum Chromate (I I I) $TaCrO_4$		
see Chromium (I I I) Tantalate $CrTaO_4$	j	106-8674
Tantalum Cobaltate (I I) Ta_2CoO_6	j	106-1795
Tantalum Cuprate (I I) Ta_2CuO_6	j	106-8763
Tantalum Ferrate (I I I) $TaFeO_4$		
see Iron (I I I) Tantalate $FeTaO_4$	j	110-8249
Tantalum Ferrate (I I) Ta_2FeO_6	j	110-8266
Tantalum mono-Germanide $TaGe$	j	111-8170
Tantalum di-Germanide $TaGe_2$	jlqt	111-8146
di-Tantalum Germanide Ta_2Ge	jlqt	111-8204
penta-Tantalum tri-Germanide Ta_5Ge_3	jlqt	111-8147
Tantalum Germanium Silicide $TaGeSi$	j	111-8171
Tantalum Germanium Silicide $TaGe_xSi_{2-x}$	j	111-8172
Tantalum - Gold $TaAu$	j	102-8143
Tantalum Lead Oxide Ta_2PbO_6		
see Lead (I I) Tantalate $PbTa_2O_6$	b	122-0414
Tantalum Manganate (I I) Ta_2MnO_6	j	119-8114
Tantalum Molybdenum Selenide $Ta_xMo_{1-x}Se_2$	j	119-8117
Tantalum Nickelate (I I) Ta_2NiO_6	j	120-8168
Tantalum di-Niobium Stannide $TaNb_2Sn$	j	120-8139
Tantalum Niobium Stannide $Ta_xNb_{3-x}Sn$	j	120-8138
di-Tantalum Niobium Stannide Ta_2NbSn	j	120-8140
Tantalum Niobium Vanadium Stannide $TaNbVSn$	j	120-8141
Tantalum Niobium Vanadium Stannide $Ta_xNb_2VSn_{1-x}$	j	120-8142
Tantalum mono-Nitride TaN	jlt	120-0051
Tantalum Nitride TaN_x	j	120-8084
di-Tantalum Nitride Ta_2N	jt	120-0073
tri-Tantalum penta-Nitride Ta_3N_5	j	120-8087
tetra-Tantalum penta-Nitride Ta_4N_5	j	120-8094
penta-Tantalum hexa-Nitride Ta_5N_6	j	120-8095
Tantalum Oxide TaO_{1-x}	jst	122-8054
Tantalum penta-Oxide Ta_2O_5	abcdfhijlmoqrst	122-0017
Tantalum mono-Phosphide TaP	j	123-8097
Tantalum tri-Rhenide $TaRe_3$	j	125-8038
Tantalum di-Selenide $TaSe_2$	dhijlrt	126-8098
Tantalum Selenide $TaSe_{2-x}$	jloqt	126-8101
Tantalum di-Selenide, Intercalated $TaSe_2$	j	126-8153
Tantalum Selenide Sulfide $TaSe_xS_{1-x}$	abj	126-8097
Tantalum Selenide Sulfide, Intercalated $TaSe_xS_{2-x}$	j	126-8152
Tantalum di-Silicide $TaSi_2$	dij	126-8063
penta-Tantalum tri-Silicide Ta_5Si_3	ij	126-8064
Tantalum di-Sulfide TaS_2	adefhijloqrt	126-0038
Tantalum di-Sulfide, Intercalated TaS_2	jkqt	126-8071
Tantalum mono-Telluride $TaTe$	j	127-8020
Tantalum di-Telluride $TaTe_2$	j	127-8021
Tantalum Tungsten Carbide $Ta_xW_{1-x}C$	j	106-1576
see also Tantalum Monocarbide $\geq$ Tungsten Monocarbide		508-0457
see also Tungsten Monocarbide $\geq$ Tantalum Monocarbide		508-0280
Tantalum Tungsten Selenide $Ta_xW_{1-x}Se_2$	j	126-8102

Substance Name	Property	Number
Tantalum Vanadate (I I I) $TaVO_4$		
see Vanadium (I I I) Tantalate $VTaO_4$	j	122-8118
di-Tellurium Bromide Te_2Br	f	104-8425
Tellurium di-Chloride $TeCl_2$	j	106-8110
Tellurium tetra-Chloride $TeCl_4$	j	106-0160
tri-Tellurium di-Chloride Te_3Cl_2	fj	106-8783
Tellurium hexa-Fluoride TeF_6	h	110-0141
Tellurium mono-Iodide TeI	fj	114-8087
di-Tellurium Iodide Te_2I	fj	114-8088
Tellurium di-Oxide TeO_2	abfhjrsv	122-0105
Tellurium Selenide $TeSe$	afrt	126-8100
Tellurium Selenide $TeSe_{1-x}$	t	126-8119
tri-Terbium (I I I) penta-Aluminate $Tb_3Al_5O_{12}$	m	102-8372
Terbium di-Aluminide $TbAl_2$	n	102-8367
Terbium Antimonide $TbSb$	hnq	126-8007
Terbium Arsenate $TbAsO_4$	hq	102-8125
Terbium Arsenide $TbAs$	f	102-8352
Terbium hexa-Boride TbB_6	j	104-8393
Terbium dodeca-Boride TbB_{12}	qu	104-8141
Terbium - Cerium - Ruthenium $Tb_xCe_{1-x}Ru_2$	jq	106-8648
Terbium - Cobalt $TbCo_2$	q	106-8602
Terbium - Cobalt $TbCo_5$	np	106-8526
Terbium - Cobalt - Germanium $TbCo_2Ge_2$	q	106-8174
Terbium Cobalt Germanium Ferrate $Tb_3Co_xGe_yFe_{5-x-y}O_{12}$	npq	106-8371
Terbium Europium Yttrium Iron Gallium Oxide $Tb_xEu_yY_{3-x-y}Fe_zGa_{5-z}O_{12}$		
see Yttrium Terbium Europium Gallium Ferrate $Y_xTb_yEu_{3-x-y}Ga_zFe_{5-z}O_{12}$	n	110-8178
Terbium Ferrate $TbFeO_3$	n	110-0361
tri-Terbium Ferrate $Tb_3Fe_5O_{12}$	ps	110-0195
Terbium Gadolinium Ferrate $Tb_xGd_{3-x}Fe_5O_{12}$	abnps	110-8053
Terbium - Gold $TbAu_2$	q	102-8110
Terbium Hydride Oxide $TbOOH$		
see Terbium Hydroperoxide $TbOOH$	k	112-8074
Terbium Hydroperoxide $TbOOH$	k	112-8074
Terbium Hydroxide $Tb(OH)_3$	hq	112-8026
Terbium - Iron $TbFe_2$	npq	110-8067
Terbium - Iron $TbFe_3$	nq	110-8099
Terbium - Iron Tb_2Fe_{17}	nq	110-8100
Terbium di-Manganese di-Germanide $TbMn_2Ge_2$	nq	111-8182
Terbium (I I I) tri-Molybdate (V I) $Tb_2Mo_3O_{12}$	bs	119-8032
Terbium Nitride TbN	df	120-8117
Terbium sesqui-Oxide Tb_2O_3	abqs	122-0449
tetra-Terbium hepta-Oxide Tb_4O_7	ajq	122-0326
Terbium Oxide Hydroxide $TbOOH$		
see Terbium Hydroperoxide $TbOOH$	k	112-8074
Terbium - Palladium $TbPd_3$	q	123-8072
Terbium Peroxide		
see tetra-Terbium hepta-Oxide Tb_4O_7	ajq	122-0326
Terbium Phosphate $TbPO_4$	ahq	122-8092
Terbium - Rhodium Tb_7Rh_3	q	125-8028
Terbium mono-Selenide $TbSe$	q	126-8128
Terbium Silicate	s	122-8140
Terbium - Silver $TbAg_2$	q	102-8389
Terbium mono-Sulfide TbS	q	126-8129
Terbium mono-Telluride $TbTe$	q	127-8019
Terbium Vanadate (I I I) $TbVO_3$	q	122-8085
Terbium Vanadate (V) $TbVO_4$	hm	122-8034
Terbium Yttrium Antimonide $Tb_xY_{1-x}Sb$	mq	126-8053
Terbium Yttrium Ferrate $Tb_xY_{3-x}Fe_5O_{12}$		
see Yttrium Terbium Ferrate $Y_xTb_{3-x}Fe_5O_{12}$	nq	110-8276
Terbium Yttrium Sulfoxylate $Tb_xY_{2-x}SO_2$	m	122-8065
Terbium - Zinc $TbZn$	np	127-8009
Terbium - Zinc $TbZn_2$	p	127-8001
Terbium - Zinc $TbZn_{12}$	jq	127-8005
Terbium - Zinc Tb_2Zn_{17}	q	127-8012
Thallium Alum $TlAl(SO_4)_2$		
see Thallium Aluminum Sulfate $TlAl(SO_4)_2$	s	102-0395
tri-Thallium Aluminide Tl_3Al	jlq	102-8284
Thallium Aluminum Sulfate $TlAl(SO_4)_2$	s	102-0395

Property: **a.** Absorption coefficient; **b.** Dielectric constant; **c.** Dielectric strength; **d.** Energy band structure; **e.** Effective mass; **f.** Energy gap; **g.** Electric hysteresis; **h.** Energy level; **i.** Electron emission properties; **j.** Electrical resistivity; **k.** Magnetoelectric properties; **l.** Hall coefficient; **m.** Luminescence properties; **n.** Magnetic hysteresis; **o.** Mobility; **p.** Magnetomechanical properties; **q.** Magnetic susceptibility; **r.** Photoelectronic properties; **s.** Refractive index; **t.** Thermoelectric properties; **u.** Work function; **v.** Piezoelectric properties.

Substance Name	Property	Number
hepta- Thallium di- Antimonide Tl_7Sb_2	j	126-8096
Thallium Antimony di- Selenide $TlSbSe_2$		
see Thallium di- Selenoantimonate $TlSbSe_2$	abj	126-8103
Thallium Antimony di- Sulfide $TlSbS_2$		
see Thallium di- Thioantimonate $TlSbS_2$	afjt	126-8104
Thallium Antimony di- Telluride $TlSbTe_2$		
see Thallium di- Telluroantimonate $TlSbTe_2$	jklt	126-8094
Thallium Arsenide di- Selenide $TlAsSe_2$		
see Thallium di- Selenoarsenate $TlAsSe_2$	r	102-8181
tri- Thallium Arsenide tri- Selenide Tl_3AsSe_3		
see tri- Thallium tri- Selenoarsenate Tl_3AsSe_3	apsv	102-8090
Thallium Arsenide di- Sulfide $TlAsS_2$		
see Thallium di- Thioarsenate $TlAsS_2$	afj	102-8203
Thallium Arsenide Sulfide $Tl_xAs_{2-x}S_2$	af	102-8470
tri- Thallium Arsenide tetra- Sulfide Tl_3AsS_4		
see tri- Thallium tetra- Thioarsenate Tl_3AsS_4	ps	102-8238
Thallium Arsenide di- Telluride $TlAsTe_2$		
see Thallium di- Telluroarsenate $TlAsTe_2$	j	102-8204
Thallium Arsenide Telluride Selenide $Tl_xAs_{1-x}Te_ySe_{1-y}$	jklot	102-8172
Thallium Arsenide Telluride Selenide $Tl_2As_2Te_3Se$	ars	102-8401
Thallium Azide TlN_3	abfrs	120-8022
Thallium - Bismuth $TlBi_2$	fj	104-8268
Thallium Bismuth di- Selenide $TlBiSe_2$		
see Thallium di- Selenobismuthate $TlBiSe_2$	fjkt	104-8220
Thallium Bismuth di- Sulfide $TlBiS_2$		
see Thallium di- Thiobismuthate $TlBiS_2$	fjt	104-8219
Thallium Bismuth di- Telluride $TlBiTe_2$		
see Thallium di- Tellurobismuthate $TlBiTe_2$	fjt	104-8218
Thallium (I) Bromide $TlBr$	abdefhjmst	104-0067
Thallium (I) Chloride $TlCl$	abdefhjmqst	106-0157
Thallium (I) Fluoride TlF	b	110-0146
Thallium Gallium di- Selenide $TlGaSe_2$		
see Thallium di- Selenogallate $TlGaSe_2$	afhjmrs	111-8190
Thallium Gallium di- Sulfide $TlGaS_2$		
see Thallium di- Thiogallate $TlGaS_2$	fm	111-0089
di- Thallium Germanium tri- Telluride Tl_2GeTe_3		
see di- Thallium tri- Tellurogermanate Tl_2GeTe_3	jqt	111-8018
Thallium Indium di- Sulfide $TlInS_2$		
see Thallium di- Thioindate $TlInS_2$	fm	114-0090
Thallium Indium Telluride $Tl_xIn_{2-x}Te_3$	jt	114-8058
Thallium (I) Iodide TlI	abdfjs	114-0055
Thallium Iodide Bromide $Tl_5I_3Br_2$	ahs	104-0434
see also K R S - 5		104-8191
see also Thallium (I) Iodide $\geq$ Thallium (I) Bromide		508-0009
Thallium Lead Telluride $Tl_xPb_{1-x}Te$	jot	123-8066
Thallium (I) Nitrate $TlNO_3$	bj	120-0047
Thallium mono- Nitride TlN	af	120-0129
Thallium Nitrite $TlNO_2$	j	120-0154
tri- Thallium Phosphide tetra- Selenide Tl_3PSe_4		
see tri- Thallium tetra- Selenophosphate Tl_3PSe_4	s	123-0051
Thallium Selenide $TlSe$	afjlt	126-8051
Thallium Selenide $TlSe_x$	fhjt	126-8107
di- Thallium Selenide Tl_2Se	fjklt	126-8034
Thallium Selenide $Tl_{2+x}Se$	o	126-8146
Thallium di- Selenoantimonate $TlSbSe_2$	abj	126-8103
Thallium di- Selenoarsenate $TlAsSe_2$	r	102-8181
tri- Thallium tri- Selenoarsenate Tl_3AsSe_3	apsv	102-8090
Thallium di- Selenobismuthate $TlBiSe_2$	fjkt	104-8220
Thallium di- Selenogallate $TlGaSe_2$	afhjmrs	111-8190
tri- Thallium tetra- Selenophosphate Tl_3PSe_4	s	123-0051
Thallium (I) Sulfate Tl_2SO_4	abf	122-0421
di- Thallium Sulfide Tl_2S	fjrt	126-0043
Thallium Telluride $TlTe$	jkl	127-8003
di- Thallium Telluride Tl_2Te	fhjlot	127-8002
Thallium sesqui- Telluride Tl_2Te_3	afjlt	127-8008
Thallium Telluride $Tl_{2+x}Te$	o	127-8024
Thallium di- Telluroantimonate $TlSbTe_2$	jklt	126-8094
Thallium di- Telluroarsenate $TlAsTe_2$	j	102-8204

Substance Name	Property	Number
Thallium di- Tellurobismuthate $TlBiTe_2$	fjt	104-8218
di- Thallium tri- Tellurogermanate Tl_2GeTe_3	jqt	111-8018
Thallium di- Thioantimonate $TlSbS_2$	afjt	126-8104
Thallium di- Thioarsenate $TlAsS_2$	afj	102-8203
tri- Thallium tetra- Thioarsenate Tl_3AsS_4	ps	102-8238
Thallium di- Thiobismuthate $TlBiS_2$	fjt	104-8219
Thallium di- Thiogallate $TlGaS_2$	fm	111-0089
Thallium di- Thioindate $TlInS_2$	fm	114-0090
tri- Thallium tetra- Thiovanadate Tl_3VS_4	s	126-0063
Thallium (I I I) Vanadate (V) $TlVO_4$	h	122-8139
Thermalox 995 BeO	i	104-8349
see also Beryllium Oxide BeO		104-0002
Thioboric Acid HBS	pq	104-8225
Thiocarbonyl Selenide $CSSe$	hi	106-8306
Thiophosphoryl Chloride $PSCl_3$	hm	106-8431
Thiothionyl Fluoride SSF_2		
see di- Sulfur di- Fluoride S_2F_2	i	110-0288
Thorium mono- Antimonide $ThSb$	q	126-8008
Thorium Bismuth di- Telluride $ThBiTe_2$		
see Thorium di- Tellurobismuthate $ThBiTe_2$	fjt	104-8217
Thorium Borate ThB_2O_5	s	104-8327
Thorium tetra- Boride ThB_4	j	104-8095
Thorium hexa- Boride ThB_6	j	104-8096
Thorium di- Carbide ThC_2	iju	106-0744
Thorium tetra- Chloride $ThCl_4$	j	106-0345
Thorium - Cobalt $ThCo_5$	hnq	106-8509
Thorium - Cobalt Th_2Co_{17}	q	106-8603
Thorium - Cobalt - Iron $ThCo_xFe_{8-x}$	n	106-8723
Thorium - Cobalt - Iron $ThCo_4Fe$	nq	106-8715
di- Thorium Cupride Th_2Cu	j	106-8693
Thorium - Erbium - Cobalt $Th_xEr_{1-x}Co_5$	hnq	106-8397
Thorium tetra- Fluoride ThF_4	abjs	110-0002
Thorium - Gadolinium - Cobalt $Th_xGd_{1-x}Co_5$	hnq	106-8399
Thorium - Gadolinium - Iron $Th_xGd_{1-x}Fe_3$	n	110-8179
Thorium - Gadolinium - Ruthenium $Th_xGd_{1-x}Ru_2$	j	111-8104
Thorium - Holmium - Cobalt $Th_xHo_{1-x}Co_5$	hnq	106-8398
tetra- Thorium 15- Hydride Th_4H_{15}	jq	112-8064
Thorium - Iron $ThFe_3$	n	110-8180
Thorium - Lanthanum - Ruthenium $Th_xLa_{1-x}Ru_2$	j	118-8046
Thorium - Lutetium - Iron $Th_xLu_{1-x}Fe_3$	nq	110-8072
Thorium - Manganese $ThMn_{12}$	j	119-8055
Thorium di- Manganese di- Germanide $ThMn_2Ge_2$	nq	111-8184
Thorium - Nickel $ThNi_5$		
see Thorium penta- Nickelide $ThNi_5$	nq	120-8170
Thorium Nickel tetra- Cobaltide $ThNiCo_4$	nq	106-8719
Thorium Nickel Cobaltide $ThNi_xCo_{5-x}$	nq	106-8718
Thorium di- Nickel tri- Cobaltide $ThNi_2Co_3$	nq	106-8720
Thorium tri- Nickel di- Cobaltide $ThNi_3Co_2$	nq	106-8721
Thorium tetra- Nickel Cobaltide $ThNi_4Co$	nq	106-8722
Thorium penta- Nickelide $ThNi_5$	nq	120-8170
Thorium mono- Oxide ThO	h	122-8071
Thorium di- Oxide ThO_2	abdfhijmoqsu	122-0003
tri- Thorium tetra- Phosphide Th_3P_4	j	123-0036
Thorium - Rhodium $ThRh_3$	jq	125-8024
Thorium - Ruthenium $ThRu_2$	j	125-8031
Thorium Silicate $ThSiO_4$	h	122-0402
Thorium di- Tellurobismuthate $ThBiTe_2$	fjt	104-8217
Thorium Yttrium Cobaltide $Th_xY_{1-x}Co_5$	nq	106-8714
Thorium - Yttrium - Cobalt - Iron $Th_xY_{1-x}Co_4Fe$	nq	106-8716
Thorium - Yttrium - Iron $Th_xY_{1-x}Fe_3$	nq	110-8071
Thorium Zirconate $ThZrO_3$	j	122-8136
Thulium Antimonide $TmSb$	jpqt	126-8010
Thulium Arsenate $TmAsO_4$	h	102-8126
Thulium Arsenide $TmAs$	f	102-8356
Thulium dodeca- Boride TmB_{12}	qu	104-8145
Thulium - Cadmium $TmCd$	jkq	106-8211
Thulium - Cobalt $TmCo_2$	q	106-8376
Thulium - Cobalt Tm_2Co_{17}	np	106-8688
Thulium - Cobalt - Germanium $TmCo_2Ge_2$	q	106-8177
Thulium Europium Yttrium Iron Gallium Oxide $Tm_xEu_yY_{3-x-y}Fe_{5-z}Ga_zO_{12}$		
see Yttrium Thulium Europium Gallium Ferrate $Y_{3-x-y}Tm_xEu_yGa_zFe_{5-z}O_{12}$	n	109-8025
Thulium Ferrite $TmFeO_3$	npq	110-0200

Property: **a.** Absorption coefficient; **b.** Dielectric constant; **c.** Dielectric strength; **d.** Energy band structure; **e.** Effective mass; **f.** Energy gap; **g.** Electric hysteresis; **h.** Energy level; **i.** Electron emission properties; **j.** Electrical resistivity; **k.** Magnetoelectric properties; **l.** Hall coefficient; **m.** Luminescence properties; **n.** Magnetic hysteresis; **o.** Mobility; **p.** Magnetomechanical properties; **q.** Magnetic susceptibility; **r.** Photoelectronic properties; **s.** Refractive index; **t.** Thermoelectric properties; **u.** Work function; **v.** Piezoelectric properties.

Substance Name	Property	Number
Thulium Gadolinium Yttrium Iron Gallium Oxide		
$Tm_xGd_yY_{3-x-y}Fe_{5-z}Ga_zO_{12}$		
see Yttrium Thulium Gadolinium Gallium Ferrate		
$Y_{3-x-y}Tm_xGd_yGa_zFe_{5-z}O_{12}$	anps	110-8044
tri-Thulium (III) penta-Gallate $Tm_3Ga_5O_{12}$		
$Tm_3Ga_5O_{12}$	h	111-8030
Thulium-Gold $TmAu_2$	q	102-8122
Thulium-Iron $TmFe_2$	npq	110-8069
Thulium-Iron Tm_2Fe_{17}	q	110-8078
Thulium Lanthanum Sulfoxylate $Tm_xLa_{2-x}SO_2$	m	118-8036
Thulium Neodymium Cobaltide $Tm_xNd_{1-x}Co_5$	n	106-8728
Thulium Nitride TmN	df	120-8118
Thulium sesqui-Oxide Tm_2O_3	bjs	122-0340
Thulium Praseodymium Cobaltide $Tm_xPr_{1-x}Co_5$	n	106-8729
Thulium mono-Selenide $TmSe$	jnq	126-8120
Thulium sesqui-Selenide Tm_2Se_3	q	126-8121
tri-Thulium tetra-Selenide Tm_3Se_4	q	126-8122
penta-Thulium hexa-Selenide Tm_5Se_6	q	126-8123
Thulium mono-Sulfide TmS	jq	126-8124
Thulium sesqui-Sulfide Tm_2S_3	q	126-8125
penta-Thulium hexa-Sulfide Tm_5S_6	q	126-8126
Thulium mono-Telluride $TmTe$	djq	127-8016
Thulium tri-Telluride $TmTe_3$	q	127-8017
Thulium sesqui-Telluride Tm_2Te_3	q	127-8018
Thulium Vanadate (III) $TmVO_3$	q	122-8084
Thulium Vanadate (V) $TmVO_4$	hmpq	122-8035
Thulium Yttrium Iron Gallium Oxide		
$TmY_2Fe_4GaO_{12}$		
see Yttrium Thulium Gallium Ferrate		
$Y_2TmGaFe_4O_{12}$	s	110-8277
Thulium-Zinc Tm_2Zn_{17}	q	127-8013
Tin Antimonide $SnSb$	bjqt	126-8011
Tin tetra-Bromide $SnBr_4$	q	104-0127
Tin di-Chloride $SnCl_2$	j	106-0303
Tin tetra-Chloride $SnCl_4$	bjq	106-0152
Tin Germanium Telluride $Sn_xGe_{1-x}Te$	jloq	111-8074
see also Tin Monotelluride ≥ Germanium Monotelluride		508-0505
Tin tetra-Iodide SnI_4	oq	114-0045
Tin mono-Oxide SnO	jt	122-0098
Tin di-Oxide SnO_2	befhijmoqrst	122-0053
see also Tinstone SnO_2		521-0470
Tin mono-Selenide $SnSe$	aefjost	126-8035
Tin di-Selenide $SnSe_2$	defhijlost	126-8055
Tin sesqui-Selenide Sn_2Se_3	jt	126-8085
Tin Selenide Sulfide $SnSe_xS_{1-x}$	fo	126-8136
Tin Selenide Sulfide $SnSe_xS_{2-x}$	fs	126-8137
Tin mono-Sulfide SnS	abefjost	126-0001
Tin di-Sulfide SnS_2	dfijlmoqs	126-0002
Tin mono-Telluride $SnTe$	abdefhjlnoqstu	126-8037
Tin Telluride Selenide $SnTe_{1-x}Se_x$	fjlt	126-8067
Tin Telluride Sulfide $SnTe_{1-x}S_x$	jlot	126-8068
Titanium tri-Aluminide $TiAl_3$	j	102-8318
tri-Titanium Aluminide Ti_3Al	jq	102-8184
tetra-Titanium Aluminide Ti_4Al	j	102-8460
Titanium Bismuth Ferrate $Ti_3Bi_9Fe_5O_9$	q	104-8122
Titanium Bismuth Oxide $TiBi_{12}O_{20}$		
see dodeca-Bismuth (III) Titanate (IV)		
$Bi_{12}TiO_{20}$	fhs	104-8123
tri-Titanium Bismuth Oxide $Ti_3Bi_4O_{12}$		
see tetra-Bismuth (III) tri-Titanate (IV)		
$Bi_4Ti_3O_{12}$	bgjnoq	104-0337
Titanium di-Boride TiB_2	eijloqtu	104-8099
Titanium Boride TiB_{2-x}	jlt	104-8269
Titanium Cadmium Oxide $TiCdO_3$		
see Cadmium Titanate (IV) $CdTiO_3$	bg	106-8293
Titanium mono-Carbide TiC	dehijloqtu	106-0125
Titanium Carbide TiC_{1-x}	ijklqtu	106-1027
Titanium Carbide Nitride TiC_xN_{1-x}	jt	106-8567
Titanium tetra-Chloride $TiCl_4$	bh	106-0153
Titanium Chromium Oxide $Ti_xCr_{2-x}O_3$	q	106-8680
Titanium-Cobalt $TiCo$	jq	106-8206
Titanium Cobalt Antimonide $TiCoSb$	q	106-8191
Titanium Cobalt Ferrite $Ti_xCo_yFe_{3-x-y}O_4$	fjot	106-8208
Titanium-Cobalt-Iron $TiCo_xFe_{1-x}$	q	106-8207

Substance Name	Property	Number
Titanium Cobalt Iron Oxide		
$Ti_xCo_yFe_{3-x-y}O_4$		
see Titanium Cobalt Ferrite $Ti_xCo_yFe_{3-x-y}O_4$	fjot	106-8208
Titanium Complexes		
see hexa-Chlorotitanium (3-) Ion $TiCl_6$	q	106-8215
Titanium (IV) Ferrate (II) $TiFeO_3$	j	110-8185
see also Ilmenite $TiFeO_3$		521-8032
Titanium (IV) di-Ferrate (II) $TiFe_2O_4$	pq	110-8208
Titanium Ferrite $Ti_xFe_{3-x}O_4$	p	110-8225
Titanium tri-Fluoride TiF_3	i	110-8084
Titanium mono-Germanide $TiGe$	jlqt	111-8200
Titanium di-Germanide $TiGe_2$	jlqt	111-8201
penta-Titanium tri-Germanide Ti_5Ge_3	jlqt	111-8139
Titanium mono-Hydride TiH	j	112-8089
Titanium Hydride TiH_{1-x}	j	112-8090
Titanium tri-Iodide TiI_3	fj	114-8076
Titanium-Iron $TiFe$	adhj	110-8165
Titanium-Iron Ti_2Fe	j	110-8166
Titanium Iron Antimonide $TiFeSb$	q	110-8061
Titanium di-Iron Antimonide $TiFe_2Sb$	q	110-8062
tri-Titanium penta-Iron nona-Bismuth 27-Oxide		
$Ti_3Fe_5Bi_9O_{27}$		
see Titanium Bismuth Ferrate $Ti_3Bi_9Fe_5O_9$	q	104-8122
Titanium Iron tri-Oxide $TiFeO_3$		
see Titanium (IV) Ferrate (II) $TiFeO_3$	j	110-8185
Titanium di-Iron tetra-Selenide		
$TiFe_2Se_4$		
see di-Iron tetra-Selenotitanate Fe_2TiSe_4	q	110-8081
Titanium di-Iron tetra-Sulfide		
$TiFe_2S_4$		
see di-Iron tetra-Thiotitanate Fe_2TiS_4	n	110-8218
Titanium Iron Sulfide $TiFe_{1-x}S_2$		
see Iron Thiotitanate $Fe_{1-x}TiS_2$	nq	110-8050
di-Titanium Iron tetra-Sulfide		
Ti_2FeS_4		
see Iron tetra-Thiodititanate $FeTi_2S_4$	q	110-8097
Titanium Lead Oxide		
see Lead (II) Titanate (II) $PbTiO_2$	b	122-8116
Titanium Lead Oxide $TiPbO_3$		
see Lead (II) Titanate (IV) $PbTiO_3$	abfgjpqstv	122-0013
Titanium-Nickel $TiNi$	f	120-8127
Titanium-Nickel $TiNi_3$	f	120-8085
Titanium-Nickel Ti_2Ni	j	120-8105
Titanium Nickel Antimonide $TiNiSb$	q	120-8033
Titanium (IV) Nickelate (II) $TiNiO_3$		
see Nickel (II) Titanate (IV) $NiTiO_3$	j	120-8161
Titanium Niobide $TiNb$	jkn	120-8047
Titanium Niobium Carbide $Ti_xNb_{1-x}C$	q	106-8560
see also Niobium Monocarbide ≥ Titanium Monocarbide		508-0502
Titanium Niobium Nitride $Ti_xNb_{1-x}N_{1-y}$	m	120-8045
Titanium Niobium Selenide $Ti_xNb_{1-x}Se_2$	j	120-8080
Titanium mono-Nitride TiN	dhijltu	120-0023
Titanium Nitride TiN_{1-x}	j	120-0165
Titanium mono-Oxide TiO	adfhjqst	122-0046
Titanium di-Oxide TiO_2	a-jloqrstu	122-0005
see also Anatase TiO_2		521-8074
see also Rutile TiO_2		521-0092
Titanium Oxide TiO_{2-x}	abfjoqt	122-0314
Titanium sesqui-Oxide Ti_2O_3	bdfjqt	122-0047
tri-Titanium Oxide Ti_3O	jt	122-0201
tri-Titanium penta-Oxide Ti_3O_5	ehjo	122-8108
tetra-Titanium hepta-Oxide Ti_4O_7	ehjo	122-0425
penta-Titanium nona-Oxide Ti_5O_9	ehj	122-8109
hexa-Titanium Oxide Ti_6O	jt	122-0450
hexa-Titanium undeca-Oxide Ti_6O_{11}	ehjo	122-8110
octa-Titanium 15-Oxide Ti_8O_{15}	ehjo	122-8111
Titanium mono-Phosphide TiP	j	123-8095
Titanium di-Selenide $TiSe_2$	dfhj	126-8090
Titanium Silicide $TiSi$	du	126-8109
Titanium di-Silicide $TiSi_2$	dijtu	126-8061
penta-Titanium tri-Silicide Ti_5Si_3	diju	126-8062
Titanium mono-Sulfide TiS	jlt	126-0036
Titanium di-Sulfide TiS_2	abdfhjors	126-0004
Titanium sesqui-Sulfide Ti_2S_3	fjlot	126-0037

Property: a. Absorption coefficient; **b.** Dielectric constant; **c.** Dielectric strength; **d.** Energy band structure; **e.** Effective mass; **f.** Energy gap; **g.** Electric hysteresis; **h.** Energy level; **i.** Electron emission properties; **j.** Electrical resistivity; **k.** Magnetoelectric properties; **l.** Hall coefficient; **m.** Luminescence properties; **n.** Magnetic hysteresis; **o.** Mobility; **p.** Magnetomechanical properties; **q.** Magnetic susceptibility; **r.** Photoelectronic properties; **s.** Refractive index; **t.** Thermoelectric properties; **u.** Work function; **v.** Piezoelectric properties.

Substance Name	Formula	Property	Number
Titanium (I I I) Tantalate	$Ti Ta O_4$	j	122-8117
Titanium Tantalum Cadmium Lead Oxide	$Ti_x Ta Cd_{1-x} Pb_2 O_6$	n	106-8827
Titanium Tantalum Carbide	$Ti_x Ta_{1-x} C$	jqt	106-8561
Titanium Tantalum Sulfide	$Ti_x Ta_{1-x} S_2$	bdjors	126-8092
Titanium tetra- Thioferrate	$Ti Fe_2 S_4$		
see di- Iron tetra- Thiotitanate	$Fe_2 Ti S_4$	n	110-8218
Titanium Vanadium sesqui- Oxide	$Ti_x V_{2-x} O_3$	jq	122-8053
Tris(penta- Fluoroethyl)amine	$N(C_2 F_5)_3$		
see Tris- (penta- Fluoroethyl)amine	$N(C_2 F_5)_3$	c	106-8578
di- Tungsten tri- Arsenide	$W_2 As_3$	j	102-8429
Tungsten Bismuth Oxide	$W Bi_6 O_{12}$		
see hexa- Bismuth (I I I) Tungstate (V I)	$Bi_6 W O_{12}$	j	104-8172
Tungsten mono- Boride	$W B$	j	104-8390
Tungsten di- Boride	$W B_2$	q	104-8100
Tungsten penta- Boride	$W_2 B_5$	jloqu	104-8115
Tungsten Cadmium tetra- Oxide	$W Cd O_4$		
see Cadmium Tungstate (V I)	$Cd W O_4$	am	106-8430
Tungsten mono- Carbide	$W C$	iju	106-0310
di- Tungsten Carbide	$W_2 C$	it	106-0423
Tungsten hexa- Chloride	$W Cl_6$	u	106-0353
Tungsten - Cobalt	$W Co$		
see Tungsten mono- Cobaltide	$W Co$	n	106-8778
Tungsten Cobalt Ferrate	$W Co_x Fe_{18-x} O_{27}$	fjlqt	106-8811
Tungsten mono- Cobaltide	$W Co$	n	106-8778
Tungsten Cobalt Lead Oxide	$W Co Pb_2 O_6$		
see di- Lead (I I) Cobalt (I I) Tungstate (V I)	$Pb_2 Co W O_6$	b	106-8250
Tungsten Cobalt Oxide	$W Co O_4$		
see Cobalt (I I) Tungstate (V I)	$Co W O_4$	abhq	106-8244
Tungsten Cobalt Zinc Oxide	$W Co_x Zn_{1-x} O_4$		
see Cobalt Zinc Tungstate	$Co_x Zn_{1-x} W O_4$	q	106-8657
Tungsten hexa- Fluoride	$W F_6$	u	110-0156
Tungsten Iron Lead Oxide	$W_x Fe_{1-x} Pb O_3$		
see Lead Tungsten Ferrate	$Pb W_x Fe_{1-x} O_3$	q	110-8142
Tungsten Lead Ferrate	$W_x Pb Fe_{1-x} O_3$		
see Lead Tungsten Ferrate	$Pb W_x Fe_{1-x} O_3$	q	110-8142
Tungsten Lead Oxide	$W Pb O_4$		
see Lead (I I) Tungstate (V I)	$Pb W O_4$	bh	122-0054
Tungsten Manganese tetra- Oxide	$W Mn O_4$		
see Manganese (I I) Tungstate (V I)	$Mn W O_4$	b	119-8034
Tungsten Molybdenum Telluride	$W_x Mo_{1-x} Te_2$	fj	119-8085
Tungsten Nickel Oxide	$W Ni O_4$		
see Nickel (I I) Tungstate (V I)	$Ni W O_4$	abh	120-8038
Tungsten Nitride	$W N$	j	120-8073
di- Tungsten Nitride	$W_2 N$	j	120-8171
Tungsten tri- Oxide	$W O_3$	abfgjrv	122-0012
Tungsten penta- Oxide	$W_2 O_5$	s	122-0367
Tungsten mono- Phosphide	$W P$	j	123-8036
Tungsten di- Selenide	$W Se_2$	defhjlot	126-8059
Tungsten di- Selenide, Intercalated	$W Se_2$	j	126-8106
Tungsten di- Silicide	$W Si_2$	djt	126-8038
Tungsten di- Sulfide	$W S_2$	hj	126-8039
Tungsten di- Sulfide, Intercalated	$W S_2$	j	126-8105
Tungsten di- Telluride	$W Te_2$	j	127-8022
Tungsten Telluride Selenide	$W Te Se$	j	126-8143
Tungsten Telluride Selenide	$W Te_x Se_{2-x}$	j	126-8144
Tungsten Zinc Oxide	$W Zn O_4$		
see Zinc Tungstate (V I)	$Zn W O_4$	abm	122-0199
Ultrasil Fused Silica		ab	122-8061
see also Silica, Fused			122-8045
Uranium di- Aluminide	$U Al_2$	jq	102-8159
Uranium tri- Aluminide	$U Al_3$	j	102-8233
Uranium tetra- Aluminide	$U Al_4$	jq	102-8234
Uranium mono- Antimonide	$U Sb$	jqt	126-8012
Uranium di- Antimonide	$U Sb_2$	jqt	126-8013
tri- Uranium tetra- Antimonide	$U_3 Sb_4$	jqt	126-8014
tetra- Uranium tri- Antimonide	$U_4 Sb_3$	jqt	126-8015
Uranium Arsenide	$U As$	hjnqt	102-8192
Uranium di- Arsenide	$U As_2$	q	102-8193
tri- Uranium tetra- Arsenide	$U_3 As_4$	ejklt	102-8071
Uranium Arsenide Phosphide	$U As_x P_{1-x}$	q	102-8236
Uranium Arsenide Sulfide	$U As_x S_{1-x}$	q	102-8237
Uranium di- Bismuthide	$U Bi_2$	q	104-8197
Uranium tetra- Boride	$U B_4$	u	104-8305
Uranium dodeca- Boride	$U B_{12}$	qu	104-8185
Uranium Boride Deuteride	$U(B D_4)_4$		
see Uranium Hydroborate, Deuterated	$U(B D_4)_4$	h	104-8128
Uranium Boride Hydride	$U(B H_4)_4$		
see Uranium Hydroborate	$U(B H_4)_4$	h	104-8127
Uranium tri- Bromide	$U Br_3$	q	104-8226
Uranium - Cadmium	$U Cd_{11}$	q	106-8181
Uranium mono- Carbide	$U C$	aijsu	106-0417
Uranium di- Carbide	$U C_2$	j	106-0420
Uranium sesqui- Carbide	$U_2 C_3$	jq	106-0612
Uranium Carbide Oxide	$U_x C_y O_{1-x-y}$	j	106-8791
Uranium tri- Chloride	$U Cl_3$	q	106-8422
Uranium tetra- Chloride	$U Cl_4$	hjq	106-0131
Uranium Chloride Oxide	$U O_2 Cl_2$		
see Uranyl Chloride	$U O_2 Cl_2$	j	106-8709
Uranium - Copper	$U Cu_5$	jqt	106-8182
Uranium di- Ferride	$U Fe_2$	j	110-8264
hexa- Uranium Ferride	$U_6 Fe$	j	110-8152
Uranium - Gallium	$U Ga_3$	j	111-8093
Uranium Germanium Telluride	$U Ge Te$		
see Uranium Tellurogermanide	$U Ge Te$	nq	111-8054
Uranium Hydroborate	$U(B H_4)_4$	h	104-8127
Uranium Hydroborate, Deuterated	$U(B D_4)_4$	h	104-8128
Uranium - Indium	$U In_3$	jq	114-8060
Uranium tri- Iodide	$U I_3$	q	114-0003
Uranium - Iron	$U Fe_2$		
see Uranium di- Ferride	$U Fe_2$	j	110-8264
Uranium - Iron	$U_6 Fe$		
see hexa- Uranium Ferride	$U_6 Fe$	j	110-8152
Uranium Iron Lead Oxide	$U_x Fe_{1-x} Pb O_3$		
see Lead Uranium Ferrate	$Pb U_x Fe_{1-x} O_3$	nq	110-8139
Uranium Lead Ferrate	$U_x Pb Fe_{1-x} O_3$		
see Lead Uranium Ferrate	$Pb U_x Fe_{1-x} O_3$	nq	110-8139
Uranium Molybdenum Hydrogen Oxide	$H_8 U Mo_{12} O_{42}$		
see Molybdouranic Acid	$H_8(U Mo_{12} O_{42})$	q	112-8033
Uranium Molybdenum Oxide	$(U O_2) Mo O_4$		
see Uranyl Molybdate	$(U O_2) Mo O_4$	m	119-8065
Uranium Nickel tetra- Cupride	$U Ni Cu_4$	jqt	106-8769
Uranium Nickel Cupride	$U Ni_x Cu_{5-x}$	jqt	106-8771
Uranium tetra- Nickel Cupride	$U Ni_4 Cu$	t	106-8770
Uranium penta- Nickelide	$U Ni_5$	jqt	120-8173
Uranium mono- Nitride	$U N$	jqt	120-0057
Uranium mono- Oxide	$U O$	h	122-8072
Uranium di- Oxide	$U O_2$	abdfhjost	122-0008
Uranium tri- Oxide	$U O_3$	h	122-0032
Uranium Oxide	$U O_{2-x}$	j	122-8090
Uranium sesqui- Oxide	$U_2 O_3$	j	122-8127
tetra- Uranium nona- Oxide	$U_4 O_9$	fj	122-0025
Uranium - Palladium	$U Pd_3$	jq	123-8060
Uranium mono- Phosphide	$U P$	ehjnqt	123-0025
Uranium di- Phosphide	$U P_2$	q	123-0041
tri- Uranium tetra- Phosphide	$U_3 P_4$	eklnpqt	123-0026
Uranium Phosphide Selenide	$U P_x Se_{1-x}$	q	123-8067
Uranium Phosphide Sulfide	$U P_x S_{1-x}$	q	123-8062
Uranium - Platinum	$U Pt$	q	123-8044
Uranium - Rhodium	$U Rh_3$	jq	125-8025
Uranium di- Selenide	$U Se_2$	nq	126-8077
tri- Uranium penta- Selenide	$U_3 Se_5$	nq	126-8155
Uranium Selenide Sulfide	$U Se S$		
see Uranium Thioselenide	$U Se S$	q	126-8133
Uranium tri- Silicide	$U Si_3$	j	126-8141
tri- Uranium Silicide	$U_3 Si$	j	126-8142
Uranium tri- Stannide	$U Sn_3$	jq	126-8091
Uranium mono- Sulfide	$U S$	hjq	126-0011
Uranium di- Sulfide	$U S_2$	nq	126-0046
tri- Uranium penta- Sulfide	$U_3 S_5$	nq	126-8154
Uranium di- Telluride	$U Te_2$	q	127-8006
hepta- Uranium dodeca- Telluride	$U_7 Te_{12}$	nq	127-8007

Property: a. Absorption coefficient; **b.** Dielectric constant; **c.** Dielectric strength; **d.** Energy band structure; **e.** Effective mass; **f.** Energy gap; **g.** Electric hysteresis; **h.** Energy level; **i.** Electron emission properties; **j.** Electrical resistivity; **k.** Magnetoelectric properties; **l.** Hall coefficient; **m.** Luminescence properties; **n.** Magnetic hysteresis; **o.** Mobility; **p.** Magnetomechanical properties; **q.** Magnetic susceptibility; **r.** Photoelectronic properties; **s.** Refractive index; **t.** Thermoelectric properties; **u.** Work function; **v.** Piezoelectric properties.

Substance Name	Property	Number
Uranium Telluride Sulfide $U\,Te\,S$		
see Uranium Thiotelluride $U\,Te\,S$	q	126-8134
Uranium Tellurogermanide $U\,Ge\,Te$	nq	111-8054
Uranium - Thallium $U\,Tl_3$	q	127-8014
Uranium Thioselenide $U\,Se\,S$	q	126-8133
Uranium Thiotelluride $U\,Te\,S$	q	126-8134
Uranium - Tin $U\,Sn_3$		
see Uranium tri- Stannide $U\,Sn_3$	jq	126-8091
Uranium - Titanium $U_2\,Ti$	f	127-8011
Uranium Tungsten Iron Lead Oxide		
$U_x\,W_y\,Fe_{1-x-y}\,Pb\,O_3$		
see Lead Uranium Tungsten Ferrate		
$Pb\,U_x\,W_y\,Fe_{1-x-y}\,O_3$	bq	110-8141
Uranium Tungsten Lead Ferrate		
$U_x\,W_y\,Pb\,Fe_{1-x-y}\,O_3$		
see Lead Uranium Tungsten Ferrate		
$Pb\,U_x\,W_y\,Fe_{1-x-y}\,O_3$	bq	110-8141
Uranium - Yttrium $U\,Y_2$	n	128-8002
Uranium - Zinc $U_2\,Zn_{17}$	q	128-8001
Uranium Zirconium Carbide $U_x\,Zr_{1-x}\,C$	j	106-8705
Uranyl Chloride $U\,O_2\,Cl_2$	j	106-8709
Uranyl Molybdate $(U\,O_2)\,Mo\,O_4$	m	119-8065
Uranyl Nitrate $U\,O_2(N\,O_3)_2$	m	120-8035
Uranyl Tungstate $(U\,O_2)\,W\,O_4$	m	122-8075
50 V Ch Z Ferrite (Russian)		
see Ferrite 50 V Ch Z (Russian)	bq	110-8188
Vanadium (V) Aluminate $V\,Al\,O_4$		
see Aluminum Vanadate (V) $Al\,V\,O_4$	a	102-8481
Vanadium Aluminate $V_x\,Al_{2-x}\,O_4$		
see Aluminum Vanadate $Al_x\,V_{2-x}\,O_4$	q	102-8365
hexa- Vanadium (V) tetra- Aluminate		
$V_6\,Al_4\,O_{21}$		
see tetra- Aluminum hexa- Vanadate (V) $Al_4\,V_6\,O_{21}$	a	102-8482
Vanadium tri- Aluminide $V\,Al_3$	j	102-8222
tri- Vanadium Aluminide $V_3\,Al$	j	102-8473
Vanadium Aluminide Germanide $V_3\,Al_x\,Ge_{1-x}$	j	102-8474
see also tri- Vanadium Aluminide $\geq$ tri- Vanadium Germanide		508-0512
see also tri- Vanadium Germanide $\geq$ tri- Vanadium Aluminide		508-0519
Vanadium Aluminide Silicide $V_3\,Al_x\,Si_{1-x}$	j	102-8475
see also tri- Vanadium Aluminide $\geq$ tri- Vanadium Silicide		508-0513
see also tri- Vanadium Silicide $\geq$ tri- Vanadium Aluminide		508-0514
Vanadium mono- Antimonide $V\,Sb$	jqt	126-8016
Vanadium di- Antimonide $V\,Sb_2$	jqt	126-8017
Vanadium Bismuthate $V\,Bi\,O_4$		
see Bismuth Vanadate $Bi\,V\,O_4$	b	104-8443
Vanadium (I I I) Boride $V\,B$	pq	104-8229
Vanadium di- Boride $V\,B_2$	jqu	104-8105
Vanadium Boride $V\,B_{2-x}$	q	104-8410
Vanadium Boride Nitride $V\,B_{1-x}\,N_{1-y}$	q	104-8408
Vanadium Boride Nitride $V\,B_{2-x}\,N_{1-y}$	q	104-8409
Vanadium Boride Silicide $V_3\,B_x\,Si_{1-x}$	j	104-8431
Vanadium mono- Carbide $V\,C$	djlqtu	106-0226
Vanadium Carbide $V\,C_{1-x}$	djlqtu	106-1287
di- Vanadium Carbide $V_2\,C$	j	106-0674
hexa- Vanadium penta- Carbide $V_6\,C_5$	jl	106-8315
octa- Vanadium hepta- Carbide $V_8\,C_7$	jl	106-8314
Vanadium tetra- Chloride $V\,Cl_4$	h	106-8114
Vanadium - Chromium - Germanium $V_x\,Cr_{5-x}\,Ge_3$	jlqt	106-8643
Vanadium Chromium Nitride $V_x\,Cr_{1-x}\,N$	q	106-8637
Vanadium Chromium Oxide $V_{2-x}\,Cr_x\,O_3$	abjqst	106-8237
Vanadium Chromium Oxide / $V_{1-x}\,Cr_x\,O_2$	jq	106-8331
Vanadium di- Chromium tetra- Selenide		
$V\,Cr_2\,Se_4$		
see Vanadium tetra- Selenodichromate $V\,Cr_2\,Se_4$	efjlot	106-8393
Vanadium di- Chromium Silicide $V\,Cr_2\,Si$	jt	106-8825
Vanadium Chromium Silicide $V_x\,Cr_{3-x}\,Si$	jqt	106-8824
Vanadium Chromium Silicide $V_x\,Cr_{5-x}\,Si_3$	jlqt	106-8261
Vanadium Cobaltate $V_x\,Co_{3-x}\,O_4$		
see Cobalt Vanadate $Co_x\,V_{3-x}\,O_4$	q	106-8741
Vanadium (I I I) Cobaltate (I I)		
$V_2\,Co\,O_4$		
see Cobalt (I I) Vanadate (I I I) $Co\,V_2\,O_4$	a	106-8768
Vanadium Cobalt Ferrite $V_x\,Co\,Fe_{2-x}\,O_4$	fj	106-8258

Substance Name	Property	Number
tri- Vanadium Cobaltide $V_3\,Co$	d	106-8296
Vanadium Complexes		
see Oxotetrachlorovanadate (4-) Ion $V\,O\,Cl_4$	q	106-8216
Vanadium Copper Sulfide $V\,Cu\,S$		
see Vanadium Thiocupride $V\,Cu\,S$	jqt	106-8153
Vanadium Ferrite $V_x\,Fe_{3-x}\,O_4$	q	110-8260
tri- Vanadium Gallide $V_3\,Ga$	dhjnqt	111-8058
Vanadium Gallide Aluminide $V_3\,Ga_x\,Al_{1-x}$	j	102-8476
see also tri- Vanadium Gallide $\geq$ tri- Vanadium Aluminide		508-0516
Vanadium Gallide Germanide $V_3\,Ga_x\,Ge_{1-x}$	j	111-8196
see also tri- Vanadium Gallide $\geq$ tri- Vanadium Germanide		508-0517
see also tri- Vanadium Germanide $\geq$ tri- Vanadium Gallide		508-0520
Vanadium Gallide Silicide $V_3\,Ga_x\,Si_{1-x}$	dj	111-8124
see also tri- Vanadium Gallide $\geq$ tri- Vanadium Silicide		508-0518
see also tri- Vanadium Silicide $\geq$ tri- Vanadium Gallide		508-0515
Vanadium Gallide Stannide $V_3\,Ga_x\,Sn_{1-x}$	jq	111-8123
tri- Vanadium Germanide $V_3\,Ge$	djlqt	111-8055
penta- Vanadium tri- Germanide $V_5\,Ge_3$	jlqt	111-8136
undeca- Vanadium octa- Germanide $V_{11}\,Ge_8$	jlqt	111-8203
Vanadium Germanide Silicide $V_3\,Ge_x\,Si_{1-x}$	j	111-8197
Vanadium - Gold $V\,Au_4$	q	102-8213
Vanadium - Gold $V_3\,Au$	j	102-8323
Vanadium Hydride Oxide $V\,O\,O\,H$		
see Vanadium Hydroperoxide $V\,O\,O\,H$	fjq	112-8062
Vanadium Hydroperoxide $V\,O\,O\,H$	fjq	112-8062
Vanadium (V) Indate $V\,In\,O_4$		
see Indium Vanadate (V) $In\,V\,O_4$	hm	114-8096
Vanadium Iron Zinc Oxide		
$V_x\,Fe_y\,Zn_{3-x-y}\,O_4$		
see Vanadium Zinc Ferrite $V_x\,Zn_y\,Fe_{3-x-y}\,O_4$	fjt	110-8215
di- Vanadium tri- Lead octa- Oxide		
$V_2\,Pb_3\,O_8$		
see di- Vanadium (V) tri- Plumbate (I I)		
$V_2\,Pb_3\,O_8$	b	122-0438
Vanadium Lead Phosphate $V_{2-x}\,Pb_3\,P_x\,O_8$	b	122-8133
Vanadium Manganese Antimonide $V_x\,Mn_{1-x-y}\,Sb$	nq	119-8051
Vanadium - Manganese - Gold $V_x\,Mn_{1-x}\,Au_4$	q	102-8364
Vanadium Nickel Cobalt Ferrite		
$V_x\,Ni_y\,Co_{1-y}\,Fe_{2-x}\,O_4$		
see Nickel Cobalt Vanadium Ferrite		
$Ni_x\,Co_{1-x}\,V_y\,Fe_{2-y}\,O_4$	fj	106-8259
Vanadium Nickel Iron Oxide		
$V_x\,Ni\,Fe_{2-x}\,O_4$		
see Nickel Vanadium Ferrite $Ni\,V_x\,Fe_{2-x}\,O_4$	fj	110-8079
Vanadium mono- Nitride $V\,N$	adjlqt	120-0035
Vanadium Nitride $V\,N_{1-x}$	fjqt	120-8077
Vanadium mono- Oxide $V\,O$	dfhjqt	122-0026
Vanadium di- Oxide $V\,O_2$	abdefghijkloqst	122-0112
Vanadium Oxide $V\,O_{1-x}$	fjlqt	122-8124
Vanadium Oxide $V\,O_{2-x}$	fgjqt	122-8078
di- Vanadium Oxide $V_2\,O$	befjoqst	122-8088
Vanadium sesqui- Oxide $V_2\,O_3$	abdfijloqst	122-0014
di- Vanadium tetra- Oxide $V_2\,O_4$	bfj	122-0015
Vanadium penta- Oxide $V_2\,O_5$	abfhjloqrst	122-0016
Vanadium Oxide $V_2\,O_{3-x}$	jq	122-8112
tri- Vanadium penta- Oxide $V_3\,O_5$	ajqt	122-8028
tetra- Vanadium Oxide $V_4\,O$	j	122-8089
tetra- Vanadium hepta- Oxide $V_4\,O_7$	ajqt	122-8029
penta- Vanadium nona- Oxide $V_5\,O_9$	ajqt	122-8030
hexa- Vanadium undeca- Oxide $V_6\,O_{11}$	ajqt	122-8031
hexa- Vanadium 13- Oxide $V_6\,O_{13}$	ajq	122-8093
hepta- Vanadium 13- Oxide $V_7\,O_{13}$	ajqt	122-8032
octa- Vanadium 15- Oxide $V_8\,O_{15}$	jqt	122-8033
Vanadium Oxide Hydroxide $V\,O\,O\,H$		
see Vanadium Hydroperoxide $V\,O\,O\,H$	fjq	112-8062
Vanadium mono- Phosphide $V\,P$	j	123-8096
tri- Vanadium Phosphide $V_3\,P$	j	123-8101
di- Vanadium (V) tri- Plumbate (I I)		
$V_2\,Pb_3\,O_8$	b	122-0438
Vanadium - Ruthenium $V\,Ru$	q	125-8034
Vanadium tetra- Selenodichromate $V\,Cr_2\,Se_4$	efjlot	106-8393
Vanadium di- Silicide $V\,Si_2$	adjlo	126-8041
di- Vanadium Silicide $V_2\,Si$	q	126-8042
tri- Vanadium Silicide $V_3\,Si$	dfjlnoqt	126-8047

Property: **a.** Absorption coefficient; **b.** Dielectric constant; **c.** Dielectric strength; **d.** Energy band structure; **e.** Effective mass; **f.** Energy gap; **g.** Electric hysteresis; **h.** Energy level; **i.** Electron emission properties; **j.** Electrical resistivity; **k.** Magnetoelectric properties; **l.** Hall coefficient; **m.** Luminescence properties; **n.** Magnetic hysteresis; **o.** Mobility; **p.** Magnetomechanical properties; **q.** Magnetic susceptibility; **r.** Photoelectronic properties; **s.** Refractive index; **t.** Thermoelectric properties; **u.** Work function; **v.** Piezoelectric properties.

Substance Name	*Property*	*Number*
penta- Vanadium tri- Silicide V_5Si_3	djloqtu	126-8108
Vanadium Silicide Carbide $V_3Si_xC_{1-x}$	j	106-8788
Vanadium Silicide Phosphide $V_3Si_xP_{1-x}$	j	123-8102
see also tri- Vanadium Phosphide ≥ tri- Vanadium Silicide		508-0521
see also tri- Vanadium Silicide ≥ tri- Vanadium Phosphide		508-0522
tri- Vanadium Stannide V_3Sn	djqt	126-8020
Vanadium mono- Sulfide VS	dhjq	126-8043
penta- Vanadium octa- Sulfide V_5S_8	q	126-8132
Vanadium (III) Tantalate $VTaO_4$	j	122-8118
Vanadium Thallium Sulfide $VTlS$		
see Vanadium Thiothallide $VTlS$	jqt	126-8057
Vanadium tri- Thallium tetra- Sulfide		
VTl_3S_4		
see tri- Thallium tetra- Thiovanadate Tl_3VS_4	s	126-0063
Vanadium Thiocupride $VCuS$	jqt	106-8153
Vanadium Thiothallide $VTlS$	jqt	126-8057
Vanadium - Tin V_3Sn		
see tri- Vanadium Stannide V_3Sn	djqt	126-8020
Vanadium Zinc Ferrite $V_xZn_yFe_{3-x-y}O_4$	fjt	110-8215
Vanadium Zinc Oxide $V_xZn_{3-x}O_4$		
see Zinc Vanadate $Zn_xV_{3-x}O_4$	fjt	122-8113
di- Vanadium Zinc tetra- Oxide V_2ZnO_4		
see Zinc Vanadate (III) ZnV_2O_4	aq	122-8027
Vitreous Quartz		
see Silica, Fused	abdfjmoqs	122-8045
Vycor 7905		
see Corning Glass Code 7905 (Vycor Fused Silica)	abs	122-8047
Water H_2O	abcdfhijlmqrstu	112-0001
Water, Deuterated D_2O	abhqs	108-0005
Water, mono- Deuterated HDO	a	108-0004
Xenon di- Fluoride XeF_2	i	110-8096
YAG		
see tri- Yttrium penta- Aluminate $Y_3Al_5O_{12}$	ahimstv	102-0250
YIG $Y_3Fe_5O_{12}$		
see tri- Yttrium penta- Ferrate (III)		
$Y_3Fe_5O_{12}$	abcdfhjklnopqrst	110-0194
YLF $YLiF_4$		
see Lithium tetra- Fluoroyttrate $LiYF_4$	afhms	110-0352
Ytterbium di- Aluminide $YbAl_2$	hjq	102-8218
Ytterbium tri- Aluminide $YbAl_3$	hjq	102-8217
Ytterbium di- Aluminum tetra- Sulfide		
$YbAl_2S_4$		
see Ytterbium tetra- Thiodialuminate $YbAl_2S_4$	j	102-8498
Ytterbium mono- Antimonide $YbSb$	f	126-8021
Ytterbium Arsenide $YbAs$	f	102-8357
Ytterbium Bismuth Ferrate $Yb_{3-x}Bi_xFe_5O_{12}$	q	104-8132
Ytterbium hexa- Boride YbB_6	jt	104-8139
Ytterbium dodeca- Boride YbB_{12}	qu	104-8140
Ytterbium Carbide Oxide $Yb_2O_2(CO_3)$		
see Ytterbium Oxide Carbonate $Yb_2O_2(CO_3)$	q	106-8275
Ytterbium Chromite $YbCrO_3$	q	106-1517
Ytterbium Chromium Manganite $YbCr_xMn_{1-x}O_3$	q	106-8324
Ytterbium - Cobalt - Germanium $YbCo_2Ge_2$	q	106-8178
Ytterbium Erbium Yttrium tri- Fluoride		
$Yb_xEr_yY_{1-x-y}F_3$		
see Yttrium Ytterbium Erbium tri- Fluoride		
$Y_{1-x-y}Yb_xEr_yF_3$	m	109-8030
Ytterbium Europium Yttrium Iron Aluminum Oxide		
$Yb_xEu_yY_{3-x-y}Fe_{5-z}Al_zO_{12}$		
see Yttrium Ytterbium Europium Aluminum Ferrate		
$Y_{3-x-y}Yb_xEu_yAl_zFe_{5-z}O_{12}$	n	102-8089
Ytterbium (III) Ferrate (III) $YbFeO_3$	n	110-8206
tri- Ytterbium (III) penta- Ferrate (III)		
$Yb_3Fe_5O_{12}$	q	110-0202
Ytterbium tri- Fluoride YbF_3	as	110-0351
Ytterbium Gadolinium Aluminum Ferrate		
$Yb_xGd_{3-x}Al_yFe_{5-y}O_{12}$	np	102-8491
Ytterbium Gadolinium Europium Yttrium Iron		
Gallium Aluminum Oxide		
$(YbGdEuY)_3(FeGaAl)_5O_{12}$		
see Yttrium Ytterbium Gadolinium Europium Gallium Aluminum		
Ferrate $(YYbGdEu)_3(GaAlFe)_5O_{12}$	p	102-8115
Ytterbium Gadolinium Europium Yttrium Iron		
Gallium Oxide		
$(YbGdEuY)_3(FeGa)_5O_{12}$		
see Yttrium Ytterbium Gadolinium Europium Gallium Ferrate		
$(YYbGdEu)_3(GaFe)_5O_{12}$	n	109-8026
Ytterbium Gadolinium Sulfide $Yb_xGd_{1-x}S$	q	111-8072
Ytterbium Gadolinium Yttrium Iron Aluminum Oxide		
$Yb_xGd_yY_{3-x-y}Fe_{5-z}Al_zO_{12}$		
see Yttrium Ytterbium Gadolinium Aluminum Ferrate		
$Y_{3-x-y}Yb_zGd_yAl_zFe_{5-z}O_{12}$	ns	102-8112
Ytterbium Gadolinium Yttrium Iron Gallium		
Aluminum Oxide		
$(YbGdY)_3(FeGaAl)_5O_{12}$		
see Yttrium Ytterbium Gadolinium Gallium Aluminum Ferrate		
$(YYbGd)_3(GaAlFe)_5O_{12}$	p	102-8114
Ytterbium Gadolinium Yttrium Iron Gallium Oxide		
$Yb_xGd_yY_{3-x-y}Fe_{5-z}Ga_zO_{12}$		
see Yttrium Ytterbium Gadolinium Gallium Ferrate		
$Y_{3-x-y}Yb_xGd_yGa_zFe_{5-x}O_{12}$	anq	110-8054
Ytterbium Gallium Ferrate $Yb_3Ga_xFe_{5-x}O_{12}$	q	110-8059
Ytterbium di- Gallium tetra- Selenide		
$YbGa_2Se_4$		
see Ytterbium tetra- Selenodigallate $YbGa_2Se_4$	j	111-8210
Ytterbium di- Gallium tetra- Sulfide		
$YbGa_2S_4$		
see Ytterbium tetra- Thiodigallate $YbGa_2S_4$	jm	111-8209
di- Ytterbium Germanium penta- Selenide		
Yb_2GeSe_5		
see di- Ytterbium penta- Selenogermanate Yb_2GeSe_5	fjt	111-8057
Ytterbium - Gold $YbAu$	j	102-8268
Ytterbium - Gold $YbAu_2$	j	102-8269
Ytterbium - Gold $YbAu_3$	j	102-8270
Ytterbium - Gold $YbAu_4$	j	102-8271
Ytterbium Indium tri- Sulfide $YbInS_3$		
see Ytterbium tri- Thioindate $YbInS_3$	f	114-8095
Ytterbium Iron Bismuth Oxide		
$Yb_{3-x}Fe_5Bi_xO_{12}$		
see Ytterbium Bismuth Ferrate $Yb_{3-x}Bi_xFe_5O_{12}$	q	104-8132
Ytterbium Iron Gallium Oxide		
$Yb_3Fe_{5-x}Ga_xO_{12}$		
see Ytterbium Gallium Ferrate $Yb_3Ga_xFe_{5-x}O_{12}$	q	110-8059
Ytterbium Iron Oxide $Yb_3Fe_5O_{12}$		
see tri- Ytterbium (III) penta- Ferrate (III)		
$Yb_3Fe_5O_{12}$	q	110-0202
Ytterbium Manganate $YbMnO_3$	b	119-0127
Ytterbium Manganese Ferrate $YbMn_xFe_{1-x}O_3$	q	110-8106
Ytterbium Nitride YbN	df	120-8119
Ytterbium sesqui- Oxide Yb_2O_3	bjsu	122-0208
Ytterbium Oxide Carbonate $Yb_2O_2(CO_3)$	q	106-8275
Ytterbium Scandium Ferrate $Yb_3Sc_xFe_{5-x}O_{12}$	a	110-8164
Ytterbium Selenide $YbSe$	adf	126-8089
Ytterbium tetra- Selenodigallate $YbGa_2Se_4$	j	111-8210
di- Ytterbium penta- Selenogermanate Yb_2GeSe_5	fjt	111-8057
Ytterbium Sulfide YbS	adf	126-8088
Ytterbium Sulfoxylate Yb_2SO_2	ahnpq	122-8068
Ytterbium Telluride $YbTe$	adfh	127-8010
Ytterbium tetra- Thiodialuminate $YbAl_2S_4$	j	102-8498
Ytterbium tetra- Thiodigallate $YbGa_2S_4$	jm	111-8209
Ytterbium tri- Thioindate $YbInS_3$	f	114-8095
Ytterbium Vanadate $YbVO_3$	q	122-8083
Ytterbium - Zinc $YbZn_{12}$	jq	132-8002
Ytterbium - Zinc Yb_2Zn_{17}	q	132-8003
Yttria Y_2O_3		
see Yttrium sesqui- Oxide Y_2O_3	bfhijlmpqstu	122-0037
Yttrium Aluminate $YAlO_3$	ahms	102-8074
tri- Yttrium penta- Aluminate $Y_3Al_5O_{12}$	ahimstv	102-0250
Yttrium Aluminide YAl	m	102-8076
Yttrium di- Aluminide YAl_2	j	102-8325
Yttrium Aluminum Borate $YAl_3B_4O_{12}$	h	102-8205

Property: a. Absorption coefficient; **b.** Dielectric constant; **c.** Dielectric strength; **d.** Energy band structure; **e.** Effective mass; **f.** Energy gap; **g.** Electric hysteresis; **h.** Energy level; **i.** Electron emission properties; **j.** Electrical resistivity; **k.** Magnetoelectric properties; **l.** Hall coefficient; **m.** Luminescence properties; **n.** Magnetic hysteresis; **o.** Mobility; **p.** Magnetomechanical properties; **q.** Magnetic susceptibility; **r.** Photoelectronic properties; **s.** Refractive index; **t.** Thermoelectric properties; **u.** Work function; **v.** Piezoelectric properties.

Substance Name	Property	Number
Yttrium Aluminum Ferrate $YAl_xFe_{1-x}O_3$	a	102-8226
Yttrium Aluminum Garnet see tri-Yttrium penta-Aluminate $Y_3Al_5O_{12}$	ahimstv	102-0250
Yttrium Arsenate $YAsO_4$	hp	102-0369
Yttrium Arsenide YAs	f	102-8349
Yttrium Bismuth Aluminum Ferrate $Y_xBi_{3-x}Al_yFe_{5-y}O_{12}$	an	102-8343
Yttrium Bismuth Ferrate $Y_{3-x}Bi_xFe_5O_{12}$	a	104-8155
Yttrium Bismuth Gallium Ferrate $Y_2BiGa_xFe_{5-x}O_{12}$	ans	104-8445
Yttrium Bismuth Gallium Ferrate $Y_{3-x}Bi_xGa_yFe_{5-y}O_{12}$	an	104-8293
Yttrium hexa-Boride YB_6	j	104-8137
Yttrium dodeca-Boride YB_{12}	q	104-8138
Yttrium Calcium Bismuth Ferrate $Y_{3-x-y}Ca_xBi_yFe_5O_{12}$	q	104-8181
Yttrium Calcium Bismuth Zirconium Ferrate $Y_{3-x-y}Ca_xBi_yZr_zFe_{5-z}O_{12}$	q	104-8182
Yttrium Calcium Germanium Ferrate $Y_{3-x}Ca_xGe_yFe_{5-y}O_{12}$	q	106-8321
Yttrium Calcium Silicon Ferrate $Y_{3-x}Ca_xSi_yFe_{5-y}O_{12}$	q	106-8320
Yttrium Calcium Tin Ferrate $Y_{3-x}Ca_xSn_yFe_{5-y}O_{12}$	q	106-8319
Yttrium Calcium Zirconium Ferrate $Y_{3-x}Ca_xZr_yFe_{5-y}O_{12}$	q	106-8318
Yttrium Carbide YC_{1-x}	jqt	106-8562
Yttrium sesqui-Carbide Y_2C_3	j	106-0710
Yttrium Cerium Aluminate $Y_{3-x}Ce_xAl_5O_{12}$	m	102-8146
Yttrium Cerium Ferrate $Y_{3-x}Ce_xFe_5O_{12}$	p	106-8162
Yttrium tri-Chloride YCl_3	j	106-0354
Yttrium Chromate (III) $YCrO_3$	afjq	106-1296
Yttrium Chromium Ferrate $YCr_xFe_{1-x}O_3$	q	106-8231
Yttrium Chromium Ferrate $Y_3Cr_xFe_{5-x}O_3$	q	106-8252
Yttrium-Cobalt YCo_2	q	106-8779
Yttrium-Cobalt YCo_3	q	106-8605
Yttrium-Cobalt YCo_5	npq	106-8217
Yttrium-Cobalt Y_2Co_7	q	106-8604
Yttrium-Cobalt Y_2Co_{17}	npq	106-8547
Yttrium Cobalt Aluminide $Y_2Co_xAl_{17-x}$	np	102-8431
Yttrium-Cobalt-Copper YCo_xCu_{5-x}	n	106-8743
Yttrium Cobalt Ferrate $YCo_xFe_{1-x}O_3$	pq	106-8232
Yttrium Cobalt Germanate $Y_{3-y-z}Co_{x+y}Ge_{5-x+z}O_{12}$	npq	106-8373
Yttrium-Cobalt-Germanium YCo_2Ge_2	oq	106-8171
Yttrium Cobalt Germanium Ferrate $Y_3Co_xGe_yFe_{5-x-y}O_{12}$	npq	106-8369
Yttrium-Cobalt-Iron YCo_4Fe	q	106-8717
Yttrium-Cobalt-Iron $Y_2Co_{17-x}Fe_x$	np	106-8327
Yttrium-Cobalt-Iron-Copper $YCo_xFe_yCu_{5-x-y}$	n	106-8744
Yttrium Cobalt Iron Oxide $YCo_xFe_{1-x}O_3$ see Yttrium Cobalt Ferrate $YCo_xFe_{1-x}O_3$	pq	106-8232
Yttrium Europium Aluminum Ferrate $Y_xEu_{3-x}Al_yFe_{5-y}O_{12}$	n	102-8101
Yttrium Europium Ferrate $Y_xEu_{3-x}Fe_5O_{12}$	p	109-8023
Yttrium Europium Gallium Ferrate $Y_xEu_{3-x}GaFe_4O_{12}$	s	109-8100
Yttrium Europium Gallium Ferrate $Y_xEu_{3-x}Ga_yFe_{5-y}O_{12}$	knpq	109-8017
Yttrium Ferrate (III) $YFeO_3$	npq	110-0369
tri-Yttrium penta-Ferrate (III) $Y_3Fe_5O_{12}$	abcdfhjklnopqrst	110-0194
Yttrium tri-Fluoride YF_3	hjm	110-0157
Yttrium Gadolinium Aluminum Ferrate $Y_xGd_{3-x}Al_yFe_{5-y}O_{12}$	b	102-8385
Yttrium Gadolinium Cerium Aluminate $Y_{3-x-y}Gd_xCe_yAl_5O_{12}$	m	102-8145
Yttrium Gadolinium Europium Aluminum Ferrate $Y_{3-x-y}Gd_xEu_yAl_zFe_{5-z}O_{12}$	n	102-8113
Yttrium Gadolinium Ferrate $Y_xGd_{3-x}Fe_5O_{12}$	aqs	110-8222
Yttrium Gadolinium Gallium Ferrate $Y_{3-x}Gd_xGa_yFe_{5-y}O_{12}$	npqt	110-8038
Yttrium Gadolinium Gallium Lead Ferrate $Y_{3-x-y}Gd_xGa_zPb_yFe_{5-z}O_{12}$	n	110-8056
Yttrium Gadolinium Lanthanum Gallium Ferrate $Y_{3-x-y}Gd_xLa_yGa_zFe_{5-z}O_{12}$	n	110-8055
tri-Yttrium penta-Gallate $Y_3Ga_5O_{12}$	adms	111-8087
Yttrium Gallium Aluminate $Y_3Ga_xAl_{5-x}O_{12}$	ms	102-8200
Yttrium Gallium Ferrate $Y_3Ga_xFe_{5-x}O_{12}$	afhnpqs	110-8051
Yttrium Germanium Sulfide Y_2GeS_5 see di-Yttrium penta-Thiogermanate Y_2GeS_5	fjo	111-8134
Yttrium Hydroxide $Y(OH)_3$	h	112-0303
Yttrium Indium Ferrate $Y_3In_xFe_{5-x}O_{12}$	n	110-8052
Yttrium di-Iridide YIr_2	j	114-8100
Yttrium-Iron YFe_2	jnq	110-8132
Yttrium-Iron YFe_3	nq	110-8074
Yttrium-Iron Y_2Fe_{17}	nq	110-8128
Yttrium-Iron Y_6Fe_{23}	q	110-8130
Yttrium Iron Aluminum Bismuth Oxide $Y_{3-x}Fe_{5-y}Al_yBi_xO_{12}$ see Yttrium Bismuth Aluminum Ferrate $Y_xBi_{3-x}Al_yFe_{5-y}O_{12}$	an	102-8343
Yttrium Iron Bismuth Oxide $Y_{3-x}Fe_5Bi_xO_{12}$ see Yttrium Bismuth Ferrate $Y_{3-x}Bi_xFe_5O_{12}$	a	104-8155
Yttrium Iron Gallium Bismuth Oxide $Y_{3-x}Fe_{5-y}Ga_yBi_xO_{12}$ see Yttrium Bismuth Gallium Ferrate $Y_{3-x}Bi_xGa_yFe_{5-y}O_{12}$	an	104-8293
Yttrium Iron Gallium Oxide $Y_3Fe_{5-x}Ga_xO_{12}$ see Yttrium Gallium Ferrate $Y_3Ga_xFe_{5-x}O_{12}$	afhnpqs	110-8051
Yttrium Iron Garnet $Y_3Fe_5O_{12}$ see tri-Yttrium penta-Ferrate (III) $Y_3Fe_5O_{12}$	abcdfhjklnopqrst	110-0194
Yttrium Iron Indium Oxide $Y_3Fe_{5-x}In_xO_{12}$ see Yttrium Indium Ferrate $Y_3In_xFe_{5-x}O_{12}$	n	110-8052
Yttrium Iron Silicon Oxide $Y_3Fe_{5-x}Si_xO_{12}$ see Yttrium Silicon Ferrate $Y_3Si_xFe_{5-x}O_{12}$	abnqr	110-8176
Yttrium-Lead YPb_3 see Yttrium tri-Plumbide YPb_3	q	123-8098
Yttrium Magnesium Silicon Ferrate $Y_{3-x}Mg_xSi_yFe_{5-y}O_{12}$	q	110-8104
Yttrium Manganate (III) $YMnO_3$	b	119-0126
Yttrium-Manganese-Iron $Y_6Mn_xFe_{23-x}$	nq	110-8219
Yttrium Neodymium Ferrate $Y_xNd_{3-x}Fe_5O_{12}$	np	110-8239
Yttrium-Nickel YNi_3	q	120-8056
Yttrium-Nickel YNi_5	q	120-8054
Yttrium-Nickel Y_2Ni_7	q	120-8055
Yttrium-Nickel Y_2Ni_{17}	q	120-8053
Yttrium Nickel Germanium Ferrate $Y_3Ni_xGe_yFe_{5-x-y}O_{12}$	npq	110-8127
Yttrium Niobate (V) $YNbO_3$	hm	120-8072
Yttrium Nitride YN	df	120-8115
Yttrium di-Osmide YOs_2	j	122-8144
Yttrium mono-Oxide YO	h	122-8073
Yttrium sesqui-Oxide Y_2O_3	bfhijlmpqstu	122-0037
Yttrium Oxide Y_2O_{3-x}	i	122-8024
di-Yttrium di-Oxosulfate Y_2SO_2 see di-Yttrium Sulfoxylate Y_2SO_2	hm	122-8025
di-Yttrium hexa-Oxosulfate Y_2SO_6	m	122-8064
Yttrium Phosphate YPO_4	hmpq	122-0296
Yttrium di-Platinide YPt_2	j	123-8106
Yttrium tri-Plumbide YPb_3	q	123-8098
Yttrium di-Rhenide YRe_2	j	125-8046
Yttrium di-Rhodide YRh_2	j	125-8043
Yttrium di-Ruthenide YRu_2	j	125-8045
Yttrium Ruthenium Ferrate $Y_3Ru_xFe_{5-x}O_{12}$	p	110-8058
Yttrium Samarium Gallium Ferrate $Y_{3-x}Sm_xGa_yFe_{5-y}O_{12}$	npq	110-8098
Yttrium Scandium Aluminate $Y_3Sc_2Al_3O_{12}$	s	102-8490
Yttrium Scandium Ferrate $Y_3Sc_xFe_{5-x}O_{12}$	npq	110-8103
tri-Yttrium tetra-Selenide Y_3Se_4	j	126-8127
Yttrium mono-Silicide YSi	d	126-8157

Property: **a.** Absorption coefficient; **b.** Dielectric constant; **c.** Dielectric strength; **d.** Energy band structure; **e.** Effective mass; **f.** Energy gap; **g.** Electric hysteresis; **h.** Energy level; **i.** Electron emission properties; **j.** Electrical resistivity; **k.** Magnetoelectric properties; **l.** Hall coefficient; **m.** Luminescence properties; **n.** Magnetic hysteresis; **o.** Mobility; **p.** Magnetomechanical properties; **q.** Magnetic susceptibility; **r.** Photoelectronic properties; **s.** Refractive index; **t.** Thermoelectric properties; **u.** Work function; **v.** Piezoelectric properties.

Substance Name	Property	Number
Yttrium di- Silicide YSi_2	d	126-8158
Yttrium Silicon Ferrate $Y_3Si_xFe_{5-x}O_{12}$	abnqr	110-8176
Yttrium - Silver YAg	j	102-8328
Yttrium tri- Stannide YSn_3	q	126-8145
Yttrium Sulfate Y_2SO_6		
see di- Yttrium hexa- Oxosulfate Y_2SO_6	m	122-8064
di- Yttrium Sulfoxylate Y_2SO_2	hm	122-8025
Yttrium Tantalate $YTaO_4$	h	122-8077
Yttrium sesqui- Telluride Y_2Te_3	j	127-8023
Yttrium Terbium Europium Gallium Ferrate $Y_xTb_yEu_{3-x-y}Ga_zFe_{5-z}O_{12}$	n	110-8178
Yttrium Terbium Ferrate $Y_xTb_{3-x}Fe_5O_{12}$	nq	110-8276
di- Yttrium penta- Thiogermanate Y_2GeS_5	fjo	111-8134
Yttrium Thulium Europium Gallium Ferrate $Y_{3-x-y}Tm_xEu_yGa_zFe_{5-z}O_{12}$	n	109-8025
Yttrium Thulium Gadolinium Gallium Ferrate $Y_{3-x-y}Tm_xGd_yGa_zFe_{5-z}O_{12}$	anps	110-8044
Yttrium Thulium Gallium Ferrate $Y_2TmGaFe_4O_{12}$	s	110-8277
Yttrium - Tin YSn_3		
see Yttrium tri- Stannide YSn_3	q	126-8145
Yttrium Vanadate (I I I) YVO_3	jq	122-8080
Yttrium Vanadate (V) YVO_4	bhmpq	122-8038
Yttrium Ytterbium Erbium tri- Fluoride $Y_{1-x-y}Yb_xEr_yF_3$	m	109-8030
Yttrium Ytterbium Europium Aluminum Ferrate $Y_{3-x-y}Yb_xEu_yAl_zFe_{5-z}O_{12}$	n	102-8089
Yttrium Ytterbium Gadolinium Aluminum Ferrate $Y_{3-x-y}Yb_zGd_yAl_zFe_{5-z}O_{12}$	ns	102-8112
Yttrium Ytterbium Gadolinium Europium Gallium Aluminum Ferrate $(YYbGdEu)_3(GaAlFe)_5O_{12}$	p	102-8115
Yttrium Ytterbium Gadolinium Europium Gallium Ferrate $(YYbGdEu)_3(GaFe)_5O_{12}$	n	109-8026
Yttrium Ytterbium Gadolinium Gallium Aluminum Ferrate $(YYbGd)_3(GaAlFe)_5O_{12}$	p	102-8114
Yttrium Ytterbium Gadolinium Gallium Ferrate $Y_{3-x-y}Yb_xGd_yGa_zFe_{5-x}O_{12}$	anq	110-8054
Yttrium - Zinc YZn	dehjlo	132-8001
Zinc Aluminate $ZnAl_2O_4$	h	102-0185
Zinc mono- Antimonide $ZnSb$	aefjklost	126-8026
Zinc di- Arsenide $ZnAs_2$	fj	102-8332
tri- Zinc di- Arsenide Zn_3As_2	fhjklot	102-8310
Zinc Arsenide Phosphide $Zn_3As_xP_{2-x}$	j	102-8484
see also tri- Zinc Diarsenide $\geq$ tri- Zinc Diphosphide		508-0544
see also tri- Zinc Diphosphide $\geq$ tri- Zinc Diarsenide		508-0545
Zinc di- Arsenidogermanate $ZnGeAs_2$	defjost	102-8179
Zinc Arsenidophosphidosilicate $ZnSiAsP$	h	102-8384
Zinc Arsenidophosphidosilicate $ZnSiAs_xP_{2-x}$	fh	102-8119
Zinc di- Arsenidosilicate $ZnSiAs_2$	abefhjklorst	102-8084
Zinc di- Arsenidostannate $ZnSnAs_2$	aefjlost	102-8180
Zinc Borate $Zn_4B_6O_{13}$	i	104-8442
Zinc Bromide $ZnBr_2$	bj	104-0213
Zinc Carbide ZnC	u	106-8548
Zinc Carbonate $ZnCO_3$	s	106-0495
Zinc Chloride $ZnCl_2$	bj	106-0180
Zinc Ferrite $ZnFe_2O_4$	jnq	110-8254
Zinc Ferrite $Zn_xFe_{3-x}O_4$	j	110-8048
Zinc Fluoride ZnF_2	abhjnp	110-0020
Zinc Gallate $ZnGa_2O_4$	hm	111-8034
Zinc Germanium di- Arsenide $ZnGeAs_2$		
see Zinc di- Arsenidogermanate $ZnGeAs_2$	defjost	102-8179
Zinc Germanium di- Phosphide $ZnGeP_2$		
see Zinc di- Phosphidogermanate $ZnGeP_2$	abdfhijlostv	111-0050
Zinc di- Indium tetra- Selenide $ZnIn_2Se_4$		
see Zinc tetra- Selenodiindate $ZnIn_2Se_4$	fr	114-8042
Zinc di- Indium tetra- Sulfide $ZnIn_2S_4$		
see Zinc tetra- Thiodiindate $ZnIn_2S_4$	adjmrs	114-8066
Zinc di- Indium tetra- Telluride $ZnIn_2Te_4$		
see Zinc tetra- Tellurodiindate $ZnIn_2Te_4$	fr	114-8043
Zinc Iodide ZnI_2	j	114-0053
Zinc Oxide ZnO	a-fhijklmoqrstuv	122-0023

Substance Name	Property	Number
Zinc Phosphate $Zn_3(PO_4)_2$	m	122-8114
Zinc Phosphide ZnP_2	adfjmot	123-0048
tri- Zinc di- Phosphide Zn_3P_2	dfhjl	123-8104
Zinc di- Phosphidogermanate $ZnGeP_2$	abdfhijlostv	111-0050
Zinc di- Phosphidosilicate $ZnSiP_2$	aefhijlmors	123-0032
Zinc di- Phosphidostannate $ZnSnP_2$	efjos	123-0042
Zinc Selenide $ZnSe$	a-fhijlmoqrstuv	126-8052
see also Irtran 4 (Kodak) $ZnSe$		126-8074
Zinc Selenide Sulfide $ZnSe_xS_{1-x}$	fhjms	126-8048
see also Zinc Selenide $\geq$ Zinc Sulfide		508-0173
see also Zinc Sulfide $\geq$ Zinc Selenide		508-0172
Zinc tetra- Selenodichromate $ZnCr_2Se_4$	fjqt	106-8270
Zinc tetra- Selenodiindate $ZnIn_2Se_4$	fr	114-8042
Zinc Silicate Zn_2SiO_4	m	122-0027
Zinc Silicon di- Arsenide $ZnSiAs_2$		
see Zinc di- Arsenidosilicate $ZnSiAs_2$	abefhjklorst	102-8084
Zinc Silicon Arsenide Phosphide $ZnSiAsP$		
see Zinc Arsenidophosphidosilicate $ZnSiAsP$	h	102-8384
Zinc Silicon Arsenide Phosphide $ZnSiAs_xP_{2-x}$		
see Zinc Arsenidophosphidosilicate $ZnSiAs_xP_{2-x}$	fh	102-8119
Zinc Silicon Phosphide $ZnSiP_2$		
see Zinc di- Phosphidosilicate $ZnSiP_2$	aefhijlmors	123-0032
Zinc Sulfide ZnS	abdefhijmoqrstuv	126-0005
see also Irtran 2 (Kodak) ZnS		126-8073
see also Wurtzite ZnS		521-8026
see also Zinc Blende ZnS		521-0086
Zinc Telluride $ZnTe$	abdefhijlmoq-v	127-8004
Zinc Telluride Selenide $ZnTe_xSe_{1-x}$	afhjmos	126-8049
see also Zinc Selenide $\geq$ Zinc Telluride		508-0530
see also Zinc Telluride $\geq$ Zinc Selenide		508-0529
Zinc Telluride Sulfide $ZnTe_xS_{1-x}$	fhms	126-8050
see also Zinc Sulfide $\geq$ Zinc Telluride		508-0525
see also Zinc Telluride $\geq$ Zinc Sulfide		508-0526
Zinc tetra- Tellurodiindate $ZnIn_2Te_4$	fr	114-8043
Zinc tetra- Thiodiindate $ZnIn_2S_4$	adjmrs	114-8066
Zinc Tin di- Antimonide $ZnSnSb_2$	adfjlo	126-8060
Zinc Tin di- Arsenide $ZnSnAs_2$		
see Zinc di- Arsenidostannate $ZnSnAs_2$	aefjlost	102-8180
Zinc Tin di- Phosphide $ZnSnP_2$		
see Zinc di- Phosphidostannate $ZnSnP_2$	efjos	123-0042
Zinc Tungstate (V I) $ZnWO_4$	abm	122-0199
Zinc Vanadate (I I I) ZnV_2O_4	aq	122-8027
Zinc Vanadate $Zn_xV_{3-x}O_4$	fjt	122-8113
Zirconia		
see Zirconium di- Oxide ZrO_2	abcfhijmoqstu	122-0004
Zirconium Boride ZrB	iu	104-8284
Zirconium di- Boride ZrB_2	abejloqrstu	104-8156
Zirconium dodeca- Boride ZrB_{12}	jqu	104-8146
Zirconium mono- Carbide ZrC	ijlqtu	106-0308
Zirconium Carbide ZrC_{1-x}	ijkloqtu	106-0937
Zirconium Carbide Oxide ZrC_xO_{1-x}	j	106-8762
Zirconium tetra- Chloride $ZrCl_4$	fj	106-0100
tri- Zirconium Cobalt Oxide Zr_3CoO		
see Cobalt Zirconate $CoZr_3O$	q	106-8656
Zirconium di- Ferride $ZrFe_2$	jq	110-8262
tri- Zirconium Ferride Zr_3Fe	q	110-8230
Zirconium mono- Germanide $ZrGe$	jlqt	111-8202
Zirconium di- Germanide $ZrGe_2$	jlqt	111-8140
tri- Zirconium Germanide Zr_3Ge	jlqt	111-8141
penta- Zirconium tri- Germanide Zr_5Ge_3	jlqt	111-8142
Zirconium - Gold Zr_3Au	j	102-8322
Zirconium Hydrogen Chloride $ZrHCl_3$	b	106-8354
Zirconium - Iron $ZrFe_2$		
see Zirconium di- Ferride $ZrFe_2$	jq	110-8262
Zirconium - Iron Zr_3Fe		
see tri- Zirconium Ferride Zr_3Fe	q	110-8230
Zirconium Lead Oxide $ZrPbO_3$		
see Lead (I I) Zirconate $PbZrO_3$	bcgj	122-0292
tri- Zirconium Nickel Oxide Zr_3NiO	q	120-8120
Zirconium Niobide $ZrNb$	n	120-8048
Zirconium Niobium Carbide $Zr_xNb_{1-x}C$	jloqt	106-8333
Zirconium Niobium Carbide $Zr_xNb_{1-x}C_{1-y}$	jloqt	106-8334

Property: a. Absorption coefficient; **b.** Dielectric constant; **c.** Dielectric strength; **d.** Energy band structure; **e.** Effective mass; **f.** Energy gap; **g.** Electric hysteresis; **h.** Energy level; **i.** Electron emission properties; **j.** Electrical resistivity; **k.** Magnetoelectric properties; **l.** Hall coefficient; **m.** Luminescence properties; **n.** Magnetic hysteresis; **o.** Mobility; **p.** Magnetomechanical properties; **q.** Magnetic susceptibility; **r.** Photoelectronic properties; **s.** Refractive index; **t.** Thermoelectric properties; **u.** Work function; **v.** Piezoelectric properties.

Substance Name	Property	Number
Zirconium Niobium Indide $Zr_x Nb_3 In_{1-x}$		
see Niobium Indium Zirconide $Nb_3 In_x Zr_{1-x}$	j	114-8082
Zirconium mono-Nitride $Zr N$	ijltu	120-0017
Zirconium Nitride $Zr N_{1-x}$	q	120-8098
Zirconium mono-Oxide $Zr O$	ahs	122-0139
Zirconium di-Oxide $Zr O_2$	abcfhijmoqstu	122-0004
Zirconium Oxide $Zr O_{2-x}$	i	122-0338
Zirconium - Rhodium $Zr_2 Rh$	j	125-8030
Zirconium - Rhodium $Zr_3 Rh$	j	125-8032
Zirconium Silicate $Zr Si O_4$	hjs	122-8070
see also Zircon $Zr Si O_4$		521-0250
Zirconium mono-Silicide $Zr Si$	d	126-8150
Zirconium di-Silicide $Zr Si_2$	dij	126-8065
di-Zirconium Silicide $Zr_2 Si$	d	126-8151
penta-Zirconium tri-Silicide $Zr_5 Si_3$	dij	126-8066
Zirconium di-Sulfide $Zr S_2$	bfjlot	126-0022
Zirconium tri-Sulfide $Zr S_3$	aj	126-8084
Zirconium Sulfide $Zr S_{1-x}$	j	126-8054
Zirconium Tantalum Sulfide $Zr_x Ta_{1-x} S_2$	j	126-8093
Zirconium Telluride $Zr Te_2$	b	127-8015
Zirconium Titanium Lead Oxide		
$Zr_{1-x} Ti_x Pb O_3$		
see Lead Zirconium Titanate $Pb Zr_x Ti_{1-x} O_3$	bcgjnqrtv	122-0196
Zirconium Titanium Lead Tin Oxide		
$Zr_x Ti_y Pb Sn_{1-x-y} O_3$		
see Lead Tin Zirconium Titanate		
$Pb Sn_x Zr_y Ti_{1-x-y} O_3$	g	122-8042
Zirconium Titanium Niobium Lead Oxide		
$Zr_x Ti_y Nb_z Pb_{1-x-y-z} O_3$		
see Lead Zirconium Titanium Niobate		
$Pb_x Zr_y Ti_z Nb_{1-x-y-z} O_3$	qs	120-8126
Zirconium Tungsten Carbide $Zr_x W_{1-x} C$	j	106-1577
see also Tungsten Monocarbide ≥ Zirconium Monocarbide		508-0458
see also Zirconium Monocarbide ≥ Tungsten Monocarbide		508-0279
Zirconium - Vanadium $Zr V_2$	jq	129-8001
Zirconium - Vanadium - Ruthenium $Zr V_x Ru_{2-x}$	q	125-8035
Zirconium - Zinc $Zr Zn_2$	dhpq	133-8001
Zirconium - Zinc $Zr Zn_{22}$	j	133-8002

Part B
SEARCH PARAMETERS

PART B

USE OF SEARCH PARAMETERS

Part B is arranged in 22 chapters, each chapter representing a specific property. Within each chapter the ordering sequence is substance number, physical state, and accession number. The last column gives the EPIC accession number pertaining to the document retrieved. The sample code designations for the various search parameters need not be memorized since they are interpreted at the bottom of each page of this part of the volume.

It is readily evident that substance numbers link this portion of the volume with the *Materials Directory* (Part A), and the EPIC accession numbers provide the link to the *Bibliography* (Part C). The general procedure for retrieval of references in making literature searches is as follows:

1. Locate and record the seven-digit substance number from the *Materials Directory* (Part A) for the material desired and note if desired properties are listed.
2. Locate seven-digit substance number in appropriate property chapters in *Search Parameters* (Part B). [*Note:* some cross-references (see also entry) may be in a different volume.]
3. Use as many of the five search parameters (physical state, subject, language, temperature, and year) as desired to locate and record EPIC accession numbers of interest.
4. Use the selected EPIC accession numbers to locate the complete bibliographic citations in the *Bibliography* (Part C).

Chapter 1 Absorption Coefficient

Substance Number	Phys. State	Subject	Language	Temperature	Year	EPIC Number
100-0045	D	S	E	N	1975	95469
0045	S	D	E	L	1974	55726
0045	S	T	E	L	1974	55726
0045	S	S	E	N	1973	56767
0045	S	S	E	N	1972	60888
0045	S	S	E	N	1974	62289
0045	S	S	E	N	1974	62306
0045	S	T	E	N	1960	64411
0045	S	S	E	N	1974	64477
0045	S	S	E	N	1973	68847
0045	S	S	E	N	1971	70398
0045	S	S	E	N	1973	82686
0045	S	S	E	N	1975	97348
0045	S	S	E	N	1976	101494
0045	S	S	E	N	1975	102056
0045	S	S	E	N	1975	103142
0045	T	S	E	N	1973	82686
0045	T	S	E	N	1975	103142
0055	A	T	E	N	1973	55113
0055	A	S	E	N	1972	62387
0055	A	T	E	N	1975	88214
0055	A	T	E	N	1974	92433
0055	A	S	E	N	1974	93380
0055	A	T	E	N	1975	93382
0055	A	T	E	N	1975	93531
0055	D	T	R	N	1973	50227
0055	D	T	E	N	1973	50228
0055	D	T	R	N	1973	51557
0055	D	T	E	N	1973	53688
0055	D	T	E	N	1973	55729
0055	D	T	E	N	1970	59691
0055	D	T	R	N	1972	62703
0055	D	T	E	L	1972	63848
0055	D	T	E	N	1972	65300
0055	D	T	R	N	1970	70339
0055	D	T	E	N	1971	70652
0055	D	T	E	N	1971	79434
0055	D	T	R	N	1975	93621
0055	D	S	E	N	1975	95469
0055	D	T	R	N	1975	95776
0055	D	T	E	N	1975	95777
0055	D	T	E	N	1975	102035
0055	P	T	R	N	1971	63424
0055	P	T	E	N	1971	67075
0055	S	T	R	N	1973	50273
0055	S	T	E	N	1973	50274
0055	S	T	R	N	1973	50309
0055	S	T	E	N	1973	50310
0055	S	T	R	N	1973	50682
0055	S	T	E	N	1973	52024
0055	S	T	E	N	1973	52428
0055	S	T	R	N	1973	52888
0055	S	T	E	N	1974	52889
0055	S	E	E	N	1972	53519
0055	S	T	E	N	1973	53573
0055	S	T	E	N	1973	53939
0055	S	T	R	N	1973	54183
0055	S	T	E	N	1973	54184
0055	S	T	R	N	1973	54466
0055	S	T	E	N	1973	54467
0055	S	T	R	N	1973	54978
0055	S	T	E	N	1974	54979
0055	S	T	R	L	1973	55294
0055	S	T	R	N	1973	55294
0055	S	T	E	N	1972	55728
0055	S	S	E	N	1973	56749
0055	S	S	E	N	1973	56767
0055	S	T	R	N	1974	58090
0055	S	T	E	N	1974	58091
0055	S	S	E	N	1974	58810
0055	S	T	E	L	1974	59268
0055	S	T	E	N	1974	59268
0055	S	S	E	N	1974	59353
0055	S	T	G	N	1971	59433
0055	S	T	E	N	1971	59614
0055	S	T	R	N	1972	60721
0055	S	T	E	N	1973	60722
0055	S	T	R	L	1974	61409
0055	S	E	R	L	1971	61558
0055	S	T	R	N	1974	61970
0055	S	T	E	N	1974	61971
0055	S	T	E	N	1969	62248
0055	S	S	E	N	1974	62289
0055	S	S	E	N	1974	62306
0055	S	T	R	N	1972	62687
0055	S	T	R	N	1973	62706
0055	S	T	R	N	1972	62713
0055	S	T	R	N	1973	62730
0055	S	S	E	N	1973	62815
0055	S	T	R	N	1972	62853
0055	S	T	R	N	1972	62858
0055	S	T	E	N	1970	63585
0055	S	T	E	N	1970	63586
0055	S	T	E	N	1971	63593
0055	S	T	R	N	1972	63697

Substance Number	Phys. State	Subject	Language	Temperature	Year	EPIC Number
100-0055	S	T	R	N	1972	63699
0055	S	T	E	N	1972	63811
0055	S	T	E	N	1972	64415
0055	S	S	E	N	1974	64477
0055	S	S	E	N	1973	64495
0055	S	T	R	N	1974	64576
0055	S	T	R	N	1970	64844
0055	S	T	E	N	1970	64845
0055	S	T	E	N	1973	65179
0055	S	T	E	N	1973	65181
0055	S	T	E	L	1974	65250
0055	S	T	E	N	1974	65250
0055	S	T	E	N	1973	65302
0055	S	T	E	N	1973	65309
0055	S	T	E	N	1973	65326
0055	S	T	E	N	1972	65339
0055	S	T	E	N	1972	65341
0055	S	E	E	N	1975	65439
0055	S	E	E	L	1971	65909
0055	S	T	R	N	1973	66431
0055	S	T	E	N	1974	66432
0055	S	S	E	N	1968	67894
0055	S	S	E	N	1971	70398
0055	S	T	E	N	1971	70499
0055	S	T	E	L	1970	70646
0055	S	T	E	N	1970	70646
0055	S	T	E	N	1971	70647
0055	S	S	E	N	1971	70669
0055	S	T	E	N	1971	70669
0055	S	T	G	N	1974	71582
0055	S	T	R	N	1974	78324
0055	S	T	E	N	1975	78325
0055	S	E	G	L	1971	78856
0055	S	E	G	N	1971	78856
0055	S	T	E	N	1975	85290
0055	S	T	E	L	1973	86425
0055	S	T	R	N	1975	86845
0055	S	T	E	N	1975	86846
0055	S	T	E	N	1974	86907
0055	S	S	R	N	1973	87035
0055	S	S	E	N	1973	87036
0055	S	T	R	L	1974	87296
0055	S	T	E	L	1975	87297
0055	S	T	R	N	1974	89251
0055	S	T	E	N	1974	89252
0055	S	T	E	N	1975	91991
0055	S	T	E	L	1974	95265
0055	S	E	E	N	1975	96639
0055	S	T	E	N	1975	96639
0055	S	S	E	N	1975	97348
0055	S	E	R	N	1976	99127
0055	S	T	R	N	1976	99127
0055	S	T	E	N	1975	99140
0055	S	E	E	N	1976	99855
0055	S	T	E	N	1976	99855
0055	S	T	E	N	1976	100631
0055	S	T	E	N	1976	101470
0055	S	T	E	N	1976	101849
0055	S	S	E	N	1975	102056
0055	S	S	E	N	1976	102151
0055	S	S	E	N	1975	103142
0055	S	T	E	N	1976	103155
0055	T	E	R	N	1973	54397
0055	T	T	R	N	1973	54397
0055	T	E	E	N	1973	54398
0055	T	T	E	N	1973	54398
0055	T	T	E	N	1972	63961
0055	T	T	O	N	1974	88134
0055	T	E	E	N	1976	99741
0055	T	S	E	N	1975	103142
8003	D	T	R	N	1972	49455
8003	D	D	E	N	1973	57871
8003	D	T	E	N	1973	57871
8003	D	T	E	N	1974	58090
8003	D	T	E	L	1973	62286
8003	D	T	E	N	1973	62286
8003	D	T	E	N	1974	62306
8003	D	S	E	N	1975	99263
8003	D	S	E	L	1976	99913
8003	S	T	E	N	1973	52040
8003	S	T	E	N	1974	53620
8003	S	T	E	N	1974	53621
8003	S	E	E	N	1974	54352
8003	S	T	E	N	1973	55153
8003	S	S	E	N	1973	56749
8003	S	S	E	N	1973	56767
8003	S	D	E	N	1974	58822
8003	S	T	E	N	1974	58822
8003	S	S	E	N	1974	59353
8003	S	T	R	N	1971	59579
8003	S	T	E	N	1971	61328
8003	S	S	E	N	1974	62289
8003	S	T	E	N	1974	62306
8003	S	T	E	N	1974	62314
8003	S	S	E	N	1972	62384

Substance Number	Phys. State	Subject	Language	Temperature	Year	EPIC Number
100-8003	S	T	E	N	1972	62384
8003	S	T	E	N	1974	62547
8003	S	S	E	N	1973	62815
8003	S	T	E	N	1972	63978
8003	S	T	E	N	1954	64426
8003	S	S	E	N	1974	64477
8003	S	S	E	N	1973	64495
8003	S	T	E	N	1973	68849
8003	S	T	E	N	1973	68851
8003	S	T	E	N	1973	68852
8003	S	T	E	N	1973	68855
8003	S	S	E	N	1971	70398
8003	S	T	R	N	1973	70949
8003	S	T	E	N	1973	91481
8003	S	T	E	N	1974	93376
8003	S	T	E	N	1974	96710
8003	S	E	E	N	1976	97298
8003	S	T	E	N	1976	99984
8003	S	S	E	N	1975	101010
8003	S	T	E	N	1975	101010
8003	S	T	E	L	1975	101014
8003	S	T	E	N	1975	101014
8003	S	T	E	N	1975	101015
8003	S	S	E	N	1975	101020
8003	S	S	E	N	1975	101026
8003	S	S	E	N	1975	101034
8003	S	E	E	N	1976	102042
8003	S	S	E	N	1975	102056
8003	S	T	E	N	1976	103350
8007	S	S	E	N	1973	60558
8007	S	T	E	L	1974	68690
8007	S	S	R	N	1973	87035
8007	S	S	E	N	1973	87036
8007	S	S	E	N	1975	101020
8007	S	S	E	N	1975	101033
8007	S	T	E	N	1975	101033
8007	S	S	E	N	1975	101034
8007	T	E	E	N	1976	99741
8008	A	S	E	N	1974	93380
8008	A	S	E	N	1974	94637
8008	A	T	E	N	1975	101030
8008	S	S	E	N	1973	60558
8008	S	T	G	N	1954	66199
8008	S	T	E	L	1974	68690
8008	S	E	G	L	1971	78856
8008	S	E	G	N	1971	78856
8008	S	T	R	N	1975	86845
8008	S	T	E	N	1975	86846
8008	S	S	R	N	1973	87035
8008	S	S	E	N	1973	87036
8008	S	T	E	N	1975	101012
8008	S	S	E	N	1975	101033
8008	S	T	E	N	1975	101033
8008	S	S	E	N	1975	101034
8008	T	S	E	N	1974	94637
8009	S	D	R	N	1973	55068
8009	S	D	E	N	1974	55069
8010	S	S	E	N	1972	53175
8010	T	S	E	N	1972	53175
8015	S	S	E	N	1972	53175
8015	T	S	E	N	1972	53175
8016	A	S	E	N	1975	101027
8016	A	S	E	N	1975	101029
8016	S	S	E	N	1972	59933
8021	S	S	E	N	1972	60888
8043	S	S	E	N	1969	75843
8050	S	E	E	N	1976	97298
8050	S	S	E	N	1975	101010
8050	S	T	E	N	1975	101010
8050	S	S	E	N	1975	101034
8059	S	S	E	N	1972	60888
8074	S	S	E	N	1973	60558
102-0002	D	D	E	L	1974	54565
0002	D	D	E	N	1974	54565
0002	D	S	E	N	1973	56749
0002	L	D	E	H	1967	66317
0002	S	S	E	H	1972	53512
0002	S	S	E	N	1972	53512
0002	S	D	E	N	1974	54024
0002	S	S	E	N	1973	56749
0002	S	D	E	N	1974	57303
0002	S	S	E	N	1974	57303
0002	S	D	E	N	1973	58212
0002	S	S	E	N	1973	58212
0002	S	S	E	N	1974	59353
0002	S	S	E	N	1973	64495
0002	S	S	E	N	1970	65877
0002	S	D	E	N	1972	66229
0002	S	T	E	N	1972	66229
0002	S	T	E	N	1967	66317
0002	S	S	E	N	1965	68323
0002	S	D	E	N	1972	68832
0002	S	D	E	N	1973	68841
0002	S	S	E	N	1964	75892

Phys. State: **A.** Amorphous; **C.** Superconductive; **D.** Doped; **F.** Fibrous or Whisker; **G.** Gas; **I.** Ionized or Plasma; **L.** Liquid; **P.** Powder or Particle; **S.** Solid; **T.** Thin Film
Subject: **D.** Data; **E.** Experiment; **S.** Survey (Review, Compendium, etc.); **T.** Theory
Language: **E.** English; **F.** French; **G.** German; **O.** Other Languages; **R.** Russian
Temperature: **L.** Low (0 to 75K); **N.** Normal (75 to 1273K); **H.** High (above 1273K)

Absorption Coefficient

Substance Number	Phys. State	Subject	Language	Temperature	Year	EPIC Number
102-0002	S	S	E	N	1971	87883
0002	S	D	E	N	1975	88493
0002	S	S	E	N	1975	93181
0002	S	D	E	N	1975	93328
0002	S	D	E	N	1975	94479
0002	S	S	E	N	1974	94636
0002	S	S	E	N	1975	101034
0002	S	D	E	N	1976	101441
0002	S	D	E	N	1975	101668
0002	S	E	E	N	1975	101668
0002	S	S	E	N	1975	101668
0002	S	D	E	N	1976	101851
0002	S	E	E	N	1976	101851
0002	S	T	E	N	1976	101851
0002	S	D	E	N	1976	102042
0002	S	E	E	N	1976	102042
0002	T	D	R	N	1971	61559
0002	T	E	R	N	1971	61559
0002	T	D	E	N	1970	62185
0002	T	T	E	N	1970	62185
0002	T	D	E	N	1971	62190
0002	T	S	E	N	1971	62190
0002	T	D	E	N	1971	65910
0002	T	E	E	N	1971	65910
0002	T	D	E	N	1969	66514
0002	T	T	E	N	1969	66514
0002	T	D	E	N	1974	81418
0002	T	D	E	N	1975	96486
0005	S	D	E	N	1974	58589
0009	D	D	E	L	1974	101643
0009	D	D	E	N	1974	101643
0009	D	T	E	L	1974	101643
0009	D	T	E	N	1974	101643
0009	S	S	E	N	1974	59353
0009	S	D	E	N	1969	62324
0009	S	S	E	N	1973	62815
0009	S	S	E	L	1972	63847
0009	S	S	E	N	1973	64495
0009	S	S	E	N	1924	73267
0009	S	T	E	N	1938	74974
0009	S	S	E	N	1971	87883
0009	T	D	O	L	1965	61141
0009	T	D	O	N	1965	61141
0009	T	S	O	L	1965	61141
0009	T	S	O	N	1965	61141
0010	D	D	R	L	1974	90739
0010	D	D	E	L	1974	95949
0010	L	D	E	N	1963	75554
0010	S	D	E	N	1973	54214
0010	S	T	E	N	1973	54214
0010	S	S	E	N	1974	59353
0010	S	D	R	N	1971	59579
0010	S	T	R	N	1971	59579
0010	S	D	E	N	1971	61328
0010	S	T	E	N	1971	61328
0010	S	S	E	N	1973	62815
0010	S	D	R	N	1972	63699
0010	S	S	E	L	1972	63847
0010	S	S	E	N	1973	64495
0010	S	D	E	N	1972	65341
0010	S	S	E	N	1924	73267
0010	S	D	E	N	1974	80503
0010	S	S	E	N	1974	80503
0010	S	S	E	N	1971	87883
0010	S	D	R	L	1974	90739
0010	S	D	E	L	1974	95949
0010	S	D	E	N	1976	101813
0010	S	E	E	N	1976	101813
0010	S	S	E	N	1976	102567
0010	T	D	O	L	1965	61141
0010	T	D	O	N	1965	61141
0010	T	S	O	L	1965	61141
0010	T	S	O	N	1965	61141
0013	D	D	R	N	1973	51950
0013	D	D	E	N	1973	54435
0013	S	S	E	N	1974	94636
0013	T	T	E	N	1969	95705
0041	S	D	R	N	1973	56785
0041	S	D	R	N	1971	60185
0041	S	D	E	N	1972	63772
0041	S	E	E	N	1975	65439
0041	S	D	E	N	1976	100761
0041	S	T	E	N	1976	100761
0041	T	D	E	N	1974	65107
0086	A	D	E	N	1973	50526
0086	A	E	E	N	1973	50526
0086	A	D	E	N	1973	55107
0086	A	D	E	N	1974	55244
0086	A	D	E	N	1972	63962
0086	A	S	E	L	1974	65584
0086	A	S	E	N	1974	65584
0086	A	S	E	N	1964	75166
0086	A	D	E	N	1974	84126
0086	A	S	E	N	1971	84631
0086	A	S	E	N	1974	94637
0086	A	S	E	N	1975	101027
0086	A	D	E	N	1975	101028
0086	A	T	E	L	1975	101028
0086	A	T	E	N	1975	101028
0086	A	S	E	N	1975	101029
0086	D	S	E	N	1975	101027

Substance Number	Phys. State	Subject	Language	Temperature	Year	EPIC Number
102-0086	S	D	E	N	1973	49533
0086	S	D	E	N	1973	50526
0086	S	E	E	N	1973	50526
0086	S	S	E	L	1973	53568
0086	S	D	R	N	1973	54193
0086	S	D	E	N	1973	54194
0086	S	D	R	N	1972	54687
0086	S	D	E	N	1974	55244
0086	S	S	E	N	1972	59933
0086	S	T	E	N	1975	66680
0086	S	D	E	N	1973	68845
0086	S	S	E	N	1971	70398
0086	S	S	E	N	1971	84631
0086	S	D	E	L	1974	85935
0086	S	D	E	N	1974	85935
0086	S	S	E	N	1971	87883
0086	S	D	E	N	1975	93161
0086	S	D	E	N	1975	93997
0086	S	S	E	N	1976	99986
0086	S	D	E	N	1976	101822
0086	S	S	E	N	1976	101822
0086	S	D	E	N	1976	101828
0086	T	D	E	N	1973	55107
0086	T	D	E	N	1974	65105
0086	T	D	E	N	1974	68831
0086	T	D	E	N	1975	88516
0086	T	D	E	N	1975	93315
0086	T	S	E	N	1974	94637
0086	T	D	E	N	1975	98067
0086	T	T	E	N	1975	98067
0086	T	D	E	N	1976	99986
0086	T	E	E	N	1976	99986
0086	T	D	E	N	1976	101813
0086	T	E	E	N	1976	101813
0086	T	D	E	N	1976	101822
0086	T	D	E	N	1976	101827
0086	T	D	E	N	1976	101828
0086	T	S	E	N	1976	102567
0105	S	T	E	N	1970	59683
0105	S	D	E	N	1967	85339
0105	T	D	R	N	1973	53779
0105	T	D	E	N	1973	55350
0105	T	D	E	N	1973	62595
0105	T	D	E	H	1975	88514
0105	T	D	E	N	1975	88514
0105	T	D	E	N	1975	93630
0120	T	D	O	N	1973	56806
0244	D	D	E	N	1974	65111
0244	D	T	E	N	1974	65111
0244	S	D	E	N	1974	65111
0244	S	T	E	N	1974	65111
0244	S	D	E	N	1972	65878
0244	S	T	E	N	1972	65878
0248	S	D	E	L	1970	66515
0248	S	D	E	N	1970	66515
0248	S	S	E	L	1974	88203
0250	D	D	E	N	1973	50396
0250	D	D	E	N	1973	53727
0250	D	D	E	N	1974	53918
0250	D	D	E	N	1974	60671
0250	D	D	R	N	1972	60727
0250	D	D	E	N	1973	60728
8001	D	S	E	N	1973	53427
8001	D	D	R	N	1972	62717
8001	D	D	E	N	1973	65313
8001	S	S	E	N	1973	52024
8001	S	S	E	N	1972	53246
8001	S	T	E	N	1972	53246
8001	S	S	E	N	1973	53427
8001	S	S	E	N	1974	58040
8001	S	D	E	N	1974	60657
8001	S	T	E	N	1974	60657
8001	S	T	E	N	1972	63811
8001	S	D	G	N	1954	66199
8001	S	T	G	N	1954	66199
8001	S	D	R	L	1973	71681
8001	S	D	R	N	1973	71681
8001	S	D	E	L	1973	82265
8001	S	D	E	N	1973	82265
8001	S	S	E	N	1962	87668
8001	S	S	E	N	1966	87830
8001	S	T	E	N	1975	93330
8001	S	S	E	N	1975	102056
8001	T	D	E	N	1976	99553
8001	T	E	E	N	1976	99553
8016	T	D	E	N	1973	50716
8031	A	D	E	N	1973	50526
8031	A	E	E	N	1973	50526
8031	A	D	E	N	1973	51915
8031	A	D	E	N	1973	55107
8031	A	S	O	N	1972	58591
8031	A	S	E	N	1970	59557
8031	A	D	E	N	1974	60536
8031	A	D	E	L	1972	60911
8031	A	D	E	N	1972	63823
8031	A	S	E	N	1974	65584
8031	A	S	E	N	1964	75166
8031	A	S	E	N	1971	84631
8031	A	D	E	L	1974	90615
8031	A	D	E	N	1974	92433
8031	A	S	E	N	1974	94637

Substance Number	Phys. State	Subject	Language	Temperature	Year	EPIC Number
102-8031	A	S	E	N	1975	101029
8031	A	S	E	L	1975	101031
8031	D	D	E	N	1973	51915
8031	D	S	E	N	1973	53051
8031	D	D	E	N	1972	63823
8031	D	D	E	N	1973	68845
8031	D	D	E	N	1975	90805
8031	L	D	E	N	1975	90805
8031	L	D	E	N	1975	90990
8031	L	S	E	N	1975	90990
8031	L	D	R	N	1976	103396
8031	L	T	R	N	1976	103396
8031	L	D	E	N	1976	103397
8031	L	T	E	N	1976	103397
8031	S	D	R	N	1973	49763
8031	S	D	E	N	1973	50526
8031	S	E	E	N	1973	50526
8031	S	D	E	N	1973	51795
8031	S	S	E	L	1973	53568
8031	S	S	E	N	1970	59557
8031	S	S	E	N	1972	59933
8031	S	D	E	N	1974	65583
8031	S	S	E	N	1974	65583
8031	S	D	E	N	1973	68845
8031	S	S	E	N	1971	84631
8031	S	D	E	N	1975	90805
8031	S	D	E	N	1972	98639
8031	S	S	E	N	1975	102056
8031	S	D	R	N	1976	103396
8031	S	T	R	N	1976	103396
8031	S	D	E	N	1976	103397
8031	S	T	E	N	1976	103397
8031	T	D	E	N	1973	55107
8031	T	D	E	L	1972	60911
8031	T	S	E	N	1972	83589
8035	S	D	E	N	1974	60664
8035	S	S	E	N	1967	75171
8035	T	D	E	N	1973	51925
8035	T	D	E	N	1967	75171
8041	A	D	E	N	1973	54224
8041	A	D	E	N	1974	86019
8041	A	T	E	N	1974	93381
8041	A	S	E	N	1974	94637
8041	A	D	E	N	1975	100036
8041	A	T	E	N	1975	101030
8041	D	D	E	L	1973	50753
8041	D	D	E	N	1973	50753
8041	D	T	E	N	1973	52457
8041	D	D	R	N	1973	52521
8041	D	S	R	N	1973	52521
8041	D	D	E	N	1972	52988
8041	D	D	E	N	1972	53068
8041	D	S	E	N	1972	53248
8041	D	D	E	N	1972	53274
8041	D	D	E	N	1972	53302
8041	D	D	E	N	1973	53442
8041	D	T	E	N	1973	53442
8041	D	D	E	N	1972	53519
8041	D	E	E	N	1972	53519
8041	D	D	E	N	1974	53638
8041	D	D	E	N	1974	53901
8041	D	D	E	N	1974	53914
8041	D	E	E	N	1974	53914
8041	D	T	E	N	1974	53914
8041	D	D	E	N	1973	54221
8041	D	E	E	N	1973	54221
8041	D	D	E	N	1974	54559
8041	D	T	E	N	1972	55096
8041	D	D	E	L	1974	55237
8041	D	D	E	N	1974	55237
8041	D	T	E	N	1974	55237
8041	D	D	E	N	1973	55835
8041	D	E	E	N	1973	55835
8041	D	D	E	N	1973	55840
8041	D	E	E	N	1973	55840
8041	D	S	E	N	1973	55840
8041	D	D	E	N	1974	57762
8041	D	S	E	N	1974	57762
8041	D	D	E	N	1974	57994
8041	D	D	E	N	1973	58212
8041	D	S	E	N	1971	59711
8041	D	D	E	N	1974	60508
8041	D	D	E	N	1971	60546
8041	D	D	E	N	1973	60575
8041	D	D	E	N	1971	60690
8041	D	T	E	N	1971	60690
8041	D	D	E	N	1974	60692
8041	D	T	E	N	1974	60692
8041	D	D	E	N	1972	61061
8041	D	S	E	N	1972	61061
8041	D	D	E	N	1974	61356
8041	D	S	E	N	1974	61356
8041	D	T	E	N	1974	61356
8041	D	D	E	N	1970	62255
8041	D	D	E	N	1970	62262
8041	D	E	E	N	1970	62262
8041	D	D	E	N	1969	62324
8041	D	D	R	N	1974	62529
8041	D	D	R	N	1973	62726
8041	D	D	E	N	1975	63348
8041	D	S	E	N	1975	63348

Phys. State: **A.** Amorphous; **C.** Superconductive; **D.** Doped; **F.** Fibrous or Whisker; **G.** Gas; **I.** Ionized or Plasma; **L.** Liquid; **P.** Powder or Particle; **S.** Solid; **T.** Thin Film
Subject: **D.** Data; **E.** Experiment; **S.** Survey (Review, Compendium, etc.); **T.** Theory
Language: **E.** English; **F.** French; **G.** German; **O.** Other Languages; **R.** Russian
Temperature: **L.** Low (0 to 75K); **N.** Normal (75 to 1273K); **H.** High (above 1273K)

Substance Number	Phys. State	Sub-ject	Lan-guage	Temper-ature	Year	EPIC Number
102-8041	D	T	E	N	1975	63348
8041	D	D	R	N	1970	63458
8041	D	D	E	N	1972	63761
8041	D	D	E	L	1972	63848
8041	D	T	E	L	1972	63848
8041	D	D	E	N	1974	64432
8041	D	D	E	N	1974	65110
8041	D	S	E	N	1974	65110
8041	D	D	E	N	1973	65322
8041	D	D	E	N	1973	65543
8041	D	D	E	N	1972	66215
8041	D	D	R	N	1972	66298
8041	D	S	R	N	1972	66298
8041	D	D	E	N	1972	66299
8041	D	S	E	N	1972	66299
8041	D	D	E	N	1975	66716
8041	D	E	E	N	1975	66716
8041	D	D	E	N	1975	72540
8041	D	D	E	N	1968	74639
8041	D	T	E	N	1968	74639
8041	D	D	E	N	1974	87448
8041	D	S	E	N	1962	87673
8041	D	S	E	N	1964	87701
8041	D	S	E	N	1970	87879
8041	D	D	E	N	1975	89296
8041	D	T	E	N	1975	89296
8041	D	D	E	N	1975	89778
8041	D	S	E	N	1975	89778
8041	D	T	E	N	1975	89778
8041	D	D	E	N	1975	93322
8041	D	D	R	L	1975	96810
8041	D	D	R	N	1975	96810
8041	D	T	R	L	1975	96810
8041	D	T	R	N	1975	96810
8041	D	D	E	N	1976	99243
8041	D	D	E	N	1976	100869
8041	D	S	E	N	1976	100869
8041	D	T	E	N	1976	100869
8041	D	D	E	N	1975	101039
8041	D	E	E	N	1975	101039
8041	D	D	E	N	1976	102278
8041	D	D	E	L	1975	103608
8041	D	D	E	N	1975	103608
8041	D	T	E	L	1975	103608
8041	D	T	E	N	1975	103608
8041	L	D	E	N	1973	54221
8041	S	D	R	N	1973	50077
8041	S	D	E	N	1973	51430
8041	S	D	E	N	1973	51650
8041	S	D	E	N	1973	51795
8041	S	S	E	N	1973	52024
8041	S	D	R	N	1972	52261
8041	S	T	E	N	1972	53095
8041	S	D	E	N	1972	53171
8041	S	D	E	N	1972	53244
8041	S	E	E	N	1972	53244
8041	S	S	E	N	1972	53244
8041	S	S	E	N	1972	53246
8041	S	T	E	N	1972	53246
8041	S	S	E	N	1972	53247
8041	S	D	E	N	1972	53259
8041	S	D	E	N	1972	53274
8041	S	E	E	N	1973	53405
8041	S	T	E	N	1973	53405
8041	S	D	E	N	1973	53442
8041	S	D	E	N	1973	53446
8041	S	D	E	N	1972	53519
8041	S	E	E	N	1972	53519
8041	S	S	E	N	1973	53782
8041	S	D	E	N	1974	53917
8041	S	S	E	N	1973	53939
8041	S	D	E	N	1973	53943
8041	S	D	E	N	1974	54024
8041	S	D	R	N	1973	54204
8041	S	D	E	N	1973	54214
8041	S	T	E	N	1973	54214
8041	S	D	E	N	1973	54221
8041	S	T	E	L	1974	54601
8041	S	D	R	N	1973	54645
8041	S	S	E	N	1973	54773
8041	S	T	R	N	1973	54990
8041	S	T	E	N	1974	54991
8041	S	D	E	N	1973	55085
8041	S	D	E	N	1972	55101
8041	S	D	E	L	1974	55237
8041	S	D	R	N	1973	55294
8041	S	S	E	N	1972	55728
8041	S	D	E	N	1974	57966
8041	S	S	E	N	1974	58040
8041	S	S	E	N	1974	58810
8041	S	T	E	N	1974	58825
8041	S	D	E	N	1974	59268
8041	S	D	R	N	1974	59281
8041	S	D	R	N	1970	59532
8041	S	T	R	N	1970	59532
8041	S	D	R	L	1973	59722
8041	S	D	E	L	1973	59723
8041	S	D	E	N	1971	59984
8041	S	D	E	N	1974	60373
8041	S	D	E	N	1971	60546
8041	S	T	E	N	1973	60575

Substance Number	Phys. State	Sub-ject	Lan-guage	Temper-ature	Year	EPIC Number
102-8041	S	D	E	N	1974	60657
8041	S	T	E	N	1974	60657
8041	S	D	E	N	1974	60692
8041	S	T	E	N	1974	60692
8041	S	D	E	N	1973	60754
8041	S	D	E	N	1972	61061
8041	S	D	E	L	1974	61185
8041	S	D	E	N	1974	61185
8041	S	E	E	L	1974	61185
8041	S	E	E	N	1974	61185
8041	S	S	E	N	1974	61185
8041	S	D	G	N	1971	62077
8041	S	T	E	N	1972	62200
8041	S	D	E	N	1969	62248
8041	S	E	E	N	1969	62248
8041	S	S	E	N	1971	62264
8041	S	S	E	N	1969	62273
8041	S	D	E	N	1973	62296
8041	S	D	E	N	1974	62307
8041	S	D	E	N	1974	62323
8041	S	D	E	N	1974	62602
8041	S	T	E	N	1974	62602
8041	S	D	R	N	1972	62710
8041	S	S	R	L	1972	62710
8041	S	D	E	L	1975	63292
8041	S	D	E	N	1975	63292
8041	S	D	E	N	1975	63348
8041	S	S	E	N	1975	63348
8041	S	T	E	N	1975	63348
8041	S	T	R	N	1972	63469
8041	S	D	E	N	1970	63586
8041	S	T	E	N	1970	63586
8041	S	D	R	N	1972	63698
8041	S	T	R	N	1972	63698
8041	S	D	E	N	1972	63761
8041	S	T	E	N	1972	63811
8041	S	T	E	N	1973	63838
8041	S	D	E	N	1974	64493
8041	S	T	E	N	1972	65147
8041	S	D	E	N	1970	65158
8041	S	D	E	N	1974	65242
8041	S	D	E	N	1973	65306
8041	S	S	E	L	1973	65306
8041	S	D	E	N	1972	65340
8041	S	T	E	N	1972	65340
8041	S	D	E	N	1975	65438
8041	S	T	E	N	1975	65438
8041	S	S	E	N	1975	65507
8041	S	D	G	N	1954	66199
8041	S	T	G	N	1954	66199
8041	S	D	E	N	1972	66215
8041	S	T	E	N	1972	66222
8041	S	T	R	N	1973	66431
8041	S	T	E	N	1974	66432
8041	S	D	E	N	1975	66716
8041	S	E	E	N	1975	66716
8041	S	D	E	N	1975	68602
8041	S	D	E	L	1974	68690
8041	S	T	E	L	1974	68690
8041	S	D	E	N	1973	68846
8041	S	S	E	N	1971	70669
8041	S	T	E	N	1971	70669
8041	S	D	G	N	1974	71582
8041	S	S	G	N	1974	71582
8041	S	D	R	N	1974	72651
8041	S	T	R	N	1974	72651
8041	S	D	E	N	1975	72700
8041	S	T	E	N	1975	72700
8041	S	D	E	N	1966	75146
8041	S	D	E	L	1969	75248
8041	S	D	E	N	1969	75248
8041	S	D	E	L	1968	75883
8041	S	D	E	N	1968	75883
8041	S	D	G	L	1971	78856
8041	S	D	G	N	1971	78856
8041	S	E	G	L	1971	78856
8041	S	E	G	N	1971	78856
8041	S	D	E	N	1973	85957
8041	S	E	E	N	1973	85957
8041	S	T	E	N	1973	85957
8041	S	S	E	N	1973	86380
8041	S	D	E	N	1974	87448
8041	S	S	E	N	1962	87673
8041	S	S	E	L	1964	87701
8041	S	S	E	N	1964	87701
8041	S	S	E	N	1974	87759
8041	S	S	E	N	1970	87879
8041	S	S	E	N	1971	87883
8041	S	D	E	N	1974	88485
8041	S	S	E	L	1975	90112
8041	S	T	E	N	1975	90112
8041	S	D	E	N	1975	91718
8041	S	E	E	N	1975	91718
8041	S	D	E	L	1975	91863
8041	S	T	E	L	1975	91863
8041	S	D	R	N	1966	91926
8041	S	D	E	N	1974	93257
8041	S	T	E	N	1974	93257
8041	S	T	E	N	1975	93326
8041	S	T	E	N	1974	93327
8041	S	T	E	N	1975	93330

Substance Number	Phys. State	Sub-ject	Lan-guage	Temper-ature	Year	EPIC Number
102-8041	S	D	E	N	1975	94150
8041	S	T	R	N	1974	96773
8041	S	T	E	N	1975	96774
8041	S	D	E	N	1975	97730
8041	S	E	E	N	1975	97730
8041	S	S	E	N	1975	97730
8041	S	T	E	N	1975	99140
8041	S	D	F	N	1976	99169
8041	S	E	F	N	1976	99169
8041	S	D	R	N	1976	99536
8041	S	S	R	N	1976	99536
8041	S	T	R	N	1976	99536
8041	S	D	E	N	1976	99856
8041	S	S	E	N	1976	99856
8041	S	T	E	N	1976	99856
8041	S	T	E	N	1975	101012
8041	S	D	E	N	1975	101019
8041	S	S	E	N	1975	101020
8041	S	D	E	N	1975	101024
8041	S	E	E	N	1975	101024
8041	S	T	E	N	1975	101030
8041	S	S	E	N	1975	101032
8041	S	S	E	N	1975	101034
8041	S	S	E	N	1976	101374
8041	S	D	E	N	1976	101470
8041	S	S	E	N	1976	101470
8041	S	T	E	N	1976	101470
8041	S	D	E	N	1975	101663
8041	S	E	E	N	1975	101663
8041	S	S	E	N	1975	101663
8041	S	D	E	N	1976	101823
8041	S	T	E	N	1976	101823
8041	S	D	E	N	1975	101890
8041	S	T	E	N	1975	101890
8041	S	S	E	N	1975	102056
8041	S	D	E	L	1976	102146
8041	S	S	E	L	1976	102146
8041	S	S	E	N	1976	102151
8041	S	T	E	N	1976	102151
8041	S	D	E	L	1976	103155
8041	S	D	E	N	1976	103155
8041	S	S	E	L	1976	103155
8041	S	S	E	N	1976	103155
8041	S	T	E	N	1976	103155
8041	T	D	E	N	1974	53638
8041	T	E	E	N	1974	53638
8041	T	D	E	N	1973	54224
8041	T	D	R	L	1973	55330
8041	T	T	R	L	1973	55330
8041	T	D	E	L	1974	59266
8041	T	T	E	L	1974	59266
8041	T	D	E	N	1969	59773
8041	T	D	O	N	1972	59928
8041	T	D	E	N	1974	62550
8041	T	S	E	L	1964	87701
8041	T	S	E	N	1964	87701
8041	T	S	E	N	1974	94637
8041	T	E	E	N	1976	99741
8041	T	D	E	N	1976	99871
8041	T	T	E	N	1976	99871
8041	T	D	E	N	1975	101039
8041	T	E	E	N	1975	101039
8054	A	T	E	N	1975	101030
8054	D	D	R	N	1973	50744
8054	D	D	E	N	1974	53638
8054	D	D	R	L	1974	62428
8054	D	D	R	N	1974	62428
8054	D	D	E	L	1974	65331
8054	D	D	E	N	1974	65331
8054	D	D	E	N	1973	78977
8054	D	D	E	N	1975	89778
8054	D	S	E	N	1975	89778
8054	D	T	E	N	1975	89778
8054	P	D	R	N	1971	63424
8054	P	T	R	N	1971	63424
8054	P	D	E	N	1971	67075
8054	P	T	E	N	1971	67075
8054	S	D	R	N	1973	49762
8054	S	S	E	N	1973	52024
8054	S	S	E	N	1972	53246
8054	S	T	E	N	1972	53246
8054	S	D	E	N	1973	53788
8054	S	E	E	N	1973	53788
8054	S	S	E	L	1974	53913
8054	S	D	E	N	1974	53917
8054	S	S	E	N	1973	53939
8054	S	D	R	N	1973	56785
8054	S	D	R	N	1974	58604
8054	S	T	R	N	1974	58604
8054	S	D	R	N	1971	60185
8054	S	D	R	L	1974	62428
8054	S	D	R	N	1974	62428
8054	S	D	E	L	1972	63772
8054	S	D	E	N	1972	63772
8054	S	T	E	N	1972	63811
8054	S	D	E	L	1974	65331
8054	S	D	E	N	1974	65331
8054	S	D	G	N	1963	65981
8054	S	D	G	N	1954	66199
8054	S	T	G	N	1954	66199
8054	S	D	G	N	1974	71582

Phys. State: **A.** Amorphous; **C.** Superconductive; **D.** Doped; **F.** Fibrous or Whisker; **G.** Gas; **I.** Ionized or Plasma; **L.** Liquid; **P.** Powder or Particle; **S.** Solid; **T.** Thin Film
Subject: **D.** Data; **E.** Experiment; **S.** Survey (Review, Compendium, etc.); **T.** Theory
Language: **E.** English; **F.** French; **G.** German; **O.** Other Languages; **R.** Russian
Temperature: **L.** Low (0 to 75K); **N.** Normal (75 to 1273K); **H.** High (above 1273K)

Substance Number	Phys. State	Subject	Language	Temperature	Year	EPIC Number
102-8054	S	S	E	N	1962	87667
8054	S	S	E	N	1971	87883
8054	S	T	E	N	1974	93327
8054	S	D	R	L	1975	97056
8054	S	D	E	L	1975	97057
8054	S	S	E	N	1972	97249
8054	S	S	E	N	1962	97977
8054	S	T	E	N	1975	99140
8054	S	D	E	N	1976	100761
8054	S	T	E	N	1976	100761
8054	S	D	E	N	1975	101019
8054	S	T	E	N	1975	101030
8054	S	D	E	N	1976	101470
8054	S	T	E	N	1976	101470
8054	S	D	E	N	1976	101823
8054	S	T	E	N	1976	101823
8054	S	S	E	N	1975	102056
8054	T	D	E	N	1974	53638
8054	T	E	E	N	1974	53638
8054	T	D	E	N	1974	58893
8054	T	D	E	N	1973	59311
8054	T	S	E	N	1971	60965
8065	S	D	R	N	1974	86779
8065	S	S	R	N	1974	86779
8065	S	D	E	N	1974	90050
8065	S	S	E	N	1974	90050
8066	S	S	R	N	1974	86779
8066	S	S	E	N	1974	90050
8069	A	D	E	L	1968	75884
8069	A	D	E	N	1968	75884
8069	S	D	R	N	1972	52260
8069	S	D	E	N	1972	53335
8069	S	D	E	N	1974	62059
8069	S	T	E	N	1974	62059
8069	S	D	E	N	1968	75884
8069	S	D	R	N	1973	93280
8074	D	D	E	N	1972	53093
8074	D	D	E	L	1972	53097
8074	D	D	E	N	1972	53097
8074	D	D	E	N	1974	53720
8074	D	T	E	N	1974	53720
8074	D	D	E	N	1972	85903
8074	S	D	E	N	1972	53093
8074	S	D	E	N	1975	68705
8074	S	T	E	N	1975	68705
8074	S	D	E	N	1972	85903
8075	S	S	E	L	1974	88203
8078	A	S	E	N	1974	94637
8084	S	D	R	N	1972	52261
8090	S	D	E	N	1972	53090
8094	D	D	E	N	1973	51749
8094	D	T	E	N	1975	101890
8094	S	T	E	N	1974	53918
8094	S	D	E	N	1975	65438
8094	S	S	E	N	1975	65438
8094	S	D	E	N	1975	101890
8094	S	T	E	N	1975	101890
8094	T	D	E	N	1973	51749
8094	T	D	E	N	1976	99871
8094	T	T	E	N	1976	99871
8094	T	D	E	N	1975	101039
8094	T	E	E	N	1975	101039
8095	D	D	E	N	1973	52782
8095	D	T	E	N	1974	58825
8095	D	D	E	N	1975	86754
8095	D	T	E	N	1975	86754
8095	S	D	R	N	1972	50731
8095	S	T	R	L	1973	55341
8095	S	T	E	N	1974	59279
8095	S	D	E	N	1972	63998
8095	S	S	E	N	1965	87703
8095	S	D	R	L	1973	101917
8095	S	D	R	N	1973	101917
8095	S	S	R	L	1973	101917
8095	S	T	R	L	1973	101917
8095	S	T	R	N	1973	101917
8095	S	D	E	L	1973	101918
8095	S	D	E	N	1973	101918
8095	S	S	E	L	1973	101918
8095	S	T	E	L	1973	101918
8095	S	T	E	N	1973	101918
8095	T	D	E	N	1976	99741
8095	T	E	E	N	1976	99741
8098	S	D	E	N	1973	52785
8098	T	D	E	N	1973	51190
8106	T	S	E	N	1974	54594
8132	D	D	E	L	1974	58029
8132	S	D	E	N	1974	53917
8132	S	D	E	L	1974	58029
8132	S	D	E	L	1970	66515
8132	S	D	E	N	1970	66515
8132	S	D	G	L	1971	78856
8132	S	D	G	N	1971	78856
8132	S	E	G	L	1971	78856
8132	S	E	G	N	1971	78856
8132	T	D	E	N	1976	99553
8132	T	E	E	N	1976	99553
8133	A	S	E	N	1974	65584
8133	A	S	E	N	1964	75166
8133	A	S	E	N	1971	84631
8133	L	D	E	N	1975	90990

Substance Number	Phys. State	Subject	Language	Temperature	Year	EPIC Number
102-8133	L	S	E	N	1975	90990
8133	S	S	E	N	1971	84631
8134	S	S	E	N	1970	87822
8134	S	S	E	N	1972	87890
8139	D	D	E	N	1974	55242
8139	S	D	E	N	1972	65878
8139	S	T	E	N	1972	65878
8139	S	D	E	L	1973	88610
8139	S	D	E	N	1973	88610
8142	D	D	E	N	1974	53638
8142	S	E	E	N	1975	65439
8142	T	D	E	N	1974	53638
8142	T	E	E	N	1974	53638
8148	T	D	R	N	1970	52207
8149	T	D	R	N	1970	52207
8150	T	D	R	N	1970	52207
8151	T	D	R	N	1970	52207
8152	T	D	R	N	1970	52207
8163	L	D	E	N	1975	90990
8163	L	S	E	N	1975	90990
8171	A	D	E	N	1972	53186
8171	A	T	E	N	1972	53186
8171	T	D	E	N	1972	53186
8171	T	T	E	N	1972	53186
8180	S	D	E	N	1975	94550
8183	A	S	E	N	1975	101029
8186	D	D	E	N	1972	53519
8186	S	D	E	N	1972	53519
8187	A	S	E	N	1974	54059
8189	D	D	E	L	1973	57497
8190	L	D	E	N	1973	51457
8191	L	D	E	N	1973	51457
8199	I	D	E	H	1973	50832
8199	I	T	E	H	1973	50832
8201	I	D	E	N	1974	53706
8201	I	E	E	N	1974	53706
8203	A	D	E	N	1974	84126
8224	S	D	R	N	1973	54383
8224	S	D	E	N	1973	54384
8226	S	D	R	N	1973	55068
8226	S	D	E	N	1974	55069
8228	S	D	E	N	1972	65878
8228	S	T	E	N	1972	65878
8232	S	D	E	N	1974	60664
8235	S	D	E	N	1972	65878
8235	S	T	E	N	1972	65878
8248	P	D	R	N	1971	63424
8248	P	T	R	N	1971	63424
8248	P	D	E	N	1971	67075
8248	P	T	E	N	1971	67075
8260	S	T	R	L	1973	57818
8260	S	T	E	L	1974	57819
8314	S	D	E	N	1975	91619
8331	A	D	R	N	1974	62436
8331	A	D	E	N	1974	67079
8331	T	D	R	N	1974	62436
8331	T	D	E	N	1974	67079
8333	S	D	F	N	1974	81628
8337	S	D	E	N	1972	65878
8337	S	T	E	N	1972	65878
8343	S	D	R	N	1973	56696
8371	S	D	R	N	1973	49763
8371	S	D	R	N	1976	103396
8371	S	T	R	N	1976	103396
8371	S	D	E	N	1976	103397
8371	S	T	E	N	1976	103397
8393	S	D	E	L	1975	86741
8393	S	D	E	N	1975	86741
8396	L	D	E	N	1975	90990
8396	L	S	E	N	1975	90990
8400	S	S	E	N	1964	65975
8401	A	D	E	N	1974	92433
8437	S	D	E	N	1968	68207
8443	S	D	E	N	1975	91619
8466	S	D	E	L	1970	63884
8466	S	D	E	N	1970	63884
8470	A	D	E	N	1974	84126
8470	A	S	E	N	1974	84126
8471	S	D	E	N	1965	100013
8471	S	T	E	N	1965	100013
8481	S	D	R	N	1974	93434
8481	S	T	R	N	1974	93434
8481	S	D	E	N	1974	93435
8481	S	T	E	N	1974	93435
8482	S	D	R	N	1974	93434
8482	S	T	R	N	1974	93434
8482	S	D	E	N	1974	93435
8482	S	T	E	N	1974	93435
104-0002	S	D	E	N	1973	52006
0002	S	S	E	N	1971	87883
0006	D	D	E	N	1972	50486
0006	D	E	E	N	1972	50486
0006	D	D	E	N	1973	50565
0006	D	D	E	N	1973	50633
0006	D	T	E	N	1973	52028
0006	D	D	E	N	1973	53785
0006	D	D	E	L	1973	53790
0006	D	D	E	N	1973	53790
0006	D	S	E	N	1973	56362
0006	D	D	E	N	1974	59393

Substance Number	Phys. State	Subject	Language	Temperature	Year	EPIC Number
104-0006	D	D	E	N	1972	60077
0006	D	D	R	N	1974	60407
0006	D	D	E	N	1974	60408
0006	D	D	E	N	1973	60586
0006	D	D	E	N	1971	61262
0006	D	S	E	N	1971	61262
0006	D	D	R	N	1974	62006
0006	D	D	E	N	1974	62007
0006	D	D	E	L	1973	62286
0006	D	D	E	N	1973	62286
0006	D	D	R	N	1971	66296
0006	D	D	E	N	1971	66297
0006	D	D	E	L	1975	66689
0006	D	D	E	N	1970	70490
0006	D	T	E	N	1970	70490
0006	D	D	E	L	1964	75090
0006	D	D	R	N	1974	77830
0006	D	T	R	N	1974	77830
0006	D	D	E	L	1974	80552
0006	D	S	E	N	1974	87215
0006	D	T	E	N	1974	87215
0006	D	D	R	L	1963	91918
0006	D	D	E	N	1974	95926
0006	D	T	E	N	1974	95926
0006	D	D	E	L	1976	99234
0006	D	T	E	L	1976	99234
0006	D	S	E	N	1975	99263
0006	D	D	R	L	1975	100849
0006	D	D	R	N	1975	100849
0006	D	T	R	L	1975	100849
0006	D	T	R	N	1975	100849
0006	D	D	E	L	1976	100850
0006	D	D	E	N	1976	100850
0006	D	T	E	L	1976	100850
0006	D	T	E	N	1976	100850
0006	D	D	E	N	1976	103336
0006	D	T	E	N	1976	103336
0006	L	D	R	N	1973	55759
0006	L	D	E	N	1973	57778
0006	L	D	R	N	1971	66296
0006	L	D	E	N	1971	66297
0006	L	D	E	N	1972	75340
0006	S	D	E	N	1972	49936
0006	S	D	E	N	1973	50565
0006	S	S	E	N	1974	52799
0006	S	D	E	N	1972	53244
0006	S	E	E	N	1972	53244
0006	S	S	E	N	1972	53244
0006	S	S	E	N	1972	53246
0006	S	T	E	N	1972	53246
0006	S	S	E	N	1972	53247
0006	S	S	E	N	1972	53248
0006	S	T	E	N	1973	53789
0006	S	D	E	N	1973	54214
0006	S	T	E	N	1973	54214
0006	S	D	E	N	1973	54653
0006	S	S	E	N	1973	54773
0006	S	D	E	N	1973	54775
0006	S	D	E	N	1972	55100
0006	S	T	E	N	1972	55100
0006	S	S	E	L	1972	55357
0006	S	S	E	N	1972	55357
0006	S	D	R	N	1973	55759
0006	S	D	E	N	1973	57710
0006	S	D	E	N	1973	57778
0006	S	D	E	N	1974	57912
0006	S	D	E	N	1973	58212
0006	S	S	E	N	1973	58212
0006	S	D	E	N	1974	58821
0006	S	D	E	N	1974	58941
0006	S	D	E	L	1974	58962
0006	S	D	E	N	1974	58962
0006	S	S	E	L	1974	58962
0006	S	S	E	N	1973	59375
0006	S	D	E	L	1973	59611
0006	S	D	E	N	1973	59611
0006	S	S	E	L	1973	59611
0006	S	S	E	N	1973	59611
0006	S	D	E	L	1970	59675
0006	S	D	R	N	1974	60407
0006	S	D	E	N	1974	60408
0006	S	D	R	N	1974	60463
0006	S	D	E	N	1974	60464
0006	S	D	E	N	1973	60582
0006	S	D	E	N	1974	60657
0006	S	T	E	N	1974	60657
0006	S	S	E	N	1974	60672
0006	S	D	E	N	1971	61706
0006	S	E	E	N	1971	61706
0006	S	D	R	N	1974	62006
0006	S	D	E	N	1974	62007
0006	S	D	E	N	1973	62274
0006	S	S	E	N	1973	62274
0006	S	D	E	L	1973	62286
0006	S	D	E	N	1973	62286
0006	S	D	E	N	1973	62296
0006	S	D	E	N	1974	62306
0006	S	D	E	N	1974	62307
0006	S	D	E	N	1974	62323
0006	S	D	E	N	1969	62324
0006	S	D	R	N	1973	62862

Phys. State: **A.** Amorphous; **C.** Superconductive; **D.** Doped; **F.** Fibrous or Whisker; **G.** Gas; **I.** Ionized or Plasma; **L.** Liquid; **P.** Powder or Particle; **S.** Solid; **T.** Thin Film
Subject: **D.** Data; **E.** Experiment; **S.** Survey (Review, Compendium, etc.); **T.** Theory
Language: **E.** English; **F.** French; **G.** German; **O.** Other Languages; **R.** Russian
Temperature: **L.** Low (0 to 75K); **N.** Normal (75 to 1273K); **H.** High (above 1273K)

Substance Number	Phys. State	Subject	Language	Temperature	Year	EPIC Number
104-0006	S	S	E	N	1949	63242
0006	S	D	E	L	1975	63327
0006	S	D	E	N	1975	63327
0006	S	S	E	N	1975	63327
0006	S	S	E	N	1970	63588
0006	S	D	R	N	1970	64286
0006	S	D	E	N	1974	64489
0006	S	T	E	N	1974	64489
0006	S	D	E	N	1973	65167
0006	S	S	E	N	1975	65501
0006	S	T	E	N	1974	65612
0006	S	D	E	N	1974	67107
0006	S	D	E	N	1970	68416
0006	S	D	E	N	1972	68832
0006	S	T	E	N	1973	68847
0006	S	D	E	N	1973	68852
0006	S	D	E	N	1973	68859
0006	S	D	E	N	1973	68870
0006	S	S	E	N	1924	73267
0006	S	S	E	L	1965	74575
0006	S	D	E	N	1938	74974
0006	S	T	E	N	1938	74974
0006	S	D	E	N	1972	75340
0006	S	S	E	N	1963	75839
0006	S	D	E	N	1969	85421
0006	S	D	E	N	1974	87448
0006	S	S	E	N	1974	87759
0006	S	S	E	N	1971	87883
0006	S	D	E	N	1975	89451
0006	S	S	E	N	1975	89451
0006	S	T	E	N	1975	89451
0006	S	D	E	N	1975	93160
0006	S	E	E	N	1975	93160
0006	S	D	E	N	1975	93316
0006	S	D	E	N	1974	93346
0006	S	T	E	N	1974	93346
0006	S	D	E	N	1975	93379
0006	S	D	E	N	1975	93559
0006	S	D	R	N	1974	94022
0006	S	D	E	N	1975	94023
0006	S	D	E	N	1975	94479
0006	S	S	E	N	1975	97220
0006	S	S	E	N	1976	97296
0006	S	D	E	N	1976	97297
0006	S	S	E	N	1976	97297
0006	S	D	E	N	1976	97298
0006	S	D	E	N	1964	98864
0006	S	E	E	N	1964	98864
0006	S	D	F	N	1976	99169
0006	S	E	F	N	1976	99169
0006	S	D	E	N	1976	99870
0006	S	D	E	N	1976	100019
0006	S	E	E	N	1976	100019
0006	S	D	E	N	1975	101013
0006	S	T	E	N	1975	101013
0006	S	T	E	L	1975	101014
0006	S	T	E	N	1975	101014
0006	S	S	E	N	1975	101034
0006	S	D	E	L	1976	101287
0006	S	D	E	N	1976	101287
0006	S	S	E	L	1976	101287
0006	S	S	E	N	1976	101287
0006	S	D	E	N	1976	101441
0006	S	D	E	N	1975	101652
0006	S	E	E	N	1975	101652
0006	S	S	E	N	1975	101652
0006	S	D	E	N	1975	101660
0006	S	T	E	N	1975	101660
0006	S	D	E	N	1975	101661
0006	S	T	E	N	1975	101661
0006	S	D	E	N	1976	101714
0006	S	E	E	N	1976	101714
0006	S	T	E	N	1976	101714
0006	S	S	E	N	1976	101811
0006	S	D	E	N	1976	101843
0006	S	S	E	L	1976	101843
0006	S	S	E	N	1976	101843
0006	S	T	E	N	1976	101843
0006	S	D	E	L	1976	101844
0006	S	D	E	N	1976	101844
0006	S	T	E	L	1976	101844
0006	S	T	E	N	1976	101844
0006	S	D	E	N	1976	101847
0006	S	E	E	N	1976	101847
0006	S	S	E	N	1976	101847
0006	S	T	E	N	1976	101847
0006	S	D	E	N	1976	101850
0006	S	E	E	N	1976	101850
0006	S	D	E	N	1976	101851
0006	S	E	E	N	1976	101851
0006	S	T	E	N	1976	101851
0006	S	D	E	N	1976	101857
0006	S	S	E	N	1976	101857
0006	S	D	E	N	1976	102042
0006	S	E	E	N	1976	102042
0006	S	S	E	N	1975	102056
0006	S	D	E	N	1974	102101
0006	S	E	E	N	1974	102101
0006	S	D	E	N	1976	103154
0006	S	S	E	N	1976	103154
0006	S	T	E	N	1976	103154
104-0006	T	S	O	L	1965	61141
0006	T	S	O	N	1965	61141
0006	T	D	E	N	1970	62185
0006	T	T	E	N	1970	62185
0007	D	D	E	N	1966	64254
0007	S	D	E	N	1972	63601
0007	S	D	E	N	1966	64254
0007	S	D	E	N	1972	64535
0007	S	S	E	N	1967	68374
0007	S	S	E	N	1966	87803
0007	T	D	E	N	1972	61068
0007	T	S	E	N	1967	68374
0007	T	D	E	L	1976	100007
0007	T	D	E	N	1976	100007
0007	T	S	E	N	1976	100007
0007	T	T	E	L	1976	100007
0007	T	T	E	N	1976	100007
0013	D	D	R	N	1974	58074
0013	D	D	E	N	1974	58075
0013	S	D	E	N	1973	50150
0013	S	S	E	N	1972	53246
0013	S	T	E	N	1972	53246
0013	S	D	R	N	1974	58074
0013	S	D	E	N	1974	58075
0013	S	D	R	N	1974	58110
0013	S	D	E	N	1974	58111
0013	S	D	R	N	1974	62010
0013	S	S	R	N	1974	62010
0013	S	T	R	N	1974	62010
0013	S	D	E	N	1974	62011
0013	S	S	E	N	1974	62011
0013	S	T	E	N	1974	62011
0013	S	D	R	N	1974	66788
0013	S	T	R	N	1974	66788
0013	S	D	E	N	1975	66789
0013	S	T	E	N	1975	66789
0013	S	S	E	N	1975	96170
0015	D	D	R	N	1975	65357
0015	D	T	R	N	1975	65357
0015	S	D	E	N	1970	64545
0016	G	S	R	N	1972	65883
0016	G	T	R	N	1972	65883
0016	G	S	E	N	1972	65884
0016	G	T	E	N	1972	65884
0021	A	D	E	N	1975	90859
0021	A	S	E	N	1975	90859
0021	A	T	E	N	1975	90859
0021	T	D	R	N	1972	55491
0021	T	D	E	N	1975	90859
0021	T	S	E	N	1975	90859
0021	T	T	E	N	1975	90859
0025	S	S	E	N	1975	91759
0025	S	T	E	N	1975	91759
0031	D	D	E	N	1973	50633
0031	D	D	E	L	1972	62285
0031	D	D	E	L	1973	62286
0031	D	D	E	N	1973	62286
0031	D	D	E	L	1975	89453
0031	D	T	E	L	1975	89453
0031	D	D	E	N	1976	101592
0031	D	E	E	N	1976	101592
0031	D	S	E	N	1976	101592
0031	D	T	E	N	1976	101592
0031	S	D	E	N	1973	50566
0031	S	S	E	N	1973	50566
0031	S	D	E	N	1971	61706
0031	S	E	E	N	1971	61706
0031	S	D	E	L	1973	62286
0031	S	D	E	N	1973	62286
0031	S	D	E	N	1969	62324
0031	S	S	E	N	1970	63588
0031	S	T	E	N	1974	65612
0031	S	D	E	N	1971	75192
0031	S	S	E	N	1971	75192
0031	S	D	E	N	1975	96982
0031	T	D	E	N	1970	62185
0031	T	T	E	N	1970	62185
0050	G	S	R	N	1972	65883
0050	G	T	R	N	1972	65883
0050	G	S	E	N	1972	65884
0050	G	T	E	N	1972	65884
0051	G	S	E	N	1974	52808
0051	S	D	E	N	1973	55109
0052	D	D	O	N	1974	87930
0052	D	E	O	N	1974	87930
0053	D	D	E	L	1973	57138
0053	D	D	R	N	1974	77830
0053	D	T	R	N	1974	77830
0053	D	D	E	L	1975	93527
0053	D	D	E	N	1974	95926
0053	D	T	E	N	1974	95926
0053	S	D	E	L	1974	58962
0053	S	D	E	L	1975	63327
0053	S	D	E	N	1975	63327
0053	S	S	E	N	1975	65501
0053	S	T	E	N	1974	65612
0053	S	D	E	N	1973	68870
0053	S	D	E	N	1975	90068
0053	S	S	R	N	1976	103163
0053	S	T	R	N	1976	103163
0053	S	S	E	N	1976	103164
104-0053	S	T	E	N	1976	103164
0053	T	D	E	N	1970	62185
0053	T	T	E	N	1970	62185
0053	T	S	R	N	1976	103163
0053	T	S	E	N	1976	103164
0055	S	D	E	N	1974	54348
0055	S	E	E	N	1974	54348
0067	L	D	E	N	1929	73248
0067	S	D	O	L	1970	101002
0067	T	D	E	N	1970	62185
0067	T	T	E	N	1970	62185
0069	S	D	R	N	1973	54395
0069	S	D	E	N	1973	54396
0069	S	D	E	N	1969	62324
0069	T	D	R	N	1973	54395
0069	T	D	E	N	1973	54396
0069	T	D	E	N	1973	101946
0069	T	T	E	N	1973	101946
0104	S	S	E	N	1972	53246
0104	S	T	E	N	1972	53246
0104	S	S	E	N	1972	53248
0104	S	D	E	N	1974	53863
0104	S	D	E	N	1974	54024
0104	S	D	E	N	1973	58212
0104	S	S	E	N	1973	58212
0104	S	S	E	N	1974	59353
0104	S	D	E	N	1974	60255
0104	S	D	E	N	1974	62305
0104	S	D	E	N	1974	62306
0104	S	D	E	L	1975	63327
0104	S	D	E	N	1975	63327
0104	S	S	E	N	1975	63327
0104	S	D	E	N	1972	68832
0104	S	D	E	N	1973	68841
0104	S	D	E	N	1973	68865
0104	S	D	E	N	1952	73261
0104	S	D	E	L	1967	74607
0104	S	D	E	N	1967	74607
0104	S	E	E	L	1967	74607
0104	S	E	E	N	1967	74607
0104	S	D	E	N	1974	84584
0104	S	D	R	L	1974	87288
0104	S	D	E	L	1975	87289
0104	S	S	E	N	1971	87883
0104	S	D	E	N	1975	88493
0104	S	D	E	N	1975	89371
0104	S	S	E	N	1975	89371
0104	S	D	E	N	1975	93328
0104	S	D	E	N	1975	93334
0104	S	D	E	N	1975	93378
0104	S	D	E	N	1975	94479
0104	S	D	E	N	1976	97297
0104	S	S	E	N	1976	97297
0104	S	D	E	N	1976	99118
0104	S	E	E	N	1976	99118
0104	S	S	E	N	1976	99118
0104	S	T	E	N	1976	99118
0104	S	D	E	N	1976	99870
0104	S	S	E	N	1976	99870
0104	S	D	E	N	1975	101016
0104	S	D	E	N	1975	101017
0104	S	S	E	L	1975	101017
0104	S	D	E	N	1975	101668
0104	S	S	E	N	1975	101668
0104	S	T	E	N	1975	101669
0104	S	D	E	N	1976	101796
0104	S	E	E	N	1976	101796
0104	S	D	E	N	1976	101811
0104	S	S	E	N	1976	101811
0104	S	D	E	N	1976	101826
0104	S	D	E	N	1976	101837
0104	S	E	E	N	1976	101837
0104	S	T	E	N	1976	101837
0104	S	D	E	N	1976	101851
0104	S	E	E	N	1976	101851
0104	S	T	E	N	1976	101851
0104	S	D	E	N	1976	101852
0104	S	E	E	N	1976	101852
0104	S	S	E	N	1976	101852
0104	S	T	E	N	1976	101852
0104	S	D	E	N	1976	101862
0104	S	D	E	N	1976	102042
0104	S	E	E	N	1976	102042
0104	S	D	E	N	1975	102056
0104	S	D	E	N	1976	103590
0104	S	T	E	N	1976	103590
0104	T	D	E	N	1974	68831
0104	T	D	E	N	1975	98067
0104	T	E	E	N	1975	98067
0104	T	S	E	N	1976	101374
0104	T	D	E	N	1976	101813
0104	T	E	E	N	1976	101813
0105	S	D	E	N	1973	54214
0105	S	T	E	N	1973	54214
0105	S	S	E	N	1975	65501
0105	S	T	E	N	1975	65501
0106	D	T	E	N	1974	54662
0106	D	D	E	L	1973	62286
0106	D	D	E	N	1973	62286
0106	D	D	E	L	1971	101559
0106	D	T	E	L	1971	101559

Phys. State: **A.** Amorphous; **C.** Superconductive; **D.** Doped; **F.** Fibrous or Whisker; **G.** Gas; **I.** Ionized or Plasma; **L.** Liquid; **P.** Powder or Particle; **S.** Solid; **T.** Thin Film
Subject: **D.** Data; **E.** Experiment; **S.** Survey (Review, Compendium, etc.); **T.** Theory
Language: **E.** English; **F.** French; **G.** German; **O.** Other Languages; **R.** Russian
Temperature: **L.** Low (0 to 75K); **N.** Normal (75 to 1273K); **H.** High (above 1273K)

Substance Number	Phys. State	Subject	Language	Temperature	Year	EPIC Number
104-0106	S	D	E	N	1973	50566
0106	S	S	E	N	1973	50566
0106	S	S	E	N	1972	53244
0106	S	S	E	N	1972	53247
0106	S	S	E	N	1973	54773
0106	S	D	E	N	1971	61706
0106	S	E	E	N	1971	61706
0106	S	D	E	L	1973	62286
0106	S	D	E	N	1973	62286
0106	S	D	E	N	1969	62324
0106	S	D	E	N	1966	64257
0106	S	T	E	N	1974	65612
0106	S	S	E	N	1971	87883
0106	S	D	R	N	1974	89256
0106	S	D	E	N	1974	89257
0106	T	D	E	N	1970	62185
0106	T	T	E	N	1970	62185
0146	D	D	E	L	1973	51836
0146	D	D	E	N	1973	51836
0196	S	D	R	N	1972	79283
0295	T	D	E	N	1970	62185
0295	T	T	E	N	1970	62185
0295	T	S	E	N	1966	64254
0302	S	D	E	N	1973	94148
0302	S	T	E	N	1973	94148
0331	S	D	R	L	1972	60701
0331	S	D	E	L	1973	60702
0331	S	D	R	L	1974	63054
0331	S	T	R	L	1974	63054
0331	S	D	E	L	1975	63055
0331	S	T	E	L	1975	63055
0431	S	D	R	L	1973	52856
0431	S	D	R	N	1973	52856
0431	S	D	E	L	1973	52857
0431	S	D	E	N	1973	52857
0434	S	S	E	N	1974	52799
0434	S	S	E	N	1972	53244
0434	S	S	E	N	1972	53247
0533	S	D	R	N	1973	52852
0533	S	D	E	L	1973	52853
0533	S	D	E	N	1972	54618
8007	T	D	O	N	1971	67028
8015	A	D	E	N	1972	53402
8016	T	D	E	N	1974	68159
8045	S	S	R	N	1972	62298
8045	S	S	E	N	1973	62299
8045	S	S	E	N	1966	66068
8045	T	S	E	N	1966	66068
8069	T	D	E	N	1973	50382
8106	S	D	E	N	1974	53860
8110	S	D	R	N	1973	53543
8110	S	D	E	N	1973	53544
8110	S	S	R	N	1974	58082
8110	S	S	E	N	1974	58083
8121	S	D	R	L	1973	50179
8121	S	D	R	N	1973	50179
8121	S	D	E	L	1973	50180
8121	S	D	E	N	1973	50180
8125	S	D	E	N	1973	50407
8133	D	D	E	N	1973	50555
8155	T	D	E	N	1973	51189
8156	T	D	E	N	1973	57279
8156	T	T	E	N	1973	57279
8164	S	D	E	N	1973	51802
8171	S	D	R	N	1973	57822
8171	S	D	E	N	1973	57823
8180	S	D	E	N	1973	52779
8183	S	D	E	N	1974	58057
8183	S	S	E	N	1974	58057
8189	S	D	E	N	1972	53244
8189	S	E	E	N	1972	53244
8189	S	D	E	N	1973	54653
8189	S	D	E	N	1973	54775
8189	S	D	E	N	1974	57912
8191	S	S	E	N	1974	52799
8191	S	S	E	N	1972	53244
8191	S	S	E	N	1972	53247
8191	S	S	E	N	1973	54773
8191	S	S	E	N	1974	64477
8191	S	D	E	N	1972	68832
8191	S	S	E	N	1971	70398
8191	S	S	E	N	1974	87759
8191	S	T	O	N	1974	87783
8191	S	S	E	N	1971	87883
8191	S	S	E	N	1975	97348
8191	S	S	E	N	1975	101034
8191	S	D	E	N	1976	101441
8191	S	D	E	N	1976	102042
8191	S	E	E	N	1976	102042
8192	S	S	E	N	1972	53244
8192	S	S	E	N	1972	53247
8192	S	S	E	N	1971	87883
8195	A	D	R	N	1971	58968
8195	A	D	E	N	1971	58969
8195	S	D	R	N	1971	58968
8195	S	D	E	N	1971	58969
8198	S	D	E	N	1973	51829
8198	S	D	R	N	1973	54504
8198	S	D	E	N	1973	54505
8198	S	D	R	N	1973	55068
8198	S	D	E	N	1974	55069

Substance Number	Phys. State	Subject	Language	Temperature	Year	EPIC Number
104-8213	A	D	E	N	1974	53726
8213	A	E	E	N	1974	53726
8213	T	D	E	N	1974	53726
8213	T	E	E	N	1974	53726
8215	S	D	E	N	1973	59166
8215	T	D	E	N	1973	59166
8231	S	D	E	N	1974	54037
8231	S	D	E	N	1975	66621
8231	S	E	E	N	1975	66621
8231	S	T	E	N	1975	66621
8238	D	D	R	N	1973	55176
8238	D	D	E	N	1974	55177
8242	S	D	E	N	1973	62296
8242	S	D	E	N	1974	62323
8242	S	D	E	N	1974	64489
8242	S	T	E	N	1974	64489
8242	S	D	E	N	1974	87448
8242	S	D	E	N	1975	101661
8242	S	S	E	N	1975	101661
8251	D	D	E	N	1974	57989
8257	D	T	R	N	1970	52334
8259	S	D	E	L	1973	58912
8259	S	D	E	N	1973	58912
8259	S	D	F	N	1975	96044
8259	S	E	F	N	1975	96044
8259	S	T	F	N	1975	96044
8265	G	S	E	N	1973	53059
8266	G	S	E	N	1973	53059
8293	T	D	E	N	1973	55542
8316	S	D	E	N	1975	96701
8316	S	T	E	N	1975	96701
8423	A	D	E	N	1975	90859
8423	A	T	E	N	1975	90859
8423	T	D	E	N	1975	90859
8423	T	T	E	N	1975	90859
8432	S	D	E	N	1976	101851
8432	S	E	E	N	1976	101851
8432	S	T	E	N	1976	101851
8445	T	D	R	N	1974	66752
8445	T	D	E	N	1975	66753
106-0001	G	D	E	N	1971	63677
0001	G	E	E	N	1971	63677
0002	G	D	E	N	1971	63677
0002	G	E	E	N	1971	63677
0003	G	T	E	N	1973	50969
0003	G	D	E	N	1972	53253
0003	G	D	R	N	1973	54369
0003	G	T	R	N	1973	54369
0003	G	D	E	N	1973	54370
0003	G	T	E	N	1973	54370
0003	G	T	R	N	1973	56859
0003	G	D	E	N	1974	57914
0003	G	E	E	N	1974	57914
0003	G	S	E	N	1974	57914
0003	G	D	E	H	1974	61333
0003	G	D	E	N	1974	61333
0003	G	E	E	H	1974	61333
0003	G	E	E	N	1974	61333
0003	G	D	E	N	1971	63677
0003	G	E	E	N	1971	63677
0003	G	D	R	N	1972	67400
0003	G	D	E	N	1966	85734
0003	G	D	R	H	1974	87314
0003	G	D	R	N	1974	87314
0003	G	S	R	H	1974	87314
0003	G	S	R	N	1974	87314
0003	G	D	E	H	1974	87315
0003	G	D	E	N	1974	87315
0003	G	S	E	H	1974	87315
0003	G	S	E	N	1974	87315
0003	G	D	E	N	1976	101446
0003	G	S	E	N	1976	101446
0003	G	T	E	N	1976	101446
0003	G	T	E	N	1976	101465
0003	G	S	E	N	1975	103142
0004	S	S	E	N	1974	59353
0004	S	S	E	N	1973	62815
0004	S	S	E	N	1973	64495
0005	S	D	F	N	1958	75815
0005	S	T	F	N	1958	75815
0005	S	S	E	N	1971	87883
0006	A	D	E	N	1973	60693
0006	D	D	E	N	1972	50486
0006	D	E	E	N	1972	50486
0006	D	D	E	N	1973	50633
0006	D	D	E	N	1972	50943
0006	D	D	E	N	1973	51581
0006	D	T	E	N	1973	52028
0006	D	D	R	N	1973	52902
0006	D	D	E	N	1974	52903
0006	D	D	E	L	1973	53580
0006	D	D	R	N	1973	53661
0006	D	D	E	N	1974	53662
0006	D	D	E	N	1973	53785
0006	D	D	E	L	1973	53790
0006	D	D	E	N	1973	53790
0006	D	D	E	N	1974	54564
0006	D	D	E	N	1973	54775
0006	D	D	E	N	1973	54807
0006	D	D	R	N	1973	55221

Substance Number	Phys. State	Subject	Language	Temperature	Year	EPIC Number
106-0006	D	D	E	N	1974	55222
0006	D	D	E	N	1974	55254
0006	D	D	E	L	1973	55608
0006	D	D	E	N	1973	55608
0006	D	T	E	L	1973	55608
0006	D	T	E	N	1973	55608
0006	D	S	E	N	1973	56362
0006	D	D	R	L	1973	56574
0006	D	D	R	N	1973	56574
0006	D	T	R	N	1973	56574
0006	D	D	E	L	1973	57404
0006	D	S	E	L	1973	57404
0006	D	T	E	L	1973	57404
0006	D	D	E	N	1974	57912
0006	D	S	E	N	1974	57968
0006	D	T	E	N	1974	58696
0006	D	S	E	N	1973	59375
0006	D	D	E	N	1974	59393
0006	D	D	E	N	1972	60077
0006	D	D	R	N	1974	60487
0006	D	S	R	N	1974	60487
0006	D	D	E	N	1974	60488
0006	D	S	E	N	1974	60488
0006	D	D	E	N	1973	60586
0006	D	T	E	N	1973	60588
0006	D	D	E	L	1973	60590
0006	D	D	E	N	1973	60754
0006	D	D	E	N	1973	60868
0006	D	D	E	N	1971	61262
0006	D	S	E	N	1971	61262
0006	D	D	E	L	1974	61371
0006	D	S	E	L	1974	61371
0006	D	T	E	L	1974	61371
0006	D	D	E	L	1974	61372
0006	D	T	E	L	1974	61372
0006	D	D	R	N	1972	62099
0006	D	S	R	N	1972	62099
0006	D	D	E	L	1973	62286
0006	D	D	E	N	1973	62286
0006	D	D	E	N	1974	62305
0006	D	D	E	N	1974	62306
0006	D	T	E	N	1974	62315
0006	D	D	E	N	1974	62535
0006	D	D	E	N	1974	62555
0006	D	D	R	N	1972	62850
0006	D	D	E	N	1972	63824
0006	D	D	E	N	1972	65169
0006	D	T	E	N	1974	65257
0006	D	D	R	N	1971	66296
0006	D	D	E	N	1971	66297
0006	D	D	E	L	1975	66689
0006	D	D	E	N	1972	67086
0006	D	S	E	N	1972	67086
0006	D	S	E	N	1973	68817
0006	D	D	E	N	1973	68842
0006	D	D	E	N	1973	68859
0006	D	D	E	N	1973	68867
0006	D	D	E	N	1973	68868
0006	D	D	E	N	1973	68870
0006	D	D	E	N	1971	70653
0006	D	D	R	N	1973	71644
0006	D	D	E	L	1973	72152
0006	D	S	E	L	1973	72152
0006	D	D	E	L	1964	75090
0006	D	S	R	N	1974	77830
0006	D	D	E	N	1971	80226
0006	D	D	E	L	1974	80552
0006	D	D	E	N	1974	80552
0006	D	D	E	N	1973	81520
0006	D	D	O	N	1970	83843
0006	D	D	E	N	1975	87197
0006	D	D	E	N	1974	88513
0006	D	D	E	N	1975	89292
0006	D	D	R	L	1963	91918
0006	D	D	E	N	1974	93147
0006	D	D	E	L	1975	93283
0006	D	D	E	N	1975	93283
0006	D	D	E	N	1975	93335
0006	D	D	E	N	1975	93386
0006	D	D	E	L	1975	93527
0006	D	D	E	N	1975	93527
0006	D	D	R	N	1974	94022
0006	D	D	E	N	1975	94023
0006	D	D	E	N	1976	95369
0006	D	E	E	N	1976	95369
0006	D	S	E	N	1974	95926
0006	D	D	E	N	1974	96710
0006	D	T	E	N	1974	96710
0006	D	T	E	N	1975	99137
0006	D	D	R	L	1975	100849
0006	D	D	R	N	1975	100849
0006	D	T	R	L	1975	100849
0006	D	T	R	N	1975	100849
0006	D	D	E	L	1976	100850
0006	D	D	E	N	1976	100850
0006	D	T	E	L	1976	100850
0006	D	T	E	N	1976	100850
0006	D	D	E	N	1975	101018
0006	D	D	R	N	1976	101471
0006	D	T	R	N	1976	101471
0006	D	E	E	N	1976	101562

Phys. State: **A.** Amorphous; **C.** Superconductive; **D.** Doped; **F.** Fibrous or Whisker; **G.** Gas; **I.** Ionized or Plasma; **L.** Liquid; **P.** Powder or Particle; **S.** Solid; **T.** Thin Film
Subject: **D.** Data; **E.** Experiment; **S.** Survey (Review, Compendium, etc.); **T.** Theory
Language: **E.** English; **F.** French; **G.** German; **O.** Other Languages; **R.** Russian
Temperature: **L.** Low (0 to 75K); **N.** Normal (75 to 1273K); **H.** High (above 1273K)

Substance Number	Phys. State	Subject	Language	Temperature	Year	EPIC Number
106-0006	D	D	E	N	1975	101676
0006	D	D	E	N	1975	101677
0006	D	T	E	N	1975	101677
0006	D	D	E	N	1976	101821
0006	D	E	E	N	1976	101821
0006	D	T	E	N	1976	101821
0006	D	D	E	N	1976	101829
0006	D	T	E	N	1976	101829
0006	D	D	E	N	1976	101858
0006	D	T	E	N	1976	101858
0006	D	D	E	N	1976	101859
0006	D	T	E	N	1976	101859
0006	D	D	E	N	1972	101925
0006	D	T	E	N	1972	101925
0006	D	D	E	N	1976	102037
0006	D	T	E	N	1976	102037
0006	D	S	E	N	1976	102567
0006	D	D	E	N	1976	103336
0006	D	T	E	N	1976	103336
0006	L	D	R	N	1973	55759
0006	L	D	E	N	1973	57778
0006	L	D	R	N	1971	66296
0006	L	D	E	N	1971	66297
0006	S	D	E	N	1972	49936
0006	S	D	R	N	1973	51380
0006	S	D	E	N	1973	51381
0006	S	D	E	N	1973	51581
0006	S	S	E	N	1974	52799
0006	S	D	E	N	1972	53090
0006	S	D	E	N	1972	53244
0006	S	E	E	N	1972	53244
0006	S	S	E	N	1972	53244
0006	S	S	E	N	1972	53246
0006	S	T	E	N	1972	53246
0006	S	S	E	N	1972	53247
0006	S	D	E	N	1973	53579
0006	S	D	E	N	1974	53619
0006	S	S	E	N	1974	53619
0006	S	T	E	N	1973	53789
0006	S	D	E	N	1974	54024
0006	S	D	E	N	1973	54214
0006	S	T	E	N	1973	54214
0006	S	D	E	N	1974	54352
0006	S	E	E	N	1974	54352
0006	S	D	E	N	1973	54653
0006	S	S	E	N	1973	54773
0006	S	D	E	N	1973	54775
0006	S	D	E	N	1972	55100
0006	S	T	E	N	1972	55100
0006	S	D	E	N	1972	55152
0006	S	S	E	L	1972	55357
0006	S	S	E	N	1972	55357
0006	S	D	R	N	1973	55759
0006	S	D	R	N	1973	55777
0006	S	D	E	H	1973	55841
0006	S	D	E	N	1973	55841
0006	S	T	E	H	1973	55841
0006	S	T	E	N	1973	55841
0006	S	D	R	N	1972	56208
0006	S	D	E	N	1973	57710
0006	S	D	E	N	1973	57778
0006	S	D	E	N	1974	57912
0006	S	D	E	N	1973	58212
0006	S	S	E	N	1973	58212
0006	S	T	E	L	1974	58821
0006	S	T	E	N	1974	58821
0006	S	D	E	L	1973	59611
0006	S	D	E	N	1973	59611
0006	S	S	E	L	1973	59611
0006	S	S	E	N	1973	59611
0006	S	D	E	N	1971	59626
0006	S	D	E	L	1970	59675
0006	S	D	E	N	1974	60380
0006	S	D	R	N	1974	60463
0006	S	D	E	N	1974	60464
0006	S	D	E	N	1973	60582
0006	S	D	E	L	1974	60657
0006	S	D	E	N	1974	60657
0006	S	T	E	L	1974	60657
0006	S	T	E	N	1974	60657
0006	S	D	E	N	1974	60672
0006	S	S	E	N	1974	60672
0006	S	D	E	N	1973	60693
0006	S	D	E	N	1973	60694
0006	S	D	E	N	1973	60754
0006	S	S	E	N	1973	60837
0006	S	D	E	N	1973	60867
0006	S	S	E	N	1973	60867
0006	S	D	G	N	1972	61011
0006	S	D	E	N	1971	61262
0006	S	S	E	N	1971	61262
0006	S	D	E	N	1971	61706
0006	S	E	E	N	1971	61706
0006	S	D	E	N	1969	62248
0006	S	D	E	N	1973	62274
0006	S	S	E	N	1973	62274
0006	S	D	E	N	1972	62275
0006	S	S	E	N	1972	62275
0006	S	D	E	L	1973	62286
0006	S	D	E	N	1973	62286
0006	S	D	E	N	1974	62295

Substance Number	Phys. State	Subject	Language	Temperature	Year	EPIC Number
106-0006	S	D	E	N	1974	62305
0006	S	D	E	N	1974	62309
0006	S	D	E	N	1974	62313
0006	S	S	E	N	1974	62314
0006	S	D	E	N	1974	62316
0006	S	D	E	N	1969	62324
0006	S	D	E	N	1973	62325
0006	S	D	E	N	1974	62525
0006	S	S	E	N	1974	62525
0006	S	D	R	N	1973	62862
0006	S	S	E	N	1949	63242
0006	S	E	E	N	1975	63256
0006	S	T	E	N	1975	63256
0006	S	D	E	L	1975	63327
0006	S	D	E	N	1975	63327
0006	S	E	E	N	1975	63327
0006	S	S	E	N	1975	63327
0006	S	D	E	N	1975	63328
0006	S	E	E	N	1975	63328
0006	S	S	E	N	1970	63588
0006	S	D	E	N	1972	63824
0006	S	D	R	N	1970	64286
0006	S	D	E	N	1974	64494
0006	S	D	E	N	1974	65105
0006	S	D	E	N	1973	65167
0006	S	S	E	N	1975	65501
0006	S	S	E	N	1975	65507
0006	S	T	E	N	1974	65612
0006	S	D	E	N	1974	65616
0006	S	D	E	N	1970	68416
0006	S	S	E	N	1973	68817
0006	S	D	E	N	1972	68832
0006	S	D	E	N	1973	68841
0006	S	D	E	N	1973	68842
0006	S	D	E	N	1973	68843
0006	S	D	E	N	1973	68844
0006	S	D	E	N	1973	68849
0006	S	D	E	N	1973	68850
0006	S	D	E	N	1973	68851
0006	S	D	E	N	1973	68853
0006	S	D	E	N	1973	68857
0006	S	D	E	N	1973	68859
0006	S	D	E	N	1973	68866
0006	S	D	E	N	1973	68869
0006	S	D	E	N	1973	68870
0006	S	D	E	N	1973	68871
0006	S	S	E	N	1972	68907
0006	S	D	E	L	1973	72152
0006	S	S	E	L	1973	72152
0006	S	S	G	N	1942	73252
0006	S	S	E	N	1924	73267
0006	S	D	E	N	1938	74974
0006	S	T	E	N	1938	74974
0006	S	D	F	N	1958	75815
0006	S	T	F	N	1958	75815
0006	S	S	R	N	1974	77920
0006	S	D	O	N	1970	83843
0006	S	D	E	N	1969	85421
0006	S	D	E	N	1975	87197
0006	S	D	E	N	1974	87448
0006	S	S	E	N	1974	87759
0006	S	S	E	N	1971	87883
0006	S	D	E	N	1974	88274
0006	S	D	E	N	1974	88485
0006	S	D	E	N	1975	88493
0006	S	D	E	N	1974	88513
0006	S	D	E	N	1975	89292
0006	S	D	E	N	1975	89451
0006	S	S	E	N	1975	89451
0006	S	T	E	N	1975	89451
0006	S	D	E	N	1975	89669
0006	S	E	E	N	1975	89669
0006	S	S	E	N	1975	91730
0006	S	D	E	N	1975	92033
0006	S	E	E	N	1975	92033
0006	S	D	E	N	1974	93147
0006	S	D	E	N	1975	93161
0006	S	D	E	N	1975	93177
0006	S	D	E	N	1975	93187
0006	S	D	E	N	1975	93316
0006	S	D	E	N	1975	93318
0006	S	D	E	N	1974	93325
0006	S	D	E	N	1975	93335
0006	S	D	E	N	1974	93346
0006	S	T	E	N	1974	93346
0006	S	D	E	N	1974	93374
0006	S	D	E	N	1975	94099
0006	S	D	E	N	1975	94150
0006	S	D	E	N	1975	94479
0006	S	S	E	N	1974	94516
0006	S	D	E	N	1976	95369
0006	S	E	E	N	1976	95369
0006	S	E	E	N	1975	97222
0006	S	S	E	N	1975	97222
0006	S	T	E	N	1975	97222
0006	S	D	E	N	1976	97225
0006	S	D	E	N	1976	97227
0006	S	D	E	N	1976	97230
0006	S	S	E	N	1976	97297
0006	S	D	E	N	1976	97298
0006	S	D	E	N	1975	98390

Substance Number	Phys. State	Subject	Language	Temperature	Year	EPIC Number
106-0006	S	T	E	N	1975	98390
0006	S	D	E	N	1976	98408
0006	S	E	E	N	1976	98408
0006	S	T	E	N	1976	98408
0006	S	E	E	N	1976	99549
0006	S	D	E	N	1976	99870
0006	S	S	E	N	1976	99870
0006	S	D	E	N	1976	99984
0006	S	T	E	N	1976	99984
0006	S	D	E	N	1976	100786
0006	S	T	E	N	1976	100786
0006	S	S	E	L	1975	101010
0006	S	S	E	N	1975	101010
0006	S	S	E	N	1975	101011
0006	S	T	E	N	1975	101011
0006	S	T	E	L	1975	101014
0006	S	T	E	N	1975	101014
0006	S	D	E	N	1975	101018
0006	S	D	E	N	1975	101026
0006	S	S	E	N	1975	101034
0006	S	D	E	N	1975	101035
0006	S	E	E	N	1975	101035
0006	S	D	E	N	1975	101041
0006	S	E	E	N	1975	101041
0006	S	S	E	N	1976	101374
0006	S	S	E	N	1976	101377
0006	S	D	E	N	1976	101441
0006	S	E	E	N	1976	101562
0006	S	D	R	N	1975	101612
0006	S	T	R	N	1975	101612
0006	S	D	E	N	1976	101613
0006	S	T	E	N	1976	101613
0006	S	D	E	N	1975	101660
0006	S	T	E	N	1975	101660
0006	S	S	E	N	1975	101661
0006	S	D	E	N	1975	101663
0006	S	E	E	N	1975	101663
0006	S	D	E	N	1975	101665
0006	S	E	E	N	1975	101665
0006	S	T	E	N	1975	101665
0006	S	D	E	N	1975	101667
0006	S	T	E	N	1975	101667
0006	S	D	E	N	1975	101675
0006	S	T	E	N	1975	101675
0006	S	D	E	N	1975	101676
0006	S	D	E	N	1976	101714
0006	S	E	E	N	1976	101714
0006	S	T	E	N	1976	101714
0006	S	D	E	N	1976	101796
0006	S	E	E	N	1976	101796
0006	S	D	E	N	1976	101808
0006	S	D	E	N	1976	101810
0006	S	T	E	N	1976	101810
0006	S	S	E	N	1976	101811
0006	S	D	E	N	1976	101812
0006	S	T	E	N	1976	101812
0006	S	D	E	N	1976	101813
0006	S	E	E	N	1976	101813
0006	S	D	E	N	1976	101821
0006	S	E	E	N	1976	101821
0006	S	T	E	N	1976	101821
0006	S	D	E	N	1976	101829
0006	S	T	E	N	1976	101829
0006	S	T	E	N	1976	101830
0006	S	E	E	N	1976	101834
0006	S	D	E	N	1976	101835
0006	S	E	E	N	1976	101835
0006	S	S	E	N	1976	101835
0006	S	T	E	N	1976	101835
0006	S	D	E	N	1976	101844
0006	S	T	E	N	1976	101844
0006	S	D	E	N	1976	101847
0006	S	E	E	N	1976	101847
0006	S	S	E	N	1976	101847
0006	S	T	E	N	1976	101847
0006	S	D	E	N	1976	101849
0006	S	E	E	N	1976	101849
0006	S	S	E	N	1976	101849
0006	S	T	E	N	1976	101849
0006	S	D	E	N	1976	101850
0006	S	E	E	N	1976	101850
0006	S	D	E	N	1976	101851
0006	S	E	E	N	1976	101851
0006	S	T	E	N	1976	101851
0006	S	D	E	N	1972	101925
0006	S	T	E	N	1972	101925
0006	S	D	E	N	1976	102042
0006	S	E	E	N	1976	102042
0006	S	S	E	N	1975	102056
0006	S	S	E	N	1976	102567
0006	S	D	E	N	1976	103154
0006	S	S	E	N	1976	103154
0006	S	T	E	N	1976	103154
0006	S	D	E	N	1976	103402
0006	S	E	E	N	1976	103402
0006	S	T	E	N	1976	103402
0006	S	D	E	N	1976	103590
0006	S	T	E	N	1976	103590
0006	S	D	E	N	1976	103591
0006	S	T	E	N	1976	103591
0006	T	D	E	N	1973	60693

Phys. State: **A.** Amorphous; **C.** Superconductive; **D.** Doped; **F.** Fibrous or Whisker; **G.** Gas; **I.** Ionized or Plasma; **L.** Liquid; **P.** Powder or Particle; **S.** Solid; **T.** Thin Film
Subject: **D.** Data; **E.** Experiment; **S.** Survey (Review, Compendium, etc.); **T.** Theory
Language: **E.** English; **F.** French; **G.** German; **O.** Other Languages; **R.** Russian
Temperature: **L.** Low (0 to 75K); **N.** Normal (75 to 1273K); **H.** High (above 1273K)

Substance Number	Phys. State	Subject	Language	Temperature	Year	EPIC Number
106-0006	T	D	E	N	1970	62185
0006	T	T	E	N	1970	62185
0006	T	D	E	N	1974	68831
0006	T	D	E	N	1975	93177
0006	T	D	E	N	1976	99920
0006	T	E	E	N	1976	99920
0006	T	T	E	N	1976	99920
0006	T	D	E	N	1975	101655
0006	T	T	E	N	1976	101808
0006	T	D	E	N	1976	101833
0008	G	D	E	N	1965	75866
0008	G	T	E	N	1965	75866
0008	G	D	E	L	1967	75868
0008	G	T	E	L	1967	75868
0008	G	S	E	N	1975	103142
0008	S	D	E	L	1965	75866
0008	S	E	E	L	1965	75866
0008	S	T	E	L	1965	75866
0008	S	D	E	L	1967	75868
0008	S	T	E	L	1967	75868
0008	S	S	E	L	1962	75890
0009	D	D	R	N	1973	54419
0009	D	D	E	N	1973	54420
0009	D	D	E	N	1974	93376
0009	L	D	E	N	1973	53703
0009	L	D	R	N	1973	54419
0009	L	D	E	N	1973	54420
0011	L	D	E	N	1969	62324
0011	L	S	R	N	1972	65883
0011	L	T	R	N	1972	65883
0011	L	S	E	N	1972	65884
0011	L	T	E	N	1972	65884
0011	L	S	E	N	1924	73267
0018	S	D	E	N	1973	52188
0021	G	D	E	N	1971	63677
0021	G	E	E	N	1971	63677
0023	S	S	E	N	1974	58014
0024	D	D	E	N	1973	51799
0024	D	D	E	N	1973	53785
0024	D	D	E	L	1973	55608
0024	D	D	E	N	1973	55608
0024	D	T	E	L	1973	55608
0024	D	T	E	N	1973	55608
0024	D	S	E	N	1973	56362
0024	D	D	E	L	1973	57138
0024	D	E	E	L	1973	57138
0024	D	T	E	L	1973	57404
0024	D	D	E	N	1971	61262
0024	D	D	R	N	1972	62099
0024	D	S	R	N	1972	62099
0024	D	D	E	N	1974	62758
0024	D	D	E	N	1972	67086
0024	D	S	E	N	1972	67086
0024	D	D	E	N	1971	70653
0024	D	D	R	N	1974	77830
0024	D	T	R	N	1974	77830
0024	D	D	E	N	1975	90068
0024	D	S	E	N	1975	90068
0024	D	T	E	N	1975	91874
0024	D	D	E	L	1975	93527
0024	D	D	E	N	1975	93527
0024	D	D	E	N	1974	95926
0024	D	T	E	N	1974	95926
0024	D	D	E	N	1975	96659
0024	D	T	E	N	1975	96659
0024	D	D	E	L	1968	98671
0024	D	D	E	N	1976	102041
0024	D	S	E	N	1976	102041
0024	D	T	E	N	1976	102041
0024	D	D	E	N	1976	103336
0024	D	T	E	N	1976	103336
0024	L	D	E	N	1972	75340
0024	S	S	E	N	1973	50936
0024	S	T	E	N	1973	52040
0024	S	S	E	N	1972	53244
0024	S	S	E	N	1972	53246
0024	S	T	E	N	1972	53246
0024	S	S	E	N	1972	53247
0024	S	S	E	N	1972	53248
0024	S	D	E	N	1974	53619
0024	S	S	E	N	1974	53619
0024	S	D	E	N	1974	53620
0024	S	T	E	N	1973	53789
0024	S	D	E	N	1974	54024
0024	S	D	E	N	1973	54214
0024	S	T	E	N	1973	54214
0024	S	S	E	N	1973	54773
0024	S	D	E	N	1972	55100
0024	S	T	E	N	1972	55100
0024	S	S	E	L	1972	55357
0024	S	S	E	N	1972	55357
0024	S	D	R	N	1973	55777
0024	S	D	E	H	1973	55841
0024	S	D	E	N	1973	55841
0024	S	T	E	H	1973	55841
0024	S	T	E	N	1973	55841
0024	S	S	E	N	1973	56749
0024	S	D	E	N	1973	58212
0024	S	S	E	N	1973	58212
0024	S	D	E	N	1974	58821
0024	S	D	E	N	1974	58822
106-0024	S	T	E	N	1974	58822
0024	S	D	E	L	1974	58962
0024	S	D	E	L	1973	59611
0024	S	D	E	N	1973	59611
0024	S	S	E	L	1973	59611
0024	S	S	E	N	1973	59611
0024	S	D	E	L	1970	59675
0024	S	T	E	N	1970	59683
0024	S	D	R	N	1973	59726
0024	S	D	E	N	1973	59727
0024	S	D	R	N	1974	60463
0024	S	D	E	N	1974	60464
0024	S	D	E	L	1974	60657
0024	S	T	E	L	1974	60657
0024	S	D	E	N	1974	60672
0024	S	S	E	N	1974	60672
0024	S	D	G	N	1972	61011
0024	S	E	R	N	1971	61548
0024	S	D	R	N	1974	61934
0024	S	D	E	N	1974	61935
0024	S	D	E	N	1969	62248
0024	S	D	E	N	1973	62274
0024	S	S	E	N	1973	62274
0024	S	T	E	N	1973	62274
0024	S	D	E	N	1972	62275
0024	S	S	E	N	1972	62275
0024	S	D	E	N	1969	62324
0024	S	D	E	N	1974	62547
0024	S	S	E	N	1974	62547
0024	S	T	E	N	1974	62547
0024	S	D	R	N	1973	62862
0024	S	D	R	N	1974	63022
0024	S	T	R	N	1974	63022
0024	S	D	E	N	1974	63023
0024	S	T	E	N	1974	63023
0024	S	S	E	N	1949	63242
0024	S	D	E	L	1975	63327
0024	S	D	E	N	1975	63327
0024	S	S	E	N	1975	63327
0024	S	D	E	N	1975	63332
0024	S	S	E	N	1975	63332
0024	S	D	E	N	1973	65167
0024	S	S	E	N	1975	65501
0024	S	T	E	N	1974	65612
0024	S	E	E	N	1971	65901
0024	S	D	E	N	1972	68832
0024	S	D	E	N	1973	68843
0024	S	T	E	N	1973	68847
0024	S	D	E	N	1973	68849
0024	S	D	E	N	1973	68850
0024	S	D	E	N	1973	68851
0024	S	D	E	N	1973	68871
0024	S	D	E	L	1973	72152
0024	S	S	E	N	1924	73267
0024	S	D	E	N	1938	74974
0024	S	T	E	N	1938	74974
0024	S	D	E	N	1972	75340
0024	S	D	F	N	1958	75815
0024	S	T	F	N	1958	75815
0024	S	S	E	N	1972	86318
0024	S	T	E	N	1972	86318
0024	S	D	E	N	1975	87185
0024	S	S	E	N	1974	87759
0024	S	T	O	N	1974	87783
0024	S	S	E	N	1971	87883
0024	S	D	E	N	1975	88493
0024	S	S	E	N	1975	91730
0024	S	D	E	N	1975	92033
0024	S	E	E	N	1975	92033
0024	S	D	E	N	1975	93160
0024	S	E	E	N	1975	93160
0024	S	D	E	N	1975	93316
0024	S	D	E	N	1974	93339
0024	S	D	E	N	1975	93379
0024	S	D	E	N	1975	93386
0024	S	D	R	N	1974	94022
0024	S	D	E	N	1975	94023
0024	S	S	E	N	1976	97297
0024	S	D	E	N	1976	97298
0024	S	D	E	N	1975	98390
0024	S	D	F	N	1976	99169
0024	S	E	F	N	1976	99169
0024	S	E	E	N	1976	99549
0024	S	D	E	N	1976	100019
0024	S	E	E	N	1976	100019
0024	S	S	E	N	1975	101010
0024	S	D	E	N	1975	101013
0024	S	T	E	N	1975	101013
0024	S	D	E	N	1975	101018
0024	S	S	E	N	1975	101034
0024	S	D	E	N	1975	101035
0024	S	E	E	N	1975	101035
0024	S	D	E	L	1976	101287
0024	S	D	E	N	1976	101287
0024	S	S	E	L	1976	101287
0024	S	S	E	N	1976	101287
0024	S	S	E	N	1976	101374
0024	S	D	E	N	1976	101441
0024	S	D	E	N	1975	101665
0024	S	E	E	N	1975	101665
0024	S	T	E	N	1975	101665
106-0024	S	D	E	N	1976	101714
0024	S	E	E	N	1976	101714
0024	S	T	E	N	1976	101714
0024	S	S	E	N	1976	101811
0024	S	T	E	N	1976	101830
0024	S	D	E	N	1976	101843
0024	S	S	E	L	1976	101843
0024	S	S	E	N	1976	101843
0024	S	T	E	N	1976	101843
0024	S	D	E	N	1976	101847
0024	S	E	E	N	1976	101847
0024	S	S	E	N	1976	101847
0024	S	T	E	N	1976	101847
0024	S	D	E	N	1976	101850
0024	S	E	E	N	1976	101850
0024	S	D	E	N	1976	101851
0024	S	E	E	N	1976	101851
0024	S	T	E	N	1976	101851
0024	S	D	E	N	1976	102042
0024	S	E	E	N	1976	102042
0024	S	S	E	N	1975	102056
0024	S	D	E	N	1976	103590
0024	S	T	E	N	1976	103590
0024	T	S	O	N	1965	61141
0024	T	D	E	N	1970	62185
0024	T	T	E	N	1970	62185
0024	T	T	E	N	1973	63774
0026	D	D	E	N	1973	52079
0026	D	D	R	N	1973	54496
0026	D	D	E	N	1973	54497
0026	D	D	E	N	1974	62327
0026	D	T	E	N	1974	62327
0026	D	D	E	N	1973	63527
0026	D	D	E	L	1974	65038
0026	D	D	E	N	1975	68675
0026	D	E	E	L	1975	68675
0026	D	D	E	N	1974	70528
0026	D	D	R	L	1975	89648
0026	D	T	R	L	1975	89648
0026	D	D	E	L	1975	89649
0026	D	T	E	L	1975	89649
0026	D	D	R	N	1975	93622
0026	D	T	R	N	1975	93622
0026	D	D	R	N	1975	93623
0026	D	T	R	N	1975	93623
0026	D	D	E	N	1975	93628
0026	D	S	E	N	1975	99263
0026	D	D	R	N	1975	101124
0026	D	T	R	N	1975	101124
0026	D	D	E	N	1975	101125
0026	D	T	E	N	1975	101125
0026	D	D	E	L	1973	101947
0026	D	T	E	L	1973	101947
0026	D	D	E	N	1975	102032
0026	D	T	E	N	1975	102032
0026	D	D	E	N	1975	102033
0026	D	T	E	N	1975	102033
0026	P	D	E	N	1976	97225
0026	S	S	E	N	1972	53246
0026	S	T	E	N	1972	53246
0026	S	S	E	N	1972	53248
0026	S	S	E	N	1972	53512
0026	S	D	E	N	1974	54024
0026	S	D	E	N	1973	58212
0026	S	S	E	N	1973	58212
0026	S	S	E	N	1974	59353
0026	S	D	E	N	1973	61754
0026	S	D	E	N	1971	62186
0026	S	D	E	N	1974	62305
0026	S	S	E	N	1949	63242
0026	S	D	E	L	1975	63327
0026	S	D	E	N	1975	63327
0026	S	S	E	N	1975	63327
0026	S	S	E	N	1970	65877
0026	S	D	E	N	1972	68832
0026	S	D	E	N	1973	68841
0026	S	D	E	N	1973	68865
0026	S	S	E	L	1974	70528
0026	S	S	E	N	1974	70528
0026	S	D	E	N	1952	73261
0026	S	S	E	N	1924	73267
0026	S	D	E	L	1967	74607
0026	S	D	E	N	1967	74607
0026	S	E	E	L	1967	74607
0026	S	E	E	N	1967	74607
0026	S	D	R	L	1974	87288
0026	S	D	E	L	1975	87289
0026	S	S	E	N	1971	87883
0026	S	D	E	N	1975	88493
0026	S	D	E	N	1974	88513
0026	S	D	E	N	1975	89371
0026	S	S	E	N	1975	89371
0026	S	D	E	N	1975	93316
0026	S	D	E	N	1975	93324
0026	S	D	E	N	1975	93328
0026	S	D	E	N	1975	93334
0026	S	D	E	N	1975	93378
0026	S	D	R	N	1975	93622
0026	S	T	R	N	1975	93622
0026	S	D	E	N	1975	94479
0026	S	D	E	N	1976	97225

Phys. State: **A.** Amorphous; **C.** Superconductive; **D.** Doped; **F.** Fibrous or Whisker; **G.** Gas; **I.** Ionized or Plasma; **L.** Liquid; **P.** Powder or Particle; **S.** Solid; **T.** Thin Film
Subject: **D.** Data; **E.** Experiment; **S.** Survey (Review, Compendium, etc.); **T.** Theory
Language: **E.** English; **F.** French; **G.** German; **O.** Other Languages; **R.** Russian
Temperature: **L.** Low (0 to 75K); **N.** Normal (75 to 1273K); **H.** High (above 1273K)

Substance Number	Phys. State	Subject	Language	Temperature	Year	EPIC Number
106-0026	S	S	E	N	1976	97297
0026	S	D	E	N	1976	97298
0026	S	D	E	N	1976	99118
0026	S	E	E	N	1976	99118
0026	S	S	E	N	1976	99118
0026	S	T	E	N	1976	99118
0026	S	D	E	N	1976	99870
0026	S	D	E	N	1975	101016
0026	S	D	E	N	1975	101017
0026	S	S	E	L	1975	101017
0026	S	S	E	N	1975	101034
0026	S	D	E	N	1976	101441
0026	S	D	E	N	1976	101650
0026	S	D	E	N	1975	101664
0026	S	E	E	N	1975	101664
0026	S	T	E	N	1975	101664
0026	S	D	E	N	1975	101668
0026	S	S	E	N	1975	101668
0026	S	D	E	N	1975	101669
0026	S	T	E	N	1975	101669
0026	S	D	E	N	1975	101670
0026	S	E	E	N	1975	101670
0026	S	D	E	N	1976	101714
0026	S	E	E	N	1976	101714
0026	S	T	E	N	1976	101714
0026	S	D	E	N	1976	101796
0026	S	E	E	N	1976	101796
0026	S	D	E	N	1976	101808
0026	S	S	E	N	1976	101811
0026	S	D	E	N	1976	101824
0026	S	E	E	N	1976	101824
0026	S	D	E	N	1976	101826
0026	S	D	E	N	1976	101837
0026	S	E	E	N	1976	101837
0026	S	T	E	N	1976	101837
0026	S	D	E	N	1976	101850
0026	S	E	E	N	1976	101850
0026	S	D	E	N	1976	101851
0026	S	E	E	N	1976	101851
0026	S	T	E	N	1976	101851
0026	S	D	E	N	1976	101852
0026	S	E	E	N	1976	101852
0026	S	T	E	N	1976	101852
0026	S	D	E	N	1976	101861
0026	S	E	E	N	1976	101861
0026	S	D	E	N	1976	101862
0026	S	D	E	L	1973	101947
0026	S	T	E	L	1973	101947
0026	S	D	E	N	1975	102033
0026	S	T	E	N	1975	102033
0026	S	D	E	N	1976	102042
0026	S	E	E	N	1976	102042
0026	S	D	E	N	1976	103590
0026	S	T	E	N	1976	103590
0026	T	D	E	N	1975	63255
0026	T	S	E	N	1976	101374
0026	T	D	E	N	1976	101824
0026	T	E	E	N	1976	101824
0031	T	D	E	N	1970	62185
0031	T	T	E	N	1970	62185
0033	S	D	E	N	1973	52188
0035	A	D	E	N	1974	91879
0035	A	S	E	N	1974	91879
0035	A	S	E	N	1974	93380
0035	A	T	E	N	1974	93381
0035	D	D	R	N	1973	52842
0035	D	D	E	N	1973	52843
0035	D	D	R	N	1973	55310
0035	D	D	R	N	1973	59077
0035	D	D	E	N	1973	59078
0035	D	D	E	N	1974	59235
0035	D	D	R	N	1973	59724
0035	D	D	E	N	1973	59725
0035	D	S	R	N	1974	68712
0035	D	S	E	N	1974	68713
0035	D	S	E	N	1965	87702
0035	D	D	E	N	1976	99748
0035	D	S	E	N	1976	99748
0035	D	T	E	N	1976	99748
0035	S	D	R	N	1973	51400
0035	S	D	E	N	1973	51401
0035	S	D	R	N	1973	57365
0035	S	D	R	N	1972	58225
0035	S	D	R	N	1971	62097
0035	S	S	R	N	1971	62097
0035	S	T	R	N	1971	62097
0035	S	D	R	N	1971	62098
0035	S	S	E	N	1975	63320
0035	S	D	R	N	1972	63478
0035	S	D	E	N	1971	64880
0035	S	S	E	N	1971	64880
0035	S	T	E	N	1971	64880
0035	S	S	E	N	1974	65250
0035	S	D	R	L	1968	65348
0035	S	D	R	N	1968	65348
0035	S	D	E	L	1969	65349
0035	S	D	E	N	1969	65349
0035	S	D	E	N	1968	65353
0035	S	D	E	N	1973	65354
0035	S	D	R	N	1974	65403
0035	S	T	R	N	1974	65403

Substance Number	Phys. State	Subject	Language	Temperature	Year	EPIC Number
106-0035	S	D	E	N	1975	65404
0035	S	T	E	N	1975	65404
0035	S	D	R	N	1972	65864
0035	S	D	E	N	1972	65865
0035	S	D	R	L	1972	65866
0035	S	D	R	N	1972	65866
0035	S	D	E	L	1972	65867
0035	S	D	E	N	1972	65867
0035	S	D	E	N	1972	65927
0035	S	D	R	N	1972	66184
0035	S	S	R	N	1972	66184
0035	S	D	E	N	1973	66185
0035	S	S	E	N	1973	66185
0035	S	D	R	N	1972	66186
0035	S	D	E	N	1973	66187
0035	S	D	E	N	1971	67085
0035	S	D	R	N	1973	67554
0035	S	E	R	N	1973	67554
0035	S	D	R	N	1974	68712
0035	S	T	R	N	1974	68712
0035	S	D	E	N	1974	68713
0035	S	T	E	N	1974	68713
0035	S	S	E	L	1965	87702
0035	S	S	E	N	1965	87702
0035	S	S	E	N	1968	87828
0035	S	S	E	N	1971	87883
0035	S	D	R	N	1964	91888
0035	S	T	R	N	1964	91888
0035	S	D	E	N	1976	99748
0035	S	T	E	N	1976	99748
0035	T	D	E	N	1970	62185
0035	T	T	E	N	1970	62185
0035	T	D	E	H	1974	66690
0035	T	D	E	N	1974	66690
0035	T	S	E	N	1974	66690
0035	T	T	E	H	1974	66690
0035	T	T	E	N	1974	66690
0035	T	D	E	N	1974	91879
0035	T	S	E	N	1974	91879
0035	T	D	E	N	1975	95534
0036	T	D	R	N	1973	54996
0036	T	D	E	N	1974	54997
0036	T	D	E	N	1970	62185
0036	T	T	E	N	1970	62185
0036	T	D	E	N	1973	68874
0036	T	D	E	N	1967	75871
0036	T	T	E	N	1967	75871
0045	D	D	R	N	1972	60725
0045	D	D	E	N	1973	60726
0046	S	D	E	N	1973	52188
0052	G	D	E	N	1973	52636
0057	S	S	E	N	1971	70661
0057	T	D	E	L	1973	57559
0057	T	S	E	L	1973	57559
0057	T	S	E	N	1966	68325
0057	T	D	E	N	1968	85433
0058	S	T	R	N	1970	53229
0058	S	T	E	N	1972	53230
0060	S	D	R	N	1973	54395
0060	S	D	E	N	1973	54396
0060	S	D	E	N	1969	62324
0060	T	D	R	N	1973	54395
0060	T	D	E	N	1973	101946
0060	T	T	E	N	1973	101946
0068	S	D	E	N	1972	49919
0081	S	D	E	N	1972	49919
0081	S	D	E	N	1974	58048
0090	S	D	E	N	1973	52485
0104	S	D	E	N	1973	52061
0104	S	D	E	N	1972	59903
0104	S	S	E	N	1971	60103
0104	T	D	E	N	1970	61741
0104	T	S	E	N	1971	87872
0114	S	D	E	L	1973	55558
0114	S	D	E	N	1973	55558
0126	D	D	O	N	1974	87930
0126	D	E	O	N	1974	87930
0126	S	D	E	N	1973	52485
0127	S	D	R	N	1973	50082
0127	S	D	E	N	1973	51428
0127	S	S	R	N	1974	60469
0127	S	S	E	N	1974	60470
0127	S	S	E	N	1962	65952
0127	S	T	E	N	1962	65952
0127	S	D	R	L	1975	87532
0127	S	D	R	N	1975	87532
0127	S	T	R	L	1975	87532
0127	S	T	R	N	1975	87532
0127	S	D	E	L	1975	87533
0127	S	D	E	N	1975	87533
0127	S	T	E	L	1975	87533
0127	S	T	E	N	1975	87533
0127	S	S	E	N	1972	99463
0132	L	D	R	N	1973	61564
0132	L	E	R	N	1973	61564
0132	L	D	E	N	1973	65915
0132	L	E	E	N	1973	65915
0141	S	D	E	N	1974	54348
0141	S	E	E	N	1974	54348
0147	G	D	E	N	1971	63677
0147	G	E	E	N	1971	63677

Substance Number	Phys. State	Subject	Language	Temperature	Year	EPIC Number
106-0156	S	D	E	N	1973	52510
0156	S	E	E	N	1973	52510
0157	S	D	F	N	1958	75815
0157	S	T	F	N	1958	75815
0157	S	D	O	L	1970	101002
0157	T	D	E	N	1975	101021
0158	S	E	E	N	1973	57613
0158	S	D	E	L	1974	61441
0158	S	D	E	N	1974	61441
0158	S	E	E	L	1974	61441
0158	S	E	E	N	1974	61441
0158	S	D	E	N	1969	62324
0158	S	S	E	N	1972	63600
0158	S	T	E	N	1972	63600
0158	S	S	E	N	1970	87822
0158	S	S	E	N	1971	87883
0158	S	S	E	N	1972	87890
0158	S	D	E	L	1975	96701
0158	S	D	E	N	1975	96701
0158	S	T	E	L	1975	96701
0158	S	T	E	N	1975	96701
0158	T	D	E	L	1973	57799
0158	T	S	E	L	1973	57799
0158	T	S	E	N	1961	64344
0159	S	D	E	N	1973	54214
0159	S	T	E	N	1973	54214
0159	S	S	E	N	1975	65501
0159	S	T	E	N	1975	65501
0159	S	D	E	N	1970	83792
0159	S	S	E	N	1970	83792
0165	D	D	E	N	1973	50633
0165	D	D	E	L	1973	57138
0165	D	D	E	N	1973	57138
0165	D	D	E	L	1973	62286
0165	D	D	E	N	1973	62286
0165	D	D	E	N	1974	62479
0165	D	T	E	L	1975	66689
0165	D	D	E	L	1974	80552
0165	D	D	E	N	1974	89309
0165	D	D	E	L	1975	89453
0165	D	T	E	L	1975	89453
0165	D	D	R	L	1975	100849
0165	D	D	R	N	1975	100849
0165	D	T	R	L	1975	100849
0165	D	T	R	N	1975	100849
0165	D	D	E	L	1976	100850
0165	D	D	E	N	1976	100850
0165	D	T	E	L	1976	100850
0165	D	T	E	N	1976	100850
0165	D	D	E	N	1976	101592
0165	D	E	E	N	1976	101592
0165	D	S	E	N	1976	101592
0165	D	T	E	N	1976	101592
0165	D	D	E	N	1976	103336
0165	D	T	E	N	1976	103336
0165	S	D	E	N	1973	50133
0165	S	D	E	N	1973	50566
0165	S	S	E	N	1973	50566
0165	S	D	E	N	1973	54214
0165	S	T	E	N	1973	54214
0165	S	S	E	L	1972	55357
0165	S	S	E	N	1972	55357
0165	S	D	E	L	1970	59675
0165	S	D	E	N	1971	61706
0165	S	E	E	N	1971	61706
0165	S	D	E	L	1973	62286
0165	S	D	E	N	1973	62286
0165	S	D	E	N	1969	62324
0165	S	D	E	N	1974	62479
0165	S	D	E	L	1975	63327
0165	S	D	E	N	1975	63327
0165	S	S	E	N	1975	63327
0165	S	S	E	N	1970	63588
0165	S	S	E	N	1975	65501
0165	S	T	E	N	1974	65612
0165	S	D	E	N	1971	75192
0165	S	S	E	N	1971	75192
0165	S	D	E	N	1975	93316
0165	S	D	E	L	1975	96982
0165	S	D	E	L	1976	101287
0165	S	D	E	N	1976	101287
0165	S	S	E	L	1976	101287
0165	S	S	E	N	1976	101287
0165	S	D	E	N	1976	101843
0165	S	S	E	L	1976	101843
0165	S	S	E	N	1976	101843
0165	S	T	E	N	1976	101843
0165	T	D	E	N	1970	62185
0165	T	T	E	N	1970	62185
0168	G	S	E	N	1973	53059
0192	S	D	E	N	1973	56142
0192	S	D	R	N	1972	79248
0192	S	D	E	N	1972	90275
0192	T	D	E	N	1975	96486
0203	D	T	E	N	1974	54662
0203	D	D	E	L	1973	62286
0203	D	D	E	N	1973	62286
0203	D	D	E	L	1971	63597
0203	D	S	E	L	1971	63597
0203	D	T	E	L	1971	63597
0203	S	D	E	N	1973	50566

Substance Number	Phys. State	Subject	Language	Temperature	Year	EPIC Number
106-0203	S	S	E	N	1973	50566
0203	S	S	E	N	1972	55357
0203	S	D	E	N	1971	61706
0203	S	E	E	N	1971	61706
0203	S	D	E	L	1973	62286
0203	S	D	E	N	1973	62286
0203	S	D	E	N	1969	62324
0203	S	T	E	N	1974	65612
0203	S	D	E	N	1976	99905
0203	S	S	E	N	1976	99905
0203	S	T	E	N	1976	99905
0204	S	D	E	N	1974	54348
0204	S	E	E	N	1974	54348
0227	S	S	E	N	1974	101158
0231	D	D	E	L	1975	90777
0231	D	T	E	L	1975	90777
0231	G	D	E	N	1971	63677
0231	G	E	E	N	1971	63677
0231	G	D	E	N	1975	90777
0231	G	T	E	N	1975	90777
0234	D	D	E	L	1973	60596
0234	S	D	E	N	1974	54348
0234	S	E	E	N	1974	54348
0234	S	D	E	L	1974	61445
0237	S	D	E	N	1971	61706
0237	S	E	E	N	1971	61706
0238	D	T	E	N	1974	54662
0238	D	D	E	L	1973	57622
0238	D	T	E	L	1973	57622
0238	D	D	E	L	1973	62286
0238	D	D	E	N	1973	62286
0238	D	D	E	L	1971	63597
0238	D	S	E	L	1971	63597
0238	D	T	E	L	1971	63597
0238	D	D	E	N	1976	99923
0238	D	T	E	N	1976	99923
0238	D	D	E	L	1971	101559
0238	D	T	E	L	1971	101559
0238	G	D	E	N	1974	54330
0238	G	E	E	N	1974	54330
0238	P	D	E	N	1976	99923
0238	P	T	E	N	1976	99923
0238	S	D	E	N	1973	50566
0238	S	S	E	N	1973	50566
0238	S	S	E	N	1972	53244
0238	S	S	E	N	1972	53247
0238	S	S	E	N	1973	54773
0238	S	D	E	L	1973	55351
0238	S	D	E	N	1973	55351
0238	S	E	E	L	1973	55351
0238	S	E	E	N	1973	55351
0238	S	T	E	L	1973	55351
0238	S	T	E	N	1973	55351
0238	S	D	E	N	1971	61706
0238	S	E	E	N	1971	61706
0238	S	D	R	N	1974	62012
0238	S	D	E	N	1974	62013
0238	S	D	E	L	1973	62286
0238	S	D	E	N	1973	62286
0238	S	D	E	N	1975	63296
0238	S	T	E	N	1974	65612
0238	S	S	E	L	1965	75847
0238	S	S	E	N	1965	75847
0238	S	S	R	L	1973	87035
0238	S	S	E	L	1973	87036
0238	T	S	E	L	1973	60584
0238	T	D	E	N	1970	62185
0238	T	T	E	N	1970	62185
0240	L	D	R	N	1973	61564
0240	L	E	R	N	1973	61564
0240	L	D	E	N	1973	65915
0240	L	E	E	N	1973	65915
0240	S	D	E	N	1973	52188
0327	T	D	E	N	1974	60654
0363	A	T	E	N	1975	96894
0363	A	D	E	N	1976	100416
0363	A	S	E	N	1976	100416
0363	D	T	R	L	1973	51559
0363	D	T	R	N	1973	51559
0363	D	T	E	L	1974	53690
0363	D	T	E	N	1974	53690
0363	D	D	E	N	1972	63849
0363	D	T	E	N	1972	63849
0363	D	S	E	L	1963	64232
0363	D	S	E	N	1963	64232
0363	D	D	E	N	1970	64857
0363	D	D	E	N	1975	65427
0363	D	S	E	N	1967	66156
0363	D	D	E	N	1975	89311
0363	D	D	E	N	1957	89723
0363	D	S	E	N	1975	99263
0363	L	D	R	N	1973	54294
0363	S	D	E	N	1973	52776
0363	S	T	E	N	1974	53614
0363	S	D	E	N	1974	53615
0363	S	T	R	N	1973	54294
0363	S	D	E	N	1973	54295
0363	S	T	E	N	1973	54295
0363	S	S	R	N	1973	54976
0363	S	S	E	N	1974	54977
0363	S	D	E	N	1973	56775

Substance Number	Phys. State	Subject	Language	Temperature	Year	EPIC Number
106-0363	S	E	E	N	1973	56775
0363	S	S	E	N	1974	58014
0363	S	D	R	N	1974	58090
0363	S	D	E	N	1974	58091
0363	S	D	R	N	1974	58210
0363	S	D	E	N	1974	59206
0363	S	D	E	N	1973	59409
0363	S	D	E	N	1970	59694
0363	S	D	E	N	1973	60636
0363	S	S	E	N	1973	60636
0363	S	D	E	L	1974	61361
0363	S	T	E	L	1974	61361
0363	S	S	E	L	1974	61441
0363	S	S	E	N	1974	61441
0363	S	T	E	N	1971	61758
0363	S	T	E	N	1971	61760
0363	S	T	E	N	1971	61763
0363	S	D	R	N	1974	61970
0363	S	E	R	N	1974	61970
0363	S	D	E	N	1974	61971
0363	S	E	E	N	1974	61971
0363	S	D	R	N	1973	62163
0363	S	D	E	N	1969	62248
0363	S	D	E	N	1969	62324
0363	S	D	R	N	1972	62713
0363	S	D	R	N	1972	62853
0363	S	T	R	N	1972	62853
0363	S	S	E	N	1973	63506
0363	S	T	E	N	1972	63811
0363	S	S	E	N	1963	64232
0363	S	D	E	N	1970	64857
0363	S	D	E	N	1973	65179
0363	S	T	E	N	1973	65179
0363	S	D	E	N	1973	65309
0363	S	S	E	N	1967	66156
0363	S	S	E	N	1972	70404
0363	S	D	E	N	1970	70576
0363	S	T	E	N	1970	70576
0363	S	T	E	N	1970	70645
0363	S	D	R	N	1974	71817
0363	S	D	E	N	1975	71966
0363	S	D	R	L	1974	81216
0363	S	S	R	L	1974	81216
0363	S	D	E	L	1974	87147
0363	S	D	E	N	1974	87147
0363	S	S	E	N	1971	87883
0363	S	S	R	L	1975	89630
0363	S	S	E	L	1975	89631
0363	S	D	E	L	1974	92375
0363	S	S	E	L	1974	92375
0363	S	D	R	L	1975	92860
0363	S	T	R	L	1975	92860
0363	S	T	E	N	1975	93349
0363	S	D	E	L	1975	93520
0363	S	D	E	N	1975	93520
0363	S	D	E	L	1976	96883
0363	S	T	E	L	1976	96883
0363	S	S	E	N	1976	97315
0363	S	D	E	N	1975	97414
0363	S	E	E	N	1975	97414
0363	S	T	E	N	1975	97414
0363	S	D	R	N	1975	98289
0363	S	T	R	N	1975	98289
0363	S	D	E	N	1976	99570
0363	S	T	E	N	1976	99570
0363	S	D	E	N	1976	100416
0363	S	S	E	N	1976	100416
0363	S	D	E	N	1976	101470
0363	S	T	E	N	1976	101470
0363	S	D	E	N	1976	101823
0363	S	T	E	N	1976	101823
0363	T	D	R	N	1972	56936
0363	T	D	R	N	1974	61992
0363	T	T	R	N	1974	61992
0363	T	D	E	N	1974	61993
0363	T	T	E	N	1974	61993
0363	T	D	E	N	1972	63961
0363	T	T	E	N	1972	63961
0363	T	S	E	N	1963	64232
0363	T	D	E	N	1975	65427
0363	T	S	E	N	1967	66156
0363	T	T	R	N	1974	66754
0363	T	T	E	N	1975	66755
0363	T	D	E	N	1974	68253
0363	T	D	R	L	1966	75862
0363	T	D	R	N	1966	75862
0363	T	D	E	L	1966	76050
0363	T	D	E	N	1966	76050
0363	T	D	E	N	1962	89724
0363	T	D	E	N	1962	89789
0363	T	D	E	N	1975	96894
0363	T	D	E	N	1976	99658
0363	T	E	E	N	1976	99658
0363	T	T	E	N	1976	99658
0363	T	D	E	N	1976	100416
0363	T	D	R	N	1975	101623
0363	T	T	R	N	1975	101623
0363	T	D	E	N	1975	101624
0363	T	T	E	N	1975	101624
0385	D	D	E	L	1972	53338
0385	D	D	E	N	1973	57641

Substance Number	Phys. State	Subject	Language	Temperature	Year	EPIC Number
106-0385	D	T	E	N	1973	57641
0385	D	D	E	N	1973	60632
0385	D	E	E	N	1973	60632
0385	S	D	E	N	1973	55364
0385	S	E	E	N	1973	55364
0385	S	S	E	N	1973	55364
0385	S	S	E	N	1973	56749
0385	S	S	E	N	1972	63847
0385	S	D	F	N	1974	88179
0387	S	S	E	N	1972	53248
0387	S	D	E	N	1973	56142
0387	T	D	E	N	1975	96486
0387	T	D	E	N	1976	101813
0387	T	E	E	N	1976	101813
0387	T	D	E	N	1976	101815
0387	T	D	E	N	1976	101816
0387	T	S	E	N	1976	102567
0417	S	D	E	N	1972	64098
0610	D	S	E	N	1973	56749
0610	D	D	E	N	1975	63295
0610	S	D	E	N	1973	52779
0791	S	D	E	N	1974	65111
0791	S	T	E	N	1974	65111
0941	S	D	R	N	1973	52259
1085	S	D	E	N	1974	60664
1256	S	D	R	N	1972	52263
1256	S	D	E	N	1973	55874
1256	S	D	E	N	1973	60802
1256	S	D	E	N	1969	62324
1256	S	D	E	N	1974	87146
1256	S	D	E	N	1974	101330
1296	S	D	R	N	1973	55068
1296	S	D	E	N	1974	55069
1299	S	D	E	N	1973	51151
1299	S	S	E	N	1974	60259
1519	S	D	E	N	1974	53915
8001	S	D	R	N	1972	54155
8001	S	D	E	N	1972	54156
8001	S	D	E	L	1964	85398
8001	S	D	E	N	1964	85398
8008	S	D	R	N	1974	77941
8008	S	S	R	N	1974	77941
8008	S	D	E	N	1974	94517
8008	S	S	E	N	1974	94517
8014	S	S	E	N	1960	65977
8040	D	D	E	N	1973	56566
8040	D	E	E	N	1973	56566
8040	D	T	E	N	1973	56566
8040	D	D	E	N	1972	63849
8040	D	T	E	N	1972	63849
8040	D	D	E	L	1971	64324
8040	D	D	E	N	1971	64324
8040	D	D	R	N	1974	87062
8040	D	D	E	N	1974	87063
8040	S	D	R	N	1973	52530
8040	S	D	E	N	1972	53244
8040	S	E	E	N	1972	53244
8040	S	S	E	N	1972	53388
8040	S	D	R	L	1973	54646
8040	S	D	E	L	1974	55190
8040	S	D	E	N	1974	57771
8040	S	D	R	L	1974	58088
8040	S	D	E	L	1974	58089
8040	S	D	E	N	1974	58223
8040	S	T	E	N	1974	58223
8040	S	D	R	N	1972	58225
8040	S	D	R	N	1972	62718
8040	S	D	E	N	1971	64324
8040	S	S	E	L	1971	64324
8040	S	D	R	N	1974	64570
8040	S	E	R	N	1974	64570
8040	S	D	E	N	1973	65314
8040	S	D	R	N	1973	71715
8040	S	T	R	N	1975	77041
8040	S	T	E	N	1975	77042
8040	S	D	E	N	1973	81843
8040	S	D	R	N	1974	87062
8040	S	D	E	N	1974	87063
8040	S	S	E	L	1963	87710
8040	S	S	E	N	1963	87710
8040	S	D	E	N	1974	88316
8040	S	E	E	N	1974	88316
8040	S	D	E	N	1976	101470
8040	S	T	E	N	1976	101470
8040	S	D	E	N	1976	101823
8040	S	T	E	N	1976	101823
8040	T	D	R	N	1970	61532
8040	T	D	E	N	1974	68253
8040	T	S	E	N	1963	87710
8040	T	D	E	N	1975	91012
8041	D	D	E	N	1972	53184
8041	D	D	E	N	1972	53245
8041	D	D	E	N	1974	55248
8041	D	S	E	N	1974	55248
8041	D	T	E	N	1974	55248
8041	D	D	R	N	1972	57864
8041	D	D	E	N	1973	58213
8041	D	T	E	N	1973	58213
8041	D	D	R	N	1974	59418
8041	D	D	E	N	1969	62248
8041	D	D	E	N	1974	62323

Phys. State: **A.** Amorphous; **C.** Superconductive; **D.** Doped; **F.** Fibrous or Whisker; **G.** Gas; **I.** Ionized or Plasma; **L.** Liquid; **P.** Powder or Particle; **S.** Solid; **T.** Thin Film
Subject: **D.** Data; **E.** Experiment; **S.** Survey (Review, Compendium, etc.); **T.** Theory
Language: **E.** English; **F.** French; **G.** German; **O.** Other Languages; **R.** Russian
Temperature: **L.** Low (0 to 75K); **N.** Normal (75 to 1273K); **H.** High (above 1273K)

Substance Number	Phys. State	Subject	Language	Temperature	Year	EPIC Number
106-8041	D	D	R	L	1972	62705
8041	D	D	R	N	1972	62705
8041	D	S	R	N	1972	62705
8041	D	D	E	N	1974	64488
8041	D	D	E	N	1974	64490
8041	D	D	E	L	1973	65301
8041	D	D	E	N	1973	65301
8041	D	S	E	N	1973	65301
8041	D	S	E	N	1970	65877
8041	D	D	E	N	1972	67638
8041	D	S	E	N	1967	68371
8041	D	D	E	N	1975	72582
8041	D	T	E	N	1975	72582
8041	D	D	E	N	1974	87448
8041	D	D	E	N	1975	89778
8041	D	S	E	N	1975	89778
8041	D	T	E	N	1975	89778
8041	D	D	E	N	1975	93355
8041	D	D	E	N	1975	93356
8041	D	D	E	N	1975	97218
8041	D	D	E	N	1975	97219
8041	D	D	E	L	1976	99175
8041	D	D	E	N	1976	99175
8041	D	S	E	N	1976	99175
8041	D	T	E	L	1976	99175
8041	D	T	E	N	1976	99175
8041	D	S	E	N	1976	101374
8041	D	D	E	N	1976	101841
8041	D	T	E	N	1976	101841
8041	D	D	E	N	1976	101842
8041	D	E	E	N	1976	101842
8041	S	D	R	N	1973	51272
8041	S	S	E	N	1974	52799
8041	S	D	E	N	1972	53244
8041	S	E	E	N	1972	53244
8041	S	S	E	N	1972	53244
8041	S	D	E	N	1972	53245
8041	S	S	E	N	1972	53245
8041	S	S	E	N	1972	53246
8041	S	T	E	N	1972	53246
8041	S	S	E	N	1972	53247
8041	S	S	E	N	1972	53248
8041	S	S	E	N	1972	53359
8041	S	D	E	N	1972	53392
8041	S	D	E	N	1974	54024
8041	S	D	E	N	1973	54214
8041	S	T	E	N	1973	54214
8041	S	D	E	N	1974	54310
8041	S	S	E	N	1973	54773
8041	S	D	E	N	1973	56149
8041	S	E	E	N	1973	56149
8041	S	D	E	N	1973	58212
8041	S	D	E	N	1973	58213
8041	S	S	E	N	1973	59375
8041	S	S	E	N	1973	60837
8041	S	S	E	N	1973	60838
8041	S	D	R	L	1970	61009
8041	S	D	R	N	1970	61009
8041	S	D	E	N	1969	62273
8041	S	D	E	N	1973	62322
8041	S	D	E	N	1973	62325
8041	S	E	E	N	1975	63256
8041	S	T	E	N	1975	63256
8041	S	S	E	N	1975	65507
8041	S	S	E	N	1970	65877
8041	S	S	E	L	1967	68371
8041	S	S	E	N	1967	68371
8041	S	S	E	N	1973	68817
8041	S	D	E	N	1973	68844
8041	S	S	E	N	1973	68863
8041	S	D	E	N	1963	68878
8041	S	T	E	N	1970	70645
8041	S	D	G	N	1974	71582
8041	S	S	G	N	1974	71582
8041	S	D	E	L	1969	75248
8041	S	D	E	N	1969	75248
8041	S	T	R	N	1975	77041
8041	S	T	E	N	1975	77042
8041	S	D	E	N	1975	80964
8041	S	E	E	N	1975	80964
8041	S	D	E	N	1972	86370
8041	S	D	E	N	1972	86371
8041	S	S	E	N	1962	87659
8041	S	S	E	N	1974	87759
8041	S	S	E	N	1971	87883
8041	S	D	E	N	1974	89232
8041	S	D	E	L	1975	91863
8041	S	T	E	L	1975	91863
8041	S	D	E	N	1959	92621
8041	S	D	E	N	1975	93320
8041	S	D	E	N	1975	93335
8041	S	D	E	N	1975	93352
8041	S	D	E	L	1975	95668
8041	S	D	E	N	1975	95668
8041	S	S	E	N	1976	97315
8041	S	T	E	N	1975	99140
8041	S	E	E	N	1976	99549
8041	S	S	E	N	1976	99549
8041	S	S	E	N	1975	101032
8041	S	S	E	N	1975	101034
8041	S	D	E	N	1975	101036

Substance Number	Phys. State	Subject	Language	Temperature	Year	EPIC Number
106-8041	S	E	E	N	1975	101036
8041	S	D	E	N	1976	101470
8041	S	T	E	N	1976	101470
8041	S	T	E	N	1975	101674
8041	S	S	E	N	1975	101678
8041	S	T	E	N	1975	101678
8041	S	D	E	N	1976	101823
8041	S	T	E	N	1976	101823
8041	S	D	E	L	1976	101840
8041	S	D	E	N	1976	101840
8041	S	T	E	L	1976	101840
8041	S	T	E	N	1976	101840
8041	S	S	E	N	1975	102056
8041	T	S	E	N	1973	60838
8041	T	D	R	N	1970	61532
8041	T	D	R	N	1974	61988
8041	T	T	R	N	1974	61988
8041	T	D	E	N	1974	61989
8041	T	T	E	N	1974	61989
8041	T	D	R	N	1974	61992
8041	T	T	R	N	1974	61992
8041	T	D	E	N	1974	61993
8041	T	T	E	N	1974	61993
8041	T	D	E	N	1974	68253
8041	T	D	E	N	1974	68831
8041	T	D	R	N	1972	76519
8041	T	T	R	N	1972	76519
8041	T	T	E	N	1974	89232
8041	T	D	E	N	1972	91552
8041	T	T	E	N	1972	91552
8041	T	D	E	N	1975	98067
8041	T	T	E	N	1975	98067
8041	T	D	E	N	1975	101021
8050	T	D	G	N	1970	66848
8101	S	D	E	N	1973	52485
8127	S	D	R	N	1974	61980
8127	S	D	E	N	1974	61981
8128	D	T	R	N	1975	95776
8128	D	T	E	N	1975	95777
8128	S	D	E	N	1973	53406
8128	S	D	E	N	1973	55149
8128	S	S	E	N	1967	68371
8128	S	T	E	N	1972	76043
8128	S	S	E	N	1975	76733
8128	S	T	R	N	1971	77234
8128	S	S	E	N	1966	87831
8128	S	D	R	L	1972	89950
8128	S	D	R	N	1972	89950
8128	S	T	R	L	1972	89950
8128	S	T	R	N	1972	89950
8128	T	S	E	N	1967	68371
8132	S	D	R	N	1974	58210
8132	S	D	E	N	1974	59206
8132	S	D	E	N	1972	63849
8132	S	T	E	N	1972	63849
8155	S	D	R	N	1972	52263
8155	S	D	E	N	1969	62324
8200	S	D	R	N	1973	52259
8200	S	D	R	N	1974	66448
8200	S	T	R	N	1974	66448
8200	S	D	E	N	1974	66449
8200	S	T	E	N	1974	66449
8200	S	D	E	N	1971	85443
8209	S	T	E	N	1974	65111
8209	S	D	E	N	1972	65878
8209	S	T	E	N	1972	65878
8225	D	D	E	L	1973	51848
8226	S	D	E	N	1973	50574
8226	S	D	E	N	1973	51151
8227	S	D	E	N	1973	51151
8227	S	D	E	L	1975	65440
8227	S	T	E	L	1975	65440
8234	S	D	R	N	1973	51561
8234	S	E	R	N	1973	51561
8234	S	D	E	N	1974	53692
8234	S	E	E	N	1974	53692
8234	S	T	R	N	1975	77041
8234	S	T	E	N	1975	77042
8236	S	D	F	N	1971	83537
8237	S	D	E	N	1972	53110
8244	S	D	R	L	1974	68630
8244	S	T	R	L	1974	68630
8244	S	D	E	L	1974	68631
8244	S	T	E	L	1974	68631
8300	S	D	E	N	1973	52314
8312	S	D	E	N	1973	52652
8338	S	D	E	N	1973	53415
8338	S	S	E	N	1974	58346
8340	S	D	E	N	1973	53415
8340	S	S	E	N	1974	58346
8342	S	D	E	N	1972	65878
8342	S	T	E	N	1972	65878
8342	S	D	E	N	1975	94550
8344	S	D	E	N	1973	53415
8357	S	S	E	N	1972	53512
8357	S	D	E	N	1971	62600
8358	S	S	E	N	1973	54773
8358	S	D	E	N	1969	62248
8358	S	D	E	N	1971	62600
8358	S	S	E	N	1973	68817
8358	S	D	E	N	1968	75247

Substance Number	Phys. State	Subject	Language	Temperature	Year	EPIC Number
106-8383	S	D	E	L	1973	51477
8383	S	D	E	N	1973	51477
8383	S	E	E	L	1973	51477
8383	S	E	E	N	1973	51477
8388	S	D	R	N	1974	77941
8388	S	S	R	N	1974	77941
8388	S	D	E	N	1974	94517
8388	S	S	E	N	1974	94517
8407	S	D	E	N	1974	62328
8407	S	T	E	N	1974	62328
8416	G	D	E	N	1974	54330
8416	G	E	E	N	1974	54330
8430	D	D	R	N	1973	54389
8430	D	D	E	N	1973	54390
8432	S	D	R	N	1973	54440
8432	S	D	E	N	1973	54441
8457	S	D	E	N	1972	65878
8457	S	T	E	N	1972	65878
8468	S	D	R	L	1973	57805
8468	S	D	E	L	1974	57806
8485	S	S	E	N	1974	58014
8487	S	D	E	N	1975	86744
8487	S	T	E	N	1975	86744
8488	S	D	E	N	1973	62296
8488	S	D	E	N	1974	65105
8488	S	D	E	N	1974	87448
8497	S	D	E	N	1965	100013
8497	S	T	E	N	1965	100013
8517	G	D	E	N	1971	63677
8531	S	D	R	N	1973	51564
8531	S	D	E	N	1974	53695
8532	G	S	E	N	1973	58999
8532	L	S	E	N	1973	58999
8536	S	S	E	N	1974	66380
8540	D	D	E	N	1974	61187
8549	S	D	R	N	1974	66730
8549	S	T	R	N	1974	66730
8549	S	D	E	N	1975	66731
8549	S	T	E	N	1975	66731
8557	S	D	R	N	1973	55068
8557	S	D	E	N	1974	55069
8575	S	D	E	L	1973	55558
8575	S	D	E	N	1973	55558
8591	S	D	R	N	1974	66730
8591	S	T	R	N	1974	66730
8591	S	D	E	N	1975	66731
8591	S	T	E	N	1975	66731
8596	S	D	R	N	1974	90242
8596	S	D	E	N	1974	90243
8611	S	D	E	N	1966	85403
8671	S	D	E	N	1974	94147
8681	S	D	E	L	1973	65772
8681	S	D	E	N	1973	65772
8681	S	T	E	L	1973	65772
8681	S	T	E	N	1973	65772
8694	T	S	E	N	1971	87872
8736	S	D	R	N	1974	77922
8736	S	T	R	N	1974	77922
8736	S	D	E	N	1974	94514
8736	S	T	E	N	1974	94514
8742	S	D	E	N	1968	68207
8748	S	D	E	N	1975	101018
8751	S	D	E	N	1974	94145
8751	S	T	E	N	1974	94145
8768	S	D	R	N	1974	90242
8768	S	D	E	N	1974	90243
8784	S	D	E	N	1965	100013
8784	S	T	E	N	1965	100013
8785	S	D	E	N	1965	100013
8785	S	T	E	N	1965	100013
8789	S	D	E	N	1976	101851
8789	S	E	E	N	1976	101851
8789	S	T	E	N	1976	101851
8789	S	D	E	N	1976	101861
8789	S	E	E	N	1976	101861
8790	T	D	E	N	1976	101833
8795	S	D	R	N	1972	76553
8795	S	T	R	N	1972	76553
8795	S	D	E	N	1972	91547
8795	S	T	E	N	1972	91547
8796	S	D	R	N	1972	76553
8796	S	T	R	N	1972	76553
8796	S	D	E	N	1972	91547
8796	S	T	E	N	1972	91547
8797	S	D	R	N	1972	76553
8797	S	T	R	N	1972	76553
8797	S	D	E	N	1972	91547
8797	S	T	E	N	1972	91547
8817	G	D	E	H	1974	65887
8817	G	E	E	H	1974	65887
8817	G	T	E	H	1974	65887
108-0004	G	S	E	N	1975	103142
0005	G	D	E	N	1973	52482
0005	S	S	E	L	1962	75890
0029	D	D	E	N	1974	87215
0029	D	S	E	N	1974	87215
0029	D	T	E	N	1974	87215
0029	S	D	R	N	1974	58128
0029	S	D	E	N	1974	58129
0029	S	D	E	N	1974	60355

Phys. State: **A.** Amorphous; **C.** Superconductive; **D.** Doped; **F.** Fibrous or Whisker; **G.** Gas; **I.** Ionized or Plasma; **L.** Liquid; **P.** Powder or Particle; **S.** Solid; **T.** Thin Film
Subject: **D.** Data; **E.** Experiment; **S.** Survey (Review, Compendium, etc.); **T.** Theory
Language: **E.** English; **F.** French; **G.** German; **O.** Other Languages; **R.** Russian
Temperature: **L.** Low (0 to 75K); **N.** Normal (75 to 1273K); **H.** High (above 1273K)

Substance Number	Phys. State	Subject	Language	Temperature	Year	EPIC Number
108-0029	S	T	E	N	1974	60355
8054	S	T	E	N	1975	63297
109-0025	D	S	E	N	1973	53052
0025	D	D	E	N	1974	54573
0025	D	S	E	L	1975	90863
0025	D	S	E	N	1975	90863
0025	S	D	E	N	1973	50888
0025	S	D	E	N	1972	52969
0025	S	S	E	N	1973	53052
0025	S	D	E	N	1972	53158
0025	S	D	E	L	1968	53358
0025	S	D	E	N	1974	54573
0025	S	D	E	N	1971	57182
0025	S	S	E	N	1974	60259
0025	S	S	E	L	1970	75905
0025	S	S	E	N	1970	75905
0029	D	D	E	N	1973	49670
0029	S	D	E	N	1973	49670
8008	D	S	E	N	1973	65763
8008	S	S	E	N	1973	65763
8013	A	D	E	N	1974	57970
8013	T	D	E	N	1974	57970
8018	D	D	E	L	1973	50866
8018	D	D	E	N	1973	50866
8019	S	D	E	N	1971	57182
8020	S	D	E	N	1971	57182
8020	S	D	E	N	1973	62310
8020	S	D	R	N	1975	86839
8020	S	D	E	N	1975	86840
8020	T	T	E	L	1974	58008
8020	T	D	R	N	1974	64236
8020	T	D	E	N	1973	64237
8021	S	D	E	N	1971	57182
8034	S	D	E	N	1972	53158
8034	S	D	E	N	1974	54573
8064	S	D	R	N	1975	86839
8064	S	D	E	N	1975	86840
8066	S	D	E	N	1974	87145
8080	S	D	E	N	1975	86759
8082	S	D	E	N	1975	63304
8082	S	T	E	N	1975	63304
110-0002	S	S	E	N	1972	53248
0002	S	D	E	N	1973	55086
0002	S	D	E	N	1974	60255
0002	S	S	E	N	1973	60838
0002	S	D	E	N	1975	87441
0002	S	D	E	N	1975	93161
0002	S	D	E	N	1975	93315
0002	S	D	E	N	1976	101828
0002	T	S	E	N	1973	60838
0002	T	D	E	N	1974	65105
0002	T	E	E	N	1973	65537
0002	T	T	E	N	1973	65537
0002	T	D	E	N	1974	68823
0002	T	D	E	N	1974	68831
0002	T	D	E	N	1973	68875
0002	T	D	E	N	1975	93315
0002	T	D	G	N	1975	93698
0002	T	T	E	N	1975	101656
0002	T	D	E	N	1976	101813
0002	T	E	E	N	1976	101813
0002	T	D	E	N	1976	101825
0002	T	D	E	N	1976	101827
0002	T	D	E	N	1976	101828
0002	T	D	E	N	1976	102015
0002	T	S	E	N	1976	102567
0002	T	D	E	N	1976	103592
0002	T	E	E	N	1976	103592
0004	G	S	R	N	1972	65883
0004	G	T	R	N	1972	65883
0004	G	S	E	N	1972	65884
0004	G	T	E	N	1972	65884
0007	S	S	E	N	1974	58014
0011	A	D	R	N	1973	54502
0011	A	D	E	N	1973	54503
0011	A	D	E	N	1973	56636
0011	S	D	E	N	1972	49919
0011	S	D	R	N	1973	54502
0011	S	D	E	N	1973	54503
0011	S	D	E	N	1973	56636
0011	S	D	E	N	1974	57915
0012	S	S	R	N	1972	65883
0012	S	T	R	N	1972	65883
0012	S	S	E	N	1972	65884
0012	S	T	E	N	1972	65884
0018	D	D	E	L	1974	58055
0018	D	E	E	L	1974	58055
0018	S	D	R	N	1974	58100
0018	S	S	R	N	1974	58100
0018	S	D	E	N	1974	58101
0018	S	S	E	N	1974	58101
0018	S	D	E	L	1974	59322
0018	S	D	E	N	1974	59322
0018	S	T	E	L	1974	59322
0018	S	T	E	N	1974	59322
0018	S	D	E	L	1971	93296
0019	S	T	E	L	1970	63653
0020	D	D	E	L	1974	58055
0020	D	E	E	L	1974	58055
110-0020	D	D	E	L	1973	64537
0021	S	D	R	N	1973	52513
0021	S	D	E	N	1976	101813
0021	S	E	E	N	1976	101813
0021	S	S	E	N	1976	102567
0021	T	D	E	N	1976	101825
0021	T	D	E	N	1976	101827
0021	T	D	E	N	1973	101946
0021	T	T	E	N	1973	101946
0023	D	D	E	L	1973	50531
0023	D	D	E	N	1973	50531
0023	D	E	E	L	1973	50531
0023	D	E	E	N	1973	50531
0023	D	D	E	N	1974	58819
0023	D	D	E	L	1973	64537
0023	D	D	E	N	1975	68675
0023	D	E	E	L	1975	68675
0023	S	D	E	N	1973	50531
0023	S	E	E	N	1973	50531
0023	S	D	E	N	1972	53135
0023	S	S	E	N	1972	53512
0023	S	D	E	N	1974	54024
0023	S	D	E	N	1974	54313
0023	S	D	E	N	1973	58212
0023	S	S	E	N	1974	59353
0023	S	D	R	N	1974	61433
0023	S	D	E	N	1974	62306
0023	S	D	E	L	1969	64549
0023	S	D	E	N	1974	65922
0023	S	D	E	N	1972	68832
0023	S	D	E	N	1973	68841
0023	S	S	E	N	1971	87883
0023	S	D	E	N	1975	88493
0023	S	D	E	N	1975	93328
0023	S	S	E	N	1975	101034
0023	S	D	E	N	1976	101441
0023	S	D	E	N	1975	101668
0023	S	E	E	N	1975	101668
0023	S	S	E	N	1975	101668
0023	S	D	E	N	1976	101837
0023	S	E	E	N	1976	101837
0023	S	T	E	N	1976	101837
0023	S	D	E	N	1976	101851
0023	S	E	E	N	1976	101851
0023	S	T	E	N	1976	101851
0023	S	D	E	N	1976	102042
0023	S	E	E	N	1976	102042
0023	T	D	F	N	1973	53787
0023	T	E	F	N	1973	53787
0023	T	D	E	N	1974	58961
0023	T	D	E	N	1970	62185
0023	T	T	E	N	1970	62185
0023	T	D	E	N	1971	64338
0023	T	S	E	N	1971	87883
0023	T	D	G	N	1975	93698
0024	D	D	E	N	1973	56362
0024	D	E	E	N	1973	56362
0024	D	T	E	N	1974	59398
0024	D	D	E	N	1970	60915
0024	D	D	E	N	1975	63337
0024	D	T	E	N	1975	63337
0024	D	D	E	N	1976	101596
0024	D	T	E	N	1976	101596
0024	L	D	E	N	1974	58441
0024	L	E	E	N	1974	58441
0024	L	D	E	N	1972	75340
0024	L	D	E	N	1963	75554
0024	S	D	E	N	1973	50545
0024	S	D	E	N	1972	53135
0024	S	S	E	N	1972	53246
0024	S	T	E	N	1972	53246
0024	S	T	E	N	1973	53789
0024	S	D	E	N	1974	54606
0024	S	D	R	N	1973	54984
0024	S	D	E	N	1974	54985
0024	S	D	E	N	1972	55100
0024	S	T	E	N	1972	55100
0024	S	D	E	N	1974	55252
0024	S	S	E	N	1972	55357
0024	S	D	E	N	1973	57334
0024	S	T	E	N	1973	57334
0024	S	D	R	N	1974	58128
0024	S	D	E	N	1974	58129
0024	S	D	E	N	1973	58212
0024	S	S	E	N	1973	58212
0024	S	D	E	N	1974	58441
0024	S	E	E	N	1974	58441
0024	S	D	E	N	1974	59398
0024	S	D	E	L	1973	59611
0024	S	D	E	N	1973	59611
0024	S	S	E	L	1973	59611
0024	S	S	E	N	1973	59611
0024	S	D	R	N	1974	60463
0024	S	D	E	N	1974	60464
0024	S	D	E	N	1974	60657
0024	S	T	E	N	1974	60657
0024	S	S	E	N	1974	60672
0024	S	D	E	N	1974	61198
0024	S	T	E	N	1974	61198
0024	S	S	E	N	1973	62274
0024	S	D	E	N	1974	62306
110-0024	S	S	E	N	1972	62384
0024	S	T	E	N	1972	62384
0024	S	D	E	N	1974	62457
0024	S	S	E	N	1949	63242
0024	S	D	E	L	1975	63327
0024	S	D	E	N	1975	63327
0024	S	S	E	N	1975	63327
0024	S	D	E	N	1975	63337
0024	S	T	E	N	1975	63337
0024	S	D	E	L	1972	63788
0024	S	D	E	N	1972	63788
0024	S	D	E	L	1966	64256
0024	S	D	E	N	1966	64256
0024	S	S	E	H	1966	64256
0024	S	S	E	L	1966	64256
0024	S	S	E	N	1966	64256
0024	S	D	E	N	1975	65501
0024	S	S	E	N	1975	65501
0024	S	T	E	N	1975	65501
0024	S	D	E	N	1970	68205
0024	S	D	E	N	1972	68832
0024	S	D	E	N	1973	68841
0024	S	D	E	L	1973	70149
0024	S	D	E	N	1973	70149
0024	S	S	E	L	1973	70149
0024	S	S	E	N	1973	70149
0024	S	D	E	L	1966	74594
0024	S	D	E	N	1966	74594
0024	S	D	E	N	1972	75340
0024	S	S	E	N	1971	87883
0024	S	D	E	L	1974	87984
0024	S	D	E	N	1974	87984
0024	S	S	E	L	1974	87984
0024	S	S	E	N	1974	87984
0024	S	D	E	N	1975	93316
0024	S	D	E	N	1975	93379
0024	S	S	E	N	1976	97297
0024	S	D	E	N	1975	101013
0024	S	T	E	N	1975	101013
0024	S	S	E	N	1976	101304
0024	S	D	E	N	1976	101441
0024	S	T	E	N	1975	101662
0024	S	S	E	N	1976	101811
0024	S	D	E	N	1976	101851
0024	S	E	E	N	1976	101851
0024	S	T	E	N	1976	101851
0024	S	D	E	N	1973	101924
0024	S	E	E	N	1973	101924
0024	S	D	E	N	1976	102042
0024	S	E	E	N	1976	102042
0024	S	S	E	N	1975	102056
0024	S	T	E	N	1976	103350
0024	T	D	E	N	1970	62185
0024	T	T	E	N	1970	62185
0025	T	D	E	N	1972	53113
0028	S	D	R	N	1974	90242
0028	S	D	E	N	1974	90243
0036	D	D	R	N	1973	52337
0036	D	D	E	N	1974	62315
0036	D	S	E	N	1974	62315
0036	D	D	E	N	1976	97298
0036	D	D	E	N	1976	101441
0036	D	D	E	N	1976	101714
0036	D	E	E	N	1976	101714
0036	D	T	E	N	1976	101714
0036	D	D	E	N	1976	101850
0036	D	E	E	N	1976	101850
0036	D	D	E	N	1976	101851
0036	D	E	E	N	1976	101851
0036	D	T	E	N	1976	101851
0036	D	D	E	N	1976	102042
0036	D	E	E	N	1976	102042
0036	S	T	E	N	1973	52040
0036	S	D	E	N	1973	54214
0036	S	T	E	N	1973	54214
0036	S	D	E	L	1974	57861
0036	S	S	E	L	1974	57861
0036	S	S	E	N	1974	57861
0036	S	T	E	L	1974	57861
0036	S	T	E	N	1974	57861
0036	S	D	E	N	1974	57862
0036	S	D	E	L	1974	58962
0036	S	D	R	N	1974	60463
0036	S	D	E	N	1974	60464
0036	S	D	E	N	1973	62274
0036	S	D	E	N	1972	62275
0036	S	S	E	N	1972	62275
0036	S	S	E	N	1974	62316
0036	S	S	E	N	1949	63242
0036	S	D	E	L	1975	63327
0036	S	D	E	N	1975	63327
0036	S	S	E	N	1975	63327
0036	S	S	E	N	1975	65501
0036	S	D	E	L	1970	66152
0036	S	D	E	N	1970	66152
0036	S	D	E	N	1973	68843
0036	S	D	E	N	1973	68850
0036	S	D	E	N	1973	68852
0036	S	D	E	N	1974	86121
0036	S	S	E	N	1974	86121
0036	S	S	E	N	1971	87883

Phys. State: **A.** Amorphous; **C.** Superconductive; **D.** Doped; **F.** Fibrous or Whisker; **G.** Gas; **I.** Ionized or Plasma; **L.** Liquid; **P.** Powder or Particle; **S.** Solid; **T.** Thin Film
Subject: **D.** Data; **E.** Experiment; **S.** Survey (Review, Compendium, etc.); **T.** Theory
Language: **E.** English; **F.** French; **G.** German; **O.** Other Languages; **R.** Russian
Temperature: **L.** Low (0 to 75K); **N.** Normal (75 to 1273K); **H.** High (above 1273K)

Substance Number	Phys. State	Subject	Language	Temperature	Year	EPIC Number
110-0036	S	D	E	N	1975	88493
0036	S	S	E	N	1975	91730
0036	S	D	E	L	1975	93160
0036	S	D	E	N	1975	93160
0036	S	E	E	L	1975	93160
0036	S	E	E	N	1975	93160
0036	S	D	E	N	1975	93316
0036	S	D	E	N	1975	93328
0036	S	S	E	N	1976	97297
0036	S	D	E	N	1974	99119
0036	S	S	E	N	1974	99119
0036	S	T	E	N	1974	99119
0036	S	D	E	N	1976	100019
0036	S	E	E	N	1976	100019
0036	S	D	E	L	1975	101015
0036	S	D	E	N	1975	101015
0036	S	D	E	N	1976	101441
0036	S	D	E	N	1975	101668
0036	S	E	E	N	1975	101668
0036	S	S	E	N	1975	101668
0036	S	D	E	N	1975	101671
0036	S	E	E	N	1975	101671
0036	S	S	E	N	1975	101671
0036	S	S	E	N	1976	101811
0036	S	D	E	N	1976	101851
0036	S	E	E	N	1976	101851
0036	S	T	E	N	1976	101851
0036	S	D	E	N	1976	102042
0036	S	E	E	N	1976	102042
0036	S	S	E	N	1975	102056
0036	T	D	E	N	1970	62185
0036	T	T	E	N	1970	62185
0036	T	T	E	N	1972	70543
0037	L	D	E	N	1963	75554
0037	S	D	E	N	1973	54214
0037	S	T	E	N	1973	54214
0037	S	D	E	N	1973	57710
0037	S	D	E	N	1971	61706
0037	S	E	E	N	1971	61706
0037	S	D	E	N	1969	62324
0037	S	D	E	L	1975	63327
0037	S	D	E	N	1975	63327
0037	S	S	E	N	1975	63327
0037	S	S	E	N	1975	65501
0037	S	S	E	N	1975	91730
0037	S	T	E	L	1975	101014
0037	S	T	E	N	1975	101014
0040	G	D	E	N	1972	53249
0040	G	E	E	N	1972	53249
0040	G	S	E	N	1972	53249
0040	S	S	R	N	1972	65883
0040	S	T	R	N	1972	65883
0040	S	S	E	N	1972	65884
0040	S	T	E	N	1972	65884
0045	S	S	R	N	1972	65883
0045	S	T	R	N	1972	65883
0045	S	S	E	N	1972	65884
0045	S	T	E	N	1972	65884
0061	S	D	R	N	1973	51378
0061	S	E	R	N	1973	51378
0061	S	D	E	N	1973	51379
0061	S	E	E	N	1973	51379
0061	S	D	E	N	1971	61706
0061	S	E	E	N	1971	61706
0061	S	D	E	N	1969	62324
0061	S	D	E	N	1971	75192
0061	S	S	E	N	1971	75192
0065	S	D	R	N	1973	55068
0065	S	D	E	N	1974	55069
0083	D	D	E	N	1973	52942
0083	D	D	E	L	1975	62976
0083	D	T	E	L	1975	62976
0083	D	D	E	N	1975	86759
0083	T	D	E	N	1975	96486
0083	T	D	E	N	1976	101815
0090	T	D	E	N	1975	96486
0090	T	D	E	N	1976	101815
0107	T	D	E	N	1974	68831
0132	D	D	E	N	1970	59602
0132	D	D	E	N	1975	66518
0132	D	T	E	N	1975	66518
0132	P	D	E	N	1976	97225
0132	S	S	E	N	1972	53246
0132	S	T	E	N	1972	53246
0132	S	D	E	N	1974	54024
0132	S	D	E	N	1973	58212
0132	S	S	E	N	1973	58212
0132	S	S	E	N	1974	59353
0132	S	D	E	N	1974	62306
0132	S	D	E	L	1975	63327
0132	S	D	E	N	1975	63327
0132	S	S	E	N	1975	63327
0132	S	D	E	N	1972	68832
0132	S	D	E	N	1973	68841
0132	S	D	E	N	1973	68865
0132	S	S	E	L	1974	70528
0132	S	D	E	L	1967	74607
0132	S	D	E	N	1967	74607
0132	S	E	E	L	1967	74607
0132	S	E	E	N	1967	74607
0132	S	D	E	N	1974	84584
110-0132	S	D	R	L	1974	87288
0132	S	D	E	L	1975	87289
0132	S	D	E	N	1975	88493
0132	S	D	E	N	1974	88513
0132	S	D	E	N	1975	89371
0132	S	S	E	N	1975	89371
0132	S	D	E	N	1975	93316
0132	S	D	E	N	1975	93324
0132	S	D	E	N	1975	93328
0132	S	D	E	N	1975	93334
0132	S	D	E	N	1975	93378
0132	S	D	E	N	1975	94479
0132	S	D	E	N	1976	97225
0132	S	S	E	N	1976	97297
0132	S	D	E	N	1976	99118
0132	S	E	E	N	1976	99118
0132	S	S	E	N	1976	99118
0132	S	T	E	N	1976	99118
0132	S	D	E	N	1975	101016
0132	S	D	E	N	1975	101017
0132	S	S	E	L	1975	101017
0132	S	S	E	N	1975	101034
0132	S	D	E	N	1976	101441
0132	S	D	E	N	1975	101668
0132	S	S	E	N	1975	101668
0132	S	D	E	N	1975	101669
0132	S	T	E	N	1975	101669
0132	S	D	E	N	1975	101670
0132	S	E	E	N	1975	101670
0132	S	D	E	N	1976	101808
0132	S	S	E	N	1976	101811
0132	S	D	E	N	1976	101837
0132	S	E	E	N	1976	101837
0132	S	T	E	N	1976	101837
0132	S	D	E	N	1976	101851
0132	S	E	E	N	1976	101851
0132	S	T	E	N	1976	101851
0132	S	D	E	N	1976	101852
0132	S	E	E	N	1976	101852
0132	S	S	E	N	1976	101852
0132	S	T	E	N	1976	101852
0132	S	D	E	N	1976	101861
0132	S	E	E	N	1976	101861
0132	S	D	E	N	1976	101862
0132	S	D	E	N	1976	102042
0132	S	E	E	N	1976	102042
0132	S	D	E	N	1976	103590
0132	S	T	E	N	1976	103590
0132	T	S	E	N	1976	101374
0132	T	D	E	N	1976	101825
0132	T	D	E	N	1976	101827
0194	D	D	E	N	1973	51189
0194	D	D	E	N	1973	52438
0194	D	D	E	N	1971	57169
0194	D	D	E	N	1974	57985
0194	D	D	E	N	1965	68546
0194	D	T	E	N	1965	68546
0194	D	D	R	N	1975	90148
0194	D	D	E	N	1975	90149
0194	S	D	R	N	1973	50259
0194	S	D	E	N	1973	50260
0194	S	S	E	N	1972	53175
0194	S	D	R	N	1973	55068
0194	S	D	E	N	1974	55069
0194	S	D	E	N	1974	58050
0194	S	D	E	N	1965	68546
0194	S	T	E	N	1965	68546
0194	S	D	E	N	1965	75938
0194	S	T	E	N	1965	75938
0194	S	D	R	N	1975	90148
0194	S	D	E	N	1975	90149
0194	T	D	E	N	1973	51189
0194	T	D	E	N	1974	54111
0194	T	D	E	N	1974	57985
0269	G	D	E	N	1975	90120
0269	G	E	E	N	1975	90120
0269	G	T	E	N	1975	90120
0279	D	S	R	N	1973	53657
0279	D	S	E	N	1974	53658
0279	D	D	R	N	1973	54373
0279	D	D	E	N	1973	54374
0279	D	D	E	N	1974	58819
0279	D	D	E	L	1975	68675
0279	D	D	E	N	1975	68675
0279	S	D	E	N	1975	68675
0299	S	D	E	N	1973	52314
0299	S	D	E	L	1974	57306
0351	T	D	E	N	1974	68831
0351	T	D	E	N	1976	101827
0352	D	D	E	L	1973	55156
0352	D	D	E	L	1975	62977
0352	D	D	E	N	1975	62977
0352	D	T	E	L	1975	62977
0352	D	T	E	N	1975	62977
0352	S	S	E	N	1973	53430
0352	S	D	E	N	1973	68839
8018	D	D	E	N	1973	52957
8039	S	D	E	N	1973	52314
8039	S	D	R	L	1973	57805
8039	S	D	E	L	1974	57806
8044	A	D	E	N	1974	57970
110-8044	D	D	E	N	1974	54111
8044	T	D	E	N	1974	54111
8044	T	D	E	N	1974	57970
8051	S	D	R	N	1973	55068
8051	S	D	E	N	1974	55069
8051	S	D	E	N	1974	58050
8051	S	D	R	N	1975	90148
8051	S	D	E	N	1975	90149
8051	T	D	R	N	1974	66752
8051	T	D	E	N	1975	66753
8053	S	D	E	N	1974	54111
8054	A	D	E	N	1974	57970
8054	T	D	E	N	1973	51123
8054	T	D	E	N	1974	57970
8090	S	D	E	N	1965	68546
8090	S	T	E	N	1965	68546
8093	S	D	E	N	1973	52314
8094	D	D	R	N	1973	54373
8094	D	D	E	N	1973	54374
8112	T	D	R	N	1974	60411
8112	T	D	E	N	1974	60412
8118	S	S	E	N	1972	53512
8118	S	D	E	N	1971	62600
8126	S	D	E	N	1973	51891
8135	S	D	E	N	1974	53749
8136	S	D	E	N	1974	53749
8137	D	S	R	N	1973	53657
8137	D	S	E	N	1974	53658
8156	S	D	R	N	1973	51951
8156	S	D	E	N	1973	54436
8157	S	D	R	N	1973	51951
8157	S	D	E	N	1973	54436
8158	S	D	R	N	1973	51951
8158	S	D	E	N	1973	54436
8159	S	D	R	N	1973	55068
8159	S	D	E	N	1974	55069
8164	T	D	E	N	1974	54111
8165	S	D	E	N	1975	86742
8169	D	D	E	L	1973	55156
8170	D	D	E	L	1973	55156
8176	S	D	E	N	1971	57169
8214	T	D	E	N	1974	81418
8222	S	D	E	N	1965	75938
8222	S	T	E	N	1965	75938
8234	S	D	E	N	1975	87154
8253	S	D	R	N	1974	90242
8253	S	D	E	N	1974	90243
8274	S	D	E	N	1976	101851
8274	S	E	E	N	1976	101851
8274	S	T	E	N	1976	101851
111-0001	S	D	E	N	1973	51795
0006	A	D	R	N	1973	54377
0006	A	D	E	N	1973	54378
0006	A	D	E	L	1975	95569
0006	S	D	R	N	1973	54377
0006	S	D	E	N	1973	54378
0006	S	D	R	N	1974	63444
0006	S	T	R	N	1974	63444
0006	S	D	E	N	1970	64545
0006	S	D	E	N	1971	65044
0006	S	D	E	N	1975	86744
0006	S	T	E	N	1975	86744
0006	S	D	E	N	1974	93445
0006	S	T	E	N	1974	93445
0008	A	D	E	N	1974	54026
0008	A	T	E	N	1974	65585
0008	A	T	E	N	1975	101030
0008	D	D	E	N	1973	52772
0008	D	D	E	N	1974	54026
0008	D	S	E	N	1974	54026
0008	D	D	E	L	1974	54555
0008	D	D	E	N	1974	54555
0008	D	D	E	N	1974	54558
0008	D	T	E	N	1974	59358
0008	D	D	E	N	1970	62194
0008	D	D	R	N	1974	63040
0008	D	D	E	N	1975	63041
0008	D	D	E	L	1969	65350
0008	D	D	E	N	1969	65350
0008	D	D	E	L	1971	70519
0008	D	D	E	N	1971	70519
0008	D	E	E	N	1971	70519
0008	D	D	E	N	1969	75184
0008	D	E	E	N	1969	75184
0008	D	T	E	N	1969	75184
0008	D	D	R	L	1974	76160
0008	D	D	R	N	1974	76160
0008	D	D	E	L	1975	76161
0008	D	D	E	N	1975	76161
0008	D	S	E	N	1965	87703
0008	D	T	E	N	1975	89296
0008	D	D	E	N	1975	89778
0008	D	S	E	N	1975	89778
0008	D	T	E	N	1975	89778
0008	D	D	R	N	1974	89999
0008	D	D	E	N	1975	90000
0008	D	D	E	N	1975	96448
0008	S	S	E	N	1973	51795
0008	S	S	E	N	1973	52024
0008	S	D	E	N	1973	52772

Phys. State: **A.** Amorphous; **C.** Superconductive; **D.** Doped; **F.** Fibrous or Whisker; **G.** Gas; **I.** Ionized or Plasma; **L.** Liquid; **P.** Powder or Particle; **S.** Solid; **T.** Thin Film
Subject: **D.** Data; **E.** Experiment; **S.** Survey (Review, Compendium, etc.); **T.** Theory
Language: **E.** English; **F.** French; **G.** German; **O.** Other Languages; **R.** Russian
Temperature: **L.** Low (0 to 75K); **N.** Normal (75 to 1273K); **H.** High (above 1273K)

Substance Number	Phys. State	Subject	Language	Temperature	Year	EPIC Number
111-0008	S	D	E	N	1974	53917
0008	S	D	E	N	1974	54026
0008	S	D	E	N	1974	54558
0008	S	D	E	N	1974	55721
0008	S	E	E	N	1974	55721
0008	S	T	E	N	1974	55721
0008	S	T	E	N	1972	55728
0008	S	T	E	N	1974	58825
0008	S	D	E	N	1974	58958
0008	S	E	E	N	1974	58958
0008	S	S	E	N	1974	58958
0008	S	D	R	N	1971	59188
0008	S	D	E	N	1971	59189
0008	S	D	E	N	1973	60575
0008	S	S	E	N	1973	60575
0008	S	T	E	N	1973	60575
0008	S	D	E	N	1974	60657
0008	S	T	E	N	1974	60657
0008	S	D	E	N	1972	60932
0008	S	E	E	N	1972	60932
0008	S	D	R	N	1973	62100
0008	S	D	E	N	1970	62194
0008	S	S	E	N	1971	62264
0008	S	T	E	N	1972	63811
0008	S	T	E	N	1974	65585
0008	S	D	E	N	1964	68792
0008	S	E	E	N	1971	70519
0008	S	T	E	N	1971	70669
0008	S	D	E	N	1969	75184
0008	S	T	E	N	1969	75184
0008	S	S	E	N	1962	87669
0008	S	S	E	N	1965	87703
0008	S	S	E	L	1974	88203
0008	S	D	E	N	1975	89266
0008	S	E	E	N	1975	89266
0008	S	D	E	N	1973	89715
0008	S	S	E	L	1975	90112
0008	S	S	E	N	1975	90112
0008	S	S	E	N	1975	93323
0008	S	T	E	N	1974	93327
0008	S	T	E	N	1975	93330
0008	S	D	E	N	1976	99177
0008	S	T	E	N	1976	99177
0008	S	T	E	N	1976	99364
0008	S	T	E	N	1975	101030
0008	S	D	E	N	1976	101211
0008	S	D	R	L	1973	101917
0008	S	D	R	N	1973	101917
0008	S	T	R	L	1973	101917
0008	S	T	R	N	1973	101917
0008	S	D	E	L	1973	101918
0008	S	D	E	N	1973	101918
0008	S	T	E	L	1973	101918
0008	S	T	E	N	1973	101918
0008	S	S	E	N	1975	102056
0008	T	D	R	N	1971	59188
0008	T	D	E	N	1971	59189
0008	T	D	E	N	1970	62194
0008	T	T	E	N	1974	65585
0008	T	D	E	N	1976	99741
0008	T	E	E	N	1976	99741
0021	S	D	E	N	1973	62246
0021	S	S	E	N	1973	62246
0021	S	D	E	N	1974	62548
0021	S	D	E	N	1973	63804
0021	S	S	R	L	1974	66446
0021	S	S	R	N	1974	66446
0021	S	S	E	L	1974	66447
0021	S	S	E	N	1974	66447
0021	S	S	E	L	1975	91290
0021	S	S	E	N	1975	91290
0021	T	D	E	N	1973	54206
0021	T	D	E	N	1970	63881
0029	S	D	R	N	1975	99712
0029	S	D	E	N	1975	99713
0029	S	D	E	L	1976	102163
0029	S	T	E	L	1976	102163
0046	S	D	E	N	1972	53169
0046	S	E	E	N	1972	53169
0050	S	D	R	N	1974	62020
0050	S	T	R	N	1974	62020
0050	S	D	E	N	1974	62021
0050	S	T	E	N	1974	62021
0050	S	D	E	N	1975	94550
0098	A	D	E	N	1975	101028
0098	A	T	E	N	1975	101028
0101	P	D	E	N	1975	68673
0101	P	T	E	N	1975	68673
8002	A	S	E	N	1974	94637
8002	A	S	E	N	1972	97249
8002	A	T	E	N	1975	101030
8002	D	T	R	N	1973	62730
8002	D	D	E	L	1961	64497
8002	D	D	R	N	1974	64959
8002	D	T	E	N	1973	65326
8002	D	D	E	N	1975	68432
8002	D	S	E	N	1966	87831
8002	D	D	E	N	1975	89778
8002	D	S	E	N	1975	89778
8002	D	T	E	N	1975	89778
8002	D	D	E	N	1975	94627

Substance Number	Phys. State	Subject	Language	Temperature	Year	EPIC Number
111-8002	D	T	E	N	1975	94627
8002	S	D	E	N	1973	51795
8002	S	S	E	N	1973	52024
8002	S	D	E	N	1974	53917
8002	S	D	E	N	1974	60657
8002	S	T	E	N	1974	60657
8002	S	D	F	N	1973	63636
8002	S	T	E	N	1972	63811
8002	S	D	E	N	1961	64496
8002	S	D	E	L	1961	64497
8002	S	D	E	N	1961	64497
8002	S	D	E	L	1962	65951
8002	S	T	E	L	1962	65951
8002	S	D	E	N	1963	65981
8002	S	D	G	N	1954	66199
8002	S	T	G	N	1954	66199
8002	S	S	E	N	1962	87670
8002	S	S	E	N	1966	87831
8002	S	T	E	N	1974	93327
8002	S	T	E	N	1975	93330
8002	S	S	E	N	1972	97249
8002	S	T	E	N	1975	101030
8002	S	D	E	N	1976	101470
8002	S	T	E	N	1976	101470
8002	S	D	E	N	1976	101823
8002	S	T	E	N	1976	101823
8002	S	S	E	N	1975	102056
8002	S	D	E	L	1976	103586
8002	S	E	E	L	1976	103586
8002	S	T	E	L	1976	103586
8002	T	S	E	N	1974	94637
8007	S	D	E	N	1973	49616
8007	S	D	E	N	1973	51795
8007	S	D	R	N	1969	53201
8007	S	D	E	N	1972	53202
8007	S	S	E	N	1973	56247
8007	S	S	E	N	1974	61360
8007	S	T	E	N	1974	61360
8007	S	D	E	N	1972	63763
8007	S	D	E	L	1962	63880
8007	S	D	E	N	1962	63880
8007	S	D	E	L	1975	65493
8007	S	T	E	L	1975	65493
8007	S	D	E	N	1974	66691
8007	S	T	E	N	1974	66691
8007	S	D	E	N	1975	96246
8007	S	T	E	N	1975	96246
8007	S	D	R	N	1975	99712
8007	S	D	E	N	1975	99713
8007	S	D	E	L	1976	100631
8007	S	D	E	N	1976	100631
8007	S	T	E	L	1976	100631
8007	S	T	E	N	1976	100631
8008	S	D	E	N	1973	51795
8008	T	D	R	N	1970	61533
8008	T	T	R	N	1970	61533
8009	S	D	E	N	1973	51795
8009	S	D	R	N	1969	53201
8009	S	D	E	N	1972	53202
8009	S	D	E	N	1973	57453
8009	S	D	R	N	1972	62689
8009	S	S	R	L	1972	62689
8009	S	D	E	L	1962	63880
8009	S	D	E	N	1962	63880
8009	S	D	E	N	1972	64417
8009	S	S	E	L	1972	64417
8010	S	D	E	N	1973	51795
8014	S	D	R	N	1974	63444
8014	S	T	R	N	1974	63444
8014	S	D	E	N	1974	93445
8014	S	T	E	N	1974	93445
8015	A	D	E	N	1973	50526
8015	A	E	E	N	1973	50526
8015	A	S	E	N	1974	94637
8015	S	D	E	N	1973	50526
8015	S	E	E	N	1973	50526
8015	S	D	E	N	1973	51795
8015	S	D	E	N	1973	53584
8015	S	D	E	N	1975	86744
8015	S	T	E	N	1975	86744
8015	T	D	E	N	1973	55106
8019	S	D	E	N	1964	59770
8019	S	T	E	N	1964	59770
8021	A	S	E	N	1974	65584
8021	A	S	E	N	1971	84631
8021	A	D	E	N	1976	99925
8021	A	T	E	N	1976	99925
8021	T	T	R	N	1973	52562
8021	T	T	E	N	1973	57787
8021	T	S	E	N	1971	84631
8021	T	D	E	N	1976	99925
8021	T	T	E	N	1976	99925
8023	D	D	E	N	1974	57750
8023	S	D	E	N	1974	57750
8026	D	D	E	N	1975	86754
8026	D	T	E	N	1975	86754
8026	D	D	E	N	1976	101211
8026	S	D	E	N	1976	101211
8031	A	S	E	N	1974	94637
8031	T	S	E	N	1974	94637
8036	S	D	E	N	1973	50958

Substance Number	Phys. State	Subject	Language	Temperature	Year	EPIC Number
111-8038	S	D	E	N	1973	52785
8038	T	D	E	N	1973	51191
8073	S	D	R	N	1969	53201
8073	S	D	E	N	1972	53202
8075	A	S	E	N	1974	94637
8075	T	D	E	N	1973	55106
8075	T	D	E	N	1971	62269
8075	T	S	E	N	1974	94637
8078	A	D	E	N	1973	50526
8078	A	E	E	N	1973	50526
8078	S	D	E	N	1973	50526
8078	S	E	E	N	1973	50526
8079	A	D	E	N	1973	50526
8079	A	E	E	N	1973	50526
8079	A	D	E	N	1975	86744
8079	A	T	E	N	1975	86744
8079	S	D	E	N	1973	50526
8079	S	E	E	N	1973	50526
8079	S	D	E	N	1973	51795
8079	S	D	E	N	1973	53584
8079	T	T	R	N	1973	52562
8079	T	T	E	N	1973	57787
8079	T	D	E	N	1975	98067
8079	T	T	E	N	1975	98067
8087	D	D	E	N	1973	53727
8087	D	D	E	N	1974	58050
8108	A	D	E	N	1974	57991
8108	A	D	E	N	1975	96723
8108	T	D	E	N	1975	96723
8116	S	D	R	N	1972	52262
8127	D	D	R	N	1974	90221
8127	D	D	E	N	1975	90222
8132	S	D	E	N	1973	56122
8187	S	D	E	N	1968	68207
8190	S	D	R	N	1972	78186
8190	T	D	R	N	1972	78186
112-0001	D	D	O	N	1974	87930
0001	D	E	O	N	1974	87930
0001	G	D	E	N	1973	51879
0001	G	D	E	N	1973	52482
0001	G	D	E	N	1972	52995
0001	G	D	E	N	1972	53271
0001	G	T	R	N	1968	53333
0001	G	T	E	N	1973	53334
0001	G	D	R	N	1973	54446
0001	G	E	R	N	1973	54446
0001	G	S	R	N	1973	54446
0001	G	T	R	N	1973	54446
0001	G	D	E	N	1973	54447
0001	G	E	E	N	1973	54447
0001	G	S	E	N	1973	54447
0001	G	T	E	N	1973	54447
0001	G	D	R	N	1973	55694
0001	G	D	E	N	1974	55796
0001	G	T	R	N	1973	56859
0001	G	D	E	N	1973	57834
0001	G	D	R	H	1974	87314
0001	G	D	R	N	1974	87314
0001	G	S	R	H	1974	87314
0001	G	S	R	N	1974	87314
0001	G	D	E	H	1974	87315
0001	G	D	E	N	1974	87315
0001	G	S	E	H	1974	87315
0001	G	S	E	N	1974	87315
0001	G	T	E	N	1976	101465
0001	I	D	E	N	1972	68127
0001	L	D	E	N	1973	50969
0001	L	D	E	N	1973	51941
0001	L	S	E	N	1972	53361
0001	L	D	E	N	1972	53488
0001	L	E	E	N	1972	53488
0001	L	S	E	N	1972	53488
0001	L	T	E	N	1972	53488
0001	L	D	E	N	1973	53703
0001	L	D	E	N	1974	53741
0001	L	T	E	N	1974	53741
0001	L	S	E	N	1974	54549
0001	L	D	E	N	1973	57543
0001	L	E	E	N	1973	57543
0001	L	D	E	N	1973	59134
0001	L	D	E	N	1971	59615
0001	L	E	E	N	1971	59615
0001	L	D	E	N	1974	60354
0001	L	T	E	N	1974	60354
0001	L	E	R	N	1971	61555
0001	L	E	E	N	1971	65906
0001	L	S	E	N	1974	85293
0001	L	D	O	N	1974	87930
0001	L	E	O	N	1974	87930
0001	L	D	G	N	1894	89952
0001	L	D	E	N	1976	100174
0001	L	E	E	N	1976	100174
0001	L	T	E	N	1976	100174
0001	L	S	E	N	1975	103142
0001	S	D	E	N	1973	50146
0001	S	S	E	N	1972	53074
0001	S	D	E	N	1972	53361
0001	S	E	E	N	1972	53361
0001	S	T	E	N	1972	53361
0001	S	S	E	L	1962	75890

Phys. State: **A.** Amorphous; **C.** Superconductive; **D.** Doped; **F.** Fibrous or Whisker; **G.** Gas; **I.** Ionized or Plasma; **L.** Liquid; **P.** Powder or Particle; **S.** Solid; **T.** Thin Film
Subject: **D.** Data; **E.** Experiment; **S.** Survey (Review, Compendium, etc.); **T.** Theory
Language: **E.** English; **F.** French; **G.** German; **O.** Other Languages; **R.** Russian
Temperature: **L.** Low (0 to 75K); **N.** Normal (75 to 1273K); **H.** High (above 1273K)

Substance Number	Phys. State	Sub-ject	Lan-guage	Temper-ature	Year	EPIC Number
112-0004	G	S	R	N	1972	65883
0004	G	T	R	N	1972	65883
0004	G	S	E	N	1972	65884
0004	G	T	E	N	1972	65884
0007	G	S	E	N	1973	51441
0010	D	S	E	N	1968	75835
0010	G	D	E	N	1974	67252
0010	G	D	E	N	1973	100963
0010	G	S	E	N	1973	100963
0010	G	T	E	N	1973	100963
0010	L	S	E	N	1968	75835
0010	S	D	E	N	1973	54727
0010	S	D	E	N	1973	55795
0010	S	S	E	L	1962	75890
0021	S	D	R	N	1974	93444
0021	S	T	R	N	1974	93444
0021	S	D	E	N	1974	93445
0021	S	T	E	N	1974	93445
0028	S	D	E	N	1973	51503
0028	S	E	E	N	1973	51503
0028	S	D	E	N	1973	59093
0028	S	S	E	N	1973	59093
0035	S	D	E	N	1970	68244
0035	S	D	R	N	1975	90134
0035	S	D	E	N	1975	90135
0038	S	D	F	N	1974	64247
0038	S	T	F	N	1974	64247
0098	D	D	E	N	1974	87215
0098	D	S	E	N	1974	87215
0098	D	T	E	N	1974	87215
0098	S	D	R	N	1974	58128
0098	S	D	E	N	1974	58129
0402	S	S	E	N	1975	101023
0402	T	D	E	N	1975	90114
0402	T	T	E	N	1975	90114
8020	S	D	R	N	1973	51564
8020	S	D	E	N	1974	53695
8025	S	D	R	N	1973	51272
8025	S	D	E	L	1972	53409
8025	S	D	E	N	1972	53409
8025	S	D	O	N	1971	60023
8025	S	S	E	N	1967	68371
8025	S	D	E	N	1963	68878
8049	S	D	R	N	1974	93444
8049	S	T	R	N	1974	93444
8049	S	D	E	N	1974	93445
8049	S	T	E	N	1974	93445
8052	G	D	E	N	1974	54312
8052	G	E	E	N	1974	54312
8052	G	S	E	N	1974	54312
8078	S	T	E	N	1975	63297
8095	S	D	E	N	1973	94481
8095	S	T	E	N	1973	94481
114-0001	D	D	E	N	1972	50486
0001	D	E	E	N	1972	50486
0001	D	D	E	N	1973	50633
0001	D	T	E	N	1973	52028
0001	D	D	E	N	1973	52474
0001	D	D	E	N	1973	53581
0001	D	E	E	N	1973	53581
0001	D	D	E	L	1973	53790
0001	D	D	E	N	1973	53790
0001	D	D	R	N	1973	54393
0001	D	D	E	N	1973	54394
0001	D	D	R	N	1973	54411
0001	D	D	E	N	1973	54412
0001	D	D	R	N	1972	54640
0001	D	D	E	L	1974	55251
0001	D	D	R	L	1973	57818
0001	D	D	E	L	1974	57819
0001	D	D	R	N	1974	58084
0001	D	D	E	N	1974	58085
0001	D	S	E	N	1974	58696
0001	D	T	E	N	1974	58696
0001	D	D	E	N	1974	59393
0001	D	D	E	N	1973	60586
0001	D	D	E	L	1974	61391
0001	D	D	E	L	1972	61498
0001	D	D	E	N	1972	61498
0001	D	S	E	L	1972	61498
0001	D	S	E	N	1972	61498
0001	D	T	E	L	1972	61498
0001	D	T	E	N	1972	61498
0001	D	D	E	L	1973	62286
0001	D	D	E	N	1973	62286
0001	D	D	E	L	1973	62811
0001	D	T	E	L	1973	62811
0001	D	D	R	N	1971	66296
0001	D	D	E	N	1971	66297
0001	D	D	E	L	1975	66689
0001	D	S	R	N	1974	77830
0001	D	D	E	L	1974	94215
0001	D	T	E	L	1974	94215
0001	D	S	E	N	1974	95926
0001	D	S	E	L	1976	99913
0001	D	D	E	N	1976	103336
0001	D	T	E	N	1976	103336
0001	L	D	R	N	1971	66296
0001	L	D	E	N	1971	66297
0001	S	S	E	N	1972	53244

Substance Number	Phys. State	Sub-ject	Lan-guage	Temper-ature	Year	EPIC Number
114-0001	S	S	E	N	1972	53247
0001	S	D	E	N	1973	54214
0001	S	T	E	N	1973	54214
0001	S	D	R	N	1972	54640
0001	S	S	E	N	1973	54773
0001	S	S	E	L	1972	55357
0001	S	S	E	N	1972	55357
0001	S	D	E	N	1973	57710
0001	S	T	R	N	1974	58227
0001	S	S	E	N	1974	58696
0001	S	D	E	L	1974	58962
0001	S	D	E	N	1974	58962
0001	S	S	E	L	1974	58962
0001	S	S	E	N	1974	58962
0001	S	D	E	L	1970	59675
0001	S	D	R	N	1974	60463
0001	S	D	E	N	1974	60464
0001	S	D	E	N	1974	61390
0001	S	S	E	N	1974	61390
0001	S	D	E	N	1971	61706
0001	S	E	E	N	1971	61706
0001	S	D	E	L	1973	62286
0001	S	D	E	N	1973	62286
0001	S	D	E	L	1973	62811
0001	S	T	E	L	1973	62811
0001	S	D	R	N	1973	62862
0001	S	D	E	L	1975	63327
0001	S	D	E	N	1975	63327
0001	S	S	E	N	1975	63327
0001	S	S	E	N	1970	63588
0001	S	D	E	N	1973	65167
0001	S	S	E	N	1975	65501
0001	S	T	E	N	1974	65612
0001	S	S	E	N	1924	73267
0001	S	D	E	N	1969	85421
0001	S	S	R	L	1973	87035
0001	S	S	R	N	1973	87035
0001	S	S	E	L	1973	87036
0001	S	S	E	N	1973	87036
0001	S	S	E	N	1971	87883
0001	S	D	E	L	1975	89451
0001	S	D	E	N	1975	89451
0001	S	S	E	L	1975	89451
0001	S	S	E	N	1975	89451
0001	S	T	E	L	1975	89451
0001	S	T	E	N	1975	89451
0001	S	D	E	N	1975	90871
0001	S	D	E	N	1975	93316
0001	S	T	E	N	1975	101011
0001	S	T	E	L	1975	101014
0001	S	T	E	N	1975	101014
0001	S	D	E	L	1976	101287
0001	S	D	E	N	1976	101287
0001	S	S	E	L	1976	101287
0001	S	S	E	N	1976	101287
0001	S	D	E	N	1976	101843
0001	S	S	E	L	1976	101843
0001	S	S	E	N	1976	101843
0001	S	T	E	N	1976	101843
0001	S	S	E	L	1975	102056
0001	S	S	E	N	1975	102056
0001	T	D	E	N	1970	62185
0001	T	T	E	N	1970	62185
0001	T	D	E	N	1975	101021
0002	D	D	E	N	1973	50633
0002	D	D	E	L	1972	62285
0002	D	D	E	L	1973	62286
0002	D	D	E	N	1973	62286
0002	D	D	E	N	1976	101592
0002	D	E	E	N	1976	101592
0002	D	S	E	N	1976	101592
0002	D	T	E	N	1976	101592
0002	S	D	E	N	1973	50566
0002	S	S	E	N	1973	50566
0002	S	D	E	N	1973	60649
0002	S	E	E	N	1973	60649
0002	S	T	E	N	1973	60649
0002	S	D	E	N	1974	61390
0002	S	S	E	N	1974	61390
0002	S	D	E	N	1971	61706
0002	S	E	E	N	1971	61706
0002	S	D	E	L	1973	62286
0002	S	D	E	N	1973	62286
0002	S	S	E	N	1970	63588
0002	S	T	E	N	1974	65612
0002	S	D	E	N	1971	75192
0002	S	S	E	N	1971	75192
0002	T	D	E	N	1970	62185
0002	T	T	E	N	1970	62185
0006	A	D	E	L	1974	66395
0006	A	T	E	L	1974	66395
0006	S	D	E	L	1973	51835
0006	S	S	E	L	1974	65584
0006	S	D	E	L	1974	90911
0006	S	T	E	L	1974	90911
0006	S	S	E	L	1975	91289
0009	D	D	R	N	1970	50950
0009	D	D	E	N	1973	52779
0009	D	E	E	N	1973	53581
0009	D	D	E	L	1964	75090
0009	D	D	R	L	1963	91918

Substance Number	Phys. State	Sub-ject	Lan-guage	Temper-ature	Year	EPIC Number
114-0009	S	D	R	N	1970	50950
0009	S	D	E	L	1974	58962
0009	S	D	E	N	1974	61390
0009	S	S	E	N	1974	61390
0009	S	S	E	N	1975	65501
0009	S	T	E	N	1974	65612
0009	S	S	E	N	1963	75839
0009	S	D	E	N	1976	101287
0009	S	D	E	N	1976	101843
0009	S	T	E	N	1976	101843
0009	S	D	E	N	1976	103350
0009	S	S	E	N	1976	103350
0009	S	T	E	N	1976	103350
0009	T	D	E	N	1970	62185
0009	T	T	E	N	1970	62185
0010	S	T	E	N	1975	65501
0010	S	D	E	L	1974	86203
0015	D	D	E	N	1975	92132
0015	T	D	E	N	1975	90860
0015	T	T	E	N	1975	90860
0015	T	D	E	N	1975	92132
0017	S	S	E	N	1973	52024
0017	S	D	E	N	1974	53915
0017	S	D	E	N	1974	53917
0017	S	S	E	N	1973	53939
0017	S	T	E	L	1974	54601
0017	S	D	R	N	1973	56785
0017	S	S	E	N	1974	58040
0017	S	D	R	N	1971	60185
0017	S	D	R	N	1974	62528
0017	S	D	E	N	1972	63772
0017	S	T	E	N	1972	63811
0017	S	D	E	N	1974	64431
0017	S	D	G	N	1954	66199
0017	S	T	G	N	1954	66199
0017	S	S	E	N	1962	87660
0017	S	D	E	L	1975	91863
0017	S	T	E	L	1975	91863
0017	S	D	E	N	1974	93257
0017	S	T	E	N	1974	93257
0017	S	S	E	N	1972	97249
0017	S	S	E	N	1963	98002
0017	S	T	E	N	1975	99140
0017	S	D	E	L	1976	99245
0017	S	E	E	L	1976	99245
0017	S	D	E	N	1976	100761
0017	S	T	E	N	1976	100761
0017	S	D	E	N	1976	101211
0017	S	D	E	N	1976	101470
0017	S	T	E	N	1976	101470
0017	S	D	E	N	1976	101823
0017	S	T	E	N	1976	101823
0017	T	D	R	L	1973	55327
0017	T	D	R	N	1973	55327
0017	T	D	E	L	1974	59263
0017	T	D	E	N	1974	59263
0046	S	D	E	N	1969	62324
0055	L	D	E	N	1929	73248
0055	T	D	E	N	1973	68874
0055	T	D	E	N	1975	101655
0055	T	D	E	N	1976	101813
0055	T	E	E	N	1976	101813
0055	T	D	E	N	1976	101814
0055	T	T	E	N	1976	101814
0055	T	S	E	N	1976	102567
0060	S	D	R	N	1973	51714
0060	S	S	E	N	1973	63666
0060	T	D	R	N	1974	66586
0060	T	D	E	N	1974	66587
8001	A	S	E	N	1970	59557
8001	A	S	E	N	1974	94637
8001	D	D	E	N	1972	53255
8001	D	D	R	N	1973	57229
8001	D	D	E	L	1969	62248
8001	D	D	E	N	1969	62248
8001	D	E	E	L	1969	62248
8001	D	E	E	N	1969	62248
8001	D	S	E	N	1963	87679
8001	D	S	E	N	1965	87781
8001	D	D	E	N	1975	89778
8001	D	S	E	N	1975	89778
8001	D	T	E	N	1975	89778
8001	I	E	E	N	1973	55115
8001	I	S	E	N	1973	55115
8001	S	D	E	N	1973	51212
8001	S	D	R	N	1972	51263
8001	S	S	E	N	1973	52024
8001	S	S	E	N	1973	52464
8001	S	S	E	N	1972	53244
8001	S	S	E	N	1972	53247
8001	S	T	E	N	1973	53564
8001	S	D	E	L	1974	53606
8001	S	D	E	N	1974	53606
8001	S	S	E	L	1974	53606
8001	S	S	E	N	1974	53606
8001	S	D	E	N	1973	53788
8001	S	E	E	N	1973	53788
8001	S	D	E	N	1973	53939
8001	S	S	E	N	1973	53939
8001	S	T	E	L	1974	54601
8001	S	S	E	N	1973	54773

Phys. State: **A.** Amorphous; **C.** Superconductive; **D.** Doped; **F.** Fibrous or Whisker; **G.** Gas; **I.** Ionized or Plasma; **L.** Liquid; **P.** Powder or Particle; **S.** Solid; **T.** Thin Film
Subject: **D.** Data; **E.** Experiment; **S.** Survey (Review, Compendium, etc.); **T.** Theory
Language: **E.** English; **F.** French; **G.** German; **O.** Other Languages; **R.** Russian
Temperature: **L.** Low (0 to 75K); **N.** Normal (75 to 1273K); **H.** High (above 1273K)

Substance Number	Phys. State	Subject	Language	Temperature	Year	EPIC Number
114-8001	S	T	R	N	1973	54970
8001	S	T	E	N	1974	54971
8001	S	T	R	N	1973	54990
8001	S	T	E	N	1974	54991
8001	S	T	R	N	1973	55340
8001	S	D	R	N	1973	57229
8001	S	D	E	L	1974	58040
8001	S	T	E	N	1974	59278
8001	S	D	G	N	1971	59433
8001	S	S	E	N	1970	59557
8001	S	S	E	N	1974	60259
8001	S	D	E	N	1971	61459
8001	S	D	R	L	1974	62427
8001	S	S	R	L	1972	62703
8001	S	T	R	L	1972	62703
8001	S	T	R	N	1972	62858
8001	S	T	E	N	1972	63811
8001	S	D	E	N	1972	63955
8001	S	E	E	N	1972	63955
8001	S	T	E	N	1973	65181
8001	S	S	E	L	1972	65300
8001	S	T	E	L	1972	65300
8001	S	D	E	L	1974	65330
8001	S	D	G	N	1954	66199
8001	S	T	G	N	1954	66199
8001	S	D	E	N	1975	66682
8001	S	D	G	N	1974	71582
8001	S	D	R	L	1973	71670
8001	S	E	R	L	1973	71670
8001	S	D	E	L	1966	74593
8001	S	D	E	L	1973	82405
8001	S	E	E	L	1973	82405
8001	S	S	E	N	1963	87679
8001	S	S	E	L	1965	87781
8001	S	S	E	N	1965	87781
8001	S	D	E	N	1975	101019
8001	S	D	E	N	1976	101470
8001	S	S	E	N	1976	101470
8001	S	T	E	N	1976	101470
8001	S	D	E	N	1976	101823
8001	S	T	E	N	1976	101823
8001	S	D	E	N	1976	103155
8001	S	S	E	N	1976	103155
8001	S	T	E	N	1976	103155
8001	T	S	E	N	1973	53451
8001	T	D	E	N	1971	63892
8001	T	T	R	N	1975	77007
8001	T	T	E	N	1975	77008
8001	T	S	E	N	1965	87781
8001	T	S	E	N	1974	94637
8010	S	E	R	N	1973	62591
8010	S	S	R	N	1973	62591
8010	S	T	R	N	1973	62591
8010	S	E	E	N	1974	62592
8010	S	S	E	N	1974	62592
8010	S	T	E	N	1974	62592
8010	S	D	R	N	1972	63472
8010	S	D	E	N	1972	65150
8012	S	D	R	N	1972	63472
8012	S	D	E	N	1972	65150
8012	S	S	E	N	1962	87661
8021	S	D	E	L	1975	93528
8021	S	D	E	N	1975	93528
8021	S	T	E	L	1975	93528
8021	S	T	E	N	1975	93528
8024	G	D	E	N	1974	54330
8024	G	E	E	N	1974	54330
8050	S	D	E	N	1973	52474
8064	S	D	R	N	1972	63472
8064	S	D	E	N	1972	65150
8066	S	D	R	N	1972	56997
8067	S	D	R	L	1976	102038
8067	S	D	R	N	1976	102038
8067	S	T	R	L	1976	102038
8067	S	T	R	N	1976	102038
8067	S	D	E	L	1976	102039
8067	S	D	E	N	1976	102039
8067	S	T	E	L	1976	102039
8067	S	T	E	N	1976	102039
116-0030	S	S	E	N	1974	66380
8003	S	D	R	N	1974	77941
8003	S	S	R	N	1974	77941
8003	S	D	E	N	1974	94517
8003	S	S	E	N	1974	94517
8017	S	D	E	N	1975	96224
8017	S	T	E	N	1975	96224
8026	S	D	R	N	1974	77941
8026	S	S	R	N	1974	77941
8026	S	D	E	N	1974	94517
8026	S	S	E	N	1974	94517
8030	S	D	F	N	1974	87699
118-0037	D	D	E	N	1973	52748
0037	D	D	E	N	1974	53896
0037	D	D	E	N	1974	62740
0037	D	D	E	N	1975	96224
0037	D	T	E	N	1975	96224
0037	S	D	E	N	1973	52748
0037	S	D	E	L	1974	60517
0037	S	D	E	N	1974	60517
118-0037	S	S	E	N	1971	87883
0037	S	D	E	L	1975	91288
0037	S	D	E	N	1975	91288
0037	S	S	E	L	1975	91288
0037	S	S	E	N	1975	91288
0037	S	T	E	L	1975	91288
0037	S	T	E	N	1975	91288
0041	D	D	E	N	1973	52748
0041	S	D	E	N	1973	52168
0041	S	E	E	N	1973	52168
0041	S	D	E	N	1973	52748
8018	S	D	E	N	1973	52123
8018	S	D	E	N	1974	90311
8048	S	D	R	N	1974	58128
8048	S	D	E	N	1974	58129
8061	S	D	E	N	1974	61202
119-0001	S	D	E	N	1974	60658
0001	S	S	E	N	1975	63300
0001	S	D	E	N	1971	75337
0002	D	D	E	L	1973	53586
0002	D	D	E	N	1973	53586
0002	D	D	E	N	1975	62975
0002	D	E	E	N	1975	62975
0002	D	S	E	N	1969	87723
0002	S	D	E	N	1973	52085
0002	S	S	E	N	1972	53512
0002	S	D	E	N	1973	53583
0002	S	D	E	N	1974	54024
0002	S	S	E	N	1974	59353
0002	S	D	R	N	1974	60463
0002	S	D	E	N	1974	60464
0002	S	S	E	N	1973	62815
0002	S	S	E	N	1949	63242
0002	S	D	E	N	1975	63297
0002	S	T	E	N	1975	63297
0002	S	D	E	N	1975	63332
0002	S	S	E	N	1975	63332
0002	S	D	E	N	1974	63390
0002	S	S	E	N	1974	63390
0002	S	T	E	N	1974	63390
0002	S	D	E	H	1966	64256
0002	S	D	E	L	1966	64256
0002	S	D	E	N	1966	64256
0002	S	S	E	N	1973	64495
0002	S	S	E	H	1970	65877
0002	S	S	E	L	1970	65877
0002	S	S	E	N	1970	65877
0002	S	D	E	N	1965	65978
0002	S	S	E	N	1965	65978
0002	S	D	E	H	1966	74594
0002	S	D	E	L	1966	74594
0002	S	D	E	N	1966	74594
0002	S	S	E	N	1971	87883
0002	S	D	E	N	1975	88493
0002	S	S	E	N	1975	93181
0002	S	S	E	H	1975	93182
0002	S	S	E	N	1975	93182
0002	S	D	E	N	1975	93328
0002	S	S	E	N	1974	94636
0002	S	D	E	N	1955	99794
0002	S	T	E	N	1955	99794
0002	S	S	E	N	1975	101034
0002	S	D	E	N	1976	101441
0002	S	D	E	N	1975	101668
0002	S	E	E	N	1975	101668
0002	S	S	E	N	1975	101668
0002	S	D	E	N	1976	101851
0002	S	E	E	N	1976	101851
0002	S	T	E	N	1976	101851
0002	S	D	E	N	1976	102042
0002	S	E	E	N	1976	102042
0002	T	D	E	N	1970	62185
0002	T	T	E	N	1970	62185
0002	T	D	E	N	1971	64338
0002	T	D	E	N	1975	96486
0005	S	D	E	N	1974	60654
0008	S	D	E	N	1974	58048
0008	S	D	E	L	1974	58055
0008	S	E	E	L	1974	58055
0008	T	D	E	N	1970	62185
0008	T	T	E	N	1970	62185
0015	T	D	E	N	1974	56621
0026	S	D	E	N	1972	49919
0043	S	D	E	L	1972	51976
0043	S	S	E	N	1974	58014
0043	S	D	E	N	1974	58048
0049	D	D	R	L	1973	52351
0049	D	D	R	N	1973	52351
8001	A	D	E	N	1974	58018
8001	S	D	E	N	1974	58040
8001	S	S	E	N	1974	58040
8002	D	S	E	N	1962	87672
8002	S	S	E	N	1962	87672
8035	S	D	R	N	1972	60735
8035	S	S	R	N	1972	60735
8035	S	D	E	N	1973	60736
8035	S	S	E	N	1973	60736
8048	S	S	E	N	1972	53512
8048	S	D	E	N	1971	62600
8052	S	D	E	N	1973	51891
119-8056	S	D	E	N	1974	53749
8080	S	D	E	N	1971	75337
8080	S	S	E	N	1974	86505
8081	S	D	R	N	1972	52262
8087	S	S	E	N	1975	85290
8087	S	T	E	N	1975	85290
120-0001	A	S	E	N	1971	65066
0001	A	T	E	N	1971	65066
0001	D	T	E	N	1971	65066
0001	S	D	E	N	1972	49919
0001	T	S	E	N	1974	54111
0001	T	D	E	N	1970	62185
0001	T	T	E	N	1970	62185
0001	T	T	E	N	1968	64270
0001	T	D	E	N	1975	66619
0002	G	D	E	N	1973	51253
0002	G	D	R	H	1973	54428
0002	G	D	R	N	1973	54428
0002	G	S	R	H	1973	54428
0002	G	T	R	H	1973	54428
0002	G	D	E	H	1973	54429
0002	G	D	E	N	1973	54429
0002	G	S	E	H	1973	54429
0002	G	T	E	H	1973	54429
0002	G	D	E	N	1973	56124
0002	S	S	E	L	1962	75890
0003	S	D	E	N	1972	53207
0003	G	D	E	N	1975	90703
0003	G	S	E	N	1975	103142
0006	S	S	E	N	1974	58014
0006	S	D	E	N	1974	58051
0009	L	D	E	N	1963	75554
0009	S	D	R	N	1972	64288
0009	S	T	R	N	1972	64288
0009	S	D	E	N	1972	68417
0009	S	T	E	N	1972	68417
0010	S	D	R	N	1972	79248
0010	S	D	E	N	1972	90275
0024	D	D	R	L	1973	55180
0024	D	S	R	L	1973	55180
0024	D	D	E	L	1974	55181
0024	D	S	E	L	1974	55181
0032	S	S	E	N	1974	66380
0035	T	D	R	N	1972	54159
0035	T	D	E	N	1972	54160
0043	L	D	R	N	1973	61564
0043	L	E	R	N	1973	61564
0043	L	D	E	N	1973	65915
0043	L	E	E	N	1973	65915
0081	S	D	F	N	1958	75815
0081	S	T	F	N	1958	75815
0129	T	D	R	N	1973	90563
0203	S	S	E	N	1974	66380
0221	A	D	E	N	1974	52811
0221	T	D	E	N	1974	52811
0233	S	D	E	L	1974	58797
0233	S	D	E	N	1974	58797
0233	T	D	E	N	1975	94546
0233	T	S	E	N	1975	94546
0233	T	T	E	N	1975	94546
8022	S	D	E	L	1974	58797
8022	S	D	E	N	1974	58797
8024	A	D	R	N	1973	56943
8024	S	D	G	N	1974	91890
8024	S	E	G	N	1974	91890
8024	S	S	G	N	1974	91890
8024	T	D	R	N	1973	56943
8024	T	D	E	N	1973	57595
8024	T	D	R	N	1973	70971
8024	T	T	R	N	1973	70971
8024	T	D	E	N	1973	96085
8024	T	T	E	N	1973	96085
8024	T	D	R	N	1974	98023
8024	T	T	R	N	1974	98023
8024	T	D	E	N	1974	98024
8024	T	T	E	N	1974	98024
8038	S	D	R	L	1974	68630
8038	S	T	R	L	1974	68630
8038	S	D	E	L	1974	68631
8038	S	T	E	L	1974	68631
8042	S	D	E	N	1974	60658
8042	S	D	E	N	1971	75337
8044	S	D	R	L	1973	70953
8044	S	T	R	L	1973	70953
8044	S	D	E	L	1973	91478
8044	S	T	E	L	1973	91478
8052	S	D	E	N	1973	51891
8088	D	T	R	N	1970	52334
8097	S	D	E	N	1971	75337
8107	T	D	E	N	1974	81418
8128	D	D	E	N	1974	63254
8128	D	S	E	N	1974	63254
8128	D	T	E	N	1974	63254
122-0003	T	D	E	N	1974	81418
0004	D	D	E	N	1973	51752
0004	S	S	E	N	1964	65975
0004	S	S	E	N	1975	93181
0004	S	S	E	N	1975	93182
0004	S	D	R	N	1974	93444

Phys. State: **A.** Amorphous; **C.** Superconductive; **D.** Doped; **F.** Fibrous or Whisker; **G.** Gas; **I.** Ionized or Plasma; **L.** Liquid; **P.** Powder or Particle; **S.** Solid; **T.** Thin Film
Subject: **D.** Data; **E.** Experiment; **S.** Survey (Review, Compendium, etc.); **T.** Theory
Language: **E.** English; **F.** French; **G.** German; **O.** Other Languages; **R.** Russian
Temperature: **L.** Low (0 to 75K); **N.** Normal (75 to 1273K); **H.** High (above 1273K)

Substance Number	Phys. State	Subject	Language	Temperature	Year	EPIC Number
122-0004	S	T	R	N	1974	93444
0004	S	D	E	N	1974	93445
0004	S	T	E	N	1974	93445
0004	T	D	G	N	1975	93698
0004	T	D	E	N	1975	96486
0005	D	E	E	N	1972	53165
0005	S	D	E	N	1972	49919
0005	S	D	E	N	1972	53113
0005	S	D	E	H	1972	53167
0005	S	D	E	N	1972	53167
0005	S	S	E	N	1972	53512
0005	S	D	R	N	1974	63444
0005	S	T	R	N	1974	63444
0005	S	T	R	N	1974	66762
0005	S	T	E	N	1975	66763
0005	S	D	F	N	1958	75815
0005	S	T	F	N	1958	75815
0005	S	S	E	N	1966	87831
0005	S	S	E	N	1971	87883
0005	S	D	E	N	1974	93445
0005	S	T	E	N	1974	93445
0005	T	D	E	N	1973	54809
0005	T	D	G	N	1975	93698
0008	S	D	E	N	1962	98644
0008	S	T	E	N	1962	98644
0008	S	D	E	N	1963	98655
0008	T	D	E	N	1972	64098
0008	T	S	E	N	1972	64098
0009	A	D	E	N	1974	57286
0009	A	S	E	N	1974	57286
0009	A	D	E	L	1975	95569
0009	A	D	E	N	1976	99319
0009	D	D	R	N	1973	50197
0009	D	D	E	N	1973	50198
0009	D	D	E	N	1973	60892
0009	D	D	E	N	1975	65504
0009	D	T	E	N	1975	65504
0009	D	D	R	N	1974	66438
0009	D	S	R	N	1974	66438
0009	D	D	E	N	1974	66439
0009	D	S	E	N	1974	66439
0009	D	D	E	N	1974	90322
0009	F	D	F	N	1974	63406
0009	F	E	F	N	1974	63406
0009	F	T	F	N	1974	63406
0009	F	D	E	N	1975	65504
0009	F	T	E	N	1975	65504
0009	F	D	E	N	1974	90322
0009	F	D	E	N	1974	93191
0009	F	E	E	N	1974	93191
0009	F	T	E	N	1974	93191
0009	F	S	E	N	1975	101027
0009	S	D	E	N	1973	52505
0009	S	S	E	N	1974	52806
0009	S	D	E	N	1973	53452
0009	S	D	E	N	1972	53498
0009	S	S	E	N	1972	53512
0009	S	D	E	N	1973	60892
0009	S	D	R	N	1974	63444
0009	S	T	R	N	1974	63444
0009	S	T	R	N	1968	64541
0009	S	T	E	N	1968	64542
0009	S	D	E	N	1972	64547
0009	S	T	E	N	1972	64547
0009	S	D	R	N	1970	64846
0009	S	D	E	N	1970	64847
0009	S	D	G	N	1959	64940
0009	S	D	G	H	1956	64941
0009	S	D	G	N	1956	64941
0009	S	D	R	N	1974	66438
0009	S	D	E	N	1974	66439
0009	S	D	E	N	1969	75962
0009	S	E	E	N	1969	75962
0009	S	S	E	N	1971	87883
0009	S	D	E	N	1974	93445
0009	S	T	E	N	1974	93445
0009	T	D	R	N	1972	51298
0009	T	D	R	N	1973	52203
0009	T	D	R	N	1973	52679
0009	T	D	E	N	1973	52793
0009	T	D	E	N	1973	54454
0009	T	D	R	N	1973	56028
0009	T	D	R	N	1971	61559
0009	T	E	R	N	1971	61559
0009	T	T	R	N	1971	61559
0009	T	D	E	N	1972	63536
0009	T	D	R	N	1972	65446
0009	T	T	R	N	1972	65446
0009	T	D	E	N	1972	65447
0009	T	T	E	N	1972	65447
0009	T	D	E	N	1971	65910
0009	T	E	E	N	1971	65910
0009	T	T	E	N	1971	65910
0009	T	D	R	N	1974	66438
0009	T	S	R	N	1974	66438
0009	T	D	E	N	1974	66439
0009	T	S	E	N	1974	66439
0009	T	D	G	N	1962	75921
0009	T	D	E	N	1974	92149
0009	T	E	E	N	1974	92149
0009	T	D	E	N	1975	92867
122-0009	T	D	G	N	1975	93698
0009	T	D	O	N	1973	101913
0009	T	D	E	N	1973	101949
0009	T	T	E	N	1973	101949
0010	G	S	R	N	1972	65883
0010	G	T	R	N	1972	65883
0010	G	S	E	N	1972	65884
0010	G	T	E	N	1972	65884
0012	S	D	E	L	1975	90692
0013	T	D	R	N	1974	90192
0013	T	D	E	N	1975	90193
0014	D	D	E	N	1972	53110
0014	S	D	E	N	1972	53110
0016	S	D	E	N	1972	49919
0016	S	D	R	N	1974	63126
0016	S	T	R	N	1974	63126
0016	S	D	E	N	1975	63127
0016	S	T	E	N	1975	63127
0016	S	T	E	N	1974	71206
0016	S	D	R	N	1974	93434
0016	S	T	R	N	1974	93434
0016	S	D	E	N	1974	93435
0016	S	T	E	N	1974	93435
0016	S	D	E	N	1973	100961
0016	S	T	E	N	1973	100961
0016	T	D	E	N	1975	66711
0016	T	T	E	N	1975	66711
0017	T	D	R	N	1974	62804
0017	T	D	E	N	1974	65343
0019	A	D	E	N	1972	53112
0019	S	D	E	N	1972	53112
0019	S	D	E	N	1972	53386
0023	D	D	E	L	1974	59358
0023	D	D	E	L	1974	65617
0023	D	D	E	N	1974	65617
0023	D	S	E	N	1963	87709
0023	D	S	E	N	1974	99215
0023	S	D	E	L	1973	57486
0023	S	D	E	N	1973	57486
0023	S	D	E	N	1974	62493
0023	S	T	E	N	1972	63811
0023	S	T	E	N	1970	70645
0023	S	S	E	N	1963	87709
0023	S	S	E	N	1974	99215
0023	T	S	E	N	1963	87709
0023	T	D	E	L	1975	92849
0023	T	D	E	L	1976	103149
0023	T	T	E	L	1976	103149
0023	T	T	E	N	1976	103149
0030	D	D	E	N	1973	50965
0030	D	D	R	N	1973	55203
0030	D	D	E	N	1974	55204
0030	D	D	E	N	1975	65497
0030	D	T	E	N	1975	65497
0030	S	S	E	N	1974	54111
0030	S	D	R	N	1973	55203
0030	S	D	E	N	1974	55204
0030	S	D	E	N	1973	60645
0030	S	E	E	N	1973	60645
0030	S	D	E	N	1975	65497
0030	S	T	E	N	1975	65497
0030	S	S	E	N	1971	87883
0030	S	D	E	N	1975	88493
0030	S	D	E	L	1975	91288
0030	S	D	E	N	1975	91288
0030	S	T	E	L	1975	91288
0030	S	T	E	N	1975	91288
0030	S	D	E	N	1975	93328
0030	S	D	E	N	1976	101441
0030	S	D	E	N	1975	101668
0030	S	E	E	N	1975	101668
0030	S	S	E	N	1975	101668
0030	S	D	E	N	1976	101851
0030	S	E	E	N	1976	101851
0030	S	T	E	N	1976	101851
0030	S	D	E	N	1976	102042
0030	S	E	E	N	1976	102042
0038	S	D	R	N	1972	79248
0038	S	D	E	N	1972	90275
0038	T	D	E	N	1975	90658
0046	S	D	R	N	1974	63444
0046	S	T	R	N	1974	63444
0046	S	D	E	N	1974	93445
0046	S	T	E	N	1974	93445
0046	T	D	E	N	1973	54809
0050	S	D	E	N	1973	51772
0050	S	S	E	N	1967	66368
0050	T	T	E	N	1973	54774
0050	T	D	E	N	1972	59438
0050	T	T	E	N	1972	59438
0050	T	S	E	N	1967	66368
0050	T	D	E	N	1975	92802
0050	T	T	E	N	1975	92802
0064	S	D	E	N	1972	49919
0095	S	D	E	N	1973	51795
0096	A	S	E	N	1974	83966
0096	A	S	E	N	1975	90806
0096	S	S	E	N	1973	60892
0096	S	S	E	N	1971	62264
0096	S	D	R	N	1974	63444
0096	S	T	R	N	1974	63444
122-0096	S	D	E	N	1974	93445
0096	S	T	E	N	1974	93445
0096	S	T	E	N	1976	99966
0096	T	D	G	N	1962	75921
0096	T	S	G	N	1962	75921
0096	T	S	E	N	1975	90806
0096	T	D	E	N	1975	92867
0096	T	T	E	N	1976	99011
0105	T	D	O	N	1973	56266
0112	S	D	E	N	1972	53110
0139	S	D	R	N	1974	93444
0139	S	T	R	N	1974	93444
0139	S	D	E	N	1974	93445
0139	S	T	E	N	1974	93445
0139	T	S	E	N	1971	63564
0139	T	D	E	N	1974	81418
0199	D	D	R	N	1973	54389
0199	D	D	E	N	1973	54390
0314	S	D	E	H	1972	53167
0326	T	D	R	N	1970	63932
0421	S	D	E	N	1973	90094
0449	S	D	R	N	1972	79248
0449	S	D	E	N	1972	90275
8004	G	D	R	N	1974	65725
8004	G	D	E	N	1974	65726
8012	T	D	E	N	1973	53458
8012	T	T	E	N	1976	101295
8027	S	D	R	N	1974	90242
8027	S	D	E	N	1974	90243
8028	S	D	E	N	1974	61379
8029	S	D	E	N	1974	61379
8030	S	D	E	N	1974	61379
8031	S	D	E	N	1974	61379
8032	S	D	E	N	1974	61379
8044	T	D	E	N	1972	53416
8045	A	D	E	N	1974	57286
8045	A	D	R	N	1974	66438
8045	A	D	E	N	1974	66439
8045	A	S	E	N	1975	96148
8045	A	D	E	N	1976	99625
8045	A	T	E	N	1976	99625
8045	A	D	E	N	1959	99666
8045	A	T	E	N	1959	99666
8045	D	D	E	N	1974	57798
8045	D	S	E	N	1974	57798
8045	D	D	E	N	1975	86883
8045	D	E	E	H	1975	86883
8045	D	E	E	N	1975	86883
8045	F	S	E	N	1975	101027
8045	L	D	E	N	1974	53864
8045	L	E	E	N	1974	53864
8045	S	D	R	H	1973	51949
8045	S	D	E	N	1973	53452
8045	S	D	E	N	1972	53498
8045	S	D	E	H	1973	54432
8045	S	D	E	N	1973	55512
8045	S	D	E	N	1973	57334
8045	S	T	E	N	1973	57334
8045	S	D	E	N	1974	57798
8045	S	D	R	N	1973	59413
8045	S	T	R	N	1973	59413
8045	S	D	E	N	1974	62317
8045	S	E	E	N	1974	62317
8045	S	S	E	N	1949	63242
8045	S	S	E	N	1973	64543
8045	S	D	E	N	1973	64544
8045	S	D	E	N	1970	64545
8045	S	S	E	N	1970	64545
8045	S	D	E	N	1973	65286
8045	S	S	E	N	1970	65877
8045	S	S	E	N	1970	66180
8045	S	D	E	N	1973	87482
8045	S	S	E	N	1971	87883
8045	S	D	E	N	1976	101304
8045	S	E	E	N	1975	101665
8045	S	T	E	N	1975	101665
8045	S	D	E	N	1936	101914
8045	S	E	E	N	1936	101914
8045	S	T	E	N	1936	101914
8045	S	D	E	N	1973	101924
8045	S	E	E	N	1973	101924
8045	T	D	E	N	1965	64850
8046	S	D	E	N	1972	53498
8046	S	D	E	N	1972	64547
8046	S	T	E	N	1972	64547
8046	S	D	E	N	1973	65897
8046	S	D	E	N	1969	75962
8046	S	E	E	N	1969	75962
8047	S	S	E	N	1972	53512
8049	S	S	E	N	1972	53512
8052	F	D	E	N	1975	101038
8052	F	E	E	N	1975	101038
8052	F	D	E	N	1975	101040
8052	F	E	E	N	1975	101040
8052	S	D	E	N	1973	53452
8052	S	T	E	N	1974	64540
8052	S	D	E	N	1973	65897
8052	S	S	E	N	1975	101034
8058	S	D	E	L	1975	91765
8058	S	D	E	N	1975	91765
8061	S	D	E	N	1969	75962

Phys. State: A. Amorphous; C. Superconductive; D. Doped; F. Fibrous or Whisker; G. Gas; I. Ionized or Plasma; L. Liquid; P. Powder or Particle; S. Solid; T. Thin Film
Subject: D. Data; E. Experiment; S. Survey (Review, Compendium, etc.); T. Theory
Language: E. English; F. French; G. German; O. Other Languages; R. Russian
Temperature: L. Low (0 to 75K); N. Normal (75 to 1273K); H. High (above 1273K)

Substance Number	Phys. State	Subject	Language	Temperature	Year	EPIC Number
122-8061	S	E	E	N	1969	75962
8062	S	D	E	N	1969	75962
8062	S	E	E	N	1969	75962
8068	S	D	F	L	1971	59041
8076	S	D	E	N	1973	60892
8076	S	S	E	N	1973	60892
8076	T	D	G	N	1962	75921
8076	T	D	E	N	1969	95705
8086	S	D	E	N	1973	65897
8092	S	D	E	L	1974	61156
8093	S	D	E	N	1974	61379
8094	S	S	E	H	1972	53512
8094	S	S	E	N	1972	53512
8098	A	D	E	L	1975	95569
8101	L	D	E	N	1976	100047
8101	L	E	E	N	1976	100047
8101	L	T	E	N	1976	100047
8101	S	D	E	N	1973	53452
8101	S	D	E	N	1972	53498
8101	S	D	E	N	1976	100047
8101	S	E	E	N	1976	100047
8101	S	S	E	N	1976	100047
8101	S	T	E	N	1976	100047
8102	S	D	E	N	1972	53498
8102	S	D	E	N	1975	100436
8102	S	E	E	N	1975	100436
8130	A	D	E	L	1975	95569
8131	S	S	E	N	1973	64543
123-0003	S	D	E	N	1973	51070
0003	S	T	R	N	1972	62858
0003	S	T	E	N	1973	65181
0003	S	S	E	L	1966	68361
0003	S	S	E	N	1966	68361
0003	S	D	G	N	1974	71582
0003	S	S	E	N	1971	87883
0003	S	D	E	N	1976	101470
0003	S	T	E	N	1976	101470
0003	S	D	E	N	1976	101823
0003	S	T	E	N	1976	101823
0003	T	S	E	N	1970	59601
0003	T	S	E	N	1966	68361
0032	S	T	E	N	1974	59352
0032	S	D	R	N	1974	62020
0032	S	T	R	N	1974	62020
0032	S	D	E	N	1974	62021
0032	S	T	E	N	1974	62021
0032	S	D	E	N	1972	65878
0032	S	T	E	N	1972	65878
0048	D	D	E	N	1971	85443
0048	S	D	E	N	1971	85443
8017	S	T	R	N	1972	62858
8017	S	T	E	N	1973	65181
8017	S	S	E	N	1962	87674
8017	S	S	E	L	1975	96245
8017	S	T	E	L	1975	96245
8017	S	D	E	N	1976	101823
8017	S	T	E	N	1976	101823
8017	T	S	E	N	1962	87674
8018	D	D	R	N	1973	50672
8018	D	D	R	N	1973	50972
8018	D	D	E	N	1973	52418
8018	D	D	R	N	1974	71470
8018	D	D	E	N	1975	71506
8018	S	D	E	N	1973	53853
8018	S	T	R	N	1972	62858
8018	S	D	E	N	1971	65041
8018	S	S	E	N	1971	65041
8018	S	T	E	N	1973	65181
8018	S	D	E	N	1975	65441
8018	S	E	E	N	1975	65441
8018	S	T	E	N	1975	65441
8018	S	S	E	L	1970	68114
8018	S	S	E	N	1970	68114
8018	S	D	E	N	1973	68901
8018	S	D	G	N	1974	71582
8018	S	S	E	L	1962	87671
8018	S	S	E	N	1962	87671
8018	S	S	E	N	1966	87831
8018	S	D	E	N	1976	101470
8018	S	T	E	N	1976	101470
8018	S	D	E	N	1976	101823
8018	S	T	E	N	1976	101823
8018	T	S	R	N	1973	52679
8018	T	D	E	N	1972	53263
8018	T	S	E	N	1973	54454
8018	T	D	E	N	1974	61179
8018	T	S	E	N	1974	61179
8018	T	D	R	N	1972	62707
8018	T	D	E	N	1973	65303
8018	T	D	R	N	1974	71470
8018	T	D	E	N	1975	71506
8018	T	D	E	N	1975	90976
8025	T	D	R	N	1972	76540
8025	T	D	E	N	1972	91592
8039	S	D	E	N	1973	88343
8039	S	T	E	N	1973	88343
8050	D	D	R	N	1974	92259
8050	D	D	E	N	1975	92260
8051	D	D	R	N	1974	92259
8051	D	D	E	N	1975	92260
123-8051	S	D	E	N	1972	53271
8051	S	S	E	N	1970	68114
8051	S	S	E	N	1975	76733
8051	S	D	E	N	1973	88343
8051	S	T	E	N	1973	88343
8051	S	D	R	N	1974	92259
8051	S	D	E	N	1975	92260
8051	S	D	E	N	1976	100173
8051	S	T	E	N	1976	100173
8051	T	D	E	N	1972	53263
8051	T	D	R	N	1972	62707
8051	T	D	E	N	1973	65303
8058	S	E	E	L	1974	60379
8058	S	T	E	L	1974	60379
8068	A	D	R	N	1974	62436
8068	A	D	E	N	1974	67079
8068	T	D	R	N	1974	62436
8068	T	D	E	N	1974	67079
8074	S	D	R	N	1974	92259
8074	S	D	E	N	1975	92260
8099	T	D	R	N	1972	76540
8099	T	D	E	N	1972	91592
8100	T	D	R	N	1972	76540
8100	T	D	E	N	1972	91592
125-8014	S	D	R	N	1974	77941
8014	S	S	R	N	1974	77941
8014	S	D	E	N	1974	94517
8014	S	S	E	N	1974	94517
126-0001	S	D	E	N	1972	100962
0001	S	T	E	N	1972	100962
0004	S	D	E	N	1974	60658
0005	D	D	E	L	1973	50533
0005	D	T	E	L	1973	50533
0005	D	D	E	N	1973	52496
0005	D	S	R	N	1973	54298
0005	D	S	E	N	1973	54299
0005	D	D	E	L	1974	59358
0005	D	D	E	L	1974	61188
0005	D	D	E	N	1970	64857
0005	D	D	E	L	1974	81762
0005	D	T	E	L	1974	81762
0005	D	D	E	N	1974	87226
0005	D	E	E	N	1974	87226
0005	D	D	R	N	1974	89483
0005	D	E	R	N	1974	89483
0005	D	S	R	N	1974	89483
0005	D	T	R	N	1974	89483
0005	D	D	E	N	1975	89778
0005	D	S	E	N	1975	89778
0005	D	T	E	N	1975	89778
0005	D	D	E	N	1974	99259
0005	D	E	E	N	1974	99259
0005	D	S	E	N	1974	99259
0005	D	T	E	N	1974	99259
0005	S	S	E	N	1972	53246
0005	S	T	E	N	1972	53246
0005	S	S	E	N	1972	53248
0005	S	D	E	N	1973	54214
0005	S	T	E	N	1973	54214
0005	S	S	E	N	1974	58014
0005	S	D	E	N	1974	60255
0005	S	D	E	N	1974	60657
0005	S	T	E	N	1974	60657
0005	S	D	E	N	1973	61472
0005	S	D	E	N	1973	62325
0005	S	S	E	N	1970	65877
0005	S	D	E	L	1975	66683
0005	S	D	E	N	1975	66683
0005	S	E	E	L	1975	66683
0005	S	E	E	N	1975	66683
0005	S	S	E	N	1924	73267
0005	S	D	F	N	1958	75815
0005	S	T	F	N	1958	75815
0005	S	D	E	N	1960	85819
0005	S	D	E	N	1975	86744
0005	S	T	E	N	1975	86744
0005	S	S	R	N	1973	87035
0005	S	S	E	N	1973	87036
0005	S	S	E	N	1963	87711
0005	S	S	E	L	1966	87712
0005	S	S	E	N	1966	87712
0005	S	S	E	N	1971	87883
0005	S	D	E	L	1975	91637
0005	S	D	E	N	1975	91637
0005	S	D	E	N	1975	93315
0005	S	T	E	N	1975	93330
0005	S	D	E	L	1976	99875
0005	S	T	E	L	1976	99875
0005	S	D	E	N	1976	101595
0005	S	S	E	N	1976	101595
0005	S	T	E	N	1976	101595
0005	S	D	E	N	1976	101828
0005	S	S	E	N	1975	102056
0005	T	D	E	N	1973	52214
0005	T	S	R	N	1973	54298
0005	T	S	E	N	1973	54299
0005	T	D	E	N	1974	58961
0005	T	D	E	L	1974	61188
0005	T	D	F	N	1974	61449
126-0005	T	T	F	N	1974	61449
0005	T	D	R	N	1974	61992
0005	T	T	R	N	1974	61992
0005	T	D	E	N	1974	61993
0005	T	T	E	N	1974	61993
0005	T	D	E	N	1970	62185
0005	T	T	E	N	1970	62185
0005	T	D	E	N	1973	65537
0005	T	E	E	N	1973	65537
0005	T	T	E	N	1973	65537
0005	T	D	E	N	1974	68253
0005	T	D	E	N	1974	68831
0005	T	D	E	N	1973	68875
0005	T	S	E	N	1963	87711
0005	T	S	E	N	1966	87712
0005	T	D	E	N	1975	93315
0005	T	D	E	N	1975	93485
0005	T	D	G	N	1975	93698
0005	T	D	E	N	1975	96486
0005	T	E	E	N	1976	99658
0005	T	T	E	N	1976	99658
0005	T	D	E	N	1973	101646
0005	T	E	E	N	1973	101646
0005	T	D	E	N	1976	101816
0005	T	D	E	N	1976	101828
0014	S	D	R	N	1974	86494
0014	S	T	R	N	1974	86494
0017	S	D	R	N	1972	79283
0038	S	D	E	N	1974	60658
8026	S	D	E	L	1964	61307
8026	S	D	E	N	1964	61307
8026	S	D	E	N	1964	85438
8030	A	D	E	N	1972	53386
8030	T	D	E	N	1972	53386
8032	S	S	R	N	1972	62298
8032	S	S	E	N	1973	62299
8035	D	D	E	L	1972	100962
8035	D	T	E	L	1972	100962
8035	S	D	E	L	1972	100962
8035	S	D	E	N	1972	100962
8035	S	T	E	L	1972	100962
8035	S	T	E	N	1972	100962
8037	S	S	E	N	1970	68114
8037	T	S	E	N	1970	68114
8041	S	D	E	N	1976	97227
8049	S	S	E	N	1974	52799
8049	S	S	E	N	1973	59375
8051	S	D	R	N	1975	100322
8051	S	T	R	N	1975	100322
8051	S	D	E	N	1975	100323
8051	S	T	E	N	1975	100323
8052	A	D	E	N	1973	60693
8052	D	D	E	N	1973	52087
8052	D	D	E	N	1972	61505
8052	D	D	E	N	1974	64488
8052	D	D	E	N	1970	64857
8052	D	D	E	L	1966	74595
8052	D	D	E	N	1974	87448
8052	D	D	E	N	1975	89778
8052	D	S	E	N	1975	89778
8052	D	T	E	N	1975	89778
8052	D	D	E	N	1975	97218
8052	S	S	E	N	1974	52799
8052	S	D	E	N	1972	53244
8052	S	E	E	N	1972	53244
8052	S	S	E	N	1972	53244
8052	S	D	E	N	1972	53245
8052	S	S	E	N	1972	53245
8052	S	S	E	N	1972	53246
8052	S	T	E	N	1972	53246
8052	S	S	E	N	1972	53247
8052	S	S	E	N	1972	53248
8052	S	D	E	N	1974	54024
8052	S	D	E	N	1973	54214
8052	S	T	E	N	1973	54214
8052	S	S	E	N	1973	54773
8052	S	D	E	N	1973	58212
8052	S	D	R	N	1974	59347
8052	S	S	E	N	1973	59375
8052	S	D	E	N	1974	60255
8052	S	D	E	L	1974	60657
8052	S	T	E	L	1974	60657
8052	S	D	E	N	1973	60693
8052	S	S	E	N	1973	60837
8052	S	D	E	N	1973	61472
8052	S	S	E	N	1971	62264
8052	S	D	E	N	1974	62302
8052	S	E	E	N	1974	62302
8052	S	D	E	N	1973	62325
8052	S	D	E	N	1974	62602
8052	S	T	E	N	1974	62602
8052	S	E	E	N	1975	63256
8052	S	T	E	N	1975	63256
8052	S	D	E	N	1965	64255
8052	S	T	E	N	1965	64255
8052	S	D	E	N	1974	64488
8052	S	D	E	N	1970	64857
8052	S	D	E	N	1974	64885
8052	S	D	E	N	1974	65105
8052	S	S	E	N	1975	65507
8052	S	S	E	N	1970	65877

Phys. State: **A.** Amorphous; **C.** Superconductive; **D.** Doped; **F.** Fibrous or Whisker; **G.** Gas; **I.** Ionized or Plasma; **L.** Liquid; **P.** Powder or Particle; **S.** Solid; **T.** Thin Film
Subject: **D.** Data; **E.** Experiment; **S.** Survey (Review, Compendium, etc.); **T.** Theory
Language: **E.** English; **F.** French; **G.** German; **O.** Other Languages; **R.** Russian
Temperature: **L.** Low (0 to 75K); **N.** Normal (75 to 1273K); **H.** High (above 1273K)

Substance Number	Phys. State	Subject	Language	Temperature	Year	EPIC Number
126-8052	S	D	E	N	1973	68153
8052	S	S	E	L	1963	68313
8052	S	S	E	N	1963	68313
8052	S	S	E	N	1973	68817
8052	S	D	E	N	1974	68823
8052	S	D	E	N	1972	68832
8052	S	D	E	N	1973	68844
8052	S	D	E	N	1973	68845
8052	S	D	E	N	1973	68875
8052	S	T	E	N	1970	70645
8052	S	D	E	N	1961	73251
8052	S	S	E	N	1974	87759
8052	S	S	E	N	1971	87883
8052	S	D	E	N	1974	88485
8052	S	D	E	N	1975	88493
8052	S	D	E	N	1975	93161
8052	S	D	E	N	1975	93315
8052	S	D	E	N	1975	93316
8052	S	T	E	N	1975	93330
8052	S	D	E	N	1975	93343
8052	S	D	E	N	1974	93373
8052	S	D	E	N	1975	94479
8052	S	D	E	N	1974	94636
8052	S	D	R	N	1975	96306
8052	S	D	E	N	1975	96307
8052	S	D	E	N	1976	97298
8052	S	D	E	N	1976	99549
8052	S	E	E	N	1976	99549
8052	S	D	E	N	1975	101018
8052	S	S	E	N	1975	101034
8052	S	D	E	N	1976	101441
8052	S	D	E	N	1976	101470
8052	S	T	E	N	1976	101470
8052	S	S	E	N	1976	101494
8052	S	D	R	N	1975	101610
8052	S	T	R	N	1975	101610
8052	S	D	E	N	1976	101611
8052	S	T	E	N	1976	101611
8052	S	T	E	N	1975	101662
8052	S	D	E	N	1975	101663
8052	S	S	E	N	1975	101663
8052	S	D	E	N	1975	101666
8052	S	E	E	N	1975	101666
8052	S	D	E	N	1975	101672
8052	S	T	E	N	1975	101672
8052	S	D	E	N	1975	101673
8052	S	S	E	N	1975	101678
8052	S	T	E	N	1975	101678
8052	S	D	E	N	1976	101714
8052	S	E	E	N	1976	101714
8052	S	T	E	N	1976	101714
8052	S	S	E	N	1976	101808
8052	S	D	E	N	1976	101828
8052	S	D	E	N	1976	101837
8052	S	E	E	N	1976	101837
8052	S	T	E	N	1976	101837
8052	S	S	E	N	1976	101838
8052	S	T	E	N	1976	101848
8052	S	D	E	N	1976	101850
8052	S	E	E	N	1976	101850
8052	S	D	E	N	1976	101851
8052	S	E	E	N	1976	101851
8052	S	S	E	N	1976	101851
8052	S	T	E	N	1976	101851
8052	S	D	E	N	1976	101860
8052	S	E	E	N	1976	101860
8052	S	D	E	N	1976	102042
8052	S	E	E	N	1976	102042
8052	S	S	E	N	1975	102056
8052	S	S	E	N	1976	102151
8052	S	T	E	N	1976	102151
8052	S	D	E	N	1974	102245
8052	S	D	E	N	1976	103590
8052	S	T	E	N	1976	103590
8052	T	D	E	N	1973	60693
8052	T	D	R	N	1970	61532
8052	T	D	R	N	1974	61992
8052	T	T	R	N	1974	61992
8052	T	D	E	N	1974	61993
8052	T	T	E	N	1974	61993
8052	T	D	E	N	1974	65105
8052	T	D	E	N	1974	68253
8052	T	S	E	N	1963	68313
8052	T	D	E	N	1973	68875
8052	T	D	E	N	1975	93315
8052	T	D	G	N	1975	93698
8052	T	D	E	N	1975	98067
8052	T	T	E	N	1975	98067
8052	T	D	E	N	1976	101813
8052	T	E	E	N	1976	101813
8052	T	D	E	N	1976	101817
8052	T	E	E	N	1976	101817
8052	T	T	E	N	1976	101817
8052	T	D	E	N	1976	101828
8052	T	D	E	N	1976	101833
8052	T	D	E	N	1976	101846
8052	T	T	E	N	1976	101846
8052	T	D	E	N	1976	102015
8052	T	S	E	N	1976	102567
8052	T	D	E	N	1976	103592
8052	T	E	E	N	1976	103592
126-8060	S	D	E	L	1973	50910
8060	S	D	E	N	1973	50910
8060	S	D	R	N	1973	51723
8060	S	D	E	L	1973	53415
8060	S	D	E	N	1973	53415
8070	S	S	E	N	1975	91600
8073	S	D	E	N	1971	62600
8074	S	S	E	N	1972	53244
8074	S	S	E	N	1972	53247
8074	S	S	E	N	1973	54773
8074	S	S	R	N	1974	59347
8074	S	D	E	N	1969	62248
8074	S	D	E	N	1971	62600
8074	S	S	E	N	1974	64885
8074	S	S	E	N	1970	65877
8074	S	T	E	N	1975	101662
8076	S	D	E	N	1973	50567
8076	S	E	E	N	1973	50567
8080	T	D	E	N	1974	53602
8080	T	S	E	N	1974	53602
8084	S	D	E	N	1973	94481
8084	S	T	E	N	1973	94481
8088	T	S	E	N	1974	53602
8088	T	D	E	N	1974	54336
8089	T	S	E	L	1974	53602
8089	T	D	E	N	1974	54336
8097	S	T	E	L	1974	62465
8100	A	D	E	N	1974	84459
8100	A	D	E	N	1974	86009
8100	T	D	E	N	1974	84459
8100	T	D	E	N	1974	86009
8103	S	D	R	N	1975	86853
8103	S	D	E	N	1975	86854
8104	S	D	R	N	1975	86853
8104	S	S	R	N	1975	86853
8104	S	D	E	N	1975	86854
8104	S	S	E	N	1975	86854
8110	S	S	E	N	1975	91600
127-8004	D	D	E	N	1975	63362
8004	D	D	E	L	1970	63651
8004	D	D	E	N	1970	63651
8004	D	D	E	N	1970	64857
8004	D	D	E	N	1975	89778
8004	D	S	E	N	1975	89778
8004	D	T	E	N	1975	89778
8004	S	T	E	L	1974	54601
8004	S	D	E	N	1974	60657
8004	S	T	E	N	1974	60657
8004	S	S	E	N	1973	60838
8004	S	D	E	N	1973	61472
8004	S	D	E	N	1972	63492
8004	S	D	E	L	1970	63651
8004	S	S	E	N	1970	63651
8004	S	S	E	N	1962	87666
8004	S	D	E	N	1974	93257
8004	S	T	E	N	1974	93257
8004	S	T	E	N	1975	93330
8004	S	S	E	N	1975	101032
8004	T	D	R	L	1972	58947
8004	T	D	R	N	1972	58947
8004	T	D	E	N	1968	59520
8004	T	S	E	N	1973	60838
8004	T	D	R	N	1970	61532
8004	T	D	E	N	1974	68253
8004	T	D	E	N	1974	68831
8004	T	D	R	N	1975	97638
8004	T	T	R	N	1975	97638
8004	T	D	E	N	1975	97639
8004	T	T	E	N	1975	97639
8008	S	D	R	N	1972	66991
8008	T	D	R	N	1972	66991
8010	T	D	E	L	1974	53602
8010	T	D	E	N	1974	53602
8010	T	S	E	N	1974	53602
8010	T	D	E	N	1974	54336

Phys. State: **A.** Amorphous; **C.** Superconductive; **D.** Doped; **F.** Fibrous or Whisker; **G.** Gas; **I.** Ionized or Plasma; **L.** Liquid; **P.** Powder or Particle; **S.** Solid; **T.** Thin Film
Subject: **D.** Data; **E.** Experiment; **S.** Survey (Review, Compendium, etc.); **T.** Theory
Language: **E.** English; **F.** French; **G.** German; **O.** Other Languages; **R.** Russian
Temperature: **L.** Low (0 to 75K); **N.** Normal (75 to 1273K); **H.** High (above 1273K)

Chapter 2 Dielectric Constant

Substance Number	Phys. State	Subject	Language	Temperature	Year	EPIC Number
100-0045	D	S	E	N	1975	95469
0045	L	D	E	N	1973	51764
0045	L	E	E	N	1973	51764
0045	L	S	E	N	1973	51764
0045	L	S	E	N	1972	87876
0045	S	S	E	L	1973	51442
0045	S	S	E	N	1973	51442
0045	S	S	E	N	1972	53114
0045	S	S	E	N	1972	53142
0045	S	S	E	N	1973	56767
0045	S	S	O	N	1969	59542
0045	S	S	E	N	1974	65104
0045	S	S	E	N	1973	82686
0045	S	T	E	N	1976	103351
0045	T	S	E	N	1973	82686
0045	T	S	E	N	1971	87880
0055	A	T	E	N	1972	53276
0055	A	T	E	N	1975	88214
0055	D	T	E	L	1974	58042
0055	D	T	E	N	1974	58042
0055	D	T	R	N	1974	66726
0055	D	T	E	N	1975	66727
0055	D	S	E	N	1975	95469
0055	S	T	R	N	1973	50215
0055	S	T	E	N	1973	50216
0055	S	T	E	N	1973	52024
0055	S	T	E	N	1973	52084
0055	S	T	R	N	1973	52830
0055	S	T	E	N	1973	52831
0055	S	S	R	N	1971	53278
0055	S	S	E	N	1972	53279
0055	S	T	E	N	1973	53562
0055	S	T	E	N	1974	53609
0055	S	S	E	N	1973	53986
0055	S	S	E	N	1974	54081
0055	S	T	E	N	1974	54341
0055	S	T	E	L	1974	54592
0055	S	T	R	N	1973	54974
0055	S	T	E	N	1974	54975
0055	S	S	E	N	1973	56767
0055	S	T	E	L	1974	58042
0055	S	T	E	N	1974	58042
0055	S	S	O	N	1969	59542
0055	S	T	O	N	1972	59998
0055	S	T	E	N	1974	60665
0055	S	T	R	N	1972	60707
0055	S	T	E	N	1973	60708
0055	S	T	E	N	1974	61382
0055	S	D	E	N	1971	62260
0055	S	T	E	N	1971	62260
0055	S	S	E	N	1973	62815
0055	S	S	E	N	1974	62816
0055	S	S	E	N	1974	65104
0055	S	S	E	N	1972	66310
0055	S	S	E	N	1972	67891
0055	S	T	E	N	1968	74648
0055	S	T	E	N	1956	75076
0055	S	T	R	N	1974	81235
0055	S	T	E	L	1973	86425
0055	S	T	E	N	1975	86756
0055	S	S	E	N	1975	90838
0055	S	T	E	N	1974	92365
0055	S	E	E	N	1975	92880
0055	S	E	E	N	1975	94595
0055	S	T	E	N	1975	94595
0055	S	T	E	N	1976	103351
0055	T	E	E	N	1972	49814
0055	T	T	E	L	1973	55193
0055	T	T	E	L	1974	55194
8003	D	T	R	N	1972	49455
8003	S	D	E	N	1973	50566
8003	S	T	E	N	1973	50566
8003	S	T	E	N	1974	53621
8003	S	S	E	N	1974	54603
8003	S	T	R	N	1974	58064
8003	S	T	E	N	1974	58065
8003	S	S	E	N	1974	59353
8003	S	S	E	N	1974	61390
8003	S	S	E	N	1973	62815
8003	S	S	E	N	1974	62816
8003	S	S	E	N	1974	65104
8003	S	D	E	N	1974	65612
8003	S	S	E	N	1972	75135
8003	S	S	E	L	1965	75847
8003	S	S	E	N	1965	75847
8003	S	T	E	N	1976	103351
8007	S	S	O	N	1969	59542
8007	S	S	E	N	1974	62816
8007	S	S	E	N	1969	68271
8007	S	S	E	L	1972	87823
8007	S	S	E	N	1972	87823
8007	S	S	E	N	1975	90838
8008	S	T	E	N	1973	57392
8008	S	S	O	N	1969	59542
8008	S	S	E	N	1974	62816

Substance Number	Phys. State	Subject	Language	Temperature	Year	EPIC Number
100-8008	S	S	E	L	1971	87884
8008	S	S	E	N	1971	87884
8008	S	S	E	N	1972	87889
8008	S	S	E	N	1975	90838
8016	S	S	E	N	1973	60755
8021	S	S	E	N	1972	60888
8031	S	T	E	N	1973	57392
8038	S	S	O	N	1969	59542
8038	S	S	E	L	1969	68115
8038	S	S	E	N	1969	68115
8038	S	S	E	N	1972	87824
8041	S	S	O	N	1969	59542
8058	S	D	E	N	1974	57962
8058	S	T	E	N	1974	57962
8059	S	S	E	N	1972	60888
8059	S	S	E	L	1965	75847
8059	S	S	E	N	1965	75847
8072	S	S	E	N	1967	98889
102-0002	A	S	E	N	1972	52403
0002	D	S	E	N	1964	87713
0002	S	S	E	N	1973	51442
0002	S	D	O	N	1973	52506
0002	S	D	E	N	1974	54023
0002	S	D	E	N	1974	57831
0002	S	D	E	N	1973	59291
0002	S	D	E	N	1967	59799
0002	S	D	E	N	1973	65652
0002	S	D	O	N	1974	66386
0002	S	S	E	N	1964	87713
0002	S	S	E	N	1968	87819
0002	S	S	E	N	1969	87870
0002	S	D	E	N	1974	90091
0002	S	S	E	N	1967	98889
0002	T	D	R	N	1973	51408
0002	T	D	E	N	1973	51409
0002	T	D	O	N	1973	56496
0002	T	D	R	N	1971	56742
0002	T	D	E	N	1973	57731
0002	T	S	E	N	1968	87866
0002	T	D	E	N	1973	90575
0002	T	D	E	N	1970	100000
0002	T	S	E	N	1970	100000
0002	T	T	E	N	1970	100000
0009	S	S	E	N	1973	51442
0009	S	T	R	N	1972	55891
0009	S	D	E	N	1974	60265
0009	S	D	E	N	1973	60579
0009	S	S	E	N	1974	62816
0009	S	D	E	N	1972	63847
0009	S	D	E	L	1969	71197
0009	S	D	E	N	1969	71197
0009	S	E	E	L	1969	71197
0009	S	E	E	N	1969	71197
0009	S	S	E	N	1938	74974
0009	S	S	E	N	1967	98664
0010	S	S	E	N	1973	51442
0010	S	T	R	N	1972	55891
0010	S	D	E	N	1967	59799
0010	S	D	E	N	1974	60265
0010	S	S	E	N	1974	62816
0010	S	D	E	N	1972	63847
0010	S	D	E	L	1969	71197
0010	S	D	E	N	1969	71197
0010	S	E	E	L	1969	71197
0010	S	E	E	N	1969	71197
0010	S	D	E	N	1974	80503
0010	S	S	E	N	1974	80503
0010	S	S	E	N	1967	98664
0018	S	D	E	N	1973	53506
0024	S	S	E	N	1973	51442
0024	S	S	E	N	1967	98664
0027	S	D	R	N	1973	52387
0027	S	D	E	N	1973	55648
0030	S	S	E	N	1973	51442
0030	S	D	E	N	1973	57879
0031	S	S	E	N	1973	51442
0032	S	S	E	N	1973	51442
0034	L	S	E	N	1967	98664
0038	L	S	E	N	1967	98664
0041	S	S	E	N	1972	87889
0041	T	D	E	N	1974	65107
0054	S	S	E	N	1973	51442
0054	S	D	E	N	1974	54054
0054	S	S	E	N	1974	54054
0054	S	D	E	N	1974	58047
0054	S	S	E	N	1975	68617
0054	S	S	E	N	1970	87822
0054	S	S	E	N	1972	87890
0054	S	S	E	N	1976	101320
0086	S	D	E	N	1973	59293
0086	S	D	E	N	1975	66680
0086	S	S	E	N	1975	66680
0086	S	T	E	N	1975	66680
0105	P	S	E	N	1971	87884

Substance Number	Phys. State	Subject	Language	Temperature	Year	EPIC Number
102-0105	S	S	E	N	1972	52968
0105	S	D	R	N	1973	53779
0105	S	D	E	N	1973	55350
0105	S	D	R	N	1971	59379
0105	S	S	E	N	1970	59683
0105	S	S	E	N	1966	87830
0105	S	S	E	N	1971	87884
0105	T	D	R	N	1973	51626
0105	T	D	E	N	1973	53352
0105	T	D	R	N	1971	58853
0105	T	S	E	N	1971	87884
0105	T	D	E	N	1973	91486
0183	S	S	E	N	1973	51442
0183	S	S	E	N	1967	98664
0210	S	S	E	N	1973	51442
0248	S	S	E	N	1972	52968
0281	S	S	E	N	1973	51442
0281	S	S	E	N	1976	101320
0282	S	S	E	N	1973	51442
0282	S	D	E	N	1974	58047
0282	S	D	E	N	1975	68617
0282	S	S	E	N	1976	101320
0296	S	D	E	N	1973	51930
0342	S	D	E	N	1973	50816
0342	S	S	E	N	1973	51442
0362	S	S	E	N	1973	51442
0389	S	S	E	N	1973	51442
8001	S	S	E	N	1973	51442
8001	S	S	E	N	1972	52968
8001	S	D	E	N	1974	58808
8001	S	D	E	N	1974	60265
8001	S	S	E	N	1962	87668
8001	S	S	E	N	1966	87830
8001	S	S	E	N	1971	87884
8001	S	S	R	N	1975	101515
8001	S	S	E	N	1975	101516
8018	S	S	E	N	1972	87889
8023	S	S	E	N	1973	51442
8027	S	S	E	N	1973	51442
8027	S	S	E	N	1975	68617
8027	S	S	E	N	1970	87822
8027	S	S	E	N	1976	101320
8028	S	S	E	N	1972	87890
8031	A	S	E	N	1964	75166
8031	D	D	O	N	1974	90008
8031	S	D	E	N	1973	55877
8031	T	D	R	N	1972	51269
8035	S	S	E	L	1973	51442
8035	S	D	E	N	1974	60664
8035	S	D	E	N	1975	68777
8041	A	D	E	N	1973	54224
8041	A	S	E	N	1974	67182
8041	A	D	E	N	1972	70674
8041	A	S	E	N	1972	70674
8041	A	S	E	N	1974	89269
8041	D	D	E	N	1974	57988
8041	D	T	E	N	1974	60692
8041	D	S	E	N	1974	61356
8041	D	T	E	N	1974	63367
8041	D	D	R	N	1975	96810
8041	D	T	R	N	1975	96810
8041	D	D	E	N	1975	103608
8041	D	T	E	N	1975	103608
8041	S	D	E	N	1972	49419
8041	S	D	E	N	1972	49814
8041	S	S	E	L	1973	51442
8041	S	S	E	N	1973	51442
8041	S	D	R	N	1972	52261
8041	S	S	E	N	1972	52968
8041	S	S	E	N	1972	53227
8041	S	E	E	N	1973	53405
8041	S	T	E	N	1973	53405
8041	S	E	E	N	1973	53443
8041	S	S	E	N	1973	53939
8041	S	S	R	N	1973	55334
8041	S	D	E	N	1974	58808
8041	S	D	E	N	1968	59151
8041	S	T	E	N	1968	59151
8041	S	S	E	N	1974	59272
8041	S	S	E	N	1970	59674
8041	S	D	E	N	1974	60265
8041	S	T	E	N	1974	60692
8041	S	D	E	N	1973	60754
8041	S	D	E	N	1971	62264
8041	S	D	E	N	1973	62296
8041	S	D	E	N	1974	62307
8041	S	T	E	N	1971	63783
8041	S	S	E	N	1974	67182
8041	S	T	E	N	1975	68602
8041	S	S	E	N	1972	70674
8041	S	S	R	N	1974	72651
8041	S	S	E	N	1975	72700
8041	S	D	E	L	1969	75248
8041	S	D	E	N	1969	75248
8041	S	S	E	N	1966	75395

Phys. State: A. Amorphous; C. Superconductive; D. Doped; F. Fibrous or Whisker; G. Gas; I. Ionized or Plasma; L. Liquid; P. Powder or Particle; S. Solid; T. Thin Film
Subject: D. Data; E. Experiment; S. Survey (Review, Compendium, etc.); T. Theory
Language: E. English; F. French; G. German; O. Other Languages; R. Russian
Temperature: L. Low (0 to 75K); N. Normal (75 to 1273K); H. High (above 1273K)

Substance Number	Phys. State	Subject	Language	Temperature	Year	EPIC Number
102-8041	S	S	E	N	1965	75847
8041	S	D	E	N	1974	87448
8041	S	S	E	L	1962	87673
8041	S	S	E	N	1962	87673
8041	S	S	E	L	1964	87701
8041	S	S	E	N	1964	87701
8041	S	S	E	N	1970	87822
8041	S	S	E	N	1970	87879
8041	S	S	E	L	1971	87884
8041	S	S	E	N	1971	87884
8041	S	D	E	N	1972	87889
8041	S	D	E	N	1975	96613
8041	S	D	R	N	1974	96773
8041	S	T	R	N	1974	96773
8041	S	D	E	N	1975	96774
8041	S	T	E	N	1975	96774
8041	S	D	E	L	1976	100412
8041	S	D	E	N	1976	100412
8041	S	S	E	N	1976	100412
8041	S	T	E	L	1976	100412
8041	S	T	E	N	1976	100412
8041	S	S	E	N	1976	101470
8041	S	S	R	N	1975	101515
8041	S	S	E	N	1975	101516
8041	S	S	E	N	1976	101823
8041	S	S	E	L	1976	103155
8041	S	S	E	N	1976	103155
8041	T	D	E	N	1973	52588
8041	T	D	E	N	1973	54224
8041	T	D	E	N	1974	62550
8054	A	D	E	N	1972	70674
8054	A	S	E	N	1972	70674
8054	A	S	E	N	1974	89269
8054	D	D	R	N	1971	51572
8054	D	T	E	L	1973	53572
8054	D	T	E	N	1973	53572
8054	S	S	E	L	1973	51442
8054	S	S	E	N	1973	51442
8054	S	S	E	N	1972	52968
8054	S	S	E	L	1974	53913
8054	S	S	E	N	1973	53939
8054	S	S	R	N	1973	55328
8054	S	D	E	N	1974	58808
8054	S	S	E	N	1974	59264
8054	S	S	E	N	1970	59674
8054	S	D	E	N	1971	65041
8054	S	S	E	N	1974	67182
8054	S	S	E	N	1962	87667
8054	S	S	E	N	1971	87884
8054	S	S	E	N	1972	87889
8054	S	S	E	N	1972	97249
8054	S	S	E	N	1976	101470
8054	S	S	R	N	1975	101515
8054	S	S	E	N	1975	101516
8054	S	S	E	N	1976	101823
8054	T	D	E	N	1974	58893
8054	T	D	E	N	1974	65107
8069	A	D	E	N	1968	75884
8069	S	D	E	N	1968	75884
8078	S	D	E	N	1971	49617
8084	S	D	R	N	1972	52261
8085	S	D	R	N	1972	49824
8086	S	D	R	N	1972	49824
8094	S	S	E	N	1972	53227
8094	S	S	E	N	1975	65438
8094	S	S	E	N	1972	87889
8095	S	S	E	N	1972	53227
8095	S	S	E	N	1972	87889
8095	S	D	E	N	1975	96613
8095	S	S	E	N	1975	96613
8106	S	D	E	N	1972	53178
8132	S	S	E	N	1972	52968
8132	T	S	E	N	1971	87884
8134	S	S	E	N	1973	51442
8134	S	D	E	N	1974	60359
8134	S	T	E	N	1974	60359
8134	S	S	E	N	1970	87822
8134	S	S	E	N	1972	87890
8135	S	S	E	N	1973	51442
8136	S	S	E	N	1973	51442
8137	S	S	E	N	1973	51442
8137	S	D	R	N	1973	52876
8137	S	D	E	N	1974	52877
8137	S	D	E	N	1975	68617
8137	S	D	E	N	1975	87162
8137	S	D	E	N	1974	90316
8137	S	S	E	N	1976	101320
8138	S	S	E	N	1973	51442
8139	D	D	E	N	1974	55242
8142	S	S	E	N	1972	87889
8166	S	D	R	N	1973	52876
8166	S	D	E	N	1974	52877
8166	S	D	E	N	1974	90316
8166	S	S	E	N	1976	101320
8171	A	D	E	N	1972	53186
8171	T	D	E	N	1972	53186
8190	L	D	E	N	1973	51457
8191	L	D	E	N	1973	51457
8232	S	D	E	N	1974	60664
8281	S	S	R	N	1973	56262
8281	S	D	E	N	1973	59291
102-8281	S	S	E	N	1973	76721
8281	T	D	F	N	1973	54648
8313	S	S	G	N	1959	65983
8313	S	S	E	N	1963	65984
8314	S	D	E	N	1975	91619
8359	S	D	E	N	1973	56972
8359	S	S	E	N	1969	87870
8375	S	D	R	N	1971	49958
8385	S	D	R	N	1971	58548
8387	S	D	E	N	1973	59293
8420	T	S	E	N	1972	87889
8432	S	S	E	H	1965	98850
8432	S	S	E	N	1965	98850
8437	S	D	E	N	1968	68207
8439	S	S	E	N	1976	101320
8443	S	D	E	N	1975	91619
8488	S	D	E	N	1973	66202
8488	S	T	E	N	1973	66202
104-0002	S	S	E	N	1973	51442
0002	S	S	E	N	1972	52968
0002	S	D	E	N	1972	53476
0002	S	D	E	N	1974	54023
0002	S	S	E	N	1969	68271
0002	S	S	E	N	1963	87681
0002	S	S	E	N	1968	87819
0002	S	S	E	N	1969	87870
0002	S	S	E	H	1965	98850
0002	S	S	E	N	1965	98850
0002	S	S	E	N	1967	98889
0002	S	S	E	N	1964	101390
0006	D	D	E	L	1973	56334
0006	D	D	E	N	1974	59393
0006	D	D	E	L	1969	71197
0006	D	D	E	N	1969	71197
0006	D	E	E	L	1969	71197
0006	D	E	E	N	1969	71197
0006	D	D	E	N	1971	80226
0006	D	D	E	N	1976	103336
0006	D	T	E	N	1976	103336
0006	S	D	E	L	1973	50820
0006	S	D	E	N	1973	50820
0006	S	S	E	L	1973	51442
0006	S	S	E	N	1973	51442
0006	S	T	E	N	1974	53743
0006	S	D	E	N	1967	59799
0006	S	D	E	N	1974	60265
0006	S	D	R	N	1974	60463
0006	S	D	E	N	1974	60464
0006	S	D	E	N	1973	60582
0006	S	S	E	N	1973	60840
0006	S	S	E	N	1973	64495
0006	S	D	E	L	1969	71197
0006	S	D	E	N	1969	71197
0006	S	E	E	L	1969	71197
0006	S	E	E	N	1969	71197
0006	S	S	E	N	1938	74974
0006	S	D	E	N	1972	75135
0006	S	T	E	N	1972	75135
0006	S	S	E	N	1963	75839
0006	S	T	R	L	1974	80388
0006	S	T	R	N	1974	80388
0006	S	D	E	L	1974	81475
0006	S	D	E	N	1974	81475
0006	S	D	E	N	1973	82666
0006	S	T	E	N	1973	82666
0006	S	D	E	N	1969	85421
0006	S	D	E	N	1975	93559
0006	S	T	E	L	1974	95834
0006	S	T	E	N	1974	95834
0006	S	D	E	L	1965	98883
0006	S	D	E	N	1965	98883
0007	S	S	E	N	1973	51442
0007	S	D	E	N	1974	54023
0007	S	D	E	N	1973	55579
0007	S	D	R	N	1971	59379
0007	S	D	E	N	1972	63787
0007	S	T	E	N	1972	63787
0007	S	D	E	N	1966	64254
0007	S	S	E	N	1967	68374
0007	S	S	E	H	1966	87803
0007	S	S	E	N	1966	87803
0007	S	S	E	N	1969	87870
0007	S	S	E	N	1971	87884
0007	S	S	E	H	1965	98850
0007	S	S	E	N	1967	98893
0007	S	S	E	N	1972	102094
0007	T	D	E	N	1972	53473
0007	T	S	E	N	1966	87803
0007	T	S	E	N	1971	87884
0008	G	S	E	N	1964	87719
0008	L	S	E	N	1964	87719
0008	S	S	E	N	1964	87719
0013	A	D	E	N	1972	60165
0013	D	D	E	N	1971	50467
0013	D	D	R	N	1973	51621
0013	D	T	R	N	1973	51621
0013	D	D	O	N	1973	52219
0013	D	D	O	N	1973	56801
0013	D	D	E	N	1973	79050
0013	D	T	E	N	1973	79050
104-0013	D	D	E	N	1973	90475
0013	S	D	E	N	1973	50150
0013	S	S	E	N	1973	51442
0013	S	S	E	N	1973	52192
0013	S	D	O	N	1973	52323
0013	S	D	R	N	1972	52515
0013	S	D	E	N	1974	54109
0013	S	E	E	N	1974	54109
0013	S	S	E	N	1974	54109
0013	S	T	E	N	1974	54109
0013	S	S	E	N	1974	54577
0013	S	D	R	N	1973	55022
0013	S	D	E	N	1974	55023
0013	S	D	R	N	1973	55064
0013	S	T	R	N	1973	55064
0013	S	D	E	N	1974	55065
0013	S	T	E	N	1974	55065
0013	S	D	E	N	1973	56462
0013	S	D	E	N	1973	56528
0013	S	D	O	N	1973	56816
0013	S	D	R	N	1973	56880
0013	S	D	R	N	1973	56881
0013	S	T	R	N	1973	56882
0013	S	D	F	N	1973	57928
0013	S	T	F	N	1973	57928
0013	S	S	R	N	1973	58747
0013	S	S	E	N	1974	60335
0013	S	T	E	N	1974	60335
0013	S	D	E	N	1974	61363
0013	S	T	E	N	1974	61363
0013	S	T	R	N	1974	61960
0013	S	T	E	N	1974	61961
0013	S	D	E	N	1973	65762
0013	S	T	E	N	1973	65762
0013	S	D	R	N	1973	68038
0013	S	D	E	N	1973	68039
0013	S	D	R	N	1971	76481
0013	S	T	R	N	1971	76481
0013	S	S	E	N	1967	85905
0013	S	S	E	L	1965	87791
0013	S	S	E	N	1965	87791
0013	S	S	E	N	1969	87870
0013	S	S	E	N	1971	87880
0013	S	D	G	N	1974	90255
0013	S	D	E	N	1974	90345
0013	S	T	E	N	1974	90345
0013	S	D	E	N	1974	90351
0013	S	T	E	N	1974	90351
0013	S	D	E	N	1974	90356
0013	S	T	E	N	1974	90361
0013	S	D	E	N	1971	91525
0013	S	T	E	N	1971	91525
0013	S	S	E	N	1965	98850
0013	T	D	R	N	1973	51614
0013	T	D	E	N	1972	60165
0013	T	D	R	N	1974	66796
0013	T	T	R	N	1974	66796
0013	T	D	E	N	1975	66797
0013	T	T	E	N	1975	66797
0013	T	D	O	N	1973	67817
0013	T	D	E	N	1967	85905
0013	T	T	E	N	1967	85905
0013	T	S	E	N	1971	87880
0015	S	S	E	N	1972	51985
0015	S	D	E	N	1973	60755
0015	S	S	E	N	1973	60755
0015	S	T	E	N	1973	60755
0015	S	D	G	N	1963	75747
0015	S	E	G	N	1963	75747
0015	S	S	E	N	1964	101393
0021	S	S	E	N	1973	51442
0022	S	S	E	N	1973	51442
0022	S	D	E	N	1974	54337
0022	S	S	E	N	1970	87822
0025	S	S	E	N	1973	51442
0025	S	S	E	N	1967	98664
0031	S	D	E	L	1973	50566
0031	S	T	E	L	1973	50566
0031	S	S	E	N	1973	51442
0031	S	D	E	N	1967	59799
0031	S	D	E	N	1974	60265
0031	S	D	E	L	1969	71197
0031	S	D	E	N	1969	71197
0031	S	E	E	L	1969	71197
0031	S	E	E	N	1969	71197
0031	S	D	E	N	1971	75192
0031	S	S	E	N	1971	75192
0031	S	D	E	N	1973	82666
0031	S	T	E	N	1973	82666
0038	S	S	E	N	1973	51442
0038	S	S	E	N	1967	98664
0039	S	S	E	N	1973	51442
0040	G	S	E	N	1967	98664
0040	S	D	E	N	1973	50419
0043	S	D	E	L	1973	53712
0049	S	S	E	N	1973	51442
0049	S	D	R	N	1974	66728
0049	S	D	E	N	1975	66729
0049	S	S	E	N	1969	68271
0049	S	S	E	N	1975	96477
0052	S	S	E	N	1973	51442

Phys. State: **A.** Amorphous; **C.** Superconductive; **D.** Doped; **F.** Fibrous or Whisker; **G.** Gas; **I.** Ionized or Plasma; **L.** Liquid; **P.** Powder or Particle; **S.** Solid; **T.** Thin Film
Subject: **D.** Data; **E.** Experiment; **S.** Survey (Review, Compendium, etc.); **T.** Theory
Language: **E.** English; **F.** French; **G.** German; **O.** Other Languages; **R.** Russian
Temperature: **L.** Low (0 to 75K); **N.** Normal (75 to 1273K); **H.** High (above 1273K)

Substance Number	Phys. State	Subject	Language	Temperature	Year	EPIC Number
104-0052	S	T	R	N	1972	55891
0053	S	S	E	N	1973	51442
0053	S	T	E	N	1974	53743
0053	S	D	E	N	1967	59799
0053	S	D	E	N	1974	60265
0053	S	D	E	L	1969	71197
0053	S	D	E	N	1969	71197
0053	S	E	E	L	1969	71197
0053	S	E	E	N	1969	71197
0053	S	D	E	N	1972	75135
0053	S	T	E	N	1972	75135
0053	S	T	R	L	1974	80388
0053	S	T	R	N	1974	80388
0053	S	D	E	N	1973	82666
0053	S	T	E	N	1973	82666
0053	S	D	E	L	1970	85417
0053	S	T	E	L	1974	95834
0053	S	T	E	N	1974	95834
0055	S	S	E	N	1973	51442
0055	S	S	E	N	1967	98664
0056	S	D	E	N	1973	50419
0067	S	D	E	L	1971	50513
0067	S	D	E	N	1971	50513
0067	S	S	E	N	1973	51442
0067	S	D	E	N	1967	59799
0067	S	D	E	N	1973	60579
0067	S	D	E	N	1971	65020
0067	S	D	E	L	1969	71197
0067	S	D	E	N	1969	71197
0067	S	E	E	L	1969	71197
0067	S	E	E	N	1969	71197
0067	S	D	E	N	1975	86748
0067	S	S	E	N	1975	86748
0067	S	D	O	L	1970	101002
0069	S	S	E	N	1973	51442
0069	S	D	R	N	1973	54395
0069	S	D	E	N	1973	54396
0069	S	D	E	N	1963	60560
0069	T	D	R	N	1973	54395
0069	T	D	E	N	1973	101946
0069	T	T	E	N	1973	101946
0104	S	S	E	N	1973	51442
0104	S	S	R	N	1973	56262
0104	S	D	E	N	1967	59799
0104	S	D	R	N	1974	60399
0104	S	D	E	N	1974	60400
0104	S	D	E	N	1963	60560
0104	S	D	E	N	1967	74607
0104	S	S	E	N	1967	74607
0104	S	D	E	N	1972	75135
0104	S	S	E	N	1972	75135
0104	S	S	E	N	1973	76721
0104	S	D	E	N	1974	84584
0104	S	D	R	L	1974	87288
0104	S	D	E	L	1975	87289
0104	S	D	E	L	1976	101501
0104	S	D	E	N	1976	101501
0104	S	T	E	L	1976	101501
0104	S	T	E	N	1976	101501
0105	S	S	E	N	1973	51442
0105	S	D	E	N	1974	60265
0105	S	D	E	L	1969	71197
0105	S	D	E	N	1969	71197
0105	S	E	E	L	1969	71197
0105	S	E	E	N	1969	71197
0105	S	D	E	N	1973	82666
0105	S	T	E	N	1973	82666
0105	S	D	E	L	1970	85417
0106	S	D	E	L	1973	50566
0106	S	T	E	L	1973	50566
0106	S	S	E	N	1973	51442
0106	S	D	E	N	1967	59799
0106	S	D	E	L	1969	71197
0106	S	D	E	N	1969	71197
0106	S	E	E	L	1969	71197
0106	S	E	E	N	1969	71197
0106	S	D	E	N	1973	82666
0106	S	T	E	N	1973	82666
0129	S	S	E	N	1973	51442
0146	S	S	E	N	1973	51442
0146	S	S	E	N	1967	98664
0188	S	S	E	N	1973	51442
0188	S	S	E	N	1969	87870
0196	S	S	E	N	1973	51442
0196	S	S	E	N	1969	68271
0213	L	D	F	N	1971	61324
0233	S	S	E	N	1973	51442
0294	S	D	E	N	1973	49712
0295	S	D	E	N	1972	63787
0295	S	T	E	N	1972	63787
0302	S	S	E	N	1973	51442
0302	S	D	E	N	1973	94148
0306	S	S	E	N	1969	87870
0337	S	S	E	N	1973	51442
0337	S	D	R	N	1974	62000
0337	S	T	R	N	1974	62000
0337	S	D	E	N	1974	62001
0337	S	T	E	N	1974	62001
0337	S	S	E	N	1969	87870
0337	T	S	E	N	1973	53758
0384	S	S	E	N	1973	51442
104-0386	S	D	E	L	1975	90067
0386	S	D	E	N	1974	90443
0386	S	D	E	N	1975	91784
0386	T	D	R	N	1972	49809
0529	S	S	E	N	1973	51442
0533	S	S	E	N	1973	51442
0533	S	S	E	N	1970	87822
0533	S	S	E	N	1972	87890
8016	S	D	E	N	1974	60303
8045	S	D	E	N	1973	57479
8045	S	S	R	N	1972	62298
8045	S	S	E	N	1973	62299
8045	S	S	E	N	1966	66068
8110	S	D	F	N	1972	49777
8110	S	S	E	N	1973	51442
8110	S	D	R	N	1974	58082
8110	S	D	E	N	1974	58083
8110	S	S	E	N	1970	87822
8110	S	S	E	N	1972	87890
8110	S	D	E	N	1975	90683
8111	S	D	F	N	1972	49777
8112	S	D	F	N	1972	49777
8118	S	D	E	N	1973	50034
8119	S	D	E	N	1973	50034
8120	S	D	E	N	1973	50034
8153	S	D	E	N	1974	53989
8156	T	D	E	N	1973	57279
8156	T	T	E	N	1973	57279
8160	S	T	R	N	1973	51360
8160	S	T	E	N	1973	51361
8161	D	T	R	N	1973	52500
8161	D	T	E	N	1974	63246
8161	S	T	R	N	1973	51360
8161	S	T	E	N	1973	51361
8161	S	T	R	N	1973	52500
8161	S	T	E	N	1974	63246
8163	S	S	E	N	1973	51442
8164	S	S	E	N	1973	51442
8164	S	D	E	N	1973	51802
8165	S	S	E	N	1973	51442
8166	S	S	E	N	1973	51442
8167	S	S	E	N	1973	51442
8168	S	S	E	N	1973	51442
8169	S	S	E	N	1973	51442
8169	S	D	E	N	1974	68409
8169	S	T	E	N	1974	68409
8170	S	S	E	N	1973	51442
8170	S	D	E	L	1974	90307
8170	S	D	E	N	1974	90307
8171	D	D	E	N	1973	66096
8171	S	D	R	N	1973	52904
8171	S	D	E	N	1974	52905
8171	S	D	O	L	1973	54850
8171	S	D	O	N	1973	54850
8171	S	D	O	L	1973	65654
8171	S	D	O	N	1973	65654
8174	S	D	E	N	1973	51917
8183	S	D	E	N	1974	58057
8183	S	D	E	L	1975	87156
8183	S	D	E	N	1975	87156
8183	S	D	E	L	1974	90077
8186	S	D	E	N	1972	53114
8187	S	D	E	N	1972	53114
8189	D	D	R	N	1971	67039
8191	S	S	E	N	1966	87841
8216	S	D	E	N	1973	52576
8223	D	D	E	N	1974	53989
8312	S	D	G	N	1973	57075
8321	S	D	E	N	1974	62605
8322	S	D	E	N	1974	62605
8354	S	D	E	N	1975	90268
8355	S	D	E	L	1974	90307
8355	S	D	E	N	1974	90307
8356	S	T	E	N	1974	90349
8361	S	D	E	N	1975	90683
8421	S	D	E	N	1974	88201
8443	S	D	R	N	1974	65397
8443	S	T	R	N	1974	65397
8443	S	D	E	N	1975	65398
8443	S	T	E	N	1975	65398
106-0001	G	S	E	N	1964	87719
0001	L	S	E	N	1964	87719
0001	S	S	E	N	1964	87719
0002	G	S	E	N	1967	98664
0002	L	D	E	N	1972	49780
0002	L	D	R	N	1973	51085
0002	L	D	E	N	1973	51764
0002	L	D	E	N	1974	57944
0002	L	E	E	N	1974	57944
0002	L	D	E	N	1973	65917
0002	L	E	E	N	1973	65917
0002	L	S	E	N	1967	98664
0003	G	T	E	N	1973	50969
0003	G	S	E	N	1967	87855
0003	G	S	E	N	1967	98664
0003	L	S	E	N	1967	98664
0004	S	S	E	N	1973	51442
0004	S	D	E	N	1974	60265
0004	S	S	E	N	1974	62816
0004	S	D	R	N	1974	66728
106-0004	S	D	E	N	1975	66729
0004	S	S	E	N	1969	68271
0004	S	S	E	N	1975	96477
0005	S	S	E	N	1973	51442
0005	S	D	F	N	1958	75815
0005	S	S	E	N	1963	75831
0005	S	S	E	N	1967	98664
0006	D	D	R	N	1973	51623
0006	D	D	R	N	1973	53650
0006	D	D	E	N	1973	53651
0006	D	D	E	N	1974	57955
0006	D	T	E	N	1974	57955
0006	D	D	E	N	1973	78997
0006	D	D	E	N	1971	80226
0006	D	S	E	N	1975	93283
0006	D	T	E	N	1976	103336
0006	S	S	E	L	1973	51442
0006	S	S	E	N	1973	51442
0006	S	D	O	N	1972	51544
0006	S	D	R	N	1973	51623
0006	S	T	E	N	1974	53743
0006	S	D	E	N	1974	54603
0006	S	S	E	N	1974	57955
0006	S	S	E	N	1967	59799
0006	S	D	E	N	1974	60265
0006	S	D	E	N	1973	60582
0006	S	D	E	L	1973	60643
0006	S	D	E	N	1973	60643
0006	S	S	E	N	1973	60643
0006	S	S	E	N	1973	64495
0006	S	D	E	N	1971	65020
0006	S	D	E	L	1973	67803
0006	S	D	E	L	1969	71197
0006	S	D	E	N	1969	71197
0006	S	E	E	L	1969	71197
0006	S	E	E	N	1969	71197
0006	S	S	E	N	1938	74974
0006	S	D	E	L	1972	75135
0006	S	T	E	L	1972	75135
0006	S	D	F	N	1958	75815
0006	S	S	E	N	1965	75847
0006	S	D	E	N	1973	78997
0006	S	T	R	L	1974	80388
0006	S	T	R	N	1974	80388
0006	S	S	E	L	1974	81475
0006	S	S	E	N	1974	81475
0006	S	D	E	N	1973	82666
0006	S	T	E	N	1973	82666
0006	S	D	E	N	1969	85421
0006	S	T	E	L	1974	95834
0006	S	T	E	N	1974	95834
0006	S	S	E	N	1967	98664
0006	S	D	E	L	1965	98883
0006	S	D	E	N	1965	98883
0007	L	S	E	N	1967	98664
0008	G	S	E	N	1965	87791
0008	G	S	E	N	1967	98664
0008	S	D	E	N	1974	54311
0008	S	S	E	N	1974	54311
0008	T	D	E	N	1974	54311
0008	T	S	E	N	1974	54311
0009	G	S	E	N	1967	98664
0009	G	S	E	N	1966	101379
0009	L	T	E	N	1973	52393
0009	L	D	E	N	1973	53703
0009	L	T	E	N	1973	53703
0009	L	S	E	N	1974	85293
0009	S	D	E	N	1973	50419
0011	G	S	E	N	1967	98664
0011	L	D	E	N	1972	49780
0011	L	S	E	N	1967	98664
0015	S	S	E	N	1973	51442
0018	S	D	E	L	1973	53712
0021	G	S	E	N	1964	87719
0024	D	D	R	N	1973	51623
0024	D	D	E	N	1973	51799
0024	D	D	E	N	1972	55087
0024	D	D	E	L	1969	71197
0024	D	D	E	N	1969	71197
0024	D	E	E	L	1969	71197
0024	D	E	E	N	1969	71197
0024	D	D	E	N	1973	78997
0024	D	T	E	N	1976	103336
0024	S	D	E	L	1973	50566
0024	S	S	E	L	1973	50566
0024	S	T	E	L	1973	50566
0024	S	D	E	N	1973	50831
0024	S	S	E	L	1973	51442
0024	S	S	E	N	1973	51442
0024	S	D	O	N	1972	51544
0024	S	T	E	N	1972	53115
0024	S	T	E	N	1974	53743
0024	S	T	R	N	1972	55891
0024	S	D	E	N	1974	57960
0024	S	E	E	N	1974	57960
0024	S	S	E	N	1974	57960
0024	S	S	E	N	1970	59683
0024	S	D	E	N	1967	59799
0024	S	D	E	N	1974	60265
0024	S	D	E	L	1973	60643
0024	S	D	E	N	1973	60643

Phys. State: **A.** Amorphous; **C.** Superconductive; **D.** Doped; **F.** Fibrous or Whisker; **G.** Gas; **I.** Ionized or Plasma; **L.** Liquid; **P.** Powder or Particle; **S.** Solid; **T.** Thin Film
Subject: **D.** Data; **E.** Experiment; **S.** Survey (Review, Compendium, etc.); **T.** Theory
Language: **E.** English; **F.** French; **G.** German; **O.** Other Languages; **R.** Russian
Temperature: **L.** Low (0 to 75K); **N.** Normal (75 to 1273K); **H.** High (above 1273K)

Substance Number	Phys. State	Sub-ject	Lan-guage	Temper-ature	Year	EPIC Number
106-0024	S	S	E	N	1973	60643
0024	S	S	E	N	1973	60840
0024	S	E	R	N	1971	61548
0024	S	D	E	N	1975	63332
0024	S	D	E	N	1971	65020
0024	S	E	E	N	1971	65901
0024	S	D	E	L	1969	71197
0024	S	D	E	N	1969	71197
0024	S	E	E	L	1969	71197
0024	S	E	E	N	1969	71197
0024	S	S	E	N	1938	74974
0024	S	D	E	L	1972	75135
0024	S	T	E	L	1972	75135
0024	S	D	F	N	1958	75815
0024	S	T	R	L	1974	80388
0024	S	T	R	N	1974	80388
0024	S	S	E	L	1974	81475
0024	S	S	E	N	1974	81475
0024	S	D	E	N	1973	82666
0024	S	T	E	N	1973	82666
0024	S	D	E	N	1971	83801
0024	S	S	E	N	1971	83801
0024	S	T	E	L	1974	95834
0024	S	T	E	N	1974	95834
0024	S	S	E	N	1967	98664
0024	S	D	E	L	1965	98883
0024	S	D	E	N	1965	98883
0026	D	D	E	N	1972	55087
0026	D	D	E	N	1975	63299
0026	D	T	E	N	1975	63299
0026	S	D	E	L	1973	50566
0026	S	S	E	L	1973	50566
0026	S	T	E	L	1973	50566
0026	S	S	E	N	1973	51442
0026	S	D	E	N	1967	59799
0026	S	D	R	N	1974	60399
0026	S	D	E	N	1974	60400
0026	S	D	E	N	1975	63299
0026	S	T	E	N	1975	63299
0026	S	D	E	N	1967	74607
0026	S	S	E	N	1967	74607
0026	S	D	E	N	1972	75135
0026	S	S	E	N	1972	75135
0026	S	D	R	L	1974	87288
0026	S	D	E	L	1975	87289
0026	S	S	E	N	1967	98664
0026	S	D	E	N	1976	101501
0026	S	T	E	N	1976	101501
0031	S	S	E	N	1973	51442
0035	P	S	E	N	1965	87702
0035	S	S	E	L	1973	51442
0035	S	S	E	N	1973	51442
0035	S	S	E	N	1972	52968
0035	S	D	E	N	1975	63320
0035	S	D	E	N	1972	63787
0035	S	T	E	N	1972	63787
0035	S	S	E	N	1968	65353
0035	S	S	E	L	1965	87702
0035	S	S	E	N	1965	87702
0035	S	S	E	L	1968	87828
0035	S	S	E	N	1968	87828
0035	S	S	E	L	1971	87887
0035	S	S	E	N	1971	87887
0035	T	S	E	N	1965	87702
0039	G	S	E	N	1964	87719
0045	S	S	E	N	1973	51442
0045	S	S	E	N	1967	98664
0046	L	D	R	N	1973	50644
0050	S	S	E	N	1973	51442
0050	S	S	E	N	1967	98664
0051	S	S	E	N	1973	51442
0051	S	S	E	N	1967	98664
0057	P	S	E	N	1966	68325
0057	S	D	E	N	1973	52412
0057	S	S	E	N	1972	52968
0057	S	D	E	N	1974	54578
0057	S	S	E	N	1969	68271
0057	T	D	E	N	1973	57559
0057	T	S	E	N	1966	68325
0057	T	D	E	N	1968	85433
0058	S	D	E	N	1974	81289
0058	S	T	E	N	1974	81289
0060	S	S	E	N	1973	51442
0060	S	D	R	N	1973	54395
0060	S	D	E	N	1973	54396
0060	S	D	E	N	1963	60560
0060	S	S	E	N	1967	98664
0060	T	D	R	N	1973	54395
0060	T	D	E	N	1973	54396
0060	T	D	E	N	1973	101946
0060	T	T	E	N	1973	101946
0061	S	S	E	N	1973	51442
0061	S	S	E	N	1967	98664
0063	S	S	E	N	1973	51442
0063	S	S	E	N	1967	98664
0066	G	S	E	N	1964	87719
0068	S	S	E	N	1973	51442
0068	S	D	E	N	1974	57960
0068	S	E	E	N	1974	57960
0068	S	S	E	N	1974	57960
0068	S	S	E	N	1967	98664

Substance Number	Phys. State	Sub-ject	Lan-guage	Temper-ature	Year	EPIC Number
106-0081	S	S	E	N	1973	51442
0104	S	D	E	N	1973	52061
0104	S	D	E	N	1972	59903
0108	S	S	E	N	1973	51442
0116	S	S	E	N	1973	51442
0117	S	S	E	N	1973	51442
0127	S	S	E	N	1973	51442
0127	S	D	E	N	1974	57960
0127	S	E	E	N	1974	57960
0127	S	S	E	N	1974	57960
0127	S	S	R	N	1974	60469
0127	S	S	E	N	1974	60470
0129	L	S	E	N	1964	65932
0132	S	S	E	N	1973	51442
0132	S	S	E	N	1967	98664
0135	S	S	E	N	1973	51442
0147	G	S	E	N	1964	87719
0147	L	S	E	N	1964	87719
0152	L	S	E	N	1967	98664
0153	L	S	E	N	1967	98664
0156	S	S	E	N	1973	51442
0156	S	D	E	N	1974	54057
0156	S	S	E	N	1974	54057
0156	S	T	E	N	1974	54057
0157	S	S	E	N	1973	51442
0157	S	D	E	N	1967	59799
0157	S	D	E	N	1973	60579
0157	S	D	E	L	1969	71197
0157	S	D	E	N	1969	71197
0157	S	E	E	L	1969	71197
0157	S	E	E	N	1969	71197
0157	S	D	F	N	1958	75815
0157	S	S	E	N	1967	98664
0157	S	D	O	L	1970	101002
0158	S	S	E	N	1973	51442
0158	S	S	E	N	1972	52968
0158	S	D	E	N	1974	54346
0158	S	S	E	N	1970	87822
0158	S	S	E	N	1972	87890
0159	S	S	E	N	1973	51442
0159	S	D	E	N	1974	60265
0159	S	D	E	L	1969	71197
0159	S	D	E	N	1969	71197
0159	S	E	E	L	1969	71197
0159	S	E	E	N	1969	71197
0159	S	D	E	N	1973	82666
0159	S	T	E	N	1973	82666
0165	D	D	E	N	1974	57141
0165	D	T	E	N	1976	103336
0165	S	D	E	L	1973	50566
0165	S	T	E	L	1973	50566
0165	S	S	E	N	1973	51442
0165	S	D	E	N	1974	54603
0165	S	D	E	N	1967	59799
0165	S	D	E	N	1974	60265
0165	S	D	E	N	1971	65020
0165	S	D	E	L	1969	71197
0165	S	D	E	N	1969	71197
0165	S	E	E	L	1969	71197
0165	S	E	E	N	1969	71197
0165	S	D	E	N	1971	75192
0165	S	S	E	N	1971	75192
0165	S	D	E	N	1973	82666
0165	S	T	E	N	1973	82666
0180	L	D	F	N	1971	61324
0182	L	S	E	N	1967	98664
0183	L	S	E	N	1967	98664
0184	L	S	E	N	1967	98664
0192	D	D	E	N	1974	57748
0192	S	S	E	N	1973	51442
0192	S	D	R	N	1972	79248
0192	S	D	E	N	1972	90275
0203	S	D	E	N	1973	50566
0203	S	T	E	N	1973	50566
0203	S	S	E	N	1973	51442
0203	S	T	E	N	1975	63324
0203	S	D	E	L	1969	71197
0203	S	D	E	N	1969	71197
0203	S	E	E	L	1969	71197
0203	S	E	E	N	1969	71197
0203	S	D	E	N	1973	82666
0203	S	T	E	N	1973	82666
0203	S	S	E	N	1976	99905
0204	S	D	R	N	1973	52387
0204	S	D	E	N	1973	55648
0218	D	D	R	N	1972	51267
0218	S	D	R	N	1971	50718
0218	S	D	R	N	1972	51267
0218	S	S	E	N	1973	51442
0218	S	D	R	N	1973	51725
0218	S	D	R	N	1973	55046
0218	S	D	E	N	1974	55047
0218	S	D	E	N	1974	62605
0218	S	D	O	N	1974	66386
0218	S	S	E	N	1965	75847
0218	S	S	E	N	1969	87870
0227	S	S	E	N	1973	51442
0227	S	S	E	N	1967	98664
0231	G	S	E	N	1964	87719
0233	G	S	E	N	1964	87719
0234	S	D	E	N	1973	50155

Substance Number	Phys. State	Sub-ject	Lan-guage	Temper-ature	Year	EPIC Number
106-0234	S	S	E	N	1973	51442
0234	S	D	E	N	1974	61445
0237	S	D	E	L	1969	71197
0237	S	D	E	N	1969	71197
0237	S	E	E	L	1969	71197
0237	S	E	E	N	1969	71197
0237	S	D	E	N	1973	82666
0237	S	T	E	N	1973	82666
0238	S	D	E	L	1973	50566
0238	S	T	E	L	1973	50566
0238	S	S	E	N	1973	51442
0238	S	D	O	N	1972	51544
0238	S	D	E	L	1973	55351
0238	S	D	E	N	1973	55351
0238	S	S	E	L	1973	55351
0238	S	S	E	N	1973	55351
0238	S	S	R	N	1973	56262
0238	S	D	E	N	1967	59799
0238	S	D	E	N	1973	60585
0238	S	S	E	N	1973	60585
0238	S	D	E	L	1969	71197
0238	S	D	E	N	1969	71197
0238	S	E	E	L	1969	71197
0238	S	E	E	N	1969	71197
0238	S	S	E	N	1973	76721
0238	S	D	E	N	1973	82666
0238	S	T	E	N	1973	82666
0251	S	S	E	N	1973	51442
0251	S	S	E	N	1967	98664
0296	S	S	E	N	1967	98664
0317	S	S	E	N	1973	51442
0317	S	D	E	N	1973	67802
0318	S	S	E	N	1973	51442
0326	S	S	E	N	1969	87870
0327	T	D	E	N	1974	60654
0363	D	S	E	N	1963	64232
0363	P	S	E	N	1967	66156
0363	S	D	R	N	1973	50215
0363	S	D	E	N	1973	50216
0363	S	S	E	L	1973	51442
0363	S	S	E	N	1973	51442
0363	S	D	E	N	1973	51922
0363	S	D	E	N	1973	52412
0363	S	S	E	N	1972	52968
0363	S	S	E	N	1974	54075
0363	S	D	E	N	1973	60579
0363	S	T	R	N	1972	60707
0363	S	T	E	N	1973	60708
0363	S	S	E	N	1963	64232
0363	S	D	E	N	1975	65498
0363	S	S	R	N	1970	66024
0363	S	S	E	N	1970	66025
0363	S	S	E	N	1967	66156
0363	S	S	E	N	1969	68271
0363	S	S	E	N	1975	68601
0363	S	T	E	N	1970	70645
0363	S	S	E	N	1974	87147
0363	S	S	E	N	1970	87822
0363	S	D	R	L	1975	89630
0363	S	D	E	L	1975	89631
0363	S	S	E	N	1975	95584
0363	S	S	E	N	1976	101470
0363	S	S	E	N	1976	101823
0363	T	D	R	N	1974	61992
0363	T	T	R	N	1974	61992
0363	T	D	E	N	1974	61993
0363	T	T	E	N	1974	61993
0384	S	S	E	N	1973	51442
0385	D	D	E	N	1972	53238
0385	D	E	E	N	1972	53238
0385	D	T	E	N	1972	53238
0385	S	S	E	N	1973	51442
0385	S	D	E	N	1973	55364
0385	S	S	E	N	1973	55364
0385	S	D	E	N	1972	63847
0385	S	D	E	N	1967	74607
0385	S	S	E	N	1967	74607
0385	S	D	F	N	1974	88179
0401	S	S	E	N	1973	51442
0409	S	S	E	N	1973	51442
0494	S	S	E	N	1973	51442
0494	S	S	E	N	1967	98664
0496	S	S	E	N	1973	51442
0496	S	S	E	N	1967	98664
0508	S	S	E	N	1973	51442
0508	S	S	E	N	1969	68271
0610	S	S	E	N	1973	51442
0758	S	S	E	N	1973	51442
0768	S	S	E	N	1973	51442
0794	S	S	E	N	1973	51442
1019	S	D	E	N	1971	49617
1084	L	D	E	N	1964	65932
1085	S	D	E	N	1974	60664
1256	S	D	E	N	1973	51809
1256	S	D	E	N	1974	101330
1419	S	S	E	N	1973	51442
8033	D	D	R	N	1971	67327
8033	S	D	R	N	1971	67327
8033	S	D	R	N	1975	74174
8033	S	D	E	N	1975	91460
8040	D	S	E	N	1963	87710

Phys. State: **A.** Amorphous; **C.** Superconductive; **D.** Doped; **F.** Fibrous or Whisker; **G.** Gas; **I.** Ionized or Plasma; **L.** Liquid; **P.** Powder or Particle; **S.** Solid; **T.** Thin Film
Subject: **D.** Data; **E.** Experiment; **S.** Survey (Review, Compendium, etc.); **T.** Theory
Language: **E.** English; **F.** French; **G.** German; **O.** Other Languages; **R.** Russian
Temperature: **L.** Low (0 to 75K); **N.** Normal (75 to 1273K); **H.** High (above 1273K)

Substance Number	Phys. State	Subject	Language	Temperature	Year	EPIC Number
106-8040	S	D	R	N	1973	50215
8040	S	D	E	N	1973	50216
8040	S	D	R	N	1972	51100
8040	S	D	F	N	1973	51107
8040	S	D	R	L	1973	51384
8040	S	D	R	N	1973	51384
8040	S	D	E	L	1973	51385
8040	S	D	E	N	1973	51385
8040	S	S	E	N	1973	51442
8040	S	D	E	N	1973	52412
8040	S	S	E	N	1972	52968
8040	S	D	E	N	1973	53462
8040	S	S	R	N	1972	53547
8040	S	S	E	N	1973	53548
8040	S	S	E	L	1974	53604
8040	S	D	R	N	1972	58690
8040	S	T	R	N	1972	60707
8040	S	T	E	N	1973	60708
8040	S	S	R	N	1970	66024
8040	S	S	E	N	1970	66025
8040	S	S	E	N	1969	68271
8040	S	S	E	N	1963	87710
8040	S	S	E	N	1975	95584
8040	S	S	E	N	1976	101470
8040	S	S	E	N	1976	101823
8041	D	S	E	N	1973	58213
8041	D	D	R	N	1974	60481
8041	D	D	E	N	1974	60482
8041	S	D	R	N	1973	51272
8041	S	S	E	N	1973	51442
8041	S	D	E	N	1973	52412
8041	S	S	E	N	1972	52968
8041	S	S	E	N	1972	53359
8041	S	D	E	N	1974	53601
8041	S	S	E	N	1974	53601
8041	S	D	E	N	1974	54310
8041	S	D	E	N	1974	58808
8041	S	D	E	N	1974	60265
8041	S	D	R	N	1974	60481
8041	S	D	E	N	1974	60482
8041	S	D	E	N	1973	60579
8041	S	D	E	N	1972	63632
8041	S	S	E	N	1969	68271
8041	S	S	E	L	1967	68371
8041	S	S	E	N	1967	68371
8041	S	T	E	N	1970	70645
8041	S	D	E	N	1968	74648
8041	S	D	E	L	1969	75248
8041	S	D	E	N	1969	75248
8041	S	D	E	N	1974	87448
8041	S	S	E	N	1962	87659
8041	S	D	E	N	1975	93320
8041	S	D	E	L	1976	100412
8041	S	D	E	N	1976	100412
8041	S	S	E	L	1976	100412
8041	S	S	E	N	1976	100412
8041	S	T	E	L	1976	100412
8041	S	T	E	N	1976	100412
8041	S	S	E	N	1976	101470
8041	S	S	E	N	1976	101823
8041	T	D	R	N	1974	61988
8041	T	T	R	N	1974	61988
8041	T	D	E	N	1974	61989
8041	T	T	E	N	1974	61989
8041	T	D	R	N	1974	61992
8041	T	T	R	N	1974	61992
8041	T	D	E	N	1974	61993
8041	T	T	E	N	1974	61993
8041	T	S	E	N	1967	68371
8128	S	S	E	N	1974	54554
8128	S	S	E	L	1974	61351
8128	S	S	E	N	1974	61351
8128	S	S	E	L	1967	68371
8128	S	S	E	N	1967	68371
8128	S	S	E	L	1972	87823
8128	S	S	E	N	1972	87823
8132	S	D	E	N	1971	61077
8132	S	S	E	L	1972	87823
8132	S	S	E	N	1972	87823
8135	S	D	E	N	1971	49617
8154	T	D	R	N	1971	76494
8154	T	D	E	N	1971	91578
8209	S	D	E	N	1974	53603
8209	S	S	E	N	1974	62028
8213	S	S	E	N	1973	51442
8213	S	S	E	N	1967	98664
8214	S	D	E	N	1973	51049
8226	S	D	E	N	1973	50574
8235	S	D	R	N	1972	51286
8236	S	S	E	N	1973	51442
8237	S	D	E	N	1972	53110
8239	S	S	E	N	1973	51442
8240	S	S	E	N	1973	51442
8241	S	S	E	N	1973	51442
8241	S	S	E	N	1970	87822
8241	S	S	E	N	1972	87890
8242	S	S	E	N	1973	51442
8242	S	D	R	N	1974	60471
8242	S	D	E	N	1974	60472
8243	S	S	E	N	1973	51442
8244	S	S	E	N	1973	51442
106-8245	S	S	E	N	1973	51442
8246	S	S	E	N	1973	51442
8247	S	S	E	N	1973	51442
8248	S	S	E	N	1973	51442
8249	S	S	E	N	1973	51442
8250	S	S	E	N	1973	51442
8251	S	S	E	N	1973	51442
8293	S	D	E	L	1973	52051
8293	S	D	E	N	1973	52051
8293	S	D	R	N	1974	63102
8293	S	T	R	N	1974	63102
8293	S	D	E	N	1975	63103
8293	S	T	E	N	1975	63103
8300	S	D	E	N	1973	52314
8312	S	D	E	N	1973	52652
8354	L	D	E	N	1973	53457
8358	S	S	E	N	1968	75247
8415	S	D	E	N	1974	54350
8415	S	T	E	N	1974	54350
8462	S	D	E	L	1974	58816
8462	S	D	E	N	1974	58816
8469	S	D	E	N	1971	61077
8473	S	D	E	N	1974	55119
8517	G	S	E	N	1964	87719
8517	L	S	E	N	1964	87719
8654	S	D	E	N	1974	62605
8654	S	S	E	N	1969	87870
8731	L	S	E	N	1967	98664
8742	S	D	E	N	1968	68207
8750	S	D	R	N	1973	52665
8750	S	D	E	N	1974	63233
8764	S	D	R	N	1971	76482
8764	S	T	R	N	1971	76482
8764	S	D	E	N	1971	91527
8764	S	T	E	N	1971	91527
8772	S	D	E	N	1975	92178
8772	S	T	E	N	1975	92178
8773	S	D	E	N	1975	92178
8773	S	T	E	N	1975	92178
108-0005	L	D	E	N	1974	60356
0005	L	E	E	N	1974	60356
0005	L	S	E	N	1951	98663
0005	L	S	E	N	1967	98664
0014	S	S	E	N	1973	51442
0014	S	S	R	N	1974	63112
0014	S	T	R	N	1974	63112
0014	S	S	E	N	1975	63113
0014	S	T	E	N	1975	63113
0014	S	S	E	N	1970	87822
0014	S	S	E	N	1972	87890
0014	S	D	E	N	1974	90316
0014	S	S	E	N	1976	101320
0029	S	S	E	N	1973	51442
0029	S	D	E	L	1974	54099
0029	S	D	E	N	1974	54099
0052	S	D	R	N	1972	79248
0052	S	D	E	N	1972	90275
0101	S	S	E	N	1973	51442
0114	S	S	E	N	1973	51442
0114	S	S	E	N	1976	101320
8006	S	D	E	N	1973	50419
8014	S	D	R	N	1973	51358
8014	S	D	E	N	1973	51359
8015	S	D	R	N	1973	51358
8015	S	D	E	N	1973	51359
8017	S	S	E	N	1973	51442
8025	S	D	R	N	1973	67526
8035	S	S	E	L	1973	62376
8045	S	D	E	N	1973	57118
8055	S	D	E	N	1974	90316
109-0001	S	D	R	N	1972	79248
0001	S	D	E	N	1972	90275
0007	S	D	R	N	1972	79248
0007	S	D	E	N	1972	90275
0019	S	S	E	N	1973	51442
0025	S	D	E	N	1973	51185
0025	S	S	E	N	1973	53052
0029	D	D	E	N	1973	49670
0029	S	D	E	N	1973	49670
8019	S	S	E	N	1974	62347
8020	S	D	E	L	1973	51185
8020	S	D	E	N	1973	51185
8020	S	S	E	N	1973	51442
8028	S	S	E	N	1973	51442
8051	S	S	E	N	1973	53052
8071	S	D	E	N	1973	56526
8099	S	D	E	N	1973	66202
8099	S	T	E	N	1973	66202
110-0002	S	D	E	N	1976	99911
0011	S	S	E	N	1973	51442
0011	S	D	E	N	1975	63344
0011	S	T	E	N	1975	63344
0017	S	D	E	N	1974	81289
0017	S	T	E	N	1974	81289
0018	S	D	E	N	1974	81289
0018	S	T	E	N	1974	81289
0019	S	D	E	N	1974	81289
0019	S	T	E	N	1974	81289
110-0020	D	T	E	N	1973	57730
0020	S	D	E	N	1974	81289
0020	S	T	E	N	1974	81289
0021	S	S	E	N	1973	51442
0021	S	D	R	N	1973	52513
0021	S	D	E	L	1976	101501
0021	S	D	E	N	1976	101501
0021	S	T	E	L	1976	101501
0021	S	T	E	N	1976	101501
0021	T	D	E	N	1973	101946
0021	T	T	E	N	1973	101946
0023	S	D	E	N	1974	57984
0023	S	D	E	N	1973	59291
0023	S	D	E	N	1960	64749
0023	S	D	E	N	1974	81289
0023	S	T	E	N	1974	81289
0023	S	D	E	N	1974	81763
0023	S	S	E	N	1974	81763
0023	S	T	E	N	1974	81763
0023	S	S	E	N	1976	101192
0023	T	D	E	N	1971	64338
0023	T	S	E	N	1957	95707
0024	L	D	E	N	1974	58441
0024	S	D	O	N	1972	49960
0024	S	S	E	N	1973	51442
0024	S	D	O	N	1972	51544
0024	S	D	E	N	1974	54098
0024	S	D	E	N	1974	54606
0024	S	S	E	N	1974	54606
0024	S	D	E	N	1974	55252
0024	S	S	E	N	1974	55252
0024	S	S	R	N	1973	56262
0024	S	D	E	N	1974	58441
0024	S	D	E	N	1974	58817
0024	S	S	E	N	1974	58817
0024	S	D	E	N	1967	59799
0024	S	D	E	N	1974	60265
0024	S	D	E	L	1973	60643
0024	S	D	E	N	1973	60643
0024	S	S	E	N	1973	60643
0024	S	D	E	N	1975	63322
0024	S	D	E	N	1972	63788
0024	S	S	E	L	1972	63788
0024	S	S	E	N	1972	63788
0024	S	D	E	L	1966	64256
0024	S	D	E	N	1966	64256
0024	S	D	E	L	1973	70149
0024	S	D	E	N	1973	70149
0024	S	S	E	L	1973	70149
0024	S	S	E	N	1973	70149
0024	S	T	E	L	1973	70149
0024	S	T	E	N	1973	70149
0024	S	D	E	L	1969	71197
0024	S	D	E	N	1969	71197
0024	S	E	E	L	1969	71197
0024	S	E	E	N	1969	71197
0024	S	D	E	L	1966	74594
0024	S	D	E	N	1966	74594
0024	S	T	E	N	1972	75135
0024	S	S	E	N	1973	76721
0024	S	S	E	L	1974	81475
0024	S	S	E	N	1974	81475
0024	S	D	E	N	1973	82666
0024	S	T	E	N	1973	82666
0024	S	D	E	N	1967	85322
0024	S	D	E	N	1975	91733
0024	S	D	E	N	1975	100030
0024	S	D	E	N	1976	102400
0024	S	S	E	N	1976	102400
0024	S	T	E	N	1976	102400
0025	S	S	E	N	1973	51442
0028	D	D	E	N	1973	52172
0030	S	S	E	N	1973	51442
0030	S	S	E	N	1967	98664
0036	S	S	E	N	1973	51442
0036	S	D	R	N	1974	58064
0036	S	S	R	N	1974	58064
0036	S	D	E	N	1974	58065
0036	S	S	E	N	1974	58065
0036	S	D	E	N	1967	59799
0036	S	D	E	N	1974	60265
0036	S	D	E	L	1969	71197
0036	S	D	E	N	1969	71197
0036	S	E	E	L	1969	71197
0036	S	E	E	N	1969	71197
0036	S	D	E	N	1972	75135
0036	S	T	E	N	1972	75135
0036	S	D	E	N	1970	75188
0036	S	T	E	N	1970	75188
0036	S	D	E	N	1973	82666
0036	S	T	E	N	1973	82666
0036	S	D	E	L	1975	91733
0036	S	D	E	N	1975	100030
0036	T	T	E	N	1972	70543
0037	S	D	E	L	1973	50820
0037	S	D	E	N	1973	50820
0037	S	S	E	N	1973	51442
0037	S	D	E	N	1974	60265
0037	S	D	E	L	1969	71197
0037	S	D	E	N	1969	71197
0037	S	E	E	L	1969	71197

Phys. State: **A.** Amorphous; **C.** Superconductive; **D.** Doped; **F.** Fibrous or Whisker; **G.** Gas; **I.** Ionized or Plasma; **L.** Liquid; **P.** Powder or Particle; **S.** Solid; **T.** Thin Film
Subject: **D.** Data; **E.** Experiment; **S.** Survey (Review, Compendium, etc.); **T.** Theory
Language: **E.** English; **F.** French; **G.** German; **O.** Other Languages; **R.** Russian
Temperature: **L.** Low (0 to 75K); **N.** Normal (75 to 1273K); **H.** High (above 1273K)

Substance Number	Phys. State	Subject	Language	Temperature	Year	EPIC Number
110-0037	S	E	E	N	1969	71197
0037	S	D	E	N	1973	82666
0037	S	T	E	N	1973	82666
0037	S	D	E	L	1975	91733
0037	S	D	E	N	1975	100030
0040	G	S	E	N	1964	87717
0061	S	S	E	N	1973	51442
0061	S	D	E	N	1974	60265
0061	S	D	E	L	1969	71197
0061	S	D	E	N	1969	71197
0061	S	E	E	L	1969	71197
0061	S	E	E	N	1969	71197
0061	S	D	E	N	1971	75192
0061	S	S	E	N	1971	75192
0061	S	D	E	N	1973	82666
0061	S	T	E	N	1973	82666
0083	S	S	R	N	1973	56262
0083	S	S	E	N	1973	76721
0132	S	S	E	N	1973	51442
0132	S	D	R	N	1974	60399
0132	S	D	E	N	1974	60400
0132	S	D	E	N	1967	74607
0132	S	S	E	N	1967	74607
0132	S	D	E	N	1972	75135
0132	S	D	E	N	1974	84584
0132	S	D	R	L	1974	87288
0132	S	D	E	L	1975	87289
0132	S	D	E	N	1976	101501
0132	S	T	E	N	1976	101501
0146	S	S	E	N	1973	51442
0194	S	D	E	N	1973	50872
0194	S	D	E	N	1973	51937
0194	T	D	E	N	1974	54111
0236	S	D	E	N	1973	49525
0269	L	T	E	N	1973	52579
0299	S	D	E	N	1973	52314
8039	S	D	E	N	1973	52314
8042	T	D	R	N	1972	49980
8053	S	S	E	N	1974	54111
8053	S	D	E	N	1973	66202
8053	S	T	E	N	1973	66202
8070	S	D	R	N	1972	56960
8073	D	D	R	N	1973	52114
8073	D	D	E	N	1973	54921
8073	S	D	E	N	1971	63486
8073	S	E	E	N	1971	63486
8076	S	D	F	N	1973	51500
8093	S	D	E	N	1973	52314
8112	T	D	R	N	1974	60411
8112	T	D	E	N	1974	60412
8118	S	S	R	N	1973	56262
8118	S	D	E	N	1974	57984
8118	S	D	E	N	1973	59291
8118	S	D	E	N	1971	62600
8118	S	D	E	N	1960	64749
8118	S	S	E	N	1973	76721
8140	S	D	E	L	1973	52623
8140	S	D	E	N	1973	52623
8141	S	D	E	L	1973	52623
8141	S	D	E	N	1973	52623
8176	S	D	R	N	1975	90152
8176	S	E	R	N	1975	90152
8176	S	D	E	N	1975	90153
8176	S	E	R	N	1975	90153
8188	S	D	R	N	1974	60429
8188	S	D	E	N	1974	60430
8251	S	D	F	N	1974	90494
111-0003	S	D	R	N	1972	79248
0003	S	D	E	N	1972	90275
0006	S	S	E	N	1973	51442
0006	S	T	E	N	1975	62678
0006	S	S	E	N	1969	68115
0006	S	D	R	N	1974	77928
0006	S	D	E	N	1974	94506
0008	A	S	E	N	1974	54026
0008	A	S	E	N	1974	67182
0008	A	D	E	N	1972	70674
0008	A	S	E	N	1972	70674
0008	A	S	E	N	1974	89269
0008	D	S	E	N	1974	54026
0008	D	S	E	N	1969	65350
0008	S	S	E	L	1973	51442
0008	S	S	E	N	1973	51442
0008	S	S	E	N	1972	52968
0008	S	S	E	N	1974	54026
0008	S	D	E	L	1973	57529
0008	S	D	E	N	1974	58808
0008	S	D	E	N	1974	58958
0008	S	S	E	N	1974	59353
0008	S	S	E	N	1970	59674
0008	S	D	E	N	1974	60265
0008	S	D	E	N	1971	62264
0008	S	S	E	N	1974	67182
0008	S	S	E	N	1972	70674
0008	S	S	E	N	1962	87669
0008	S	S	E	N	1965	87703
0008	S	D	E	N	1975	87747
0008	S	S	E	N	1970	87822
0008	S	S	E	L	1971	87884
0008	S	S	E	N	1971	87884
111-0008	S	S	E	N	1972	87889
0008	S	S	E	N	1974	89269
0008	S	T	E	N	1975	90032
0008	S	D	E	N	1975	96613
0008	S	S	R	N	1975	101515
0008	S	S	E	N	1975	101516
0021	S	S	E	N	1972	52968
0021	S	D	E	N	1973	63804
0021	S	S	R	N	1974	66446
0021	S	S	E	N	1974	66447
0021	S	S	E	N	1971	87884
0021	T	S	E	N	1974	58028
0046	S	S	E	N	1973	51442
0046	S	T	G	N	1973	51929
0050	S	D	E	N	1974	53603
0050	S	D	E	N	1974	62064
0050	S	T	E	N	1974	62064
8002	A	D	E	N	1972	70674
8002	A	S	E	N	1972	70674
8002	A	S	E	N	1974	89269
8002	S	S	E	L	1973	51442
8002	S	S	E	N	1973	51442
8002	S	S	E	N	1972	52968
8002	S	D	E	N	1974	58808
8002	S	S	E	N	1970	59674
8002	S	D	E	N	1974	60265
8002	S	D	F	N	1973	63636
8002	S	S	E	N	1974	67182
8002	S	S	E	N	1972	70674
8002	S	S	E	N	1962	87670
8002	S	S	E	N	1971	87884
8002	S	S	E	N	1976	101470
8002	S	S	R	N	1975	101515
8002	S	S	E	N	1975	101516
8002	S	S	E	N	1976	101823
8007	S	S	E	N	1974	61360
8008	S	D	E	N	1975	68673
8008	S	T	E	N	1975	68673
8008	T	D	R	N	1970	61533
8009	S	D	E	N	1973	57453
8009	S	D	R	N	1972	62689
8009	S	D	E	N	1972	64417
8019	S	D	E	N	1964	59770
8019	S	T	E	N	1964	59770
8021	A	D	E	N	1972	53266
8021	S	S	E	N	1972	52968
8021	T	D	E	N	1972	53266
8021	T	S	E	L	1969	68115
8021	T	S	E	N	1969	68115
8031	S	S	E	N	1972	87889
8042	S	S	E	N	1973	51442
8042	S	D	E	N	1972	93293
8042	S	S	E	N	1972	93293
8061	S	D	R	L	1973	52870
8061	S	D	R	N	1973	52870
8061	S	D	E	L	1973	52871
8061	S	D	E	N	1973	52871
8061	S	D	R	L	1974	58094
8061	S	D	R	N	1974	58094
8061	S	D	E	L	1974	58095
8061	S	D	E	N	1974	58095
8061	S	D	R	N	1974	87294
8061	S	D	E	N	1975	87295
8061	S	D	R	N	1974	90204
8061	S	D	E	N	1975	90205
8061	T	D	R	L	1973	52870
8061	T	D	R	N	1973	52870
8061	T	D	E	L	1973	52871
8061	T	D	E	N	1973	52871
8068	S	D	R	N	1974	58526
8068	S	T	R	N	1974	58526
8068	S	D	E	N	1974	66302
8068	S	T	E	N	1974	66302
8068	S	D	R	N	1974	90204
8068	S	D	E	N	1975	90205
8125	S	D	E	N	1974	58322
8125	S	D	E	N	1974	61362
8128	T	D	E	N	1974	83981
8129	T	D	E	N	1974	83981
8155	S	D	R	N	1974	90204
8155	S	D	E	N	1975	90205
8156	S	D	R	N	1974	90204
8156	S	D	E	N	1975	90205
8162	S	S	E	N	1972	87824
8187	S	D	E	N	1968	68207
8194	S	D	E	N	1974	62062
8194	S	T	E	N	1974	62062
112-0001	D	D	O	N	1972	51230
0001	D	D	O	N	1972	51231
0001	D	D	E	N	1973	53053
0001	D	D	E	N	1972	53212
0001	D	D	E	N	1975	65428
0001	D	E	E	N	1975	65428
0001	D	T	E	N	1975	65428
0001	G	S	E	N	1967	98664
0001	L	D	R	N	1972	49852
0001	L	D	E	N	1973	50969
0001	L	D	E	N	1973	51304
0001	L	E	E	N	1973	51304
0001	L	T	E	N	1973	51304
112-0001	L	S	E	N	1973	51764
0001	L	D	R	N	1972	52265
0001	L	D	R	N	1945	53233
0001	L	D	E	N	1972	53234
0001	L	S	E	N	1972	53275
0001	L	D	E	N	1973	53703
0001	L	T	E	N	1973	53703
0001	L	D	E	N	1974	54320
0001	L	S	E	N	1974	54320
0001	L	T	E	N	1974	54320
0001	L	D	E	N	1974	57960
0001	L	E	E	N	1974	57960
0001	L	S	E	N	1974	57960
0001	L	S	E	N	1972	59932
0001	L	D	E	N	1974	60354
0001	L	D	E	N	1974	60356
0001	L	E	E	N	1974	60356
0001	L	S	E	N	1974	60356
0001	L	E	R	N	1971	61555
0001	L	D	E	N	1971	65020
0001	L	D	G	N	1973	65549
0001	L	E	G	N	1973	65549
0001	L	E	E	N	1971	65906
0001	L	T	E	N	1974	66879
0001	L	S	E	N	1974	85293
0001	L	D	E	N	1975	90092
0001	L	S	E	N	1951	98663
0001	L	S	E	N	1967	98664
0001	L	S	E	N	1962	99561
0001	S	D	E	N	1973	50912
0001	S	S	E	N	1973	51442
0001	S	D	E	N	1972	53212
0001	S	S	E	N	1972	53275
0001	S	D	R	N	1972	53432
0001	S	D	E	N	1973	53433
0001	S	D	E	N	1973	58134
0001	S	S	E	N	1972	59932
0001	S	D	E	N	1974	61171
0001	S	E	E	N	1974	61171
0001	S	S	E	N	1974	61171
0001	S	D	E	N	1971	65020
0001	S	D	E	N	1975	65428
0001	S	E	E	N	1975	65428
0001	S	T	E	N	1975	65428
0001	S	S	E	N	1967	98664
0001	S	S	E	N	1962	99561
0004	G	S	E	N	1967	98664
0008	S	S	E	N	1973	51442
0008	S	D	E	N	1973	57879
0010	G	S	E	N	1967	87855
0010	G	S	E	N	1967	98664
0010	L	S	E	N	1967	98664
0011	S	S	E	N	1969	68271
0021	S	S	E	N	1969	87870
0021	T	D	E	N	1975	68613
0028	D	D	E	N	1974	64715
0028	D	T	E	N	1974	64715
0028	S	S	E	N	1973	51442
0028	S	D	E	N	1973	52624
0028	S	D	E	N	1974	54054
0028	S	S	E	N	1974	54054
0028	S	S	E	N	1974	54577
0028	S	T	E	N	1974	57310
0028	S	D	R	N	1972	60705
0028	S	T	R	N	1972	60705
0028	S	D	E	N	1973	60706
0028	S	T	E	N	1973	60706
0028	S	S	E	N	1975	68617
0028	S	S	E	N	1970	87822
0028	S	S	E	N	1972	87890
0028	S	D	E	N	1974	90316
0028	S	T	E	N	1974	90337
0028	S	S	E	N	1976	101320
0033	D	D	R	N	1973	55054
0033	D	D	E	N	1974	55055
0033	S	S	E	N	1973	51442
0033	S	D	E	N	1973	67800
0034	G	S	E	N	1967	98664
0034	S	D	E	N	1973	50419
0035	D	D	R	N	1973	55054
0035	D	D	E	N	1974	55055
0035	S	S	E	N	1973	51442
0035	S	D	R	N	1971	66129
0035	S	D	R	N	1973	71655
0035	S	S	R	N	1975	74174
0035	S	D	R	N	1975	90134
0035	S	D	E	N	1975	90135
0035	S	S	E	N	1975	91460
0035	S	D	E	N	1973	91464
0035	S	D	E	N	1975	91944
0035	S	T	E	N	1975	91944
0035	S	D	E	N	1974	100965
0035	S	S	E	N	1974	100965
0035	S	T	E	N	1974	100965
0038	S	S	E	N	1973	51442
0038	S	S	E	N	1975	68617
0038	S	S	R	N	1975	74174
0038	S	S	E	N	1970	87822
0038	S	S	E	N	1972	87890
0038	S	S	E	N	1975	91460
0038	S	S	E	N	1976	101320

Phys. State: **A.** Amorphous; **C.** Superconductive; **D.** Doped; **F.** Fibrous or Whisker; **G.** Gas; **I.** Ionized or Plasma; **L.** Liquid; **P.** Powder or Particle; **S.** Solid; **T.** Thin Film
Subject: **D.** Data; **E.** Experiment; **S.** Survey (Review, Compendium, etc.); **T.** Theory
Language: **E.** English; **F.** French; **G.** German; **O.** Other Languages; **R.** Russian
Temperature: **L.** Low (0 to 75K); **N.** Normal (75 to 1273K); **H.** High (above 1273K)

Substance Number	Phys. State	Subject	Language	Temperature	Year	EPIC Number
112-0096	S	S	E	N	1973	51442
0098	S	S	E	N	1973	51442
0275	S	S	E	N	1973	51442
0402	S	D	E	N	1973	50571
0402	S	S	E	N	1973	51442
0402	S	D	E	N	1973	55889
0402	S	S	E	N	1969	68271
0481	S	D	R	N	1972	79248
0481	S	D	E	N	1972	90275
0569	S	D	E	N	1973	60640
0583	S	D	E	N	1973	50873
0583	S	D	R	N	1973	51358
0583	S	D	E	N	1973	51359
0583	S	S	E	N	1973	51442
0583	S	D	E	N	1974	57310
0583	S	D	E	N	1975	68617
0583	S	D	E	N	1974	90316
0583	S	S	E	N	1976	101320
0604	S	S	E	N	1973	51442
0629	S	S	E	N	1973	51442
0637	S	S	E	N	1973	51442
0671	S	S	E	N	1973	51442
8020	S	S	E	N	1973	51442
8020	S	S	R	N	1972	53547
8020	S	S	E	N	1973	53548
8024	S	D	E	N	1971	49617
8025	S	D	R	N	1973	51272
8025	S	S	E	N	1972	52968
8025	S	D	E	L	1974	53599
8025	S	D	E	N	1974	53599
8025	S	T	E	N	1974	53599
8025	S	S	E	L	1969	68271
8025	S	S	E	N	1969	68271
8034	S	S	E	N	1973	51442
8069	S	D	E	N	1973	60640
8070	S	D	E	N	1973	60640
8071	S	D	E	N	1973	60640
114-0001	D	D	E	N	1963	64750
0001	D	D	E	N	1971	80226
0001	D	T	E	N	1976	103336
0001	S	D	E	L	1973	50820
0001	S	D	E	N	1973	50820
0001	S	S	E	N	1973	51442
0001	S	D	E	N	1967	59799
0001	S	D	E	N	1974	60265
0001	S	D	E	L	1969	71197
0001	S	D	E	N	1969	71197
0001	S	E	E	L	1969	71197
0001	S	E	E	N	1969	71197
0001	S	D	E	N	1972	75135
0001	S	T	E	N	1972	75135
0001	S	T	R	L	1974	80388
0001	S	T	R	N	1974	80388
0001	S	D	E	N	1973	82666
0001	S	T	E	N	1973	82666
0001	S	D	E	N	1969	85421
0001	S	T	E	L	1974	95834
0001	S	T	E	N	1974	95834
0001	S	S	E	N	1967	98664
0002	S	D	E	L	1973	50566
0002	S	T	E	L	1973	50566
0002	S	S	E	N	1973	51442
0002	S	D	E	N	1967	59799
0002	S	D	E	N	1974	60265
0002	S	D	E	L	1969	71197
0002	S	D	E	N	1969	71197
0002	S	E	E	L	1969	71197
0002	S	E	E	N	1969	71197
0002	S	D	E	N	1971	75192
0002	S	S	E	N	1971	75192
0002	S	D	E	N	1973	82666
0002	S	T	E	N	1973	82666
0006	S	S	E	N	1973	51442
0006	S	S	E	L	1975	91289
0009	D	D	E	N	1973	55620
0009	S	S	E	N	1973	51442
0009	S	D	E	N	1974	53621
0009	S	T	E	N	1974	53621
0009	S	D	E	N	1973	55620
0009	S	D	R	N	1974	58064
0009	S	S	R	N	1974	58064
0009	S	D	E	N	1974	58065
0009	S	S	E	N	1974	58065
0009	S	D	E	N	1974	60265
0009	S	D	E	L	1969	71197
0009	S	D	E	N	1969	71197
0009	S	E	E	L	1969	71197
0009	S	E	E	N	1969	71197
0009	S	T	E	N	1972	75135
0009	S	S	E	N	1963	75839
0009	S	T	R	L	1974	80388
0009	S	T	R	N	1974	80388
0009	S	D	E	N	1973	82666
0009	S	T	E	N	1973	82666
0009	S	D	E	L	1970	85417
0009	S	T	E	L	1974	95834
0009	S	T	E	N	1974	95834
0010	S	S	E	N	1973	51442
0010	S	D	E	N	1973	82666
0010	S	T	E	N	1973	82666

Substance Number	Phys. State	Subject	Language	Temperature	Year	EPIC Number
114-0010	S	D	E	L	1970	85417
0015	D	D	E	N	1975	92132
0015	T	D	E	N	1975	92132
0017	A	D	E	N	1972	70674
0017	A	S	E	N	1972	70674
0017	A	S	E	N	1974	89269
0017	S	S	E	N	1973	51442
0017	S	S	E	N	1972	52968
0017	S	S	E	N	1973	53939
0017	S	D	E	N	1974	58808
0017	S	S	E	N	1970	59674
0017	S	D	E	N	1974	60265
0017	S	S	E	N	1974	67182
0017	S	D	E	N	1972	70674
0017	S	S	E	N	1972	70674
0017	S	S	E	N	1962	87660
0017	S	S	E	N	1971	87884
0017	S	S	E	N	1963	98002
0017	S	S	E	N	1976	101470
0017	S	S	R	N	1975	101515
0017	S	S	E	N	1975	101516
0017	S	S	E	N	1976	101823
0017	T	D	E	N	1974	65107
0018	S	S	E	N	1973	51442
0055	S	S	E	N	1973	51442
0060	D	D	R	N	1973	57378
0060	S	S	E	N	1973	51442
0060	S	D	E	N	1973	53574
0060	S	S	E	N	1973	53574
0060	S	S	E	N	1974	54577
0060	S	D	R	N	1973	55012
0060	S	D	E	N	1974	55013
0060	S	D	R	N	1974	63128
0060	S	T	R	N	1974	63128
0060	S	D	E	N	1975	63129
0060	S	T	E	N	1975	63129
0077	S	S	E	N	1973	51442
8001	A	S	E	N	1970	59557
8001	A	D	E	N	1972	70674
8001	A	S	E	N	1972	70674
8001	A	S	E	N	1974	89269
8001	D	S	E	N	1965	87781
8001	S	S	E	L	1973	51442
8001	S	D	E	N	1973	51833
8001	S	S	E	N	1972	52968
8001	S	D	E	N	1972	53159
8001	S	S	E	N	1972	53299
8001	S	S	E	N	1973	53564
8001	S	S	E	N	1973	53939
8001	S	S	E	L	1974	54339
8001	S	D	E	N	1974	54596
8001	S	S	R	N	1973	55328
8001	S	D	E	N	1974	58808
8001	S	S	E	N	1974	59264
8001	S	S	E	N	1970	59557
8001	S	S	E	N	1970	59674
8001	S	D	E	N	1974	60265
8001	S	S	E	N	1963	60679
8001	S	D	E	N	1971	62260
8001	S	S	E	N	1973	65539
8001	S	S	E	L	1974	66375
8001	S	D	E	N	1968	74648
8001	S	S	E	N	1963	87679
8001	S	S	E	L	1965	87781
8001	S	S	E	N	1965	87781
8001	S	S	E	L	1971	87884
8001	S	S	E	N	1971	87884
8001	S	D	R	L	1975	99492
8001	S	S	R	L	1975	99492
8001	S	T	R	L	1975	99492
8001	S	D	E	L	1975	99493
8001	S	S	E	L	1975	99493
8001	S	T	E	L	1975	99493
8001	S	S	E	N	1976	101470
8001	S	S	R	N	1975	101515
8001	S	S	E	N	1975	101516
8001	S	S	E	N	1976	101823
8001	S	S	E	N	1976	103155
8047	S	S	E	N	1973	51442
8069	T	D	E	N	1974	83981
116-0001	S	D	E	N	1973	49986
0001	S	S	E	N	1973	51442
0001	S	S	E	N	1967	98664
0005	S	S	E	N	1973	51442
0005	S	D	E	N	1973	51580
0005	S	D	E	N	1973	53838
0005	S	S	E	N	1967	98664
0012	S	S	E	N	1973	51442
0017	D	D	E	L	1977	103589
0017	D	D	E	N	1977	103589
0017	S	S	E	N	1973	51442
0017	S	D	E	L	1973	57638
0017	S	S	E	L	1967	75838
0017	S	S	E	N	1967	75838
0024	S	S	E	N	1973	51442
0031	S	D	E	N	1972	49479
0031	S	S	E	N	1973	51442
0043	S	S	E	N	1973	51442
8017	S	D	O	N	1972	50641
8017	S	D	E	N	1975	63258

Substance Number	Phys. State	Subject	Language	Temperature	Year	EPIC Number
116-8017	S	S	E	N	1970	87822
8017	S	S	E	N	1972	87890
8017	S	S	E	N	1965	98850
8018	S	S	E	N	1973	51442
8019	S	S	E	N	1973	51442
8020	S	S	E	N	1973	51442
8021	S	S	E	N	1973	51442
8022	S	S	E	N	1973	51442
8023	S	S	E	N	1973	51442
8024	S	D	E	N	1973	51834
8024	S	D	E	N	1975	62865
8025	D	D	E	N	1975	91963
8025	S	D	E	N	1972	53065
8025	S	D	E	N	1975	91963
8043	S	D	E	N	1973	55968
8043	S	T	E	N	1973	55968
8044	S	D	E	N	1975	68590
8044	S	T	E	N	1975	68590
118-0020	S	D	R	N	1972	79248
0020	S	D	E	N	1972	90275
0026	S	D	R	N	1972	50651
0037	S	D	R	H	1973	51366
0037	S	D	R	N	1973	51366
0037	S	D	E	H	1973	51367
0037	S	D	E	N	1973	51367
0037	S	S	E	N	1973	51442
0037	S	S	E	N	1973	52192
0037	S	D	R	N	1974	68660
0037	S	S	R	N	1974	68660
0037	S	T	R	N	1974	68660
0037	S	D	E	N	1975	68661
0037	S	S	E	N	1975	68661
0037	S	T	E	N	1975	68661
0037	S	S	E	N	1970	87822
0037	S	S	E	N	1972	87890
0037	T	D	E	N	1974	90072
0041	S	S	E	N	1973	51442
0041	S	S	E	N	1973	52192
0041	S	S	E	N	1974	54577
0041	S	S	E	N	1970	87822
0041	S	S	E	N	1972	87890
0042	S	S	E	N	1973	51442
0042	S	D	E	N	1973	51580
0070	S	S	E	N	1973	51442
8018	S	D	E	N	1973	51258
8018	S	D	E	N	1973	52123
8018	S	D	E	N	1974	54551
8018	S	D	E	N	1973	56462
8018	S	D	E	N	1975	85756
8020	S	S	E	N	1973	51442
8038	S	D	E	N	1973	52192
8070	S	D	R	N	1971	49958
8075	S	D	E	N	1974	63253
8075	S	D	E	N	1974	90358
8076	S	D	E	N	1974	63253
8089	S	S	E	N	1969	87870
119-0001	S	D	E	N	1973	52076
0002	P	D	E	N	1973	55521
0002	S	S	E	N	1973	51442
0002	S	D	E	N	1973	52412
0002	S	D	E	N	1973	53583
0002	S	S	E	N	1973	53583
0002	S	D	E	N	1974	57984
0002	S	D	E	N	1973	59291
0002	S	D	E	N	1974	60265
0002	S	D	R	N	1974	60463
0002	S	D	E	N	1974	60464
0002	S	D	E	L	1973	60643
0002	S	D	E	N	1973	60643
0002	S	S	E	N	1973	60643
0002	S	D	E	N	1974	62065
0002	S	T	E	N	1974	62065
0002	S	S	E	N	1974	62816
0002	S	D	E	N	1975	63332
0002	S	D	E	H	1966	64256
0002	S	D	E	L	1966	64256
0002	S	D	E	N	1966	64256
0002	S	D	E	N	1965	65978
0002	S	S	E	N	1965	65978
0002	S	D	E	N	1970	68210
0002	S	S	E	N	1969	68271
0002	S	D	E	H	1966	74594
0002	S	D	E	L	1966	74594
0002	S	D	E	N	1966	74594
0002	S	S	E	N	1963	87682
0002	S	S	E	N	1969	87723
0002	S	S	E	N	1969	87870
0002	S	S	E	H	1965	98850
0002	S	S	E	N	1965	98850
0002	S	S	E	N	1967	98889
0002	S	D	R	N	1976	103366
0002	S	T	R	N	1976	103366
0002	S	D	E	N	1976	103367
0002	S	T	E	N	1976	103367
0002	T	D	E	N	1971	64338
0003	S	S	E	N	1973	51442
0005	S	D	E	N	1974	60654
0007	S	S	E	N	1973	51442
0008	D	D	E	N	1964	60562

Phys. State: **A.** Amorphous; **C.** Superconductive; **D.** Doped; **F.** Fibrous or Whisker; **G.** Gas; **I.** Ionized or Plasma; **L.** Liquid; **P.** Powder or Particle; **S.** Solid; **T.** Thin Film
Subject: **D.** Data; **E.** Experiment; **S.** Survey (Review, Compendium, etc.); **T.** Theory
Language: **E.** English; **F.** French; **G.** German; **O.** Other Languages; **R.** Russian
Temperature: **L.** Low (0 to 75K); **N.** Normal (75 to 1273K); **H.** High (above 1273K)

Substance Number	Phys. State	Subject	Language	Temperature	Year	EPIC Number
119-0008	S	S	E	N	1973	51442
0010	S	S	E	N	1973	51442
0015	S	D	E	N	1972	54704
0021	S	S	E	N	1973	51442
0021	S	S	E	N	1969	87870
0049	S	S	E	N	1973	51442
0050	S	S	E	N	1973	51442
0073	S	S	E	N	1973	51442
0105	S	S	E	N	1973	51442
0126	S	S	E	N	1973	51442
0127	S	S	E	N	1973	51442
8009	S	S	E	N	1962	87662
8010	S	D	E	N	1973	57127
8032	S	S	E	N	1973	51442
8033	S	S	E	N	1973	51442
8034	S	S	E	N	1973	51442
8035	S	S	E	N	1973	51442
8035	S	D	R	N	1973	54500
8035	S	D	E	N	1973	54501
8036	S	S	E	N	1973	51442
8048	S	S	R	N	1973	56262
8048	S	D	E	N	1974	57984
8048	S	S	E	N	1974	57984
8048	S	D	E	N	1973	59291
8048	S	S	E	N	1973	76721
8103	S	D	R	N	1974	65413
8103	S	T	R	N	1974	65413
8103	S	D	E	N	1975	65414
8103	S	T	E	N	1975	65414
8115	S	D	R	N	1971	76482
8115	S	T	R	N	1971	76482
8115	S	D	E	N	1971	91527
8115	S	T	E	N	1971	91527
120-0001	A	S	E	N	1972	52403
0001	S	S	E	N	1973	51442
0001	S	S	E	N	1974	54111
0001	S	D	E	N	1970	68210
0003	G	S	E	N	1967	98664
0003	L	S	E	N	1967	98664
0004	S	S	E	N	1966	87721
0004	S	S	E	N	1969	87870
0006	S	D	E	N	1974	58051
0009	L	D	F	N	1973	51497
0009	L	E	F	N	1973	51497
0009	L	D	F	N	1974	62084
0009	S	S	E	N	1973	51442
0009	S	D	E	N	1968	75725
0009	S	S	E	N	1967	98664
0010	S	D	R	N	1972	79248
0010	S	D	E	N	1972	90275
0016	S	S	E	N	1973	51442
0016	S	D	E	N	1973	51580
0016	S	D	R	N	1973	52387
0016	S	D	E	N	1973	52580
0016	S	D	E	N	1973	55648
0024	S	S	E	N	1973	51442
0024	S	S	E	N	1974	54577
0031	S	S	E	N	1973	51442
0036	S	D	E	N	1973	55968
0036	S	T	E	N	1973	55968
0043	S	S	E	N	1973	51442
0047	S	D	E	N	1973	57879
0075	S	S	E	N	1973	51442
0080	S	S	E	N	1973	51442
0081	S	S	E	N	1973	51442
0081	S	D	F	N	1958	75815
0081	S	S	E	N	1967	98664
0197	S	S	E	N	1973	51442
0221	A	S	E	N	1971	87885
0233	S	D	E	N	1971	49617
0235	S	T	R	N	1973	51360
0235	S	T	E	N	1973	51361
0235	S	S	E	N	1973	51442
0235	S	S	E	N	1965	98850
8022	S	D	E	N	1971	49617
8024	A	D	R	N	1971	59379
8024	A	S	E	N	1971	87885
8024	S	D	E	N	1972	52979
8024	S	D	E	N	1973	53756
8024	S	D	E	N	1974	54023
8024	S	S	E	N	1968	87805
8024	S	S	E	N	1971	87885
8024	S	S	E	N	1967	98893
8024	T	S	E	N	1973	51442
8024	T	D	E	N	1973	57595
8024	T	S	E	N	1968	87805
8024	T	S	E	N	1968	87866
8024	T	S	E	N	1971	87885
8024	T	S	E	N	1972	87888
8024	T	D	R	N	1974	98023
8024	T	T	R	N	1974	98023
8024	T	D	E	N	1974	98024
8024	T	T	E	N	1974	98024
8025	S	D	F	N	1972	49777
8026	S	D	F	N	1972	49777
8027	S	D	F	N	1972	49777
8036	S	S	E	N	1973	51442
8037	S	S	E	N	1973	51442
8038	S	S	E	N	1973	51442
8039	S	S	E	N	1973	51442

Substance Number	Phys. State	Subject	Language	Temperature	Year	EPIC Number
120-8040	S	S	E	N	1973	51442
8042	S	D	E	N	1973	52076
8042	S	D	E	L	1974	62465
8114	S	D	R	N	1973	51725
8169	S	D	R	N	1971	76482
8169	S	T	R	N	1971	76482
8169	S	D	E	N	1971	91527
8169	S	T	E	N	1971	91527
8181	S	D	E	L	1976	101344
8181	S	T	E	L	1976	101344
8181	S	D	E	L	1977	103589
122-0003	S	S	E	N	1973	51442
0003	S	S	E	N	1969	87870
0004	S	S	E	N	1973	51442
0004	S	S	E	N	1969	87870
0005	D	D	E	H	1971	65761
0005	D	T	E	H	1971	65761
0005	S	S	E	N	1973	51442
0005	S	S	E	N	1972	53252
0005	S	D	R	L	1973	53648
0005	S	D	R	N	1973	53648
0005	S	D	E	L	1974	53649
0005	S	D	E	N	1974	53649
0005	S	D	E	H	1974	58818
0005	S	D	E	N	1974	58818
0005	S	T	E	H	1974	58818
0005	S	T	E	N	1974	58818
0005	S	T	E	N	1975	62678
0005	S	D	E	H	1971	65761
0005	S	T	E	H	1971	65761
0005	S	S	E	N	1955	65933
0005	S	D	F	N	1958	75815
0005	S	S	E	N	1974	87606
0005	S	S	E	N	1969	87870
0005	S	S	E	N	1967	98889
0005	T	S	E	N	1972	53371
0005	T	D	O	N	1973	56496
0005	T	D	R	N	1972	56958
0005	T	S	E	N	1968	87866
0008	S	S	E	N	1973	51442
0009	A	D	E	N	1974	53904
0009	A	D	R	L	1971	59379
0009	A	S	E	N	1973	60634
0009	A	S	E	N	1971	87885
0009	A	D	E	N	1976	99319
0009	A	S	E	N	1976	99319
0009	A	S	E	N	1976	99625
0009	A	T	E	N	1976	99625
0009	S	S	E	N	1973	51442
0009	S	D	E	N	1974	53904
0009	S	T	E	N	1974	54101
0009	S	D	E	N	1973	59291
0009	S	D	R	H	1971	59379
0009	S	S	E	N	1973	60634
0009	S	D	E	N	1973	60755
0009	S	S	E	N	1973	60755
0009	S	T	E	N	1973	60755
0009	S	D	G	N	1963	75747
0009	S	E	G	N	1963	75747
0009	S	S	G	N	1963	75747
0009	T	D	E	N	1973	50748
0009	T	D	R	N	1972	51298
0009	T	D	E	N	1973	52306
0009	T	D	R	N	1973	52679
0009	T	D	E	N	1973	54454
0009	T	D	R	N	1973	56028
0009	T	D	E	N	1973	57729
0009	T	D	R	L	1971	59379
0009	T	D	E	N	1972	63537
0009	T	S	E	N	1968	87866
0010	G	S	E	N	1967	98664
0010	L	S	E	N	1967	98664
0011	L	S	E	N	1967	98664
0012	S	S	E	N	1973	51442
0013	D	D	O	N	1972	49897
0013	D	D	E	N	1974	90358
0013	S	D	O	N	1972	49897
0013	S	S	E	N	1973	51442
0013	S	T	E	N	1972	53221
0013	S	D	E	N	1972	53802
0013	S	D	R	N	1974	86817
0013	S	S	R	N	1974	86817
0013	S	T	R	N	1974	86817
0013	S	S	E	N	1969	87870
0013	S	D	E	N	1975	92635
0013	S	S	E	N	1975	92635
0013	S	T	E	N	1975	92635
0014	D	D	E	N	1972	53110
0014	S	D	E	N	1972	53110
0015	S	S	E	N	1971	87881
0016	P	S	E	N	1971	87881
0016	S	D	E	N	1971	49793
0016	S	D	E	N	1972	52977
0016	S	D	R	N	1974	63088
0016	S	T	R	N	1974	63088
0016	S	D	E	N	1975	63089
0016	S	T	E	N	1975	63089
0016	S	S	E	N	1971	87881
0017	S	S	E	N	1973	51442
0017	T	D	E	N	1973	50764

Substance Number	Phys. State	Subject	Language	Temperature	Year	EPIC Number
122-0017	T	S	E	N	1973	63510
0017	T	S	E	N	1968	87866
0019	S	S	E	N	1973	51442
0023	D	D	E	N	1974	57753
0023	S	S	E	N	1973	51442
0023	S	D	E	N	1973	52412
0023	S	S	E	N	1972	52968
0023	S	D	R	N	1973	55706
0023	S	D	E	N	1974	57753
0023	S	D	R	N	1972	58690
0023	S	D	E	N	1974	62493
0023	S	S	E	N	1972	63847
0023	S	D	E	N	1975	65498
0023	S	S	R	N	1970	66024
0023	S	S	E	N	1970	66025
0023	S	S	E	N	1969	68271
0023	S	T	E	N	1970	70645
0023	S	S	E	L	1963	87709
0023	S	S	E	N	1963	87709
0023	S	S	E	N	1970	87822
0023	S	S	E	N	1969	87870
0023	S	S	E	N	1965	98850
0023	S	S	E	N	1967	98889
0023	T	D	E	N	1972	53094
0023	T	T	E	L	1976	103149
0030	S	S	E	N	1973	51442
0030	S	D	R	N	1973	53668
0030	S	S	R	N	1973	53668
0030	S	T	R	N	1973	53668
0030	S	D	E	N	1974	53669
0030	S	S	E	N	1974	53669
0030	S	T	E	N	1974	53669
0030	S	S	E	N	1974	54111
0030	S	T	R	N	1973	58704
0030	S	D	E	N	1973	60645
0030	S	D	R	N	1972	60719
0030	S	T	R	N	1972	60719
0030	S	D	E	N	1973	60720
0030	S	T	E	N	1973	60720
0030	S	T	R	L	1974	61958
0030	S	T	R	N	1974	61958
0030	S	T	E	L	1974	61959
0030	S	T	E	N	1974	61959
0030	S	D	E	N	1971	65020
0030	S	S	E	N	1969	87870
0030	S	D	E	L	1975	90067
0030	S	T	E	N	1974	90343
0030	S	D	E	L	1977	103589
0030	S	D	E	N	1977	103589
0030	T	D	R	L	1974	61958
0030	T	D	R	N	1974	61958
0030	T	T	R	L	1974	61958
0030	T	T	R	N	1974	61958
0030	T	D	E	L	1974	61959
0030	T	D	E	N	1974	61959
0030	T	T	E	L	1974	61959
0030	T	T	E	N	1974	61959
0031	S	S	E	N	1973	51442
0031	S	D	R	N	1974	66728
0031	S	D	E	N	1975	66729
0031	S	S	E	N	1969	68271
0031	S	S	E	N	1975	96477
0037	S	S	E	N	1973	51442
0037	S	D	R	N	1972	79248
0037	S	D	E	N	1972	90275
0038	S	D	R	N	1972	79248
0038	S	D	E	N	1972	90275
0047	S	S	E	N	1973	51442
0050	P	S	E	N	1967	66368
0050	S	S	E	N	1973	51442
0050	S	S	E	N	1967	66368
0050	S	S	E	N	1969	68115
0050	S	S	E	N	1967	98664
0050	T	D	E	N	1974	53643
0051	S	S	E	N	1967	66368
0051	S	S	E	N	1969	68115
0053	S	S	E	N	1973	51442
0053	S	T	E	N	1975	62678
0053	S	S	E	N	1969	68115
0054	S	S	E	N	1973	51442
0064	S	D	E	N	1973	60755
0067	S	S	E	N	1967	66368
0067	S	S	E	N	1969	68115
0096	A	S	E	N	1972	52403
0096	S	S	E	N	1973	51442
0096	T	S	E	N	1968	87866
0105	S	D	E	N	1972	93290
0112	S	D	E	N	1972	53110
0112	S	S	E	N	1971	87881
0112	T	S	E	N	1971	87881
0132	S	S	E	N	1973	51442
0133	S	D	R	L	1973	70818
0133	S	D	R	N	1973	70818
0133	S	D	E	L	1973	91574
0133	S	D	E	N	1973	91574
0196	D	D	E	N	1972	49820
0196	D	D	E	N	1973	56462
0196	D	D	E	N	1974	90572
0196	S	D	E	N	1972	53076
0196	S	D	E	N	1972	53162
0196	S	T	R	N	1973	53668

Phys. State: **A.** Amorphous; **C.** Superconductive; **D.** Doped; **F.** Fibrous or Whisker; **G.** Gas; **I.** Ionized or Plasma; **L.** Liquid; **P.** Powder or Particle; **S.** Solid; **T.** Thin Film
Subject: **D.** Data; **E.** Experiment; **S.** Survey (Review, Compendium, etc.); **T.** Theory
Language: **E.** English; **F.** French; **G.** German; **O.** Other Languages; **R.** Russian
Temperature: **L.** Low (0 to 75K); **N.** Normal (75 to 1273K); **H.** High (above 1273K)

Substance Number	Phys. State	Subject	Language	Temperature	Year	EPIC Number
122-0196	S	T	E	N	1974	53669
0196	S	D	E	N	1974	55119
0196	S	D	E	N	1973	56462
0196	S	D	E	N	1974	57957
0196	S	T	E	N	1974	57957
0196	S	D	R	N	1972	58713
0196	S	D	G	N	1974	90255
0196	S	D	E	N	1974	90312
0196	S	D	E	N	1974	90572
0196	S	S	E	N	1965	98850
0198	S	S	E	N	1973	51442
0199	S	S	E	N	1973	51442
0208	S	D	R	N	1972	79248
0208	S	D	E	N	1972	90275
0208	T	S	E	N	1973	51442
0292	D	D	R	N	1973	51291
0292	S	S	E	N	1973	51442
0292	S	D	E	N	1973	56462
0292	S	D	E	N	1974	58816
0292	S	S	E	N	1969	87870
0314	S	D	E	N	1972	53102
0314	S	E	E	N	1972	53102
0314	T	D	R	N	1972	56958
0340	S	D	R	N	1972	79248
0340	S	D	E	N	1972	90275
0414	S	S	E	N	1973	51442
0421	S	S	E	N	1973	51442
0438	S	D	R	N	1974	68662
0438	S	T	R	N	1974	68662
0438	S	D	E	N	1975	68663
0438	S	T	E	N	1975	68663
0438	S	D	R	L	1973	70818
0438	S	D	R	N	1973	70818
0438	S	D	E	L	1973	91574
0438	S	D	E	N	1973	91574
0449	S	D	R	N	1972	79248
0449	S	D	E	N	1972	90275
8036	S	S	E	N	1967	98664
8038	S	S	E	N	1973	51442
8045	A	D	E	N	1974	57286
8045	A	S	E	N	1976	99625
8045	A	T	E	N	1976	99625
8045	S	D	E	N	1974	54023
8045	S	D	E	N	1972	55087
8045	S	D	E	N	1973	55579
8045	S	S	R	N	1973	56262
8045	S	D	E	N	1960	64749
8045	S	S	E	N	1971	66193
8045	S	S	E	N	1973	76721
8045	S	S	E	N	1969	87870
8045	S	D	R	N	1974	92292
8045	S	T	R	N	1974	92292
8045	S	D	E	N	1974	92293
8045	S	T	E	N	1974	92293
8045	S	S	E	H	1965	98850
8045	S	S	E	N	1965	98850
8045	S	S	E	N	1967	98889
8046	A	D	E	N	1974	53904
8046	S	D	E	N	1974	53904
8046	S	D	E	N	1972	55087
8046	S	S	E	N	1971	65759
8046	S	S	E	N	1968	87819
8046	S	S	E	N	1966	101404
8047	S	D	E	N	1960	64749
8048	A	D	E	N	1974	53904
8048	S	D	E	N	1974	53904
8048	S	S	E	N	1974	53904
8048	S	D	E	N	1972	55087
8049	A	D	E	N	1974	53904
8049	S	D	E	N	1974	53904
8052	A	D	E	N	1974	53904
8052	S	D	E	N	1974	53904
8052	S	D	E	N	1972	55087
8056	D	D	E	N	1973	55278
8057	A	D	E	N	1974	53904
8057	S	D	E	N	1974	53904
8057	S	S	E	N	1974	53904
8058	A	D	E	N	1974	53904
8058	S	D	E	N	1974	53904
8058	S	D	E	N	1972	55087
8059	A	D	E	N	1974	53904
8059	S	D	E	N	1974	53904
8060	A	D	E	N	1974	53904
8060	S	D	E	N	1974	53904
8060	S	D	E	N	1972	55087
8061	A	D	E	N	1974	53904
8061	S	D	E	N	1974	53904
8061	S	D	E	N	1972	55087
8062	A	D	E	N	1974	53904
8062	S	D	E	N	1974	53904
8062	S	D	E	N	1972	55087
8067	S	D	E	N	1973	52576
8079	D	D	E	N	1974	57957
8079	D	T	E	N	1974	57957
8088	P	S	E	N	1971	87881
8088	S	S	E	L	1971	87881
8088	S	S	E	N	1971	87881
8095	S	S	E	N	1974	53904
8096	S	S	E	N	1974	53904
8097	S	S	E	N	1974	53904
8098	S	S	E	N	1974	53904

Substance Number	Phys. State	Subject	Language	Temperature	Year	EPIC Number
122-8098	S	D	E	N	1972	55087
8099	S	S	E	N	1974	53904
8099	S	D	E	N	1972	55087
8100	S	S	E	N	1974	53904
8100	S	D	E	N	1972	55087
8101	S	S	E	N	1974	53904
8101	S	D	E	N	1972	55087
8102	S	S	E	N	1974	53904
8102	S	D	E	N	1972	55087
8103	S	S	E	N	1974	53904
8103	S	D	E	N	1972	55087
8115	S	D	E	N	1974	62605
8115	S	S	E	N	1969	87870
8116	D	D	E	N	1975	59847
8129	S	D	E	N	1972	55087
8133	S	D	R	L	1973	70818
8133	S	D	R	N	1973	70818
8133	S	D	E	L	1973	91574
8133	S	D	E	N	1973	91574
8141	S	D	E	L	1977	103589
8141	S	D	E	N	1977	103589
123-0003	S	S	E	N	1973	51442
0003	S	S	E	N	1972	52968
0003	S	D	E	L	1973	53786
0003	S	S	E	N	1969	68115
0003	S	S	E	N	1966	68361
0003	S	S	E	N	1967	98664
0003	S	S	E	N	1976	101470
0003	S	S	E	N	1976	101823
0003	T	S	E	N	1966	68361
8017	S	S	E	N	1973	51442
8017	S	D	E	L	1973	52463
8017	S	D	E	N	1973	52463
8017	S	S	E	N	1972	52968
8017	S	D	E	L	1973	53786
8017	S	D	E	N	1975	63285
8017	S	S	E	L	1969	68115
8017	S	S	E	N	1969	68115
8017	S	S	E	N	1962	87674
8017	S	S	E	L	1975	96245
8017	S	S	E	N	1976	101823
8017	S	D	E	N	1976	102168
8018	S	S	E	L	1973	51442
8018	S	S	E	N	1973	51442
8018	S	S	E	N	1972	52968
8018	S	D	E	L	1973	53786
8018	S	S	E	N	1973	55157
8018	S	D	E	N	1975	63285
8018	S	S	E	N	1975	63285
8018	S	S	E	N	1975	63321
8018	S	D	E	N	1971	65045
8018	S	S	E	N	1971	65045
8018	S	S	E	L	1970	68114
8018	S	S	E	N	1970	68114
8018	S	S	E	L	1969	68115
8018	S	S	E	N	1969	68115
8018	S	S	E	N	1962	87671
8018	S	D	E	L	1975	100034
8018	S	S	E	N	1976	101470
8018	S	S	E	N	1976	101823
8018	S	D	E	L	1976	102173
8018	S	D	E	N	1976	102173
8018	T	S	E	N	1970	68114
8039	S	S	E	N	1972	87824
8039	S	D	E	N	1976	102168
8051	S	D	E	N	1973	65985
8058	S	S	E	N	1974	61199
126-0001	S	S	E	N	1969	68115
0004	S	D	E	N	1973	60640
0005	D	D	R	N	1973	54298
0005	D	T	R	N	1973	54298
0005	D	D	E	N	1973	54299
0005	D	T	E	N	1973	54299
0005	D	S	E	N	1963	87711
0005	D	S	E	N	1966	87712
0005	P	S	E	N	1963	87711
0005	S	S	E	N	1973	51442
0005	S	D	E	N	1973	52412
0005	S	S	E	N	1972	52968
0005	S	D	E	N	1974	58808
0005	S	S	E	N	1974	59353
0005	S	D	E	N	1974	60265
0005	S	D	E	L	1973	61472
0005	S	D	E	N	1973	61472
0005	S	S	E	N	1973	61472
0005	S	D	E	N	1975	66683
0005	S	S	E	N	1975	66683
0005	S	S	E	N	1969	68271
0005	S	D	F	N	1958	75815
0005	S	S	E	N	1963	87711
0005	S	S	E	N	1970	87822
0005	T	D	R	N	1973	54298
0005	T	T	R	N	1973	54298
0005	T	D	E	N	1973	54299
0005	T	T	E	N	1973	54299
0005	T	D	R	N	1974	61992
0005	T	T	R	N	1974	61992
0005	T	D	E	N	1974	61993
0005	T	T	E	N	1974	61993

Substance Number	Phys. State	Subject	Language	Temperature	Year	EPIC Number
126-0005	T	S	E	N	1963	87711
0014	S	D	R	N	1973	50838
0014	S	S	E	N	1973	51442
0014	S	D	R	N	1974	58098
0014	S	D	E	N	1974	58099
0014	S	D	R	N	1974	63032
0014	S	T	R	N	1974	63032
0014	S	D	E	N	1974	63033
0014	S	T	E	N	1974	63033
0017	S	S	E	N	1973	51442
0017	S	S	E	N	1969	68271
0022	S	D	E	N	1973	60640
8011	S	S	E	N	1973	51442
8030	A	D	E	N	1972	53112
8030	S	S	E	N	1973	51442
8030	S	D	E	N	1972	53112
8032	S	S	R	N	1972	62298
8032	S	S	E	N	1973	62299
8037	S	S	E	N	1973	51442
8037	S	S	E	N	1972	52968
8037	S	S	E	L	1970	68114
8037	S	S	E	N	1970	68114
8037	S	S	E	L	1969	68115
8037	S	S	E	N	1969	68115
8046	T	D	E	N	1974	83981
8052	S	S	E	N	1973	51442
8052	S	D	E	N	1973	52412
8052	S	S	E	N	1972	52968
8052	S	S	R	N	1972	53547
8052	S	S	E	N	1973	53548
8052	S	D	E	N	1974	58808
8052	S	S	E	N	1974	59353
8052	S	D	E	N	1974	60265
8052	S	D	E	L	1973	61472
8052	S	D	E	N	1973	61472
8052	S	S	E	N	1973	61472
8052	S	D	E	N	1971	62264
8052	S	D	E	N	1965	64255
8052	S	S	E	N	1969	68271
8052	S	S	E	N	1963	68313
8052	S	T	E	N	1970	70645
8052	S	D	E	N	1974	87448
8052	S	S	E	N	1970	87822
8052	S	D	E	L	1976	100412
8052	S	D	E	N	1976	100412
8052	S	T	E	L	1976	100412
8052	S	T	E	N	1976	100412
8052	S	S	E	N	1976	101470
8052	S	D	E	N	1976	101848
8052	T	D	R	N	1974	61992
8052	T	T	R	N	1974	61992
8052	T	D	E	N	1974	61993
8052	T	T	E	N	1974	61993
8073	S	S	R	N	1973	56262
8073	S	D	E	N	1971	62600
8073	S	D	E	N	1960	64749
8073	S	S	E	N	1973	76721
8074	S	S	R	N	1973	56262
8074	S	D	E	N	1971	62600
8074	S	S	E	N	1973	76721
8092	S	S	E	N	1974	58804
8097	S	D	E	N	1974	62465
8103	S	S	R	N	1975	86853
8103	S	S	E	N	1975	86854
127-8004	A	D	E	N	1973	51484
8004	S	S	E	N	1973	51442
8004	S	D	E	N	1973	52412
8004	S	S	E	N	1972	52968
8004	S	D	E	N	1974	58808
8004	S	D	E	N	1974	60265
8004	S	D	E	L	1973	61472
8004	S	D	E	N	1973	61472
8004	S	S	E	N	1973	61472
8004	S	D	E	N	1972	63492
8004	S	S	E	N	1972	63492
8004	S	S	E	L	1969	68271
8004	S	S	E	N	1969	68271
8004	S	S	E	N	1970	87822
8004	T	D	E	N	1973	51484
8015	S	D	E	N	1973	60640

Phys. State: **A.** Amorphous; **C.** Superconductive; **D.** Doped; **F.** Fibrous or Whisker; **G.** Gas; **I.** Ionized or Plasma; **L.** Liquid; **P.** Powder or Particle; **S.** Solid; **T.** Thin Film
Subject: **D.** Data; **E.** Experiment; **S.** Survey (Review, Compendium, etc.); **T.** Theory
Language: **E.** English; **F.** French; **G.** German; **O.** Other Languages; **R.** Russian
Temperature: **L.** Low (0 to 75K); **N.** Normal (75 to 1273K); **H.** High (above 1273K)

Chapter 3 Dielectric Strength

Substance Number	Phys. State	Subject	Language	Temperature	Year	EPIC Number
100-0045	L	S	O	N	1964	53395
0045	L	S	E	N	1972	53396
0045	L	S	E	N	1972	87876
0045	T	S	E	N	1971	87880
0055	A	D	E	N	1974	54091
0055	D	T	E	N	1974	61432
0055	S	S	E	N	1968	67894
8003	S	S	E	N	1974	70440
102-0002	D	S	E	N	1964	87713
0002	S	D	R	L	1973	55174
0002	S	D	R	N	1973	55174
0002	S	S	R	L	1973	55174
0002	S	S	R	N	1973	55174
0002	S	D	E	L	1974	55175
0002	S	D	E	N	1974	55175
0002	S	S	E	L	1974	55175
0002	S	S	E	N	1974	55175
0002	S	D	O	H	1974	66386
0002	S	D	O	N	1974	66386
0002	S	D	E	N	1970	67476
0002	S	S	E	N	1964	87713
0002	S	S	E	N	1968	87819
0002	S	S	E	N	1967	87864
0002	S	S	E	N	1967	98897
0002	T	D	G	N	1973	51458
0002	T	D	R	N	1973	51628
0002	T	D	R	N	1972	51979
0002	T	D	E	N	1972	53252
0002	T	D	E	N	1972	53299
0002	T	D	R	N	1973	55225
0002	T	D	E	N	1974	55226
0002	T	D	R	N	1972	58840
0002	T	D	R	N	1975	90295
0002	T	D	E	N	1974	90540
0002	T	D	E	N	1973	90575
0002	T	D	E	N	1970	100000
0002	T	S	E	N	1970	100000
0010	S	T	E	N	1973	56645
0105	T	D	R	N	1973	51626
0105	T	D	R	N	1971	58853
0105	T	D	E	N	1973	91486
0105	T	D	E	N	1975	93630
8031	A	D	E	H	1974	65598
8031	S	D	R	N	1973	55325
8031	S	D	E	N	1974	59261
8041	D	T	E	N	1974	61432
8041	S	S	E	N	1975	65457
8041	S	D	E	N	1975	92079
8041	T	D	E	N	1973	52588
8054	S	S	E	N	1975	65457
8106	S	D	E	N	1972	53178
8171	A	D	E	N	1972	53186
8171	T	D	E	N	1972	53186
8313	S	S	G	N	1959	65983
8313	S	S	E	N	1963	65984
104-0002	S	D	E	N	1972	53476
0002	S	S	E	N	1963	87681
0002	S	S	E	N	1968	87819
0006	S	T	E	N	1974	56613
0006	S	D	O	N	1971	65845
0006	S	T	O	N	1971	65845
0006	S	D	E	N	1976	99987
0006	S	E	E	N	1976	99987
0006	S	S	E	N	1976	99987
0007	S	S	E	N	1966	87803
0007	T	D	E	N	1972	53473
0007	T	S	E	N	1966	87803
0008	G	S	E	N	1964	87719
0013	S	D	E	N	1973	56462
0013	S	T	R	N	1974	68646
0013	S	T	E	N	1975	68647
0013	T	D	E	N	1972	60165
0053	S	D	E	N	1976	99987
0053	S	E	E	N	1976	99987
0053	S	S	E	N	1976	99987
106-0001	G	D	R	N	1973	55692
0001	G	S	E	N	1964	87719
0002	L	S	R	N	1954	53377
0002	L	S	E	N	1972	53378
0003	G	D	E	N	1973	51640
0006	S	D	E	N	1976	99987
0006	S	E	E	N	1976	99987
0006	S	S	E	N	1976	99987
0021	G	S	E	N	1964	87719
0024	S	S	E	N	1975	65457
0024	S	D	O	N	1971	65845
0024	S	T	O	N	1971	65845
0024	S	D	E	N	1976	99987
0024	S	E	E	N	1976	99987
0034	G	S	E	N	1964	87719
0039	G	D	R	N	1973	55692
0039	G	S	E	N	1964	87719
106-0066	G	S	E	N	1964	87719
0147	D	S	E	N	1964	87719
0147	G	S	E	N	1964	87719
0158	S	S	E	N	1970	87822
0166	G	S	E	N	1964	87719
0231	G	D	R	N	1973	55692
0231	G	S	E	N	1964	87719
0233	G	S	E	N	1964	87719
0363	S	D	R	N	1973	52537
0363	S	D	E	N	1974	53664
0363	S	S	E	N	1975	65457
0363	T	T	R	N	1973	51555
0363	T	T	E	N	1973	53686
8041	S	S	E	N	1973	60838
8475	G	S	E	N	1964	87719
8476	G	S	E	N	1964	87719
8477	G	S	E	N	1964	87719
8478	G	S	E	N	1964	87719
8479	G	S	E	N	1964	87719
8481	G	S	E	N	1964	87719
8517	G	S	E	N	1964	87719
8577	G	D	R	N	1973	55692
8578	G	D	R	N	1973	55692
8579	G	D	R	N	1973	55692
8689	G	S	E	N	1964	87719
8690	G	S	E	N	1964	87719
8691	G	S	E	N	1964	87719
8692	G	S	E	N	1964	87719
108-8025	S	S	E	N	1970	87822
8025	S	S	E	N	1972	87890
110-0011	T	D	R	N	1973	51628
0024	S	D	E	N	1974	67247
0036	S	D	E	N	1976	99987
0036	S	E	E	N	1976	99987
0036	S	S	E	N	1976	99987
0037	S	D	E	N	1976	99987
0037	S	E	E	N	1976	99987
0037	S	S	E	N	1976	99987
0040	D	D	E	N	1974	67241
0040	G	D	E	N	1972	51588
0040	G	T	E	N	1972	51593
0040	G	D	E	N	1972	51594
0040	G	T	E	N	1972	51594
0040	G	D	E	N	1972	51595
0040	G	D	E	N	1972	51596
0040	G	D	G	N	1973	53055
0040	G	D	E	N	1973	55522
0040	G	D	R	N	1973	55692
0040	G	D	E	N	1973	66899
0040	G	D	E	N	1974	67232
0040	G	D	E	N	1974	67234
0040	G	D	E	N	1974	67235
0040	G	D	E	N	1974	67238
0040	G	T	E	N	1974	67238
0040	G	D	E	N	1974	67240
0040	G	D	E	N	1974	67241
0040	G	D	E	N	1974	67244
0040	G	S	E	N	1964	87717
0040	L	D	E	N	1974	67240
0194	S	D	E	N	1973	51920
111-0008	S	S	E	N	1975	65457
8195	S	D	E	N	1975	100607
8195	S	T	E	N	1975	100607
112-0001	L	D	R	N	1945	53233
0001	L	D	E	N	1972	53234
0001	L	S	R	N	1954	53377
0001	L	S	E	N	1972	53378
0001	L	D	R	N	1974	58660
0001	L	D	R	N	1971	67038
0001	L	D	E	N	1974	67515
0001	S	D	R	N	1945	53233
0001	S	D	E	N	1972	53234
114-0001	S	D	E	N	1976	99987
0001	S	E	E	N	1976	99987
0001	S	S	E	N	1976	99987
0009	S	S	E	N	1976	99987
8001	S	D	R	N	1973	51631
8001	S	S	E	N	1975	65457
8001	T	D	E	N	1975	90858
8001	T	T	E	N	1975	90858
118-0037	S	D	E	N	1973	50557
8018	S	D	E	N	1973	56462
119-0002	S	S	E	N	1963	87682
0002	S	S	E	N	1969	87723
120-0001	D	D	E	N	1975	63350
0001	D	T	E	N	1975	63350
0001	T	D	R	N	1973	51628
120-0001	T	D	E	N	1975	63350
0001	T	T	E	N	1975	63350
0003	G	D	E	N	1972	51589
0003	G	D	E	N	1973	56514
0004	T	D	E	N	1972	53252
0221	A	S	E	N	1971	87885
8024	A	S	E	N	1971	87885
8024	S	D	R	L	1973	55174
8024	S	D	R	N	1973	55174
8024	S	S	R	L	1973	55174
8024	S	S	R	N	1973	55174
8024	S	D	E	L	1974	55175
8024	S	D	E	N	1974	55175
8024	S	S	E	L	1974	55175
8024	S	S	E	N	1974	55175
8024	T	S	E	N	1971	87885
8024	T	D	R	N	1974	98023
8024	T	D	E	N	1974	98024
122-0004	T	D	E	N	1972	53252
0005	T	D	E	N	1972	53252
0005	T	S	E	N	1972	53371
0009	A	S	E	N	1971	87885
0009	D	D	E	N	1973	57725
0009	D	T	E	N	1973	57725
0009	S	D	E	N	1974	54045
0009	S	D	R	L	1973	55174
0009	S	D	R	N	1973	55174
0009	S	S	R	L	1973	55174
0009	S	S	R	N	1973	55174
0009	S	D	E	L	1974	55175
0009	S	D	E	N	1974	55175
0009	S	S	E	L	1974	55175
0009	S	S	E	N	1974	55175
0009	S	S	E	N	1975	65457
0009	T	D	E	N	1973	52587
0009	T	D	R	N	1973	55225
0009	T	D	E	N	1974	55226
0009	T	D	E	N	1973	60891
0009	T	D	E	N	1974	62833
0009	T	D	E	N	1972	63537
0009	T	D	E	N	1975	65457
0009	T	T	E	N	1975	65457
0009	T	S	E	N	1968	87866
0009	T	D	E	N	1975	90856
0009	T	T	E	N	1975	90856
0009	T	S	E	N	1976	101374
0017	T	S	E	N	1968	87866
0019	T	D	E	N	1972	53252
0023	S	S	E	N	1975	65457
0030	S	E	E	L	1977	103589
0096	S	D	R	L	1973	55174
0096	S	D	R	N	1973	55174
0096	S	S	R	L	1973	55174
0096	S	S	R	N	1973	55174
0096	S	D	E	L	1974	55175
0096	S	D	E	N	1974	55175
0096	S	S	E	L	1974	55175
0096	S	S	E	N	1974	55175
0096	T	D	R	N	1973	66036
0096	T	D	E	N	1973	66037
0096	T	S	E	N	1968	87866
0196	D	D	E	N	1973	56462
0196	S	D	E	N	1972	53076
0196	S	D	E	N	1973	56462
0196	S	D	E	N	1975	63345
0196	S	D	E	N	1975	63346
0196	S	S	E	N	1975	63346
0196	S	T	E	N	1975	63346
0196	S	D	E	N	1975	66617
0196	S	T	E	N	1975	66617
0292	S	D	E	N	1973	56462
8046	S	S	E	N	1968	87819
126-0014	L	D	E	N	1972	76041
0014	L	D	R	N	1971	76069
8052	S	S	E	N	1975	65457

Phys. State: **A.** Amorphous; **C.** Superconductive; **D.** Doped; **F.** Fibrous or Whisker; **G.** Gas; **I.** Ionized or Plasma; **L.** Liquid; **P.** Powder or Particle; **S.** Solid; **T.** Thin Film
Subject: **D.** Data; **E.** Experiment; **S.** Survey (Review, Compendium, etc.); **T.** Theory
Language: **E.** English; **F.** French; **G.** German; **O.** Other Languages; **R.** Russian
Temperature: **L.** Low (0 to 75K); **N.** Normal (75 to 1273K); **H.** High (above 1273K)

Chapter 4 Energy Band Structure

Substance Number	Phys. State	Sub-ject	Lan-guage	Temper-ature	Year	EPIC Number
100-0045	G	T	E	N	1974	54036
0055	A	T	E	N	1973	51774
0055	A	E	E	N	1972	53113
0055	A	S	E	N	1972	53251
0055	A	S	E	N	1973	53426
0055	A	T	E	N	1973	55113
0055	A	T	E	N	1973	65596
0055	A	S	O	N	1974	65614
0055	A	T	E	N	1962	65961
0055	A	T	E	N	1967	74602
0055	A	S	E	N	1975	95324
0055	A	T	E	N	1976	100646
0055	D	D	E	N	1973	50756
0055	D	T	E	N	1975	65494
0055	D	T	E	N	1962	65947
0055	D	T	E	N	1971	70652
0055	D	T	R	N	1975	95776
0055	D	T	E	N	1975	95777
0055	L	S	E	N	1970	75833
0055	S	S	E	N	1973	50777
0055	S	T	E	N	1973	50925
0055	S	T	E	N	1973	51470
0055	S	T	R	N	1973	51552
0055	S	T	E	N	1973	51791
0055	S	T	E	N	1972	53176
0055	S	S	E	N	1972	53200
0055	S	T	E	N	1973	53562
0055	S	S	E	N	1974	53607
0055	S	T	E	N	1973	53683
0055	S	D	E	N	1974	53917
0055	S	T	E	N	1974	53917
0055	S	S	E	N	1974	54081
0055	S	T	E	N	1974	54086
0055	S	T	R	N	1972	54286
0055	S	T	E	N	1972	54287
0055	S	T	E	N	1974	54339
0055	S	D	E	N	1974	54345
0055	S	T	E	N	1974	55241
0055	S	S	E	N	1973	56284
0055	S	S	E	N	1973	56749
0055	S	S	E	N	1973	56765
0055	S	E	R	N	1973	56900
0055	S	S	E	N	1973	58565
0055	S	S	E	N	1973	58572
0055	S	S	E	N	1974	58810
0055	S	T	E	N	1958	59568
0055	S	T	R	N	1971	59580
0055	S	T	E	N	1970	59810
0055	S	D	E	N	1975	59831
0055	S	T	E	N	1975	59831
0055	S	T	E	N	1973	60628
0055	S	T	E	N	1971	61329
0055	S	T	E	N	1974	61352
0055	S	T	E	N	1970	61493
0055	S	T	E	N	1970	61494
0055	S	S	E	N	1969	61512
0055	S	T	E	N	1971	61678
0055	S	S	O	N	1974	62496
0055	S	T	E	N	1975	63303
0055	S	T	E	N	1974	64457
0055	S	T	E	N	1971	65080
0055	S	S	O	N	1974	65614
0055	S	T	E	N	1962	65939
0055	S	T	E	N	1962	65946
0055	S	T	E	N	1962	65948
0055	S	T	E	N	1962	65955
0055	S	T	R	N	1974	66452
0055	S	T	E	N	1974	66453
0055	S	T	E	N	1975	66685
0055	S	S	E	N	1974	66865
0055	S	T	E	L	1970	70646
0055	S	T	E	N	1975	75197
0055	S	T	E	N	1970	75905
0055	S	T	R	N	1974	78324
0055	S	T	E	N	1975	78325
0055	S	S	E	N	1971	84631
0055	S	T	E	N	1975	85290
0055	S	S	E	N	1973	87614
0055	S	S	E	N	1973	87615
0055	S	S	E	N	1972	87656
0055	S	E	E	N	1974	90402
0055	S	T	R	N	1974	92325
0055	S	T	E	N	1975	92326
0055	S	T	E	N	1975	92822
0055	S	T	E	N	1975	98207
0055	S	T	E	N	1976	101470
0055	T	E	E	N	1973	51016
0055	T	T	E	N	1972	61768
0055	T	T	E	N	1967	74602
0055	T	T	E	N	1976	100222
8003	S	S	E	N	1974	54603
8003	S	T	E	N	1973	61074
8003	S	S	E	N	1966	64257
8003	S	S	E	N	1968	74624
8003	S	T	E	L	1970	85417

Substance Number	Phys. State	Sub-ject	Lan-guage	Temper-ature	Year	EPIC Number
100-8003	S	S	E	N	1975	86762
8003	S	S	E	N	1975	86763
8005	S	D	E	N	1972	50460
8005	S	S	E	N	1973	58566
8006	S	D	R	N	1972	50470
8007	S	T	E	N	1974	57322
8007	S	S	E	N	1973	58180
8007	S	S	O	N	1974	62496
8007	S	D	E	N	1975	87171
8007	S	S	E	N	1972	87823
8007	S	T	E	N	1975	90874
8008	S	S	E	N	1973	50772
8008	S	T	E	N	1974	57322
8008	S	S	E	N	1973	58180
8008	S	S	O	N	1974	62496
8008	S	S	R	N	1975	86845
8008	S	S	E	N	1975	86846
8008	S	D	E	N	1975	87171
8008	S	S	E	N	1971	87884
8008	S	S	E	N	1972	87889
8008	S	T	E	N	1975	90874
8009	S	T	E	N	1973	53420
8016	S	T	E	N	1970	59810
8021	S	S	E	N	1973	58566
8025	S	S	E	N	1973	58566
8025	S	S	E	N	1974	87606
8034	S	T	E	N	1973	57655
8038	S	S	E	N	1972	87824
8043	S	S	E	N	1973	58566
8043	S	S	E	N	1969	75843
8047	S	D	E	N	1975	87171
8059	S	S	E	N	1973	51467
8071	S	S	E	N	1972	56585
102-0002	S	D	E	N	1974	65241
0002	T	D	E	N	1972	52981
0002	T	T	E	N	1975	66723
0005	S	D	R	N	1973	52318
0005	S	D	E	N	1974	61388
0009	S	D	E	N	1972	53215
0009	S	S	E	N	1975	86758
0010	S	D	E	N	1972	53215
0010	S	S	E	N	1975	86758
0010	T	T	O	N	1965	61141
0041	S	S	E	N	1972	87889
0041	T	D	E	N	1974	65107
0086	D	D	E	N	1973	52191
0086	S	S	E	N	1973	60634
0105	S	D	E	N	1972	53466
0248	S	D	E	N	1972	53099
0248	S	D	E	N	1971	65042
8001	D	S	E	N	1971	87884
8001	S	D	E	N	1973	50925
8001	S	S	E	N	1973	53427
8001	S	D	E	N	1974	58137
8001	S	S	E	N	1972	66310
8001	S	S	E	N	1962	87668
8001	S	S	E	N	1971	87884
8001	S	S	E	N	1972	87889
8005	S	D	E	N	1974	57319
8018	S	S	E	N	1972	87889
8031	A	S	E	N	1974	58811
8031	S	S	E	N	1974	58811
8035	S	D	E	N	1974	60664
8041	D	D	R	N	1972	49888
8041	D	D	R	N	1973	52532
8041	D	T	E	N	1972	53113
8041	D	D	E	N	1974	57773
8041	D	D	E	N	1971	59711
8041	D	D	E	N	1975	72540
8041	D	D	E	N	1975	90109
8041	D	T	E	N	1975	90109
8041	D	S	E	N	1975	97860
8041	D	D	E	N	1976	100869
8041	D	T	E	N	1976	100869
8041	S	D	E	N	1973	49684
8041	S	D	E	N	1973	50925
8041	S	D	E	N	1973	50928
8041	S	D	E	N	1973	51790
8041	S	T	E	N	1973	51805
8041	S	D	E	N	1973	52449
8041	S	D	E	N	1973	52782
8041	S	D	E	N	1972	53099
8041	S	S	E	N	1972	53227
8041	S	D	E	N	1974	53607
8041	S	D	E	N	1974	53610
8041	S	D	E	N	1974	54081
8041	S	S	E	N	1974	54094
8041	S	S	R	N	1973	55307
8041	S	T	E	N	1972	55728
8041	S	D	R	N	1973	56900
8041	S	S	E	N	1974	58810
8041	S	S	E	N	1974	59232
8041	S	D	R	N	1970	59532
8041	S	D	E	N	1971	60546

Substance Number	Phys. State	Sub-ject	Lan-guage	Temper-ature	Year	EPIC Number
102-8041	S	T	E	N	1973	60575
8041	S	T	E	N	1973	60627
8041	S	T	E	N	1970	61493
8041	S	S	E	N	1969	61512
8041	S	D	E	N	1971	65042
8041	S	S	E	N	1971	65048
8041	S	T	E	L	1975	65475
8041	S	S	O	N	1966	66022
8041	S	S	E	N	1967	66023
8041	S	S	E	N	1972	66310
8041	S	D	E	N	1975	66684
8041	S	S	E	N	1975	66684
8041	S	T	E	N	1975	66684
8041	S	T	E	N	1975	68602
8041	S	S	E	N	1975	73247
8041	S	T	E	N	1975	73247
8041	S	S	E	N	1973	86380
8041	S	D	E	N	1975	86754
8041	S	S	E	N	1975	86757
8041	S	D	R	N	1975	86831
8041	S	D	E	N	1975	86832
8041	S	D	E	N	1975	87171
8041	S	S	E	N	1962	87673
8041	S	S	E	N	1964	87701
8041	S	S	E	L	1971	87884
8041	S	S	E	N	1971	87884
8041	S	S	E	N	1972	87889
8041	S	S	E	N	1974	88203
8041	S	D	R	N	1974	90369
8041	S	D	E	N	1975	90874
8041	S	S	E	N	1975	90874
8041	S	T	E	N	1975	90874
8041	S	S	E	N	1975	91218
8041	T	D	R	N	1973	55306
8041	T	D	E	N	1974	59231
8054	D	D	R	N	1973	50055
8054	D	D	E	N	1973	51411
8054	S	D	R	N	1973	49762
8054	S	D	R	N	1973	50055
8054	S	D	E	N	1973	50925
8054	S	D	E	N	1973	51411
8054	S	D	E	N	1974	53607
8054	S	D	E	N	1974	53610
8054	S	T	E	N	1974	55241
8054	S	D	E	N	1971	65080
8054	S	T	E	N	1971	65080
8054	S	S	E	N	1972	66310
8054	S	S	E	N	1962	87667
8054	S	S	E	N	1972	87889
8054	T	D	E	N	1974	65107
8058	F	S	E	N	1975	91972
8058	S	T	E	N	1968	53357
8066	S	D	R	N	1973	52557
8069	S	D	E	N	1973	50559
8069	S	D	E	N	1972	53335
8069	S	D	E	N	1974	62059
8069	S	T	E	N	1974	62059
8069	S	D	R	N	1973	93280
8070	S	D	E	N	1975	87180
8094	S	S	E	N	1972	53227
8094	S	S	E	N	1972	87889
8094	S	S	E	N	1974	88203
8094	T	D	R	N	1973	50057
8094	T	D	E	N	1973	51413
8094	T	S	E	N	1972	87889
8095	S	S	E	N	1972	53227
8095	S	D	E	N	1975	59831
8095	S	D	E	N	1975	86754
8095	S	S	E	N	1965	87703
8095	S	S	E	N	1972	87889
8095	S	S	E	L	1974	88203
8096	S	D	R	N	1972	56991
8104	S	D	E	L	1973	50482
8104	S	D	E	N	1973	50482
8106	A	T	E	N	1976	100646
8132	S	S	E	N	1972	53227
8132	S	S	E	N	1972	87889
8132	S	S	E	N	1974	88203
8133	A	T	E	N	1976	100646
8142	S	S	E	N	1972	87889
8142	T	S	E	N	1972	87889
8171	A	D	E	N	1972	53186
8171	T	D	E	N	1972	53186
8173	S	D	E	N	1972	53215
8179	S	D	R	N	1973	55307
8179	S	D	E	N	1974	59232
8187	A	T	E	N	1974	54059
8187	S	T	E	N	1974	54059
8229	S	D	E	N	1974	57326
8229	S	T	E	N	1974	57326
8231	S	D	E	N	1974	57326
8231	S	T	E	N	1974	57326
8235	D	D	E	N	1974	54092
8235	S	D	E	L	1974	54092
8235	S	D	E	N	1974	54092

Phys. State: A. Amorphous; C. Superconductive; D. Doped; F. Fibrous or Whisker; G. Gas; I. Ionized or Plasma; L. Liquid; P. Powder or Particle; S. Solid; T. Thin Film
Subject: D. Data; E. Experiment; S. Survey (Review, Compendium, etc.); T. Theory
Language: E. English; F. French; G. German; O. Other Languages; R. Russian
Temperature: L. Low (0 to 75K); N. Normal (75 to 1273K); H. High (above 1273K)

Substance Number	Phys. State	Subject	Language	Temperature	Year	EPIC Number
102-8235	S	D	O	N	1973	67248
8243	A	S	E	N	1974	58811
8255	S	D	E	N	1971	65083
8278	S	D	E	N	1973	57461
8283	S	S	E	N	1971	65062
8283	S	D	E	N	1971	65083
8283	S	S	E	N	1971	65083
8287	S	S	E	N	1971	65069
8314	S	D	E	N	1975	91619
8333	S	S	E	N	1972	87889
8374	S	D	E	N	1974	62044
8399	S	D	E	N	1974	57326
8399	S	T	E	N	1974	57326
8420	T	S	E	N	1972	87889
8437	S	D	E	N	1974	62044
8443	S	D	E	N	1975	91619
8458	F	D	E	N	1975	91972
8483	S	D	R	N	1974	77917
8483	S	T	R	N	1974	77917
8483	S	D	E	N	1974	94485
8483	S	T	E	N	1974	94485
104-0002	S	T	R	N	1975	89660
0002	S	T	E	N	1975	89661
0006	D	D	E	L	1975	66689
0006	S	D	E	N	1974	54604
0006	S	D	E	N	1974	58941
0006	S	S	E	N	1974	58941
0006	S	D	E	L	1970	59675
0006	S	D	E	N	1966	64258
0006	S	S	E	N	1966	64258
0006	S	D	E	N	1975	86757
0007	S	D	R	N	1973	56044
0007	S	D	E	N	1972	63601
0007	S	S	E	N	1972	63601
0007	S	D	E	N	1972	63787
0007	S	T	E	N	1972	63787
0007	S	D	E	N	1966	64254
0007	S	D	E	N	1972	64535
0007	S	S	E	N	1972	64535
0007	S	T	E	N	1975	65499
0007	S	S	E	N	1967	68374
0007	T	D	E	N	1976	100007
0007	T	T	E	N	1976	100007
0013	S	D	E	N	1973	50150
0022	S	D	E	N	1973	51007
0022	S	D	F	N	1973	51779
0022	S	D	E	N	1974	61388
0022	S	S	E	N	1974	61388
0022	S	D	E	N	1975	66684
0022	S	T	E	N	1975	66684
0031	S	D	E	N	1966	64258
0031	S	S	E	N	1966	64258
0031	S	D	E	N	1975	86757
0049	S	D	E	N	1975	86757
0051	S	D	E	N	1973	55109
0053	S	D	E	N	1966	64258
0053	S	S	E	N	1966	64258
0053	S	S	E	N	1975	65501
0053	S	D	E	N	1975	86757
0053	S	D	E	N	1975	86763
0067	S	D	E	N	1975	86748
0069	S	D	R	N	1973	54395
0069	S	D	E	N	1973	54396
0104	S	S	E	N	1974	84584
0104	S	D	R	L	1974	87288
0104	S	D	E	L	1975	87289
0105	S	D	E	N	1966	64258
0105	S	D	E	N	1975	86757
0105	S	D	E	N	1975	86763
0106	S	D	E	N	1971	61706
0106	S	D	E	L	1966	64257
0106	S	D	E	N	1966	64258
0106	S	S	E	N	1966	64258
0196	S	D	E	N	1975	86757
0295	S	D	R	N	1973	50367
0295	S	D	E	N	1973	50368
0295	S	D	E	N	1972	63787
0295	S	T	E	N	1972	63787
0331	S	D	R	L	1973	49848
0331	S	D	E	L	1973	54526
0331	S	T	R	L	1972	60701
0331	S	T	E	L	1972	60702
0331	S	T	R	L	1974	63054
0331	S	T	E	L	1975	63055
0431	S	D	R	N	1973	52856
0431	S	D	E	N	1973	52857
8032	S	D	E	N	1975	86757
8033	S	D	E	N	1975	86757
8042	S	D	E	L	1973	51069
8042	S	D	E	N	1973	52184
8045	S	T	R	N	1971	49758
8045	S	D	R	L	1973	50295
8045	S	D	E	L	1973	50296
8045	S	S	R	N	1972	62298
8045	S	T	E	N	1973	62299
8045	S	D	E	N	1972	63966
8045	S	D	E	N	1962	65955
8045	S	T	E	N	1962	65955
8045	S	T	G	N	1975	91993
8108	S	S	E	N	1966	66068
104-8109	T	T	R	N	1975	101557
8109	T	T	E	N	1975	101558
8153	S	D	E	N	1974	53989
8159	S	D	E	N	1975	66701
8159	S	T	E	N	1975	66701
8257	D	D	R	N	1970	52334
8258	D	D	R	N	1970	52334
8296	S	D	E	N	1974	62044
8426	S	D	E	N	1974	62044
8447	S	D	R	N	1974	66760
8447	S	T	R	N	1974	66760
8447	S	D	E	N	1975	66761
8447	S	T	E	N	1975	66761
106-0004	S	D	E	N	1975	80826
0004	S	D	E	N	1975	86757
0006	D	D	E	L	1975	66689
0006	D	T	E	L	1975	66689
0006	S	D	E	N	1974	54604
0006	S	D	E	L	1970	59675
0006	S	D	E	N	1975	63328
0006	S	D	E	N	1966	64258
0006	S	S	E	N	1966	64258
0006	S	S	E	N	1975	65501
0006	S	D	E	N	1967	74601
0006	S	T	E	N	1967	74601
0006	S	D	E	N	1975	86757
0006	S	D	E	N	1975	86763
0006	S	S	E	N	1975	91730
0006	T	D	E	N	1974	54347
0024	D	T	E	N	1974	62758
0024	S	D	E	L	1970	59675
0024	S	D	R	N	1974	61934
0024	S	D	E	N	1974	61935
0024	S	T	E	N	1971	64069
0024	S	D	E	N	1966	64258
0024	S	S	E	N	1966	64258
0024	S	T	E	N	1973	65271
0024	S	S	E	N	1975	65501
0024	S	D	E	N	1971	83801
0024	S	T	E	N	1971	83801
0024	S	D	E	N	1975	86757
0024	S	D	E	N	1975	86763
0024	S	S	E	N	1975	91730
0024	T	D	E	N	1974	54347
0024	T	T	O	N	1965	61141
0026	D	D	E	N	1975	68675
0026	S	D	R	N	1973	55197
0026	S	D	E	N	1974	55198
0026	S	D	R	L	1974	87288
0026	S	D	E	L	1975	87289
0026	S	D	R	N	1974	92220
0026	S	T	R	N	1974	92220
0026	S	D	E	N	1974	92221
0026	S	T	E	N	1974	92221
0026	S	S	E	N	1974	98834
0031	S	D	E	N	1974	65241
0035	D	D	E	N	1974	53634
0035	S	D	R	N	1973	55223
0035	S	S	R	N	1973	55223
0035	S	D	E	N	1974	55224
0035	S	S	E	N	1974	55224
0035	S	D	R	N	1971	62097
0035	S	S	R	N	1971	62098
0035	S	D	E	N	1975	63320
0035	S	S	E	N	1975	63320
0035	S	D	E	N	1972	63787
0035	S	T	E	N	1972	63787
0035	S	D	E	N	1971	64880
0035	S	D	R	N	1968	65348
0035	S	D	E	N	1969	65349
0035	S	S	E	N	1971	67085
0035	S	S	E	N	1965	87702
0035	S	S	E	N	1971	87887
0035	S	D	R	N	1974	90369
0036	S	D	E	N	1973	51007
0036	S	D	E	N	1974	61388
0036	S	S	E	N	1974	61388
0047	S	S	E	N	1975	91289
0057	T	S	E	N	1968	85433
0060	S	D	R	N	1973	54395
0060	S	D	E	N	1973	54396
0081	S	D	E	N	1975	65487
0081	S	S	E	N	1975	65487
0081	S	D	E	N	1975	80826
0095	S	D	E	N	1975	65487
0104	S	T	E	N	1973	52061
0125	S	D	E	N	1975	90034
0125	S	S	E	N	1964	93287
0127	S	T	E	N	1972	55728
0157	S	D	E	N	1972	49632
0157	S	S	O	N	1971	67877
0157	S	T	O	N	1971	67877
0157	S	D	E	N	1975	86748
0158	S	D	E	N	1972	49630
0158	S	D	E	N	1973	49709
0158	S	D	E	N	1973	50532
0158	S	D	E	N	1973	51007
0158	S	D	E	N	1974	61388
0158	S	S	E	N	1974	61388
0158	T	D	E	N	1961	64344
106-0159	S	D	E	N	1966	64258
0159	S	D	E	N	1970	83792
0159	S	T	E	N	1970	83792
0159	S	D	E	N	1975	86757
0159	S	D	E	N	1975	86763
0159	S	S	E	N	1975	91730
0159	T	D	E	N	1974	54347
0165	S	D	E	N	1973	49665
0165	S	D	E	L	1970	59675
0165	S	D	E	N	1966	64258
0165	S	S	E	N	1966	64258
0165	S	D	E	N	1975	86757
0203	S	D	E	N	1973	49665
0203	S	D	E	N	1966	64258
0226	S	S	E	N	1974	94480
0237	S	D	E	N	1966	64258
0237	S	S	E	N	1975	86763
0238	S	D	E	N	1973	60585
0238	S	T	E	N	1973	60585
0238	S	D	E	N	1966	64258
0309	S	D	E	N	1974	58023
0363	D	D	E	N	1974	60290
0363	S	D	E	N	1973	50911
0363	S	S	E	L	1972	52975
0363	S	S	E	N	1972	53388
0363	S	D	E	N	1974	53607
0363	S	T	E	N	1974	53614
0363	S	T	R	N	1973	54970
0363	S	T	E	N	1974	54971
0363	S	S	E	N	1974	57323
0363	S	D	E	N	1973	57560
0363	S	S	E	N	1973	57560
0363	S	D	E	N	1970	59694
0363	S	T	E	L	1974	61361
0363	S	T	R	N	1974	61970
0363	S	S	E	N	1963	64232
0363	S	T	E	N	1965	64273
0363	S	S	E	N	1967	66156
0363	S	S	E	N	1972	87823
0363	S	T	E	N	1975	93350
0363	T	S	R	L	1966	75862
0363	T	S	R	N	1966	75862
0363	T	T	R	L	1966	75862
0363	T	T	R	N	1966	75862
0363	T	D	E	N	1966	76050
0363	T	S	E	L	1966	76050
0363	T	S	E	N	1966	76050
0363	T	T	E	L	1966	76050
0385	S	S	E	N	1974	98834
0508	S	D	E	N	1975	86757
0590	S	D	E	N	1975	86757
0941	S	D	R	N	1973	52916
0941	S	D	E	N	1974	52917
0941	S	D	E	N	1972	53335
1085	S	D	E	N	1974	60664
1204	S	D	R	N	1974	77917
1204	S	T	R	N	1974	77917
1204	S	D	E	N	1974	94485
1204	S	T	E	N	1974	94485
1256	S	D	E	N	1974	101330
1256	S	S	E	N	1974	101330
1287	S	D	E	N	1973	50999
8001	S	D	O	N	1973	51968
8001	S	D	E	N	1973	57135
8001	S	D	O	N	1973	58530
8008	S	D	R	N	1974	77941
8008	S	T	R	N	1974	77941
8008	S	D	E	N	1974	94517
8008	S	T	E	N	1974	94517
8014	S	S	E	N	1960	65977
8040	S	D	E	N	1973	52092
8040	S	S	E	L	1972	52975
8040	S	S	E	N	1972	53388
8040	S	D	E	N	1974	53607
8040	S	D	E	N	1974	62277
8040	S	S	E	N	1963	87710
8040	T	S	E	N	1971	60964
8041	D	D	E	N	1974	54034
8041	D	T	E	N	1974	54034
8041	D	D	E	N	1974	62323
8041	S	D	E	N	1973	49684
8041	S	D	E	N	1973	50507
8041	S	T	E	N	1973	50507
8041	S	D	E	N	1973	50925
8041	S	D	E	N	1973	50928
8041	S	D	E	N	1973	52092
8041	S	D	R	N	1973	52318
8041	S	D	E	N	1974	53607
8041	S	D	E	N	1974	53610
8041	S	D	E	N	1972	63632
8041	S	S	E	N	1967	68371
8041	S	D	R	N	1971	76463
8041	S	D	R	N	1974	90369
8041	S	D	E	N	1971	91585
8041	S	D	E	N	1975	94613
8041	T	S	E	N	1967	68371
8045	S	D	E	N	1975	86757
8047	S	D	R	N	1974	86642
8047	S	T	R	N	1974	86642
8047	S	D	E	N	1975	92632
8047	S	T	E	N	1975	92632

Phys. State: **A.** Amorphous; **C.** Superconductive; **D.** Doped; **F.** Fibrous or Whisker; **G.** Gas; **I.** Ionized or Plasma; **L.** Liquid; **P.** Powder or Particle; **S.** Solid; **T.** Thin Film
Subject: **D.** Data; **E.** Experiment; **S.** Survey (Review, Compendium, etc.); **T.** Theory
Language: **E.** English; **F.** French; **G.** German; **O.** Other Languages; **R.** Russian
Temperature: **L.** Low (0 to 75K); **N.** Normal (75 to 1273K); **H.** High (above 1273K)

Substance Number	Phys. State	Subject	Language	Temperature	Year	EPIC Number
106-8048	S	D	E	N	1975	86757
8072	S	D	E	N	1973	52956
8123	S	D	E	N	1974	90281
8127	S	D	E	N	1974	54033
8127	S	S	E	N	1972	87823
8128	D	T	R	N	1975	95776
8128	D	T	E	N	1975	95777
8128	S	T	R	N	1973	55014
8128	S	T	E	N	1974	55015
8128	S	S	E	N	1967	68371
8128	S	S	E	N	1972	87823
8128	T	S	E	N	1972	87823
8129	S	D	E	N	1974	58823
8129	S	T	E	N	1974	58823
8132	S	S	E	N	1972	87823
8134	S	S	E	N	1972	87823
8143	S	D	R	N	1974	86642
8143	S	T	R	N	1974	86642
8143	S	D	E	N	1975	92632
8143	S	T	E	N	1975	92632
8154	S	D	R	N	1973	50068
8154	S	D	E	N	1973	51422
8155	S	D	R	N	1973	50068
8155	S	D	E	N	1973	51422
8200	S	D	R	N	1974	77917
8200	S	T	R	N	1974	77917
8200	S	D	E	N	1974	94485
8200	S	T	E	N	1974	94485
8209	S	D	E	N	1974	58823
8209	S	T	E	N	1974	58823
8234	S	D	R	N	1973	51561
8234	S	D	E	N	1974	53692
8262	S	D	R	N	1974	86642
8262	S	T	R	N	1974	86642
8262	S	D	E	N	1975	92632
8262	S	T	E	N	1975	92632
8289	S	D	E	N	1973	51864
8289	S	D	E	N	1974	62044
8290	T	D	E	N	1973	51876
8296	S	D	R	N	1973	52275
8299	D	D	E	N	1974	58823
8299	D	T	E	N	1974	58823
8299	S	D	E	N	1974	58823
8299	S	T	E	N	1974	58823
8312	S	T	E	N	1970	75905
8388	S	D	E	N	1973	53644
8388	S	D	R	N	1974	77941
8388	S	T	R	N	1974	77941
8388	S	D	E	N	1974	94517
8388	S	T	E	N	1974	94517
8403	S	T	E	N	1968	75990
8438	S	T	E	N	1974	93998
8521	S	D	R	N	1974	86642
8521	S	T	R	N	1974	86642
8521	S	D	E	N	1975	92632
8521	S	T	E	N	1975	92632
8545	S	D	R	N	1974	86642
8545	S	T	R	N	1974	86642
8545	S	D	E	N	1975	92632
8545	S	T	E	N	1975	92632
8611	S	D	R	N	1974	77917
8611	S	T	R	N	1974	77917
8611	S	D	E	N	1974	94485
8611	S	T	E	N	1974	94485
8671	S	D	E	N	1974	94147
8751	S	D	E	N	1974	94145
8751	S	T	E	N	1974	94145
8756	S	D	R	N	1974	86642
8756	S	T	R	N	1974	86642
8756	S	D	E	N	1975	92632
8756	S	T	E	N	1975	92632
8757	S	D	R	N	1974	86642
8757	S	T	R	N	1974	86642
8757	S	D	E	N	1975	92632
8757	S	T	E	N	1975	92632
8799	S	D	R	N	1974	77917
8799	S	T	R	N	1974	77917
8799	S	D	E	N	1974	94485
8799	S	T	E	N	1974	94485
8817	G	D	E	H	1974	65887
8817	G	S	E	H	1974	65887
8817	G	T	E	H	1974	65887
8847	S	T	E	N	1968	75990
8848	S	T	E	N	1968	75990
108-8047	S	D	E	N	1975	86757
109-0025	S	D	E	L	1973	50887
0025	S	D	E	N	1973	50887
0025	S	D	E	N	1971	65043
0025	S	S	E	N	1971	65043
0025	S	S	E	N	1975	91600
8019	S	T	E	N	1974	62347
8019	S	D	E	N	1971	65043
8019	S	S	E	N	1971	65043
8019	S	S	E	N	1975	91600
8020	S	D	E	N	1971	65043
8020	S	S	E	N	1971	65043
8020	S	S	E	N	1970	75905
8020	S	S	E	N	1975	91600
8021	S	S	E	N	1975	91600
109-8078	S	D	E	N	1975	86757
8079	S	D	E	N	1975	86757
8082	S	D	E	N	1975	63304
8096	S	D	R	N	1974	86642
8096	S	T	R	N	1974	86642
8096	S	D	E	N	1975	92632
8096	S	T	E	N	1975	92632
110-0010	D	D	E	N	1973	88617
0011	S	D	E	N	1974	65241
0021	S	S	E	N	1974	98834
0023	D	D	E	N	1975	68675
0023	S	D	E	N	1976	101192
0023	S	S	E	N	1976	101192
0023	S	T	E	N	1976	101192
0024	S	D	E	N	1973	50151
0024	S	D	E	N	1973	50545
0024	S	D	E	N	1974	54604
0024	S	D	E	N	1974	55252
0024	S	D	E	N	1973	60594
0024	S	D	E	N	1973	60623
0024	S	D	E	N	1975	63322
0024	S	T	E	N	1975	63322
0024	S	D	E	N	1966	64258
0024	S	S	E	N	1975	65501
0024	S	D	E	N	1967	85322
0024	S	D	E	N	1975	86757
0024	S	S	E	N	1975	86763
0024	S	S	E	N	1975	91730
0024	S	S	E	N	1975	91733
0024	S	D	E	N	1976	102400
0025	S	D	E	N	1972	53113
0030	S	D	E	N	1975	80826
0036	S	D	E	N	1972	49910
0036	S	D	E	N	1966	64258
0036	S	D	E	N	1975	86757
0036	S	S	E	N	1975	86763
0036	S	S	E	N	1975	91730
0037	S	D	E	N	1974	54604
0037	S	D	E	N	1966	64258
0037	S	D	E	N	1975	86757
0037	S	S	E	N	1975	86763
0037	S	S	E	N	1975	91730
0061	S	D	E	N	1966	64258
0061	S	S	E	N	1971	75192
0061	S	D	E	N	1975	86757
0061	S	S	E	N	1975	86763
0132	S	S	E	N	1974	84584
0132	S	D	R	L	1974	87288
0132	S	D	E	L	1975	87289
0194	S	D	E	N	1974	58050
0269	S	D	E	N	1973	50787
0279	D	D	E	N	1975	68675
0299	S	D	E	N	1974	57306
8015	S	D	R	N	1974	86642
8015	S	T	R	N	1974	86642
8015	S	D	E	N	1975	92632
8015	S	T	E	N	1975	92632
8020	S	S	E	N	1974	98834
8041	S	D	E	N	1972	49921
8063	S	D	R	N	1974	86642
8063	S	T	R	N	1974	86642
8063	S	D	E	N	1975	92632
8063	S	T	E	N	1975	92632
8064	S	D	E	N	1973	50790
8064	S	D	R	N	1974	86642
8064	S	T	R	N	1974	86642
8064	S	D	E	N	1975	92632
8064	S	T	E	N	1975	92632
8165	S	D	E	N	1975	86742
8165	S	S	E	N	1975	86742
111-0006	S	D	E	N	1971	65044
0008	D	D	E	N	1973	52782
0008	D	T	E	N	1974	53927
0008	D	D	E	N	1973	57403
0008	D	T	E	N	1969	75184
0008	S	D	E	N	1973	50925
0008	S	D	E	N	1973	50928
0008	S	S	E	L	1973	51760
0008	S	S	E	N	1972	53227
0008	S	D	E	N	1974	53607
0008	S	D	E	N	1974	53610
0008	S	D	E	N	1974	54081
0008	S	D	E	N	1973	55161
0008	S	D	E	N	1974	55721
0008	S	D	E	N	1975	59578
0008	S	T	E	N	1973	60575
0008	S	D	R	N	1973	62100
0008	S	S	E	N	1972	66310
0008	S	D	R	N	1974	81026
0008	S	D	E	N	1975	86754
0008	S	D	R	N	1975	86831
0008	S	D	E	N	1975	86832
0008	S	S	E	N	1962	87669
0008	S	S	E	N	1965	87703
0008	S	S	E	N	1972	87889
0008	S	D	E	N	1973	89715
0008	S	S	E	N	1975	91218
0008	S	D	E	N	1975	92633
0021	S	D	E	N	1972	53466
111-0021	S	S	E	N	1973	62246
0021	S	D	E	N	1974	62548
0021	S	S	R	N	1974	66446
0021	S	T	R	N	1974	66446
0021	S	S	E	N	1974	66447
0021	S	T	E	N	1974	66447
0021	S	S	E	N	1975	91290
0050	S	D	E	N	1973	56407
0050	S	T	E	N	1973	56408
0050	S	D	E	N	1974	58030
0050	S	D	E	N	1974	62064
0050	S	T	E	N	1974	62064
0052	S	D	E	N	1975	86757
8002	D	D	E	N	1970	68209
8002	S	D	E	L	1973	50578
8002	S	D	E	N	1973	50578
8002	S	D	E	N	1973	50925
8002	S	D	E	L	1973	53561
8002	S	D	E	N	1974	53607
8002	S	T	E	N	1973	60627
8002	S	S	E	N	1969	61512
8002	S	S	F	N	1973	63636
8002	S	S	E	N	1961	64497
8002	S	T	E	N	1961	64497
8002	S	S	R	N	1974	64959
8002	S	S	E	N	1972	66310
8002	S	S	E	N	1975	66685
8002	S	T	E	N	1975	66685
8002	S	S	E	N	1975	68432
8002	S	D	E	N	1968	74648
8002	S	S	E	N	1972	87889
8002	S	D	R	N	1974	90369
8002	S	S	E	N	1972	97249
8007	S	S	E	N	1973	56247
8007	S	D	E	N	1973	56333
8007	S	D	E	N	1974	58436
8007	S	D	E	N	1974	63373
8007	S	D	E	N	1974	90915
8007	S	S	E	N	1975	96246
8021	A	D	E	N	1973	49710
8021	A	D	E	N	1972	53266
8021	A	D	E	N	1976	99925
8021	A	T	E	N	1976	99925
8021	S	D	E	N	1973	49710
8021	S	T	E	N	1971	67166
8021	T	D	E	N	1972	53266
8021	T	D	E	N	1976	99925
8021	T	T	L	N	1976	99925
8026	S	D	E	N	1973	55161
8026	S	D	E	N	1975	86754
8026	S	S	E	N	1972	87889
8026	S	S	E	N	1975	91218
8031	S	T	E	N	1973	52098
8031	S	S	E	N	1972	87889
8037	S	D	E	N	1972	65879
8037	S	T	F	N	1962	65958
8055	S	D	R	N	1973	52275
8058	C	D	E	L	1974	61152
8058	S	D	R	N	1973	52275
8058	S	D	E	N	1975	90033
8071	S	D	E	N	1971	65043
8075	T	D	E	N	1971	53513
8078	T	D	E	N	1971	53513
8087	D	D	E	N	1974	58050
8124	C	D	E	L	1974	61152
8151	S	D	E	N	1970	66928
112-0001	G	D	E	N	1973	53558
0001	S	D	E	N	1973	50934
0001	S	T	E	N	1973	50934
0025	S	D	E	N	1975	63329
0025	S	T	E	N	1975	63329
0098	S	D	E	N	1975	63329
0098	S	T	E	N	1975	63329
0402	S	D	E	N	1973	57560
0402	S	S	E	N	1973	57560
0569	S	D	E	N	1973	51862
0698	S	S	E	N	1971	65073
8020	S	D	R	N	1973	51281
8020	S	D	E	N	1973	52092
8020	S	T	E	N	1974	54086
8025	D	T	E	N	1976	101450
8025	S	D	E	N	1973	49739
8025	S	D	E	N	1973	50507
8025	S	T	E	N	1973	50507
8025	S	D	E	N	1973	52092
8025	S	T	E	N	1974	53599
8025	S	D	E	N	1974	53607
8025	S	T	R	L	1974	63000
8025	S	T	E	L	1974	63001
8025	T	T	E	N	1974	66692
8032	S	D	R	N	1973	51281
8044	S	D	E	N	1971	75781
8044	S	T	E	N	1971	75781
8053	S	D	E	N	1973	53558
8075	S	D	E	N	1975	86757
8096	S	D	R	N	1974	86642
8096	S	T	R	N	1974	86642
8096	S	D	E	N	1975	92632
8096	S	T	E	N	1975	92632

Phys. State: **A.** Amorphous; **C.** Superconductive; **D.** Doped; **F.** Fibrous or Whisker; **G.** Gas; **I.** Ionized or Plasma; **L.** Liquid; **P.** Powder or Particle; **S.** Solid; **T.** Thin Film
Subject: **D.** Data; **E.** Experiment; **S.** Survey (Review, Compendium, etc.); **T.** Theory
Language: **E.** English; **F.** French; **G.** German; **O.** Other Languages; **R.** Russian
Temperature: **L.** Low (0 to 75K); **N.** Normal (75 to 1273K); **H.** High (above 1273K)

Substance Number	Phys. State	Subject	Language	Temperature	Year	EPIC Number
114-0001	D	D	E	L	1975	66689
0001	S	D	E	N	1973	50165
0001	S	D	E	N	1974	54604
0001	S	D	E	L	1970	59675
0001	S	S	E	N	1974	61390
0001	S	D	E	N	1966	64258
0001	S	S	E	N	1966	64258
0001	S	S	E	N	1969	85421
0001	S	D	E	N	1975	86757
0002	S	D	E	N	1973	50165
0002	S	D	E	N	1966	64258
0002	S	D	E	N	1975	86757
0006	S	D	E	N	1974	54089
0006	S	T	R	L	1973	55403
0006	S	T	E	L	1974	57814
0006	S	D	E	N	1974	63373
0006	S	S	E	N	1975	91289
0009	S	D	E	N	1973	50165
0009	S	D	E	N	1966	64258
0009	S	D	E	N	1975	86757
0010	S	D	E	N	1966	64258
0010	S	D	E	N	1975	86757
0017	S	D	E	N	1973	50925
0017	S	D	E	N	1974	53607
0017	S	D	E	N	1973	55161
0017	S	S	E	N	1972	66310
0017	S	D	E	N	1975	86754
0017	S	S	E	N	1962	87660
0017	S	S	E	N	1972	87889
0017	S	S	E	N	1975	91218
0017	T	D	E	N	1974	65107
0055	S	D	E	N	1975	86748
0060	S	D	E	N	1973	53574
0060	S	T	E	N	1973	53574
0060	T	D	E	N	1973	55876
8001	D	D	E	N	1973	54670
8001	D	T	R	N	1972	61908
8001	D	S	E	N	1975	87741
8001	S	D	E	N	1973	49684
8001	S	D	R	L	1973	50061
8001	S	D	R	N	1973	50646
8001	S	D	E	N	1973	50925
8001	S	D	E	N	1973	50928
8001	S	D	E	L	1973	51417
8001	S	D	R	N	1973	51558
8001	S	S	R	N	1973	51558
8001	S	T	E	N	1973	52025
8001	S	D	R	N	1973	52318
8001	S	S	E	N	1972	53299
8001	S	D	E	N	1974	53607
8001	S	D	E	N	1974	53610
8001	S	D	E	N	1973	53689
8001	S	S	E	N	1973	53689
8001	S	S	E	N	1974	54094
8001	S	T	R	N	1973	54970
8001	S	T	E	N	1974	54971
8001	S	S	E	N	1974	55241
8001	S	T	E	N	1974	55241
8001	S	T	E	N	1972	55728
8001	S	T	E	N	1970	61493
8001	S	T	E	N	1974	64457
8001	S	D	R	L	1974	65371
8001	S	T	R	L	1974	65371
8001	S	D	E	L	1975	65372
8001	S	T	E	L	1975	65372
8001	S	S	O	N	1966	66022
8001	S	S	E	N	1967	66023
8001	S	S	E	N	1972	66310
8001	S	S	E	N	1975	66685
8001	S	T	E	N	1975	66685
8001	S	D	E	N	1975	87172
8001	S	S	E	N	1963	87679
8001	S	S	E	L	1965	87781
8001	S	S	E	N	1965	87781
8001	S	S	E	N	1971	87884
8001	S	S	E	N	1972	87889
8001	T	D	E	N	1973	54670
8001	T	S	E	N	1965	87781
8010	S	D	R	N	1972	63472
8010	S	D	E	N	1972	65150
8041	S	T	R	N	1972	49568
8054	S	D	E	N	1972	53295
8066	S	D	R	N	1972	56997
116-0017	S	D	E	N	1972	49921
0017	S	D	E	N	1973	51208
8003	S	D	R	N	1974	77941
8003	S	T	R	N	1974	77941
8003	S	D	E	N	1974	94517
8003	S	T	E	N	1974	94517
8016	S	D	E	N	1972	49921
8026	S	D	E	N	1974	53644
8026	S	D	R	N	1974	77941
8026	S	T	R	N	1974	77941
8026	S	D	E	N	1974	94517
8026	S	T	E	N	1974	94517
118-0008	S	D	E	N	1975	86757
0026	S	D	R	N	1974	86642
0026	S	T	R	N	1974	86642
0026	S	D	E	N	1975	92632
118-0026	S	T	E	N	1975	92632
0037	D	S	E	N	1974	62740
8005	S	D	E	N	1972	53295
8071	S	D	E	N	1975	86757
8092	S	D	R	N	1974	86642
8092	S	T	R	N	1974	86642
8092	S	D	E	N	1975	92632
8092	S	T	E	N	1975	92632
8097	S	D	R	N	1974	86642
8097	S	T	R	N	1974	86642
8097	S	D	E	N	1975	92632
8097	S	T	E	N	1975	92632
8098	S	D	R	N	1974	86642
8098	S	T	R	N	1974	86642
8098	S	D	E	N	1975	92632
8098	S	T	E	N	1975	92632
119-0001	C	D	E	L	1975	89571
0001	S	D	E	N	1973	50539
0001	S	D	E	N	1973	51862
0001	S	T	E	N	1973	57400
0001	S	D	E	N	1971	75337
0001	S	T	E	N	1973	75570
0001	S	D	E	L	1972	101321
0001	S	S	E	L	1972	101321
0002	S	D	E	N	1973	53583
0002	S	D	E	N	1974	60673
0002	S	S	E	N	1974	60673
0002	S	T	E	N	1974	60673
0002	S	D	E	N	1974	62065
0002	S	T	E	N	1974	62065
0002	S	D	E	N	1974	65241
0002	S	D	E	N	1975	86757
0002	S	S	E	N	1969	87723
0008	S	D	E	N	1975	80826
0015	S	D	E	N	1974	65241
0041	S	D	E	N	1973	51646
0064	S	D	E	N	1975	86757
8002	S	D	E	N	1972	65879
8002	S	T	F	N	1962	65958
8008	S	D	E	N	1975	86757
8009	S	D	E	N	1972	65879
8015	S	D	R	N	1974	86642
8015	S	T	R	N	1974	86642
8015	S	D	E	N	1975	92632
8015	S	T	E	N	1975	92632
8016	S	D	R	N	1974	86642
8016	S	T	R	N	1974	86642
8016	S	D	E	N	1975	92632
8016	S	T	E	N	1975	92632
8019	S	T	R	N	1974	60409
8019	S	T	E	N	1974	60410
8019	S	D	R	N	1974	86642
8019	S	T	R	N	1974	86642
8019	S	D	E	N	1975	92632
8019	S	T	E	N	1975	92632
8031	S	D	R	N	1974	86642
8031	S	T	R	N	1974	86642
8031	S	D	E	N	1975	92632
8031	S	T	E	N	1975	92632
8057	S	D	E	N	1972	65879
8058	S	D	R	N	1974	86642
8058	S	T	R	N	1974	86642
8058	S	D	E	N	1975	92632
8058	S	T	E	N	1975	92632
8080	S	T	E	N	1973	75570
8082	S	D	R	N	1974	86642
8082	S	T	R	N	1974	86642
8082	S	D	E	N	1975	92632
8082	S	T	E	N	1975	92632
8091	S	T	E	N	1970	75905
8112	S	D	R	N	1974	86642
8112	S	T	R	N	1974	86642
8112	S	D	E	N	1975	92632
8112	S	T	E	N	1975	92632
8113	S	D	R	N	1974	86642
8113	S	T	R	N	1974	86642
8113	S	D	E	N	1975	92632
8113	S	T	E	N	1975	92632
120-0001	A	S	E	N	1971	65066
0001	S	T	E	N	1968	53357
0001	S	S	E	N	1975	65487
0006	S	D	E	N	1973	51017
0006	S	D	E	N	1974	58051
0006	S	S	E	N	1974	58051
0006	S	D	E	N	1974	58052
0023	S	S	E	N	1964	93287
0035	S	S	E	N	1974	94480
0045	S	S	E	N	1974	58023
0045	S	D	G	N	1971	66334
0045	S	D	E	N	1975	80826
0056	S	D	E	N	1975	86757
0166	S	D	E	N	1975	86757
0172	S	D	E	N	1973	50539
0211	S	D	E	N	1975	86757
8006	S	D	R	N	1972	50470
8024	S	S	E	N	1971	87885
8042	S	D	E	N	1973	51862
8042	S	D	E	N	1971	75337
8115	S	D	E	N	1975	86757
120-8116	S	D	E	N	1975	86757
8117	S	D	E	N	1975	86757
8118	S	D	E	N	1975	86757
8119	S	D	E	N	1975	86757
8147	S	D	R	N	1974	86642
8147	S	T	R	N	1974	86642
8147	S	D	E	N	1975	92632
8147	S	T	E	N	1975	92632
8167	S	D	R	N	1974	86642
8167	S	T	R	N	1974	86642
8167	S	D	E	N	1975	92632
8167	S	T	E	N	1975	92632
8178	S	D	E	N	1974	62044
122-0003	S	D	E	N	1974	62048
0003	S	T	E	N	1974	62048
0005	D	T	E	N	1973	50756
0005	D	E	E	N	1972	53163
0005	S	S	E	N	1972	53166
0008	S	D	E	N	1974	62048
0008	S	T	E	N	1974	62048
0009	S	T	E	N	1973	55905
0009	S	D	E	N	1974	58803
0009	S	S	E	N	1973	60634
0009	T	D	R	N	1972	51298
0014	S	D	E	N	1973	50516
0014	S	D	E	N	1974	54593
0014	S	T	E	N	1975	86761
0017	T	D	E	N	1974	62032
0023	D	D	E	H	1974	53916
0023	D	D	E	N	1974	53916
0023	S	D	E	N	1973	52075
0023	S	D	E	N	1974	53607
0023	S	D	E	H	1974	53916
0023	S	D	E	N	1974	53916
0023	S	D	E	N	1974	62493
0023	S	D	E	N	1975	63293
0023	S	D	R	N	1974	81407
0023	S	D	E	N	1974	95806
0023	S	S	E	N	1974	99215
0026	S	D	E	N	1973	57573
0026	S	D	E	N	1975	80826
0026	S	D	E	N	1974	94480
0026	S	S	E	N	1974	94480
0026	S	T	E	N	1974	94480
0030	D	D	E	N	1974	90339
0030	S	D	E	N	1972	49921
0030	S	D	E	N	1973	60591
0030	S	T	E	N	1973	60591
0031	S	D	E	N	1975	86757
0046	S	D	E	N	1975	80826
0047	D	D	E	L	1973	52020
0047	S	S	E	N	1970	75833
0047	S	S	E	N	1975	86761
0047	S	T	E	N	1975	86761
0084	S	S	E	N	1973	55968
0112	S	D	E	N	1972	49907
0112	S	D	E	N	1973	50522
0112	S	S	E	N	1972	53261
0112	S	D	E	N	1972	56074
0112	S	D	E	N	1973	60633
0112	T	D	E	L	1972	53271
8045	S	D	E	N	1968	64538
8045	S	S	E	N	1968	64538
123-0003	S	S	E	N	1972	53200
0003	S	D	E	N	1973	53786
0003	S	S	E	N	1966	68361
0048	S	D	R	N	1974	77917
0048	S	T	R	N	1974	77917
0048	S	D	E	N	1974	94485
0048	S	T	E	N	1974	94485
8017	D	D	E	N	1974	90402
8017	S	T	E	N	1973	52461
8017	S	D	E	N	1973	53786
8017	S	D	E	N	1975	63284
8017	S	D	E	N	1975	63285
8017	S	S	E	N	1975	63285
8017	S	T	E	N	1975	63285
8017	S	S	E	N	1972	87824
8018	S	D	E	N	1973	51070
8018	S	D	E	N	1974	53736
8018	S	S	E	N	1973	53786
8018	S	D	E	N	1972	59070
8018	S	D	E	N	1975	63284
8018	S	D	E	N	1975	63285
8018	S	S	E	N	1975	63285
8018	S	T	E	N	1975	63285
8018	S	S	E	N	1972	63827
8018	S	D	E	N	1971	65045
8018	S	S	E	N	1970	68114
8018	S	S	E	N	1972	87824
8039	S	D	R	N	1973	50066
8039	S	D	E	N	1973	51420
8039	S	T	E	N	1973	52461
8039	S	S	E	N	1972	53321
8039	S	D	E	N	1976	102168
8051	S	D	E	N	1974	61383
8074	S	S	E	N	1972	87824
8104	S	T	R	N	1974	77917
8104	S	D	E	N	1974	94485

Phys. State: **A.** Amorphous; **C.** Superconductive; **D.** Doped; **F.** Fibrous or Whisker; **G.** Gas; **I.** Ionized or Plasma; **L.** Liquid; **P.** Powder or Particle; **S.** Solid; **T.** Thin Film
Subject: **D.** Data; **E.** Experiment; **S.** Survey (Review, Compendium, etc.); **T.** Theory
Language: **E.** English; **F.** French; **G.** German; **O.** Other Languages; **R.** Russian
Temperature: **L.** Low (0 to 75K); **N.** Normal (75 to 1273K); **H.** High (above 1273K)

Substance Number	Phys. State	Subject	Language	Temperature	Year	EPIC Number
123-8104	S	T	E	N	1974	94485
125-8014	S	D	R	N	1974	77941
8014	S	T	R	N	1974	77941
8014	S	D	E	N	1974	94517
8014	S	T	E	N	1974	94517
8039	S	D	R	N	1974	86642
8039	S	T	R	N	1974	86642
8039	S	D	E	N	1975	92632
8039	S	T	E	N	1975	92632
126-0002	S	D	E	N	1973	57406
0004	S	D	E	N	1973	50898
0004	S	D	E	N	1974	53598
0005	D	T	E	N	1970	64857
0005	S	D	E	N	1973	50507
0005	S	T	E	N	1973	50507
0005	S	D	E	N	1973	50925
0005	S	D	E	N	1974	53607
0005	S	S	E	N	1974	53610
0005	S	D	R	N	1973	55207
0005	S	D	E	N	1974	55208
0005	S	T	E	N	1973	57655
0005	S	T	E	N	1973	57737
0005	S	D	E	N	1975	63293
0005	S	D	E	N	1975	87171
0005	S	S	E	N	1963	87711
0005	S	S	E	N	1972	87823
0005	S	T	E	N	1975	93580
0005	T	S	F	N	1974	61449
0005	T	T	F	N	1974	86060
0017	S	D	E	N	1975	86757
0025	S	D	E	N	1973	57706
0025	S	S	E	N	1975	91600
0038	S	D	E	N	1973	51862
0038	S	S	E	N	1975	65484
0038	S	D	E	N	1975	66668
0038	S	S	E	N	1975	66668
0038	S	T	E	N	1975	66668
0038	S	S	E	L	1972	70535
0038	S	S	E	N	1972	70535
8020	S	D	R	N	1973	52275
8030	A	D	E	N	1973	57646
8030	T	D	E	N	1973	57646
8032	S	D	E	N	1973	52195
8037	S	S	E	N	1970	68114
8037	T	D	E	N	1972	53416
8038	S	D	R	N	1974	86642
8038	S	T	R	N	1974	86642
8038	S	D	E	N	1975	92632
8038	S	T	E	N	1975	92632
8041	S	D	R	N	1974	86642
8041	S	T	R	N	1974	86642
8041	S	D	E	N	1975	92632
8041	S	T	E	N	1975	92632
8043	S	D	E	N	1974	61369
8043	S	T	E	N	1974	61369
8046	S	D	E	N	1973	50537
8047	C	D	E	L	1974	61152
8047	S	D	R	N	1973	52275
8047	S	D	E	N	1972	53111
8047	S	D	R	N	1974	86642
8047	S	T	R	N	1974	86642
8047	S	D	E	N	1975	92632
8047	S	T	E	N	1975	92632
8052	D	D	E	N	1970	64857
8052	D	T	E	N	1970	64857
8052	D	S	E	L	1966	74595
8052	S	D	E	N	1973	49684
8052	S	D	E	N	1973	50507
8052	S	T	E	N	1973	50507
8052	S	D	E	N	1973	50925
8052	S	D	E	N	1973	50928
8052	S	D	E	N	1972	53099
8052	S	D	E	N	1974	53607
8052	S	S	E	N	1974	53610
8052	S	D	E	N	1973	57560
8052	S	S	E	N	1973	57560
8052	S	D	E	N	1965	64255
8052	S	D	E	N	1971	65042
8052	S	D	E	N	1975	66684
8052	S	T	E	N	1975	66684
8052	S	D	R	N	1974	90369
8052	S	D	E	N	1975	90874
8052	S	S	E	N	1975	90874
8052	S	T	E	N	1975	90874
8055	S	D	E	N	1973	57406
8055	S	D	E	N	1974	63373
8059	S	D	R	N	1973	52563
8059	S	D	E	N	1973	57788
8060	S	D	R	N	1973	51723
8061	S	D	R	N	1974	86642
8061	S	T	R	N	1974	86642
8061	S	D	E	N	1975	92632
8061	S	T	E	N	1975	92632
8062	S	D	R	N	1974	86642
8062	S	T	R	N	1974	86642
8062	S	D	E	N	1975	92632
8062	S	T	E	N	1975	92632
8063	S	D	R	N	1974	86642
8063	S	T	R	N	1974	86642
126-8063	S	D	E	N	1975	92632
8063	S	T	E	N	1975	92632
8065	S	D	R	N	1974	86642
8065	S	T	R	N	1974	86642
8065	S	D	E	N	1975	92632
8065	S	T	E	N	1975	92632
8066	S	D	R	N	1974	86642
8066	S	T	R	N	1974	86642
8066	S	D	E	N	1975	92632
8066	S	T	E	N	1975	92632
8070	S	S	E	N	1975	91600
8079	S	D	E	N	1975	86757
8080	S	D	E	N	1975	86757
8088	S	S	E	N	1975	91600
8089	S	S	E	N	1975	91600
8090	S	D	E	N	1974	53598
8092	S	S	E	N	1975	66668
8098	S	D	E	N	1975	65484
8098	S	D	E	N	1975	66668
8098	S	T	E	N	1975	66668
8108	S	D	R	N	1974	86642
8108	S	T	R	N	1974	86642
8108	S	D	E	N	1975	92632
8108	S	T	E	N	1975	92632
8109	S	D	R	N	1974	86642
8109	S	T	R	N	1974	86642
8109	S	D	E	N	1975	92632
8109	S	T	E	N	1975	92632
8110	S	S	E	N	1975	91600
8147	S	D	R	N	1974	86642
8147	S	T	R	N	1974	86642
8147	S	D	E	N	1975	92632
8147	S	T	E	N	1975	92632
8148	S	D	R	N	1974	86642
8148	S	T	R	N	1974	86642
8148	S	D	E	N	1975	92632
8148	S	T	E	N	1975	92632
8149	S	D	R	N	1974	86642
8149	S	T	R	N	1974	86642
8149	S	D	E	N	1975	92632
8149	S	T	E	N	1975	92632
8150	S	D	R	N	1974	86642
8150	S	T	R	N	1974	86642
8150	S	D	E	N	1975	92632
8150	S	T	E	N	1975	92632
8151	S	D	R	N	1974	86642
8151	S	T	R	N	1974	86642
8151	S	D	E	N	1975	92632
8151	S	T	E	N	1975	92632
8157	S	D	R	N	1974	86642
8157	S	T	R	N	1974	86642
8157	S	D	E	N	1975	92632
8157	S	T	E	N	1975	92632
8158	S	D	R	N	1974	86642
8158	S	T	R	N	1974	86642
8158	S	D	E	N	1975	92632
8158	S	T	E	N	1975	92632
8159	S	D	R	N	1974	86642
8159	S	T	R	N	1974	86642
8159	S	D	E	N	1975	92632
8159	S	T	E	N	1975	92632
127-8004	D	T	E	N	1970	64857
8004	S	D	E	N	1973	50507
8004	S	T	E	N	1973	50507
8004	S	D	E	N	1973	50925
8004	S	D	E	N	1973	52092
8004	S	D	E	N	1974	53607
8004	S	D	E	N	1974	53610
8004	S	T	R	N	1973	54970
8004	S	T	E	N	1974	54971
8004	S	T	R	N	1972	58947
8004	S	S	E	N	1962	87666
8004	T	T	R	N	1972	58947
8010	S	S	E	N	1975	91600
8010	T	T	E	N	1974	53602
8016	S	S	E	N	1975	91600
132-8001	S	D	E	N	1975	90465
8001	S	T	E	N	1975	90465
133-8001	S	D	E	N	1974	54116
8001	S	S	E	N	1974	54116

Phys. State: **A.** Amorphous; **C.** Superconductive; **D.** Doped; **F.** Fibrous or Whisker; **G.** Gas; **I.** Ionized or Plasma; **L.** Liquid; **P.** Powder or Particle; **S.** Solid; **T.** Thin Film
Subject: **D.** Data; **E.** Experiment; **S.** Survey (Review, Compendium, etc.); **T.** Theory
Language: **E.** English; **F.** French; **G.** German; **O.** Other Languages; **R.** Russian
Temperature: **L.** Low (0 to 75K); **N.** Normal (75 to 1273K); **H.** High (above 1273K)

Chapter 5 Effective Mass

Substance Number	Phys. State	Subject	Language	Temperature	Year	EPIC Number
100-0045	S	S	R	N	1974	83872
0055	D	T	E	N	1975	65494
0055	S	E	R	N	1973	50682
0055	S	T	E	N	1973	51050
0055	S	E	E	N	1973	52428
0055	S	T	E	N	1973	52697
0055	S	S	R	N	1971	53278
0055	S	S	E	N	1972	53279
0055	S	T	R	N	1972	54286
0055	S	T	E	N	1972	54287
0055	S	T	E	N	1974	54602
0055	S	S	E	N	1974	57325
0055	S	T	E	N	1974	58033
0055	S	T	E	N	1974	58034
0055	S	T	R	N	1971	59580
0055	S	S	E	N	1970	59681
0055	S	T	E	N	1971	61329
0055	S	D	E	L	1974	61435
0055	S	D	E	N	1974	61435
0055	S	T	E	N	1971	62260
0055	S	S	E	N	1974	64464
0055	S	T	R	N	1974	64576
0055	S	T	E	N	1975	66686
0055	S	S	E	N	1973	67175
0055	S	T	R	N	1969	67765
0055	S	S	E	N	1972	67891
0055	S	S	R	N	1974	83872
0055	S	T	E	N	1974	86907
0055	S	T	R	N	1975	90674
0055	S	S	E	N	1974	91448
0055	T	T	E	N	1975	65496
8003	D	E	E	N	1973	57701
8003	S	S	E	N	1974	54603
8007	S	S	E	N	1969	68271
8007	S	S	E	L	1972	87823
8007	S	S	E	N	1972	87823
8008	S	D	R	N	1971	66993
8008	S	T	R	N	1971	66993
8008	S	T	R	N	1971	66997
8008	S	S	E	L	1971	87884
8008	S	S	E	N	1971	87884
8008	S	S	E	N	1972	87889
8008	T	S	E	N	1969	87821
8038	S	S	E	L	1969	68115
8038	S	S	E	N	1969	68115
8038	S	S	E	N	1972	87824
102-0009	S	D	E	L	1973	50577
0009	S	S	E	N	1972	63847
0010	S	S	E	N	1972	63847
0041	S	S	E	N	1972	87889
0041	T	D	E	N	1974	65107
0041	T	D	E	N	1975	65464
0120	S	D	R	N	1973	50724
0120	S	D	E	N	1973	53025
8001	D	D	R	N	1972	62717
8001	D	D	E	N	1973	65313
8001	D	S	E	N	1962	87668
8001	S	S	E	N	1973	53427
8001	S	D	E	N	1974	58137
8001	S	S	E	N	1972	67891
8001	S	S	E	N	1962	87668
8001	S	S	E	N	1966	87830
8001	S	S	E	N	1971	87884
8018	S	S	E	N	1973	51865
8018	S	T	E	N	1973	51865
8018	S	S	E	N	1972	87889
8018	T	S	E	N	1973	64100
8035	S	S	E	N	1972	51526
8035	S	D	E	N	1965	53356
8035	S	D	E	L	1974	53622
8035	S	D	E	N	1974	53622
8041	D	D	R	N	1972	49888
8041	D	D	E	L	1973	50931
8041	D	D	R	N	1973	52520
8041	D	D	R	N	1973	52532
8041	D	T	R	N	1973	52532
8041	D	D	R	N	1970	53088
8041	D	D	E	N	1972	53089
8041	D	D	E	N	1974	57761
8041	D	D	E	N	1974	57773
8041	D	T	E	N	1974	57773
8041	D	D	R	N	1972	58203
8041	D	D	E	N	1974	61356
8041	D	S	E	N	1962	87673
8041	D	S	E	L	1964	87701
8041	D	S	E	N	1964	87701
8041	D	D	R	N	1975	96810
8041	D	D	E	N	1975	103608
8041	S	D	E	N	1973	50579
8041	S	D	R	N	1973	50706
8041	S	D	E	N	1973	51055
8041	S	D	R	N	1972	52261
8041	S	S	E	N	1973	53570
8041	S	S	E	L	1974	54080

Substance Number	Phys. State	Subject	Language	Temperature	Year	EPIC Number
102-8041	S	D	R	N	1973	55294
8041	S	S	R	N	1973	55334
8041	S	D	E	N	1973	57396
8041	S	D	E	N	1973	57568
8041	S	D	E	N	1973	57610
8041	S	D	E	N	1974	58038
8041	S	E	E	N	1974	58038
8041	S	S	E	N	1974	58038
8041	S	S	E	L	1974	58935
8041	S	D	E	N	1974	59268
8041	S	S	E	N	1974	59272
8041	S	S	E	N	1973	60581
8041	S	S	E	N	1974	61373
8041	S	D	E	N	1974	62063
8041	S	D	E	N	1974	65242
8041	S	S	E	N	1975	65457
8041	S	T	R	N	1971	66997
8041	S	D	R	N	1971	66998
8041	S	T	R	N	1969	67765
8041	S	S	E	N	1972	67891
8041	S	S	R	N	1974	72651
8041	S	S	E	N	1975	72700
8041	S	D	E	N	1975	73247
8041	S	S	E	N	1975	73247
8041	S	D	R	N	1975	81273
8041	S	S	R	N	1975	81273
8041	S	S	E	N	1962	87673
8041	S	S	E	L	1964	87701
8041	S	S	E	N	1964	87701
8041	S	S	E	L	1971	87884
8041	S	S	E	N	1971	87884
8041	S	S	E	N	1972	87889
8041	S	D	E	N	1975	94088
8041	S	S	E	N	1975	94088
8041	S	S	E	N	1976	99243
8041	S	S	E	N	1976	101470
8041	S	S	E	N	1976	101823
8041	S	S	E	L	1976	103155
8041	S	S	E	N	1976	103155
8041	T	S	E	N	1971	60965
8041	T	S	E	N	1969	87821
8041	T	S	E	N	1971	87884
8054	D	D	R	N	1973	50055
8054	D	D	E	N	1973	51411
8054	D	D	R	N	1971	51572
8054	D	D	E	N	1973	52088
8054	D	D	R	N	1974	62428
8054	D	D	E	N	1974	65331
8054	S	T	R	N	1973	50055
8054	S	D	E	N	1973	51411
8054	S	T	E	N	1973	51411
8054	S	D	E	L	1973	52697
8054	S	S	E	L	1974	53913
8054	S	D	E	N	1974	62063
8054	S	S	E	N	1974	64457
8054	S	S	E	N	1975	65457
8054	S	S	E	N	1972	67891
8054	S	S	E	L	1962	87667
8054	S	S	E	N	1962	87667
8054	S	S	E	L	1971	87884
8054	S	S	E	N	1971	87884
8054	S	S	E	N	1972	87889
8054	S	S	E	N	1976	101470
8054	S	S	E	N	1976	101823
8054	T	S	E	N	1971	60965
8054	T	D	E	N	1974	65107
8054	T	S	E	L	1971	87884
8054	T	S	E	N	1971	87884
8065	S	D	R	N	1973	50067
8065	S	D	E	N	1973	51421
8065	S	D	E	N	1973	51423
8066	S	D	R	N	1973	52557
8069	S	D	E	N	1972	53335
8069	S	D	R	N	1972	56986
8069	S	D	E	N	1974	62059
8069	S	T	E	N	1974	62059
8069	S	S	E	N	1975	94550
8071	S	D	E	N	1972	49487
8083	S	D	R	N	1973	51606
8084	S	D	R	N	1972	52261
8084	S	D	R	N	1973	55338
8084	S	D	E	N	1974	59276
8084	S	S	E	N	1975	94550
8094	S	D	R	N	1973	50069
8094	S	S	E	N	1972	53227
8094	T	S	E	N	1972	87889
8095	D	D	E	N	1974	55245
8095	S	S	E	N	1972	53227
8095	S	D	R	N	1975	81273
8095	S	S	R	N	1975	81273
8095	S	S	E	N	1972	87889
8095	S	D	E	N	1975	94088
8095	S	S	E	N	1975	94088
8096	D	D	R	N	1972	50105
8096	S	D	E	N	1975	94550

Substance Number	Phys. State	Subject	Language	Temperature	Year	EPIC Number
102-8108	S	D	R	N	1973	50724
8108	S	D	E	N	1973	53025
8132	S	S	E	N	1971	87884
8133	S	S	E	N	1972	67891
8142	S	S	E	N	1973	51865
8142	S	T	E	N	1973	51865
8142	S	D	E	L	1971	52970
8142	S	S	E	N	1972	87889
8179	S	S	E	N	1975	94550
8180	S	D	E	N	1975	94550
8232	S	D	E	L	1974	53622
8278	S	D	E	N	1973	57461
8379	S	S	E	N	1971	87884
8420	T	S	E	N	1972	87889
8438	S	D	E	N	1974	88681
104-0006	S	D	R	L	1974	66728
0006	S	D	E	L	1975	66729
0049	S	D	R	N	1974	66728
0049	S	D	E	N	1975	66729
0049	S	S	R	H	1974	66744
0049	S	S	R	N	1974	66744
0049	S	S	E	H	1975	66745
0049	S	S	E	N	1975	66745
0049	S	S	E	N	1969	68271
0067	S	D	O	L	1970	101002
0249	S	S	E	N	1971	87364
0331	S	D	R	L	1973	49848
0331	S	D	E	L	1973	54526
8042	D	S	E	N	1966	66068
8042	S	D	E	L	1973	51069
8042	S	D	E	N	1973	52184
8042	S	S	R	N	1972	62298
8042	S	S	E	N	1973	62299
8045	C	S	R	L	1975	86849
8045	C	S	E	L	1975	86850
8045	D	S	E	N	1966	66068
8045	S	S	R	N	1972	62298
8045	S	S	E	N	1973	62299
8045	S	D	E	N	1972	63966
8045	S	S	E	N	1972	63966
8045	S	S	E	N	1975	96857
8099	S	D	R	N	1972	51232
8108	D	T	O	N	1971	59997
8108	D	S	E	N	1966	66068
8108	S	S	E	N	1971	59999
8109	D	T	O	N	1971	59997
8109	T	D	R	N	1975	101557
8109	T	D	E	N	1975	101558
8156	S	D	R	N	1972	51232
8157	S	D	R	N	1972	51232
8194	S	S	R	N	1972	62298
8194	S	S	E	N	1973	62299
8224	S	S	R	L	1971	54264
8224	S	S	E	L	1972	54265
8231	S	D	E	N	1974	54037
8360	S	D	O	N	1974	90531
106-0004	S	D	R	N	1974	66728
0004	S	D	E	N	1975	66729
0004	S	S	R	H	1974	66744
0004	S	S	R	N	1974	66744
0004	S	S	E	H	1975	66745
0004	S	S	E	N	1975	66745
0006	S	D	E	N	1974	54603
0035	D	S	R	N	1973	59077
0035	D	S	E	N	1973	59078
0035	D	S	E	N	1965	87702
0035	S	D	R	N	1973	50187
0035	S	D	E	N	1973	50188
0035	S	D	E	N	1968	65353
0035	S	S	E	N	1968	65353
0035	S	D	E	N	1973	65354
0035	S	S	E	N	1973	65354
0035	S	S	E	H	1965	87702
0035	S	S	E	N	1965	87702
0035	S	S	E	N	1968	87828
0035	S	S	E	N	1971	87887
0035	S	S	R	H	1972	94899
0035	S	S	E	H	1973	95896
0036	T	D	R	N	1973	54996
0036	T	D	E	N	1974	54997
0057	S	S	E	N	1969	68271
0057	S	S	E	N	1966	68325
0057	T	S	E	N	1971	60964
0057	T	S	E	N	1966	68325
0104	S	D	E	N	1973	52061
0104	S	T	E	N	1973	52061
0104	S	D	R	N	1972	59068
0104	S	D	E	N	1972	59069
0104	S	S	E	N	1971	87872
0125	S	S	R	H	1972	94899
0125	S	S	E	H	1973	95896
0127	S	S	E	N	1974	65250
0157	S	D	O	L	1970	101002

Phys. State: **A.** Amorphous; **C.** Superconductive; **D.** Doped; **F.** Fibrous or Whisker; **G.** Gas; **I.** Ionized or Plasma; **L.** Liquid; **P.** Powder or Particle; **S.** Solid; **T.** Thin Film
Subject: **D.** Data; **E.** Experiment; **S.** Survey (Review, Compendium, etc.); **T.** Theory
Language: **E.** English; **F.** French; **G.** German; **O.** Other Languages; **R.** Russian
Temperature: **L.** Low (0 to 75K); **N.** Normal (75 to 1273K); **H.** High (above 1273K)

Substance Number	Phys. State	Subject	Language	Temperature	Year	EPIC Number
106-0158	S	D	E	N	1973	49709
0158	S	D	E	N	1974	57143
0165	S	D	E	N	1974	54603
0327	T	D	E	N	1974	60654
0363	D	S	E	N	1963	64232
0363	D	S	E	N	1967	66156
0363	S	S	E	N	1974	54075
0363	S	S	E	N	1974	61182
0363	S	S	E	N	1963	64232
0363	S	D	E	N	1975	65491
0363	S	S	E	L	1967	66156
0363	S	S	E	N	1967	66156
0363	S	S	E	N	1972	67891
0363	S	S	E	N	1969	68271
0363	S	S	E	N	1975	68601
0363	S	D	E	N	1970	70645
0363	S	S	E	N	1970	70645
0363	S	S	E	N	1972	87823
0363	S	S	E	N	1975	95584
0363	S	S	E	N	1976	101470
0363	S	S	E	N	1976	101823
0363	T	S	E	N	1974	53750
0363	T	S	E	N	1971	60964
0385	S	S	E	N	1972	63847
0941	S	D	E	N	1972	53335
1085	D	D	E	L	1974	53622
1085	S	D	E	L	1974	53622
1085	S	D	E	N	1973	56345
1256	S	D	E	N	1973	50829
1256	S	D	E	N	1974	101330
8001	S	D	E	N	1973	57135
8040	D	S	E	N	1963	87710
8040	S	S	E	L	1974	53604
8040	S	D	R	N	1973	55300
8040	S	D	E	N	1974	59225
8040	S	S	E	N	1969	68271
8040	S	D	R	N	1973	71715
8040	S	D	E	N	1973	81843
8040	S	S	E	L	1963	87710
8040	S	S	E	N	1963	87710
8040	S	S	E	N	1972	87823
8040	S	S	E	N	1975	95584
8040	S	S	E	N	1976	101470
8040	S	S	E	N	1976	101823
8040	T	S	E	N	1971	60964
8040	T	S	E	N	1963	87710
8041	D	S	E	N	1973	58213
8041	D	S	E	N	1967	68371
8041	P	S	E	N	1967	68371
8041	S	S	E	N	1971	60102
8041	S	S	E	N	1974	62323
8041	S	S	E	N	1972	67891
8041	S	S	E	L	1969	68271
8041	S	S	E	N	1969	68271
8041	S	S	E	N	1967	68371
8041	S	D	E	N	1970	70645
8041	S	S	E	N	1970	70645
8041	S	S	E	N	1962	87659
8041	S	S	E	N	1972	87823
8041	S	S	E	N	1976	101470
8041	S	S	E	N	1976	101823
8041	T	S	E	N	1971	60964
8041	T	S	E	N	1967	68371
8074	S	D	R	N	1973	50355
8074	S	D	E	N	1973	50356
8075	S	D	R	N	1970	67624
8081	S	D	R	N	1973	55711
8084	S	D	R	N	1972	59068
8084	S	D	E	N	1972	59069
8127	S	S	E	N	1972	87823
8128	D	S	E	L	1972	87823
8128	S	D	E	N	1973	50542
8128	S	D	R	N	1971	52298
8128	S	D	E	N	1971	52299
8128	S	D	E	N	1973	53406
8128	S	S	E	N	1974	54554
8128	S	S	R	N	1973	55014
8128	S	S	E	N	1974	55015
8128	S	D	E	N	1971	60102
8128	S	S	E	L	1974	61351
8128	S	S	E	N	1967	68371
8128	S	S	R	N	1973	70817
8128	S	S	E	L	1972	87823
8128	S	S	E	N	1972	87823
8128	S	S	E	N	1966	87831
8128	S	S	E	N	1973	91573
8128	S	D	R	L	1976	103167
8128	S	D	R	N	1976	103167
8128	S	D	E	L	1976	103168
8128	S	D	E	N	1976	103168
8132	S	S	E	N	1972	87823
8134	S	S	E	N	1972	87823
8143	S	D	E	N	1972	49865
8143	S	D	R	N	1973	50355
8143	S	D	E	N	1973	50356
8228	S	D	E	N	1973	51176
8289	S	D	E	N	1973	51864
8342	S	S	E	N	1975	94550
8391	S	D	R	N	1971	76489
8391	S	D	E	N	1971	91568
8393	S	D	E	N	1971	91568

Substance Number	Phys. State	Subject	Language	Temperature	Year	EPIC Number
106-8394	S	D	R	N	1971	76489
8394	S	D	E	N	1971	91568
8529	D	D	R	N	1973	55326
8529	D	D	E	N	1974	59262
8529	S	D	R	N	1973	56861
8529	S	T	R	N	1973	56861
8529	S	D	E	N	1973	57295
8529	S	T	E	N	1973	57295
8531	S	D	E	N	1974	57587
8580	S	S	E	N	1972	87823
108-0079	S	D	E	N	1974	54324
109-8019	S	S	E	N	1974	62347
110-0024	S	S	E	L	1972	63788
0024	S	S	E	N	1972	63788
111-0008	D	T	E	N	1973	56392
0008	D	S	E	N	1974	63393
0008	D	D	E	N	1969	65350
0008	D	S	E	N	1969	65350
0008	D	D	E	N	1969	75184
0008	S	D	E	N	1974	62277
0008	S	S	E	N	1975	65457
0008	S	D	E	N	1969	75184
0008	S	S	E	N	1962	87669
0008	S	S	E	N	1965	87703
0008	S	S	E	L	1971	87884
0008	S	S	E	N	1971	87884
0008	S	D	R	N	1976	99887
0008	S	T	R	N	1976	99887
0008	S	D	E	N	1976	101356
0008	S	T	E	N	1976	101356
0021	D	D	E	N	1972	53081
0021	S	S	E	N	1973	63804
0021	S	S	R	N	1974	66446
0021	S	S	E	N	1974	66447
0021	S	S	E	N	1975	91290
0021	T	S	E	N	1971	87884
8002	D	D	E	N	1974	61358
8002	D	D	E	L	1975	65494
8002	D	T	E	L	1975	65494
8002	S	D	E	L	1973	51869
8002	S	D	E	N	1974	62063
8002	S	S	R	N	1973	62706
8002	S	S	R	N	1974	64959
8002	S	S	E	N	1973	65302
8002	S	S	E	N	1972	67891
8002	S	S	E	N	1975	68432
8002	S	S	E	L	1962	87670
8002	S	S	E	N	1962	87670
8002	S	S	E	N	1971	87884
8002	S	S	E	N	1972	87889
8002	S	S	E	N	1976	101470
8002	S	S	E	N	1976	101823
8007	S	D	R	N	1969	53201
8007	S	D	E	N	1972	53202
8007	S	S	E	N	1973	56247
8007	S	T	E	N	1973	56247
8007	S	D	E	N	1974	61354
8009	S	D	R	N	1969	53201
8009	S	D	E	N	1972	53202
8009	S	D	R	N	1972	62689
8009	S	D	E	N	1972	64417
8021	S	S	E	N	1969	68115
8021	T	D	E	N	1973	57468
8031	D	D	R	N	1969	67413
8031	S	S	E	N	1973	51865
8031	S	T	E	N	1973	51865
8031	S	D	R	N	1969	67413
8031	S	S	E	N	1972	87889
8071	S	D	E	N	1974	54324
8154	S	D	R	N	1970	67423
8157	S	D	O	N	1974	90531
8158	S	D	O	N	1974	90531
8162	S	S	E	N	1972	87824
112-0011	T	S	E	N	1971	60964
0402	T	S	E	N	1971	60964
8020	S	D	R	N	1973	51281
8020	S	D	E	L	1974	54086
8020	S	D	E	N	1974	54086
8020	S	S	E	L	1974	54086
8020	S	S	E	N	1974	54086
8020	S	D	E	N	1974	60534
8020	S	S	E	N	1974	64457
8020	S	S	E	N	1969	68271
8020	T	S	E	N	1971	60964
8025	D	D	R	N	1971	52298
8025	D	D	E	N	1971	52299
8025	D	D	E	L	1974	53599
8025	D	D	E	N	1974	53599
8025	D	D	E	N	1976	101450
8025	S	D	E	L	1973	51870
8025	S	D	E	L	1973	51871
8025	S	D	R	N	1971	52298
8025	S	D	E	N	1971	52299
8025	S	D	E	N	1972	53409
8025	S	D	O	N	1971	60023
8025	S	S	E	N	1974	64457

Substance Number	Phys. State	Subject	Language	Temperature	Year	EPIC Number
112-8025	S	D	R	N	1969	67411
8025	S	S	E	L	1969	68271
8025	S	S	E	N	1969	68271
8025	T	S	E	N	1971	60964
8032	S	D	R	N	1973	51281
8032	S	S	E	N	1972	87823
8083	S	S	E	N	1972	87823
8087	S	S	E	L	1972	87823
8087	S	S	E	N	1972	87823
114-0001	S	D	E	N	1974	54603
0001	S	D	R	L	1974	66728
0001	S	D	E	L	1975	66729
0002	S	D	E	N	1974	54603
0015	T	D	E	N	1973	65550
0017	D	S	E	N	1971	87884
0017	D	S	E	N	1962	97977
0017	D	S	E	N	1963	98002
0017	S	S	E	L	1974	54080
0017	S	D	E	N	1973	55161
0017	S	D	E	N	1973	57396
0017	S	D	E	N	1973	57568
0017	S	S	R	N	1974	87312
0017	S	S	E	N	1975	87313
0017	S	S	E	N	1962	87660
0017	S	S	E	N	1971	87884
0017	S	D	E	L	1975	91725
0017	S	S	E	L	1975	91725
0017	S	S	E	N	1962	97977
0017	S	S	E	N	1963	98002
0017	S	S	E	N	1976	101470
0017	S	S	E	N	1976	101823
0017	T	D	E	N	1974	65107
8001	D	D	R	N	1974	58068
8001	D	S	R	N	1974	58068
8001	D	D	E	N	1974	58069
8001	D	S	E	N	1974	58069
8001	D	D	R	N	1974	66647
8001	D	D	E	N	1974	66648
8001	D	S	E	N	1963	87679
8001	D	S	E	N	1975	87741
8001	D	S	E	L	1965	87781
8001	D	S	E	N	1965	87781
8001	S	D	E	N	1973	51050
8001	S	D	E	N	1973	51833
8001	S	T	E	N	1973	51833
8001	S	D	R	N	1973	52523
8001	S	D	R	L	1973	52543
8001	S	S	R	L	1973	52543
8001	S	S	E	N	1973	52702
8001	S	S	E	N	1972	53299
8001	S	S	E	N	1973	53564
8001	S	D	E	L	1974	53605
8001	S	D	E	N	1974	53605
8001	S	D	E	L	1974	53677
8001	S	S	E	L	1974	53677
8001	S	S	E	L	1974	54339
8001	S	S	E	N	1974	55241
8001	S	S	R	N	1973	55319
8001	S	D	R	N	1973	55340
8001	S	S	E	N	1973	56765
8001	S	D	E	N	1974	57764
8001	S	D	E	N	1974	58038
8001	S	E	E	N	1974	58038
8001	S	S	E	N	1974	58038
8001	S	S	E	N	1974	59254
8001	S	D	E	N	1974	59278
8001	S	D	E	N	1974	62063
8001	S	D	E	N	1974	63375
8001	S	S	E	N	1974	64457
8001	S	T	E	L	1970	64851
8001	S	D	E	N	1974	65239
8001	S	S	E	N	1975	65457
8001	S	S	E	N	1973	65539
8001	S	S	O	L	1966	66022
8001	S	S	O	N	1966	66022
8001	S	S	E	L	1967	66023
8001	S	S	E	N	1967	66023
8001	S	D	E	L	1974	66375
8001	S	D	E	N	1975	66682
8001	S	T	R	N	1971	66997
8001	S	S	E	N	1972	67891
8001	S	D	R	N	1973	68518
8001	S	S	R	N	1973	68518
8001	S	S	E	N	1975	68679
8001	S	D	E	L	1966	74593
8001	S	S	E	N	1960	75859
8001	S	D	E	L	1975	86751
8001	S	S	E	L	1963	87679
8001	S	S	E	N	1963	87679
8001	S	S	E	L	1965	87781
8001	S	S	E	N	1965	87781
8001	S	S	E	L	1971	87884
8001	S	S	E	N	1971	87884
8001	S	S	E	N	1972	87889
8001	S	S	R	L	1974	88331
8001	S	S	E	L	1974	88332
8001	S	D	E	N	1974	90399
8001	S	S	E	N	1976	101470
8001	S	S	E	N	1976	101823
8001	S	S	E	N	1976	103155

Phys. State: **A.** Amorphous; **C.** Superconductive; **D.** Doped; **F.** Fibrous or Whisker; **G.** Gas; **I.** Ionized or Plasma; **L.** Liquid; **P.** Powder or Particle; **S.** Solid; **T.** Thin Film
Subject: **D.** Data; **E.** Experiment; **S.** Survey (Review, Compendium, etc.); **T.** Theory
Language: **E.** English; **F.** French; **G.** German; **O.** Other Languages; **R.** Russian
Temperature: **L.** Low (0 to 75K); **N.** Normal (75 to 1273K); **H.** High (above 1273K)

Substance Number	Phys. State	Subject	Language	Temperature	Year	EPIC Number
114-8001	T	S	E	N	1971	60965
8001	T	S	E	N	1975	65496
8001	T	T	E	N	1975	65496
8012	S	S	E	N	1962	87661
8018	S	S	R	N	1973	87035
8018	S	S	E	N	1973	87036
119-0001	S	D	E	N	1975	63300
0002	S	D	E	N	1974	62065
0002	S	T	E	N	1974	62065
0005	S	D	E	N	1974	60654
8002	D	S	E	N	1962	87672
8002	S	S	E	N	1962	87672
8026	S	D	R	N	1973	50355
8026	S	D	E	N	1973	50356
120-0001	S	S	E	N	1962	69937
0001	S	T	R	N	1975	90674
0106	S	D	E	N	1974	54324
8079	S	D	R	N	1973	52563
8079	S	D	E	N	1973	57788
122-0005	D	T	E	N	1973	50756
0005	S	S	E	N	1964	60562
0009	T	D	E	N	1975	65457
0023	D	S	E	L	1963	87709
0023	D	S	E	N	1963	87709
0023	S	D	E	N	1975	63293
0023	S	S	E	N	1972	63847
0023	S	S	E	N	1969	68271
0023	S	D	E	N	1970	70645
0023	S	S	E	N	1970	70645
0023	T	S	E	N	1971	60964
0031	S	D	R	N	1974	66728
0031	S	D	E	N	1975	66729
0031	S	S	R	H	1974	66744
0031	S	S	E	N	1974	66744
0031	S	S	E	H	1975	66745
0031	S	S	E	N	1975	66745
0050	S	D	R	N	1972	50688
0050	S	S	E	N	1969	68115
0050	T	D	E	N	1974	53643
0053	S	D	E	N	1973	50398
0053	S	S	E	N	1969	68115
0053	T	S	E	N	1966	87833
0112	S	S	E	N	1972	53261
0112	S	S	E	N	1971	87881
0112	T	S	E	N	1971	87881
0425	S	S	E	N	1975	80497
8088	S	S	E	N	1971	87881
8108	S	S	E	N	1975	80497
8109	S	S	E	N	1975	80497
8110	S	S	E	N	1975	80497
8111	S	S	E	N	1975	80497
123-0003	S	S	E	N	1972	53200
0003	S	S	E	N	1972	67891
0003	S	S	E	L	1969	68115
0003	S	S	E	N	1969	68115
0003	S	S	E	L	1966	68361
0003	S	S	E	N	1966	68361
0003	S	D	R	N	1975	94600
0003	S	D	E	N	1975	100283
0003	S	S	E	N	1976	101470
0003	S	S	E	N	1976	101823
0003	T	S	E	N	1966	68361
0025	S	D	E	N	1973	51176
0026	S	D	E	N	1972	49487
0032	S	S	E	N	1975	94550
0042	S	S	E	N	1975	94550
8004	S	D	E	N	1973	52053
8017	S	T	E	N	1973	52461
8017	S	D	E	N	1975	63284
8017	S	S	E	N	1975	63284
8017	S	S	E	L	1969	68115
8017	S	S	E	N	1969	68115
8017	S	S	E	N	1962	87674
8017	S	S	E	L	1975	96245
8017	S	S	E	N	1976	101823
8017	S	D	E	N	1976	102168
8017	S	T	E	N	1976	102168
8018	D	D	E	N	1972	49874
8018	D	T	E	N	1962	65963
8018	D	S	R	N	1974	71470
8018	D	S	E	N	1975	71506
8018	S	D	E	N	1973	53853
8018	S	D	E	N	1972	59070
8018	S	D	R	N	1968	60749
8018	S	D	E	N	1974	60750
8018	S	S	R	N	1974	63131
8018	S	S	E	N	1975	63132
8018	S	D	E	N	1975	63284
8018	S	S	E	N	1975	63284
8018	S	T	E	N	1962	65963
8018	S	S	E	L	1970	68114
8018	S	S	E	N	1970	68114
8018	S	S	E	L	1969	68115
8018	S	S	E	N	1969	68115
8018	S	D	E	N	1966	75147
8018	S	S	E	L	1962	87671
8018	S	S	E	N	1962	87671
123-8018	S	D	R	N	1966	91929
8018	S	D	E	L	1975	100034
8018	S	S	E	N	1976	101470
8018	S	S	E	N	1976	101823
8018	T	D	E	N	1974	61179
8018	T	S	R	N	1974	71470
8018	T	S	E	N	1975	71506
8018	T	D	E	N	1975	90976
8039	S	D	R	N	1973	50066
8039	S	D	E	N	1973	51420
8039	S	T	E	N	1973	52461
8039	S	S	E	N	1972	87824
8039	S	D	E	N	1976	102168
8039	T	D	E	N	1972	53321
8051	S	D	E	N	1972	53271
8051	S	D	E	L	1968	53358
8051	S	D	E	N	1974	61383
8051	S	D	F	N	1972	61662
8051	S	D	R	N	1974	63131
8051	S	D	E	N	1975	63132
8051	S	D	E	N	1973	65985
8051	S	S	E	L	1970	68114
8051	S	S	E	N	1970	68114
8051	S	S	E	L	1972	87824
8051	S	S	E	N	1972	87824
8094	S	S	E	N	1972	87824
126-0001	S	S	E	N	1969	68115
0005	D	S	E	L	1974	61188
0005	D	S	E	N	1963	87711
0005	S	D	E	L	1973	51060
0005	S	D	E	N	1973	51060
0005	S	D	E	N	1974	58036
0005	S	S	E	N	1974	58036
0005	S	D	E	N	1975	63293
0005	S	D	E	N	1975	66683
0005	S	S	E	L	1969	68271
0005	S	S	E	N	1966	87712
0005	T	S	E	N	1971	60964
0038	S	D	E	N	1974	58804
8026	S	D	E	N	1964	61307
8032	D	D	E	N	1973	54934
8032	S	D	E	N	1972	100970
8032	S	T	E	N	1972	100970
8035	S	S	E	N	1969	68115
8037	S	S	E	L	1970	68114
8037	S	S	E	N	1970	68114
8037	S	S	E	N	1969	68115
8052	S	D	E	N	1974	60751
8052	S	S	E	N	1969	68271
8052	S	S	E	N	1963	68313
8052	S	D	E	N	1970	70645
8052	S	S	E	N	1970	70645
8052	S	D	E	N	1961	73251
8052	S	S	E	N	1976	101470
8052	T	S	E	N	1971	60964
8055	S	D	E	N	1972	49935
8055	S	S	E	N	1969	68115
8059	D	D	R	N	1973	52563
8059	D	D	E	N	1973	57788
8059	S	D	R	N	1973	52563
8059	S	S	R	N	1973	52563
8059	S	D	E	N	1973	57788
8059	S	S	E	N	1973	57788
127-8004	S	S	E	N	1972	63492
8004	S	S	E	N	1969	68271
8004	T	S	E	N	1971	60964
132-8001	S	D	E	N	1973	51859
8001	S	D	E	N	1974	54071

Phys. State: A. Amorphous; C. Superconductive; D. Doped; F. Fibrous or Whisker; G. Gas; I. Ionized or Plasma; L. Liquid; P. Powder or Particle; S. Solid; T. Thin Film
Subject: D. Data; E. Experiment; S. Survey (Review, Compendium, etc.); T. Theory
Language: E. English; F. French; G. German; O. Other Languages; R. Russian
Temperature: L. Low (0 to 75K); N. Normal (75 to 1273K); H. High (above 1273K)

Chapter 6 Energy Gap

Substance Number	Phys. State	Subject	Language	Temperature	Year	EPIC Number
100-0045	D	S	E	N	1975	95469
0045	S	S	E	L	1973	50808
0045	S	S	E	N	1973	50808
0045	S	S	E	N	1973	55967
0045	S	S	E	N	1973	56749
0045	S	S	E	N	1973	56767
0045	S	S	O	N	1969	59542
0045	S	S	E	N	1972	59933
0045	S	S	O	N	1970	60098
0045	S	S	E	N	1972	60888
0045	S	S	E	N	1974	62306
0045	S	S	E	H	1967	62829
0045	S	S	E	N	1967	62829
0045	S	S	R	N	1974	83872
0045	S	S	E	N	1975	91217
0045	S	S	E	N	1974	91448
0045	S	S	E	N	1976	97315
0055	A	D	E	N	1971	49794
0055	A	T	E	N	1973	51782
0055	A	S	E	N	1972	52414
0055	A	S	E	N	1972	53251
0055	A	T	E	N	1973	55740
0055	A	S	O	N	1972	58591
0055	A	S	E	N	1970	59557
0055	A	S	E	N	1971	60961
0055	A	S	E	N	1972	62387
0055	A	T	E	N	1972	62387
0055	A	T	E	N	1975	93531
0055	C	T	R	L	1974	60413
0055	C	T	E	L	1974	60414
0055	D	T	R	N	1973	51557
0055	D	T	E	N	1973	53688
0055	D	T	R	N	1971	54260
0055	D	T	E	N	1972	54261
0055	D	T	E	N	1974	61432
0055	D	T	E	N	1975	65494
0055	D	T	E	N	1962	65947
0055	D	T	R	N	1970	70339
0055	D	T	E	N	1971	79434
0055	D	T	R	N	1975	87534
0055	D	T	E	N	1975	87535
0055	D	T	R	N	1975	93621
0055	D	S	E	N	1975	95469
0055	D	T	R	N	1975	95776
0055	D	T	E	N	1975	95777
0055	D	T	E	N	1975	102035
0055	S	T	E	N	1972	49490
0055	S	T	E	N	1973	49620
0055	S	T	R	N	1972	49757
0055	S	S	E	N	1973	50526
0055	S	T	E	N	1973	51050
0055	S	T	E	N	1973	51782
0055	S	S	E	N	1972	53200
0055	S	S	R	N	1971	53278
0055	S	S	E	N	1972	53279
0055	S	T	E	N	1973	53562
0055	S	S	E	N	1974	53607
0055	S	T	E	N	1974	54094
0055	S	T	R	N	1971	54268
0055	S	T	E	N	1972	54269
0055	S	T	R	N	1972	54286
0055	S	T	E	N	1972	54287
0055	S	T	E	N	1974	54602
0055	S	T	R	N	1973	54978
0055	S	T	E	N	1974	54979
0055	S	D	E	H	1973	55112
0055	S	T	E	N	1973	55157
0055	S	T	E	N	1972	55728
0055	S	S	E	N	1973	56767
0055	S	S	E	N	1974	58808
0055	S	T	E	N	1968	59164
0055	S	T	G	L	1973	59319
0055	S	T	E	N	1974	59353
0055	S	S	O	N	1969	59542
0055	S	S	E	N	1970	59557
0055	S	T	E	N	1970	59588
0055	S	S	E	N	1970	59681
0055	S	T	E	N	1970	59810
0055	S	S	E	N	1974	60265
0055	S	D	E	N	1971	60678
0055	S	T	E	N	1973	60976
0055	S	T	E	N	1947	61287
0055	S	T	E	N	1970	61493
0055	S	S	E	N	1970	61494
0055	S	T	E	N	1970	61494
0055	S	T	R	N	1971	61519
0055	S	T	R	N	1973	62706
0055	S	T	E	N	1973	62815
0055	S	T	E	N	1971	63219
0055	S	T	R	N	1972	63697
0055	S	S	E	L	1974	64464
0055	S	S	E	N	1974	64464
0055	S	T	E	N	1973	65302
0055	S	T	E	N	1972	65339
0055	S	T	E	L	1975	65494
100-0055	S	T	E	N	1975	65494
0055	S	T	E	N	1975	66685
0055	S	S	E	N	1972	67891
0055	S	T	E	N	1975	75197
0055	S	S	E	N	1971	76033
0055	S	T	E	N	1971	76033
0055	S	S	R	N	1971	77244
0055	S	T	R	N	1971	77244
0055	S	T	R	N	1974	78324
0055	S	T	E	N	1975	78325
0055	S	S	R	N	1974	83872
0055	S	S	E	N	1966	85844
0055	S	T	E	N	1974	86068
0055	S	E	R	N	1974	90002
0055	S	E	E	N	1975	90004
0055	S	S	E	N	1974	91448
0055	S	T	R	N	1974	92325
0055	S	T	E	N	1975	92326
0055	S	S	E	N	1976	97315
0055	S	T	E	N	1975	98207
0055	S	E	R	N	1976	99127
0055	S	T	R	N	1976	99127
0055	S	E	E	N	1976	99855
0055	S	T	E	N	1976	99855
0055	S	S	E	N	1975	100825
0055	T	T	R	N	1973	50064
0055	T	S	E	N	1971	60965
0055	T	S	E	N	1974	87639
0055	T	S	E	N	1974	89230
8003	D	T	R	N	1972	49455
8003	S	S	E	N	1974	53607
8003	S	S	E	N	1974	54603
8003	S	T	E	N	1973	57683
8003	S	E	G	N	1973	58175
8003	S	S	E	H	1970	59588
8003	S	S	E	N	1970	59588
8003	S	S	E	N	1974	62306
8003	S	S	E	N	1975	86762
8003	S	S	E	N	1975	86763
8006	S	D	R	N	1972	50470
8007	S	S	E	N	1972	52983
8007	S	T	E	N	1973	57398
8007	S	S	O	N	1969	59542
8007	S	S	E	N	1973	60558
8007	S	S	E	L	1969	68271
8007	S	S	E	N	1969	68271
8007	S	T	E	N	1973	72085
8007	S	S	E	L	1972	87823
8007	S	S	E	N	1972	87823
8007	S	D	E	N	1975	91146
8007	T	S	E	N	1974	97255
8008	S	S	E	N	1973	50772
8008	S	S	E	N	1972	52983
8008	S	T	E	N	1973	57392
8008	S	S	O	N	1969	59542
8008	S	S	E	N	1973	60558
8008	S	S	E	L	1971	87884
8008	S	S	E	N	1971	87884
8008	S	S	E	N	1972	87889
8008	S	T	E	N	1972	90612
8008	S	S	E	N	1974	93385
8008	S	S	E	N	1965	98852
8008	S	T	R	N	1975	101515
8008	S	T	E	N	1975	101516
8008	T	S	E	N	1969	87821
8013	D	D	R	N	1973	52534
8013	D	D	E	N	1974	53647
8016	S	T	E	N	1970	59810
8016	S	S	E	N	1965	101536
8021	A	S	E	N	1974	94637
8021	S	S	R	N	1967	53069
8021	S	S	E	N	1972	53070
8021	S	S	E	N	1972	60888
8025	S	T	E	N	1974	64890
8026	S	S	E	N	1974	93338
8026	S	S	E	N	1974	93340
8026	S	S	E	N	1974	93341
8029	S	T	E	N	1974	64890
8031	S	T	E	N	1973	57392
8031	S	S	E	N	1972	65878
8038	S	S	O	N	1969	59542
8038	S	S	E	L	1969	68115
8038	S	S	E	N	1969	68115
8038	S	S	E	N	1972	87824
8038	T	S	E	N	1972	87824
8040	S	T	E	N	1974	64890
8040	S	S	E	N	1969	75843
8041	S	S	O	N	1969	59542
8043	S	S	E	N	1969	75843
8059	S	S	E	N	1972	60888
8071	S	S	E	N	1973	57843
8071	S	S	E	N	1972	65878
8071	S	S	E	L	1973	88610
8071	S	S	E	N	1973	88610
8074	S	S	E	N	1973	60558
102-0002	A	D	R	H	1972	76523
0002	A	D	E	H	1972	91509
0002	L	T	R	H	1971	76473
0002	L	T	E	H	1971	91499
0002	S	S	E	N	1973	56749
0002	S	D	E	H	1974	57300
0002	S	S	E	H	1974	57300
0002	S	S	E	N	1974	57300
0002	S	D	E	N	1975	101667
0002	T	D	R	N	1973	51408
0002	T	D	E	N	1973	51409
0005	S	D	E	N	1974	54600
0005	S	D	E	N	1974	58589
0005	S	D	E	N	1975	86758
0005	S	S	E	N	1975	86758
0009	D	D	E	N	1975	90105
0009	D	T	E	N	1975	90105
0009	S	D	E	N	1972	53215
0009	S	D	E	N	1975	86758
0009	S	S	E	N	1975	86758
0009	T	D	O	L	1965	61141
0009	T	D	O	N	1965	61141
0010	S	D	E	N	1972	53215
0010	S	D	E	N	1975	86758
0010	S	S	E	N	1975	86758
0010	T	D	O	L	1965	61141
0010	T	D	O	N	1965	61141
0010	T	T	O	N	1965	61141
0041	S	S	E	N	1972	87889
0041	T	D	E	L	1974	65107
0041	T	D	E	N	1974	65107
0041	T	D	E	N	1975	65464
0054	S	D	E	N	1973	51852
0086	A	D	E	N	1972	63962
0086	A	S	E	N	1974	65584
0086	A	S	E	N	1964	75166
0086	A	D	E	N	1974	84126
0086	L	D	R	H	1973	52538
0086	L	D	R	N	1973	52538
0086	L	D	E	H	1974	53667
0086	L	D	E	N	1974	53667
0086	S	D	R	L	1973	52538
0086	S	D	R	L	1974	53667
0086	S	D	R	N	1973	54193
0086	S	D	E	N	1973	54194
0086	S	D	R	N	1972	54687
0086	S	D	E	N	1974	55244
0086	S	D	E	N	1973	56527
0086	S	S	E	L	1974	86455
0086	S	S	E	N	1974	86455
0086	T	D	E	N	1973	55106
0105	S	S	E	N	1972	52968
0105	S	S	E	N	1972	53466
0105	S	D	R	N	1973	53779
0105	S	D	E	N	1973	55350
0105	S	D	R	N	1971	59379
0105	S	D	E	N	1974	65738
0105	S	D	E	N	1967	85339
0105	S	S	E	N	1966	87830
0105	S	S	E	N	1971	87884
0105	T	D	E	N	1973	53352
0105	T	S	E	N	1971	87884
0105	T	T	R	N	1973	90563
0105	T	D	E	N	1975	93630
0120	T	D	R	N	1973	54861
0244	S	D	E	N	1973	52302
0244	S	E	E	N	1973	52302
0244	S	D	E	N	1972	65878
0244	S	S	E	N	1972	65878
0244	S	T	E	N	1972	65878
0248	S	S	E	N	1972	52968
0248	S	D	E	N	1972	53099
0248	S	D	E	L	1973	53569
0248	S	D	E	N	1973	53569
0248	S	D	E	N	1971	61508
0248	S	D	E	N	1971	65042
0248	S	D	E	L	1970	66515
0248	S	D	E	N	1970	66515
0248	S	S	E	N	1970	66515
0248	S	S	E	N	1975	66684
0248	S	T	E	N	1975	66684
0248	S	S	E	N	1966	87830
0248	S	S	E	N	1971	87884
0248	S	S	E	N	1972	87889
0248	S	S	E	L	1974	88203
0248	S	D	E	N	1975	90718
0248	S	S	E	N	1975	90718
0248	S	S	E	N	1975	93384
0248	T	D	R	L	1973	55339
0248	T	S	R	L	1973	55339
0248	T	D	E	L	1974	59277
0248	T	S	E	N	1971	60965
0248	T	S	E	N	1969	87821
0248	T	D	E	N	1976	99553
0281	S	D	E	N	1973	51852

Phys. State: **A.** Amorphous; **C.** Superconductive; **D.** Doped; **F.** Fibrous or Whisker; **G.** Gas; **I.** Ionized or Plasma; **L.** Liquid; **P.** Powder or Particle; **S.** Solid; **T.** Thin Film
Subject: **D.** Data; **E.** Experiment; **S.** Survey (Review, Compendium, etc.); **T.** Theory
Language: **E.** English; **F.** French; **G.** German; **O.** Other Languages; **R.** Russian
Temperature: **L.** Low (0 to 75K); **N.** Normal (75 to 1273K); **H.** High (above 1273K)

Substance Number	Phys. State	Subject	Language	Temperature	Year	EPIC Number
102-0382	S	D	R	N	1972	49823
8001	D	D	R	N	1972	62717
8001	D	D	E	N	1973	65313
8001	D	S	E	L	1962	87668
8001	S	S	E	N	1972	52968
8001	S	S	E	N	1973	53427
8001	S	D	E	N	1973	53560
8001	S	S	E	N	1972	55728
8001	S	D	E	N	1974	58808
8001	S	T	E	N	1974	58808
8001	S	D	R	N	1966	59587
8001	S	D	E	N	1966	63247
8001	S	S	O	N	1966	66022
8001	S	S	E	N	1967	66023
8001	S	D	G	N	1954	66199
8001	S	S	G	N	1954	66199
8001	S	S	E	N	1975	66684
8001	S	T	E	N	1975	66684
8001	S	D	R	L	1973	71681
8001	S	D	R	N	1973	71681
8001	S	D	F	N	1974	81628
8001	S	S	F	N	1974	81628
8001	S	D	E	L	1973	82265
8001	S	D	E	N	1973	82265
8001	S	S	E	L	1962	87668
8001	S	S	E	N	1962	87668
8001	S	S	E	N	1966	87830
8001	S	S	E	N	1971	87884
8001	S	S	E	N	1972	87889
8001	S	D	E	N	1975	90718
8001	S	S	E	N	1975	90718
8001	S	D	R	N	1975	101515
8001	S	S	R	N	1975	101515
8001	S	T	R	N	1975	101515
8001	S	D	E	N	1975	101516
8001	S	S	E	N	1975	101516
8001	S	T	E	N	1975	101516
8001	T	S	E	N	1971	60965
8001	T	S	E	N	1969	87821
8001	T	D	E	N	1976	99553
8001	T	E	E	N	1976	99553
8005	C	D	E	L	1975	100026
8012	S	D	R	N	1974	81141
8012	S	D	E	N	1975	92631
8012	S	D	E	N	1976	102175
8018	S	S	E	N	1973	51865
8018	S	T	E	N	1973	51865
8018	S	S	E	N	1972	87889
8018	T	D	E	L	1973	64100
8018	T	T	E	L	1973	64100
8018	T	T	E	N	1973	64100
8018	T	S	E	N	1972	87889
8031	A	D	E	N	1972	53276
8031	A	D	R	N	1974	60421
8031	A	D	E	N	1974	60422
8031	A	D	E	N	1974	60536
8031	A	D	E	N	1974	62603
8031	A	D	E	N	1972	63823
8031	A	S	E	N	1974	65584
8031	A	D	E	H	1974	65598
8031	A	S	E	N	1964	75166
8031	A	S	E	N	1974	84007
8031	D	D	E	N	1973	49533
8031	D	S	E	N	1973	53051
8031	D	D	R	N	1974	60421
8031	D	D	E	N	1974	60422
8031	D	D	E	N	1972	63823
8031	D	S	E	N	1974	86455
8031	L	D	E	N	1974	84032
8031	L	S	E	N	1975	90990
8031	L	D	R	N	1976	103396
8031	L	D	E	N	1976	103397
8031	S	D	R	N	1973	49763
8031	S	D	E	N	1972	53195
8031	S	D	R	N	1973	55325
8031	S	D	E	N	1973	55877
8031	S	D	E	N	1974	59261
8031	S	D	R	N	1974	60421
8031	S	D	E	N	1974	60422
8031	S	D	E	L	1974	84032
8031	S	S	E	L	1974	86455
8031	S	S	E	N	1974	86455
8031	S	D	R	N	1976	103396
8031	S	T	R	N	1976	103396
8031	S	D	E	N	1976	103397
8031	S	T	E	N	1976	103397
8031	T	D	E	N	1973	55106
8035	S	D	E	N	1972	51526
8035	S	S	E	N	1972	51526
8035	S	D	E	N	1965	53356
8035	S	D	E	N	1974	53622
8035	S	S	E	N	1974	53622
8035	S	D	E	N	1974	60664
8035	S	S	E	N	1974	60664
8035	S	D	E	N	1975	68777
8035	S	S	E	N	1967	75171
8035	S	D	E	N	1966	85844
8035	S	S	E	N	1966	85844
8035	T	S	E	N	1967	75171
8041	A	S	E	N	1972	53251
8041	A	D	E	N	1973	56525
102-8041	A	D	E	N	1974	60533
8041	A	D	E	N	1972	60905
8041	A	D	E	N	1972	66227
8041	A	D	E	N	1974	68692
8041	A	S	E	N	1974	83952
8041	D	D	E	L	1972	49928
8041	D	D	E	N	1973	50700
8041	D	D	E	N	1973	51866
8041	D	D	E	N	1972	53302
8041	D	S	E	N	1973	53565
8041	D	D	E	N	1974	53638
8041	D	S	E	N	1973	53782
8041	D	D	E	N	1974	53902
8041	D	D	R	N	1973	55336
8041	D	S	R	N	1973	55336
8041	D	D	E	N	1973	55835
8041	D	D	E	L	1973	57739
8041	D	D	E	N	1974	57966
8041	D	S	E	N	1974	58826
8041	D	D	E	N	1974	59274
8041	D	S	E	N	1974	59274
8041	D	S	E	N	1971	59711
8041	D	T	E	N	1971	59711
8041	D	S	E	N	1972	60677
8041	D	D	E	N	1971	60690
8041	D	D	E	N	1974	61180
8041	D	T	E	N	1974	61432
8041	D	S	E	N	1970	62251
8041	D	D	E	N	1970	62255
8041	D	D	R	N	1974	62529
8041	D	D	R	N	1973	62726
8041	D	D	E	N	1972	63761
8041	D	D	E	L	1972	63848
8041	D	S	E	L	1972	63848
8041	D	D	E	N	1974	64432
8041	D	D	E	N	1973	65322
8041	D	S	E	N	1975	66715
8041	D	D	E	L	1958	75961
8041	D	D	E	N	1958	75961
8041	D	S	E	N	1964	87701
8041	D	D	R	L	1975	96810
8041	D	D	R	N	1975	96810
8041	D	T	E	N	1976	100869
8041	D	D	E	L	1975	103608
8041	D	D	E	N	1975	103608
8041	S	D	R	N	1971	49969
8041	S	D	E	N	1973	50752
8041	S	D	E	N	1973	50928
8041	S	D	R	N	1972	52261
8041	S	S	E	N	1972	52968
8041	S	D	E	N	1972	53099
8041	S	S	E	N	1972	53227
8041	S	S	E	N	1972	53251
8041	S	D	E	N	1972	53302
8041	S	D	E	N	1973	53560
8041	S	S	E	N	1973	53570
8041	S	D	E	N	1974	53610
8041	S	D	E	N	1974	53917
8041	S	S	E	N	1973	53939
8041	S	S	E	N	1974	54082
8041	S	S	E	N	1974	54085
8041	S	D	E	N	1974	54094
8041	S	D	R	N	1973	54361
8041	S	S	R	N	1973	54361
8041	S	D	E	N	1973	54362
8041	S	S	E	N	1973	54362
8041	S	D	E	N	1974	54600
8041	S	D	E	N	1974	54608
8041	S	D	R	N	1973	55294
8041	S	S	R	N	1973	55308
8041	S	S	R	N	1973	55338
8041	S	S	E	N	1973	56749
8041	S	D	E	N	1973	56818
8041	S	S	E	N	1974	57322
8041	S	D	E	N	1973	57396
8041	S	D	E	N	1973	57610
8041	S	D	E	N	1973	57732
8041	S	D	E	N	1974	57966
8041	S	D	E	N	1974	58038
8041	S	S	E	N	1974	58038
8041	S	D	G	N	1973	58175
8041	S	E	G	N	1973	58175
8041	S	D	E	N	1974	58808
8041	S	T	E	N	1974	58808
8041	S	D	E	L	1974	58935
8041	S	S	E	N	1974	58958
8041	S	S	E	N	1974	59233
8041	S	D	E	N	1974	59268
8041	S	S	E	N	1974	59276
8041	S	D	E	N	1970	59674
8041	S	D	R	L	1973	59722
8041	S	D	E	L	1973	59723
8041	S	T	E	N	1971	59984
8041	S	D	E	N	1974	60265
8041	S	D	E	N	1974	60308
8041	S	D	E	N	1974	60533
8041	S	S	E	N	1974	60533
8041	S	D	E	N	1971	60546
8041	S	S	E	N	1971	60546
8041	S	D	E	N	1963	60679
8041	S	T	E	N	1974	60692
102-8041	S	D	E	N	1972	60905
8041	S	D	E	N	1971	61508
8041	S	S	E	N	1969	61512
8041	S	D	E	N	1974	62063
8041	S	T	E	N	1974	62063
8041	S	D	E	N	1969	62248
8041	S	D	E	N	1971	62264
8041	S	D	E	N	1975	63348
8041	S	D	E	N	1972	63761
8041	S	D	E	N	1973	63838
8041	S	D	E	N	1972	63962
8041	S	D	E	N	1974	64493
8041	S	S	E	N	1971	65041
8041	S	D	E	N	1971	65042
8041	S	D	E	N	1975	65434
8041	S	S	E	N	1975	65434
8041	S	D	E	N	1975	65438
8041	S	D	G	N	1954	66199
8041	S	S	E	N	1975	66684
8041	S	T	E	N	1975	66684
8041	S	D	R	N	1971	66998
8041	S	D	E	N	1975	68602
8041	S	S	E	L	1975	68602
8041	S	S	E	N	1975	68602
8041	S	D	G	N	1974	71582
8041	S	D	E	N	1975	73247
8041	S	S	E	N	1975	73247
8041	S	D	E	L	1968	75883
8041	S	D	E	N	1968	75883
8041	S	S	E	L	1968	75883
8041	S	S	E	N	1968	75883
8041	S	S	E	N	1970	82820
8041	S	S	E	N	1973	86380
8041	S	S	R	N	1975	86877
8041	S	S	E	N	1975	86878
8041	S	S	E	L	1962	87673
8041	S	S	E	N	1962	87673
8041	S	S	E	L	1964	87701
8041	S	S	E	N	1964	87701
8041	S	S	E	N	1965	87703
8041	S	S	E	L	1971	87884
8041	S	S	E	N	1971	87884
8041	S	S	E	N	1972	87889
8041	S	S	E	L	1975	90112
8041	S	S	E	N	1975	90112
8041	S	D	R	N	1975	90136
8041	S	T	R	N	1975	90136
8041	S	D	E	N	1975	90137
8041	S	T	E	N	1975	90137
8041	S	D	E	N	1975	90718
8041	S	S	E	N	1975	90718
8041	S	D	E	N	1975	91718
8041	S	E	E	N	1975	91718
8041	S	T	E	N	1975	91718
8041	S	S	E	N	1972	97249
8041	S	D	E	N	1975	97730
8041	S	D	E	N	1976	100761
8041	S	T	E	N	1976	100761
8041	S	S	E	N	1976	100869
8041	S	S	E	N	1976	101470
8041	S	D	R	N	1975	101515
8041	S	S	R	N	1975	101515
8041	S	T	R	N	1975	101515
8041	S	D	E	N	1975	101516
8041	S	S	E	N	1975	101516
8041	S	T	E	N	1975	101516
8041	S	T	E	N	1975	101723
8041	S	S	E	N	1976	101823
8041	S	D	E	L	1976	103155
8041	S	D	E	N	1976	103155
8041	T	D	E	N	1974	53638
8041	T	D	R	N	1973	55306
8041	T	D	E	N	1973	56525
8041	T	D	E	N	1974	59231
8041	T	S	E	N	1971	60965
8041	T	D	E	N	1975	66624
8041	T	T	E	N	1975	66624
8041	T	D	E	N	1974	68692
8041	T	S	E	N	1974	83952
8041	T	S	E	N	1964	87701
8041	T	S	E	N	1969	87821
8041	T	S	E	L	1971	87884
8041	T	S	E	N	1976	101298
8049	S	S	E	N	1972	53470
8054	D	D	R	N	1973	50055
8054	D	D	E	N	1973	51411
8054	D	S	E	N	1973	53572
8054	D	D	E	N	1974	53638
8054	D	D	R	N	1973	55893
8054	D	D	R	N	1974	62428
8054	D	D	E	N	1974	65331
8054	D	S	E	N	1962	87667
8054	P	D	R	N	1971	63424
8054	P	D	E	N	1971	67075
8054	S	D	R	N	1973	50055
8054	S	D	E	N	1973	51411
8054	S	S	E	N	1972	52968
8054	S	D	E	N	1973	53560
8054	S	D	E	N	1974	53610
8054	S	S	E	L	1974	53913
8054	S	D	E	N	1974	53917

Phys. State: **A.** Amorphous; **C.** Superconductive; **D.** Doped; **F.** Fibrous or Whisker; **G.** Gas; **I.** Ionized or Plasma; **L.** Liquid; **P.** Powder or Particle; **S.** Solid; **T.** Thin Film
Subject: **D.** Data; **E.** Experiment; **S.** Survey (Review, Compendium, etc.); **T.** Theory
Language: **E.** English; **F.** French; **G.** German; **O.** Other Languages; **R.** Russian
Temperature: **L.** Low (0 to 75K); **N.** Normal (75 to 1273K); **H.** High (above 1273K)

Substance Number	Phys. State	Sub-ject	Lan-guage	Temper-ature	Year	EPIC Number
102-8054	S	S	E	N	1973	53939
8054	S	D	E	N	1974	55241
8054	S	D	E	N	1973	57732
8054	S	D	E	N	1974	58808
8054	S	T	E	N	1974	58808
8054	S	D	E	N	1970	59674
8054	S	D	E	L	1974	60284
8054	S	D	E	N	1974	60284
8054	S	E	E	L	1974	60284
8054	S	E	E	N	1974	60284
8054	S	S	E	L	1974	60284
8054	S	S	E	N	1974	60284
8054	S	T	E	L	1974	60284
8054	S	T	E	N	1974	60284
8054	S	S	E	N	1973	60580
8054	S	D	E	N	1974	62063
8054	S	T	E	N	1974	62063
8054	S	D	G	N	1954	66199
8054	S	S	G	N	1954	66199
8054	S	S	E	N	1975	66684
8054	S	T	E	N	1975	66684
8054	S	D	G	N	1974	71582
8054	S	S	E	L	1962	87667
8054	S	S	E	N	1962	87667
8054	S	S	E	L	1971	87884
8054	S	S	E	N	1971	87884
8054	S	S	E	L	1972	87889
8054	S	S	E	N	1972	87889
8054	S	D	R	N	1975	90136
8054	S	T	R	N	1975	90136
8054	S	D	E	N	1975	90137
8054	S	T	E	N	1975	90137
8054	S	D	E	N	1975	90718
8054	S	S	E	N	1975	90718
8054	S	D	R	L	1975	97056
8054	S	D	E	L	1975	97057
8054	S	S	E	N	1972	97249
8054	S	D	E	N	1976	100761
8054	S	S	E	L	1976	100761
8054	S	S	E	N	1976	100761
8054	S	T	E	N	1976	100761
8054	S	S	E	N	1976	101470
8054	S	D	R	N	1975	101515
8054	S	S	R	N	1975	101515
8054	S	T	R	N	1975	101515
8054	S	D	E	N	1975	101516
8054	S	S	E	N	1975	101516
8054	S	T	E	N	1975	101516
8054	S	S	E	L	1976	101823
8054	T	D	E	N	1974	53638
8054	T	S	E	N	1971	60965
8054	T	D	E	N	1973	64100
8054	T	D	E	N	1974	65107
8054	T	S	E	L	1971	87884
8054	T	S	E	N	1972	87889
8065	S	D	R	N	1973	50067
8065	S	D	R	N	1973	50069
8065	S	D	E	N	1973	51421
8066	S	D	R	N	1973	52557
8066	S	D	R	N	1974	86779
8066	S	S	R	N	1974	86779
8066	S	D	E	N	1974	90050
8066	S	S	E	N	1974	90050
8069	A	D	R	N	1971	67773
8069	A	D	E	L	1968	75884
8069	A	D	E	N	1968	75884
8069	A	D	R	N	1973	83375
8069	A	D	E	N	1973	90273
8069	S	D	R	N	1972	52260
8069	S	D	E	N	1972	53335
8069	S	D	R	N	1973	54199
8069	S	D	E	N	1973	54200
8069	S	D	R	N	1972	56981
8069	S	D	R	N	1972	56983
8069	S	D	E	N	1974	62059
8069	S	D	E	N	1968	75884
8069	S	D	R	N	1973	83375
8069	S	D	E	N	1973	90273
8069	S	S	E	N	1975	94550
8075	S	D	E	N	1973	49530
8075	S	S	E	N	1972	87889
8075	S	S	E	L	1974	88203
8078	S	D	E	N	1971	49617
8083	A	D	R	N	1971	67773
8083	S	D	R	N	1972	76530
8083	S	T	R	N	1972	76530
8083	S	D	E	N	1972	91535
8083	S	T	E	N	1972	91535
8083	S	S	E	N	1975	94550
8084	S	D	E	N	1973	50789
8084	S	D	E	N	1973	51051
8084	S	D	R	N	1972	52261
8084	S	S	R	N	1973	55338
8084	S	S	E	N	1974	59276
8084	S	S	E	N	1975	94550
8094	D	D	E	N	1973	51749
8094	D	D	E	N	1970	62253
8094	D	T	R	N	1973	62733
8094	D	T	E	N	1974	65329
8094	D	T	E	N	1975	101890
8094	S	S	E	N	1972	53227
102-8094	S	D	R	N	1973	55308
8094	S	D	E	N	1974	59233
8094	S	T	E	N	1974	60692
8094	S	D	E	N	1975	65438
8094	S	S	E	N	1975	65438
8094	S	S	E	N	1972	87889
8094	S	D	R	N	1974	90002
8094	S	E	R	N	1974	90002
8094	S	D	E	N	1975	90004
8094	S	E	E	N	1975	90004
8094	T	D	R	N	1973	50057
8094	T	D	E	N	1973	51413
8094	T	D	E	N	1973	51749
8095	D	T	E	N	1975	63351
8095	S	D	R	N	1972	50731
8095	S	S	E	N	1972	53227
8095	S	T	R	L	1973	55341
8095	S	T	E	N	1974	59279
8095	S	D	E	N	1975	59831
8095	S	S	E	N	1973	86380
8095	S	S	E	N	1965	87703
8095	S	S	E	N	1972	87889
8095	S	S	E	L	1974	88203
8095	S	D	R	L	1973	101917
8095	S	D	R	N	1973	101917
8095	S	S	R	L	1973	101917
8095	S	T	R	L	1973	101917
8095	S	T	R	N	1973	101917
8095	S	D	E	L	1973	101918
8095	S	D	E	N	1973	101918
8095	S	S	E	L	1973	101918
8095	S	T	E	L	1973	101918
8095	S	T	E	N	1973	101918
8095	T	S	E	N	1972	87889
8096	S	D	R	N	1970	55102
8096	S	D	E	N	1972	55103
8096	S	D	R	N	1972	56981
8096	S	D	R	N	1974	66560
8096	S	D	E	N	1974	66561
8096	S	S	E	N	1975	94550
8104	S	D	E	L	1973	50482
8104	S	D	E	N	1973	50482
8106	A	D	E	N	1974	62603
8106	A	D	E	N	1970	66929
8106	A	S	E	N	1976	100646
8106	S	D	E	N	1974	54594
8106	T	D	E	N	1974	54594
8106	T	D	E	N	1970	66929
8119	S	D	E	N	1973	50789
8132	S	S	E	N	1972	52968
8132	S	S	E	N	1972	53227
8132	S	D	E	L	1973	53569
8132	S	D	E	N	1973	53569
8132	S	D	E	N	1974	53917
8132	S	D	E	L	1974	58029
8132	S	D	E	N	1971	61508
8132	S	D	E	L	1970	66515
8132	S	D	E	N	1970	66515
8132	S	S	E	N	1970	66515
8132	S	S	E	N	1975	66684
8132	S	T	E	N	1975	66684
8132	S	S	E	N	1966	87830
8132	S	S	E	N	1971	87884
8132	S	S	E	N	1972	87889
8132	S	D	E	N	1975	90718
8132	S	S	E	N	1975	90718
8132	T	S	E	N	1971	60965
8132	T	S	E	N	1969	87821
8132	T	D	E	N	1976	99553
8132	T	E	E	N	1976	99553
8133	A	D	E	N	1971	62269
8133	A	D	E	N	1974	62603
8133	A	D	E	N	1974	63399
8133	A	S	E	N	1974	65584
8133	A	S	E	N	1964	75166
8133	A	D	E	N	1974	84007
8133	A	S	E	N	1976	100646
8133	L	S	E	N	1975	90990
8133	S	S	E	L	1974	86455
8133	S	S	E	N	1974	86455
8133	T	D	E	N	1973	55106
8133	T	D	E	N	1971	62269
8133	T	D	E	N	1974	84007
8139	S	D	E	L	1974	53722
8139	S	D	E	L	1973	57712
8139	S	D	E	N	1973	57712
8139	S	D	E	N	1974	60309
8139	S	D	E	N	1972	65878
8139	S	S	E	N	1972	65878
8139	S	T	E	N	1972	65878
8139	S	D	E	L	1973	88610
8139	S	D	E	N	1973	88610
8141	L	D	E	N	1973	51768
8141	S	D	E	N	1973	51522
8141	S	D	E	N	1971	59951
8142	D	D	E	N	1974	53638
8142	S	D	E	N	1973	50752
8142	S	S	E	N	1973	51865
8142	S	T	E	N	1973	51865
8142	S	D	E	N	1975	65434
8142	S	S	E	N	1975	65434
102-8142	S	S	E	N	1973	86380
8142	S	S	E	L	1972	87889
8142	S	S	E	N	1972	87889
8142	T	D	E	N	1974	53638
8148	T	D	R	N	1970	52207
8149	T	D	R	N	1970	52207
8150	T	D	R	N	1970	52207
8151	T	D	R	N	1970	52207
8152	T	D	R	N	1970	52207
8163	A	D	E	N	1972	53376
8163	L	S	E	N	1975	90990
8171	A	D	E	N	1972	53186
8171	S	D	E	N	1972	53195
8171	T	D	E	N	1972	53186
8173	S	D	E	N	1972	53215
8173	S	D	E	N	1975	86758
8173	S	S	E	N	1975	86758
8179	S	D	R	N	1970	55102
8179	S	D	E	N	1972	55103
8179	S	D	R	N	1973	55307
8179	S	D	R	N	1972	56981
8179	S	D	R	N	1972	56982
8179	S	D	E	N	1974	59232
8179	S	S	E	N	1975	94550
8180	S	D	R	N	1973	55074
8180	S	D	E	N	1974	55075
8180	S	D	R	N	1970	55102
8180	S	D	E	N	1972	55103
8180	S	D	E	N	1975	94550
8188	A	D	R	N	1973	83375
8188	A	D	E	N	1973	90273
8188	S	D	E	N	1970	63884
8188	S	D	E	N	1966	85844
8190	L	D	E	N	1973	51457
8191	L	D	E	N	1973	51457
8196	T	D	E	L	1974	57978
8203	A	D	E	N	1974	84126
8214	T	D	E	N	1973	55106
8227	T	D	E	N	1973	55106
8228	S	D	R	N	1970	55102
8228	S	D	E	N	1972	55103
8228	S	D	E	N	1972	65878
8228	S	S	E	N	1972	65878
8228	S	T	E	N	1972	65878
8229	S	D	R	N	1970	55102
8229	S	D	E	N	1972	55103
8229	S	D	E	N	1974	57326
8230	S	D	R	N	1970	55102
8230	S	D	E	N	1972	55103
8231	S	D	R	N	1970	55102
8231	S	D	E	N	1972	55103
8231	S	D	E	N	1974	57326
8232	S	D	E	N	1974	53622
8232	S	S	E	N	1974	53622
8232	S	D	E	N	1974	60664
8232	S	S	E	N	1974	60664
8235	S	D	E	N	1974	54092
8235	S	D	E	N	1972	65878
8235	S	S	E	N	1972	65878
8235	S	T	E	N	1972	65878
8248	P	D	R	N	1971	63424
8248	P	D	E	N	1971	67075
8248	S	S	E	N	1973	53415
8248	S	D	R	N	1970	55102
8248	S	D	E	N	1972	55103
8249	S	S	E	N	1973	53415
8249	S	D	R	N	1970	55102
8249	S	D	R	N	1972	55103
8306	D	T	R	N	1972	78825
8306	D	T	E	N	1972	93207
8306	S	T	R	N	1972	78825
8306	S	T	E	N	1972	93207
8310	S	D	E	N	1973	53799
8310	S	D	E	N	1975	68777
8310	S	D	E	N	1966	85844
8310	S	S	E	N	1966	85844
8310	T	D	O	N	1969	65841
8311	S	D	E	N	1973	56364
8311	S	T	E	N	1975	68777
8314	S	S	E	N	1975	72449
8331	A	D	R	N	1974	62436
8331	A	D	E	N	1974	67079
8331	S	D	O	N	1973	51964
8331	T	D	R	N	1974	62436
8331	T	D	E	N	1974	67079
8332	S	D	E	N	1966	85844
8332	S	S	E	N	1966	85844
8333	S	D	F	N	1974	81628
8333	S	S	F	N	1974	81628
8333	S	S	E	N	1972	87889
8337	S	D	E	N	1972	65878
8337	S	S	E	N	1972	65878
8337	S	T	E	N	1972	65878
8344	S	D	E	N	1969	85351
8344	S	S	E	N	1969	85351
8345	S	D	E	N	1969	85351
8345	S	S	E	N	1969	85351
8346	S	D	E	N	1969	85351
8346	S	S	E	N	1969	85351
8347	S	D	E	N	1969	85351
8347	S	S	E	N	1969	85351

Phys. State: **A.** Amorphous; **C.** Superconductive; **D.** Doped; **F.** Fibrous or Whisker; **G.** Gas; **I.** Ionized or Plasma; **L.** Liquid; **P.** Powder or Particle; **S.** Solid; **T.** Thin Film
Subject: **D.** Data; **E.** Experiment; **S.** Survey (Review, Compendium, etc.); **T.** Theory
Language: **E.** English; **F.** French; **G.** German; **O.** Other Languages; **R.** Russian
Temperature: **L.** Low (0 to 75K); **N.** Normal (75 to 1273K); **H.** High (above 1273K)

Substance Number	Phys. State	Subject	Language	Temperature	Year	EPIC Number
102-8348	S	S	E	N	1969	85351
8349	S	S	E	N	1969	85351
8350	S	S	E	N	1969	85351
8351	S	S	E	N	1969	85351
8352	S	S	E	N	1969	85351
8353	S	D	E	N	1969	85351
8353	S	S	E	N	1969	85351
8354	S	S	E	N	1969	85351
8355	S	S	E	N	1969	85351
8356	S	D	E	N	1969	85351
8356	S	S	E	N	1969	85351
8357	S	D	E	N	1969	85351
8357	S	S	E	N	1969	85351
8358	S	S	E	N	1969	85351
8359	L	D	O	N	1973	67598
8371	S	D	R	N	1973	49763
8371	S	D	R	N	1976	103396
8371	S	T	R	N	1976	103396
8371	S	D	E	N	1976	103397
8371	S	T	E	N	1976	103397
8379	S	S	E	N	1971	87884
8379	T	D	E	N	1974	58343
8383	A	D	E	N	1974	84007
8383	A	S	E	N	1974	84007
8395	L	S	E	N	1975	90990
8396	T	D	E	N	1973	65288
8399	S	D	E	N	1974	57326
8420	S	S	E	N	1972	87889
8420	T	S	E	N	1972	87889
8434	A	D	R	N	1971	67773
8436	A	D	R	N	1971	67773
8455	S	D	R	N	1972	76530
8455	S	T	R	N	1972	76530
8455	S	D	E	N	1972	91535
8455	S	T	E	N	1972	91535
8466	S	D	E	L	1970	63884
8466	S	D	E	N	1970	63884
8467	S	D	E	N	1970	63884
8468	S	D	E	N	1970	63884
8470	A	D	E	N	1974	84126
104-0002	S	S	E	N	1972	52968
0002	S	S	E	N	1969	68271
0002	S	S	R	N	1974	80408
0002	S	S	E	N	1974	95255
0006	L	D	E	N	1975	91295
0006	L	S	E	N	1975	91295
0006	S	D	E	L	1973	50820
0006	S	D	E	N	1973	50820
0006	S	D	E	N	1973	53560
0006	S	D	E	L	1974	58962
0006	S	T	R	N	1974	60447
0006	S	T	E	N	1974	60448
0006	S	D	E	L	1968	74624
0006	S	D	E	N	1968	74624
0006	S	D	E	N	1975	86757
0006	S	D	E	N	1975	101667
0007	S	D	R	N	1973	56044
0007	S	D	R	N	1972	56873
0007	S	T	E	N	1974	58431
0007	S	D	R	N	1971	59379
0007	S	D	E	N	1972	63601
0007	S	S	E	N	1972	63601
0007	S	D	E	N	1972	63787
0007	S	D	E	N	1972	64535
0007	S	S	E	N	1972	64535
0007	S	S	E	N	1975	65499
0007	S	D	E	N	1975	65500
0007	S	T	E	N	1975	65500
0007	S	S	E	H	1967	68374
0007	S	S	E	L	1967	68374
0007	S	S	E	N	1967	68374
0007	S	S	E	N	1966	87803
0007	S	S	E	L	1971	87884
0007	S	S	E	N	1971	87884
0007	S	S	E	N	1972	102094
0007	T	D	E	N	1972	61068
0007	T	T	R	N	1973	90563
0007	T	D	E	N	1976	100007
0013	S	D	R	N	1973	50643
0013	S	T	R	N	1973	50643
0013	S	D	R	N	1973	54982
0013	S	D	E	N	1974	54983
0013	S	D	R	N	1972	59071
0013	S	D	E	N	1972	59072
0013	S	S	R	N	1974	62010
0013	S	S	E	N	1974	62011
0013	S	T	R	N	1974	66788
0013	S	T	E	N	1975	66789
0013	S	D	R	N	1971	76481
0013	S	D	E	N	1971	91525
0013	T	S	R	N	1974	90192
0013	T	S	E	N	1975	90193
0015	A	S	R	N	1973	71659
0015	A	S	E	N	1973	91454
0021	A	D	E	N	1975	90859
0021	T	D	E	N	1974	62566
0021	T	D	E	N	1975	90859
0031	D	T	E	L	1975	89453
0031	S	D	E	L	1968	74624
0031	S	D	E	N	1968	74624

Substance Number	Phys. State	Subject	Language	Temperature	Year	EPIC Number
104-0031	S	D	E	N	1975	86757
0031	S	D	E	N	1975	96982
0049	S	D	R	N	1974	66728
0049	S	D	E	N	1975	66729
0049	S	D	R	H	1974	66744
0049	S	D	R	N	1974	66744
0049	S	S	R	H	1974	66744
0049	S	S	E	N	1974	66744
0049	S	T	R	H	1974	66744
0049	S	T	R	N	1974	66744
0049	S	D	E	H	1975	66745
0049	S	D	E	N	1975	66745
0049	S	S	E	H	1975	66745
0049	S	S	E	N	1975	66745
0049	S	T	E	H	1975	66745
0049	S	T	E	N	1975	66745
0049	S	S	E	N	1969	68271
0049	S	D	E	N	1975	86757
0049	S	S	E	N	1975	96477
0053	L	D	E	N	1975	91295
0053	S	D	E	N	1973	53560
0053	S	D	E	L	1974	58962
0053	S	T	R	N	1974	60447
0053	S	T	E	N	1974	60448
0053	S	D	E	N	1975	86757
0053	S	D	E	N	1975	86763
0053	S	D	E	N	1975	101667
0055	S	D	E	N	1974	54348
0067	S	S	E	N	1975	86748
0067	S	D	O	L	1970	101002
0069	S	D	R	N	1973	54395
0069	S	D	E	N	1973	54396
0069	S	D	E	N	1973	57728
0069	S	D	E	N	1963	60560
0104	S	D	E	N	1963	60560
0104	S	D	R	L	1974	87288
0104	S	D	E	L	1975	87289
0104	S	S	E	N	1974	98834
0104	S	D	E	N	1975	101667
0105	S	S	E	N	1974	62066
0105	S	S	R	N	1974	63016
0105	S	S	E	N	1974	63017
0105	S	D	E	N	1975	86757
0105	S	D	E	N	1975	86763
0105	S	D	E	N	1975	101667
0109	S	D	R	N	1975	84594
0109	S	T	R	N	1975	84594
0109	S	D	E	N	1975	93217
0109	S	T	E	N	1975	93217
0196	S	D	E	N	1973	53588
0196	S	S	E	L	1969	68271
0196	S	D	E	N	1975	86757
0249	S	S	E	N	1971	87364
0294	S	D	E	N	1973	49712
0295	S	D	E	N	1972	63787
0295	S	D	E	N	1966	64254
0295	S	S	E	N	1966	64254
0295	S	S	E	N	1971	87884
0295	T	S	E	N	1971	60965
0306	S	S	E	N	1973	86375
0331	S	T	R	L	1974	63054
0331	S	T	E	L	1975	63055
0431	S	D	R	L	1973	52856
0431	S	D	R	N	1973	52856
0431	S	D	E	L	1973	52857
0431	S	D	E	N	1973	52857
0471	S	D	E	N	1976	96888
0533	S	S	R	N	1973	54986
0533	S	S	E	N	1974	54987
8010	S	T	F	N	1973	57472
8015	A	D	E	N	1975	63643
8015	A	S	E	N	1975	63643
8032	S	D	E	N	1973	53588
8032	S	S	E	L	1969	68271
8032	S	D	E	N	1975	86757
8033	S	D	E	N	1973	53588
8033	S	S	E	N	1969	68271
8033	S	D	E	N	1975	86757
8042	S	D	F	N	1973	55915
8042	S	S	E	N	1971	59999
8042	S	S	E	N	1974	62277
8042	S	S	R	N	1972	62298
8042	S	S	E	N	1973	62299
8042	S	S	E	N	1966	66068
8042	T	S	E	N	1966	66068
8045	C	S	R	L	1975	86849
8045	C	S	E	L	1975	86850
8045	S	D	E	L	1973	52072
8045	S	S	E	N	1971	59999
8045	S	S	E	N	1974	62277
8045	S	S	R	N	1972	62298
8045	S	S	E	N	1973	62299
8045	S	S	R	N	1974	63082
8045	S	S	E	N	1975	63083
8045	S	S	E	N	1966	66068
8045	S	S	E	N	1975	96857
8045	T	S	E	N	1966	66068
8055	S	D	R	N	1973	52566
8055	S	D	E	N	1973	57791
8108	S	S	E	N	1971	59999
8108	S	S	E	N	1975	63083

Substance Number	Phys. State	Subject	Language	Temperature	Year	EPIC Number
104-8108	S	S	E	N	1966	66068
8108	T	S	E	N	1966	66068
8109	S	D	R	N	1972	62298
8109	S	D	E	N	1973	62299
8109	T	D	R	L	1975	101557
8109	T	D	R	N	1975	101557
8109	T	D	E	L	1975	101558
8109	T	D	E	N	1975	101558
8118	S	D	E	N	1973	50034
8119	S	D	E	N	1973	50034
8120	S	D	E	N	1973	50034
8121	S	D	R	N	1973	50179
8121	S	D	E	N	1973	50180
8123	S	S	R	N	1973	54986
8123	S	S	E	N	1974	54987
8164	S	D	E	N	1973	51802
8171	S	D	R	N	1973	52904
8171	S	D	E	N	1974	52905
8171	S	D	R	N	1973	57822
8171	S	D	E	N	1974	57823
8183	S	D	E	N	1972	53400
8183	S	D	E	N	1975	87156
8194	D	S	E	N	1972	56769
8194	S	D	R	N	1972	62298
8194	S	D	E	N	1973	62299
8195	A	D	R	N	1971	58968
8195	A	D	E	N	1971	58969
8195	S	D	R	N	1971	58968
8195	S	D	E	N	1971	58969
8196	S	D	R	N	1973	49847
8196	S	D	E	N	1973	54520
8202	S	D	E	N	1973	50752
8213	A	D	E	N	1974	53726
8213	T	D	E	N	1974	53726
8217	A	D	E	N	1971	60140
8217	S	D	E	N	1971	60140
8217	T	D	E	N	1971	60140
8218	A	D	R	N	1971	60139
8218	S	D	R	N	1971	60139
8218	T	D	R	N	1971	60139
8219	A	D	R	N	1971	60139
8219	A	D	E	N	1971	60140
8219	S	D	R	N	1971	60139
8219	S	D	E	N	1971	60140
8219	T	D	R	N	1971	60139
8219	T	D	E	N	1971	60140
8220	A	D	R	N	1971	60139
8220	A	D	E	N	1971	60140
8220	S	D	R	N	1971	60139
8220	S	D	E	N	1971	60140
8220	T	D	R	N	1971	60139
8220	T	D	E	N	1971	60140
8224	S	D	R	L	1971	54264
8224	S	D	E	L	1972	54265
8224	S	D	R	L	1973	55044
8224	S	D	E	L	1974	55045
8231	S	D	R	N	1973	49847
8231	S	D	E	N	1973	54520
8231	S	S	R	N	1973	54986
8231	S	S	E	N	1974	54987
8232	S	D	R	N	1973	49847
8232	S	D	E	N	1973	54520
8233	S	D	R	N	1973	49847
8233	S	D	E	N	1973	54520
8234	S	D	R	N	1973	49847
8234	S	D	E	N	1973	54520
8235	S	D	R	N	1973	49847
8235	S	D	E	N	1973	54520
8236	S	D	R	N	1973	49847
8236	S	D	E	N	1973	54520
8255	S	S	E	N	1971	59999
8268	C	D	E	L	1974	61151
8268	C	S	E	L	1974	61151
8299	S	D	E	N	1974	56084
8304	S	S	E	N	1969	85351
8316	S	D	E	N	1975	96701
8316	S	T	E	N	1975	96701
8366	S	S	E	N	1971	87884
8403	L	D	R	N	1971	76462
8403	L	D	E	N	1971	91582
8404	L	D	R	N	1971	76462
8404	L	D	E	N	1971	91582
8405	L	D	R	N	1971	76462
8405	L	D	E	N	1971	91582
8425	S	D	E	N	1974	62504
8427	S	S	R	N	1974	63082
8427	S	S	E	N	1975	63083
8428	S	S	R	N	1974	63082
8428	S	S	E	N	1975	63083
8429	S	D	R	N	1974	63082
8429	S	D	E	N	1975	63083
8438	S	S	E	N	1974	65212
8439	S	D	E	N	1974	65212
8441	S	D	E	N	1974	65212
8446	S	D	E	N	1976	102175
8447	S	T	R	N	1974	66760
8447	S	T	E	N	1975	66761
8448	S	S	E	N	1972	49784
8449	S	S	E	N	1972	49784
8450	S	S	E	N	1972	49784
8451	S	S	E	N	1972	49784

Phys. State: **A.** Amorphous; **C.** Superconductive; **D.** Doped; **F.** Fibrous or Whisker; **G.** Gas; **I.** Ionized or Plasma; **L.** Liquid; **P.** Powder or Particle; **S.** Solid; **T.** Thin Film
Subject: **D.** Data; **E.** Experiment; **S.** Survey (Review, Compendium, etc.); **T.** Theory
Language: **E.** English; **F.** French; **G.** German; **O.** Other Languages; **R.** Russian
Temperature: **L.** Low (0 to 75K); **N.** Normal (75 to 1273K); **H.** High (above 1273K)

Substance Number	Phys. State	Sub-ject	Lan-guage	Temper-ature	Year	EPIC Number
104-8452	S	S	E	N	1972	49784
8453	S	S	E	N	1972	49784
8454	S	S	E	N	1972	49784
8455	S	S	E	N	1972	49784
106-0002	L	S	E	N	1970	59588
0004	S	D	R	N	1974	66728
0004	S	D	E	N	1975	66729
0004	S	D	R	H	1974	66744
0004	S	D	R	N	1974	66744
0004	S	S	E	H	1974	66744
0004	S	S	E	N	1974	66744
0004	S	T	R	H	1974	66744
0004	S	T	R	N	1974	66744
0004	S	D	E	H	1975	66745
0004	S	D	E	N	1975	66745
0004	S	S	E	H	1975	66745
0004	S	S	E	N	1975	66745
0004	S	T	E	H	1975	66745
0004	S	T	E	N	1975	66745
0004	S	S	E	L	1969	68271
0004	S	S	E	N	1969	68271
0004	S	D	E	N	1975	86757
0004	S	S	E	N	1975	96477
0006	D	D	R	N	1973	54498
0006	D	D	E	N	1973	54499
0006	D	D	R	N	1973	55042
0006	D	D	E	N	1974	55043
0006	D	S	E	N	1972	55357
0006	D	D	E	N	1974	57955
0006	D	D	E	N	1971	80226
0006	L	D	E	N	1975	91295
0006	L	S	E	N	1975	91295
0006	S	D	E	N	1973	53560
0006	S	S	E	N	1972	55357
0006	S	D	E	L	1974	58962
0006	S	S	E	N	1952	59642
0006	S	T	R	N	1974	60447
0006	S	T	E	N	1974	60448
0006	S	D	R	N	1974	62004
0006	S	D	E	N	1974	62005
0006	S	D	E	N	1967	74601
0006	S	T	E	N	1967	74601
0006	S	D	E	L	1968	74624
0006	S	D	E	N	1968	74624
0006	S	S	E	L	1970	85417
0006	S	D	E	N	1975	86757
0006	S	D	E	N	1975	86763
0006	S	D	E	N	1975	91730
0006	S	S	E	N	1975	91730
0006	S	D	E	N	1975	101667
0024	D	D	E	N	1975	91874
0024	L	D	E	N	1975	91295
0024	S	D	E	N	1973	53560
0024	S	S	E	N	1973	56749
0024	S	S	E	N	1973	56765
0024	S	D	E	L	1974	58962
0024	S	S	E	H	1970	59588
0024	S	S	E	N	1952	59642
0024	S	T	R	N	1974	60447
0024	S	T	E	N	1974	60448
0024	S	D	E	L	1968	74624
0024	S	D	E	N	1968	74624
0024	S	D	E	N	1971	83801
0024	S	S	E	N	1971	83801
0024	S	S	E	L	1970	85417
0024	S	D	E	N	1975	86757
0024	S	D	E	N	1975	86763
0024	S	D	E	N	1975	91730
0024	S	S	E	N	1975	91730
0024	S	D	E	N	1975	101667
0024	T	T	O	N	1965	61141
0026	S	D	E	N	1973	57728
0026	S	S	E	N	1974	98834
0026	S	D	E	N	1975	101667
0031	S	D	E	N	1975	80826
0033	S	T	E	N	1975	90031
0035	A	S	E	N	1971	60960
0035	A	D	E	N	1974	91879
0035	D	T	R	N	1973	59724
0035	D	T	E	N	1973	59725
0035	D	S	E	L	1974	62060
0035	D	T	E	L	1974	62060
0035	D	S	E	L	1965	87702
0035	D	D	E	N	1976	99748
0035	S	S	E	N	1972	52968
0035	S	D	E	L	1972	53982
0035	S	S	R	N	1971	62097
0035	S	D	R	N	1971	62098
0035	S	S	R	N	1971	62098
0035	S	D	E	N	1975	63320
0035	S	S	E	N	1975	63320
0035	S	D	E	N	1972	63787
0035	S	S	E	N	1971	64880
0035	S	D	R	L	1968	65348
0035	S	S	R	L	1968	65348
0035	S	D	E	L	1969	65349
0035	S	S	E	L	1969	65349
0035	S	D	E	N	1968	65353
0035	S	S	R	N	1972	65864
0035	S	S	E	N	1972	65865
106-0035	S	D	R	N	1972	66184
0035	S	S	R	N	1972	66184
0035	S	D	E	N	1973	66185
0035	S	S	E	N	1973	66185
0035	S	D	E	N	1971	67085
0035	S	S	E	N	1971	67085
0035	S	S	E	L	1965	87702
0035	S	S	E	N	1965	87702
0035	S	S	E	L	1968	87828
0035	S	S	E	N	1968	87828
0035	S	S	E	L	1971	87887
0035	S	S	E	N	1971	87887
0035	T	D	R	N	1973	58531
0035	T	S	E	N	1971	60960
0035	T	D	E	N	1974	66690
0035	T	S	E	N	1974	66690
0035	T	T	E	N	1974	66690
0035	T	D	E	N	1974	91879
0035	T	D	E	N	1975	95534
0036	L	D	R	N	1973	55758
0036	L	D	E	N	1973	57781
0036	T	D	R	N	1973	54996
0036	T	D	E	N	1974	54997
0057	D	S	E	N	1966	68325
0057	S	S	E	N	1972	52968
0057	S	S	E	L	1969	68271
0057	S	S	E	N	1969	68271
0057	S	S	E	N	1966	68325
0057	T	S	E	N	1971	60964
0057	T	S	E	N	1966	68325
0057	T	D	E	N	1968	85433
0060	S	D	R	N	1973	54395
0060	S	D	E	N	1973	54396
0060	S	D	E	N	1973	57728
0060	S	D	E	N	1963	60560
0068	S	D	E	N	1975	80826
0077	S	D	R	N	1973	52377
0077	S	D	E	N	1973	57490
0081	S	S	E	N	1973	56286
0081	S	D	E	N	1974	58048
0081	S	T	E	N	1974	58048
0081	S	D	E	N	1975	80826
0100	S	D	R	N	1973	52377
0100	S	D	E	N	1973	57490
0104	D	D	R	N	1973	51556
0104	D	D	E	N	1973	51921
0104	D	D	E	N	1973	53687
0104	L	D	R	H	1973	51562
0104	L	D	E	H	1974	53693
0104	L	D	R	N	1971	76462
0104	L	D	E	N	1971	91582
0104	S	D	E	N	1973	51921
0104	S	S	E	N	1972	59933
0104	S	S	E	N	1971	87872
0127	S	D	E	N	1975	63342
0141	S	D	E	N	1974	54348
0156	D	D	E	N	1973	52127
0157	S	S	E	N	1975	86748
0157	S	S	R	N	1973	87035
0157	S	S	E	N	1973	87036
0157	S	D	O	L	1970	101002
0158	L	D	R	N	1973	55758
0158	L	D	E	N	1973	57781
0158	S	D	E	N	1973	49709
0158	S	S	E	N	1972	52968
0158	S	D	R	N	1973	54361
0158	S	S	R	N	1973	54361
0158	S	D	E	N	1973	54362
0158	S	S	E	N	1973	54362
0158	S	S	R	N	1973	87035
0158	S	S	E	N	1973	87036
0158	S	D	E	L	1975	96701
0158	S	D	E	N	1975	96701
0158	S	T	E	L	1975	96701
0158	S	T	E	N	1975	96701
0158	T	S	E	N	1961	64344
0159	S	S	E	N	1974	62066
0159	S	S	R	N	1974	63016
0159	S	S	E	N	1974	63017
0159	S	S	E	L	1970	85417
0159	S	D	E	N	1975	86757
0159	S	D	E	N	1975	86763
0159	S	D	E	N	1975	91730
0159	S	S	E	N	1975	91730
0159	S	D	E	N	1975	101667
0165	L	D	E	N	1975	91295
0165	L	S	E	N	1975	91295
0165	S	D	E	N	1973	53560
0165	S	D	E	L	1968	74624
0165	S	D	E	N	1968	74624
0165	S	S	E	L	1970	85417
0165	S	D	E	N	1975	86757
0165	S	D	E	N	1975	96982
0165	S	D	E	N	1975	101667
0192	S	D	E	N	1973	57837
0204	S	D	E	N	1974	54348
0234	S	D	E	N	1974	54348
0234	S	S	E	N	1974	98834
0237	S	S	E	N	1975	86763
0237	S	D	E	N	1975	101667
0309	S	D	E	N	1975	68687
106-0363	D	D	E	N	1973	49614
0363	D	D	E	N	1974	60290
0363	D	S	E	N	1963	64232
0363	D	S	E	N	1967	66156
0363	D	D	E	N	1970	70573
0363	D	S	E	N	1970	70573
0363	D	D	R	N	1975	97671
0363	D	D	E	N	1975	97672
0363	S	D	E	N	1973	50911
0363	S	D	E	N	1973	51220
0363	S	D	R	H	1972	52252
0363	S	D	R	N	1972	52252
0363	S	S	E	N	1972	52968
0363	S	S	E	L	1972	52975
0363	S	S	E	N	1972	53388
0363	S	D	E	N	1974	53615
0363	S	D	R	N	1971	56217
0363	S	D	R	N	1974	58210
0363	S	D	E	N	1974	59206
0363	S	D	E	N	1973	59409
0363	S	D	E	N	1971	60103
0363	S	D	E	N	1973	60636
0363	S	D	E	L	1974	61361
0363	S	S	E	L	1974	61361
0363	S	S	E	N	1970	61494
0363	S	D	E	N	1971	61758
0363	S	D	E	N	1971	61760
0363	S	S	E	N	1971	61760
0363	S	D	E	N	1971	61763
0363	S	T	E	N	1974	61971
0363	S	D	R	N	1973	62163
0363	S	D	E	N	1969	62248
0363	S	S	E	N	1973	62480
0363	S	S	E	L	1963	64232
0363	S	S	E	N	1963	64232
0363	S	S	E	L	1967	66156
0363	S	S	E	N	1967	66156
0363	S	S	E	L	1969	68271
0363	S	S	E	N	1969	68271
0363	S	S	E	N	1970	82820
0363	S	S	E	N	1966	85844
0363	S	S	E	N	1972	87823
0363	S	S	E	N	1975	96148
0363	S	D	E	N	1976	100416
0363	S	S	E	N	1976	100416
0363	S	S	E	N	1976	101470
0363	S	S	E	N	1976	101823
0363	T	D	R	N	1973	51555
0363	T	D	E	N	1973	53686
0363	T	D	E	N	1974	53750
0363	T	D	E	N	1973	58586
0363	T	S	E	N	1971	60964
0363	T	S	E	N	1963	64232
0363	T	S	E	N	1967	66156
0363	T	T	R	N	1974	66754
0363	T	D	E	N	1975	66755
0363	T	S	E	N	1976	97315
0363	T	S	E	N	1976	102978
0363	T	S	E	N	1976	103588
0385	D	D	E	L	1969	74658
0385	D	D	E	N	1969	74658
0385	S	S	E	N	1973	56749
0385	S	D	E	N	1973	57728
0385	S	S	E	N	1974	98834
0508	D	D	E	N	1972	50848
0508	S	D	E	N	1973	53588
0508	S	D	E	N	1974	67654
0508	S	S	E	L	1969	68271
0508	S	S	E	N	1969	68271
0508	S	D	E	N	1975	86757
0508	T	D	E	N	1972	50848
0590	S	D	E	N	1975	86757
0610	S	T	E	N	1973	57743
0941	A	D	R	N	1973	83375
0941	A	D	E	N	1973	90273
0941	S	D	R	N	1973	52259
0941	S	D	R	N	1972	52264
0941	S	D	R	N	1973	52916
0941	S	D	E	N	1974	52917
0941	S	D	E	N	1972	53335
0941	S	D	R	N	1972	56981
0941	S	D	R	N	1974	66574
0941	S	D	E	N	1974	66575
0941	S	D	R	N	1973	83375
0941	S	D	E	N	1973	90273
0941	S	S	E	N	1975	94550
0956	S	D	R	N	1973	57006
1019	S	D	E	N	1971	49617
1025	S	D	E	N	1974	56084
1079	S	D	R	N	1967	53069
1079	S	D	E	N	1972	53070
1083	S	D	R	N	1973	50037
1083	S	D	R	N	1971	76477
1083	S	D	E	N	1971	91523
1085	S	D	E	N	1974	53622
1085	S	S	E	N	1974	53622
1085	S	D	E	N	1974	60664
1085	S	S	E	N	1974	60664
1085	S	D	E	N	1966	85844
1249	S	D	R	N	1971	76477
1249	S	D	E	N	1971	91523

Phys. State: **A.** Amorphous; **C.** Superconductive; **D.** Doped; **F.** Fibrous or Whisker; **G.** Gas; **I.** Ionized or Plasma; **L.** Liquid; **P.** Powder or Particle; **S.** Solid; **T.** Thin Film
Subject: **D.** Data; **E.** Experiment; **S.** Survey (Review, Compendium, etc.); **T.** Theory
Language: **E.** English; **F.** French; **G.** German; **O.** Other Languages; **R.** Russian
Temperature: **L.** Low (0 to 75K); **N.** Normal (75 to 1273K); **H.** High (above 1273K)

Substance Number	Phys. State	Subject	Language	Temperature	Year	EPIC Number
106-1256	S	D	R	N	1972	52263
1256	S	D	E	N	1973	55874
1256	S	D	E	N	1973	60802
1256	S	S	E	N	1973	60802
1256	S	D	E	N	1974	87146
1256	S	D	E	N	1974	101330
1296	S	D	R	N	1971	76477
1296	S	D	E	N	1971	91523
1485	S	D	R	N	1971	76477
1485	S	D	E	N	1971	91523
1519	S	D	E	N	1974	53915
1519	S	S	E	N	1974	53915
1519	S	D	R	N	1972	56999
1519	S	S	E	N	1975	94550
1804	S	D	R	N	1973	70822
1804	S	D	E	N	1973	91587
1809	S	D	R	N	1974	93455
1809	S	T	R	N	1974	93455
1809	S	D	E	N	1974	93456
1809	S	T	E	N	1974	93456
8001	S	D	E	N	1973	57135
8001	S	D	E	L	1964	85398
8001	S	D	E	N	1964	85398
8008	S	D	R	N	1974	77941
8008	S	T	R	N	1974	77941
8008	S	D	E	N	1974	94517
8008	S	T	E	N	1974	94517
8014	S	S	E	L	1960	65977
8014	S	S	E	N	1960	65977
8040	D	D	E	N	1973	56566
8040	D	D	R	N	1974	87062
8040	D	D	E	N	1974	87063
8040	S	D	R	N	1973	51561
8040	S	D	E	N	1973	52654
8040	S	S	E	N	1972	52968
8040	S	S	E	L	1972	52975
8040	S	D	R	N	1969	53223
8040	S	D	E	N	1972	53224
8040	S	S	E	N	1972	53388
8040	S	S	R	N	1972	53547
8040	S	S	E	N	1973	53548
8040	S	D	E	L	1974	53604
8040	S	S	E	L	1974	53604
8040	S	D	E	N	1974	53692
8040	S	D	R	N	1970	61027
8040	S	T	R	N	1974	61986
8040	S	T	E	N	1974	61987
8040	S	D	R	N	1974	64570
8040	S	S	R	N	1974	64570
8040	S	S	E	L	1969	68271
8040	S	S	E	N	1969	68271
8040	S	D	R	N	1975	77041
8040	S	S	R	N	1975	77041
8040	S	D	E	N	1975	77042
8040	S	S	E	N	1975	77042
8040	S	S	E	N	1966	85844
8040	S	D	R	N	1974	87062
8040	S	D	E	N	1974	87063
8040	S	S	E	L	1963	87710
8040	S	S	E	N	1963	87710
8040	S	S	E	N	1972	87823
8040	S	D	E	N	1974	88316
8040	S	S	E	N	1974	88316
8040	S	S	E	N	1976	101470
8040	S	S	E	N	1976	101823
8040	T	S	E	N	1971	60964
8040	T	S	E	N	1963	87710
8040	T	D	E	N	1975	91012
8041	D	D	E	N	1972	49494
8041	D	D	R	L	1972	57864
8041	D	D	R	N	1972	57864
8041	D	D	E	N	1969	62248
8041	D	T	E	N	1974	62323
8041	D	S	E	L	1967	68371
8041	D	S	E	N	1967	68371
8041	D	S	E	N	1962	87659
8041	S	D	E	N	1972	49493
8041	S	D	E	N	1972	49494
8041	S	D	R	N	1973	50261
8041	S	D	E	N	1973	50262
8041	S	D	E	N	1973	50928
8041	S	D	E	N	1973	51216
8041	S	D	R	N	1973	51272
8041	S	D	R	N	1973	51561
8041	S	D	E	N	1973	51648
8041	S	S	E	N	1972	52968
8041	S	D	E	N	1973	53560
8041	S	D	E	L	1973	53588
8041	S	D	E	N	1974	53610
8041	S	D	E	N	1974	53692
8041	S	D	E	N	1974	54600
8041	S	S	R	N	1973	55014
8041	S	S	E	N	1974	55015
8041	S	D	E	N	1963	60679
8041	S	D	R	N	1969	61845
8041	S	S	E	N	1971	65041
8041	S	D	R	N	1969	68271
8041	S	D	R	N	1971	68351
8041	S	S	E	H	1967	68371
8041	S	S	E	L	1967	68371
8041	S	S	E	N	1967	68371
106-8041	S	D	G	N	1974	71582
8041	S	S	E	N	1973	72085
8041	S	D	R	N	1975	77041
8041	S	S	R	N	1975	77041
8041	S	T	R	N	1975	77041
8041	S	D	E	N	1975	77042
8041	S	S	E	N	1975	77042
8041	S	T	E	N	1975	77042
8041	S	D	E	N	1975	80964
8041	S	E	E	N	1975	80964
8041	S	S	E	N	1970	82820
8041	S	D	E	N	1966	85431
8041	S	S	E	N	1962	87659
8041	S	S	E	L	1972	87823
8041	S	S	E	N	1972	87823
8041	S	D	E	N	1972	90612
8041	S	D	E	N	1959	92621
8041	S	D	E	L	1975	95668
8041	S	D	E	N	1975	95668
8041	S	S	E	N	1976	97315
8041	S	S	E	N	1976	101470
8041	S	S	E	N	1976	101823
8041	S	D	E	L	1976	101840
8041	S	D	E	N	1976	101840
8041	T	S	E	N	1971	60964
8041	T	D	R	N	1970	61532
8041	T	D	E	N	1970	61743
8041	T	D	R	N	1969	61845
8041	T	S	E	L	1967	68371
8041	T	S	E	N	1967	68371
8041	T	D	R	N	1972	76519
8041	T	T	R	N	1972	76519
8041	T	D	E	N	1972	91552
8041	T	T	E	N	1972	91552
8045	S	D	E	N	1973	53588
8045	S	S	E	L	1969	68271
8045	S	D	E	N	1975	86757
8048	S	D	E	N	1973	53588
8048	S	S	E	L	1969	68271
8048	S	D	E	N	1975	86757
8074	S	D	R	N	1973	50355
8074	S	D	E	N	1973	50356
8081	L	D	R	H	1973	51562
8081	L	D	E	H	1974	53693
8081	L	D	R	N	1971	76462
8081	L	D	E	N	1971	91582
8084	L	D	R	H	1973	51562
8084	L	D	E	H	1974	53693
8084	L	D	R	N	1971	76462
8084	L	D	E	N	1971	91582
8127	S	D	E	N	1973	51648
8127	S	D	R	N	1974	61980
8127	S	D	E	N	1974	61981
8127	S	S	E	L	1972	87823
8127	S	S	E	N	1972	87823
8128	D	T	R	N	1975	95776
8128	D	T	E	N	1975	95777
8128	S	D	E	L	1973	53406
8128	S	D	E	N	1973	53406
8128	S	D	E	L	1973	53588
8128	S	S	E	N	1974	54554
8128	S	S	R	N	1973	55014
8128	S	T	R	N	1973	55014
8128	S	S	E	N	1974	55015
8128	S	T	E	N	1974	55015
8128	S	D	E	N	1973	55149
8128	S	D	E	N	1973	58248
8128	S	D	E	N	1971	60102
8128	S	S	E	L	1974	61351
8128	S	D	E	N	1973	66893
8128	S	S	E	L	1967	68371
8128	S	S	E	N	1967	68371
8128	S	S	E	L	1972	87823
8128	S	S	E	N	1972	87823
8128	S	S	E	N	1966	87831
8128	S	D	R	L	1976	103167
8128	S	D	R	N	1976	103167
8128	S	D	E	L	1976	103168
8128	S	D	E	N	1976	103168
8128	T	S	E	N	1967	68371
8129	S	D	E	N	1973	49585
8132	S	D	E	N	1971	61077
8132	S	S	E	N	1970	61494
8132	S	S	R	N	1973	87035
8132	S	S	E	N	1973	87036
8132	S	S	E	N	1972	87823
8133	S	S	R	N	1973	87035
8133	S	S	E	N	1973	87036
8133	S	S	E	N	1972	87823
8134	S	D	R	N	1971	56217
8134	S	S	R	N	1973	87035
8134	S	S	E	N	1973	87036
8134	T	S	E	N	1972	87823
8134	T	D	E	N	1976	102978
8134	T	D	E	N	1976	103588
8134	T	S	E	N	1976	103588
8135	S	D	E	N	1971	49617
8143	S	D	R	N	1973	50355
8143	S	D	E	N	1973	50356
8149	S	D	E	N	1973	50815
8149	S	D	E	N	1973	53318
106-8154	D	D	R	N	1973	51551
8154	D	D	E	N	1973	53682
8154	T	D	R	N	1972	56995
8154	T	D	R	N	1971	76494
8154	T	D	E	N	1971	91578
8155	S	D	R	N	1972	52263
8200	S	D	R	N	1974	66448
8200	S	D	E	N	1974	66449
8200	S	D	E	N	1971	85443
8208	S	D	E	N	1973	50815
8209	S	D	E	N	1973	52302
8209	S	E	E	N	1973	52302
8209	S	D	E	N	1974	62028
8209	S	S	E	N	1974	62028
8209	S	T	E	N	1974	62028
8209	S	D	E	N	1972	65878
8209	S	S	E	N	1972	65878
8209	S	T	E	N	1972	65878
8209	T	D	E	N	1974	53635
8234	S	D	R	N	1973	51561
8234	S	D	E	N	1974	53692
8234	S	D	R	N	1972	58674
8234	S	D	R	N	1975	77041
8234	S	S	R	N	1975	77041
8234	S	D	E	N	1975	77042
8234	S	S	E	N	1975	77042
8234	S	S	E	N	1972	87823
8236	S	D	R	N	1973	51325
8258	S	D	R	N	1970	51710
8259	S	D	R	N	1970	51710
8260	S	D	R	N	1970	51710
8270	S	D	R	N	1973	58519
8271	S	D	E	N	1975	66627
8271	S	S	E	N	1975	96148
8271	T	D	E	N	1975	97322
8289	S	D	E	N	1973	51864
8290	T	D	E	N	1973	51876
8299	S	D	E	N	1973	52302
8299	S	E	E	N	1973	52302
8299	T	D	E	N	1975	90115
8299	T	T	E	N	1975	90115
8299	T	D	E	N	1975	97322
8312	S	D	R	N	1973	58519
8335	S	D	R	N	1969	53223
8335	S	D	E	N	1972	53224
8338	S	D	E	N	1973	53415
8338	S	D	R	N	1970	55102
8338	S	D	E	N	1972	55103
8340	S	D	E	N	1973	53415
8340	S	D	R	N	1970	55102
8340	S	D	E	N	1972	55103
8342	S	D	E	N	1972	65878
8342	S	S	E	N	1972	65878
8342	S	T	E	N	1972	65878
8342	S	D	E	N	1975	94550
8344	S	D	E	N	1973	53415
8344	S	D	R	N	1970	55102
8344	S	D	E	N	1972	55103
8344	S	D	E	N	1973	56160
8356	S	D	E	N	1972	55089
8358	S	D	E	N	1969	62248
8386	S	D	E	L	1972	53698
8387	S	S	E	L	1972	53698
8388	S	D	R	N	1974	77941
8388	S	T	R	N	1974	77941
8388	S	D	E	N	1972	80067
8388	S	D	E	N	1974	94517
8388	S	T	E	N	1974	94517
8392	S	D	E	N	1967	75175
8393	S	D	E	N	1967	75175
8394	S	D	R	N	1973	58519
8394	S	D	E	N	1967	75175
8433	S	D	R	N	1973	49847
8433	S	D	E	N	1973	54520
8438	S	T	E	N	1974	93998
8439	S	D	R	N	1972	60709
8439	S	D	E	N	1973	60710
8439	S	D	R	N	1974	63161
8439	S	D	E	N	1975	63162
8453	S	D	R	N	1970	55102
8453	S	D	E	N	1972	55103
8454	S	D	R	N	1970	55102
8454	S	D	E	N	1972	55103
8455	S	D	R	N	1970	55102
8455	S	D	E	N	1972	55103
8455	S	D	R	N	1972	76551
8455	S	D	E	N	1972	91546
8456	S	D	R	N	1970	55102
8456	S	D	E	N	1972	55103
8457	S	D	R	N	1970	55102
8457	S	D	E	N	1972	55103
8457	S	D	E	N	1972	65878
8457	S	S	E	N	1972	65878
8457	S	T	E	N	1972	65878
8458	S	D	R	N	1970	55102
8458	S	D	E	N	1972	55103
8458	S	D	R	N	1972	76551
8458	S	D	E	N	1972	91546
8459	S	D	R	N	1970	55102
8459	S	D	E	N	1972	55103
8469	S	D	E	N	1971	61077

Phys. State: **A.** Amorphous; **C.** Superconductive; **D.** Doped; **F.** Fibrous or Whisker; **G.** Gas; **I.** Ionized or Plasma; **L.** Liquid; **P.** Powder or Particle; **S.** Solid; **T.** Thin Film
Subject: **D.** Data; **E.** Experiment; **S.** Survey (Review, Compendium, etc.); **T.** Theory
Language: **E.** English; **F.** French; **G.** German; **O.** Other Languages; **R.** Russian
Temperature: **L.** Low (0 to 75K); **N.** Normal (75 to 1273K); **H.** High (above 1273K)

Substance Number	Phys. State	Subject	Language	Temperature	Year	EPIC Number
106-8471	S	D	R	N	1971	59995
8528	D	D	R	N	1973	55295
8528	D	D	E	N	1974	59271
8529	S	D	R	N	1973	56861
8529	S	D	E	N	1973	57295
8531	S	D	R	N	1973	51564
8531	S	D	E	N	1974	53695
8531	S	D	E	N	1974	57587
8531	S	S	E	N	1972	87823
8531	T	S	E	N	1972	87823
8534	S	D	E	N	1974	66363
8535	S	D	E	N	1974	66363
8536	S	S	E	N	1974	66380
8549	S	D	R	N	1973	58519
8565	S	D	R	N	1972	60709
8565	S	D	E	N	1973	60710
8580	S	D	E	N	1973	55872
8580	S	S	E	N	1972	87823
8580	T	D	E	N	1973	57259
8581	S	D	E	N	1973	55917
8589	T	D	R	N	1973	56055
8611	S	D	E	N	1966	85403
8658	S	D	R	N	1973	58870
8766	S	S	E	N	1975	90115
8766	S	S	E	N	1975	97322
8783	S	D	E	N	1974	62504
8795	S	D	R	N	1972	76553
8795	S	D	E	N	1972	91547
8796	S	D	R	N	1972	76553
8796	S	D	E	N	1972	91547
8811	S	D	R	N	1974	65411
8811	S	D	E	N	1975	65412
108-0029	S	D	E	N	1974	54099
0029	S	D	R	N	1974	58128
0029	S	D	E	N	1974	58129
0029	S	D	E	N	1974	62066
8044	S	D	R	N	1973	56317
8047	S	D	E	N	1975	86757
8061	S	S	E	N	1972	49784
109-0001	S	D	R	N	1973	54869
0025	D	D	E	N	1973	50887
0025	D	S	E	N	1973	53052
0025	D	D	E	N	1974	54573
0025	D	S	E	L	1975	90863
0025	D	S	E	N	1975	90863
0025	S	D	E	N	1972	49906
0025	S	D	E	N	1973	50887
0025	S	D	E	L	1973	50888
0025	S	S	E	N	1973	53052
0025	S	S	E	N	1972	53158
0025	S	D	E	N	1973	53587
0025	S	D	E	N	1974	54573
0025	S	S	E	L	1970	75905
0025	S	S	E	N	1970	75905
0040	S	D	R	H	1973	70815
0040	S	D	R	N	1973	70815
0040	S	D	E	H	1973	91572
0040	S	D	E	N	1973	91572
0060	S	D	R	N	1973	70822
0060	S	D	E	N	1973	91587
8019	S	D	R	N	1973	52564
8019	S	D	E	N	1973	57789
8020	S	D	R	N	1975	86839
8020	S	D	E	N	1975	86840
8021	S	D	R	N	1973	52564
8021	S	D	E	N	1973	57789
8034	S	D	E	N	1972	53158
8040	S	D	R	N	1973	52564
8040	S	D	E	N	1973	57789
8041	S	D	R	N	1973	52564
8041	S	D	E	N	1973	57789
8042	S	D	R	N	1973	52564
8042	S	D	E	N	1973	57789
8064	S	D	R	N	1975	86839
8064	S	D	E	N	1975	86840
8071	S	D	E	N	1973	56526
8074	S	S	E	N	1969	85351
8078	S	D	E	N	1975	86757
8079	S	D	E	N	1975	86757
8082	S	D	E	N	1975	63304
8102	S	S	E	N	1972	49784
110-0010	S	D	R	N	1966	59587
0010	S	D	E	N	1966	63247
0011	S	D	E	N	1975	80826
0021	S	D	E	N	1973	57728
0021	S	S	E	N	1974	98834
0023	S	D	R	N	1974	63056
0023	S	T	R	N	1974	63056
0023	S	D	E	N	1975	63057
0023	S	T	E	N	1975	63057
0023	S	D	R	N	1972	76520
0023	S	T	R	N	1972	76520
0023	S	D	E	N	1972	91553
0023	S	T	E	N	1972	91553
0023	S	D	E	N	1976	101192
0023	S	S	E	N	1976	101192
0023	S	T	E	N	1976	101192
0023	S	D	E	N	1975	101667

Substance Number	Phys. State	Subject	Language	Temperature	Year	EPIC Number
110-0023	T	D	E	N	1974	58961
0024	L	D	E	N	1973	57594
0024	S	D	E	N	1973	50151
0024	S	D	E	N	1973	50545
0024	S	D	E	N	1974	55252
0024	S	S	E	N	1974	55252
0024	S	D	R	N	1974	58128
0024	S	D	E	N	1974	58129
0024	S	D	E	N	1974	59398
0024	S	T	E	L	1974	59398
0024	S	D	E	N	1973	60594
0024	S	D	E	N	1973	60623
0024	S	S	E	N	1973	60623
0024	S	S	E	N	1974	62066
0024	S	D	E	N	1974	62306
0024	S	D	E	N	1974	62457
0024	S	S	R	N	1974	63016
0024	S	S	E	N	1974	63017
0024	S	D	E	N	1975	63322
0024	S	S	E	N	1975	63322
0024	S	S	E	N	1975	65501
0024	S	D	E	N	1967	85322
0024	S	D	E	N	1975	86757
0024	S	S	E	N	1975	86763
0024	S	D	E	N	1975	91730
0024	S	S	E	N	1975	91730
0024	S	D	E	N	1975	97579
0024	S	S	E	N	1975	97579
0024	S	D	E	N	1975	101667
0024	S	D	E	N	1976	102400
0024	S	S	E	N	1976	102400
0025	S	D	E	N	1972	53113
0025	S	D	R	N	1974	88553
0025	S	D	E	N	1974	94190
0030	S	S	E	N	1973	56286
0034	S	D	R	N	1973	51325
0036	L	D	O	H	1973	53826
0036	L	D	O	N	1973	53826
0036	L	D	E	N	1973	57594
0036	S	D	E	N	1973	53560
0036	S	S	E	N	1973	56749
0036	S	D	E	N	1975	86757
0036	S	S	E	N	1975	86763
0036	S	D	E	N	1975	91730
0036	S	S	E	N	1975	91730
0036	S	D	E	N	1975	101667
0037	S	D	E	L	1973	50820
0037	S	D	E	N	1973	50820
0037	S	D	E	N	1973	53560
0037	S	D	E	L	1974	58962
0037	S	D	E	N	1974	62457
0037	S	D	E	N	1975	86757
0037	S	S	E	N	1975	86763
0037	S	D	E	N	1975	91730
0037	S	S	E	N	1975	91730
0037	S	D	E	N	1975	101667
0061	S	D	E	N	1975	86757
0061	S	S	E	N	1975	86763
0061	S	D	E	N	1975	101667
0132	S	S	E	N	1974	98834
0132	S	D	E	N	1975	101667
0194	D	T	E	N	1974	57985
0194	S	D	E	N	1973	50872
0194	S	D	E	L	1974	58050
0194	S	D	E	N	1974	58050
0194	S	S	E	N	1974	58050
0194	T	T	E	N	1974	57985
0269	S	D	E	N	1973	50787
0352	S	S	E	N	1973	86375
8046	S	D	E	N	1975	91913
8046	S	T	E	N	1975	91913
8051	S	D	E	N	1974	58050
8051	S	S	E	N	1974	58050
8079	S	D	R	N	1970	51710
8082	S	D	R	N	1973	55807
8082	S	D	E	N	1973	56370
8082	S	D	R	N	1973	66116
8135	S	D	E	N	1975	65199
8203	S	D	R	N	1973	55807
8203	S	D	R	N	1973	66116
8204	S	D	R	N	1973	55807
8204	S	D	R	N	1973	66116
8205	S	D	R	N	1973	55807
8205	S	D	E	N	1973	56370
8205	S	D	R	N	1973	66116
8215	S	D	G	N	1973	57058
8217	S	D	E	N	1973	57124
111-0006	A	S	E	N	1969	68115
0006	S	S	E	N	1970	59717
0006	S	D	E	N	1971	65044
0006	S	S	E	N	1969	68115
0008	A	S	E	N	1972	53251
0008	A	D	E	N	1974	60533
0008	A	D	E	N	1972	60905
0008	A	D	E	N	1970	62194
0008	A	D	E	N	1974	65585
0008	A	D	E	N	1972	66227
0008	D	D	E	N	1974	60516
0008	D	S	E	N	1970	62194
0008	D	D	E	L	1971	70519

Substance Number	Phys. State	Subject	Language	Temperature	Year	EPIC Number
111-0008	D	D	E	N	1971	70519
0008	D	D	R	N	1974	76160
0008	D	D	E	N	1975	76161
0008	D	D	R	N	1974	97464
0008	D	D	E	N	1975	97465
0008	S	D	R	N	1972	50732
0008	S	D	E	N	1973	50928
0008	S	S	E	L	1973	51760
0008	S	D	E	N	1973	51907
0008	S	S	E	N	1972	52968
0008	S	S	E	N	1972	53227
0008	S	S	E	N	1972	53251
0008	S	D	E	N	1973	53560
0008	S	D	E	N	1974	53610
0008	S	D	E	N	1974	53917
0008	S	D	E	N	1974	54600
0008	S	D	E	N	1974	54608
0008	S	S	E	N	1972	55728
0008	S	T	E	N	1972	55728
0008	S	D	E	N	1973	55860
0008	S	D	E	N	1973	57732
0008	S	D	E	N	1974	58808
0008	S	T	E	N	1974	58808
0008	S	D	E	N	1974	58958
0008	S	D	E	N	1970	59674
0008	S	S	E	N	1974	60516
0008	S	D	E	N	1974	60533
0008	S	S	E	N	1974	60533
0008	S	D	E	N	1972	60905
0008	S	D	E	N	1971	61508
0008	S	D	E	N	1974	62030
0008	S	D	R	N	1973	62100
0008	S	D	E	N	1970	62194
0008	S	D	E	N	1971	62264
0008	S	D	E	N	1974	62277
0008	S	D	E	N	1974	65585
0008	S	S	E	N	1975	66684
0008	S	T	E	N	1975	66684
0008	S	D	E	N	1968	75942
0008	S	T	E	L	1968	75942
0008	S	T	E	N	1968	75942
0008	S	S	E	N	1973	86380
0008	S	S	E	N	1962	87669
0008	S	S	E	L	1965	87703
0008	S	S	E	N	1965	87703
0008	S	S	E	L	1971	87884
0008	S	S	E	N	1971	87884
0008	S	S	E	N	1972	87889
0008	S	S	E	L	1974	88203
0008	S	D	E	N	1975	89266
0008	S	D	E	N	1973	89715
0008	S	T	E	N	1975	90032
0008	S	S	E	L	1975	90112
0008	S	S	E	N	1975	90112
0008	S	D	R	N	1975	90136
0008	S	T	R	N	1975	90136
0008	S	D	E	N	1975	90137
0008	S	T	E	N	1975	90137
0008	S	D	E	N	1975	90718
0008	S	S	E	N	1975	90718
0008	S	S	E	N	1972	97249
0008	S	D	E	N	1976	99177
0008	S	D	E	N	1976	99364
0008	S	T	E	N	1976	99364
0008	S	D	R	N	1975	101515
0008	S	S	R	N	1975	101515
0008	S	T	R	N	1975	101515
0008	S	D	E	N	1975	101516
0008	S	S	E	N	1975	101516
0008	S	T	E	N	1975	101516
0008	S	D	R	L	1973	101917
0008	S	D	R	N	1973	101917
0008	S	T	R	L	1973	101917
0008	S	T	R	N	1973	101917
0008	S	D	E	L	1973	101918
0008	S	D	E	N	1973	101918
0008	S	T	E	L	1973	101918
0008	S	T	E	N	1973	101918
0008	T	D	R	N	1971	59188
0008	T	D	E	N	1971	59189
0008	T	S	E	N	1971	60965
0008	T	D	E	N	1970	62194
0008	T	D	E	N	1974	65585
0008	T	S	E	N	1965	87703
0015	S	S	E	L	1969	68115
0015	S	S	E	N	1969	68115
0021	D	D	E	N	1972	53081
0021	D	D	E	N	1974	53912
0021	D	D	E	L	1974	54560
0021	D	S	E	L	1974	54560
0021	D	S	E	N	1974	54560
0021	D	S	E	N	1974	58028
0021	D	D	E	N	1974	60371
0021	S	S	E	N	1972	52968
0021	S	S	E	N	1972	53466
0021	S	D	E	L	1974	58037
0021	S	D	E	N	1974	58037
0021	S	D	E	L	1973	62246
0021	S	D	E	N	1973	62246
0021	S	S	E	N	1973	62246
0021	S	S	R	L	1974	66446

Phys. State: **A.** Amorphous; **C.** Superconductive; **D.** Doped; **F.** Fibrous or Whisker; **G.** Gas; **I.** Ionized or Plasma; **L.** Liquid; **P.** Powder or Particle; **S.** Solid; **T.** Thin Film
Subject: **D.** Data; **E.** Experiment; **S.** Survey (Review, Compendium, etc.); **T.** Theory
Language: **E.** English; **F.** French; **G.** German; **O.** Other Languages; **R.** Russian
Temperature: **L.** Low (0 to 75K); **N.** Normal (75 to 1273K); **H.** High (above 1273K)

Substance Number	Phys. State	Subject	Language	Temperature	Year	EPIC Number
111-0021	S	S	R	N	1974	66446
0021	S	S	E	L	1974	66447
0021	S	S	E	N	1974	66447
0021	S	S	E	L	1975	91290
0021	S	S	E	N	1975	91290
0021	T	D	E	N	1973	54206
0021	T	D	E	N	1970	63881
0021	T	S	E	N	1971	87884
0021	T	T	R	N	1973	90563
0029	S	D	R	L	1973	50679
0029	S	D	R	N	1973	50679
0029	S	D	E	N	1973	50776
0029	S	D	E	L	1973	52425
0029	S	D	E	N	1973	52425
0029	S	D	E	N	1962	63880
0029	S	S	E	N	1962	63880
0029	S	D	R	N	1965	76401
0029	S	D	E	L	1969	85428
0029	S	D	E	N	1969	85428
0029	S	D	E	N	1965	91742
0029	S	D	R	N	1975	99712
0029	S	S	R	N	1975	99712
0029	S	D	E	N	1975	99713
0029	S	S	E	N	1975	99713
0029	S	D	R	N	1975	100322
0029	S	D	E	N	1975	100323
0050	S	D	E	N	1973	56335
0050	S	D	E	N	1975	94550
0052	S	D	E	N	1975	86757
0089	S	D	R	N	1972	76507
0089	S	D	E	N	1972	91590
0093	S	D	R	H	1973	70815
0093	S	D	R	N	1973	70815
0093	S	D	E	H	1973	91572
0093	S	D	E	N	1973	91572
0098	S	S	E	N	1969	68115
0103	S	D	R	H	1973	70815
0103	S	D	R	N	1973	70815
0103	S	D	E	H	1973	91572
0103	S	D	R	H	1973	91572
0103	S	D	E	N	1973	91572
0104	S	D	R	H	1973	70815
0104	S	D	R	N	1973	70815
0104	S	D	E	H	1973	91572
0104	S	D	E	N	1973	91572
8002	D	D	E	N	1974	61358
8002	D	D	E	L	1961	64497
8002	D	D	E	L	1975	65494
8002	D	T	E	L	1975	65494
8002	D	T	E	N	1975	65494
8002	S	D	E	L	1973	49738
8002	S	D	E	N	1973	49738
8002	S	S	E	N	1972	52968
8002	S	D	E	N	1973	53560
8002	S	D	E	N	1974	53917
8002	S	D	E	N	1974	57322
8002	S	S	E	L	1974	57322
8002	S	S	E	N	1974	57322
8002	S	D	E	N	1974	58808
8002	S	T	E	N	1974	58808
8002	S	D	E	N	1970	59674
8002	S	D	E	L	1974	60284
8002	S	D	E	N	1974	60284
8002	S	E	E	L	1974	60284
8002	S	E	E	N	1974	60284
8002	S	S	E	L	1974	60284
8002	S	S	E	N	1974	60284
8002	S	T	E	L	1974	60284
8002	S	T	E	N	1974	60284
8002	S	S	E	N	1969	61512
8002	S	D	E	N	1974	62063
8002	S	T	E	N	1974	62063
8002	S	D	E	N	1961	64496
8002	S	D	E	L	1961	64497
8002	S	D	E	N	1961	64497
8002	S	S	R	N	1974	64959
8002	S	D	E	L	1975	65494
8002	S	T	E	L	1975	65494
8002	S	T	E	N	1975	65494
8002	S	D	E	L	1962	65951
8002	S	D	E	N	1962	65951
8002	S	S	O	L	1966	66022
8002	S	S	E	L	1967	66023
8002	S	D	G	N	1954	66199
8002	S	S	G	N	1954	66199
8002	S	S	E	N	1975	66684
8002	S	T	E	N	1975	66684
8002	S	S	E	N	1975	68432
8002	S	D	F	N	1974	81628
8002	S	S	F	N	1974	81628
8002	S	S	E	L	1962	87670
8002	S	S	E	N	1962	87670
8002	S	S	E	L	1971	87884
8002	S	S	E	N	1971	87884
8002	S	S	E	L	1972	87889
8002	S	S	E	N	1972	87889
8002	S	D	R	N	1975	90136
8002	S	T	R	N	1975	90136
8002	S	D	E	N	1975	90137
8002	S	T	E	N	1975	90137
8002	S	D	E	N	1972	90612
111-8002	S	D	E	N	1975	90718
8002	S	S	E	N	1975	90718
8002	S	S	E	N	1972	97249
8002	S	S	E	N	1976	101470
8002	S	D	R	N	1975	101515
8002	S	S	R	N	1975	101515
8002	S	T	R	N	1975	101515
8002	S	D	E	N	1975	101516
8002	S	S	E	N	1975	101516
8002	S	T	E	N	1975	101516
8002	S	S	E	L	1976	101823
8002	S	S	E	N	1976	101823
8002	S	D	E	L	1976	103586
8002	T	S	E	N	1971	60965
8002	T	S	E	N	1969	87821
8007	S	D	E	N	1973	50776
8007	S	D	R	N	1969	53201
8007	S	D	E	N	1972	53202
8007	S	S	E	N	1974	61360
8007	S	D	E	N	1972	63763
8007	S	D	E	N	1974	66691
8007	S	T	E	N	1974	66691
8007	S	D	R	N	1965	76401
8007	S	D	E	N	1969	85428
8007	S	D	E	N	1965	91742
8007	S	D	E	N	1975	96246
8007	S	S	E	N	1975	96246
8007	S	T	R	N	1975	99712
8007	S	T	E	N	1975	99713
8007	S	D	R	N	1975	100322
8007	S	D	E	N	1975	100323
8007	T	D	E	N	1973	57281
8008	S	D	R	N	1972	58561
8008	T	D	R	N	1970	61533
8009	S	D	R	N	1969	53201
8009	S	D	E	N	1972	53202
8009	S	D	R	N	1972	62689
8009	S	D	E	N	1962	63880
8009	S	D	E	N	1972	64417
8009	S	D	R	N	1975	100322
8009	S	D	E	N	1975	100323
8010	L	D	E	N	1974	79184
8010	L	S	E	N	1974	79184
8015	A	D	E	N	1973	51901
8015	A	D	E	N	1971	62269
8015	L	D	R	H	1976	103384
8015	L	D	R	N	1976	103384
8015	L	T	R	H	1976	103384
8015	L	T	R	N	1976	103384
8015	L	D	E	H	1976	103385
8015	L	D	E	N	1976	103385
8015	L	T	E	H	1976	103385
8015	L	T	E	N	1976	103385
8015	S	D	E	N	1973	53584
8015	S	S	E	L	1969	68115
8015	S	S	E	N	1969	68115
8015	T	D	E	N	1973	51901
8015	T	D	E	N	1973	55106
8019	S	D	E	N	1973	49591
8021	A	D	E	N	1973	51901
8021	A	D	E	N	1972	53266
8021	A	S	E	N	1974	65584
8021	S	S	E	N	1972	52968
8021	S	D	E	N	1971	59951
8021	S	S	E	N	1971	59951
8021	S	S	E	L	1969	68115
8021	S	S	E	N	1969	68115
8021	S	S	E	N	1972	87824
8021	T	D	E	N	1973	51901
8021	T	D	E	N	1972	53266
8021	T	D	E	N	1973	55106
8021	T	S	E	N	1974	55137
8021	T	D	E	N	1973	57468
8022	S	D	E	N	1973	50776
8022	S	D	E	N	1969	85428
8026	D	D	E	N	1974	60516
8026	S	D	E	N	1972	52989
8026	S	D	E	N	1973	55161
8026	S	S	E	N	1974	60516
8026	S	D	E	L	1974	62039
8026	S	S	E	L	1972	87889
8026	S	S	E	N	1972	87889
8026	S	D	E	N	1976	101211
8026	T	S	E	N	1972	87889
8031	S	S	E	N	1973	51865
8031	S	T	E	N	1973	51865
8031	S	S	E	L	1972	87889
8031	S	S	E	N	1972	87889
8057	S	D	R	N	1972	52209
8065	S	D	E	L	1973	53293
8065	S	D	E	N	1973	53293
8068	S	D	R	N	1974	58526
8068	S	T	R	N	1974	58526
8068	S	D	E	N	1974	66302
8068	S	T	E	N	1974	66302
8075	A	D	E	N	1973	51901
8075	A	S	E	N	1972	53376
8075	A	D	E	N	1974	53628
8075	A	D	E	N	1971	62269
8075	A	D	E	N	1972	75431
8075	T	D	E	N	1973	51901
111-8075	T	D	E	N	1971	53513
8075	T	D	E	N	1974	53628
8075	T	D	E	N	1973	55106
8075	T	D	E	N	1971	62269
8075	T	D	E	N	1972	75431
8078	S	D	E	N	1974	54594
8078	T	D	E	N	1971	53513
8078	T	D	E	N	1974	54594
8078	T	D	E	N	1973	55106
8079	A	D	E	N	1973	51901
8079	A	D	E	N	1975	86744
8079	A	T	E	N	1975	86744
8079	L	D	R	N	1974	87298
8079	L	D	E	N	1975	87299
8079	S	D	E	N	1973	53584
8079	S	S	E	N	1969	68115
8079	S	S	E	N	1972	87824
8079	T	D	E	N	1973	51901
8079	T	D	E	N	1973	55106
8098	S	D	R	N	1971	59995
8099	S	D	R	N	1971	59995
8100	S	D	R	N	1971	59995
8101	S	D	R	N	1971	59995
8108	A	D	E	N	1974	57991
8108	A	D	E	N	1975	96723
8108	A	S	E	N	1975	96723
8108	T	D	E	N	1974	57991
8108	T	D	E	N	1975	96723
8108	T	S	E	N	1975	96723
8109	A	S	E	N	1974	62603
8110	A	S	E	N	1974	62603
8114	A	D	E	N	1973	51901
8114	T	D	E	N	1973	51901
8116	S	D	R	N	1972	52262
8119	D	S	R	N	1973	55337
8119	D	S	E	N	1974	59275
8127	S	S	E	N	1972	87824
8128	T	D	E	N	1974	83981
8132	S	D	E	N	1973	56122
8133	S	D	R	N	1973	56317
8134	S	D	R	N	1973	56317
8153	S	D	R	N	1970	67414
8161	S	S	E	N	1972	87824
8162	A	S	E	N	1972	87824
8162	S	S	E	N	1972	87824
8190	S	D	R	N	1972	76507
8190	S	D	R	N	1972	78186
8190	S	D	E	N	1972	91590
8190	T	D	R	N	1972	78186
8207	S	S	E	N	1972	49784
112-0001	D	D	O	N	1972	51230
0001	L	S	E	N	1970	59588
0001	S	D	E	N	1973	50934
0011	S	S	E	N	1969	68271
0011	T	S	E	N	1971	60964
0025	S	D	E	N	1975	63329
0033	D	D	R	N	1973	55054
0033	D	D	E	N	1974	55055
0035	D	D	R	N	1973	55054
0035	D	D	E	N	1974	55055
0035	S	D	R	N	1973	52386
0035	S	D	E	N	1973	58579
0040	S	S	E	N	1974	61200
0098	S	D	R	N	1974	58128
0098	S	D	E	N	1974	58129
0098	S	D	E	N	1975	63329
0402	S	S	E	N	1969	68271
0402	S	S	E	N	1975	101023
0402	T	S	E	N	1971	60964
0402	T	D	E	N	1975	90114
0402	T	S	E	N	1975	90114
0569	S	D	E	N	1973	51862
8020	S	D	R	N	1973	51281
8020	S	D	R	N	1973	51564
8020	S	S	R	N	1972	53547
8020	S	S	E	N	1973	53548
8020	S	S	E	N	1974	53611
8020	S	D	E	N	1974	53695
8020	S	D	E	L	1974	54086
8020	S	D	E	N	1974	54086
8020	S	S	E	N	1972	87823
8020	T	S	E	N	1971	60964
8024	S	D	E	N	1971	49617
8025	D	D	E	N	1976	101450
8025	S	D	E	N	1973	49739
8025	S	D	R	N	1973	51272
8025	S	T	E	N	1973	52459
8025	S	S	E	N	1972	52968
8025	S	D	E	N	1972	53409
8025	S	D	E	L	1973	53588
8025	S	S	R	N	1973	55014
8025	S	S	E	N	1974	55015
8025	S	T	E	N	1973	57687
8025	S	D	E	N	1974	58432
8025	S	D	O	N	1971	60023
8025	S	D	E	L	1962	65963
8025	S	S	E	N	1969	68271
8025	S	S	E	N	1967	68371
8025	S	S	E	N	1973	72085
8025	T	S	E	N	1971	60964

Phys. State: **A.** Amorphous; **C.** Superconductive; **D.** Doped; **F.** Fibrous or Whisker; **G.** Gas; **I.** Ionized or Plasma; **L.** Liquid; **P.** Powder or Particle; **S.** Solid; **T.** Thin Film
Subject: **D.** Data; **E.** Experiment; **S.** Survey (Review, Compendium, etc.); **T.** Theory
Language: **E.** English; **F.** French; **G.** German; **O.** Other Languages; **R.** Russian
Temperature: **L.** Low (0 to 75K); **N.** Normal (75 to 1273K); **H.** High (above 1273K)

Substance Number	Phys. State	Subject	Language	Temperature	Year	EPIC Number
112-8032	S	D	R	N	1973	51281
8032	S	S	E	N	1972	87823
8062	S	D	F	N	1974	66369
8075	S	D	E	N	1975	86757
8083	S	S	E	N	1972	87823
8085	S	S	E	N	1972	87823
8085	T	S	E	N	1972	87823
8086	S	S	E	N	1972	87823
8087	S	S	E	N	1972	87823
8087	T	D	O	N	1972	67652
8094	C	D	E	L	1975	100026
114-0001	D	D	R	N	1973	52539
0001	D	D	E	N	1974	53672
0001	D	D	R	N	1973	54474
0001	D	D	E	N	1973	54475
0001	D	D	E	N	1973	60586
0001	D	D	E	L	1974	61391
0001	D	D	E	L	1972	61498
0001	D	D	E	N	1971	80226
0001	S	D	E	L	1973	50820
0001	S	D	E	N	1973	50820
0001	S	D	E	N	1973	53560
0001	S	D	R	N	1973	54474
0001	S	D	E	N	1973	54475
0001	S	D	E	L	1974	58962
0001	S	D	E	L	1968	74624
0001	S	D	E	N	1968	74624
0001	S	D	E	N	1975	86757
0001	S	D	E	N	1975	101667
0002	S	D	E	L	1968	74624
0002	S	D	E	N	1968	74624
0002	S	D	E	N	1975	86757
0006	S	S	E	L	1974	65584
0006	S	S	E	L	1975	91289
0009	S	D	E	N	1973	53560
0009	S	D	E	L	1974	58962
0009	S	D	E	N	1975	86757
0009	S	D	E	N	1975	101667
0010	S	S	E	N	1974	62066
0010	S	D	E	N	1975	86757
0010	S	D	E	N	1975	101667
0015	D	D	E	N	1975	92132
0015	T	D	E	N	1975	92132
0015	T	S	E	N	1975	92132
0017	A	S	E	N	1971	87884
0017	D	D	E	L	1973	57738
0017	D	D	E	N	1973	57738
0017	D	D	E	N	1974	60516
0017	D	D	E	N	1975	63562
0017	D	S	E	N	1975	63562
0017	D	S	E	N	1971	87884
0017	S	S	E	N	1972	52968
0017	S	S	E	N	1972	52989
0017	S	D	E	N	1973	53560
0017	S	D	E	N	1974	53915
0017	S	S	E	N	1974	53915
0017	S	D	E	N	1974	53917
0017	S	S	E	N	1973	53939
0017	S	D	R	N	1973	54361
0017	S	S	R	N	1973	54361
0017	S	D	E	N	1973	54362
0017	S	S	E	N	1973	54362
0017	S	D	E	N	1973	55860
0017	S	D	E	N	1973	57396
0017	S	D	E	N	1973	57732
0017	S	D	E	L	1973	57738
0017	S	D	E	N	1974	58808
0017	S	T	E	N	1974	58808
0017	S	D	E	N	1970	59674
0017	S	D	R	N	1971	60221
0017	S	S	E	N	1974	60516
0017	S	D	R	N	1974	62528
0017	S	S	R	N	1974	62528
0017	S	D	E	N	1974	64431
0017	S	S	E	N	1974	64431
0017	S	D	G	N	1954	66199
0017	S	S	E	N	1975	66684
0017	S	T	E	N	1975	66684
0017	S	S	R	N	1974	87312
0017	S	S	E	N	1975	87313
0017	S	S	E	N	1962	87660
0017	S	S	E	L	1971	87884
0017	S	S	E	N	1971	87884
0017	S	S	E	N	1972	87889
0017	S	D	R	N	1975	90136
0017	S	T	R	N	1975	90136
0017	S	D	E	N	1975	90137
0017	S	T	E	N	1975	90137
0017	S	D	E	N	1975	90718
0017	S	S	E	N	1975	90718
0017	S	D	E	L	1975	91725
0017	S	S	E	L	1975	91725
0017	S	S	E	N	1972	97249
0017	S	S	E	L	1962	97977
0017	S	S	E	N	1962	97977
0017	S	S	E	L	1963	98002
0017	S	S	E	N	1963	98002
0017	S	D	E	N	1976	100761
0017	S	S	E	L	1976	100761
0017	S	S	E	N	1976	100761
114-0017	S	T	E	N	1976	100761
0017	S	S	E	N	1976	101470
0017	S	D	R	N	1975	101515
0017	S	S	R	N	1975	101515
0017	S	T	R	N	1975	101515
0017	S	D	E	N	1975	101516
0017	S	S	E	N	1975	101516
0017	S	T	E	N	1975	101516
0017	S	S	E	N	1976	101823
0017	T	D	R	N	1973	55327
0017	T	T	R	L	1973	55327
0017	T	D	E	N	1974	59263
0017	T	T	E	L	1974	59263
0017	T	S	E	N	1971	60965
0017	T	D	E	N	1974	65107
0017	T	S	E	N	1969	87821
0017	T	S	E	N	1971	87884
0046	D	D	E	N	1973	51742
0055	S	S	E	N	1975	86748
0060	S	D	R	N	1973	51714
0060	S	D	E	N	1973	53574
0060	T	D	R	N	1974	66586
0060	T	D	E	N	1974	66587
0078	S	S	E	N	1971	87884
0078	T	T	R	N	1973	90563
0090	S	D	R	N	1972	76507
0090	S	D	E	N	1972	91590
0111	S	D	R	N	1974	93455
0111	S	T	R	N	1974	93455
0111	S	D	E	N	1974	93456
0111	S	T	E	N	1974	93456
0112	S	D	R	N	1974	93455
0112	S	T	R	N	1974	93455
0112	S	D	E	N	1974	93456
0112	S	T	E	N	1974	93456
0113	S	D	R	N	1974	93455
0113	S	T	R	N	1974	93455
0113	S	D	E	N	1974	93456
0113	S	T	E	N	1974	93456
0114	S	D	R	N	1974	93455
0114	S	T	R	N	1974	93455
0114	S	D	E	N	1974	93456
0114	S	T	E	N	1974	93456
8001	A	D	E	N	1973	50922
8001	A	S	E	N	1970	75887
8001	D	D	E	N	1973	54670
8001	D	S	R	L	1972	62704
8001	D	S	E	L	1973	65123
8001	D	D	R	N	1974	66647
8001	D	D	E	N	1974	66648
8001	D	S	E	N	1970	75887
8001	D	S	E	L	1965	87781
8001	S	D	E	N	1973	49738
8001	S	D	E	N	1973	50928
8001	S	D	E	N	1973	51050
8001	S	T	E	N	1973	52025
8001	S	S	R	L	1973	52543
8001	S	S	E	N	1972	52968
8001	S	S	E	N	1972	53299
8001	S	D	E	N	1973	53560
8001	S	D	E	N	1974	53610
8001	S	S	E	L	1974	53677
8001	S	S	E	N	1973	53939
8001	S	D	E	N	1974	54094
8001	S	S	E	L	1974	54339
8001	S	D	E	N	1974	54600
8001	S	D	E	N	1974	55241
8001	S	S	R	N	1973	55319
8001	S	S	E	N	1973	56749
8001	S	S	E	N	1973	56765
8001	S	D	E	N	1974	57322
8001	S	D	E	L	1974	58031
8001	S	D	E	N	1974	58038
8001	S	S	E	N	1974	58038
8001	S	S	E	N	1974	58040
8001	S	D	E	N	1974	58808
8001	S	T	E	N	1974	58808
8001	S	S	E	N	1974	59254
8001	S	D	E	N	1970	59674
8001	S	D	E	L	1974	60284
8001	S	D	E	N	1974	60284
8001	S	E	E	L	1974	60284
8001	S	E	E	N	1974	60284
8001	S	S	E	L	1974	60284
8001	S	S	E	N	1974	60284
8001	S	T	E	L	1974	60284
8001	S	T	E	N	1974	60284
8001	S	T	E	N	1963	60566
8001	S	S	E	N	1973	60580
8001	S	D	E	N	1963	60679
8001	S	D	E	N	1970	61493
8001	S	D	E	N	1974	62063
8001	S	T	E	N	1974	62063
8001	S	D	E	N	1969	62248
8001	S	T	E	N	1956	62960
8001	S	D	R	L	1974	65371
8001	S	D	E	L	1975	65372
8001	S	D	E	N	1973	65539
8001	S	D	G	N	1954	66199
8001	S	S	G	N	1954	66199
8001	S	D	E	N	1975	66682
114-8001	S	S	E	N	1975	66684
8001	S	T	E	N	1975	66684
8001	S	D	E	N	1972	67891
8001	S	S	E	N	1975	68679
8001	S	D	G	N	1974	71582
8001	S	D	R	L	1973	71670
8001	S	D	E	L	1966	74593
8001	S	S	E	N	1960	75859
8001	S	D	E	L	1973	82405
8001	S	S	E	L	1963	87679
8001	S	S	E	N	1963	87679
8001	S	S	E	L	1965	87781
8001	S	S	E	N	1965	87781
8001	S	S	E	L	1971	87884
8001	S	S	E	N	1971	87884
8001	S	S	E	L	1972	87889
8001	S	S	E	N	1972	87889
8001	S	S	R	L	1974	88331
8001	S	S	E	L	1974	88332
8001	S	D	R	N	1975	90136
8001	S	T	R	N	1975	90136
8001	S	D	E	N	1975	90137
8001	S	T	E	N	1975	90137
8001	S	D	E	N	1975	90718
8001	S	S	E	N	1975	90718
8001	S	S	E	N	1972	97249
8001	S	S	E	N	1976	101470
8001	S	D	R	N	1975	101515
8001	S	S	R	N	1975	101515
8001	S	T	R	N	1975	101515
8001	S	D	E	N	1975	101516
8001	S	S	E	N	1975	101516
8001	S	T	E	N	1975	101516
8001	S	D	R	L	1975	101629
8001	S	D	E	L	1975	101630
8001	S	S	E	N	1976	101823
8001	S	D	E	N	1976	103155
8001	T	D	E	N	1973	50922
8001	T	D	E	N	1973	54670
8001	T	S	E	N	1971	60965
8001	T	D	E	N	1971	63892
8001	T	D	E	N	1973	64100
8001	T	S	E	N	1965	87781
8001	T	S	E	N	1969	87821
8010	S	S	E	N	1972	61505
8010	S	D	R	N	1972	63472
8010	S	D	E	N	1972	65150
8011	L	D	R	N	1974	87298
8011	L	D	E	N	1975	87299
8012	L	D	E	N	1972	63722
8012	L	S	E	N	1972	63722
8012	L	D	R	H	1976	103384
8012	L	D	R	N	1976	103384
8012	L	T	R	H	1976	103384
8012	L	T	R	N	1976	103384
8012	L	D	E	H	1976	103385
8012	L	D	E	N	1976	103385
8012	L	T	E	H	1976	103385
8012	L	T	E	N	1976	103385
8012	S	D	R	N	1972	63472
8012	S	D	E	N	1972	65150
8012	S	S	E	N	1962	87661
8018	S	S	R	N	1973	87035
8018	S	S	E	N	1973	87036
8042	S	D	E	N	1973	50550
8042	S	S	E	N	1972	61505
8043	S	D	E	N	1973	50550
8044	C	D	E	L	1973	50953
8064	S	D	R	N	1972	63472
8064	S	D	E	N	1972	65150
8067	S	D	R	N	1975	100322
8067	S	D	E	N	1975	100323
8067	S	D	R	L	1976	102038
8067	S	D	R	N	1976	102038
8067	S	T	R	L	1976	102038
8067	S	T	R	N	1976	102038
8067	S	D	E	L	1976	102039
8067	S	D	E	N	1976	102039
8067	S	T	E	L	1976	102039
8067	S	T	E	N	1976	102039
8069	T	D	E	N	1974	83981
8070	T	D	E	N	1971	63892
8075	S	D	E	N	1974	56084
8076	S	D	E	N	1974	56084
8087	S	D	E	N	1974	62504
8088	S	D	E	N	1974	62504
8095	S	D	R	N	1974	93455
8095	S	T	R	N	1974	93455
8095	S	D	E	N	1974	93456
116-0005	S	D	E	N	1973	53838
0005	S	D	R	N	1973	57006
0017	S	D	E	N	1973	49734
0030	S	S	E	N	1974	66380
8003	S	D	R	N	1974	77941
8003	S	T	R	N	1974	77941
8003	S	D	E	N	1974	94517
8003	S	T	E	N	1974	94517
8026	S	D	R	N	1974	77941
8026	S	T	R	N	1974	77941
8026	S	D	E	N	1974	94517

Phys. State: **A.** Amorphous; **C.** Superconductive; **D.** Doped; **F.** Fibrous or Whisker; **G.** Gas; **I.** Ionized or Plasma; **L.** Liquid; **P.** Powder or Particle; **S.** Solid; **T.** Thin Film
Subject: **D.** Data; **E.** Experiment; **S.** Survey (Review, Compendium, etc.); **T.** Theory
Language: **E.** English; **F.** French; **G.** German; **O.** Other Languages; **R.** Russian
Temperature: **L.** Low (0 to 75K); **N.** Normal (75 to 1273K); **H.** High (above 1273K)

Substance Number	Phys. State	Subject	Language	Temperature	Year	EPIC Number
116-8026	S	T	E	N	1974	94517
8037	S	D	R	N	1973	58870
8038	S	D	R	N	1973	58870
118-0004	S	S	R	N	1974	63016
0004	S	S	E	N	1974	63017
0008	S	D	E	N	1975	86757
0037	D	T	E	N	1974	53896
0037	S	D	R	N	1973	55018
0037	S	D	E	N	1974	55019
0037	S	D	E	L	1974	60517
0037	S	D	E	N	1974	60517
0037	S	D	E	L	1975	91288
0037	S	D	E	N	1975	91288
0037	S	S	E	L	1975	91288
0037	S	S	E	N	1975	91288
0037	S	T	E	L	1975	91288
0037	S	T	E	N	1975	91288
0042	S	D	R	N	1973	57006
8015	C	D	E	L	1973	50953
8019	S	S	E	N	1972	53775
8028	S	S	E	N	1972	53775
8048	S	D	R	N	1974	58128
8048	S	D	E	N	1974	58129
8058	L	D	R	N	1973	51530
8058	L	D	E	N	1973	53679
8058	S	D	R	N	1973	51530
8058	S	D	E	N	1973	53679
8071	S	D	E	N	1975	86757
8072	S	D	R	N	1973	58870
8073	S	D	R	N	1973	58870
119-0001	D	D	E	L	1973	57666
0001	D	D	E	N	1973	57666
0001	S	D	E	N	1973	51862
0001	S	D	R	N	1967	53069
0001	S	D	E	N	1972	53070
0001	S	S	E	N	1973	57480
0001	S	D	E	N	1974	60658
0001	S	D	E	N	1975	63300
0001	S	D	E	N	1974	89519
0001	S	S	E	N	1974	89519
0001	S	D	E	N	1975	90460
0002	S	D	E	N	1973	53583
0002	S	S	E	N	1973	53583
0002	S	D	E	H	1970	60090
0002	S	S	E	N	1969	68271
0002	S	D	E	N	1975	86757
0002	S	S	E	N	1963	87682
0002	S	S	E	N	1969	87723
0002	S	D	E	N	1975	101667
0007	S	D	E	N	1975	80826
0008	D	D	E	N	1964	60562
0008	D	D	E	L	1974	58048
0008	S	D	E	N	1974	58048
0008	S	T	E	N	1974	58048
0041	S	D	E	N	1973	51646
0043	S	D	E	N	1974	58048
0043	S	T	E	N	1974	58048
0051	S	D	E	N	1965	58978
0064	S	D	E	N	1975	86757
8001	A	S	E	N	1974	58018
8001	S	D	E	N	1970	75407
8002	S	D	E	N	1972	53413
8002	S	T	E	N	1956	62960
8002	S	S	E	L	1962	87672
8002	S	S	E	N	1962	87672
8008	S	S	E	L	1969	68271
8008	S	D	E	N	1975	86757
8009	S	S	E	N	1962	87662
8010	S	S	E	L	1969	68271
8026	S	D	R	N	1973	50355
8026	S	D	E	N	1973	50356
8035	S	D	R	N	1972	60735
8035	S	S	R	N	1972	60735
8035	S	T	R	N	1972	60735
8035	S	D	E	N	1973	60736
8035	S	S	E	N	1973	60736
8035	S	T	E	N	1973	60736
8040	S	D	E	N	1973	52655
8041	S	D	E	N	1973	52655
8042	S	D	E	N	1973	52655
8067	S	D	R	N	1973	49847
8067	S	D	E	N	1973	54520
8081	S	D	R	N	1972	52262
8084	D	D	R	N	1973	56469
8084	D	D	E	N	1973	76678
8084	S	D	E	N	1975	90460
8085	S	S	E	N	1969	75843
8093	S	D	G	N	1973	57057
8094	S	D	G	N	1973	57057
8101	S	D	E	N	1975	90460
8120	S	S	E	N	1972	49784
120-0001	D	D	E	N	1973	52827
0001	D	D	E	N	1973	53755
0001	D	D	E	N	1975	63350
0001	S	D	R	N	1973	50634
0001	S	D	E	N	1973	52827
0001	S	D	E	N	1973	53032
0001	S	D	E	N	1973	53755

Substance Number	Phys. State	Subject	Language	Temperature	Year	EPIC Number
120-0001	S	S	E	N	1974	58051
0001	S	D	E	N	1974	65606
0001	S	S	E	N	1974	65606
0001	S	D	E	H	1971	66845
0001	S	D	E	N	1971	66845
0001	S	D	E	N	1975	80826
0004	S	S	E	H	1964	60562
0004	S	S	E	N	1964	60562
0006	S	D	E	N	1974	58051
0006	S	D	E	N	1974	58052
0009	S	D	E	N	1968	75725
0009	S	S	E	N	1968	75725
0010	S	D	R	N	1973	54869
0016	S	D	R	N	1973	57006
0024	S	D	R	N	1973	51325
0032	S	S	E	N	1974	66380
0036	S	S	E	N	1973	56765
0045	C	S	E	L	1972	87886
0045	S	D	E	N	1975	68687
0045	T	S	E	L	1972	87886
0056	S	D	E	N	1975	86757
0129	T	D	R	N	1973	90563
0129	T	T	R	N	1973	90563
0140	S	D	R	N	1967	53069
0140	S	D	E	N	1972	53070
0166	S	D	E	N	1975	86757
0190	S	S	E	N	1973	51936
0199	T	D	E	L	1973	52784
0203	S	S	E	N	1974	66380
0211	S	D	E	N	1975	86757
0233	S	D	E	N	1971	49617
0233	S	D	E	N	1974	58797
0286	S	D	R	N	1973	70822
0286	S	D	E	N	1973	91587
0287	S	D	R	N	1973	70822
0287	S	D	E	N	1973	91587
0288	S	D	R	N	1973	70822
0288	S	D	E	N	1973	91587
8006	C	T	R	L	1974	60465
8006	C	T	E	L	1974	60466
8006	C	S	E	L	1968	68372
8006	C	S	E	L	1968	68373
8006	C	S	E	L	1972	87886
8022	S	D	E	N	1971	49617
8022	S	S	E	N	1974	66380
8024	A	D	R	N	1971	59379
8024	A	S	E	N	1971	87885
8024	S	S	E	N	1971	87885
8042	S	D	E	N	1973	51862
8051	S	S	E	N	1972	53775
8077	S	S	R	N	1973	53995
8077	S	S	E	N	1973	53996
8079	S	D	R	N	1973	52563
8079	S	D	E	N	1973	57788
8085	S	S	F	N	1974	59609
8115	S	D	E	N	1975	86757
8116	S	D	E	N	1975	86757
8117	S	D	E	N	1975	86757
8118	S	D	E	N	1975	86757
8119	S	D	E	N	1975	86757
8121	S	D	R	N	1973	58870
8122	S	D	R	N	1973	58870
8127	S	D	E	N	1974	60275
8179	L	D	E	N	1974	62056
8179	L	T	E	N	1974	62056
8179	S	D	E	N	1974	62056
8179	S	T	E	N	1974	62056
8180	S	D	R	N	1976	99754
8180	S	D	E	N	1976	101631
122-0003	D	D	E	N	1973	51939
0003	S	D	E	N	1973	51939
0003	S	D	E	N	1973	53715
0003	S	D	E	H	1972	54828
0003	S	D	E	N	1972	54828
0004	D	D	E	N	1974	58340
0004	S	S	E	N	1974	55267
0005	D	D	R	N	1973	55066
0005	D	D	E	N	1974	55067
0005	D	D	E	H	1964	60562
0005	D	D	E	N	1964	60562
0005	D	S	E	N	1964	60562
0005	S	D	R	N	1973	50634
0005	S	D	E	N	1973	53032
0005	S	S	E	N	1972	53163
0005	S	S	E	N	1972	53166
0005	S	T	E	N	1972	53166
0005	S	D	R	N	1973	55066
0005	S	D	E	N	1974	55067
0005	S	D	E	N	1964	60562
0005	S	S	E	N	1964	60562
0005	S	D	R	N	1974	66762
0005	S	S	R	N	1974	66762
0005	S	T	R	N	1974	66762
0005	S	D	E	N	1975	66763
0005	S	S	E	N	1975	66763
0005	S	T	E	N	1975	66763
0005	S	S	E	N	1974	87606
0005	T	D	R	N	1972	56958
0008	S	D	F	H	1971	59552
0008	S	D	F	N	1971	59552

Substance Number	Phys. State	Subject	Language	Temperature	Year	EPIC Number
122-0008	S	D	E	N	1974	62048
0009	A	D	R	L	1971	59379
0009	A	S	R	N	1973	71659
0009	A	S	E	N	1971	87885
0009	A	S	E	N	1973	91454
0009	D	D	E	N	1973	57725
0009	S	D	R	H	1971	59379
0009	S	D	E	N	1975	101667
0009	T	D	E	N	1973	52306
0009	T	D	R	L	1971	59379
0012	S	D	E	N	1975	90692
0012	S	T	E	N	1975	90692
0013	T	D	R	N	1974	90192
0013	T	D	E	N	1975	90193
0014	S	S	E	N	1972	53110
0014	S	D	R	N	1973	70821
0014	S	D	E	N	1975	80826
0014	S	D	E	N	1973	91586
0015	S	S	E	N	1971	87881
0016	D	D	R	N	1971	76496
0016	D	D	E	N	1971	91580
0016	S	D	E	N	1971	49793
0016	S	D	R	N	1973	50219
0016	S	D	E	N	1973	50220
0016	S	D	R	N	1973	52535
0016	S	D	E	N	1974	53652
0016	S	S	E	N	1973	56765
0016	S	T	E	N	1974	71206
0016	S	S	E	L	1971	87881
0016	S	S	E	N	1971	87881
0017	S	D	E	H	1974	55261
0017	S	D	E	L	1974	55261
0017	T	D	E	N	1973	50764
0017	T	S	E	N	1974	53724
0017	T	D	E	N	1974	62032
0017	T	D	E	N	1973	63510
0023	S	S	E	N	1972	52968
0023	S	D	E	N	1973	60636
0023	S	D	E	N	1972	61767
0023	S	T	E	N	1972	61767
0023	S	S	E	N	1974	62493
0023	S	D	E	N	1975	63293
0023	S	S	E	L	1969	68271
0023	S	D	E	N	1975	80826
0023	S	S	E	H	1963	87709
0023	S	S	E	N	1963	87709
0023	T	S	E	N	1971	60964
0023	T	D	E	L	1975	92849
0025	D	D	R	N	1973	51317
0025	D	D	E	N	1973	55347
0025	S	D	R	N	1973	51317
0025	S	D	E	N	1973	55347
0026	S	S	E	N	1970	75833
0026	S	S	E	N	1971	87881
0030	D	D	E	N	1975	65497
0030	S	D	E	N	1973	49734
0030	S	D	E	N	1973	60645
0030	S	D	E	N	1975	65497
0030	S	D	E	L	1975	91288
0030	S	D	E	N	1975	91288
0030	S	T	E	L	1975	91288
0030	S	T	E	N	1975	91288
0031	S	D	R	N	1974	66728
0031	S	D	E	N	1975	66729
0031	S	D	R	H	1974	66744
0031	S	D	R	N	1974	66744
0031	S	S	E	H	1974	66744
0031	S	S	E	N	1974	66744
0031	S	T	R	H	1974	66744
0031	S	T	R	N	1974	66744
0031	S	D	E	H	1975	66745
0031	S	D	E	N	1975	66745
0031	S	S	E	H	1975	66745
0031	S	S	E	N	1975	66745
0031	S	T	E	H	1975	66745
0031	S	T	E	N	1975	66745
0031	S	S	E	L	1969	68271
0031	S	D	E	N	1975	86757
0031	S	S	E	N	1975	96477
0037	S	D	R	N	1973	54869
0037	S	S	E	N	1973	86375
0038	T	D	E	N	1975	90658
0046	S	D	E	N	1975	80826
0047	D	D	E	N	1974	62056
0047	D	T	E	N	1974	62056
0047	L	D	E	N	1974	62056
0047	L	T	E	N	1974	62056
0047	S	D	E	N	1975	80826
0050	P	S	E	L	1967	66368
0050	P	S	E	N	1967	66368
0050	S	D	R	N	1972	50688
0050	S	S	E	N	1967	66368
0050	S	S	E	N	1969	68115
0050	T	D	E	L	1974	53643
0050	T	S	E	L	1967	66368
0050	T	S	E	N	1967	66368
0050	T	D	E	N	1975	92802
0053	A	S	E	N	1976	98108
0053	D	D	E	N	1974	57302
0053	S	D	E	N	1973	50398
0053	S	S	E	N	1974	57302

Phys. State: **A.** Amorphous; **C.** Superconductive; **D.** Doped; **F.** Fibrous or Whisker; **G.** Gas; **I.** Ionized or Plasma; **L.** Liquid; **P.** Powder or Particle; **S.** Solid; **T.** Thin Film
Subject: **D.** Data; **E.** Experiment; **S.** Survey (Review, Compendium, etc.); **T.** Theory
Language: **E.** English; **F.** French; **G.** German; **O.** Other Languages; **R.** Russian
Temperature: **L.** Low (0 to 75K); **N.** Normal (75 to 1273K); **H.** High (above 1273K)

Substance Number	Phys. State	Subject	Language	Temperature	Year	EPIC Number
122-0053	S	S	E	N	1969	68115
0053	T	D	E	N	1974	57302
0053	T	S	E	N	1969	68115
0053	T	S	E	N	1966	87833
0068	T	S	E	N	1969	68115
0093	S	D	O	N	1973	51459
0096	T	S	E	N	1975	95324
0105	T	D	O	N	1973	56266
0112	S	S	E	N	1972	53110
0112	S	S	E	N	1972	53261
0112	S	D	E	N	1974	55974
0112	S	S	E	N	1971	87881
0112	T	S	E	N	1971	87881
0299	S	D	R	N	1973	57006
0314	S	D	E	N	1972	53102
0314	T	D	R	N	1972	56958
0421	S	D	E	N	1973	90094
8041	S	D	R	N	1973	54869
8045	D	D	E	N	1975	86883
8045	S	S	E	N	1974	61337
8045	S	S	E	N	1971	66193
8078	S	D	E	N	1974	55974
8078	S	S	E	N	1970	75833
8088	S	S	E	N	1971	87881
8113	S	D	G	N	1973	57059
8124	S	S	E	N	1970	75833
8124	S	D	R	H	1972	76529
8124	S	D	R	N	1972	76529
8124	S	S	E	N	1971	87881
8124	S	D	E	H	1972	91534
8124	S	D	E	N	1972	91534
8134	S	D	R	N	1973	70821
8134	S	D	E	N	1973	91586
123-0003	S	S	E	N	1972	52968
0003	S	D	E	L	1972	53200
0003	S	D	E	N	1972	53200
0003	S	S	E	L	1973	54772
0003	S	D	E	N	1973	60638
0003	S	S	E	L	1969	68115
0003	S	S	E	N	1969	68115
0003	S	S	E	N	1966	68361
0003	S	D	G	N	1974	71582
0003	S	S	E	N	1972	87824
0003	S	S	E	N	1976	101470
0003	S	S	E	L	1976	101823
0003	S	S	E	N	1976	101823
0003	T	D	R	N	1971	63462
0003	T	D	E	N	1971	65164
0003	T	S	E	N	1966	68361
0003	T	D	E	N	1971	70599
0027	L	D	E	N	1972	62523
0032	S	D	E	L	1972	49918
0032	S	D	E	N	1973	50789
0032	S	D	E	N	1974	55242
0032	S	T	E	N	1974	59352
0032	S	D	E	N	1972	65878
0032	S	S	E	N	1972	65878
0032	S	T	E	N	1972	65878
0032	S	S	E	N	1975	94550
0042	S	S	E	N	1975	94550
0048	D	D	E	N	1971	85443
0048	S	D	R	N	1972	49646
0048	S	D	E	N	1972	51526
0048	S	S	E	N	1972	51526
0048	S	D	R	N	1972	55490
0048	S	D	E	N	1971	85443
0048	S	D	E	N	1966	85844
8013	S	D	E	N	1969	85351
8013	S	S	E	N	1969	85351
8017	P	S	E	N	1972	87824
8017	S	T	E	N	1973	52461
8017	S	D	E	L	1973	52462
8017	S	D	E	N	1973	52462
8017	S	D	E	N	1973	52463
8017	S	S	E	N	1972	52968
8017	S	S	E	L	1973	54772
8017	S	D	F	N	1970	59867
8017	S	D	E	N	1973	60638
8017	S	S	E	N	1973	60638
8017	S	D	R	L	1972	63428
8017	S	D	R	N	1972	63428
8017	S	D	E	L	1973	67082
8017	S	D	E	N	1973	67082
8017	S	S	E	L	1969	68115
8017	S	S	E	N	1969	68115
8017	S	D	E	N	1975	87174
8017	S	S	E	N	1975	87174
8017	S	S	E	N	1962	87674
8017	S	S	E	N	1972	87824
8017	S	S	E	L	1975	96245
8017	S	S	E	N	1976	101823
8017	S	D	E	N	1976	102168
8017	S	T	E	N	1976	102168
8017	T	D	R	N	1971	67320
8018	C	D	E	L	1973	55157
8018	D	D	R	N	1973	58209
8018	D	D	E	N	1974	59204
8018	D	D	R	N	1972	62719
8018	D	D	E	N	1973	65315
8018	D	D	R	N	1974	71470
123-8018	D	D	E	N	1975	71506
8018	L	T	R	H	1976	103384
8018	L	T	R	N	1976	103384
8018	L	T	E	H	1976	103385
8018	L	T	E	N	1976	103385
8018	P	S	E	N	1972	87824
8018	S	S	E	N	1972	52968
8018	S	D	E	N	1973	53588
8018	S	D	E	N	1973	53853
8018	S	D	E	N	1972	59070
8018	S	S	E	N	1972	59070
8018	S	D	E	N	1973	60638
8018	S	S	E	N	1973	60638
8018	S	D	R	N	1968	60749
8018	S	D	E	N	1974	60750
8018	S	S	R	N	1974	63131
8018	S	S	E	N	1975	63132
8018	S	S	E	N	1972	63827
8018	S	D	E	N	1975	65441
8018	S	S	E	L	1970	68114
8018	S	S	E	N	1970	68114
8018	S	S	E	L	1969	68115
8018	S	S	E	N	1969	68115
8018	S	T	E	N	1975	68678
8018	S	D	G	N	1974	71582
8018	S	S	E	N	1966	75147
8018	S	D	E	N	1975	87174
8018	S	S	E	N	1975	87174
8018	S	S	E	L	1962	87671
8018	S	S	E	N	1962	87671
8018	S	S	E	N	1972	87824
8018	S	S	E	N	1966	87831
8018	S	S	R	N	1966	91929
8018	S	D	E	N	1975	91930
8018	S	S	E	N	1976	101470
8018	S	S	E	L	1976	101823
8018	T	D	O	N	1971	49563
8018	T	D	R	N	1972	49571
8018	T	D	E	N	1972	53263
8018	T	D	E	N	1968	59520
8018	T	D	R	N	1972	62707
8018	T	D	E	N	1973	65303
8018	T	D	R	N	1971	67320
8018	T	D	R	N	1974	71470
8018	T	D	E	N	1975	71506
8018	T	D	E	N	1975	90976
8018	T	D	E	N	1973	102095
8025	T	D	R	N	1972	76540
8025	T	D	E	N	1972	91592
8039	S	D	R	N	1973	50066
8039	S	D	E	N	1973	51420
8039	S	T	E	N	1973	52461
8039	S	D	E	L	1973	52462
8039	S	D	E	N	1973	52462
8039	S	D	E	N	1973	52463
8039	S	S	E	N	1972	53321
8039	S	S	E	L	1972	87824
8039	S	S	E	N	1972	87824
8039	S	S	R	N	1974	97468
8039	S	S	E	N	1975	97469
8039	S	D	E	N	1976	102168
8039	T	D	E	N	1972	53324
8039	T	D	E	N	1973	53434
8050	T	S	E	N	1972	87824
8051	D	D	E	N	1973	57597
8051	S	D	E	N	1973	53588
8051	S	T	E	N	1973	57444
8051	S	D	E	N	1974	60161
8051	S	D	E	L	1974	61383
8051	S	D	F	N	1972	61662
8051	S	S	F	N	1972	61662
8051	S	S	R	N	1974	63131
8051	S	S	E	N	1975	63132
8051	S	S	E	N	1970	68114
8051	S	S	E	L	1972	87824
8051	S	S	E	N	1972	87824
8051	S	D	R	N	1975	94942
8051	S	D	E	N	1975	95895
8051	S	D	E	N	1976	100173
8051	T	D	E	N	1972	53263
8051	T	D	E	N	1973	53434
8051	T	D	R	N	1972	62707
8051	T	D	E	N	1973	65303
8051	T	S	E	L	1972	87824
8051	T	S	E	N	1972	87824
8051	T	D	E	N	1973	102095
8051	T	S	E	N	1973	102095
8058	S	S	E	L	1973	54772
8058	S	S	E	N	1974	61199
8058	S	S	E	N	1972	87824
8065	S	D	R	N	1973	52528
8065	S	D	R	N	1973	55298
8065	S	D	E	N	1974	57769
8065	S	D	E	N	1974	59283
8068	A	D	R	N	1974	62436
8068	A	D	E	N	1974	67079
8068	T	D	R	N	1974	62436
8068	T	D	E	N	1974	67079
8069	S	D	E	N	1969	85351
8070	S	D	E	N	1969	85351
8070	S	S	E	N	1969	85351
123-8074	P	S	E	N	1972	87824
8074	S	S	E	N	1972	87824
8093	S	S	E	N	1972	87824
8094	S	S	E	N	1972	87824
8099	T	D	R	N	1972	76540
8099	T	D	E	N	1972	91592
8100	T	D	R	N	1972	76540
8100	T	D	E	N	1972	91592
8104	S	D	E	N	1973	53799
125-8014	S	D	R	N	1974	77941
8014	S	T	R	N	1974	77941
8014	S	D	E	N	1974	94517
8014	S	T	E	N	1974	94517
8036	S	D	R	N	1973	58870
126-0001	L	S	E	N	1969	68115
0001	S	S	E	N	1971	59952
0001	S	S	E	N	1969	68115
0001	S	S	E	N	1972	87824
0002	S	D	E	N	1973	57112
0002	S	S	E	N	1969	68115
0002	S	S	E	N	1972	87824
0004	S	D	E	N	1973	51856
0004	S	D	E	N	1974	53598
0004	S	S	E	N	1974	58804
0005	D	D	E	N	1973	49614
0005	D	D	R	N	1971	56220
0005	S	D	E	N	1973	51907
0005	S	S	E	N	1972	52968
0005	S	D	E	N	1973	53560
0005	S	D	E	N	1974	53610
0005	S	D	R	N	1973	54361
0005	S	S	R	N	1973	54361
0005	S	D	E	N	1973	54362
0005	S	S	E	N	1973	54362
0005	S	D	R	N	1973	55207
0005	S	D	E	N	1974	55208
0005	S	D	R	N	1971	56217
0005	S	D	E	N	1974	58036
0005	S	D	E	N	1974	58808
0005	S	T	E	N	1974	58808
0005	S	D	E	N	1975	63293
0005	S	D	E	L	1975	66683
0005	S	D	E	N	1975	66683
0005	S	E	E	L	1975	66683
0005	S	E	E	N	1975	66683
0005	S	S	E	N	1975	66683
0005	S	S	E	N	1969	68271
0005	S	S	E	N	1973	72085
0005	S	D	E	N	1960	85819
0005	S	S	E	N	1960	85819
0005	S	S	E	L	1963	87711
0005	S	S	E	N	1963	87711
0005	S	S	E	N	1966	87712
0005	S	S	E	N	1972	87823
0005	S	D	E	N	1962	89789
0005	S	D	E	L	1975	91637
0005	S	D	E	N	1975	91637
0005	S	S	E	N	1975	91637
0005	T	D	E	N	1974	58961
0005	T	S	E	N	1971	60964
0005	T	S	E	N	1963	87711
0005	T	D	E	N	1976	101298
0014	L	D	R	N	1974	90235
0014	L	D	E	N	1975	90236
0014	L	D	R	H	1976	103384
0014	L	D	R	N	1976	103384
0014	L	T	R	H	1976	103384
0014	L	T	R	N	1976	103384
0014	L	D	E	H	1976	103385
0014	L	D	E	N	1976	103385
0014	L	T	E	H	1976	103385
0014	L	T	E	N	1976	103385
0014	S	D	R	N	1973	51973
0014	T	D	E	N	1973	55106
0017	S	D	E	N	1973	53588
0017	S	S	E	L	1969	68271
0017	S	D	E	N	1975	86757
0022	S	D	R	N	1967	53069
0022	S	D	E	N	1972	53070
0037	S	D	R	N	1967	53069
0037	S	D	E	N	1972	53070
0038	S	D	E	N	1973	51862
0038	S	D	R	N	1967	53069
0038	S	D	E	N	1972	53070
0043	L	D	R	N	1971	59646
0043	L	D	E	N	1971	59647
8001	S	D	E	N	1969	85351
8001	S	S	E	N	1969	85351
8021	S	D	E	N	1969	85351
8021	S	S	E	N	1969	85351
8026	S	D	E	L	1964	61307
8026	S	D	E	N	1964	61307
8026	S	D	E	N	1964	85438
8026	S	S	E	N	1964	85438
8030	A	D	E	N	1972	49458
8030	A	D	E	N	1972	49467
8030	A	D	E	N	1973	51901
8030	A	D	E	N	1972	53112
8030	A	D	E	N	1972	53386

Phys. State: A. Amorphous; C. Superconductive; D. Doped; F. Fibrous or Whisker; G. Gas; I. Ionized or Plasma; L. Liquid; P. Powder or Particle; S. Solid; T. Thin Film
Subject: D. Data; E. Experiment; S. Survey (Review, Compendium, etc.); T. Theory
Language: E. English; F. French; G. German; O. Other Languages; R. Russian
Temperature: L. Low (0 to 75K); N. Normal (75 to 1273K); H. High (above 1273K)

Substance Number	Phys. State	Subject	Language	Temperature	Year	EPIC Number
126-8030	L	D	R	H	1976	103384
8030	L	D	R	N	1976	103384
8030	L	T	R	H	1976	103384
8030	L	T	R	N	1976	103384
8030	L	D	E	H	1976	103385
8030	L	D	E	N	1976	103385
8030	L	T	E	H	1976	103385
8030	L	T	E	N	1976	103385
8030	S	D	E	N	1972	53112
8030	S	D	E	N	1974	55249
8030	T	D	E	N	1972	49458
8030	T	D	E	N	1972	49467
8030	T	D	E	N	1973	51901
8030	T	D	E	N	1972	53386
8032	A	D	E	N	1974	62603
8032	L	D	R	N	1971	76462
8032	L	D	E	N	1971	91582
8032	L	T	R	H	1976	103384
8032	L	T	R	N	1976	103384
8032	L	T	E	H	1976	103385
8032	L	T	E	N	1976	103385
8032	S	S	R	N	1972	62298
8032	S	S	E	N	1973	62299
8034	D	D	R	N	1973	51515
8034	L	D	R	N	1973	51515
8034	L	D	R	N	1971	59646
8034	L	D	E	N	1971	59647
8035	S	S	E	N	1969	68115
8035	S	S	E	N	1972	87824
8035	S	D	E	L	1972	100962
8035	S	D	E	N	1972	100962
8037	L	T	R	H	1976	103384
8037	L	T	R	N	1976	103384
8037	L	T	E	H	1976	103385
8037	L	T	E	N	1976	103385
8037	S	S	E	N	1972	52968
8037	S	D	E	N	1973	60638
8037	S	S	E	N	1973	60638
8037	S	D	R	L	1972	63428
8037	S	D	R	N	1972	63428
8037	S	D	E	L	1973	67082
8037	S	D	E	N	1973	67082
8037	S	S	E	N	1970	68114
8037	S	S	E	L	1969	68115
8037	S	S	E	N	1969	68115
8037	S	S	E	N	1972	87824
8037	T	S	E	N	1970	68114
8046	A	D	E	N	1972	49467
8046	A	D	E	N	1973	51901
8046	T	D	E	N	1972	49467
8046	T	D	E	N	1973	51901
8047	C	D	E	L	1972	49547
8047	C	D	E	L	1973	50870
8047	C	S	E	L	1967	66157
8048	S	S	E	N	1972	87823
8048	T	D	E	N	1976	101298
8048	T	S	E	N	1976	101298
8049	S	S	E	N	1972	87823
8049	T	D	E	N	1973	50612
8050	S	S	E	N	1972	87823
8050	S	S	E	N	1976	101298
8050	T	D	E	N	1976	101298
8051	S	D	R	N	1975	100322
8051	S	T	R	N	1975	100322
8051	S	D	E	N	1975	100323
8051	S	T	E	N	1975	100323
8052	D	D	E	N	1974	53923
8052	D	D	E	N	1974	60751
8052	D	D	E	N	1972	61505
8052	D	D	E	L	1966	74595
8052	S	D	E	N	1973	50928
8052	S	D	E	N	1973	51907
8052	S	S	E	N	1972	52968
8052	S	D	E	N	1972	53099
8052	S	D	E	N	1973	53346
8052	S	S	R	N	1972	53547
8052	S	S	E	N	1973	53548
8052	S	D	E	N	1973	53560
8052	S	D	E	N	1974	53610
8052	S	D	E	N	1974	54600
8052	S	D	E	N	1974	58808
8052	S	T	E	N	1974	58808
8052	S	D	E	N	1963	60679
8052	S	D	E	N	1974	60751
8052	S	D	R	N	1969	61845
8052	S	D	E	N	1971	62264
8052	S	D	E	N	1971	65042
8052	S	S	E	N	1969	68271
8052	S	S	E	L	1963	68313
8052	S	S	E	N	1963	68313
8052	S	S	E	N	1973	72085
8052	S	S	E	N	1972	87823
8052	S	D	E	N	1975	88219
8052	S	S	E	L	1975	88219
8052	S	S	E	N	1975	88219
8052	S	D	E	N	1975	93167
8052	S	D	R	N	1975	96306
8052	S	D	E	N	1975	96307
8052	S	S	E	N	1976	101470
8052	S	D	R	N	1975	101610
8052	S	T	R	N	1975	101610
126-8052	S	D	E	N	1976	101611
8052	S	T	E	N	1976	101611
8052	T	S	E	N	1971	60964
8052	T	D	R	N	1970	61532
8052	T	S	E	L	1963	68313
8052	T	S	E	N	1963	68313
8052	T	S	E	N	1972	87823
8052	T	D	E	N	1976	101298
8052	T	S	E	N	1976	101298
8055	S	D	E	N	1972	49935
8055	S	S	E	N	1969	68115
8055	S	S	E	N	1972	87824
8059	D	D	R	N	1973	52563
8059	D	D	E	N	1973	57788
8059	S	D	R	N	1973	52563
8059	S	D	E	N	1973	57788
8060	S	D	E	N	1973	50910
8060	S	D	R	N	1973	51723
8060	S	D	E	N	1973	53415
8067	S	S	E	N	1972	87824
8070	S	S	E	N	1972	53775
8072	S	D	E	N	1971	53360
8072	S	D	E	N	1973	53855
8074	S	D	E	N	1969	62248
8076	S	D	E	N	1973	50567
8079	S	D	E	N	1973	53588
8079	S	S	E	L	1969	68271
8079	S	D	E	N	1975	86757
8080	S	D	E	N	1973	53588
8080	S	S	E	L	1969	68271
8080	S	D	E	N	1975	86757
8083	C	D	E	L	1974	58045
8088	T	D	E	N	1974	54336
8089	T	D	E	N	1974	54336
8090	S	D	E	N	1974	53598
8100	A	D	E	N	1974	86009
8100	T	D	E	N	1974	86009
8104	S	D	R	N	1975	86853
8104	S	D	E	N	1975	86854
8104	T	D	R	N	1973	56300
8107	S	D	E	N	1974	84453
8136	S	S	E	N	1972	87824
8137	S	S	E	N	1972	87824
127-8002	L	D	E	N	1974	54095
8002	L	S	E	N	1974	54095
8002	L	T	E	N	1974	54095
8002	L	D	R	N	1971	59646
8002	L	D	E	N	1971	59647
8004	A	D	E	N	1973	51484
8004	D	D	R	L	1973	50084
8004	D	D	R	N	1973	50084
8004	D	D	E	L	1973	51435
8004	D	D	E	N	1973	51435
8004	S	D	E	N	1973	51648
8004	S	S	E	N	1972	52968
8004	S	D	E	N	1971	53243
8004	S	D	E	N	1973	53560
8004	S	D	E	N	1974	53610
8004	S	D	E	N	1974	54033
8004	S	D	R	N	1973	54361
8004	S	S	R	N	1973	54361
8004	S	D	E	N	1973	54362
8004	S	S	E	N	1973	54362
8004	S	D	E	N	1974	58808
8004	S	T	E	N	1974	58808
8004	S	D	R	N	1969	61845
8004	S	D	E	N	1972	63492
8004	S	S	E	N	1972	63492
8004	S	S	E	N	1969	68271
8004	S	S	E	N	1973	72085
8004	S	S	E	N	1962	87666
8004	S	S	E	N	1972	87823
8004	S	D	E	N	1972	90612
8004	T	D	E	N	1973	51484
8004	T	D	R	L	1972	58947
8004	T	D	R	N	1972	58947
8004	T	S	E	N	1971	60964
8004	T	D	R	N	1970	61532
8004	T	D	R	N	1969	61845
8004	T	D	E	N	1976	101298
8008	T	D	R	N	1972	66991
8010	T	D	E	N	1974	54336
8011	S	D	F	N	1974	59609

Phys. State: **A.** Amorphous; **C.** Superconductive; **D.** Doped; **F.** Fibrous or Whisker; **G.** Gas; **I.** Ionized or Plasma; **L.** Liquid; **P.** Powder or Particle; **S.** Solid; **T.** Thin Film
Subject: **D.** Data; **E.** Experiment; **S.** Survey (Review, Compendium, etc.); **T.** Theory
Language: **E.** English; **F.** French; **G.** German; **O.** Other Languages; **R.** Russian
Temperature: **L.** Low (0 to 75K); **N.** Normal (75 to 1273K); **H.** High (above 1273K)

Chapter 7 Electric Hysteresis

Substance Number	Phys. State	Subject	Language	Temperature	Year	EPIC Number
100-0045	S	S	R	N	1971	53063
0045	S	S	E	N	1972	53064
0045	S	S	E	N	1973	58179
0055	S	T	E	N	1975	91784
8028	S	D	E	N	1973	56593
102-0002	T	T	R	H	1975	91366
0002	T	T	E	H	1975	95225
0054	S	S	E	N	1970	87822
0054	S	S	E	N	1972	87890
0054	S	S	E	N	1976	101320
0281	S	S	E	N	1976	101320
0282	S	S	E	N	1976	101320
0342	S	D	E	N	1972	49480
0342	S	D	E	N	1973	50816
8027	S	S	E	N	1970	87822
8027	S	S	E	N	1970	87871
8027	S	S	E	N	1976	101320
8137	S	T	R	N	1973	52876
8137	S	T	E	N	1974	52877
8137	S	D	E	N	1974	90316
8137	S	T	E	N	1974	90316
8137	S	D	E	N	1974	90338
8137	S	S	E	N	1976	101320
8166	S	T	R	N	1973	52876
8166	S	T	E	N	1974	52877
8166	S	D	E	N	1974	90316
8166	S	T	E	N	1974	90316
8166	S	T	E	L	1974	90340
8166	S	S	E	N	1976	101320
8412	S	S	E	N	1970	87871
8412	S	S	E	N	1976	101320
8413	S	S	E	N	1970	87871
8414	S	S	E	N	1970	87871
8439	S	S	E	N	1976	101320
104-0002	S	D	E	N	1973	57106
0013	D	D	E	N	1971	50467
0013	D	D	O	N	1973	56801
0013	P	D	E	N	1973	57471
0013	S	D	R	N	1973	50347
0013	S	D	E	N	1973	50348
0013	S	D	E	N	1973	51824
0013	S	D	R	N	1972	52515
0013	S	D	E	N	1974	54547
0013	S	S	E	N	1974	54577
0013	S	T	R	N	1973	55022
0013	S	T	E	N	1974	55023
0013	S	D	R	N	1973	55064
0013	S	D	E	N	1974	55065
0013	S	D	R	N	1972	56005
0013	S	D	E	N	1973	56462
0013	S	S	R	N	1973	56875
0013	S	S	R	N	1973	56876
0013	S	S	R	N	1973	56878
0013	S	T	R	N	1973	56879
0013	S	D	R	N	1973	56880
0013	S	T	R	N	1973	56885
0013	S	S	O	N	1973	57208
0013	S	D	E	N	1974	60335
0013	S	D	R	N	1973	68038
0013	S	D	E	N	1973	68039
0013	S	S	E	N	1967	85905
0013	S	S	E	N	1971	87880
0013	S	D	G	N	1974	90255
0013	S	D	E	N	1974	90347
0013	S	D	E	N	1974	90352
0013	S	D	E	N	1974	90354
0013	S	S	E	N	1965	98850
0013	T	D	R	N	1973	51614
0013	T	D	R	N	1974	65389
0013	T	T	R	N	1974	65389
0013	T	D	E	N	1975	65390
0013	T	T	E	N	1975	65390
0013	T	D	E	N	1967	85905
0040	S	D	E	N	1973	50419
0337	D	D	E	N	1974	54027
0337	S	T	E	N	1974	54027
0386	S	T	R	N	1973	52854
0386	S	T	E	N	1973	52855
0386	S	D	E	L	1975	90067
0386	S	T	E	N	1975	91784
0386	T	E	R	N	1972	49809
8110	S	D	E	N	1974	54028
8110	S	S	E	N	1970	87822
8110	S	S	E	N	1972	87890
8110	S	D	E	N	1975	90683
8160	S	T	R	N	1973	51360
8160	S	T	E	N	1973	51361
8161	S	T	R	N	1973	51360
8161	S	T	E	N	1973	51361
8169	S	S	E	N	1970	87871
8171	D	D	E	N	1973	66096
8171	S	D	E	N	1973	51462
8171	S	D	R	N	1973	52904
104-8171	S	D	E	N	1974	52905
8171	S	D	O	L	1973	54850
8171	S	D	O	N	1973	54850
8171	S	D	O	L	1973	65654
8171	S	D	O	N	1973	65654
8175	S	D	R	N	1973	51934
8175	S	D	E	N	1973	63232
8188	S	D	E	N	1972	53114
8237	S	D	E	N	1974	54547
8318	T	D	E	N	1973	58178
8357	S	D	E	N	1974	90359
8358	S	D	E	N	1974	90359
8361	S	D	E	N	1975	90683
8364	S	S	E	N	1970	87871
8365	S	S	E	N	1970	87871
106-0006	S	D	R	N	1972	52240
0218	S	D	R	L	1973	55046
0218	S	D	E	L	1974	55047
8245	S	S	E	N	1970	87871
8293	S	D	E	L	1973	52051
8773	S	D	E	N	1975	92178
8773	S	T	E	N	1975	92178
108-0014	S	D	E	N	1973	66101
0014	S	S	E	N	1970	87822
0014	S	S	E	N	1972	87890
0014	S	D	E	N	1974	90316
0014	S	T	E	N	1974	90316
0014	S	T	E	L	1974	90340
0014	S	S	E	N	1976	101320
0114	S	S	E	N	1970	87871
0114	S	S	E	N	1976	101320
8014	S	D	R	N	1973	51358
8014	S	D	E	N	1973	51359
8015	S	D	R	N	1973	51358
8015	S	D	E	N	1973	51359
8025	S	T	R	N	1973	52854
8025	S	T	E	N	1973	52855
8025	S	D	R	N	1973	67526
8055	S	D	E	N	1974	90316
8055	S	T	E	N	1974	90316
8055	S	T	E	L	1974	90340
8055	S	S	E	N	1976	101320
8056	S	S	E	N	1970	87871
110-8252	S	S	E	N	1970	87871
111-0046	S	D	G	N	1973	51928
0046	S	D	G	N	1970	52694
0046	S	D	E	N	1974	54028
0046	S	D	R	N	1973	56014
0046	S	D	E	N	1973	57103
0046	S	D	E	N	1974	90308
8061	S	D	R	N	1974	90204
8061	S	D	E	N	1975	90205
8061	T	D	R	N	1973	52870
8061	T	D	E	N	1973	52871
8068	D	D	E	N	1972	53114
8068	S	D	E	N	1972	53114
8068	S	D	E	N	1973	57120
8068	S	D	R	N	1974	90204
8068	S	D	E	N	1975	90205
8069	S	D	E	N	1972	53114
8070	S	D	E	N	1972	53114
8119	D	T	R	N	1973	55337
8119	D	T	E	N	1974	59275
8135	S	D	E	N	1974	57144
112-0028	S	D	E	N	1973	50782
0028	S	D	E	N	1973	52624
0028	S	S	E	N	1974	54577
0028	S	T	E	N	1974	63580
0028	S	D	R	N	1973	67524
0028	S	T	O	N	1974	67738
0028	S	S	E	N	1970	87822
0028	S	S	E	N	1972	87890
0028	S	T	E	N	1974	90315
0028	S	D	E	N	1974	90316
0028	S	T	E	N	1974	90316
0028	S	T	E	N	1974	90337
0028	S	T	E	L	1974	90340
0028	S	D	E	N	1974	90352
0028	S	S	E	N	1976	101320
0033	S	D	E	N	1974	64508
0033	S	D	E	N	1973	67800
0033	S	S	E	N	1970	87871
0034	S	D	E	L	1973	50419
0035	S	D	R	N	1971	66129
0035	S	D	R	N	1973	71655
0035	S	S	E	N	1970	87871
0035	S	D	E	N	1973	91464
0035	S	D	E	N	1975	91944
0035	S	T	E	N	1975	91944
0038	S	S	E	N	1970	87822
112-0038	S	S	E	N	1970	87871
0038	S	S	E	N	1976	101320
0275	S	S	E	N	1970	87871
0583	S	D	E	N	1973	50873
0583	S	D	R	N	1973	51358
0583	S	D	E	N	1973	51359
0583	S	D	E	N	1974	90316
0583	S	T	E	L	1974	90340
0583	S	S	E	N	1976	101320
0604	S	S	E	N	1970	87871
8034	S	D	E	N	1973	57119
8051	S	D	R	N	1973	55020
8051	S	D	E	N	1974	55021
8051	S	S	R	N	1973	62863
8051	S	S	E	N	1973	65166
8080	S	S	E	N	1970	87871
8081	S	S	E	N	1970	87871
8082	S	S	E	N	1970	87871
8097	S	D	E	N	1975	91944
8097	S	T	E	N	1975	91944
114-0018	S	D	E	N	1973	57448
0018	S	T	R	N	1973	58523
0060	S	D	R	N	1973	51932
0060	S	D	E	N	1973	53574
0060	S	S	E	N	1974	54577
0060	S	D	R	N	1973	55012
0060	S	D	E	N	1974	55013
0060	S	T	R	N	1974	63128
0060	S	T	E	N	1975	63129
0060	S	D	E	N	1973	63230
0060	S	T	E	L	1974	90340
116-0017	S	S	E	L	1972	87890
0031	S	D	E	N	1973	52291
0031	S	D	E	N	1973	56642
0031	S	S	E	N	1972	87890
0031	S	T	R	N	1974	90202
0031	S	T	E	N	1975	90203
0031	S	D	E	N	1974	90354
8017	S	D	O	N	1972	50641
8017	S	T	R	N	1973	52854
8017	S	T	E	N	1973	52855
8017	S	S	E	N	1970	87822
8017	S	S	E	N	1972	87890
8017	S	S	E	N	1965	98850
8040	S	T	E	L	1974	90340
8044	S	D	E	N	1975	68590
8044	S	T	E	N	1975	68590
118-0037	S	S	R	N	1973	56887
0037	S	S	E	H	1970	87822
0037	S	S	E	H	1972	87890
0037	S	D	E	N	1974	90346
0041	S	S	E	N	1972	87890
0041	P	D	E	N	1973	67801
0041	S	D	E	N	1974	54028
0041	S	S	E	N	1974	54577
0041	S	S	R	N	1973	56887
0041	S	S	E	N	1970	87822
0041	S	S	E	N	1972	87890
8018	S	D	E	N	1973	52123
8018	S	E	E	N	1973	52123
8018	S	D	E	N	1973	56462
8018	S	S	E	N	1974	66864
8018	S	D	E	N	1975	85756
8018	T	T	F	N	1973	54648
8059	D	T	R	H	1974	60431
8059	D	T	E	H	1974	60432
8059	S	T	R	H	1974	60431
8059	S	T	E	H	1974	60432
8088	S	D	E	H	1974	90504
8088	S	D	E	N	1974	90504
119-0015	S	S	E	N	1970	87871
8103	S	S	E	N	1970	87871
120-0024	S	S	E	N	1974	54577
0024	S	D	E	N	1973	55873
0197	S	D	E	N	1973	53796
0197	S	S	E	N	1970	87871
0235	S	T	R	N	1973	51360
0235	S	T	E	N	1973	51361
0235	S	S	E	N	1965	98850
8039	S	D	E	N	1974	62679
8104	S	D	E	N	1973	56156
8181	S	D	E	L	1976	101344
122-0005	S	T	E	N	1974	58818
0009	S	D	E	N	1974	54028
0012	S	D	E	N	1974	90352
0013	S	D	E	N	1973	51633
0013	S	D	E	N	1972	53802
0013	S	S	E	N	1956	75730
0013	S	S	E	N	1970	87871

Phys. State: **A.** Amorphous; **C.** Superconductive; **D.** Doped; **F.** Fibrous or Whisker; **G.** Gas; **I.** Ionized or Plasma; **L.** Liquid; **P.** Powder or Particle; **S.** Solid; **T.** Thin Film
Subject: **D.** Data; **E.** Experiment; **S.** Survey (Review, Compendium, etc.); **T.** Theory
Language: **E.** English; **F.** French; **G.** German; **O.** Other Languages; **R.** Russian
Temperature: **L.** Low (0 to 75K); **N.** Normal (75 to 1273K); **H.** High (above 1273K)

Substance Number	Phys. State	Sub-ject	Lan-guage	Temper-ature	Year	EPIC Number
122-0013	S	T	E	N	1974	90353
0030	S	T	E	N	1973	51672
0030	S	D	O	L	1972	67461
0030	S	D	O	N	1972	67461
0030	S	D	E	L	1975	90067
0112	S	D	E	N	1974	55974
0196	D	D	E	N	1972	49820
0196	D	D	E	N	1972	53292
0196	D	E	E	N	1972	53292
0196	D	D	E	N	1973	56462
0196	D	D	E	N	1974	90572
0196	S	D	E	N	1973	56462
0196	S	T	E	N	1974	57957
0196	S	T	E	N	1975	63345
0196	S	D	G	N	1974	90255
0196	S	D	E	N	1974	90572
0196	S	S	E	N	1965	98850
0292	S	D	E	N	1973	56462
0292	S	S	O	N	1973	57208
0292	S	S	E	N	1970	87871
8042	D	D	E	N	1973	52756
8042	S	D	E	N	1973	52756
8043	S	T	R	N	1973	52854
8043	S	T	E	N	1973	52855
8056	D	D	E	N	1973	55278
8067	S	D	E	N	1973	52576
8078	S	D	E	N	1974	55974
8079	D	T	E	N	1974	57957
8123	S	S	E	N	1970	87871
123-8018	D	D	E	L	1970	66918
8018	S	D	E	L	1970	66918
8051	S	D	E	L	1970	66918

Phys. State: **A.** Amorphous; **C.** Superconductive; **D.** Doped; **F.** Fibrous or Whisker; **G.** Gas; **I.** Ionized or Plasma; **L.** Liquid; **P.** Powder or Particle; **S.** Solid; **T.** Thin Film
Subject: **D.** Data; **E.** Experiment; **S.** Survey (Review, Compendium, etc.); **T.** Theory
Language: **E.** English; **F.** French; **G.** German; **O.** Other Languages; **R.** Russian
Temperature: **L.** Low (0 to 75K); **N.** Normal (75 to 1273K); **H.** High (above 1273K)

Chapter 8 Energy Level

Substance Number	Phys. State	Subject	Language	Temperature	Year	EPIC Number
100-0003	D	D	R	N	1973	52326
0045	G	D	E	N	1973	51491
0045	G	S	E	N	1973	51491
0045	G	T	E	N	1973	51491
0045	G	T	E	N	1974	54036
0045	G	S	R	N	1972	65883
0045	G	S	E	N	1972	65884
0045	G	S	E	H	1964	87578
0045	I	S	E	N	1974	88611
0045	I	S	E	N	1974	88612
0045	I	S	E	N	1974	88613
0045	L	D	E	N	1973	51491
0045	L	S	E	N	1973	51491
0045	L	T	E	N	1973	51491
0045	L	S	R	N	1972	65883
0045	L	S	E	N	1972	65884
0045	S	S	E	N	1973	56767
0045	S	S	E	N	1971	65050
0045	S	S	R	N	1972	65883
0045	S	S	E	N	1972	65884
0045	S	S	E	N	1974	90711
0055	A	T	E	N	1973	51774
0055	A	T	E	N	1972	53113
0055	A	E	E	N	1972	53276
0055	A	T	E	N	1972	53276
0055	A	S	E	N	1974	55137
0055	A	T	E	N	1973	55740
0055	A	S	O	N	1972	58591
0055	A	S	E	N	1973	59623
0055	A	S	E	N	1971	60961
0055	A	T	E	N	1972	62387
0055	A	T	R	N	1972	62723
0055	A	T	E	N	1974	63399
0055	A	T	E	N	1971	65067
0055	A	T	E	N	1973	65319
0055	A	T	E	N	1962	65961
0055	C	S	E	L	1973	56284
0055	D	D	E	N	1973	50756
0055	D	S	E	N	1972	53200
0055	D	T	R	N	1971	54260
0055	D	T	E	N	1972	54261
0055	D	T	R	N	1973	55331
0055	D	T	E	N	1974	59267
0055	D	S	R	N	1972	62703
0055	D	S	R	N	1972	62704
0055	D	T	R	N	1972	62723
0055	D	T	R	N	1973	62727
0055	D	T	E	L	1972	63848
0055	D	S	E	N	1973	65123
0055	D	S	E	N	1972	65300
0055	D	T	E	N	1973	65319
0055	D	T	E	N	1973	65323
0055	D	T	E	N	1962	65947
0055	D	T	R	N	1974	78247
0055	D	T	E	N	1975	78261
0055	D	E	E	N	1974	90402
0055	L	T	E	N	1973	55740
0055	L	S	E	N	1970	75833
0055	S	T	R	N	1973	50072
0055	S	T	R	N	1973	50073
0055	S	E	R	N	1973	50205
0055	S	E	E	N	1973	50206
0055	S	T	E	N	1973	50925
0055	S	E	E	N	1973	51465
0055	S	T	R	N	1973	51552
0055	S	E	E	N	1973	51758
0055	S	T	E	N	1973	51791
0055	S	E	E	N	1973	51910
0055	S	S	O	N	1973	52180
0055	S	T	R	N	1973	52373
0055	S	T	E	N	1973	52697
0055	S	S	E	N	1972	53132
0055	S	T	E	N	1972	53176
0055	S	S	E	N	1972	53324
0055	S	T	E	N	1973	53562
0055	S	S	E	N	1974	53607
0055	S	T	E	N	1973	53683
0055	S	D	E	N	1974	53917
0055	S	T	E	N	1974	53917
0055	S	T	E	N	1974	54040
0055	S	D	E	N	1974	54081
0055	S	S	E	N	1974	54083
0055	S	T	E	N	1974	54085
0055	S	D	E	N	1974	54094
0055	S	S	E	N	1974	54094
0055	S	T	E	N	1974	54094
0055	S	T	R	N	1973	54183
0055	S	T	E	N	1973	54184
0055	S	T	R	N	1971	54268
0055	S	T	E	N	1972	54269
0055	S	T	E	N	1974	54339
0055	S	T	E	H	1973	55112
0055	S	S	E	N	1974	55137
0055	S	T	R	N	1973	55191
0055	S	T	E	N	1974	55192
100-0055	S	T	R	N	1973	55287
0055	S	T	R	N	1973	55294
0055	S	T	R	N	1973	55332
0055	S	S	E	N	1973	56284
0055	S	S	E	L	1973	56765
0055	S	S	E	N	1973	56767
0055	S	T	E	N	1974	57002
0055	S	T	E	N	1974	57980
0055	S	T	E	N	1974	58034
0055	S	T	E	N	1974	59245
0055	S	T	E	N	1974	59268
0055	S	T	E	N	1974	59269
0055	S	T	G	L	1973	59319
0055	S	T	E	N	1970	59810
0055	S	T	E	N	1971	60102
0055	S	T	E	N	1964	60562
0055	S	T	E	N	1973	60629
0055	S	T	E	N	1973	60630
0055	S	D	E	N	1971	60678
0055	S	T	R	N	1972	60707
0055	S	T	E	N	1973	60708
0055	S	T	R	N	1972	60721
0055	S	T	E	N	1973	60722
0055	S	T	E	N	1947	61287
0055	S	T	E	N	1974	61352
0055	S	T	R	L	1973	61454
0055	S	S	E	N	1970	61494
0055	S	T	E	N	1970	61494
0055	S	T	E	N	1974	63209
0055	S	E	E	N	1975	63405
0055	S	S	E	L	1971	64456
0055	S	T	E	N	1974	64457
0055	S	T	E	N	1971	65042
0055	S	T	E	N	1974	65250
0055	S	T	E	L	1962	65945
0055	S	T	E	N	1962	65946
0055	S	T	E	N	1962	65960
0055	S	S	R	N	1974	66558
0055	S	S	E	N	1974	66559
0055	S	T	E	N	1975	66685
0055	S	S	E	N	1973	67175
0055	S	D	E	N	1972	67891
0055	S	T	E	N	1971	76033
0055	S	T	R	N	1971	77244
0055	S	S	R	N	1974	83872
0055	S	S	E	N	1975	86765
0055	S	T	E	N	1975	86765
0055	S	T	R	N	1975	90012
0055	S	T	E	N	1975	90133
0055	S	T	E	N	1974	90403
0055	S	T	R	N	1975	90674
0055	S	S	E	N	1974	91448
0055	S	T	E	N	1975	91605
0055	S	T	E	N	1975	92822
0055	S	T	E	N	1974	92943
0055	S	T	E	N	1975	93512
0055	S	T	E	N	1975	98207
0055	T	T	R	N	1968	75362
0055	T	T	E	N	1969	91450
8003	D	T	R	N	1974	58124
8003	D	T	E	N	1974	58125
8003	S	S	E	N	1973	51467
8003	S	T	E	L	1973	53582
8003	S	S	E	N	1974	54603
8003	S	T	E	L	1970	59675
8003	S	T	E	L	1973	60592
8003	S	T	E	N	1973	60592
8003	S	D	E	N	1970	63588
8003	S	S	E	N	1970	63588
8003	S	S	E	N	1966	63913
8003	S	T	E	N	1975	66687
8003	S	S	E	N	1968	74624
8003	S	T	E	N	1968	74624
8003	S	S	E	N	1975	86758
8007	S	D	E	N	1975	87171
8007	S	T	E	N	1975	96242
8008	D	S	E	N	1971	87884
8008	S	T	E	N	1973	57392
8008	S	D	E	N	1975	87171
8008	T	S	E	N	1969	87821
8011	S	D	R	N	1973	52327
8016	S	T	E	N	1970	59810
8017	S	T	E	N	1974	54110
8031	S	T	E	N	1973	57392
8043	S	S	E	N	1969	75843
8047	S	D	E	N	1975	87171
8059	S	S	E	N	1973	51467
8062	G	D	E	N	1975	92059
8062	G	S	E	N	1975	92059
102-0002	A	S	E	N	1972	52403
0002	D	D	E	N	1973	50785
0002	D	D	E	N	1974	54323
0002	D	D	E	L	1974	54565
0002	D	D	E	N	1974	54565
102-0002	D	S	E	N	1974	54565
0002	D	S	E	N	1973	56749
0002	S	S	E	N	1973	56749
0002	S	S	E	N	1974	94145
0002	T	D	E	N	1972	53262
0005	S	D	E	N	1974	54600
0005	S	S	E	N	1974	54600
0005	S	D	E	N	1974	58589
0005	S	D	E	N	1974	61388
0005	S	D	E	N	1975	86758
0009	D	T	E	N	1975	90105
0009	S	E	E	N	1973	49671
0009	S	D	E	N	1972	63847
0009	S	S	E	N	1972	63847
0009	S	D	E	N	1975	86758
0010	S	D	E	N	1973	50837
0010	S	D	E	N	1972	63847
0010	S	S	E	N	1972	63847
0010	S	D	E	N	1975	86758
0013	D	D	R	N	1973	51950
0013	D	D	R	N	1973	52352
0013	D	D	E	N	1973	54435
0033	S	S	E	N	1974	94145
0038	S	D	E	N	1974	54305
0041	T	T	E	N	1975	65464
0105	D	D	O	N	1974	90530
0105	T	T	E	N	1967	85339
0119	S	D	E	N	1974	54305
0182	S	D	E	N	1974	54305
0185	S	S	E	N	1974	94145
0191	D	D	R	L	1973	54357
0191	D	D	R	N	1973	54357
0191	D	D	E	L	1973	54358
0191	D	D	E	N	1973	54358
0248	S	T	R	N	1973	51376
0248	S	T	E	N	1973	51377
0248	S	S	E	N	1966	87830
0248	S	D	E	N	1975	90718
0248	S	S	E	N	1975	90718
0250	D	D	E	N	1973	52164
0250	D	S	E	N	1972	53131
0250	D	D	E	N	1973	53727
0250	D	D	E	N	1974	53918
0250	D	T	E	N	1974	53918
0250	D	D	R	N	1973	54375
0250	D	D	E	N	1973	54376
0250	D	D	E	N	1974	57987
0250	D	D	E	N	1974	60671
0250	D	S	E	N	1974	60671
0250	D	D	R	N	1972	60727
0250	D	D	E	N	1973	60728
0250	D	D	E	N	1969	101680
0297	D	D	R	N	1973	70823
0297	D	D	E	N	1973	91588
0317	G	D	E	N	1973	52751
0342	S	D	R	L	1973	52914
0342	S	D	E	L	1974	52915
0369	D	D	E	N	1974	57305
8001	A	D	E	N	1974	54345
8001	D	D	E	N	1973	53427
8001	D	S	E	N	1973	53427
8001	D	D	R	L	1973	58200
8001	D	D	R	N	1973	58200
8001	D	D	E	L	1974	59205
8001	D	D	E	N	1974	59205
8001	D	S	E	N	1962	87668
8001	D	S	E	N	1966	87830
8001	D	S	E	N	1971	87884
8001	S	D	E	N	1973	50925
8001	S	S	E	N	1973	53427
8001	S	S	E	N	1974	54081
8001	S	D	E	N	1974	54345
8001	S	D	R	N	1973	55223
8001	S	D	E	N	1974	55224
8001	S	S	E	N	1972	55728
8001	S	D	E	N	1975	90718
8001	S	S	E	N	1975	90718
8001	T	S	E	N	1969	87821
8005	S	D	E	N	1974	57319
8005	S	T	E	N	1974	57319
8018	T	D	E	N	1973	64100
8031	A	D	E	N	1972	53276
8031	A	S	E	N	1974	61387
8031	A	S	E	N	1971	84631
8031	D	D	R	N	1974	60421
8031	D	D	E	N	1974	60422
8031	S	S	E	N	1971	84631
8035	S	D	E	N	1974	60664
8041	A	D	E	N	1974	54345
8041	D	D	E	N	1972	49555
8041	D	D	R	N	1972	49647
8041	D	D	R	L	1973	50080
8041	D	D	R	N	1973	50081
8041	D	D	E	N	1973	50154
8041	D	D	R	L	1973	50221

Phys. State: **A.** Amorphous; **C.** Superconductive; **D.** Doped; **F.** Fibrous or Whisker; **G.** Gas; **I.** Ionized or Plasma; **L.** Liquid; **P.** Powder or Particle; **S.** Solid; **T.** Thin Film
Subject: **D.** Data; **E.** Experiment; **S.** Survey (Review, Compendium, etc.); **T.** Theory
Language: **E.** English; **F.** French; **G.** German; **O.** Other Languages; **R.** Russian
Temperature: **L.** Low (0 to 75K); **N.** Normal (75 to 1273K); **H.** High (above 1273K)

Substance Number	Phys. State	Sub-ject	Lan-guage	Temper-ature	Year	EPIC Number
102-8041	D	D	E	L	1973	50222
8041	D	D	R	N	1973	50723
8041	D	D	E	N	1973	50904
8041	D	D	E	L	1973	50931
8041	D	D	E	N	1973	51427
8041	D	D	E	N	1973	51433
8041	D	D	E	N	1973	51643
8041	D	D	R	N	1973	51704
8041	D	D	E	N	1973	51790
8041	D	T	E	N	1973	52090
8041	D	D	E	N	1973	52290
8041	D	T	R	N	1973	52520
8041	D	D	R	N	1973	52521
8041	D	T	R	N	1973	52529
8041	D	D	R	N	1973	52532
8041	D	D	E	L	1973	52651
8041	D	D	E	N	1973	52937
8041	D	D	E	N	1973	53024
8041	D	T	E	N	1972	53113
8041	D	D	E	N	1972	53138
8041	D	D	E	N	1972	53143
8041	D	D	E	N	1972	53271
8041	D	D	E	N	1973	53565
8041	D	D	E	N	1974	54559
8041	D	T	E	N	1973	54771
8041	D	D	E	N	1974	55237
8041	D	D	E	N	1974	55245
8041	D	D	R	N	1973	55336
8041	D	S	R	N	1973	55336
8041	D	D	R	N	1973	55342
8041	D	D	E	N	1973	56372
8041	D	D	R	N	1973	57367
8041	D	D	E	N	1973	57440
8041	D	T	E	N	1973	57469
8041	D	T	E	N	1974	57761
8041	D	D	E	N	1974	57762
8041	D	T	E	N	1974	57770
8041	D	D	E	N	1974	57773
8041	D	D	E	N	1974	58326
8041	D	D	R	N	1972	58674
8041	D	D	E	N	1974	59274
8041	D	S	E	N	1974	59274
8041	D	D	E	N	1974	59284
8041	D	D	E	N	1971	59711
8041	D	T	E	N	1971	59711
8041	D	S	E	L	1972	60677
8041	D	D	E	N	1971	60690
8041	D	S	E	N	1972	61061
8041	D	T	E	N	1972	61061
8041	D	T	E	N	1974	61180
8041	D	T	E	N	1974	61356
8041	D	S	E	N	1970	61494
8041	D	S	E	N	1970	62251
8041	D	S	E	N	1969	62252
8041	D	S	E	N	1970	62255
8041	D	D	R	N	1973	62726
8041	D	D	R	H	1970	63458
8041	D	D	R	N	1970	63458
8041	D	D	E	H	1970	65158
8041	D	D	E	N	1970	65158
8041	D	D	E	N	1973	65322
8041	D	D	R	N	1970	66268
8041	D	D	R	N	1970	66270
8041	D	T	R	N	1974	66450
8041	D	T	E	N	1974	66451
8041	D	D	E	N	1975	66715
8041	D	S	E	N	1975	66715
8041	D	D	O	N	1971	66801
8041	D	D	R	N	1970	67712
8041	D	D	R	N	1969	67766
8041	D	D	E	N	1970	68189
8041	D	D	E	N	1968	74639
8041	D	S	E	N	1962	87673
8041	D	S	E	L	1964	87701
8041	D	S	E	N	1964	87701
8041	D	S	E	L	1971	87884
8041	D	S	E	N	1971	87884
8041	D	D	E	N	1975	90007
8041	D	D	E	N	1975	97860
8041	D	D	E	N	1976	100869
8041	D	T	E	N	1976	100869
8041	G	D	E	N	1973	56372
8041	S	D	E	N	1972	49555
8041	S	D	R	N	1972	49647
8041	S	D	R	N	1973	50054
8041	S	D	E	N	1973	50925
8041	S	D	E	N	1973	51465
8041	S	E	E	N	1973	51465
8041	S	D	E	N	1973	51790
8041	S	D	E	N	1973	51910
8041	S	E	E	N	1973	51910
8041	S	S	O	N	1973	52180
8041	S	S	E	N	1973	53570
8041	S	D	E	N	1974	53607
8041	S	D	E	N	1974	54081
8041	S	S	E	N	1974	54085
8041	S	D	E	N	1974	54094
8041	S	D	E	N	1974	54345
8041	S	D	R	N	1973	54361
8041	S	S	R	N	1973	54361
8041	S	D	E	N	1973	54362
102-8041	S	S	E	N	1973	54362
8041	S	D	E	N	1974	54600
8041	S	S	E	N	1974	54600
8041	S	D	E	L	1974	54601
8041	S	D	E	N	1974	54601
8041	S	D	E	N	1974	54604
8041	S	D	E	N	1974	54608
8041	S	S	E	N	1974	54608
8041	S	T	R	N	1973	54990
8041	S	T	E	N	1974	54991
8041	S	D	R	N	1973	55305
8041	S	D	R	L	1973	55316
8041	S	S	R	L	1973	55316
8041	S	S	R	N	1973	55334
8041	S	D	E	N	1971	55377
8041	S	S	E	N	1974	58038
8041	S	D	E	L	1974	58935
8041	S	D	E	N	1974	59230
8041	S	D	E	L	1974	59241
8041	S	S	E	L	1974	59241
8041	S	D	E	N	1974	59272
8041	S	D	R	N	1973	59722
8041	S	S	R	N	1973	59722
8041	S	T	R	N	1973	59722
8041	S	D	E	N	1973	59723
8041	S	S	E	N	1973	59723
8041	S	T	E	N	1973	59723
8041	S	D	E	N	1971	60546
8041	S	S	E	N	1971	60546
8041	S	D	E	N	1973	60575
8041	S	D	E	N	1973	60581
8041	S	T	E	N	1973	60627
8041	S	D	E	N	1974	62063
8041	S	T	E	N	1974	62063
8041	S	S	E	N	1970	62262
8041	S	D	E	N	1973	63838
8041	S	S	E	N	1971	65048
8041	S	D	E	N	1975	65438
8041	S	T	E	N	1972	66214
8041	S	D	R	N	1970	67712
8041	S	T	R	N	1974	72651
8041	S	T	E	N	1975	72700
8041	S	D	E	N	1968	74648
8041	S	D	E	N	1966	75146
8041	S	D	R	N	1975	81273
8041	S	S	E	N	1973	86380
8041	S	T	E	L	1975	86752
8041	S	D	R	N	1975	86877
8041	S	D	E	N	1975	86878
8041	S	D	E	N	1975	87171
8041	S	S	E	N	1964	87701
8041	S	D	E	L	1975	89446
8041	S	T	E	L	1975	89446
8041	S	D	E	N	1975	90025
8041	S	D	E	N	1975	90718
8041	S	S	E	N	1975	90718
8041	S	T	E	N	1975	91718
8041	S	T	E	L	1975	91863
8041	S	D	R	N	1966	91926
8041	S	D	E	N	1975	94088
8041	S	D	R	N	1974	96773
8041	S	S	R	N	1974	96773
8041	S	D	E	N	1975	96774
8041	S	S	E	N	1975	96774
8041	S	S	E	N	1972	97249
8041	S	D	E	N	1975	97730
8041	S	S	E	N	1975	97730
8041	T	D	E	N	1973	51410
8041	T	D	E	L	1973	51432
8041	T	D	O	N	1973	51511
8041	T	D	E	N	1975	63405
8041	T	D	R	N	1969	67766
8041	T	D	E	N	1970	68189
8041	T	S	E	N	1964	87701
8041	T	S	E	N	1969	87821
8041	T	S	E	N	1971	87884
8054	A	D	E	N	1974	54345
8054	D	D	R	N	1973	50055
8054	D	D	R	N	1973	50080
8054	D	D	E	N	1973	51411
8054	D	D	E	N	1973	51433
8054	D	T	E	N	1973	53572
8054	D	D	R	N	1973	58156
8054	D	S	E	N	1972	61061
8054	D	D	R	L	1974	62428
8054	D	D	R	N	1974	62428
8054	D	D	E	L	1974	65331
8054	D	D	E	N	1974	65331
8054	D	D	R	N	1974	66562
8054	D	D	E	N	1974	66563
8054	D	S	E	N	1962	87667
8054	D	S	E	N	1971	87884
8054	S	D	R	N	1973	50055
8054	S	D	E	N	1973	50925
8054	S	D	E	N	1973	51411
8054	S	D	E	N	1973	52697
8054	S	S	E	L	1973	52697
8054	S	D	E	N	1974	53607
8054	S	D	E	N	1974	54081
8054	S	D	E	N	1974	54345
8054	S	D	R	N	1974	58604
102-8054	S	T	R	N	1974	58604
8054	S	D	E	N	1974	62063
8054	S	T	E	N	1974	62063
8054	S	D	E	N	1968	74648
8054	S	S	E	N	1962	87667
8054	S	D	E	N	1975	90718
8054	S	S	E	N	1975	90718
8054	S	S	E	N	1972	97249
8056	S	D	E	N	1972	52995
8069	S	D	E	N	1973	50559
8070	S	D	E	N	1975	87180
8074	D	D	E	N	1972	49856
8074	D	D	E	N	1973	52405
8074	D	D	E	N	1970	52699
8074	D	D	E	L	1972	53097
8074	D	D	E	L	1972	53126
8074	D	S	E	N	1973	65763
8074	D	S	E	N	1972	85903
8074	S	T	E	N	1975	68705
8075	T	D	R	L	1973	55339
8075	T	D	E	L	1974	59277
8084	D	D	R	N	1973	55338
8084	D	D	R	N	1974	67749
8084	S	D	E	N	1973	51051
8084	S	D	R	N	1973	55338
8084	S	D	E	N	1974	59276
8084	S	D	R	N	1974	67759
8084	S	D	E	N	1975	86764
8094	D	D	R	N	1973	50083
8094	D	D	E	N	1973	51434
8094	T	D	R	N	1973	50057
8094	T	D	R	N	1973	50083
8094	T	D	E	N	1973	51413
8094	T	D	E	N	1973	51434
8095	D	D	E	N	1973	52782
8095	D	D	E	N	1974	53717
8095	D	D	E	L	1974	53737
8095	D	D	E	N	1974	53737
8095	D	D	E	N	1974	54035
8095	D	T	E	N	1974	54035
8095	D	S	E	N	1974	55245
8095	D	D	E	N	1975	86754
8095	D	S	E	L	1972	87889
8095	D	S	E	N	1972	87889
8095	D	D	E	L	1974	88285
8095	S	S	E	N	1972	53227
8095	S	D	E	N	1974	53721
8095	S	D	E	N	1975	63356
8095	S	T	E	N	1975	63356
8095	S	D	R	N	1975	81273
8095	S	S	E	N	1965	87703
8095	S	D	E	N	1975	94088
8096	D	D	R	N	1973	51730
8096	D	S	E	N	1973	79154
8106	A	S	E	N	1974	54594
8106	A	T	E	N	1974	54594
8106	T	D	E	N	1974	54594
8119	S	D	E	N	1975	86764
8120	D	D	E	N	1973	50869
8125	S	S	E	N	1973	51205
8126	S	S	E	N	1973	51205
8127	S	S	E	N	1973	51205
8132	S	T	R	N	1973	51376
8132	S	T	E	N	1973	51377
8132	S	D	E	N	1970	66515
8132	S	D	E	N	1975	90718
8132	S	S	E	N	1975	90718
8139	S	D	E	N	1973	51461
8139	S	D	E	L	1974	53722
8139	S	D	E	N	1974	60309
8162	S	D	E	N	1973	52451
8173	S	D	E	N	1975	86758
8187	A	D	E	N	1974	54059
8187	A	S	E	N	1974	54059
8187	S	T	E	N	1974	54059
8187	S	D	E	N	1973	57667
8189	D	D	E	L	1970	59866
8189	S	D	E	L	1975	68702
8192	S	D	E	N	1974	54113
8205	D	D	E	N	1973	52164
8217	S	T	E	N	1973	52303
8218	S	T	E	N	1973	52303
8223	S	D	E	N	1973	57667
8230	S	D	E	N	1974	62033
8232	S	D	E	N	1974	60664
8235	S	D	E	N	1974	54092
8243	A	D	E	N	1974	58811
8243	A	S	E	N	1974	58811
8243	S	D	E	N	1974	58811
8243	S	S	E	N	1974	58811
8248	S	D	E	N	1974	58811
8259	S	D	E	N	1974	57975
8278	S	D	E	N	1973	57461
8283	S	D	E	N	1971	65061
8283	S	T	E	N	1971	65061
8286	S	T	E	N	1971	65069
8288	S	T	E	N	1971	65069
8310	S	D	E	N	1973	53799
8384	S	D	E	N	1975	86764
8392	S	D	E	N	1975	68681
8392	S	T	E	N	1975	68681

Phys. State: **A.** Amorphous; **C.** Superconductive; **D.** Doped; **F.** Fibrous or Whisker; **G.** Gas; **I.** Ionized or Plasma; **L.** Liquid; **P.** Powder or Particle; **S.** Solid; **T.** Thin Film
Subject: **D.** Data; **E.** Experiment; **S.** Survey (Review, Compendium, etc.); **T.** Theory
Language: **E.** English; **F.** French; **G.** German; **O.** Other Languages; **R.** Russian
Temperature: **L.** Low (0 to 75K); **N.** Normal (75 to 1273K); **H.** High (above 1273K)

Substance Number	Phys. State	Subject	Language	Temperature	Year	EPIC Number
102-8393	S	D	E	L	1974	60668
8393	S	D	E	N	1974	60668
8393	S	T	E	L	1974	60668
8393	S	T	E	N	1974	60668
8393	S	D	E	L	1975	63298
8393	S	D	E	N	1975	63298
8393	S	S	E	N	1975	63298
8393	S	D	E	L	1975	86741
8393	S	D	E	N	1975	86741
8396	T	D	E	N	1973	65288
8448	S	S	E	N	1974	94145
8449	S	S	E	N	1974	94145
104-0002	S	D	G	N	1970	52691
0002	S	D	R	N	1975	89660
0002	S	D	E	N	1975	89661
0006	D	D	E	N	1973	50410
0006	D	D	E	N	1973	50565
0006	D	T	E	N	1973	52028
0006	D	D	E	N	1973	52629
0006	D	D	E	L	1974	53990
0006	D	T	E	L	1974	53990
0006	D	D	R	N	1973	54359
0006	D	D	E	N	1973	54360
0006	D	D	R	L	1973	54401
0006	D	S	R	L	1973	54401
0006	D	D	E	L	1973	54402
0006	D	S	E	L	1973	54402
0006	D	D	E	N	1974	59393
0006	D	S	E	N	1974	59393
0006	D	T	E	N	1974	59393
0006	D	D	E	N	1973	60586
0006	D	S	E	L	1973	60646
0006	S	D	E	N	1973	49708
0006	S	D	E	N	1972	49936
0006	S	D	E	N	1973	50565
0006	S	D	R	N	1973	54359
0006	S	D	E	N	1973	54360
0006	S	D	E	N	1974	54604
0006	S	S	E	N	1972	55728
0006	S	D	E	N	1974	58821
0006	S	S	E	N	1971	59626
0006	S	D	E	L	1970	59675
0006	S	S	E	N	1973	60558
0006	S	D	E	N	1973	60582
0006	S	S	E	N	1971	61706
0006	S	T	E	N	1971	61706
0006	S	D	E	N	1966	64258
0006	S	T	E	N	1966	64258
0006	S	D	E	N	1972	70677
0006	S	S	E	N	1972	70677
0006	S	T	E	L	1965	74575
0006	S	D	E	L	1968	74624
0006	S	D	E	N	1968	74624
0006	S	D	E	N	1969	85421
0006	S	S	E	N	1969	85421
0006	S	D	E	N	1975	86762
0006	S	D	R	N	1974	90087
0007	S	T	R	N	1973	51376
0007	S	T	E	N	1973	51377
0007	S	D	E	N	1972	63787
0007	S	D	E	N	1972	64535
0007	S	S	E	N	1972	64535
0007	S	D	E	N	1975	65499
0007	S	T	E	N	1975	65499
0007	S	D	E	N	1975	65500
0007	S	T	E	N	1975	65500
0007	T	D	E	N	1976	100007
0007	T	S	E	N	1976	100007
0007	T	T	E	N	1976	100007
0013	S	D	E	N	1973	50150
0016	G	T	R	N	1972	65883
0016	G	T	E	N	1972	65884
0022	S	D	E	N	1974	61388
0022	S	T	E	N	1975	90967
0031	D	D	E	L	1973	50142
0031	D	D	E	N	1973	50142
0031	D	T	E	L	1975	89453
0031	S	D	E	N	1974	58821
0031	S	S	E	N	1971	61706
0031	S	D	E	N	1966	64258
0031	S	T	E	N	1966	64258
0031	S	D	E	N	1972	70677
0031	S	S	E	N	1972	70677
0031	S	D	E	L	1968	74624
0031	S	D	E	N	1968	74624
0031	S	D	E	N	1971	75192
0031	S	S	E	N	1971	75192
0031	S	D	E	N	1975	86762
0039	G	D	E	N	1974	54315
0039	G	S	E	N	1974	54315
0043	S	S	E	N	1975	93528
0049	G	D	E	N	1974	54315
0049	G	S	E	N	1974	54315
0049	S	S	R	N	1973	51370
0049	S	S	E	N	1973	51371
0049	S	D	R	H	1974	66744
0049	S	D	R	N	1974	66744
0049	S	T	R	H	1974	66744
0049	S	T	R	N	1974	66744
0049	S	D	E	H	1975	66745

Substance Number	Phys. State	Subject	Language	Temperature	Year	EPIC Number
104-0049	S	D	E	N	1975	66745
0049	S	T	E	H	1975	66745
0049	S	T	E	N	1975	66745
0049	S	D	R	N	1972	76508
0049	S	D	E	N	1972	91530
0050	G	T	R	N	1972	65883
0050	G	T	E	N	1972	65884
0053	D	D	E	L	1973	50142
0053	D	D	E	N	1973	50142
0053	D	D	E	L	1973	60646
0053	D	D	E	N	1973	60646
0053	D	T	E	N	1973	60647
0053	D	D	E	N	1975	93527
0053	S	D	E	N	1974	54604
0053	S	D	E	L	1973	60646
0053	S	D	E	N	1966	64258
0053	S	T	E	N	1966	64258
0053	S	D	E	N	1975	65501
0067	S	D	O	L	1970	101002
0069	S	D	R	L	1973	54395
0069	S	D	R	N	1973	54395
0069	S	S	R	N	1973	54395
0069	S	D	E	L	1973	54396
0069	S	D	E	N	1973	54396
0069	S	S	E	N	1973	54396
0094	S	D	E	N	1974	54305
0104	D	D	E	N	1973	50979
0104	D	D	R	N	1973	51350
0104	D	D	E	N	1973	51351
0104	D	D	R	L	1973	52848
0104	D	D	E	L	1973	52849
0104	D	D	E	N	1974	53589
0104	D	D	R	N	1973	54448
0104	D	D	E	N	1973	54449
0104	S	D	R	N	1974	60441
0104	S	D	E	N	1974	60442
0104	S	D	E	N	1972	70677
0104	S	D	E	N	1974	84584
0104	S	D	R	N	1974	87288
0104	S	D	E	N	1975	87289
0104	S	S	E	N	1974	98834
0105	S	D	R	N	1974	63016
0105	S	D	E	N	1974	63017
0105	S	D	E	N	1966	64258
0105	S	T	E	N	1966	64258
0105	S	D	E	N	1975	65501
0106	I	D	R	N	1974	67820
0106	S	D	E	N	1966	64258
0106	S	T	E	N	1966	64258
0106	S	D	E	N	1975	86762
0146	S	D	E	N	1973	52631
0295	S	T	R	N	1973	51376
0295	S	T	E	N	1973	51377
0295	S	D	E	N	1972	63787
0302	S	D	E	N	1973	94148
0306	D	D	E	N	1972	68077
0331	S	D	R	L	1973	49848
0331	S	D	E	L	1973	54526
0331	S	D	R	L	1972	60701
0331	S	T	R	L	1972	60701
0331	S	D	E	L	1973	60702
0331	S	T	E	L	1973	60702
0331	S	T	R	L	1974	63054
0331	S	T	E	L	1975	63055
0384	D	D	R	N	1973	54494
0384	D	D	E	N	1973	54495
0386	D	D	E	N	1974	60363
0434	S	D	E	N	1973	52703
0434	S	E	E	N	1973	52703
0533	S	D	R	N	1973	54986
0533	S	D	E	N	1974	54987
8015	A	D	E	N	1974	58018
8042	S	D	E	L	1973	51069
8042	S	D	E	N	1973	52184
8042	S	D	E	L	1973	59900
8042	S	S	E	L	1973	59900
8042	S	S	E	N	1966	66068
8042	T	S	E	N	1966	66068
8045	D	D	E	L	1973	52709
8045	D	S	E	N	1966	66068
8045	S	D	E	L	1973	52072
8045	S	T	E	L	1973	52072
8045	S	D	E	L	1973	52709
8045	S	D	E	N	1972	63966
8045	S	D	E	N	1975	96857
8045	T	S	E	N	1966	66068
8108	T	S	E	N	1966	66068
8123	S	D	R	N	1973	54986
8123	S	D	E	N	1974	54987
8126	I	D	E	N	1973	50410
8127	S	D	E	N	1973	50417
8128	S	D	E	N	1973	50417
8129	D	D	E	N	1973	50417
8130	D	D	E	N	1973	50417
8133	D	D	E	N	1973	50555
8153	S	D	E	N	1974	53989
8159	S	T	E	N	1975	66701
8191	S	D	E	N	1973	52703
8191	S	E	E	N	1973	52703
8199	S	T	E	N	1973	51900
8199	T	T	E	N	1973	51900

Substance Number	Phys. State	Subject	Language	Temperature	Year	EPIC Number
104-8213	A	D	E	N	1974	53726
8213	T	D	E	N	1974	53726
8215	S	D	E	N	1973	59166
8224	S	S	R	N	1974	58072
8224	S	S	E	N	1974	58073
8228	D	D	R	N	1973	54494
8228	D	D	E	N	1973	54495
8231	S	D	E	N	1974	54037
8231	S	T	E	N	1974	54037
8231	S	D	R	N	1973	54986
8231	S	D	E	N	1974	54987
8238	D	D	R	N	1973	55176
8238	D	D	E	N	1974	55177
8247	S	T	E	N	1974	58006
8248	S	T	E	N	1974	58006
8249	S	T	E	N	1974	58006
8250	S	T	E	N	1974	58006
8251	D	D	E	N	1974	57989
8259	S	D	E	N	1973	58912
8265	G	S	E	N	1973	53059
8360	S	D	O	N	1974	90531
106-0003	G	D	R	N	1973	51330
0003	G	T	R	N	1973	51330
0003	G	S	E	N	1973	51467
0003	G	D	E	N	1973	52480
0003	G	S	E	N	1973	56749
0003	G	D	E	N	1973	64877
0003	G	T	E	N	1973	64877
0003	I	D	R	N	1971	54280
0003	I	D	E	N	1972	54281
0004	D	D	E	N	1973	50135
0004	G	D	E	N	1974	54315
0004	G	S	E	N	1974	54315
0004	S	S	E	N	1973	49664
0004	S	T	E	N	1973	49664
0004	S	D	R	H	1974	66744
0004	S	D	R	N	1974	66744
0004	S	T	R	H	1974	66744
0004	S	T	R	N	1974	66744
0004	S	D	E	H	1975	66745
0004	S	D	E	N	1975	66745
0004	S	T	E	H	1975	66745
0004	S	T	E	N	1975	66745
0005	D	D	E	N	1973	50135
0006	D	D	E	N	1973	50410
0006	D	D	E	N	1973	50979
0006	D	T	E	N	1973	52028
0006	D	D	E	N	1973	52629
0006	D	D	E	L	1973	53580
0006	D	D	R	N	1973	53650
0006	D	D	E	N	1973	53651
0006	D	D	R	N	1973	53661
0006	D	D	E	N	1974	53662
0006	D	D	R	L	1973	54401
0006	D	S	R	L	1973	54401
0006	D	D	E	L	1973	54402
0006	D	S	E	L	1973	54402
0006	D	D	R	N	1973	54498
0006	D	D	E	N	1973	54499
0006	D	D	E	N	1974	55254
0006	D	S	E	N	1972	55357
0006	D	D	R	N	1973	56574
0006	D	T	R	N	1973	56574
0006	D	D	E	L	1973	57113
0006	D	D	R	N	1974	58124
0006	D	T	R	N	1974	58124
0006	D	D	E	N	1974	58125
0006	D	T	E	N	1974	58125
0006	D	D	E	N	1974	59393
0006	D	S	E	N	1974	59393
0006	D	T	E	N	1974	59393
0006	D	D	E	N	1973	60586
0006	D	D	E	N	1973	60588
0006	D	D	E	L	1973	60590
0006	D	T	E	L	1973	60590
0006	D	S	E	L	1973	60646
0006	D	T	E	L	1974	61372
0006	D	T	E	N	1974	62555
0006	D	D	E	L	1975	66689
0006	D	S	E	L	1975	66689
0006	D	D	E	N	1974	80552
0006	D	S	E	N	1974	80552
0006	D	T	E	N	1974	80552
0006	S	D	E	N	1973	49708
0006	S	D	E	N	1972	49936
0006	S	D	E	N	1973	53579
0006	S	D	R	N	1973	54490
0006	S	D	E	N	1973	54491
0006	S	D	E	N	1974	54603
0006	S	D	E	N	1974	54604
0006	S	D	E	L	1974	58821
0006	S	T	E	L	1974	58821
0006	S	S	E	N	1971	59626
0006	S	D	E	L	1970	59675
0006	S	D	E	N	1973	60582
0006	S	D	E	L	1973	60592
0006	S	D	E	N	1973	60592
0006	S	S	E	L	1973	60592
0006	S	S	E	N	1973	60592
0006	S	T	E	L	1973	60592

Phys. State: **A.** Amorphous; **C.** Superconductive; **D.** Doped; **F.** Fibrous or Whisker; **G.** Gas; **I.** Ionized or Plasma; **L.** Liquid; **P.** Powder or Particle; **S.** Solid; **T.** Thin Film
Subject: **D.** Data; **E.** Experiment; **S.** Survey (Review, Compendium, etc.); **T.** Theory
Language: **E.** English; **F.** French; **G.** German; **O.** Other Languages; **R.** Russian
Temperature: **L.** Low (0 to 75K); **N.** Normal (75 to 1273K); **H.** High (above 1273K)

Substance Number	Phys. State	Subject	Language	Temperature	Year	EPIC Number
106-0006	S	T	E	N	1973	60592
0006	S	S	E	N	1971	61706
0006	S	T	E	N	1971	61706
0006	S	S	E	N	1974	62314
0006	S	D	E	N	1975	63328
0006	S	E	E	N	1975	63328
0006	S	T	E	N	1975	63328
0006	S	T	E	N	1975	63334
0006	S	D	E	N	1966	64258
0006	S	T	E	N	1966	64258
0006	S	D	E	N	1972	70677
0006	S	S	E	N	1972	70677
0006	S	D	E	N	1967	74601
0006	S	S	E	N	1967	74601
0006	S	T	E	N	1967	74601
0006	S	D	E	L	1968	74624
0006	S	D	E	N	1968	74624
0006	S	S	R	N	1974	77920
0006	S	D	E	N	1969	85421
0006	S	S	E	N	1969	85421
0006	S	D	E	N	1975	86762
0006	S	T	E	N	1975	89669
0006	S	D	E	N	1975	91730
0006	S	S	E	N	1974	94516
0006	T	D	E	N	1974	54347
0008	G	D	R	N	1973	51330
0008	G	T	R	N	1973	51330
0008	G	S	E	N	1973	53954
0008	G	D	E	N	1973	64877
0008	G	T	E	N	1973	64877
0011	G	T	R	N	1973	51330
0011	L	D	R	N	1973	51330
0011	L	D	E	N	1973	64877
0011	L	T	E	N	1973	64877
0011	L	T	R	N	1972	65883
0011	L	T	E	N	1972	65884
0011	S	D	R	N	1973	54371
0011	S	D	E	N	1973	54372
0018	S	D	E	N	1973	52188
0018	S	S	E	N	1975	93528
0024	D	D	E	L	1973	50142
0024	D	D	E	N	1973	50142
0024	D	D	E	N	1973	50979
0024	D	D	E	N	1973	52629
0024	D	S	E	L	1974	55255
0024	D	D	E	N	1975	91874
0024	D	D	E	N	1976	102041
0024	D	T	E	N	1976	102041
0024	S	T	E	N	1974	53619
0024	S	D	E	N	1974	54604
0024	S	S	E	N	1973	56749
0024	S	D	E	N	1974	58821
0024	S	S	E	N	1971	59626
0024	S	D	E	L	1970	59675
0024	S	S	E	N	1973	60558
0024	S	D	E	N	1966	64258
0024	S	T	E	N	1966	64258
0024	S	D	E	N	1975	65501
0024	S	D	E	N	1972	70677
0024	S	S	E	N	1972	70677
0024	S	D	E	L	1968	74624
0024	S	D	E	N	1968	74624
0024	S	D	E	N	1975	91730
0024	T	D	E	N	1974	54347
0026	D	D	R	N	1973	49561
0026	D	D	E	N	1972	49687
0026	D	D	E	N	1973	50135
0026	D	D	E	N	1972	50860
0026	D	D	E	N	1973	50979
0026	D	D	E	N	1973	52079
0026	D	D	R	N	1973	52325
0026	D	D	E	L	1973	52429
0026	D	D	R	L	1973	52848
0026	D	D	E	L	1973	52849
0026	D	D	E	N	1968	53357
0026	D	D	E	N	1974	53589
0026	D	S	E	N	1974	53589
0026	D	D	R	N	1973	54448
0026	D	S	R	N	1973	54448
0026	D	D	E	N	1973	54449
0026	D	S	E	N	1973	54449
0026	D	D	R	L	1973	54476
0026	D	D	E	L	1973	54477
0026	D	D	E	N	1973	54510
0026	D	D	E	N	1974	62327
0026	D	T	E	N	1974	62327
0026	D	D	E	N	1973	63527
0026	D	D	E	L	1974	65038
0026	D	D	R	N	1975	86871
0026	D	D	E	N	1975	86872
0026	D	D	E	N	1975	93628
0026	S	D	R	N	1973	55197
0026	S	D	E	N	1974	55198
0026	S	S	E	N	1973	56749
0026	S	D	E	N	1972	70677
0026	S	D	R	N	1974	87288
0026	S	S	R	N	1974	87288
0026	S	D	E	N	1975	87289
0026	S	S	E	N	1975	87289
0026	S	D	R	N	1974	92220
0026	S	T	R	N	1974	92220
106-0026	S	D	E	N	1974	92221
0026	S	T	E	N	1974	92221
0026	S	S	E	N	1974	98834
0033	S	D	E	N	1973	52188
0035	D	D	E	L	1973	50143
0035	D	D	E	N	1973	50143
0035	D	D	R	N	1973	51733
0035	D	D	E	L	1974	54106
0035	D	D	E	L	1974	54582
0035	D	D	R	N	1973	59077
0035	D	D	E	N	1973	59078
0035	D	D	E	L	1974	60670
0035	D	T	E	L	1974	60670
0035	D	T	E	L	1974	62060
0035	D	D	E	N	1973	79186
0035	D	S	E	N	1965	87702
0035	D	S	E	L	1971	87887
0035	D	S	E	N	1971	87887
0035	P	S	E	N	1965	87702
0035	S	D	R	N	1973	55223
0035	S	D	E	N	1974	55224
0035	S	D	R	N	1973	57375
0035	S	S	E	N	1973	60593
0035	S	T	E	N	1973	60593
0035	S	D	R	N	1971	62097
0035	S	T	R	N	1971	62097
0035	S	D	R	N	1974	63028
0035	S	T	R	N	1974	63028
0035	S	D	E	N	1974	63029
0035	S	T	E	N	1974	63029
0035	S	S	E	N	1975	63320
0035	S	D	E	N	1972	63787
0035	S	D	E	N	1971	64880
0035	S	T	E	N	1971	64880
0035	S	D	R	L	1968	65348
0035	S	D	E	L	1969	65349
0035	S	D	E	N	1973	65354
0035	S	S	E	N	1973	65354
0035	S	S	R	N	1972	65864
0035	S	S	E	N	1972	65865
0035	S	S	R	N	1972	65866
0035	S	S	E	N	1972	65867
0035	S	D	R	N	1974	68712
0035	S	D	E	N	1974	68713
0035	S	S	E	N	1965	87702
0035	S	S	E	N	1966	87803
0036	S	D	E	N	1974	61388
0036	T	D	R	N	1973	54996
0036	T	D	E	N	1974	54997
0045	D	D	E	N	1973	52631
0045	D	D	R	N	1972	60725
0045	D	D	E	N	1973	60726
0046	S	D	E	N	1973	52188
0047	S	S	E	N	1975	91289
0057	P	S	E	N	1966	68325
0057	T	S	E	N	1966	68325
0058	S	D	R	N	1973	51316
0058	S	D	E	N	1973	55171
0058	S	S	E	N	1975	68703
0060	S	D	R	L	1973	54395
0060	S	D	R	N	1973	54395
0060	S	S	R	N	1973	54395
0060	S	D	E	L	1973	54396
0060	S	D	E	N	1973	54396
0060	S	S	E	N	1973	54396
0081	D	D	E	N	1973	50864
0081	S	D	E	N	1973	49735
0081	S	T	E	N	1974	58048
0081	S	S	E	N	1975	63331
0081	S	D	E	N	1975	65487
0081	S	S	E	N	1975	65487
0081	S	S	E	N	1975	68703
0095	S	D	E	N	1975	65487
0104	D	D	E	N	1970	61741
0104	D	T	E	N	1970	61741
0104	S	D	E	N	1972	59903
0104	T	D	E	N	1970	61741
0125	S	S	E	N	1964	93287
0127	D	T	O	N	1973	59372
0127	S	D	R	N	1973	50082
0127	S	D	E	N	1973	51428
0127	S	S	E	N	1972	55728
0127	S	D	E	N	1975	63342
0127	S	T	E	N	1975	63342
0129	G	D	E	N	1973	51637
0131	S	D	E	N	1974	54314
0131	S	S	E	N	1974	54314
0153	L	T	E	N	1973	53408
0156	D	D	E	N	1973	52127
0157	S	D	E	N	1972	49632
0157	S	D	O	L	1970	101002
0158	D	D	E	L	1972	49667
0158	S	D	E	N	1972	49630
0158	S	D	R	N	1973	54361
0158	S	S	R	N	1973	54361
0158	S	D	E	N	1973	54362
0158	S	D	E	N	1974	61388
0159	D	D	R	N	1973	57353
0159	S	D	E	N	1974	58821
0159	S	D	R	N	1974	63016
0159	S	D	E	N	1974	63017
106-0159	S	D	E	N	1966	64258
0159	S	T	E	N	1966	64258
0159	S	D	E	N	1975	65501
0159	T	D	E	N	1974	54347
0165	D	D	E	N	1974	62479
0165	D	S	E	N	1974	62479
0165	D	D	E	N	1974	89309
0165	S	D	E	N	1973	52004
0165	S	D	E	N	1974	54603
0165	S	D	E	N	1974	58821
0165	S	D	E	L	1970	59675
0165	S	D	E	N	1971	61706
0165	S	D	E	N	1966	64258
0165	S	T	E	N	1966	64258
0165	S	D	E	L	1968	74624
0165	S	D	E	N	1968	74624
0165	S	D	E	N	1971	75192
0165	S	S	E	N	1971	75192
0165	S	D	E	N	1975	86762
0168	G	S	E	N	1973	53059
0192	G	D	E	N	1974	54315
0192	G	S	E	N	1974	54315
0203	I	D	R	N	1974	67820
0203	S	D	E	N	1966	64258
0203	S	T	E	N	1966	64258
0203	S	D	E	N	1975	86762
0205	S	D	E	N	1974	59384
0231	G	D	R	N	1973	51330
0231	G	T	R	N	1973	51330
0231	G	D	E	N	1973	64877
0231	G	T	E	N	1973	64877
0234	D	D	E	L	1973	60596
0234	D	T	E	L	1973	60596
0234	S	S	E	N	1973	58912
0237	I	D	R	N	1974	67820
0237	S	S	E	N	1971	61706
0237	S	D	E	N	1966	64258
0237	S	T	E	N	1966	64258
0237	S	D	E	N	1975	86762
0238	I	D	R	N	1974	67820
0238	S	T	E	L	1973	53582
0238	S	S	E	N	1973	60585
0238	S	D	E	N	1966	64258
0238	S	T	E	N	1966	64258
0238	S	D	E	N	1975	86762
0238	T	D	E	N	1973	60584
0240	S	D	E	N	1973	52188
0240	S	T	E	N	1974	61398
0259	D	D	E	N	1973	50867
0259	D	S	E	N	1973	50889
0259	D	S	E	N	1973	50890
0259	D	S	E	N	1974	53589
0259	D	D	E	N	1973	57538
0259	D	D	E	N	1974	65758
0259	D	S	E	N	1974	65758
0259	D	T	E	N	1974	65758
0296	S	D	E	N	1974	54305
0309	S	D	E	N	1974	58023
0309	S	T	E	N	1974	58023
0309	S	D	E	N	1974	59384
0309	S	D	E	N	1975	68687
0309	S	T	E	N	1975	68687
0363	D	D	E	N	1973	49614
0363	D	D	R	N	1973	51550
0363	D	T	R	L	1973	51559
0363	D	T	R	N	1973	51559
0363	D	D	E	N	1971	53487
0363	D	D	E	N	1973	53681
0363	D	T	E	L	1974	53690
0363	D	T	E	N	1974	53690
0363	D	D	E	L	1973	55163
0363	D	D	E	N	1973	55163
0363	D	S	E	N	1973	55163
0363	D	S	E	N	1963	64232
0363	D	T	E	N	1975	65427
0363	D	S	E	L	1967	66156
0363	D	S	E	N	1967	66156
0363	D	D	E	N	1970	66927
0363	D	T	E	N	1972	67036
0363	D	D	E	L	1966	74595
0363	D	D	E	N	1975	89311
0363	D	T	E	N	1975	89311
0363	D	D	R	N	1975	97671
0363	D	S	R	N	1975	97671
0363	D	T	R	N	1975	97671
0363	D	D	E	N	1975	97672
0363	D	S	E	N	1975	97672
0363	D	T	E	N	1975	97672
0363	S	D	E	N	1972	49485
0363	S	D	R	L	1973	50074
0363	S	D	E	N	1973	50638
0363	S	D	E	N	1973	50911
0363	S	D	E	L	1973	51425
0363	S	D	E	N	1973	51874
0363	S	D	R	N	1972	52252
0363	S	D	R	N	1973	52882
0363	S	D	E	N	1974	52883
0363	S	T	E	N	1972	53239
0363	S	S	E	N	1972	53388
0363	S	D	E	N	1974	53607
0363	S	D	E	L	1974	53614

Phys. State: **A.** Amorphous; **C.** Superconductive; **D.** Doped; **F.** Fibrous or Whisker; **G.** Gas; **I.** Ionized or Plasma; **L.** Liquid; **P.** Powder or Particle; **S.** Solid; **T.** Thin Film
Subject: **D.** Data; **E.** Experiment; **S.** Survey (Review, Compendium, etc.); **T.** Theory
Language: **E.** English; **F.** French; **G.** German; **O.** Other Languages; **R.** Russian
Temperature: **L.** Low (0 to 75K); **N.** Normal (75 to 1273K); **H.** High (above 1273K)

Substance Number	Phys. State	Subject	Language	Temperature	Year	EPIC Number
106-0363	S	D	R	L	1972	54233
0363	S	D	E	N	1974	54345
0363	S	D	E	L	1973	54718
0363	S	S	E	N	1974	57323
0363	S	D	E	N	1974	57325
0363	S	D	E	N	1973	57560
0363	S	S	E	N	1973	57560
0363	S	D	R	N	1974	58210
0363	S	D	E	N	1974	59206
0363	S	T	E	N	1973	59409
0363	S	T	E	N	1974	60377
0363	S	T	R	N	1972	60707
0363	S	T	E	N	1973	60708
0363	S	D	E	L	1974	61361
0363	S	T	E	L	1974	61361
0363	S	D	E	N	1971	61758
0363	S	S	E	N	1971	61758
0363	S	D	E	N	1971	61760
0363	S	T	E	N	1971	61760
0363	S	D	E	N	1971	61763
0363	S	D	R	N	1974	61970
0363	S	D	E	N	1974	61971
0363	S	T	R	N	1973	62163
0363	S	D	E	N	1971	63879
0363	S	S	E	N	1963	64232
0363	S	T	E	N	1975	65476
0363	S	T	E	N	1975	65491
0363	S	S	E	L	1967	66156
0363	S	S	E	N	1967	66156
0363	S	D	E	L	1975	66688
0363	S	T	E	L	1975	66688
0363	S	S	R	N	1974	66742
0363	S	T	R	N	1974	66742
0363	S	S	E	N	1975	66743
0363	S	T	E	N	1975	66743
0363	S	S	E	N	1975	68674
0363	S	T	E	N	1975	68674
0363	S	T	E	N	1971	70600
0363	S	D	E	N	1968	74648
0363	S	D	E	N	1974	87147
0363	S	S	E	N	1974	87147
0363	S	D	E	N	1975	88215
0363	S	D	E	N	1975	90062
0363	S	T	E	N	1975	90469
0363	S	D	E	N	1975	92725
0363	S	S	E	N	1975	95584
0363	T	D	E	N	1974	53635
0363	T	D	E	N	1973	53686
0363	T	D	R	N	1972	56936
0363	T	D	O	N	1973	65693
0363	T	D	R	N	1972	67466
0363	T	T	E	N	1974	90590
0385	D	D	E	N	1973	50979
0385	D	D	E	N	1973	57641
0385	D	T	E	N	1973	57641
0385	S	D	E	N	1972	63847
0385	S	S	E	N	1972	63847
0385	S	S	E	N	1974	98834
0413	D	D	E	N	1973	50135
0498	S	D	E	L	1973	50880
0508	D	D	R	N	1972	58771
0508	S	D	R	N	1972	58772
0610	D	D	R	N	1973	50343
0610	D	D	E	N	1973	50344
0610	D	D	R	N	1973	54450
0610	D	D	E	N	1973	54451
0610	D	D	R	N	1973	54494
0610	D	D	E	N	1973	54495
0610	D	D	E	L	1973	55120
0610	D	D	E	N	1975	63295
0610	S	T	E	N	1973	57743
0639	S	D	E	N	1974	59384
0652	S	D	E	N	1973	53439
0768	D	D	R	N	1973	54494
0768	D	D	E	N	1973	54495
0941	S	D	R	N	1972	52264
0941	S	D	R	N	1974	66574
0941	S	D	E	N	1974	66575
1085	S	D	E	N	1974	60664
1256	S	T	E	N	1973	60802
1256	S	D	E	N	1974	87146
1256	S	S	E	N	1974	87146
8001	D	D	R	N	1972	56734
8040	D	D	E	L	1972	52975
8040	D	D	R	N	1973	55296
8040	D	D	E	N	1974	59280
8040	D	D	E	N	1971	64324
8040	D	D	R	N	1974	87062
8040	D	D	E	N	1974	87063
8040	D	S	E	N	1963	87710
8040	S	D	R	L	1973	50297
8040	S	D	E	L	1973	50298
8040	S	D	R	N	1973	52530
8040	S	T	R	N	1973	52530
8040	S	D	E	N	1973	52773
8040	S	T	E	N	1972	53239
8040	S	S	E	N	1972	53388
8040	S	D	E	N	1974	53607
8040	S	D	E	N	1974	54345
8040	S	T	R	L	1973	54646
8040	S	T	E	L	1974	55190

Substance Number	Phys. State	Subject	Language	Temperature	Year	EPIC Number
106-8040	S	D	R	N	1973	55296
8040	S	D	E	N	1973	56398
8040	S	D	E	N	1974	57325
8040	S	D	E	N	1974	57771
8040	S	T	E	N	1974	57771
8040	S	D	E	N	1974	58223
8040	S	D	R	N	1972	58678
8040	S	D	E	N	1974	59280
8040	S	D	E	N	1972	59904
8040	S	T	R	N	1972	60707
8040	S	T	E	N	1973	60708
8040	S	S	R	N	1974	61986
8040	S	S	E	N	1974	61987
8040	S	S	E	N	1971	64324
8040	S	D	R	N	1971	67724
8040	S	D	R	N	1974	87062
8040	S	D	E	N	1974	87063
8040	S	S	E	N	1963	87710
8040	S	S	E	N	1975	95584
8040	T	D	E	N	1973	50749
8041	A	D	E	N	1974	54345
8041	D	D	E	N	1972	49494
8041	D	D	R	N	1973	51625
8041	D	D	E	N	1973	52153
8041	D	D	E	N	1972	53391
8041	D	D	E	N	1974	54034
8041	D	T	E	N	1974	54034
8041	D	T	E	N	1974	55248
8041	D	S	E	N	1973	58213
8041	D	T	R	N	1974	59418
8041	D	D	E	N	1974	62323
8041	D	D	R	N	1972	62705
8041	D	D	E	N	1973	65301
8041	D	D	E	N	1972	67638
8041	D	S	E	N	1967	68371
8041	D	D	E	N	1973	79080
8041	D	S	E	N	1962	87659
8041	D	D	E	N	1975	97219
8041	S	D	E	N	1972	49493
8041	S	D	E	N	1972	49494
8041	S	D	E	N	1973	50507
8041	S	D	E	N	1973	50925
8041	S	D	E	L	1973	51216
8041	S	D	E	N	1973	51216
8041	S	S	R	N	1973	52522
8041	S	D	E	N	1974	53607
8041	S	D	E	N	1974	54081
8041	S	D	E	N	1974	54345
8041	S	D	E	N	1974	54600
8041	S	S	E	N	1974	54600
8041	S	D	E	N	1974	57325
8041	S	S	E	N	1974	57763
8041	S	D	E	N	1970	60042
8041	S	S	E	N	1970	60042
8041	S	D	R	N	1974	61980
8041	S	T	R	N	1974	61980
8041	S	D	E	N	1974	61981
8041	S	T	E	N	1974	61981
8041	S	D	E	N	1972	63632
8041	S	S	E	N	1972	63632
8041	S	D	E	N	1975	65477
8041	S	D	E	N	1972	67636
8041	S	D	E	N	1972	67637
8041	S	D	E	N	1972	67639
8041	S	D	R	N	1971	67723
8041	S	S	E	N	1967	68371
8041	S	D	E	N	1968	74648
8041	S	D	R	N	1971	76463
8041	S	S	E	N	1962	87659
8041	S	D	E	N	1971	91585
8041	S	T	E	L	1975	91863
8041	T	D	R	N	1973	51625
8041	T	D	E	N	1973	53451
8041	T	D	R	N	1972	56939
8041	T	D	R	N	1972	76519
8041	T	S	R	N	1972	76519
8041	T	D	E	N	1973	79080
8041	T	D	E	N	1972	91552
8041	T	S	E	N	1972	91552
8059	S	S	E	N	1975	68703
8070	S	S	E	N	1975	68703
8114	L	T	E	N	1973	53408
8123	S	D	E	N	1974	90281
8127	D	D	E	L	1970	49613
8127	S	D	R	N	1974	61980
8127	S	S	R	N	1974	61980
8127	S	T	R	N	1974	61980
8127	S	D	E	N	1974	61981
8127	S	S	E	N	1974	61981
8127	S	T	E	N	1974	61981
8128	S	D	R	N	1973	55014
8128	S	T	R	N	1973	55014
8128	S	D	E	N	1974	55015
8128	S	T	E	N	1974	55015
8128	S	D	E	N	1973	55149
8132	D	D	E	L	1970	49613
8132	S	S	R	N	1974	61980
8132	S	S	E	N	1974	61981
8133	D	D	E	L	1970	49613
8133	S	S	R	N	1974	61980
8133	S	S	E	N	1974	61981

Substance Number	Phys. State	Subject	Language	Temperature	Year	EPIC Number
106-8134	D	D	E	L	1970	49613
8134	S	S	R	N	1974	61980
8134	S	S	E	N	1974	61981
8155	D	D	R	N	1971	67048
8209	S	D	E	N	1973	50903
8209	S	D	E	N	1974	62028
8225	D	D	E	L	1973	51848
8226	S	D	E	N	1973	50574
8227	S	D	E	L	1975	65440
8227	S	T	E	L	1975	65440
8234	S	D	R	N	1973	51561
8234	S	S	R	N	1973	51561
8234	S	D	E	N	1974	53692
8234	S	S	E	N	1974	53692
8234	S	D	R	N	1972	58674
8234	S	S	R	N	1974	61980
8234	S	S	E	N	1974	61981
8244	S	D	R	L	1974	68630
8244	S	D	E	L	1974	68631
8289	S	D	E	N	1973	51864
8289	S	D	E	N	1974	54587
8303	G	D	E	N	1973	52479
8304	D	D	E	L	1973	52489
8305	G	D	E	N	1973	52491
8306	G	D	E	N	1973	52491
8307	G	D	E	N	1973	52491
8342	D	D	R	N	1973	55292
8342	D	D	R	N	1972	55492
8342	D	D	E	N	1974	56990
8342	D	D	R	N	1972	56990
8342	D	D	E	N	1974	59251
8342	S	D	R	N	1972	56988
8351	D	D	E	N	1973	53439
8353	S	D	E	N	1973	53439
8383	S	D	R	N	1973	51316
8383	S	D	E	N	1973	55171
8383	S	S	E	N	1974	94145
8395	S	D	E	N	1973	59166
8397	S	T	E	L	1973	52649
8398	S	T	E	L	1973	52649
8399	S	T	E	L	1973	52649
8404	S	D	E	L	1974	53988
8404	S	D	E	N	1974	53988
8405	S	D	E	L	1974	53988
8406	S	D	E	L	1974	53988
8406	S	D	E	N	1974	53988
8407	S	D	E	L	1974	53988
8407	S	D	E	N	1974	62328
8407	S	T	E	N	1974	62328
8408	S	D	E	L	1974	53988
8409	S	D	E	L	1974	53988
8410	S	D	E	L	1974	53988
8410	S	D	E	N	1974	53988
8411	S	D	E	L	1974	53988
8411	S	D	E	N	1974	53988
8412	S	D	E	L	1974	53988
8413	S	D	E	L	1974	53988
8417	S	D	E	L	1974	54327
8418	S	D	E	L	1974	54327
8419	S	D	E	L	1974	54327
8420	S	D	E	L	1974	54327
8420	S	D	E	N	1974	54327
8421	D	D	E	L	1974	54327
8427	D	D	R	N	1973	54494
8427	D	D	E	N	1973	54495
8428	D	D	R	N	1973	54506
8428	D	D	E	N	1973	54507
8431	S	D	R	N	1973	54417
8431	S	D	E	N	1973	54418
8432	D	D	E	N	1973	50135
8440	S	D	R	N	1973	51316
8440	S	D	E	N	1973	55171
8441	S	D	R	N	1973	51316
8441	S	D	E	N	1973	55171
8442	S	D	R	N	1973	51316
8442	S	D	E	N	1973	55171
8443	S	D	R	N	1973	51316
8443	S	D	E	N	1973	55171
8444	S	D	R	N	1973	51316
8444	S	D	E	N	1973	55171
8445	S	D	R	N	1973	51316
8445	S	D	E	N	1973	55171
8446	S	D	R	N	1973	51316
8446	S	D	E	N	1973	55171
8447	S	D	R	N	1973	51316
8447	S	D	E	N	1973	55171
8448	S	D	R	N	1973	51316
8448	S	D	E	N	1973	55171
8449	S	D	R	N	1973	51316
8449	S	D	E	N	1973	55171
8450	S	D	R	N	1973	51316
8450	S	D	E	N	1973	55171
8451	S	D	R	N	1973	51316
8451	S	D	E	N	1973	55171
8452	D	D	E	N	1973	50135
8461	S	S	E	N	1974	54108
8462	D	T	E	N	1974	58816
8495	S	S	E	N	1970	61209
8496	S	S	E	N	1970	61209
8497	S	S	E	N	1970	61209
8509	S	T	E	L	1973	52649

Phys. State: **A.** Amorphous; **C.** Superconductive; **D.** Doped; **F.** Fibrous or Whisker; **G.** Gas; **I.** Ionized or Plasma; **L.** Liquid; **P.** Powder or Particle; **S.** Solid; **T.** Thin Film
Subject: **D.** Data; **E.** Experiment; **S.** Survey (Review, Compendium, etc.); **T.** Theory
Language: **E.** English; **F.** French; **G.** German; **O.** Other Languages; **R.** Russian
Temperature: **L.** Low (0 to 75K); **N.** Normal (75 to 1273K); **H.** High (above 1273K)

Substance Number	Phys. State	Sub-ject	Lan-guage	Temper-ature	Year	EPIC Number
106-8513	G	D	E	N	1974	54315
8528	D	S	R	N	1973	55295
8528	D	S	E	N	1974	59271
8531	S	D	R	N	1973	51564
8531	S	D	E	N	1974	53695
8536	S	S	E	N	1974	66380
8537	G	S	E	N	1973	53059
8538	S	D	E	L	1974	61159
8539	S	D	E	L	1974	61159
8540	D	D	E	N	1974	61187
8563	S	S	E	N	1970	61209
8576	S	D	E	L	1972	55593
8580	S	S	R	N	1974	61980
8580	S	S	E	N	1974	61981
8658	S	D	R	N	1973	58870
8671	I	D	E	N	1974	66959
8671	S	D	E	N	1974	94147
8671	S	S	E	N	1974	94147
8671	S	T	E	N	1974	94147
8679	D	D	R	N	1973	67365
8751	S	D	E	N	1974	94145
8751	S	T	E	N	1974	94145
8817	G	D	E	H	1974	65887
8817	G	T	E	H	1974	65887
108-0005	G	D	E	N	1973	52482
0021	G	D	E	N	1973	52481
0029	S	D	E	N	1974	60355
0029	S	T	E	N	1974	60355
0079	S	D	E	N	1974	54324
8012	S	S	E	N	1973	51205
8016	G	S	E	N	1973	51439
8026	I	D	E	N	1972	53146
8029	S	T	E	N	1973	52658
109-0025	D	S	E	N	1973	53052
0025	S	D	E	L	1973	50887
0025	S	D	E	N	1973	50887
0025	S	D	E	L	1973	50888
0025	S	S	E	N	1973	53052
0025	S	D	E	N	1973	53587
0025	S	D	E	N	1971	57182
0025	S	T	E	N	1974	61395
0025	S	S	E	N	1971	65043
8012	S	D	E	L	1972	49857
8012	S	D	E	N	1972	49857
8019	S	D	E	N	1971	57182
8019	S	T	E	N	1974	62347
8019	S	S	E	N	1971	65043
8020	S	D	E	N	1971	57182
8020	S	S	E	N	1971	65043
8021	S	D	E	N	1971	57182
8053	D	D	E	N	1974	57305
8054	D	D	E	N	1974	57305
8056	S	D	E	L	1974	61159
8057	S	T	E	N	1974	61395
8058	S	T	E	N	1974	61395
8059	S	T	E	N	1974	61395
8061	S	D	E	L	1974	61159
8062	S	D	E	L	1974	61159
8066	S	D	E	N	1974	87145
8075	S	D	E	L	1971	57503
8082	S	D	E	N	1975	63304
110-0004	G	T	R	N	1972	65883
0004	G	T	E	N	1972	65884
0010	S	D	E	N	1972	52995
0012	S	T	R	N	1972	65883
0012	S	T	E	N	1972	65884
0017	S	D	E	N	1973	50624
0017	S	T	E	N	1973	52408
0017	S	S	E	N	1975	68703
0018	S	T	E	N	1973	52408
0018	S	D	E	N	1973	60648
0018	S	S	E	N	1973	60648
0018	S	D	E	N	1975	63331
0018	S	S	E	N	1975	63331
0018	S	S	E	N	1975	68703
0018	S	D	E	L	1971	93296
0018	S	T	E	L	1971	93296
0019	S	S	E	N	1975	68703
0020	D	D	E	L	1974	58055
0020	D	D	E	L	1973	64537
0020	S	S	E	N	1975	63331
0021	D	D	R	L	1973	52848
0021	D	D	E	L	1973	52849
0021	S	S	E	N	1974	98834
0023	D	D	E	L	1974	58819
0023	D	D	E	N	1974	58819
0023	D	D	E	L	1973	64537
0023	S	D	E	L	1969	64549
0023	S	D	E	N	1976	101192
0023	S	S	E	N	1976	101192
0023	S	T	E	N	1976	101192
0024	S	S	E	N	1973	60558
0024	S	D	E	N	1973	60594
0024	S	D	E	N	1974	62457
0024	S	D	R	N	1974	63016
0024	S	D	E	N	1974	63017
0024	S	D	E	N	1966	64258
0024	S	T	E	N	1966	64258
110-0024	S	D	E	N	1975	65501
0024	S	D	E	N	1972	70677
0024	S	S	E	N	1972	70677
0024	S	D	E	N	1967	85322
0024	S	D	E	N	1975	97579
0024	S	D	E	N	1976	102400
0024	S	S	E	N	1976	102400
0025	S	D	E	N	1972	53113
0030	S	D	E	N	1974	53749
0030	S	D	E	N	1975	91840
0030	S	T	E	N	1975	91840
0036	D	D	R	N	1973	52337
0036	S	D	E	N	1974	54604
0036	S	D	E	N	1966	64258
0036	S	T	E	N	1966	64258
0036	S	D	E	N	1975	65501
0036	S	D	E	N	1975	91730
0037	S	D	E	N	1974	54604
0037	S	D	E	N	1971	61706
0037	S	T	E	N	1971	61706
0037	S	D	E	N	1974	62457
0037	S	D	E	N	1966	64258
0037	S	T	E	N	1966	64258
0037	S	D	E	N	1975	86762
0037	S	D	E	N	1975	91730
0040	G	D	E	N	1973	52478
0040	G	D	E	N	1975	92059
0040	G	S	E	N	1975	92059
0040	S	T	R	N	1972	65883
0040	S	T	E	N	1972	65884
0041	S	D	E	N	1974	54328
0045	S	T	R	N	1972	65883
0045	S	T	E	N	1972	65884
0061	S	D	E	N	1971	61706
0061	S	D	E	N	1966	64258
0061	S	T	E	N	1966	64258
0061	S	D	E	N	1971	75192
0061	S	S	E	N	1971	75192
0061	S	D	E	N	1975	86762
0065	S	S	E	N	1975	68703
0083	D	D	E	L	1972	53126
0083	D	D	E	L	1973	55120
0083	D	D	E	L	1975	62976
0083	D	T	E	L	1975	62976
0083	D	D	E	N	1975	86759
0132	D	D	E	N	1973	50979
0132	D	D	R	N	1973	51350
0132	D	D	E	N	1973	51351
0132	D	D	R	L	1973	52848
0132	D	D	E	L	1973	52849
0132	D	D	E	N	1974	53589
0132	D	D	R	N	1973	54448
0132	D	D	E	N	1973	54449
0132	D	D	E	N	1970	59602
0132	D	D	E	N	1974	62327
0132	D	T	E	N	1974	62327
0132	D	D	E	N	1975	66518
0132	D	T	E	N	1975	66518
0132	D	D	R	N	1975	86871
0132	D	D	E	N	1975	86872
0132	D	D	R	N	1974	60441
0132	S	D	E	N	1974	60442
0132	S	D	E	N	1972	70677
0132	S	D	E	N	1974	84584
0132	S	D	R	N	1974	87288
0132	S	D	E	N	1975	87289
0132	S	S	E	N	1974	98834
0141	G	D	E	N	1973	52478
0157	D	D	E	N	1971	66204
0157	D	T	E	N	1971	66204
0194	D	D	E	L	1973	55120
0194	S	D	E	N	1973	50872
0194	S	T	E	N	1973	51937
0194	T	S	E	N	1974	54111
0219	G	D	E	N	1973	51637
0224	L	D	E	N	1973	49538
0269	G	S	E	N	1973	51467
0269	G	D	E	N	1973	52481
0269	G	T	E	N	1974	54038
0269	G	D	E	N	1974	54316
0269	G	E	E	N	1974	54316
0269	G	T	E	N	1974	54316
0279	D	D	R	N	1973	53657
0279	D	D	E	N	1974	53658
0279	D	D	E	N	1974	54108
0279	D	D	R	N	1973	55038
0279	D	D	E	N	1974	55039
0279	D	D	R	N	1973	55176
0279	D	D	E	N	1974	55177
0279	D	D	E	L	1974	58819
0279	D	D	E	N	1974	58819
0298	G	D	E	N	1973	51637
0299	S	D	E	N	1974	57306
0299	S	T	E	N	1974	57306
0343	G	D	E	N	1973	52479
0352	D	T	E	N	1973	53430
0352	D	D	E	L	1973	55156
0352	D	S	E	N	1973	55156
0352	D	D	E	L	1975	62977
0352	D	D	E	N	1975	62977
0352	D	T	E	L	1975	62977
110-0352	D	T	E	N	1975	62977
0352	D	D	E	N	1973	68839
0352	D	S	E	N	1973	86375
0377	G	D	E	N	1973	52479
0377	G	D	E	N	1973	62303
8018	D	D	E	N	1973	52957
8020	S	S	E	N	1974	98834
8039	S	T	R	N	1973	50243
8039	S	T	E	N	1973	50244
8041	S	D	R	N	1975	86875
8041	S	S	R	N	1975	86875
8041	S	D	E	N	1975	86876
8041	S	S	E	N	1975	86876
8051	D	D	F	N	1973	51780
8066	S	D	E	L	1973	50868
8066	S	D	E	N	1973	50868
8095	D	D	E	L	1973	52489
8135	S	D	E	N	1974	53749
8137	D	D	R	N	1973	53657
8137	D	D	E	N	1974	53658
8137	D	D	R	N	1973	55038
8137	D	D	E	N	1974	55039
8155	S	D	E	N	1974	54328
8155	S	T	E	N	1974	54328
8165	S	D	E	N	1975	86742
8165	S	T	E	N	1975	86742
8169	D	D	E	L	1973	55156
8169	D	S	E	N	1973	55156
8170	D	D	E	L	1973	55156
8170	D	S	E	N	1973	55156
8189	S	D	E	L	1974	61159
8192	S	D	E	L	1974	61159
8193	S	D	E	L	1974	61159
8194	S	D	E	L	1974	61159
8195	S	D	E	L	1974	61159
8196	S	D	E	L	1974	61159
111-0006	S	D	E	N	1971	65044
0008	A	D	E	N	1974	54345
0008	D	D	E	N	1973	51758
0008	D	E	E	N	1973	51758
0008	D	D	E	N	1974	53927
0008	D	D	E	L	1974	54555
0008	D	D	E	N	1974	55245
0008	D	T	E	N	1973	56392
0008	D	D	E	N	1973	57403
0008	D	T	E	L	1974	58814
0008	D	D	E	N	1970	59690
0008	D	S	E	N	1970	59690
0008	D	D	E	N	1974	61181
0008	D	D	R	N	1974	63040
0008	D	S	R	N	1974	63040
0008	D	D	E	N	1975	63041
0008	D	S	E	N	1975	63041
0008	D	D	E	L	1969	65350
0008	D	S	E	N	1969	65350
0008	D	D	R	N	1974	66598
0008	D	D	E	N	1974	66599
0008	D	D	E	N	1975	66714
0008	D	T	E	N	1975	66714
0008	D	D	E	L	1971	70519
0008	D	D	E	N	1971	70519
0008	D	S	E	N	1971	70519
0008	D	D	R	N	1974	76160
0008	D	D	E	N	1975	76161
0008	D	D	R	N	1972	76547
0008	D	S	R	N	1972	76547
0008	D	T	R	N	1974	80751
0008	D	S	E	N	1962	87669
0008	D	S	E	L	1965	87703
0008	D	S	E	N	1965	87703
0008	D	S	E	H	1971	87884
0008	D	S	E	L	1971	87884
0008	D	S	E	N	1971	87884
0008	D	D	R	N	1974	89999
0008	D	S	R	N	1974	89999
0008	D	D	E	N	1975	90000
0008	D	S	E	N	1975	90000
0008	D	D	E	N	1972	91597
0008	D	S	E	N	1972	91597
0008	D	T	E	N	1974	95262
0008	D	D	R	N	1974	97464
0008	D	S	R	N	1974	97464
0008	D	D	E	N	1975	97465
0008	D	S	E	N	1975	97465
0008	S	D	R	N	1973	50205
0008	S	D	E	N	1973	50206
0008	S	D	E	N	1973	50925
0008	S	S	E	L	1973	51760
0008	S	S	O	N	1973	52180
0008	S	D	O	N	1973	52208
0008	S	D	E	N	1974	53607
0008	S	D	E	N	1974	54081
0008	S	D	E	N	1974	54345
0008	S	D	E	N	1974	54600
0008	S	S	E	N	1974	54600
0008	S	D	E	N	1974	54608
0008	S	S	E	N	1974	54608
0008	S	S	E	N	1972	55728
0008	S	D	E	N	1973	60575
0008	S	D	R	N	1973	62100

Phys. State: **A.** Amorphous; **C.** Superconductive; **D.** Doped; **F.** Fibrous or Whisker; **G.** Gas; **I.** Ionized or Plasma; **L.** Liquid; **P.** Powder or Particle; **S.** Solid; **T.** Thin Film
Subject: **D.** Data; **E.** Experiment; **S.** Survey (Review, Compendium, etc.); **T.** Theory
Language: **E.** English; **F.** French; **G.** German; **O.** Other Languages; **R.** Russian
Temperature: **L.** Low (0 to 75K); **N.** Normal (75 to 1273K); **H.** High (above 1273K)

Substance Number	Phys. State	Subject	Language	Temperature	Year	EPIC Number
111-0008	S	S	R	N	1973	62100
0008	S	D	E	N	1974	62277
0008	S	T	E	N	1975	65476
0008	S	D	E	L	1975	65492
0008	S	D	R	N	1970	67629
0008	S	D	E	N	1975	68674
0008	S	S	E	N	1975	68674
0008	S	T	E	N	1975	68674
0008	S	D	E	N	1968	74648
0008	S	D	R	N	1974	81026
0008	S	S	E	N	1962	87669
0008	S	S	E	N	1965	87703
0008	S	D	E	N	1973	89715
0008	S	S	E	N	1973	89715
0008	S	T	E	N	1975	90032
0008	S	D	E	N	1975	90718
0008	S	S	E	N	1975	90718
0008	S	D	E	N	1975	92633
0008	S	S	E	N	1972	97249
0008	T	D	R	L	1973	55339
0008	T	D	E	L	1974	59277
0008	T	D	E	N	1975	66714
0008	T	S	E	N	1975	66714
0008	T	T	E	N	1975	66714
0008	T	D	R	N	1971	67719
0008	T	S	E	N	1965	87703
0021	D	D	E	N	1974	53912
0021	D	D	E	N	1974	54560
0021	D	S	E	N	1973	62246
0021	D	S	R	N	1974	66446
0021	D	S	E	N	1974	66447
0021	S	D	E	L	1974	58037
0021	S	D	E	N	1974	62548
0021	S	S	R	L	1974	66446
0021	S	T	R	N	1974	66446
0021	S	S	E	L	1974	66447
0021	S	T	E	N	1974	66447
0021	T	D	E	N	1973	54206
0021	T	D	E	N	1974	58028
0021	T	T	E	N	1974	58028
0029	S	D	E	N	1969	85428
0029	S	D	E	L	1976	102163
0029	S	T	E	L	1976	102163
0050	D	D	E	N	1973	50558
0050	S	D	E	N	1973	50558
8002	A	D	E	N	1974	54345
8002	D	D	R	N	1973	50080
8002	D	D	E	L	1973	50483
8002	D	D	E	N	1973	51433
8002	D	S	E	N	1972	61061
8002	D	D	E	L	1974	61358
8002	D	D	R	N	1974	64959
8002	D	D	E	N	1975	68432
8002	D	S	E	N	1971	87884
8002	D	S	E	N	1975	94627
8002	S	D	E	L	1973	50483
8002	S	D	E	N	1973	50923
8002	S	D	E	N	1973	50925
8002	S	D	E	L	1973	52283
8002	S	D	E	N	1974	53607
8002	S	D	E	N	1974	54081
8002	S	D	E	N	1974	54345
8002	S	D	E	N	1974	54661
8002	S	T	E	N	1973	60627
8002	S	S	F	N	1973	63636
8002	S	T	E	N	1961	64497
8002	S	T	E	L	1962	65951
8002	S	D	E	N	1968	74648
8002	S	D	E	N	1975	90718
8002	S	S	E	N	1975	90718
8002	S	S	E	N	1972	97249
8002	S	D	E	L	1976	103586
8002	T	S	E	N	1969	87821
8007	D	D	R	N	1973	66119
8007	D	D	R	N	1970	67421
8007	S	T	E	N	1973	51795
8007	S	T	E	N	1973	56247
8007	S	S	R	L	1974	58062
8007	S	S	E	L	1974	58063
8007	S	D	E	N	1974	61354
8007	S	D	E	L	1975	65493
8007	S	D	E	N	1975	65493
8007	S	T	E	L	1975	65493
8007	S	T	E	N	1975	65493
8007	S	S	E	N	1974	66691
8007	S	D	E	N	1969	85428
8007	S	D	E	L	1976	102163
8007	S	T	E	L	1976	102163
8009	D	D	R	N	1970	67421
8009	S	T	E	N	1973	51795
8015	A	D	E	N	1973	51901
8015	T	D	E	N	1973	51901
8015	T	T	E	N	1973	55106
8021	A	D	E	N	1973	49710
8021	A	D	E	N	1973	51901
8021	A	D	E	N	1972	53374
8021	A	D	E	N	1973	60682
8021	S	D	E	N	1973	49710
8021	S	D	E	N	1973	60682
8021	T	D	E	N	1973	51901
8022	S	D	E	N	1969	85428

Substance Number	Phys. State	Subject	Language	Temperature	Year	EPIC Number
111-8022	S	D	E	L	1976	102163
8022	S	T	E	L	1976	102163
8026	S	D	E	N	1976	101211
8028	D	D	R	L	1973	50277
8028	D	D	R	N	1973	50277
8028	D	D	E	L	1973	50278
8028	D	D	E	N	1973	50278
8030	S	D	E	N	1973	50415
8031	S	D	E	N	1974	54661
8034	D	D	E	L	1973	50865
8034	D	T	E	L	1973	50865
8034	D	D	E	N	1973	51010
8037	S	D	E	N	1973	51072
8051	D	D	R	N	1974	92274
8051	D	D	E	N	1974	92275
8058	S	D	E	N	1975	90033
8071	S	D	E	N	1974	54324
8071	S	S	E	N	1971	65043
8075	A	D	E	N	1973	51901
8075	A	S	E	N	1972	53376
8075	T	D	E	N	1973	51901
8075	T	D	E	N	1971	53513
8075	T	T	E	N	1973	55106
8078	A	S	E	N	1974	54594
8078	A	T	E	N	1974	54594
8078	T	D	E	N	1971	53513
8079	A	D	E	N	1973	51901
8079	T	D	E	N	1973	51901
8094	S	T	E	N	1974	54110
8108	A	T	E	N	1974	57991
8108	T	T	E	N	1974	57991
8119	D	D	R	N	1973	55337
8119	D	D	E	N	1974	59275
8127	D	T	R	N	1974	90221
8127	D	T	E	N	1975	90222
8153	S	D	R	N	1970	67414
8157	S	D	O	N	1974	90531
8158	S	D	O	N	1974	90531
8190	S	D	R	N	1972	78186
8190	T	D	R	N	1972	78186
8192	S	D	R	N	1971	76488
8192	S	T	R	N	1971	76488
8192	S	D	E	N	1971	91569
8192	S	T	E	N	1971	91569
8206	S	T	E	N	1975	68676
112-0001	G	D	E	N	1973	51765
0001	G	D	E	N	1973	52482
0001	I	D	E	N	1973	52672
0001	I	E	E	N	1973	52672
0001	I	T	E	N	1973	52672
0001	L	S	E	N	1973	51467
0001	L	D	E	N	1974	58802
0001	S	D	E	N	1973	50934
0001	S	T	E	N	1973	50934
0001	S	S	R	N	1973	51370
0001	S	S	E	N	1973	51371
0004	G	S	E	N	1973	51439
0004	G	T	R	N	1972	65883
0004	G	T	E	N	1972	65884
0010	G	S	E	N	1973	51467
0010	I	D	E	N	1974	60353
0010	I	T	E	N	1974	60353
0021	G	D	E	N	1974	54315
0021	G	S	E	N	1974	54315
0025	S	T	E	N	1975	63329
0098	D	D	R	N	1973	51952
0098	D	D	E	N	1973	54437
0098	S	T	E	N	1975	63329
0303	D	D	E	L	1972	49857
0303	D	D	E	N	1972	49857
0402	S	D	E	N	1974	53607
0402	S	D	E	N	1974	54345
0402	S	D	E	N	1973	57560
0402	S	S	E	N	1973	57560
0402	S	S	E	N	1975	101023
8020	S	D	E	N	1974	53611
8020	S	D	E	N	1974	54345
8020	S	D	E	N	1968	74648
8025	S	D	R	L	1973	50062
8025	S	D	E	L	1973	51418
8025	S	T	E	L	1974	53599
8025	S	T	E	N	1974	53599
8025	S	D	E	N	1974	53607
8025	S	D	E	N	1974	54345
8025	S	D	E	N	1973	57454
8025	S	D	O	N	1971	60023
8025	S	D	E	N	1968	74648
8026	D	D	E	L	1972	49857
8026	D	D	E	N	1972	49857
8026	D	D	E	N	1973	51172
8049	G	D	E	N	1974	54315
8049	G	S	E	N	1974	54315
8050	S	D	E	N	1974	54306
8053	T	D	E	N	1973	53558
8061	D	D	E	N	1974	57305
8065	S	S	E	N	1974	86505
114-0001	D	D	R	N	1972	49654
0001	D	D	E	L	1973	50142
0001	D	D	E	N	1973	50142

Substance Number	Phys. State	Subject	Language	Temperature	Year	EPIC Number
114-0001	D	T	E	N	1973	52028
0001	D	D	R	L	1973	54401
0001	D	S	R	L	1973	54401
0001	D	D	E	L	1973	54402
0001	D	S	E	L	1973	54402
0001	D	D	R	N	1973	54411
0001	D	D	E	N	1973	54412
0001	D	T	E	N	1974	55250
0001	D	D	R	N	1974	58084
0001	D	D	E	N	1974	58085
0001	D	D	E	N	1974	59393
0001	D	S	E	N	1974	59393
0001	D	T	E	N	1974	59393
0001	D	D	E	N	1973	60586
0001	D	S	E	L	1972	61498
0001	S	T	E	L	1973	53582
0001	S	D	E	N	1974	54603
0001	S	D	E	N	1974	54604
0001	S	S	E	N	1972	55728
0001	S	D	E	N	1974	58821
0001	S	D	E	L	1970	59675
0001	S	D	E	N	1974	61390
0001	S	D	E	N	1971	61706
0001	S	S	E	N	1971	61706
0001	S	T	E	N	1971	61706
0001	S	D	E	N	1966	64258
0001	S	T	E	N	1966	64258
0001	S	D	E	N	1972	70677
0001	S	S	E	N	1972	70677
0001	S	D	E	L	1968	74624
0001	S	D	E	N	1968	74624
0001	S	D	E	N	1969	85421
0001	S	S	E	N	1969	85421
0001	S	D	E	N	1975	86762
0002	D	D	E	L	1973	50142
0002	D	D	E	N	1973	50142
0002	S	D	E	N	1974	54603
0002	S	D	E	N	1974	58821
0002	S	S	E	N	1973	60558
0002	S	D	E	N	1974	61390
0002	S	S	E	N	1971	61706
0002	S	D	E	N	1966	64258
0002	S	T	E	N	1966	64258
0002	S	D	E	N	1972	70677
0002	S	S	E	N	1972	70677
0002	S	D	E	L	1968	74624
0002	S	D	E	N	1968	74624
0002	S	D	E	N	1971	75192
0002	S	S	E	N	1971	75192
0002	S	D	E	N	1975	86762
0006	S	T	E	N	1974	54089
0006	S	S	E	N	1975	91289
0009	D	D	E	L	1973	50142
0009	D	D	E	N	1973	50142
0009	D	D	R	L	1973	54401
0009	D	D	E	L	1973	54402
0009	D	D	E	N	1975	62876
0009	S	D	E	N	1974	54604
0009	S	D	E	N	1974	61390
0009	S	D	E	N	1966	64258
0009	S	T	E	N	1966	64258
0009	S	D	E	N	1975	65501
0010	S	D	E	N	1966	64258
0010	S	T	E	N	1966	64258
0010	S	D	E	N	1975	65501
0017	A	D	E	N	1974	54345
0017	D	S	E	N	1962	87660
0017	D	S	E	N	1971	87884
0017	S	D	R	N	1973	50205
0017	S	D	E	N	1973	50206
0017	S	D	E	N	1973	50923
0017	S	D	E	N	1973	50925
0017	S	D	E	N	1974	53607
0017	S	D	E	N	1974	54081
0017	S	D	E	N	1974	54345
0017	S	D	R	N	1973	54361
0017	S	S	R	N	1973	54361
0017	S	D	E	N	1973	54362
0017	S	S	E	N	1973	54362
0017	S	T	E	L	1974	54601
0017	S	T	E	N	1974	54601
0017	S	D	R	N	1973	55305
0017	S	D	E	N	1974	59230
0017	S	D	R	N	1974	62528
0017	S	S	R	N	1974	62528
0017	S	D	E	N	1974	64431
0017	S	S	E	N	1974	64431
0017	S	D	E	N	1968	74648
0017	S	T	R	N	1974	87312
0017	S	T	E	N	1975	87313
0017	S	S	E	N	1962	87660
0017	S	D	E	N	1975	90718
0017	S	S	E	N	1975	90718
0017	S	D	E	L	1975	91725
0017	S	T	E	L	1975	91863
0017	S	S	E	N	1972	97249
0017	S	S	E	N	1963	98002
0059	S	D	E	N	1974	54305
0060	S	D	E	N	1973	53574
0060	S	D	E	N	1973	63666
8001	A	D	E	N	1974	54345

Phys. State: A. Amorphous; C. Superconductive; D. Doped; F. Fibrous or Whisker; G. Gas; I. Ionized or Plasma; L. Liquid; P. Powder or Particle; S. Solid; T. Thin Film
Subject: D. Data; E. Experiment; S. Survey (Review, Compendium, etc.); T. Theory
Language: E. English; F. French; G. German; O. Other Languages; R. Russian
Temperature: L. Low (0 to 75K); N. Normal (75 to 1273K); H. High (above 1273K)

Substance Number	Phys. State	Subject	Language	Temperature	Year	EPIC Number
114-8001	D	D	R	N	1973	50209
8001	D	D	E	N	1973	50210
8001	D	S	E	N	1974	54081
8001	D	D	R	L	1973	54292
8001	D	T	R	N	1973	54292
8001	D	D	E	L	1973	54293
8001	D	T	E	N	1973	54293
8001	D	S	E	N	1972	61061
8001	D	T	E	N	1973	61770
8001	D	S	E	N	1963	87679
8001	D	S	E	L	1965	87781
8001	D	S	E	N	1965	87781
8001	D	S	E	L	1971	87884
8001	D	S	E	N	1971	87884
8001	S	D	E	N	1973	50548
8001	S	D	E	N	1973	50925
8001	S	D	E	N	1973	51212
8001	S	D	E	N	1973	51833
8001	S	D	E	L	1973	52283
8001	S	D	R	N	1973	52523
8001	S	T	R	L	1973	52525
8001	S	D	E	L	1973	52702
8001	S	D	E	N	1973	52702
8001	S	T	E	L	1973	52702
8001	S	T	E	N	1973	52702
8001	S	D	E	N	1974	53606
8001	S	T	E	N	1974	53606
8001	S	D	E	N	1974	53607
8001	S	T	E	N	1973	53782
8001	S	S	E	N	1973	53939
8001	S	D	E	N	1974	54081
8001	S	D	E	N	1974	54094
8001	S	D	E	N	1974	54345
8001	S	D	E	N	1974	54600
8001	S	S	E	N	1974	54600
8001	S	T	R	N	1973	54990
8001	S	T	E	N	1974	54991
8001	S	T	R	N	1973	55340
8001	S	S	E	N	1973	56749
8001	S	D	E	N	1974	57764
8001	S	T	E	L	1974	57766
8001	S	D	E	L	1974	58031
8001	S	D	E	N	1974	58038
8001	S	T	E	N	1974	59278
8001	S	D	E	N	1974	60537
8001	S	D	R	N	1972	60721
8001	S	D	E	N	1973	60722
8001	S	D	E	N	1974	62063
8001	S	T	E	N	1974	62063
8001	S	T	R	L	1974	62427
8001	S	D	R	L	1974	63036
8001	S	D	E	L	1974	63037
8001	S	T	E	L	1974	65330
8001	S	D	R	L	1974	65371
8001	S	T	R	L	1974	65371
8001	S	D	E	L	1975	65372
8001	S	T	E	L	1975	65372
8001	S	D	E	N	1975	66682
8001	S	T	E	L	1975	66682
8001	S	T	E	N	1975	66682
8001	S	T	E	L	1966	74593
8001	S	D	E	N	1968	74648
8001	S	D	E	N	1975	87172
8001	S	S	E	N	1975	87172
8001	S	S	E	L	1963	87679
8001	S	S	E	N	1965	87781
8001	S	D	E	N	1975	90718
8001	S	S	E	N	1975	90718
8001	S	S	E	N	1972	97249
8001	T	D	R	N	1975	77007
8001	T	D	E	N	1975	77008
8021	S	D	E	N	1975	93528
8054	S	D	E	L	1975	68702
8057	S	T	E	N	1973	52658
8096	S	D	R	N	1972	68553
8096	S	D	E	N	1972	68554
116-0017	D	D	E	N	1974	54351
0030	S	S	E	N	1974	66380
8017	D	D	E	N	1974	54351
8037	S	D	R	N	1973	58870
8038	S	D	R	N	1973	58870
118-0037	D	D	E	N	1974	53896
0037	D	T	E	N	1974	53896
8005	S	D	E	L	1975	68702
8015	D	D	R	N	1974	92274
8015	D	D	E	N	1974	92275
8016	D	D	E	N	1973	51034
8021	D	D	R	N	1973	52560
8021	D	D	E	N	1973	57785
8025	S	T	E	N	1975	68676
8027	D	D	E	N	1972	53520
8040	G	D	E	N	1974	54315
8040	G	S	E	N	1974	54315
8041	D	D	R	N	1973	54494
8041	D	D	E	N	1973	54495
8042	D	D	R	N	1973	54494
8042	D	D	E	N	1973	54495
8043	D	D	R	N	1973	54494
8043	D	D	E	N	1973	54495
118-8044	S	D	E	N	1974	54965
8044	S	S	E	L	1974	54965
8045	D	D	R	N	1973	55195
8045	D	D	E	N	1974	55196
8055	S	D	E	L	1975	68702
8060	D	D	R	N	1974	60501
8060	D	D	E	N	1974	60502
8061	S	T	E	N	1974	61202
8072	S	D	R	N	1973	58870
8073	S	D	R	N	1973	58870
8096	D	D	R	N	1974	92274
8096	D	D	E	N	1974	92275
119-0001	S	D	E	N	1973	52549
0001	S	D	E	N	1974	60658
0001	S	T	E	N	1974	89519
0001	S	D	E	N	1975	90460
0001	S	D	E	L	1972	101321
0002	D	D	E	N	1973	53586
0002	D	S	E	L	1973	53586
0002	D	D	E	N	1974	54108
0002	D	T	E	N	1974	54108
0002	D	D	E	N	1975	62975
0002	D	T	E	N	1975	62975
0002	D	S	E	N	1966	63913
0002	S	D	E	N	1970	52696
0002	S	D	E	N	1973	53583
0002	S	S	E	N	1973	53583
0002	S	T	E	N	1973	53583
0002	S	D	E	N	1974	62065
0002	S	S	E	N	1974	62065
0002	S	T	E	N	1974	62065
0002	S	S	E	N	1966	63913
0002	S	S	E	N	1969	87723
0008	D	T	E	N	1964	60562
0008	S	D	E	N	1973	49735
0008	S	D	E	N	1974	53749
0010	S	T	E	N	1973	52408
0050	D	D	R	N	1973	54494
0050	D	D	E	N	1973	54495
0051	S	D	E	N	1972	52995
0073	D	D	R	N	1973	54494
0073	D	D	E	N	1973	54495
8002	D	S	E	L	1962	87672
8002	S	D	E	N	1973	51072
8009	S	D	E	N	1973	51072
8020	S	D	E	N	1973	52549
8035	S	D	R	N	1973	55048
8035	S	D	E	N	1974	55049
8080	C	D	E	L	1975	89571
8080	S	D	E	N	1973	59309
8080	S	S	E	N	1974	86505
8084	S	D	E	N	1975	90460
8084	S	D	E	L	1972	101321
8101	S	D	E	N	1975	90460
8101	S	D	E	L	1972	101321
8103	S	D	R	N	1974	65413
8103	S	D	E	N	1975	65414
120-0001	A	S	E	N	1972	52403
0001	A	S	E	N	1971	65066
0001	D	D	E	N	1971	52970
0001	S	D	E	N	1973	49735
0001	S	S	E	N	1975	63331
0001	S	D	E	N	1975	65487
0001	S	S	E	N	1975	65487
0001	S	S	E	N	1975	68703
0001	S	T	R	N	1975	90674
0001	T	D	E	N	1972	52501
0002	G	D	E	N	1973	52477
0002	G	D	E	N	1973	52479
0002	I	D	E	N	1973	50769
0002	I	D	E	N	1972	53134
0002	I	S	E	N	1976	98747
0003	G	D	E	N	1973	52477
0005	G	D	E	N	1974	54315
0006	S	S	E	N	1974	58051
0006	S	D	E	N	1974	58052
0006	S	T	E	N	1974	58052
0014	G	D	E	N	1973	52477
0014	G	D	E	N	1973	52479
0023	S	S	R	N	1973	53995
0023	S	S	E	N	1973	53996
0023	S	S	E	N	1964	93287
0024	D	D	R	L	1973	55180
0024	D	D	E	L	1974	55181
0032	S	D	E	N	1974	54096
0032	S	T	E	N	1974	54096
0032	S	D	E	N	1973	60642
0032	S	T	E	N	1973	60642
0032	S	S	E	N	1974	66380
0042	S	T	E	N	1975	65476
0045	S	D	E	N	1974	58023
0045	S	D	G	N	1971	66334
0045	S	D	E	N	1975	68687
0045	S	T	E	N	1975	68687
0106	S	D	E	N	1974	54324
0166	S	D	E	N	1973	51194
0203	S	S	E	N	1974	66380
8021	S	D	E	N	1974	53593
8024	S	S	E	N	1971	87885
120-8024	T	D	E	N	1973	57595
8024	T	S	E	N	1973	57595
8038	S	D	R	L	1974	68630
8038	S	D	E	L	1974	68631
8071	G	D	E	N	1974	54315
8072	D	D	R	N	1973	54494
8072	D	D	E	N	1973	54495
8079	S	D	R	N	1973	52563
8079	S	T	R	N	1973	52563
8079	S	D	E	N	1973	57788
8079	S	T	E	N	1973	57788
8121	S	D	R	N	1973	58870
8122	S	D	R	N	1973	58870
8182	S	D	E	N	1975	65463
8182	S	T	E	N	1975	65463
122-0003	G	D	E	N	1974	54315
0003	G	S	E	N	1974	54315
0003	S	D	R	N	1974	77924
0003	S	T	R	N	1974	77924
0003	S	D	E	N	1974	94512
0003	S	T	E	N	1974	94512
0004	G	D	E	N	1974	54315
0004	G	S	E	N	1974	54315
0005	D	T	E	N	1973	50756
0005	D	E	E	N	1972	53163
0005	D	E	E	N	1972	53164
0005	D	D	E	N	1973	67807
0005	G	D	E	N	1974	54315
0005	G	S	E	N	1974	54315
0008	G	D	E	N	1974	54315
0008	G	S	E	N	1974	54315
0008	S	S	E	N	1974	98834
0009	S	D	E	N	1973	50626
0009	S	T	E	N	1973	53585
0009	S	D	E	N	1974	54101
0009	S	T	E	N	1974	58802
0009	S	D	E	N	1974	58803
0009	S	S	E	N	1974	58803
0009	S	T	E	N	1974	66308
0009	T	D	R	N	1973	52679
0009	T	D	E	N	1974	53903
0009	T	T	E	N	1974	53903
0009	T	D	E	N	1973	54454
0009	T	D	E	N	1974	58041
0009	T	T	E	N	1975	86753
0010	G	S	E	N	1973	51467
0010	G	D	E	N	1973	51942
0010	G	T	R	N	1972	65883
0010	G	T	E	N	1972	65884
0010	I	D	E	H	1975	68596
0010	I	S	E	H	1975	68596
0010	I	T	E	H	1975	68596
0016	D	D	R	N	1973	53670
0016	D	D	E	N	1974	53671
0017	D	T	E	N	1974	62032
0017	T	D	E	N	1974	53724
0017	T	D	E	N	1974	62032
0017	T	T	E	N	1973	63510
0023	D	D	G	N	1973	57678
0023	D	S	E	N	1963	87709
0023	S	D	E	N	1974	53607
0023	S	D	E	H	1974	53916
0023	S	D	E	N	1974	59358
0023	S	D	E	N	1973	60636
0023	S	D	E	N	1972	61767
0023	S	D	E	N	1972	63847
0023	S	S	E	N	1972	63847
0023	S	S	E	N	1975	68674
0023	S	T	E	N	1975	68674
0023	S	D	E	N	1968	74648
0023	S	S	E	N	1974	99215
0023	T	D	E	N	1973	57273
0026	S	D	E	N	1974	94480
0026	S	T	E	N	1974	94480
0030	D	D	E	N	1973	50965
0030	D	D	E	N	1973	53578
0030	D	E	E	N	1973	53578
0030	D	T	E	N	1973	53578
0030	S	S	E	N	1974	54595
0030	S	D	R	N	1973	55203
0030	S	D	E	N	1974	55204
0030	S	D	E	N	1973	56523
0030	S	T	E	N	1973	60591
0030	S	D	E	N	1973	60645
0030	S	S	E	N	1973	60645
0031	S	D	R	H	1974	66744
0031	S	D	R	N	1974	66744
0031	S	T	R	H	1974	66744
0031	S	T	R	N	1974	66744
0031	S	D	E	H	1975	66745
0031	S	D	E	N	1975	66745
0031	S	T	E	H	1975	66745
0031	S	T	E	N	1975	66745
0031	S	D	R	N	1972	76508
0031	S	D	E	N	1972	91530
0032	G	D	E	N	1974	54315
0032	G	S	E	N	1974	54315
0037	S	D	R	N	1974	77924
0037	S	T	R	N	1974	77924
0037	S	D	E	N	1974	94512

Phys. State: **A.** Amorphous; **C.** Superconductive; **D.** Doped; **F.** Fibrous or Whisker; **G.** Gas; **I.** Ionized or Plasma; **L.** Liquid; **P.** Powder or Particle; **S.** Solid; **T.** Thin Film
Subject: **D.** Data; **E.** Experiment; **S.** Survey (Review, Compendium, etc.); **T.** Theory
Language: **E.** English; **F.** French; **G.** German; **O.** Other Languages; **R.** Russian
Temperature: **L.** Low (0 to 75K); **N.** Normal (75 to 1273K); **H.** High (above 1273K)

Substance Number	Phys. State	Subject	Language	Temperature	Year	EPIC Number
122-0037	S	T	E	N	1974	94512
0046	G	D	E	N	1974	54315
0046	G	S	E	N	1974	54315
0050	D	S	E	N	1967	66368
0050	T	T	E	N	1973	54774
0050	T	S	E	N	1967	66368
0053	D	D	E	N	1969	68246
0053	S	D	E	N	1973	50398
0053	T	D	O	N	1973	56768
0054	D	D	R	N	1973	54494
0054	D	D	E	N	1973	54495
0077	G	D	E	N	1974	54315
0096	A	S	E	N	1972	52403
0096	S	D	E	N	1973	53585
0105	S	D	E	N	1975	90079
0105	T	D	O	N	1973	56266
0112	S	D	E	N	1972	56074
0112	S	T	E	N	1973	60633
0139	G	D	E	N	1974	54315
0139	G	S	E	N	1974	54315
0198	D	D	R	N	1973	54494
0198	D	D	E	N	1973	54495
0296	D	D	R	N	1973	52560
0296	D	D	R	N	1973	55195
0296	D	S	R	N	1973	55195
0296	D	T	R	N	1973	55195
0296	D	D	E	N	1974	55196
0296	D	S	E	N	1974	55196
0296	D	T	E	N	1974	55196
0296	D	D	E	L	1974	57305
0296	D	D	E	N	1974	57305
0296	D	S	E	L	1974	57305
0296	D	S	E	N	1974	57305
0296	D	D	E	N	1973	57785
0296	D	D	E	L	1974	61156
0402	D	D	E	N	1974	57305
0425	S	D	E	N	1975	80497
8004	S	D	E	N	1973	51636
8013	S	D	E	N	1975	65429
8021	S	D	E	N	1973	51636
8025	D	D	R	N	1974	92274
8025	D	D	E	N	1974	92275
8034	S	S	E	N	1973	51205
8035	S	S	E	N	1973	51205
8038	D	D	E	L	1974	57305
8038	D	D	E	N	1974	57305
8038	D	S	E	L	1974	57305
8038	D	S	E	N	1974	57305
8038	D	D	R	N	1973	70946
8038	D	T	R	N	1973	70946
8038	D	D	E	N	1973	91485
8038	D	T	E	N	1973	91485
8038	S	D	R	N	1972	68553
8038	S	D	E	N	1972	68554
8068	S	D	F	L	1971	59041
8070	D	D	E	N	1974	57305
8070	D	D	E	N	1975	63265
8070	D	T	E	N	1975	63265
8071	G	D	E	N	1974	54315
8071	G	S	E	N	1974	54315
8072	G	D	E	N	1974	54315
8072	G	S	E	N	1974	54315
8073	G	D	E	N	1974	54315
8073	G	S	E	N	1974	54315
8074	G	D	E	N	1974	54315
8077	D	D	R	N	1973	54494
8077	D	D	E	N	1973	54495
8091	D	D	E	N	1974	57305
8091	S	D	R	N	1972	68553
8091	S	D	E	N	1972	68554
8092	S	D	E	L	1974	61156
8108	S	D	E	N	1975	80497
8109	S	D	E	N	1975	80497
8110	S	D	E	N	1975	80497
8111	S	D	E	N	1975	80497
8139	S	D	R	N	1972	68553
8139	S	D	E	N	1972	68554
123-0003	D	S	E	N	1966	68361
0003	S	D	E	N	1972	53200
0003	S	S	E	N	1974	53607
0003	S	S	E	N	1973	53851
0003	S	D	E	N	1973	60638
0003	S	D	E	N	1975	65495
0003	S	T	E	N	1975	65495
0003	S	S	E	N	1966	68361
0003	T	D	R	N	1973	55323
0003	T	D	E	N	1974	59259
0003	T	S	E	N	1966	68361
0014	S	D	E	N	1974	53593
0025	S	D	E	N	1974	53593
0025	S	D	E	N	1974	54113
0032	S	D	G	N	1973	51683
0032	S	D	E	N	1973	52054
0032	S	T	E	N	1974	59352
0032	S	D	E	N	1975	86764
8017	D	D	E	N	1974	90402
8017	S	T	E	N	1973	52461
8017	S	D	E	N	1974	53607
8017	S	D	E	N	1973	60638
8017	S	D	E	N	1975	87174
123-8017	S	S	E	N	1962	87674
8018	D	D	R	N	1973	50672
8018	D	D	E	N	1973	52418
8018	D	S	E	N	1970	68114
8018	D	S	E	N	1969	68115
8018	S	D	E	N	1974	53607
8018	S	S	E	N	1973	56749
8018	S	T	R	N	1973	58155
8018	S	D	E	N	1972	59070
8018	S	D	E	N	1973	60638
8018	S	D	E	N	1971	65045
8018	S	S	E	N	1975	65495
8018	S	T	E	N	1975	68678
8018	S	D	E	N	1975	87174
8018	T	D	R	N	1974	93120
8018	T	D	E	N	1975	93121
8039	S	T	E	N	1973	52461
8039	S	D	R	N	1974	97468
8039	S	D	E	N	1975	97469
8046	D	D	E	L	1974	54965
8050	D	D	R	N	1974	92259
8050	D	D	E	N	1975	92260
8051	D	D	R	N	1974	92259
8051	D	D	E	N	1975	92260
8051	S	D	E	N	1973	65985
8058	S	S	E	N	1974	61199
8065	S	D	R	N	1973	55298
8065	S	D	E	N	1974	59283
8073	S	D	E	L	1971	57503
8104	S	D	E	N	1973	53799
125-8036	S	D	R	N	1973	58870
126-0004	S	D	E	N	1973	51856
0004	S	D	E	N	1974	53598
0005	D	D	E	N	1973	49584
0005	D	D	E	N	1973	49614
0005	D	D	O	N	1973	51989
0005	D	T	R	N	1973	52380
0005	D	D	E	N	1973	52941
0005	D	T	E	L	1974	54084
0005	D	T	E	N	1973	57493
0005	D	D	R	N	1972	58771
0005	D	D	E	N	1974	60751
0005	D	T	E	N	1974	60751
0005	D	D	E	L	1974	61188
0005	D	T	R	N	1974	66782
0005	D	D	E	N	1975	66783
0005	D	D	E	L	1966	74595
0005	D	D	E	L	1974	81762
0005	D	D	E	N	1974	87226
0005	D	S	E	N	1963	87711
0005	D	S	E	N	1966	87712
0005	S	D	E	N	1973	50925
0005	S	D	E	L	1973	51060
0005	S	D	E	N	1973	51060
0005	S	D	E	N	1974	53607
0005	S	D	E	N	1974	54081
0005	S	D	R	N	1973	54361
0005	S	S	R	N	1973	54361
0005	S	D	E	N	1973	54362
0005	S	S	E	N	1973	54362
0005	S	D	R	N	1973	55207
0005	S	D	E	N	1974	55208
0005	S	D	R	N	1972	56942
0005	S	D	E	N	1974	59358
0005	S	D	R	N	1974	60445
0005	S	T	R	N	1974	60445
0005	S	D	E	N	1974	60446
0005	S	T	E	N	1974	60446
0005	S	S	E	N	1972	63503
0005	S	D	E	N	1973	67531
0005	S	E	E	N	1973	67531
0005	S	D	E	N	1968	74648
0005	S	D	E	N	1975	87171
0005	S	S	E	L	1963	87711
0005	S	S	E	N	1966	87712
0005	S	T	E	L	1976	99875
0005	T	D	R	N	1973	56315
0011	S	D	E	N	1974	54113
0017	D	D	E	N	1972	49838
0017	D	D	R	N	1972	58771
0025	S	D	E	N	1973	57706
0038	S	T	E	N	1975	66668
0038	S	S	E	N	1972	70535
8007	S	D	E	L	1974	61394
8007	S	D	E	N	1974	61394
8030	S	T	E	N	1974	55249
8032	D	D	R	N	1973	55822
8037	S	D	E	N	1973	60638
8039	S	D	E	L	1972	101321
8043	S	D	E	N	1974	61369
8043	S	T	E	N	1974	61369
8048	D	D	E	L	1970	49613
8049	D	D	E	L	1970	49613
8050	D	D	E	L	1970	49613
8052	D	D	E	N	1973	51020
8052	D	D	E	N	1971	53243
8052	D	D	E	N	1974	53923
8052	D	S	E	N	1963	68313
8052	D	D	E	L	1966	74595
126-8052	D	S	E	L	1966	74595
8052	D	D	G	N	1975	90552
8052	S	D	E	N	1973	50925
8052	S	D	E	N	1973	53346
8052	S	D	E	N	1974	53607
8052	S	D	E	N	1974	54081
8052	S	D	E	N	1974	54345
8052	S	D	E	N	1974	54600
8052	S	S	E	N	1974	54600
8052	S	D	E	N	1974	54604
8052	S	D	E	N	1974	55257
8052	S	S	E	N	1974	55257
8052	S	D	E	N	1974	57325
8052	S	D	E	N	1973	57560
8052	S	S	E	N	1973	57560
8052	S	D	E	N	1973	68345
8052	S	S	E	N	1975	68674
8052	S	T	E	N	1975	68674
8052	S	D	E	N	1968	74648
8052	S	D	E	N	1973	88610
8052	S	E	E	N	1975	97217
8052	T	S	E	N	1963	68313
8055	S	D	E	N	1972	49935
8059	D	D	R	N	1973	52563
8059	D	T	R	N	1973	52563
8059	D	D	E	N	1973	57788
8059	D	T	E	N	1973	57788
8059	S	D	R	N	1973	52563
8059	S	T	R	N	1973	52563
8059	S	D	E	N	1973	57788
8059	S	T	E	N	1973	57788
8059	S	D	E	L	1972	101321
8090	S	D	E	N	1974	53598
8098	S	D	E	N	1974	62465
8098	S	T	E	N	1975	66668
8107	S	D	E	N	1974	84453
8156	S	T	E	N	1975	68676
127-8002	L	T	E	N	1974	54095
8004	A	D	E	N	1974	54345
8004	D	D	R	N	1973	50084
8004	D	D	E	N	1973	51435
8004	D	D	E	N	1973	53844
8004	D	T	E	L	1970	63651
8004	D	D	E	N	1970	67143
8004	D	S	E	N	1962	87666
8004	D	D	O	N	1973	90098
8004	S	D	E	L	1973	50845
8004	S	D	E	N	1973	50925
8004	S	D	E	N	1973	52152
8004	S	D	E	N	1971	53243
8004	S	D	E	N	1974	53607
8004	S	D	E	N	1974	54081
8004	S	D	E	N	1974	54345
8004	S	D	R	N	1973	54361
8004	S	S	R	N	1973	54361
8004	S	D	E	N	1973	54362
8004	S	S	E	N	1973	54362
8004	S	D	E	N	1973	57629
8004	S	D	R	N	1974	61980
8004	S	T	R	N	1974	61980
8004	S	D	E	N	1974	61981
8004	S	T	E	N	1974	61981
8004	S	D	E	N	1972	63492
8004	S	T	E	N	1975	65476
8004	S	D	E	N	1970	67143
8004	S	S	E	N	1975	68674
8004	S	T	E	N	1975	68674
8004	S	D	E	N	1968	74648
8010	T	D	E	N	1974	53602
8010	T	T	E	N	1974	53602
132-8001	S	D	E	N	1973	51859
8001	S	D	E	N	1975	90465
8001	S	T	E	N	1975	90465
133-8001	S	D	E	N	1974	54116
8001	S	S	E	N	1974	54116
8001	S	S	E	N	1973	56286

Phys. State: **A.** Amorphous; **C.** Superconductive; **D.** Doped; **F.** Fibrous or Whisker; **G.** Gas; **I.** Ionized or Plasma; **L.** Liquid; **P.** Powder or Particle; **S.** Solid; **T.** Thin Film
Subject: **D.** Data; **E.** Experiment; **S.** Survey (Review, Compendium, etc.); **T.** Theory
Language: **E.** English; **F.** French; **G.** German; **O.** Other Languages; **R.** Russian
Temperature: **L.** Low (0 to 75K); **N.** Normal (75 to 1273K); **H.** High (above 1273K)

Chapter 9 Electron Emission Properties

Substance Number	Phys. State	Sub-ject	Lan-guage	Temper-ature	Year	EPIC Number
100-0045	G	E	E	N	1973	52595
0045	S	S	O	N	1973	50602
0045	S	T	R	N	1973	51688
0045	S	T	E	N	1973	63180
0055	A	S	E	N	1971	60961
0055	A	T	E	N	1972	64085
0055	D	T	E	N	1971	68133
0055	D	T	R	N	1974	77934
0055	D	T	E	N	1974	94494
0055	S	T	R	N	1973	51552
0055	S	T	R	N	1973	52160
0055	S	S	E	N	1974	53607
0055	S	T	E	N	1973	53683
0055	S	S	R	N	1973	53794
0055	S	T	R	N	1973	54968
0055	S	T	E	N	1974	54969
0055	S	T	E	N	1973	60628
0055	S	T	R	N	1974	63157
0055	S	T	E	N	1975	63158
0055	S	T	E	N	1975	63303
0055	S	S	F	N	1971	64995
0055	S	T	R	N	1972	65696
0055	S	T	E	N	1972	65697
0055	S	T	E	N	1973	66038
0055	S	T	E	N	1974	66110
0055	S	T	E	N	1974	66819
0055	S	T	E	N	1974	66821
0055	S	E	F	N	1971	67646
0055	T	S	E	N	1974	87639
0055	T	T	O	N	1974	88134
8003	S	T	R	N	1971	59579
8003	S	T	E	N	1971	61328
8003	S	S	E	N	1974	66806
8003	S	T	R	N	1974	77919
8003	S	T	E	N	1974	94518
8007	S	S	E	N	1969	68271
8008	S	S	F	N	1971	64995
8008	S	S	E	N	1971	87884
8008	S	S	E	N	1972	87889
8029	S	D	E	N	1973	56720
8038	S	S	E	N	1969	68115
8063	S	T	R	N	1974	77922
8063	S	T	E	N	1974	94514
102-0002	A	S	E	N	1972	52403
0002	D	S	E	N	1973	56749
0002	D	D	E	N	1974	66828
0002	D	D	R	H	1975	95124
0002	D	D	R	N	1975	95124
0002	D	D	E	H	1976	95907
0002	D	D	E	N	1976	95907
0002	S	D	E	H	1973	49433
0002	S	D	R	N	1972	49971
0002	S	D	E	N	1973	51225
0002	S	D	E	N	1974	58827
0002	S	S	E	N	1974	58827
0002	S	D	E	H	1970	60090
0002	S	E	E	H	1970	60090
0002	S	D	R	N	1974	67821
0002	S	D	E	N	1972	68992
0002	T	D	E	N	1972	52981
0002	T	D	E	N	1972	53133
0002	T	E	E	N	1972	53133
0002	T	D	E	N	1974	62785
0002	T	D	E	H	1973	65547
0002	T	D	E	N	1973	65547
0002	T	T	E	H	1973	65547
0002	T	T	E	N	1973	65547
0002	T	D	E	N	1975	66619
0002	T	E	E	N	1975	66619
0002	T	D	O	N	1974	67787
0002	T	D	R	N	1974	77932
0002	T	T	R	N	1974	77932
0002	T	S	E	N	1975	90038
0002	T	D	R	H	1975	91366
0002	T	D	E	N	1974	94499
0002	T	T	E	N	1974	94499
0002	T	D	R	H	1975	95124
0002	T	D	R	N	1975	95124
0002	T	D	E	H	1975	95225
0002	T	D	E	H	1976	95907
0002	T	D	E	N	1976	95907
0005	S	D	E	N	1974	54600
0009	D	D	R	N	1974	61996
0009	D	T	R	N	1974	61996
0009	D	D	E	N	1974	61997
0009	D	T	E	N	1974	61997
0009	D	D	E	N	1975	90105
0009	D	T	E	N	1975	90105
0009	S	D	R	N	1974	61996
0009	S	T	R	N	1974	61996
0009	S	D	E	N	1974	61997
0009	S	T	E	N	1974	61997
0010	S	T	R	N	1971	59579
0010	S	T	E	N	1971	61328

Substance Number	Phys. State	Sub-ject	Lan-guage	Temper-ature	Year	EPIC Number
102-0011	S	D	E	N	1973	57557
0015	S	D	E	N	1974	58827
0015	S	S	E	N	1974	58827
0041	S	D	E	N	1972	53066
0041	S	D	E	N	1974	53917
0041	S	S	E	N	1972	87889
0248	S	D	E	N	1975	93384
0250	D	D	E	N	1974	53918
0250	D	S	E	N	1969	101680
8001	S	D	R	N	1973	55223
8001	S	D	E	N	1974	55224
8001	S	S	E	N	1971	87884
8031	A	D	E	N	1972	53373
8031	S	D	E	N	1974	54097
8031	S	D	R	N	1974	58112
8031	S	D	E	N	1974	58113
8031	T	D	E	N	1972	53373
8040	T	D	O	N	1973	58722
8041	D	D	R	N	1972	50696
8041	D	T	E	N	1973	52759
8041	D	D	E	N	1972	53217
8041	D	S	E	N	1972	53227
8041	D	D	E	N	1972	53228
8041	D	T	E	N	1974	53910
8041	D	T	E	N	1972	55098
8041	D	E	E	N	1971	59711
8041	D	D	E	N	1974	61180
8041	D	D	E	N	1974	63367
8041	D	D	E	N	1964	66316
8041	D	T	E	N	1964	66316
8041	D	D	G	N	1972	67785
8041	D	S	E	N	1964	87701
8041	D	S	E	N	1972	87889
8041	D	D	E	N	1976	100869
8041	D	T	E	N	1976	100869
8041	L	D	E	N	1974	53730
8041	S	D	E	N	1973	50928
8041	S	D	E	N	1973	51464
8041	S	T	E	N	1973	51805
8041	S	D	R	N	1973	52278
8041	S	D	E	N	1973	52758
8041	S	D	R	N	1973	52892
8041	S	D	E	N	1974	52893
8041	S	D	E	N	1972	53066
8041	S	D	E	N	1972	53477
8041	S	D	E	N	1974	53607
8041	S	D	E	N	1974	53917
8041	S	D	E	N	1974	54600
8041	S	D	E	N	1974	54604
8041	S	T	E	N	1972	55165
8041	S	D	E	N	1973	56417
8041	S	D	E	N	1973	57557
8041	S	D	E	N	1974	60372
8041	S	D	R	N	1973	62623
8041	S	E	R	N	1973	62623
8041	S	T	E	N	1975	63685
8041	S	D	E	N	1973	65002
8041	S	D	E	N	1973	65120
8041	S	E	E	N	1973	65120
8041	S	D	E	N	1972	66214
8041	S	T	E	N	1972	66214
8041	S	D	R	N	1970	66271
8041	S	D	E	N	1975	66708
8041	S	T	E	N	1975	66708
8041	S	D	E	N	1970	66847
8041	S	T	E	N	1972	67004
8041	S	D	R	N	1973	67548
8041	S	D	R	N	1974	68636
8041	S	T	R	N	1974	68636
8041	S	D	E	N	1975	68637
8041	S	T	E	N	1975	68637
8041	S	T	E	N	1974	80374
8041	S	D	R	N	1975	86877
8041	S	D	E	N	1975	86878
8041	S	S	E	N	1964	87701
8041	S	S	E	N	1971	87884
8041	S	E	R	L	1975	91272
8041	S	E	R	N	1975	91272
8041	S	E	E	L	1975	95909
8041	S	E	E	N	1975	95909
8041	T	D	E	N	1972	53217
8041	T	D	E	N	1972	53228
8041	T	D	E	N	1972	53470
8054	D	T	R	N	1972	55366
8054	D	T	E	N	1973	60745
8054	S	D	E	N	1974	53607
8054	S	D	R	N	1973	54968
8054	S	D	E	N	1974	54969
8054	S	D	E	N	1973	57557
8054	S	S	E	N	1971	87884
8070	S	D	E	N	1975	87180
8094	D	D	E	N	1972	53228
8094	S	D	E	N	1973	52758
8094	S	S	E	N	1972	53227
8094	S	D	E	N	1974	53918

Substance Number	Phys. State	Sub-ject	Lan-guage	Temper-ature	Year	EPIC Number
102-8094	S	D	E	N	1974	60372
8094	S	S	E	N	1972	87889
8095	D	D	E	N	1973	52782
8095	D	D	E	N	1974	54035
8095	D	D	E	N	1973	54776
8095	D	S	E	N	1973	54776
8095	D	D	E	N	1964	66316
8095	D	S	E	N	1972	87889
8095	S	S	E	N	1972	53227
8095	S	D	E	N	1974	53917
8096	S	D	E	N	1974	58030
8096	S	T	E	N	1974	58030
8104	S	D	E	N	1974	53917
8139	S	D	E	N	1973	51461
8142	D	D	E	N	1972	53199
8142	S	D	R	N	1973	56581
8142	S	S	E	N	1972	87889
8199	I	D	E	H	1971	52201
8199	I	E	E	H	1971	52201
8255	S	D	E	N	1971	65083
8283	S	D	E	N	1971	65083
8392	S	D	E	N	1975	87180
8420	S	S	E	N	1972	87889
8457	S	D	R	H	1974	97477
8457	S	D	R	N	1974	97477
8457	S	D	E	H	1974	97478
8457	S	D	E	N	1974	97478
104-0002	D	D	E	N	1971	65810
0002	D	T	E	N	1974	66813
0002	D	D	E	N	1974	66825
0002	P	D	E	N	1974	66810
0002	S	D	E	N	1973	50554
0002	S	D	E	N	1973	52322
0002	S	E	E	N	1973	52322
0002	S	D	E	N	1973	52690
0002	S	D	G	N	1970	52691
0002	S	D	E	N	1971	65812
0002	S	T	E	N	1974	66104
0002	S	T	E	N	1974	66811
0002	S	D	E	N	1974	66812
0002	S	T	E	N	1974	66813
0002	S	T	E	N	1974	66817
0002	S	D	E	N	1974	66826
0002	S	S	R	N	1973	67353
0002	S	D	R	N	1974	80408
0002	S	D	R	N	1975	89660
0002	S	T	R	N	1975	89660
0002	S	D	E	N	1975	89661
0002	S	T	E	N	1975	89661
0002	S	D	E	N	1974	95255
0002	T	S	R	N	1973	67353
0006	D	D	R	N	1972	54873
0006	D	D	R	L	1973	56574
0006	D	D	R	N	1973	56574
0006	D	D	R	N	1972	57038
0006	D	D	R	N	1970	67317
0006	D	D	E	L	1976	99234
0006	F	D	R	N	1972	57039
0006	S	D	E	N	1972	49936
0006	S	D	E	N	1974	54604
0006	S	D	E	L	1965	74575
0006	T	D	R	N	1973	67543
0006	T	D	R	N	1973	67544
0007	S	S	E	H	1967	68374
0007	S	S	E	N	1967	68374
0007	S	S	E	H	1971	87884
0013	S	D	R	N	1973	54982
0013	S	D	E	N	1974	54983
0022	S	D	E	N	1973	51007
0025	S	D	E	N	1974	66814
0025	S	T	E	N	1974	66817
0031	D	D	R	N	1970	67420
0031	T	D	R	N	1970	67420
0049	S	D	R	N	1973	51370
0049	S	T	R	N	1973	51370
0049	S	D	E	N	1973	51371
0049	S	T	E	N	1973	51371
0049	S	D	E	N	1972	53256
0049	S	D	E	N	1974	53627
0049	S	S	E	N	1969	68271
0049	S	D	R	H	1972	76508
0049	S	D	R	N	1972	76508
0049	S	E	R	N	1972	76508
0049	S	D	R	N	1974	77912
0049	S	T	R	N	1974	77912
0049	S	D	E	H	1972	91530
0049	S	D	E	N	1972	91530
0049	S	E	E	N	1972	91530
0049	S	D	E	N	1974	94503
0049	S	T	E	N	1974	94503
0049	S	D	E	N	1976	100580
0049	T	D	R	N	1973	67350
0049	T	D	R	N	1973	67548
0049	T	D	R	N	1971	76354

Phys. State: **A.** Amorphous; **C.** Superconductive; **D.** Doped; **F.** Fibrous or Whisker; **G.** Gas; **I.** Ionized or Plasma; **L.** Liquid; **P.** Powder or Particle; **S.** Solid; **T.** Thin Film
Subject: **D.** Data; **E.** Experiment; **S.** Survey (Review, Compendium, etc.); **T.** Theory
Language: **E.** English; **F.** French; **G.** German; **O.** Other Languages; **R.** Russian
Temperature: **L.** Low (0 to 75K); **N.** Normal (75 to 1273K); **H.** High (above 1273K)

Substance Number	Phys. State	Subject	Language	Temperature	Year	EPIC Number
104-0049	T	D	R	N	1971	76365
0049	T	E	E	N	1971	85671
0049	T	D	E	N	1971	85675
0053	S	D	E	N	1974	54604
0053	S	D	E	N	1975	90068
0055	S	D	E	N	1974	54348
0055	S	E	E	N	1974	54348
0055	S	S	E	N	1974	54348
0086	L	D	E	N	1973	51739
0196	S	D	E	N	1974	53627
0196	S	S	E	N	1969	68271
0485	S	D	E	N	1973	52584
8007	T	D	O	N	1971	67028
8032	S	D	E	N	1974	53627
8032	S	S	E	N	1969	68271
8033	S	D	E	N	1974	53627
8033	S	S	E	N	1969	68271
8045	S	S	E	N	1966	66068
8069	S	S	R	N	1970	53179
8069	S	S	E	N	1972	53180
8069	S	D	R	H	1972	58305
8069	S	S	E	H	1974	60367
8069	S	D	R	N	1973	71959
8069	S	D	E	N	1973	82778
8069	S	D	E	H	1974	89508
8069	T	D	E	N	1974	90583
8099	S	S	E	N	1974	93387
8231	S	D	E	N	1975	66621
8231	S	T	E	N	1975	66621
8251	D	D	E	N	1974	57989
8257	D	T	R	N	1970	52334
8258	D	T	R	N	1970	52334
8267	G	S	E	N	1973	53059
8270	S	D	E	N	1951	72552
8270	S	E	E	N	1951	72552
8270	S	T	E	N	1951	72552
8271	S	D	E	N	1951	72552
8271	S	E	E	N	1951	72552
8271	S	T	E	N	1951	72552
8284	S	S	E	N	1974	93387
8296	S	D	E	N	1973	55851
8303	S	D	G	H	1969	86378
8303	S	D	E	H	1972	86379
8349	S	D	E	N	1971	65810
8401	S	D	O	N	1974	67789
8442	D	D	E	L	1974	65217
8442	D	T	E	L	1974	65217
8447	S	D	R	N	1974	66760
8447	S	T	R	N	1974	66760
8447	S	D	E	N	1975	66761
8447	S	T	E	N	1975	66761
106-0003	G	S	E	N	1973	52593
0003	G	D	E	N	1971	63677
0003	G	E	E	N	1971	63677
0004	S	D	E	N	1974	53627
0004	T	D	R	N	1973	58287
0006	D	D	R	N	1972	54873
0006	D	D	R	L	1973	56574
0006	D	D	R	N	1973	56574
0006	D	S	R	N	1972	62850
0006	D	D	E	N	1972	63824
0006	D	S	E	N	1972	65169
0006	S	D	E	N	1972	49936
0006	S	S	E	N	1974	54348
0006	S	D	E	N	1974	54604
0006	S	S	E	L	1972	55357
0006	S	S	E	N	1972	55357
0006	S	D	E	N	1972	63824
0006	S	D	R	N	1974	68652
0006	S	T	R	N	1974	68652
0006	S	D	E	N	1975	68653
0006	S	T	E	N	1975	68653
0006	S	D	R	N	1974	77920
0006	S	T	R	N	1974	77920
0006	S	D	E	N	1974	94516
0006	S	T	E	N	1974	94516
0006	S	D	E	N	1975	101663
0006	T	D	O	N	1971	49564
0006	T	D	R	N	1972	49569
0006	T	D	R	N	1973	50100
0006	T	D	E	N	1974	54347
0006	T	E	E	N	1974	54347
0006	T	D	R	N	1973	67543
0006	T	D	R	N	1973	67544
0008	G	S	E	N	1973	52593
0008	G	D	E	N	1971	63677
0008	G	E	E	N	1971	63677
0008	T	D	E	N	1974	54061
0009	D	D	R	N	1973	54419
0009	D	D	E	N	1973	54420
0009	L	D	R	N	1973	54419
0009	L	D	E	N	1973	54420
0023	S	D	E	N	1974	58014
0024	D	D	E	N	1973	50032
0024	D	D	E	N	1973	53042
0024	D	D	R	N	1972	54895
0024	D	D	R	N	1972	57038
0024	D	D	R	N	1970	67317
0024	D	D	R	N	1973	67552
0024	D	D	E	N	1975	90068
106-0024	F	D	R	N	1972	57039
0024	S	D	R	L	1973	52868
0024	S	D	R	N	1973	52868
0024	S	D	E	L	1973	52869
0024	S	D	E	N	1973	52869
0024	S	S	E	N	1974	54348
0024	S	D	E	N	1974	54604
0024	S	S	E	N	1973	60835
0024	S	D	E	N	1974	66109
0024	S	D	R	N	1973	70905
0024	S	E	R	N	1973	70905
0024	S	T	R	N	1973	70905
0024	S	D	E	N	1973	91746
0024	S	E	E	N	1973	91746
0024	S	T	E	N	1973	91746
0024	T	D	E	N	1974	54347
0024	T	E	E	N	1974	54347
0026	D	D	E	N	1971	65811
0026	S	D	E	N	1971	65811
0026	S	D	R	N	1974	68652
0026	S	T	R	N	1974	68652
0026	S	D	E	N	1975	68653
0026	S	T	E	N	1975	68653
0026	T	D	O	N	1971	49564
0031	S	D	E	N	1973	49700
0031	S	D	E	N	1973	52584
0031	T	D	E	N	1972	68992
0033	S	D	E	N	1973	52473
0033	T	D	E	N	1973	49700
0035	F	D	E	H	1975	62877
0035	S	D	R	N	1973	55223
0035	S	D	E	N	1974	55224
0035	S	S	E	H	1965	87702
0035	S	S	E	N	1965	87702
0035	S	S	E	N	1971	87887
0035	T	T	E	N	1974	90647
0036	S	D	E	N	1973	51007
0049	G	S	E	N	1973	52591
0051	S	T	E	N	1974	66817
0057	S	S	E	N	1969	68271
0057	S	S	E	N	1966	68325
0063	S	D	E	N	1973	52584
0064	S	D	E	N	1973	49700
0064	S	D	E	N	1973	52584
0068	S	D	E	N	1974	58827
0068	S	S	E	N	1974	58827
0125	S	D	R	H	1972	49817
0125	S	D	R	H	1973	52392
0125	S	D	E	H	1973	54539
0125	S	D	R	H	1973	71960
0125	S	D	E	H	1973	82779
0127	S	E	R	N	1972	50693
0127	S	D	E	N	1974	58827
0127	S	S	E	N	1974	58827
0127	S	T	E	N	1975	63342
0127	T	D	E	N	1972	68992
0129	G	D	E	N	1973	51637
0133	S	D	E	N	1973	52584
0141	S	D	E	N	1974	54348
0141	S	E	E	N	1974	54348
0158	S	D	E	N	1973	51007
0158	S	D	E	N	1974	61388
0159	S	S	E	N	1974	54348
0159	T	D	E	N	1974	54347
0159	T	E	E	N	1974	54347
0165	S	D	E	N	1973	52004
0165	S	S	E	N	1974	54348
0165	S	D	E	L	1975	96982
0165	S	D	E	N	1975	96982
0203	S	T	E	N	1974	66817
0204	S	D	E	N	1974	54348
0204	S	E	E	N	1974	54348
0231	G	S	E	N	1973	52591
0234	S	D	E	N	1974	54348
0234	S	E	E	N	1974	54348
0237	T	S	E	N	1972	87889
0238	P	D	E	N	1974	66809
0238	S	D	E	N	1972	53183
0238	S	S	E	N	1972	53183
0238	S	T	E	N	1972	53183
0238	S	D	E	N	1973	60587
0238	S	T	E	N	1973	60587
0238	S	D	E	N	1974	66809
0238	S	D	R	N	1970	67837
0238	T	D	E	N	1973	56646
0238	T	D	E	N	1973	60584
0308	D	D	R	N	1973	52392
0308	D	D	E	N	1973	54539
0308	S	D	R	N	1973	52392
0308	S	S	R	N	1970	53179
0308	S	S	E	N	1972	53180
0308	S	D	E	N	1973	54539
0308	S	D	R	H	1973	71960
0308	S	D	E	H	1973	82779
0308	S	D	R	H	1976	99762
0308	S	T	R	H	1976	99762
0308	S	D	E	H	1976	101355
0308	S	T	E	H	1976	101355
0309	S	S	E	H	1966	87721
0309	S	S	E	N	1966	87721
0310	S	D	R	H	1972	49817
106-0328	S	D	E	N	1973	52584
0363	D	D	E	L	1973	55163
0363	D	D	E	N	1973	55163
0363	D	T	E	N	1973	55163
0363	S	D	R	N	1973	52537
0363	S	D	E	N	1974	53607
0363	S	D	E	N	1974	53664
0363	S	D	R	N	1972	54895
0363	S	D	E	N	1973	57560
0363	S	D	E	N	1974	58014
0363	S	D	E	L	1974	60377
0363	S	D	E	N	1974	60377
0363	S	E	E	L	1974	60377
0363	S	E	E	N	1974	60377
0363	S	T	E	N	1971	61758
0363	S	D	E	N	1971	61760
0363	S	T	E	N	1965	64273
0363	S	S	E	N	1967	66156
0363	S	S	E	N	1969	68271
0363	S	D	E	N	1975	75197
0363	S	D	R	N	1974	77923
0363	S	T	R	N	1974	77923
0363	S	T	E	N	1974	80374
0363	S	D	E	N	1974	94513
0363	S	T	E	N	1974	94513
0363	S	S	E	N	1976	97315
0417	S	S	R	N	1970	53179
0417	S	S	E	N	1972	53180
0423	S	D	R	N	1974	77932
0423	S	T	R	N	1974	77932
0423	S	D	E	N	1974	94499
0423	S	T	E	N	1974	94499
0508	S	D	E	N	1974	53627
0610	D	S	E	N	1973	56749
0610	D	S	E	N	1969	101680
0744	S	S	R	N	1970	53179
0744	S	S	E	N	1972	53180
0762	G	S	E	N	1973	52591
0937	S	S	R	N	1970	53179
0937	S	S	E	N	1972	53180
1027	S	D	R	H	1972	49817
1058	S	D	E	N	1973	52584
1083	D	D	R	H	1973	51333
1083	D	D	E	N	1973	54126
1083	S	D	R	H	1973	51333
1083	S	D	E	H	1973	54126
1273	S	D	E	N	1973	52584
1378	S	D	E	N	1973	52584
1418	S	D	E	N	1973	52584
1430	S	D	E	N	1973	52584
8008	D	D	O	N	1974	67789
8008	S	T	O	N	1971	67029
8008	S	D	R	N	1974	77922
8008	S	T	R	N	1974	77922
8008	S	D	E	N	1974	94514
8008	S	T	E	N	1974	94514
8040	S	D	E	N	1973	52092
8040	S	D	E	N	1974	53607
8040	S	D	R	N	1972	54895
8040	S	S	E	N	1969	68271
8040	S	T	E	N	1975	90027
8041	D	D	R	N	1970	67420
8041	S	D	E	N	1972	49493
8041	S	D	E	N	1973	50928
8041	S	D	E	N	1973	52092
8041	S	D	R	N	1973	52318
8041	S	D	E	N	1974	53607
8041	S	D	E	N	1974	54600
8041	S	D	E	N	1972	63632
8041	S	S	E	N	1969	68271
8041	S	S	E	N	1967	68371
8041	S	S	E	N	1976	97315
8041	T	D	R	N	1970	67420
8045	S	D	E	N	1974	53627
8048	S	D	E	N	1974	53627
8050	T	D	E	N	1972	53217
8050	T	S	E	N	1972	87889
8063	S	D	R	N	1973	51370
8063	S	T	R	N	1973	51370
8063	S	D	E	N	1973	51371
8063	S	T	E	N	1973	51371
8229	S	D	E	N	1973	52584
8255	S	D	E	N	1973	51583
8289	S	T	E	N	1974	54587
8290	T	D	E	N	1973	51876
8305	G	D	E	N	1973	52491
8306	G	D	E	N	1973	52491
8307	G	D	E	N	1973	52491
8308	S	D	E	N	1973	52584
8309	S	D	E	N	1973	52584
8310	S	D	E	N	1973	52584
8311	S	D	E	N	1973	52584
8388	S	D	E	N	1974	53644
8388	S	D	E	N	1972	80067
8388	S	E	E	N	1972	80067
8485	S	D	E	N	1974	58014
8711	T	D	G	N	1957	86339
8711	T	D	E	N	1973	86340
8736	S	D	O	N	1974	67788
8736	S	D	R	N	1974	77922
8736	S	T	R	N	1974	77922

Phys. State: A. Amorphous; C. Superconductive; D. Doped; F. Fibrous or Whisker; G. Gas; I. Ionized or Plasma; L. Liquid; P. Powder or Particle; S. Solid; T. Thin Film
Subject: D. Data; E. Experiment; S. Survey (Review, Compendium, etc.); T. Theory
Language: E. English; F. French; G. German; O. Other Languages; R. Russian
Temperature: L. Low (0 to 75K); N. Normal (75 to 1273K); H. High (above 1273K)

Substance Number	Phys. State	Subject	Language	Temperature	Year	EPIC Number
106-8736	S	D	E	N	1974	94514
8736	S	T	E	N	1974	94514
8809	S	D	E	N	1963	64751
8809	S	E	E	N	1963	64751
108-0014	S	D	E	N	1973	66101
0021	G	D	E	N	1973	52481
0029	S	D	R	N	1974	58128
0029	S	D	E	N	1974	58129
109-0025	D	D	E	N	1973	50607
0025	S	D	E	N	1973	50607
0025	S	D	E	N	1973	53587
0025	S	T	E	N	1973	57651
8020	S	T	E	N	1973	57651
8051	S	S	E	L	1975	90863
110-0007	S	D	E	N	1974	58014
0017	S	D	E	N	1973	49700
0017	S	T	E	N	1973	52408
0018	S	T	E	N	1973	52408
0018	S	D	E	N	1975	63331
0019	S	D	E	N	1973	52473
0019	T	D	E	N	1973	49700
0023	S	D	E	N	1974	58827
0023	S	S	E	N	1974	58827
0024	D	D	E	N	1973	56375
0024	D	D	R	N	1972	57038
0024	D	D	E	N	1971	65811
0024	D	D	E	N	1974	66828
0024	F	D	R	N	1972	57039
0024	G	D	E	N	1975	96972
0024	G	E	E	N	1975	96972
0024	L	D	E	N	1974	58441
0024	L	E	E	N	1974	58441
0024	P	D	E	N	1975	92754
0024	P	T	E	N	1975	92754
0024	S	D	E	N	1973	49700
0024	S	D	E	N	1974	54604
0024	S	S	E	N	1974	55252
0024	S	D	R	N	1974	58128
0024	S	D	E	N	1974	58129
0024	S	D	E	N	1974	58441
0024	S	E	E	N	1974	58441
0024	S	D	R	N	1974	63016
0024	S	D	E	N	1974	63017
0024	S	D	E	N	1971	65811
0024	S	T	E	N	1974	66105
0024	S	D	E	N	1974	66808
0024	S	D	R	N	1974	68652
0024	S	T	R	N	1974	68652
0024	S	D	E	N	1975	68653
0024	S	T	E	N	1975	68653
0024	T	D	E	N	1974	66807
0024	T	D	E	N	1975	96972
0024	T	E	E	N	1975	96972
0036	S	D	E	N	1974	54604
0036	S	D	R	N	1972	54895
0036	S	D	E	N	1974	66808
0037	S	D	E	N	1974	54604
0045	S	D	E	N	1974	58255
0219	G	D	E	N	1973	51637
0224	L	D	E	N	1973	49538
0269	G	D	E	N	1973	52481
0288	G	D	G	N	1973	50022
0298	G	D	E	N	1973	51637
0343	G	D	E	N	1973	52479
0377	G	D	E	N	1973	52479
8041	S	D	E	N	1973	52473
8084	S	D	E	N	1973	51792
8096	G	S	E	N	1973	52591
8135	T	D	G	N	1957	86339
8135	T	D	E	N	1973	86340
8187	G	S	E	N	1973	53059
111-0001	S	D	E	N	1973	57557
0008	D	S	E	N	1972	53227
0008	D	D	E	N	1973	54776
0008	D	S	E	N	1973	54776
0008	D	D	E	N	1973	57726
0008	D	D	E	N	1974	58001
0008	D	D	E	N	1974	61186
0008	D	S	E	L	1971	70519
0008	D	S	E	N	1971	70519
0008	D	S	E	N	1965	87703
0008	D	S	E	N	1972	87889
0008	S	D	E	N	1973	50928
0008	S	D	E	N	1973	52758
0008	S	D	R	N	1973	52892
0008	S	D	E	N	1974	52893
0008	S	D	E	N	1974	53607
0008	S	D	E	N	1974	54600
0008	S	D	E	N	1973	54776
0008	S	D	E	N	1973	57557
0008	S	D	R	N	1973	62623
0008	S	E	R	N	1973	62623
0008	S	D	E	N	1973	65120
0008	S	E	E	N	1973	65120
0008	S	T	E	N	1974	80374
0008	S	D	R	N	1974	81026
0008	S	S	E	N	1971	87884
111-0008	S	D	E	N	1975	91930
0008	S	E	E	N	1975	91930
0008	S	D	E	N	1975	92633
0008	T	D	E	N	1975	66708
0008	T	T	E	N	1975	66708
0050	S	D	E	N	1974	58030
0050	S	T	E	N	1974	58030
8002	S	D	E	N	1973	50923
8002	S	D	E	N	1974	53607
8002	S	D	E	N	1973	57557
8002	S	D	F	N	1973	63636
8002	S	S	E	N	1971	87884
8007	S	D	E	N	1974	58436
8007	S	D	E	N	1974	90915
8007	S	T	E	N	1974	90915
8021	A	D	E	N	1973	49710
8021	A	D	E	N	1972	53374
8021	A	D	E	N	1973	60682
8021	A	S	E	N	1974	65584
8021	S	D	E	N	1973	49710
8021	S	D	E	N	1973	60682
8021	S	S	E	N	1974	65584
8026	S	D	E	N	1972	53477
8037	S	D	E	N	1973	51072
8037	S	D	E	N	1973	52073
112-0001	G	D	E	N	1971	63677
0001	G	E	E	N	1971	63677
0001	I	D	R	N	1972	68402
0004	G	D	E	N	1971	63677
0004	G	E	E	N	1971	63677
0010	D	D	E	N	1973	49600
0010	G	D	E	N	1971	63677
0010	G	E	E	N	1971	63677
0010	L	D	E	N	1973	49600
0098	S	D	R	N	1974	58128
0098	S	D	E	N	1974	58129
0247	S	D	R	H	1974	93037
0247	S	D	R	N	1974	93037
0247	S	E	R	H	1974	93037
0247	S	E	R	N	1974	93037
0247	S	D	E	H	1975	93038
0247	S	D	E	N	1975	93038
0247	S	E	E	H	1975	93038
0247	S	E	E	N	1975	93038
0402	S	D	E	N	1973	57560
8020	S	D	E	N	1973	52092
8025	S	D	E	N	1973	52092
8025	S	S	E	N	1967	68371
114-0001	D	E	E	N	1973	53581
0001	D	D	R	L	1973	56574
0001	D	D	R	N	1973	56574
0001	S	D	E	N	1973	51032
0001	S	D	E	N	1974	54604
0002	T	D	E	N	1973	50165
0009	S	D	E	N	1974	54604
0017	D	D	E	N	1973	57740
0017	D	S	E	N	1973	57740
0017	S	D	E	N	1973	50923
0017	S	D	E	N	1974	53607
0017	S	D	E	L	1974	54080
0017	S	D	E	N	1974	60774
0017	S	D	E	N	1970	66847
0017	S	S	E	N	1971	87884
0060	S	D	R	N	1974	58112
0060	S	D	E	N	1974	58113
8001	D	D	E	N	1973	61770
8001	S	D	E	N	1973	50928
8001	S	D	R	N	1973	52318
8001	S	D	E	N	1974	53607
8001	S	D	E	N	1974	54600
8001	S	S	E	N	1965	87781
8001	S	S	E	N	1971	87884
8001	T	D	E	N	1975	90858
8001	T	T	E	N	1975	90858
8041	S	D	R	N	1972	49568
116-0005	S	D	E	N	1974	66818
0005	S	E	E	N	1974	66818
8026	S	D	E	N	1974	53644
118-0002	T	D	R	N	1972	50694
0037	S	D	E	N	1972	51229
0037	S	S	E	N	1973	60835
0037	S	D	E	N	1974	66103
8048	S	D	R	N	1974	58128
8048	S	D	E	N	1974	58129
119-0002	P	S	E	N	1966	63913
0002	P	S	E	H	1969	87723
0002	P	S	E	N	1969	87723
0002	S	D	E	N	1970	52696
0002	S	D	E	N	1974	53627
0002	S	T	R	N	1973	58294
0002	S	D	E	N	1974	58827
0002	S	S	E	N	1974	58827
0002	S	D	R	N	1972	60713
0002	S	E	R	N	1972	60713
0002	S	T	R	N	1972	60713
0002	S	D	E	N	1973	60714
119-0002	S	E	E	N	1973	60714
0002	S	T	E	N	1973	60714
0002	S	S	E	N	1966	63913
0002	S	S	R	N	1973	67353
0002	S	S	E	H	1963	87682
0002	S	S	E	N	1963	87682
0002	S	S	E	N	1969	87723
0002	T	D	R	N	1972	49569
0002	T	D	R	N	1973	50704
0002	T	S	E	N	1966	63913
0002	T	S	E	N	1969	87723
0008	T	D	E	N	1972	68992
0010	S	T	E	N	1973	52408
0043	S	D	E	N	1974	58014
0064	S	D	E	N	1974	53627
8002	S	D	E	N	1973	51072
8002	S	D	E	N	1973	52073
8008	S	D	E	N	1974	53627
8009	S	D	E	N	1973	51072
8009	S	D	E	N	1973	52073
8019	S	D	F	N	1973	51294
8031	S	D	F	N	1973	51294
8079	S	D	R	N	1973	58734
8079	S	D	E	N	1974	68941
120-0001	A	S	E	N	1972	52403
0001	D	D	E	N	1971	52970
0001	D	D	R	N	1973	58291
0001	D	D	R	N	1973	58292
0001	S	D	E	N	1973	49700
0001	S	D	E	N	1975	90821
0001	S	E	E	N	1975	90821
0001	S	T	E	N	1975	90821
0001	T	D	E	N	1973	52473
0001	T	D	E	N	1975	66619
0001	T	T	E	N	1975	66619
0001	T	D	E	N	1975	90071
0002	G	D	E	N	1973	52479
0002	G	D	E	N	1971	63677
0002	G	E	E	N	1971	63677
0002	I	D	E	N	1973	50769
0002	I	D	R	N	1972	68402
0003	G	D	E	N	1971	63677
0003	G	E	E	N	1971	63677
0006	S	D	E	N	1973	52473
0006	S	D	E	N	1974	58014
0014	G	D	E	N	1973	52479
0016	S	D	E	N	1974	58014
0017	S	D	R	H	1974	93037
0017	S	D	R	N	1974	93037
0017	S	E	R	H	1974	93037
0017	S	E	R	N	1974	93037
0017	S	D	E	H	1975	93038
0017	S	D	E	N	1975	93038
0017	S	E	E	N	1975	93038
0023	S	D	R	H	1974	93037
0023	S	D	R	N	1974	93037
0023	S	E	R	H	1974	93037
0023	S	E	R	N	1974	93037
0023	S	D	E	H	1975	93038
0023	S	D	E	N	1975	93038
0023	S	E	E	H	1975	93038
0023	S	E	E	N	1975	93038
8024	S	D	R	N	1974	77911
8024	S	T	R	N	1974	77911
8024	S	D	E	N	1974	94505
8024	S	T	E	N	1974	94505
8088	D	T	R	N	1970	52334
122-0003	S	S	R	N	1970	53179
0003	S	S	E	N	1972	53180
0003	T	D	R	H	1973	52392
0003	T	D	E	H	1973	54539
0003	T	D	R	H	1973	71960
0003	T	D	E	H	1973	82779
0003	T	D	E	H	1972	86959
0003	T	D	E	N	1972	86959
0004	S	S	F	N	1972	49541
0004	S	D	E	H	1970	60090
0004	S	E	E	H	1970	60090
0004	S	S	E	N	1974	93387
0005	S	D	E	N	1963	64751
0005	S	E	E	N	1963	64751
0005	S	D	E	H	1975	88237
0009	S	D	E	N	1973	50626
0009	S	D	O	N	1973	52309
0009	S	D	E	N	1973	52771
0009	S	D	E	N	1973	53585
0009	S	S	E	N	1973	53585
0009	S	S	E	N	1974	58803
0009	S	S	E	N	1975	89502
0009	T	D	E	N	1974	54079
0009	T	D	E	N	1975	65457
0009	T	D	E	N	1975	72538
0009	T	D	E	N	1975	86753
0010	G	D	E	N	1973	51942
0011	S	D	E	N	1974	56544
0014	S	D	F	N	1973	49543
0017	T	D	E	N	1973	52128
0017	T	T	E	N	1973	63510
0017	T	D	E	N	1975	68614

Phys. State: **A.** Amorphous; **C.** Superconductive; **D.** Doped; **F.** Fibrous or Whisker; **G.** Gas; **I.** Ionized or Plasma; **L.** Liquid; **P.** Powder or Particle; **S.** Solid; **T.** Thin Film
Subject: **D.** Data; **E.** Experiment; **S.** Survey (Review, Compendium, etc.); **T.** Theory
Language: **E.** English; **F.** French; **G.** German; **O.** Other Languages; **R.** Russian
Temperature: **L.** Low (0 to 75K); **N.** Normal (75 to 1273K); **H.** High (above 1273K)

Substance Number	Phys. State	Sub-ject	Lan-guage	Temper-ature	Year	EPIC Number
122-0017	T	T	E	N	1975	68614
0023	D	D	E	N	1975	92755
0023	D	T	E	N	1975	92755
0023	S	D	E	N	1974	53607
0023	S	D	E	N	1972	61767
0023	S	D	E	N	1974	66102
0023	S	S	E	N	1969	68271
0023	S	D	E	N	1975	92755
0023	S	T	E	N	1975	92755
0031	S	D	R	N	1973	51370
0031	S	T	R	N	1973	51370
0031	S	D	E	N	1973	51371
0031	S	T	E	N	1973	51371
0031	S	D	E	N	1974	53627
0031	S	E	R	N	1972	76508
0031	S	E	E	N	1972	91530
0031	T	S	R	N	1970	53179
0031	T	S	E	N	1972	53180
0037	S	D	E	H	1975	88237
0037	S	D	F	H	1971	103193
0037	S	E	F	H	1971	103193
0037	S	T	F	H	1971	103193
0037	T	D	R	H	1972	50705
0037	T	D	R	H	1973	52392
0037	T	D	E	H	1973	54539
0037	T	D	R	H	1973	71960
0037	T	D	E	H	1973	82779
0050	S	D	E	N	1973	53822
0050	S	S	E	N	1967	68368
0050	T	S	E	N	1967	66368
0053	S	D	E	N	1972	53271
0067	S	D	E	N	1973	53822
0068	S	D	E	N	1973	53822
0096	A	S	E	N	1972	52403
0096	S	D	E	N	1973	53585
0096	T	D	O	N	1974	67787
0096	T	D	E	N	1972	68992
0096	T	D	R	N	1974	77932
0096	T	T	R	N	1974	77932
0096	T	D	E	N	1974	94499
0096	T	T	E	N	1974	94499
0112	S	S	E	N	1971	87881
0132	S	D	E	N	1974	66814
0132	S	T	E	N	1974	66817
0338	S	S	F	N	1972	49541
8004	S	D	E	N	1973	51636
8021	S	D	E	N	1973	51636
8024	S	S	F	N	1972	49541
8138	T	D	E	N	1963	64751
8138	T	E	E	N	1963	64751
123-0003	S	S	E	N	1969	68115
0003	S	S	E	N	1966	68361
0032	S	D	E	N	1974	59352
8017	S	D	F	N	1970	59867
8018	S	D	E	N	1973	51218
8018	S	D	E	N	1973	55157
8018	S	D	E	N	1971	62195
8018	S	D	E	N	1975	63284
8018	S	D	E	N	1975	91930
8018	S	E	E	N	1975	91930
8058	S	D	E	L	1974	60379
126-0002	S	D	E	N	1973	57405
0005	D	D	E	N	1973	52120
0005	D	D	E	L	1974	81762
0005	D	T	E	L	1974	81762
0005	D	S	E	N	1966	87712
0005	S	D	E	N	1973	52120
0005	S	D	O	N	1973	52307
0005	S	D	E	N	1974	53607
0005	S	D	E	N	1974	58014
0005	S	S	E	N	1969	68271
0005	S	S	E	N	1966	87712
0005	T	D	E	N	1973	52120
0017	S	D	E	N	1974	53627
0038	S	D	E	N	1975	65484
0038	S	E	E	N	1975	65484
0038	S	T	E	N	1975	65484
8030	A	D	E	N	1972	49458
8030	A	D	E	N	1974	55249
8030	A	E	E	N	1974	55249
8030	A	D	E	N	1973	57646
8030	S	D	E	N	1972	53112
8030	S	D	E	N	1974	55249
8030	S	E	E	N	1974	55249
8030	T	D	E	N	1972	49458
8030	T	D	E	N	1973	57646
8052	D	D	E	N	1974	53923
8052	S	D	E	N	1973	50928
8052	S	D	E	N	1974	53607
8052	S	D	E	N	1974	54600
8052	S	D	E	N	1974	54604
8052	S	D	E	N	1973	57560
8052	S	D	E	N	1975	101673
8052	S	T	E	N	1975	101673
8055	S	D	E	N	1973	57405
8061	S	D	F	N	1973	51294
8062	S	D	F	N	1973	51294
8063	S	D	F	N	1973	51294
8064	S	D	F	N	1973	51294
126-8065	S	D	F	N	1973	51294
8066	S	D	F	N	1973	51294
8066	T	D	E	H	1973	52231
8066	T	D	E	N	1973	52231
8079	S	D	E	N	1974	53627
8079	S	S	E	N	1969	68271
8080	S	D	E	N	1974	53627
8080	S	S	E	N	1969	68271
8098	S	D	E	N	1975	65484
8098	S	T	E	N	1975	65484
127-8004	S	D	E	N	1973	52092
8004	S	D	E	N	1974	53607
8004	S	S	E	N	1969	68271

Phys. State: **A.** Amorphous; **C.** Superconductive; **D.** Doped; **F.** Fibrous or Whisker; **G.** Gas; **I.** Ionized or Plasma; **L.** Liquid; **P.** Powder or Particle; **S.** Solid; **T.** Thin Film
Subject: **D.** Data; **E.** Experiment; **S.** Survey (Review, Compendium, etc.); **T.** Theory
Language: **E.** English; **F.** French; **G.** German; **O.** Other Languages; **R.** Russian
Temperature: **L.** Low (0 to 75K); **N.** Normal (75 to 1273K); **H.** High (above 1273K)

Chapter 10 Electrical Resistivity

Substance Number	Phys. State	Subject	Language	Temperature	Year	EPIC Number
100-0045	A	T	E	N	1973	52475
0045	C	S	E	L	1972	53503
0045	C	S	E	L	1974	59378
0045	C	S	E	L	1971	61514
0045	C	S	E	L	1963	62161
0045	C	S	E	L	1975	75601
0045	L	S	E	H	1971	84631
0045	L	S	E	N	1971	84631
0045	L	S	E	N	1972	87876
0045	L	S	E	N	1968	98632
0045	S	E	E	H	1972	50025
0045	S	S	E	N	1973	55967
0045	S	S	E	N	1972	56587
0045	S	S	E	N	1972	59933
0045	S	T	E	N	1960	64411
0045	S	S	E	N	1973	82686
0045	S	S	E	H	1971	84631
0045	S	S	E	N	1971	84631
0045	S	S	R	N	1971	87444
0045	S	S	E	N	1974	87445
0045	T	S	E	N	1973	82686
0045	T	S	E	N	1971	87880
0055	A	D	E	N	1971	49794
0055	A	T	E	N	1973	51774
0055	A	T	E	N	1973	51861
0055	A	S	E	N	1972	52414
0055	A	T	E	N	1972	53195
0055	A	T	E	N	1972	53311
0055	A	S	E	N	1973	53314
0055	A	S	E	N	1973	53429
0055	A	T	E	N	1973	53448
0055	A	T	E	N	1974	54091
0055	A	T	O	N	1973	55275
0055	A	T	E	N	1973	55740
0055	A	T	E	L	1973	57475
0055	A	T	E	N	1974	58805
0055	A	T	E	N	1974	58806
0055	A	S	E	N	1970	59557
0055	A	D	R	N	1971	59598
0055	A	E	R	N	1971	59598
0055	A	T	E	N	1973	59623
0055	A	T	E	N	1971	59721
0055	A	S	E	N	1971	60961
0055	A	T	E	N	1974	61386
0055	A	T	E	L	1973	61452
0055	A	D	E	N	1971	62174
0055	A	E	E	N	1971	62174
0055	A	T	E	N	1972	62387
0055	A	T	R	L	1972	62723
0055	A	T	R	N	1972	62723
0055	A	T	E	N	1974	63399
0055	A	S	E	N	1972	64074
0055	A	T	E	N	1972	64085
0055	A	T	E	L	1973	65319
0055	A	T	E	N	1973	65319
0055	A	S	O	N	1974	65614
0055	A	T	E	N	1973	65771
0055	A	S	E	N	1971	84631
0055	A	S	E	N	1974	86448
0055	A	T	E	N	1974	86448
0055	A	T	E	N	1974	86453
0055	A	T	E	N	1975	88214
0055	A	T	E	N	1975	93561
0055	A	T	E	L	1975	94551
0055	A	T	E	N	1975	94551
0055	A	T	E	N	1975	97520
0055	A	T	E	N	1976	100646
0055	C	T	E	L	1973	55193
0055	C	T	E	L	1974	55194
0055	C	T	R	L	1974	60413
0055	C	T	E	L	1974	60414
0055	C	T	R	L	1974	60451
0055	C	T	E	L	1974	60452
0055	C	T	R	L	1974	60479
0055	C	T	E	L	1974	60480
0055	C	T	E	L	1973	60611
0055	C	T	R	L	1968	75362
0055	C	T	R	L	1975	86857
0055	C	T	E	L	1975	86858
0055	C	T	E	L	1969	91450
0055	D	T	E	L	1973	50583
0055	D	T	E	N	1973	51005
0055	D	T	E	N	1973	53461
0055	D	T	R	N	1971	54260
0055	D	T	E	N	1972	54261
0055	D	D	E	N	1962	59755
0055	D	T	R	L	1974	60413
0055	D	T	E	L	1974	60414
0055	D	T	R	L	1974	60479
0055	D	T	E	L	1974	60480
0055	D	E	E	H	1971	60928
0055	D	E	E	N	1971	60928
0055	D	E	R	N	1972	61562
0055	D	T	R	N	1973	62585
0055	D	T	E	N	1974	62586
100-0055	D	T	R	N	1972	62703
0055	D	S	R	N	1972	62704
0055	D	T	R	N	1973	62727
0055	D	S	E	N	1973	65123
0055	D	T	E	N	1972	65300
0055	D	T	E	N	1973	65323
0055	D	E	E	N	1972	65913
0055	D	T	R	N	1974	67747
0055	D	T	R	N	1974	71344
0055	D	T	E	N	1975	71345
0055	D	T	R	N	1975	87534
0055	D	T	E	N	1975	87535
0055	D	E	R	H	1974	93417
0055	D	E	R	N	1974	93417
0055	D	E	E	H	1974	93418
0055	D	E	E	N	1974	93418
0055	L	T	E	N	1973	55740
0055	L	E	O	N	1972	61015
0055	L	E	E	H	1971	62243
0055	L	S	E	N	1967	75838
0055	L	S	E	N	1974	84318
0055	L	S	E	N	1971	84631
0055	L	S	E	H	1969	94149
0055	L	S	E	N	1969	94149
0055	L	E	R	H	1975	95126
0055	L	E	R	N	1975	95126
0055	L	S	R	N	1966	95131
0055	L	S	E	N	1966	96497
0055	L	E	E	H	1975	97093
0055	L	E	E	N	1975	97093
0055	P	E	R	N	1973	68007
0055	P	E	E	N	1973	68008
0055	S	E	R	N	1971	49756
0055	S	T	R	N	1973	50283
0055	S	T	E	N	1973	50284
0055	S	E	E	N	1973	50806
0055	S	T	R	N	1973	51563
0055	S	E	G	N	1973	51683
0055	S	E	R	N	1972	52222
0055	S	T	E	N	1973	52304
0055	S	T	R	N	1970	52675
0055	S	S	E	N	1972	53200
0055	S	T	E	N	1973	53562
0055	S	T	E	N	1974	53600
0055	S	T	E	N	1974	53694
0055	S	S	R	N	1973	53794
0055	S	S	E	N	1973	53986
0055	S	T	R	N	1971	54276
0055	S	T	E	N	1972	54277
0055	S	T	E	N	1974	54339
0055	S	T	R	N	1973	54974
0055	S	T	E	N	1974	54975
0055	S	E	E	H	1973	55112
0055	S	T	E	L	1974	55247
0055	S	T	E	N	1974	55247
0055	S	S	O	N	1973	55353
0055	S	T	R	N	1971	55362
0055	S	E	E	N	1973	55588
0055	S	E	E	N	1973	55859
0055	S	T	E	N	1973	55859
0055	S	E	E	N	1973	56718
0055	S	T	E	L	1973	57475
0055	S	T	E	N	1974	57584
0055	S	T	E	N	1974	57980
0055	S	T	R	N	1974	58090
0055	S	T	E	N	1974	58091
0055	S	S	E	N	1973	58565
0055	S	T	E	N	1974	58805
0055	S	S	E	N	1974	58806
0055	S	T	E	N	1974	58806
0055	S	E	E	N	1965	58978
0055	S	T	E	N	1950	59014
0055	S	T	E	N	1950	59015
0055	S	T	R	N	1969	59075
0055	S	T	E	N	1970	59076
0055	S	E	E	N	1968	59164
0055	S	T	E	N	1968	59164
0055	S	E	E	L	1969	59174
0055	S	E	E	N	1969	59174
0055	S	E	E	L	1958	59175
0055	S	E	E	N	1958	59175
0055	S	E	E	L	1959	59176
0055	S	E	E	N	1959	59176
0055	S	E	E	L	1965	59177
0055	S	E	E	N	1965	59177
0055	S	E	E	N	1959	59185
0055	S	T	E	N	1959	59185
0055	S	T	G	L	1973	59319
0055	S	T	E	N	1970	59479
0055	S	T	E	N	1963	59484
0055	S	T	E	N	1964	59485
0055	S	S	E	N	1970	59557
0055	S	T	E	N	1958	59568
0055	S	E	E	N	1974	59573
0055	S	T	E	N	1974	59573
100-0055	S	T	R	N	1971	59580
0055	S	T	E	N	1970	59588
0055	S	T	E	N	1970	59698
0055	S	T	E	N	1969	59716
0055	S	S	E	N	1970	59810
0055	S	D	R	N	1970	59994
0055	S	E	R	N	1970	59994
0055	S	T	R	N	1970	59994
0055	S	T	O	N	1972	59998
0055	S	T	O	N	1970	60020
0055	S	E	R	N	1971	60216
0055	S	E	R	N	1971	60217
0055	S	T	E	N	1973	60629
0055	S	D	E	N	1971	60678
0055	S	T	R	N	1972	60723
0055	S	T	E	N	1973	60724
0055	S	S	O	N	1972	61007
0055	S	T	O	N	1972	61007
0055	S	E	R	N	1961	61104
0055	S	T	R	N	1961	61104
0055	S	E	E	N	1961	61105
0055	S	T	E	N	1961	61105
0055	S	T	R	N	1967	61228
0055	S	E	G	N	1974	61268
0055	S	T	E	N	1971	61329
0055	S	T	E	N	1974	61421
0055	S	T	E	N	1974	61443
0055	S	T	R	L	1973	61454
0055	S	T	E	N	1970	61493
0055	S	S	E	N	1969	61512
0055	S	S	E	N	1970	62250
0055	S	D	E	N	1971	62260
0055	S	E	E	N	1971	62260
0055	S	T	E	N	1971	62260
0055	S	D	E	N	1971	62263
0055	S	T	E	N	1971	62266
0055	S	D	E	N	1971	62272
0055	S	E	E	N	1971	62272
0055	S	T	E	N	1971	62272
0055	S	E	E	N	1974	62308
0055	S	T	R	N	1974	62513
0055	S	T	R	N	1972	62698
0055	S	T	R	N	1972	62720
0055	S	E	E	N	1974	62826
0055	S	S	E	N	1963	63138
0055	S	E	E	N	1971	63197
0055	S	E	E	N	1971	63198
0055	S	T	E	H	1974	63375
0055	S	T	E	L	1974	63375
0055	S	T	R	N	1971	63465
0055	S	E	E	N	1973	63542
0055	S	T	E	N	1973	63542
0055	S	E	E	N	1968	63912
0055	S	T	E	N	1972	64429
0055	S	S	E	L	1971	64456
0055	S	T	R	N	1970	64854
0055	S	T	E	N	1971	64855
0055	S	T	E	N	1971	65154
0055	S	T	R	N	1973	65191
0055	S	T	E	N	1974	65192
0055	S	T	E	N	1973	65316
0055	S	S	O	N	1974	65614
0055	S	S	E	N	1962	65939
0055	S	T	E	N	1962	65939
0055	S	T	E	L	1974	66375
0055	S	T	R	N	1973	66433
0055	S	T	E	N	1974	66434
0055	S	T	R	N	1974	66435
0055	S	T	E	N	1974	66436
0055	S	T	R	N	1974	66452
0055	S	T	E	N	1974	66453
0055	S	T	E	N	1975	66686
0055	S	S	E	N	1974	66974
0055	S	E	R	N	1972	67630
0055	S	S	E	N	1968	67894
0055	S	E	E	N	1968	67895
0055	S	E	G	N	1968	67895
0055	S	T	E	N	1972	70530
0055	S	T	E	H	1970	70568
0055	S	T	E	N	1971	70608
0055	S	T	E	N	1971	70662
0055	S	T	E	N	1961	74508
0055	S	T	E	N	1931	74971
0055	S	T	E	N	1971	76033
0055	S	T	E	N	1971	76193
0055	S	E	R	N	1972	76387
0055	S	T	R	N	1972	76387
0055	S	T	R	N	1971	77244
0055	S	T	R	N	1971	77301
0055	S	T	R	N	1974	81141
0055	S	T	R	N	1974	81202
0055	S	E	E	N	1972	83168
0055	S	T	E	N	1972	83168
0055	S	T	E	N	1971	84752
0055	S	E	R	N	1975	85355

Phys. State: **A.** Amorphous; **C.** Superconductive; **D.** Doped; **F.** Fibrous or Whisker; **G.** Gas; **I.** Ionized or Plasma; **L.** Liquid; **P.** Powder or Particle; **S.** Solid; **T.** Thin Film
Subject: **D.** Data; **E.** Experiment; **S.** Survey (Review, Compendium, etc.); **T.** Theory
Language: **E.** English; **F.** French; **G.** German; **O.** Other Languages; **R.** Russian
Temperature: **L.** Low (0 to 75K); **N.** Normal (75 to 1273K); **H.** High (above 1273K)

Substance Number	Phys. State	Subject	Language	Temperature	Year	EPIC Number
100-0055	S	T	E	L	1974	86010
0055	S	T	E	N	1974	86010
0055	S	T	E	N	1974	86068
0055	S	E	O	N	1974	86432
0055	S	T	E	N	1974	86454
0055	S	T	E	N	1975	87173
0055	S	S	R	N	1971	87444
0055	S	S	E	N	1974	87445
0055	S	S	E	N	1973	87614
0055	S	T	R	N	1975	90012
0055	S	D	E	N	1975	90018
0055	S	T	E	N	1975	90133
0055	S	T	E	N	1975	91605
0055	S	E	E	N	1975	92370
0055	S	T	E	N	1974	92401
0055	S	T	E	N	1975	92631
0055	S	E	G	L	1975	92648
0055	S	E	G	N	1975	92648
0055	S	T	E	N	1975	93561
0055	S	S	E	H	1969	94149
0055	S	S	E	N	1969	94149
0055	S	T	E	N	1975	95509
0055	S	T	E	N	1975	96738
0055	S	E	E	L	1975	96816
0055	S	E	E	N	1975	96816
0055	S	T	E	N	1976	99749
0055	S	T	R	L	1975	100328
0055	S	T	E	L	1975	100329
0055	T	E	E	N	1972	49814
0055	T	T	R	N	1973	50064
0055	T	T	E	N	1973	51902
0055	T	E	E	N	1972	53299
0055	T	T	E	L	1973	55193
0055	T	T	E	L	1974	55194
0055	T	T	E	N	1972	55375
0055	T	E	O	N	1972	56460
0055	T	T	O	N	1973	57348
0055	T	E	E	N	1973	58586
0055	T	T	R	N	1965	59462
0055	T	T	E	N	1965	59463
0055	T	T	R	N	1964	59464
0055	T	T	E	N	1964	59465
0055	T	E	R	N	1971	59575
0055	T	D	R	N	1971	59598
0055	T	E	R	N	1971	59598
0055	T	T	R	L	1974	60451
0055	T	T	E	L	1974	60452
0055	T	S	E	N	1971	60961
0055	T	D	R	N	1970	61000
0055	T	E	R	N	1970	61000
0055	T	S	E	N	1972	61768
0055	T	D	E	N	1971	62174
0055	T	E	E	N	1971	62174
0055	T	D	E	N	1974	62297
0055	T	E	E	N	1974	62297
0055	T	T	R	N	1971	63465
0055	T	T	R	N	1971	63468
0055	T	S	E	N	1972	64074
0055	T	T	E	N	1971	65154
0055	T	T	E	N	1971	65157
0055	T	T	E	N	1975	73337
0055	T	T	R	L	1975	86857
0055	T	T	E	L	1975	86858
0055	T	T	O	N	1974	88134
0055	T	T	E	N	1975	90876
0055	T	S	E	N	1975	94588
8003	D	T	R	N	1972	49455
8003	D	T	G	N	1973	52362
8003	D	T	F	N	1973	53873
8003	L	D	R	N	1973	67558
8003	L	T	R	N	1973	67558
8003	L	S	E	H	1968	98632
8003	L	S	E	N	1968	98632
8003	S	T	G	N	1973	52362
8003	S	T	E	H	1973	57614
8003	S	S	E	H	1970	59588
8003	S	S	E	N	1970	59588
8005	D	D	E	N	1974	55739
8005	S	S	R	N	1973	55479
8007	S	E	R	N	1972	52255
8007	S	S	E	N	1969	68271
8007	S	S	E	L	1972	87823
8007	S	S	E	N	1972	87823
8008	S	S	E	N	1971	87884
8008	S	S	E	N	1972	87889
8008	T	S	E	N	1969	87821
8009	S	T	E	N	1973	53420
8009	S	S	E	L	1974	58928
8009	S	S	E	N	1974	58928
8010	S	S	E	N	1972	53175
8011	S	T	E	L	1973	51024
8013	D	D	R	H	1973	52534
8013	D	D	R	N	1973	52534
8013	D	D	E	H	1974	53647
8013	D	D	E	N	1974	53647
8015	S	S	E	N	1972	53175
8016	A	S	E	N	1972	53375
8016	A	S	E	N	1973	54768
8016	A	S	E	N	1975	95324
8016	S	S	E	N	1969	59800
8016	S	S	E	N	1970	59810
100-8016	S	S	E	N	1972	59933
8016	S	S	E	N	1973	60755
8016	S	S	G	N	1971	66491
8016	S	T	R	N	1970	67690
8016	S	S	E	N	1965	101536
8016	T	S	E	N	1973	54768
8017	C	S	E	L	1972	53503
8017	C	S	E	L	1971	61514
8017	C	S	E	L	1963	62161
8017	C	S	E	L	1966	87721
8017	S	T	E	L	1971	70649
8017	S	T	E	N	1975	91299
8017	S	S	R	N	1959	98151
8022	S	S	E	N	1967	75838
8026	S	S	E	N	1967	98895
8027	S	S	R	N	1972	56475
8027	S	S	E	H	1967	98888
8027	S	S	E	N	1967	98888
8027	S	S	E	H	1967	98890
8029	S	T	E	N	1975	80826
8029	S	S	E	H	1967	97982
8029	S	S	E	N	1967	97982
8030	S	S	R	N	1972	56731
8031	S	S	E	N	1975	100825
8035	S	S	E	N	1967	98892
8036	S	S	E	N	1967	98894
8038	C	S	E	L	1969	68115
8038	S	S	E	L	1969	68115
8038	S	S	E	N	1969	68115
8038	S	S	E	N	1972	87824
8040	S	S	E	L	1969	75843
8040	S	S	E	N	1969	75843
8043	C	S	E	L	1969	75843
8043	S	S	E	L	1969	75843
8043	S	S	E	N	1969	75843
8044	L	S	O	N	1973	58738
8048	S	T	R	N	1971	66284
8050	L	D	R	H	1973	67558
8050	L	D	R	N	1973	67558
8050	L	T	R	H	1973	67558
8050	L	T	R	N	1973	67558
8050	L	S	E	H	1968	98632
8050	L	S	E	N	1968	98632
8052	L	D	R	N	1973	67558
8052	L	T	R	N	1973	67558
8053	L	D	R	N	1973	67558
8053	L	T	R	N	1973	67558
8054	L	D	R	H	1973	67558
8054	L	D	R	N	1973	67558
8054	L	T	R	H	1973	67558
8054	L	T	R	N	1973	67558
8055	L	D	R	H	1973	67558
8055	L	D	R	N	1973	67558
8055	L	T	R	H	1973	67558
8055	L	T	R	N	1973	67558
8056	L	D	R	H	1973	67558
8056	L	D	R	N	1973	67558
8056	L	T	R	H	1973	67558
8056	L	T	R	N	1973	67558
8057	S	T	R	N	1973	67856
8059	L	S	E	N	1968	98632
8061	S	T	E	L	1976	102104
8067	C	S	E	L	1972	53503
8067	S	S	E	N	1969	75843
8068	S	S	E	N	1964	93287
8068	S	S	E	N	1967	98891
8068	S	S	E	N	1955	98904
8069	C	S	E	L	1972	87886
8069	S	S	E	L	1972	87886
8069	S	S	E	N	1972	87886
8070	L	S	E	N	1968	98632
8071	S	S	E	N	1975	100825
8072	S	S	E	H	1967	98889
8072	S	S	E	N	1967	98889
8075	C	S	E	L	1971	57148
8075	S	D	E	L	1971	57148
8076	C	S	E	L	1971	57148
8076	S	D	E	L	1971	57148
102-0001	L	S	E	N	1968	98632
0002	A	S	E	N	1972	52403
0002	A	D	E	H	1972	76523
0002	A	E	R	H	1972	76523
0002	A	S	R	N	1972	76523
0002	A	D	E	H	1972	91509
0002	A	E	E	H	1972	91509
0002	A	S	E	N	1972	91509
0002	D	D	E	H	1974	57300
0002	D	E	E	H	1974	57300
0002	D	S	E	H	1974	57300
0002	D	S	E	H	1964	87713
0002	D	S	E	L	1964	87713
0002	D	S	E	N	1964	87713
0002	L	D	R	H	1971	76473
0002	L	E	R	H	1971	76473
0002	L	D	E	H	1971	91499
0002	L	E	E	H	1971	91499
0002	L	D	R	H	1976	99798
0002	L	E	R	H	1976	99798
0002	P	D	E	N	1974	61342
0002	P	S	E	N	1974	61342
102-0002	S	E	E	H	1973	49433
0002	S	S	E	N	1973	56749
0002	S	D	E	H	1974	57300
0002	S	D	E	N	1974	57300
0002	S	E	E	H	1974	57300
0002	S	E	E	N	1974	57300
0002	S	S	E	H	1974	57300
0002	S	S	E	N	1974	57300
0002	S	T	E	H	1974	57300
0002	S	D	E	N	1974	57831
0002	S	D	R	N	1969	59128
0002	S	D	E	N	1969	59129
0002	S	S	E	H	1970	60090
0002	S	S	E	N	1970	60090
0002	S	D	G	N	1971	60095
0002	S	E	G	N	1971	60095
0002	S	S	E	H	1962	65974
0002	S	S	E	N	1962	65974
0002	S	D	O	H	1974	66386
0002	S	D	O	N	1974	66386
0002	S	S	E	N	1964	87713
0002	S	S	E	N	1968	87819
0002	S	S	E	H	1966	87846
0002	S	S	E	N	1966	87846
0002	S	S	E	N	1967	87864
0002	S	D	E	N	1975	93162
0002	S	S	E	H	1967	97982
0002	S	S	E	N	1967	97982
0002	S	S	E	H	1967	98889
0002	S	S	E	N	1967	98889
0002	T	D	R	N	1973	51408
0002	T	D	E	N	1973	51409
0002	T	D	E	N	1972	53252
0002	T	D	E	N	1972	53299
0002	T	D	E	N	1972	53532
0002	T	D	E	N	1961	65971
0002	T	S	E	N	1972	83589
0002	T	D	E	N	1973	90575
0002	T	T	E	N	1970	100000
0005	L	S	E	N	1968	98632
0005	S	D	E	N	1972	49876
0005	S	S	E	H	1974	55267
0005	S	S	E	N	1974	55267
0005	S	S	E	N	1973	56765
0009	L	D	E	N	1972	49474
0009	L	S	E	N	1968	98632
0009	S	S	E	N	1973	58913
0009	S	D	E	N	1975	63326
0009	S	E	E	N	1975	63326
0010	D	D	R	N	1973	50189
0010	D	D	E	N	1973	50190
0010	L	D	E	N	1972	49474
0010	L	S	E	N	1968	98632
0010	S	D	R	N	1973	50189
0010	S	D	E	N	1973	50190
0010	S	S	E	N	1973	58913
0010	S	D	E	N	1975	63326
0010	S	E	E	N	1975	63326
0013	S	S	E	H	1967	97983
0013	S	S	E	N	1967	97983
0013	S	S	E	H	1967	98889
0013	S	S	E	N	1967	98889
0016	L	D	R	N	1973	51347
0016	L	D	E	N	1973	55345
0018	S	D	E	N	1973	53506
0018	S	D	E	N	1974	65737
0030	L	S	E	N	1972	51438
0030	L	S	E	N	1968	98632
0030	S	D	E	N	1973	57879
0031	T	D	F	N	1973	49416
0031	T	D	E	N	1974	62407
0031	T	S	E	N	1967	87860
0035	L	S	E	N	1968	98632
0041	S	D	R	N	1971	60185
0041	S	S	E	N	1972	87889
0041	T	D	E	L	1974	65107
0041	T	D	E	N	1974	65107
0041	T	E	E	N	1974	65107
0041	T	D	E	L	1975	65464
0041	T	D	E	N	1975	65464
0054	S	D	E	N	1973	51852
0054	S	S	E	N	1972	87890
0086	A	D	E	N	1972	49466
0086	A	D	R	N	1973	70819
0086	A	T	R	N	1973	70819
0086	A	S	E	N	1967	75838
0086	A	D	E	N	1973	91575
0086	A	T	E	N	1973	91575
0086	D	S	E	N	1967	75838
0086	L	D	R	H	1973	52538
0086	L	D	R	N	1973	52538
0086	L	D	E	H	1974	53667
0086	L	D	E	N	1974	53667
0086	S	S	R	N	1970	53106
0086	S	S	E	N	1972	53107
0086	S	D	E	N	1973	56527
0086	S	S	E	N	1972	59933
0086	S	S	E	N	1974	61340
0086	S	D	R	N	1973	70819
0086	S	T	R	N	1973	70819
0086	S	D	E	N	1973	91575

Phys. State: **A.** Amorphous; **C.** Superconductive; **D.** Doped; **F.** Fibrous or Whisker; **G.** Gas; **I.** Ionized or Plasma; **L.** Liquid; **P.** Powder or Particle; **S.** Solid; **T.** Thin Film
Subject: **D.** Data; **E.** Experiment; **S.** Survey (Review, Compendium, etc.); **T.** Theory
Language: **E.** English; **F.** French; **G.** German; **O.** Other Languages; **R.** Russian
Temperature: **L.** Low (0 to 75K); **N.** Normal (75 to 1273K); **H.** High (above 1273K)

Substance Number	Phys. State	Subject	Language	Temperature	Year	EPIC Number
102-0086	S	T	E	N	1973	91575
0086	T	D	E	N	1972	49466
0105	C	S	E	L	1974	59378
0105	D	D	O	N	1974	90530
0105	P	D	O	N	1974	90530
0105	S	D	E	N	1974	65738
0105	S	S	G	H	1974	80980
0105	S	S	G	N	1974	80980
0105	S	D	E	N	1967	85339
0105	S	S	E	N	1966	87830
0105	S	S	E	N	1971	87884
0105	T	D	R	N	1973	51626
0105	T	D	E	N	1973	53352
0105	T	D	R	N	1971	58853
0105	T	T	E	N	1967	85339
0105	T	S	E	N	1971	87884
0105	T	D	E	N	1973	91486
0120	L	D	R	N	1973	52540
0120	L	D	E	N	1974	53675
0120	L	S	E	N	1967	87860
0120	L	S	E	H	1968	98632
0120	L	S	E	N	1968	98632
0120	S	D	R	N	1973	50724
0120	S	D	E	N	1973	53025
0120	S	D	F	N	1970	59704
0120	S	E	F	N	1970	59704
0120	S	D	E	N	1936	61578
0120	S	E	E	N	1952	65344
0120	S	S	E	N	1952	65344
0120	S	T	E	N	1952	65344
0120	S	S	E	L	1967	87860
0120	S	S	E	N	1967	87860
0120	T	D	R	N	1973	54861
0120	T	D	O	N	1973	56806
0191	S	S	E	H	1976	103180
0191	S	S	E	N	1976	103180
0246	C	S	E	L	1973	56765
0248	S	S	E	N	1966	87830
0248	S	S	E	N	1971	87884
0248	T	S	E	N	1969	87821
0248	T	T	E	N	1976	99553
0281	S	D	E	N	1973	51852
0296	S	D	E	N	1973	51930
0348	S	S	E	H	1974	55267
0348	S	S	E	N	1974	55267
0348	S	S	E	N	1973	56765
0348	S	S	R	N	1974	63050
0348	S	S	E	N	1975	63051
0382	S	D	R	N	1972	49823
8001	C	S	E	L	1969	75904
8001	C	S	E	N	1971	87884
8001	S	D	E	N	1973	53427
8001	D	D	R	N	1966	59587
8001	D	E	R	N	1966	59587
8001	D	D	E	N	1966	63247
8001	D	E	E	N	1966	63247
8001	D	S	E	N	1962	87668
8001	D	S	E	N	1966	87830
8001	D	S	E	N	1971	87884
8001	D	S	E	N	1967	97985
8001	L	S	E	H	1971	87884
8001	L	S	R	H	1974	92307
8001	L	S	E	N	1974	92308
8001	S	D	E	N	1973	53427
8001	S	S	E	N	1973	53427
8001	S	D	R	N	1966	59587
8001	S	E	R	N	1966	59587
8001	S	D	E	N	1966	63247
8001	S	E	E	N	1966	63247
8001	S	D	G	N	1954	66199
8001	S	S	E	N	1962	87668
8001	S	S	E	L	1966	87830
8001	S	S	E	N	1966	87830
8001	S	S	E	H	1971	87884
8001	S	S	E	N	1971	87884
8001	S	S	R	N	1974	92307
8001	S	S	E	N	1974	92308
8001	S	S	E	N	1967	97985
8002	S	D	E	N	1936	61578
8005	C	D	E	L	1975	100026
8005	L	D	G	N	1959	59037
8005	S	D	E	N	1936	61578
8006	L	D	G	N	1959	59037
8007	L	D	G	N	1959	59037
8012	S	D	R	H	1973	50321
8012	S	D	R	N	1973	50321
8012	S	D	E	H	1973	50322
8012	S	D	E	N	1973	50322
8012	S	D	R	H	1972	94899
8012	S	D	R	N	1972	94899
8012	S	D	E	H	1973	95896
8012	S	D	E	N	1973	95896
8012	S	S	E	N	1967	97985
8012	S	D	E	N	1974	101642
8012	S	D	E	N	1976	102175
8018	S	S	E	N	1972	87889
8027	S	S	E	N	1970	87822
8028	S	S	E	N	1972	87890
8031	A	D	E	N	1972	49466
8031	A	D	E	N	1972	53276
8031	A	S	E	N	1973	53314
102-8031	A	S	E	N	1973	53429
8031	A	S	E	N	1973	54769
8031	A	S	O	N	1972	58591
8031	A	S	E	N	1970	59557
8031	A	D	R	N	1974	60421
8031	A	D	E	N	1974	60422
8031	A	D	E	N	1972	63823
8031	A	D	E	H	1974	65598
8031	A	D	E	N	1973	67288
8031	A	S	E	N	1964	75166
8031	A	S	E	N	1974	84007
8031	A	S	E	N	1971	84631
8031	A	D	E	N	1975	90770
8031	A	S	E	N	1975	90770
8031	A	T	E	N	1975	90770
8031	D	D	E	N	1973	49533
8031	D	D	R	N	1974	60421
8031	D	D	E	N	1974	60422
8031	D	D	E	N	1972	63823
8031	D	D	O	N	1974	90008
8031	L	D	R	H	1973	55217
8031	L	D	R	N	1973	55217
8031	L	D	E	H	1974	55218
8031	L	D	E	N	1974	55218
8031	L	S	E	N	1970	59557
8031	L	S	E	N	1972	60899
8031	L	D	R	N	1971	78826
8031	L	T	R	N	1971	78826
8031	L	D	E	N	1974	84032
8031	L	D	E	N	1971	93209
8031	L	T	E	N	1971	93209
8031	L	D	R	N	1976	103396
8031	L	D	E	N	1976	103397
8031	S	D	E	N	1973	51769
8031	S	T	E	N	1973	52650
8031	S	S	R	N	1970	53106
8031	S	S	E	N	1972	53107
8031	S	D	R	N	1973	55325
8031	S	D	E	N	1973	55877
8031	S	D	E	N	1973	56120
8031	S	T	E	N	1973	56120
8031	S	D	E	N	1974	59261
8031	S	S	E	N	1972	59933
8031	S	D	R	N	1974	60421
8031	S	D	E	N	1974	60422
8031	S	D	E	H	1972	67201
8031	S	D	E	N	1972	67201
8031	S	S	E	N	1964	75166
8031	S	S	E	N	1972	98639
8031	T	D	E	N	1972	49466
8031	T	S	E	N	1973	54769
8031	T	S	E	N	1972	83589
8035	S	D	E	N	1973	51048
8035	S	D	E	N	1972	51526
8035	S	S	E	N	1972	51526
8035	S	E	E	L	1969	59174
8035	S	E	E	N	1969	59174
8035	S	D	E	N	1975	94550
8040	S	D	R	N	1912	91893
8040	T	D	O	N	1973	58722
8041	A	D	E	N	1972	49464
8041	A	S	E	N	1971	49794
8041	A	D	E	N	1973	56525
8041	A	D	E	N	1974	68692
8041	A	S	E	N	1970	75887
8041	A	S	E	N	1974	83952
8041	D	D	R	N	1972	49888
8041	D	D	E	L	1972	49928
8041	D	D	R	L	1973	50079
8041	D	D	R	N	1973	50079
8041	D	D	R	N	1973	50081
8041	D	D	E	N	1973	50700
8041	D	D	E	N	1973	51427
8041	D	D	E	L	1973	51432
8041	D	D	E	N	1973	51432
8041	D	D	R	N	1973	51704
8041	D	D	E	L	1973	51866
8041	D	D	E	N	1973	51866
8041	D	D	E	N	1973	52460
8041	D	D	R	N	1973	52529
8041	D	D	R	N	1973	52561
8041	D	D	E	N	1973	52937
8041	D	D	E	N	1972	52973
8041	D	D	E	N	1972	52982
8041	D	D	E	N	1972	53068
8041	D	D	R	N	1970	53088
8041	D	D	E	N	1972	53089
8041	D	D	E	L	1972	53113
8041	D	D	E	N	1972	53113
8041	D	D	E	N	1972	53171
8041	D	D	E	L	1972	53270
8041	D	D	E	N	1972	53270
8041	D	D	E	N	1972	53274
8041	D	D	E	N	1972	53302
8041	D	D	E	N	1973	53352
8041	D	D	E	N	1972	53390
8041	D	D	E	L	1973	53414
8041	D	D	E	N	1973	53414
8041	D	D	E	N	1972	53484
8041	D	T	E	N	1972	53484
8041	D	D	E	N	1971	53515
102-8041	D	D	E	N	1972	53519
8041	D	D	E	N	1974	53735
8041	D	D	E	N	1974	53745
8041	D	D	E	N	1974	53902
8041	D	T	E	N	1974	53902
8041	D	D	E	N	1973	54221
8041	D	D	E	N	1973	54771
8041	D	D	E	N	1973	55085
8041	D	D	R	N	1973	55342
8041	D	D	E	N	1973	55835
8041	D	D	E	N	1974	57770
8041	D	D	E	N	1973	57786
8041	D	T	E	N	1974	58826
8041	D	D	E	N	1974	59284
8041	D	D	E	L	1970	59695
8041	D	D	E	N	1970	59695
8041	D	S	E	L	1972	60677
8041	D	S	E	N	1972	60677
8041	D	D	E	N	1973	60748
8041	D	D	E	N	1974	61185
8041	D	S	E	N	1969	61512
8041	D	D	E	N	1971	61678
8041	D	D	E	N	1964	62127
8041	D	D	E	N	1970	62262
8041	D	D	R	N	1973	62726
8041	D	D	E	N	1974	63116
8041	D	T	E	N	1974	63116
8041	D	D	E	N	1975	63363
8041	D	S	R	N	1970	63458
8041	D	S	E	N	1970	65158
8041	D	D	E	N	1973	65322
8041	D	D	E	N	1975	65434
8041	D	S	E	N	1975	65434
8041	D	T	E	N	1964	66316
8041	D	D	R	N	1974	66450
8041	D	D	E	N	1974	66451
8041	D	D	R	N	1972	67630
8041	D	D	R	N	1969	67766
8041	D	D	E	N	1973	68864
8041	D	D	E	L	1958	75961
8041	D	D	E	N	1958	75961
8041	D	D	R	N	1975	81166
8041	D	T	R	N	1975	81166
8041	D	D	R	N	1974	83498
8041	D	D	E	N	1974	86454
8041	D	S	E	N	1974	86454
8041	D	S	E	N	1962	87673
8041	D	S	E	L	1964	87701
8041	D	S	E	N	1964	87701
8041	D	S	E	N	1971	87884
8041	D	S	E	L	1975	90393
8041	D	D	E	N	1974	92391
8041	D	D	E	N	1975	93322
8041	D	D	E	N	1975	94087
8041	D	T	E	N	1975	94087
8041	D	D	E	N	1973	101327
8041	L	S	E	H	1964	87701
8041	L	S	R	H	1974	92307
8041	L	S	E	H	1974	92308
8041	P	D	R	N	1973	56966
8041	P	D	R	N	1969	67767
8041	S	D	E	N	1972	49419
8041	S	D	E	N	1972	49814
8041	S	D	R	N	1973	50054
8041	S	D	R	N	1973	50077
8041	S	D	R	N	1973	50083
8041	S	D	E	N	1972	51086
8041	S	D	R	N	1972	51102
8041	S	D	E	N	1973	51410
8041	S	D	E	N	1973	51430
8041	S	D	E	N	1973	51434
8041	S	T	E	L	1973	52026
8041	S	D	E	N	1970	52693
8041	S	T	E	N	1970	52693
8041	S	D	R	N	1973	52838
8041	S	D	E	N	1973	52839
8041	S	D	E	N	1972	52973
8041	S	D	E	N	1972	52982
8041	S	D	E	N	1972	53171
8041	S	D	E	L	1972	53184
8041	S	D	E	N	1972	53274
8041	S	D	E	N	1972	53302
8041	S	D	E	N	1973	53446
8041	S	D	E	N	1974	53910
8041	S	D	E	N	1974	54221
8041	S	D	R	N	1973	54947
8041	S	D	E	N	1973	55095
8041	S	D	E	N	1972	55101
8041	S	D	E	N	1973	55161
8041	S	D	R	L	1973	55305
8041	S	D	E	N	1971	55377
8041	S	D	E	N	1973	56771
8041	S	S	E	N	1973	56771
8041	S	D	R	N	1972	56957
8041	S	D	E	L	1974	57002
8041	S	D	E	N	1974	57002
8041	S	D	E	N	1974	58038
8041	S	D	E	L	1974	58935
8041	S	D	E	L	1974	59230
8041	S	D	E	N	1971	60690
8041	S	E	E	N	1971	60690

Phys. State: **A.** Amorphous; **C.** Superconductive; **D.** Doped; **F.** Fibrous or Whisker; **G.** Gas; **I.** Ionized or Plasma; **L.** Liquid; **P.** Powder or Particle; **S.** Solid; **T.** Thin Film
Subject: **D.** Data; **E.** Experiment; **S.** Survey (Review, Compendium, etc.); **T.** Theory
Language: **E.** English; **F.** French; **G.** German; **O.** Other Languages; **R.** Russian
Temperature: **L.** Low (0 to 75K); **N.** Normal (75 to 1273K); **H.** High (above 1273K)

Substance Number	Phys. State	Sub-ject	Lan-guage	Temper-ature	Year	EPIC Number
102-8041	S	T	E	N	1974	60692
8041	S	D	E	N	1973	60754
8041	S	D	E	N	1974	61185
8041	S	S	E	N	1969	61512
8041	S	D	E	N	1971	61678
8041	S	D	E	N	1969	62248
8041	S	D	E	N	1970	62262
8041	S	S	E	N	1971	62264
8041	S	D	E	N	1974	62323
8041	S	E	G	N	1970	62372
8041	S	D	E	N	1974	63116
8041	S	T	E	N	1974	63116
8041	S	D	E	N	1975	63292
8041	S	D	R	N	1972	63469
8041	S	D	E	N	1972	63538
8041	S	S	E	L	1974	64464
8041	S	S	E	N	1974	64464
8041	S	D	E	N	1974	64493
8041	S	D	E	N	1972	65147
8041	S	D	R	L	1973	66551
8041	S	D	E	L	1974	66552
8041	S	D	R	N	1971	66998
8041	S	D	R	N	1970	67035
8041	S	D	R	N	1969	67767
8041	S	D	R	N	1974	68636
8041	S	D	E	N	1975	68637
8041	S	D	E	N	1973	68846
8041	S	D	E	N	1973	68864
8041	S	D	R	N	1974	72651
8041	S	D	E	N	1975	72700
8041	S	D	E	N	1966	75146
8041	S	S	E	N	1973	86380
8041	S	D	E	N	1974	87448
8041	S	S	E	N	1962	87673
8041	S	S	E	H	1964	87701
8041	S	S	E	L	1971	87884
8041	S	S	E	N	1971	87884
8041	S	D	R	N	1966	91926
8041	S	D	E	N	1975	92079
8041	S	S	R	N	1974	92307
8041	S	S	E	N	1974	92308
8041	S	D	G	L	1975	92648
8041	S	D	G	N	1975	92648
8041	S	E	G	L	1975	92648
8041	S	E	G	N	1975	92648
8041	S	D	E	N	1975	101024
8041	T	D	E	N	1973	49528
8041	T	D	R	L	1972	49973
8041	T	D	R	N	1972	49973
8041	T	D	R	L	1973	50079
8041	T	D	R	N	1973	50079
8041	T	D	R	N	1973	50676
8041	T	D	E	L	1973	51432
8041	T	D	E	N	1973	51432
8041	T	D	O	N	1973	51511
8041	T	D	E	N	1973	52422
8041	T	D	R	L	1973	52832
8041	T	D	R	N	1973	52832
8041	T	D	E	L	1973	52833
8041	T	D	E	N	1973	52833
8041	T	D	E	N	1973	53352
8041	T	D	E	N	1973	56525
8041	T	T	R	N	1971	60141
8041	T	T	E	N	1971	60142
8041	T	S	E	L	1971	60965
8041	T	S	E	N	1971	60965
8041	T	D	E	N	1974	62550
8041	T	S	R	N	1972	62704
8041	T	D	E	N	1970	62952
8041	T	E	E	N	1970	62952
8041	T	T	E	N	1970	62952
8041	T	S	E	N	1973	65123
8041	T	D	R	N	1974	66578
8041	T	D	E	N	1974	66579
8041	T	D	R	N	1969	67766
8041	T	D	E	N	1974	68692
8041	T	S	E	N	1974	83952
8041	T	S	E	N	1964	87701
8041	T	S	E	N	1968	87819
8041	T	S	E	N	1969	87821
8041	T	S	E	N	1971	87884
8041	T	D	E	N	1962	89724
8041	T	D	E	N	1974	90083
8054	D	D	E	N	1972	51091
8054	D	D	R	N	1973	58156
8054	D	S	E	N	1962	87667
8054	D	D	E	N	1963	98648
8054	L	S	E	N	1971	87884
8054	L	S	R	N	1974	92307
8054	L	S	E	N	1974	92308
8054	S	D	E	L	1971	53516
8054	S	D	E	N	1971	53516
8054	S	D	E	N	1972	55164
8054	S	S	E	N	1972	55164
8054	S	E	E	L	1958	59175
8054	S	E	E	N	1958	59175
8054	S	D	R	N	1972	62693
8054	S	D	E	N	1972	64420
8054	S	D	G	N	1954	66199
8054	S	S	E	N	1962	87667
8054	S	S	E	N	1971	87884

Substance Number	Phys. State	Sub-ject	Lan-guage	Temper-ature	Year	EPIC Number
102-8054	S	S	R	N	1974	92307
8054	S	S	E	N	1974	92308
8054	S	S	E	N	1967	97985
8054	S	D	E	N	1963	98648
8054	T	S	E	N	1973	53451
8054	T	T	E	N	1966	59478
8054	T	S	E	N	1971	87884
8058	F	D	E	N	1975	91972
8058	F	E	E	N	1975	91972
8058	F	S	E	N	1975	91972
8058	F	T	E	N	1975	91972
8065	D	D	R	N	1974	84840
8065	L	S	E	N	1967	87860
8065	S	D	R	N	1974	84840
8065	S	D	R	N	1974	86779
8065	S	S	E	N	1967	87860
8065	S	D	E	N	1974	90050
8066	L	D	E	H	1972	49461
8066	L	D	E	N	1972	49461
8066	S	D	E	N	1972	49461
8066	S	D	R	N	1973	52557
8066	S	D	R	N	1973	58197
8066	S	D	R	N	1974	86779
8066	S	D	E	N	1974	90050
8068	T	D	F	N	1973	49416
8069	A	D	R	N	1971	67725
8069	A	D	R	N	1971	67773
8069	A	D	E	N	1968	75884
8069	L	D	E	N	1972	49463
8069	L	D	R	N	1972	56981
8069	L	D	R	N	1973	64519
8069	S	D	E	N	1972	53335
8069	S	D	R	N	1972	56981
8069	S	D	R	N	1972	56983
8069	S	D	R	N	1972	56992
8069	S	D	R	N	1973	64519
8069	S	S	E	N	1975	94550
8070	A	D	E	N	1972	49466
8070	T	D	E	N	1972	49466
8071	S	D	E	N	1973	56374
8072	L	D	G	H	1957	61325
8072	S	T	E	N	1972	49495
8072	S	D	E	N	1973	56172
8080	S	D	E	L	1973	49768
8080	S	D	E	N	1973	49768
8081	S	D	E	L	1973	49768
8081	S	D	E	N	1973	49768
8082	S	D	E	L	1973	49768
8082	S	D	E	N	1973	49768
8083	A	D	R	N	1971	67725
8083	A	D	R	N	1971	67773
8083	S	S	E	N	1975	94550
8084	L	D	R	H	1974	66570
8084	L	D	E	H	1974	66571
8084	S	D	E	N	1973	51051
8084	S	D	R	N	1973	55338
8084	S	D	E	N	1974	59276
8084	S	D	R	N	1974	66570
8084	S	D	E	N	1974	66571
8084	S	D	R	N	1974	67759
8084	S	D	E	N	1975	94550
8085	S	D	R	N	1972	49824
8086	S	D	R	N	1972	49824
8087	S	D	E	N	1973	49860
8087	S	S	E	H	1974	55267
8087	S	S	E	N	1974	55267
8087	S	D	E	N	1975	90396
8088	S	D	E	N	1973	49862
8093	L	D	G	H	1914	100892
8093	L	D	G	N	1914	100892
8094	S	D	E	N	1974	53918
8094	S	D	R	N	1973	55308
8094	S	D	R	N	1972	56957
8094	S	D	E	N	1974	59233
8094	T	D	R	N	1973	50057
8094	T	D	E	N	1973	51413
8095	D	S	E	N	1965	87703
8095	S	D	E	N	1974	53721
8095	S	D	R	N	1972	56957
8095	S	S	E	N	1965	87703
8096	L	D	R	N	1972	56981
8096	L	D	R	N	1973	64519
8096	S	D	R	N	1973	50201
8096	S	D	E	N	1973	50202
8096	S	D	R	N	1970	55102
8096	S	D	E	N	1972	55103
8096	S	D	R	N	1972	56981
8096	S	D	R	N	1972	56992
8096	S	D	R	N	1973	64519
8096	S	D	E	N	1975	94550
8100	C	D	E	L	1973	51579
8100	C	D	F	L	1973	57624
8100	C	S	E	L	1974	59378
8100	C	D	E	L	1975	75624
8100	C	E	E	L	1975	75624
8100	C	S	F	L	1974	87919
8100	S	S	E	L	1966	87721
8105	S	S	G	N	1959	65983
8105	S	S	E	N	1963	65984
8106	A	D	E	N	1973	65201
8106	A	T	E	N	1973	65201

Substance Number	Phys. State	Sub-ject	Lan-guage	Temper-ature	Year	EPIC Number
102-8106	A	D	E	N	1973	67288
8106	A	T	E	N	1976	100646
8106	L	D	R	H	1973	55217
8106	L	D	R	N	1973	55217
8106	L	D	E	H	1974	55218
8106	L	D	E	N	1974	55218
8106	S	S	R	N	1970	53106
8106	S	S	E	N	1972	53107
8106	S	D	E	N	1972	53178
8107	L	D	R	H	1972	95056
8107	L	D	E	H	1972	95814
8107	S	D	E	N	1973	50605
8107	S	D	E	N	1973	52031
8108	S	D	R	N	1973	50724
8108	S	D	E	N	1973	53025
8109	S	D	E	L	1973	59111
8117	L	D	R	N	1972	50967
8117	L	D	G	H	1914	100892
8117	L	D	G	N	1914	100892
8117	S	D	R	N	1972	50967
8117	S	D	E	N	1973	51980
8118	S	D	R	N	1973	50742
8118	S	D	E	N	1973	79081
8128	S	D	E	L	1973	51213
8128	S	D	E	N	1973	51213
8128	S	S	E	L	1974	58928
8128	S	S	E	N	1974	58928
8129	S	D	E	L	1973	51213
8129	S	D	E	N	1973	51213
8132	S	S	E	N	1971	87884
8132	T	T	E	N	1976	99553
8133	A	S	E	N	1973	53314
8133	A	S	E	N	1973	53429
8133	A	D	E	N	1973	67288
8133	A	D	E	N	1973	67289
8133	A	D	E	N	1974	84007
8133	A	T	E	N	1976	100646
8133	D	D	E	N	1975	65858
8133	L	D	E	H	1971	62269
8133	L	D	E	N	1971	62269
8133	L	D	E	N	1975	65858
8133	S	S	R	N	1970	53106
8133	S	S	E	N	1972	53107
8133	T	D	E	N	1974	84007
8134	S	S	E	N	1972	87890
8139	S	D	E	N	1974	53722
8139	S	D	E	N	1974	60309
8139	S	D	E	N	1973	88610
8140	S	S	E	H	1962	65974
8140	S	S	E	N	1962	65974
8141	L	D	E	N	1973	51768
8141	L	D	E	N	1975	90018
8141	S	D	R	N	1973	55771
8141	S	D	E	N	1971	59951
8141	S	D	E	N	1975	90018
8141	S	S	E	N	1967	97985
8142	D	D	E	N	1975	65434
8142	T	S	E	N	1972	87889
8143	T	D	E	N	1973	51734
8144	S	D	E	N	1973	55786
8156	S	S	E	L	1974	58928
8156	S	S	E	N	1974	58928
8157	S	S	E	L	1974	58928
8157	S	S	E	N	1974	58928
8158	S	S	E	L	1974	58928
8158	S	S	E	N	1974	58928
8159	S	D	E	L	1973	52430
8159	S	D	E	N	1973	52430
8159	S	D	E	L	1974	54072
8159	S	D	E	N	1974	54072
8159	S	D	E	N	1974	54076
8159	S	D	E	L	1972	70545
8159	S	D	E	N	1972	70545
8159	S	D	E	L	1976	95560
8160	S	D	E	L	1973	52430
8160	S	D	E	N	1973	52430
8160	S	D	E	L	1974	54072
8160	S	D	E	N	1974	54072
8160	S	D	E	N	1974	54076
8160	S	D	E	L	1972	70545
8160	S	D	E	N	1972	70545
8160	S	D	E	L	1976	95560
8161	S	D	E	L	1973	52430
8161	S	D	E	N	1973	52430
8163	A	D	E	N	1972	53376
8163	S	D	E	N	1973	52780
8163	S	T	E	N	1973	52780
8164	A	D	R	N	1973	51078
8164	A	D	E	N	1973	52821
8164	S	S	E	N	1974	86455
8165	A	D	R	N	1973	51078
8165	A	D	E	N	1973	52821
8168	S	S	E	L	1972	54881
8168	S	S	E	N	1972	54881
8168	S	T	E	L	1972	54881
8168	S	T	E	N	1972	54881
8168	S	S	E	L	1970	59594
8168	S	S	E	N	1970	59594
8169	C	D	E	L	1973	51579
8169	C	D	E	L	1971	53075
8169	C	D	R	L	1973	55213

Phys. State: **A.** Amorphous; **C.** Superconductive; **D.** Doped; **F.** Fibrous or Whisker; **G.** Gas; **I.** Ionized or Plasma; **L.** Liquid; **P.** Powder or Particle; **S.** Solid; **T.** Thin Film
Subject: **D.** Data; **E.** Experiment; **S.** Survey (Review, Compendium, etc.); **T.** Theory
Language: **E.** English; **F.** French; **G.** German; **O.** Other Languages; **R.** Russian
Temperature: **L.** Low (0 to 75K); **N.** Normal (75 to 1273K); **H.** High (above 1273K)

Substance Number	Phys. State	Subject	Language	Temperature	Year	EPIC Number
102-8169	C	S	R	L	1973	55213
8169	C	D	E	L	1974	55214
8169	C	S	E	L	1974	55214
8169	C	D	E	L	1974	60358
8169	C	S	O	L	1973	62410
8169	C	D	F	L	1975	63413
8169	C	T	F	L	1975	63413
8169	C	S	E	L	1974	64981
8169	C	D	E	L	1975	66719
8169	C	E	E	L	1975	66719
8169	C	T	E	L	1975	66719
8169	C	D	E	L	1975	75624
8169	C	E	E	L	1975	75624
8169	C	D	E	L	1972	75852
8169	C	T	E	L	1972	75852
8169	C	D	E	L	1975	87153
8169	C	T	E	L	1975	87153
8169	C	S	E	L	1966	87721
8169	C	S	E	L	1972	87886
8169	C	S	E	L	1976	97924
8169	C	S	E	L	1976	97925
8169	S	D	E	L	1971	53075
8169	S	S	E	L	1972	87886
8169	S	S	E	N	1972	87886
8169	T	D	R	L	1973	55213
8169	T	S	R	L	1973	55213
8169	T	D	E	L	1974	55214
8169	T	S	E	L	1974	55214
8171	A	D	E	N	1972	53186
8171	T	D	E	N	1972	53186
8172	A	D	E	N	1972	53187
8172	A	S	E	N	1972	53187
8172	S	D	E	N	1974	53908
8172	S	E	E	N	1974	53908
8172	S	T	E	N	1974	53908
8173	L	S	E	N	1968	98632
8174	C	S	E	L	1972	53272
8174	S	S	E	L	1972	53272
8174	S	S	E	N	1972	53272
8179	L	D	R	N	1972	56981
8179	S	D	R	N	1970	55102
8179	S	D	E	N	1972	55103
8179	S	D	R	N	1972	56981
8179	S	S	E	N	1975	94550
8180	L	D	R	H	1973	55074
8180	L	D	E	H	1974	55075
8180	L	D	R	N	1973	64519
8180	S	D	R	N	1973	55074
8180	S	D	E	N	1974	55075
8180	S	D	R	N	1970	55102
8180	S	D	E	N	1972	55103
8180	S	D	E	N	1972	56980
8180	S	D	R	N	1973	64519
8180	S	D	E	N	1975	94550
8184	S	D	E	N	1965	64251
8186	D	D	E	N	1972	53519
8187	A	D	E	L	1969	72525
8187	A	D	E	N	1969	72525
8187	L	D	G	H	1957	61325
8187	P	D	E	N	1971	70587
8187	P	T	E	N	1971	70587
8187	S	D	E	L	1973	56572
8187	S	D	E	N	1973	56572
8187	S	E	E	L	1973	56572
8187	S	E	E	N	1973	56572
8187	S	S	E	N	1954	59563
8187	S	S	E	N	1971	59622
8187	S	D	E	L	1970	59684
8187	S	D	E	N	1970	59684
8187	S	S	E	L	1970	59684
8187	S	S	E	N	1970	59684
8187	S	D	G	N	1971	59718
8187	S	D	E	L	1971	63591
8187	S	S	E	L	1971	63591
8187	S	T	E	L	1971	63591
8187	S	D	G	N	1936	75374
8187	S	T	G	N	1936	75374
8187	S	D	E	N	1938	85455
8187	S	E	E	N	1938	85455
8187	S	T	E	N	1938	85455
8187	S	S	E	N	1966	87843
8187	S	S	R	N	1974	88600
8187	S	D	E	L	1971	89783
8187	S	D	E	N	1971	89783
8187	S	S	E	N	1975	90846
8187	S	T	E	N	1976	101754
8188	S	D	E	N	1970	63884
8188	S	T	E	N	1970	63884
8189	C	D	E	L	1973	55121
8189	C	S	E	L	1974	59378
8189	C	S	E	L	1974	88040
8189	D	D	E	N	1973	50538
8189	D	D	E	L	1973	55121
8189	S	D	E	N	1973	50538
8190	L	D	E	N	1973	51457
8190	L	E	E	N	1973	51457
8191	L	D	E	N	1973	51457
8191	L	E	E	N	1973	51457
8192	S	D	E	L	1974	61168
8192	S	D	E	N	1974	61168
8192	S	S	E	N	1974	61168
102-8194	C	D	E	L	1973	51579
8195	S	D	R	N	1972	54683
8195	S	D	E	L	1973	63624
8195	S	S	E	L	1973	63624
8195	S	S	E	L	1973	63637
8195	S	D	E	L	1975	66703
8195	S	D	E	N	1975	66703
8195	S	T	R	N	1974	91206
8195	S	T	E	N	1975	103292
8196	C	D	E	L	1973	51895
8196	C	S	E	L	1973	51895
8196	C	D	E	L	1974	57978
8196	C	S	E	L	1974	57978
8196	T	D	E	L	1973	51895
8197	C	S	E	L	1973	51895
8197	L	D	G	H	1959	59037
8197	L	D	G	N	1959	59037
8198	C	S	E	L	1973	51895
8198	L	D	G	H	1959	59037
8198	L	D	G	N	1959	59037
8202	L	S	E	N	1971	65065
8203	A	T	R	N	1973	53665
8203	A	T	E	N	1974	53666
8203	L	T	R	N	1973	53665
8203	L	T	E	N	1974	53666
8203	S	T	R	N	1973	53665
8203	S	T	E	N	1974	53666
8204	A	T	R	N	1973	53665
8204	A	T	E	N	1974	53666
8204	L	D	R	N	1973	53665
8204	L	T	R	N	1973	53665
8204	L	D	E	N	1974	53666
8204	L	T	E	N	1974	53666
8204	S	T	R	N	1973	53665
8204	S	T	E	N	1974	53666
8215	L	D	G	H	1957	59036
8215	L	D	G	N	1957	59036
8217	C	S	E	L	1973	52303
8217	S	D	E	L	1973	52303
8217	S	D	E	N	1973	52303
8218	S	D	E	N	1973	52303
8219	S	S	E	N	1958	75842
8220	S	S	E	N	1967	97985
8221	S	S	E	N	1958	75842
8222	S	D	E	L	1974	54354
8222	S	S	E	L	1974	54354
8222	S	T	E	L	1974	54354
8222	S	D	E	L	1974	64980
8222	S	D	E	N	1974	64980
8223	D	D	R	N	1973	55444
8223	S	S	E	N	1971	59622
8223	S	D	E	N	1971	61726
8223	S	S	E	N	1966	87843
8223	S	D	E	N	1975	90846
8225	S	D	E	L	1974	54963
8225	S	D	E	N	1974	54963
8228	L	D	R	N	1971	76499
8228	L	T	R	N	1971	76499
8228	L	D	E	N	1971	91563
8228	L	T	E	N	1971	91563
8228	S	D	R	N	1970	55102
8228	S	D	E	N	1972	55103
8228	S	D	R	N	1971	76499
8228	S	T	R	N	1971	76499
8228	S	D	E	N	1971	91563
8228	S	T	E	N	1971	91563
8229	S	D	R	N	1970	55102
8229	S	D	E	N	1972	55103
8230	S	D	R	N	1970	55102
8230	S	D	E	N	1972	55103
8230	S	T	E	N	1974	62033
8231	S	D	R	N	1970	55102
8231	S	D	E	N	1972	55103
8231	S	S	E	N	1967	97985
8233	S	S	E	N	1974	54072
8233	S	D	E	N	1976	95560
8234	S	S	E	L	1974	54072
8234	S	S	E	N	1974	54072
8234	S	D	E	L	1976	95560
8239	S	D	E	N	1943	61285
8240	S	D	E	N	1973	51980
8240	S	D	E	N	1943	61285
8240	S	D	E	N	1936	61578
8240	S	E	E	N	1952	65344
8240	S	T	E	N	1952	65344
8241	S	D	E	N	1943	61285
8244	L	D	G	H	1957	61325
8248	S	D	R	N	1970	55102
8248	S	D	E	N	1972	55103
8249	S	D	R	N	1970	55102
8249	S	D	E	N	1972	55103
8250	S	D	E	N	1973	57735
8253	S	D	E	N	1973	57735
8255	C	D	E	L	1973	55129
8256	C	D	E	L	1973	55129
8257	C	D	E	L	1973	57497
8259	S	D	E	L	1974	57975
8259	S	D	E	N	1974	57975
8261	S	S	E	L	1972	54881
8261	S	S	E	N	1972	54881
8261	S	T	E	L	1972	54881
102-8261	S	T	E	N	1972	54881
8261	S	S	E	L	1970	59594
8261	S	S	E	N	1970	59594
8262	S	S	E	N	1970	59588
8268	S	D	E	L	1975	63269
8269	S	D	E	L	1975	63269
8270	S	D	E	L	1975	63269
8271	S	D	E	L	1975	63269
8278	S	D	E	N	1936	61578
8278	S	E	E	N	1952	65344
8278	S	T	E	N	1952	65344
8279	S	D	E	N	1936	61578
8279	S	E	E	N	1952	65344
8279	S	T	E	N	1952	65344
8280	S	D	E	N	1936	61578
8280	S	E	E	N	1952	65344
8280	S	T	E	N	1952	65344
8282	S	D	E	N	1936	61578
8282	S	E	E	N	1952	65344
8282	S	T	E	N	1952	65344
8283	C	D	E	L	1975	99454
8283	C	E	E	L	1975	99454
8283	S	S	E	N	1974	64980
8284	S	D	E	L	1971	65065
8287	S	D	E	L	1971	89783
8287	S	D	E	N	1971	89783
8287	S	D	R	L	1956	89787
8287	S	D	R	N	1956	89787
8287	S	D	E	L	1956	89788
8287	S	D	E	N	1956	89788
8288	S	D	R	L	1956	89787
8288	S	D	R	N	1956	89787
8288	S	D	E	L	1956	89788
8288	S	D	E	N	1956	89788
8289	S	D	E	N	1936	61578
8290	S	D	E	N	1936	61578
8291	S	D	E	N	1936	61578
8292	S	D	E	N	1936	61578
8293	A	S	E	N	1973	54768
8293	T	S	E	N	1973	54768
8294	S	D	E	N	1973	51980
8295	S	D	E	N	1973	51980
8303	S	S	E	N	1973	56765
8303	S	D	E	N	1953	75543
8303	S	E	E	N	1953	75543
8306	D	D	R	N	1972	78825
8306	D	T	R	N	1972	78825
8306	D	D	E	N	1972	93207
8306	D	T	E	N	1972	93207
8306	S	S	E	H	1974	55267
8306	S	S	E	N	1974	55267
8306	S	D	R	N	1972	78825
8306	S	T	R	N	1972	78825
8306	S	D	E	N	1972	93207
8306	S	T	E	N	1972	93207
8307	S	S	E	H	1974	55267
8307	S	S	E	N	1974	55267
8308	S	S	E	H	1974	55267
8308	S	S	E	N	1974	55267
8310	S	D	E	N	1973	53799
8310	S	T	E	N	1973	53799
8310	S	T	E	N	1972	57000
8310	S	D	E	N	1975	94550
8310	T	T	E	N	1972	57000
8310	T	D	O	N	1969	65841
8311	S	D	E	N	1973	56364
8312	C	S	E	L	1973	56765
8314	L	D	E	N	1975	72449
8315	S	D	E	L	1974	64980
8315	S	D	E	N	1974	64980
8315	T	T	E	N	1974	89525
8316	S	D	E	L	1974	64980
8316	S	D	E	N	1974	64980
8317	S	D	E	L	1974	64980
8317	S	D	E	N	1974	64980
8318	S	D	E	L	1974	64980
8318	S	D	E	N	1974	64980
8319	S	D	E	L	1974	64980
8319	S	D	E	N	1974	64980
8320	S	D	E	L	1974	64980
8320	S	D	E	N	1974	64980
8321	C	S	E	L	1974	64981
8322	C	S	E	L	1974	64981
8323	C	S	E	L	1974	64981
8324	C	S	E	L	1974	88040
8325	C	S	E	L	1959	75729
8325	C	S	E	L	1974	88040
8326	C	S	E	L	1974	88040
8327	C	S	E	L	1974	88040
8328	C	S	E	L	1974	88040
8329	C	S	E	L	1974	88040
8330	S	D	R	L	1956	89787
8330	S	D	R	N	1956	89787
8330	S	D	E	L	1956	89788
8330	S	D	E	N	1956	89788
8332	S	T	E	N	1974	57880
8333	S	S	E	N	1972	87889
8333	T	D	F	N	1974	57941
8335	L	D	R	N	1973	64519
8335	S	D	R	N	1973	64519
8339	S	D	R	N	1973	55771

Phys. State: **A.** Amorphous; **C.** Superconductive; **D.** Doped; **F.** Fibrous or Whisker; **G.** Gas; **I.** Ionized or Plasma; **L.** Liquid; **P.** Powder or Particle; **S.** Solid; **T.** Thin Film
Subject: **D.** Data; **E.** Experiment; **S.** Survey (Review, Compendium, etc.); **T.** Theory
Language: **E.** English; **F.** French; **G.** German; **O.** Other Languages; **R.** Russian
Temperature: **L.** Low (0 to 75K); **N.** Normal (75 to 1273K); **H.** High (above 1273K)

Substance Number	Phys. State	Subject	Language	Temperature	Year	EPIC Number
102-8341	S	D	E	N	1973	56479
8346	S	D	E	N	1969	85351
8359	L	D	O	N	1973	67598
8374	S	D	E	N	1973	57714
8374	S	D	E	N	1974	88681
8377	S	D	E	N	1974	70392
8378	S	D	E	N	1974	70392
8380	L	D	E	H	1975	90018
8380	S	D	E	N	1975	90018
8381	D	D	E	N	1975	90018
8381	L	D	E	N	1975	90018
8381	S	D	E	N	1975	90018
8382	L	D	E	N	1975	90018
8382	S	D	E	N	1975	90018
8383	A	D	E	N	1974	84007
8383	A	S	E	N	1974	84007
8394	C	D	E	L	1975	99454
8394	C	E	E	L	1975	99454
8396	A	S	E	N	1964	75166
8396	S	S	E	N	1964	75166
8397	C	D	E	L	1974	60305
8398	C	D	E	L	1974	60358
8405	S	D	R	N	1971	66977
8409	C	S	E	L	1968	68372
8409	C	S	E	L	1968	68373
8409	S	S	E	L	1966	87721
8410	C	S	E	L	1965	87791
8415	C	S	E	L	1966	87721
8415	C	S	E	L	1972	87886
8416	C	S	E	L	1966	87721
8416	S	S	E	L	1972	87886
8416	S	S	E	N	1972	87886
8417	C	S	E	L	1976	97924
8417	S	S	E	L	1966	87721
8417	S	S	E	L	1972	87886
8417	S	S	E	N	1972	87886
8417	S	D	E	L	1976	100572
8417	S	D	E	N	1976	100572
8417	S	E	E	L	1976	100572
8417	S	E	E	N	1976	100572
8420	S	S	E	N	1972	87889
8420	T	S	E	N	1972	87889
8421	C	S	E	L	1966	87721
8421	S	S	E	L	1966	87721
8422	S	S	E	N	1967	97983
8423	S	S	E	N	1967	97983
8424	S	S	E	N	1967	97983
8425	S	S	E	N	1967	97983
8426	S	S	E	H	1967	97983
8426	S	S	E	N	1967	97983
8427	S	S	E	N	1967	97985
8428	S	S	E	N	1967	97985
8429	S	S	E	N	1967	97985
8430	S	S	E	N	1967	97985
8432	S	D	E	N	1969	98858
8434	A	D	R	N	1971	67725
8434	A	D	R	N	1971	67773
8435	A	D	R	N	1971	67725
8436	A	D	R	N	1971	67773
8437	S	D	E	N	1974	88681
8438	L	D	R	H	1972	95056
8438	L	D	E	H	1972	95814
8438	S	D	E	N	1974	88681
8442	C	S	E	L	1966	87721
8444	L	D	R	H	1972	95056
8444	L	D	E	H	1972	95814
8445	L	D	R	H	1972	95056
8445	L	D	E	H	1972	95814
8446	L	D	R	H	1972	95056
8446	L	D	E	H	1972	95814
8447	L	D	R	H	1972	95056
8447	L	D	E	H	1972	95814
8450	C	D	R	L	1974	81228
8450	C	D	E	L	1974	92358
8453	S	D	R	L	1972	76538
8453	S	D	R	N	1972	76538
8453	S	D	E	L	1972	91520
8453	S	D	E	N	1972	91520
8454	S	D	R	L	1972	76538
8454	S	D	R	N	1972	76538
8454	S	D	E	L	1972	91520
8454	S	D	E	N	1972	91520
8456	S	D	G	L	1975	98087
8456	S	E	G	L	1975	98087
8456	S	E	G	N	1975	98087
8458	F	D	E	N	1975	91972
8458	F	E	E	N	1975	91972
8458	F	T	E	N	1975	91972
8460	S	D	E	N	1975	91299
8460	S	T	E	N	1975	91299
8466	S	D	E	N	1970	63884
8467	S	D	E	N	1970	63884
8468	S	D	E	N	1970	63884
8472	L	D	G	H	1914	100892
8472	L	D	G	N	1914	100892
8473	C	D	E	L	1975	66720
8473	C	T	E	L	1975	66720
8473	C	D	E	L	1976	100720
8473	C	E	E	L	1976	100720
8473	T	D	E	L	1975	66720
8473	T	T	E	L	1975	66720

Substance Number	Phys. State	Subject	Language	Temperature	Year	EPIC Number
102-8474	C	D	E	L	1976	100720
8474	C	E	E	L	1976	100720
8475	C	D	E	L	1976	100720
8475	C	E	E	L	1976	100720
8476	C	D	E	L	1976	100720
8476	C	E	E	L	1976	100720
8477	S	D	E	L	1976	100785
8477	S	D	E	N	1976	100785
8477	S	T	E	L	1976	100785
8477	S	T	E	N	1976	100785
8478	S	D	E	L	1976	100572
8478	S	D	E	N	1976	100572
8478	S	E	E	L	1976	100572
8478	S	E	E	N	1976	100572
8479	C	D	E	L	1976	97925
8479	C	T	E	L	1976	97925
8480	S	D	R	N	1972	78827
8480	S	T	R	N	1972	78827
8480	S	D	E	N	1972	93210
8480	S	T	E	N	1972	93210
8484	S	D	E	N	1973	53799
8484	S	T	E	N	1973	53799
8485	C	D	F	L	1973	57624
8486	C	D	F	L	1973	57624
8492	S	S	E	H	1976	103180
8492	S	S	E	N	1976	103180
8493	S	S	E	H	1976	103180
8493	S	S	E	N	1976	103180
8494	S	S	E	H	1976	103180
8494	S	S	E	N	1976	103180
8495	S	S	E	H	1976	103180
8495	S	S	E	N	1976	103180
8496	S	D	E	N	1974	57750
8497	S	D	E	N	1974	57750
8498	S	D	E	N	1974	57750
8503	S	D	E	N	1974	57750
104-0002	S	D	E	N	1972	53476
0002	S	S	E	H	1962	65974
0002	S	S	E	N	1962	65974
0002	S	S	E	H	1969	68271
0002	S	S	E	N	1969	68271
0002	S	S	E	N	1963	87681
0002	S	S	E	N	1968	87819
0002	S	S	E	H	1966	87846
0002	S	S	E	N	1966	87846
0002	S	D	E	N	1975	93162
0002	S	T	E	H	1975	95378
0002	S	S	E	H	1967	97982
0002	S	S	E	N	1967	97982
0002	S	S	E	H	1962	98647
0002	S	S	E	H	1967	98889
0002	S	S	E	N	1967	98889
0002	S	S	E	H	1955	98900
0006	D	T	R	N	1973	56574
0006	D	D	E	N	1974	59393
0006	D	T	E	N	1976	103336
0006	F	D	R	N	1973	56306
0006	L	D	E	N	1972	49474
0006	L	D	E	N	1975	91295
0006	L	S	E	N	1975	91295
0006	L	S	E	N	1968	98632
0006	S	D	E	N	1973	62296
0006	S	D	E	N	1975	93559
0007	A	S	E	L	1975	95324
0007	D	S	E	N	1972	102094
0007	S	D	G	N	1971	60095
0007	S	E	G	N	1971	60095
0007	S	D	E	N	1966	64254
0007	S	S	E	H	1962	65974
0007	S	S	E	H	1967	68374
0007	S	S	E	N	1967	68374
0007	S	S	E	H	1966	87803
0007	S	S	E	N	1966	87803
0007	S	S	E	N	1971	87884
0007	S	S	E	H	1967	97984
0007	S	S	E	N	1967	98893
0007	T	D	E	N	1972	53473
0007	T	D	F	N	1973	54648
0007	T	S	E	N	1966	87803
0007	T	S	E	N	1969	87821
0013	C	S	R	L	1974	68646
0013	C	S	E	L	1975	68647
0013	D	D	R	H	1972	49828
0013	D	D	R	N	1972	49828
0013	D	D	E	N	1973	50125
0013	D	D	E	N	1973	50126
0013	D	D	R	N	1973	51621
0013	D	T	R	N	1973	51621
0013	D	T	R	N	1973	52898
0013	D	T	E	N	1974	52899
0013	D	D	E	N	1973	53884
0013	D	D	R	N	1974	58110
0013	D	D	E	N	1974	58111
0013	D	D	E	N	1974	61339
0013	D	S	E	N	1974	61339
0013	D	D	O	N	1972	66150
0013	D	D	E	N	1973	79050
0013	D	T	E	N	1973	79050
0013	D	D	O	N	1975	90089
0013	D	T	E	N	1974	90362

Substance Number	Phys. State	Subject	Language	Temperature	Year	EPIC Number
104-0013	D	D	E	N	1973	90475
0013	D	S	E	N	1967	97983
0013	S	D	E	N	1971	50468
0013	S	D	O	N	1973	52323
0013	S	D	E	N	1973	56462
0013	S	D	E	N	1973	56528
0013	S	D	R	N	1974	58110
0013	S	D	E	N	1974	58111
0013	S	D	R	N	1972	59071
0013	S	D	E	N	1972	59072
0013	S	S	E	N	1972	59933
0013	S	S	E	N	1974	61339
0013	S	S	E	N	1967	97983
0013	T	D	E	N	1972	60165
0013	T	D	E	N	1967	85905
0013	T	D	O	N	1975	90089
0015	S	S	E	N	1972	51985
0015	S	S	E	H	1966	87803
0015	S	S	E	N	1966	87803
0015	S	S	E	H	1964	101393
0015	S	S	E	N	1964	101393
0021	L	S	R	H	1966	95131
0021	L	S	E	H	1966	96497
0021	L	S	E	N	1968	98632
0021	S	S	R	N	1966	95131
0021	S	S	E	N	1966	96497
0021	S	S	E	N	1976	103180
0022	L	S	E	N	1968	98632
0022	S	D	E	N	1973	57727
0031	L	D	E	N	1972	49474
0031	L	S	E	N	1968	98632
0038	L	S	E	N	1972	51438
0040	L	D	E	N	1973	50419
0040	L	S	E	N	1967	98664
0049	S	D	E	N	1974	53627
0049	S	D	R	N	1974	66728
0049	S	D	E	N	1975	66729
0049	S	D	R	H	1974	66744
0049	S	D	R	N	1974	66744
0049	S	T	R	H	1974	66744
0049	S	T	R	N	1974	66744
0049	S	D	E	H	1975	66745
0049	S	D	E	N	1975	66745
0049	S	T	E	H	1975	66745
0049	S	T	E	N	1975	66745
0049	S	D	R	H	1972	76508
0049	S	D	R	N	1972	76508
0049	S	E	R	N	1972	76508
0049	S	S	E	N	1966	87846
0049	S	D	E	H	1972	91530
0049	S	D	E	N	1972	91530
0049	S	E	E	N	1972	91530
0049	S	S	E	N	1975	96477
0049	S	S	E	N	1967	97982
0049	S	S	E	N	1967	98889
0049	T	S	E	N	1975	96477
0050	S	S	E	N	1976	99185
0052	L	S	E	N	1968	98632
0053	L	D	E	N	1972	49474
0053	L	D	E	N	1975	91295
0053	L	S	E	N	1975	91295
0053	L	S	E	N	1968	98632
0055	L	D	R	N	1973	51347
0055	L	D	R	N	1969	52400
0055	L	D	E	N	1973	52401
0055	L	D	E	N	1973	55345
0055	L	D	E	H	1975	90985
0055	L	D	E	N	1975	90985
0055	L	S	E	H	1975	90985
0055	L	S	E	N	1975	90985
0055	L	T	E	H	1975	90985
0055	L	T	E	N	1975	90985
0055	L	S	E	H	1968	98632
0055	L	S	E	N	1968	98632
0067	L	S	E	N	1968	98632
0069	D	D	E	N	1973	50169
0069	L	S	E	N	1968	98632
0069	S	D	E	N	1973	50169
0077	L	S	E	N	1968	98632
0081	L	D	G	H	1973	52507
0081	L	D	G	N	1973	52507
0081	L	S	E	N	1968	98632
0093	L	D	E	N	1975	80277
0093	L	E	E	N	1975	80277
0093	L	S	E	N	1968	98632
0103	L	S	E	N	1968	98632
0104	D	D	E	N	1973	51057
0104	S	D	E	N	1973	51057
0104	S	D	F	N	1972	53541
0104	S	T	F	N	1972	53541
0104	S	D	E	N	1963	60560
0104	S	D	O	N	1973	67579
0104	S	S	E	N	1976	103180
0105	L	D	E	N	1972	49474
0105	L	S	E	N	1968	98632
0106	L	D	E	N	1972	49474
0106	L	S	E	N	1968	98632
0109	S	D	R	N	1975	84594
0109	S	T	R	N	1975	84594
0109	S	S	E	N	1966	87803
0109	S	D	E	N	1975	93217

Phys. State: **A.** Amorphous; **C.** Superconductive; **D.** Doped; **F.** Fibrous or Whisker; **G.** Gas; **I.** Ionized or Plasma; **L.** Liquid; **P.** Powder or Particle; **S.** Solid; **T.** Thin Film
Subject: **D.** Data; **E.** Experiment; **S.** Survey (Review, Compendium, etc.); **T.** Theory
Language: **E.** English; **F.** French; **G.** German; **O.** Other Languages; **R.** Russian
Temperature: **L.** Low (0 to 75K); **N.** Normal (75 to 1273K); **H.** High (above 1273K)

Substance Number	Phys. State	Subject	Language	Temperature	Year	EPIC Number
104-0109	S	T	E	N	1975	93217
0110	L	S	E	N	1968	98632
0118	L	S	E	N	1968	98632
0146	S	D	E	N	1973	52631
0149	L	D	R	N	1974	90235
0149	L	T	R	N	1974	90235
0149	L	D	E	N	1975	90236
0149	L	T	E	N	1975	90236
0149	L	S	E	N	1968	98632
0171	C	D	E	L	1974	64714
0185	L	S	E	H	1968	98632
0185	L	S	E	N	1968	98632
0186	L	S	E	H	1968	98632
0186	L	S	E	N	1968	98632
0187	L	S	E	H	1968	98632
0187	L	S	E	N	1968	98632
0188	S	S	E	H	1962	65974
0188	S	S	E	N	1962	65974
0196	S	D	E	N	1974	53627
0213	L	D	F	N	1971	61324
0213	L	S	E	N	1968	98632
0249	S	S	E	N	1971	87364
0249	S	D	R	H	1972	94899
0249	S	D	R	N	1972	94899
0249	S	D	E	H	1973	95896
0249	S	D	E	N	1973	95896
0295	S	S	E	N	1971	87884
0306	L	S	E	N	1968	98632
0309	L	S	E	N	1968	98632
0331	L	D	R	N	1974	90235
0331	L	T	R	N	1974	90235
0331	L	D	E	N	1975	90236
0331	L	T	E	N	1975	90236
0331	L	S	E	N	1968	98632
0331	S	D	R	N	1971	59648
0331	S	D	E	N	1971	59649
0337	T	S	E	N	1973	53758
0386	D	D	E	N	1974	60363
0386	D	S	E	N	1967	97983
0386	T	D	R	N	1972	49809
0409	S	D	R	N	1971	76503
0409	S	T	R	N	1971	76503
0409	S	D	E	N	1971	91564
0409	S	T	E	N	1971	91564
0435	L	S	E	N	1972	51438
0435	L	S	E	N	1968	98632
0471	S	D	E	N	1976	96888
0471	S	E	E	N	1976	96888
0533	S	S	E	N	1970	87822
0533	S	S	E	N	1972	87890
0572	S	D	R	N	1971	76503
0572	S	T	R	N	1971	76503
0572	S	D	E	N	1971	91564
0572	S	T	E	N	1971	91564
0573	S	D	R	N	1971	76503
0573	S	T	R	N	1971	76503
0573	S	D	E	N	1971	91564
0573	S	T	E	N	1971	91564
0574	S	D	R	N	1971	76503
0574	S	T	R	N	1971	76503
0574	S	D	E	N	1971	91564
0574	S	T	E	N	1971	91564
0575	S	D	R	N	1971	76503
0575	S	T	R	N	1971	76503
0575	S	D	E	N	1971	91564
0575	S	T	E	N	1971	91564
8010	L	D	O	N	1973	50499
8010	S	D	R	N	1967	72953
8010	S	S	E	N	1971	87884
8011	C	S	E	L	1971	87884
8011	F	D	E	N	1975	68616
8011	F	T	E	N	1975	68616
8011	L	D	E	N	1975	88234
8011	S	S	E	N	1971	87884
8011	S	D	E	N	1976	100267
8011	S	T	E	N	1976	100267
8013	C	S	E	L	1965	87791
8015	A	D	E	N	1975	63643
8015	S	S	E	N	1960	65977
8031	S	S	E	N	1967	97985
8032	S	D	E	N	1974	53627
8032	S	S	E	N	1969	68271
8033	S	D	E	N	1974	53627
8033	S	S	E	N	1969	68271
8042	D	D	R	N	1972	62716
8042	D	S	R	N	1972	62716
8042	D	D	E	N	1973	65312
8042	D	S	E	N	1973	65312
8042	D	S	E	N	1966	66068
8042	L	D	R	H	1969	61867
8042	L	D	R	N	1969	61867
8042	S	D	R	N	1973	57802
8042	S	D	E	N	1974	57803
8042	S	D	R	N	1971	59648
8042	S	D	E	N	1971	59649
8042	S	D	F	N	1971	61672
8042	S	D	R	N	1966	62300
8042	S	D	E	N	1974	62301
8042	S	D	R	N	1972	62716
8042	S	D	E	N	1973	65312
8042	S	S	E	L	1966	66068

Substance Number	Phys. State	Subject	Language	Temperature	Year	EPIC Number
104-8042	S	S	E	N	1966	66068
8042	S	D	E	N	1975	96857
8042	T	D	E	N	1974	57959
8044	L	S	E	N	1968	98632
8045	C	S	E	L	1972	62298
8045	C	S	E	L	1973	62299
8045	C	D	R	L	1975	86849
8045	C	S	R	L	1975	86849
8045	C	D	E	L	1975	86850
8045	C	S	E	L	1975	86850
8045	D	D	O	N	1972	61133
8045	D	D	R	L	1972	62298
8045	D	D	R	N	1972	62298
8045	D	D	E	L	1973	62299
8045	D	S	E	L	1966	66068
8045	D	S	E	N	1966	66068
8045	D	D	E	L	1974	88264
8045	D	D	E	N	1974	88264
8045	D	T	E	L	1974	88264
8045	D	T	E	N	1974	88264
8045	D	S	E	N	1967	97985
8045	L	D	R	N	1973	52540
8045	L	D	E	N	1974	53675
8045	L	D	R	H	1969	61867
8045	L	D	R	N	1969	61867
8045	L	S	R	N	1972	62298
8045	L	S	E	N	1973	62299
8045	L	D	R	N	1972	63429
8045	L	S	E	H	1966	66068
8045	L	S	E	N	1966	66068
8045	L	D	E	N	1973	67081
8045	L	D	R	H	1974	87298
8045	L	D	R	N	1974	87298
8045	L	D	E	H	1975	87299
8045	L	D	E	N	1975	87299
8045	L	D	R	H	1976	103384
8045	L	D	R	N	1976	103384
8045	L	D	E	H	1976	103385
8045	L	D	E	N	1976	103385
8045	S	D	R	L	1973	50295
8045	S	D	E	L	1973	50296
8045	S	D	E	L	1973	52072
8045	S	T	E	L	1973	52072
8045	S	S	E	N	1972	56769
8045	S	D	R	N	1971	61826
8045	S	E	R	N	1971	61826
8045	S	D	E	N	1971	61827
8045	S	E	E	N	1971	61827
8045	S	S	E	N	1974	62277
8045	S	S	R	N	1972	62298
8045	S	S	E	N	1973	62299
8045	S	D	R	N	1966	62300
8045	S	D	E	N	1974	62301
8045	S	S	E	L	1966	66068
8045	S	S	E	N	1966	66068
8045	S	D	R	N	1972	76534
8045	S	D	E	L	1974	80630
8045	S	D	E	N	1974	80630
8045	S	T	E	L	1974	80630
8045	S	T	E	N	1974	80630
8045	S	S	E	N	1972	87891
8045	S	D	E	N	1974	87918
8045	S	D	E	N	1972	91537
8045	S	D	G	N	1975	91993
8045	S	S	E	N	1967	97985
8045	S	D	E	N	1975	98084
8045	S	E	E	N	1975	98084
8045	S	D	E	N	1968	98762
8049	S	S	E	N	1967	97985
8052	S	S	E	N	1967	97985
8053	S	D	R	N	1966	76422
8053	S	D	E	N	1966	91741
8055	S	D	R	N	1973	52566
8055	S	T	R	N	1973	52566
8055	S	D	E	N	1973	57791
8055	S	T	E	N	1973	57791
8066	L	S	E	N	1968	98632
8068	S	D	R	N	1973	52566
8068	S	T	R	N	1973	52566
8068	S	D	E	N	1973	57791
8068	S	T	E	N	1973	57791
8068	S	D	R	H	1971	76476
8068	S	D	R	L	1971	76476
8068	S	D	R	N	1971	76476
8068	S	S	R	N	1971	76476
8068	S	D	E	H	1971	91521
8068	S	D	E	L	1971	91521
8068	S	D	E	N	1971	91521
8068	S	S	E	N	1971	91521
8069	C	D	E	L	1973	52186
8069	S	D	E	N	1973	50382
8069	S	E	R	N	1973	51629
8069	S	D	E	N	1973	52186
8069	S	D	R	N	1974	67946
8069	S	D	E	N	1974	67947
8069	S	S	E	N	1967	97985
8069	T	D	E	N	1973	50382
8079	L	S	E	N	1968	98632
8081	S	D	R	N	1973	52566
8081	S	T	R	N	1973	52566
8081	S	D	E	N	1973	57791

Substance Number	Phys. State	Subject	Language	Temperature	Year	EPIC Number
104-8081	S	T	E	N	1973	57791
8083	C	S	E	L	1966	87721
8083	C	S	E	L	1972	87886
8083	S	D	E	N	1964	72756
8083	S	E	E	N	1964	72756
8083	S	S	E	N	1964	72756
8083	S	S	E	N	1966	87721
8083	S	S	E	N	1972	87886
8088	L	S	E	N	1968	98632
8090	S	D	E	N	1964	72756
8090	S	E	E	N	1964	72756
8090	S	S	E	N	1964	72756
8090	S	D	R	H	1971	76493
8090	S	D	R	N	1971	76493
8090	S	D	E	H	1971	91577
8090	S	D	E	N	1971	91577
8095	S	S	E	H	1967	97985
8096	S	S	E	N	1967	97985
8099	S	D	R	H	1972	51232
8099	S	D	R	N	1972	51232
8099	S	D	R	N	1972	51265
8099	S	D	E	N	1972	51266
8099	S	S	F	N	1969	65459
8099	S	S	E	H	1962	65974
8099	S	S	E	N	1962	65974
8099	S	D	E	H	1964	72756
8099	S	D	E	N	1964	72756
8099	S	E	E	H	1964	72756
8099	S	E	E	N	1964	72756
8099	S	S	E	N	1964	72756
8099	S	D	R	H	1971	76493
8099	S	D	R	N	1971	76493
8099	S	S	E	N	1966	87803
8099	S	D	E	H	1971	91577
8099	S	D	E	N	1971	91577
8099	S	S	E	H	1967	97985
8099	S	S	E	N	1967	97985
8105	S	D	R	N	1972	51265
8105	S	D	E	N	1972	51266
8106	D	D	R	N	1972	56015
8106	S	D	E	N	1973	49520
8108	D	D	R	N	1972	52222
8108	D	D	R	N	1973	54907
8108	D	D	O	N	1971	59997
8108	D	D	R	N	1972	62298
8108	D	D	E	N	1973	62299
8108	D	S	E	N	1966	66068
8108	D	D	E	N	1968	98762
8108	S	D	R	N	1972	49727
8108	S	D	R	N	1973	54907
8108	S	S	E	N	1972	56769
8108	S	D	R	N	1971	58992
8108	S	D	E	N	1972	59135
8108	S	T	E	N	1972	59135
8108	S	D	E	N	1971	59999
8108	S	E	E	N	1971	59999
8108	S	S	R	N	1972	62298
8108	S	S	E	N	1973	62299
8108	S	S	E	L	1966	66068
8108	S	S	E	N	1966	66068
8108	S	D	O	N	1970	86322
8108	S	D	E	N	1973	86323
8108	S	D	E	N	1974	90003
8108	S	S	E	N	1967	97985
8108	S	D	E	N	1968	98762
8108	T	D	R	N	1974	87931
8108	T	D	R	N	1974	89245
8108	T	D	E	N	1974	89246
8108	T	D	R	N	1975	93405
8108	T	D	E	N	1975	93406
8109	D	D	O	N	1971	59997
8109	S	D	R	N	1972	49727
8109	S	D	R	N	1973	52541
8109	S	D	E	N	1974	53676
8109	S	S	E	N	1972	56769
8109	S	D	E	N	1972	59135
8109	S	T	E	N	1972	59135
8109	S	D	R	N	1971	60192
8109	S	S	R	N	1972	62298
8109	S	S	E	N	1973	62299
8109	S	T	R	N	1972	85970
8109	S	D	O	N	1970	86322
8109	S	D	E	N	1973	86323
8109	S	S	E	N	1967	97985
8109	T	D	R	N	1973	52541
8109	T	D	E	N	1974	53676
8109	T	T	R	N	1973	62861
8109	T	T	E	N	1973	65168
8109	T	D	R	L	1975	101557
8109	T	D	R	N	1975	101557
8109	T	D	E	L	1975	101558
8109	T	D	E	N	1975	101558
8110	S	D	R	N	1974	58082
8110	S	D	E	N	1974	58083
8110	S	S	E	N	1970	87822
8110	S	S	E	N	1972	87890
8114	S	D	O	N	1972	49812
8114	S	D	R	N	1972	51265
8114	S	D	E	N	1972	51266
8115	S	D	O	N	1972	49812
8115	S	D	R	N	1972	51265

Phys. State: **A.** Amorphous; **C.** Superconductive; **D.** Doped; **F.** Fibrous or Whisker; **G.** Gas; **I.** Ionized or Plasma; **L.** Liquid; **P.** Powder or Particle; **S.** Solid; **T.** Thin Film
Subject: **D.** Data; **E.** Experiment; **S.** Survey (Review, Compendium, etc.); **T.** Theory
Language: **E.** English; **F.** French; **G.** German; **O.** Other Languages; **R.** Russian
Temperature: **L.** Low (0 to 75K); **N.** Normal (75 to 1273K); **H.** High (above 1273K)

Substance Number	Phys. State	Subject	Language	Temperature	Year	EPIC Number
104-8115	S	D	E	N	1972	51266
8115	S	D	R	N	1971	76493
8115	S	D	E	N	1971	91577
8116	S	D	E	N	1974	57750
8117	S	D	E	N	1973	50023
8136	D	D	F	N	1974	55973
8136	S	D	F	N	1973	50942
8136	S	D	F	N	1974	55973
8136	S	T	F	N	1973	57939
8136	S	S	E	N	1967	97985
8137	C	D	E	L	1973	52186
8137	S	D	E	N	1973	52186
8137	S	S	E	N	1967	97985
8139	S	D	F	N	1973	50942
8139	S	T	F	N	1973	57939
8139	S	S	E	N	1967	97985
8146	S	S	E	N	1967	97985
8156	S	D	R	H	1972	51232
8156	S	D	R	N	1972	51232
8156	S	D	R	N	1972	51265
8156	S	D	E	N	1972	51266
8156	S	D	E	H	1964	72756
8156	S	D	E	N	1964	72756
8156	S	E	E	H	1964	72756
8156	S	E	E	N	1964	72756
8156	S	S	E	N	1964	72756
8156	S	D	R	H	1971	76493
8156	S	D	R	N	1971	76493
8156	S	S	E	N	1966	87803
8156	S	D	E	H	1971	91577
8156	S	D	E	N	1971	91577
8156	S	S	E	H	1967	97985
8156	S	S	E	N	1967	97985
8156	T	D	E	N	1961	65971
8157	S	D	R	H	1972	51232
8157	S	D	R	N	1972	51232
8157	S	D	E	N	1964	72756
8157	S	E	E	N	1964	72756
8157	S	S	E	N	1964	72756
8157	S	S	E	H	1967	97985
8157	S	S	E	N	1967	97985
8158	D	D	E	N	1974	58551
8158	S	D	R	L	1972	51237
8158	S	S	E	L	1972	54886
8158	S	S	E	N	1972	54886
8158	S	D	E	N	1974	58551
8158	S	S	E	N	1967	97985
8159	S	D	R	N	1972	51237
8159	S	D	R	N	1972	51265
8159	S	D	E	N	1972	51266
8159	S	S	F	N	1969	65459
8159	S	D	R	N	1966	76422
8159	S	D	R	H	1971	76493
8159	S	D	R	N	1971	76493
8159	S	S	E	N	1966	87803
8159	S	D	E	H	1971	91577
8159	S	D	E	N	1971	91577
8159	S	D	E	N	1966	91741
8172	S	D	E	N	1973	51635
8176	S	D	E	N	1973	52048
8183	C	S	E	L	1973	56765
8183	S	D	E	N	1972	52993
8183	S	D	E	N	1972	53400
8183	S	S	E	N	1973	56765
8183	S	D	E	L	1974	67506
8183	S	D	E	N	1974	67506
8184	S	D	E	N	1972	52993
8189	D	D	R	N	1971	67039
8189	S	D	R	N	1971	67726
8194	S	S	E	N	1972	56769
8194	S	D	R	N	1971	60192
8194	S	S	R	N	1972	62298
8194	S	S	E	N	1973	62299
8194	S	D	E	N	1972	68995
8199	S	D	E	N	1973	51900
8199	T	D	E	N	1973	51900
8204	D	S	E	N	1967	97983
8204	S	D	E	L	1973	50754
8204	S	D	E	N	1973	50754
8205	C	D	R	L	1973	51273
8206	C	D	R	L	1973	51273
8207	C	D	R	L	1973	51273
8207	S	S	E	H	1966	87721
8207	S	S	E	N	1966	87721
8207	S	D	E	N	1964	93286
8208	C	D	R	L	1973	51273
8208	S	D	E	H	1964	93286
8208	S	D	E	N	1964	93286
8209	C	D	R	L	1973	51273
8209	S	D	E	H	1964	93286
8209	S	D	E	N	1964	93286
8210	C	D	R	L	1973	51273
8211	C	D	R	L	1973	51273
8212	C	D	R	L	1973	51273
8214	D	D	R	N	1973	53673
8214	D	D	E	N	1974	53674
8214	S	D	R	N	1973	53673
8214	S	D	E	N	1974	53674
8214	S	D	R	N	1971	59648
8214	S	D	E	N	1971	59649
8214	S	D	R	N	1971	76497
104-8214	S	T	R	N	1971	76497
8214	S	D	E	N	1971	91542
8214	S	T	E	N	1971	91542
8217	A	D	E	N	1971	60140
8217	S	D	E	N	1971	60140
8217	T	D	E	N	1971	60140
8218	A	D	R	N	1971	60139
8218	S	D	R	N	1971	60139
8218	S	D	R	N	1970	61240
8218	T	D	R	N	1971	60139
8219	A	D	R	N	1971	60139
8219	A	D	E	N	1971	60140
8219	S	D	R	N	1971	60139
8219	S	D	E	N	1971	60140
8219	S	D	R	N	1970	61240
8219	T	D	R	N	1971	60139
8219	T	D	E	N	1971	60140
8220	A	D	R	N	1971	60139
8220	A	D	E	N	1971	60140
8220	S	D	R	N	1971	60139
8220	S	D	E	N	1971	60140
8220	S	D	R	N	1970	61240
8220	T	D	R	N	1971	60139
8220	T	D	E	N	1971	60140
8224	S	D	R	L	1971	54264
8224	S	D	E	L	1972	54265
8224	S	D	O	N	1974	58922
8224	S	S	O	N	1974	58922
8224	S	D	R	N	1972	94907
8224	S	D	E	N	1973	95897
8230	C	S	E	L	1966	87721
8230	C	S	E	L	1972	87886
8230	S	S	E	N	1966	87721
8230	S	S	E	L	1972	87886
8230	S	S	E	N	1972	87886
8237	D	S	E	N	1967	97983
8239	S	S	E	N	1967	97985
8242	S	D	E	N	1973	62296
8252	C	S	E	L	1971	59607
8253	C	S	E	L	1971	59607
8254	S	D	F	N	1972	60959
8254	S	D	E	N	1971	61219
8256	L	S	E	N	1974	62782
8268	C	D	E	L	1974	61151
8268	C	S	E	L	1974	61151
8269	D	D	R	H	1971	65450
8269	D	D	R	N	1971	65450
8269	D	D	E	H	1971	65451
8269	D	D	E	N	1971	65451
8269	S	D	R	H	1971	65450
8269	S	D	R	N	1971	65450
8269	S	D	E	H	1971	65451
8269	S	D	E	N	1971	65451
8270	T	S	E	N	1975	96477
8272	S	D	R	N	1973	62447
8281	S	D	R	N	1966	76422
8281	S	D	E	N	1966	91741
8286	L	S	O	N	1972	54007
8287	L	S	O	N	1972	54007
8288	L	S	O	N	1972	54007
8289	L	S	O	N	1972	54007
8290	S	D	F	N	1973	54832
8291	S	D	F	N	1973	54832
8294	S	D	R	N	1973	55817
8294	S	D	R	N	1971	76497
8294	S	T	R	N	1971	76497
8294	S	D	E	N	1971	91542
8294	S	T	E	N	1971	91542
8294	T	D	R	N	1973	55817
8297	S	D	E	N	1973	55866
8299	S	D	E	N	1974	56084
8303	S	D	G	H	1969	86378
8303	S	D	G	N	1969	86378
8303	S	D	E	H	1972	86379
8303	S	D	E	N	1972	86379
8304	S	D	E	N	1969	85351
8306	S	D	E	N	1964	93286
8318	T	D	E	N	1973	58178
8320	L	D	E	H	1975	90018
8320	S	D	E	N	1975	90018
8323	L	D	E	N	1975	90018
8323	S	D	E	N	1975	90018
8344	C	S	E	L	1966	87721
8344	C	S	E	L	1972	87886
8354	S	D	E	N	1975	90268
8360	S	D	O	N	1974	90531
8362	C	S	E	L	1968	68372
8363	C	S	E	L	1965	87791
8366	S	S	E	N	1971	87884
8367	C	S	E	L	1971	87884
8368	C	S	E	L	1966	87721
8368	C	S	E	L	1972	87886
8371	C	S	E	L	1966	87721
8372	S	S	E	N	1967	97983
8373	S	S	E	N	1967	97983
8374	S	S	E	N	1967	97983
8375	D	S	E	N	1967	97983
8376	D	S	E	N	1967	97983
8377	D	S	E	N	1967	97983
8378	S	S	E	N	1967	97983
8379	S	S	E	N	1967	97983
104-8380	S	S	E	N	1967	97983
8381	S	S	E	N	1967	97983
8382	S	S	E	N	1967	97983
8383	S	S	E	N	1967	97983
8384	D	S	E	N	1967	97983
8385	S	S	E	N	1967	97983
8386	D	S	E	N	1967	97983
8387	S	S	E	N	1967	97983
8388	S	S	E	N	1967	97983
8389	S	S	E	N	1967	97984
8390	S	S	E	H	1967	97985
8390	S	S	E	N	1967	97985
8391	S	S	E	N	1967	97985
8392	S	S	E	N	1967	97985
8393	S	S	E	N	1967	97985
8394	S	S	E	N	1967	97985
8395	S	S	E	L	1967	97985
8395	S	S	E	N	1967	97985
8396	S	S	E	N	1967	97985
8397	S	S	E	N	1967	97985
8398	S	S	E	N	1955	98902
8406	S	D	R	N	1966	76422
8406	S	D	E	N	1966	91741
8407	S	D	R	N	1966	76422
8407	S	D	E	N	1966	91741
8418	S	D	R	N	1971	76486
8418	S	D	E	N	1971	91505
8419	S	D	R	N	1971	76486
8419	S	D	E	N	1971	91505
8420	S	D	R	H	1971	76476
8420	S	D	R	L	1971	76476
8420	S	D	R	N	1971	76476
8420	S	D	E	H	1971	91521
8420	S	D	E	L	1971	91521
8420	S	D	E	N	1971	91521
8424	S	D	E	N	1975	87287
8430	S	D	E	N	1975	93162
8431	C	D	E	L	1976	100720
8431	C	E	E	L	1976	100720
8433	S	S	E	H	1962	65974
8433	S	S	E	N	1962	65974
8437	S	D	R	N	1971	76503
8437	S	T	R	N	1971	76503
8437	S	D	E	N	1971	91564
8437	S	T	E	N	1971	91564
8438	S	S	E	N	1974	65212
8439	S	D	E	N	1974	65212
8439	S	T	E	N	1974	65212
8441	S	D	E	N	1974	65212
8441	S	T	E	N	1974	65212
8446	S	D	E	N	1976	102175
8448	S	D	E	N	1972	49784
8449	S	D	E	N	1972	49784
8450	S	D	E	N	1972	49784
8451	S	D	E	N	1972	49784
8452	S	D	E	N	1972	49784
8453	S	D	E	N	1972	49784
8454	S	D	E	N	1972	49784
8455	S	D	E	N	1972	49784
8456	S	D	E	N	1974	57750
8457	S	D	E	N	1974	57750
8458	S	D	E	N	1974	57750
106-0002	L	S	E	N	1970	59588
0003	I	D	E	H	1971	93277
0004	L	D	R	H	1970	61774
0004	S	D	E	N	1974	53627
0004	S	D	F	H	1974	55972
0004	S	D	R	N	1974	66728
0004	S	D	E	N	1975	66729
0004	S	D	R	H	1974	66744
0004	S	D	R	N	1974	66744
0004	S	T	R	H	1974	66744
0004	S	T	R	N	1974	66744
0004	S	D	E	H	1975	66745
0004	S	D	E	N	1975	66745
0004	S	T	E	H	1975	66745
0004	S	T	E	N	1975	66745
0004	S	S	E	N	1969	68271
0004	S	S	E	N	1966	87846
0004	S	S	E	N	1975	96477
0004	S	S	E	N	1967	97982
0004	S	S	E	H	1967	98889
0004	S	S	E	N	1967	98889
0006	D	D	R	N	1973	50361
0006	D	D	E	N	1973	50362
0006	D	D	E	N	1973	51581
0006	D	D	E	N	1973	52064
0006	D	D	R	N	1973	52866
0006	D	D	E	N	1973	52867
0006	D	D	R	N	1973	55221
0006	D	T	R	N	1973	56574
0006	D	D	R	N	1973	57354
0006	D	D	R	N	1974	60487
0006	D	D	E	N	1974	60488
0006	D	D	R	N	1970	66138
0006	D	D	R	N	1971	66296
0006	D	D	E	N	1971	66297
0006	D	D	O	N	1970	83843
0006	F	D	R	N	1973	56306
0006	L	D	E	N	1972	49474

Phys. State: **A.** Amorphous; **C.** Superconductive; **D.** Doped; **F.** Fibrous or Whisker; **G.** Gas; **I.** Ionized or Plasma; **L.** Liquid; **P.** Powder or Particle; **S.** Solid; **T.** Thin Film
Subject: **D.** Data; **E.** Experiment; **S.** Survey (Review, Compendium, etc.); **T.** Theory
Language: **E.** English; **F.** French; **G.** German; **O.** Other Languages; **R.** Russian
Temperature: **L.** Low (0 to 75K); **N.** Normal (75 to 1273K); **H.** High (above 1273K)

Substance Number	Phys. State	Sub-ject	Lan-guage	Temper-ature	Year	EPIC Number
106-0006	L	D	R	N	1973	54917
0006	L	D	R	N	1973	58164
0006	L	D	R	N	1971	66296
0006	L	D	E	N	1971	66297
0006	L	S	E	N	1974	85293
0006	L	D	E	N	1975	90985
0006	L	T	E	N	1975	90985
0006	L	D	E	N	1975	91295
0006	L	S	E	N	1975	91295
0006	L	S	E	N	1968	98632
0006	S	D	R	N	1973	50361
0006	S	D	E	N	1973	50362
0006	S	D	E	N	1973	51581
0006	S	D	E	N	1973	52064
0006	S	D	R	N	1973	52866
0006	S	D	E	N	1973	52867
0006	S	D	R	N	1973	57354
0006	S	T	E	N	1973	57614
0006	S	D	E	N	1972	58980
0006	S	D	R	N	1974	60487
0006	S	D	E	N	1974	60488
0006	S	D	G	N	1972	61011
0006	S	D	R	N	1974	62004
0006	S	T	R	N	1974	62004
0006	S	D	E	N	1974	62005
0006	S	T	E	N	1974	62005
0006	S	S	E	N	1965	75847
0006	S	D	O	N	1970	83843
0006	S	D	R	N	1974	93419
0006	S	S	R	N	1974	93419
0006	S	T	R	N	1974	93419
0006	S	D	E	N	1975	93420
0006	S	S	E	N	1975	93420
0006	S	T	E	N	1975	93420
0009	L	S	E	N	1967	98664
0009	L	S	E	N	1966	101379
0018	L	S	E	N	1968	98632
0023	C	S	E	L	1936	67892
0024	C	S	E	L	1972	62375
0024	D	D	E	N	1972	49545
0024	D	D	E	N	1973	50032
0024	D	D	E	N	1973	50709
0024	D	D	E	N	1973	51799
0024	D	D	E	N	1973	52064
0024	D	D	R	N	1973	56008
0024	D	T	R	N	1973	56008
0024	D	D	E	N	1974	63234
0024	D	T	E	N	1974	63234
0024	D	D	R	N	1970	66138
0024	D	D	E	N	1975	91874
0024	D	T	E	N	1975	91874
0024	D	D	E	N	1975	96659
0024	F	D	R	N	1973	56306
0024	L	D	E	N	1972	49474
0024	L	D	G	N	1973	50014
0024	L	D	R	N	1973	51347
0024	L	D	R	N	1973	54917
0024	L	D	E	N	1973	55345
0024	L	D	R	N	1973	58164
0024	L	D	E	N	1975	91295
0024	L	S	E	N	1975	91295
0024	L	S	E	H	1968	98632
0024	L	S	E	N	1968	98632
0024	S	D	E	N	1973	50709
0024	S	D	E	N	1973	52064
0024	S	D	E	N	1973	54820
0024	S	D	R	N	1973	56008
0024	S	T	R	N	1973	56008
0024	S	S	E	N	1973	56749
0024	S	S	E	N	1973	56765
0024	S	D	G	N	1972	61011
0024	S	D	E	N	1974	63234
0024	S	T	E	N	1974	63234
0024	S	D	E	N	1975	96659
0026	D	D	R	N	1969	67326
0026	L	D	R	N	1971	56148
0026	S	D	F	N	1972	53541
0026	S	T	F	N	1972	53541
0026	S	S	E	H	1974	55267
0026	S	S	E	N	1974	55267
0026	S	D	R	N	1973	56322
0026	S	D	R	N	1970	56913
0026	S	S	E	N	1976	103180
0031	A	S	E	N	1975	95324
0031	D	S	E	H	1967	97982
0031	S	S	E	H	1967	97982
0031	S	S	E	N	1967	97982
0031	S	S	E	H	1967	98889
0031	S	S	E	N	1967	98889
0031	T	D	E	N	1961	65971
0035	A	S	E	N	1971	60960
0035	A	D	E	N	1974	67205
0035	A	S	E	L	1975	95324
0035	D	S	E	L	1965	87702
0035	D	S	E	N	1965	87702
0035	D	S	E	N	1968	87828
0035	S	D	R	H	1973	50187
0035	S	D	R	N	1973	50187
0035	S	D	E	H	1973	50188
0035	S	D	E	N	1973	50188
0035	S	D	R	N	1973	51523
106-0035	S	D	R	N	1973	51618
0035	S	D	R	L	1972	54938
0035	S	D	R	N	1972	54938
0035	S	D	R	N	1972	63478
0035	S	D	R	N	1974	64485
0035	S	T	R	N	1974	64485
0035	S	D	E	N	1972	65927
0035	S	D	R	N	1974	66572
0035	S	D	E	N	1974	66573
0035	S	S	E	H	1965	87702
0035	S	S	E	L	1965	87702
0035	S	S	E	N	1965	87702
0035	S	S	E	N	1966	87803
0035	S	S	E	N	1968	87828
0035	S	S	E	N	1971	87887
0035	S	D	R	N	1964	91888
0035	S	S	E	H	1967	97984
0035	S	S	E	N	1967	97984
0035	S	S	E	H	1955	98912
0035	S	S	E	N	1955	98912
0035	T	D	F	N	1973	54648
0035	T	D	R	N	1973	58531
0035	T	S	E	N	1971	60960
0035	T	D	E	N	1974	66690
0035	T	D	E	N	1974	67205
0035	T	S	E	N	1968	87828
0035	T	T	E	N	1974	90647
0036	L	D	R	N	1973	55758
0036	L	D	E	N	1973	57781
0036	L	D	E	N	1973	60580
0036	S	D	R	N	1973	55802
0036	S	D	E	N	1973	57727
0036	T	D	R	N	1972	49937
0045	D	D	E	N	1973	52631
0045	L	D	E	N	1973	65637
0045	S	D	E	N	1973	52631
0047	L	S	E	N	1968	98632
0050	L	D	E	N	1973	51744
0050	L	E	E	N	1973	51744
0050	L	S	E	H	1968	98632
0050	L	S	E	N	1968	98632
0057	P	S	E	N	1966	68325
0057	S	S	E	N	1969	68271
0057	S	S	E	N	1966	68325
0057	T	S	E	N	1966	68325
0057	T	D	E	N	1968	85433
0059	D	D	E	N	1973	57633
0059	S	D	E	N	1973	51882
0059	S	D	E	N	1973	57633
0060	L	D	O	N	1973	56236
0060	L	S	E	N	1968	98632
0060	S	D	E	N	1963	60560
0061	L	D	E	N	1973	51744
0061	L	E	E	N	1973	51744
0061	L	S	E	N	1968	98632
0062	S	D	R	N	1972	51265
0062	S	D	E	N	1972	51266
0062	S	D	R	N	1973	70259
0062	S	D	R	N	1971	76493
0062	S	D	E	N	1971	91577
0062	S	D	E	N	1973	93221
0064	L	S	E	N	1968	98632
0068	S	D	E	N	1974	53752
0068	S	E	E	N	1974	53752
0068	S	T	E	N	1974	53752
0068	S	T	R	N	1973	68020
0068	S	T	E	N	1973	68021
0077	S	T	R	N	1973	52377
0077	S	T	E	N	1973	57490
0081	D	D	E	N	1964	60562
0081	D	T	R	H	1974	80753
0081	D	T	R	N	1974	80753
0081	D	T	E	H	1974	95260
0081	D	T	E	N	1974	95260
0081	S	D	E	H	1971	49788
0081	S	D	E	N	1973	51787
0081	S	S	E	H	1974	54022
0081	S	D	R	N	1973	55772
0081	S	D	E	N	1964	60562
0081	S	D	E	N	1974	68956
0081	S	D	E	N	1975	80965
0081	S	S	E	H	1975	80965
0081	S	S	E	N	1975	80965
0081	S	S	E	N	1967	98889
0095	D	T	R	H	1974	80753
0095	D	T	R	N	1974	80753
0095	D	T	E	H	1974	95260
0095	D	T	E	N	1974	95260
0100	S	T	R	N	1973	52377
0100	S	T	E	N	1973	57490
0104	D	D	R	N	1973	51556
0104	D	D	E	N	1973	51921
0104	D	D	E	N	1973	53687
0104	D	D	E	N	1970	61741
0104	D	T	E	N	1970	61741
0104	L	D	R	H	1973	51562
0104	L	S	R	H	1973	51562
0104	L	T	R	H	1973	51562
0104	L	D	R	H	1970	53296
0104	L	D	E	H	1972	53297
0104	L	D	E	H	1974	53693
106-0104	L	S	E	H	1974	53693
0104	L	T	E	H	1974	53693
0104	L	S	E	H	1971	87872
0104	L	D	R	H	1975	91346
0104	L	S	E	H	1968	98632
0104	L	D	E	H	1914	100892
0104	L	D	G	H	1914	100892
0104	S	D	R	N	1973	51556
0104	S	D	R	H	1973	51562
0104	S	T	R	H	1973	51562
0104	S	D	E	N	1973	51921
0104	S	D	R	H	1970	53296
0104	S	D	R	N	1970	53296
0104	S	D	E	H	1972	53297
0104	S	D	E	N	1972	53297
0104	S	D	E	N	1973	53687
0104	S	D	E	H	1974	53693
0104	S	T	E	H	1974	53693
0104	S	D	R	N	1972	59068
0104	S	D	E	N	1972	59069
0104	S	D	F	N	1970	59704
0104	S	E	E	N	1952	65344
0104	S	T	E	N	1952	65344
0104	S	S	E	H	1971	87872
0104	S	S	E	N	1971	87872
0104	T	D	E	N	1970	61741
0125	C	S	E	L	1964	93287
0125	S	D	E	N	1973	50707
0125	S	D	R	N	1972	51265
0125	S	D	E	N	1972	51266
0125	S	S	F	H	1969	65459
0125	S	S	E	H	1962	65974
0125	S	S	E	N	1962	65974
0125	S	D	R	H	1969	78213
0125	S	D	R	N	1969	78213
0125	S	S	R	H	1969	78213
0125	S	S	R	N	1969	78213
0125	S	T	R	H	1969	78213
0125	S	T	R	N	1969	78213
0125	S	S	E	N	1966	87803
0125	S	D	E	N	1964	93287
0125	S	S	E	N	1964	93287
0125	S	S	E	H	1967	97984
0125	S	S	E	N	1967	97984
0125	T	D	F	N	1973	54648
0125	T	D	R	N	1973	57030
0125	T	D	R	N	1973	58183
0126	L	S	E	N	1968	98632
0127	S	D	R	N	1973	50082
0127	S	D	R	N	1972	50693
0127	S	D	E	N	1973	51428
0127	S	S	E	N	1973	56765
0127	S	D	R	N	1974	60469
0127	S	D	E	N	1974	60470
0127	S	D	E	N	1975	63342
0127	S	S	E	N	1966	87846
0129	L	S	E	N	1964	65932
0131	L	S	E	N	1968	98632
0141	L	S	E	N	1968	98632
0152	S	S	E	N	1973	52315
0156	D	D	E	N	1973	52127
0157	L	S	E	N	1968	98632
0158	L	D	R	N	1973	55758
0158	L	D	E	N	1973	57781
0158	L	S	E	H	1968	98632
0158	L	S	E	N	1968	98632
0158	S	D	E	N	1973	57727
0158	S	S	E	N	1970	87822
0158	S	S	E	N	1972	87890
0159	L	D	E	N	1972	49474
0159	L	D	R	N	1969	52400
0159	L	D	E	N	1973	52401
0159	L	D	R	N	1973	54917
0159	L	D	R	N	1973	58164
0159	L	S	E	N	1968	98632
0160	L	S	E	N	1968	98632
0165	D	D	E	N	1973	56168
0165	D	D	E	N	1974	57141
0165	D	D	E	N	1974	65109
0165	L	D	E	N	1972	49474
0165	L	D	R	N	1973	54917
0165	L	D	E	N	1975	91295
0165	L	S	E	N	1975	91295
0165	L	S	E	N	1968	98632
0165	S	D	E	N	1974	65109
0168	S	S	E	N	1966	101407
0180	L	D	O	N	1973	56236
0180	L	D	F	N	1971	61324
0180	L	S	E	N	1968	98632
0183	L	S	E	N	1967	98664
0183	S	S	E	N	1973	52315
0192	D	D	E	H	1973	51747
0192	D	D	E	N	1973	51747
0192	D	D	E	H	1972	55088
0192	D	D	E	N	1972	55088
0192	D	T	E	H	1972	55088
0192	D	T	E	N	1972	55088
0192	P	S	E	N	1967	97982
0192	S	T	F	N	1974	67731
0192	S	S	E	H	1967	97982
0192	S	S	E	N	1967	97982

Phys. State: **A.** Amorphous; **C.** Superconductive; **D.** Doped; **F.** Fibrous or Whisker; **G.** Gas; **I.** Ionized or Plasma; **L.** Liquid; **P.** Powder or Particle; **S.** Solid; **T.** Thin Film
Subject: **D.** Data; **E.** Experiment; **S.** Survey (Review, Compendium, etc.); **T.** Theory
Language: **E.** English; **F.** French; **G.** German; **O.** Other Languages; **R.** Russian
Temperature: **L.** Low (0 to 75K); **N.** Normal (75 to 1273K); **H.** High (above 1273K)

Substance Number	Phys. State	Subject	Language	Temperature	Year	EPIC Number
106-0192	S	S	E	H	1967	98889
0192	S	S	E	N	1967	98889
0192	T	D	E	N	1961	65971
0203	D	D	E	N	1974	65109
0203	L	D	E	N	1972	49474
0203	L	S	E	N	1975	72449
0203	L	S	E	N	1968	98632
0203	S	D	E	N	1974	65109
0204	L	D	E	H	1975	90985
0204	L	D	E	N	1975	90985
0204	L	S	E	H	1975	90985
0204	L	S	E	N	1975	90985
0204	L	T	E	H	1975	90985
0204	L	T	E	N	1975	90985
0204	L	S	E	N	1968	98632
0205	C	S	E	L	1974	53921
0205	C	T	E	L	1972	54238
0205	C	D	E	L	1974	59384
0205	C	S	E	L	1974	59384
0205	C	S	E	L	1964	93287
0205	S	D	R	N	1972	51265
0205	S	D	E	N	1972	51266
0205	S	D	R	N	1971	76493
0205	S	D	R	H	1969	78213
0205	S	D	R	N	1969	78213
0205	S	S	R	H	1969	78213
0205	S	S	R	N	1969	78213
0205	S	T	R	H	1969	78213
0205	S	T	R	N	1969	78213
0205	S	S	E	N	1966	87803
0205	S	D	E	N	1971	91577
0205	S	D	E	N	1964	93287
0205	S	S	E	N	1964	93287
0205	S	S	E	H	1967	97984
0205	S	S	E	N	1967	97984
0205	T	D	F	N	1973	54648
0205	T	D	E	N	1961	65971
0218	D	D	R	N	1972	51267
0218	S	D	R	N	1972	51267
0218	S	S	E	N	1967	97983
0218	S	S	E	H	1976	103180
0218	S	S	E	N	1976	103180
0226	C	S	E	L	1964	93287
0226	S	S	E	N	1966	87803
0226	S	D	E	N	1964	93287
0226	S	S	E	N	1964	93287
0226	S	S	E	H	1967	97984
0226	S	S	E	N	1967	97984
0227	L	S	E	N	1968	98632
0234	L	D	E	H	1975	90985
0234	L	D	E	N	1975	90985
0234	L	S	E	H	1975	90985
0234	L	S	E	N	1975	90985
0234	L	T	E	H	1975	90985
0234	L	T	E	N	1975	90985
0234	L	S	E	H	1968	98632
0234	L	S	E	N	1968	98632
0234	S	D	E	N	1973	50155
0237	L	D	R	H	1972	52242
0237	L	S	E	N	1968	98632
0238	D	D	E	N	1973	52064
0238	L	D	E	N	1972	49474
0238	L	S	E	N	1968	98632
0238	S	D	E	N	1973	52064
0239	L	S	E	N	1968	98632
0251	L	S	E	N	1968	98632
0252	L	S	E	N	1968	98632
0259	L	S	E	N	1968	98632
0268	L	D	O	N	1972	67586
0268	L	S	E	N	1968	98632
0298	L	S	E	N	1968	98632
0303	L	S	E	N	1968	98632
0308	C	T	E	L	1972	54238
0308	C	T	E	L	1974	88049
0308	C	S	E	L	1964	93287
0308	F	D	R	N	1972	56477
0308	S	D	E	N	1973	50707
0308	S	D	R	N	1972	51265
0308	S	D	E	N	1972	51266
0308	S	D	E	N	1969	72727
0308	S	D	R	N	1971	76493
0308	S	S	E	N	1966	87803
0308	S	D	E	N	1971	91577
0308	S	D	R	H	1966	93279
0308	S	D	R	N	1966	93279
0308	S	D	E	N	1964	93287
0308	S	S	E	N	1964	93287
0308	S	S	E	H	1967	97984
0308	S	S	E	N	1967	97984
0308	S	S	E	N	1955	98662
0308	T	D	F	N	1973	54648
0308	T	D	R	N	1973	57030
0308	T	D	R	N	1973	58183
0308	T	D	E	N	1961	65971
0309	C	T	E	L	1972	54238
0309	C	D	E	L	1974	59384
0309	C	S	E	L	1974	59384
0309	C	S	E	L	1966	87721
0309	C	S	E	L	1972	87886
0309	C	T	E	L	1974	88049
0309	C	S	E	L	1964	93287
106-0309	P	S	E	N	1966	87721
0309	S	D	R	L	1973	50743
0309	S	D	R	N	1972	51265
0309	S	D	E	N	1972	51266
0309	S	S	F	N	1969	65459
0309	S	D	R	N	1973	70259
0309	S	D	E	L	1973	79073
0309	S	S	E	N	1966	87721
0309	S	S	E	L	1972	87886
0309	S	S	E	N	1972	87886
0309	S	D	E	N	1973	93221
0309	S	D	R	H	1966	93279
0309	S	D	R	N	1966	93279
0309	S	D	E	N	1964	93287
0309	S	S	E	N	1964	93287
0309	S	S	E	H	1967	97984
0309	S	S	E	N	1967	97984
0309	T	D	F	N	1973	54648
0309	T	D	R	N	1973	57030
0309	T	D	R	N	1973	58183
0310	S	D	R	N	1972	51265
0310	S	D	E	N	1972	51266
0310	S	S	F	N	1969	65459
0310	S	D	R	N	1971	76493
0310	S	D	E	N	1971	91577
0310	S	S	E	H	1967	97984
0310	S	S	E	N	1967	97984
0328	L	S	E	N	1968	98632
0328	S	S	E	L	1970	75833
0328	S	S	E	N	1970	75833
0337	L	S	E	H	1968	98632
0337	L	S	E	N	1968	98632
0345	L	S	E	N	1968	98632
0354	L	S	E	N	1968	98632
0363	D	D	R	N	1973	50090
0363	D	D	R	N	1972	52253
0363	D	D	E	N	1973	52656
0363	D	D	E	N	1972	53177
0363	D	D	E	N	1971	53243
0363	D	T	E	N	1973	55163
0363	D	D	O	N	1972	59839
0363	D	T	O	N	1972	59839
0363	D	D	E	N	1972	60922
0363	D	S	E	N	1963	64232
0363	D	S	E	N	1967	66156
0363	D	D	E	N	1972	70404
0363	D	D	E	N	1971	76193
0363	D	T	E	N	1971	76193
0363	D	D	R	N	1971	77301
0363	D	T	R	N	1971	77301
0363	D	D	E	N	1957	89723
0363	D	D	E	N	1962	89789
0363	D	D	R	N	1972	90411
0363	D	D	O	N	1974	90631
0363	D	S	E	N	1967	97984
0363	P	S	E	N	1967	66156
0363	P	D	O	N	1975	90376
0363	P	E	O	N	1975	90376
0363	S	D	E	N	1972	49934
0363	S	T	R	N	1973	50102
0363	S	D	R	N	1972	51099
0363	S	D	R	N	1973	51271
0363	S	D	E	N	1973	51874
0363	S	D	E	N	1973	51922
0363	S	D	R	H	1972	52252
0363	S	D	R	N	1972	52252
0363	S	D	R	N	1972	52253
0363	S	D	E	N	1973	52776
0363	S	D	E	N	1973	53320
0363	S	D	R	N	1973	55058
0363	S	D	E	N	1974	55059
0363	S	D	R	N	1971	56217
0363	S	D	O	N	1973	57346
0363	S	D	R	N	1973	57825
0363	S	D	E	N	1974	57826
0363	S	D	R	N	1974	58090
0363	S	D	E	N	1974	58091
0363	S	T	R	N	1974	60415
0363	S	T	E	N	1974	60416
0363	S	D	R	N	1972	60703
0363	S	D	E	L	1973	60704
0363	S	D	E	N	1972	60922
0363	S	D	E	N	1971	61760
0363	S	D	E	N	1971	61763
0363	S	D	E	N	1971	62312
0363	S	D	E	N	1973	62480
0363	S	S	E	L	1963	64232
0363	S	S	E	N	1963	64232
0363	S	D	E	N	1974	64986
0363	S	S	E	L	1967	66156
0363	S	S	E	N	1967	66156
0363	S	D	R	N	1973	67387
0363	S	S	E	N	1969	68271
0363	S	S	E	N	1972	87823
0363	S	D	E	N	1974	88174
0363	S	T	E	N	1975	88215
0363	S	D	R	N	1972	90411
0363	S	D	E	N	1975	90511
0363	S	T	E	N	1975	90653
0363	S	S	E	N	1967	97984
0363	T	D	R	N	1973	50090
106-0363	T	D	E	N	1973	50791
0363	T	D	E	N	1973	50905
0363	T	D	E	N	1972	51284
0363	T	T	R	N	1973	51555
0363	T	D	E	N	1973	51914
0363	T	T	E	N	1973	53686
0363	T	D	E	N	1974	54033
0363	T	D	R	N	1972	55386
0363	T	T	R	N	1972	55386
0363	T	D	R	N	1972	56944
0363	T	D	E	N	1973	58586
0363	T	D	R	N	1969	59075
0363	T	D	E	N	1970	59076
0363	T	D	E	N	1974	60286
0363	T	D	E	N	1972	64092
0363	T	S	E	N	1963	64232
0363	T	D	R	N	1973	65571
0363	T	D	E	N	1973	65572
0363	T	S	E	N	1967	66156
0363	T	T	R	N	1974	66754
0363	T	T	E	N	1975	66755
0363	T	D	E	N	1972	75456
0363	T	T	E	N	1972	75456
0363	T	D	E	N	1974	88174
0363	T	D	E	N	1962	89724
0363	T	D	R	N	1973	90437
0363	T	D	E	N	1974	90590
0363	T	S	E	N	1974	97255
0363	T	S	E	N	1976	97315
0363	T	D	R	N	1975	101623
0363	T	T	R	N	1975	101623
0363	T	D	E	N	1975	101624
0363	T	T	E	N	1975	101624
0384	L	S	E	N	1972	51438
0384	L	S	E	N	1968	98632
0385	D	D	E	N	1972	53238
0385	D	T	E	N	1972	53238
0385	D	S	E	N	1973	56765
0385	D	D	E	L	1969	74658
0385	D	D	E	N	1969	74658
0385	D	E	E	L	1969	74658
0385	D	E	E	N	1969	74658
0401	L	D	F	N	1973	54829
0401	L	S	E	N	1968	98632
0409	L	D	E	N	1973	51744
0409	L	E	E	N	1973	51744
0409	L	S	E	N	1968	98632
0417	D	S	E	H	1976	102007
0417	D	S	E	N	1976	102007
0417	S	S	E	N	1968	64269
0417	S	S	E	H	1967	97984
0417	S	S	E	N	1967	97984
0417	S	S	E	H	1976	102007
0417	S	S	E	N	1976	102007
0420	S	S	E	H	1967	97984
0420	S	S	E	H	1976	102007
0420	S	S	E	N	1976	102007
0452	S	S	E	N	1964	93287
0505	L	D	R	N	1971	76462
0505	L	D	E	N	1971	91582
0507	L	S	E	H	1968	98632
0507	L	S	E	N	1968	98632
0508	S	D	E	N	1974	53627
0508	S	D	E	N	1974	67654
0523	S	D	E	N	1972	53078
0523	S	S	E	N	1973	56765
0575	S	D	E	H	1973	52827
0575	S	D	E	N	1973	52827
0608	L	D	O	N	1972	67586
0608	L	S	E	N	1968	98632
0610	S	D	E	H	1973	50443
0610	S	D	E	N	1973	50443
0610	S	D	R	N	1973	67359
0612	S	S	E	H	1976	102007
0612	S	S	E	N	1976	102007
0621	L	D	O	N	1972	67586
0621	L	S	E	N	1968	98632
0626	L	D	O	N	1972	67586
0626	L	S	E	N	1968	98632
0628	L	S	E	N	1968	98632
0639	C	S	E	L	1974	53921
0639	C	T	E	L	1972	54238
0639	C	D	E	L	1974	59384
0639	C	S	E	L	1974	59384
0639	C	S	E	L	1964	93287
0639	S	D	E	N	1964	93287
0639	S	S	E	N	1964	93287
0639	S	S	E	H	1967	97984
0639	S	S	E	N	1967	97984
0639	T	D	F	N	1973	54648
0639	T	D	E	N	1961	65971
0640	S	D	R	N	1972	51265
0640	S	D	E	N	1972	51266
0640	S	S	E	H	1967	97984
0640	S	S	E	N	1967	97984
0673	S	D	E	H	1974	59354
0673	T	D	E	N	1974	89522
0674	C	D	E	L	1976	100720
0674	C	E	E	L	1976	100720
0710	C	T	E	L	1973	55125
0744	L	E	E	H	1971	62243

Phys. State: **A.** Amorphous; **C.** Superconductive; **D.** Doped; **F.** Fibrous or Whisker; **G.** Gas; **I.** Ionized or Plasma; **L.** Liquid; **P.** Powder or Particle; **S.** Solid; **T.** Thin Film
Subject: **D.** Data; **E.** Experiment; **S.** Survey (Review, Compendium, etc.); **T.** Theory
Language: **E.** English; **F.** French; **G.** German; **O.** Other Languages; **R.** Russian
Temperature: **L.** Low (0 to 75K); **N.** Normal (75 to 1273K); **H.** High (above 1273K)

Substance Number	Phys. State	Subject	Language	Temperature	Year	EPIC Number
106-0744	S	S	E	H	1967	97984
0750	S	S	E	N	1967	97984
0750	S	S	E	H	1976	102007
0750	S	S	E	N	1976	102007
0768	S	D	R	N	1973	67359
0927	S	D	E	N	1973	57431
0927	S	S	E	L	1969	75843
0927	S	S	E	N	1969	75843
0937	D	D	R	N	1971	76469
0937	D	D	E	N	1971	91495
0937	S	D	R	L	1973	50743
0937	S	D	R	H	1973	52724
0937	S	D	R	N	1973	52724
0937	S	D	E	H	1973	52725
0937	S	D	E	N	1973	52725
0937	S	D	R	N	1975	70607
0937	S	D	R	N	1970	76459
0937	S	T	R	N	1970	76459
0937	S	D	R	N	1971	76469
0937	S	D	R	N	1971	76485
0937	S	S	R	N	1971	76485
0937	S	D	E	L	1973	79073
0937	S	D	R	N	1974	86079
0937	S	D	E	N	1975	86080
0937	S	D	E	N	1971	91495
0937	S	D	E	N	1971	91504
0937	S	S	E	N	1971	91504
0937	S	D	E	N	1970	91514
0937	S	T	E	N	1970	91514
0937	S	D	E	N	1975	93225
0941	A	D	R	N	1972	58202
0941	A	T	R	N	1972	58202
0941	L	D	R	N	1972	56981
0941	L	D	R	N	1974	66574
0941	L	D	E	N	1974	66575
0941	S	D	R	N	1973	52259
0941	S	D	R	N	1972	52264
0941	S	D	E	N	1972	53335
0941	S	D	R	N	1973	54953
0941	S	D	R	N	1972	56981
0941	S	D	R	N	1974	66574
0941	S	D	E	N	1974	66575
0941	S	D	E	N	1975	94550
0956	L	D	R	N	1973	57006
0956	L	S	E	H	1968	98632
0956	S	D	R	N	1973	57006
0961	L	S	E	N	1972	51438
0961	L	S	E	N	1968	98632
1001	C	S	E	L	1966	87721
1001	S	D	E	H	1974	59354
1025	S	D	E	N	1974	56084
1027	S	D	R	L	1973	50743
1027	S	D	R	N	1973	55826
1027	S	D	R	L	1971	76491
1027	S	D	R	N	1971	76491
1027	S	D	E	L	1973	79073
1027	S	D	E	L	1971	91570
1027	S	D	E	N	1971	91570
1027	S	D	E	N	1964	93287
1027	S	S	E	N	1964	93287
1062	C	D	R	L	1972	63967
1062	C	S	R	L	1972	63967
1062	C	T	R	L	1972	63967
1062	C	D	E	L	1972	68424
1062	C	S	E	L	1972	68424
1062	C	T	E	L	1972	68424
1062	C	S	E	L	1966	87721
1062	S	D	R	N	1975	70607
1062	S	S	E	N	1966	87721
1062	S	D	E	N	1975	93225
1079	S	D	R	N	1967	53069
1079	S	D	E	N	1972	53070
1079	S	D	F	L	1973	55965
1079	S	D	F	N	1973	55965
1079	S	D	E	L	1973	57110
1079	S	D	E	N	1973	57110
1083	S	D	R	N	1973	50037
1083	S	D	E	H	1974	60532
1083	S	D	E	N	1974	60532
1083	S	D	R	H	1971	76477
1083	S	D	R	N	1971	76477
1083	S	D	E	H	1971	91523
1083	S	D	E	N	1971	91523
1084	L	D	E	N	1964	65932
1085	S	D	E	N	1973	56345
1085	S	D	E	N	1975	94550
1249	S	D	R	H	1971	76477
1249	S	D	R	N	1971	76477
1249	S	D	E	H	1971	91523
1249	S	D	E	N	1971	91523
1256	D	D	E	N	1972	49878
1256	S	D	E	N	1972	49878
1256	S	D	E	N	1973	51809
1287	S	D	E	L	1973	52754
1287	S	D	E	N	1973	52754
1287	S	D	R	N	1965	76400
1287	S	T	R	N	1965	76400
1287	S	D	E	N	1965	91743
1287	S	T	E	N	1965	91743
1287	S	D	E	N	1964	93287
1287	S	S	E	N	1964	93287

Substance Number	Phys. State	Subject	Language	Temperature	Year	EPIC Number
106-1290	S	S	E	N	1966	101407
1296	S	D	R	H	1971	76477
1296	S	D	R	N	1971	76477
1296	S	D	E	H	1971	91523
1296	S	D	E	N	1971	91523
1418	S	D	R	N	1973	57239
1430	S	D	R	N	1973	57239
1485	S	D	R	H	1971	76477
1485	S	D	E	N	1971	76477
1485	S	D	E	H	1971	91523
1485	S	D	E	N	1971	91523
1487	S	S	E	L	1969	75843
1487	S	S	E	N	1969	75843
1519	D	S	E	N	1974	53915
1519	D	D	E	N	1971	75767
1519	S	D	E	N	1974	53915
1519	S	S	E	N	1974	53915
1519	S	D	E	N	1971	75767
1519	S	S	E	N	1975	94550
1544	D	D	E	N	1974	58321
1544	D	T	E	N	1974	58321
1576	S	D	R	N	1973	70259
1576	S	D	R	N	1971	76493
1576	S	D	E	N	1971	91577
1576	S	D	E	N	1973	93221
1577	S	D	R	N	1971	76493
1577	S	D	E	N	1971	91577
1795	S	D	R	N	1971	76484
1795	S	S	R	N	1971	76484
1795	S	D	E	N	1971	91524
1795	S	S	E	N	1971	91524
1796	S	D	R	N	1971	76484
1796	S	D	E	N	1971	91524
1804	S	D	R	N	1973	70822
1804	S	T	R	N	1973	70822
1804	S	D	E	N	1973	91587
1804	S	T	E	N	1973	91587
8001	D	D	E	N	1973	53451
8001	D	D	R	N	1973	54954
8001	D	D	R	N	1972	55493
8001	D	D	R	N	1972	76511
8001	D	T	R	N	1972	76511
8001	D	D	R	N	1972	76512
8001	D	D	E	N	1972	91555
8001	D	T	E	N	1972	91555
8001	D	D	E	N	1972	91556
8001	L	D	R	N	1973	52540
8001	L	D	E	N	1974	53675
8001	L	S	G	H	1967	58994
8001	L	S	G	N	1967	58994
8001	L	D	R	N	1971	60193
8001	L	E	R	N	1971	60193
8001	L	D	E	H	1975	81640
8001	L	D	E	N	1975	81640
8001	L	S	E	N	1975	81640
8001	S	D	E	L	1973	51041
8001	S	D	R	N	1973	55288
8001	S	D	E	N	1974	59247
8001	S	D	R	N	1971	61477
8001	S	D	E	N	1974	63117
8001	S	T	E	N	1974	63117
8001	S	D	E	N	1971	65921
8001	S	D	R	N	1972	76505
8001	S	T	R	N	1972	76505
8001	S	D	R	N	1972	76511
8001	S	T	R	N	1972	76511
8001	S	D	R	N	1972	76518
8001	S	T	R	N	1972	76518
8001	S	D	E	N	1972	91528
8001	S	T	E	N	1972	91528
8001	S	D	E	N	1972	91539
8001	S	T	E	N	1972	91539
8001	S	D	E	N	1972	91555
8001	S	T	E	N	1972	91555
8001	T	S	E	N	1973	53451
8001	T	D	R	N	1972	76511
8001	T	T	R	N	1972	76511
8001	T	D	E	N	1972	91555
8001	T	T	E	N	1972	91555
8018	S	D	R	N	1966	62300
8018	S	D	E	N	1974	62301
8024	S	D	E	N	1936	61578
8025	C	S	E	L	1965	87791
8025	L	D	G	N	1957	59036
8025	L	D	G	H	1914	100892
8025	L	D	G	N	1914	100892
8033	D	D	R	N	1971	67327
8033	D	D	R	N	1975	74174
8033	D	T	R	N	1975	74174
8033	D	D	E	N	1975	91460
8033	D	T	E	N	1975	91460
8033	S	D	E	N	1972	49858
8033	S	T	E	N	1973	51884
8033	S	D	R	N	1971	67327
8033	S	D	R	N	1975	74174
8033	S	T	R	N	1975	74174
8033	S	D	E	N	1975	91460
8033	S	T	E	N	1975	91460
8040	D	D	R	N	1972	52254
8040	D	D	R	N	1972	52257
8040	D	E	E	N	1973	56566

Substance Number	Phys. State	Subject	Language	Temperature	Year	EPIC Number
106-8040	D	T	E	N	1973	56566
8040	D	D	E	N	1971	64324
8040	D	S	E	N	1963	87710
8040	S	D	R	N	1972	49816
8040	S	D	E	N	1973	50941
8040	S	E	E	N	1973	50941
8040	S	D	R	N	1973	51384
8040	S	D	E	N	1973	51385
8040	S	D	R	N	1972	52254
8040	S	D	R	N	1972	52256
8040	S	D	R	N	1972	52257
8040	S	D	R	N	1972	52267
8040	S	D	R	N	1973	52530
8040	S	D	E	N	1973	52654
8040	S	D	E	N	1973	52773
8040	S	D	R	N	1969	53223
8040	S	D	E	N	1972	53224
8040	S	D	E	N	1973	53462
8040	S	S	R	N	1972	53547
8040	S	S	E	N	1973	53548
8040	S	D	E	L	1974	53625
8040	S	D	E	N	1974	53625
8040	S	D	O	N	1973	57355
8040	S	D	R	N	1973	57356
8040	S	D	E	N	1974	57771
8040	S	D	R	L	1972	58678
8040	S	D	R	N	1972	58678
8040	S	D	E	N	1972	59904
8040	S	T	E	N	1972	59904
8040	S	D	R	N	1970	61027
8040	S	D	R	N	1974	61986
8040	S	D	E	N	1974	61987
8040	S	D	E	N	1971	62312
8040	S	D	E	N	1971	64324
8040	S	S	E	H	1969	68271
8040	S	S	E	N	1969	68271
8040	S	S	E	N	1963	87710
8040	T	D	O	N	1973	51445
8040	T	D	E	N	1973	53451
8040	T	T	O	N	1971	61481
8040	T	S	E	N	1963	87710
8040	T	S	E	N	1972	87823
8041	A	D	E	N	1972	49782
8041	D	D	E	N	1972	49494
8041	D	D	O	N	1973	49552
8041	D	D	R	N	1973	51625
8041	D	D	E	N	1973	52653
8041	D	D	E	N	1972	53245
8041	D	D	E	N	1974	53601
8041	D	D	E	N	1974	54034
8041	D	E	E	N	1974	54034
8041	D	D	R	N	1973	55309
8041	D	S	E	N	1973	56749
8041	D	D	E	N	1974	59234
8041	D	S	E	N	1971	60964
8041	D	D	E	N	1974	62323
8041	D	T	E	N	1974	62323
8041	D	T	R	N	1973	62727
8041	D	D	E	N	1974	64490
8041	D	T	E	N	1973	65323
8041	D	D	E	N	1975	65462
8041	D	S	E	N	1967	68371
8041	D	D	G	N	1971	70363
8041	D	D	R	N	1973	70820
8041	D	T	R	N	1973	70820
8041	D	D	R	N	1972	76526
8041	D	T	R	N	1972	76526
8041	D	D	E	N	1973	79080
8041	D	S	E	N	1962	87659
8041	D	D	E	N	1972	91512
8041	D	T	E	N	1972	91512
8041	D	D	E	N	1973	91576
8041	D	T	E	N	1973	91576
8041	D	D	R	N	1974	93457
8041	D	T	R	N	1974	93457
8041	D	D	E	N	1974	93458
8041	D	T	E	N	1974	93458
8041	D	S	E	N	1967	97985
8041	L	D	E	N	1973	60580
8041	S	D	E	N	1972	49494
8041	S	D	O	N	1973	49552
8041	S	D	E	N	1972	53245
8041	S	S	E	N	1972	53359
8041	S	D	E	N	1974	53601
8041	S	D	O	N	1973	57922
8041	S	D	E	N	1974	57976
8041	S	D	R	L	1972	58680
8041	S	D	R	N	1972	58680
8041	S	D	E	N	1969	62273
8041	S	D	E	N	1971	62312
8041	S	D	E	N	1974	62323
8041	S	D	R	N	1971	67723
8041	S	S	E	N	1969	68271
8041	S	S	E	N	1967	68371
8041	S	D	R	N	1973	70820
8041	S	T	R	N	1973	70820
8041	S	D	E	N	1969	75248
8041	S	D	R	N	1971	76463
8041	S	D	E	N	1966	85431
8041	S	D	E	N	1972	86371
8041	S	S	E	N	1962	87659

Phys. State: **A.** Amorphous; **C.** Superconductive; **D.** Doped; **F.** Fibrous or Whisker; **G.** Gas; **I.** Ionized or Plasma; **L.** Liquid; **P.** Powder or Particle; **S.** Solid; **T.** Thin Film
Subject: **D.** Data; **E.** Experiment; **S.** Survey (Review, Compendium, etc.); **T.** Theory
Language: **E.** English; **F.** French; **G.** German; **O.** Other Languages; **R.** Russian
Temperature: **L.** Low (0 to 75K); **N.** Normal (75 to 1273K); **H.** High (above 1273K)

Substance Number	Phys. State	Subject	Language	Temperature	Year	EPIC Number
106-8041	S	S	E	N	1972	87823
8041	S	D	E	N	1973	91576
8041	S	T	E	N	1973	91576
8041	S	D	E	N	1971	91585
8041	S	D	E	N	1975	93167
8041	S	E	E	N	1975	93167
8041	S	D	E	N	1975	93320
8041	S	S	E	N	1976	97315
8041	S	S	E	N	1967	97985
8041	S	D	E	N	1975	101672
8041	T	D	E	N	1972	49782
8041	T	D	E	N	1973	51268
8041	T	D	R	N	1973	51625
8041	T	D	E	N	1968	59520
8041	T	S	E	N	1971	60964
8041	T	D	R	N	1973	71653
8041	T	T	R	N	1973	71653
8041	T	D	R	N	1972	76519
8041	T	D	E	N	1973	79080
8041	T	D	E	N	1974	88072
8041	T	D	E	N	1974	88174
8041	T	D	E	N	1973	91466
8041	T	T	E	N	1973	91466
8041	T	D	E	N	1972	91552
8041	T	S	E	N	1974	97255
8045	S	D	E	N	1974	53627
8048	S	D	E	N	1974	53627
8049	S	D	E	N	1972	49915
8064	S	S	E	N	1967	97984
8074	D	D	R	N	1973	50355
8074	D	D	E	N	1973	50356
8074	L	D	R	H	1973	50975
8074	L	D	E	H	1973	50976
8074	S	D	R	N	1973	50355
8074	S	D	E	N	1973	50356
8074	S	S	E	N	1967	97985
8075	L	D	R	H	1973	50975
8075	L	D	E	H	1973	50976
8075	S	S	R	N	1972	56731
8075	S	D	R	L	1970	67624
8075	S	D	R	N	1970	67624
8076	L	D	R	H	1973	50975
8076	L	D	E	H	1973	50976
8081	D	D	R	N	1973	52556
8081	L	D	R	H	1973	51562
8081	L	T	R	H	1973	51562
8081	L	D	R	H	1970	53296
8081	L	D	E	H	1972	53297
8081	L	D	E	H	1974	53693
8081	L	T	E	H	1974	53693
8081	L	S	E	N	1967	87860
8081	L	D	R	H	1975	91346
8081	S	D	R	H	1973	51562
8081	S	T	R	H	1973	51562
8081	S	D	R	H	1970	53296
8081	S	D	R	N	1970	53296
8081	S	D	E	H	1972	53297
8081	S	D	E	N	1972	53297
8081	S	D	E	H	1974	53693
8081	S	T	E	H	1974	53693
8081	S	D	R	N	1973	55711
8081	S	D	F	N	1970	59704
8081	S	E	F	N	1970	59704
8081	S	S	E	N	1967	87860
8081	S	D	R	N	1974	93465
8081	S	D	E	N	1974	93466
8081	T	D	R	N	1973	52570
8081	T	D	E	N	1973	79103
8084	L	D	R	H	1973	51562
8084	L	S	R	H	1973	51562
8084	L	T	R	H	1973	51562
8084	L	D	R	H	1970	53296
8084	L	D	E	H	1972	53297
8084	L	D	E	H	1974	53693
8084	L	S	E	H	1974	53693
8084	L	T	E	H	1974	53693
8084	L	D	R	H	1975	91346
8084	S	D	R	N	1972	49759
8084	S	D	R	H	1973	51562
8084	S	T	R	H	1973	51562
8084	S	D	R	H	1970	53296
8084	S	D	R	N	1970	53296
8084	S	D	E	H	1972	53297
8084	S	D	E	N	1972	53297
8084	S	D	E	H	1974	53693
8084	S	T	E	H	1974	53693
8084	S	D	R	N	1972	59068
8084	S	D	E	N	1972	59069
8084	S	D	R	L	1972	60544
8084	S	D	R	N	1972	60544
8084	S	D	E	L	1972	60545
8084	S	D	E	N	1972	60545
8084	S	E	R	N	1975	94018
8084	S	E	E	N	1975	94019
8089	L	S	E	N	1968	98632
8090	L	S	E	N	1968	98632
8091	L	S	E	N	1968	98632
8110	L	S	E	N	1968	98632
8117	S	D	R	N	1971	50664
8118	S	D	E	N	1973	49529
8119	S	D	E	N	1973	49529

Substance Number	Phys. State	Subject	Language	Temperature	Year	EPIC Number
106-8119	S	S	E	L	1973	54004
8119	S	S	E	N	1973	54004
8120	S	D	O	L	1973	49534
8120	S	D	O	N	1973	49534
8120	S	S	E	L	1969	75843
8120	S	S	E	N	1969	75843
8121	S	D	O	L	1973	49534
8121	S	D	O	N	1973	49534
8121	S	D	E	N	1973	57115
8122	S	D	O	L	1973	49534
8122	S	D	O	N	1973	49534
8122	S	D	E	N	1973	57115
8127	S	D	R	N	1972	58679
8127	S	S	E	N	1972	87823
8128	S	D	E	L	1972	49933
8128	S	D	E	N	1972	49933
8128	S	D	E	L	1972	53184
8128	S	D	E	N	1972	53401
8128	S	D	E	L	1973	53852
8128	S	D	E	N	1973	53852
8128	S	D	E	N	1973	55149
8128	S	D	E	L	1969	59174
8128	S	D	E	N	1969	59174
8128	S	E	E	L	1969	59174
8128	S	E	E	N	1969	59174
8128	S	T	E	L	1969	59174
8128	S	T	E	N	1969	59174
8128	S	D	E	N	1974	61351
8128	S	S	E	N	1967	68371
8128	S	T	R	N	1973	70817
8128	S	D	R	L	1974	86221
8128	S	D	R	N	1974	86221
8128	S	S	E	N	1972	87823
8128	S	T	E	N	1973	91573
8128	S	D	E	L	1974	92626
8128	S	D	E	N	1974	92626
8128	T	D	R	N	1972	49717
8128	T	D	E	N	1973	51923
8128	T	D	E	N	1974	66692
8128	T	S	E	N	1972	87823
8128	T	D	R	N	1974	90409
8132	D	S	E	L	1972	87823
8132	S	D	E	N	1971	61077
8132	S	S	E	L	1972	87823
8133	S	S	E	N	1972	87823
8134	D	S	E	N	1972	87823
8134	S	D	R	N	1971	56217
8134	S	S	E	N	1972	87823
8138	C	D	E	L	1972	53355
8138	S	D	G	N	1973	49769
8139	C	D	E	L	1972	53355
8139	S	D	G	N	1973	49769
8140	C	D	E	L	1972	53355
8140	S	D	G	N	1973	49769
8142	S	D	E	N	1974	57750
8143	A	T	R	N	1971	63423
8143	A	T	E	N	1971	67074
8143	D	D	R	N	1973	50355
8143	D	D	E	N	1973	50356
8143	S	D	E	N	1972	49865
8143	S	D	R	N	1973	50355
8143	S	D	E	N	1973	50356
8143	S	S	R	N	1972	56731
8143	S	S	E	N	1967	97985
8143	T	D	R	N	1973	58553
8143	T	T	R	N	1971	63423
8143	T	T	E	N	1971	67074
8144	S	D	E	N	1972	49878
8145	C	D	E	L	1973	55121
8145	C	S	E	L	1959	75729
8145	D	D	E	L	1973	55121
8146	T	D	R	N	1972	49937
8149	S	D	E	L	1973	50004
8149	S	D	E	N	1973	50004
8149	S	D	E	N	1973	50815
8149	S	D	E	N	1973	51909
8149	S	D	E	L	1972	53113
8149	S	D	E	N	1972	53113
8149	S	D	E	N	1973	53318
8150	S	D	E	N	1973	50005
8151	S	D	E	N	1973	50023
8152	S	D	E	N	1973	50023
8153	S	D	F	N	1973	50026
8154	T	D	R	N	1972	56995
8154	T	D	R	N	1971	76494
8154	T	D	E	N	1971	91578
8156	L	D	R	N	1973	52540
8156	L	D	E	N	1974	53675
8157	S	D	E	N	1971	68078
8163	S	D	R	N	1973	50325
8163	S	D	E	N	1973	50326
8164	S	D	R	N	1973	50355
8164	S	D	E	N	1973	50356
8165	S	D	R	N	1973	50355
8165	S	D	E	N	1973	50356
8182	S	D	E	L	1975	92154
8182	S	D	E	N	1975	92154
8183	S	D	E	N	1973	50097
8184	S	D	E	N	1973	50097
8185	S	D	E	N	1973	50097
8193	S	D	F	N	1973	50620

Substance Number	Phys. State	Subject	Language	Temperature	Year	EPIC Number
106-8194	S	D	R	N	1973	50652
8195	S	D	R	N	1973	50652
8196	S	D	R	N	1973	50652
8197	S	D	R	N	1973	50652
8200	S	D	R	N	1973	50681
8200	S	D	E	N	1973	52427
8201	S	D	F	L	1973	55965
8201	S	D	F	N	1973	55965
8204	S	D	E	L	1973	55279
8204	S	D	E	N	1973	55279
8206	S	D	E	H	1973	50780
8206	S	D	E	N	1973	50780
8208	S	D	E	N	1973	50815
8209	S	D	E	L	1973	50903
8209	S	D	E	N	1973	50903
8209	S	D	E	N	1974	62028
8209	S	E	E	N	1974	62028
8209	T	D	E	N	1974	53635
8211	S	D	E	L	1973	50921
8214	S	D	E	N	1971	49792
8214	S	E	E	N	1971	49792
8234	S	T	R	N	1973	51561
8234	S	T	E	N	1974	53692
8234	S	D	R	N	1974	60415
8234	S	D	E	N	1974	60416
8234	S	S	E	N	1972	87823
8237	S	S	E	N	1972	53110
8237	S	D	E	N	1974	57860
8238	L	S	E	N	1972	51438
8243	S	D	R	N	1971	76484
8243	S	S	R	N	1971	76484
8243	S	D	E	N	1971	91524
8243	S	S	E	N	1971	91524
8258	S	D	R	N	1970	51710
8259	S	D	R	N	1970	51710
8260	S	D	R	N	1970	51710
8261	S	D	R	N	1973	51732
8261	S	D	E	N	1973	79136
8262	A	T	R	N	1971	63423
8262	A	T	E	N	1971	67074
8262	S	D	R	N	1973	51732
8262	S	D	R	N	1971	76478
8262	S	D	E	N	1973	79136
8262	S	D	E	N	1971	91502
8262	T	T	R	N	1971	63423
8262	T	T	E	N	1971	67074
8263	S	D	F	N	1973	51741
8270	S	D	R	N	1973	58519
8271	S	D	E	N	1975	66627
8271	S	S	E	N	1975	96148
8271	T	D	E	N	1975	97322
8286	C	D	E	L	1972	49904
8287	C	D	E	L	1972	49904
8289	S	D	E	N	1936	61578
8289	S	D	E	L	1971	63591
8289	S	S	E	L	1971	63591
8289	S	T	E	L	1971	63591
8289	S	E	E	N	1952	65344
8289	S	T	E	N	1952	65344
8299	T	D	E	N	1975	90115
8299	T	T	E	N	1975	90115
8299	T	D	E	N	1975	97322
8302	S	S	E	N	1974	61168
8312	C	D	E	L	1968	53357
8312	D	D	E	N	1973	55670
8312	D	D	R	N	1974	66790
8312	D	T	R	N	1974	66790
8312	D	D	E	N	1975	66791
8312	D	T	E	N	1975	66791
8312	S	D	E	N	1968	53357
8312	S	D	E	N	1968	53358
8312	S	D	R	N	1973	58519
8312	S	D	R	N	1974	66790
8312	S	T	R	N	1974	66790
8312	S	D	E	N	1975	66791
8312	S	T	E	N	1975	66791
8314	S	D	E	L	1973	52754
8314	S	D	E	N	1973	52754
8315	S	D	E	L	1973	52754
8315	S	D	E	N	1973	52754
8322	S	D	E	N	1973	52943
8325	S	D	E	N	1972	52993
8325	S	D	E	L	1972	53250
8325	S	D	E	N	1972	53250
8331	S	D	E	L	1972	53113
8331	S	D	E	N	1972	53113
8333	S	D	R	N	1971	53129
8333	S	D	E	N	1972	53130
8333	S	D	R	N	1973	54689
8333	S	T	R	N	1973	54689
8334	S	D	R	N	1971	53129
8334	S	D	E	N	1972	53130
8334	S	D	R	N	1975	70607
8334	S	D	E	N	1975	93225
8335	S	D	F	N	1970	84029
8335	S	D	R	N	1974	93465
8335	S	T	R	N	1974	93465
8335	S	D	E	N	1974	93466
8335	S	T	E	N	1974	93466
8335	T	T	O	N	1971	61478
8336	S	S	E	L	1972	53272

Phys. State: **A.** Amorphous; **C.** Superconductive; **D.** Doped; **F.** Fibrous or Whisker; **G.** Gas; **I.** Ionized or Plasma; **L.** Liquid; **P.** Powder or Particle; **S.** Solid; **T.** Thin Film
Subject: **D.** Data; **E.** Experiment; **S.** Survey (Review, Compendium, etc.); **T.** Theory
Language: **E.** English; **F.** French; **G.** German; **O.** Other Languages; **R.** Russian
Temperature: **L.** L[illegible] (0 to 75K); **N.** Normal (75 to 1273K); **H.** High (above 1273K)

Substance Number	Phys. State	Subject	Language	Temperature	Year	EPIC Number
106-8336	S	S	E	N	1972	53272
8337	C	S	E	L	1972	53272
8337	S	S	E	L	1972	53272
8337	S	S	E	N	1972	53272
8338	S	D	E	N	1973	53415
8338	S	D	R	N	1970	55102
8338	S	D	E	N	1972	55103
8338	S	S	E	N	1974	58346
8340	S	D	R	N	1970	55102
8340	S	D	E	N	1972	55103
8342	D	D	R	N	1972	55492
8342	S	D	E	N	1975	94550
8343	S	D	E	L	1973	53404
8343	S	D	E	N	1973	53404
8344	S	D	E	N	1973	53415
8344	S	D	R	N	1970	55102
8344	S	D	E	N	1972	55103
8347	S	S	E	N	1973	53420
8347	S	T	E	N	1973	61070
8347	S	D	E	H	1973	65651
8347	S	D	E	N	1973	65651
8347	S	T	E	H	1973	65651
8347	S	T	E	N	1973	65651
8348	S	S	E	N	1973	53420
8348	S	T	E	N	1973	61070
8348	S	D	E	H	1973	65651
8348	S	D	E	N	1973	65651
8348	S	T	E	H	1973	65651
8348	S	T	E	N	1973	65651
8349	S	S	E	N	1973	53420
8349	S	T	E	N	1973	61070
8349	S	D	E	H	1973	65651
8349	S	D	E	N	1973	65651
8349	S	T	E	H	1973	65651
8349	S	T	E	N	1973	65651
8350	S	D	E	N	1973	53439
8352	S	D	E	N	1973	53439
8356	D	D	E	H	1972	53535
8356	D	D	E	N	1972	53535
8356	D	D	E	H	1970	67274
8356	D	D	E	N	1970	67274
8356	D	D	E	H	1971	67275
8356	D	D	E	N	1971	67275
8356	D	D	E	H	1972	67276
8356	D	D	E	N	1972	67276
8356	S	D	E	H	1972	53535
8356	S	D	E	N	1972	53535
8356	S	D	E	H	1972	55089
8356	S	D	E	N	1972	55089
8356	S	E	E	H	1972	55089
8356	S	E	E	N	1972	55089
8356	S	D	E	H	1974	57749
8356	S	D	E	H	1971	67273
8356	S	D	E	N	1971	67273
8356	S	D	E	H	1970	67274
8356	S	D	E	N	1970	67274
8360	S	D	E	L	1973	55279
8360	S	D	E	N	1973	55279
8361	S	D	E	N	1971	49792
8361	S	E	E	N	1971	49792
8363	S	D	E	L	1973	51821
8363	S	D	E	N	1973	51821
8364	S	D	E	N	1973	51890
8365	S	D	E	N	1973	51890
8366	S	D	E	N	1973	51890
8375	S	S	E	L	1972	54881
8375	S	S	E	N	1972	54881
8375	S	T	E	L	1972	54881
8375	S	T	E	N	1972	54881
8375	S	S	E	L	1970	59594
8375	S	S	E	N	1970	59594
8384	S	D	E	L	1973	50817
8384	S	D	E	N	1973	50817
8385	C	D	E	L	1973	57082
8388	S	D	E	N	1974	53644
8389	S	D	E	N	1973	59156
8390	S	D	E	N	1973	59156
8391	S	D	F	L	1973	55965
8391	S	D	F	N	1973	55965
8391	S	D	E	N	1973	59156
8391	S	D	R	N	1971	76489
8391	S	T	R	N	1971	76489
8391	S	D	E	N	1971	91568
8391	S	T	E	N	1971	91568
8392	S	D	E	N	1973	59156
8392	S	D	E	N	1967	75175
8393	S	D	E	N	1973	59156
8393	S	D	E	N	1967	75175
8393	S	D	E	N	1971	91568
8393	S	T	E	N	1971	91568
8394	S	D	R	N	1973	58519
8394	S	D	E	N	1973	59156
8394	S	D	E	N	1967	75175
8394	S	D	R	N	1971	76489
8394	S	T	R	N	1971	76489
8394	S	D	E	N	1971	91568
8394	S	T	E	N	1971	91568
8414	S	D	E	N	1974	53919
8416	L	S	E	N	1968	98632
8423	S	D	G	N	1932	60555
8424	S	D	G	N	1932	60555
106-8425	S	D	G	N	1932	60555
8438	S	T	E	N	1974	93998
8439	S	D	R	N	1972	60709
8439	S	D	E	N	1973	60710
8439	S	D	R	N	1974	63161
8439	S	D	E	N	1975	63162
8439	S	S	E	N	1967	97983
8453	S	D	R	N	1970	55102
8453	S	D	E	N	1972	55103
8453	S	D	F	N	1974	90493
8454	S	D	R	N	1970	55102
8454	S	D	E	N	1972	55103
8455	L	D	R	N	1972	76551
8455	L	T	R	N	1972	76551
8455	L	D	E	N	1972	91546
8455	L	T	E	N	1972	91546
8455	S	D	R	N	1970	55102
8455	S	D	E	N	1972	55103
8455	S	D	R	N	1972	76551
8455	S	T	R	N	1972	76551
8455	S	D	E	N	1972	91546
8455	S	T	E	N	1972	91546
8456	S	D	R	N	1970	55102
8456	S	D	E	N	1972	55103
8456	S	D	F	N	1974	90493
8457	S	D	R	N	1970	55102
8457	S	D	E	N	1972	55103
8458	L	D	R	N	1972	76551
8458	L	T	R	N	1972	76551
8458	L	D	E	N	1972	91546
8458	L	T	E	N	1972	91546
8458	S	D	R	N	1970	55102
8458	S	D	E	N	1972	55103
8458	S	D	R	N	1972	76551
8458	S	T	R	N	1972	76551
8458	S	D	E	N	1972	91546
8458	S	T	E	N	1972	91546
8459	S	D	R	N	1970	55102
8459	S	D	E	N	1972	55103
8460	S	D	R	L	1973	53995
8460	S	D	R	N	1973	53995
8460	S	D	E	L	1973	53996
8460	S	D	E	N	1973	53996
8467	S	D	R	N	1973	55288
8467	S	D	E	N	1974	59247
8467	S	D	R	N	1968	61308
8467	S	D	E	N	1968	61309
8469	S	D	E	N	1971	61077
8471	S	D	R	N	1971	59995
8473	S	D	E	N	1974	55119
8485	L	S	E	H	1968	98632
8488	S	D	E	N	1973	62296
8491	S	S	E	L	1973	54004
8491	S	S	E	N	1973	54004
8494	S	S	E	N	1971	59881
8494	S	T	G	N	1971	61890
8495	C	S	E	L	1970	61209
8495	C	S	E	L	1976	99156
8495	S	S	E	N	1971	59881
8495	S	S	E	N	1970	61209
8495	S	D	E	N	1971	61219
8495	S	S	E	N	1976	99185
8496	C	S	E	L	1970	61209
8496	S	S	E	N	1971	59881
8496	S	S	E	N	1970	61209
8497	C	S	E	L	1970	61209
8497	S	S	E	N	1971	59881
8497	S	S	E	N	1970	61209
8498	S	T	R	N	1970	64854
8498	S	T	E	N	1971	64855
8499	S	D	E	N	1936	61578
8499	S	E	E	N	1952	65344
8499	S	T	E	N	1952	65344
8500	S	D	E	N	1936	61578
8500	S	E	E	N	1952	65344
8500	S	T	E	N	1952	65344
8501	S	D	E	N	1936	61578
8502	S	D	E	N	1936	61578
8503	S	D	E	N	1936	61578
8504	C	S	E	L	1966	87721
8504	C	D	E	L	1975	90381
8504	C	D	E	L	1975	90382
8504	F	D	E	L	1975	90381
8504	T	D	E	L	1975	90382
8506	C	D	E	L	1973	52186
8506	S	D	E	L	1973	52186
8512	L	D	R	H	1973	52569
8512	L	D	E	H	1973	78966
8512	S	S	E	H	1958	75842
8512	S	S	E	L	1958	75842
8512	S	S	E	N	1958	75842
8519	S	D	E	L	1971	63591
8519	S	S	E	L	1971	63591
8519	S	T	E	L	1971	63591
8521	A	T	R	N	1971	63423
8521	A	T	E	N	1971	67074
8521	S	S	E	N	1967	97985
8521	T	T	R	N	1971	63423
8521	T	T	E	N	1971	67074
8522	S	S	E	N	1973	56765
8523	S	S	E	N	1960	65977
106-8524	S	S	E	N	1960	65977
8527	T	D	R	N	1973	56329
8528	D	D	R	N	1973	55295
8528	D	D	E	N	1974	59271
8529	S	D	R	N	1973	56861
8529	S	D	E	N	1973	57295
8529	S	D	R	N	1974	58280
8529	S	D	E	N	1974	77075
8531	S	S	E	N	1972	87823
8531	T	S	E	N	1972	87823
8532	S	D	R	N	1973	51962
8532	S	D	E	N	1973	55346
8535	S	T	E	N	1974	66363
8541	S	D	E	N	1971	61219
8545	A	T	R	N	1971	63423
8545	A	T	E	N	1971	67074
8545	S	D	R	N	1972	68551
8545	S	T	R	N	1972	68551
8545	S	D	E	N	1972	68552
8545	S	T	E	N	1972	68552
8545	T	T	R	N	1971	63423
8545	T	T	E	N	1971	67074
8549	S	D	R	N	1973	58519
8553	S	D	R	N	1971	67825
8559	C	D	R	L	1972	63967
8559	C	S	R	L	1972	63967
8559	C	T	R	L	1972	63967
8559	C	D	E	L	1972	68424
8559	C	S	E	L	1972	68424
8559	C	T	E	L	1972	68424
8559	S	D	R	L	1973	50743
8559	S	D	E	L	1973	79073
8561	S	D	E	N	1964	93287
8561	S	S	E	N	1964	93287
8562	S	D	E	N	1964	93287
8562	S	S	E	N	1964	93287
8563	C	S	E	L	1970	61209
8564	D	S	E	N	1974	87606
8564	S	S	E	N	1974	87606
8565	S	D	R	N	1972	60709
8565	S	D	E	N	1973	60710
8565	S	D	R	N	1974	67753
8567	S	T	R	N	1973	54689
8580	S	S	E	N	1972	87823
8580	T	S	E	N	1972	87823
8584	S	D	F	L	1973	55965
8584	S	D	F	N	1973	55965
8585	S	D	F	L	1973	55965
8585	S	D	F	N	1973	55965
8586	S	D	F	L	1973	55965
8586	S	D	F	N	1973	55965
8587	S	D	F	L	1973	55966
8587	S	D	F	N	1973	55966
8588	S	D	E	N	1975	62658
8589	T	D	R	N	1973	56055
8595	S	D	E	L	1973	56353
8595	S	D	E	N	1973	56353
8596	S	S	E	N	1967	97983
8606	S	D	E	N	1973	56706
8607	S	D	E	N	1973	56706
8608	S	D	E	N	1973	56706
8609	S	D	E	N	1973	56706
8611	S	D	E	N	1966	85403
8612	S	D	R	N	1972	56998
8625	S	D	E	L	1973	57110
8625	S	D	E	N	1973	57110
8633	S	D	R	N	1973	57239
8641	S	D	R	N	1973	51609
8642	S	D	R	N	1973	51724
8642	S	D	R	N	1971	66283
8642	S	D	R	N	1971	76478
8642	S	D	E	N	1971	91502
8643	S	D	R	N	1973	51724
8644	D	D	E	N	1973	53834
8644	S	D	E	H	1973	65651
8644	S	D	E	N	1973	65651
8644	S	T	E	H	1973	65651
8644	S	T	E	N	1973	65651
8645	T	D	R	L	1973	53928
8645	T	D	R	N	1973	53928
8646	D	D	R	N	1974	58280
8646	D	D	E	N	1974	77075
8646	S	D	R	N	1974	58280
8646	S	D	E	N	1974	77075
8648	C	D	E	L	1974	61410
8648	C	T	E	L	1974	61410
8648	C	T	E	L	1974	63380
8650	L	D	R	N	1971	76462
8650	L	D	E	H	1975	90018
8650	L	D	E	N	1971	91582
8650	S	D	E	N	1975	90018
8651	L	D	E	N	1975	90018
8651	S	D	E	N	1975	90018
8652	L	D	E	N	1975	90018
8652	S	D	E	N	1975	90018
8653	L	D	R	N	1971	76462
8653	L	D	E	N	1975	90018
8653	L	D	E	N	1971	91582
8653	S	D	E	N	1975	90018
8654	S	S	E	H	1962	65974
8654	S	S	E	N	1962	65974

Phys. State: **A.** Amorphous; **C.** Superconductive; **D.** Doped; **F.** Fibrous or Whisker; **G.** Gas; **I.** Ionized or Plasma; **L.** Liquid; **P.** Powder or Particle; **S.** Solid; **T.** Thin Film
Subject: **D.** Data; **E.** Experiment; **S.** Survey (Review, Compendium, etc.); **T.** Theory
Language: **E.** English; **F.** French; **G.** German; **O.** Other Languages; **R.** Russian
Temperature: **L.** Low (0 to 75K); **N.** Normal (75 to 1273K); **H.** High (above 1273K)

Substance Number	Phys. State	Subject	Language	Temperature	Year	EPIC Number
106-8658	S	D	R	N	1973	58870
8660	T	D	E	N	1974	60374
8669	S	D	R	N	1971	66283
8669	S	D	R	N	1972	66285
8674	S	D	R	N	1971	67332
8675	S	D	R	N	1973	67359
8686	S	D	F	N	1974	90493
8687	S	D	F	N	1974	90493
8693	C	S	E	L	1965	87791
8694	S	D	E	N	1975	90841
8694	S	S	E	N	1975	90841
8694	S	T	E	N	1975	90841
8694	T	S	E	N	1971	87872
8696	S	S	E	N	1967	97983
8697	S	S	E	N	1967	97983
8698	S	S	E	N	1967	97983
8699	S	S	E	N	1967	97983
8700	S	S	E	H	1967	97983
8700	S	S	E	N	1967	97983
8701	S	S	E	H	1967	97983
8701	S	S	E	N	1967	97983
8702	S	S	E	N	1967	97983
8703	S	S	E	N	1967	97984
8703	S	S	E	N	1976	102007
8704	S	S	E	N	1967	97984
8704	S	S	E	H	1976	102007
8704	S	S	E	N	1976	102007
8705	S	S	E	H	1967	97984
8705	S	S	E	N	1967	97984
8706	D	S	E	H	1967	97984
8706	D	S	E	N	1967	97984
8706	S	S	E	H	1967	97984
8706	S	S	E	N	1967	97984
8707	D	S	E	H	1967	97984
8707	D	S	E	N	1967	97984
8707	S	S	E	N	1967	97984
8708	L	S	E	N	1968	98632
8709	L	S	E	N	1968	98632
8710	L	S	E	N	1968	98632
8711	T	D	G	N	1957	86339
8711	T	D	E	N	1973	86340
8712	C	D	E	L	1974	91401
8730	L	S	E	N	1967	98664
8731	L	S	E	N	1967	98664
8734	S	D	R	N	1971	67726
8735	S	D	R	N	1974	67740
8735	S	D	R	N	1974	67753
8738	S	D	R	N	1971	67825
8749	S	D	E	N	1953	75543
8749	S	E	E	N	1953	75543
8754	C	D	R	L	1974	81228
8754	C	D	E	L	1974	92358
8755	C	D	R	L	1974	81228
8755	C	D	E	L	1974	92358
8759	S	D	R	N	1971	76478
8759	S	D	E	N	1971	91502
8762	S	D	R	N	1970	76459
8762	S	T	R	N	1970	76459
8762	S	D	E	N	1970	91514
8762	S	T	E	N	1970	91514
8763	S	D	R	N	1971	76484
8763	S	D	E	N	1971	91524
8766	S	S	E	N	1975	90115
8766	S	S	E	N	1975	97322
8766	T	D	E	N	1975	97322
8767	S	S	E	N	1976	103180
8769	S	D	E	L	1975	92154
8771	S	D	E	N	1975	92154
8783	S	D	E	N	1974	62504
8786	L	D	G	H	1914	100892
8786	L	D	G	N	1914	100892
8787	L	D	G	H	1914	100892
8787	L	D	G	N	1914	100892
8788	C	D	E	L	1976	100720
8788	C	E	E	L	1976	100720
8791	S	S	E	H	1976	102007
8791	S	S	E	N	1976	102007
8792	S	T	R	N	1974	86647
8806	S	D	E	N	1974	58321
8806	S	T	E	N	1974	58321
8807	S	D	E	N	1974	58321
8807	S	T	E	N	1974	58321
8808	S	D	E	N	1974	58321
8808	S	T	E	N	1974	58321
8811	S	D	R	N	1974	65411
8811	S	T	R	N	1974	65411
8811	S	D	E	N	1975	65412
8811	S	T	E	N	1975	65412
8818	S	D	R	N	1971	66283
8819	S	D	R	N	1971	66283
8820	S	D	R	N	1971	66283
8823	S	D	R	N	1974	65623
8823	S	T	R	N	1974	65623
8823	S	D	E	N	1974	68419
8823	S	T	E	N	1974	68419
8824	S	D	R	N	1972	68551
8824	S	T	R	N	1972	68551
8824	S	D	E	N	1972	68552
8824	S	T	E	N	1972	68552
8825	S	D	R	N	1972	68551
8825	S	T	R	N	1972	68551
106-8825	S	D	E	N	1972	68552
8825	S	T	E	N	1972	68552
8828	S	S	E	N	1976	103180
8829	S	S	E	H	1976	103180
8829	S	S	E	N	1976	103180
8831	S	D	E	N	1974	57750
8832	S	D	E	H	1973	65651
8832	S	D	E	N	1973	65651
8832	S	T	E	H	1973	65651
8832	S	T	E	N	1973	65651
8836	C	S	E	L	1959	75729
8837	C	S	E	L	1959	75729
8838	C	S	E	L	1959	75729
108-0014	S	D	E	N	1973	66101
0014	S	S	E	N	1970	87822
0014	S	S	E	N	1972	87890
0029	S	D	E	N	1974	54099
0029	S	D	E	N	1974	62066
0029	S	S	E	N	1974	62066
0029	S	T	E	N	1974	62066
0052	S	D	F	H	1975	90267
0079	S	D	E	L	1974	54324
0079	S	D	E	N	1974	54324
8001	S	T	E	N	1973	49991
8025	S	S	E	N	1970	87822
8025	S	S	E	N	1972	87890
8028	C	D	E	L	1972	57080
8043	S	D	E	N	1973	56161
8044	S	D	R	N	1973	56317
8057	S	S	E	N	1967	97985
8060	C	D	E	L	1973	58635
8060	C	T	E	L	1973	58635
8060	C	D	E	L	1975	92664
8060	C	T	E	L	1975	92664
8060	C	D	E	L	1975	96258
8060	C	T	E	L	1975	96258
8061	S	D	E	N	1972	49784
109-0001	S	D	F	H	1973	54836
0001	S	D	R	N	1973	54869
0025	D	D	E	N	1973	50887
0025	D	D	E	N	1974	54573
0025	S	D	E	N	1973	50887
0025	S	D	E	N	1973	50888
0025	S	D	E	L	1972	52969
0025	S	D	E	N	1972	52969
0025	S	D	E	L	1972	53158
0025	S	D	E	N	1972	53158
0025	S	D	R	L	1974	60439
0025	S	D	R	N	1974	60439
0025	S	D	E	L	1974	60440
0025	S	D	E	N	1974	60440
0025	T	D	E	L	1974	60295
0025	T	D	E	N	1974	60295
0025	T	E	E	L	1974	60295
0025	T	E	E	N	1974	60295
0029	D	D	E	N	1973	49670
0029	S	D	E	N	1973	49670
0040	S	D	R	H	1973	70815
0040	S	D	R	N	1973	70815
0040	S	D	E	H	1973	91572
0040	S	D	E	N	1973	91572
0060	S	D	R	N	1973	70822
0060	S	T	R	N	1973	70822
0060	S	D	E	N	1973	91587
0060	S	T	E	N	1973	91587
8019	S	D	R	N	1973	52564
8019	S	D	E	N	1973	57789
8019	S	D	E	N	1973	62310
8019	S	D	E	L	1974	62346
8019	S	D	E	N	1974	62346
8019	S	T	E	L	1974	62346
8019	S	T	E	N	1974	62346
8019	S	D	E	N	1974	62347
8019	S	T	E	N	1974	62347
8020	D	S	E	N	1967	75838
8020	S	D	E	N	1973	62310
8020	S	D	R	N	1975	86839
8020	S	D	E	N	1975	86840
8020	T	D	R	N	1973	64236
8020	T	T	R	N	1973	64236
8020	T	D	E	N	1973	64237
8020	T	T	E	N	1973	64237
8021	S	D	R	N	1973	52564
8021	S	D	E	N	1973	57789
8021	S	D	E	N	1973	62310
8029	S	D	F	L	1973	51499
8029	S	D	F	N	1973	51499
8031	S	D	E	L	1973	55943
8031	S	D	E	L	1974	58909
8031	S	D	E	N	1974	58909
8034	S	D	E	L	1972	53158
8034	S	D	E	N	1972	53158
8040	S	D	R	N	1973	52564
8040	S	D	E	N	1973	57789
8041	S	D	R	N	1973	52564
8041	S	D	E	N	1973	57789
8042	S	D	R	N	1973	52564
8042	S	D	E	N	1973	57789
8051	S	D	R	L	1974	60439
109-8051	S	D	R	N	1974	60439
8051	S	D	E	L	1974	60440
8051	S	D	E	N	1974	60440
8064	S	D	R	N	1975	86839
8064	S	D	E	N	1975	86840
8068	S	D	E	N	1973	56161
8071	S	D	E	N	1973	56526
8083	S	S	E	N	1967	97985
8084	S	S	E	N	1967	97985
8085	S	S	E	N	1967	97985
8087	S	D	R	N	1973	67865
8102	S	D	E	N	1972	49784
8103	S	D	E	N	1974	57750
8104	S	D	E	N	1974	57750
8105	S	D	E	N	1974	57750
8106	S	D	E	N	1974	57750
8107	C	S	E	L	1959	75729
110-0002	S	D	E	N	1976	99911
0007	L	S	E	H	1968	98632
0007	L	D	E	H	1914	100892
0007	S	D	R	N	1972	50091
0007	S	D	R	N	1967	53069
0007	S	D	E	N	1972	53070
0010	D	S	E	L	1969	75843
0010	D	S	E	N	1969	75843
0010	S	D	R	N	1966	59587
0010	S	E	R	N	1966	59587
0010	S	D	E	N	1966	63247
0010	S	E	E	N	1966	63247
0011	D	D	R	N	1973	55830
0011	D	D	E	N	1960	60561
0011	D	S	E	N	1967	97982
0011	S	D	O	N	1973	50981
0011	S	S	E	H	1974	54022
0011	S	S	E	N	1974	54022
0011	S	D	R	N	1973	55830
0011	S	S	E	N	1966	87846
0011	S	D	E	H	1975	95378
0011	S	D	E	N	1975	95378
0011	S	E	E	H	1975	95378
0011	S	E	E	N	1975	95378
0011	T	D	E	N	1970	67623
0018	L	S	E	H	1968	98632
0018	L	S	E	N	1968	98632
0020	L	S	E	N	1968	98632
0021	L	S	E	N	1968	98632
0021	S	D	E	N	1973	57728
0021	S	D	E	N	1975	90266
0021	T	D	E	N	1973	57744
0023	S	D	R	N	1974	63056
0023	S	T	R	N	1974	63056
0023	S	D	E	N	1975	63057
0023	S	T	E	N	1975	63057
0023	S	D	R	N	1972	76520
0023	S	T	R	N	1972	76520
0023	S	D	E	N	1972	91553
0023	S	T	E	N	1972	91553
0024	D	D	E	N	1975	63337
0024	D	T	E	N	1975	63337
0024	D	D	R	N	1970	67349
0024	L	D	R	H	1972	52242
0024	L	D	E	N	1973	57594
0024	L	D	E	N	1974	58441
0024	L	S	E	H	1968	98632
0024	L	S	E	N	1968	98632
0024	S	D	F	N	1972	53541
0024	S	T	F	N	1972	53541
0024	S	T	E	N	1974	54098
0024	S	D	R	N	1973	54984
0024	S	D	E	N	1974	54985
0024	S	D	E	N	1974	58441
0024	S	D	E	N	1975	63337
0024	S	T	E	N	1975	63337
0024	S	D	E	N	1975	97579
0024	S	S	E	N	1975	97579
0024	S	T	E	N	1975	97579
0025	D	D	E	L	1972	53113
0025	D	D	E	N	1972	53113
0025	S	D	E	L	1973	50004
0025	S	D	E	N	1973	50004
0025	S	D	E	N	1972	53113
0025	S	D	R	N	1974	88553
0025	S	D	E	N	1974	94190
0025	T	E	R	N	1972	49972
0025	T	D	E	N	1970	67623
0028	S	S	E	N	1967	97983
0028	T	E	E	N	1973	51762
0030	S	D	F	N	1973	52169
0036	D	S	E	N	1972	59933
0036	D	D	E	N	1970	75188
0036	D	T	E	N	1970	75188
0036	L	D	R	H	1972	52242
0036	L	D	O	H	1973	53826
0036	L	D	O	N	1973	53826
0036	L	D	E	N	1973	57594
0036	L	S	E	H	1968	98632
0036	L	S	E	N	1968	98632
0036	S	D	E	N	1970	75188
0036	S	T	E	N	1970	75188
0037	L	D	R	H	1972	52242

Phys. State: **A.** Amorphous; **C.** Superconductive; **D.** Doped; **F.** Fibrous or Whisker; **G.** Gas; **I.** Ionized or Plasma; **L.** Liquid; **P.** Powder or Particle; **S.** Solid; **T.** Thin Film
Subject: **D.** Data; **E.** Experiment; **S.** Survey (Review, Compendium, etc.); **T.** Theory
Language: **E.** English; **F.** French; **G.** German; **O.** Other Languages; **R.** Russian
Temperature: **L.** Low (0 to 75K); **N.** Normal (75 to 1273K); **H.** High (above 1273K)

Substance Number	Phys. State	Sub-ject	Lan-guage	Temper-ature	Year	EPIC Number
110-0037	L	S	E	H	1968	98632
0037	L	S	E	N	1968	98632
0040	G	D	G	H	1966	59223
0040	L	D	E	N	1974	67240
0061	L	D	R	H	1972	52242
0083	D	D	E	N	1973	57736
0083	S	S	E	N	1976	103180
0083	T	D	E	N	1973	52469
0083	T	D	E	N	1973	57736
0083	T	T	E	N	1973	57736
0125	S	S	E	N	1976	99185
0132	S	D	F	N	1972	53541
0132	S	T	F	N	1972	53541
0132	S	S	E	N	1976	103180
0157	S	D	E	N	1973	50573
0194	D	T	E	N	1972	53192
0194	D	T	E	N	1974	57985
0194	S	D	E	N	1973	50872
0194	S	D	E	N	1973	51920
0194	S	D	E	N	1973	51937
0194	T	T	E	N	1974	57985
0236	S	D	E	N	1973	49525
0236	S	D	E	N	1974	55263
0236	S	E	E	N	1974	55263
8015	L	D	R	H	1973	50975
8015	L	D	E	H	1973	50976
8015	S	S	E	N	1967	97985
8017	S	D	E	N	1973	50573
8036	S	D	E	N	1973	49520
8037	S	D	E	N	1973	49520
8040	S	D	F	N	1972	49774
8042	T	D	R	N	1972	49980
8042	T	D	R	N	1972	49981
8042	T	D	R	N	1972	58195
8046	S	D	F	N	1972	49774
8046	S	D	E	L	1973	50004
8046	S	D	E	N	1973	50004
8046	S	D	E	N	1973	50005
8046	S	D	E	L	1972	53113
8046	S	D	E	N	1972	53113
8046	S	S	E	N	1970	75905
8046	S	D	E	N	1975	91913
8046	S	T	E	N	1975	91913
8047	S	D	E	L	1973	50004
8047	S	D	E	N	1973	50004
8047	S	D	E	N	1973	51839
8048	S	D	E	N	1973	50005
8063	L	D	R	H	1973	50975
8063	L	D	E	H	1973	50976
8064	L	D	R	H	1973	50975
8064	L	D	E	H	1973	50976
8064	S	S	R	N	1972	56731
8070	S	D	E	N	1971	49792
8070	S	E	E	N	1971	49792
8070	S	D	R	N	1972	56960
8073	D	D	R	N	1973	52114
8073	D	D	G	N	1972	54629
8073	D	D	E	N	1973	54630
8073	D	D	E	N	1973	54921
8073	S	D	E	N	1971	49792
8073	S	E	E	N	1971	49792
8073	S	S	E	N	1973	51186
8073	S	D	E	N	1971	63486
8073	S	E	E	N	1971	63486
8077	S	D	G	N	1950	53501
8077	S	D	E	N	1972	53502
8079	S	D	R	N	1970	51710
8082	S	D	R	N	1973	55807
8082	S	D	E	N	1973	56343
8082	S	D	E	N	1973	56370
8082	S	D	R	N	1973	66116
8083	S	D	E	N	1973	56370
8102	S	D	R	N	1973	50645
8102	S	D	E	N	1972	53186
8102	S	D	E	L	1970	59684
8102	S	D	E	N	1970	59684
8102	S	D	E	N	1974	66368
8102	S	D	E	H	1973	101641
8102	S	D	E	N	1973	101641
8102	S	E	E	H	1973	101641
8102	S	E	E	N	1973	101641
8112	S	D	R	N	1973	50742
8112	S	S	E	N	1970	75905
8112	S	D	E	N	1973	79081
8116	S	S	E	L	1972	53272
8116	S	S	E	N	1972	53272
8117	S	D	G	N	1950	53501
8117	S	D	E	N	1972	53502
8119	S	D	E	N	1971	49792
8119	S	E	E	N	1971	49792
8120	S	D	E	N	1971	49792
8120	S	E	E	N	1971	49792
8121	S	D	E	N	1971	49792
8121	S	E	E	N	1971	49792
8121	T	E	E	N	1973	51762
8123	S	D	F	N	1973	51110
8123	S	D	E	N	1974	53624
8124	S	D	E	L	1973	51821
8124	S	D	E	N	1973	51821
8132	S	D	E	L	1975	92137
8132	S	D	E	N	1975	92137
110-8134	S	D	E	L	1973	50817
8134	S	D	E	N	1973	50817
8135	L	S	E	H	1968	98632
8135	S	D	E	H	1974	53749
8135	S	D	E	N	1974	53749
8135	S	D	E	L	1975	65199
8135	S	D	E	N	1975	65199
8135	T	D	G	N	1957	86339
8135	T	D	E	N	1973	86340
8136	S	D	E	H	1974	53749
8136	S	D	E	N	1974	53749
8152	C	D	E	L	1973	52186
8152	C	D	E	L	1973	55132
8152	S	D	E	N	1973	52186
8165	S	D	E	L	1974	58944
8165	S	D	E	N	1974	58944
8166	C	D	E	L	1974	58944
8166	S	D	E	L	1974	58944
8166	S	D	E	N	1974	58944
8185	S	S	E	N	1967	97983
8197	S	S	E	N	1972	63980
8203	S	D	R	N	1973	55807
8203	S	D	R	N	1973	66116
8204	S	D	R	N	1973	55807
8204	S	D	R	N	1973	66116
8205	S	D	R	N	1973	55807
8205	S	D	E	N	1973	56370
8205	S	D	R	N	1973	66116
8205	S	D	E	N	1971	68080
8211	S	D	E	N	1973	56161
8215	S	D	G	N	1973	57058
8216	S	D	E	N	1973	57124
8217	S	D	E	N	1973	57124
8234	C	D	E	L	1975	87154
8249	S	D	R	N	1971	67332
8253	S	S	E	N	1967	97983
8254	S	D	R	N	1974	67753
8254	S	S	E	N	1967	97983
8259	S	D	R	N	1973	50742
8259	S	D	E	N	1973	79081
8261	S	D	E	L	1975	92137
8261	S	D	E	N	1975	92137
8262	S	S	R	H	1972	78759
8262	S	S	R	N	1972	78759
8262	S	D	E	L	1975	92137
8262	S	D	E	N	1975	92137
8262	S	S	E	H	1972	93228
8262	S	S	E	N	1972	93228
8263	S	D	E	L	1975	92137
8263	S	D	E	N	1975	92137
8264	S	S	E	N	1975	92137
8266	S	D	R	N	1971	76484
8266	S	D	E	N	1971	91524
8267	S	D	R	N	1971	76484
8267	S	D	E	N	1971	91524
8280	S	S	E	N	1976	103180
8283	S	D	E	L	1971	65747
8283	S	D	E	N	1971	65747
8283	S	T	E	L	1971	65747
8283	S	T	E	N	1971	65747
111-0001	S	D	E	N	1973	50805
0001	S	D	E	N	1973	53044
0003	S	D	F	H	1975	90267
0006	L	S	E	H	1968	98632
0006	P	S	E	H	1969	68115
0006	P	S	E	N	1969	68115
0006	S	S	E	N	1969	68115
0008	D	D	R	N	1973	50071
0008	D	D	R	N	1973	55321
0008	D	D	E	N	1974	58327
0008	D	T	E	N	1974	58327
0008	D	D	E	N	1974	58958
0008	D	D	E	N	1974	59257
0008	D	D	E	N	1971	61678
0008	D	D	R	N	1974	76160
0008	D	D	E	N	1975	76161
0008	D	S	E	N	1962	87669
0008	D	S	E	N	1965	87703
0008	D	D	E	N	1975	96448
0008	S	D	R	N	1973	50205
0008	S	D	E	N	1973	50206
0008	S	D	R	N	1972	50732
0008	S	D	E	N	1973	51907
0008	S	T	E	N	1973	55161
0008	S	S	E	N	1973	55835
0008	S	D	E	N	1973	55860
0008	S	D	E	N	1974	58958
0008	S	D	E	N	1974	62030
0008	S	D	R	N	1971	66936
0008	S	S	E	N	1962	87669
0008	S	S	E	N	1965	87703
0008	S	S	E	N	1971	87884
0008	T	D	R	N	1971	59188
0008	T	D	E	N	1971	59189
0008	T	D	R	N	1971	67719
0015	L	S	E	N	1968	98632
0015	S	S	E	N	1969	68115
0021	C	S	R	L	1974	66446
0021	C	S	E	L	1974	66447
0021	C	S	E	L	1971	87884
111-0021	D	D	E	N	1973	52644
0021	D	D	E	N	1974	60371
0021	S	D	E	N	1973	62246
0021	S	E	E	N	1973	62246
0021	S	S	R	N	1974	66446
0021	S	S	E	N	1974	66447
0021	S	S	E	N	1971	87884
0021	T	D	E	N	1973	53394
0021	T	D	E	N	1973	53529
0021	T	D	E	N	1973	54206
0021	T	D	E	N	1974	58028
0029	S	D	R	N	1965	76401
0029	S	D	E	N	1965	91742
0046	S	D	E	N	1972	53240
0050	D	D	E	N	1973	50558
0050	S	D	E	N	1973	50558
0050	S	D	E	N	1973	56335
0050	S	D	E	N	1975	94550
0093	S	D	R	H	1973	70815
0093	S	D	R	N	1973	70815
0093	S	D	E	H	1973	91572
0093	S	D	E	N	1973	91572
0103	S	D	R	H	1973	70815
0103	S	D	R	N	1973	70815
0103	S	D	E	H	1973	91572
0103	S	D	R	H	1973	91572
0103	S	D	E	N	1973	91572
0104	S	D	R	H	1973	70815
0104	S	D	R	N	1973	70815
0104	S	D	E	H	1973	91572
0104	S	D	E	N	1973	91572
8002	A	S	E	N	1971	49794
8002	A	S	E	N	1970	75887
8002	C	S	E	L	1969	75904
8002	C	S	E	L	1971	87884
8002	D	D	E	L	1973	57692
8002	D	D	E	N	1973	57692
8002	D	D	E	L	1974	61358
8002	D	D	E	N	1974	61358
8002	D	S	E	N	1969	61512
8002	D	D	E	N	1975	66679
8002	D	D	R	N	1972	76506
8002	D	D	R	N	1972	76521
8002	D	D	E	L	1975	87176
8002	D	D	E	N	1975	87176
8002	D	S	E	N	1962	87670
8002	D	D	E	N	1972	91507
8002	D	D	E	N	1972	91529
8002	D	D	E	N	1975	94627
8002	D	S	E	N	1967	97985
8002	L	S	E	N	1962	87670
8002	L	S	E	N	1971	87884
8002	L	S	R	N	1974	92307
8002	L	S	E	N	1974	92308
8002	S	D	E	L	1973	50578
8002	S	D	E	N	1973	50578
8002	S	D	E	N	1972	53519
8002	S	D	E	N	1974	54661
8002	S	D	R	N	1973	55713
8002	S	D	E	L	1973	57565
8002	S	D	E	N	1973	57565
8002	S	T	E	N	1956	62960
8002	S	D	G	N	1954	66199
8002	S	S	E	L	1962	87670
8002	S	S	E	N	1962	87670
8002	S	S	E	L	1971	87884
8002	S	S	E	N	1971	87884
8002	S	S	R	N	1974	92307
8002	S	S	E	N	1974	92308
8002	S	S	E	N	1967	97985
8007	S	D	R	N	1969	53201
8007	S	D	E	N	1972	53202
8007	S	D	R	N	1973	55322
8007	S	D	E	N	1974	59258
8007	S	D	E	N	1974	61354
8007	S	D	R	N	1965	76401
8007	S	D	E	N	1965	91742
8007	T	D	E	N	1973	57281
8007	T	E	E	N	1976	101201
8007	T	T	E	N	1976	101201
8008	S	D	R	N	1972	58561
8009	L	D	R	N	1973	52540
8009	L	D	E	N	1974	53675
8009	S	D	R	N	1969	53201
8009	S	D	E	N	1972	53202
8010	L	S	E	N	1974	62782
8010	L	D	E	N	1972	63722
8010	S	S	E	N	1970	75833
8014	T	D	R	N	1973	86004
8014	T	E	R	N	1973	86004
8015	A	D	E	N	1973	51901
8015	L	D	R	H	1974	87298
8015	L	D	E	H	1975	87299
8015	L	D	R	H	1976	103384
8015	L	D	R	N	1976	103384
8015	L	D	E	H	1976	103385
8015	L	D	E	N	1976	103385
8015	S	S	E	N	1969	68115
8015	T	D	E	N	1973	51901
8015	T	D	E	N	1973	55106
8016	L	D	R	N	1973	49578

Phys. State: **A.** Amorphous; **C.** Superconductive; **D.** Doped; **F.** Fibrous or Whisker; **G.** Gas; **I.** Ionized or Plasma; **L.** Liquid; **P.** Powder or Particle; **S.** Solid; **T.** Thin Film
Subject: **D.** Data; **E.** Experiment; **S.** Survey (Review, Compendium, etc.); **T.** Theory
Language: **E.** English; **F.** French; **G.** German; **O.** Other Languages; **R.** Russian
Temperature: **L.** Low (0 to 75K); **N.** Normal (75 to 1273K); **H.** High (above 1273K)

Substance Number	Phys. State	Subject	Language	Temperature	Year	EPIC Number
111-8016	S	D	R	N	1973	49578
8017	L	D	R	N	1973	49578
8017	S	D	R	N	1973	49578
8018	L	D	R	N	1973	49578
8018	S	D	R	N	1973	49578
8019	S	D	E	N	1973	49591
8019	S	D	E	N	1972	53519
8020	S	T	E	N	1974	57985
8021	A	D	E	N	1973	51901
8021	A	S	E	N	1973	54768
8021	A	D	E	N	1974	55137
8021	A	S	E	N	1971	84631
8021	A	D	E	N	1976	99925
8021	A	T	E	N	1976	99925
8021	D	D	E	L	1973	52437
8021	D	D	E	N	1974	54572
8021	D	E	R	N	1972	61562
8021	D	E	E	N	1972	65913
8021	D	S	E	N	1967	97985
8021	L	D	R	N	1973	52540
8021	L	D	E	N	1974	53675
8021	L	D	R	H	1974	87298
8021	L	D	R	N	1974	87298
8021	L	D	E	H	1975	87299
8021	L	D	E	N	1975	87299
8021	S	D	E	N	1974	54572
8021	S	D	E	N	1974	55137
8021	S	D	R	L	1973	55199
8021	S	D	R	N	1973	55199
8021	S	D	E	L	1974	55200
8021	S	D	E	N	1974	55200
8021	S	D	G	L	1971	59513
8021	S	D	G	N	1971	59513
8021	S	S	G	L	1971	59513
8021	S	S	G	N	1971	59513
8021	S	D	E	N	1971	59951
8021	S	S	E	N	1969	68115
8021	S	D	R	N	1975	75092
8021	S	D	E	N	1975	91748
8021	S	D	R	N	1974	93451
8021	S	E	R	N	1974	93451
8021	S	T	R	N	1974	93451
8021	S	D	E	N	1974	93452
8021	S	E	E	N	1974	93452
8021	S	T	E	N	1974	93452
8021	S	S	E	L	1967	97985
8021	S	S	E	N	1967	97985
8021	S	D	R	N	1975	100839
8021	S	T	R	N	1975	100839
8021	S	D	E	N	1976	100840
8021	S	T	E	N	1976	100840
8021	T	D	E	N	1973	51901
8021	T	T	R	N	1973	52562
8021	T	D	R	N	1973	52896
8021	T	D	E	N	1974	52897
8021	T	S	E	N	1973	54768
8021	T	D	E	N	1973	55106
8021	T	D	E	N	1974	55137
8021	T	T	E	N	1974	55137
8021	T	T	E	N	1973	57787
8021	T	S	E	N	1971	84631
8021	T	D	E	N	1976	99925
8021	T	T	E	N	1976	99925
8023	S	D	E	N	1974	57750
8024	C	S	E	L	1959	75729
8025	S	D	E	N	1973	49999
8026	S	T	E	N	1973	55161
8031	S	D	E	N	1974	54661
8031	S	T	E	N	1975	61807
8031	S	S	E	N	1972	87889
8037	A	D	E	N	1975	68677
8037	A	T	E	N	1975	68677
8037	S	S	E	N	1967	97985
8037	T	D	E	N	1975	68677
8037	T	T	E	N	1975	68677
8041	S	D	R	H	1972	55387
8041	S	D	R	N	1972	55387
8041	S	D	E	L	1973	63624
8041	S	S	E	L	1973	63624
8041	S	D	E	H	1974	88429
8041	S	D	E	N	1974	88429
8043	S	D	E	L	1974	58909
8043	S	D	E	N	1974	58909
8044	S	S	E	L	1972	54881
8044	S	S	E	N	1972	54881
8044	S	T	E	L	1972	54881
8044	S	T	E	N	1972	54881
8044	S	S	E	L	1970	59594
8044	S	S	E	N	1970	59594
8044	S	T	E	L	1970	59594
8044	S	T	E	N	1970	59594
8044	S	T	E	L	1971	60950
8044	S	T	E	N	1971	60950
8044	S	D	E	L	1973	65773
8044	S	D	E	N	1973	65773
8044	S	T	E	L	1973	65773
8044	S	T	E	N	1973	65773
8055	C	D	R	L	1975	86851
8055	C	S	R	L	1975	86851
8055	C	D	E	L	1975	86852
8055	C	S	E	L	1975	86852

Substance Number	Phys. State	Subject	Language	Temperature	Year	EPIC Number
111-8055	C	D	E	L	1976	100720
8055	C	E	E	L	1976	100720
8055	C	T	E	L	1976	100720
8055	S	S	E	L	1967	66157
8055	S	S	E	N	1967	66157
8055	S	D	R	N	1971	66283
8055	S	D	R	N	1972	66285
8057	S	D	R	N	1972	52209
8058	C	D	E	L	1974	61152
8058	C	S	E	L	1974	61152
8058	C	D	E	L	1974	61194
8058	C	T	E	L	1974	61194
8058	C	S	O	L	1973	62410
8058	C	S	E	L	1974	64981
8058	C	D	E	L	1975	68710
8058	C	T	E	L	1975	68710
8058	C	D	E	L	1975	75624
8058	C	E	E	L	1975	75624
8058	C	D	E	L	1976	100720
8058	C	E	E	L	1976	100720
8058	C	T	E	L	1976	100720
8058	S	S	E	L	1967	66157
8058	S	S	E	N	1967	66157
8062	C	S	E	L	1959	75729
8063	C	S	E	L	1959	75729
8063	S	S	E	L	1972	54881
8063	S	S	E	N	1972	54881
8063	S	T	E	L	1972	54881
8063	S	T	E	N	1972	54881
8063	S	S	E	L	1970	59594
8063	S	S	E	N	1970	59594
8064	C	S	E	L	1959	75729
8064	S	S	E	L	1972	54881
8064	S	S	E	N	1972	54881
8064	S	T	E	L	1972	54881
8064	S	T	E	N	1972	54881
8064	S	S	E	L	1970	59594
8064	S	S	E	N	1970	59594
8065	S	D	E	L	1972	52969
8065	S	D	E	N	1972	52969
8065	S	D	E	L	1972	53158
8065	S	D	E	N	1972	53158
8065	S	D	E	L	1973	53293
8065	S	D	E	N	1973	53293
8066	S	D	E	L	1972	52969
8066	S	D	E	N	1972	52969
8066	S	D	E	N	1972	53010
8066	S	D	E	L	1972	53158
8066	S	D	E	N	1972	53158
8067	S	D	E	N	1972	53010
8067	S	D	E	L	1972	53158
8067	S	D	E	N	1972	53158
8068	S	D	R	N	1974	58526
8068	S	D	E	N	1974	66302
8071	S	D	E	N	1974	54324
8073	L	S	E	N	1974	62782
8074	S	D	E	N	1976	99351
8074	S	T	E	N	1976	99351
8074	T	D	E	N	1972	53416
8075	A	D	E	N	1973	51901
8075	A	D	E	N	1974	53628
8075	A	E	E	N	1974	53628
8075	A	D	E	N	1971	62269
8075	A	D	E	N	1972	75431
8075	T	D	E	N	1973	51901
8075	T	D	E	N	1971	53513
8075	T	D	E	N	1974	53628
8075	T	E	E	N	1974	53628
8075	T	D	E	N	1973	55106
8075	T	D	E	N	1972	75431
8075	T	S	E	N	1974	94637
8076	S	D	E	L	1973	53404
8076	S	D	E	N	1973	53404
8077	S	D	E	N	1972	53500
8078	T	D	E	N	1971	53513
8079	A	D	E	N	1973	51901
8079	L	D	R	H	1974	87298
8079	L	D	R	N	1974	87298
8079	L	D	E	H	1975	87299
8079	L	D	E	N	1975	87299
8079	S	S	E	N	1969	68115
8079	T	D	E	N	1973	51901
8079	T	T	R	N	1973	52562
8079	T	T	E	N	1973	57787
8080	A	D	E	N	1973	51901
8080	T	D	E	N	1973	51901
8092	S	D	E	N	1974	54572
8093	S	S	E	L	1974	54072
8093	S	S	E	N	1974	54072
8093	S	D	E	N	1976	95560
8095	S	S	E	N	1974	59386
8096	S	D	E	N	1974	59386
8098	S	D	R	N	1971	59995
8099	S	D	R	N	1971	59995
8100	S	D	R	N	1971	59995
8101	S	D	R	N	1971	59995
8102	C	T	E	L	1973	55125
8102	C	T	E	L	1974	57993
8102	C	S	E	L	1974	64981
8102	C	T	E	L	1975	68709
8102	C	S	E	L	1975	75601

Substance Number	Phys. State	Subject	Language	Temperature	Year	EPIC Number
111-8102	C	D	E	L	1975	75624
8102	C	E	E	L	1975	75624
8102	C	D	R	L	1974	81213
8102	C	E	R	L	1974	81213
8102	C	T	R	L	1974	81213
8102	C	S	E	L	1966	87721
8102	C	S	F	L	1974	87919
8102	C	D	E	L	1975	90384
8102	C	D	E	L	1975	90387
8102	C	D	E	L	1975	91953
8102	C	E	E	L	1975	91953
8102	C	T	E	L	1975	91953
8102	C	D	E	L	1974	92395
8102	C	E	E	L	1974	92395
8102	C	T	E	L	1974	92395
8102	C	S	E	L	1976	103404
8102	T	T	E	L	1974	57993
8102	T	S	E	L	1975	75601
8102	T	D	E	L	1975	90384
8102	T	D	E	L	1975	90387
8102	T	D	E	L	1975	91953
8102	T	E	E	L	1975	91953
8102	T	T	E	L	1975	91953
8103	C	S	E	L	1973	55121
8104	C	D	E	L	1973	55121
8106	S	T	E	N	1973	57662
8107	C	D	E	L	1974	57993
8107	C	S	E	L	1966	87721
8107	S	D	R	N	1971	66283
8107	S	D	R	N	1972	66285
8107	T	D	E	L	1974	57993
8108	A	D	E	N	1975	96723
8108	C	S	E	L	1969	68115
8108	T	D	E	N	1975	96723
8108	T	D	R	N	1976	101176
8108	T	S	R	N	1976	101176
8108	T	D	E	N	1976	101886
8108	T	S	E	N	1976	101886
8112	L	D	E	N	1972	63722
8117	S	D	E	N	1972	63827
8118	C	S	E	L	1974	59378
8118	C	D	E	L	1974	60358
8118	C	D	R	L	1974	63076
8118	C	E	R	L	1974	63076
8118	C	D	E	L	1975	63077
8118	C	E	E	L	1975	63077
8118	C	S	E	L	1974	64981
8118	C	D	E	L	1975	75624
8118	C	E	E	L	1975	75624
8118	C	S	E	L	1966	87721
8118	C	S	E	L	1972	87886
8118	C	D	E	L	1975	91953
8118	C	E	E	L	1975	91953
8118	C	S	E	L	1975	91953
8118	C	T	E	L	1975	91953
8118	C	S	E	L	1976	97925
8118	T	D	R	L	1974	63076
8118	T	E	R	L	1974	63076
8118	T	D	E	L	1975	63077
8118	T	E	E	L	1975	63077
8118	T	D	E	L	1975	91953
8118	T	E	E	L	1975	91953
8118	T	S	E	L	1975	91953
8118	T	T	E	L	1975	91953
8119	D	D	R	N	1973	55337
8119	D	D	E	N	1974	59275
8123	C	D	E	L	1974	61152
8123	C	S	E	L	1974	61152
8123	C	D	E	L	1975	68710
8123	C	T	E	L	1975	68710
8124	C	D	E	L	1974	61152
8124	C	S	E	L	1974	61152
8124	C	D	E	L	1976	100720
8124	C	E	E	L	1976	100720
8126	C	S	E	L	1974	64981
8126	S	D	R	N	1971	66283
8126	S	D	R	N	1972	66285
8127	D	S	E	N	1972	87824
8127	S	S	E	N	1972	87824
8128	T	D	E	N	1974	83981
8133	S	D	R	N	1973	56317
8134	S	D	R	N	1973	56317
8136	S	D	R	N	1973	51724
8136	S	D	R	N	1971	66283
8136	S	D	R	N	1972	66285
8139	S	D	R	N	1971	66283
8139	S	D	R	N	1972	66285
8140	S	D	R	N	1971	66283
8140	S	D	R	N	1972	66285
8141	S	D	R	N	1971	66283
8141	S	D	R	N	1972	66285
8142	S	D	R	N	1971	66283
8142	S	D	R	N	1972	66285
8143	S	D	R	N	1971	66283
8143	S	D	R	N	1972	66285
8144	S	D	R	N	1971	66283
8144	S	D	R	N	1972	66285
8145	C	S	E	L	1966	87721
8145	S	D	R	N	1971	66283
8145	S	D	R	N	1972	66285
8145	S	S	E	N	1966	87721

Phys. State: A. Amorphous; C. Superconductive; D. Doped; F. Fibrous or Whisker; G. Gas; I. Ionized or Plasma; L. Liquid; P. Powder or Particle; S. Solid; T. Thin Film
Subject: D. Data; E. Experiment; S. Survey (Review, Compendium, etc.); T. Theory
Language: E. English; F. French; G. German; O. Other Languages; R. Russian
Temperature: L. Low (0 to 75K); N. Normal (75 to 1273K); H. High (above 1273K)

Substance Number	Phys. State	Sub-ject	Lan-guage	Temper-ature	Year	EPIC Number
111-8145	S	S	E	N	1967	97985
8146	S	D	R	N	1971	66283
8146	S	D	R	N	1972	66285
8146	S	S	E	N	1967	97985
8147	S	D	R	N	1971	66283
8147	S	D	R	N	1972	66285
8148	S	D	R	N	1972	66285
8149	S	D	R	N	1971	66283
8149	S	D	R	N	1972	66285
8150	S	D	R	N	1971	66283
8150	S	D	R	N	1972	66285
8152	S	D	R	N	1973	67379
8153	S	D	R	N	1970	67414
8154	S	D	R	N	1970	67423
8157	S	D	O	N	1974	90531
8158	S	D	O	N	1974	90531
8160	C	S	E	L	1968	68372
8160	C	S	E	L	1968	68373
8160	C	S	E	L	1966	87721
8162	A	S	E	N	1972	87824
8162	S	S	E	N	1972	87824
8163	C	S	E	L	1966	87721
8164	C	S	E	L	1966	87721
8165	C	S	E	L	1966	87721
8166	C	S	E	L	1966	87721
8168	S	S	E	N	1966	87721
8168	S	S	E	N	1967	97985
8169	S	S	E	H	1967	97985
8169	S	S	E	N	1967	97985
8170	S	S	E	N	1967	97985
8171	S	S	E	N	1967	97985
8172	S	S	E	N	1967	97985
8173	S	S	E	N	1967	97985
8174	S	S	E	N	1967	97985
8175	S	S	E	N	1967	97985
8176	S	S	E	N	1967	97985
8177	L	S	E	N	1968	98632
8181	S	D	E	L	1975	90116
8181	S	D	E	N	1975	90116
8181	S	D	E	L	1974	92436
8181	S	D	E	N	1974	92436
8187	S	D	R	N	1972	55387
8187	S	D	E	N	1974	88429
8188	S	D	R	H	1972	55387
8188	S	D	R	N	1972	55387
8188	S	D	E	H	1974	88429
8188	S	D	E	N	1974	88429
8189	S	D	R	N	1972	55387
8189	S	D	E	N	1974	88429
8190	S	D	R	N	1972	78186
8190	T	D	R	N	1972	78186
8191	C	D	R	L	1974	81228
8191	C	D	E	L	1974	92358
8193	C	S	E	L	1974	63380
8193	C	T	E	L	1974	63380
8195	S	D	E	N	1975	100607
8195	S	T	E	N	1975	100607
8196	C	D	E	L	1976	100720
8196	C	E	E	L	1976	100720
8197	C	D	E	L	1976	100720
8197	C	E	E	L	1976	100720
8198	C	D	E	L	1976	97925
8198	C	S	E	L	1976	97925
8198	C	T	E	L	1976	97925
8199	C	D	F	L	1973	57624
8200	S	D	R	N	1971	66283
8201	S	D	R	N	1971	66283
8202	S	D	R	N	1971	66283
8203	S	D	R	N	1971	66283
8204	S	D	R	N	1971	66283
8207	S	D	E	N	1972	49784
8208	S	D	E	N	1974	57750
8209	S	D	E	N	1974	57750
8210	S	D	E	N	1974	57750
8211	C	S	E	L	1959	75729
112-0001	D	D	O	N	1972	51230
0001	D	D	O	N	1972	51231
0001	D	T	E	N	1974	90535
0001	G	D	E	H	1974	66880
0001	G	T	E	H	1974	66880
0001	L	D	R	N	1972	49852
0001	L	D	R	N	1972	58760
0001	L	S	E	N	1974	85293
0001	L	D	E	N	1975	90092
0001	L	S	E	N	1967	98664
0001	L	S	E	N	1962	99561
0001	S	D	E	N	1973	50912
0001	S	T	E	N	1973	51030
0001	S	S	E	N	1972	53074
0001	S	D	E	N	1972	53213
0001	S	D	R	N	1972	53432
0001	S	D	E	N	1973	53433
0001	S	T	E	N	1974	90535
0004	L	S	E	N	1967	98664
0008	S	D	E	N	1973	57879
0010	D	S	E	N	1968	75835
0010	L	D	R	N	1973	51348
0010	L	D	E	N	1973	57487
0010	L	S	E	N	1968	75835
0010	L	S	E	N	1974	85293
112-0010	S	D	R	N	1973	51348
0010	S	D	E	N	1973	57487
0021	S	S	E	H	1967	97982
0021	S	S	E	N	1967	97982
0021	S	S	E	H	1967	98889
0021	S	S	E	N	1967	98889
0021	T	D	E	N	1961	65971
0028	S	D	O	N	1971	56210
0028	S	S	E	N	1970	87822
0028	S	S	E	L	1972	87890
0028	S	S	E	N	1972	87890
0033	S	D	R	N	1973	55054
0033	S	D	E	N	1974	55055
0034	L	D	E	N	1973	50419
0034	L	S	E	N	1967	98664
0035	D	D	R	N	1973	55054
0035	D	D	E	N	1974	55055
0035	S	D	R	N	1973	52386
0035	S	D	R	N	1973	55054
0035	S	D	E	N	1974	55055
0035	S	D	E	N	1973	58579
0038	D	D	R	N	1973	55054
0038	D	D	E	N	1974	55055
0038	S	S	E	N	1970	87822
0038	S	S	E	N	1972	87890
0040	L	D	E	N	1973	50462
0040	L	D	E	N	1975	80277
0040	L	E	E	N	1975	80277
0040	L	D	E	N	1975	92112
0040	L	E	E	N	1975	92112
0040	L	S	E	N	1968	98632
0040	S	D	E	N	1975	92112
0040	S	E	E	N	1975	92112
0098	L	S	E	N	1968	98632
0098	S	S	E	N	1974	62066
0240	S	D	E	L	1973	56356
0240	S	D	E	N	1973	56356
0247	S	D	R	H	1972	59050
0247	S	D	R	N	1972	59050
0247	S	S	R	H	1972	59050
0247	S	S	R	N	1972	59050
0247	S	D	E	H	1972	59051
0247	S	D	E	N	1972	59051
0247	S	S	E	H	1972	59051
0247	S	S	E	N	1972	59051
0247	S	S	E	N	1964	93287
0247	S	S	E	H	1967	97984
0247	S	S	E	N	1967	97984
0402	S	S	E	N	1969	68271
0402	S	D	E	N	1975	101023
0481	D	D	F	H	1973	50619
0481	S	D	F	H	1973	50619
0577	C	D	E	L	1973	52099
0577	C	D	E	L	1972	57080
0577	S	D	E	L	1973	56356
0577	S	D	E	N	1973	56356
0698	S	S	E	N	1967	97984
8001	S	S	E	N	1967	97985
8008	S	T	E	N	1973	57662
8020	S	S	R	N	1972	53547
8020	S	S	E	N	1973	53548
8020	S	D	R	H	1952	62370
8020	S	D	R	N	1952	62370
8020	S	S	E	N	1969	68271
8020	S	S	E	N	1972	87823
8020	T	S	E	N	1972	87823
8022	C	S	E	L	1966	87721
8022	C	S	E	L	1972	87886
8022	S	S	E	L	1966	87721
8025	D	D	E	N	1976	101450
8025	S	D	R	L	1973	50062
8025	S	D	R	N	1973	50062
8025	S	D	E	L	1973	51418
8025	S	D	E	N	1973	51418
8025	S	D	R	N	1973	51721
8025	S	E	E	L	1958	59175
8025	S	E	E	N	1958	59175
8025	S	D	R	H	1952	62370
8025	S	D	R	N	1952	62370
8025	S	D	R	L	1974	63000
8025	S	T	R	L	1974	63000
8025	S	D	E	L	1974	63001
8025	S	T	E	L	1974	63001
8025	S	D	E	L	1962	65962
8025	S	D	E	N	1962	65962
8025	S	T	E	L	1962	65962
8025	S	T	E	N	1962	65962
8025	S	D	R	N	1969	66486
8025	S	D	R	N	1969	67411
8025	S	S	E	N	1969	68271
8025	S	S	E	N	1967	68371
8025	T	D	E	L	1971	54903
8025	T	D	E	N	1971	54903
8025	T	D	E	N	1974	66692
8032	S	S	E	L	1972	87823
8032	S	S	E	N	1972	87823
8053	L	S	E	N	1968	98632
8055	C	T	E	L	1973	55125
8055	C	D	E	L	1973	56672
8055	C	S	E	L	1973	56672
8055	C	D	E	L	1974	58934
112-8055	C	S	E	L	1974	58934
8055	S	D	E	N	1973	56672
8056	C	D	E	L	1973	56672
8056	C	S	E	L	1973	56672
8056	C	D	E	L	1974	58934
8056	S	D	E	N	1973	56672
8062	S	T	F	L	1974	66369
8062	S	T	F	N	1974	66369
8064	C	S	E	L	1972	63819
8064	C	D	E	L	1972	75996
8064	S	D	E	L	1972	75996
8064	S	D	E	N	1972	75996
8065	C	S	E	L	1974	86505
8067	S	D	E	L	1973	55961
8067	S	D	E	N	1973	55961
8067	S	D	E	L	1974	58360
8067	S	D	E	N	1974	58360
8067	S	D	E	L	1975	90637
8067	S	D	E	N	1975	90637
8067	S	E	E	L	1975	90637
8067	S	E	E	N	1975	90637
8067	S	T	E	L	1975	90637
8067	S	T	E	N	1975	90637
8079	C	D	E	L	1973	58635
8079	C	T	E	L	1973	58635
8079	S	D	E	L	1975	93537
8079	S	D	E	N	1975	93537
8083	S	S	E	L	1972	87823
8083	S	S	E	N	1972	87823
8084	S	S	E	L	1972	87823
8084	S	S	E	N	1972	87823
8085	S	S	E	N	1972	87823
8087	S	S	E	N	1972	87823
8087	T	S	E	N	1972	87823
8088	S	S	E	N	1967	97984
8089	S	S	E	N	1967	97984
8090	S	S	E	N	1967	97984
8091	S	S	E	N	1967	97985
8092	S	S	E	N	1967	97985
8093	L	S	E	N	1968	98632
8094	C	D	E	L	1975	100026
8100	C	S	E	L	1959	75729
8101	C	S	E	L	1959	75729
114-0001	D	D	E	N	1973	52064
0001	D	D	E	N	1963	64750
0001	F	D	R	N	1973	56306
0001	L	D	E	N	1972	49474
0001	L	S	E	N	1968	98632
0001	S	D	E	N	1973	52064
0002	L	D	E	N	1972	49474
0002	L	S	E	N	1968	98632
0009	D	E	E	N	1973	53581
0009	L	D	E	N	1975	91295
0009	L	S	E	N	1975	91295
0009	L	S	E	N	1968	98632
0010	L	D	E	N	1972	49474
0010	L	S	E	N	1968	98632
0011	L	S	E	H	1968	98632
0011	L	S	E	N	1968	98632
0015	D	D	E	N	1975	90860
0015	D	S	E	N	1975	92132
0015	S	D	E	N	1973	55964
0015	T	D	E	N	1973	56604
0015	T	D	R	N	1971	76465
0015	T	D	E	N	1975	90860
0015	T	D	E	N	1971	91584
0017	A	S	E	N	1971	87884
0017	D	D	E	N	1972	53463
0017	D	T	E	N	1973	57740
0017	D	D	E	N	1975	63562
0017	D	T	E	N	1975	63562
0017	D	D	R	N	1971	66936
0017	D	S	E	N	1962	97977
0017	D	S	E	N	1963	98002
0017	S	D	R	N	1973	50205
0017	S	D	E	N	1973	50206
0017	S	D	E	N	1974	53915
0017	S	D	E	N	1973	55860
0017	S	D	G	N	1954	66199
0017	S	S	E	N	1962	87660
0017	S	S	E	L	1971	87884
0017	S	S	E	N	1971	87884
0017	S	S	E	N	1962	97977
0017	S	S	E	N	1967	97984
0017	S	S	E	N	1963	98002
0017	T	D	R	L	1973	52832
0017	T	D	R	N	1973	52832
0017	T	D	E	L	1973	52833
0017	T	D	E	N	1973	52833
0017	T	S	E	N	1971	87884
0028	L	D	E	N	1976	101193
0028	L	S	E	N	1976	101193
0028	L	T	E	N	1976	101193
0046	D	D	E	N	1973	51742
0046	D	D	E	N	1973	55786
0046	L	D	E	N	1976	101193
0046	L	S	E	N	1976	101193
0046	L	T	E	N	1976	101193
0053	L	S	E	N	1968	98632
0055	L	S	E	H	1968	98632

Phys. State: **A.** Amorphous; **C.** Superconductive; **D.** Doped; **F.** Fibrous or Whisker; **G.** Gas; **I.** Ionized or Plasma; **L.** Liquid; **P.** Powder or Particle; **S.** Solid; **T.** Thin Film
Subject: **D.** Data; **E.** Experiment; **S.** Survey (Review, Compendium, etc.); **T.** Theory
Language: **E.** English; **F.** French; **G.** German; **O.** Other Languages; **R.** Russian
Temperature: **L.** Low (0 to 75K); **N.** Normal (75 to 1273K); **H.** High (above 1273K)

Substance Number	Phys. State	Sub-ject	Lan-guage	Temper-ature	Year	EPIC Number
114-0055	L	S	E	N	1968	98632
0055	S	S	E	N	1975	86748
0059	L	D	E	N	1975	80277
0059	L	E	E	N	1975	80277
0060	D	D	R	N	1974	58120
0060	D	D	E	N	1974	58121
0060	S	D	R	N	1974	58120
0060	S	D	E	N	1974	58121
0078	F	D	R	N	1973	56854
0078	S	S	E	N	1971	87884
0078	T	D	R	N	1972	51234
0079	L	D	E	N	1972	49474
0088	L	S	E	N	1968	98632
0112	S	D	R	N	1974	93455
0112	S	T	R	N	1974	93455
0112	S	D	E	N	1974	93456
0112	S	T	E	N	1974	93456
0113	S	D	R	N	1974	93455
0113	S	T	R	N	1974	93455
0113	S	D	E	N	1974	93456
0113	S	T	E	N	1974	93456
8001	A	D	E	N	1973	50922
8001	A	S	E	N	1970	59557
8001	A	S	E	N	1970	75887
8001	A	D	E	N	1974	87770
8001	C	S	E	L	1969	75904
8001	C	D	E	L	1974	87770
8001	C	S	E	L	1965	87781
8001	C	S	E	L	1971	87884
8001	D	D	R	N	1972	52357
8001	D	D	R	N	1965	61106
8001	D	D	E	N	1965	61107
8001	D	S	R	L	1972	62704
8001	D	T	R	N	1973	62727
8001	D	S	E	N	1974	64457
8001	D	S	E	L	1973	65123
8001	D	T	E	N	1973	65323
8001	D	S	E	N	1970	75887
8001	D	S	E	L	1975	87741
8001	D	S	E	N	1975	87741
8001	D	S	E	L	1965	87781
8001	D	S	E	N	1965	87781
8001	D	D	E	N	1975	90870
8001	D	T	E	N	1975	90870
8001	L	D	R	N	1973	52540
8001	L	D	E	N	1974	53675
8001	L	T	R	N	1971	61554
8001	L	D	R	H	1952	62370
8001	L	D	R	N	1952	62370
8001	L	T	E	N	1971	65904
8001	L	S	R	N	1974	92307
8001	L	S	E	N	1974	92308
8001	S	D	R	N	1973	51558
8001	S	D	R	L	1973	51700
8001	S	D	R	N	1973	51700
8001	S	D	R	L	1973	52525
8001	S	D	R	L	1973	52543
8001	S	D	E	L	1973	52933
8001	S	D	E	N	1973	52933
8001	S	S	E	N	1972	53299
8001	S	T	E	L	1973	53564
8001	S	T	E	N	1973	53564
8001	S	D	E	L	1974	53677
8001	S	D	E	N	1973	53689
8001	S	D	R	L	1973	54179
8001	S	D	R	N	1973	54179
8001	S	D	E	L	1973	54180
8001	S	D	E	N	1973	54180
8001	S	T	R	N	1973	55319
8001	S	D	R	L	1973	55320
8001	S	S	R	L	1973	55320
8001	S	D	E	L	1974	57766
8001	S	D	E	N	1974	58038
8001	S	E	E	L	1958	59175
8001	S	E	E	N	1958	59175
8001	S	T	E	N	1974	59254
8001	S	D	E	L	1974	59256
8001	S	S	E	L	1974	59256
8001	S	S	E	N	1970	59557
8001	S	D	E	N	1973	60685
8001	S	T	E	N	1973	60685
8001	S	D	E	N	1970	61493
8001	S	E	R	N	1971	61554
8001	S	T	R	N	1971	61554
8001	S	D	E	N	1969	62248
8001	S	D	E	N	1971	62260
8001	S	D	R	N	1952	62370
8001	S	S	E	L	1974	64464
8001	S	S	E	N	1974	64464
8001	S	D	R	L	1974	65371
8001	S	D	E	L	1975	65372
8001	S	E	E	N	1971	65904
8001	S	T	E	N	1971	65904
8001	S	S	O	N	1966	66022
8001	S	S	E	N	1967	66023
8001	S	D	G	N	1954	66199
8001	S	D	E	L	1974	66375
8001	S	T	E	L	1974	66375
8001	S	D	R	L	1974	66600
8001	S	D	E	L	1974	66601
8001	S	T	E	N	1975	66682
114-8001	S	D	R	L	1974	66734
8001	S	T	R	L	1974	66734
8001	S	D	E	L	1975	66735
8001	S	T	E	L	1975	66735
8001	S	D	R	L	1974	66736
8001	S	T	R	L	1974	66736
8001	S	D	E	L	1975	66737
8001	S	T	E	L	1975	66737
8001	S	S	E	L	1963	87679
8001	S	S	E	N	1963	87679
8001	S	D	E	N	1974	87770
8001	S	S	E	L	1965	87781
8001	S	S	E	N	1965	87781
8001	S	S	E	L	1971	87884
8001	S	S	E	N	1971	87884
8001	S	S	E	N	1972	87891
8001	S	S	R	N	1974	92307
8001	S	S	E	N	1974	92308
8001	S	S	E	L	1967	97985
8001	S	S	E	N	1967	97985
8001	S	D	R	L	1975	101629
8001	S	E	R	L	1975	101629
8001	S	T	R	L	1975	101629
8001	S	D	E	L	1975	101630
8001	S	E	E	L	1975	101630
8001	S	T	E	L	1975	101630
8001	T	D	R	L	1973	50671
8001	T	D	E	N	1973	50922
8001	T	D	E	L	1973	52417
8001	T	S	E	N	1973	53451
8001	T	S	E	N	1971	60965
8001	T	S	E	N	1975	65496
8001	T	D	E	N	1974	87770
8001	T	S	E	N	1965	87781
8001	T	S	E	N	1969	87821
8008	L	S	E	N	1968	98632
8010	D	D	R	N	1971	67054
8010	S	T	R	N	1972	63472
8010	S	T	E	N	1972	65150
8010	S	D	R	N	1972	76548
8010	S	D	E	N	1972	91598
8011	C	S	E	L	1972	62375
8011	L	D	R	N	1973	52540
8011	L	D	E	N	1974	53675
8011	L	D	E	N	1972	63722
8011	L	D	R	H	1974	87298
8011	L	D	R	N	1974	87298
8011	L	D	E	H	1975	87299
8011	L	D	E	N	1975	87299
8011	L	S	R	N	1974	92307
8011	L	S	E	N	1974	92308
8011	S	D	R	N	1973	62447
8011	S	S	R	N	1974	92307
8011	S	S	E	N	1974	92308
8012	A	S	E	N	1962	87661
8012	L	D	E	N	1972	63722
8012	L	D	R	H	1974	87298
8012	L	D	E	H	1975	87299
8012	L	S	E	N	1976	101193
8012	L	T	E	N	1976	101193
8012	L	D	R	H	1976	103384
8012	L	D	R	N	1976	103384
8012	L	D	E	H	1976	103385
8012	L	D	E	N	1976	103385
8012	S	T	R	N	1972	63472
8012	S	T	E	N	1972	65150
8012	S	S	E	N	1970	75833
8012	S	S	E	N	1962	87661
8012	S	S	E	N	1967	97985
8018	L	S	E	N	1968	98632
8020	L	S	E	N	1968	98632
8024	L	S	E	N	1968	98632
8034	L	S	E	N	1968	98632
8041	S	D	R	N	1972	49568
8044	C	D	E	L	1973	52186
8044	S	D	E	N	1973	52186
8048	S	D	E	N	1973	55786
8049	S	D	E	N	1973	51831
8051	S	D	R	N	1971	76497
8051	S	T	R	N	1971	76497
8051	S	D	E	N	1971	91542
8051	S	T	E	N	1971	91542
8054	C	D	E	L	1973	52186
8054	C	S	E	L	1975	68702
8054	S	D	E	N	1973	52186
8055	C	S	E	L	1973	50527
8058	S	D	G	N	1971	59640
8059	S	D	E	L	1974	54072
8059	S	D	E	N	1974	54072
8059	S	D	E	N	1974	54076
8059	S	D	E	N	1976	95560
8060	S	S	E	N	1974	54072
8060	S	D	E	N	1976	95560
8063	L	D	E	N	1972	63722
8064	S	T	R	N	1972	63472
8064	S	T	E	N	1972	65150
8065	S	D	E	N	1972	63827
8066	S	D	R	N	1972	56997
8067	L	D	R	H	1974	87298
8067	L	D	R	N	1974	87298
8067	L	D	E	H	1975	87299
114-8067	L	D	E	N	1975	87299
8067	L	D	E	N	1972	101939
8067	L	T	E	N	1972	101939
8067	S	D	R	N	1974	87298
8067	S	D	E	N	1975	87299
8067	S	D	E	N	1972	101939
8067	S	T	E	N	1972	101939
8068	C	S	E	L	1974	64981
8069	T	D	E	N	1974	83981
8075	S	D	E	N	1974	56084
8076	S	D	E	N	1974	56084
8079	C	S	E	L	1968	68372
8079	C	S	E	L	1966	87721
8080	C	S	E	L	1966	87721
8082	C	S	E	L	1966	87721
8083	C	S	E	L	1966	87721
8084	C	S	E	L	1966	87721
8084	C	S	E	L	1976	97924
8085	C	S	E	L	1966	87721
8086	S	S	E	N	1967	97985
8087	S	D	E	N	1974	62504
8088	S	D	E	N	1974	62504
8089	L	D	E	N	1976	101193
8089	L	S	E	N	1976	101193
8089	L	T	E	N	1976	101193
8090	C	S	E	L	1976	97924
8091	C	S	E	L	1976	97924
8097	S	D	E	N	1974	57750
8098	S	D	E	N	1974	57750
8099	C	S	E	L	1959	75729
8100	C	S	E	L	1959	75729
8101	C	S	E	L	1959	75729
8102	C	S	E	L	1959	75729
8103	C	S	E	L	1959	75729
116-0001	L	D	G	N	1973	49778
0001	L	S	E	N	1972	51438
0001	L	S	E	N	1968	98632
0001	S	D	F	N	1972	49470
0005	L	D	R	N	1973	57006
0005	L	S	E	H	1968	98632
0005	S	D	E	N	1973	53838
0005	S	D	R	N	1973	57006
0012	L	S	E	N	1972	51438
0012	L	S	E	N	1968	98632
8010	L	D	R	N	1971	78826
8010	L	T	R	N	1971	78826
8010	L	D	E	N	1971	93209
8010	L	T	E	N	1971	93209
8012	L	D	E	N	1973	54890
8013	L	D	E	N	1973	54890
8014	L	D	E	N	1973	54890
8017	D	S	E	N	1970	87822
8017	S	D	O	N	1972	50641
8017	S	S	E	N	1972	87890
8025	D	D	E	N	1975	91963
8025	S	D	E	N	1975	91963
8026	S	D	E	N	1974	53644
8027	S	S	E	N	1973	56765
8028	S	S	E	L	1973	56765
8028	S	S	E	N	1973	56765
8031	L	D	E	N	1973	54890
8037	S	D	R	N	1973	58870
8038	S	D	R	N	1973	58870
8039	S	S	R	N	1973	67360
118-0002	T	D	R	N	1972	50694
0003	S	D	R	N	1971	49963
0003	S	S	E	N	1966	87846
0003	S	S	E	H	1967	98889
0003	S	S	E	N	1967	98889
0004	L	D	G	N	1973	49778
0004	L	S	E	N	1972	51438
0004	L	S	E	N	1968	98632
0020	S	D	F	H	1973	54836
0028	C	D	E	L	1975	63276
0031	L	S	E	N	1972	51438
0031	L	S	E	N	1968	98632
0037	D	D	E	N	1973	52748
0037	S	D	E	N	1973	50557
0037	S	S	E	N	1970	87822
0037	S	S	E	H	1972	87890
0037	S	S	E	N	1972	87890
0042	L	D	R	N	1973	57006
0042	L	S	E	N	1968	98632
0042	S	D	R	N	1973	57006
8005	C	D	E	L	1973	56353
8005	C	S	E	L	1974	62805
8005	C	D	E	L	1975	68702
8005	C	S	E	L	1975	68702
8005	C	T	E	L	1975	68702
8005	D	D	E	L	1975	68702
8005	D	T	E	L	1975	68702
8005	S	D	E	L	1973	56353
8005	S	D	E	N	1973	56353
8017	S	S	E	L	1967	97985
8017	S	S	E	N	1967	97985
8018	S	D	E	N	1973	56462
8019	S	S	E	N	1972	53775
8019	S	D	R	L	1974	58116
8019	S	D	E	L	1974	58117

Phys. State: **A.** Amorphous; **C.** Superconductive; **D.** Doped; **F.** Fibrous or Whisker; **G.** Gas; **I.** Ionized or Plasma; **L.** Liquid; **P.** Powder or Particle; **S.** Solid; **T.** Thin Film
Subject: **D.** Data; **E.** Experiment; **S.** Survey (Review, Compendium, etc.); **T.** Theory
Language: **E.** English; **F.** French; **G.** German; **O.** Other Languages; **R.** Russian
Temperature: **L.** Low (0 to 75K); **N.** Normal (75 to 1273K); **H.** High (above 1273K)

Substance Number	Phys. State	Sub-ject	Lan-guage	Temper-ature	Year	EPIC Number
118-8026	S	S	E	N	1973	53420
8026	S	T	E	N	1973	61070
8028	S	S	E	N	1972	53775
8030	C	D	E	L	1973	56077
8030	C	S	E	L	1959	75729
8046	C	D	E	L	1973	55121
8047	C	D	E	L	1973	55121
8047	C	S	E	L	1959	75729
8047	D	D	E	L	1973	55121
8051	C	D	E	L	1975	63276
8052	S	S	E	L	1973	54004
8052	S	S	E	N	1973	54004
8053	C	S	E	L	1974	62805
8054	C	S	E	L	1974	62805
8055	C	S	E	L	1974	62805
8055	C	D	E	L	1975	68702
8055	C	S	E	L	1975	68702
8055	C	T	E	L	1975	68702
8056	C	S	E	L	1974	62805
8057	S	D	E	N	1974	58909
8058	L	D	R	N	1973	51530
8058	L	S	R	N	1973	51530
8058	L	D	E	N	1973	53679
8058	L	S	E	N	1973	53679
8058	S	D	R	N	1973	51530
8058	S	S	R	N	1973	51530
8058	S	D	E	N	1973	53679
8058	S	S	E	N	1973	53679
8059	S	S	R	H	1974	60431
8059	S	S	E	H	1974	60432
8062	S	D	E	N	1967	75838
8063	C	D	E	L	1972	53189
8064	S	S	E	N	1974	87606
8064	S	S	E	H	1967	97983
8064	S	S	E	N	1967	97983
8065	D	D	E	N	1973	55659
8065	S	D	E	N	1973	55659
8066	D	D	E	N	1973	55794
8072	S	D	R	N	1973	58870
8073	S	D	R	N	1973	58870
8077	C	D	E	L	1975	63276
8078	C	D	E	L	1975	63276
8079	C	D	E	L	1975	63276
8080	C	D	E	L	1975	63276
8081	C	D	E	L	1975	63276
8082	C	D	E	L	1975	63276
8083	C	D	E	L	1975	63276
8084	C	D	E	L	1975	63276
8085	C	D	E	L	1975	63276
8086	C	D	E	L	1975	63276
8087	S	S	R	N	1973	67360
8090	S	S	E	N	1967	97983
8091	S	S	E	N	1967	97985
8092	S	S	E	N	1967	97985
8093	S	S	E	N	1967	97985
8094	L	S	E	N	1968	98632
8095	C	S	E	L	1975	75606
8097	S	T	R	N	1974	86647
8098	S	T	R	N	1974	86647
8099	S	D	E	N	1975	91299
8099	S	T	E	N	1975	91299
8103	C	S	E	L	1959	75729
8104	C	S	E	L	1959	75729
8105	C	S	E	L	1959	75729
8106	C	S	E	L	1959	75729
119-0001	A	D	E	L	1974	66395
0001	A	T	E	L	1974	66395
0001	C	D	E	L	1973	57666
0001	C	D	E	L	1975	89571
0001	D	D	E	N	1973	57666
0001	S	D	R	N	1972	50572
0001	S	D	R	N	1967	53069
0001	S	D	E	N	1972	53070
0001	S	D	E	N	1973	57666
0001	S	E	E	N	1952	65344
0001	S	T	E	N	1952	65344
0001	S	D	E	N	1975	90460
0002	D	D	E	H	1973	50441
0002	D	D	E	N	1973	50441
0002	D	D	R	N	1972	53061
0002	D	D	E	N	1973	53062
0002	P	D	E	N	1973	55521
0002	S	T	E	N	1972	50009
0002	S	D	E	H	1973	52313
0002	S	D	R	N	1972	53061
0002	S	D	E	N	1973	53062
0002	S	D	E	N	1974	53627
0002	S	S	E	N	1970	59588
0002	S	D	E	H	1970	60090
0002	S	S	E	H	1970	60090
0002	S	S	E	H	1962	65974
0002	S	D	E	N	1970	68210
0002	S	S	E	H	1969	68271
0002	S	S	E	N	1969	68271
0002	S	S	E	H	1963	87682
0002	S	S	E	N	1963	87682
0002	S	S	E	H	1969	87723
0002	S	S	E	N	1969	87723
0002	S	S	E	H	1966	87846
0002	S	S	E	N	1966	87846

Substance Number	Phys. State	Sub-ject	Lan-guage	Temper-ature	Year	EPIC Number
119-0002	S	D	E	H	1975	95378
0002	S	E	E	H	1975	95378
0002	S	T	E	H	1975	95378
0002	S	S	E	H	1967	97982
0002	S	S	E	N	1967	97982
0002	S	S	E	H	1962	98647
0002	S	S	E	H	1967	98889
0002	S	S	E	N	1967	98889
0008	D	D	E	N	1964	60562
0008	D	E	E	H	1964	60562
0008	D	E	E	N	1964	60562
0008	D	T	R	H	1975	90140
0008	D	T	R	N	1975	90140
0008	D	T	E	H	1975	90141
0008	D	T	E	N	1975	90141
0008	S	D	E	H	1971	49788
0008	S	D	E	H	1974	53749
0008	S	D	E	N	1974	53749
0008	S	S	E	H	1974	54022
0008	S	S	E	N	1974	54022
0008	S	D	E	N	1964	60562
0008	S	S	E	N	1974	87606
0008	S	D	E	N	1967	98889
0008	S	S	F	H	1976	99799
0008	S	S	F	N	1976	99799
0008	T	D	E	N	1974	54020
0010	P	D	G	N	1975	90506
0010	S	D	E	N	1972	67192
0015	L	S	E	N	1968	98632
0021	S	S	E	H	1967	97983
0021	S	S	E	N	1967	97983
0026	S	S	E	N	1966	87846
0041	S	D	E	N	1969	72658
0041	S	S	E	N	1967	97984
0051	S	D	E	N	1965	58978
0051	S	E	E	N	1965	58978
0064	S	D	E	N	1974	53627
8001	A	S	E	N	1972	53402
8001	S	S	E	H	1960	65977
8001	S	S	E	N	1960	65977
8001	S	S	E	N	1967	97985
8002	A	D	E	N	1975	68677
8002	A	T	E	N	1975	68677
8002	D	S	E	N	1962	87672
8002	L	S	R	N	1974	92307
8002	L	S	E	N	1974	92308
8002	S	D	E	N	1972	53413
8002	S	T	E	N	1956	62960
8002	S	S	E	N	1962	87672
8002	S	S	R	N	1974	92307
8002	S	S	E	N	1974	92308
8002	S	S	E	L	1967	97985
8002	S	S	E	N	1967	97985
8002	T	D	E	N	1975	68677
8002	T	T	E	N	1975	68677
8003	S	D	R	N	1974	63090
8003	S	T	R	N	1974	63090
8003	S	D	E	N	1975	63091
8003	S	T	E	N	1975	63091
8003	S	S	E	N	1967	97985
8008	S	D	E	N	1974	53627
8009	D	S	E	N	1962	87662
8009	L	S	R	H	1974	92307
8009	L	S	E	H	1974	92308
8009	S	S	E	N	1962	87662
8009	S	S	R	N	1974	92307
8009	S	S	E	N	1974	92308
8009	S	S	E	L	1967	97985
8009	S	S	E	N	1967	97985
8015	S	S	E	N	1967	97985
8016	S	S	E	H	1967	97985
8016	S	S	E	N	1967	97985
8019	S	D	F	N	1973	51294
8019	S	D	E	N	1972	56855
8019	S	S	F	N	1969	65459
8019	S	S	E	H	1967	97985
8019	S	S	E	N	1967	97985
8020	C	D	E	L	1974	79190
8020	C	S	E	L	1974	79190
8020	P	D	E	L	1974	79190
8027	S	S	E	H	1967	97983
8027	S	S	E	N	1967	97983
8031	S	D	F	N	1973	51294
8031	S	D	E	H	1973	52231
8031	S	D	E	N	1973	52231
8033	S	D	R	N	1971	76484
8033	S	S	R	N	1971	76484
8033	S	D	E	N	1971	91524
8033	S	S	E	N	1971	91524
8037	S	D	E	L	1973	50003
8040	D	D	R	L	1973	55056
8040	D	D	R	N	1973	55056
8040	D	D	E	L	1974	55057
8040	D	D	E	N	1974	55057
8040	S	D	E	N	1973	52655
8040	S	D	R	L	1973	55056
8040	S	D	R	N	1973	55056
8040	S	D	E	L	1974	55057
8040	S	D	E	N	1974	55057
8041	S	D	E	N	1973	52655
8042	S	D	E	N	1973	52655

Substance Number	Phys. State	Sub-ject	Lan-guage	Temper-ature	Year	EPIC Number
119-8043	S	S	E	L	1972	53272
8043	S	S	E	N	1972	53272
8044	S	S	E	L	1972	53272
8044	S	S	E	N	1972	53272
8045	S	D	E	N	1973	53318
8047	S	D	R	N	1973	50645
8047	S	D	R	N	1973	51686
8047	S	D	E	N	1973	63173
8047	S	D	G	N	1936	75374
8047	S	T	G	N	1936	75374
8047	S	S	E	N	1958	75842
8047	S	S	E	L	1967	97985
8047	S	S	E	N	1967	97985
8050	S	D	E	L	1973	51821
8050	S	D	E	N	1973	51821
8053	C	D	R	L	1973	51273
8054	C	D	R	L	1973	51273
8054	C	D	E	L	1972	62806
8054	S	D	G	N	1929	60551
8054	S	D	E	N	1936	61578
8055	C	D	R	L	1973	51273
8056	S	D	O	N	1973	65518
8057	D	S	E	N	1967	97985
8057	L	D	G	N	1957	59036
8057	L	S	R	N	1974	92307
8057	L	S	E	N	1974	92308
8057	S	D	E	L	1974	57958
8057	S	D	E	N	1974	57958
8057	S	D	E	N	1936	61578
8057	S	S	R	N	1974	92307
8057	S	S	E	N	1974	92308
8057	S	S	E	N	1967	97985
8058	S	D	R	L	1973	55078
8058	S	D	R	N	1973	55078
8058	S	D	E	L	1974	55079
8058	S	D	E	N	1974	55079
8066	T	D	R	N	1973	54381
8066	T	D	E	N	1973	54382
8069	C	D	E	L	1973	55125
8070	C	D	E	L	1973	55125
8070	C	S	E	L	1975	75606
8071	C	D	E	L	1973	55125
8072	C	T	E	L	1973	55125
8073	C	D	E	L	1972	62806
8074	C	D	E	L	1972	62806
8075	C	D	E	L	1972	62806
8076	C	D	E	L	1972	62806
8077	S	D	E	N	1936	61578
8080	C	D	E	L	1973	59309
8080	C	D	E	L	1971	60954
8080	C	T	E	L	1971	60954
8080	C	D	E	L	1973	75570
8080	C	S	E	L	1974	86505
8080	C	D	E	L	1975	89571
8080	C	S	E	L	1976	103259
8080	S	D	E	N	1973	57666
8082	C	S	E	L	1974	64981
8083	C	S	E	L	1974	64981
8084	C	T	E	L	1974	79190
8084	D	D	R	N	1973	56469
8084	D	S	E	N	1969	75843
8084	D	D	E	N	1973	76678
8084	D	D	R	N	1974	93453
8084	D	T	R	N	1974	93453
8084	D	D	E	N	1974	93454
8084	D	T	E	N	1974	93454
8084	S	D	R	N	1973	56469
8084	S	S	E	N	1969	75843
8084	S	D	E	N	1973	76678
8084	S	D	E	N	1975	90460
8084	S	D	R	N	1974	93453
8084	S	T	R	N	1974	93453
8084	S	D	E	N	1974	93454
8084	S	T	E	N	1974	93454
8084	S	S	E	N	1967	97985
8085	S	S	E	N	1969	75843
8086	C	D	E	L	1974	79190
8091	D	S	E	H	1967	97985
8091	D	S	E	N	1967	97985
8091	S	T	R	N	1972	56907
8093	S	D	G	N	1973	57057
8094	S	D	G	N	1973	57057
8095	L	S	E	N	1968	98632
8101	A	D	E	L	1974	66395
8101	A	T	E	L	1974	66395
8101	S	D	E	N	1975	90460
8101	S	S	E	N	1967	97985
8102	C	S	E	L	1965	87791
8104	C	S	E	L	1972	87886
8105	S	S	E	H	1967	97983
8105	S	S	E	N	1967	97983
8106	S	S	E	N	1967	97984
8107	S	S	E	N	1967	97985
8108	S	S	E	H	1967	97985
8108	S	S	E	N	1967	97985
8109	S	D	E	N	1967	85908
8110	C	S	E	L	1975	75606
8111	C	D	R	L	1974	81228
8111	C	D	E	L	1974	92358
8114	S	D	R	N	1971	76484
8114	S	S	R	N	1971	76484

Phys. State: **A.** Amorphous; **C.** Superconductive; **D.** Doped; **F.** Fibrous or Whisker; **G.** Gas; **I.** Ionized or Plasma; **L.** Liquid; **P.** Powder or Particle; **S.** Solid; **T.** Thin Film
Subject: **D.** Data; **E.** Experiment; **S.** Survey (Review, Compendium, etc.); **T.** Theory
Language: **E.** English; **F.** French; **G.** German; **O.** Other Languages; **R.** Russian
Temperature: **L.** Low (0 to 75K); **N.** Normal (75 to 1273K); **H.** High (above 1273K)

Substance Number	Phys. State	Subject	Language	Temperature	Year	EPIC Number
119-8114	S	D	E	N	1971	91524
8114	S	S	E	N	1971	91524
8116	S	D	R	L	1974	63024
8116	S	D	E	L	1974	63025
8117	S	D	R	N	1974	93453
8117	S	T	R	N	1974	93453
8117	S	D	E	N	1974	93454
8117	S	T	E	N	1974	93454
8118	S	D	R	N	1974	93453
8118	S	T	R	N	1974	93453
8118	S	D	E	N	1974	93454
8118	S	T	E	N	1974	93454
8119	A	D	E	N	1975	68677
8119	A	T	E	N	1975	68677
8119	T	D	E	N	1975	68677
8119	T	T	E	N	1975	68677
8120	S	D	E	N	1972	49784
120-0001	A	S	E	N	1972	52403
0001	D	D	R	H	1973	51632
0001	D	D	R	N	1973	51632
0001	D	D	E	N	1973	52640
0001	D	D	E	H	1973	52827
0001	D	D	E	N	1973	52827
0001	D	D	E	H	1973	53755
0001	D	D	E	N	1973	53755
0001	D	T	E	H	1973	53755
0001	D	T	E	N	1973	53755
0001	D	S	E	N	1973	56765
0001	D	D	E	N	1975	63350
0001	D	T	E	N	1975	63350
0001	D	D	E	H	1972	66933
0001	D	D	E	N	1972	66933
0001	D	D	E	H	1971	67432
0001	D	D	E	N	1971	67432
0001	D	S	E	N	1974	87606
0001	S	D	E	H	1971	49788
0001	S	D	R	N	1971	49982
0001	S	D	R	N	1971	49983
0001	S	D	R	H	1973	51632
0001	S	D	R	N	1973	51632
0001	S	D	E	N	1973	51787
0001	S	D	E	N	1973	52768
0001	S	D	E	H	1973	52827
0001	S	D	O	N	1971	53046
0001	S	D	E	H	1973	53435
0001	S	T	E	H	1973	53435
0001	S	D	E	H	1973	53755
0001	S	D	E	N	1973	53755
0001	S	T	E	H	1973	53755
0001	S	T	E	N	1973	53755
0001	S	D	E	N	1960	60561
0001	S	D	E	N	1974	65606
0001	S	T	E	N	1974	65606
0001	S	D	E	H	1971	66845
0001	S	D	E	N	1971	66845
0001	S	D	E	H	1972	66933
0001	S	D	E	N	1972	66933
0001	S	D	E	H	1971	67432
0001	S	D	E	N	1971	67432
0001	S	D	E	N	1970	68210
0001	S	T	E	N	1970	75905
0001	S	S	E	N	1966	87846
0001	S	T	E	N	1975	91134
0001	S	D	E	N	1967	98889
0001	S	S	E	H	1967	98889
0001	T	D	E	N	1975	63350
0001	T	T	E	N	1975	63350
0004	D	D	E	H	1973	55117
0004	D	D	E	N	1973	55117
0004	D	D	E	N	1973	57844
0004	D	S	E	N	1966	87721
0004	S	D	E	H	1973	55117
0004	S	D	E	N	1973	55117
0004	S	D	E	H	1973	57844
0004	S	D	E	N	1973	57844
0004	S	S	E	H	1966	87721
0004	S	S	E	N	1966	87721
0004	T	D	E	L	1972	49465
0004	T	D	E	N	1972	49465
0004	T	D	E	N	1972	53252
0006	L	S	E	H	1968	98632
0006	L	S	E	N	1968	98632
0006	S	D	E	N	1973	56164
0006	S	D	E	N	1974	58051
0006	S	S	E	N	1974	58051
0006	S	S	E	L	1975	66700
0006	S	T	E	L	1975	66700
0007	S	S	E	N	1965	101534
0009	L	D	G	N	1973	49778
0009	L	S	E	N	1972	51438
0009	L	S	E	N	1968	98632
0009	S	D	E	N	1968	75725
0009	S	E	E	N	1968	75725
0010	S	D	R	N	1973	54869
0016	L	D	R	N	1973	57006
0016	L	S	E	N	1968	98632
0016	S	D	R	N	1973	57006
0017	C	D	R	L	1975	86851
0017	C	S	R	L	1975	86851
0017	C	D	E	L	1975	86852
120-0017	C	S	E	L	1975	86852
0017	C	S	E	L	1964	93287
0017	S	D	R	H	1972	59050
0017	S	D	R	N	1972	59050
0017	S	S	R	H	1972	59050
0017	S	S	R	N	1972	59050
0017	S	D	E	H	1972	59051
0017	S	D	E	N	1972	59051
0017	S	S	E	H	1972	59051
0017	S	S	E	N	1972	59051
0017	S	S	E	H	1962	65974
0017	S	S	E	N	1962	65974
0017	S	S	E	N	1966	87803
0017	S	D	E	N	1964	93287
0017	S	S	E	N	1964	93287
0017	S	S	E	N	1955	98662
0017	S	S	E	H	1967	98893
0017	S	S	E	N	1967	98893
0017	T	D	E	N	1961	65971
0023	C	S	E	L	1964	93287
0023	S	S	E	N	1963	62914
0023	S	S	F	N	1969	65459
0023	S	S	E	N	1963	65968
0023	S	S	E	H	1962	65974
0023	S	S	E	N	1962	65974
0023	S	S	E	N	1966	87803
0023	S	D	E	N	1964	93287
0023	S	S	E	N	1964	93287
0023	S	S	E	H	1967	97984
0023	S	S	E	L	1967	97984
0023	S	S	E	N	1967	97984
0023	S	S	E	N	1967	98893
0023	T	D	E	N	1963	62914
0023	T	D	E	N	1961	65971
0024	L	S	E	N	1972	51438
0024	L	S	E	N	1968	98632
0035	C	D	E	L	1972	54619
0035	C	S	E	L	1964	93287
0035	S	D	R	H	1973	53995
0035	S	D	R	N	1973	53995
0035	S	D	E	H	1973	53996
0035	S	D	E	N	1973	53996
0035	S	D	E	N	1972	54619
0035	S	D	E	N	1964	93287
0035	S	S	E	N	1964	93287
0035	T	D	R	N	1972	54159
0035	T	D	E	N	1972	54160
0036	S	D	E	N	1973	51858
0036	S	D	E	N	1972	53013
0036	S	S	E	N	1973	56765
0042	D	D	G	N	1973	51307
0042	S	D	G	N	1973	51307
0042	S	D	E	H	1973	55117
0044	C	D	E	L	1974	53590
0045	C	D	E	L	1974	53921
0045	C	T	E	L	1973	55125
0045	C	D	O	L	1971	61479
0045	C	D	E	L	1972	62375
0045	C	E	E	L	1972	62375
0045	C	S	E	L	1972	62375
0045	C	D	R	L	1975	86851
0045	C	S	R	L	1975	86851
0045	C	D	E	L	1975	86852
0045	C	S	E	L	1975	86852
0045	C	S	E	L	1966	87721
0045	C	S	E	L	1972	87886
0045	C	S	F	L	1974	87919
0045	C	S	E	L	1964	93287
0045	C	S	E	L	1967	97984
0045	S	S	E	L	1966	87721
0045	S	S	E	N	1972	87886
0045	S	D	E	N	1964	93287
0045	S	S	E	N	1964	93287
0045	S	S	E	L	1967	97984
0045	S	S	E	N	1967	97984
0045	T	D	R	N	1972	54159
0045	T	T	R	N	1972	54159
0045	T	D	E	N	1972	54160
0045	T	T	E	N	1972	54160
0045	T	D	E	L	1973	55126
0045	T	D	E	L	1973	57438
0045	T	D	O	L	1971	61479
0045	T	D	E	L	1972	62375
0045	T	S	E	L	1972	87886
0045	T	S	E	N	1972	87886
0047	L	S	E	N	1972	51438
0047	L	S	E	N	1968	98632
0047	S	D	E	N	1973	57879
0051	C	D	E	L	1975	91954
0051	C	E	E	L	1975	91954
0051	P	D	E	N	1974	86051
0051	S	D	E	N	1964	93287
0051	S	S	E	N	1964	93287
0051	S	S	E	N	1967	97984
0051	T	D	O	N	1972	51984
0051	T	D	R	N	1972	54159
0051	T	D	E	N	1972	54160
0051	T	D	E	N	1973	59572
0051	T	T	E	N	1973	59572
0051	T	D	E	N	1971	64072
0051	T	D	E	N	1971	65760
120-0051	T	D	E	N	1973	66509
0051	T	D	E	N	1970	67469
0051	T	D	E	N	1974	86051
0051	T	D	E	L	1975	91954
0051	T	E	E	L	1975	91954
0057	S	D	E	L	1968	64268
0057	S	D	E	N	1968	64268
0057	S	T	E	L	1968	64268
0057	S	S	E	N	1968	64269
0066	S	S	E	N	1973	53431
0073	P	D	E	N	1974	86051
0073	T	D	E	N	1973	59572
0073	T	T	E	N	1973	59572
0073	T	T	E	N	1972	63504
0073	T	D	E	N	1971	64072
0073	T	D	E	N	1973	66509
0073	T	D	E	N	1974	86051
0073	T	D	E	N	1974	89522
0073	T	D	E	N	1975	91956
0073	T	E	E	N	1975	91956
0073	T	S	E	N	1975	91956
0075	L	D	G	N	1973	49778
0075	L	S	E	N	1972	51438
0075	L	S	E	N	1968	98632
0075	S	D	R	N	1973	57238
0106	S	D	E	N	1974	54324
0140	S	D	R	N	1967	53069
0140	S	D	E	N	1972	53070
0154	L	S	E	N	1972	51438
0165	S	D	R	N	1970	53058
0172	C	D	E	L	1972	55092
0172	C	D	E	L	1975	62979
0172	C	S	E	L	1972	87886
0172	S	T	E	L	1975	62979
0172	S	S	E	N	1972	87886
0199	C	D	E	L	1973	52186
0199	C	D	E	L	1974	53921
0199	C	S	E	L	1966	87721
0199	S	D	E	N	1973	52186
0199	S	S	E	L	1966	87721
0199	S	S	E	N	1966	87721
0286	S	D	R	N	1973	70822
0286	S	T	R	N	1973	70822
0286	S	D	E	N	1973	91587
0286	S	T	E	N	1973	91587
0287	S	D	R	N	1973	70822
0287	S	T	R	N	1973	70822
0287	S	D	E	N	1973	91587
0287	S	T	E	N	1973	91587
0288	S	D	R	N	1973	70822
0288	S	T	R	N	1973	70822
0288	S	D	E	N	1973	91587
0288	S	T	E	N	1973	91587
8001	S	D	R	L	1972	100974
8001	S	D	R	N	1972	100974
8003	C	S	E	L	1966	87721
8003	C	S	E	L	1972	87886
8005	C	S	E	L	1968	68373
8005	C	S	E	L	1972	87886
8005	S	S	E	L	1968	68373
8005	S	S	E	L	1972	87886
8006	C	D	E	L	1974	53641
8006	C	T	E	L	1973	55125
8006	C	S	R	L	1973	55213
8006	C	S	E	L	1974	55214
8006	C	D	E	L	1974	57794
8006	C	T	E	L	1974	57794
8006	C	D	E	L	1974	60358
8006	C	D	E	L	1974	60388
8006	C	D	R	L	1974	60465
8006	C	D	E	L	1974	60466
8006	C	S	O	L	1973	62410
8006	C	D	R	L	1973	62435
8006	C	E	R	L	1973	62435
8006	C	T	R	L	1973	62435
8006	C	D	E	L	1974	63435
8006	C	D	G	L	1971	64184
8006	C	T	G	L	1971	64184
8006	C	S	E	L	1974	64981
8006	C	D	E	L	1971	65081
8006	C	S	E	L	1971	65081
8006	C	T	E	L	1971	65081
8006	C	D	E	L	1973	66134
8006	C	E	E	L	1973	66134
8006	C	T	E	L	1973	66134
8006	C	D	E	L	1975	66698
8006	C	T	E	L	1975	66698
8006	C	D	R	L	1973	68040
8006	C	D	E	L	1973	68041
8006	C	S	E	L	1968	68372
8006	C	S	E	L	1968	68373
8006	C	D	E	L	1975	75624
8006	C	E	E	L	1975	75624
8006	C	S	E	L	1966	87721
8006	C	S	E	L	1965	87791
8006	C	S	E	L	1972	87886
8006	C	S	F	L	1974	87919
8006	C	T	E	L	1974	88053
8006	C	E	E	L	1974	89286
8006	C	S	E	L	1974	89286
8006	C	D	E	L	1975	91953

Phys. State: **A.** Amorphous; **C.** Superconductive; **D.** Doped; **F.** Fibrous or Whisker; **G.** Gas; **I.** Ionized or Plasma; **L.** Liquid; **P.** Powder or Particle; **S.** Solid; **T.** Thin Film
Subject: **D.** Data; **E.** Experiment; **S.** Survey (Review, Compendium, etc.); **T.** Theory
Language: **E.** English; **F.** French; **G.** German; **O.** Other Languages; **R.** Russian
Temperature: **L.** Low (0 to 75K); **N.** Normal (75 to 1273K); **H.** High (above 1273K)

Substance Number	Phys. State	Subject	Language	Temperature	Year	EPIC Number
120-8006	C	E	E	L	1975	91953
8006	C	S	E	L	1975	91953
8006	C	T	E	L	1975	91953
8006	C	D	E	L	1974	92665
8006	C	E	E	L	1974	92665
8006	C	S	E	L	1965	98851
8006	C	S	E	L	1976	99156
8006	C	S	E	L	1976	103404
8006	D	D	E	L	1974	53641
8006	D	D	E	L	1974	60388
8006	D	D	R	L	1973	62435
8006	D	E	R	L	1973	62435
8006	D	T	R	L	1973	62435
8006	D	D	E	L	1973	66134
8006	D	E	E	L	1973	66134
8006	D	T	E	L	1973	66134
8006	D	D	E	L	1975	66698
8006	D	T	E	L	1975	66698
8006	S	S	O	N	1973	62410
8006	S	S	E	L	1968	68373
8006	S	S	E	N	1968	68373
8006	S	S	E	L	1966	87721
8006	S	S	E	L	1972	87886
8006	S	S	E	L	1965	98851
8006	S	S	E	N	1965	98851
8006	S	T	E	L	1976	102104
8006	T	S	R	L	1973	55213
8006	T	S	E	L	1974	55214
8006	T	D	E	L	1975	91953
8006	T	E	E	L	1975	91953
8006	T	S	E	L	1975	91953
8006	T	T	E	L	1975	91953
8007	C	S	E	L	1968	68373
8013	S	D	R	N	1971	66935
8017	L	D	R	H	1973	50975
8017	L	D	E	H	1973	50976
8019	S	S	E	N	1967	98889
8021	S	D	E	L	1972	49502
8021	S	D	E	N	1972	49502
8021	S	D	E	L	1974	54963
8021	S	D	E	N	1974	54963
8023	D	D	E	L	1973	49621
8023	D	D	E	N	1973	49621
8023	D	D	E	L	1975	92020
8023	D	D	E	N	1975	92020
8023	S	D	E	L	1975	92020
8023	S	D	E	N	1975	92020
8024	A	D	R	N	1973	56943
8024	A	S	E	N	1971	87885
8024	S	T	E	N	1974	60322
8024	S	D	R	H	1971	76470
8024	S	T	R	H	1971	76470
8024	S	S	E	N	1968	87805
8024	S	S	E	N	1971	87885
8024	S	D	E	H	1971	91494
8024	S	T	E	H	1971	91494
8024	S	S	E	N	1967	98893
8024	T	D	R	N	1973	56943
8024	T	D	E	N	1973	57595
8024	T	S	E	N	1971	87885
8024	T	D	R	N	1974	98023
8024	T	D	E	N	1974	98024
8028	S	D	E	L	1972	49875
8028	S	D	E	N	1972	49875
8034	S	D	E	L	1973	50606
8034	S	D	E	N	1973	50606
8034	S	D	E	L	1974	54072
8034	S	D	E	N	1974	54072
8034	S	D	E	N	1974	54076
8034	S	D	E	N	1976	95560
8037	S	D	R	N	1971	76484
8037	S	S	R	N	1971	76484
8037	S	D	E	N	1971	91524
8037	S	S	E	N	1971	91524
8041	S	D	E	L	1973	49658
8041	S	D	E	N	1973	49658
8041	S	D	E	L	1973	51936
8041	S	D	E	N	1973	51936
8042	A	D	E	L	1974	66395
8042	A	T	E	L	1974	66395
8042	C	D	E	L	1972	55092
8042	C	D	E	L	1973	57600
8042	C	D	E	L	1974	62037
8042	C	S	E	L	1974	62037
8042	C	T	E	L	1974	62037
8042	C	D	E	L	1975	62979
8042	C	T	E	L	1975	62979
8042	C	S	E	L	1966	87721
8042	C	S	E	L	1972	87886
8042	D	D	R	N	1974	93453
8042	D	T	R	N	1974	93453
8042	D	D	E	N	1974	93454
8042	D	T	E	N	1974	93454
8042	S	D	E	N	1972	56855
8042	S	S	E	L	1969	75843
8042	S	S	E	N	1969	75843
8042	S	S	E	N	1966	87721
8042	S	S	E	L	1972	87886
8042	S	S	E	N	1972	87886
8042	S	D	R	N	1974	93453
8042	S	T	R	N	1974	93453

Substance Number	Phys. State	Subject	Language	Temperature	Year	EPIC Number
120-8042	S	D	E	N	1974	93454
8042	S	T	E	N	1974	93454
8042	S	S	E	N	1967	97985
8047	C	D	E	L	1975	63357
8047	C	T	E	L	1975	63357
8049	S	D	E	L	1973	53404
8049	S	D	E	N	1973	53404
8050	S	S	E	N	1973	53420
8050	S	T	E	N	1973	61070
8051	S	S	E	N	1972	53775
8051	T	S	E	N	1972	53775
8058	C	D	R	L	1973	51273
8064	S	D	E	N	1973	51936
8066	S	D	E	L	1974	54963
8066	S	D	E	N	1974	54963
8067	C	D	E	L	1974	53921
8067	C	D	E	L	1972	62375
8067	S	S	E	N	1972	87886
8068	C	D	E	L	1974	53921
8069	C	D	E	L	1974	53921
8070	C	D	E	L	1974	53921
8071	A	D	R	N	1973	56038
8071	P	D	R	N	1973	56038
8073	T	D	R	N	1973	54381
8073	T	D	E	N	1973	54382
8074	S	D	R	N	1973	55008
8074	S	D	E	N	1974	55009
8077	S	D	R	H	1973	53995
8077	S	D	R	N	1973	53995
8077	S	D	E	H	1973	53996
8077	S	D	E	N	1973	53996
8078	S	D	E	L	1974	54055
8078	S	D	E	N	1974	54055
8079	S	D	R	N	1973	52563
8079	S	D	E	N	1973	57788
8080	S	D	E	L	1974	58804
8080	S	D	E	N	1974	58804
8081	C	T	E	L	1973	55125
8081	C	S	E	L	1975	68709
8081	C	S	E	L	1966	87721
8081	C	S	E	L	1972	87886
8082	S	D	E	L	1975	63305
8082	S	D	E	N	1975	63305
8083	S	D	E	L	1975	63305
8083	S	D	E	N	1975	63305
8084	P	D	E	N	1974	86051
8084	T	D	E	N	1975	57831
8084	T	T	E	N	1974	57831
8084	T	D	E	N	1974	86051
8087	P	D	E	N	1974	86051
8087	T	S	E	N	1972	63504
8087	T	D	E	N	1974	86051
8093	C	S	E	L	1974	64981
8093	C	S	E	L	1966	87721
8094	P	D	E	N	1974	86051
8094	T	D	E	N	1974	86051
8095	P	D	E	N	1974	86051
8095	T	D	E	N	1974	86051
8099	L	D	E	N	1973	54890
8100	L	D	E	N	1973	54890
8101	L	D	E	N	1973	54890
8102	P	D	R	N	1973	56038
8103	P	D	R	N	1973	56038
8105	C	D	O	L	1973	56265
8105	T	D	O	L	1973	56265
8105	T	D	O	N	1973	56265
8106	S	D	E	L	1973	56353
8106	S	D	E	N	1973	56353
8108	S	D	R	N	1972	56998
8121	S	D	R	N	1973	58870
8122	S	D	R	N	1973	58870
8125	L	S	E	N	1968	98632
8131	S	D	E	L	1975	63305
8132	S	D	R	N	1971	66935
8133	S	D	R	N	1971	66935
8134	S	S	R	N	1973	67360
8136	S	D	R	N	1971	90517
8137	C	S	E	L	1968	68372
8137	C	S	E	L	1968	68373
8137	C	S	E	L	1966	87721
8138	C	S	E	L	1968	68372
8139	C	S	E	L	1968	68372
8140	C	S	E	L	1968	68372
8141	C	S	E	L	1968	68372
8141	C	S	E	L	1968	68373
8141	S	S	E	L	1968	68373
8141	S	S	E	N	1968	68373
8142	C	S	E	L	1968	68372
8143	C	S	E	L	1968	68372
8144	C	S	E	L	1968	68372
8145	C	S	E	L	1968	68373
8146	C	S	E	L	1968	68373
8147	S	S	E	N	1966	87721
8147	S	S	E	N	1967	97985
8148	S	S	E	N	1966	87721
8148	S	S	E	N	1972	87886
8148	S	S	E	N	1967	97984
8149	C	S	E	L	1972	87886
8149	S	S	E	L	1966	87721
8149	S	S	E	N	1966	87721
8149	S	S	E	N	1972	87886

Substance Number	Phys. State	Subject	Language	Temperature	Year	EPIC Number
120-8149	S	S	E	N	1967	97985
8150	C	S	E	L	1966	87721
8150	C	S	E	L	1972	87886
8151	S	S	E	N	1966	87721
8152	S	S	E	N	1966	87721
8153	S	S	E	N	1966	87721
8154	S	S	E	N	1966	87721
8156	S	S	E	N	1966	87721
8157	C	S	E	L	1966	87721
8158	S	S	E	N	1966	87721
8159	C	S	E	L	1966	87721
8160	C	S	E	L	1966	87721
8161	S	S	E	N	1967	97983
8162	S	S	E	N	1967	97985
8163	L	S	E	N	1968	98632
8166	C	S	R	L	1973	70836
8166	C	S	E	L	1973	93232
8167	C	T	E	L	1975	68709
8168	S	D	R	N	1971	76484
8168	S	S	R	N	1971	76484
8168	S	D	E	N	1971	91524
8168	S	S	E	N	1971	91524
8171	C	D	E	L	1975	91954
8171	C	E	E	L	1975	91954
8171	T	D	E	L	1975	91954
8171	T	E	E	L	1975	91954
8172	C	D	E	L	1975	91965
8172	C	T	E	L	1975	91965
8172	T	D	E	L	1975	91965
8172	T	T	E	L	1975	91965
8173	S	D	E	L	1975	92154
8173	S	D	E	N	1975	92154
8174	S	D	R	N	1972	100974
8175	S	D	R	N	1972	100974
8176	S	D	R	N	1972	100974
8177	C	D	E	L	1975	62979
8177	C	T	E	L	1975	62979
8179	S	D	E	N	1974	62056
8179	S	T	E	N	1974	62056
8184	C	S	E	L	1959	75729
8185	C	S	E	L	1959	75729
8186	C	S	E	L	1959	75729
8187	C	S	E	L	1959	75729
122-0003	D	D	E	H	1973	51939
0003	D	D	E	N	1973	51939
0003	D	S	E	H	1974	55267
0003	D	S	E	N	1974	55267
0003	S	E	E	H	1973	49433
0003	S	D	E	H	1973	51939
0003	S	D	E	N	1973	51939
0003	S	D	E	H	1973	53287
0003	S	D	E	N	1973	53287
0003	S	D	E	H	1973	53715
0003	S	D	E	N	1973	53715
0003	S	E	E	H	1973	53715
0003	S	E	E	N	1973	53715
0003	S	D	E	H	1974	53861
0003	S	D	E	N	1974	53861
0003	S	D	E	H	1972	54828
0003	S	D	E	N	1972	54828
0003	S	E	E	H	1972	54828
0003	S	E	E	N	1972	54828
0003	S	S	E	H	1972	54828
0003	S	S	E	N	1972	54828
0003	S	S	E	H	1974	55267
0003	S	S	E	N	1974	55267
0003	S	D	E	H	1973	56099
0003	S	D	E	N	1973	56099
0003	S	S	E	H	1962	65974
0003	S	D	F	N	1974	67731
0003	S	T	F	N	1974	67731
0003	S	S	E	H	1966	87846
0003	S	S	E	N	1966	87846
0003	S	T	E	H	1975	95378
0003	S	S	E	H	1967	97982
0003	S	S	E	N	1967	97982
0003	S	S	E	H	1967	98889
0003	S	S	E	N	1967	98889
0003	S	S	F	H	1976	99799
0003	S	S	F	N	1976	99799
0004	A	S	E	N	1975	95324
0004	C	D	E	L	1970	59668
0004	D	D	E	N	1974	58340
0004	S	D	O	N	1972	49950
0004	S	D	G	H	1973	50015
0004	S	D	E	H	1973	53287
0004	S	D	E	N	1972	53403
0004	S	D	E	N	1974	58340
0004	S	S	E	H	1970	60090
0004	S	S	E	H	1966	87846
0004	S	S	E	N	1966	87846
0004	S	T	E	H	1975	95378
0004	S	S	E	H	1967	97982
0004	S	S	E	H	1962	98647
0004	S	S	E	H	1967	98889
0004	S	S	E	N	1967	98889
0004	S	S	F	N	1976	99799
0004	T	D	E	N	1972	53252
0004	T	D	E	N	1961	65971
0005	D	D	G	N	1973	51307

Phys. State: **A.** Amorphous; **C.** Superconductive; **D.** Doped; **F.** Fibrous or Whisker; **G.** Gas; **I.** Ionized or Plasma; **L.** Liquid; **P.** Powder or Particle; **S.** Solid; **T.** Thin Film
Subject: **D.** Data; **E.** Experiment; **S.** Survey (Review, Compendium, etc.); **T.** Theory
Language: **E.** English; **F.** French; **G.** German; **O.** Other Languages; **R.** Russian
Temperature: **L.** Low (0 to 75K); **N.** Normal (75 to 1273K); **H.** High (above 1273K)

Substance Number	Phys. State	Subject	Language	Temperature	Year	EPIC Number
122-0005	D	D	R	N	1973	55066
0005	D	D	E	N	1974	55067
0005	D	D	E	H	1964	60562
0005	D	D	E	N	1964	60562
0005	D	S	E	N	1964	60562
0005	D	D	E	H	1971	65761
0005	D	T	E	H	1971	65761
0005	D	S	E	H	1974	87606
0005	D	S	E	N	1974	87606
0005	S	D	R	N	1973	50648
0005	S	D	E	N	1972	53165
0005	S	D	R	N	1973	55066
0005	S	D	E	N	1974	55067
0005	S	D	E	H	1964	60562
0005	S	D	E	N	1964	60562
0005	S	E	E	H	1964	60562
0005	S	E	E	N	1964	60562
0005	S	S	E	N	1964	60562
0005	S	D	O	N	1973	64997
0005	S	D	E	H	1971	65761
0005	S	T	E	H	1971	65761
0005	S	S	E	H	1966	87846
0005	S	S	E	N	1966	87846
0005	S	D	E	H	1975	88237
0005	S	S	E	H	1967	97982
0005	S	S	E	N	1967	97982
0005	S	S	E	H	1967	98889
0005	S	S	E	N	1967	98889
0005	T	D	E	N	1972	53252
0008	L	D	E	H	1964	98555
0008	S	S	E	N	1973	56765
0008	S	D	R	N	1972	56921
0008	S	D	F	N	1971	59552
0008	S	D	F	N	1971	59553
0008	S	T	F	N	1971	59553
0008	S	D	E	N	1974	62048
0008	S	D	E	N	1972	63549
0008	S	E	E	N	1972	63549
0008	S	D	E	N	1972	68079
0008	S	S	E	H	1966	87846
0008	S	S	E	N	1966	87846
0008	S	S	E	H	1967	97982
0008	S	S	E	N	1967	97982
0008	S	D	E	N	1962	98644
0009	A	E	E	N	1973	57733
0009	A	S	E	N	1971	87885
0009	D	D	E	N	1973	57725
0009	D	T	E	N	1973	57725
0009	D	D	E	N	1973	57733
0009	D	E	E	N	1973	57733
0009	D	S	E	N	1973	57733
0009	D	D	E	N	1972	66213
0009	L	D	R	H	1970	61774
0009	S	D	R	N	1973	51983
0009	S	T	E	N	1973	52771
0009	S	D	E	N	1973	52781
0009	S	D	E	N	1974	54045
0009	S	S	E	N	1974	54045
0009	S	E	E	N	1974	54552
0009	S	D	E	N	1973	55144
0009	S	D	O	H	1974	66386
0009	S	D	O	N	1974	66386
0009	S	S	E	H	1966	87846
0009	S	S	E	N	1966	87846
0009	S	S	E	H	1967	87864
0009	S	S	E	N	1967	87864
0009	S	T	E	H	1975	95378
0009	S	S	E	H	1967	97982
0009	S	S	E	N	1967	97982
0009	T	D	E	N	1972	53370
0009	T	D	E	N	1973	57725
0009	T	T	E	N	1973	57725
0009	T	E	E	N	1973	57733
0009	T	T	E	N	1972	63537
0009	T	D	E	N	1972	66213
0009	T	D	R	N	1973	86004
0009	T	E	R	N	1973	86004
0009	T	D	E	N	1975	86753
0012	D	S	E	N	1967	75838
0012	S	D	E	N	1972	51448
0012	S	D	E	N	1975	90692
0012	S	T	E	N	1975	90692
0013	D	D	O	N	1972	49897
0013	S	D	R	N	1972	49829
0013	S	D	O	N	1972	49897
0014	D	D	E	N	1971	57195
0014	D	D	E	N	1974	57860
0014	D	D	E	L	1973	60600
0014	D	D	E	N	1973	60600
0014	D	S	E	L	1973	60600
0014	D	S	E	N	1973	60600
0014	S	S	E	N	1973	51150
0014	S	S	E	N	1972	53110
0014	S	D	E	N	1972	53261
0014	S	S	E	N	1972	53261
0014	S	S	E	N	1973	56286
0014	S	S	E	N	1971	57195
0014	S	D	E	N	1974	57860
0014	S	S	E	L	1973	60600
0014	S	S	E	N	1973	60600
0014	S	S	E	N	1972	63980

Substance Number	Phys. State	Subject	Language	Temperature	Year	EPIC Number
122-0014	S	D	R	N	1973	70821
0014	S	S	E	L	1970	75833
0014	S	S	E	N	1970	75833
0014	S	T	E	N	1975	91134
0014	S	D	E	N	1973	91586
0014	S	S	E	N	1974	94480
0014	S	S	E	H	1967	97982
0014	S	S	E	N	1967	97982
0014	S	S	E	H	1967	98889
0014	S	S	E	N	1967	98889
0014	T	D	E	N	1972	53110
0014	T	S	E	N	1972	53110
0015	S	S	E	N	1971	87881
0016	A	S	E	N	1971	87881
0016	D	D	R	N	1974	63046
0016	D	T	R	N	1974	63046
0016	D	D	E	N	1975	63047
0016	D	T	E	N	1975	63047
0016	D	D	R	N	1971	76496
0016	D	S	R	N	1971	76496
0016	D	D	F	N	1975	90787
0016	D	E	F	H	1975	90787
0016	D	E	F	N	1975	90787
0016	D	S	F	H	1975	90787
0016	D	S	F	N	1975	90787
0016	D	D	E	N	1971	91580
0016	D	S	E	N	1971	91580
0016	L	S	E	N	1971	87881
0016	L	S	R	H	1966	95131
0016	L	S	E	N	1966	96497
0016	L	S	E	N	1968	98632
0016	S	D	E	N	1973	52769
0016	S	D	E	N	1972	52977
0016	S	D	R	N	1973	55820
0016	S	D	E	N	1972	60793
0016	S	T	E	N	1972	60793
0016	S	D	R	N	1974	63126
0016	S	T	R	N	1974	63126
0016	S	D	E	N	1975	63127
0016	S	T	E	N	1975	63127
0016	S	S	E	N	1971	87881
0016	S	D	R	N	1975	90146
0016	S	T	R	N	1975	90146
0016	S	D	E	N	1975	90147
0016	S	T	E	N	1975	90147
0016	S	D	F	N	1975	90787
0016	S	S	R	N	1966	95131
0016	S	S	E	N	1966	96497
0016	S	T	E	N	1975	97574
0016	S	S	E	H	1967	97982
0016	S	S	E	N	1967	97982
0016	S	S	E	N	1966	101404
0016	T	T	R	N	1974	66756
0016	T	T	E	N	1975	66757
0016	T	S	E	N	1971	87881
0017	S	D	E	H	1974	55261
0017	S	D	E	N	1974	55261
0017	S	S	E	N	1967	98889
0017	T	D	R	N	1972	50655
0017	T	D	E	N	1973	54669
0017	T	E	E	N	1973	54669
0017	T	D	E	L	1971	62230
0017	T	D	E	N	1971	62230
0017	T	S	E	N	1971	62230
0017	T	T	E	N	1973	63510
0017	T	D	E	N	1975	68614
0017	T	T	E	N	1975	68614
0017	T	S	E	N	1968	87866
0019	D	D	F	N	1973	49544
0019	L	D	F	N	1973	49544
0019	L	S	E	N	1968	98632
0019	T	D	E	N	1972	53252
0023	D	D	E	N	1973	50747
0023	D	D	G	L	1973	51338
0023	D	D	G	N	1973	51338
0023	D	D	R	N	1973	55899
0023	D	D	E	L	1974	56620
0023	D	D	E	N	1974	56620
0023	D	D	E	N	1973	57273
0023	D	D	E	N	1975	64818
0023	D	S	E	N	1963	87709
0023	D	S	E	L	1967	97982
0023	D	S	E	N	1967	97982
0023	I	D	E	N	1974	53916
0023	I	E	E	N	1974	53916
0023	P	S	E	L	1963	87709
0023	P	S	E	N	1963	87709
0023	S	D	E	N	1973	62386
0023	S	S	E	N	1969	68271
0023	S	S	E	L	1963	87709
0023	S	S	E	N	1963	87709
0023	S	D	G	L	1975	90686
0023	S	D	G	N	1975	90686
0023	S	T	G	L	1975	90686
0023	S	S	E	H	1967	97982
0023	S	S	E	N	1967	97982
0023	S	S	E	H	1967	98889
0023	S	S	E	N	1967	98889
0023	T	D	E	N	1973	50747
0023	T	D	R	N	1973	51345
0023	T	D	E	N	1973	52632

Substance Number	Phys. State	Subject	Language	Temperature	Year	EPIC Number
122-0023	T	D	E	N	1972	53094
0023	T	D	E	N	1973	53352
0023	T	D	E	N	1973	53451
0023	T	D	E	N	1973	53848
0023	T	D	R	N	1973	55899
0023	T	D	O	N	1973	56872
0023	T	D	E	N	1973	57273
0023	T	D	E	N	1975	92849
0025	D	D	R	N	1973	51317
0025	D	D	E	N	1973	55347
0025	S	D	R	N	1973	51317
0025	S	D	E	N	1973	51775
0025	S	D	E	N	1973	55347
0026	S	D	R	N	1974	63060
0026	S	D	E	N	1975	63061
0026	S	S	E	N	1970	75833
0026	S	S	E	L	1971	87881
0026	S	S	E	N	1971	87881
0026	S	S	E	N	1974	94480
0028	T	D	E	N	1972	64075
0030	C	S	E	L	1967	75838
0030	C	S	E	L	1969	75904
0030	D	D	E	N	1973	50965
0030	D	D	E	N	1973	53578
0030	D	D	E	N	1975	65497
0030	S	D	E	N	1973	53578
0030	S	D	E	N	1974	54595
0030	S	D	R	N	1973	55203
0030	S	D	E	N	1974	55204
0030	S	D	E	N	1975	65497
0030	S	S	E	N	1967	97983
0030	S	S	E	H	1976	103180
0030	S	S	E	N	1976	103180
0031	S	D	R	N	1971	49963
0031	S	D	E	N	1974	53627
0031	S	D	F	H	1974	55972
0031	S	D	R	N	1974	66728
0031	S	D	E	N	1975	66729
0031	S	D	R	H	1974	66744
0031	S	D	R	N	1974	66744
0031	S	T	R	H	1974	66744
0031	S	T	R	N	1974	66744
0031	S	D	E	H	1975	66745
0031	S	D	E	N	1975	66745
0031	S	T	E	H	1975	66745
0031	S	T	E	N	1975	66745
0031	S	S	E	H	1969	68271
0031	S	D	R	H	1972	76508
0031	S	D	R	N	1972	76508
0031	S	E	R	N	1972	76508
0031	S	S	E	N	1966	87846
0031	S	D	E	H	1972	91530
0031	S	D	E	N	1972	91530
0031	S	E	E	N	1972	91530
0031	S	S	E	N	1975	96477
0031	S	S	E	N	1967	97982
0031	S	D	R	N	1973	54869
0037	S	S	F	H	1971	103193
0037	T	D	E	N	1972	53532
0046	S	D	R	N	1974	63060
0046	S	D	E	N	1975	63061
0046	T	D	E	N	1963	62914
0046	T	S	E	N	1963	62914
0047	D	D	E	N	1974	62056
0047	D	T	E	N	1974	62056
0047	S	T	E	N	1971	52970
0047	S	S	E	N	1972	54886
0047	S	D	E	N	1974	62056
0047	S	T	E	N	1974	62056
0047	S	S	E	H	1970	75833
0047	S	S	E	N	1970	75833
0050	D	S	E	N	1967	66368
0050	L	S	E	N	1968	98632
0050	P	S	E	N	1967	66368
0050	S	D	R	N	1972	50690
0050	S	S	E	N	1969	68115
0050	S	S	E	N	1966	87846
0050	T	S	E	N	1967	66368
0051	S	S	E	N	1967	66368
0051	S	S	E	N	1969	68115
0053	C	S	E	L	1966	87833
0053	D	D	E	N	1974	57302
0053	D	S	E	N	1966	87833
0053	P	S	E	N	1966	87833
0053	S	D	E	N	1973	50398
0053	S	D	E	N	1974	57797
0053	S	S	E	N	1969	68115
0053	S	S	E	H	1967	98889
0053	S	S	E	N	1967	98889
0053	T	D	E	N	1973	50138
0053	T	D	O	N	1973	56768
0053	T	D	E	N	1974	57302
0053	T	D	R	N	1971	76465
0053	T	S	E	N	1966	87833
0053	T	D	E	N	1971	91584
0067	S	S	E	N	1967	66368
0067	S	S	E	N	1969	68115
0068	S	D	G	N	1973	49660
0068	S	S	E	N	1967	66368
0068	S	S	E	N	1969	68115
0068	T	S	E	N	1969	68115

Phys. State: **A.** Amorphous; **C.** Superconductive; **D.** Doped; **F.** Fibrous or Whisker; **G.** Gas; **I.** Ionized or Plasma; **L.** Liquid; **P.** Powder or Particle; **S.** Solid; **T.** Thin Film
Subject: **D.** Data; **E.** Experiment; **S.** Survey (Review, Compendium, etc.); **T.** Theory
Language: **E.** English; **F.** French; **G.** German; **O.** Other Languages; **R.** Russian
Temperature: **L.** Low (0 to 75K); **N.** Normal (75 to 1273K); **H.** High (above 1273K)

Substance Number	Phys. State	Sub-ject	Lan-guage	Temper-ature	Year	EPIC Number
122-0077	S	D	F	N	1973	49866
0084	S	D	E	L	1974	60652
0084	S	D	E	N	1974	60652
0084	S	T	E	L	1974	60652
0084	S	T	E	N	1974	60652
0089	S	D	E	N	1972	52974
0093	A	S	E	N	1973	53314
0093	A	S	E	N	1973	53429
0093	S	D	O	N	1973	51459
0093	S	D	R	H	1973	51615
0093	S	D	R	N	1973	51615
0093	S	T	E	N	1973	51877
0093	S	D	R	N	1973	70821
0093	S	D	E	N	1973	91586
0096	A	S	E	N	1972	52403
0096	A	S	E	L	1975	95324
0096	D	D	F	N	1973	50617
0096	T	D	F	N	1973	50617
0096	T	D	R	N	1973	86004
0096	T	E	R	N	1973	86004
0096	T	S	E	N	1975	95324
0097	S	D	F	H	1975	90267
0098	S	D	R	L	1974	65377
0098	S	D	R	N	1974	65377
0098	S	D	E	L	1975	65378
0098	S	D	E	N	1975	65378
0098	S	D	R	N	1974	67757
0105	L	S	E	N	1968	98632
0105	S	D	E	N	1975	90079
0112	A	D	E	N	1972	68076
0112	S	S	E	N	1972	53110
0112	S	D	E	L	1972	53113
0112	S	D	E	N	1972	53113
0112	S	D	E	N	1972	53261
0112	S	S	E	N	1972	53261
0112	S	S	E	N	1973	56765
0112	S	S	E	N	1971	87881
0112	S	D	R	N	1974	90433
0112	S	S	E	N	1974	94480
0112	T	S	E	N	1972	53110
0112	T	D	E	L	1972	53113
0112	T	D	E	N	1972	53113
0112	T	D	E	L	1972	53271
0112	T	D	E	N	1974	54556
0112	T	D	R	N	1972	56946
0112	T	D	R	N	1972	60739
0112	T	T	R	N	1972	60739
0112	T	D	E	N	1973	60740
0112	T	T	E	N	1973	60740
0112	T	D	E	N	1972	68076
0112	T	S	E	N	1971	87881
0196	D	D	E	N	1973	56462
0196	S	D	E	N	1974	55119
0196	S	D	E	N	1973	56462
0196	S	T	E	N	1975	63345
0201	S	D	E	N	1965	64246
0208	S	D	F	H	1973	54836
0292	S	D	E	N	1973	56462
0299	L	D	R	N	1973	57006
0299	L	S	E	H	1968	98632
0299	S	D	R	N	1973	57006
0314	S	D	E	H	1972	53102
0314	S	D	E	N	1972	53102
0314	S	E	E	N	1972	53102
0314	S	D	R	N	1974	63060
0314	S	D	E	N	1975	63061
0326	T	D	R	N	1970	63932
0340	S	D	F	H	1973	54836
0397	S	D	F	N	1973	49866
0425	S	D	E	N	1975	80497
0425	S	S	E	N	1975	80497
0450	S	D	E	N	1965	64246
8026	T	D	E	N	1974	62293
8026	T	E	E	N	1974	62293
8028	S	S	E	N	1973	51150
8028	S	S	E	N	1971	87881
8029	S	S	E	N	1973	51150
8029	S	S	E	N	1971	87881
8030	S	S	E	N	1973	51150
8030	S	S	E	N	1971	87881
8031	S	S	E	N	1973	51150
8031	S	S	E	N	1971	87881
8032	S	S	E	L	1973	51150
8032	S	S	E	N	1973	51150
8032	S	S	E	N	1971	87881
8033	S	S	E	L	1973	51150
8033	S	S	E	N	1973	51150
8041	S	D	R	N	1973	54869
8045	S	S	E	N	1971	66193
8045	S	S	E	H	1967	97982
8045	S	S	E	N	1967	97982
8045	S	S	E	N	1967	97983
8045	S	S	E	H	1967	98889
8045	S	S	E	N	1967	98889
8046	S	S	E	N	1971	66193
8046	S	S	E	N	1968	87819
8046	S	S	E	N	1966	101404
8053	D	D	R	L	1975	86869
8053	D	D	R	N	1975	86869
8053	D	D	E	L	1975	86870
8053	D	D	E	N	1975	86870

Substance Number	Phys. State	Sub-ject	Lan-guage	Temper-ature	Year	EPIC Number
122-8053	S	D	E	L	1973	60578
8053	S	D	E	N	1973	60578
8053	S	D	E	L	1973	60600
8053	S	D	E	N	1973	60600
8054	T	D	E	N	1973	54669
8054	T	E	E	N	1973	54669
8054	T	D	E	N	1972	64079
8070	S	S	E	H	1962	65974
8078	S	D	R	N	1974	63060
8078	S	D	E	N	1975	63061
8078	S	S	E	N	1970	75833
8078	T	D	E	N	1974	54556
8080	S	S	R	L	1974	58122
8080	S	S	E	N	1974	58123
8087	S	D	E	N	1975	65429
8088	A	S	E	N	1971	87881
8088	S	D	R	N	1971	64150
8088	S	T	R	N	1971	64150
8088	S	D	E	N	1971	68412
8088	S	T	E	N	1971	68412
8088	S	S	E	N	1971	87881
8088	T	S	E	N	1971	87881
8089	S	D	R	N	1971	64150
8089	S	T	R	N	1971	64150
8089	S	D	E	N	1971	68412
8089	S	T	E	N	1971	68412
8090	S	D	E	H	1973	56099
8090	S	D	E	N	1973	56099
8090	S	D	E	H	1974	58902
8090	S	D	E	N	1974	58902
8090	S	T	E	H	1974	58902
8090	S	T	E	N	1974	58902
8090	S	S	E	N	1967	97982
8093	S	S	E	N	1971	87881
8105	T	S	E	N	1972	83589
8108	S	D	E	N	1975	80497
8108	S	S	E	N	1975	80497
8109	S	D	E	N	1975	80497
8109	S	S	E	N	1975	80497
8110	S	D	E	N	1975	80497
8110	S	S	E	N	1975	80497
8111	S	D	E	N	1975	80497
8111	S	S	E	N	1975	80497
8112	P	D	E	N	1971	57195
8112	P	T	E	N	1971	57195
8113	S	D	G	N	1973	57059
8115	S	S	E	H	1962	65974
8115	S	S	E	N	1962	65974
8117	S	D	R	N	1971	67332
8118	S	D	R	N	1971	67332
8120	S	D	R	N	1973	67379
8122	S	S	E	N	1967	66368
8122	S	S	E	N	1969	68115
8124	S	S	E	N	1970	75833
8124	S	D	R	H	1972	76529
8124	S	D	R	N	1972	76529
8124	S	S	E	L	1971	87881
8124	S	S	E	N	1971	87881
8124	S	D	E	H	1972	91534
8124	S	D	E	N	1972	91534
8127	S	S	E	N	1967	97982
8134	S	D	R	N	1973	70821
8134	S	D	E	N	1973	91586
8136	S	S	E	H	1962	65974
8136	S	S	E	N	1962	65974
8142	C	S	E	L	1959	75729
8143	C	S	E	L	1959	75729
8144	C	S	E	L	1959	75729
8145	C	S	E	L	1959	75729
123-0003	D	D	R	N	1972	51098
0003	L	D	R	H	1974	87298
0003	L	D	E	H	1975	87299
0003	L	S	E	H	1968	98632
0003	S	D	E	L	1972	53200
0003	S	D	E	N	1972	53200
0003	S	D	E	N	1973	56346
0003	S	D	E	N	1971	62260
0003	S	D	R	N	1966	62300
0003	S	D	E	N	1974	62301
0003	S	D	R	N	1971	67314
0003	S	D	R	N	1974	67748
0003	S	S	E	N	1969	68115
0003	S	S	E	L	1966	68361
0003	S	S	E	N	1966	68361
0003	T	D	R	N	1973	55323
0003	T	D	E	N	1974	59259
0003	T	S	E	N	1966	68361
0025	S	D	E	L	1974	61168
0025	S	D	E	N	1974	61168
0025	S	S	E	N	1974	61168
0027	L	D	E	N	1972	62523
0032	S	D	G	N	1973	51683
0032	S	E	G	N	1973	51683
0032	S	D	E	N	1973	52054
0032	S	S	E	N	1975	94550
0036	C	S	E	L	1972	62375
0042	S	S	E	N	1975	94550
0048	S	D	R	N	1972	49646
0048	S	D	E	N	1972	51526
0048	S	S	E	N	1972	51526

Substance Number	Phys. State	Sub-ject	Lan-guage	Temper-ature	Year	EPIC Number
123-0048	S	D	R	N	1972	55490
8004	S	D	E	N	1973	52053
8005	S	E	E	L	1969	59174
8005	S	E	E	N	1969	59174
8013	S	D	E	N	1969	85351
8014	S	D	E	L	1973	56353
8014	S	D	E	N	1973	56353
8017	D	D	E	N	1974	57986
8017	L	D	R	H	1974	87298
8017	L	D	E	H	1975	87299
8017	S	D	E	N	1973	52462
8017	S	D	R	N	1974	58895
8017	S	E	E	L	1958	59175
8017	S	E	E	N	1958	59175
8017	S	D	E	N	1936	61578
8017	S	D	R	N	1966	62300
8017	S	D	E	N	1974	62301
8017	S	D	E	N	1974	64884
8017	S	S	E	N	1969	68115
8017	S	D	R	N	1971	76500
8017	S	T	R	N	1971	76500
8017	S	S	E	N	1962	87674
8017	S	D	E	N	1971	91566
8017	S	T	E	N	1971	91566
8017	S	D	R	N	1974	97481
8017	S	D	E	N	1974	97482
8017	T	D	E	N	1974	57986
8017	T	S	E	N	1962	87674
8018	C	S	E	L	1973	55157
8018	C	T	E	L	1973	55157
8018	C	S	E	L	1973	62485
8018	C	S	E	L	1970	68114
8018	C	S	E	L	1969	68115
8018	D	T	E	L	1972	53500
8018	D	D	E	N	1974	53736
8018	D	D	R	N	1973	58209
8018	D	D	E	N	1972	59135
8018	D	T	E	N	1972	59135
8018	D	D	E	N	1974	59204
8018	D	D	R	N	1973	59370
8018	D	D	R	N	1972	62320
8018	D	D	E	N	1974	62321
8018	D	D	E	L	1973	62485
8018	D	S	E	N	1970	68114
8018	D	D	E	N	1962	73285
8018	D	D	E	N	1972	83516
8018	D	S	E	N	1962	87671
8018	D	S	E	N	1967	97985
8018	D	D	R	N	1975	99646
8018	D	D	E	N	1975	103293
8018	L	D	R	N	1973	52540
8018	L	D	E	N	1974	53675
8018	L	D	R	H	1974	87298
8018	L	D	E	H	1975	87299
8018	L	D	R	H	1976	103384
8018	L	D	R	N	1976	103384
8018	L	D	E	H	1976	103385
8018	L	D	E	N	1976	103385
8018	S	D	E	N	1973	52078
8018	S	D	R	N	1974	57869
8018	S	T	R	L	1973	58155
8018	S	T	R	N	1973	58155
8018	S	D	R	N	1973	58209
8018	S	D	E	N	1974	59204
8018	S	D	R	N	1973	59370
8018	S	D	R	N	1968	60749
8018	S	D	E	N	1974	60750
8018	S	D	E	N	1971	62195
8018	S	D	R	N	1966	62300
8018	S	D	E	N	1974	62301
8018	S	D	R	N	1973	62729
8018	S	S	E	N	1975	63321
8018	S	D	R	N	1969	63449
8018	S	T	R	N	1969	63449
8018	S	D	E	N	1969	63450
8018	S	T	E	N	1969	63450
8018	S	D	E	N	1972	63827
8018	S	D	E	N	1974	64881
8018	S	D	E	N	1973	65325
8018	S	S	E	N	1960	65977
8018	S	S	E	L	1970	68114
8018	S	S	E	N	1970	68114
8018	S	S	E	L	1969	68115
8018	S	S	E	N	1969	68115
8018	S	T	R	N	1972	85970
8018	S	T	E	N	1972	85971
8018	S	S	E	L	1962	87671
8018	S	S	E	N	1962	87671
8018	S	D	R	N	1974	93120
8018	S	D	E	N	1975	93121
8018	S	D	E	N	1961	97244
8018	S	T	E	N	1961	97244
8018	S	T	R	N	1975	97658
8018	S	T	E	N	1975	97659
8018	T	D	O	N	1971	49563
8018	T	D	R	N	1972	49571
8018	T	T	E	N	1974	58606
8018	T	D	R	N	1974	58894
8018	T	D	E	N	1968	59520
8018	T	D	R	N	1973	62729
8018	T	D	E	N	1974	64883

Phys. State: **A.** Amorphous; **C.** Superconductive; **D.** Doped; **F.** Fibrous or Whisker; **G.** Gas; **I.** Ionized or Plasma; **L.** Liquid; **P.** Powder or Particle; **S.** Solid; **T.** Thin Film
Subject: **D.** Data; **E.** Experiment; **S.** Survey (Review, Compendium, etc.); **T.** Theory
Language: **E.** English; **F.** French; **G.** German; **O.** Other Languages; **R.** Russian
Temperature: **L.** Low (0 to 75K); **N.** Normal (75 to 1273K); **H.** High (above 1273K)

Substance Number	Phys. State	Subject	Language	Temperature	Year	EPIC Number
123-8018	T	D	E	N	1973	65325
8018	T	S	E	N	1970	68114
8018	T	S	E	N	1962	87671
8018	T	D	R	N	1974	93120
8018	T	D	E	N	1975	93121
8036	S	S	E	N	1967	97984
8039	S	D	E	L	1971	52970
8039	S	D	E	N	1971	52970
8039	S	D	R	N	1974	58895
8039	S	D	E	N	1974	64884
8039	S	S	E	L	1972	87824
8039	S	S	E	N	1972	87824
8039	T	D	E	N	1973	53434
8040	C	D	E	L	1973	52186
8040	S	D	E	L	1973	50590
8040	S	D	E	N	1973	50590
8040	S	D	E	N	1973	52186
8041	S	D	E	L	1973	50590
8041	S	D	E	N	1973	50590
8042	S	D	E	L	1973	50590
8042	S	D	E	N	1973	50590
8043	S	D	E	L	1973	50606
8043	S	D	E	N	1973	50606
8047	S	D	E	N	1973	57742
8050	S	D	R	N	1973	50725
8050	S	D	E	N	1973	53026
8051	D	D	E	N	1973	53423
8051	S	D	R	N	1973	50725
8051	S	D	E	N	1973	53026
8051	S	D	R	N	1973	55823
8051	S	D	E	N	1974	60382
8051	S	D	R	L	1974	63131
8051	S	D	R	N	1974	63131
8051	S	D	E	L	1975	63132
8051	S	D	E	N	1975	63132
8051	S	S	E	L	1970	68114
8051	S	S	E	N	1970	68114
8051	S	S	E	N	1972	87824
8051	S	D	R	N	1975	94942
8051	S	D	E	N	1975	95895
8051	T	D	E	L	1974	60283
8051	T	D	E	N	1974	60283
8051	T	S	E	N	1970	68114
8051	T	D	R	N	1974	80749
8051	T	S	E	N	1972	87824
8051	T	D	E	N	1974	95251
8056	S	D	E	L	1974	54072
8056	S	D	E	N	1974	54072
8056	S	D	E	N	1974	54076
8056	S	D	E	N	1976	95560
8057	S	D	E	L	1974	54072
8057	S	D	E	N	1974	54072
8057	S	D	E	N	1974	54076
8057	S	D	E	L	1976	95560
8059	S	D	E	L	1974	54055
8059	S	D	E	N	1974	54055
8060	S	S	E	N	1974	54055
8061	S	D	E	L	1974	54072
8061	S	D	E	N	1974	54072
8061	S	D	E	L	1976	95560
8065	S	D	R	N	1973	52528
8065	S	D	E	N	1974	57769
8066	S	D	E	N	1972	63827
8070	S	D	E	N	1969	85351
8074	D	S	E	N	1972	87824
8075	S	D	E	L	1975	63276
8075	S	D	E	N	1975	63276
8094	S	S	E	N	1972	87824
8095	S	S	E	N	1967	97984
8096	S	S	E	N	1967	97984
8097	S	S	E	N	1967	97984
8101	C	D	E	L	1976	100720
8101	C	E	E	L	1976	100720
8102	C	D	E	L	1976	100720
8102	C	E	E	L	1976	100720
8103	S	T	R	N	1974	86647
8104	S	D	E	N	1973	53799
8104	S	T	E	N	1973	53799
8106	C	S	E	L	1959	75729
8107	C	S	E	L	1959	75729
8108	C	S	E	L	1959	75729
8109	C	S	E	L	1959	75729
125-8024	S	D	E	L	1973	50606
8024	S	D	E	N	1973	50606
8025	S	D	E	L	1973	50606
8025	S	D	E	N	1973	50606
8029	C	D	E	L	1973	52186
8029	S	D	E	N	1973	52186
8030	C	D	E	L	1973	52186
8030	S	D	E	N	1973	52186
8031	C	D	E	L	1973	55121
8031	D	D	E	L	1973	55121
8032	C	S	E	L	1974	64981
8033	S	S	R	N	1972	56731
8036	S	D	R	N	1973	58870
8037	S	S	E	N	1967	97985
8038	C	S	R	L	1973	70836
8038	C	S	E	L	1973	93232
8043	C	S	E	L	1959	75729
8044	C	S	E	L	1959	75729

Substance Number	Phys. State	Subject	Language	Temperature	Year	EPIC Number
125-8045	C	S	E	L	1959	75729
8046	C	S	E	L	1959	75729
126-0001	L	S	E	N	1969	68115
0001	L	D	R	H	1974	87298
0001	L	D	E	H	1975	87299
0001	L	S	E	H	1968	98632
0001	L	S	E	N	1968	98632
0001	S	S	E	N	1969	68115
0001	S	S	E	N	1972	87824
0001	T	D	E	N	1969	59589
0001	T	T	E	N	1969	59589
0002	S	D	E	N	1973	57112
0002	S	S	E	N	1969	68115
0004	S	D	E	L	1974	58804
0004	S	D	E	N	1974	58804
0004	S	S	E	L	1974	58804
0004	S	S	E	N	1974	58804
0005	D	D	E	N	1973	51938
0005	D	D	R	N	1971	56220
0005	D	D	E	N	1974	60751
0005	S	D	R	N	1971	56217
0005	S	D	E	N	1973	61450
0005	S	D	R	N	1974	67748
0005	S	S	E	N	1969	68271
0005	S	T	E	N	1960	85819
0005	S	S	E	N	1963	87711
0005	S	S	E	N	1966	87712
0005	S	S	E	N	1967	97984
0005	T	D	E	N	1972	64092
0011	S	S	E	N	1963	98656
0014	L	D	E	N	1972	60899
0014	L	D	E	N	1972	76041
0014	L	T	E	N	1972	76041
0014	L	D	R	N	1971	76069
0014	L	T	R	N	1971	76069
0014	L	D	R	H	1974	87298
0014	L	D	E	H	1975	87299
0014	L	D	R	N	1974	90235
0014	L	T	R	N	1974	90235
0014	L	D	E	N	1975	90236
0014	L	T	E	N	1975	90236
0014	L	S	E	N	1968	98632
0014	L	D	R	H	1976	103384
0014	L	D	R	N	1976	103384
0014	L	D	E	H	1976	103385
0014	L	D	E	N	1976	103385
0014	S	D	E	N	1973	50496
0014	S	D	R	N	1974	58098
0014	S	D	E	N	1974	58099
0017	S	D	E	N	1974	53627
0022	S	D	R	N	1967	53069
0022	S	D	E	N	1972	53070
0025	S	S	E	N	1975	91600
0036	S	D	R	N	1967	53069
0036	S	D	E	N	1972	53070
0037	S	D	R	N	1967	53069
0037	S	D	E	N	1972	53070
0038	C	D	E	L	1972	55092
0038	C	D	E	L	1975	62979
0038	C	T	E	L	1975	62979
0038	C	S	E	L	1974	70494
0038	C	D	E	L	1972	70535
0038	C	D	E	L	1974	79190
0038	C	D	E	L	1975	96691
0038	C	T	E	L	1975	96691
0038	S	D	R	N	1967	53069
0038	S	D	E	N	1972	53070
0038	S	D	E	L	1975	62979
0038	S	T	E	L	1975	62979
0038	S	S	E	L	1974	70494
0038	S	S	E	N	1974	70494
0038	S	D	E	L	1972	70535
0038	S	D	E	N	1972	70535
0038	S	D	E	N	1974	90613
0038	S	S	E	L	1976	103263
0038	S	S	E	N	1976	103263
0043	L	D	R	N	1972	52246
0043	L	D	R	N	1971	59646
0043	L	D	E	N	1971	59647
0043	L	S	E	N	1970	59699
0043	L	D	R	N	1972	66992
0043	S	D	R	N	1972	66992
0059	S	D	R	N	1972	76557
0059	S	T	R	N	1972	76557
0059	S	D	E	N	1972	91550
0059	S	T	E	N	1972	91550
8010	S	D	R	N	1973	55687
8011	S	D	R	N	1973	55687
8011	S	D	E	N	1936	61578
8011	T	D	E	N	1975	59955
8012	S	D	R	N	1973	55687
8013	S	D	R	N	1973	55687
8014	S	D	R	N	1973	55687
8015	S	D	R	N	1973	55687
8016	S	D	R	N	1973	55687
8017	S	D	R	N	1973	55687
8020	C	D	E	L	1974	61152
8020	C	S	E	L	1974	64981
8020	C	D	E	L	1975	68710
8020	C	T	E	L	1975	68710

Substance Number	Phys. State	Subject	Language	Temperature	Year	EPIC Number
126-8020	S	S	E	L	1967	66157
8020	S	S	E	N	1967	66157
8026	L	S	G	N	1967	58994
8026	L	D	R	N	1971	60193
8026	L	E	R	N	1971	60193
8026	S	D	R	N	1971	58851
8026	S	D	E	N	1964	61307
8026	S	E	E	N	1964	61307
8026	S	D	R	N	1966	62300
8026	S	D	E	N	1974	62301
8026	S	S	E	N	1967	97985
8030	A	D	E	N	1972	49458
8030	A	D	E	N	1973	51901
8030	A	D	E	N	1972	53112
8030	A	D	E	N	1972	53386
8030	D	D	E	N	1972	49462
8030	D	S	R	N	1972	59001
8030	D	S	E	N	1972	59002
8030	D	S	E	N	1970	59699
8030	L	D	E	N	1972	49462
8030	L	D	R	H	1973	56862
8030	L	D	R	N	1973	56862
8030	L	D	E	H	1973	57296
8030	L	D	E	N	1973	57296
8030	L	S	R	N	1972	59001
8030	L	S	E	N	1972	59002
8030	L	S	E	N	1970	59699
8030	L	D	R	H	1969	61867
8030	L	D	R	N	1969	61867
8030	L	D	R	H	1970	68540
8030	L	D	R	N	1970	68540
8030	L	T	R	H	1970	68540
8030	L	T	R	N	1970	68540
8030	L	D	R	H	1974	87298
8030	L	D	E	H	1975	87299
8030	L	D	R	H	1976	103384
8030	L	D	R	N	1976	103384
8030	L	D	E	H	1976	103385
8030	L	D	E	N	1976	103385
8030	T	D	E	N	1972	49458
8030	T	D	E	N	1973	51901
8030	T	D	E	N	1972	53386
8032	D	D	R	N	1972	50174
8032	D	D	E	N	1973	54934
8032	D	D	R	N	1970	55104
8032	D	D	E	N	1972	55105
8032	D	D	R	N	1973	55822
8032	D	S	E	N	1972	56769
8032	D	D	E	N	1972	100970
8032	D	D	G	N	1976	101451
8032	D	T	G	N	1976	101451
8032	L	D	R	N	1973	52540
8032	L	D	E	N	1974	53675
8032	L	D	R	H	1969	61867
8032	L	D	R	N	1969	61867
8032	L	D	R	H	1974	87298
8032	L	D	E	H	1975	87299
8032	L	D	R	H	1976	103384
8032	L	D	R	N	1976	103384
8032	L	D	E	H	1976	103385
8032	L	D	E	N	1976	103385
8032	S	D	R	N	1970	55104
8032	S	D	E	N	1972	55105
8032	S	D	F	N	1971	61672
8032	S	S	E	N	1974	62277
8032	S	D	R	N	1972	62298
8032	S	D	E	N	1973	62299
8032	S	D	R	N	1966	62300
8032	S	D	E	N	1974	62301
8032	S	D	R	N	1972	76548
8032	S	D	E	N	1972	91598
8032	S	D	E	N	1975	96857
8032	S	S	E	N	1967	97985
8032	S	D	E	N	1972	100970
8032	T	D	R	N	1972	50174
8034	D	D	R	N	1973	51515
8034	D	D	R	N	1974	66637
8034	D	D	E	N	1974	66638
8034	D	D	E	N	1969	75372
8034	L	D	R	N	1973	51515
8034	L	D	R	N	1972	52246
8034	L	D	R	N	1971	59646
8034	L	D	E	N	1971	59647
8034	L	S	E	N	1970	59699
8034	L	D	R	N	1974	66637
8034	L	D	E	N	1974	66638
8034	L	D	R	N	1972	66992
8034	L	D	E	N	1969	75372
8034	S	D	O	N	1973	52666
8034	S	D	R	N	1972	66992
8035	L	D	R	N	1973	50726
8035	L	D	E	N	1973	53027
8035	S	S	E	N	1969	68115
8035	S	S	E	N	1972	87824
8035	T	D	E	N	1969	59589
8037	C	S	E	L	1972	62375
8037	D	D	E	N	1973	51543
8037	L	D	R	H	1974	87298
8037	L	D	E	H	1975	87299
8037	L	D	R	H	1976	103384
8037	L	D	R	N	1976	103384

Phys. State: **A.** Amorphous; **C.** Superconductive; **D.** Doped; **F.** Fibrous or Whisker; **G.** Gas; **I.** Ionized or Plasma; **L.** Liquid; **P.** Powder or Particle; **S.** Solid; **T.** Thin Film
Subject: **D.** Data; **E.** Experiment; **S.** Survey (Review, Compendium, etc.); **T.** Theory
Language: **E.** English; **F.** French; **G.** German; **O.** Other Languages; **R.** Russian
Temperature: **L.** Low (0 to 75K); **N.** Normal (75 to 1273K); **H.** High (above 1273K)

Substance Number	Phys. State	Subject	Language	Temperature	Year	EPIC Number
126-8037	L	D	E	H	1976	103385
8037	L	D	E	N	1976	103385
8037	S	D	E	L	1973	50003
8037	S	D	E	N	1973	51543
8037	S	S	E	N	1970	68114
8037	S	S	E	L	1969	68115
8037	S	S	E	N	1969	68115
8037	S	D	R	N	1974	86780
8037	S	S	E	N	1972	87824
8037	S	D	E	N	1974	90054
8037	S	D	R	N	1974	97481
8037	S	D	E	N	1974	97482
8037	S	S	E	N	1967	97985
8037	T	D	R	N	1972	49570
8037	T	D	E	N	1972	53416
8037	T	T	E	N	1969	59589
8038	S	D	E	N	1972	56855
8038	T	D	E	N	1973	57742
8039	C	T	E	L	1974	79157
8041	S	S	E	N	1967	66157
8041	S	T	R	N	1974	86647
8043	S	D	E	N	1975	90480
8046	A	D	E	N	1973	51901
8046	T	D	E	N	1973	51901
8047	C	D	E	L	1974	61152
8047	C	S	E	L	1974	61152
8047	C	D	E	L	1974	61400
8047	C	S	O	L	1973	62410
8047	C	D	F	L	1975	63413
8047	C	T	F	L	1975	63413
8047	C	D	G	L	1971	64184
8047	C	T	G	L	1971	64184
8047	C	S	E	L	1974	64981
8047	C	D	E	L	1971	65081
8047	C	S	E	L	1971	65081
8047	C	T	E	L	1971	65081
8047	C	S	E	L	1967	66157
8047	C	D	E	L	1975	66720
8047	C	T	E	L	1975	66720
8047	C	D	E	L	1975	68710
8047	C	T	E	L	1975	68710
8047	C	D	E	L	1975	75624
8047	C	E	E	L	1975	75624
8047	C	D	R	L	1974	80750
8047	C	D	R	L	1975	86851
8047	C	S	R	L	1975	86851
8047	C	D	E	L	1975	86852
8047	C	S	E	L	1975	86852
8047	C	T	E	L	1974	88053
8047	C	S	E	L	1975	91953
8047	C	D	E	L	1974	95263
8047	C	D	E	L	1976	100720
8047	C	E	E	L	1976	100720
8047	C	T	E	L	1976	100720
8047	S	D	R	L	1973	52860
8047	S	D	R	N	1973	52860
8047	S	D	E	L	1973	52861
8047	S	D	E	N	1973	52861
8047	S	S	E	L	1967	66157
8047	S	S	E	N	1967	66157
8047	S	D	E	L	1974	88620
8047	S	D	E	L	1976	102104
8047	S	T	E	L	1976	102104
8047	T	S	E	L	1967	66157
8047	T	D	E	L	1975	66720
8047	T	T	E	L	1975	66720
8047	T	S	E	L	1975	91953
8048	D	D	E	N	1973	50765
8048	S	S	E	N	1972	87823
8049	S	S	E	N	1972	87823
8051	L	D	R	N	1972	66992
8051	S	D	O	N	1972	49652
8051	S	D	R	N	1972	66992
8052	D	D	E	N	1972	52965
8052	D	D	E	N	1971	53243
8052	D	D	E	N	1974	53923
8052	D	D	R	N	1972	58681
8052	D	D	E	L	1974	60751
8052	D	D	E	N	1974	60751
8052	D	T	E	N	1974	60751
8052	D	S	E	N	1963	68313
8052	P	D	R	N	1973	56966
8052	S	D	E	N	1973	50806
8052	S	E	E	N	1973	50806
8052	S	D	R	N	1972	52267
8052	S	D	E	N	1971	53243
8052	S	D	E	N	1973	53346
8052	S	D	G	N	1970	53379
8052	S	D	E	N	1972	53380
8052	S	S	R	N	1972	53547
8052	S	S	E	N	1973	53548
8052	S	D	R	N	1972	58681
8052	S	S	E	N	1969	68271
8052	S	D	E	N	1973	68345
8052	S	S	E	N	1972	87823
8052	S	D	E	N	1973	88610
8052	S	D	E	L	1975	93167
8052	S	D	E	N	1975	93167
8052	S	E	E	N	1975	93167
8052	S	D	E	N	1975	101672
8052	T	S	E	N	1963	68313
126-8052	T	D	F	N	1975	90442
8052	T	D	E	N	1975	93167
8054	S	D	E	L	1972	49905
8055	L	D	R	N	1973	50726
8055	L	D	E	N	1973	53027
8055	S	D	E	N	1972	49935
8055	S	S	E	N	1969	68115
8055	S	D	R	N	1971	76500
8055	S	T	R	N	1971	76500
8055	S	D	E	N	1971	91566
8055	S	T	E	N	1971	91566
8057	S	D	F	N	1973	50026
8058	S	D	E	L	1974	58909
8058	S	D	E	N	1974	58909
8059	C	T	E	L	1974	79190
8059	D	D	R	N	1972	50654
8059	D	D	R	N	1973	52563
8059	D	D	E	N	1973	57788
8059	D	S	E	N	1969	75843
8059	S	D	R	N	1973	52563
8059	S	D	E	N	1973	57788
8059	S	S	E	N	1967	97985
8060	S	D	E	N	1973	50910
8060	S	D	E	N	1973	53415
8061	S	D	F	N	1973	51294
8061	S	D	E	N	1972	56855
8062	S	D	F	N	1973	51294
8063	S	D	F	N	1973	51294
8063	S	S	E	N	1967	97985
8064	S	D	F	N	1973	51294
8065	C	D	R	L	1973	51273
8065	S	D	F	N	1973	51294
8066	S	D	F	N	1973	51294
8067	S	D	R	N	1973	51601
8067	S	S	E	N	1972	87824
8068	S	D	R	N	1973	51601
8068	S	S	E	N	1972	87824
8069	S	D	E	N	1972	52964
8070	S	S	E	N	1972	53775
8070	S	S	E	N	1975	91600
8071	C	D	E	L	1972	52993
8071	C	D	E	L	1974	55229
8071	C	D	E	L	1973	61430
8071	C	D	E	L	1973	61451
8071	C	D	E	N	1973	61451
8071	C	D	E	L	1975	62979
8071	C	T	E	L	1975	62979
8071	C	D	E	L	1972	70535
8071	C	D	E	L	1974	79190
8071	C	S	E	L	1974	79190
8071	C	D	E	L	1974	89390
8071	C	D	E	L	1975	96691
8071	C	T	E	L	1975	96691
8071	S	D	E	L	1973	55111
8071	S	D	E	N	1973	55111
8071	S	S	E	L	1973	55111
8071	S	S	E	N	1973	55111
8071	S	S	E	L	1971	63751
8071	S	D	E	L	1972	70535
8071	S	D	E	N	1972	70535
8072	A	D	E	H	1973	53855
8075	L	D	E	N	1972	49462
8079	S	D	E	N	1974	53627
8080	S	D	E	N	1974	53627
8083	C	T	E	L	1974	58045
8083	S	D	R	N	1975	91201
8083	S	D	E	N	1975	94197
8083	S	S	E	N	1967	97985
8084	S	S	E	H	1970	59588
8084	S	S	E	N	1970	59588
8085	T	D	E	N	1969	59589
8085	T	T	E	N	1969	59589
8086	L	D	G	N	1970	62078
8090	S	D	E	L	1974	58804
8090	S	D	E	N	1974	58804
8091	S	S	E	L	1974	54072
8091	S	S	E	N	1974	54072
8091	S	D	E	L	1976	95560
8092	S	D	E	N	1974	58804
8092	S	S	E	L	1974	58804
8092	S	S	E	N	1974	58804
8093	S	D	E	L	1974	58804
8093	S	D	E	N	1974	58804
8094	A	D	O	N	1970	60019
8094	S	D	R	N	1973	55285
8094	S	D	E	N	1974	59242
8094	S	D	O	N	1970	60019
8094	S	D	R	N	1970	61240
8094	T	D	O	N	1970	60019
8095	D	D	R	N	1973	61824
8095	D	D	E	N	1973	61825
8095	S	D	R	N	1973	61824
8095	S	D	E	N	1973	61825
8096	S	E	E	N	1952	65344
8096	S	T	E	N	1952	65344
8097	C	D	E	L	1975	62979
8097	C	T	E	L	1975	62979
8097	C	D	E	L	1975	96691
8097	C	T	E	L	1975	96691
8097	S	D	E	L	1974	62465
8097	S	D	E	N	1974	62465
126-8098	C	D	E	L	1975	62979
8098	C	D	E	L	1975	96691
8098	C	S	E	L	1975	96691
8098	C	T	E	L	1975	96691
8098	D	D	R	N	1974	93453
8098	D	T	R	N	1974	93453
8098	D	D	E	N	1974	93454
8098	D	T	E	N	1974	93454
8098	S	T	E	L	1975	62979
8098	S	S	E	L	1970	75833
8098	S	S	E	N	1970	75833
8098	S	D	R	N	1974	93453
8098	S	T	R	N	1974	93453
8098	S	D	E	N	1974	93454
8098	S	T	E	N	1974	93454
8098	S	S	E	N	1967	97985
8099	S	S	E	N	1960	65977
8101	S	S	E	N	1969	75843
8102	S	S	E	N	1967	97985
8103	S	D	R	N	1970	61240
8104	T	D	R	N	1973	56300
8105	C	D	E	L	1974	79190
8106	C	D	E	L	1974	79190
8107	L	S	E	N	1974	84453
8108	S	D	R	N	1973	51732
8108	S	S	E	N	1967	66157
8108	S	D	E	N	1973	79136
8110	S	S	E	N	1975	91600
8118	S	D	R	N	1972	56998
8120	S	D	E	L	1975	63276
8120	S	D	E	N	1975	63276
8124	S	D	E	L	1975	63276
8124	S	D	E	N	1975	63276
8127	C	D	E	L	1975	63276
8135	S	D	R	N	1971	90517
8138	S	S	E	N	1967	97984
8139	S	S	E	N	1967	97984
8140	S	S	E	N	1967	97985
8141	S	S	E	N	1967	97985
8142	S	S	E	N	1967	97985
8143	S	S	E	N	1967	97985
8144	S	S	E	N	1967	97985
8152	C	D	E	L	1975	96691
8152	C	T	E	L	1975	96691
8153	C	D	E	L	1975	62979
8153	C	T	E	L	1975	62979
127-8002	D	D	R	N	1973	51346
8002	D	D	R	N	1973	52745
8002	D	D	E	N	1974	52746
8002	D	D	E	N	1973	59208
8002	D	D	R	N	1972	67958
8002	D	D	E	N	1972	67959
8002	L	D	R	N	1973	51346
8002	L	D	R	N	1972	52246
8002	L	D	R	N	1973	52745
8002	L	D	E	N	1974	52746
8002	L	S	E	N	1974	54095
8002	L	S	R	N	1972	59001
8002	L	S	E	N	1972	59002
8002	L	D	E	N	1973	59208
8002	L	D	R	N	1971	59646
8002	L	D	E	N	1971	59647
8002	L	S	E	N	1970	59699
8002	L	D	E	N	1972	63722
8002	L	D	R	N	1972	66992
8002	L	D	R	N	1972	67958
8002	L	D	E	N	1974	86452
8002	S	D	R	N	1972	66992
8002	S	D	E	N	1972	67959
8003	L	D	R	N	1973	52540
8003	L	D	E	N	1974	53675
8003	S	D	E	L	1973	50804
8003	S	D	E	N	1973	50804
8003	S	D	E	L	1973	56152
8003	S	D	E	N	1973	56152
8004	A	D	E	N	1972	49782
8004	A	D	E	N	1973	51484
8004	D	D	E	N	1973	53844
8004	D	S	E	N	1962	87666
8004	L	D	E	N	1973	60580
8004	S	D	O	N	1973	57922
8004	S	S	E	N	1969	68271
8004	S	S	E	N	1962	87666
8004	S	S	E	N	1972	87823
8004	T	D	E	N	1972	49782
8004	T	D	E	N	1973	51484
8004	T	D	E	N	1973	56591
8004	T	D	E	N	1968	59520
8005	S	D	E	L	1974	58909
8005	S	D	E	N	1974	58909
8008	L	D	R	N	1973	52540
8008	L	D	E	N	1974	53675
8008	L	D	E	N	1972	63722
8008	S	D	G	N	1971	59640
8016	S	D	E	N	1975	63276
8020	S	S	E	N	1967	97985
8021	S	S	E	N	1967	97985
8022	S	S	E	N	1967	97985
8023	S	S	E	N	1967	97985

Phys. State: **A.** Amorphous; **C.** Superconductive; **D.** Doped; **F.** Fibrous or Whisker; **G.** Gas; **I.** Ionized or Plasma; **L.** Liquid; **P.** Powder or Particle; **S.** Solid; **T.** Thin Film
Subject: **D.** Data; **E.** Experiment; **S.** Survey (Review, Compendium, etc.); **T.** Theory
Language: **E.** English; **F.** French; **G.** German; **O.** Other Languages; **R.** Russian
Temperature: **L.** Low (0 to 75K); **N.** Normal (75 to 1273K); **H.** High (above 1273K)

Substance Number	Phys. State	Subject	Language	Temperature	Year	EPIC Number
129-8001	C	D	E	L	1973	56672
8001	C	S	E	L	1973	56672
8001	C	D	E	L	1974	58934
8001	C	S	E	L	1974	58934
8001	S	D	E	N	1973	56672
132-8001	S	D	E	L	1974	54071
8001	S	D	E	N	1974	54071
8002	S	D	E	N	1974	58909
133-8002	C	D	R	L	1973	51273

Phys. State: **A.** Amorphous; **C.** Superconductive; **D.** Doped; **F.** Fibrous or Whisker; **G.** Gas; **I.** Ionized or Plasma; **L.** Liquid; **P.** Powder or Particle; **S.** Solid; **T.** Thin Film
Subject: **D.** Data; **E.** Experiment; **S.** Survey (Review, Compendium, etc.); **T.** Theory
Language: **E.** English; **F.** French; **G.** German; **O.** Other Languages; **R.** Russian
Temperature: **L.** Low (0 to 75K); **N.** Normal (75 to 1273K); **H.** High (above 1273K)

Chapter 11 Magnetoelectric Properties

Substance Number	Phys. State	Sub-ject	Lan-guage	Temper-ature	Year	EPIC Number
100-0045	S	S	E	L	1975	92677
0045	S	S	E	N	1975	92677
0055	A	T	R	N	1972	62723
0055	A	T	E	N	1973	65319
0055	A	T	E	N	1973	65771
0055	A	T	E	N	1974	86448
0055	A	T	E	N	1976	100646
0055	C	T	E	L	1975	96735
0055	D	T	E	N	1973	57395
0055	D	S	R	L	1972	62704
0055	D	S	E	L	1973	65123
0055	S	T	R	N	1973	50056
0055	S	T	R	N	1973	50674
0055	S	T	E	N	1973	51412
0055	S	T	E	N	1973	52083
0055	S	T	E	N	1973	52420
0055	S	E	E	N	1973	52778
0055	S	T	R	N	1973	52880
0055	S	T	E	N	1974	52881
0055	S	T	E	N	1974	53600
0055	S	T	E	N	1974	53609
0055	S	S	E	N	1973	53986
0055	S	T	R	N	1971	54276
0055	S	T	E	N	1972	54277
0055	S	T	E	N	1974	54343
0055	S	T	R	N	1973	55191
0055	S	T	E	N	1974	55192
0055	S	T	R	N	1973	55333
0055	S	T	E	N	1974	59270
0055	S	T	E	N	1958	59568
0055	S	T	R	N	1971	59580
0055	S	T	R	N	1972	60021
0055	S	T	R	N	1974	60433
0055	S	T	E	N	1974	60434
0055	S	T	E	N	1971	61329
0055	S	T	E	N	1970	61493
0055	S	S	E	L	1971	64456
0055	S	T	E	N	1974	65239
0055	S	T	E	N	1962	65942
0055	S	T	E	N	1962	65956
0055	S	E	O	N	1974	66483
0055	S	E	O	N	1971	67030
0055	S	T	R	N	1970	67419
0055	S	T	E	N	1974	67618
0055	S	S	E	N	1971	76189
0055	S	T	E	N	1971	76189
0055	S	S	R	N	1971	77339
0055	S	T	R	N	1971	77339
0055	S	T	E	N	1975	78758
0055	S	T	E	N	1975	90111
0055	S	T	E	N	1975	90555
0055	S	T	R	N	1975	90673
0055	S	E	F	N	1975	91781
0055	S	T	F	N	1975	91781
0055	S	T	E	N	1975	92037
0055	S	E	G	L	1975	92648
0055	S	E	G	N	1975	92648
0055	S	T	E	N	1974	92943
0055	S	T	R	N	1974	93080
0055	S	T	E	N	1975	95509
0055	S	T	E	N	1975	96737
0055	S	T	E	N	1975	96738
0055	S	T	E	L	1976	98423
0055	S	T	E	N	1976	98423
0055	S	T	R	N	1975	99063
0055	S	T	E	N	1975	99064
0055	T	E	E	N	1972	53299
0055	T	T	R	N	1974	60397
0055	T	T	E	N	1974	60398
0055	T	T	E	N	1975	65496
0055	T	T	R	N	1968	75362
0055	T	T	E	N	1969	91450
0055	T	T	R	N	1972	94894
0055	T	T	E	N	1972	95899
0055	T	T	R	N	1975	96340
0055	T	T	E	N	1975	96341
8003	S	T	E	N	1973	57702
8008	S	T	E	N	1974	67290
8008	S	T	R	N	1974	93080
8008	S	T	E	N	1975	93081
8013	D	D	R	N	1973	52534
8013	D	D	E	N	1974	53647
102-0002	D	D	E	N	1973	50785
0041	T	D	E	N	1974	65107
8001	S	S	E	N	1962	87668
8035	S	D	E	N	1973	51048
8041	D	D	R	N	1972	49888
8041	D	D	E	L	1972	49928
8041	D	D	R	L	1973	50079
8041	D	D	R	N	1973	50079
8041	D	D	E	L	1973	51042
8041	D	D	E	L	1973	51432
8041	D	D	E	N	1973	51432
8041	D	D	R	L	1973	54950
102-8041	D	D	R	N	1973	54950
8041	D	D	E	L	1958	75961
8041	D	S	E	L	1964	87701
8041	D	S	E	N	1964	87701
8041	D	D	E	N	1974	90398
8041	D	T	E	N	1974	90398
8041	S	D	O	N	1973	51960
8041	S	D	R	L	1973	54950
8041	S	D	R	N	1973	54950
8041	S	D	E	N	1972	56330
8041	S	D	E	L	1973	56440
8041	S	D	R	N	1974	58659
8041	S	S	R	L	1972	62704
8041	S	S	E	L	1973	65123
8041	S	D	R	L	1973	66551
8041	S	D	E	L	1974	66552
8041	S	D	R	N	1972	66984
8041	S	T	E	N	1974	67290
8041	S	D	E	N	1970	68209
8041	S	D	R	N	1975	81273
8041	S	S	E	N	1962	87673
8041	S	S	E	L	1964	87701
8041	S	S	E	N	1964	87701
8041	S	D	G	L	1975	92648
8041	S	D	G	N	1975	92648
8041	S	E	G	L	1975	92648
8041	S	E	G	N	1975	92648
8041	S	D	E	N	1975	94088
8041	T	D	R	L	1973	50079
8041	T	D	R	N	1973	50079
8041	T	D	R	N	1973	50676
8041	T	D	E	L	1973	51432
8041	T	D	E	N	1973	51432
8041	T	D	R	N	1973	51702
8041	T	D	E	N	1973	52422
8041	T	D	R	L	1973	52832
8041	T	D	R	N	1973	52832
8041	T	D	E	L	1973	52833
8041	T	D	E	N	1973	52833
8041	T	D	E	N	1973	52935
8041	T	E	R	N	1972	61563
8041	T	E	E	N	1972	65914
8054	S	D	E	N	1972	55164
8054	S	S	E	N	1962	87667
8054	T	S	E	L	1973	53451
8054	T	S	E	N	1973	53451
8066	S	D	R	N	1973	51553
8066	S	D	R	N	1973	52557
8066	S	D	E	N	1973	53684
8071	S	D	E	N	1972	49487
8071	S	D	E	N	1973	56374
8084	S	D	R	N	1973	55338
8084	S	D	E	N	1974	59276
8095	S	D	R	N	1975	81273
8095	S	D	E	N	1975	94088
8106	A	T	E	N	1976	100646
8133	A	T	E	N	1976	100646
8142	S	D	E	N	1973	54758
8172	A	D	E	N	1972	53187
8195	S	D	E	L	1973	56440
8195	S	D	E	N	1973	56440
8195	S	D	E	L	1975	66703
8195	S	D	E	N	1975	66703
8195	S	S	E	L	1975	66703
8195	S	S	E	N	1975	66703
8195	S	T	E	L	1975	66703
8195	S	T	E	N	1975	66703
8197	S	D	E	L	1971	75948
8197	S	D	E	N	1971	75948
8198	S	D	E	L	1971	75948
8198	S	D	E	N	1971	75948
8220	S	S	E	L	1958	75842
8220	S	S	E	N	1958	75842
8310	S	D	E	L	1973	57114
8374	S	D	E	N	1973	57714
8502	S	D	E	L	1971	75948
8502	S	D	E	N	1971	75948
104-8042	L	D	R	N	1972	52220
8042	S	D	E	L	1973	51069
8042	S	S	E	N	1966	66068
8045	D	S	E	N	1966	66068
8045	L	D	R	N	1972	52220
8045	S	D	R	N	1971	49758
8045	S	D	R	L	1973	50295
8045	S	D	E	L	1973	50296
8045	S	D	E	L	1973	52072
8045	S	D	R	L	1972	62298
8045	S	D	E	L	1973	62299
8045	S	D	E	L	1972	63966
8045	S	S	E	N	1966	66068
8045	S	D	G	N	1975	91993
8109	T	D	R	N	1975	101557
8109	T	D	E	N	1975	101558
8220	S	D	R	N	1970	61240
104-8224	S	D	R	L	1971	54264
8224	S	D	E	L	1972	54265
8224	S	D	R	L	1973	55044
8224	S	D	R	N	1973	55044
8224	S	D	E	L	1974	55045
8224	S	D	E	N	1974	55045
8317	S	T	E	N	1974	57720
106-0035	D	S	E	N	1965	87702
0035	S	S	E	L	1965	87702
0035	S	S	E	N	1965	87702
0035	S	S	E	L	1968	87828
0035	S	S	E	N	1968	87828
0057	S	S	E	N	1966	68325
0309	S	D	R	L	1973	50743
0309	S	D	E	L	1973	79073
0363	D	S	E	N	1963	64232
0363	D	S	E	N	1967	66156
0363	S	T	E	N	1974	61182
0363	S	S	E	L	1967	66156
0363	S	S	E	N	1967	66156
0937	S	D	R	L	1973	50743
0937	S	D	E	L	1973	79073
1027	S	D	R	L	1973	50743
1027	S	D	R	L	1971	76491
1027	S	D	E	L	1973	79073
1027	S	D	E	L	1971	91570
1516	S	T	E	N	1973	52954
8040	S	T	R	N	1973	55300
8040	S	T	E	N	1974	59225
8041	D	S	E	N	1967	68371
8041	D	S	E	N	1962	87659
8128	S	D	R	N	1973	55014
8128	S	D	E	N	1974	55015
8128	S	D	R	N	1973	55409
8128	S	D	E	N	1974	57830
8128	S	D	E	L	1962	65962
8128	S	T	E	L	1962	65962
8128	S	S	E	N	1967	68371
8128	S	D	E	N	1974	90401
8128	S	D	R	L	1976	103167
8128	S	D	R	N	1976	103167
8128	S	D	E	L	1976	103168
8128	S	D	E	N	1976	103168
8147	S	D	E	N	1973	49998
8148	S	D	E	N	1973	49998
8211	S	D	E	L	1973	50921
8312	D	T	R	N	1974	66790
8312	D	T	E	N	1975	66791
8312	S	D	E	N	1975	65456
8312	S	E	E	N	1975	65456
8312	S	D	R	N	1974	66790
8312	S	T	R	N	1974	66790
8312	S	D	E	N	1975	66791
8312	S	T	E	N	1975	66791
8323	S	T	E	N	1973	52954
8363	S	D	E	L	1973	51821
8400	S	T	E	N	1973	52101
8436	S	D	E	N	1973	51828
8436	S	D	E	N	1973	57695
8439	S	D	R	N	1974	63161
8439	S	D	E	N	1975	63162
8467	S	D	R	N	1968	61308
8467	S	D	E	N	1968	61309
8531	S	D	E	N	1974	57587
8559	S	D	R	L	1973	50743
8812	S	D	E	N	1975	65456
8812	S	E	E	N	1975	65456
108-0087	S	T	E	N	1973	52954
8046	S	D	E	N	1973	57658
109-0025	S	D	E	L	1973	50887
0025	S	D	E	N	1973	50887
0025	T	D	E	N	1973	57643
0025	T	D	E	N	1974	60295
0025	T	E	E	N	1974	60295
8017	D	D	R	N	1974	58092
8017	D	D	E	N	1974	58093
8019	S	D	E	L	1974	62346
8019	S	D	E	N	1974	62346
8019	S	T	E	L	1974	62346
8019	S	T	E	N	1974	62346
8076	S	D	E	N	1973	57658
110-0025	S	D	E	N	1973	56393
0028	T	T	R	N	1974	60493
0028	T	T	E	N	1974	60494
0194	D	D	R	N	1974	58092
0194	D	D	E	N	1974	58093
0194	S	D	R	N	1974	58092
0194	S	D	E	N	1974	58093
8042	T	T	R	N	1974	60493
8042	T	T	E	N	1974	60494
8119	T	D	R	N	1974	60493

Phys. State: **A.** Amorphous; **C.** Superconductive; **D.** Doped; **F.** Fibrous or Whisker; **G.** Gas; **I.** Ionized or Plasma; **L.** Liquid; **P.** Powder or Particle; **S.** Solid; **T.** Thin Film
Subject: **D.** Data; **E.** Experiment; **S.** Survey (Review, Compendium, etc.); **T.** Theory
Language: **E.** English; **F.** French; **G.** German; **O.** Other Languages; **R.** Russian
Temperature: **L.** Low (0 to 75K); **N.** Normal (75 to 1273K); **H.** High (above 1273K)

Magnetoelectric Properties

Substance Number	Phys. State	Subject	Language	Temperature	Year	EPIC Number
110-8119	T	D	E	N	1974	60494
8124	S	D	E	L	1973	51821
111-0008	S	S	E	N	1965	87703
8002	D	D	E	N	1974	61358
8002	D	D	E	L	1975	65494
8002	S	D	E	N	1973	53561
8002	S	T	E	L	1973	53561
8002	S	T	E	N	1973	53561
8002	S	D	E	L	1961	64496
8002	S	D	E	N	1961	64496
8002	S	T	E	L	1961	64496
8002	S	T	E	N	1961	64496
8002	S	S	E	N	1962	87670
8007	S	D	F	L	1963	58997
8007	S	D	F	N	1963	58997
8007	S	E	F	L	1963	58997
8007	S	E	F	N	1963	58997
8021	A	S	E	N	1970	59557
8021	D	D	E	L	1973	52437
8021	L	D	R	N	1972	52220
8021	S	D	E	L	1973	52437
8031	S	D	E	N	1973	52098
8035	S	D	E	L	1973	50884
8041	S	D	E	N	1973	56440
112-8020	S	D	E	L	1974	53611
8025	D	D	E	N	1976	101450
8025	D	E	E	N	1976	101450
8025	D	T	E	N	1976	101450
8025	S	D	R	L	1973	50062
8025	S	D	E	L	1973	51418
8025	S	D	R	N	1973	55409
8025	S	D	E	N	1974	57830
8042	S	D	E	N	1976	98423
8042	S	T	E	L	1976	98423
8042	S	T	E	N	1976	98423
8067	S	D	E	L	1973	55961
8067	S	D	E	L	1974	58360
8067	S	D	E	N	1974	58360
8074	S	D	E	N	1973	57658
114-0017	S	D	R	N	1973	51702
0017	S	D	E	N	1973	52935
0017	S	S	E	N	1962	87660
0017	S	S	E	N	1963	98002
0017	T	D	R	L	1973	52832
0017	T	D	R	N	1973	52832
0017	T	D	E	L	1973	52833
0017	T	D	E	N	1973	52833
8001	A	S	E	N	1970	59557
8001	A	D	E	L	1974	87770
8001	C	D	E	L	1974	87770
8001	D	D	R	L	1973	50209
8001	D	D	R	N	1973	50209
8001	D	D	E	L	1973	50210
8001	D	D	E	N	1973	50210
8001	D	T	R	N	1973	52372
8001	D	T	E	N	1974	63212
8001	D	S	E	N	1974	64457
8001	D	D	R	N	1973	68518
8001	D	T	R	N	1973	68518
8001	D	S	E	N	1975	87741
8001	S	D	R	N	1973	50646
8001	S	D	R	L	1973	50683
8001	S	D	E	N	1973	52098
8001	S	T	E	N	1973	52197
8001	S	D	R	L	1973	52525
8001	S	T	E	L	1973	52702
8001	S	T	E	N	1973	52704
8001	S	D	E	L	1973	52928
8001	S	D	R	N	1973	54173
8001	S	D	E	N	1973	54174
8001	S	D	E	L	1974	54339
8001	S	T	R	N	1973	54956
8001	S	D	R	N	1972	56959
8001	S	T	E	N	1974	57590
8001	S	D	E	L	1974	57766
8001	S	D	E	N	1974	60287
8001	S	T	E	N	1974	60287
8001	S	D	E	L	1963	60566
8001	S	D	E	N	1956	62960
8001	S	D	R	L	1974	63036
8001	S	T	R	L	1974	63036
8001	S	D	E	L	1974	63037
8001	S	T	E	L	1974	63037
8001	S	D	E	N	1974	65239
8001	S	T	E	N	1974	65239
8001	S	D	R	L	1974	65371
8001	S	T	R	L	1974	65371
8001	S	D	E	L	1975	65372
8001	S	T	E	L	1975	65372
8001	S	S	O	L	1966	66022
8001	S	S	O	N	1966	66022
8001	S	S	E	L	1967	66023
8001	S	S	E	N	1967	66023
8001	S	D	R	N	1974	66580
8001	S	D	E	N	1974	66581
8001	S	D	R	L	1974	66600
8001	S	D	E	L	1974	66601
8001	S	D	R	L	1974	66732
114-8001	S	T	R	L	1974	66732
8001	S	D	E	L	1975	66733
8001	S	T	E	L	1975	66733
8001	S	D	R	L	1974	66734
8001	S	T	R	L	1974	66734
8001	S	D	E	L	1975	66735
8001	S	T	E	L	1975	66735
8001	S	D	R	L	1974	66736
8001	S	T	R	L	1974	66736
8001	S	D	E	L	1975	66737
8001	S	T	E	L	1975	66737
8001	S	D	R	N	1973	68518
8001	S	T	R	N	1973	68518
8001	S	S	E	L	1971	76189
8001	S	S	E	N	1971	76189
8001	S	S	R	L	1971	77339
8001	S	S	R	N	1971	77339
8001	S	D	E	L	1975	86751
8001	S	S	E	N	1963	87679
8001	S	S	E	L	1965	87781
8001	S	S	E	N	1965	87781
8001	S	T	E	N	1975	90111
8001	S	D	E	N	1975	96737
8001	S	T	E	N	1975	96737
8001	T	D	E	N	1972	53299
8001	T	S	E	N	1972	53299
8001	T	T	E	N	1975	65496
8010	S	D	E	L	1974	59583
8010	S	D	E	N	1974	59583
8062	S	D	E	N	1972	60930
118-8065	D	D	E	N	1973	55659
8065	S	D	E	N	1973	55659
119-0041	S	D	E	L	1969	72658
0041	S	D	E	N	1969	72658
8002	D	S	E	N	1962	87672
8050	S	D	E	L	1973	51821
120-0045	C	D	E	L	1974	57997
0045	C	S	E	L	1974	57997
0045	T	D	E	L	1974	57997
0045	T	S	E	L	1974	57997
0199	C	D	E	L	1974	57997
0199	T	D	E	L	1974	57997
8006	C	S	O	L	1973	62410
8042	C	D	E	L	1974	62037
8047	C	D	E	L	1975	63357
8047	C	T	E	L	1975	63357
122-0023	S	S	E	N	1963	87709
0030	D	D	E	N	1974	90339
0112	S	D	E	N	1972	53261
123-0003	S	S	E	L	1966	68361
0003	S	S	E	N	1966	68361
0026	S	D	E	N	1972	49487
8004	S	D	E	N	1973	52053
8005	S	D	E	N	1974	56627
8017	D	D	E	N	1974	57986
8017	S	S	E	L	1962	87674
8017	S	S	E	N	1962	87674
8017	T	D	E	N	1974	57986
8017	T	E	E	N	1974	57986
8018	D	D	R	N	1973	59370
8018	S	D	E	N	1972	59070
8018	S	S	E	N	1972	59070
8018	S	T	E	N	1972	59070
8018	S	D	R	N	1973	59370
8018	S	D	R	N	1968	60749
8018	S	T	R	N	1968	60749
8018	S	D	E	N	1974	60750
8018	S	T	E	N	1974	60750
8018	S	S	E	N	1974	64457
8018	S	S	E	L	1970	68114
8018	S	S	E	N	1970	68114
8018	S	D	E	N	1966	75147
8018	S	S	E	L	1962	87671
8018	S	S	E	N	1962	87671
8018	S	D	R	N	1966	91929
8039	S	D	R	N	1973	50066
8039	S	D	E	N	1973	51420
8051	S	D	E	N	1974	60369
8051	S	E	E	N	1974	60369
8051	S	D	E	N	1973	65985
126-8026	S	D	R	N	1971	58851
8034	S	D	O	N	1973	52666
8071	C	D	E	L	1973	61451
8071	C	T	E	L	1973	61451
8071	C	D	E	L	1974	88597
8094	S	D	R	N	1973	55285
8094	S	D	E	N	1974	59242
8094	S	D	R	N	1970	61240
127-8003	S	D	E	L	1973	50804
8003	S	D	E	N	1973	50804

Phys. State: **A.** Amorphous; **C.** Superconductive; **D.** Doped; **F.** Fibrous or Whisker; **G.** Gas; **I.** Ionized or Plasma; **L.** Liquid; **P.** Powder or Particle; **S.** Solid; **T.** Thin Film
Subject: **D.** Data; **E.** Experiment; **S.** Survey (Review, Compendium, etc.); **T.** Theory
Language: **E.** English; **F.** French; **G.** German; **O.** Other Languages; **R.** Russian
Temperature: **L.** Low (0 to 75K); **N.** Normal (75 to 1273K); **H.** High (above 1273K)

Chapter 12 Hall Coefficient

Substance Number	Phys. State	Subject	Language	Temperature	Year	EPIC Number
100-0045	S	S	E	N	1973	55967
0055	A	T	E	N	1973	51774
0055	A	T	E	N	1975	86750
0055	A	T	E	N	1976	100646
0055	D	T	E	N	1973	53461
0055	D	E	E	H	1971	60928
0055	D	E	E	N	1971	60928
0055	D	E	R	N	1972	61562
0055	D	E	E	N	1972	65913
0055	D	T	R	N	1974	67747
0055	D	T	R	N	1974	72313
0055	D	T	E	N	1975	72358
0055	D	E	R	H	1974	93417
0055	D	E	R	N	1974	93417
0055	D	E	E	H	1974	93418
0055	D	E	E	N	1974	93418
0055	L	S	R	N	1972	59001
0055	L	S	E	N	1972	59002
0055	L	S	R	N	1966	95131
0055	L	S	E	N	1966	96497
0055	S	E	R	N	1973	50095
0055	S	E	E	H	1973	50148
0055	S	E	E	N	1973	50148
0055	S	E	E	L	1973	50794
0055	S	E	E	N	1973	50794
0055	S	T	R	N	1973	51372
0055	S	T	E	N	1973	51373
0055	S	E	G	N	1973	51683
0055	S	E	E	N	1973	52657
0055	S	S	E	N	1972	53200
0055	S	T	E	N	1972	53299
0055	S	S	E	N	1973	53986
0055	S	T	E	N	1974	54040
0055	S	T	R	N	1972	54286
0055	S	T	E	N	1972	54287
0055	S	E	E	N	1973	55588
0055	S	T	E	N	1973	57390
0055	S	T	E	N	1973	58630
0055	S	E	E	N	1965	58978
0055	S	E	E	N	1968	59164
0055	S	T	E	N	1968	59164
0055	S	E	E	H	1956	59167
0055	S	E	E	L	1956	59167
0055	S	E	E	N	1956	59167
0055	S	E	E	L	1969	59174
0055	S	E	E	N	1969	59174
0055	S	E	E	L	1958	59175
0055	S	E	E	N	1958	59175
0055	S	E	E	L	1965	59177
0055	S	E	E	N	1965	59177
0055	S	E	E	N	1959	59185
0055	S	T	E	N	1959	59185
0055	S	T	E	N	1958	59568
0055	S	E	E	N	1974	59573
0055	S	T	E	N	1974	59573
0055	S	T	O	N	1970	60020
0055	S	E	E	N	1966	60796
0055	S	T	E	N	1966	60796
0055	S	T	E	N	1970	61493
0055	S	S	E	N	1970	61494
0055	S	T	R	N	1970	64854
0055	S	T	E	N	1971	64855
0055	S	E	O	N	1971	67030
0055	S	T	O	N	1972	67588
0055	S	E	R	N	1973	68005
0055	S	E	E	N	1973	68006
0055	S	T	E	N	1975	68679
0055	S	E	R	N	1972	76387
0055	S	T	R	N	1972	76387
0055	S	T	E	N	1975	78758
0055	S	E	E	N	1972	83168
0055	S	T	E	N	1972	83168
0055	S	E	E	L	1975	96816
0055	S	E	E	N	1975	96816
0055	S	T	E	N	1975	98207
0055	T	T	R	N	1973	50064
0055	T	E	E	N	1973	58586
0055	T	S	E	N	1972	61768
8005	S	S	R	N	1973	55480
8013	D	D	R	N	1973	52534
8013	D	D	E	N	1974	53647
8027	S	S	R	N	1972	56475
8040	S	S	E	N	1969	75843
8043	S	S	E	N	1969	75843
8057	S	T	R	N	1973	67856
8068	S	S	E	N	1964	93287
102-0041	S	D	R	N	1971	60185
0041	T	D	E	L	1974	65107
0041	T	D	E	N	1974	65107
0041	T	E	E	N	1974	65107
0041	T	D	E	N	1975	65464
0120	L	D	R	N	1973	52540
0120	L	D	E	N	1974	53675
0120	S	D	R	N	1973	50724
102-0120	S	D	E	N	1973	53025
0348	S	D	E	N	1973	52657
0348	S	E	E	N	1973	52657
8001	D	D	E	N	1973	53427
8001	D	D	R	N	1972	62717
8001	D	D	E	N	1973	65313
8001	D	S	E	N	1962	87668
8001	S	S	E	N	1973	53427
8001	S	S	E	N	1962	87668
8001	S	S	E	N	1966	87830
8012	S	D	R	N	1973	50321
8012	S	D	E	N	1973	50322
8012	S	D	R	N	1974	81141
8012	S	D	E	N	1975	92631
8035	S	D	E	N	1973	51048
8035	S	D	E	N	1972	51526
8035	S	E	E	L	1969	59174
8035	S	E	E	N	1969	59174
8035	S	D	E	N	1975	94550
8041	D	D	R	N	1972	49647
8041	D	D	R	N	1972	49888
8041	D	D	E	L	1973	51866
8041	D	D	E	N	1973	51866
8041	D	D	E	N	1973	52460
8041	D	D	E	N	1972	52982
8041	D	D	R	N	1970	53088
8041	D	D	E	N	1972	53089
8041	D	D	E	L	1972	53138
8041	D	D	E	N	1972	53138
8041	D	D	E	N	1972	53143
8041	D	D	E	N	1972	53171
8041	D	D	E	N	1972	53302
8041	D	D	E	N	1972	53484
8041	D	D	E	L	1973	53565
8041	D	D	E	N	1973	53565
8041	D	D	E	N	1974	53638
8041	D	D	E	N	1974	53735
8041	D	E	E	N	1974	53745
8041	D	T	E	N	1974	53910
8041	D	S	E	N	1972	55099
8041	D	T	E	N	1972	55099
8041	D	T	E	N	1974	57994
8041	D	D	E	L	1970	59695
8041	D	D	E	N	1970	59695
8041	D	D	E	N	1971	60690
8041	D	E	E	N	1971	60690
8041	D	D	E	N	1964	62127
8041	D	D	E	N	1975	63363
8041	D	T	E	N	1975	63363
8041	D	D	E	N	1974	65110
8041	D	S	E	N	1974	65110
8041	D	D	R	N	1969	67766
8041	D	D	R	N	1975	81166
8041	D	T	R	N	1975	81166
8041	D	S	E	N	1962	87673
8041	D	S	E	L	1964	87701
8041	D	S	E	N	1964	87701
8041	D	D	E	N	1975	94087
8041	D	T	E	N	1975	94087
8041	S	D	R	N	1972	49647
8041	S	D	R	N	1972	51102
8041	S	D	E	N	1972	52982
8041	S	D	E	N	1972	53171
8041	S	D	E	L	1972	53184
8041	S	D	R	N	1972	54286
8041	S	D	E	N	1972	54287
8041	S	D	R	N	1973	54947
8041	S	D	R	L	1973	55305
8041	S	D	R	N	1973	55305
8041	S	D	E	N	1971	55377
8041	S	D	E	N	1973	57396
8041	S	T	E	N	1973	58630
8041	S	D	E	L	1974	59230
8041	S	D	E	N	1974	59230
8041	S	T	E	N	1973	60748
8041	S	D	E	N	1973	60754
8041	S	S	E	L	1974	64464
8041	S	S	E	N	1974	64464
8041	S	D	E	N	1972	66263
8041	S	D	R	N	1971	66998
8041	S	D	R	N	1970	67035
8041	S	D	E	N	1973	68192
8041	S	D	E	N	1966	75146
8041	S	S	E	N	1973	86380
8041	S	S	E	N	1962	87673
8041	S	S	E	L	1964	87701
8041	S	S	E	N	1964	87701
8041	S	D	R	N	1966	91926
8041	T	D	R	N	1973	50676
8041	T	D	E	N	1973	52422
8041	T	D	E	N	1973	52589
8041	T	D	R	L	1973	52832
8041	T	D	E	L	1973	52833
8041	T	D	E	N	1973	52833
8041	T	S	E	L	1971	60965
102-8041	T	S	E	N	1971	60965
8041	T	D	R	N	1969	67766
8041	T	D	R	N	1972	76536
8041	T	T	R	N	1972	76536
8041	T	D	E	N	1972	91519
8041	T	T	E	N	1972	91519
8054	D	D	E	N	1972	51091
8054	D	D	E	N	1974	53638
8054	D	D	R	N	1973	58156
8054	D	D	E	N	1966	60796
8054	D	S	E	N	1962	87667
8054	S	D	E	N	1972	51091
8054	S	D	E	L	1971	53516
8054	S	D	E	N	1971	53516
8054	S	E	E	L	1958	59175
8054	S	E	E	N	1958	59175
8054	S	D	E	L	1964	59758
8054	S	D	E	N	1966	60796
8054	S	E	E	N	1966	60796
8054	S	T	E	N	1966	60796
8054	S	D	E	N	1972	66263
8054	S	S	E	N	1962	87667
8054	T	S	E	N	1973	53451
8054	T	S	E	N	1971	60965
8065	S	D	R	N	1974	86779
8065	S	D	E	N	1974	90050
8066	L	D	E	H	1972	49461
8066	L	D	E	N	1972	49461
8066	S	D	E	N	1972	49461
8066	S	D	R	N	1973	52557
8066	S	D	R	N	1973	58197
8066	S	D	R	N	1974	86779
8066	S	D	E	N	1974	90050
8069	S	D	E	N	1972	53335
8069	S	D	R	N	1972	56992
8071	S	D	E	N	1972	49487
8084	S	D	R	N	1973	55338
8084	S	D	E	N	1974	59276
8084	S	D	R	N	1974	67759
8084	S	D	E	N	1975	94550
8094	D	D	G	N	1973	50835
8095	S	S	E	N	1965	87703
8096	D	D	R	N	1972	50105
8096	D	D	R	N	1973	51730
8096	D	D	E	N	1973	79154
8096	S	D	R	N	1972	56992
8106	A	T	E	N	1976	100646
8106	L	D	R	N	1973	51406
8106	L	D	E	N	1973	51407
8108	S	D	R	N	1973	50724
8108	S	D	E	N	1973	53025
8133	A	D	E	N	1973	67289
8133	A	T	E	N	1976	100646
8133	L	D	R	N	1973	51406
8133	L	D	E	N	1973	51407
8139	S	D	E	N	1974	60309
8142	D	D	E	N	1972	53199
8142	D	D	E	N	1974	53638
8172	A	D	E	N	1972	53187
8172	A	S	E	N	1972	53187
8180	S	D	E	N	1975	94550
8187	A	D	E	L	1969	72525
8187	A	D	E	N	1969	72525
8202	L	D	E	N	1973	53675
8202	L	S	E	N	1971	65065
8223	S	S	E	N	1966	87843
8241	S	D	E	N	1943	61285
8284	S	D	E	N	1971	65065
8287	S	D	R	N	1956	89787
8287	S	D	E	N	1956	89788
8288	S	D	R	N	1956	89787
8288	S	D	E	N	1956	89788
8310	S	D	E	N	1973	53799
8310	S	D	E	N	1975	94550
8311	S	D	E	N	1973	56364
8330	S	D	R	N	1956	89787
8330	S	D	E	N	1956	89788
8333	T	D	F	N	1974	57941
8374	S	D	E	N	1974	88681
8383	A	T	E	N	1974	84007
8437	S	D	E	N	1974	88681
8438	S	D	E	N	1974	88681
8453	S	D	R	L	1972	76538
8453	S	D	R	N	1972	76538
8453	S	D	E	L	1972	91520
8453	S	D	E	N	1972	91520
8454	S	D	R	L	1972	76538
8454	S	D	R	N	1972	76538
8454	S	D	E	L	1972	91520
8454	S	D	E	N	1972	91520
104-0049	S	E	R	N	1974	66728
0049	S	E	E	N	1975	66729
0409	S	D	R	N	1971	76503
0409	S	T	R	N	1971	76503

Phys. State: **A.** Amorphous; **C.** Superconductive; **D.** Doped; **F.** Fibrous or Whisker; **G.** Gas; **I.** Ionized or Plasma; **L.** Liquid; **P.** Powder or Particle; **S.** Solid; **T.** Thin Film
Subject: **D.** Data; **E.** Experiment; **S.** Survey (Review, Compendium, etc.); **T.** Theory
Language: **E.** English; **F.** French; **G.** German; **O.** Other Languages; **R.** Russian
Temperature: **L.** Low (0 to 75K); **N.** Normal (75 to 1273K); **H.** High (above 1273K)

Substance Number	Phys. State	Sub-ject	Lan-guage	Temper-ature	Year	EPIC Number
104-0409	S	D	E	N	1971	91564
0409	S	T	E	N	1971	91564
0572	S	D	R	N	1971	76503
0572	S	T	R	N	1971	76503
0572	S	D	E	N	1971	91564
0572	S	T	E	N	1971	91564
0573	S	D	R	N	1971	76503
0573	S	T	R	N	1971	76503
0573	S	D	E	N	1971	91564
0573	S	T	E	N	1971	91564
8010	S	D	R	N	1967	72953
8042	S	S	E	N	1966	66068
8043	S	D	R	N	1972	49822
8045	D	D	E	L	1973	52709
8045	D	S	E	N	1966	66068
8045	L	D	R	N	1973	52540
8045	L	D	E	N	1974	53675
8045	L	S	E	N	1972	62298
8045	L	S	E	N	1973	62299
8045	L	D	E	N	1967	64763
8045	L	D	E	N	1971	65065
8045	S	D	R	L	1973	50295
8045	S	D	E	L	1973	50296
8045	S	D	E	L	1973	52072
8045	S	D	E	L	1973	52709
8045	S	D	R	N	1972	62298
8045	S	S	R	N	1972	62298
8045	S	D	E	N	1973	62299
8045	S	S	E	N	1973	62299
8045	S	D	E	L	1972	63966
8045	S	D	E	N	1971	65065
8045	S	S	E	L	1966	66068
8045	S	S	E	N	1966	66068
8045	S	D	R	N	1972	76534
8045	S	D	E	N	1972	91537
8045	S	D	G	N	1975	91993
8045	S	D	E	N	1968	98762
8083	S	S	E	N	1966	87721
8099	S	D	R	N	1972	51232
8108	D	S	E	N	1966	66068
8108	D	D	E	N	1968	98762
8108	S	D	E	N	1971	59999
8108	S	E	E	N	1971	59999
8108	S	S	E	N	1966	66068
8108	S	D	E	N	1968	98762
8108	T	D	R	N	1975	93407
8108	T	D	E	N	1975	93408
8109	T	D	R	L	1975	101557
8109	T	D	R	N	1975	101557
8109	T	T	R	N	1975	101557
8109	T	D	E	L	1975	101558
8109	T	D	E	N	1975	101558
8109	T	T	E	N	1975	101558
8114	S	D	O	N	1972	49812
8115	S	D	O	N	1972	49812
8156	S	D	R	N	1972	51232
8157	S	D	R	N	1972	51232
8158	S	D	R	L	1972	51237
8159	S	D	R	N	1972	51237
8176	S	D	E	N	1973	52048
8224	S	D	R	N	1972	94907
8224	S	D	E	N	1973	95897
8269	D	D	R	N	1971	65450
8269	D	D	E	N	1971	65451
8269	S	D	R	N	1971	65450
8269	S	D	E	N	1971	65451
8369	S	S	E	N	1966	66068
106-0004	S	E	R	N	1974	66728
0004	S	E	E	N	1975	66729
0035	D	S	E	N	1965	87702
0035	D	D	E	N	1976	99748
0035	S	D	R	N	1974	64485
0035	S	T	R	N	1974	64485
0035	S	S	E	L	1965	87702
0035	S	S	E	N	1965	87702
0057	P	S	E	N	1966	68325
0057	S	S	E	N	1966	68325
0057	T	S	E	N	1973	57559
0081	D	T	R	N	1975	90140
0081	D	T	E	N	1975	90141
0104	S	D	R	N	1972	59068
0104	S	D	E	N	1972	59069
0104	S	S	E	N	1971	87872
0104	T	D	E	N	1970	61741
0125	S	S	E	N	1964	93287
0127	S	D	R	N	1972	50692
0127	S	E	R	N	1972	50692
0205	S	S	E	N	1964	93287
0226	S	S	E	N	1964	93287
0308	S	S	E	N	1964	93287
0309	S	D	R	L	1973	50743
0309	S	D	E	L	1973	79073
0309	S	S	E	N	1966	87721
0309	S	S	E	N	1972	87886
0309	S	S	E	N	1964	93287
0363	D	D	E	N	1973	50830
0363	D	S	E	N	1963	64232
0363	D	S	E	N	1967	66156
0363	D	D	E	N	1957	89723
0363	S	D	E	L	1974	57324

Substance Number	Phys. State	Sub-ject	Lan-guage	Temper-ature	Year	EPIC Number
106-0363	S	D	E	N	1974	57324
0363	S	D	E	N	1974	61182
0363	S	S	E	N	1963	64232
0363	S	S	E	N	1967	66156
0363	T	D	E	N	1974	53750
0363	T	S	E	N	1974	53750
0385	D	D	E	L	1969	74658
0385	D	D	E	N	1969	74658
0385	D	E	E	L	1969	74658
0385	D	E	E	N	1969	74658
0452	S	S	E	N	1964	93287
0639	S	S	E	N	1964	93287
0937	D	D	R	N	1971	76469
0937	D	D	E	N	1971	91495
0937	S	D	R	L	1973	50743
0937	S	D	R	N	1971	76469
0937	S	D	R	N	1971	76485
0937	S	S	R	N	1971	76485
0937	S	D	E	L	1973	79073
0937	S	D	E	N	1971	91495
0937	S	D	E	N	1971	91504
0937	S	S	E	N	1971	91504
0941	S	D	R	N	1973	54953
1027	S	D	R	L	1973	50743
1027	S	D	R	N	1973	56473
1027	S	D	R	N	1971	76491
1027	S	D	E	L	1973	79073
1027	S	D	E	N	1971	91570
1079	S	D	R	N	1967	53069
1079	S	D	E	N	1972	53070
1085	S	D	E	N	1973	56345
1287	S	D	E	L	1973	52754
1287	S	D	E	N	1973	52754
8001	D	D	E	N	1973	53451
8001	D	D	R	N	1973	54954
8001	D	D	R	N	1972	76511
8001	D	T	R	N	1972	76511
8001	D	D	R	N	1972	76512
8001	D	D	E	N	1972	91555
8001	D	T	E	N	1972	91555
8001	D	D	E	N	1972	91556
8001	L	D	R	N	1973	52540
8001	L	D	E	N	1974	53675
8001	L	D	E	N	1967	64763
8001	S	D	E	L	1973	51041
8001	S	D	R	N	1972	54155
8001	S	D	E	N	1972	54156
8001	S	D	R	N	1972	76511
8001	S	T	R	N	1972	76511
8001	S	D	E	N	1972	91555
8001	S	T	E	N	1972	91555
8001	T	S	E	N	1973	53451
8001	T	D	R	N	1972	76511
8001	T	T	R	N	1972	76511
8001	T	D	E	N	1972	91555
8001	T	T	E	N	1972	91555
8040	S	D	E	N	1973	50941
8040	S	S	E	N	1972	59933
8040	S	S	E	N	1963	87710
8041	D	D	E	N	1974	53601
8041	D	D	E	N	1974	64490
8041	D	D	E	N	1975	65462
8041	D	S	E	N	1967	68371
8041	D	S	E	N	1962	87659
8041	S	T	E	N	1973	56149
8041	S	D	R	L	1972	58680
8041	S	D	R	N	1972	58680
8041	S	S	E	N	1972	59933
8041	S	S	E	N	1967	68371
8041	S	S	E	N	1962	87659
8041	S	E	E	N	1975	93167
8075	S	D	R	L	1970	67624
8075	S	D	R	N	1970	67624
8081	D	D	R	N	1973	52556
8081	S	D	R	N	1973	55711
8081	S	D	R	N	1974	93465
8081	S	D	E	N	1974	93466
8084	S	D	R	N	1972	59068
8084	S	D	E	N	1972	59069
8084	S	D	R	L	1972	60544
8084	S	D	R	N	1972	60544
8084	S	D	E	L	1972	60545
8084	S	D	E	N	1972	60545
8125	S	D	R	N	1972	49559
8126	S	D	R	N	1972	49559
8127	S	D	R	N	1972	58679
8128	S	D	E	L	1972	49933
8128	S	D	E	N	1972	49933
8128	S	D	E	L	1972	53184
8128	S	D	E	N	1972	53401
8128	S	D	E	N	1973	53406
8128	S	D	E	L	1973	53852
8128	S	D	E	L	1969	59174
8128	S	D	E	N	1969	59174
8128	S	E	E	L	1969	59174
8128	S	E	E	N	1969	59174
8128	S	D	E	L	1974	61351
8128	S	D	E	N	1974	61351
8128	S	S	E	L	1967	68371
8128	S	S	E	N	1967	68371
8128	S	D	R	L	1974	86221

Substance Number	Phys. State	Sub-ject	Lan-guage	Temper-ature	Year	EPIC Number
106-8128	S	D	R	N	1974	86221
8128	S	D	E	N	1974	90401
8128	S	D	E	L	1974	92626
8128	S	D	E	N	1974	92626
8128	S	D	R	N	1976	103167
8128	S	D	E	N	1976	103168
8128	T	D	R	N	1972	49717
8128	T	D	E	N	1973	51923
8128	T	D	E	N	1974	66692
8128	T	S	E	N	1967	68371
8143	S	D	E	N	1972	49865
8156	D	D	R	N	1973	50095
8156	L	D	R	N	1973	52540
8156	L	D	E	N	1974	53675
8156	S	D	R	N	1973	50095
8157	S	D	R	N	1973	55457
8261	S	D	R	N	1973	51732
8261	S	D	E	N	1973	79136
8262	S	D	R	N	1973	51732
8262	S	D	R	N	1971	76478
8262	S	D	E	N	1973	79136
8262	S	D	E	N	1971	91502
8295	S	D	E	N	1973	52233
8299	T	D	E	N	1975	90115
8299	T	T	E	N	1975	90115
8312	S	D	E	N	1968	53358
8314	S	D	E	L	1973	52754
8314	S	D	E	N	1973	52754
8315	S	D	E	L	1973	52754
8315	S	D	E	N	1973	52754
8333	S	D	R	N	1971	53129
8333	S	D	E	N	1972	53130
8333	S	D	R	N	1973	54689
8334	S	D	R	N	1971	53129
8334	S	D	E	N	1972	53130
8335	S	D	R	N	1974	93465
8335	S	D	E	N	1974	93466
8338	S	D	E	N	1973	53415
8339	S	D	E	N	1973	53415
8340	S	D	E	L	1973	53415
8340	S	D	E	N	1973	53415
8340	S	S	E	N	1974	58346
8344	S	D	E	N	1973	53415
8364	S	D	E	N	1973	51890
8365	S	D	E	N	1973	51890
8366	S	D	E	N	1973	51890
8391	S	D	R	N	1971	76489
8391	S	T	R	N	1971	76489
8391	S	D	E	N	1971	91568
8391	S	T	E	N	1971	91568
8393	S	D	E	N	1971	91568
8393	S	T	E	N	1971	91568
8394	S	D	R	N	1971	76489
8394	S	T	R	N	1971	76489
8394	S	D	E	N	1971	91568
8394	S	T	E	N	1971	91568
8439	S	D	R	N	1972	60709
8439	S	T	R	N	1972	60709
8439	S	D	E	N	1973	60710
8439	S	T	E	N	1973	60710
8453	S	D	F	N	1974	90493
8456	S	D	F	N	1974	90493
8467	S	D	R	N	1973	55288
8467	S	D	E	N	1974	59247
8467	S	D	R	N	1968	61308
8467	S	D	E	N	1968	61309
8527	T	D	R	N	1973	56329
8529	S	D	R	N	1973	56861
8529	S	D	E	N	1973	57295
8559	S	D	R	L	1973	50743
8559	S	D	E	L	1973	79073
8565	S	D	R	N	1972	60709
8565	S	T	R	N	1972	60709
8565	S	D	E	N	1973	60710
8565	S	T	E	N	1973	60710
8611	S	D	E	N	1966	85403
8642	S	D	R	N	1973	51724
8642	S	D	R	N	1971	66283
8642	S	D	R	N	1971	76478
8642	S	D	E	N	1971	91502
8643	S	D	R	N	1973	51724
8653	D	S	E	N	1970	59699
8669	S	D	R	N	1971	66283
8686	S	D	F	N	1974	90493
8687	S	D	F	N	1974	90493
8759	S	D	R	N	1971	76478
8759	S	D	E	N	1971	91502
8766	S	S	E	N	1975	90115
8766	T	D	E	N	1975	97322
8811	S	D	R	N	1974	65411
8811	S	T	R	N	1974	65411
8811	S	D	E	N	1975	65412
8811	S	T	E	N	1975	65412
8818	S	D	R	N	1971	66283
8819	S	D	R	N	1971	66283
8820	S	D	R	N	1971	66283
108-0079	S	D	E	N	1974	54324
109-0025	S	D	E	N	1972	49906
0025	S	D	E	L	1973	50887

Phys. State: **A.** Amorphous; **C.** Superconductive; **D.** Doped; **F.** Fibrous or Whisker; **G.** Gas; **I.** Ionized or Plasma; **L.** Liquid; **P.** Powder or Particle; **S.** Solid; **T.** Thin Film
Subject: **D.** Data; **E.** Experiment; **S.** Survey (Review, Compendium, etc.); **T.** Theory
Language: **E.** English; **F.** French; **G.** German; **O.** Other Languages; **R.** Russian
Temperature: **L.** Low (0 to 75K); **N.** Normal (75 to 1273K); **H.** High (above 1273K)

Substance Number	Phys. State	Sub-ject	Lan-guage	Temper-ature	Year	EPIC Number
109-0025	S	D	E	N	1973	50887
0025	S	D	E	N	1973	50888
0025	S	D	E	L	1972	53158
0025	S	D	E	N	1972	53158
8019	S	D	E	L	1974	62346
8019	S	D	E	N	1974	62346
8019	S	T	E	L	1974	62346
8019	S	T	E	N	1974	62346
8019	S	D	E	N	1974	62347
8019	S	T	E	N	1974	62347
8034	S	D	E	L	1972	53158
8034	S	D	E	N	1972	53158
110-0007	S	D	R	N	1967	53069
0007	S	D	E	N	1972	53070
0028	D	T	R	N	1975	90140
0028	D	T	E	N	1975	90141
0194	D	T	R	N	1975	90140
0194	D	T	E	N	1975	90141
8042	T	D	R	N	1972	49981
8046	S	D	E	N	1972	49867
8102	S	D	R	N	1973	50645
8112	D	T	R	N	1975	90140
8112	D	T	E	N	1975	90141
8119	D	T	R	N	1975	90140
8119	D	T	E	N	1975	90141
8121	D	T	R	N	1975	90140
8121	D	T	E	N	1975	90141
111-0008	D	D	R	N	1972	76547
0008	D	D	E	N	1972	91597
0008	S	S	E	N	1965	87703
0008	T	D	R	N	1971	59188
0008	T	D	E	N	1971	59189
0021	T	D	E	N	1973	53394
0021	T	D	E	N	1973	53529
0050	D	D	E	N	1973	50558
0050	S	D	E	N	1973	50558
0050	S	D	E	N	1973	56335
8002	D	D	R	N	1972	51113
8002	D	D	E	L	1973	57692
8002	D	D	E	N	1973	57692
8002	D	D	E	L	1974	61358
8002	D	D	E	N	1974	61358
8002	D	S	E	L	1974	61358
8002	D	D	E	N	1975	66679
8002	D	D	R	N	1972	76506
8002	D	D	E	L	1975	87176
8002	D	D	E	N	1975	87176
8002	D	D	E	N	1972	91529
8002	D	D	E	N	1975	94627
8002	S	D	E	N	1973	50152
8002	S	D	E	L	1973	50578
8002	S	D	E	N	1973	50578
8002	S	D	E	N	1972	53519
8002	S	D	E	L	1973	53561
8002	S	D	E	N	1973	53561
8002	S	D	E	N	1974	54661
8002	S	D	R	N	1973	55710
8002	S	T	E	N	1956	62960
8002	S	D	E	N	1961	64496
8002	S	D	E	N	1961	64497
8002	S	D	E	N	1972	66263
8002	S	S	E	L	1962	87670
8002	S	S	E	N	1962	87670
8007	S	D	F	L	1963	58997
8007	S	D	F	N	1963	58997
8007	S	E	F	L	1963	58997
8007	S	E	F	N	1963	58997
8009	L	D	R	N	1973	52540
8009	L	D	E	N	1974	53675
8019	S	D	E	N	1973	49591
8019	S	D	E	N	1972	53519
8021	D	D	E	L	1973	52437
8021	D	D	R	N	1972	61562
8021	D	E	R	N	1972	61562
8021	D	D	E	N	1972	65913
8021	D	E	E	N	1972	65913
8021	D	T	R	N	1974	87069
8021	D	T	E	N	1974	87070
8021	L	D	R	N	1973	52540
8021	L	D	E	N	1974	53675
8021	S	T	R	N	1974	87069
8021	S	T	E	N	1974	87070
8021	S	D	R	N	1974	93451
8021	S	E	R	N	1974	93451
8021	S	T	R	N	1974	93451
8021	S	D	E	N	1974	93452
8021	S	E	E	N	1974	93452
8021	S	T	E	N	1974	93452
8025	S	D	E	N	1973	49999
8026	S	T	E	N	1973	55161
8031	S	D	E	N	1974	54661
8031	S	T	E	N	1975	61807
8055	S	D	R	N	1971	66283
8065	S	D	E	L	1972	52969
8065	S	D	E	N	1972	52969
8065	S	D	E	L	1972	53158
8065	S	D	E	N	1972	53158
8065	S	D	E	N	1973	53293
8066	S	D	E	N	1972	52969

Substance Number	Phys. State	Sub-ject	Lan-guage	Temper-ature	Year	EPIC Number
111-8071	S	D	E	N	1974	54324
8074	T	D	E	N	1972	53416
8079	D	D	E	N	1972	49462
8079	L	D	E	N	1972	49462
8107	S	D	R	N	1971	66283
8108	T	D	R	N	1976	101176
8108	T	S	R	N	1976	101176
8108	T	D	E	N	1976	101886
8108	T	S	E	N	1976	101886
8126	S	D	R	N	1971	66283
8127	D	D	R	N	1974	90221
8127	D	D	E	N	1975	90222
8136	S	D	R	N	1973	51724
8136	S	D	R	N	1971	66283
8139	S	D	R	N	1971	66283
8140	S	D	R	N	1971	66283
8141	S	D	R	N	1971	66283
8142	S	D	R	N	1971	66283
8143	S	D	R	N	1971	66283
8144	S	D	R	N	1971	66283
8145	S	D	R	N	1971	66283
8146	S	D	R	N	1971	66283
8147	S	D	R	N	1971	66283
8149	S	D	R	N	1971	66283
8150	S	D	R	N	1971	66283
8200	S	D	R	N	1971	66283
8201	S	D	R	N	1971	66283
8202	S	D	R	N	1971	66283
8203	S	D	R	N	1971	66283
8204	S	D	R	N	1971	66283
112-0001	S	T	E	N	1973	51030
0010	D	S	E	N	1968	75835
0010	L	S	E	N	1968	75835
0247	S	S	E	N	1964	93287
8025	D	D	E	N	1976	101450
8025	S	D	R	L	1973	50062
8025	S	D	E	L	1973	51418
8025	S	D	R	N	1973	51721
8025	S	E	E	L	1958	59175
8025	S	E	E	N	1958	59175
8025	S	D	R	L	1974	63000
8025	S	T	R	L	1974	63000
8025	S	D	E	L	1974	63001
8025	S	T	E	L	1974	63001
8025	S	D	E	L	1962	65962
8025	S	D	E	N	1962	65962
8025	S	T	E	L	1962	65962
8025	S	T	E	N	1962	65962
8025	S	D	E	L	1962	65963
8025	S	D	R	N	1969	66486
8025	S	D	R	N	1969	67411
8025	S	S	E	L	1967	68371
8025	S	S	E	N	1967	68371
8025	S	D	R	L	1972	76527
8025	S	D	R	N	1972	76527
8025	S	S	R	L	1972	76527
8025	S	S	R	N	1972	76527
8025	S	T	R	L	1972	76527
8025	S	T	R	N	1972	76527
8025	S	D	E	L	1972	91532
8025	S	D	E	N	1972	91532
8025	S	S	E	L	1972	91532
8025	S	S	E	N	1972	91532
8025	S	T	E	L	1972	91532
8025	S	T	E	N	1972	91532
8025	T	D	E	L	1971	54903
8025	T	D	E	N	1971	54903
8025	T	D	R	N	1972	56941
8025	T	D	E	N	1974	66692
114-0017	D	D	E	N	1972	53463
0017	D	S	E	N	1963	98002
0017	S	D	R	L	1973	55305
0017	S	D	R	N	1973	55305
0017	S	D	E	L	1974	59230
0017	S	D	E	N	1974	59230
0017	S	S	E	N	1962	87660
0017	S	S	E	N	1962	97977
0017	S	S	E	N	1963	98002
0017	T	D	R	L	1973	52832
0017	T	D	R	N	1973	52832
0017	T	D	E	L	1973	52833
0017	T	D	E	N	1973	52833
8001	D	D	R	L	1973	50209
8001	D	D	R	N	1973	50209
8001	D	D	E	L	1973	50210
8001	D	D	E	N	1973	50210
8001	D	D	R	N	1972	51113
8001	D	D	E	L	1963	60566
8001	D	S	E	L	1975	87741
8001	D	S	E	N	1975	87741
8001	D	S	E	L	1965	87781
8001	D	S	E	N	1965	87781
8001	L	D	R	N	1973	52540
8001	L	D	E	N	1974	53675
8001	L	S	G	N	1967	58994
8001	S	D	R	N	1973	50646
8001	S	D	R	L	1973	51390
8001	S	D	E	L	1973	51391
8001	S	D	E	N	1973	52464

Substance Number	Phys. State	Sub-ject	Lan-guage	Temper-ature	Year	EPIC Number
114-8001	S	S	E	N	1972	53299
8001	S	D	E	N	1974	53735
8001	S	D	R	L	1973	54179
8001	S	D	R	N	1973	54179
8001	S	D	E	L	1973	54180
8001	S	D	E	N	1973	54180
8001	S	D	R	N	1972	54286
8001	S	D	E	N	1972	54287
8001	S	E	E	H	1956	59167
8001	S	E	E	L	1956	59167
8001	S	E	E	N	1956	59167
8001	S	E	E	L	1958	59175
8001	S	E	E	N	1958	59175
8001	S	D	E	L	1959	59176
8001	S	D	E	N	1974	60537
8001	S	D	E	L	1963	60566
8001	S	D	E	N	1970	61493
8001	S	S	E	L	1974	64464
8001	S	S	E	N	1974	64464
8001	S	D	E	N	1974	65239
8001	S	D	R	L	1974	65371
8001	S	D	E	L	1975	65372
8001	S	S	O	N	1966	66022
8001	S	S	E	N	1967	66023
8001	S	T	E	N	1975	66682
8001	S	D	R	L	1974	66734
8001	S	T	R	L	1974	66734
8001	S	D	E	L	1975	66735
8001	S	T	E	L	1975	66735
8001	S	D	R	L	1974	66736
8001	S	T	R	L	1974	66736
8001	S	D	E	L	1975	66737
8001	S	T	E	L	1975	66737
8001	S	D	E	L	1975	68679
8001	S	T	E	N	1975	68679
8001	S	D	R	N	1971	76472
8001	S	S	R	N	1971	76472
8001	S	S	E	L	1963	87679
8001	S	S	E	N	1963	87679
8001	S	S	E	L	1965	87781
8001	S	S	E	N	1965	87781
8001	S	D	E	N	1971	91496
8001	S	S	E	N	1971	91496
8001	S	D	E	N	1975	96737
8001	S	T	E	N	1975	96737
8001	S	T	R	L	1975	101629
8001	S	T	E	L	1975	101630
8001	T	S	E	N	1973	53451
8001	T	S	E	N	1963	87679
8001	T	S	E	N	1965	87781
8011	L	D	R	N	1973	51406
8011	L	D	E	N	1973	51407
8011	L	D	R	N	1973	52540
8011	L	D	E	N	1974	53675
8012	S	S	E	N	1962	87661
8049	S	D	E	N	1973	51831
8067	L	D	E	N	1972	101939
8067	L	T	E	N	1972	101939
8067	S	D	E	N	1972	101939
8067	S	T	E	N	1972	101939
119-0001	S	D	R	N	1967	53069
0001	S	D	E	N	1972	53070
0008	D	T	R	N	1975	90140
0008	D	T	E	N	1975	90141
8002	D	S	E	N	1962	87672
8002	S	D	E	N	1972	53413
8002	S	S	E	N	1962	87672
8003	S	D	R	N	1973	55457
8009	D	S	E	N	1962	87662
8009	S	S	E	N	1962	87662
8037	S	D	E	L	1973	50003
8047	S	D	R	N	1973	50645
8084	D	S	E	N	1969	75843
8084	S	S	E	N	1969	75843
8109	S	D	E	N	1967	85908
120-0001	D	T	R	N	1975	90140
0001	D	T	E	N	1975	90141
0006	S	D	E	N	1973	56164
0017	S	S	E	N	1964	93287
0023	S	S	E	N	1964	93287
0035	S	D	E	N	1972	54619
0035	S	S	E	N	1964	93287
0036	S	D	E	N	1973	51858
0045	S	S	E	L	1972	87886
0045	S	S	E	N	1972	87886
0045	S	S	E	N	1964	93287
0051	S	S	E	N	1964	93287
0106	S	D	E	N	1974	54324
0140	S	D	R	N	1967	53069
0140	S	D	E	N	1972	53070
0199	S	S	E	N	1966	87721
8001	S	D	R	N	1972	100974
8013	S	D	R	N	1971	66935
8042	S	S	E	N	1966	87721
8132	S	D	R	N	1971	66935
8133	S	D	R	N	1971	66935
8147	S	S	E	N	1966	87721
8147	S	S	E	N	1972	87886
8174	S	D	R	N	1972	100974

Phys. State: **A.** Amorphous; **C.** Superconductive; **D.** Doped; **F.** Fibrous or Whisker; **G.** Gas; **I.** Ionized or Plasma; **L.** Liquid; **P.** Powder or Particle; **S.** Solid; **T.** Thin Film
Subject: **D.** Data; **E.** Experiment; **S.** Survey (Review, Compendium, etc.); **T.** Theory
Language: **E.** English; **F.** French; **G.** German; **O.** Other Languages; **R.** Russian
Temperature: **L.** Low (0 to 75K); **N.** Normal (75 to 1273K); **H.** High (above 1273K)

Substance Number	Phys. State	Subject	Language	Temperature	Year	EPIC Number
120-8175	S	D	R	N	1972	100974
8176	S	D	R	N	1972	100974
122-0005	D	D	E	L	1973	51875
0014	S	D	E	N	1972	53261
0014	S	E	E	N	1972	53261
0014	S	S	E	N	1972	53261
0014	S	D	E	N	1973	60600
0014	S	S	E	N	1973	60600
0016	D	D	R	N	1974	63046
0016	D	T	R	N	1974	63046
0016	D	D	E	N	1975	63047
0016	D	T	E	N	1975	63047
0017	T	T	E	N	1971	62230
0023	D	D	G	L	1973	51338
0023	D	D	G	N	1973	51338
0023	D	D	E	N	1975	64818
0023	D	S	E	L	1963	87709
0023	D	S	E	N	1963	87709
0023	S	S	E	L	1963	87709
0023	S	S	E	N	1963	87709
0023	T	D	R	N	1973	51345
0023	T	D	E	N	1973	53848
0030	D	D	E	N	1975	65497
0030	S	D	E	N	1975	65497
0031	S	E	R	N	1974	66728
0031	S	E	E	N	1975	66729
0037	S	D	E	N	1970	58979
0084	S	D	E	L	1974	60652
0084	S	D	E	N	1974	60652
0112	S	D	E	N	1972	53261
0112	S	E	E	N	1972	53261
0112	S	T	E	N	1973	60610
8044	T	D	E	N	1972	53416
8124	S	D	R	N	1972	76529
8124	S	D	E	N	1972	91534
123-0003	S	D	E	L	1972	53200
0003	S	D	E	N	1972	53200
0003	S	S	E	L	1972	53200
0003	S	S	E	N	1972	53200
0003	S	D	R	N	1971	67314
0003	S	E	R	N	1971	67314
0003	S	S	E	L	1966	68361
0003	S	S	E	N	1966	68361
0003	T	S	E	N	1966	68361
0003	T	S	E	N	1975	94588
0026	S	D	E	N	1972	49487
0032	S	D	E	N	1973	52054
8004	S	D	E	N	1973	52053
8005	S	D	E	N	1974	56627
8005	S	E	E	L	1969	59174
8005	S	E	E	N	1969	59174
8017	D	D	E	N	1974	57986
8017	S	D	E	N	1973	52462
8017	S	D	E	N	1973	52463
8017	S	D	E	L	1974	53729
8017	S	D	E	N	1974	53729
8017	S	E	E	L	1958	59175
8017	S	E	E	N	1958	59175
8017	S	S	E	L	1962	87674
8017	S	S	E	N	1962	87674
8017	T	D	E	N	1974	57986
8017	T	E	E	N	1974	57986
8018	D	D	R	N	1973	50672
8018	D	D	E	N	1973	52418
8018	D	D	E	N	1973	55921
8018	D	D	R	N	1973	58209
8018	D	D	E	N	1974	59204
8018	D	D	R	N	1973	59370
8018	D	D	R	N	1972	62320
8018	D	D	E	N	1974	62321
8018	D	D	R	N	1972	62719
8018	D	D	E	N	1973	65315
8018	D	S	E	N	1970	68114
8018	D	S	E	N	1962	87671
8018	D	D	R	N	1975	99646
8018	D	D	E	N	1975	103293
8018	L	D	R	N	1973	52540
8018	L	D	E	N	1974	53675
8018	S	D	R	N	1973	50095
8018	S	D	R	N	1973	58209
8018	S	D	E	N	1972	59070
8018	S	S	E	N	1972	59070
8018	S	T	E	N	1972	59070
8018	S	D	E	N	1974	59204
8018	S	D	R	N	1973	59370
8018	S	D	R	N	1968	60749
8018	S	D	E	N	1974	60750
8018	S	D	E	N	1971	62195
8018	S	D	R	N	1972	62298
8018	S	D	E	N	1973	62299
8018	S	S	E	N	1970	68114
8018	S	D	E	L	1973	68901
8018	S	D	E	N	1973	68901
8018	S	S	E	L	1962	87671
8018	S	S	E	N	1962	87671
8018	T	D	O	N	1971	49563
8018	T	D	R	N	1972	49571
8018	T	D	R	N	1974	58894
8018	T	S	E	N	1968	59520
123-8018	T	D	E	N	1972	61768
8018	T	D	R	N	1973	62729
8018	T	D	E	N	1974	64883
8018	T	D	E	N	1973	65325
8039	S	D	E	N	1973	52462
8039	S	D	E	N	1973	52463
8039	S	D	E	L	1974	53729
8039	S	D	E	N	1974	53729
8039	S	D	R	N	1974	97468
8039	S	D	E	N	1975	97469
8039	T	D	E	N	1972	53321
8039	T	D	E	N	1972	53324
8039	T	D	E	N	1973	53434
8051	D	D	E	N	1973	53423
8051	S	D	E	L	1968	53358
8051	S	T	E	N	1973	53423
8051	S	D	E	L	1974	60369
8051	S	D	E	N	1974	60369
8051	S	D	E	N	1974	60382
8051	S	D	E	L	1974	61383
8051	S	D	E	N	1974	61383
8051	S	D	R	L	1974	63131
8051	S	D	R	N	1974	63131
8051	S	D	E	L	1975	63132
8051	S	D	E	N	1975	63132
8051	S	D	E	N	1973	65985
8051	S	S	E	N	1970	68114
8051	T	D	E	N	1972	53303
8051	T	D	E	N	1974	88464
8104	S	D	E	N	1973	53799
126-0002	D	D	F	N	1973	58336
0002	S	D	E	N	1973	57112
0022	S	D	R	N	1967	53069
0022	S	D	E	N	1972	53070
0036	S	D	R	N	1967	53069
0036	S	D	E	N	1972	53070
0037	S	D	R	N	1967	53069
0037	S	D	E	N	1972	53070
0038	S	D	R	N	1967	53069
0038	S	D	E	N	1972	53070
0038	S	D	E	L	1972	70535
0038	S	D	E	N	1972	70535
0038	S	T	E	L	1976	103263
8026	L	D	E	N	1967	64763
8026	S	D	R	N	1971	58851
8026	S	D	E	N	1964	61307
8026	S	E	E	N	1964	61307
8030	D	D	E	N	1972	49462
8030	D	S	R	N	1972	59001
8030	D	S	E	N	1972	59002
8030	D	S	E	N	1970	59699
8030	D	D	R	N	1974	87318
8030	D	D	E	N	1974	87319
8030	L	D	E	N	1972	49462
8030	L	S	R	N	1972	59001
8030	L	S	E	N	1972	59002
8030	L	S	E	N	1970	59699
8030	L	D	R	N	1974	87318
8030	L	D	E	N	1974	87319
8032	D	D	E	N	1973	54934
8032	D	D	R	N	1970	55104
8032	D	D	E	N	1972	55105
8032	D	D	R	N	1973	55822
8032	D	D	E	N	1972	100970
8032	L	D	R	N	1973	52540
8032	L	D	E	N	1974	53675
8032	S	D	R	N	1972	62298
8032	S	D	E	N	1973	62299
8032	S	D	E	N	1972	100970
8034	S	D	O	N	1973	52666
8037	S	D	E	L	1973	50003
8037	S	S	E	N	1970	68114
8037	S	S	R	N	1974	87069
8037	S	S	E	N	1974	87070
8037	T	D	R	N	1972	49570
8037	T	D	E	N	1972	53416
8041	S	S	E	N	1967	66157
8047	S	S	E	N	1967	66157
8051	S	D	O	N	1972	49652
8052	D	D	E	N	1971	53243
8052	D	D	E	L	1974	60751
8052	D	D	E	N	1974	60751
8052	S	D	E	N	1973	68345
8052	S	E	E	N	1975	93167
8055	S	D	E	N	1972	49935
8059	D	D	R	N	1972	50654
8059	D	S	E	N	1969	75843
8060	S	D	E	N	1973	50910
8060	S	D	E	N	1973	53415
8067	S	D	R	N	1973	51601
8068	S	D	R	N	1973	51601
8069	S	D	E	N	1972	52964
8075	L	D	E	N	1972	49462
8094	S	D	R	N	1973	55285
8094	S	D	E	N	1974	59242
8098	S	S	E	L	1970	75833
8098	S	S	E	N	1970	75833
8101	S	S	E	N	1969	75843
8108	S	D	R	N	1973	51732
8108	S	S	E	N	1967	66157
126-8108	S	D	E	N	1973	79136
127-8002	L	D	E	N	1972	49460
8002	L	S	R	N	1972	59001
8002	L	S	E	N	1972	59002
8002	L	D	E	N	1974	86452
8003	L	D	R	N	1973	52540
8003	L	D	E	N	1974	53675
8003	S	D	E	L	1973	50804
8003	S	D	E	N	1973	50804
8003	S	D	E	L	1973	56152
8003	S	D	E	N	1973	56152
8004	S	S	E	N	1962	87666
8004	S	D	R	N	1972	90410
8008	L	D	R	N	1973	52540
8008	L	D	E	N	1974	53675
132-8001	S	D	E	L	1974	54071
8001	S	D	E	N	1974	54071

Phys. State: **A.** Amorphous; **C.** Superconductive; **D.** Doped; **F.** Fibrous or Whisker; **G.** Gas; **I.** Ionized or Plasma; **L.** Liquid; **P.** Powder or Particle; **S.** Solid; **T.** Thin Film
Subject: **D.** Data; **E.** Experiment; **S.** Survey (Review, Compendium, etc.); **T.** Theory
Language: **E.** English; **F.** French; **G.** German; **O.** Other Languages; **R.** Russian
Temperature: **L.** Low (0 to 75K); **N.** Normal (75 to 1273K); **H.** High (above 1273K)

Chapter 13 Luminescence Properties

Substance Number	Phys. State	Subject	Language	Temperature	Year	EPIC Number
100-0045	G	S	E	N	1972	53128
0045	G	D	E	N	1974	54036
0045	S	E	E	N	1972	66910
0055	D	T	R	N	1973	50677
0055	D	T	R	N	1973	50678
0055	D	T	E	N	1973	52423
0055	D	T	E	N	1973	52424
0055	D	S	E	L	1972	53388
0055	D	T	R	N	1973	55331
0055	D	T	E	N	1974	59267
0055	S	T	R	N	1973	50720
0055	S	S	E	N	1973	51759
0055	S	E	E	N	1973	52783
0055	S	S	E	N	1971	53243
0055	S	T	R	N	1973	54978
0055	S	T	E	N	1974	54979
0055	S	T	E	N	1970	61494
0055	S	E	R	N	1971	61550
0055	S	T	E	N	1974	62068
0055	S	T	E	N	1970	62256
0055	S	T	E	N	1975	62913
0055	S	E	E	N	1971	65905
0055	S	E	E	N	1972	66910
0055	S	T	R	N	1974	81218
0055	S	T	E	N	1974	92378
8003	D	T	E	N	1972	49806
8003	D	T	R	N	1973	49842
8003	D	T	E	N	1973	50862
8003	D	T	E	N	1973	54512
8003	D	D	R	N	1973	66541
8003	D	D	E	N	1974	66542
8003	S	S	R	N	1973	50109
8003	S	T	E	N	1973	50490
8003	S	S	R	N	1971	51305
8003	S	T	E	L	1973	53582
8003	S	S	E	N	1973	54519
8003	S	S	R	N	1973	57017
8003	S	T	E	N	1975	66687
8003	S	T	E	N	1973	67808
8003	S	T	R	N	1973	70949
8003	S	T	E	N	1973	91481
8007	D	T	E	N	1973	50489
8007	S	S	E	N	1973	50774
8007	S	S	E	N	1971	53243
8033	D	D	E	N	1973	57528
8071	S	S	E	N	1972	56585
102-0002	D	D	E	L	1974	54323
0002	D	D	E	N	1974	54323
0002	D	T	E	N	1974	54323
0002	D	D	E	L	1974	54565
0002	D	D	E	N	1974	54565
0002	D	D	R	N	1973	58698
0002	D	D	E	N	1974	66828
0002	D	D	R	N	1974	90190
0002	D	D	E	N	1974	90191
0002	S	D	E	N	1971	49803
0002	S	D	R	N	1973	58698
0002	S	D	R	N	1974	75232
0002	S	T	R	N	1974	75232
0002	S	D	R	N	1974	84223
0002	S	T	R	N	1974	84223
0002	S	D	E	N	1974	91473
0002	S	T	E	N	1974	91473
0002	S	D	E	N	1974	91474
0002	S	T	E	N	1974	91474
0002	T	D	R	N	1972	51527
0002	T	D	R	N	1973	71654
0002	T	T	R	N	1973	71654
0002	T	D	E	N	1973	91465
0002	T	T	E	N	1973	91465
0005	P	D	E	N	1972	66930
0005	S	T	R	N	1973	54871
0005	S	D	R	N	1974	67988
0005	S	D	E	N	1974	67989
0009	D	T	R	N	1973	54871
0009	D	D	R	N	1973	58865
0009	P	D	E	N	1972	66930
0009	S	D	E	N	1973	49671
0010	L	D	E	N	1963	75554
0010	L	E	E	N	1963	75554
0010	S	D	E	N	1973	50837
0010	S	D	O	N	1960	53290
0010	S	D	E	N	1973	53291
0013	D	D	R	N	1973	52352
0016	D	D	R	N	1973	51320
0086	A	D	E	L	1973	56395
0086	A	S	E	L	1974	65584
0086	A	S	E	N	1974	65584
0086	A	S	E	L	1974	86455
0086	S	D	E	L	1973	53568
0086	S	D	E	L	1973	56395
0086	S	S	E	N	1974	65584
0086	S	S	E	L	1974	86455
0086	T	S	E	N	1974	65584

Substance Number	Phys. State	Subject	Language	Temperature	Year	EPIC Number
102-0105	D	D	R	N	1973	49575
0105	D	D	E	N	1973	50030
0105	D	D	R	N	1973	50122
0105	D	D	E	N	1973	50488
0105	D	D	E	N	1973	54513
0105	D	D	E	N	1973	79432
0105	D	D	O	N	1974	90530
0105	P	D	O	N	1974	90530
0191	D	D	F	N	1973	52619
0191	D	D	R	L	1973	54357
0191	D	D	R	N	1973	54357
0191	D	D	E	L	1973	54358
0191	D	D	E	N	1973	54358
0191	D	D	E	N	1974	57751
0248	S	D	E	L	1973	53569
0248	S	D	E	N	1973	53569
0248	S	S	E	N	1966	87830
0248	T	D	R	L	1973	55339
0248	T	D	E	L	1974	59277
0250	D	T	R	N	1973	49842
0250	D	D	R	N	1973	50107
0250	D	D	E	N	1973	50396
0250	D	D	R	N	1970	50951
0250	D	D	E	N	1973	51743
0250	D	D	E	N	1973	52164
0250	D	D	E	N	1972	53131
0250	D	D	E	L	1973	53727
0250	D	D	E	N	1974	53727
0250	D	T	E	N	1974	53727
0250	D	D	E	N	1974	53918
0250	D	T	E	N	1973	54512
0250	D	D	R	L	1973	56901
0250	D	D	E	N	1974	57987
0250	D	D	R	N	1973	58699
0250	D	D	E	N	1974	60671
0250	D	E	E	N	1974	60671
0250	D	D	R	N	1972	60727
0250	D	D	E	N	1973	60728
0250	D	D	R	N	1972	86383
0250	D	T	R	N	1972	86383
0250	D	D	E	N	1969	101680
0250	D	T	E	N	1969	101680
0250	S	D	R	N	1973	50107
0297	D	D	R	N	1973	52330
0297	D	D	R	N	1973	70823
0297	D	D	E	N	1973	91588
0303	D	D	E	N	1973	51047
0342	S	D	R	L	1973	52914
0342	S	D	E	L	1974	52915
8001	D	D	R	N	1973	51292
8001	D	D	R	L	1973	58200
8001	D	D	R	N	1973	58200
8001	D	D	E	L	1974	59205
8001	D	D	E	N	1974	59205
8031	A	D	E	L	1973	56395
8031	A	S	E	L	1974	86455
8031	A	S	E	L	1975	101031
8031	S	D	E	N	1973	50544
8031	S	D	E	L	1973	53568
8031	S	D	E	L	1973	56395
8031	S	S	E	L	1974	86455
8041	D	D	R	N	1972	49647
8041	D	D	E	N	1973	50131
8041	D	D	E	N	1973	50400
8041	D	D	R	N	1972	50471
8041	D	D	E	L	1973	50850
8041	D	D	E	L	1973	50904
8041	D	D	E	N	1973	50904
8041	D	D	E	L	1973	50931
8041	D	T	E	L	1973	51042
8041	D	D	R	N	1973	51547
8041	D	D	E	N	1973	51750
8041	D	D	E	N	1973	51916
8041	D	D	E	N	1973	52044
8041	D	T	E	N	1973	52457
8041	D	D	R	N	1973	52520
8041	D	D	R	N	1973	52561
8041	D	D	E	L	1973	52651
8041	D	D	E	N	1973	52783
8041	D	D	E	N	1973	52924
8041	D	D	E	N	1973	53015
8041	D	D	E	N	1972	53171
8041	D	D	E	N	1972	53184
8041	D	D	E	N	1972	53271
8041	D	D	E	N	1972	53302
8041	D	D	E	L	1972	53465
8041	D	D	E	N	1974	53730
8041	D	D	E	L	1974	53745
8041	D	D	R	N	1973	54957
8041	D	S	E	N	1974	55237
8041	D	D	R	N	1973	55306
8041	D	D	R	N	1973	55312
8041	D	D	R	N	1973	55336
8041	D	D	R	N	1973	56213
8041	D	D	E	N	1974	56629

Substance Number	Phys. State	Subject	Language	Temperature	Year	EPIC Number
102-8041	D	D	E	L	1973	57579
8041	D	D	E	L	1973	57739
8041	D	D	E	N	1973	57739
8041	D	D	E	N	1973	57740
8041	D	D	E	N	1974	57761
8041	D	D	E	N	1973	57786
8041	D	D	E	N	1974	57994
8041	D	T	E	N	1974	57994
8041	D	D	R	N	1971	58700
8041	D	D	E	N	1974	59231
8041	D	D	E	N	1974	59237
8041	D	D	E	N	1974	59274
8041	D	D	E	L	1974	60508
8041	D	E	E	L	1974	60508
8041	D	D	E	N	1974	60516
8041	D	D	E	N	1974	61180
8041	D	S	E	N	1970	62251
8041	D	S	E	N	1969	62252
8041	D	D	E	N	1970	62253
8041	D	D	E	N	1969	62254
8041	D	D	E	N	1970	62255
8041	D	T	R	N	1973	62726
8041	D	D	E	N	1975	63348
8041	D	S	E	N	1975	63348
8041	D	D	R	N	1973	63482
8041	D	D	E	N	1973	65161
8041	D	T	E	N	1973	65322
8041	D	D	E	N	1973	65543
8041	D	D	R	N	1970	66268
8041	D	D	R	N	1970	66270
8041	D	D	E	N	1964	66316
8041	D	D	R	L	1974	81226
8041	D	D	R	N	1974	81226
8041	D	T	R	L	1974	81226
8041	D	T	R	N	1974	81226
8041	D	D	R	N	1974	83498
8041	D	T	R	N	1974	83498
8041	D	S	E	L	1964	87701
8041	D	S	E	N	1964	87701
8041	D	D	R	N	1974	90210
8041	D	D	E	N	1975	90211
8041	D	D	E	L	1974	92356
8041	D	D	E	N	1974	92356
8041	D	T	E	L	1974	92356
8041	D	T	E	N	1974	92356
8041	D	D	E	N	1974	92391
8041	D	T	E	N	1974	92391
8041	D	D	E	N	1975	97860
8041	D	D	E	N	1976	100869
8041	S	D	E	N	1973	49594
8041	S	D	R	N	1972	49647
8041	S	D	E	L	1973	49715
8041	S	D	R	N	1972	49815
8041	S	D	R	N	1971	49969
8041	S	D	R	N	1972	50471
8041	S	D	E	N	1973	50579
8041	S	D	E	N	1973	50701
8041	S	D	E	N	1973	50857
8041	S	D	E	L	1973	50904
8041	S	D	E	N	1973	50904
8041	S	D	E	N	1973	51750
8041	S	D	E	L	1973	52030
8041	S	E	E	N	1973	52783
8041	S	D	E	N	1973	53015
8041	S	D	E	N	1972	53095
8041	S	D	E	N	1972	53171
8041	S	D	E	N	1972	53259
8041	S	D	E	N	1972	53302
8041	S	D	E	L	1973	53570
8041	S	D	E	N	1973	53570
8041	S	D	E	L	1974	53745
8041	S	D	E	N	1974	54309
8041	S	D	R	N	1973	54947
8041	S	D	E	N	1973	55095
8041	S	D	E	L	1974	55243
8041	S	S	E	L	1974	55243
8041	S	D	E	N	1971	55377
8041	S	D	E	N	1974	56653
8041	S	D	E	L	1973	57579
8041	S	T	R	N	1972	58683
8041	S	T	E	N	1974	58825
8041	S	S	E	N	1974	60516
8041	S	D	E	L	1974	61373
8041	S	D	E	N	1974	61373
8041	S	D	R	N	1972	64490
8041	S	D	R	L	1972	66490
8041	S	D	E	N	1975	66713
8041	S	T	E	N	1975	66713
8041	S	D	O	N	1974	66874
8041	S	D	R	N	1974	67986
8041	S	D	E	N	1974	67987
8041	S	D	E	L	1975	86752
8041	S	T	E	L	1975	86752
8041	S	S	E	L	1964	87701
8041	S	S	E	N	1964	87701

Phys. State: **A.** Amorphous; **C.** Superconductive; **D.** Doped; **F.** Fibrous or Whisker; **G.** Gas; **I.** Ionized or Plasma; **L.** Liquid; **P.** Powder or Particle; **S.** Solid; **T.** Thin Film
Subject: **D.** Data; **E.** Experiment; **S.** Survey (Review, Compendium, etc.); **T.** Theory
Language: **E.** English; **F.** French; **G.** German; **O.** Other Languages; **R.** Russian
Temperature: **L.** Low (0 to 75K); **N.** Normal (75 to 1273K); **H.** High (above 1273K)

Substance Number	Phys. State	Subject	Language	Temperature	Year	EPIC Number
102-8041	S	S	E	N	1974	88203
8041	S	D	E	L	1975	90112
8041	S	D	E	N	1975	90112
8041	S	T	E	L	1975	90112
8041	S	T	E	N	1975	90112
8041	T	D	E	N	1973	52589
8041	T	D	R	N	1973	55306
8041	T	D	E	N	1974	59231
8041	T	D	E	N	1975	66624
8041	T	T	E	N	1975	66624
8041	T	D	R	N	1974	92311
8041	T	T	R	N	1974	92311
8041	T	D	E	N	1975	92312
8041	T	T	E	N	1975	92312
8054	S	D	R	N	1973	54197
8054	S	D	E	N	1973	54198
8054	T	S	E	N	1971	60965
8070	S	D	E	L	1975	90035
8070	S	D	E	N	1975	90035
8074	D	D	E	N	1973	49711
8074	D	D	E	N	1972	49856
8074	D	D	E	L	1973	52405
8074	D	D	E	N	1973	52405
8074	D	D	E	N	1973	52635
8074	D	D	E	N	1970	52699
8074	D	D	E	N	1973	53008
8074	D	D	E	N	1972	53093
8074	D	D	E	L	1972	53097
8074	D	D	E	N	1972	53097
8074	D	D	E	N	1972	53126
8074	D	D	E	N	1974	53720
8074	D	T	E	N	1974	53720
8074	D	D	R	N	1973	58158
8074	D	D	E	N	1974	58652
8074	D	D	E	N	1972	85903
8075	D	D	E	N	1973	49530
8075	S	D	E	N	1972	53081
8075	T	D	R	L	1973	55339
8075	T	D	E	L	1974	59277
8076	D	D	R	N	1972	49573
8094	D	D	R	N	1973	50083
8094	D	D	G	N	1973	50835
8094	D	D	E	N	1973	51434
8094	D	D	R	N	1973	55312
8094	D	D	E	N	1974	59237
8094	D	D	E	N	1970	62253
8094	S	D	R	N	1972	49815
8094	S	S	E	N	1972	49835
8094	S	D	E	N	1973	50857
8094	S	D	E	N	1973	52783
8094	S	E	E	N	1973	52783
8094	S	S	E	L	1972	53227
8094	S	S	E	N	1972	53227
8094	S	D	E	N	1974	53918
8094	S	D	E	N	1974	54309
8094	S	T	E	N	1975	62913
8094	S	S	E	N	1974	88203
8094	T	D	R	N	1973	50083
8094	T	D	E	N	1973	51434
8095	D	D	E	N	1973	51221
8095	D	D	E	N	1973	52782
8095	D	S	E	N	1972	53227
8095	D	D	E	N	1972	53368
8095	D	D	E	N	1974	53717
8095	D	D	E	L	1974	53737
8095	D	D	E	N	1974	53737
8095	D	D	E	N	1974	54035
8095	D	D	E	N	1973	54776
8095	D	S	E	N	1973	54776
8095	D	D	E	N	1974	55245
8095	D	D	R	L	1973	55315
8095	D	T	R	N	1973	55315
8095	D	T	E	N	1974	58825
8095	D	D	E	L	1974	59240
8095	D	T	E	N	1974	59240
8095	D	D	E	N	1974	60516
8095	D	D	E	N	1975	62894
8095	D	D	E	N	1975	63351
8095	D	E	E	N	1975	63351
8095	D	T	E	N	1975	63351
8095	D	D	E	N	1975	63356
8095	D	T	E	N	1975	63356
8095	D	D	E	N	1975	65468
8095	D	T	E	N	1975	65468
8095	D	D	E	L	1974	88285
8095	F	S	E	N	1974	88203
8095	S	S	E	N	1972	49835
8095	S	D	E	N	1973	50088
8095	S	D	E	N	1973	50857
8095	S	S	E	N	1973	51760
8095	S	D	E	N	1973	52050
8095	S	D	E	N	1973	52782
8095	S	D	E	L	1972	53171
8095	S	D	E	N	1972	53171
8095	S	S	E	N	1972	53227
8095	S	D	E	N	1974	53721
8095	S	D	E	N	1973	54776
8095	S	D	R	N	1973	55341
8095	S	T	R	L	1973	55341
8095	S	D	E	N	1974	59279
8095	S	T	E	L	1974	59279

Substance Number	Phys. State	Subject	Language	Temperature	Year	EPIC Number
102-8095	S	S	E	N	1974	60516
8095	S	D	E	N	1974	61540
8095	S	D	E	N	1975	63356
8095	S	T	E	N	1975	63356
8095	S	D	R	L	1972	66490
8095	S	D	R	N	1972	66490
8095	S	D	E	N	1972	66910
8095	S	S	E	N	1965	87703
8095	S	S	E	L	1974	88203
8095	S	D	E	L	1975	90112
8095	S	D	E	N	1975	90112
8095	S	T	E	L	1975	90112
8095	S	T	E	N	1975	90112
8095	T	D	E	N	1973	51221
8095	T	D	E	N	1976	99741
8095	T	E	E	N	1976	99741
8103	S	D	E	N	1973	50446
8104	S	D	E	L	1973	50482
8104	S	D	E	N	1973	50482
8105	D	D	E	N	1973	50144
8105	D	D	R	N	1973	50511
8105	D	D	E	N	1973	55962
8106	S	D	E	N	1973	50544
8106	S	D	E	L	1973	50897
8120	D	D	E	N	1973	50869
8132	D	D	E	N	1971	68126
8132	S	D	E	L	1973	53569
8132	S	S	E	N	1974	88203
8139	S	D	E	L	1974	53722
8139	S	D	E	N	1974	53722
8139	S	D	E	L	1973	88610
8142	D	D	R	N	1974	90227
8142	D	D	E	N	1975	90228
8142	S	D	E	N	1971	52970
8142	S	D	E	N	1972	52995
8142	S	D	E	N	1975	65434
8142	S	D	E	N	1975	66713
8142	S	T	E	N	1975	66713
8142	T	D	R	N	1974	90227
8142	T	D	E	N	1975	90228
8145	S	D	E	N	1973	51743
8146	S	D	E	N	1973	51743
8154	D	D	R	N	1972	52247
8185	T	D	E	N	1972	53478
8200	D	D	E	N	1973	52164
8200	D	D	E	N	1973	53727
8200	D	T	E	N	1973	53727
8224	S	D	R	N	1973	54383
8224	S	D	E	N	1973	54384
8231	S	D	E	L	1974	57326
8235	S	D	E	L	1974	54092
8260	S	T	R	L	1973	57818
8260	S	T	E	L	1974	57819
8260	S	D	R	N	1974	67988
8260	S	D	E	N	1974	67989
8283	S	D	E	N	1971	65062
8340	D	D	R	N	1973	55828
8342	S	D	R	N	1973	56678
8342	S	D	E	N	1973	76683
8370	D	D	E	N	1973	57516
8372	D	D	E	N	1973	57518
8386	D	D	R	N	1973	58699
8393	S	S	E	L	1974	60668
8393	S	S	E	N	1974	60668
8393	S	S	E	L	1975	63298
8393	S	S	E	N	1975	63298
8393	S	D	E	L	1975	86741
8393	S	S	E	N	1975	86741
8399	S	D	E	L	1974	57326
8496	S	D	E	N	1974	57750
8497	D	D	E	N	1974	57750
8503	D	D	E	N	1974	57750
104-0002	D	D	E	N	1971	67340
0002	S	D	E	N	1973	52006
0002	S	D	E	N	1973	52690
0006	D	D	E	N	1972	49481
0006	D	D	E	N	1972	50486
0006	D	E	E	N	1972	50486
0006	D	D	E	N	1973	50565
0006	D	D	E	N	1973	50633
0006	D	D	E	N	1973	50863
0006	D	D	R	N	1971	51115
0006	D	D	E	N	1973	52089
0006	D	S	R	L	1970	52229
0006	D	D	R	N	1973	52341
0006	D	D	E	L	1974	53990
0006	D	D	R	L	1973	54401
0006	D	S	R	L	1973	54401
0006	D	D	E	L	1973	54402
0006	D	S	E	L	1973	54402
0006	D	D	R	N	1973	54472
0006	D	D	E	N	1973	54473
0006	D	D	R	N	1973	56321
0006	D	D	R	N	1973	56574
0006	D	D	R	N	1974	60407
0006	D	D	E	N	1974	60408
0006	D	D	E	L	1973	60644
0006	D	D	R	N	1972	62850
0006	D	D	E	N	1972	65169
0006	D	D	E	L	1964	75090

Substance Number	Phys. State	Subject	Language	Temperature	Year	EPIC Number
104-0006	D	D	E	L	1974	80552
0006	D	D	R	L	1963	91918
0006	D	D	E	L	1976	99234
0006	D	T	E	L	1976	99234
0006	D	D	R	L	1975	100849
0006	D	D	R	N	1975	100849
0006	D	T	R	L	1975	100849
0006	D	T	R	N	1975	100849
0006	D	D	E	L	1976	100850
0006	D	D	E	N	1976	100850
0006	D	T	E	L	1976	100850
0006	D	T	E	N	1976	100850
0006	S	D	E	N	1973	50565
0006	S	T	E	N	1973	51878
0006	S	D	E	N	1973	54225
0006	S	D	R	N	1973	54359
0006	S	D	E	N	1973	54360
0006	S	D	R	N	1973	54472
0006	S	D	E	N	1973	54473
0006	S	S	E	L	1972	55357
0006	S	S	E	N	1972	55357
0006	S	D	E	N	1974	58941
0006	S	D	R	N	1974	60407
0006	S	D	E	N	1974	60408
0006	S	D	R	N	1974	60447
0006	S	D	E	N	1974	60448
0006	S	T	E	N	1974	65859
0006	S	D	R	N	1974	87308
0006	S	D	E	N	1975	87309
0006	S	D	E	N	1975	93559
0006	S	D	E	L	1976	99234
0006	S	T	E	L	1976	99234
0007	D	D	R	N	1972	56873
0007	D	S	E	N	1967	68374
0007	S	D	E	N	1975	65499
0007	S	T	E	N	1975	65499
0007	S	S	E	N	1967	68374
0007	S	S	E	N	1966	87803
0013	S	D	R	N	1973	56883
0013	S	T	R	N	1975	86881
0013	S	T	E	N	1975	86882
0022	S	D	E	N	1973	53877
0022	S	D	E	N	1974	57589
0025	D	D	R	N	1972	51297
0025	D	D	R	N	1973	52336
0025	D	D	R	N	1969	67324
0031	D	D	E	L	1973	50142
0031	D	D	E	N	1973	50142
0031	D	D	E	N	1973	50633
0031	D	D	E	N	1973	57657
0031	D	D	E	L	1973	60644
0031	S	D	E	L	1975	96982
0031	S	D	E	N	1975	96982
0052	D	D	R	N	1972	50045
0052	D	D	R	N	1972	50961
0052	D	D	O	N	1974	87930
0052	D	E	O	N	1974	87930
0053	D	D	E	L	1973	50142
0053	D	D	E	N	1973	50142
0053	D	D	R	N	1973	52341
0053	D	D	R	N	1973	52343
0053	D	D	R	N	1971	58140
0053	D	D	E	L	1964	75090
0053	D	D	R	L	1963	91918
0053	D	D	E	L	1975	93527
0053	D	D	R	N	1976	103163
0053	D	T	R	N	1976	103163
0053	D	D	E	N	1976	103164
0053	D	T	E	N	1976	103164
0053	S	D	R	N	1974	60447
0053	S	D	E	N	1974	60448
0053	S	D	E	N	1975	90068
0053	S	D	R	N	1976	103163
0053	S	S	R	N	1976	103163
0053	S	D	E	N	1976	103164
0053	S	S	E	N	1976	103164
0067	S	D	E	N	1974	57142
0067	S	D	E	N	1974	64328
0067	S	T	E	N	1974	64328
0069	S	D	E	L	1972	49883
0069	S	D	E	N	1972	49883
0104	D	D	R	N	1973	50112
0104	D	D	E	N	1973	50167
0104	D	D	E	N	1972	50860
0104	D	D	R	N	1973	51350
0104	D	D	E	N	1973	51351
0104	D	D	R	N	1973	52329
0104	D	D	E	N	1973	54523
0104	S	D	E	N	1974	68149
0106	D	D	E	N	1973	57657
0106	S	D	E	N	1973	50478
0106	S	D	R	N	1974	89256
0106	S	D	E	N	1974	89257
0118	D	D	R	N	1975	90172
0118	D	T	R	N	1975	90172
0118	D	D	E	N	1975	90173
0118	D	T	E	N	1975	90173
0146	D	D	R	N	1973	52339
0186	S	D	R	N	1972	50046
0196	S	S	E	N	1969	68271
0306	D	D	E	N	1972	68077

Phys. State: **A.** Amorphous; **C.** Superconductive; **D.** Doped; **F.** Fibrous or Whisker; **G.** Gas; **I.** Ionized or Plasma; **L.** Liquid; **P.** Powder or Particle; **S.** Solid; **T.** Thin Film
Subject: **D.** Data; **E.** Experiment; **S.** Survey (Review, Compendium, etc.); **T.** Theory
Language: **E.** English; **F.** French; **G.** German; **O.** Other Languages; **R.** Russian
Temperature: **L.** Low (0 to 75K); **N.** Normal (75 to 1273K); **H.** High (above 1273K)

Substance Number	Phys. State	Sub- ject	Lan- guage	Temper- ature	Year	EPIC Number
104-0331	S	D	R	L	1973	49848
0331	S	D	E	L	1973	54526
0331	S	D	R	L	1974	63141
0331	S	T	R	L	1974	63141
0331	S	D	E	L	1975	63142
0331	S	T	E	L	1975	63142
0384	D	D	R	N	1973	54492
0384	D	D	E	N	1973	54493
0533	S	D	E	N	1973	52779
0533	S	D	E	N	1972	54618
8076	S	D	R	N	1972	49567
8107	D	D	E	L	1973	49558
8110	D	D	R	N	1973	52335
8113	D	D	E	N	1971	49804
8113	D	D	E	N	1973	55500
8113	D	D	O	N	1972	68082
8113	D	T	O	N	1972	68082
8116	D	D	E	N	1972	49859
8116	D	D	E	N	1974	57750
8117	S	D	E	N	1973	50023
8131	I	D	E	N	1973	50418
8133	D	D	E	N	1973	50555
8134	S	D	R	N	1973	50741
8134	S	D	E	N	1973	79428
8135	D	D	E	N	1973	50861
8177	S	D	E	N	1973	52103
8178	D	D	R	N	1973	52344
8179	S	D	E	L	1970	52692
8180	S	D	E	N	1973	52779
8196	S	D	R	N	1973	49847
8196	S	D	E	N	1972	50858
8196	S	D	E	N	1973	54520
8228	D	D	R	N	1973	54492
8228	D	D	E	N	1973	54493
8228	D	D	R	N	1973	54494
8228	D	D	E	N	1973	54495
8238	D	D	R	N	1973	55176
8238	D	D	E	N	1974	55177
8273	S	D	E	N	1973	53877
8274	S	D	E	N	1973	53877
8275	S	D	E	N	1973	53877
8316	S	D	E	N	1974	57589
8348	D	D	E	N	1974	65732
8352	D	D	R	N	1973	67361
8353	S	D	R	N	1973	67362
8444	D	D	E	N	1973	65763
8457	D	D	E	N	1974	57750
106-0003	D	D	E	N	1973	53835
0003	G	D	E	N	1973	49598
0003	G	D	E	N	1973	50140
0004	D	D	R	N	1973	50122
0004	D	D	E	N	1973	50135
0004	D	D	R	N	1971	51114
0004	D	D	E	N	1973	52630
0004	D	D	E	N	1974	56623
0004	D	D	E	N	1973	57520
0004	D	D	R	N	1972	58761
0004	D	D	R	N	1972	58763
0004	D	T	R	N	1973	70950
0004	D	D	E	N	1973	79432
0004	D	T	E	N	1973	91482
0004	S	D	E	N	1973	49664
0004	S	D	E	N	1973	51634
0004	T	D	E	N	1974	56623
0005	D	D	E	N	1973	50135
0005	S	D	R	N	1972	51295
0006	D	D	E	N	1972	49481
0006	D	D	R	N	1972	49755
0006	D	T	R	N	1973	49846
0006	D	D	R	L	1973	50113
0006	D	D	R	N	1973	50239
0006	D	D	E	N	1973	50240
0006	D	D	R	N	1973	50249
0006	D	D	E	N	1973	50250
0006	D	D	E	N	1972	50486
0006	D	E	E	N	1972	50486
0006	D	D	E	N	1973	50493
0006	D	D	E	N	1973	50633
0006	D	D	E	N	1972	50856
0006	D	D	E	N	1972	50943
0006	D	D	R	N	1973	50988
0006	D	T	R	N	1973	50988
0006	D	D	R	N	1971	51115
0006	D	D	R	N	1973	51380
0006	D	D	E	N	1973	51381
0006	D	D	E	N	1973	51581
0006	D	S	R	L	1970	52229
0006	D	D	R	N	1973	52341
0006	D	D	E	L	1973	53580
0006	D	D	R	N	1973	53650
0006	D	D	E	N	1973	53651
0006	D	D	R	N	1973	53661
0006	D	D	E	N	1974	53662
0006	D	D	E	N	1973	53708
0006	D	T	E	N	1973	53708
0006	D	D	R	L	1973	54401
0006	D	S	R	L	1973	54401
0006	D	D	E	L	1973	54402
0006	D	S	E	L	1973	54402
0006	D	D	R	N	1973	54498
106-0006	D	D	E	N	1973	54499
0006	D	T	E	N	1973	54518
0006	D	D	E	L	1973	54524
0006	D	S	E	N	1973	54770
0006	D	D	R	N	1973	55042
0006	D	D	E	N	1974	55043
0006	D	D	E	N	1974	55254
0006	D	T	E	N	1974	55254
0006	D	D	R	N	1973	56574
0006	D	D	E	L	1973	57113
0006	D	D	R	N	1972	58773
0006	D	D	E	L	1973	60644
0006	D	D	E	N	1973	60868
0006	D	D	R	N	1972	62850
0006	D	D	R	L	1974	63012
0006	D	T	R	L	1974	63012
0006	D	D	E	L	1974	63013
0006	D	T	E	L	1974	63013
0006	D	D	R	N	1974	63153
0006	D	T	R	N	1974	63153
0006	D	D	E	N	1975	63154
0006	D	T	E	N	1975	63154
0006	D	D	E	N	1972	63824
0006	D	D	E	N	1972	65169
0006	D	D	R	L	1974	65379
0006	D	T	R	L	1974	65379
0006	D	D	E	L	1975	65380
0006	D	T	E	L	1975	65380
0006	D	D	R	N	1974	66778
0006	D	T	R	N	1974	66778
0006	D	D	E	N	1975	66779
0006	D	T	E	N	1975	66779
0006	D	D	R	N	1974	67403
0006	D	S	E	N	1973	68817
0006	D	D	R	N	1973	71644
0006	D	D	E	L	1964	75090
0006	D	D	E	L	1974	80552
0006	D	D	E	N	1973	81520
0006	D	D	R	L	1963	91918
0006	D	D	R	L	1975	100849
0006	D	D	R	N	1975	100849
0006	D	T	R	L	1975	100849
0006	D	T	R	N	1975	100849
0006	D	D	E	L	1976	100850
0006	D	D	E	N	1976	100850
0006	D	T	E	L	1976	100850
0006	D	T	E	N	1976	100850
0006	S	D	E	N	1973	50490
0006	S	T	R	N	1973	50988
0006	S	D	R	N	1973	51283
0006	S	D	E	N	1973	51581
0006	S	E	E	N	1972	55357
0006	S	S	E	L	1972	55357
0006	S	D	R	N	1974	60447
0006	S	D	E	N	1974	60448
0006	S	D	E	N	1973	60583
0006	S	T	E	N	1973	60583
0006	S	D	E	L	1975	63334
0006	S	D	E	N	1975	63334
0006	S	S	E	L	1975	63334
0006	S	S	E	N	1975	63334
0006	S	T	E	L	1975	63334
0006	S	T	E	N	1975	63334
0006	S	D	E	N	1972	63824
0006	S	D	E	N	1973	67808
0006	S	T	E	N	1973	67808
0006	S	D	R	N	1974	87308
0006	S	D	E	N	1975	87309
0008	D	D	E	L	1973	50476
0008	D	D	E	N	1973	53835
0008	I	D	R	H	1974	86073
0008	I	D	E	H	1975	86074
0008	S	D	E	L	1973	50476
0009	D	D	R	N	1973	54419
0009	D	D	E	N	1973	54420
0009	L	D	R	N	1973	54419
0009	L	D	E	N	1973	54420
0011	G	D	E	N	1973	51669
0024	D	D	R	N	1972	49808
0024	D	D	E	N	1973	50032
0024	D	D	E	L	1973	50142
0024	D	D	E	N	1973	50142
0024	D	D	R	N	1971	51115
0024	D	D	R	N	1973	51380
0024	D	D	E	N	1973	51381
0024	D	D	R	N	1973	52341
0024	D	D	E	N	1973	53042
0024	D	D	E	N	1973	57091
0024	D	D	E	N	1973	57426
0024	D	D	E	L	1973	60644
0024	D	D	R	N	1972	62850
0024	D	D	E	N	1972	65169
0024	D	D	R	N	1973	66120
0024	D	D	E	L	1964	75090
0024	D	D	E	N	1975	90068
0024	D	D	R	L	1963	91918
0024	D	D	E	N	1976	102041
0024	D	T	E	N	1976	102041
0024	S	D	E	N	1973	57091
0024	S	D	E	N	1973	57428
0024	S	D	E	N	1973	57513
106-0024	S	E	E	N	1973	57513
0024	S	D	R	N	1974	60447
0024	S	D	E	N	1974	60448
0024	S	D	E	N	1975	68612
0024	S	E	E	N	1975	68612
0024	S	T	E	N	1975	68612
0024	S	D	R	N	1975	90158
0024	S	T	R	N	1975	90158
0024	S	D	E	N	1975	90159
0024	S	T	E	N	1975	90159
0026	D	D	R	N	1973	49561
0026	D	D	R	N	1973	49580
0026	D	D	E	N	1973	49678
0026	D	D	E	N	1971	49800
0026	D	D	E	N	1971	49803
0026	D	D	R	N	1973	50112
0026	D	D	E	N	1973	50135
0026	D	D	E	N	1973	50480
0026	D	D	E	N	1973	50487
0026	D	D	E	N	1973	50614
0026	D	D	E	N	1972	50860
0026	D	D	E	N	1973	51211
0026	D	D	R	N	1973	51324
0026	D	D	E	N	1973	52079
0026	D	E	E	N	1973	52079
0026	D	D	R	N	1973	52329
0026	D	D	R	N	1973	52342
0026	D	D	E	L	1973	52429
0026	D	D	E	N	1973	52493
0026	D	D	E	N	1973	52583
0026	D	D	R	L	1973	52848
0026	D	D	E	L	1973	52849
0026	D	D	R	N	1973	52874
0026	D	D	E	N	1973	52875
0026	D	D	E	N	1968	53357
0026	D	D	R	N	1973	54403
0026	D	D	E	N	1973	54404
0026	D	D	R	L	1973	54444
0026	D	D	E	L	1973	54445
0026	D	D	R	L	1973	54476
0026	D	D	E	L	1973	54477
0026	D	D	R	N	1973	54496
0026	D	D	E	N	1973	54497
0026	D	D	E	N	1973	54510
0026	D	D	E	N	1973	54523
0026	D	D	R	L	1973	54992
0026	D	D	R	N	1973	54992
0026	D	T	R	L	1973	54992
0026	D	T	R	N	1973	54992
0026	D	D	E	L	1974	54993
0026	D	D	E	N	1974	54993
0026	D	T	E	L	1974	54993
0026	D	T	E	N	1974	54993
0026	D	D	R	N	1973	56318
0026	D	D	R	N	1973	56639
0026	D	D	R	N	1973	56640
0026	D	D	R	N	1973	58697
0026	D	D	E	N	1970	66920
0026	D	D	R	N	1974	67746
0026	D	D	E	N	1973	76650
0026	D	D	E	N	1973	76652
0026	D	D	R	N	1975	86871
0026	D	D	E	N	1975	86872
0026	D	D	R	N	1975	90172
0026	D	T	R	N	1975	90172
0026	D	D	E	N	1975	90173
0026	D	T	E	N	1975	90173
0026	D	D	E	L	1975	91219
0026	D	E	E	L	1975	91219
0026	D	D	R	N	1975	93623
0026	D	T	R	N	1975	93623
0026	D	D	E	N	1975	93628
0026	D	D	E	N	1975	102032
0026	D	T	E	N	1975	102032
0026	S	D	E	N	1973	49678
0026	S	D	R	N	1973	56318
0026	S	D	R	N	1973	56322
0026	S	D	R	N	1973	58697
0026	S	D	E	N	1974	68149
0026	S	D	E	L	1974	70528
0026	S	D	E	N	1974	70528
0026	S	S	E	L	1974	70528
0026	S	S	E	N	1974	70528
0035	D	S	E	N	1972	49835
0035	D	S	R	N	1973	50114
0035	D	D	E	L	1973	50143
0035	D	D	E	N	1973	50143
0035	D	D	E	N	1972	53257
0035	D	D	E	L	1974	53634
0035	D	D	E	N	1974	53634
0035	D	D	E	L	1974	54106
0035	D	T	E	L	1974	54106
0035	D	D	E	L	1974	54582
0035	D	E	E	L	1974	54582
0035	D	D	R	L	1973	56638
0035	D	D	R	N	1973	56638
0035	D	D	E	N	1973	57522
0035	D	D	E	L	1974	60670
0035	D	T	E	L	1974	60670
0035	D	S	E	L	1974	62060
0035	D	T	E	L	1974	62060

Phys. State: **A.** Amorphous; **C.** Superconductive; **D.** Doped; **F.** Fibrous or Whisker; **G.** Gas; **I.** Ionized or Plasma; **L.** Liquid; **P.** Powder or Particle; **S.** Solid; **T.** Thin Film
Subject: **D.** Data; **E.** Experiment; **S.** Survey (Review, Compendium, etc.); **T.** Theory
Language: **E.** English; **F.** French; **G.** German; **O.** Other Languages; **R.** Russian
Temperature: **L.** Low (0 to 75K); **N.** Normal (75 to 1273K); **H.** High (above 1273K)

Substance Number	Phys. State	Subject	Language	Temperature	Year	EPIC Number
106-0035	D	D	R	N	1970	67319
0035	D	D	R	L	1973	68520
0035	D	D	R	N	1973	68520
0035	D	T	R	L	1973	68520
0035	D	T	R	N	1973	68520
0035	D	D	E	L	1973	76649
0035	D	D	E	N	1973	76649
0035	D	S	E	L	1968	87828
0035	D	D	R	N	1974	90219
0035	D	D	E	N	1975	90220
0035	D	D	E	N	1976	99748
0035	D	T	E	N	1976	99748
0035	S	D	R	L	1973	50289
0035	S	D	R	N	1973	50289
0035	S	D	E	L	1973	50290
0035	S	D	E	N	1973	50290
0035	S	D	E	N	1973	51913
0035	S	E	E	L	1974	54582
0035	S	D	R	L	1973	55028
0035	S	D	R	N	1973	55028
0035	S	D	E	L	1974	55029
0035	S	D	E	N	1974	55029
0035	S	D	R	N	1973	57375
0035	S	D	R	L	1974	58114
0035	S	D	R	N	1974	58114
0035	S	D	E	L	1974	58115
0035	S	D	E	N	1974	58115
0035	S	D	R	N	1971	58702
0035	S	D	R	L	1974	63028
0035	S	D	R	N	1974	63028
0035	S	T	R	L	1974	63028
0035	S	T	R	N	1974	63028
0035	S	D	E	L	1974	63029
0035	S	D	E	N	1974	63029
0035	S	T	E	L	1974	63029
0035	S	T	E	N	1974	63029
0035	S	D	R	L	1968	65348
0035	S	D	R	N	1968	65348
0035	S	D	E	L	1969	65349
0035	S	D	E	N	1969	65349
0035	S	D	R	N	1970	67319
0035	S	D	R	L	1975	85352
0035	S	D	R	N	1975	85352
0035	S	T	R	L	1975	85352
0035	S	T	R	N	1975	85352
0035	S	S	E	N	1965	87702
0035	S	S	E	N	1966	87803
0035	S	S	E	N	1968	87828
0035	S	D	E	L	1975	94096
0035	S	D	E	N	1975	94096
0035	S	T	E	L	1975	94096
0035	S	T	E	N	1975	94096
0035	T	D	E	N	1974	90647
0035	T	T	E	N	1974	90647
0036	T	D	R	N	1972	49937
0051	D	D	R	N	1972	51297
0051	D	D	R	N	1973	52336
0051	D	D	E	N	1972	67269
0051	D	D	R	N	1969	67324
0051	D	D	R	N	1974	80748
0051	D	D	E	N	1974	95252
0051	P	D	E	N	1972	67269
0051	S	D	R	N	1974	80748
0051	S	D	E	N	1974	95252
0060	D	D	E	N	1970	67431
0060	S	D	E	L	1972	49883
0060	S	D	E	N	1972	49883
0060	S	D	E	N	1970	67431
0067	D	D	R	N	1973	52336
0093	S	D	F	N	1973	65685
0126	D	D	R	N	1972	50045
0126	D	D	R	N	1972	50961
0126	D	D	O	N	1974	87930
0126	D	E	O	N	1974	87930
0126	S	D	E	N	1973	50842
0127	S	D	R	L	1973	49845
0127	S	D	E	L	1972	49925
0127	S	D	E	N	1972	49925
0127	S	D	R	L	1973	50371
0127	S	D	E	L	1973	50372
0127	S	D	R	N	1972	50693
0127	S	E	R	N	1972	50693
0127	S	D	R	L	1973	50834
0127	S	D	E	L	1973	54517
0157	S	D	E	N	1974	57142
0158	S	D	E	L	1972	53210
0158	S	D	E	N	1973	53877
0158	S	D	E	N	1974	57589
0158	S	S	E	L	1974	61441
0158	S	S	E	N	1974	61441
0158	S	T	E	N	1974	61441
0159	D	D	R	N	1973	57353
0165	D	D	E	N	1972	49481
0165	D	D	R	L	1973	50113
0165	D	D	E	N	1973	50633
0165	D	D	E	L	1973	54524
0165	D	D	E	L	1973	60644
0165	D	D	E	L	1974	80552
0165	D	D	E	N	1974	89309
0165	D	D	R	L	1975	100849
0165	D	D	R	N	1975	100849

Substance Number	Phys. State	Subject	Language	Temperature	Year	EPIC Number
106-0165	D	T	R	L	1975	100849
0165	D	T	R	N	1975	100849
0165	D	D	E	L	1976	100850
0165	D	D	E	N	1976	100850
0165	D	T	E	L	1976	100850
0165	D	T	E	N	1976	100850
0165	S	D	R	N	1974	87308
0165	S	D	E	N	1975	87309
0165	S	D	E	L	1975	96982
0165	S	D	E	N	1975	96982
0168	G	S	E	N	1973	53059
0183	D	D	E	N	1972	53219
0183	D	T	E	N	1972	53219
0183	L	D	E	N	1972	53219
0183	L	T	E	N	1972	53219
0192	D	D	E	N	1973	57837
0192	S	D	E	N	1973	57837
0203	D	D	E	N	1973	57657
0234	D	D	E	N	1973	50492
0234	D	T	E	L	1973	57694
0238	D	D	R	N	1970	50504
0238	D	D	R	L	1971	51306
0238	D	D	R	N	1971	51306
0238	D	D	R	N	1973	52341
0238	D	D	R	N	1973	54452
0238	D	D	E	N	1973	54453
0238	D	D	R	N	1973	54728
0238	D	D	R	N	1973	56509
0238	D	D	E	L	1973	57622
0238	D	D	E	N	1973	57622
0238	D	T	E	L	1973	57622
0238	D	T	E	N	1973	57622
0238	D	D	E	N	1973	57660
0238	D	D	R	N	1974	61944
0238	D	T	R	N	1974	61944
0238	D	D	E	N	1974	61945
0238	D	T	E	N	1974	61945
0238	D	D	R	N	1973	67914
0238	D	D	E	N	1973	67915
0238	D	D	E	N	1976	99923
0238	D	E	E	N	1976	99923
0238	D	T	E	N	1976	99923
0238	P	D	E	N	1976	99923
0238	P	E	E	N	1976	99923
0238	P	T	E	N	1976	99923
0238	S	D	E	N	1973	49705
0238	S	D	E	N	1973	50478
0238	S	D	E	L	1973	50770
0238	S	D	E	L	1973	53582
0238	S	T	E	L	1973	53582
0238	S	T	E	N	1975	63296
0238	T	D	E	N	1976	99923
0238	T	T	E	N	1976	99923
0259	D	D	E	N	1973	50535
0259	D	D	E	N	1973	50867
0259	D	D	E	N	1974	65758
0259	D	T	E	N	1974	65758
0259	D	D	E	L	1970	68217
0363	D	D	E	N	1973	49614
0363	D	D	E	N	1973	50131
0363	D	D	E	N	1973	51058
0363	D	D	R	N	1973	51275
0363	D	D	R	L	1973	51559
0363	D	D	R	N	1973	51559
0363	D	D	R	N	1973	52345
0363	D	D	E	L	1972	52975
0363	D	D	E	N	1972	53144
0363	D	D	E	L	1972	53388
0363	D	D	E	L	1974	53690
0363	D	D	E	N	1974	53690
0363	D	D	E	N	1973	55163
0363	D	D	E	N	1973	56542
0363	D	D	R	N	1972	58686
0363	D	D	R	N	1972	58769
0363	D	D	O	N	1972	59839
0363	D	T	O	N	1972	59839
0363	D	D	E	L	1974	60290
0363	D	D	E	N	1974	60290
0363	D	D	R	L	1974	63143
0363	D	T	R	L	1974	63143
0363	D	D	E	L	1975	63144
0363	D	T	E	L	1975	63144
0363	D	S	E	N	1963	64232
0363	D	T	E	N	1975	65427
0363	D	S	E	N	1967	66156
0363	D	D	R	N	1974	67984
0363	D	D	E	N	1974	67985
0363	D	D	E	L	1966	74595
0363	P	S	E	N	1967	66156
0363	S	D	E	N	1973	49615
0363	S	D	R	L	1973	49844
0363	S	D	E	N	1972	49934
0363	S	D	E	L	1973	50475
0363	S	D	E	L	1973	50477
0363	S	D	E	N	1973	50477
0363	S	D	E	L	1973	50484
0363	S	D	E	N	1973	50485
0363	S	D	E	N	1973	50541
0363	S	D	E	L	1973	50631
0363	S	D	E	N	1973	50842
0363	S	D	F	N	1973	50983

Substance Number	Phys. State	Subject	Language	Temperature	Year	EPIC Number
106-0363	S	D	R	N	1973	50995
0363	S	D	E	N	1973	51021
0363	S	D	E	N	1973	51075
0363	S	D	R	L	1973	51278
0363	S	D	R	N	1973	51398
0363	S	E	R	N	1973	51398
0363	S	D	E	N	1973	51399
0363	S	E	E	N	1973	51399
0363	S	D	R	N	1972	52251
0363	S	D	E	L	1973	52289
0363	S	D	E	L	1972	52975
0363	S	D	E	N	1972	53081
0363	S	D	E	N	1972	53144
0363	S	S	E	N	1972	53220
0363	S	D	E	N	1973	53344
0363	S	D	E	L	1972	53388
0363	S	D	E	L	1974	53614
0363	S	E	E	L	1974	53614
0363	S	D	E	N	1974	53615
0363	S	E	E	N	1974	53615
0363	S	T	R	L	1972	54233
0363	S	D	E	L	1973	54516
0363	S	T	E	L	1973	54718
0363	S	D	R	L	1973	54976
0363	S	T	R	L	1973	54976
0363	S	D	E	L	1974	54977
0363	S	T	E	L	1974	54977
0363	S	D	R	L	1973	55052
0363	S	D	E	L	1974	55053
0363	S	D	R	N	1973	55993
0363	S	D	R	N	1971	56217
0363	S	D	E	N	1973	56354
0363	S	D	R	L	1973	56692
0363	S	D	R	L	1973	56697
0363	S	D	R	N	1972	57337
0363	S	D	E	N	1973	57637
0363	S	T	E	N	1973	57637
0363	S	D	E	L	1974	58035
0363	S	T	E	L	1974	58035
0363	S	T	R	N	1972	58683
0363	S	D	R	N	1972	58685
0363	S	D	R	N	1972	58686
0363	S	T	E	N	1973	59409
0363	S	S	E	L	1974	61441
0363	S	T	R	N	1973	62163
0363	S	D	R	L	1974	63143
0363	S	T	R	L	1974	63143
0363	S	D	E	L	1975	63144
0363	S	T	E	L	1975	63144
0363	S	S	E	L	1963	64232
0363	S	S	E	N	1963	64232
0363	S	D	E	N	1975	65490
0363	S	E	E	N	1975	65490
0363	S	T	E	N	1975	65490
0363	S	D	R	L	1974	65619
0363	S	T	R	L	1974	65619
0363	S	T	R	N	1974	65619
0363	S	S	E	L	1967	66156
0363	S	S	E	N	1967	66156
0363	S	D	E	L	1975	66688
0363	S	T	E	L	1975	66688
0363	S	D	R	L	1974	66742
0363	S	D	R	N	1974	66742
0363	S	T	R	L	1974	66742
0363	S	T	R	N	1974	66742
0363	S	D	E	L	1975	66743
0363	S	D	E	N	1975	66743
0363	S	T	E	L	1975	66743
0363	S	T	E	N	1975	66743
0363	S	D	G	N	1970	67881
0363	S	D	E	L	1974	68418
0363	S	T	E	L	1974	68418
0363	S	T	E	N	1974	68418
0363	S	D	R	N	1974	81227
0363	S	T	R	N	1974	81227
0363	S	D	E	N	1974	92357
0363	S	T	E	N	1974	92357
0363	S	S	E	N	1975	92725
0363	S	D	R	L	1976	99618
0363	S	D	R	N	1976	99618
0363	S	T	R	L	1976	99618
0363	S	T	R	N	1976	99618
0363	S	D	E	L	1976	99857
0363	S	D	E	N	1976	99857
0363	S	T	E	L	1976	99857
0363	S	T	E	N	1976	99857
0363	T	D	E	N	1974	53635
0363	T	D	R	N	1972	56936
0363	T	D	E	N	1974	62889
0363	T	D	E	N	1975	65427
0363	T	S	E	N	1975	65427
0363	T	S	E	L	1967	66156
0363	T	D	R	N	1972	92409
0385	D	D	E	N	1973	50167
0385	D	D	E	N	1973	50906
0385	D	D	F	N	1972	86944
0385	D	D	E	N	1973	86945
0413	D	D	R	N	1972	49754
0413	D	D	E	N	1973	50135
0413	D	D	E	N	1972	50856
0508	D	D	E	N	1972	49721

Phys. State: **A.** Amorphous; **C.** Superconductive; **D.** Doped; **F.** Fibrous or Whisker; **G.** Gas; **I.** Ionized or Plasma; **L.** Liquid; **P.** Powder or Particle; **S.** Solid; **T.** Thin Film
Subject: **D.** Data; **E.** Experiment; **S.** Survey (Review, Compendium, etc.); **T.** Theory
Language: **E.** English; **F.** French; **G.** German; **O.** Other Languages; **R.** Russian
Temperature: **L.** Low (0 to 75K); **N.** Normal (75 to 1273K); **H.** High (above 1273K)

Substance Number	Phys. State	Sub-ject	Lan-guage	Temper-ature	Year	EPIC Number
106-0508	D	D	E	N	1972	50848
0508	D	D	E	N	1973	52627
0508	D	D	E	N	1973	55618
0508	D	D	E	N	1972	55956
0508	D	D	R	N	1971	56205
0508	D	D	R	N	1972	58761
0508	D	D	R	N	1972	58762
0508	D	D	R	N	1972	58763
0508	D	D	R	N	1972	58764
0508	D	D	R	N	1972	58765
0508	D	D	R	N	1972	58767
0508	D	D	R	N	1972	58770
0508	D	D	R	N	1972	58771
0508	D	D	R	N	1972	58773
0508	T	D	E	N	1972	50848
0610	D	D	E	N	1973	49877
0610	D	D	R	N	1973	54492
0610	D	D	E	N	1973	54493
0610	D	D	R	N	1973	54494
0610	D	D	E	N	1973	54495
0610	D	D	E	N	1973	55156
0610	D	D	R	N	1972	58714
0610	D	D	E	L	1975	63295
0610	D	D	E	N	1975	63295
0610	D	E	E	N	1975	63295
0610	S	D	E	N	1973	50020
0610	S	D	R	N	1972	56738
0610	S	D	R	N	1972	56739
0610	S	D	E	N	1973	57743
0626	S	D	E	N	1973	50867
0768	D	D	R	N	1973	54478
0768	D	D	E	N	1973	54479
0768	D	D	R	N	1973	54492
0768	D	D	E	N	1973	54493
0768	D	D	R	N	1973	54494
0768	D	D	E	N	1973	54495
1256	D	D	R	N	1972	58691
1256	S	D	R	N	1970	52206
1256	S	D	R	N	1973	56678
1256	S	D	R	N	1972	58691
1256	S	D	E	N	1973	76683
1299	D	D	E	N	1973	49637
1519	D	T	E	N	1971	75767
1519	S	D	E	N	1974	53915
8040	D	D	R	N	1973	50217
8040	D	D	E	N	1973	50218
8040	D	D	R	N	1972	52118
8040	D	D	E	L	1972	52975
8040	D	D	E	N	1972	53144
8040	D	D	E	L	1972	53388
8040	D	D	E	N	1971	64324
8040	D	S	E	N	1963	87710
8040	P	S	E	N	1963	87710
8040	S	D	E	L	1973	49956
8040	S	D	R	L	1973	50217
8040	S	D	R	N	1973	50217
8040	S	D	E	L	1973	50218
8040	S	D	E	N	1973	50218
8040	S	D	E	N	1973	50485
8040	S	D	E	L	1973	50822
8040	S	D	E	N	1973	51043
8040	S	E	E	N	1973	51043
8040	S	D	E	L	1973	52080
8040	S	D	E	N	1973	52080
8040	S	D	R	N	1972	52118
8040	S	D	R	N	1972	52251
8040	S	D	E	L	1973	52708
8040	S	D	E	N	1973	52708
8040	S	D	E	L	1972	52975
8040	S	D	E	N	1972	53144
8040	S	D	E	L	1972	53388
8040	S	D	E	N	1973	53462
8040	S	D	E	L	1974	53604
8040	S	D	E	N	1974	53747
8040	S	D	R	L	1973	54646
8040	S	D	E	L	1974	55190
8040	S	D	R	L	1973	56692
8040	S	D	E	N	1973	57841
8040	S	D	R	L	1974	58088
8040	S	D	E	L	1974	58089
8040	S	T	R	N	1972	58683
8040	S	S	E	L	1974	61441
8040	S	T	E	N	1970	62256
8040	S	D	R	L	1974	63143
8040	S	T	R	L	1974	63143
8040	S	D	E	L	1975	63144
8040	S	T	E	L	1975	63144
8040	S	D	E	N	1971	64324
8040	S	S	E	N	1963	87710
8041	D	D	E	L	1974	57976
8041	D	D	E	N	1974	62323
8041	D	D	R	N	1974	67982
8041	D	D	E	N	1974	67983
8041	D	S	E	L	1967	68371
8041	D	S	E	N	1967	68371
8041	D	D	R	N	1972	68396
8041	S	D	E	L	1973	50703
8041	S	D	E	N	1973	50703
8041	S	D	E	L	1973	50846
8041	S	D	R	N	1972	52251
8041	S	D	R	N	1973	52522
106-8041	S	D	E	L	1973	56851
8041	S	D	E	N	1973	56851
8041	S	D	R	N	1973	56899
8041	S	D	E	N	1974	57763
8041	S	D	E	L	1974	57976
8041	S	D	R	L	1970	61009
8041	S	D	R	N	1970	61009
8041	S	D	R	N	1971	68353
8041	S	S	E	L	1967	68371
8041	S	D	R	N	1971	76463
8041	S	D	E	N	1971	91585
8041	T	D	R	N	1972	76519
8041	T	T	R	N	1972	76519
8041	T	D	E	N	1972	91552
8041	T	T	E	N	1972	91552
8045	D	D	E	N	1973	52627
8087	L	D	E	N	1973	52315
8127	D	D	E	L	1970	49613
8128	S	D	E	L	1972	53184
8128	S	D	E	N	1972	53184
8128	S	D	E	L	1973	53852
8128	S	S	E	N	1967	68371
8128	S	D	R	N	1973	70817
8128	S	T	R	N	1973	70817
8128	S	D	E	N	1973	91573
8128	S	T	E	N	1973	91573
8132	D	D	E	L	1970	49613
8132	D	D	R	N	1973	52345
8132	S	D	E	L	1973	52055
8132	S	D	E	N	1973	52055
8132	S	D	E	L	1972	53388
8132	S	S	E	N	1970	61494
8132	S	D	R	N	1974	81218
8132	S	T	R	N	1974	81218
8132	S	D	E	N	1974	92378
8132	S	T	E	N	1974	92378
8133	D	D	E	L	1970	49613
8134	D	D	E	L	1970	49613
8134	D	D	R	N	1972	50956
8134	D	D	R	N	1973	51276
8134	D	D	R	N	1973	52338
8134	D	D	R	N	1973	52345
8134	D	D	E	N	1972	52965
8134	D	D	O	N	1972	57344
8134	D	D	E	N	1973	57737
8134	D	E	E	N	1973	57737
8134	D	D	R	N	1972	66128
8134	D	D	E	N	1974	67255
8134	S	D	R	N	1971	56217
8134	T	D	R	N	1972	50956
8142	D	D	E	N	1972	49859
8142	D	D	E	N	1974	57750
8146	T	D	R	N	1972	49937
8151	S	D	E	N	1973	50023
8152	S	D	E	N	1973	50023
8154	D	D	R	N	1973	51551
8154	D	D	E	N	1973	53682
8155	D	D	R	N	1971	67048
8155	S	D	R	N	1971	67048
8180	I	D	E	N	1973	50418
8186	D	D	E	N	1973	50020
8187	I	T	E	N	1973	50479
8188	G	D	E	N	1973	52537
8188	I	T	E	N	1973	50479
8188	I	D	E	N	1974	63434
8192	D	D	F	N	1973	50618
8192	S	D	E	N	1974	58550
8200	S	D	R	L	1973	50681
8200	S	D	R	N	1973	50681
8200	S	D	E	L	1973	52427
8200	S	D	E	N	1973	52427
8209	D	D	E	L	1974	60509
8209	D	D	E	N	1974	60509
8209	D	T	E	L	1974	60509
8209	D	T	E	N	1974	60509
8209	T	D	E	N	1974	53635
8234	D	D	R	N	1973	51279
8264	G	D	E	N	1973	51767
8271	D	D	E	N	1975	66627
8271	D	T	E	N	1975	66627
8271	D	D	E	N	1975	75629
8271	D	T	E	N	1975	75629
8271	S	D	E	N	1975	66627
8271	S	T	E	N	1975	66627
8292	D	D	E	N	1973	52014
8301	D	D	R	N	1973	52344
8304	D	D	E	L	1973	52489
8342	S	D	R	N	1972	56988
8362	D	D	E	N	1972	50856
8383	S	D	E	L	1973	51477
8383	S	D	E	N	1973	51477
8383	S	E	E	L	1973	51477
8383	S	E	E	N	1973	51477
8407	S	D	E	L	1974	62328
8407	S	D	E	N	1974	62328
8407	S	T	E	L	1974	62328
8407	S	T	E	N	1974	62328
8414	S	D	R	N	1973	54464
8414	S	D	E	N	1973	54465
8427	D	D	R	N	1973	54478
8427	D	D	E	N	1973	54479
106-8427	D	D	R	N	1973	54494
8427	D	D	E	N	1973	54495
8428	D	D	R	N	1973	54506
8428	D	D	E	N	1973	54507
8429	S	D	R	N	1973	54508
8429	S	D	E	N	1973	54509
8430	D	D	R	N	1973	54389
8430	D	D	E	N	1973	54390
8431	S	D	R	N	1973	54417
8431	S	D	E	N	1973	54418
8432	D	D	E	N	1973	50135
8432	D	D	R	N	1973	51681
8434	S	D	R	N	1973	50721
8434	S	D	E	N	1973	54525
8452	D	D	E	N	1973	50135
8463	D	D	E	N	1973	57596
8464	D	D	E	N	1973	57596
8465	D	D	E	N	1973	57596
8520	D	D	R	N	1973	51681
8528	D	D	R	N	1973	55295
8528	D	D	E	N	1974	59271
8536	S	S	E	N	1974	66380
8552	S	D	E	N	1973	53877
8622	S	D	G	L	1973	57070
8622	S	D	G	N	1973	57070
8636	D	D	E	N	1973	57521
8676	D	D	R	N	1973	67361
8677	S	D	R	N	1973	67362
8678	S	D	R	N	1973	67362
8679	D	D	R	N	1973	67365
8745	S	D	R	L	1974	68350
8745	S	D	R	N	1974	68350
8746	S	D	R	L	1974	68350
8746	S	D	R	N	1974	68350
8747	S	D	R	L	1974	68350
8747	S	D	R	N	1974	68350
8767	D	D	R	N	1975	90172
8767	D	T	R	N	1975	90172
8767	D	D	E	N	1975	90173
8767	D	T	E	N	1975	90173
8831	D	D	E	N	1974	57750
108-8012	S	D	R	N	1973	52344
8012	S	D	R	N	1973	67371
109-0001	S	D	E	N	1974	61059
0001	S	E	E	N	1974	61059
8008	S	D	R	N	1973	51326
8008	S	D	R	N	1973	51329
8018	D	D	E	L	1973	50866
8019	S	D	E	N	1971	57181
8020	S	D	E	N	1971	57181
8021	D	D	E	N	1970	66920
8021	S	D	E	N	1971	57181
8030	S	D	E	N	1973	51736
8032	S	D	R	N	1973	52344
8032	S	D	R	N	1973	67371
8035	S	D	E	N	1972	53184
8037	D	D	F	N	1973	52167
8037	S	D	F	N	1973	52167
8054	S	D	R	N	1973	67371
8066	S	D	E	N	1974	87145
8080	S	D	E	N	1975	86759
8097	S	D	R	N	1973	70946
8097	S	T	R	N	1973	70946
8097	S	D	E	N	1973	91485
8097	S	T	E	N	1973	91485
8101	S	D	R	N	1972	68553
8101	S	T	R	N	1972	68553
8101	S	D	E	N	1972	68554
8101	S	T	E	N	1972	68554
8103	S	D	E	N	1974	57750
8105	S	D	E	N	1974	57750
110-0018	D	D	E	N	1973	57524
0023	D	D	E	L	1973	50531
0023	D	D	E	N	1973	50531
0023	D	D	E	L	1974	58819
0023	S	D	E	N	1973	50531
0023	S	D	E	N	1969	64549
0023	S	S	E	N	1969	64549
0023	S	D	E	N	1974	68149
0024	D	T	E	N	1972	49471
0024	D	T	E	N	1971	49582
0024	D	D	E	N	1971	49801
0024	D	D	R	N	1972	50657
0024	D	D	R	N	1970	50949
0024	D	D	E	N	1973	53000
0024	D	D	R	N	1972	54894
0024	D	E	R	N	1972	54894
0024	D	D	E	N	1970	60915
0024	D	T	E	N	1970	60915
0024	D	D	E	N	1974	66828
0024	D	D	E	N	1971	67341
0024	D	D	R	N	1974	90495
0024	D	D	E	N	1976	101596
0024	D	T	E	N	1976	101596
0024	S	D	E	N	1971	49802
0024	S	D	E	N	1971	49803
0024	S	D	R	N	1970	50949
0024	S	D	E	N	1973	51793

Phys. State: **A.** Amorphous; **C.** Superconductive; **D.** Doped; **F.** Fibrous or Whisker; **G.** Gas; **I.** Ionized or Plasma; **L.** Liquid; **P.** Powder or Particle; **S.** Solid; **T.** Thin Film
Subject: **D.** Data; **E.** Experiment; **S.** Survey (Review, Compendium, etc.); **T.** Theory
Language: **E.** English; **F.** French; **G.** German; **O.** Other Languages; **R.** Russian
Temperature: **L.** Low (0 to 75K); **N.** Normal (75 to 1273K); **H.** High (above 1273K)

Substance Number	Phys. State	Subject	Language	Temperature	Year	EPIC Number
110-0024	S	D	E	N	1973	53000
0024	S	T	E	N	1974	54098
0024	S	S	E	N	1972	55357
0024	S	D	R	N	1974	63016
0024	S	D	E	N	1974	63017
0024	S	D	E	N	1974	68149
0024	S	D	E	N	1970	68205
0025	T	D	E	N	1972	53113
0030	S	D	E	N	1975	91840
0030	S	T	E	N	1975	91840
0036	D	D	R	N	1973	50986
0036	D	D	R	N	1973	52337
0036	D	T	R	N	1973	52337
0036	D	D	E	N	1973	52820
0036	D	D	R	N	1972	54894
0036	D	E	R	N	1972	54894
0036	D	D	R	N	1969	67325
0045	D	D	R	N	1975	90172
0045	D	T	R	N	1975	90172
0045	D	D	E	N	1975	90173
0045	D	T	E	N	1975	90173
0083	D	D	R	N	1971	49896
0083	D	D	R	N	1970	50948
0083	D	D	E	N	1973	51737
0083	D	D	E	N	1973	52942
0083	D	D	E	N	1972	53126
0083	D	D	E	N	1973	56520
0083	D	D	E	N	1973	57740
0083	D	D	E	L	1975	62976
0083	D	E	E	L	1975	62976
0083	D	T	E	L	1975	62976
0083	D	D	E	N	1975	86759
0132	D	D	R	N	1973	50112
0132	D	D	E	N	1973	50487
0132	D	D	E	N	1972	50860
0132	D	D	R	N	1973	51350
0132	D	D	E	N	1973	51351
0132	D	D	R	N	1973	52329
0132	D	S	R	N	1973	52512
0132	D	D	R	L	1973	52848
0132	D	D	E	L	1973	52849
0132	D	D	E	N	1973	54523
0132	D	S	E	N	1974	54875
0132	D	D	E	N	1975	66518
0132	D	S	E	N	1975	66518
0132	D	T	E	N	1975	66518
0132	D	D	R	N	1975	86871
0132	D	D	E	N	1975	86872
0132	D	T	E	L	1975	91219
0132	S	D	E	L	1974	70528
0132	S	S	E	L	1974	70528
0157	D	D	E	N	1973	51735
0157	D	D	E	N	1973	51736
0157	D	D	E	N	1971	66204
0157	D	T	E	N	1971	66204
0269	G	T	E	N	1973	50543
0269	G	D	E	N	1974	54038
0269	G	D	E	N	1974	54316
0269	G	E	E	N	1974	54316
0279	D	D	R	L	1973	52340
0279	D	D	R	N	1973	52340
0279	D	D	R	N	1973	53657
0279	D	S	R	N	1973	53657
0279	D	D	E	N	1974	53658
0279	D	S	E	N	1974	53658
0279	D	D	R	L	1973	54373
0279	D	D	R	N	1973	54373
0279	D	D	E	N	1973	54374
0279	D	D	R	N	1973	55176
0279	D	D	E	N	1974	55177
0279	D	D	E	L	1974	58819
0279	D	D	E	N	1974	58819
0350	D	D	E	N	1973	51735
0352	D	D	E	N	1973	53287
0352	D	T	E	N	1973	53430
0352	D	D	E	N	1973	68839
0352	D	D	E	N	1973	88375
8018	D	D	E	L	1973	52957
8018	D	D	E	N	1973	52957
8094	D	D	R	L	1973	52340
8094	D	D	R	N	1973	52340
8094	D	D	R	N	1973	53657
8094	D	S	R	N	1973	53657
8094	D	D	E	N	1974	53658
8094	D	S	E	N	1974	53658
8094	D	D	R	L	1973	54373
8094	D	D	R	N	1973	54373
8094	D	D	E	N	1973	54374
8095	D	D	E	L	1973	52489
8115	D	D	E	N	1972	53271
8137	D	D	R	N	1973	53657
8137	D	D	E	N	1974	53658
8169	D	D	E	N	1973	55156
8209	S	D	R	N	1972	60741
8209	S	D	E	N	1973	60742
8210	S	D	R	N	1972	60741
8210	S	D	E	N	1973	60742
8221	D	D	E	N	1973	57530
111-0003	D	D	E	N	1972	50856
0003	D	D	E	N	1973	51735
111-0008	A	S	E	N	1974	54026
0008	D	D	E	N	1973	49606
0008	D	T	E	N	1973	49732
0008	D	S	E	N	1972	49835
0008	D	D	R	N	1973	50058
0008	D	T	R	N	1973	50111
0008	D	D	R	N	1973	50115
0008	D	D	R	N	1972	50733
0008	D	D	R	N	1972	50734
0008	D	D	E	N	1973	50757
0008	D	T	E	N	1973	50849
0008	D	D	E	N	1972	50859
0008	D	T	E	N	1972	50859
0008	D	D	E	N	1973	51414
0008	D	D	E	N	1973	51758
0008	D	S	E	L	1973	51760
0008	D	D	E	N	1973	52468
0008	D	D	E	N	1973	52637
0008	D	D	E	N	1973	52772
0008	D	D	G	N	1973	53019
0008	D	D	E	L	1972	53471
0008	D	D	E	N	1973	53569
0008	D	S	E	N	1974	54026
0008	D	T	E	N	1973	54522
0008	D	D	E	L	1974	54555
0008	D	D	E	N	1974	54558
0008	D	D	E	N	1973	54776
0008	D	S	E	N	1973	54776
0008	D	D	E	N	1973	56541
0008	D	D	E	N	1973	57726
0008	D	D	E	L	1974	58327
0008	D	D	E	N	1974	58327
0008	D	T	E	L	1974	58327
0008	D	T	E	N	1974	58327
0008	D	D	E	L	1974	58814
0008	D	D	E	N	1974	58814
0008	D	T	E	L	1974	58814
0008	D	T	E	N	1974	58814
0008	D	D	E	N	1974	60516
0008	D	D	E	N	1973	60626
0008	D	D	E	N	1974	61181
0008	D	D	E	N	1974	61186
0008	D	D	E	L	1969	65350
0008	D	D	E	N	1975	65468
0008	D	T	E	N	1975	65468
0008	D	D	R	L	1974	66655
0008	D	D	E	L	1974	66656
0008	D	D	E	N	1973	67813
0008	D	D	E	L	1971	70519
0008	D	D	E	N	1971	70519
0008	D	D	E	N	1973	79418
0008	D	S	E	N	1962	87669
0008	D	S	E	L	1965	87703
0008	D	S	E	N	1965	87703
0008	D	D	R	N	1974	97464
0008	D	D	E	N	1975	97465
0008	D	D	E	N	1976	101211
0008	S	D	R	N	1973	50115
0008	S	D	E	N	1973	51084
0008	S	S	E	N	1973	51760
0008	S	D	E	N	1973	51907
0008	S	D	E	N	1973	52705
0008	S	D	E	N	1973	52772
0008	S	D	E	L	1972	52996
0008	S	D	E	L	1972	53171
0008	S	D	E	N	1972	53171
0008	S	S	E	N	1974	54026
0008	S	D	E	N	1973	55860
0008	S	D	R	N	1973	56584
0008	S	D	E	L	1974	57288
0008	S	E	E	L	1974	57288
0008	S	T	E	N	1974	58825
0008	S	D	E	N	1972	60932
0008	S	E	E	N	1972	60932
0008	S	D	E	L	1975	65492
0008	S	E	E	L	1975	65492
0008	S	T	E	L	1975	65492
0008	S	D	E	N	1973	65916
0008	S	D	R	L	1972	66490
0008	S	D	R	N	1972	66490
0008	S	D	E	N	1972	66910
0008	S	D	E	N	1975	68597
0008	S	T	E	N	1975	68597
0008	S	D	E	N	1973	79418
0008	S	S	E	N	1962	87669
0008	S	S	E	L	1965	87703
0008	S	S	E	N	1965	87703
0008	S	D	E	L	1975	90112
0008	S	D	E	N	1975	90112
0008	S	T	E	L	1975	90112
0008	S	T	E	N	1975	90112
0008	S	D	E	N	1976	101211
0008	T	D	R	L	1973	50059
0008	T	D	E	L	1973	51415
0021	D	D	E	N	1973	50481
0021	D	D	E	N	1973	52644
0021	D	D	E	N	1972	53081
0021	D	D	E	N	1972	53478
0021	D	D	E	N	1974	53912
0021	D	E	E	N	1974	53912
0021	D	D	E	L	1974	54555
111-0021	D	D	E	L	1974	54560
0021	D	D	E	N	1974	54560
0021	D	D	E	N	1973	57527
0021	D	D	E	L	1974	58037
0021	D	D	E	N	1974	58037
0021	D	D	E	H	1973	62246
0021	D	D	E	N	1973	62246
0021	D	D	E	N	1970	63881
0021	D	S	R	N	1974	66446
0021	D	S	E	N	1974	66447
0021	D	S	E	N	1975	91290
0021	F	D	R	L	1974	90233
0021	F	D	R	N	1974	90233
0021	F	D	E	L	1975	90234
0021	F	D	E	N	1975	90234
0021	S	D	E	N	1973	50481
0021	S	S	E	N	1973	50773
0021	S	D	E	N	1973	52151
0021	S	S	E	L	1974	58037
0021	S	S	E	N	1974	58037
0021	S	D	E	N	1973	62246
0021	S	S	R	L	1974	66446
0021	S	S	E	L	1974	66447
0021	S	D	R	N	1974	66588
0021	S	D	E	N	1974	66589
0021	S	D	O	N	1973	66876
0021	S	D	E	N	1971	68126
0021	S	S	E	N	1975	91290
0021	T	D	E	N	1972	53478
0021	T	D	E	L	1970	63881
0021	T	D	E	N	1970	63881
0029	S	D	R	L	1973	50679
0029	S	D	R	N	1973	50679
0029	S	D	E	N	1973	50776
0029	S	D	E	L	1973	52425
0029	S	D	E	N	1973	52425
0029	S	D	E	L	1973	58651
0029	S	D	E	N	1973	58651
0089	S	T	R	N	1972	76507
0089	S	T	E	N	1972	91590
8002	D	D	E	L	1973	50483
8002	D	D	E	L	1962	65951
8002	D	D	E	N	1962	65951
8002	D	T	E	L	1962	65951
8002	D	T	E	N	1962	65951
8002	S	D	E	L	1973	50483
8002	S	D	E	L	1962	65951
8002	S	D	E	N	1962	65951
8002	S	T	E	L	1962	65951
8002	S	T	E	N	1962	65951
8002	S	D	R	L	1974	67986
8002	S	D	R	N	1974	67986
8002	S	D	E	L	1974	67987
8002	S	D	E	N	1974	67987
8007	S	D	F	L	1972	49834
8007	S	D	F	N	1972	49834
8007	S	D	R	L	1973	50065
8007	S	D	E	N	1973	50776
8007	S	D	E	L	1972	50851
8007	S	D	E	N	1972	50851
8007	S	E	E	L	1972	50851
8007	S	E	E	N	1972	50851
8007	S	D	E	L	1973	51037
8007	S	D	E	N	1973	51037
8007	S	T	R	N	1973	51314
8007	S	D	E	L	1973	52057
8007	S	D	R	L	1974	58062
8007	S	D	E	L	1974	58063
8007	S	T	E	N	1973	62171
8007	S	D	E	L	1975	65493
8007	S	D	E	N	1975	65493
8007	S	T	E	L	1975	65493
8007	S	T	E	N	1975	65493
8007	S	D	R	N	1974	65723
8007	S	D	E	N	1974	65724
8010	D	S	R	N	1973	52561
8010	D	S	E	N	1973	57786
8021	D	D	E	N	1974	58335
8022	S	D	E	N	1973	50776
8023	D	D	E	N	1972	49859
8023	D	D	E	N	1974	57750
8023	D	S	E	N	1974	57750
8026	D	D	E	L	1973	50758
8026	D	D	E	N	1973	50758
8026	D	D	E	N	1973	50766
8026	D	D	E	N	1973	50907
8026	D	D	E	N	1972	52989
8026	D	D	E	N	1972	53144
8026	D	D	E	L	1974	62039
8026	D	S	E	L	1974	62039
8026	D	D	E	N	1976	101211
8026	S	D	E	N	1973	50087
8026	S	D	E	N	1972	52989
8026	S	D	E	L	1972	53081
8026	S	D	E	N	1971	55384
8026	S	D	R	N	1973	58199
8026	S	D	E	L	1974	62039
8026	S	D	R	N	1974	66590
8026	S	D	E	N	1974	66591
8026	S	D	E	N	1976	101211
8026	S	S	E	N	1976	101211

Phys. State: **A.** Amorphous; **C.** Superconductive; **D.** Doped; **F.** Fibrous or Whisker; **G.** Gas; **I.** Ionized or Plasma; **L.** Liquid; **P.** Powder or Particle; **S.** Solid; **T.** Thin Film
Subject: **D.** Data; **E.** Experiment; **S.** Survey (Review, Compendium, etc.); **T.** Theory
Language: **E.** English; **F.** French; **G.** German; **O.** Other Languages; **R.** Russian
Temperature: **L.** Low (0 to 75K); **N.** Normal (75 to 1273K); **H.** High (above 1273K)

Substance Number	Phys. State	Subject	Language	Temperature	Year	EPIC Number
111-8026	T	D	R	L	1973	50059
8026	T	D	E	N	1973	50907
8026	T	D	E	L	1973	51415
8026	T	D	E	N	1974	58345
8034	D	D	E	L	1973	50865
8034	D	D	E	N	1973	51010
8035	D	D	R	N	1973	52344
8051	D	D	E	N	1973	51896
8051	D	T	R	N	1974	92274
8051	D	T	E	N	1974	92275
8051	S	D	R	N	1973	52331
8051	T	D	E	N	1973	51896
8056	S	D	R	N	1970	52205
8081	D	D	E	N	1972	50856
8082	S	D	E	N	1973	51892
8087	D	D	E	N	1973	53727
8087	D	T	E	N	1973	53727
8088	D	D	E	N	1973	52164
8119	D	D	R	N	1973	56898
8190	S	T	R	N	1972	76507
8190	S	T	E	N	1972	91590
8209	S	D	E	N	1974	57750
112-0001	S	D	R	N	1973	70911
0001	S	T	R	N	1973	70911
0001	S	D	E	N	1973	91745
0001	S	T	E	N	1973	91745
0010	D	D	E	N	1973	53835
0098	D	D	R	L	1973	51952
0098	D	D	R	N	1973	51952
0098	D	D	E	L	1973	54437
0098	D	D	E	N	1973	54437
0402	S	D	F	N	1973	50983
8025	S	D	E	L	1962	65963
8027	D	D	E	N	1973	50137
8028	I	D	E	N	1973	50418
8029	I	D	E	N	1973	50418
8043	S	D	R	N	1973	52344
8043	S	D	R	N	1973	67371
8044	S	D	E	N	1973	51507
8050	S	D	E	N	1974	54306
8053	A	D	E	L	1974	67259
114-0001	D	D	R	N	1972	49654
0001	D	D	E	L	1973	50142
0001	D	D	E	N	1973	50142
0001	D	D	E	N	1972	50486
0001	D	E	E	N	1972	50486
0001	D	D	E	N	1973	50633
0001	D	D	E	N	1973	50771
0001	D	D	R	N	1971	51115
0001	D	D	R	N	1973	52341
0001	D	D	R	N	1973	52539
0001	D	D	E	N	1973	53581
0001	D	D	E	N	1974	53672
0001	D	D	E	N	1972	53804
0001	D	D	R	N	1973	54393
0001	D	D	E	N	1973	54394
0001	D	D	R	L	1973	54401
0001	D	S	R	L	1973	54401
0001	D	D	E	L	1973	54402
0001	D	S	E	L	1973	54402
0001	D	D	R	N	1973	54411
0001	D	D	E	N	1973	54412
0001	D	D	R	N	1973	54474
0001	D	D	E	N	1973	54475
0001	D	T	E	N	1974	55250
0001	D	D	R	N	1973	56574
0001	D	D	R	N	1971	56575
0001	D	D	R	N	1971	56576
0001	D	D	R	L	1973	57818
0001	D	D	E	L	1974	57819
0001	D	D	R	L	1973	58532
0001	D	D	R	N	1973	58532
0001	D	D	E	L	1973	60644
0001	D	D	R	L	1974	63106
0001	D	T	R	L	1974	63106
0001	D	D	E	L	1975	63107
0001	D	T	E	L	1975	63107
0001	D	D	E	N	1963	64750
0001	D	E	E	N	1963	64750
0001	D	D	R	N	1973	66541
0001	D	D	E	N	1974	66542
0001	D	D	R	N	1974	66784
0001	D	T	R	N	1974	66784
0001	D	D	E	N	1975	66785
0001	D	T	E	N	1975	66785
0001	D	D	R	N	1974	67988
0001	D	D	E	N	1974	67989
0001	D	S	E	L	1976	99913
0001	S	D	R	N	1972	49755
0001	S	D	R	L	1973	49843
0001	S	D	R	N	1973	49843
0001	S	S	E	L	1972	50491
0001	S	S	E	N	1972	50491
0001	S	T	E	L	1972	50491
0001	S	T	E	N	1972	50491
0001	S	D	E	L	1973	50770
0001	S	D	E	L	1973	53582
0001	S	T	E	L	1973	53582
0001	S	D	R	N	1973	54474

Substance Number	Phys. State	Subject	Language	Temperature	Year	EPIC Number
114-0001	S	D	E	N	1973	54475
0001	S	D	E	L	1973	54515
0001	S	D	E	N	1973	54515
0001	S	D	E	L	1973	57104
0001	S	D	R	N	1974	60447
0001	S	D	E	N	1974	60448
0001	S	D	E	N	1963	64750
0001	S	E	E	N	1963	64750
0001	S	D	R	N	1974	66784
0001	S	S	R	N	1974	66784
0001	S	T	R	N	1974	66784
0001	S	D	E	N	1975	66785
0001	S	S	E	N	1975	66785
0001	S	T	E	N	1975	66785
0001	S	D	E	N	1975	89452
0001	S	D	E	L	1975	90059
0001	S	D	E	N	1975	90059
0002	D	D	E	L	1973	50142
0002	D	D	E	N	1973	50142
0002	D	D	E	N	1973	50633
0002	D	D	E	L	1973	60644
0002	S	D	E	L	1973	50770
0006	S	D	E	L	1973	51835
0006	S	D	R	L	1973	55403
0006	S	D	E	L	1974	57814
0006	S	D	E	N	1975	60963
0006	S	D	E	L	1974	90911
0006	S	T	E	L	1974	90911
0009	D	D	E	L	1973	50142
0009	D	D	E	N	1973	50142
0009	D	D	R	N	1970	50950
0009	D	D	R	N	1973	52341
0009	D	D	E	N	1973	53581
0009	D	D	R	L	1973	54401
0009	D	D	E	L	1973	54402
0009	D	D	R	N	1973	56509
0009	D	D	R	N	1971	58140
0009	D	D	E	N	1975	62876
0009	D	D	E	N	1971	67264
0009	D	D	R	N	1973	67914
0009	D	D	E	N	1973	67915
0009	S	D	R	N	1970	50950
0010	S	D	E	L	1974	86203
0017	D	D	E	N	1973	50089
0017	D	D	E	L	1973	57738
0017	D	D	E	N	1973	57738
0017	D	D	E	N	1973	57740
0017	D	D	E	N	1974	58437
0017	S	S	E	N	1973	51760
0017	S	D	E	N	1972	52995
0017	S	S	E	N	1972	53467
0017	S	D	E	L	1974	54080
0017	S	D	E	N	1973	55860
0017	S	D	E	L	1973	57738
0017	S	D	E	N	1974	57905
0017	S	D	R	N	1974	87312
0017	S	D	E	N	1975	87313
0017	S	D	E	L	1976	99245
0046	D	D	R	N	1970	52206
0046	S	D	R	N	1970	52206
0090	S	T	R	N	1972	76507
0090	S	T	E	N	1972	91590
8001	D	D	R	N	1973	50680
8001	D	D	E	N	1973	52426
8001	D	S	E	L	1965	87781
8001	D	S	E	N	1965	87781
8001	I	D	E	N	1973	55115
8001	S	D	R	L	1973	50061
8001	S	D	E	L	1973	51417
8001	S	D	E	L	1974	60284
8001	S	D	E	N	1974	60284
8001	S	E	E	L	1974	60284
8001	S	E	E	N	1974	60284
8001	S	S	E	L	1965	87781
8001	S	S	E	N	1965	87781
8001	T	S	E	N	1965	87781
8066	S	D	E	N	1973	57708
8096	S	D	R	N	1972	68553
8096	S	T	R	N	1972	68553
8096	S	D	E	N	1972	68554
8096	S	T	E	N	1972	68554
8097	D	D	E	N	1974	57750
116-0017	D	D	E	N	1974	54351
0017	D	E	E	N	1974	54351
0030	S	S	E	N	1974	66380
8017	D	D	E	N	1974	54351
8017	D	E	E	N	1974	54351
8017	S	D	O	N	1972	50641
8029	S	T	E	N	1974	61202
8042	S	D	R	N	1973	50121
8042	S	D	E	N	1973	79433
118-0003	D	D	E	N	1972	50856
0003	D	D	E	N	1973	52630
0003	D	D	E	N	1973	56399
0003	D	D	R	N	1973	67668
0037	S	D	R	N	1972	49884
8015	D	D	E	N	1973	51896
8015	D	D	F	N	1973	59303
8015	D	T	R	N	1974	92274

Substance Number	Phys. State	Subject	Language	Temperature	Year	EPIC Number
118-8015	D	T	E	N	1974	92275
8015	S	D	R	N	1973	52331
8015	T	D	E	N	1973	51896
8016	D	D	E	N	1973	51034
8021	D	D	E	N	1972	50856
8021	D	D	R	N	1973	52333
8022	D	D	E	N	1972	50856
8022	D	D	R	N	1973	52344
8022	S	D	E	N	1972	50856
8023	D	D	R	N	1973	52344
8031	S	D	E	N	1973	51892
8032	D	D	E	N	1972	50856
8033	D	D	E	N	1972	50856
8034	D	D	E	N	1973	51892
8034	S	D	E	N	1973	51892
8035	D	D	E	N	1973	51892
8035	S	D	E	N	1973	51892
8036	D	D	F	N	1973	52167
8037	D	D	E	N	1973	52164
8043	D	D	R	N	1973	58300
8043	D	D	R	N	1974	66878
8045	D	D	E	N	1974	58511
8060	D	D	R	N	1974	60501
8060	D	D	E	N	1974	60502
8061	S	D	E	N	1974	61202
8067	S	D	E	N	1973	56073
8068	S	D	E	L	1973	56391
8068	S	D	E	N	1973	56391
8096	D	T	R	N	1974	92274
8096	D	T	E	N	1974	92275
8100	S	D	E	N	1975	65463
8100	S	T	E	N	1975	65463
8101	D	D	E	N	1975	65463
8101	D	T	E	N	1975	65463
119-0002	D	D	E	N	1973	52630
0002	D	D	E	N	1974	56623
0002	D	D	E	N	1975	63301
0002	D	T	E	N	1975	63301
0002	S	D	E	N	1970	52696
0002	S	D	E	N	1972	53823
0002	S	D	R	N	1974	67756
0002	S	S	E	N	1969	87723
0002	T	D	E	N	1974	56623
0002	T	S	E	N	1969	87723
0050	D	D	R	N	1973	54492
0050	D	D	E	N	1973	54493
0073	D	D	R	N	1973	54494
0073	D	D	E	N	1973	54495
8027	D	D	E	N	1973	50854
8028	D	D	E	N	1973	50861
8039	D	D	R	N	1973	52344
8065	S	D	R	N	1973	54464
8065	S	D	E	N	1973	54465
8068	S	D	R	N	1973	50721
8068	S	D	E	N	1973	54525
120-0001	D	D	E	N	1970	66920
0003	G	D	F	N	1973	50027
0009	L	D	E	N	1963	75554
0009	L	E	E	N	1963	75554
0014	G	D	E	N	1973	50411
0014	G	D	E	N	1973	51738
0014	G	D	E	N	1973	56110
0014	G	D	E	N	1974	58426
0014	I	T	E	N	1973	50479
0016	S	D	R	N	1974	90496
0024	D	D	R	L	1973	55180
0024	D	D	E	L	1974	55181
0032	S	S	E	N	1974	66380
0199	C	D	E	L	1973	52784
0199	T	D	E	L	1973	52784
0203	S	S	E	N	1974	66380
8024	D	D	E	L	1974	54555
8024	S	D	E	N	1973	53756
8024	T	D	E	L	1973	49715
8032	I	T	E	N	1973	50479
8035	S	D	R	N	1973	51329
8044	S	D	R	N	1973	50721
8044	S	D	R	N	1973	52316
8044	S	D	E	N	1973	54525
8044	S	D	R	L	1973	70953
8044	S	T	R	L	1973	70953
8044	S	D	E	L	1973	91478
8044	S	T	E	L	1973	91478
8045	C	D	E	L	1973	52784
8045	T	D	E	L	1973	52784
8072	S	D	R	N	1973	67363
8088	D	D	R	N	1970	52334
8092	S	T	E	N	1974	61202
8164	S	D	R	N	1973	50121
8164	S	D	E	N	1973	79433
8182	S	D	E	N	1975	65463
8182	S	T	E	N	1975	65463
122-0003	S	D	F	N	1973	52354
0003	S	D	E	N	1970	68216
0004	S	D	R	N	1973	51322
0004	T	D	R	N	1972	51527
0009	S	D	E	N	1973	53452
0009	S	S	E	N	1974	58803

Phys. State: **A.** Amorphous; **C.** Superconductive; **D.** Doped; **F.** Fibrous or Whisker; **G.** Gas; **I.** Ionized or Plasma; **L.** Liquid; **P.** Powder or Particle; **S.** Solid; **T.** Thin Film
Subject: **D.** Data; **E.** Experiment; **S.** Survey (Review, Compendium, etc.); **T.** Theory
Language: **E.** English; **F.** French; **G.** German; **O.** Other Languages; **R.** Russian
Temperature: **L.** Low (0 to 75K); **N.** Normal (75 to 1273K); **H.** High (above 1273K)

Substance Number	Phys. State	Subject	Language	Temperature	Year	EPIC Number
122-0009	T	D	R	N	1972	51527
0009	T	D	E	N	1974	53903
0009	T	T	E	N	1974	53903
0009	T	D	E	N	1974	58041
0010	G	D	E	N	1973	50627
0010	G	D	E	N	1973	53874
0017	T	D	R	N	1972	51527
0023	D	D	E	N	1973	50714
0023	D	D	E	H	1974	53916
0023	D	D	E	L	1974	56620
0023	D	D	E	N	1974	56620
0023	D	T	R	N	1974	80752
0023	D	S	E	N	1963	87709
0023	D	T	E	N	1974	95261
0023	I	D	E	H	1974	53916
0023	P	D	R	N	1972	56947
0023	P	S	E	N	1963	87709
0023	S	D	E	N	1972	49551
0023	S	D	E	N	1971	51969
0023	S	D	G	L	1973	52187
0023	S	D	G	N	1973	52187
0023	S	D	E	N	1972	53102
0023	S	D	R	N	1974	81407
0023	S	D	E	N	1974	95806
0023	T	D	E	L	1975	92849
0027	D	D	E	N	1973	50020
0027	D	D	R	N	1973	50122
0027	D	D	E	N	1974	57751
0027	D	D	E	N	1973	79432
0030	D	D	E	N	1973	51657
0037	D	D	E	N	1973	51735
0037	D	D	F	N	1973	52167
0037	D	D	R	N	1973	52332
0037	D	D	E	N	1973	57596
0037	D	D	R	N	1973	67668
0037	T	D	E	N	1973	51918
0053	D	D	E	N	1975	63709
0053	D	D	E	N	1969	68246
0132	D	D	R	N	1972	51297
0132	D	D	R	N	1973	52336
0132	D	D	R	N	1969	67324
0198	D	D	R	N	1973	54492
0198	D	D	E	N	1973	54493
0199	D	D	R	N	1973	54389
0199	D	D	E	N	1973	54390
0296	D	D	R	N	1973	52333
0296	D	D	E	N	1974	58511
8025	D	D	E	N	1973	50136
8025	D	D	F	N	1973	52167
8025	D	T	R	N	1974	92274
8025	D	T	E	N	1974	92275
8025	S	D	R	N	1973	52331
8034	S	D	R	N	1973	52344
8034	S	D	R	N	1973	67371
8035	S	D	R	N	1973	67371
8036	D	D	R	N	1973	52336
8037	D	D	R	N	1973	52344
8038	D	D	F	N	1973	52167
8038	D	D	R	N	1973	52344
8038	D	D	F	N	1973	59303
8038	D	D	O	N	1974	65891
8038	D	T	O	N	1974	65891
8038	D	D	R	N	1973	67371
8038	D	D	R	N	1973	70946
8038	D	T	R	N	1973	70946
8038	D	D	E	N	1973	91485
8038	D	T	E	N	1973	91485
8038	S	D	R	N	1972	68553
8038	S	T	R	N	1972	68553
8038	S	D	E	N	1972	68554
8038	S	T	E	N	1972	68554
8039	S	D	R	N	1973	52344
8040	S	D	R	N	1973	52344
8040	S	D	R	N	1973	67371
8045	D	D	R	N	1973	56699
8045	D	D	E	N	1976	100620
8045	S	D	E	N	1973	53452
8045	S	D	R	N	1974	58066
8045	S	E	R	N	1974	58066
8045	S	T	R	N	1974	58066
8045	S	D	E	N	1974	58067
8045	S	E	E	N	1974	58067
8045	S	T	E	N	1974	58067
8045	S	S	E	N	1970	66180
8046	S	D	E	N	1973	53452
8050	S	D	E	N	1973	53452
8063	D	D	E	L	1972	50856
8063	S	D	E	L	1972	50856
8064	D	D	E	N	1972	50856
8065	S	D	F	N	1973	52167
8066	D	D	E	N	1973	52164
8066	D	S	E	N	1973	52164
8069	D	D	F	N	1973	52167
8075	S	D	R	N	1973	54464
8075	S	D	E	N	1973	54465
8091	S	D	R	N	1972	68553
8091	S	T	R	N	1972	68553
8091	S	D	E	N	1972	68554
8091	S	T	E	N	1972	68554
8114	D	D	E	N	1974	57751
8119	D	D	R	N	1973	67357

Substance Number	Phys. State	Subject	Language	Temperature	Year	EPIC Number
123-0003	S	S	E	L	1966	68361
0003	S	S	E	N	1966	68361
0003	T	S	E	L	1966	68361
0003	T	S	E	N	1966	68361
0032	S	D	E	L	1972	49918
0048	S	D	E	N	1971	85443
8017	S	D	E	N	1973	52463
8018	S	S	E	N	1970	68114
8039	S	D	E	N	1973	52463
8051	D	D	E	L	1968	53357
8051	D	D	E	N	1968	53357
8058	S	D	E	N	1974	61199
126-0002	S	D	E	L	1974	58641
0005	D	D	E	N	1973	49584
0005	D	D	E	N	1973	49614
0005	D	D	E	N	1973	49669
0005	D	D	E	N	1973	50020
0005	D	D	R	N	1973	50122
0005	D	D	E	N	1973	50131
0005	D	D	E	N	1973	50168
0005	D	D	E	N	1973	50393
0005	D	D	E	N	1973	50433
0005	D	T	E	N	1973	50489
0005	D	D	E	N	1973	50506
0005	D	D	R	N	1972	50647
0005	D	D	E	N	1973	50712
0005	D	D	E	N	1973	50713
0005	D	D	E	N	1973	50836
0005	D	T	E	N	1973	50849
0005	D	D	R	N	1973	51327
0005	D	D	E	N	1973	51641
0005	D	D	E	N	1973	51748
0005	D	D	E	N	1973	51938
0005	D	D	O	N	1973	51989
0005	D	D	R	N	1973	52338
0005	D	D	R	N	1973	52380
0005	D	T	E	N	1971	52970
0005	D	D	E	N	1972	52990
0005	D	D	E	L	1972	53081
0005	D	S	E	N	1971	53243
0005	D	D	E	N	1972	53254
0005	D	E	E	N	1972	53254
0005	D	T	E	N	1972	53254
0005	D	D	F	N	1973	53871
0005	D	D	E	L	1974	54084
0005	D	E	E	L	1974	54084
0005	D	D	R	N	1972	54149
0005	D	D	E	N	1972	54150
0005	D	T	R	N	1973	54298
0005	D	T	E	N	1973	54299
0005	D	D	E	N	1973	55871
0005	D	D	E	N	1973	55881
0005	D	D	R	N	1971	56218
0005	D	D	E	N	1973	56351
0005	D	T	E	N	1973	56369
0005	D	D	G	N	1973	57073
0005	D	D	E	N	1973	57493
0005	D	D	E	N	1973	57519
0005	D	S	E	N	1973	57533
0005	D	T	E	N	1973	57533
0005	D	D	E	N	1973	57737
0005	D	E	E	N	1973	57737
0005	D	D	E	N	1974	57745
0005	D	D	R	N	1972	58771
0005	D	D	R	N	1972	58773
0005	D	D	E	L	1974	60751
0005	D	D	E	N	1974	60751
0005	D	D	E	L	1974	61188
0005	D	E	E	L	1974	61188
0005	D	D	R	N	1973	65011
0005	D	D	R	N	1973	65265
0005	D	D	R	N	1973	65266
0005	D	D	E	N	1974	67255
0005	D	T	E	N	1974	67430
0005	D	D	R	N	1970	67768
0005	D	T	R	N	1973	70954
0005	D	D	E	N	1973	75855
0005	D	E	E	N	1973	75855
0005	D	D	E	N	1973	79432
0005	D	D	R	N	1974	80405
0005	D	D	R	N	1974	80406
0005	D	D	R	N	1974	80409
0005	D	T	E	N	1974	80409
0005	D	T	R	N	1974	80409
0005	D	D	E	N	1974	87226
0005	D	S	E	N	1963	87711
0005	D	S	E	N	1966	87712
0005	D	D	E	N	1973	88610
0005	D	D	E	N	1973	90522
0005	D	T	E	N	1973	91477
0005	D	D	E	N	1974	95254
0005	D	T	E	N	1974	95254
0005	D	D	E	N	1974	95257
0005	D	D	E	N	1974	95258
0005	P	D	R	N	1972	56837
0005	P	D	R	N	1972	56838
0005	P	S	E	N	1963	87711
0005	S	D	R	N	1971	49968
0005	S	D	E	N	1973	50433
0005	S	S	E	N	1973	50775

Substance Number	Phys. State	Subject	Language	Temperature	Year	EPIC Number
126-0005	S	D	E	N	1973	50843
0005	S	D	E	N	1973	50844
0005	S	D	E	N	1973	51021
0005	S	D	E	L	1973	51060
0005	S	D	E	N	1973	51060
0005	S	D	E	N	1973	51907
0005	S	S	E	N	1973	52121
0005	S	D	R	N	1972	52251
0005	S	D	E	N	1972	52995
0005	S	T	E	N	1972	53271
0005	S	T	E	N	1972	53824
0005	S	D	R	N	1973	55207
0005	S	D	E	N	1974	55208
0005	S	D	R	N	1971	56217
0005	S	D	R	N	1973	56897
0005	S	D	R	N	1972	56942
0005	S	D	R	N	1972	56948
0005	S	D	E	N	1972	61023
0005	S	E	E	N	1972	61023
0005	S	S	E	N	1970	61494
0005	S	D	E	N	1972	63503
0005	S	D	E	N	1973	67531
0005	S	D	R	N	1974	81214
0005	S	D	R	N	1974	81223
0005	S	E	R	N	1974	81223
0005	S	T	R	N	1974	81223
0005	S	D	R	N	1975	85354
0005	S	T	R	N	1975	85354
0005	S	S	E	N	1966	87712
0005	S	D	R	N	1974	92329
0005	S	D	E	N	1975	92330
0005	S	D	E	N	1975	92369
0005	S	T	E	N	1975	92369
0005	S	D	E	N	1974	92373
0005	S	D	E	N	1974	92383
0005	S	E	E	N	1974	92383
0005	S	T	E	N	1974	92383
0005	T	D	E	N	1973	50393
0005	T	D	R	N	1972	50647
0005	T	D	E	N	1972	52990
0005	T	T	R	N	1973	54298
0005	T	T	E	N	1973	54299
0005	T	D	E	N	1973	56351
0005	T	D	R	N	1972	56938
0005	T	D	E	L	1974	61188
0005	T	E	E	L	1974	61188
0005	T	D	R	N	1974	80405
0005	T	D	R	N	1974	80406
0005	T	S	E	N	1963	87711
0005	T	D	E	N	1974	95257
0005	T	D	E	N	1974	95258
0017	D	D	E	N	1972	49838
0017	D	D	E	N	1973	55614
0017	D	D	R	N	1972	58768
0017	D	D	R	N	1972	58771
0025	S	D	E	N	1972	53116
8048	D	D	E	L	1970	49613
8048	D	D	O	N	1972	49895
8048	D	D	E	N	1973	50765
8049	D	D	E	L	1970	49613
8049	S	S	E	N	1972	87823
8049	T	D	E	N	1973	50612
8049	T	E	E	N	1973	50612
8050	D	D	E	L	1970	49613
8052	D	D	E	N	1973	51020
8052	D	D	E	N	1973	51033
8052	D	D	E	N	1973	51813
8052	D	D	E	N	1973	52795
8052	D	D	E	N	1972	52965
8052	D	D	E	N	1971	53243
8052	D	T	E	N	1973	56369
8052	D	D	E	N	1974	56545
8052	D	D	E	N	1973	57534
8052	D	D	E	N	1974	59967
8052	D	D	E	L	1974	60751
8052	D	D	E	N	1974	60751
8052	D	D	E	N	1973	67067
8052	D	S	E	N	1963	68313
8052	D	D	E	N	1973	68345
8052	S	T	E	N	1973	50849
8052	S	D	E	N	1973	51907
8052	S	D	R	N	1972	52251
8052	S	D	E	L	1971	53243
8052	S	D	E	N	1971	53243
8052	S	S	R	N	1972	53547
8052	S	S	E	N	1973	53548
8052	S	D	E	L	1973	55944
8052	S	T	F	N	1974	56617
8052	S	D	F	N	1973	56703
8052	S	D	E	N	1973	57387
8052	S	T	R	N	1972	58683
8052	S	S	E	N	1970	61494
8052	S	D	E	L	1975	62640
8052	S	D	E	N	1973	67067
8052	S	D	E	N	1973	68345
8052	S	D	E	N	1973	68854
8052	S	D	R	N	1974	81218
8052	S	T	R	N	1974	81218
8052	S	D	E	N	1974	92378
8052	S	T	E	N	1974	92378
8052	S	D	E	N	1975	93358

Phys. State: **A.** Amorphous; **C.** Superconductive; **D.** Doped; **F.** Fibrous or Whisker; **G.** Gas; **I.** Ionized or Plasma; **L.** Liquid; **P.** Powder or Particle; **S.** Solid; **T.** Thin Film
Subject: **D.** Data; **E.** Experiment; **S.** Survey (Review, Compendium, etc.); **T.** Theory
Language: **E.** English; **F.** French; **G.** German; **O.** Other Languages; **R.** Russian
Temperature: **L.** Low (0 to 75K); **N.** Normal (75 to 1273K); **H.** High (above 1273K)

Substance Number	Phys. State	Subject	Language	Temperature	Year	EPIC Number
126-8052	S	D	E	N	1975	97217
8052	T	D	F	N	1975	90442
8053	S	D	E	L	1973	50847
8053	S	D	E	N	1973	50847
8069	S	D	E	N	1972	52964
8069	S	D	E	N	1972	53116
8070	S	D	E	N	1972	53116
8072	A	D	E	N	1973	53855
8072	S	D	E	N	1973	53855
8079	S	S	E	N	1969	68271
127-8004	D	D	R	L	1973	50084
8004	D	D	R	N	1973	50084
8004	D	D	E	L	1973	50845
8004	D	D	E	L	1973	51435
8004	D	D	E	N	1973	51435
8004	D	D	E	N	1973	53844
8004	D	D	F	N	1972	67271
8004	D	D	E	N	1973	90522
8004	S	D	E	L	1973	50845
8004	S	D	E	N	1973	51043
8004	S	E	E	N	1973	51043
8004	S	D	E	N	1973	52152
8004	S	D	R	N	1972	52251
8004	S	D	E	N	1971	53243
8004	S	D	R	N	1973	70952
8004	S	T	R	N	1973	70952
8004	S	D	E	N	1973	91479
8004	S	T	E	N	1973	91479

Phys. State: **A.** Amorphous; **C.** Superconductive; **D.** Doped; **F.** Fibrous or Whisker; **G.** Gas; **I.** Ionized or Plasma; **L.** Liquid; **P.** Powder or Particle; **S.** Solid; **T.** Thin Film
Subject: **D.** Data; **E.** Experiment; **S.** Survey (Review, Compendium, etc.); **T.** Theory
Language: **E.** English; **F.** French; **G.** German; **O.** Other Languages; **R.** Russian
Temperature: **L.** Low (0 to 75K); **N.** Normal (75 to 1273K); **H.** High (above 1273K)

Chapter 14 Magnetic Hysteresis

Substance Number	Phys. State	Subject	Language	Temperature	Year	EPIC Number
100-0045	S	S	E	N	1973	82686
0045	S	S	E	L	1975	92677
0045	S	S	E	N	1975	92677
0045	T	S	E	N	1973	82686
0055	S	T	R	N	1972	60723
0055	S	T	E	N	1973	60724
0055	S	T	E	N	1975	66696
8005	S	S	R	N	1973	55480
8009	S	S	G	N	1973	53840
8010	D	D	O	N	1973	67578
8010	S	S	E	N	1972	53175
8010	S	S	E	N	1973	56284
8010	S	D	O	N	1973	67578
8010	T	T	E	N	1973	50908
8010	T	S	E	N	1972	53175
8015	D	D	O	N	1973	67578
8015	S	S	E	N	1972	53175
8015	S	T	R	N	1974	66740
8015	S	T	E	N	1975	66741
8015	S	D	O	N	1973	67578
8015	T	S	E	N	1972	53175
8017	S	S	G	N	1973	53840
8049	S	S	O	N	1974	67300
8049	S	T	R	N	1973	67851
8049	S	T	E	N	1974	91408
8051	S	T	E	N	1974	91408
8058	S	T	E	N	1974	54576
8058	S	T	E	N	1974	57962
8058	S	T	E	N	1974	67211
8058	S	T	R	N	1974	68650
8058	S	T	E	N	1975	68651
8058	T	T	R	N	1974	68654
8058	T	T	E	N	1975	68655
102-0054	S	D	E	L	1974	58047
0282	S	D	E	L	1974	58047
0298	S	T	E	L	1975	90844
8041	D	D	R	L	1974	61936
8041	D	D	R	N	1974	61936
8041	D	T	R	L	1974	61936
8041	D	T	R	N	1974	61936
8041	D	D	E	L	1974	61937
8041	D	D	E	N	1974	61937
8041	D	T	E	L	1974	61937
8041	D	T	E	N	1974	61937
8041	D	D	R	N	1974	68644
8041	D	T	R	N	1974	68644
8041	D	D	E	N	1975	68645
8041	D	T	E	N	1975	68645
8069	A	D	R	N	1973	83375
8069	A	D	E	N	1973	90273
8089	T	D	E	N	1973	49989
8089	T	D	E	N	1973	51128
8089	T	D	E	N	1973	51131
8095	D	S	R	L	1973	55315
8095	D	S	E	L	1974	59240
8098	D	D	E	N	1973	51886
8098	S	D	R	N	1973	50183
8098	S	D	E	N	1973	50184
8098	S	D	E	N	1973	51886
8098	T	D	E	N	1973	51190
8101	T	D	E	N	1973	50385
8112	T	D	E	N	1973	51131
8113	T	D	E	N	1973	51131
8116	T	D	E	N	1973	51128
8118	S	D	E	N	1975	63358
8118	S	T	E	N	1975	63358
8169	S	S	O	L	1973	62410
8169	S	S	E	L	1966	87721
8187	S	S	E	N	1975	90846
8188	A	D	R	N	1973	83375
8188	A	D	E	N	1973	90273
8192	S	D	E	L	1974	54113
8192	S	S	E	L	1974	54113
8206	S	D	E	L	1973	52196
8207	S	D	E	L	1973	52196
8223	S	D	E	N	1975	90846
8223	S	S	E	N	1975	90846
8225	S	D	E	N	1974	54963
8258	S	D	E	L	1974	58053
8258	S	D	E	N	1974	58053
8261	S	D	E	L	1975	90866
8264	S	S	E	L	1973	54004
8334	P	D	E	N	1974	70390
8341	S	D	E	N	1973	56479
8343	S	D	R	N	1973	56696
8367	S	D	E	L	1973	57446
8369	S	D	F	N	1973	57509
8369	S	T	F	N	1973	57509
8369	S	D	R	L	1973	67847
8369	S	D	R	N	1973	67847
8431	S	D	E	N	1974	91413
8459	S	D	E	L	1975	90866
8461	S	D	E	N	1975	63358
8461	S	T	E	N	1975	63358
102-8462	S	D	E	N	1975	63358
8462	S	T	E	N	1975	63358
8463	S	D	E	N	1975	63358
8463	S	T	E	N	1975	63358
8464	S	D	E	N	1975	63358
8464	S	T	E	N	1975	63358
8465	S	D	E	N	1975	63358
8465	S	T	E	N	1975	63358
8491	T	D	E	N	1975	68607
8491	T	T	E	N	1975	68607
104-0006	D	D	E	L	1974	53990
0013	S	D	E	N	1974	60385
0013	S	S	E	N	1974	60385
0013	S	T	E	N	1974	60385
0013	S	D	R	N	1972	60731
0013	S	T	R	N	1972	60731
0013	S	D	E	N	1973	60732
0013	S	T	E	N	1973	60732
0013	S	S	R	N	1974	61962
0013	S	S	E	N	1974	61963
0013	S	D	R	N	1974	63159
0013	S	T	R	N	1974	63159
0013	S	D	E	N	1975	63160
0013	S	T	E	N	1975	63160
0013	S	T	R	N	1975	86881
0013	S	T	E	N	1975	86882
0095	S	D	E	L	1974	61157
0337	D	D	E	N	1974	54027
0337	S	D	E	N	1974	54027
0337	S	S	E	N	1974	54027
0337	S	T	E	N	1974	54027
0347	S	T	R	L	1974	85089
0347	S	T	R	N	1974	85089
0347	S	T	E	L	1974	91490
0347	S	T	E	N	1974	91490
0529	S	D	E	L	1973	51173
0529	S	D	E	N	1973	51173
0529	S	D	E	L	1972	53116
0529	S	D	E	N	1972	53116
8016	P	D	R	N	1973	57217
8016	S	D	E	N	1973	51169
8016	S	D	E	N	1972	53282
8016	S	D	E	N	1974	60523
8016	S	T	E	N	1974	60523
8016	S	T	E	N	1974	90278
8016	S	D	E	N	1974	90279
8016	S	T	E	N	1974	90279
8016	T	D	E	N	1973	49517
8016	T	D	R	N	1973	51516
8016	T	D	E	N	1973	51653
8016	T	D	E	N	1973	51912
8016	T	D	E	N	1973	53241
8016	T	D	E	N	1974	53893
8016	T	D	E	N	1974	53894
8016	T	S	E	N	1974	53894
8016	T	T	E	N	1974	53894
8016	T	D	R	N	1973	55465
8016	T	D	E	N	1973	55864
8016	T	D	E	N	1973	55888
8016	T	D	R	N	1974	63014
8016	T	T	R	N	1974	63014
8016	T	D	E	N	1974	63015
8016	T	T	E	N	1974	63015
8068	S	D	R	H	1971	76476
8068	S	D	R	L	1971	76476
8068	S	D	R	N	1971	76476
8068	S	D	E	H	1971	91521
8068	S	D	E	L	1971	91521
8068	S	D	E	N	1971	91521
8072	S	D	G	N	1973	50439
8106	D	D	R	N	1972	56015
8106	S	D	E	H	1973	50445
8106	S	D	E	N	1973	51655
8106	S	D	E	N	1974	53860
8106	S	D	E	H	1974	58059
8106	S	D	E	N	1974	58059
8106	S	S	E	N	1974	58059
8106	S	D	E	N	1975	65473
8106	S	S	E	N	1975	65473
8106	S	T	E	N	1975	65473
8106	S	D	O	N	1973	65663
8154	S	D	E	L	1973	51173
8154	S	D	E	N	1973	51173
8154	S	D	E	L	1972	53116
8154	S	D	E	N	1972	53116
8162	S	D	R	N	1973	51392
8162	S	D	E	N	1973	51393
8162	S	D	E	N	1974	56607
8162	S	D	R	N	1974	60467
8162	S	D	E	N	1974	60468
8162	S	D	R	N	1974	60489
8162	S	S	R	N	1974	60489
8162	S	T	R	N	1974	60489
8162	S	D	E	N	1974	60490
104-8162	S	S	E	N	1974	60490
8162	S	T	E	N	1974	60490
8169	S	D	E	N	1974	68409
8169	S	T	E	N	1974	68409
8170	S	D	R	L	1974	81236
8170	S	T	R	L	1974	81236
8170	S	D	E	L	1974	92366
8170	S	T	E	L	1974	92366
8171	S	D	E	N	1974	53895
8174	S	D	E	N	1973	51917
8198	S	D	G	N	1972	67868
8227	S	D	E	L	1974	54321
8227	S	D	E	N	1974	54321
8247	S	D	E	L	1974	58006
8249	S	D	E	L	1974	58006
8250	S	D	E	L	1974	58006
8293	T	D	E	N	1973	55542
8307	S	D	R	N	1972	56950
8308	S	D	R	N	1972	56950
8309	S	D	R	N	1972	56950
8319	D	D	E	N	1975	59585
8319	S	D	E	N	1975	59585
8333	S	D	E	L	1975	63275
8333	S	T	E	L	1975	63275
8334	S	D	E	L	1975	63275
8334	S	T	E	L	1975	63275
8335	S	D	E	L	1975	63275
8335	S	T	E	L	1975	63275
8336	S	D	E	L	1975	63275
8336	S	T	E	L	1975	63275
8337	S	D	E	L	1975	63275
8337	S	T	E	L	1975	63275
8338	S	D	E	L	1975	63275
8338	S	T	E	L	1975	63275
8359	S	D	E	L	1974	90467
8420	S	D	R	H	1971	76476
8420	S	D	R	L	1971	76476
8420	S	D	R	N	1971	76476
8420	S	D	E	H	1971	91521
8420	S	D	E	L	1971	91521
8420	S	D	E	N	1971	91521
8445	T	T	R	N	1974	66752
8445	T	T	E	N	1975	66753
106-0046	S	D	R	L	1974	81237
0046	S	S	R	L	1974	81237
0046	S	D	E	L	1974	92367
0046	S	S	E	L	1974	92367
0081	P	S	E	N	1974	63748
0113	S	D	E	L	1973	56441
0210	A	S	E	N	1973	53050
0309	S	S	E	L	1966	87721
0327	D	D	R	N	1972	49840
0327	D	D	E	N	1973	55879
0327	S	D	R	N	1972	49840
0497	D	D	E	L	1972	49912
0608	S	D	E	L	1973	51847
0622	S	D	R	L	1974	86618
0622	S	S	R	L	1974	86618
0622	S	T	R	L	1974	86618
0622	S	D	E	L	1975	94084
0622	S	S	E	L	1975	94084
0622	S	T	E	L	1975	94084
0623	S	D	R	L	1974	86618
0623	S	S	R	L	1974	86618
0623	S	T	R	L	1974	86618
0623	S	D	E	L	1975	94084
0623	S	S	E	L	1975	94084
0623	S	T	E	L	1975	94084
0872	S	D	E	L	1973	53701
0927	S	D	E	N	1973	57431
0941	A	D	R	N	1973	83375
0941	A	D	E	N	1973	90273
0941	S	D	R	N	1973	83375
0941	S	D	E	N	1973	90273
1079	S	T	E	N	1975	90470
1516	S	T	E	L	1975	90844
1522	S	D	E	L	1968	53358
1522	S	D	E	N	1968	53358
8038	S	D	E	N	1973	49504
8038	S	D	E	N	1974	92666
8038	S	T	E	N	1974	92666
8038	T	S	E	N	1974	92666
8061	S	T	R	L	1974	85089
8061	S	T	R	N	1974	85089
8061	S	T	E	L	1974	91490
8061	S	T	E	N	1974	91490
8120	S	D	O	L	1973	49534
8121	S	D	O	L	1973	49534
8123	P	D	E	N	1973	55529
8123	P	D	R	N	1972	56067
8123	P	D	E	N	1971	57194
8123	P	D	E	N	1975	90554
8123	S	S	E	N	1973	49540
8123	S	D	R	N	1973	50668

Phys. State: **A.** Amorphous; **C.** Superconductive; **D.** Doped; **F.** Fibrous or Whisker; **G.** Gas; **I.** Ionized or Plasma; **L.** Liquid; **P.** Powder or Particle; **S.** Solid; **T.** Thin Film
Subject: **D.** Data; **E.** Experiment; **S.** Survey (Review, Compendium, etc.); **T.** Theory
Language: **E.** English; **F.** French; **G.** German; **O.** Other Languages; **R.** Russian
Temperature: **L.** Low (0 to 75K); **N.** Normal (75 to 1273K); **H.** High (above 1273K)

Substance Number	Phys. State	Subject	Language	Temperature	Year	EPIC Number
106-8123	S	D	R	N	1973	50740
8123	S	D	E	N	1973	51136
8123	S	D	E	H	1973	51137
8123	S	D	E	N	1973	51137
8123	S	D	E	N	1973	51138
8123	S	D	E	N	1973	51139
8123	S	D	E	N	1973	51140
8123	S	D	E	N	1973	51143
8123	S	S	E	N	1973	51144
8123	S	D	E	N	1973	51249
8123	S	D	R	N	1973	51689
8123	S	D	E	H	1973	51754
8123	S	D	E	N	1973	51754
8123	S	D	E	N	1973	52058
8123	S	D	E	N	1970	52681
8123	S	D	E	N	1973	53001
8123	S	D	E	N	1973	53325
8123	S	D	R	N	1973	55473
8123	S	D	R	N	1973	55477
8123	S	D	E	N	1973	55524
8123	S	D	E	N	1973	55525
8123	S	D	E	N	1973	55531
8123	S	D	E	N	1973	55654
8123	S	D	O	N	1973	56807
8123	S	D	E	N	1973	58242
8123	S	D	E	L	1974	61196
8123	S	D	E	N	1974	61196
8123	S	S	E	L	1974	61196
8123	S	S	E	N	1974	61196
8123	S	T	R	N	1974	63014
8123	S	T	E	N	1974	63015
8123	S	D	R	N	1974	63044
8123	S	T	R	N	1974	63044
8123	S	D	E	N	1975	63045
8123	S	T	E	N	1975	63045
8123	S	D	E	N	1973	63182
8123	S	S	E	N	1974	63748
8123	S	D	R	N	1973	67845
8123	S	D	R	N	1973	67851
8123	S	T	R	N	1973	67851
8123	S	D	R	N	1973	67852
8123	S	D	R	N	1973	67853
8130	S	D	E	L	1973	49587
8141	S	D	R	N	1972	49840
8149	S	D	E	L	1973	51166
8149	S	D	E	N	1973	51166
8149	S	D	E	N	1973	51197
8161	S	D	R	N	1973	50257
8161	S	D	E	N	1973	50258
8161	S	D	R	L	1973	50730
8161	S	D	R	N	1973	50730
8161	S	D	E	L	1973	53031
8161	S	D	E	N	1973	53031
8190	P	D	E	N	1974	70390
8190	S	D	E	N	1973	50587
8190	S	D	E	N	1974	90280
8204	P	D	E	N	1971	57194
8204	S	D	R	N	1973	50740
8204	S	D	E	N	1973	51138
8204	S	S	E	N	1973	51144
8204	S	D	R	N	1973	51689
8204	S	D	R	N	1973	55477
8204	S	T	R	N	1974	60423
8204	S	T	E	N	1974	60424
8204	S	D	E	N	1973	63182
8204	S	D	E	L	1974	91414
8204	S	D	E	N	1974	91414
8205	S	D	R	N	1973	50740
8205	S	T	E	N	1975	65473
8205	S	D	R	N	1973	67853
8217	S	D	E	N	1973	51136
8217	S	S	E	N	1973	51144
8217	S	D	R	N	1973	51689
8217	S	D	E	N	1973	55524
8217	S	D	E	N	1973	63182
8217	S	D	O	N	1973	65656
8217	S	D	O	N	1973	67577
8218	S	D	E	N	1973	51136
8218	S	D	E	N	1973	55524
8218	S	D	E	N	1973	55530
8218	S	T	R	N	1974	60423
8218	S	T	E	N	1974	60424
8218	S	D	E	L	1974	91414
8218	S	D	E	N	1974	91414
8219	S	D	E	N	1973	51139
8219	S	D	E	N	1973	53001
8220	S	D	E	L	1973	51141
8220	S	D	E	N	1973	51141
8220	S	S	E	N	1973	51144
8221	S	S	E	N	1973	51144
8221	S	D	R	N	1973	51689
8221	S	D	E	N	1973	63182
8222	P	D	E	N	1971	57194
8222	S	S	E	N	1973	51144
8222	S	D	R	N	1973	51689
8222	S	D	E	N	1973	63182
8223	P	D	E	N	1975	90554
8223	S	S	E	N	1973	51144
8223	S	D	R	N	1973	51689
8223	S	D	E	L	1973	52649
8223	S	S	E	L	1973	54004
106-8223	S	D	E	N	1973	63182
8224	S	S	E	N	1973	51144
8227	S	T	E	N	1975	65440
8233	S	D	E	N	1973	51905
8291	S	D	E	N	1973	51905
8294	T	D	R	N	1972	49978
8312	S	D	G	N	1972	67868
8316	S	D	E	L	1973	52786
8317	S	D	E	L	1973	52786
8326	S	D	E	N	1973	52999
8326	S	D	E	N	1973	59290
8327	S	D	E	N	1973	52999
8327	S	D	E	N	1973	59290
8328	S	D	R	N	1973	50727
8328	S	D	E	N	1973	53028
8329	S	D	R	N	1973	50727
8329	S	D	E	N	1973	53028
8360	S	D	E	L	1973	58320
8360	S	D	E	N	1973	58320
8368	S	D	E	L	1973	51883
8368	S	D	E	N	1973	51883
8368	S	D	R	L	1973	55470
8369	S	D	R	N	1973	50658
8370	S	D	R	N	1973	50658
8371	S	D	R	N	1973	50658
8372	S	D	R	N	1973	50658
8373	S	D	R	N	1973	50658
8397	S	D	E	L	1973	52649
8398	S	D	E	L	1973	52649
8399	S	D	E	L	1973	52649
8400	S	T	E	N	1973	52101
8401	S	D	E	N	1973	52101
8414	C	D	E	L	1974	53919
8435	S	D	R	L	1973	55072
8435	S	D	R	N	1973	55072
8435	S	D	E	L	1974	55073
8435	S	D	E	N	1974	55073
8438	S	T	E	N	1974	93998
8439	S	D	R	N	1973	55030
8439	S	D	E	N	1974	55031
8439	S	D	R	N	1974	63161
8439	S	D	E	N	1975	63162
8439	S	D	E	N	1975	63358
8439	S	T	E	N	1975	63358
8439	S	D	R	N	1974	84222
8439	S	D	E	N	1974	91472
8466	T	D	E	N	1973	57599
8472	S	D	E	L	1973	55150
8472	S	D	E	N	1973	55150
8486	T	D	E	N	1974	57998
8490	S	S	E	L	1973	54004
8492	S	D	E	L	1973	56441
8492	S	S	E	L	1973	56441
8507	S	D	E	L	1973	52597
8507	S	D	E	N	1973	52597
8508	S	D	E	N	1973	52642
8508	S	T	E	N	1973	52642
8509	P	D	E	N	1974	91407
8509	S	D	E	L	1973	52649
8509	S	D	E	L	1975	90117
8509	S	D	E	N	1975	90117
8509	S	D	E	L	1974	91409
8509	S	D	E	N	1974	91409
8510	S	D	E	N	1974	53865
8510	T	D	E	N	1973	62748
8525	S	T	R	N	1974	60423
8525	S	T	E	N	1974	60424
8526	S	T	R	N	1974	60423
8526	S	T	E	N	1974	60424
8527	S	T	R	N	1974	60423
8527	S	T	E	N	1974	60424
8532	S	S	R	N	1973	51962
8532	S	S	E	N	1973	55346
8547	D	D	E	N	1974	91413
8547	S	D	E	N	1974	91412
8547	S	D	E	N	1974	91413
8549	S	D	R	N	1975	86867
8549	S	D	E	N	1975	86868
8549	S	D	O	N	1975	90101
8550	S	D	E	N	1973	53798
8551	S	D	F	L	1973	53867
8553	S	D	R	N	1972	53888
8553	S	D	E	N	1973	56856
8553	S	E	E	N	1973	56856
8553	S	D	R	N	1971	67825
8553	T	D	E	N	1973	58136
8554	S	D	R	N	1972	53888
8555	S	D	R	N	1972	53888
8556	S	D	R	N	1972	53888
8557	S	D	F	N	1973	56163
8565	S	D	R	N	1974	67753
8574	S	D	R	N	1972	55494
8587	S	D	F	L	1973	55966
8596	S	D	E	N	1973	56533
8627	S	D	E	N	1971	57152
8640	T	D	R	N	1972	58193
8640	T	D	R	N	1973	90667
8662	D	D	E	N	1974	60298
8662	D	T	E	N	1974	60298
8667	S	D	O	N	1973	65656
8667	S	D	O	N	1973	67577
106-8668	S	D	E	N	1973	66112
8684	S	T	E	N	1974	90301
8688	S	D	E	N	1974	91411
8713	S	D	E	L	1975	90116
8713	S	D	E	N	1975	90116
8713	S	D	E	L	1974	92436
8713	S	D	E	N	1974	92436
8714	P	D	E	N	1974	91407
8715	P	D	E	N	1974	91407
8716	P	D	E	N	1974	91407
8718	S	D	E	L	1975	90117
8718	S	D	E	N	1975	90117
8718	S	D	E	L	1974	91409
8718	S	D	E	N	1974	91409
8719	S	D	E	N	1974	91409
8720	S	D	E	L	1974	91409
8720	S	D	E	N	1974	91409
8721	S	D	E	L	1975	90117
8721	S	D	E	N	1975	90117
8721	S	D	E	L	1974	91409
8722	S	D	E	L	1975	90117
8722	S	D	E	N	1975	90117
8722	S	D	E	L	1974	91409
8723	S	D	E	N	1974	91410
8724	S	D	E	N	1974	91411
8725	S	D	E	N	1974	91411
8726	S	D	E	N	1974	91412
8727	S	D	E	N	1974	91412
8728	S	D	E	L	1974	91414
8728	S	D	E	N	1974	91414
8729	S	D	E	L	1974	91414
8729	S	D	E	N	1974	91414
8735	S	D	R	N	1974	67753
8737	S	D	R	N	1971	67824
8738	S	D	R	N	1971	67825
8739	S	D	R	N	1971	67825
8740	S	D	R	N	1971	67826
8743	S	D	O	N	1972	68348
8744	S	D	O	N	1972	68348
8750	S	T	R	N	1973	52665
8750	S	T	E	N	1974	63233
8753	S	D	E	N	1972	91596
8760	S	D	R	N	1972	76522
8760	S	T	R	N	1972	76522
8760	S	D	E	N	1972	91508
8760	S	T	E	N	1972	91508
8761	S	D	R	N	1972	76522
8761	S	T	R	N	1972	76522
8761	S	D	E	N	1972	91508
8761	S	T	E	N	1972	91508
8774	T	S	E	N	1974	92666
8774	T	T	E	N	1974	92666
8775	S	D	E	N	1974	92666
8775	S	T	E	N	1974	92666
8776	T	S	E	N	1974	92666
8777	T	S	E	N	1974	92666
8778	T	S	E	N	1974	92666
8798	S	D	R	N	1974	63149
8798	S	T	R	N	1974	63149
8798	S	D	E	N	1975	63150
8798	S	T	E	N	1975	63150
8815	S	D	E	N	1975	65472
8826	S	D	E	L	1977	103589
8827	S	D	E	L	1977	103589
108-0014	S	S	R	N	1974	63112
0014	S	S	E	N	1975	63113
0087	D	D	R	N	1974	63149
0087	D	T	R	N	1974	63149
0087	D	D	E	N	1975	63150
0087	D	T	E	N	1975	63150
0087	S	D	R	N	1973	50335
0087	S	D	E	N	1973	50336
0087	S	D	R	N	1974	81200
0087	S	T	R	N	1974	81200
0087	S	D	E	N	1974	92399
0087	S	T	E	N	1974	92399
8007	S	D	R	N	1974	81231
8007	S	T	R	N	1974	81231
8007	S	D	E	N	1974	92361
8007	S	T	E	N	1974	92361
8010	S	D	E	L	1973	53960
8010	S	D	E	N	1973	53960
8010	S	D	R	L	1973	55474
8010	S	D	E	L	1975	90866
8013	S	D	R	L	1973	51313
8013	S	D	R	N	1973	51313
8013	S	D	E	L	1973	62170
8013	S	D	E	N	1973	62170
8030	S	D	E	L	1973	52597
8030	S	D	E	N	1973	52597
8053	S	D	E	L	1974	60387
8058	S	D	E	L	1975	90116
8058	S	D	E	N	1975	90116
8058	S	D	E	L	1974	92436
8059	S	D	R	L	1974	81232
8059	S	T	R	L	1974	81232
8059	S	D	E	L	1974	92362
8059	S	T	E	L	1974	92362
109-0025	D	S	E	L	1973	53052

Phys. State: **A.** Amorphous; **C.** Superconductive; **D.** Doped; **F.** Fibrous or Whisker; **G.** Gas; **I.** Ionized or Plasma; **L.** Liquid; **P.** Powder or Particle; **S.** Solid; **T.** Thin Film
Subject: **D.** Data; **E.** Experiment; **S.** Survey (Review, Compendium, etc.); **T.** Theory
Language: **E.** English; **F.** French; **G.** German; **O.** Other Languages; **R.** Russian
Temperature: **L.** Low (0 to 75K); **N.** Normal (75 to 1273K); **H.** High (above 1273K)

Substance Number	Phys. State	Subject	Language	Temperature	Year	EPIC Number
109-0025	D	D	E	N	1974	54573
0025	S	S	E	L	1973	53052
0025	S	D	E	N	1974	54573
0025	T	D	E	L	1974	60295
0025	T	D	E	N	1974	60295
0025	T	E	E	L	1974	60295
0025	T	E	E	N	1974	60295
0029	T	D	R	N	1973	50327
0029	T	D	E	N	1973	50328
8013	T	D	E	N	1973	50385
8013	T	D	E	N	1973	50604
8014	T	D	E	N	1973	50385
8014	T	D	E	N	1973	51128
8015	S	D	E	N	1973	51153
8015	S	D	R	L	1973	55474
8016	S	D	R	L	1973	51313
8016	S	D	R	N	1973	51313
8016	S	D	E	L	1973	62170
8016	S	D	E	N	1973	62170
8017	D	D	E	N	1974	60291
8017	D	T	E	N	1974	60291
8017	T	E	E	N	1973	51125
8017	T	D	E	N	1974	60291
8017	T	T	E	N	1974	60291
8017	T	D	E	N	1974	61193
8017	T	T	E	N	1974	61193
8019	S	D	E	L	1974	62346
8019	S	D	E	N	1974	62346
8019	S	T	E	L	1974	62346
8019	S	T	E	N	1974	62346
8020	T	D	E	L	1974	58008
8020	T	S	E	L	1974	58008
8020	T	T	E	L	1974	58008
8024	T	D	E	N	1973	51127
8025	S	D	E	N	1974	60299
8025	S	T	E	N	1974	60299
8025	T	D	E	N	1973	51128
8026	T	D	E	N	1973	51131
8039	S	D	R	L	1973	55026
8039	S	D	R	N	1973	55026
8039	S	D	E	L	1974	55027
8039	S	D	E	N	1974	55027
8055	S	S	E	L	1973	53052
8058	S	D	E	L	1974	61395
8059	S	D	E	L	1974	61395
8063	S	D	E	L	1966	74596
8065	S	T	R	N	1975	86841
8065	S	T	E	N	1975	86842
8070	S	S	E	N	1973	56342
8072	S	D	E	L	1974	56610
8073	S	D	E	L	1974	56610
8086	S	D	E	L	1975	90116
8086	S	D	E	N	1975	90116
8086	S	D	E	L	1974	92436
110-0011	P	D	R	N	1973	57222
0011	S	D	R	N	1973	52567
0011	S	D	E	N	1973	55527
0011	S	D	E	N	1973	57792
0011	S	D	F	N	1973	65522
0018	D	T	E	L	1974	58055
0020	D	T	E	L	1974	58055
0025	S	D	E	L	1973	51166
0025	S	D	E	N	1973	51166
0025	S	D	F	N	1973	65522
0025	S	D	E	L	1976	102012
0026	D	D	O	N	1972	90375
0028	T	D	E	N	1973	51762
0028	T	E	E	N	1973	51762
0194	D	T	R	N	1973	55407
0194	D	T	E	N	1974	57824
0194	D	D	E	N	1974	58003
0194	D	D	G	N	1972	67868
0194	S	D	R	N	1973	50229
0194	S	D	R	N	1973	50230
0194	S	D	R	N	1973	50247
0194	S	D	E	N	1973	50248
0194	S	D	R	N	1973	50335
0194	S	D	E	N	1973	50336
0194	S	D	R	N	1973	52369
0194	S	E	R	N	1973	52369
0194	S	T	R	N	1973	52369
0194	S	D	E	N	1973	52706
0194	S	T	E	N	1973	52706
0194	S	E	E	N	1974	54561
0194	S	T	E	N	1974	54561
0194	S	D	E	N	1973	56463
0194	S	D	E	L	1974	57974
0194	S	D	E	N	1974	57974
0194	S	D	R	N	1974	60467
0194	S	D	E	N	1974	60468
0194	S	D	E	N	1974	61195
0194	S	D	E	N	1974	63207
0194	S	E	E	N	1974	63207
0194	S	T	E	N	1974	63207
0194	T	D	E	N	1973	66882
0200	S	D	R	N	1973	50335
0200	S	D	E	N	1973	50336
0200	S	D	E	N	1973	51656
0200	T	D	R	N	1973	50349
0200	T	D	E	N	1973	50350
110-0236	S	D	E	N	1973	49525
0236	S	D	E	N	1974	55263
0245	S	T	R	N	1975	86841
0245	S	T	E	N	1975	86842
0361	S	D	E	L	1975	92022
0361	S	T	E	L	1975	92022
0368	S	D	R	N	1973	50191
0368	S	D	E	N	1973	50192
0368	S	D	R	N	1973	50335
0368	S	D	E	N	1973	50336
0369	D	D	E	N	1973	51654
0369	S	D	R	N	1973	50191
0369	S	D	E	N	1973	50192
0369	S	D	R	N	1973	50335
0369	S	D	E	N	1973	50336
0369	S	D	E	N	1973	51654
0369	S	D	R	N	1973	52908
0369	S	D	E	N	1974	52909
0369	S	T	E	N	1974	54576
0369	S	T	R	N	1974	63014
0369	S	T	E	N	1974	63015
0369	S	D	R	N	1974	63084
0369	S	T	R	N	1974	63084
0369	S	D	E	N	1975	63085
0369	S	T	R	N	1974	66740
0369	S	T	E	N	1975	66741
0369	S	D	R	N	1974	66786
0369	S	T	R	N	1974	66786
0369	S	D	E	N	1975	66787
0369	S	T	E	N	1975	66787
0369	S	D	R	N	1974	81200
0369	S	T	R	N	1974	81200
0369	S	D	E	N	1974	92399
0369	S	T	E	N	1974	92399
0369	T	D	R	L	1973	50327
0369	T	D	E	N	1973	50328
0375	S	D	R	N	1973	50335
0375	S	D	E	N	1973	50336
8015	S	D	E	N	1973	52642
8015	T	D	E	N	1975	90553
8038	L	D	E	N	1973	49592
8038	S	S	E	N	1972	53175
8038	T	D	E	N	1973	49592
8038	T	D	E	N	1973	50385
8038	T	D	E	N	1974	57969
8038	T	D	E	N	1974	60521
8038	T	T	E	N	1974	60521
8042	S	D	R	N	1973	50237
8042	S	D	E	N	1973	50238
8042	S	D	E	N	1973	51121
8042	S	D	R	N	1971	58541
8042	T	D	R	H	1968	49891
8042	T	D	R	N	1968	49891
8042	T	D	R	N	1972	49977
8042	T	T	R	N	1972	49977
8042	T	D	R	N	1972	49978
8042	T	D	R	N	1972	49979
8042	T	D	R	N	1973	50285
8042	T	T	R	N	1973	50285
8042	T	D	E	N	1973	50286
8042	T	T	E	N	1973	50286
8042	T	T	R	N	1973	57816
8042	T	T	E	N	1974	57817
8042	T	D	R	N	1973	90669
8044	T	D	E	N	1973	49989
8044	T	D	E	N	1973	50385
8044	T	D	E	N	1973	51128
8044	T	D	E	N	1974	58000
8044	T	T	E	N	1974	58000
8044	T	D	E	N	1974	60392
8044	T	T	E	N	1974	60392
8046	D	D	R	N	1973	90667
8046	S	D	E	L	1973	51166
8046	S	D	E	N	1973	51166
8046	T	D	E	N	1973	58136
8046	T	D	R	N	1973	90667
8047	D	D	R	N	1971	67049
8047	T	D	R	N	1971	67049
8050	S	D	E	N	1973	50170
8051	S	D	R	N	1973	50275
8051	S	D	E	N	1973	50276
8051	S	D	E	N	1973	51658
8051	S	D	E	L	1974	57974
8051	S	D	E	N	1974	57974
8051	S	S	E	L	1974	57974
8051	S	S	E	N	1974	57974
8051	S	D	E	L	1974	60302
8051	S	D	E	N	1974	60302
8051	T	T	R	N	1974	66752
8051	T	T	E	N	1975	66753
8052	S	D	R	N	1973	50275
8052	S	D	E	N	1973	50276
8053	S	D	R	N	1973	50335
8053	S	D	E	N	1973	50336
8054	T	D	E	N	1973	50385
8054	T	D	E	N	1973	50908
8054	T	T	E	N	1973	50908
8054	T	D	E	N	1973	51123
8054	T	D	E	N	1973	51130
8055	T	D	E	N	1973	50385
8056	T	D	E	N	1973	50386
110-8060	S	D	R	L	1973	51313
8060	S	D	R	N	1973	51313
8060	S	D	E	L	1973	62170
8060	S	D	E	N	1973	62170
8063	T	D	R	N	1971	50663
8065	S	D	E	L	1973	50826
8065	S	D	E	N	1973	50826
8065	S	T	E	N	1973	50826
8067	A	D	E	L	1974	62337
8067	A	D	E	N	1974	62337
8067	A	S	E	L	1974	62337
8067	A	S	E	N	1974	62337
8067	A	T	E	L	1974	62337
8067	A	T	E	N	1974	62337
8067	A	D	E	N	1974	90284
8067	S	D	E	L	1973	53960
8067	S	D	E	N	1973	53960
8067	S	D	R	L	1973	55474
8067	S	D	E	L	1974	62337
8067	S	D	E	N	1974	62337
8067	S	T	E	N	1974	62337
8068	S	D	R	L	1973	55474
8069	S	D	R	L	1973	55474
8070	S	D	E	L	1973	51166
8070	S	D	E	N	1973	51166
8070	S	T	O	N	1973	51531
8070	S	D	E	N	1973	65519
8071	S	S	E	N	1973	54004
8071	S	D	E	N	1973	55945
8072	S	D	E	N	1973	55945
8073	D	D	R	N	1973	52114
8073	D	D	G	N	1972	54629
8073	D	D	E	N	1973	54630
8073	D	D	E	N	1973	54921
8073	S	S	E	N	1973	51186
8073	S	T	O	N	1973	51531
8073	S	D	E	N	1973	51911
8073	S	D	G	N	1972	52548
8073	S	D	R	N	1971	58542
8074	S	D	R	L	1973	51313
8074	S	D	R	N	1973	51313
8074	S	D	E	L	1973	62170
8074	S	D	E	N	1973	62170
8077	S	D	G	N	1950	53501
8077	S	D	E	N	1972	53502
8090	D	D	O	N	1975	90682
8090	S	D	E	N	1973	51911
8090	S	D	E	L	1974	55264
8090	S	D	E	N	1974	55264
8090	S	S	E	N	1974	55264
8091	D	D	O	H	1973	51954
8092	A	D	E	L	1974	62337
8092	A	D	E	N	1974	62337
8092	A	T	E	L	1974	62337
8092	A	T	E	N	1974	62337
8092	S	D	R	L	1973	55474
8092	S	D	E	L	1974	62337
8092	S	D	E	N	1974	62337
8092	S	T	E	L	1974	62337
8092	S	T	E	N	1974	62337
8098	S	D	E	N	1973	52641
8098	S	D	E	N	1974	57999
8098	T	D	E	N	1974	60392
8098	T	T	E	N	1974	60392
8099	S	D	E	L	1973	52789
8099	S	D	E	N	1973	52789
8100	S	D	E	L	1973	52789
8101	T	D	R	N	1972	50662
8102	S	D	E	N	1972	53186
8103	S	D	R	N	1974	60467
8103	S	D	E	N	1974	60468
8112	S	D	R	N	1973	51518
8112	S	D	E	N	1973	53242
8112	S	D	R	N	1973	55824
8112	S	D	E	N	1974	57888
8112	S	D	R	N	1968	102375
8112	S	T	R	N	1968	102375
8112	T	D	R	N	1973	55897
8112	T	T	R	N	1974	60411
8112	T	T	E	N	1974	60412
8113	S	D	R	N	1973	50650
8113	S	D	R	N	1973	51518
8113	S	D	E	N	1973	53242
8114	S	D	R	N	1973	51518
8114	S	D	E	N	1973	53242
8117	S	D	G	N	1950	53501
8117	S	D	E	N	1972	53502
8119	S	D	R	N	1971	67826
8119	T	T	R	N	1974	60493
8119	T	T	E	N	1974	60494
8121	S	D	R	N	1973	57026
8121	S	D	E	N	1973	65524
8121	T	D	E	N	1973	51762
8121	T	E	E	N	1973	51762
8127	S	D	R	N	1973	50658
8128	S	D	E	L	1974	56610
8132	A	D	E	L	1974	62337
8132	A	D	E	N	1974	62337
8132	A	T	E	L	1974	62337
8132	A	T	E	N	1974	62337
8132	S	D	F	L	1973	53869

Phys. State: **A.** Amorphous; **C.** Superconductive; **D.** Doped; **F.** Fibrous or Whisker; **G.** Gas; **I.** Ionized or Plasma; **L.** Liquid; **P.** Powder or Particle; **S.** Solid; **T.** Thin Film
Subject: **D.** Data; **E.** Experiment; **S.** Survey (Review, Compendium, etc.); **T.** Theory
Language: **E.** English; **F.** French; **G.** German; **O.** Other Languages; **R.** Russian
Temperature: **L.** Low (0 to 75K); **N.** Normal (75 to 1273K); **H.** High (above 1273K)

Substance Number	Phys. State	Sub-ject	Lan-guage	Temper-ature	Year	EPIC Number
110-8132	S	D	F	N	1973	53869
8132	S	D	R	L	1973	55474
8133	S	D	R	L	1973	55474
8139	S	D	E	N	1973	52623
8140	S	D	E	N	1973	52623
8143	S	D	E	L	1973	52196
8144	S	D	E	L	1973	52196
8163	S	D	E	L	1973	53960
8163	S	D	E	N	1973	53960
8171	D	D	R	N	1974	61984
8171	D	T	R	N	1974	61984
8171	D	D	E	N	1974	61985
8171	D	T	E	N	1974	61985
8171	S	D	R	N	1974	58126
8171	S	D	E	N	1974	58127
8172	S	D	R	N	1974	58126
8172	S	D	E	N	1974	58127
8176	S	D	E	N	1974	58003
8176	S	D	G	N	1972	67868
8178	S	S	E	N	1974	57971
8179	S	S	E	L	1973	54004
8179	S	S	E	N	1973	54004
8180	S	S	E	L	1973	54004
8180	S	S	E	N	1973	54004
8206	S	D	E	N	1973	55887
8212	S	D	E	N	1973	56463
8213	A	D	E	N	1972	56588
8218	S	D	E	L	1973	57129
8218	S	D	E	N	1973	57129
8219	S	D	E	L	1971	57057
8219	S	D	E	N	1971	57057
8220	S	D	E	L	1971	57057
8220	S	D	E	N	1971	57157
8226	S	D	R	N	1971	58540
8226	S	D	R	N	1971	58547
8227	S	T	R	N	1971	58545
8228	S	T	R	N	1971	58545
8229	S	D	R	N	1971	58546
8233	S	D	R	N	1971	67826
8234	C	D	E	L	1975	87154
8235	S	D	E	N	1974	60390
8238	S	D	E	L	1975	63278
8238	S	D	E	N	1975	63278
8239	S	D	R	L	1973	52370
8239	S	D	E	L	1974	63208
8240	D	D	R	L	1973	52370
8240	D	D	E	L	1974	63208
8240	S	D	R	L	1973	52370
8240	S	D	E	L	1974	63208
8245	S	D	R	N	1972	67060
8250	P	D	E	N	1974	90259
8253	S	D	E	N	1975	63358
8253	S	T	E	N	1975	63358
8253	S	D	R	N	1971	67826
8254	S	D	R	N	1974	67753
8255	S	D	R	N	1971	67824
8256	S	D	R	N	1971	67824
8257	S	D	R	N	1971	67826
8258	S	D	R	N	1971	67826
8265	S	D	R	N	1974	81234
8265	S	T	R	N	1974	81234
8265	S	D	E	N	1974	92364
8265	S	T	E	N	1974	92364
8268	S	D	E	L	1975	90801
8268	S	T	E	L	1975	90801
8269	S	D	E	L	1975	90801
8269	S	T	E	L	1975	90801
8272	S	D	E	L	1975	68711
8272	S	D	E	N	1975	68711
8272	S	E	E	L	1975	68711
8272	S	E	E	N	1975	68711
8272	S	T	E	L	1975	68711
8272	S	T	E	N	1975	68711
8275	D	D	R	N	1974	61984
8275	D	T	R	N	1974	61984
8275	D	D	E	N	1974	61985
8275	D	T	E	N	1974	61985
8276	S	T	R	N	1975	85350
8276	S	T	E	N	1976	94077
8279	S	D	R	N	1968	102375
8279	S	T	R	N	1968	102375
111-0046	S	T	E	N	1974	53898
8002	D	S	R	L	1973	55315
8002	D	S	E	L	1974	59240
8020	T	T	E	N	1974	60521
8021	D	D	E	L	1973	52437
8038	D	D	E	N	1973	51886
8038	S	D	E	N	1973	51886
8038	T	D	E	N	1973	51191
8038	T	D	E	N	1973	51192
8039	T	D	E	N	1973	51192
8044	S	D	E	L	1973	51162
8054	S	D	E	L	1973	52065
8054	S	D	E	N	1973	52065
8058	C	D	G	L	1972	53005
8058	S	S	O	L	1973	62410
8083	S	D	E	L	1975	90801
8083	S	D	E	N	1975	90801
8083	S	T	E	L	1975	90801
8083	S	T	E	N	1975	90801
111-8083	T	D	R	N	1971	49830
8092	S	D	E	L	1974	54572
8092	S	D	E	N	1974	54572
8092	S	T	E	N	1974	54572
8117	S	D	E	L	1973	57111
8138	S	D	E	L	1973	60609
8138	S	T	E	L	1973	60609
8178	S	D	E	L	1975	90116
8178	S	D	E	N	1975	90116
8178	S	D	E	L	1974	92436
8178	S	D	E	N	1974	92436
8179	S	D	E	L	1975	90116
8179	S	D	E	N	1975	90116
8179	S	D	E	L	1974	92436
8179	S	D	E	N	1974	92436
8180	S	D	E	L	1975	90116
8180	S	D	E	N	1975	90116
8180	S	D	E	L	1974	92436
8180	S	D	E	N	1974	92436
8181	S	D	E	L	1975	90116
8181	S	D	E	N	1975	90116
8181	S	D	E	L	1974	92436
8181	S	D	E	N	1974	92436
8182	S	D	E	L	1975	90116
8182	S	D	E	N	1975	90116
8182	S	D	E	L	1974	92436
8183	S	D	E	L	1975	90116
8183	S	D	E	N	1975	90116
8183	S	D	E	L	1974	92436
8184	S	D	E	L	1975	90116
8184	S	D	E	N	1975	90116
8191	S	D	R	L	1974	86222
8191	S	T	R	L	1974	86222
8191	S	D	E	L	1974	92627
8191	S	T	E	L	1974	92627
8205	S	D	E	L	1975	68609
112-0028	D	D	E	N	1974	64715
0028	D	T	E	N	1974	64715
0028	S	D	E	L	1974	58047
8022	S	S	E	L	1966	87721
8047	S	D	E	L	1973	52199
8054	T	D	E	N	1973	57599
8068	S	D	E	L	1974	56610
114-8001	D	T	R	N	1973	52372
8001	D	T	E	N	1974	63212
8033	S	D	E	L	1974	54326
116-0017	S	D	E	L	1977	103589
0017	S	D	E	N	1977	103589
8017	S	D	E	N	1975	63258
118-0037	D	E	E	N	1974	53896
0037	D	T	E	N	1974	53896
119-0008	S	T	E	L	1974	58055
0041	S	T	E	N	1971	57187
0041	S	D	E	N	1969	72658
0041	S	S	E	N	1969	72658
0041	S	D	E	N	1975	90471
8004	D	D	E	N	1974	62680
8004	S	D	E	N	1974	62680
8015	S	D	E	L	1973	51182
8037	S	D	E	L	1973	50003
8040	S	D	E	N	1973	52655
8041	S	D	E	N	1973	52655
8042	S	D	E	N	1973	52655
8047	S	D	E	N	1974	60297
8050	S	D	E	L	1973	51821
8050	S	D	E	N	1973	51821
8051	S	D	E	L	1973	51883
8051	S	D	E	N	1973	51883
8058	S	D	R	L	1974	68656
8058	S	D	R	N	1974	68656
8058	S	T	R	L	1974	68656
8058	S	T	R	N	1974	68656
8058	S	D	E	L	1975	68657
8058	S	D	E	N	1975	68657
8058	S	T	E	L	1975	68657
8058	S	T	E	N	1975	68657
8059	S	D	E	L	1973	52597
8059	S	D	E	N	1973	52597
8060	S	D	E	L	1973	52597
8060	S	D	E	N	1973	52597
8063	S	D	E	L	1973	52597
8063	S	D	E	N	1973	52597
8092	S	D	E	N	1973	56978
8096	S	D	E	L	1975	63278
120-0045	C	S	E	L	1972	62375
0045	S	S	E	L	1966	87721
8006	C	D	G	L	1972	53005
8006	C	S	E	L	1972	62375
8006	C	S	E	L	1968	68373
8006	S	S	O	L	1973	62410
8021	S	D	E	L	1974	53593
8021	S	D	E	N	1974	53593
8021	S	D	E	L	1974	54963
8021	S	D	E	N	1974	54963
8031	S	D	R	L	1973	50251
120-8031	S	D	E	L	1973	50252
8041	S	T	E	N	1973	51936
8042	C	D	E	L	1974	62037
8042	C	S	E	L	1974	62037
8047	C	D	G	L	1972	53005
8047	C	D	E	L	1975	63357
8047	C	T	E	L	1975	63357
8048	C	D	G	L	1972	53005
8065	S	D	E	L	1973	52196
8066	S	D	E	L	1974	54963
8076	S	D	R	L	1973	55026
8076	S	D	R	N	1973	55026
8076	S	D	E	L	1974	55027
8076	S	D	E	N	1974	55027
8078	S	D	E	L	1974	54055
8078	S	D	E	N	1974	54055
8078	S	S	E	L	1971	59678
8082	S	D	E	L	1974	58053
8082	S	T	E	N	1974	58053
8082	S	D	E	L	1975	63305
8083	S	D	E	L	1974	58053
8083	S	D	E	N	1974	58053
8083	S	D	E	L	1975	63305
8130	S	D	E	L	1975	63278
8131	S	D	E	L	1975	63305
8170	S	D	E	L	1975	90117
8170	S	D	E	N	1975	90117
8181	S	D	E	L	1977	103589
8181	S	D	E	N	1977	103589
122-0030	D	D	E	L	1977	103589
0030	D	D	E	N	1977	103589
0030	S	D	E	L	1977	103589
0030	S	D	E	N	1977	103589
0030	S	T	E	L	1977	103589
0096	T	T	R	N	1974	63074
0096	T	T	E	N	1975	63075
0196	S	D	E	L	1977	103589
8068	S	D	F	L	1971	59041
123-0025	S	D	E	L	1974	53593
0025	S	D	E	N	1974	53593
0026	S	D	R	N	1971	54274
0026	S	T	R	N	1971	54274
0026	S	D	E	N	1972	54275
0026	S	T	E	N	1972	54275
126-0046	S	D	E	L	1973	51889
0046	S	D	E	N	1973	51889
8007	S	S	E	L	1974	61394
8037	S	D	E	L	1973	50003
8047	S	S	O	L	1973	62410
8047	S	S	E	L	1967	66157
8047	S	S	E	N	1967	66157
8047	T	S	E	L	1967	66157
8077	S	D	E	L	1973	51889
8077	S	D	E	N	1973	51889
8120	S	D	E	L	1975	63276
8154	S	D	E	L	1974	61918
8154	S	D	E	N	1974	61918
8154	S	T	E	L	1974	61918
8154	S	T	E	N	1974	61918
8155	S	D	E	L	1974	61918
8155	S	D	E	N	1974	61918
8155	S	T	E	L	1974	61918
8155	S	T	E	N	1974	61918
127-8007	S	D	E	L	1973	51889
8007	S	D	E	N	1973	51889
8009	S	D	E	L	1973	52199
8009	S	D	E	N	1973	52199
128-8002	S	D	E	L	1973	51889

Phys. State: **A.** Amorphous; **C.** Superconductive; **D.** Doped; **F.** Fibrous or Whisker; **G.** Gas; **I.** Ionized or Plasma; **L.** Liquid; **P.** Powder or Particle; **S.** Solid; **T.** Thin Film
Subject: **D.** Data; **E.** Experiment; **S.** Survey (Review, Compendium, etc.); **T.** Theory
Language: **E.** English; **F.** French; **G.** German; **O.** Other Languages; **R.** Russian
Temperature: **L.** Low (0 to 75K); **N.** Normal (75 to 1273K); **H.** High (above 1273K)

Chapter 15 Mobility

Substance Number	Phys. State	Sub-ject	Lan-guage	Temper-ature	Year	EPIC Number
100-0045	D	S	E	N	1975	95469
0045	S	S	E	N	1973	55967
0045	S	S	O	N	1969	59542
0045	S	S	O	N	1971	60099
0045	S	S	R	N	1974	83872
0045	S	S	E	N	1974	91448
0055	A	S	E	N	1972	52414
0055	A	T	E	N	1972	53113
0055	A	S	E	N	1971	60961
0055	A	T	E	N	1974	63399
0055	A	T	E	N	1972	64085
0055	A	T	E	N	1974	67281
0055	A	S	E	N	1971	84631
0055	A	T	E	N	1976	100646
0055	D	T	E	N	1973	57562
0055	D	T	E	N	1962	65940
0055	D	S	E	N	1975	95469
0055	L	D	R	N	1973	50223
0055	L	D	E	N	1973	50224
0055	L	D	R	N	1972	59001
0055	L	S	R	N	1972	59001
0055	L	D	E	N	1972	59002
0055	L	S	E	N	1972	59002
0055	L	S	E	N	1971	84631
0055	L	T	E	H	1975	88184
0055	S	E	R	N	1973	50070
0055	S	T	R	N	1973	50283
0055	S	T	E	N	1973	50284
0055	S	E	E	L	1973	50794
0055	S	E	E	N	1973	50794
0055	S	E	E	N	1973	51424
0055	S	E	E	N	1973	52778
0055	S	T	E	N	1973	52778
0055	S	S	E	N	1972	53200
0055	S	S	R	N	1971	53278
0055	S	S	E	N	1972	53279
0055	S	S	E	N	1973	53427
0055	S	T	E	N	1973	53782
0055	S	S	E	N	1973	53986
0055	S	T	E	L	1974	54353
0055	S	T	E	N	1974	54602
0055	S	T	E	N	1973	54678
0055	S	E	O	N	1972	54762
0055	S	E	E	N	1973	56714
0055	S	T	E	N	1973	57390
0055	S	T	E	N	1973	57485
0055	S	S	O	N	1972	58591
0055	S	E	E	N	1968	59164
0055	S	T	E	N	1968	59164
0055	S	E	E	L	1958	59175
0055	S	E	E	N	1958	59175
0055	S	T	G	L	1973	59319
0055	S	S	O	N	1969	59542
0055	S	S	E	N	1970	59681
0055	S	T	E	N	1970	59810
0055	S	T	E	N	1971	60678
0055	S	E	E	N	1966	60796
0055	S	T	E	N	1966	60796
0055	S	D	E	L	1974	61435
0055	S	D	E	N	1974	61435
0055	S	T	E	L	1974	61435
0055	S	T	E	N	1974	61435
0055	S	T	E	N	1974	61443
0055	S	S	E	N	1970	61494
0055	S	E	R	N	1972	63474
0055	S	E	E	N	1972	65152
0055	S	T	R	N	1974	65419
0055	S	T	E	N	1975	65420
0055	S	T	E	N	1962	65944
0055	S	T	R	N	1974	66452
0055	S	T	E	N	1974	66453
0055	S	E	R	N	1973	66555
0055	S	E	E	N	1974	66556
0055	S	T	R	N	1974	66594
0055	S	T	E	N	1974	66595
0055	S	E	E	N	1974	66970
0055	S	S	E	N	1973	67175
0055	S	E	R	N	1970	67415
0055	S	E	R	N	1972	67630
0055	S	T	E	N	1971	70608
0055	S	T	R	N	1974	81141
0055	S	S	R	N	1974	83872
0055	S	T	E	L	1974	86010
0055	S	T	E	N	1974	86010
0055	S	S	E	N	1975	86765
0055	S	T	E	N	1975	86765
0055	S	T	R	N	1975	90012
0055	S	T	E	N	1975	90133
0055	S	S	E	N	1974	91448
0055	S	T	E	N	1975	92631
0055	S	T	R	N	1974	93080
0055	S	T	E	N	1975	93081
0055	S	T	E	L	1975	94588
0055	S	T	E	N	1975	94588
0055	S	T	E	N	1975	96738

Substance Number	Phys. State	Sub-ject	Lan-guage	Temper-ature	Year	EPIC Number
100-0055	S	T	E	N	1976	99749
0055	T	T	E	N	1973	58586
0055	T	T	E	N	1971	62260
0055	T	T	R	N	1968	75362
0055	T	T	E	N	1969	91450
0055	T	T	E	L	1975	94588
0055	T	T	E	N	1975	94588
8003	S	S	E	N	1973	55967
8007	S	S	O	N	1969	59542
8007	S	S	E	N	1969	68271
8007	S	S	E	L	1972	87823
8007	S	S	E	N	1972	87823
8008	S	S	O	N	1969	59542
8008	S	S	E	L	1971	87884
8008	S	S	E	N	1971	87884
8008	S	S	E	N	1972	87889
8008	S	T	R	N	1974	93080
8008	S	T	E	N	1975	93081
8008	T	S	E	N	1969	87821
8013	D	D	R	H	1973	52534
8013	D	D	R	N	1973	52534
8013	D	D	E	H	1974	53647
8013	D	D	E	N	1974	53647
8016	S	S	E	N	1969	59800
8016	S	T	E	N	1970	59810
8016	S	S	E	N	1972	59933
8016	S	S	E	N	1967	75838
8016	T	S	E	N	1973	53854
8038	S	S	O	N	1969	59542
8038	S	S	E	L	1969	68115
8038	S	S	E	N	1969	68115
8038	S	S	E	N	1972	87824
8038	T	S	E	N	1972	87824
8041	S	S	O	N	1969	59542
8043	S	S	E	N	1969	75843
8044	L	S	O	N	1973	58738
102-0002	S	T	E	N	1973	56971
0005	S	D	E	N	1974	58589
0005	S	E	E	N	1974	58589
0009	D	T	R	N	1972	62856
0009	D	T	E	N	1973	65177
0009	S	D	E	L	1973	50577
0009	S	D	E	N	1975	63326
0009	T	T	R	N	1972	62856
0009	T	T	E	N	1973	65177
0010	S	D	E	N	1973	56645
0041	S	D	R	N	1971	60185
0041	S	S	E	N	1972	87889
0041	T	D	E	L	1974	65107
0041	T	D	E	N	1974	65107
0041	T	D	E	N	1975	65464
0041	T	S	E	N	1972	87889
0086	S	S	E	N	1974	55244
0086	S	D	E	N	1973	56527
0086	S	S	E	N	1972	59933
0105	S	S	E	N	1966	87830
0105	S	S	E	N	1971	87884
0120	S	D	R	N	1973	50724
0120	S	D	E	N	1973	53025
0120	T	D	R	N	1973	54861
0248	S	S	E	N	1971	87884
0248	T	S	E	N	1971	60965
0248	T	S	E	N	1969	87821
0348	S	S	E	N	1973	56765
0348	S	D	O	N	1972	66262
0348	S	E	O	N	1972	66262
8001	D	D	E	N	1973	53427
8001	D	S	E	N	1971	87884
8001	S	S	E	N	1973	53427
8001	S	S	E	N	1972	67891
8001	S	S	E	N	1962	87668
8001	S	S	E	N	1966	87830
8001	S	S	E	L	1971	87884
8001	S	S	E	N	1971	87884
8001	T	S	E	N	1971	60965
8018	S	S	E	N	1972	87889
8018	T	D	E	L	1973	64100
8018	T	D	E	N	1973	64100
8031	A	D	E	N	1973	67288
8031	S	D	O	N	1972	54762
8031	S	S	E	N	1972	59933
8035	S	D	E	N	1972	51526
8035	S	S	E	N	1972	51526
8035	S	D	E	N	1974	53622
8035	T	D	R	N	1973	51082
8035	T	D	E	N	1973	56341
8041	A	S	E	N	1971	49794
8041	D	D	E	N	1972	49555
8041	D	D	E	N	1972	49783
8041	D	D	R	L	1973	50080
8041	D	D	R	N	1972	50803
8041	D	D	E	L	1973	51042
8041	D	D	E	N	1973	51042
8041	D	D	E	N	1973	51433

Substance Number	Phys. State	Sub-ject	Lan-guage	Temper-ature	Year	EPIC Number
102-8041	D	D	R	N	1973	51624
8041	D	D	R	N	1973	51704
8041	D	D	E	L	1973	51866
8041	D	D	E	N	1973	51866
8041	D	D	E	N	1973	52460
8041	D	D	R	N	1973	52520
8041	D	D	R	N	1973	52561
8041	D	D	E	N	1973	52937
8041	D	D	E	N	1972	52973
8041	D	D	E	N	1972	52982
8041	D	D	E	N	1972	53068
8041	D	D	R	N	1970	53088
8041	D	D	E	N	1972	53089
8041	D	T	E	N	1972	53113
8041	D	D	E	N	1972	53171
8041	D	S	E	N	1972	53227
8041	D	D	E	N	1972	53302
8041	D	D	E	N	1973	53352
8041	D	D	E	N	1972	53390
8041	D	D	E	L	1973	53440
8041	D	D	E	N	1972	53484
8041	D	D	E	N	1971	53515
8041	D	D	E	N	1974	53735
8041	D	D	E	N	1974	53745
8041	D	D	E	N	1974	53910
8041	D	D	E	N	1974	54087
8041	D	S	E	N	1973	54771
8041	D	D	E	N	1972	55096
8041	D	D	E	N	1972	55098
8041	D	D	R	L	1973	55303
8041	D	T	R	L	1973	55303
8041	D	D	E	N	1973	56537
8041	D	D	E	N	1973	57739
8041	D	S	E	N	1973	57739
8041	D	D	E	N	1974	57761
8041	D	D	E	N	1973	57786
8041	D	D	E	N	1974	57994
8041	D	D	E	L	1974	59228
8041	D	T	E	L	1974	59228
8041	D	D	E	L	1970	59695
8041	D	D	E	N	1970	59695
8041	D	D	E	N	1974	61180
8041	D	D	E	N	1974	62055
8041	D	D	E	N	1964	62127
8041	D	S	E	N	1970	62251
8041	D	D	E	N	1970	62262
8041	D	D	R	N	1973	62726
8041	D	D	E	N	1975	63363
8041	D	D	E	N	1971	63995
8041	D	D	E	N	1973	65322
8041	D	D	E	N	1975	65434
8041	D	D	R	N	1974	66450
8041	D	D	E	N	1974	66451
8041	D	D	E	N	1973	66481
8041	D	D	R	N	1972	67630
8041	D	D	R	N	1969	67766
8041	D	D	E	N	1970	68189
8041	D	D	E	N	1973	68864
8041	D	D	E	N	1973	78992
8041	D	S	E	N	1962	87673
8041	D	S	E	L	1964	87701
8041	D	S	E	N	1964	87701
8041	D	S	E	L	1969	87821
8041	D	D	E	N	1975	89296
8041	D	D	E	N	1976	99243
8041	D	D	E	N	1976	100869
8041	D	D	E	N	1973	101327
8041	S	D	E	N	1972	49555
8041	S	D	R	N	1973	50054
8041	S	D	E	N	1973	50752
8041	S	D	E	N	1972	51086
8041	S	D	R	N	1972	51102
8041	S	D	E	N	1973	51651
8041	S	D	O	N	1973	51960
8041	S	D	E	N	1972	52973
8041	S	D	E	N	1972	52982
8041	S	D	E	N	1972	53171
8041	S	D	E	L	1972	53184
8041	S	S	E	N	1972	53227
8041	S	D	R	N	1973	53231
8041	S	D	E	N	1972	53232
8041	S	D	E	N	1972	53302
8041	S	D	E	N	1973	53446
8041	S	D	E	N	1972	53477
8041	S	D	E	N	1973	53570
8041	S	D	E	N	1974	53745
8041	S	S	E	N	1974	53745
8041	S	D	E	N	1974	54087
8041	S	D	R	N	1973	54645
8041	S	D	E	N	1973	55095
8041	S	D	E	N	1972	55101
8041	S	D	E	N	1972	55165
8041	S	D	R	N	1973	55167
8041	S	D	E	N	1974	55168
8041	S	D	R	N	1973	55305

Phys. State: **A.** Amorphous; **C.** Superconductive; **D.** Doped; **F.** Fibrous or Whisker; **G.** Gas; **I.** Ionized or Plasma; **L.** Liquid; **P.** Powder or Particle; **S.** Solid; **T.** Thin Film
Subject: **D.** Data; **E.** Experiment; **S.** Survey (Review, Compendium, etc.); **T.** Theory
Language: **E.** English; **F.** French; **G.** German; **O.** Other Languages; **R.** Russian
Temperature: **L.** Low (0 to 75K); **N.** Normal (75 to 1273K); **H.** High (above 1273K)

Substance Number	Phys. State	Subject	Language	Temperature	Year	EPIC Number
102-8041	S	D	R	N	1973	55316
8041	S	D	E	N	1973	55627
8041	S	D	R	N	1973	56328
8041	S	D	E	N	1973	56714
8041	S	D	R	N	1972	56730
8041	S	D	R	N	1972	56957
8041	S	D	E	N	1973	57568
8041	S	D	E	N	1973	57739
8041	S	S	E	N	1974	58038
8041	S	D	E	N	1974	59230
8041	S	D	E	N	1974	59241
8041	S	D	E	N	1974	59281
8041	S	D	R	N	1973	59722
8041	S	D	E	N	1973	59723
8041	S	D	E	N	1973	60748
8041	S	D	E	N	1974	61185
8041	S	D	E	N	1974	61373
8041	S	D	E	N	1969	62248
8041	S	S	E	N	1970	62262
8041	S	S	E	N	1971	62264
8041	S	D	E	N	1974	62323
8041	S	D	E	N	1973	62582
8041	S	D	R	N	1972	62691
8041	S	D	E	N	1972	63538
8041	S	D	E	N	1973	63838
8041	S	S	E	L	1974	64464
8041	S	S	E	N	1974	64464
8041	S	D	E	N	1974	64493
8041	S	D	E	N	1974	65242
8041	S	D	R	N	1974	66659
8041	S	D	E	N	1974	66660
8041	S	T	R	N	1972	66976
8041	S	D	E	N	1972	67519
8041	S	T	E	N	1974	67619
8041	S	D	R	N	1971	67721
8041	S	S	E	N	1972	67891
8041	S	D	E	N	1970	68209
8041	S	D	R	N	1974	68636
8041	S	D	E	N	1975	68637
8041	S	D	E	N	1973	68846
8041	S	D	E	N	1973	68864
8041	S	D	R	N	1974	72651
8041	S	D	E	N	1975	72700
8041	S	D	E	N	1966	75146
8041	S	D	E	N	1966	75395
8041	S	D	R	N	1975	81273
8041	S	S	E	N	1973	86380
8041	S	D	E	N	1974	87448
8041	S	S	E	L	1964	87701
8041	S	S	E	N	1964	87701
8041	S	S	E	N	1968	87819
8041	S	S	E	N	1971	87884
8041	S	S	E	N	1972	87889
8041	S	D	R	N	1966	91926
8041	S	D	E	N	1975	94088
8041	S	D	E	N	1975	101019
8041	T	D	R	L	1972	49973
8041	T	D	R	N	1972	49973
8041	T	D	R	N	1973	50676
8041	T	D	R	N	1973	51386
8041	T	D	E	N	1973	51387
8041	T	D	E	N	1973	51410
8041	T	D	R	N	1973	51624
8041	T	D	R	L	1973	51702
8041	T	D	R	N	1973	51702
8041	T	D	E	N	1973	52422
8041	T	D	R	L	1973	52832
8041	T	D	R	N	1973	52832
8041	T	D	E	L	1973	52833
8041	T	D	E	L	1973	52935
8041	T	D	E	N	1973	52935
8041	T	D	E	N	1972	53143
8041	T	D	E	N	1974	60393
8041	T	S	E	L	1971	60965
8041	T	S	E	N	1971	60965
8041	T	D	E	N	1974	62550
8041	T	D	E	N	1970	62952
8041	T	D	R	N	1969	67766
8041	T	D	E	N	1970	68189
8041	T	D	R	N	1972	76536
8041	T	T	R	N	1972	76536
8041	T	D	E	N	1973	78992
8041	T	S	E	L	1969	87821
8041	T	S	E	N	1969	87821
8041	T	S	E	L	1971	87884
8041	T	S	E	N	1972	87889
8041	T	D	E	N	1974	90073
8041	T	D	E	N	1974	90083
8041	T	D	E	N	1972	91519
8041	T	T	E	N	1972	91519
8041	T	D	E	N	1975	93323
8054	D	D	R	N	1973	50080
8054	D	D	E	N	1973	51433
8054	D	D	R	N	1970	53316
8054	D	D	E	N	1973	53317
8054	D	D	R	N	1973	58156
8054	D	T	R	L	1973	58726
8054	D	T	R	N	1973	58726
8054	D	D	E	N	1966	60796
8054	D	D	R	L	1974	62428
8054	D	D	R	N	1974	62428
102-8054	D	D	E	L	1974	65331
8054	D	D	E	N	1974	65331
8054	D	S	E	N	1962	87667
8054	D	S	E	N	1971	87884
8054	S	D	R	N	1970	53316
8054	S	D	E	N	1973	53317
8054	S	D	E	L	1971	53516
8054	S	D	E	N	1971	53516
8054	S	D	E	N	1972	55164
8054	S	S	E	N	1972	55164
8054	S	T	E	N	1972	55164
8054	S	E	E	L	1958	59175
8054	S	E	E	N	1958	59175
8054	S	D	E	N	1966	60796
8054	S	E	E	N	1966	60796
8054	S	T	E	N	1966	60796
8054	S	D	R	N	1972	62693
8054	S	D	E	N	1972	64420
8054	S	D	R	N	1973	66121
8054	S	D	G	N	1954	66199
8054	S	S	E	N	1972	67891
8054	S	S	E	N	1962	87667
8054	S	S	E	N	1971	87884
8054	S	S	E	N	1972	87889
8054	S	D	R	N	1975	97056
8054	S	D	E	N	1975	97057
8054	S	D	E	N	1975	101019
8054	T	S	E	N	1973	53451
8054	T	S	E	N	1971	60965
8054	T	S	E	N	1974	65107
8054	T	S	E	N	1969	87821
8054	T	S	E	N	1971	87884
8054	T	S	E	N	1972	87889
8065	S	D	R	N	1973	50069
8065	S	D	E	N	1973	51423
8065	S	D	R	N	1974	86779
8065	S	D	E	N	1974	90050
8066	S	T	R	N	1973	51553
8066	S	T	E	N	1973	53684
8066	S	D	R	N	1974	86779
8066	S	D	E	N	1974	90050
8069	S	D	E	N	1972	53335
8069	S	D	R	N	1973	54199
8069	S	D	E	N	1973	54200
8069	S	S	E	N	1975	94550
8083	S	D	R	N	1972	49811
8083	S	D	E	N	1972	58866
8083	S	S	E	N	1975	94550
8084	D	D	R	N	1973	68034
8084	D	D	E	N	1973	68035
8084	S	D	R	N	1972	49811
8084	S	D	R	L	1973	55338
8084	S	D	R	N	1973	55338
8084	S	D	E	N	1972	58866
8084	S	D	E	L	1974	59276
8084	S	D	E	N	1974	59276
8084	S	D	R	N	1974	67759
8084	S	D	E	N	1975	94550
8094	D	D	E	N	1974	53910
8094	S	D	E	N	1974	53910
8094	S	D	R	N	1972	56957
8094	T	D	E	N	1975	93323
8095	D	S	E	N	1972	53227
8095	D	S	E	N	1972	87889
8095	S	S	E	N	1972	53227
8095	S	D	R	N	1972	56957
8095	S	D	R	N	1975	81273
8095	S	S	E	N	1973	86380
8095	S	S	E	N	1965	87703
8095	S	S	E	N	1972	87889
8095	S	D	E	N	1975	94088
8095	T	S	E	N	1972	87889
8096	D	D	R	N	1972	50105
8096	S	D	R	N	1973	50201
8096	S	D	E	N	1973	50202
8096	S	D	R	N	1973	51730
8096	S	D	R	N	1970	55102
8096	S	S	R	N	1970	55102
8096	S	D	E	N	1972	55103
8096	S	S	E	N	1972	55103
8096	S	D	E	N	1973	79154
8096	S	D	E	N	1975	94550
8106	A	D	E	N	1970	66929
8106	A	D	E	N	1973	67288
8106	A	T	E	N	1976	100646
8106	L	D	R	N	1973	51406
8106	L	D	E	N	1973	51407
8106	T	D	E	N	1970	66929
8108	S	D	R	N	1973	50724
8108	S	D	E	N	1973	53025
8132	D	D	E	N	1971	68126
8132	D	S	E	N	1966	87830
8132	S	S	E	N	1971	87884
8132	T	S	E	N	1971	60965
8132	T	S	E	N	1969	87821
8133	A	D	E	N	1973	67288
8133	A	D	E	N	1974	84007
8133	A	T	E	N	1976	100646
8133	L	D	R	N	1973	51406
8133	L	D	E	N	1973	51407
8133	S	S	E	N	1972	67891
102-8133	T	D	E	N	1974	84007
8139	S	D	E	N	1974	53722
8139	S	D	E	N	1974	60309
8139	S	D	E	N	1973	88610
8142	D	D	R	N	1973	51624
8142	D	D	E	N	1975	65434
8142	D	D	E	N	1973	78992
8142	S	D	E	N	1973	50752
8142	S	D	E	N	1972	52995
8142	S	D	E	N	1974	54087
8142	S	D	E	N	1975	59584
8142	S	D	R	N	1973	66121
8142	S	S	E	N	1973	86380
8142	S	S	E	N	1972	87889
8142	T	D	R	N	1973	51624
8142	T	D	E	N	1973	78992
8142	T	S	E	N	1972	87889
8171	A	D	E	N	1972	53186
8171	T	D	E	N	1972	53186
8172	A	D	E	N	1972	53187
8172	A	S	E	N	1972	53187
8179	S	D	R	N	1970	55102
8179	S	D	E	N	1972	55103
8179	S	D	R	N	1972	56982
8179	S	S	E	N	1975	94550
8180	S	D	R	N	1973	55074
8180	S	D	E	N	1974	55075
8180	S	D	R	N	1970	55102
8180	S	D	E	N	1972	55103
8180	S	D	R	N	1972	56980
8180	S	D	E	N	1975	94550
8228	S	D	R	N	1970	55102
8228	S	D	E	N	1972	55103
8229	S	D	R	N	1970	55102
8229	S	D	E	N	1972	55103
8230	S	D	R	N	1970	55102
8230	S	D	E	N	1972	55103
8230	S	D	E	L	1974	62033
8230	S	D	E	N	1974	62033
8230	S	T	E	L	1974	62033
8230	S	T	E	N	1974	62033
8231	S	D	R	N	1970	55102
8231	S	D	E	N	1972	55103
8232	S	D	E	N	1974	53622
8235	S	D	O	N	1973	67248
8248	S	D	R	N	1970	55102
8248	S	D	E	N	1972	55103
8310	S	D	E	N	1973	53799
8310	S	T	E	N	1972	57000
8310	S	D	E	N	1973	57114
8310	T	T	E	N	1972	57000
8310	T	D	O	N	1969	65841
8331	S	D	O	N	1973	51964
8333	S	S	E	N	1972	87889
8346	S	D	E	N	1969	85351
8383	A	D	E	N	1974	84007
8396	A	S	E	N	1964	75166
8396	S	S	E	N	1964	75166
8420	S	S	E	N	1972	87889
8420	T	S	E	N	1972	87889
8453	S	D	R	L	1972	76538
8453	S	D	R	N	1972	76538
8453	S	D	E	L	1972	91520
8453	S	D	E	N	1972	91520
8454	S	D	R	L	1972	76538
8454	S	D	R	N	1972	76538
8454	S	D	E	L	1972	91520
8454	S	D	E	N	1972	91520
104-0006	S	D	E	L	1974	54605
0006	S	D	E	N	1974	54605
0006	S	T	E	L	1974	54605
0006	S	T	E	N	1974	54605
0006	S	D	E	N	1974	56613
0006	S	D	E	N	1973	62296
0006	S	D	E	N	1975	64287
0006	S	S	E	L	1965	74575
0013	S	D	E	N	1971	50468
0013	S	D	R	N	1972	59071
0013	S	D	E	N	1972	59072
0013	S	D	R	N	1974	63159
0013	S	D	E	N	1975	63160
0049	S	D	R	N	1974	66728
0049	S	E	R	N	1974	66728
0049	S	S	R	N	1974	66728
0049	S	T	R	N	1974	66728
0049	S	D	E	N	1975	66729
0049	S	E	E	N	1975	66729
0049	S	S	E	N	1975	66729
0049	S	T	E	N	1975	66729
0049	S	D	R	H	1974	66744
0049	S	D	R	N	1974	66744
0049	S	T	R	H	1974	66744
0049	S	T	R	N	1974	66744
0049	S	D	E	H	1975	66745
0049	S	D	E	N	1975	66745
0049	S	T	E	H	1975	66745
0049	S	T	E	N	1975	66745
0049	S	S	E	N	1969	68271
0049	S	D	R	H	1972	76508
0049	S	D	R	N	1972	76508

Phys. State: **A.** Amorphous; **C.** Superconductive; **D.** Doped; **F.** Fibrous or Whisker; **G.** Gas; **I.** Ionized or Plasma; **L.** Liquid; **P.** Powder or Particle; **S.** Solid; **T.** Thin Film
Subject: **D.** Data; **E.** Experiment; **S.** Survey (Review, Compendium, etc.); **T.** Theory
Language: **E.** English; **F.** French; **G.** German; **O.** Other Languages; **R.** Russian
Temperature: **L.** Low (0 to 75K); **N.** Normal (75 to 1273K); **H.** High (above 1273K)

Substance Number	Phys. State	Subject	Language	Temperature	Year	EPIC Number
104-0049	S	D	E	H	1972	91530
0049	S	D	E	N	1972	91530
0049	S	S	E	N	1975	96477
0069	D	D	E	N	1973	50169
0069	S	D	E	N	1973	50169
0249	S	S	E	N	1971	87364
0295	S	S	E	N	1971	87884
0295	T	S	E	N	1971	60965
0337	T	S	E	N	1973	53758
8010	S	D	R	N	1967	72953
8010	S	S	E	N	1971	87884
8011	S	S	E	L	1971	87884
8011	S	S	E	N	1971	87884
8042	D	D	R	N	1972	62716
8042	D	S	R	N	1972	62716
8042	D	D	E	N	1973	65312
8042	D	S	E	N	1973	65312
8042	D	S	E	N	1966	66068
8042	S	D	R	N	1972	62716
8042	S	D	E	N	1973	65312
8042	S	S	E	N	1966	66068
8042	S	D	E	N	1975	96857
8043	S	D	R	N	1972	49822
8045	D	D	E	L	1973	52709
8045	D	D	R	L	1972	62298
8045	D	D	E	L	1973	62299
8045	D	S	E	L	1966	66068
8045	D	S	E	N	1966	66068
8045	D	D	E	L	1974	88264
8045	S	D	R	L	1973	50295
8045	S	D	E	L	1973	50296
8045	S	D	E	L	1973	52072
8045	S	T	E	L	1973	52072
8045	S	D	R	N	1972	62298
8045	S	S	R	N	1972	62298
8045	S	S	E	N	1973	62299
8045	S	S	E	N	1971	63594
8045	S	T	E	N	1971	63594
8045	S	S	E	N	1966	66068
8099	S	D	R	N	1972	51232
8108	D	T	O	N	1971	59997
8108	D	D	R	N	1972	62298
8108	D	S	E	N	1966	66068
8108	S	S	E	N	1971	59999
8108	S	S	E	N	1966	66068
8108	T	S	E	N	1966	66068
8108	T	D	R	N	1975	93405
8108	T	D	E	N	1975	93406
8108	T	D	R	N	1975	93407
8108	T	D	E	N	1975	93408
8109	D	T	O	N	1971	59997
8109	S	D	R	N	1972	62298
8109	S	D	E	N	1973	62299
8114	S	D	O	N	1972	49812
8115	S	D	O	N	1972	49812
8156	S	D	R	N	1972	51232
8157	S	D	R	N	1972	51232
8183	S	D	E	N	1973	54901
8184	S	D	E	N	1972	52993
8194	S	S	R	N	1972	62298
8194	S	S	E	N	1973	62299
8202	S	D	E	N	1973	50752
8224	S	S	R	L	1971	54264
8224	S	S	E	L	1972	54265
8224	S	D	R	N	1971	67046
8224	S	E	R	N	1971	67046
8242	S	D	E	N	1973	62296
8304	S	D	E	N	1969	85351
8366	S	S	E	N	1971	87884
106-0004	S	D	R	N	1974	66728
0004	S	E	R	N	1974	66728
0004	S	T	R	N	1974	66728
0004	S	D	E	N	1975	66729
0004	S	E	E	N	1975	66729
0004	S	T	E	N	1975	66729
0004	S	D	R	H	1974	66744
0004	S	D	R	N	1974	66744
0004	S	T	R	H	1974	66744
0004	S	T	R	N	1974	66744
0004	S	D	E	H	1975	66745
0004	S	D	E	N	1975	66745
0004	S	T	E	H	1975	66745
0004	S	T	E	N	1975	66745
0004	S	D	R	H	1972	76508
0004	S	D	R	N	1972	76508
0004	S	D	E	H	1972	91530
0004	S	D	E	N	1972	91530
0004	S	S	E	N	1975	96477
0006	S	D	E	N	1972	53173
0006	S	D	E	N	1972	58980
0006	S	T	E	N	1952	59642
0006	S	D	R	L	1974	63155
0006	S	D	R	N	1974	63155
0006	S	D	E	L	1975	63156
0006	S	D	E	N	1975	63156
0024	S	S	E	N	1973	56765
0024	S	T	E	N	1952	59642
0024	S	D	E	N	1971	64069
0035	D	S	R	N	1973	59077
0035	D	S	E	N	1973	59078
106-0035	D	S	E	N	1965	87702
0035	D	S	E	N	1968	87828
0035	D	D	E	N	1976	99748
0035	S	D	R	H	1973	50187
0035	S	D	R	N	1973	50187
0035	S	D	E	H	1973	50188
0035	S	D	E	N	1973	50188
0035	S	D	R	N	1972	54938
0035	S	T	R	N	1974	64485
0035	S	S	E	L	1965	87702
0035	S	S	E	N	1965	87702
0035	S	S	E	N	1968	87828
0035	S	S	E	N	1971	87887
0035	S	S	R	H	1972	94899
0035	S	S	E	H	1973	95896
0035	T	D	R	N	1973	58531
0035	T	S	E	N	1974	66690
0035	T	S	E	N	1968	87828
0035	T	D	E	N	1975	95534
0057	S	S	E	N	1969	68271
0057	S	S	E	N	1966	68325
0057	T	S	E	N	1971	60964
0057	T	S	E	N	1966	68325
0081	D	T	R	N	1975	90140
0081	D	T	E	N	1975	90141
0081	S	S	E	N	1969	49679
0081	S	D	E	H	1971	49788
0104	S	D	R	N	1972	59068
0104	S	D	E	N	1972	59069
0104	S	S	E	N	1972	59933
0104	S	S	E	N	1971	87872
0104	T	D	E	N	1972	60922
0104	T	D	E	N	1970	61741
0104	T	D	E	N	1971	63887
0125	S	S	R	H	1972	94899
0125	S	S	E	H	1973	95896
0127	S	D	R	N	1973	50082
0127	S	D	E	N	1973	51428
0127	S	D	R	N	1974	60469
0127	S	T	R	N	1974	60469
0127	S	D	E	N	1974	60470
0127	S	T	E	N	1974	60470
0127	S	D	E	N	1975	63342
0156	D	D	E	N	1973	52127
0156	D	T	E	N	1973	52127
0309	S	S	E	H	1972	87886
0363	D	D	E	N	1973	50830
0363	D	D	E	N	1973	55163
0363	D	D	E	N	1973	58586
0363	D	S	E	N	1971	60964
0363	D	S	E	L	1963	64232
0363	D	S	E	N	1963	64232
0363	D	S	E	N	1967	66156
0363	D	D	R	N	1974	67743
0363	D	D	E	N	1975	68601
0363	D	S	E	N	1975	68601
0363	D	T	E	N	1975	68601
0363	D	D	E	N	1957	89723
0363	S	D	E	L	1972	49953
0363	S	D	E	N	1972	49953
0363	S	T	R	N	1973	50102
0363	S	D	E	N	1973	51874
0363	S	D	R	N	1973	52836
0363	S	D	E	N	1973	52837
0363	S	D	E	N	1973	56394
0363	S	D	E	L	1974	57324
0363	S	D	E	N	1974	57324
0363	S	D	R	N	1973	57825
0363	S	D	E	N	1974	57826
0363	S	D	E	N	1974	61182
0363	S	T	E	N	1974	61182
0363	S	D	E	N	1969	62248
0363	S	S	E	N	1963	64232
0363	S	S	E	L	1967	66156
0363	S	S	E	N	1967	66156
0363	S	D	R	N	1974	67743
0363	S	D	G	N	1970	67881
0363	S	S	E	N	1972	67891
0363	S	S	E	L	1969	68271
0363	S	S	E	N	1969	68271
0363	S	D	E	N	1975	68601
0363	S	T	E	N	1975	68601
0363	S	S	R	N	1974	71817
0363	S	S	E	N	1975	71966
0363	T	D	R	N	1973	51555
0363	T	T	R	N	1973	51555
0363	T	D	E	N	1973	51914
0363	T	D	E	N	1973	53686
0363	T	T	E	N	1973	53686
0363	T	D	E	N	1974	53750
0363	T	D	E	N	1974	54033
0363	T	D	R	N	1972	56944
0363	T	D	R	N	1973	58586
0363	T	D	E	N	1974	60286
0363	T	S	E	N	1971	60964
0363	T	S	E	N	1963	64232
0363	T	D	R	N	1973	65571
0363	T	D	E	N	1973	65572
0363	T	S	E	N	1967	66156
0363	T	D	R	N	1970	67769
0363	T	D	R	N	1971	76498
106-0363	T	D	E	N	1962	89789
0363	T	D	E	N	1974	90590
0363	T	D	E	N	1971	91581
0363	T	S	E	N	1975	94588
0363	T	S	E	N	1976	97315
0385	D	S	E	N	1973	56765
0385	D	D	E	L	1969	74658
0385	D	D	E	N	1969	74658
0937	S	D	R	N	1971	76485
0937	S	D	E	N	1971	91504
0941	S	D	R	N	1973	54953
0941	S	S	E	N	1975	94550
1079	S	D	R	N	1967	53069
1079	S	D	E	N	1972	53070
1085	D	D	E	N	1974	53622
1085	S	D	E	N	1974	53622
1256	S	D	R	N	1972	56993
1256	S	D	E	N	1974	101330
1519	D	D	E	N	1971	63887
1519	S	D	E	N	1974	53915
1519	S	D	E	N	1971	63887
1519	S	S	E	N	1975	94550
8001	D	D	R	N	1972	76512
8001	D	D	E	N	1972	91556
8001	S	D	R	N	1973	50075
8001	S	D	E	L	1973	51041
8001	S	D	E	N	1973	51426
8001	T	S	E	N	1973	53451
8008	S	D	E	N	1974	53644
8040	D	D	R	N	1973	55296
8040	D	T	R	N	1973	55296
8040	D	D	R	N	1972	56733
8040	D	D	E	N	1974	59280
8040	D	T	E	N	1974	59280
8040	D	D	E	L	1971	64324
8040	D	D	E	N	1971	64324
8040	D	S	E	N	1963	87710
8040	S	D	R	N	1973	52530
8040	S	D	R	N	1969	53223
8040	S	D	E	N	1972	53224
8040	S	D	E	N	1974	53625
8040	S	T	E	N	1974	53625
8040	S	T	R	N	1973	55300
8040	S	T	R	N	1973	55987
8040	S	D	E	N	1974	57771
8040	S	T	E	N	1974	59225
8040	S	D	R	N	1972	62718
8040	S	D	E	N	1973	65314
8040	S	S	E	N	1969	68271
8040	S	S	E	N	1963	87710
8040	T	D	O	N	1973	51445
8040	T	D	R	N	1973	56580
8040	T	S	E	N	1971	60964
8041	D	D	O	N	1973	49552
8041	D	D	E	N	1973	52653
8041	D	S	E	N	1973	52653
8041	D	D	E	N	1974	53601
8041	D	T	E	N	1974	54034
8041	D	D	R	L	1972	57864
8041	D	D	R	N	1972	57864
8041	D	T	R	L	1972	57864
8041	D	T	R	N	1972	57864
8041	D	D	E	N	1969	62248
8041	D	D	R	N	1972	62705
8041	D	D	E	N	1973	65301
8041	D	D	E	N	1975	65462
8041	D	D	E	N	1972	67638
8041	D	T	E	N	1972	67638
8041	D	S	E	N	1967	68371
8041	D	S	E	N	1962	87659
8041	D	D	E	N	1975	93355
8041	D	D	E	N	1975	93356
8041	D	D	R	N	1974	93457
8041	D	D	E	N	1974	93458
8041	S	D	O	N	1973	49552
8041	S	D	E	N	1974	53925
8041	S	S	E	N	1974	53925
8041	S	T	R	N	1973	55987
8041	S	T	E	N	1973	57391
8041	S	D	E	N	1974	57976
8041	S	S	E	N	1974	57976
8041	S	S	E	N	1972	59933
8041	S	S	E	N	1973	60838
8041	S	S	E	N	1974	62323
8041	S	D	R	N	1972	62705
8041	S	D	E	N	1973	65301
8041	S	D	R	N	1971	67723
8041	S	S	E	N	1972	67891
8041	S	S	E	L	1969	68271
8041	S	S	E	N	1969	68271
8041	S	D	R	N	1971	68351
8041	S	S	E	L	1967	68371
8041	S	S	E	N	1967	68371
8041	S	D	R	N	1971	76463
8041	S	S	E	N	1962	87659
8041	S	D	E	N	1971	91585
8041	T	D	R	N	1973	51616
8041	T	D	E	N	1973	53451
8041	T	S	E	N	1971	60964
8041	T	D	R	N	1974	66639
8041	T	D	E	N	1974	66640

Phys. State: **A.** Amorphous; **C.** Superconductive; **D.** Doped; **F.** Fibrous or Whisker; **G.** Gas; **I.** Ionized or Plasma; **L.** Liquid; **P.** Powder or Particle; **S.** Solid; **T.** Thin Film
Subject: **D.** Data; **E.** Experiment; **S.** Survey (Review, Compendium, etc.); **T.** Theory
Language: **E.** English; **F.** French; **G.** German; **O.** Other Languages; **R.** Russian
Temperature: **L.** Low (0 to 75K); **N.** Normal (75 to 1273K); **H.** High (above 1273K)

Substance Number	Phys. State	Subject	Language	Temperature	Year	EPIC Number
106-8041	T	D	R	N	1972	76519
8041	T	T	E	N	1972	88174
8041	T	D	E	N	1972	91552
8065	S	D	E	N	1973	51890
8074	S	D	R	N	1973	50355
8074	S	D	E	N	1973	50356
8081	D	D	R	N	1973	52556
8081	L	S	E	N	1967	87860
8081	S	D	R	N	1973	55711
8081	S	S	E	N	1967	87860
8081	S	D	R	N	1974	93465
8081	S	D	E	N	1974	93466
8081	T	D	R	N	1973	52570
8081	T	D	E	N	1973	79103
8082	T	D	E	N	1973	55113
8084	S	D	R	N	1972	49759
8084	S	D	R	N	1972	59068
8084	S	D	E	N	1972	59069
8084	S	D	R	L	1972	60544
8084	S	D	R	N	1972	60544
8084	S	D	E	L	1972	60545
8084	S	D	E	N	1972	60545
8084	T	D	R	N	1973	50104
8127	S	S	E	N	1972	87823
8128	D	S	E	N	1967	68371
8128	S	D	R	N	1971	52298
8128	S	D	E	N	1971	52299
8128	S	D	E	L	1972	53184
8128	S	D	E	N	1972	53401
8128	S	D	E	N	1973	53406
8128	S	D	E	L	1973	53852
8128	S	D	E	N	1973	53852
8128	S	D	E	N	1974	53925
8128	S	S	E	N	1974	53925
8128	S	S	E	N	1974	54554
8128	S	D	R	N	1973	55014
8128	S	D	E	N	1974	55015
8128	S	D	E	N	1973	55149
8128	S	D	E	N	1973	58248
8128	S	D	E	N	1971	60102
8128	S	D	E	L	1974	61351
8128	S	D	E	N	1974	61351
8128	S	S	E	L	1974	61351
8128	S	S	E	N	1974	61351
8128	S	D	E	N	1973	66893
8128	S	S	E	L	1967	68371
8128	S	S	E	N	1967	68371
8128	S	S	E	N	1972	87823
8128	S	S	E	N	1966	87831
8128	S	D	R	L	1976	103167
8128	S	D	R	N	1976	103167
8128	S	D	E	L	1976	103168
8128	S	D	E	N	1976	103168
8128	T	D	R	N	1972	49717
8128	T	D	E	N	1973	51923
8128	T	D	E	N	1974	66692
8128	T	S	E	N	1967	68371
8128	T	S	E	N	1972	87823
8128	T	D	R	N	1974	90409
8132	S	S	E	L	1972	87823
8143	S	D	R	N	1973	50355
8143	S	D	E	N	1973	50356
8143	T	D	R	N	1973	58553
8149	S	D	E	N	1973	50815
8154	D	D	R	N	1973	51551
8154	D	D	E	N	1973	53682
8171	S	D	E	N	1973	50581
8208	S	D	E	N	1973	50815
8209	S	D	E	N	1973	50903
8209	S	D	E	L	1974	62028
8209	S	D	E	N	1974	62028
8209	S	T	E	L	1974	62028
8209	S	T	E	N	1974	62028
8234	T	S	E	N	1972	87823
8271	S	D	E	N	1975	66627
8271	S	S	E	N	1975	96148
8271	T	D	E	N	1975	97322
8295	S	D	E	N	1973	52233
8299	T	D	E	N	1975	90115
8299	T	T	E	N	1975	90115
8312	S	D	E	N	1968	53358
8333	S	D	R	N	1971	53129
8333	S	D	E	N	1972	53130
8334	S	D	R	N	1971	53129
8334	S	D	E	N	1972	53130
8335	S	D	F	N	1970	84029
8335	S	D	R	N	1974	93465
8335	S	D	E	N	1974	93466
8338	S	D	E	N	1973	53415
8338	S	D	R	N	1970	55102
8338	S	D	E	N	1972	55103
8338	S	S	E	N	1974	58346
8338	S	D	E	N	1970	65825
8339	S	D	E	N	1973	53415
8340	D	S	E	N	1974	58346
8340	S	D	E	N	1973	53415
8340	S	D	R	N	1970	55102
8340	S	D	E	N	1972	55103
8340	S	S	E	N	1974	58346
8342	D	D	R	N	1973	55292
8342	D	D	R	N	1972	55492
106-8342	D	D	E	N	1974	59251
8344	S	D	E	N	1973	53415
8344	S	D	R	N	1970	55102
8344	S	D	E	N	1972	55103
8356	S	T	E	H	1972	55089
8356	S	T	E	N	1972	55089
8358	S	D	E	N	1969	62248
8364	S	D	E	N	1973	51890
8366	S	D	E	N	1973	51890
8391	S	D	R	N	1971	76489
8391	S	T	R	N	1971	76489
8391	S	D	E	N	1971	91568
8391	S	T	E	N	1971	91568
8393	S	D	E	N	1971	91568
8393	S	T	E	N	1971	91568
8394	S	D	R	N	1971	76489
8394	S	T	R	N	1971	76489
8394	S	D	E	N	1971	91568
8394	S	T	E	N	1971	91568
8438	S	T	E	N	1974	93998
8453	S	D	R	N	1970	55102
8453	S	D	E	N	1972	55103
8454	S	D	R	N	1970	55102
8454	S	D	E	N	1972	55103
8455	S	D	R	N	1970	55102
8455	S	D	E	N	1972	55103
8456	S	D	R	N	1970	55102
8456	S	D	E	N	1972	55103
8457	S	D	R	N	1970	55102
8457	S	D	E	N	1972	55103
8458	S	D	R	N	1970	55102
8458	S	D	E	N	1972	55103
8459	S	D	R	N	1970	55102
8459	S	D	E	N	1972	55103
8467	S	D	R	N	1968	61308
8467	S	D	E	N	1968	61309
8488	S	D	E	N	1973	62296
8522	S	D	R	N	1973	68031
8522	S	D	E	N	1973	68032
8528	D	D	R	N	1973	55295
8528	D	D	E	N	1974	59271
8529	S	D	R	N	1973	56861
8529	S	T	R	N	1973	56861
8529	S	D	E	N	1973	57295
8529	S	T	E	N	1973	57295
8531	S	S	E	N	1972	87823
8694	S	S	E	N	1971	87872
8694	S	D	E	N	1975	90841
8707	S	D	R	N	1973	68031
8707	S	D	E	N	1973	68032
8766	S	S	E	N	1975	90115
8766	S	S	E	N	1975	97322
8766	T	D	E	N	1975	97322
8766	T	T	E	N	1975	97322
108-0079	S	D	E	N	1974	54324
8044	S	D	R	N	1973	56317
109-0025	D	D	E	N	1973	50887
0025	D	D	E	N	1974	54573
0025	D	S	E	N	1974	54573
0025	S	D	E	L	1973	50887
0025	S	D	E	N	1973	50887
0025	S	D	E	L	1972	53158
0025	S	D	E	N	1972	53158
0025	S	S	E	N	1974	54573
0025	S	D	R	N	1974	60439
0025	S	D	E	N	1974	60440
8019	S	D	E	L	1974	62346
8019	S	D	E	N	1974	62346
8034	S	D	E	L	1972	53158
8034	S	D	E	N	1972	53158
8051	S	D	R	N	1974	60439
8051	S	D	E	N	1974	60440
8087	S	D	R	N	1973	67865
110-0011	D	D	E	N	1960	60561
0028	D	T	R	N	1975	90140
0028	D	T	E	N	1975	90141
0194	D	T	E	N	1974	57985
0194	D	T	R	N	1975	90140
0194	D	T	E	N	1975	90141
0194	T	T	E	N	1974	57985
8042	S	D	R	N	1970	67050
8042	T	D	R	N	1972	49981
8046	S	D	E	N	1972	49867
8082	S	D	R	N	1973	55807
8082	S	D	E	N	1973	56370
8083	S	D	E	N	1973	56370
8112	D	T	R	N	1975	90140
8112	D	T	E	N	1975	90141
8119	D	T	R	N	1975	90140
8119	D	T	E	N	1975	90141
8121	D	T	R	N	1975	90140
8121	D	T	E	N	1975	90141
8203	S	D	R	N	1973	55807
8204	S	D	R	N	1973	55807
8205	S	D	R	N	1973	55807
8205	S	D	E	N	1973	56370
111-0001	S	D	E	N	1973	53044
111-0008	A	D	E	N	1974	65585
0008	D	D	E	N	1974	58327
0008	D	T	E	N	1974	58327
0008	D	D	E	N	1974	58958
0008	D	S	E	N	1969	65350
0008	D	D	E	N	1969	75184
0008	D	D	R	N	1972	76547
0008	D	S	E	N	1962	87669
0008	D	S	E	N	1965	87703
0008	D	S	E	L	1971	87884
0008	D	S	E	N	1971	87884
0008	D	D	R	N	1974	89999
0008	D	D	E	N	1975	90000
0008	D	D	E	N	1972	91597
0008	S	S	E	N	1974	53748
0008	S	D	E	N	1974	58958
0008	S	D	E	N	1974	62030
0008	S	D	R	N	1973	62100
0008	S	D	E	N	1974	62277
0008	S	D	R	N	1973	67355
0008	S	D	E	N	1969	75184
0008	S	S	E	N	1973	86380
0008	S	S	E	N	1962	87669
0008	S	S	E	N	1965	87703
0008	S	S	E	N	1971	87884
0008	S	D	E	N	1973	89715
0008	T	D	R	N	1971	59188
0008	T	D	E	N	1971	59189
0008	T	S	E	N	1971	60965
0008	T	D	E	N	1974	65585
0008	T	D	R	N	1971	67719
0008	T	S	E	N	1969	87821
0021	D	D	E	N	1972	53081
0021	D	D	E	N	1974	53912
0021	D	D	E	N	1973	62246
0021	S	D	E	N	1974	53912
0021	S	D	E	N	1974	57752
0021	S	S	E	N	1973	63804
0021	S	S	R	N	1974	66446
0021	S	S	E	N	1974	66447
0021	S	D	O	N	1973	66876
0021	S	S	E	N	1971	87884
0021	T	D	E	N	1973	53529
0021	T	D	E	N	1974	58028
0021	T	S	E	N	1974	58028
0021	T	S	R	N	1974	66446
0021	T	S	E	N	1974	66447
0021	T	D	E	N	1975	90095
0029	S	D	R	N	1965	76401
0029	S	D	E	N	1965	91742
0050	D	D	E	N	1973	50558
0050	S	D	E	N	1973	50558
0050	S	D	E	N	1973	56335
8002	A	S	E	N	1971	49794
8002	D	D	R	N	1973	50080
8002	D	D	E	N	1973	51433
8002	D	D	E	L	1974	61358
8002	D	D	E	N	1974	61358
8002	D	D	R	N	1972	76506
8002	D	S	E	N	1962	87670
8002	D	D	E	N	1972	91529
8002	D	D	E	N	1975	94627
8002	D	S	E	N	1975	94627
8002	S	D	E	L	1973	51869
8002	S	D	E	N	1973	53561
8002	S	D	R	N	1973	55710
8002	S	D	E	N	1974	58330
8002	S	D	E	N	1961	64496
8002	S	T	E	N	1961	64497
8002	S	D	G	N	1954	66199
8002	S	D	R	N	1970	66484
8002	S	T	R	N	1970	66484
8002	S	S	E	N	1972	67891
8002	S	S	E	N	1962	87670
8002	S	S	E	L	1971	87884
8002	S	S	E	N	1971	87884
8002	S	S	E	N	1972	87889
8002	S	D	E	L	1976	103586
8002	T	S	E	N	1971	60965
8002	T	S	E	N	1969	87821
8007	S	D	E	N	1972	49833
8007	S	D	R	N	1973	55322
8007	S	D	E	N	1973	56333
8007	S	D	E	N	1974	59258
8007	S	D	E	N	1974	61190
8007	S	D	E	N	1974	61354
8007	S	S	E	N	1974	61354
8007	S	D	R	N	1965	76401
8007	S	D	E	N	1965	91742
8019	D	D	E	N	1972	53519
8021	A	D	E	N	1972	53266
8021	D	D	R	N	1972	61562
8021	D	D	E	N	1972	65913
8021	S	T	R	N	1973	55199
8021	S	T	E	N	1974	55200
8021	S	D	E	N	1971	67166
8021	S	S	E	N	1972	87824
8021	T	D	E	N	1972	53266
8026	D	D	E	N	1973	50087
8026	S	T	E	N	1973	55161
8026	T	S	E	N	1972	87889

Phys. State: **A.** Amorphous; **C.** Superconductive; **D.** Doped; **F.** Fibrous or Whisker; **G.** Gas; **I.** Ionized or Plasma; **L.** Liquid; **P.** Powder or Particle; **S.** Solid; **T.** Thin Film
Subject: **D.** Data; **E.** Experiment; **S.** Survey (Review, Compendium, etc.); **T.** Theory
Language: **E.** English; **F.** French; **G.** German; **O.** Other Languages; **R.** Russian
Temperature: **L.** Low (0 to 75K); **N.** Normal (75 to 1273K); **H.** High (above 1273K)

Substance Number	Phys. State	Subject	Language	Temperature	Year	EPIC Number
111-8031	D	D	R	N	1972	56940
8031	D	S	E	N	1972	87889
8031	S	S	E	N	1972	87889
8031	S	T	E	N	1975	90651
8031	T	D	R	N	1972	56940
8031	T	D	E	N	1971	63892
8065	S	D	E	N	1973	53293
8071	S	D	E	N	1974	54324
8074	T	D	E	N	1972	53416
8079	S	S	E	N	1969	68115
8108	S	S	E	N	1969	68115
8108	S	D	R	N	1976	101176
8108	S	D	E	N	1976	101886
8108	T	D	R	N	1976	101176
8108	T	D	E	N	1976	101886
8117	S	D	E	N	1972	63827
8121	S	D	E	N	1971	67166
8122	S	D	E	N	1971	67166
8127	S	S	E	N	1972	87824
8133	S	D	R	N	1973	56317
8134	S	D	R	N	1973	56317
8153	S	D	R	N	1970	67414
8154	S	D	R	N	1970	67423
8162	S	S	E	N	1972	87824
112-0011	S	S	E	N	1969	68271
0011	T	S	E	N	1971	60964
0021	S	D	E	N	1971	49789
0040	S	D	E	N	1974	61200
0040	S	S	E	N	1974	61200
0040	S	T	E	N	1974	61200
0402	S	S	E	N	1969	68271
0402	S	S	E	N	1975	101023
0402	T	S	E	N	1971	60964
8020	S	D	E	L	1974	54086
8020	S	D	E	N	1974	54086
8020	S	D	E	N	1974	60534
8020	S	S	E	L	1974	64457
8020	T	S	E	N	1971	60964
8025	D	D	R	N	1971	52298
8025	D	D	E	N	1971	52299
8025	D	D	E	L	1974	53599
8025	D	D	E	N	1976	101450
8025	S	D	E	L	1973	51870
8025	S	D	E	L	1973	51871
8025	S	D	R	N	1971	52298
8025	S	D	E	N	1971	52299
8025	S	D	E	N	1974	58432
8025	S	E	E	L	1958	59175
8025	S	E	E	N	1958	59175
8025	S	D	R	L	1974	63000
8025	S	T	R	L	1974	63000
8025	S	D	E	L	1974	63001
8025	S	T	E	L	1974	63001
8025	S	S	E	L	1974	64457
8025	S	S	E	N	1962	65962
8025	S	T	E	N	1962	65963
8025	S	S	E	N	1969	68271
8025	S	S	E	N	1967	68371
8025	T	D	R	N	1972	56941
8025	T	S	E	N	1971	60964
8025	T	D	E	N	1974	66692
8032	S	S	E	N	1972	87823
8083	S	S	E	L	1972	87823
8083	S	S	E	N	1972	87823
8084	S	S	E	L	1972	87823
8084	S	S	E	N	1972	87823
8085	S	S	E	N	1972	87823
8085	T	S	E	N	1972	87823
8087	S	S	E	L	1972	87823
8087	S	S	E	N	1972	87823
8087	T	D	O	N	1972	67652
114-0015	T	D	E	N	1973	56604
0017	D	D	E	N	1972	53463
0017	D	D	E	N	1973	57738
0017	D	D	E	N	1973	57739
0017	D	S	E	N	1971	87884
0017	S	D	E	N	1973	51524
0017	S	D	R	L	1973	51702
0017	S	D	R	N	1973	51702
0017	S	D	E	L	1973	52935
0017	S	D	E	N	1973	52935
0017	S	D	E	N	1972	52995
0017	S	D	E	N	1974	53915
0017	S	D	E	N	1973	55161
0017	S	D	R	N	1973	55305
0017	S	D	E	N	1973	56714
0017	S	D	E	N	1973	57568
0017	S	D	E	N	1973	57738
0017	S	S	E	N	1973	57738
0017	S	D	E	N	1974	59230
0017	S	D	E	N	1974	60304
0017	S	S	E	N	1974	60304
0017	S	D	R	N	1974	62528
0017	S	D	E	N	1974	64431
0017	S	S	O	N	1966	66022
0017	S	S	E	N	1967	66023
0017	S	D	R	N	1971	66936
0017	S	S	E	N	1962	87660
0017	S	S	E	N	1971	87884
114-0017	S	S	E	N	1963	98002
0017	T	E	E	N	1972	53463
0017	T	T	E	N	1972	53463
0017	T	D	R	N	1973	55327
0017	T	D	E	N	1971	55380
0017	T	D	E	N	1974	59263
0017	T	S	E	N	1971	60965
0017	T	S	E	N	1974	65107
0017	T	S	E	N	1971	87884
0017	T	S	E	N	1972	87889
0045	S	D	E	N	1973	51783
0078	T	S	E	N	1974	58028
8001	D	D	R	N	1973	50209
8001	D	D	E	N	1973	50210
8001	D	D	R	L	1973	54292
8001	D	D	R	N	1973	54292
8001	D	D	E	L	1973	54293
8001	D	D	E	N	1973	54293
8001	D	D	R	N	1965	61106
8001	D	D	E	N	1965	61107
8001	D	D	E	N	1973	61770
8001	D	D	E	N	1971	63892
8001	D	S	E	N	1975	87741
8001	D	S	E	N	1965	87781
8001	P	D	E	N	1971	63892
8001	S	D	R	L	1973	50061
8001	S	D	R	L	1973	50646
8001	S	D	R	N	1973	50646
8001	S	D	R	L	1973	50683
8001	S	D	E	N	1973	50683
8001	S	E	R	L	1973	50683
8001	S	D	E	N	1973	51212
8001	S	D	E	L	1973	51417
8001	S	D	R	N	1973	51558
8001	S	D	E	N	1973	51649
8001	S	D	R	N	1973	52162
8001	S	D	E	N	1973	52464
8001	S	D	R	L	1973	52543
8001	S	D	E	N	1973	52628
8001	S	D	E	L	1973	52928
8001	S	D	E	N	1973	52928
8001	S	E	E	L	1973	52928
8001	S	D	E	N	1972	53271
8001	S	S	E	N	1972	53299
8001	S	D	E	N	1974	53606
8001	S	D	E	L	1974	53677
8001	S	D	E	N	1973	53689
8001	S	D	E	N	1974	53735
8001	S	D	R	L	1973	54179
8001	S	D	R	N	1973	54179
8001	S	D	E	L	1973	54180
8001	S	D	E	N	1973	54180
8001	S	D	R	L	1972	54286
8001	S	D	E	L	1972	54287
8001	S	D	R	L	1973	54952
8001	S	D	R	N	1973	54952
8001	S	S	E	L	1973	55115
8001	S	D	R	N	1973	55319
8001	S	D	R	N	1973	55340
8001	S	D	R	N	1973	56687
8001	S	S	E	L	1973	56765
8001	S	S	E	N	1973	56765
8001	S	T	E	N	1974	57590
8001	S	D	E	N	1973	57892
8001	S	S	E	N	1974	58038
8001	S	E	E	L	1958	59175
8001	S	E	E	N	1958	59175
8001	S	D	E	L	1959	59176
8001	S	D	E	N	1974	59254
8001	S	D	E	N	1974	59278
8001	S	D	E	N	1974	60279
8001	S	D	E	N	1974	60287
8001	S	D	E	N	1974	60537
8001	S	D	E	L	1963	60566
8001	S	D	E	N	1963	60566
8001	S	D	E	N	1970	61493
8001	S	D	E	N	1969	62248
8001	S	D	R	N	1974	62427
8001	S	T	E	N	1956	62960
8001	S	D	R	L	1974	63036
8001	S	D	E	L	1974	63037
8001	S	S	E	N	1972	63955
8001	S	S	E	N	1974	64457
8001	S	S	E	L	1974	64464
8001	S	S	E	N	1974	64464
8001	S	D	E	N	1974	65239
8001	S	D	E	N	1974	65330
8001	S	D	E	N	1973	65539
8001	S	S	O	N	1966	66022
8001	S	S	E	N	1967	66023
8001	S	T	R	N	1970	66269
8001	S	D	R	L	1974	66732
8001	S	D	E	L	1975	66733
8001	S	S	E	N	1972	67891
8001	S	D	E	L	1975	68679
8001	S	S	E	N	1975	68679
8001	S	D	R	L	1973	71670
8001	S	S	E	N	1960	75859
8001	S	D	R	N	1971	76472
8001	S	S	R	N	1971	76472
8001	S	D	E	L	1973	82405
114-8001	S	D	E	L	1975	86751
8001	S	D	R	N	1975	86863
8001	S	D	E	N	1975	86864
8001	S	D	E	L	1969	87324
8001	S	D	E	N	1969	87324
8001	S	S	E	L	1963	87679
8001	S	S	E	N	1963	87679
8001	S	S	E	L	1965	87781
8001	S	S	E	N	1965	87781
8001	S	S	E	L	1971	87884
8001	S	S	E	N	1971	87884
8001	S	S	E	N	1972	87889
8001	S	D	E	N	1975	90111
8001	S	T	E	N	1975	90111
8001	S	D	E	N	1975	90868
8001	S	D	E	N	1971	91496
8001	S	S	E	N	1971	91496
8001	S	D	E	N	1975	101019
8001	S	D	R	L	1975	101629
8001	S	T	R	L	1975	101629
8001	S	D	E	L	1975	101630
8001	S	T	E	L	1975	101630
8001	T	D	O	N	1972	49819
8001	T	D	E	N	1972	53299
8001	T	S	E	N	1972	53299
8001	T	D	E	N	1972	53369
8001	T	S	E	N	1973	53451
8001	T	D	R	N	1972	56945
8001	T	T	E	N	1973	57272
8001	T	D	E	N	1973	57897
8001	T	S	E	L	1971	60965
8001	T	S	E	N	1971	60965
8001	T	D	E	N	1971	62260
8001	T	D	E	N	1971	63892
8001	T	D	R	N	1971	67337
8001	T	S	E	N	1965	87781
8001	T	S	E	N	1969	87821
8011	L	D	R	N	1973	51406
8011	L	D	E	N	1973	51407
8012	D	D	R	N	1972	51988
8012	S	S	E	N	1962	87661
8065	S	D	E	N	1972	63827
116-0017	S	S	E	L	1967	75838
8028	S	S	E	N	1973	56765
119-0001	S	D	R	N	1967	53069
0001	S	D	E	N	1972	53070
0001	S	D	E	N	1975	90460
0002	S	D	E	H	1970	60090
0002	S	S	E	N	1969	68271
0002	S	S	E	N	1969	87723
0008	D	T	R	N	1975	90140
0008	D	T	E	N	1975	90141
0008	S	S	E	N	1969	49679
0008	S	D	E	H	1971	49788
0010	S	T	E	N	1972	67192
8002	D	S	E	N	1962	87672
8002	S	D	E	N	1972	53413
8002	S	S	E	N	1962	87672
8009	S	S	E	N	1962	87662
8026	S	D	R	N	1973	50355
8026	S	D	E	N	1973	50356
8084	D	S	E	N	1969	75843
8084	S	S	E	N	1969	75843
8084	S	D	E	N	1975	90460
8101	S	D	E	N	1975	90460
8109	S	D	E	N	1967	85908
120-0001	D	S	E	N	1970	75905
0001	D	T	R	N	1975	90140
0001	D	T	E	N	1975	90141
0001	S	S	E	N	1969	49679
0001	S	D	E	H	1971	49788
0001	S	D	E	N	1971	49791
0001	S	D	E	N	1975	62674
0001	S	S	E	N	1962	69937
0004	S	D	E	H	1973	55117
0004	S	D	E	N	1973	55117
0004	S	D	E	N	1973	57844
0004	S	S	E	N	1966	87721
0106	S	D	E	N	1974	54324
0140	S	D	R	N	1967	53069
0140	S	D	E	N	1972	53070
8042	S	S	E	N	1966	87721
8079	S	D	R	N	1973	52563
8079	S	D	E	N	1973	57788
8136	S	D	R	N	1971	90517
8147	S	S	E	N	1966	87721
8147	S	S	E	N	1972	87886
8151	S	S	E	N	1966	87721
122-0003	S	D	E	N	1971	49789
0004	S	D	E	N	1971	49789
0005	S	D	E	N	1964	60562
0005	S	S	E	N	1964	60562
0005	S	D	E	H	1975	88237
0008	S	D	E	N	1974	62048
0009	A	D	E	N	1973	51026
0009	D	D	E	N	1973	52781
0009	D	D	E	N	1973	57725

Phys. State: **A.** Amorphous; **C.** Superconductive; **D.** Doped; **F.** Fibrous or Whisker; **G.** Gas; **I.** Ionized or Plasma; **L.** Liquid; **P.** Powder or Particle; **S.** Solid; **T.** Thin Film
Subject: **D.** Data; **E.** Experiment; **S.** Survey (Review, Compendium, etc.); **T.** Theory
Language: **E.** English; **F.** French; **G.** German; **O.** Other Languages; **R.** Russian
Temperature: **L.** Low (0 to 75K); **N.** Normal (75 to 1273K); **H.** High (above 1273K)

Substance Number	Phys. State	Subject	Language	Temperature	Year	EPIC Number
122-0014	S	S	E	N	1972	53110
0014	S	D	E	N	1972	53261
0014	S	S	E	N	1972	53261
0016	D	D	R	N	1974	63046
0016	D	T	R	N	1974	63046
0016	D	D	E	N	1975	63047
0016	D	T	E	N	1975	63047
0016	D	D	R	N	1971	76496
0016	D	D	E	N	1971	91580
0016	S	S	E	N	1971	87881
0017	S	D	E	H	1974	55261
0017	T	D	E	N	1971	62230
0017	T	D	E	N	1973	63510
0023	D	D	R	N	1973	55899
0023	D	D	R	N	1973	57249
0023	D	D	E	N	1975	64818
0023	D	S	E	L	1963	87709
0023	D	S	E	N	1963	87709
0023	S	S	E	N	1969	68271
0023	S	S	E	L	1963	87709
0023	S	S	E	N	1963	87709
0023	S	S	E	N	1975	92849
0023	T	D	R	N	1973	51315
0023	T	D	R	N	1973	51345
0023	T	D	E	N	1973	53848
0023	T	D	R	N	1973	55899
0023	T	S	E	N	1971	60964
0023	T	D	E	N	1975	92849
0030	D	D	E	N	1975	65497
0030	S	D	E	N	1975	65497
0031	S	D	R	N	1974	66728
0031	S	E	R	N	1974	66728
0031	S	T	R	N	1974	66728
0031	S	D	E	N	1975	66729
0031	S	E	E	N	1975	66729
0031	S	T	E	N	1975	66729
0031	S	D	R	H	1974	66744
0031	S	D	R	N	1974	66744
0031	S	T	R	H	1974	66744
0031	S	T	R	N	1974	66744
0031	S	D	E	H	1975	66745
0031	S	D	E	N	1975	66745
0031	S	T	E	H	1975	66745
0031	S	T	E	N	1975	66745
0031	S	D	R	H	1972	76508
0031	S	D	R	N	1972	76508
0031	S	D	E	H	1972	91530
0031	S	D	E	N	1972	91530
0031	S	S	E	N	1975	96477
0050	S	D	R	N	1972	50688
0050	S	D	R	N	1972	50690
0050	S	S	E	N	1969	68115
0050	T	D	R	N	1975	90164
0050	T	T	R	N	1975	90164
0050	T	D	E	N	1975	90165
0050	T	T	E	N	1975	90165
0053	D	D	E	N	1973	57908
0053	S	S	E	N	1969	68115
0053	S	S	E	N	1966	87833
0053	T	S	E	N	1969	68115
0053	T	S	E	N	1966	87833
0112	P	S	E	N	1971	87881
0112	S	S	E	N	1972	53110
0112	S	D	E	N	1972	53261
0112	S	S	E	N	1972	53261
0112	S	D	E	L	1973	60610
0112	S	D	E	N	1973	60610
0112	S	S	E	N	1971	87881
0112	T	S	E	N	1973	60610
0112	T	S	E	N	1971	87881
0314	S	S	E	N	1969	49679
0314	S	D	E	N	1972	53102
0314	S	E	E	N	1972	53102
0425	S	D	E	N	1975	80497
8044	T	D	E	N	1972	53416
8045	S	S	E	N	1971	66193
8088	S	S	E	N	1971	87881
8108	S	D	E	N	1975	80497
8110	S	D	E	N	1975	80497
8111	S	D	E	N	1975	80497
123-0003	D	D	R	N	1971	63462
0003	D	D	E	N	1971	65164
0003	D	D	E	N	1974	90579
0003	S	D	E	L	1972	53200
0003	S	D	E	N	1972	53200
0003	S	S	E	L	1972	53200
0003	S	S	E	N	1972	53200
0003	S	D	E	N	1972	53271
0003	S	D	E	N	1973	56346
0003	S	D	E	N	1974	60270
0003	S	S	E	N	1972	67891
0003	S	S	E	L	1969	68115
0003	S	S	E	N	1969	68115
0003	S	S	E	L	1966	68361
0003	S	S	E	N	1966	68361
0003	T	D	R	N	1971	63462
0003	T	D	E	N	1971	65164
0003	T	S	E	N	1966	68361
0003	T	D	E	N	1974	90579
0003	T	S	E	N	1975	94588

Substance Number	Phys. State	Subject	Language	Temperature	Year	EPIC Number
123-0032	S	D	E	N	1973	52054
0032	S	S	E	N	1975	94550
0042	S	S	E	N	1975	94550
0048	S	D	R	N	1972	55490
8004	S	D	E	N	1973	52053
8013	S	D	E	N	1969	85351
8017	S	D	E	L	1973	52462
8017	S	D	E	N	1973	52462
8017	S	D	E	N	1973	52463
8017	S	D	E	L	1974	53729
8017	S	D	E	N	1974	53729
8017	S	S	E	L	1974	53729
8017	S	S	E	N	1974	53729
8017	S	E	E	L	1958	59175
8017	S	E	E	N	1958	59175
8017	S	S	E	L	1969	68115
8017	S	S	E	N	1969	68115
8017	S	S	E	L	1962	87674
8017	S	S	E	N	1962	87674
8017	S	S	E	N	1972	87824
8018	D	D	E	N	1972	49874
8018	D	S	E	N	1973	53853
8018	D	D	R	N	1972	62320
8018	D	D	E	N	1974	62321
8018	D	S	R	N	1972	62719
8018	D	T	R	N	1972	62719
8018	D	S	E	N	1973	65315
8018	D	T	E	N	1973	65315
8018	D	S	E	L	1970	68114
8018	D	S	E	N	1970	68114
8018	S	D	E	N	1973	53853
8018	S	S	E	N	1973	53853
8018	S	D	E	N	1973	55157
8018	S	D	E	N	1972	59070
8018	S	S	E	N	1972	59070
8018	S	D	R	N	1968	60749
8018	S	D	E	N	1974	60750
8018	S	S	E	L	1974	61383
8018	S	D	E	N	1971	62195
8018	S	S	E	N	1974	64457
8018	S	S	E	L	1970	68114
8018	S	S	E	N	1970	68114
8018	S	S	E	L	1969	68115
8018	S	S	E	N	1969	68115
8018	S	D	E	L	1973	68901
8018	S	D	E	N	1973	68901
8018	S	S	E	L	1962	87671
8018	S	S	E	N	1962	87671
8018	S	S	E	N	1972	87824
8018	T	D	O	N	1971	49563
8018	T	D	R	N	1972	49571
8018	T	D	R	N	1974	58894
8018	T	S	E	N	1968	59520
8018	T	D	E	N	1974	61179
8018	T	D	E	N	1972	61768
8018	T	S	E	N	1972	61768
8018	T	D	R	N	1973	62729
8018	T	S	R	N	1973	62729
8018	T	D	E	N	1974	64883
8018	T	D	E	N	1973	65325
8018	T	S	E	N	1973	65325
8018	T	S	E	N	1970	68114
8018	T	D	E	N	1973	68901
8018	T	D	R	N	1974	93120
8018	T	D	E	N	1975	93121
8039	S	D	E	L	1973	52462
8039	S	D	E	N	1973	52462
8039	S	D	E	N	1973	52463
8039	S	D	E	L	1974	53729
8039	S	D	E	N	1974	53729
8039	S	S	E	N	1972	87824
8039	T	D	E	N	1972	53321
8039	T	D	E	N	1972	53324
8039	T	D	E	N	1973	53434
8050	T	S	E	N	1972	87824
8051	D	D	E	N	1973	53423
8051	D	D	E	N	1973	57597
8051	D	S	E	N	1972	87824
8051	S	D	E	N	1972	53271
8051	S	S	E	N	1972	53321
8051	S	S	E	N	1972	53324
8051	S	D	R	N	1973	55823
8051	S	D	E	N	1974	60369
8051	S	D	E	N	1974	60382
8051	S	D	E	L	1974	61383
8051	S	D	E	N	1974	61383
8051	S	S	E	L	1974	61383
8051	S	D	E	N	1973	65985
8051	S	S	E	N	1970	68114
8051	S	S	E	L	1972	87824
8051	S	S	E	N	1972	87824
8051	S	D	E	N	1974	88465
8051	S	D	R	N	1975	94942
8051	S	D	E	N	1975	95895
8051	T	D	E	N	1972	53303
8051	T	S	E	N	1972	53321
8051	T	S	E	N	1972	53324
8051	T	D	E	L	1974	60283
8051	T	D	E	N	1974	60283
8051	T	D	E	N	1973	68901
8051	T	D	R	N	1974	80749

Substance Number	Phys. State	Subject	Language	Temperature	Year	EPIC Number
123-8051	T	S	E	N	1972	87824
8051	T	D	E	N	1974	88464
8051	T	D	E	N	1974	88465
8051	T	D	E	N	1974	95251
8066	S	D	E	N	1972	63827
8070	S	D	E	N	1969	85351
8074	S	S	E	N	1972	87824
8074	T	S	E	N	1972	87824
126-0001	S	S	E	N	1969	68115
0001	S	S	E	N	1972	87824
0002	S	D	E	N	1973	57112
0004	S	D	E	N	1974	58804
0004	S	S	E	N	1974	58804
0005	D	D	E	N	1974	60751
0005	D	S	E	N	1963	87711
0005	S	S	E	N	1975	66683
0005	S	S	E	N	1969	68271
0005	S	S	E	N	1963	87711
0005	S	S	E	N	1966	87712
0005	T	S	E	N	1971	60964
0005	T	S	E	N	1966	87712
0014	S	D	R	N	1973	51973
0022	S	D	R	N	1967	53069
0022	S	D	E	N	1972	53070
0037	S	D	R	N	1967	53069
0037	S	D	E	N	1972	53070
0038	S	D	R	N	1967	53069
0038	S	D	E	N	1972	53070
0038	S	D	E	N	1974	58804
0038	S	S	E	N	1974	58804
0038	S	D	E	L	1972	70535
0038	S	D	E	N	1972	70535
8026	S	D	E	N	1964	61307
8030	S	S	E	N	1974	55249
8032	D	D	R	N	1970	55104
8032	D	D	E	N	1972	55105
8032	D	D	G	N	1976	101451
8032	S	D	R	N	1972	62298
8032	S	D	E	N	1975	96857
8032	S	D	E	N	1972	100970
8035	S	S	E	N	1969	68115
8037	D	D	E	N	1973	51543
8037	D	D	O	N	1973	58234
8037	D	S	E	N	1970	68114
8037	S	D	E	N	1973	51543
8037	S	S	E	L	1974	61383
8037	S	S	E	L	1970	68114
8037	S	S	E	N	1970	68114
8037	S	S	E	N	1969	68115
8037	S	D	R	N	1974	86780
8037	S	S	E	N	1972	87824
8037	S	D	E	N	1974	90054
8037	T	D	R	N	1972	49570
8037	T	D	E	N	1972	53416
8041	S	S	E	N	1967	66157
8047	S	S	E	N	1967	66157
8049	D	S	E	N	1972	87823
8049	S	S	E	N	1972	87823
8052	D	D	E	N	1971	53243
8052	D	D	E	N	1974	53923
8052	D	D	E	L	1974	60751
8052	D	D	E	N	1974	60751
8052	D	S	E	N	1963	68313
8052	S	D	E	N	1971	53243
8052	S	D	E	N	1973	53346
8052	S	S	R	N	1972	53547
8052	S	S	E	N	1973	53548
8052	S	T	E	N	1973	57391
8052	S	S	E	N	1969	68271
8052	S	S	E	N	1963	68313
8052	S	D	E	N	1973	88610
8052	T	S	E	N	1971	60964
8055	S	S	E	N	1969	68115
8059	D	D	R	N	1973	52563
8059	D	D	E	N	1973	57788
8059	D	S	E	N	1969	75843
8059	S	D	R	N	1973	52563
8059	S	D	E	N	1973	57788
8060	S	D	E	N	1973	50910
8060	S	D	E	N	1973	53415
8068	S	S	E	N	1972	87824
8069	S	D	E	N	1972	52964
8074	S	D	E	N	1969	62248
8092	S	D	E	N	1974	58804
8092	S	S	E	N	1974	58804
8101	S	S	E	N	1969	75843
8108	S	S	E	N	1967	66157
8135	S	D	R	N	1971	90517
8136	S	S	E	N	1972	87824
8146	L	D	E	N	1969	75372
127-8002	L	D	E	N	1972	49460
8002	L	D	E	N	1974	86452
8004	D	D	E	N	1975	68606
8004	S	D	E	N	1968	53357
8004	S	S	E	N	1974	53748
8004	S	T	E	N	1973	57391
8004	S	S	E	N	1969	68271
8004	S	S	E	N	1962	87666
8004	T	S	E	N	1971	60964

Phys. State: **A.** Amorphous; **C.** Superconductive; **D.** Doped; **F.** Fibrous or Whisker; **G.** Gas; **I.** Ionized or Plasma; **L.** Liquid; **P.** Powder or Particle; **S.** Solid; **T.** Thin Film
Subject: **D.** Data; **E.** Experiment; **S.** Survey (Review, Compendium, etc.); **T.** Theory
Language: **E.** English; **F.** French; **G.** German; **O.** Other Languages; **R.** Russian
Temperature: **L.** Low (0 to 75K); **N.** Normal (75 to 1273K); **H.** High (above 1273K)

Substance Number	Phys. State	Subject	Language	Temperature	Year	EPIC Number
127-8024	L	D	E	N	1969	75372
8024	L	S	E	N	1969	75372
132-8001	S	D	E	L	1974	54071
8001	S	D	E	N	1974	54071

Phys. State: **A.** Amorphous; **C.** Superconductive; **D.** Doped; **F.** Fibrous or Whisker; **G.** Gas; **I.** Ionized or Plasma; **L.** Liquid; **P.** Powder or Particle; **S.** Solid; **T.** Thin Film
Subject: **D.** Data; **E.** Experiment; **S.** Survey (Review, Compendium, etc.); **T.** Theory
Language: **E.** English; **F.** French; **G.** German; **O.** Other Languages; **R.** Russian
Temperature: **L.** Low (0 to 75K); **N.** Normal (75 to 1273K); **H.** High (above 1273K)

Chapter 16 Magnetomechanical Properties

Substance Number	Phys. State	Subject	Language	Temperature	Year	EPIC Number
100-8003	S	E	E	N	1974	54352
8003	S	T	E	N	1974	54352
8009	S	D	R	N	1973	55040
8009	S	T	R	N	1973	55040
8009	S	D	E	N	1974	55041
8009	S	T	E	N	1974	55041
8009	S	T	R	N	1973	57828
8009	S	T	E	N	1974	57829
8009	S	S	E	N	1974	66343
8010	D	T	E	N	1973	58240
8010	S	S	E	N	1972	53175
8010	S	S	E	N	1974	66343
8010	T	S	E	N	1972	53175
8015	S	S	E	N	1972	53175
8015	S	T	R	N	1974	66740
8015	S	T	E	N	1975	66741
8015	T	S	E	N	1972	53175
8049	S	T	E	N	1974	91408
8051	S	T	E	N	1974	91408
8058	S	S	E	N	1974	66343
8058	S	T	E	N	1974	66343
8058	S	E	R	N	1973	67920
8058	S	E	E	N	1973	67921
8060	S	S	E	N	1974	66343
8060	T	D	E	N	1974	90426
8060	T	E	E	N	1974	90426
8060	T	T	E	N	1974	90426
102-0086	S	D	E	N	1973	55151
0369	D	D	E	L	1974	57305
0369	D	D	E	N	1974	57305
8058	S	D	R	N	1973	52884
8058	S	D	E	N	1974	52885
8090	S	D	E	N	1973	55151
8098	S	D	E	L	1973	50818
8098	S	D	E	N	1973	50818
8114	T	D	E	N	1973	51131
8115	T	D	E	N	1973	51131
8118	S	D	R	N	1973	50742
8118	S	D	E	N	1973	79081
8238	S	D	E	N	1973	55151
8334	P	D	E	N	1974	70390
8408	S	D	R	N	1974	90672
8431	S	D	E	N	1974	91413
8491	D	D	E	N	1975	68615
8491	D	T	E	N	1975	68615
8491	T	D	E	N	1975	68615
8491	T	T	E	N	1975	68615
104-0007	S	S	E	N	1972	102094
8016	S	T	E	N	1974	60523
8016	T	D	E	N	1973	51653
8016	T	D	E	N	1973	55864
8055	S	D	E	N	1974	54329
8106	S	D	E	H	1973	50445
8106	S	D	E	N	1974	53860
8162	S	D	E	N	1974	56607
8162	S	D	R	N	1974	60467
8162	S	D	E	N	1974	60468
8162	S	S	R	N	1974	60489
8162	S	S	E	N	1974	60490
8225	S	D	E	N	1974	54319
8227	S	D	E	N	1974	54321
8229	S	D	E	N	1974	54329
8230	S	D	E	N	1974	54329
8240	S	D	R	N	1973	55219
8240	S	D	E	N	1974	55220
8241	S	D	R	N	1973	55219
8241	S	D	E	N	1974	55220
8307	S	D	R	N	1972	56950
8308	S	D	R	N	1972	56950
8309	S	D	R	N	1972	56950
8350	D	D	E	N	1971	66264
8350	S	D	E	N	1971	66264
106-0006	S	E	E	N	1974	54352
0046	S	T	E	N	1973	51159
0058	S	D	R	N	1973	56894
0081	S	S	E	N	1974	63748
0363	S	S	E	N	1974	54075
8123	S	S	E	N	1973	51144
8123	S	D	R	N	1973	55473
8123	S	T	R	N	1973	57828
8123	S	T	E	N	1974	57829
8123	S	D	R	N	1974	63014
8123	S	D	E	N	1974	63015
8123	S	D	E	L	1975	63274
8123	S	D	E	N	1975	63274
8123	S	S	E	L	1975	63274
8123	S	S	E	N	1975	63274
8149	S	D	E	N	1973	51197
8157	S	D	R	N	1973	52884
8157	S	D	E	N	1974	52885
8161	S	D	R	N	1973	50257
8161	S	D	E	N	1973	50258
106-8162	S	D	R	L	1973	50301
8162	S	D	R	N	1973	50301
8162	S	D	E	L	1973	50302
8162	S	D	E	N	1973	50302
8163	S	D	R	N	1973	50325
8163	S	D	E	N	1973	50326
8190	P	D	E	N	1974	70390
8190	S	S	E	N	1973	51144
8190	S	D	R	N	1974	87310
8190	S	D	E	N	1975	87311
8190	S	D	E	L	1974	90524
8190	S	D	E	N	1974	90524
8198	S	D	R	N	1973	50660
8198	S	D	R	N	1971	58543
8199	S	D	R	N	1973	50660
8204	S	D	E	L	1973	55279
8204	S	D	E	N	1973	55279
8204	S	D	R	L	1974	60423
8204	S	D	R	N	1974	60423
8204	S	S	R	L	1974	60423
8204	S	S	R	N	1974	60423
8204	S	D	E	L	1974	60424
8204	S	D	E	N	1974	60424
8204	S	S	E	L	1974	60424
8204	S	S	E	N	1974	60424
8217	S	D	E	N	1974	90283
8218	S	D	R	N	1974	60423
8218	S	S	R	L	1974	60423
8218	S	S	R	N	1974	60423
8218	S	D	E	N	1974	60424
8218	S	S	E	L	1974	60424
8218	S	S	E	N	1974	60424
8220	S	D	E	L	1973	51141
8220	S	D	E	N	1973	51141
8220	S	S	E	N	1973	51144
8221	S	D	R	N	1973	67849
8232	S	D	R	N	1974	52920
8232	S	D	E	N	1974	52921
8233	S	D	E	N	1973	51905
8291	S	D	E	N	1973	51905
8294	T	D	R	N	1972	49978
8312	D	D	E	N	1975	60962
8326	S	D	E	N	1973	52999
8326	S	D	E	N	1973	59290
8327	S	D	E	N	1973	52999
8327	S	D	E	N	1973	59290
8360	S	D	E	L	1973	55279
8360	S	D	E	N	1973	55279
8369	S	D	R	N	1973	50658
8370	S	D	R	N	1973	50658
8371	S	D	R	N	1973	50658
8372	S	D	R	N	1973	50658
8373	S	D	R	N	1973	50658
8403	S	D	E	N	1974	60348
8403	S	D	E	N	1974	61161
8426	S	S	E	N	1974	54319
8439	S	D	R	N	1973	55030
8439	S	D	E	N	1974	55031
8486	S	T	E	N	1974	57998
8510	T	D	E	N	1973	62748
8525	S	D	R	L	1974	60423
8525	S	D	R	N	1974	60423
8525	S	S	R	L	1974	60423
8525	S	S	R	N	1974	60423
8525	S	D	E	L	1974	60424
8525	S	D	E	N	1974	60424
8525	S	S	E	L	1974	60424
8525	S	S	E	N	1974	60424
8526	S	D	R	N	1974	60423
8526	S	S	R	L	1974	60423
8526	S	S	R	N	1974	60423
8526	S	D	E	N	1974	60424
8526	S	S	E	L	1974	60424
8526	S	S	E	N	1974	60424
8527	S	D	R	N	1974	60423
8527	S	S	R	L	1974	60423
8527	S	S	R	N	1974	60423
8527	S	D	E	N	1974	60424
8527	S	S	E	L	1974	60424
8527	S	S	E	N	1974	60424
8547	D	D	E	N	1974	91413
8547	S	D	R	N	1974	87310
8547	S	S	R	N	1974	87310
8547	S	D	E	N	1975	87311
8547	S	S	E	N	1975	87311
8547	S	D	E	N	1974	91412
8547	S	D	E	N	1974	91413
8549	S	D	O	N	1975	90101
8574	S	D	R	N	1973	57361
8597	S	D	E	L	1974	90524
8597	S	D	E	N	1974	90524
8627	S	D	E	N	1971	57152
8628	S	D	E	N	1971	57153
8640	T	D	R	N	1973	90667
8684	S	T	E	N	1974	90301
106-8688	S	D	E	L	1974	90524
8688	S	D	E	N	1974	90524
8688	S	D	E	N	1974	91411
8724	S	D	E	N	1974	91411
8725	S	D	E	N	1974	91411
8726	S	D	E	N	1974	91412
8727	S	D	E	N	1974	91412
108-0087	D	D	R	N	1974	65375
0087	D	D	E	N	1975	65376
8001	S	D	E	L	1974	58010
8001	S	D	E	N	1974	58010
8007	S	D	R	N	1975	86841
8007	S	D	E	N	1975	86842
8009	S	D	E	N	1973	51035
8010	S	D	E	N	1973	51153
8010	S	T	E	N	1973	51486
8010	S	D	E	N	1974	61161
8011	S	D	E	N	1973	51153
109-0025	S	T	E	L	1973	52962
0025	S	T	E	L	1972	53260
0025	S	D	E	L	1974	54122
0025	S	T	E	L	1974	54122
0025	S	T	E	N	1974	54122
8001	S	D	E	L	1974	58010
8001	S	D	E	N	1974	58010
8011	S	D	R	N	1975	86841
8011	S	D	E	N	1975	86842
8013	L	D	E	N	1973	50586
8013	T	D	E	N	1973	50586
8015	S	D	E	N	1973	51153
8015	S	T	E	N	1973	51486
8015	S	D	E	N	1974	61161
8017	L	D	E	N	1973	50586
8017	T	D	E	N	1973	49532
8017	T	D	E	N	1973	50586
8019	S	T	E	L	1973	52962
8019	S	T	E	L	1972	53260
8020	S	T	E	L	1973	52962
8020	S	T	E	L	1972	53260
8020	T	T	E	L	1974	58008
8021	S	T	E	L	1973	52962
8022	S	D	E	L	1973	51035
8023	T	D	E	N	1973	51124
8065	D	T	E	N	1973	58240
8065	S	D	R	N	1975	86841
8065	S	D	E	N	1975	86842
8077	S	T	E	N	1973	58240
110-0011	S	D	E	N	1973	51200
0011	S	E	E	N	1973	51200
0011	S	T	R	N	1972	58792
0020	D	D	E	L	1974	58055
0020	D	D	E	L	1973	64537
0023	D	D	E	L	1973	64537
0024	S	S	E	N	1974	58015
0025	D	D	E	N	1974	58435
0025	S	D	E	N	1974	58435
0025	S	D	E	N	1974	66053
0026	S	D	E	L	1972	49879
0026	S	D	E	N	1972	49879
0026	T	D	R	N	1973	90666
0028	S	S	E	N	1974	66343
0028	T	D	E	N	1973	51762
0194	D	D	R	L	1973	50301
0194	D	D	R	N	1973	50301
0194	D	D	E	L	1973	50302
0194	D	D	E	N	1973	50302
0194	D	D	F	N	1973	51780
0194	D	T	E	N	1973	52328
0194	D	T	R	N	1973	52328
0194	D	D	E	L	1973	52438
0194	D	D	E	N	1973	52438
0194	D	D	R	N	1973	55184
0194	D	T	R	N	1973	55184
0194	D	D	E	N	1974	55185
0194	D	T	E	N	1974	55185
0194	S	D	E	N	1972	49583
0194	S	T	E	N	1973	52706
0194	S	D	R	N	1973	55184
0194	S	D	E	N	1974	55185
0194	S	D	R	N	1974	58096
0194	S	D	E	N	1974	58097
0194	S	D	R	N	1974	60467
0194	S	D	E	N	1974	60468
0194	S	S	E	N	1974	66343
0194	S	D	R	N	1975	86841
0194	S	S	R	N	1975	86841
0194	S	D	E	N	1975	86842
0194	S	S	E	N	1975	86842
0195	S	D	R	N	1975	86841
0195	S	D	E	N	1975	86842
0199	S	D	R	N	1975	86841
0199	S	D	E	N	1975	86842

Phys. State: **A.** Amorphous; **C.** Superconductive; **D.** Doped; **F.** Fibrous or Whisker; **G.** Gas; **I.** Ionized or Plasma; **L.** Liquid; **P.** Powder or Particle; **S.** Solid; **T.** Thin Film
Subject: **D.** Data; **E.** Experiment; **S.** Survey (Review, Compendium, etc.); **T.** Theory
Language: **E.** English; **F.** French; **G.** German; **O.** Other Languages; **R.** Russian
Temperature: **L.** Low (0 to 75K); **N.** Normal (75 to 1273K); **H.** High (above 1273K)

Substance Number	Phys. State	Subject	Language	Temperature	Year	EPIC Number
110-0200	S	D	E	N	1973	51656
0200	S	D	E	N	1974	60341
0245	S	D	R	N	1975	86841
0245	S	D	E	N	1975	86842
0369	D	D	R	N	1974	52920
0369	D	D	E	N	1974	52921
0369	S	D	R	N	1974	63014
0369	S	D	E	N	1974	63015
0369	S	T	R	N	1974	66740
0369	S	T	E	N	1975	66741
8014	S	E	E	N	1974	64329
8015	S	D	E	N	1973	52700
8038	L	D	E	N	1973	49714
8038	T	D	E	N	1973	49505
8038	T	D	E	N	1973	49714
8038	T	T	E	N	1974	60521
8042	T	D	R	N	1972	49978
8042	T	D	R	N	1973	56325
8042	T	D	R	N	1973	57816
8042	T	D	E	N	1974	57817
8042	T	D	R	N	1972	58194
8042	T	T	R	N	1973	90669
8044	L	D	E	N	1973	50586
8044	T	D	E	N	1973	50586
8044	T	D	E	N	1974	58000
8044	T	D	E	N	1974	60392
8046	D	D	R	N	1973	90667
8046	S	D	E	L	1973	51166
8046	S	D	E	L	1973	51196
8046	S	D	E	N	1973	51196
8046	S	T	E	N	1973	51196
8046	S	D	E	N	1971	57171
8046	T	D	R	N	1973	90667
8047	S	D	E	N	1973	54906
8051	S	D	E	L	1974	60302
8051	S	D	E	N	1974	60302
8051	S	S	E	L	1974	60302
8051	S	S	E	N	1974	60302
8053	S	T	E	N	1973	51198
8057	S	D	R	N	1974	63080
8057	S	S	R	N	1974	63080
8057	S	T	R	N	1974	63080
8057	S	D	E	N	1975	63081
8057	S	S	E	N	1975	63081
8057	S	T	E	N	1975	63081
8057	S	D	R	N	1975	86841
8057	S	D	E	N	1975	86842
8058	S	D	E	L	1973	50528
8058	S	D	E	N	1973	50528
8058	S	T	E	N	1973	50528
8058	T	D	E	N	1975	68615
8058	T	T	E	N	1975	68615
8063	T	D	R	N	1971	50663
8067	S	D	E	N	1973	51153
8067	S	T	E	N	1973	51486
8067	S	D	E	N	1974	61161
8067	S	D	E	N	1974	62036
8067	S	T	E	N	1974	62036
8067	S	S	E	N	1975	68711
8068	S	D	E	N	1973	51153
8068	S	T	E	N	1973	51486
8068	S	D	E	N	1974	61161
8068	S	D	E	N	1974	62036
8068	S	T	E	N	1974	62036
8068	S	S	E	N	1975	68711
8069	S	D	E	N	1973	51153
8069	S	T	E	N	1973	51486
8070	S	D	E	L	1973	51166
8073	S	D	G	N	1972	52548
8090	S	D	R	N	1973	57361
8092	S	D	E	N	1974	60348
8092	S	D	E	N	1974	61161
8098	S	D	E	N	1974	57999
8098	T	D	E	N	1974	53733
8098	T	D	E	N	1974	60392
8101	T	D	E	N	1973	52790
8102	T	D	E	N	1973	52790
8103	S	D	R	N	1974	60467
8103	S	D	E	N	1974	60468
8112	D	D	F	N	1973	57933
8112	S	D	R	N	1973	50742
8112	S	D	E	N	1973	79081
8112	T	D	R	N	1973	55897
8112	T	D	R	N	1973	56302
8121	T	D	E	N	1973	51762
8127	S	D	R	N	1973	50658
8133	S	D	E	N	1974	60348
8156	S	S	E	N	1973	60605
8163	S	D	E	N	1974	53594
8171	S	D	R	N	1974	58126
8171	S	D	E	N	1974	58127
8172	S	D	R	N	1974	58126
8172	S	D	E	N	1974	58127
8208	S	T	E	N	1974	58509
8224	S	S	E	N	1973	60605
8225	S	D	E	N	1974	58435
8232	S	E	E	N	1974	64329
8239	S	D	R	L	1973	52370
8239	S	D	R	N	1973	52370
8239	S	D	E	L	1974	63208
8239	S	D	E	N	1974	63208
110-8240	D	D	R	L	1973	52370
8240	D	D	R	N	1973	52370
8240	D	D	E	L	1974	63208
8240	D	D	E	N	1974	63208
8240	S	D	R	L	1973	52370
8240	S	D	R	N	1973	52370
8240	S	D	E	L	1974	63208
8240	S	D	E	N	1974	63208
8253	S	S	E	N	1974	66343
8259	S	D	R	N	1973	50742
8259	S	D	E	N	1973	79081
8272	S	D	E	N	1974	62036
8272	S	T	E	N	1974	62036
8272	S	D	E	L	1975	68711
8272	S	D	E	N	1975	68711
8272	S	E	E	L	1975	68711
8272	S	E	E	N	1975	68711
8273	S	D	R	N	1974	63080
8273	S	S	R	N	1974	63080
8273	S	T	R	N	1974	63080
8273	S	D	E	N	1975	63081
8273	S	S	E	N	1975	63081
8273	S	T	E	N	1975	63081
111-8002	D	D	E	N	1974	61358
8020	T	T	E	N	1974	60521
8106	S	D	E	L	1974	58010
8106	S	D	E	N	1974	58010
8138	S	D	E	L	1973	60609
8138	S	T	E	L	1973	60609
112-8008	S	D	E	L	1974	58010
8008	S	D	E	N	1974	58010
8020	S	D	E	L	1974	53611
8031	S	D	E	L	1973	51054
114-8078	S	D	E	N	1971	57154
118-8001	S	D	E	L	1974	58010
8001	S	D	E	N	1974	58010
119-0041	S	T	E	N	1971	57187
0041	S	D	E	L	1969	72658
0041	S	D	E	N	1969	72658
0041	S	E	E	L	1969	72658
0041	S	E	E	N	1969	72658
120-0001	S	T	R	N	1972	58792
122-0013	D	D	O	N	1972	49897
0013	S	D	O	N	1972	49897
0037	D	T	R	L	1973	57807
0037	D	T	E	L	1974	57808
0296	D	D	E	L	1974	57305
0296	D	D	E	N	1974	57305
8035	S	D	R	L	1974	63002
8035	S	T	R	N	1974	63002
8035	S	D	E	L	1974	63003
8035	S	T	E	L	1974	63003
8035	S	T	E	N	1974	63003
8038	D	D	E	L	1974	57305
8038	D	D	E	N	1974	57305
8068	S	D	F	L	1971	59041
8091	D	D	E	L	1974	57305
8091	D	D	E	N	1974	57305
123-0026	S	D	R	N	1971	54274
0026	S	T	R	N	1971	54274
0026	S	D	E	N	1972	54275
0026	S	T	E	N	1972	54275
8013	S	D	E	L	1974	58010
8013	S	D	E	N	1974	58010
8018	S	S	E	N	1970	68114
126-8001	S	D	E	L	1974	58010
8001	S	D	E	N	1974	58010
8010	S	D	E	L	1974	58010
8010	S	D	E	N	1974	58010
127-8001	S	D	E	L	1973	51054
8009	S	D	E	L	1973	52199
8009	S	D	E	N	1973	52199
133-8001	S	D	E	N	1971	57154

Phys. State: **A.** Amorphous; **C.** Superconductive; **D.** Doped; **F.** Fibrous or Whisker; **G.** Gas; **I.** Ionized or Plasma; **L.** Liquid; **P.** Powder or Particle; **S.** Solid; **T.** Thin Film
Subject: **D.** Data; **E.** Experiment; **S.** Survey (Review, Compendium, etc.); **T.** Theory
Language: **E.** English; **F.** French; **G.** German; **O.** Other Languages; **R.** Russian
Temperature: **L.** Low (0 to 75K); **N.** Normal (75 to 1273K); **H.** High (above 1273K)

Chapter 17 Magnetic Susceptibility

Substance Number	Phys. State	Subject	Language	Temperature	Year	EPIC Number
100-0045	S	S	E	N	1973	50656
0045	S	S	E	N	1972	51586
0055	A	T	E	N	1974	61357
0055	S	E	O	L	1970	49562
0055	S	E	O	N	1970	49562
0055	S	T	R	N	1974	60433
0055	S	T	E	N	1974	60434
0055	S	T	R	N	1972	60723
0055	S	T	E	N	1973	60724
0055	S	T	R	N	1972	60729
0055	S	T	E	N	1973	60730
0055	S	T	E	N	1974	61357
0055	S	S	E	L	1971	64456
0055	S	T	E	N	1974	86068
0055	S	E	R	N	1974	90206
0055	S	E	E	N	1975	90207
0055	S	T	E	N	1974	90545
0055	T	T	E	N	1973	51016
0055	T	T	R	N	1968	75362
0055	T	T	E	N	1969	91450
8004	S	T	E	N	1972	49942
8005	S	S	R	N	1973	55480
8007	S	S	E	N	1969	68271
8007	S	S	E	N	1972	87823
8008	S	S	E	N	1971	87884
8008	S	S	E	N	1972	87889
8009	S	T	E	N	1973	50882
8009	S	T	E	N	1973	53420
8009	S	T	R	N	1973	58309
8010	S	S	E	N	1972	53175
8010	T	S	E	N	1972	53175
8013	S	T	R	N	1973	52840
8013	S	T	E	N	1973	52841
8015	S	S	E	N	1972	53175
8015	T	S	E	N	1972	53175
8017	S	D	E	L	1973	51753
8017	S	D	E	N	1973	51753
8017	S	E	E	L	1973	51753
8017	S	E	E	N	1973	51753
8017	S	S	E	N	1974	54072
8017	S	T	E	N	1974	54110
8036	S	S	E	N	1967	98894
8037	L	D	R	N	1972	52223
8037	L	D	R	N	1972	52224
8037	S	D	R	N	1972	52223
8037	S	D	R	N	1972	52224
8038	L	D	R	N	1972	52223
8038	L	D	R	N	1972	52224
8038	S	D	R	N	1972	52223
8038	S	D	R	N	1972	52224
8038	S	S	E	N	1969	68115
8039	L	D	R	N	1972	52223
8039	S	D	R	N	1972	52223
8040	S	S	E	N	1969	75843
8041	S	T	R	N	1973	58309
8042	S	T	R	N	1973	58309
8043	S	S	E	N	1969	75843
8045	S	T	E	N	1974	63810
8048	S	T	R	N	1971	66284
8058	S	T	E	N	1973	55660
8064	S	S	E	N	1969	75903
8067	S	S	E	N	1969	75843
8069	S	S	E	N	1972	87886
8072	S	S	E	N	1967	98889
8075	S	D	E	L	1971	57148
8075	S	D	E	N	1971	57148
8075	S	S	E	L	1971	57148
8075	S	S	E	N	1971	57148
8075	S	S	E	L	1974	60340
8075	S	S	E	N	1974	60340
8076	S	D	E	L	1971	57148
8076	S	S	E	L	1971	57148
102-0002	D	D	E	L	1970	68214
0002	D	D	E	N	1970	68214
0002	S	D	E	N	1970	68214
0002	S	S	E	N	1967	98889
0041	S	S	E	N	1972	87889
0054	S	T	E	N	1974	54054
0054	S	D	E	N	1974	58047
0086	A	D	E	L	1972	49917
0086	A	D	E	N	1972	49917
0086	A	E	E	L	1972	49917
0086	A	E	E	N	1972	49917
0086	D	D	E	L	1972	49917
0086	D	D	E	N	1972	49917
0086	D	E	E	L	1972	49917
0086	D	E	E	N	1972	49917
0086	S	S	E	L	1973	53051
0086	S	S	E	N	1973	53051
0086	S	D	E	N	1974	61357
0086	S	S	E	N	1974	61357
0086	S	T	E	N	1974	61357
0191	D	D	R	N	1973	57025
0282	S	D	E	N	1974	58047
102-8001	S	S	E	N	1971	87884
8031	A	D	E	L	1972	49917
8031	A	D	E	N	1972	49917
8031	A	E	E	L	1972	49917
8031	A	E	E	N	1972	49917
8031	A	S	E	L	1973	53051
8031	A	S	E	N	1973	53051
8031	A	D	E	N	1974	90245
8031	D	D	E	L	1972	49917
8031	D	D	E	N	1972	49917
8031	D	E	E	L	1972	49917
8031	D	E	E	N	1972	49917
8031	D	S	E	L	1973	53051
8031	D	S	E	N	1973	53051
8031	D	D	E	N	1974	90245
8031	S	D	R	N	1972	50173
8031	S	S	E	L	1973	53051
8031	S	S	E	N	1973	53051
8031	S	D	E	N	1975	90807
8031	S	S	E	N	1975	90807
8041	D	D	R	N	1973	54955
8041	D	D	R	N	1974	68644
8041	D	T	R	N	1974	68644
8041	D	D	E	N	1975	68645
8041	D	T	E	N	1975	68645
8041	D	D	E	N	1975	97860
8041	L	S	E	H	1964	87701
8041	L	S	E	H	1971	87884
8041	P	D	R	N	1973	56966
8041	S	S	E	N	1972	53227
8041	S	D	R	N	1974	58130
8041	S	S	R	N	1974	58130
8041	S	D	E	N	1974	58131
8041	S	S	E	N	1974	58131
8041	S	D	R	N	1971	76480
8041	S	T	R	N	1971	76480
8041	S	S	E	H	1964	87701
8041	S	S	E	N	1964	87701
8041	S	S	E	N	1971	87884
8041	S	S	E	N	1972	87889
8041	S	D	R	N	1974	90206
8041	S	D	E	N	1975	90207
8041	S	D	E	N	1974	90545
8041	S	D	E	N	1971	91500
8041	S	T	E	N	1971	91500
8054	L	S	E	N	1971	87884
8054	S	D	E	L	1974	53913
8054	S	T	E	L	1974	53913
8054	S	D	R	N	1974	58130
8054	S	S	R	N	1974	58130
8054	S	D	E	N	1974	58131
8054	S	S	E	N	1974	58131
8054	S	S	R	N	1974	63131
8054	S	S	E	N	1975	63132
8054	S	S	E	N	1962	87667
8054	S	S	E	L	1971	87884
8054	S	S	E	N	1971	87884
8054	S	D	R	N	1974	90206
8054	S	D	E	N	1975	90207
8058	S	D	E	N	1968	53357
8059	S	D	R	N	1974	65383
8059	S	T	R	N	1974	65383
8059	S	D	E	N	1975	65384
8059	S	T	E	N	1975	65384
8069	A	D	R	N	1973	83375
8069	A	D	E	N	1973	90273
8069	S	D	E	N	1974	61357
8069	S	S	E	N	1974	61357
8069	S	T	E	N	1974	61357
8069	S	D	E	N	1970	63884
8069	S	D	R	N	1973	83375
8069	S	D	E	N	1973	90273
8073	P	D	E	L	1972	67267
8073	S	D	E	L	1973	49510
8077	S	D	R	N	1973	49581
8080	S	D	E	L	1973	49768
8080	S	D	E	N	1973	49768
8081	S	D	E	L	1973	49768
8081	S	D	E	N	1973	49768
8082	S	D	E	L	1973	49768
8082	S	D	E	N	1973	49768
8085	S	D	R	N	1972	49824
8086	S	D	R	N	1972	49824
8088	S	D	E	N	1973	49862
8092	L	D	R	H	1973	50052
8092	S	D	R	H	1973	50052
8092	S	D	R	N	1973	50052
8093	L	D	R	H	1973	50052
8093	S	D	R	H	1973	50052
8093	S	D	R	N	1973	50052
8095	S	S	E	N	1972	53227
8095	S	S	E	N	1972	87889
8098	D	D	E	N	1973	51886
8098	S	D	E	L	1973	50818
8098	S	D	E	N	1973	50818
102-8098	S	D	E	N	1973	51886
8099	S	D	E	L	1973	49587
8100	S	D	R	L	1973	50353
8100	S	D	R	N	1973	50353
8100	S	D	E	L	1973	50354
8100	S	D	E	N	1973	50354
8100	S	D	F	L	1973	57624
8100	S	D	F	N	1973	57624
8100	S	T	F	L	1973	57624
8100	S	T	F	N	1973	57624
8102	S	D	E	L	1973	50405
8106	S	D	E	N	1972	52976
8107	S	D	E	N	1973	50605
8107	S	D	E	N	1973	52035
8109	S	D	E	L	1973	51174
8109	S	D	E	N	1973	51174
8109	S	D	E	N	1971	57500
8110	S	D	E	L	1973	51174
8110	S	D	E	N	1973	51174
8111	S	D	E	L	1973	51174
8111	S	D	E	N	1973	51174
8117	L	D	R	H	1973	50052
8117	L	D	R	N	1973	50052
8117	S	D	R	N	1973	50052
8121	S	D	E	L	1973	51174
8122	S	D	E	L	1973	51174
8123	S	D	E	L	1973	51174
8123	S	D	E	N	1973	51174
8124	S	D	E	N	1973	51187
8125	S	D	E	L	1974	61156
8127	S	D	E	L	1974	61156
8128	D	D	O	N	1973	51224
8128	S	D	O	N	1973	52319
8130	S	D	O	N	1973	51224
8131	S	D	O	N	1973	51224
8137	S	D	E	N	1975	87162
8137	S	S	E	N	1975	87162
8140	S	D	R	N	1973	51520
8155	S	D	E	N	1973	52300
8156	S	D	O	N	1973	52319
8157	S	D	O	N	1973	52319
8157	S	D	E	L	1973	52596
8157	S	D	E	L	1971	57502
8157	S	D	E	N	1971	57502
8158	S	D	O	N	1973	52319
8159	S	D	E	L	1973	52430
8159	S	D	E	N	1973	52430
8159	S	D	E	L	1971	57179
8159	S	D	E	L	1972	70545
8159	S	D	E	N	1972	70545
8159	S	D	E	N	1976	95560
8160	S	D	E	L	1973	52430
8160	S	D	E	N	1973	52430
8160	S	D	E	L	1971	57179
8160	S	D	E	L	1972	70545
8160	S	D	E	N	1972	70545
8160	S	D	E	L	1976	95560
8161	S	D	E	L	1973	52430
8161	S	D	E	N	1973	52430
8161	S	D	E	L	1971	57179
8162	S	D	E	L	1973	52451
8162	S	D	E	N	1973	52451
8167	S	T	E	N	1973	52951
8168	S	T	E	N	1973	52951
8169	C	D	F	L	1973	57624
8169	C	D	F	L	1975	63413
8169	C	T	F	L	1975	63413
8169	D	S	E	L	1966	87721
8169	P	S	E	L	1966	87721
8169	P	S	E	L	1972	87886
8169	P	S	E	N	1972	87886
8169	S	D	E	L	1971	53075
8169	S	D	F	L	1973	57624
8169	S	D	F	N	1973	57624
8169	S	T	F	L	1973	57624
8169	S	T	F	N	1973	57624
8184	S	D	E	N	1972	53389
8184	S	D	E	H	1971	87384
8184	S	D	E	N	1971	87384
8187	S	S	R	N	1974	88600
8188	A	S	E	N	1972	49917
8188	A	D	R	N	1973	83375
8188	A	D	E	N	1973	90273
8188	S	S	E	N	1972	49917
8188	S	S	E	N	1973	53051
8188	S	D	E	N	1970	63884
8192	S	D	E	L	1973	51800
8192	S	D	E	N	1973	51800
8192	S	T	E	L	1973	51800
8192	S	T	E	N	1973	51800
8192	S	D	E	L	1974	54113
8192	S	D	E	N	1974	54113
8192	S	S	E	L	1974	54113
8192	S	S	E	N	1974	54113
8192	S	D	E	L	1974	61167

Phys. State: **A.** Amorphous; **C.** Superconductive; **D.** Doped; **F.** Fibrous or Whisker; **G.** Gas; **I.** Ionized or Plasma; **L.** Liquid; **P.** Powder or Particle; **S.** Solid; **T.** Thin Film
Subject: **D.** Data; **E.** Experiment; **S.** Survey (Review, Compendium, etc.); **T.** Theory
Language: **E.** English; **F.** French; **G.** German; **O.** Other Languages; **R.** Russian
Temperature: **L.** Low (0 to 75K); **N.** Normal (75 to 1273K); **H.** High (above 1273K)

Substance Number	Phys. State	Subject	Language	Temperature	Year	EPIC Number
102-8192	S	D	E	N	1974	61167
8192	S	S	E	L	1974	61168
8192	S	S	E	N	1974	61168
8193	S	D	E	L	1973	51800
8193	S	D	E	N	1973	51800
8193	S	T	E	L	1973	51800
8193	S	T	E	N	1973	51800
8195	D	D	E	L	1974	90649
8195	D	D	E	N	1974	90649
8195	S	D	E	N	1973	50944
8195	S	E	E	N	1973	50944
8195	S	D	E	L	1973	63637
8195	S	D	E	L	1975	66703
8195	S	S	E	L	1975	66703
8206	S	D	E	L	1973	52196
8207	S	D	E	L	1973	52196
8213	S	D	E	N	1971	57173
8213	S	T	E	N	1974	60338
8216	S	S	F	N	1973	52166
8217	S	D	E	L	1973	52303
8217	S	D	E	N	1973	52303
8218	S	D	E	L	1973	52303
8218	S	D	E	N	1973	52303
8221	S	S	E	N	1958	59561
8221	S	S	E	N	1958	75842
8223	D	D	R	N	1973	55444
8225	S	D	E	L	1974	54963
8225	S	D	E	N	1974	54963
8234	S	D	E	N	1976	95560
8236	S	D	E	L	1974	54113
8236	S	D	E	N	1974	54113
8236	S	S	E	L	1974	54113
8236	S	S	E	N	1974	54113
8236	S	D	E	L	1974	61167
8236	S	D	E	N	1974	61167
8237	S	D	E	L	1974	54113
8237	S	D	E	N	1974	54113
8237	S	S	E	L	1974	54113
8237	S	S	E	N	1974	54113
8255	S	D	E	L	1973	60573
8255	S	D	E	N	1973	60573
8255	S	S	E	L	1973	60573
8255	S	S	E	N	1973	60573
8256	S	D	E	L	1973	60573
8256	S	D	E	N	1973	60573
8256	S	S	E	L	1973	60573
8256	S	S	E	N	1973	60573
8257	S	D	E	L	1973	57497
8258	S	D	E	L	1974	58053
8258	S	D	E	N	1974	58053
8260	S	D	E	N	1974	57820
8261	S	S	E	N	1973	54004
8261	S	D	E	N	1975	90866
8265	S	S	E	N	1973	54004
8266	S	S	E	N	1973	54004
8267	S	S	E	N	1973	54004
8272	S	S	E	N	1973	54004
8273	S	S	E	N	1973	54004
8274	S	S	E	N	1973	54004
8275	S	S	E	N	1973	54004
8276	S	S	E	N	1973	54004
8284	S	D	E	N	1971	65065
8309	A	S	E	L	1973	53051
8309	A	S	E	N	1973	53051
8309	L	S	E	N	1973	53051
8309	S	S	E	L	1973	53051
8309	S	S	E	N	1973	53051
8334	P	D	E	N	1974	70390
8336	S	D	E	N	1973	55139
8338	S	D	E	N	1973	55663
8360	S	D	E	N	1971	57173
8361	S	D	E	N	1971	57173
8362	S	D	E	N	1971	57173
8364	S	D	E	N	1971	57173
8365	S	D	E	L	1971	57198
8365	S	D	E	N	1971	57198
8366	S	D	R	N	1973	57349
8368	S	D	E	N	1971	57500
8368	S	D	E	L	1974	64326
8368	S	D	E	N	1974	64326
8369	S	D	R	N	1973	67847
8373	S	D	E	L	1973	57571
8374	S	D	E	N	1973	57714
8388	S	D	E	L	1974	64326
8388	S	D	E	N	1974	64326
8389	S	D	E	L	1974	64326
8389	S	D	E	N	1974	64326
8390	S	D	E	L	1974	64326
8390	S	D	E	N	1974	64326
8391	S	D	E	L	1974	64326
8391	S	D	E	N	1974	64326
8394	L	D	E	N	1973	60573
8394	S	D	E	L	1973	60573
8394	S	D	E	N	1973	60573
8407	S	D	E	L	1974	90649
8407	S	D	E	N	1974	90649
8415	S	S	E	N	1972	87886
8418	S	S	E	N	1966	87721
8418	S	S	E	N	1972	87886
8419	S	S	E	N	1966	87721
8419	S	S	E	N	1972	87886

Substance Number	Phys. State	Subject	Language	Temperature	Year	EPIC Number
102-8450	C	D	R	L	1974	81228
8450	C	D	E	L	1974	92358
8450	S	D	R	L	1974	81228
8450	S	D	E	L	1974	92358
8458	F	D	E	N	1975	91972
8458	F	T	E	N	1975	91972
8465	S	D	E	N	1975	63358
8465	S	T	E	N	1975	63358
8466	S	D	E	N	1970	63884
8467	S	D	E	N	1970	63884
8468	S	D	E	N	1970	63884
8469	S	D	E	N	1970	63884
8477	S	D	E	L	1976	100785
8477	S	D	E	N	1976	100785
8485	S	D	F	L	1973	57624
8485	S	D	F	N	1973	57624
8485	S	T	F	L	1973	57624
8485	S	T	F	N	1973	57624
8486	S	D	F	N	1973	57624
8486	S	T	F	L	1973	57624
8486	S	T	F	N	1973	57624
8487	S	D	R	N	1974	65383
8487	S	T	R	N	1974	65383
8487	S	D	E	N	1975	65384
8487	S	T	E	N	1975	65384
8499	S	S	E	N	1969	75903
8500	S	S	E	N	1969	75903
8501	S	S	E	N	1969	75903
104-0002	S	S	E	N	1967	98889
0007	S	S	E	N	1967	68374
0007	S	S	E	N	1971	87884
0013	D	D	R	N	1974	61962
0013	D	S	R	N	1974	61962
0013	D	T	R	N	1974	61962
0013	D	D	E	N	1974	61963
0013	D	S	E	N	1974	61963
0013	D	T	E	N	1974	61963
0013	D	D	R	N	1970	76458
0013	D	T	R	N	1970	76458
0013	D	D	E	N	1970	91515
0013	D	T	E	N	1970	91515
0013	S	D	O	N	1973	52323
0013	S	S	E	N	1974	53895
0013	S	S	E	N	1974	54577
0013	S	D	R	N	1974	61962
0013	S	S	R	N	1974	61962
0013	S	T	R	N	1974	61962
0013	S	D	E	N	1974	61963
0013	S	S	E	N	1974	61963
0013	S	T	E	N	1974	61963
0013	S	D	E	N	1975	64577
0013	S	S	E	N	1975	64577
0013	S	T	E	N	1975	64577
0013	S	D	R	N	1974	65391
0013	S	S	R	N	1974	65391
0013	S	T	R	N	1974	65391
0013	S	D	E	N	1975	65392
0013	S	S	E	N	1975	65392
0013	S	T	E	N	1975	65392
0013	S	D	R	N	1974	66788
0013	S	D	E	N	1975	66789
0013	S	D	R	N	1970	76458
0013	S	T	R	N	1970	76458
0013	S	D	E	N	1970	91515
0013	S	T	E	N	1970	91515
0013	S	S	E	N	1975	96170
0013	T	S	R	N	1974	66796
0013	T	S	E	N	1975	66797
0022	S	D	R	N	1971	76480
0022	S	T	R	N	1971	76480
0022	S	D	E	N	1971	91500
0022	S	T	E	N	1971	91500
0043	S	D	E	L	1973	53712
0049	S	S	E	N	1967	98889
0095	S	D	E	L	1974	61157
0127	L	S	E	N	1974	54304
0171	S	S	E	L	1973	56441
0171	S	D	E	L	1974	62340
0171	S	D	E	L	1974	64714
0171	S	T	E	L	1974	64714
0337	D	D	E	N	1974	54027
0347	S	D	E	N	1968	53357
0386	S	D	R	N	1974	65391
0386	S	S	R	N	1974	65391
0386	S	T	R	N	1974	65391
0386	S	D	E	N	1975	65392
0386	S	S	E	N	1975	65392
0386	S	T	E	N	1975	65392
0409	S	D	R	N	1971	76503
0409	S	T	R	N	1971	76503
0409	S	D	E	N	1971	91564
0409	S	T	E	N	1971	91564
0529	S	D	E	N	1973	51173
0529	S	D	E	L	1972	53116
0529	S	D	E	N	1972	53116
0533	S	S	E	N	1972	87890
0574	S	D	R	N	1971	76503
0574	S	T	R	N	1971	76503
0574	S	D	E	N	1971	91564
0574	S	T	E	N	1971	91564

Substance Number	Phys. State	Subject	Language	Temperature	Year	EPIC Number
104-0575	S	D	R	N	1971	76503
0575	S	T	R	N	1971	76503
0575	S	D	E	N	1971	91564
0575	S	T	E	N	1971	91564
8010	L	D	R	N	1973	50946
8010	L	D	E	N	1975	88234
8010	S	D	R	N	1973	50946
8011	L	D	R	N	1973	50946
8011	L	D	E	N	1975	88234
8011	S	D	R	N	1973	50946
8016	T	D	E	N	1974	53893
8016	T	S	E	N	1973	56287
8042	S	S	E	N	1966	66068
8043	S	D	R	N	1972	49822
8045	L	D	R	N	1972	52223
8045	S	D	R	N	1972	52223
8045	S	S	E	N	1972	62298
8045	S	S	E	N	1973	62299
8045	S	S	E	N	1966	66068
8055	S	D	R	N	1973	52566
8055	S	D	E	N	1973	57791
8068	S	D	R	N	1973	52566
8068	S	D	E	N	1973	57791
8069	S	D	R	N	1971	76503
8069	S	T	R	N	1971	76503
8069	S	D	E	N	1971	91564
8069	S	T	E	N	1971	91564
8073	S	D	E	N	1973	49509
8073	S	D	E	N	1972	49889
8075	S	D	R	N	1974	93436
8075	S	T	R	N	1974	93436
8075	S	D	E	N	1974	93437
8075	S	T	E	N	1974	93437
8080	S	D	E	L	1974	54326
8080	S	D	E	N	1974	54326
8080	S	D	E	L	1972	55592
8080	S	D	E	N	1972	55592
8081	S	D	R	N	1973	52566
8081	S	D	E	N	1973	57791
8083	S	D	R	N	1974	93436
8083	S	T	R	N	1974	93436
8083	S	D	E	N	1974	93437
8083	S	T	E	N	1974	93437
8087	S	D	E	L	1974	54326
8090	S	D	R	N	1974	93436
8090	S	T	R	N	1974	93436
8090	S	D	E	N	1974	93437
8090	S	T	E	N	1974	93437
8099	S	D	R	N	1974	93436
8099	S	T	R	N	1974	93436
8099	S	D	E	N	1974	93437
8099	S	T	E	N	1974	93437
8100	S	D	R	N	1974	93436
8100	S	T	R	N	1974	93436
8100	S	D	E	N	1974	93437
8100	S	T	E	N	1974	93437
8105	S	D	R	N	1974	93436
8105	S	T	R	N	1974	93436
8105	S	D	E	N	1974	93437
8105	S	T	E	N	1974	93437
8106	S	D	E	N	1974	53860
8106	T	S	E	N	1974	58000
8107	D	D	E	L	1973	49558
8110	S	D	F	N	1972	49777
8110	S	D	E	N	1974	54028
8111	S	D	F	N	1972	49777
8112	S	D	F	N	1972	49777
8114	S	D	R	N	1974	93436
8114	S	T	R	N	1974	93436
8114	S	D	E	N	1974	93437
8114	S	T	E	N	1974	93437
8115	S	D	R	N	1974	93436
8115	S	T	R	N	1974	93436
8115	S	D	E	N	1974	93437
8115	S	T	E	N	1974	93437
8122	S	D	R	N	1973	50211
8122	S	D	E	N	1973	50212
8124	S	D	R	L	1973	50255
8124	S	D	E	L	1973	50256
8132	S	D	E	N	1972	50530
8136	C	T	E	L	1972	55092
8136	D	D	F	N	1974	55973
8138	S	D	R	N	1973	50728
8138	S	D	E	N	1973	53029
8140	S	D	R	N	1973	50728
8140	S	D	E	N	1973	53029
8141	S	D	R	N	1973	50728
8141	S	D	E	N	1973	53029
8142	S	D	R	N	1973	50728
8142	S	D	E	N	1973	53029
8143	S	D	R	N	1973	50728
8143	S	D	E	N	1973	53029
8144	S	D	R	N	1973	50728
8144	S	D	E	N	1973	53029
8145	S	D	R	N	1973	50728
8145	S	D	E	N	1973	53029
8146	S	D	R	N	1973	50728
8146	S	D	E	N	1973	53029
8147	S	D	R	N	1973	50728
8147	S	D	E	N	1973	53029
8150	S	D	E	L	1973	49512

Phys. State: **A.** Amorphous; **C.** Superconductive; **D.** Doped; **F.** Fibrous or Whisker; **G.** Gas; **I.** Ionized or Plasma; **L.** Liquid; **P.** Powder or Particle; **S.** Solid; **T.** Thin Film
Subject: **D.** Data; **E.** Experiment; **S.** Survey (Review, Compendium, etc.); **T.** Theory
Language: **E.** English; **F.** French; **G.** German; **O.** Other Languages; **R.** Russian
Temperature: **L.** Low (0 to 75K); **N.** Normal (75 to 1273K); **H.** High (above 1273K)

Substance Number	Phys. State	Subject	Language	Temperature	Year	EPIC Number
104-8150	S	D	E	N	1973	49512
8151	S	D	E	L	1973	51120
8151	S	D	E	N	1973	51120
8152	S	D	E	L	1973	51147
8152	S	D	E	N	1973	51147
8153	S	D	E	L	1973	51148
8153	S	D	E	N	1973	51148
8153	S	D	E	N	1974	53989
8154	S	D	E	N	1973	51173
8154	S	D	E	L	1972	53116
8154	S	D	E	N	1972	53116
8156	S	D	R	N	1974	93436
8156	S	T	R	N	1974	93436
8156	S	D	E	N	1974	93437
8156	S	T	E	N	1974	93437
8157	S	D	R	N	1974	93436
8157	S	T	R	N	1974	93436
8157	S	D	E	N	1974	93437
8157	S	T	E	N	1974	93437
8158	C	T	E	L	1972	55092
8158	S	D	R	L	1972	51237
8159	S	D	R	N	1972	51237
8159	S	S	E	N	1975	66701
8159	S	T	E	N	1975	66701
8159	S	D	R	N	1971	76503
8159	S	T	R	N	1971	76503
8159	S	D	E	N	1971	91564
8159	S	T	E	N	1971	91564
8159	S	D	R	N	1974	93436
8159	S	T	R	N	1974	93436
8159	S	D	E	N	1974	93437
8159	S	T	E	N	1974	93437
8162	S	D	R	N	1973	51392
8162	S	D	E	N	1973	51393
8162	S	D	E	N	1974	56607
8162	S	D	R	N	1974	60467
8162	S	D	E	N	1974	60468
8162	S	T	R	N	1974	60489
8162	S	T	E	N	1974	60490
8170	S	D	R	L	1974	81236
8170	S	D	R	N	1974	81236
8170	S	T	R	L	1974	81236
8170	S	T	R	N	1974	81236
8170	S	D	E	L	1974	92366
8170	S	D	E	N	1974	92366
8170	S	T	E	L	1974	92366
8170	S	T	E	N	1974	92366
8171	S	S	E	N	1974	53895
8171	S	D	R	N	1973	57822
8171	S	D	E	N	1974	57823
8173	S	D	E	N	1973	51885
8174	S	D	E	N	1973	51917
8181	S	D	E	N	1973	52787
8182	S	D	E	N	1973	52787
8183	S	S	E	N	1974	84846
8185	S	D	R	N	1973	50728
8185	S	D	E	N	1973	53029
8197	S	D	E	L	1973	51800
8197	S	D	E	N	1973	51800
8197	S	T	E	L	1973	51800
8197	S	T	E	N	1973	51800
8198	S	S	E	N	1973	51829
8200	S	D	E	L	1973	51888
8200	S	D	E	N	1973	51888
8200	S	E	E	L	1973	51888
8200	S	E	E	N	1973	51888
8200	S	T	E	L	1973	51888
8200	S	T	E	N	1973	51888
8200	S	D	E	L	1975	90444
8201	S	D	E	L	1973	51888
8201	S	D	E	N	1973	51888
8201	S	E	E	L	1973	51888
8201	S	E	E	N	1973	51888
8201	S	T	E	L	1973	51888
8201	S	T	E	N	1973	51888
8203	S	D	E	L	1973	51888
8203	S	D	E	N	1973	51888
8203	S	E	E	L	1973	51888
8203	S	E	E	N	1973	51888
8203	S	T	E	L	1973	51888
8203	S	T	E	N	1973	51888
8214	S	S	R	N	1971	59648
8214	S	S	E	N	1971	59649
8223	D	D	E	N	1974	53989
8225	S	D	E	N	1974	54319
8226	S	D	E	L	1974	54326
8226	S	D	E	N	1974	54326
8226	S	D	E	L	1972	55592
8226	S	D	E	N	1972	55592
8227	S	D	E	L	1974	54321
8227	S	D	E	N	1974	54321
8229	S	D	E	N	1974	54329
8230	S	D	E	N	1974	54329
8239	C	T	E	L	1972	55092
8246	S	D	R	N	1974	58070
8246	S	D	E	N	1974	58071
8247	S	D	E	N	1974	58006
8248	S	D	E	N	1974	58006
8249	S	D	E	N	1974	58006
8250	S	D	E	N	1974	58006
8254	S	D	F	N	1972	60959
104-8272	S	D	R	N	1973	62447
8278	S	D	E	N	1973	53882
8292	S	D	E	N	1973	55422
8300	S	D	E	N	1973	56162
8307	S	D	R	N	1972	56950
8308	S	D	R	N	1972	56950
8309	S	D	R	N	1972	56950
8310	S	D	R	N	1972	57004
8311	S	D	R	N	1972	57004
8313	S	D	E	L	1971	57168
8313	S	D	E	N	1971	57168
8314	S	D	R	N	1973	57349
8315	S	D	E	L	1971	57502
8315	S	D	E	N	1971	57502
8315	S	D	E	N	1975	63275
8315	S	T	E	N	1975	63275
8324	S	D	F	N	1974	62085
8325	S	D	F	N	1974	62085
8326	S	D	F	N	1974	62085
8328	S	D	E	N	1975	63275
8328	S	T	E	N	1975	63275
8329	S	D	E	L	1975	63275
8329	S	D	E	N	1975	63275
8329	S	T	E	L	1975	63275
8329	S	T	E	N	1975	63275
8330	S	D	E	L	1975	63275
8330	S	T	E	L	1975	63275
8331	S	D	E	L	1975	63275
8331	S	T	E	L	1975	63275
8332	S	D	E	L	1975	63275
8332	S	T	E	L	1975	63275
8333	S	D	E	L	1975	63275
8333	S	D	E	N	1975	63275
8333	S	T	E	L	1975	63275
8333	S	T	E	N	1975	63275
8334	S	D	E	L	1975	63275
8334	S	T	E	L	1975	63275
8335	S	D	E	L	1975	63275
8335	S	T	E	L	1975	63275
8336	S	D	E	L	1975	63275
8336	S	T	E	L	1975	63275
8337	S	D	E	L	1975	63275
8337	S	T	E	L	1975	63275
8338	S	D	E	L	1975	63275
8338	S	T	E	L	1975	63275
8339	S	D	E	N	1975	63275
8339	S	T	E	N	1975	63275
8340	S	D	E	N	1975	63275
8340	S	T	E	N	1975	63275
8341	S	D	E	N	1975	63275
8341	S	T	E	N	1975	63275
8342	S	D	E	N	1975	63275
8342	S	T	E	N	1975	63275
8343	S	D	E	L	1975	63275
8343	S	D	E	N	1975	63275
8343	S	T	E	L	1975	63275
8343	S	T	E	N	1975	63275
8351	S	D	E	N	1971	67020
8359	S	D	E	L	1974	90467
8408	S	D	R	N	1972	76549
8408	S	T	R	N	1972	76549
8408	S	D	E	N	1972	91599
8408	S	T	E	N	1972	91599
8409	S	D	R	N	1972	76549
8409	S	T	R	N	1972	76549
8409	S	D	E	N	1972	91599
8409	S	T	E	N	1972	91599
8410	S	D	R	N	1972	76549
8410	S	T	R	N	1972	76549
8410	S	D	E	N	1972	91599
8410	S	T	E	N	1972	91599
8436	S	D	R	N	1970	76453
8436	S	T	R	N	1970	76453
8436	S	D	E	N	1970	91544
8436	S	T	E	N	1970	91544
8437	S	D	R	N	1971	76503
8437	S	T	R	N	1971	76503
8437	S	D	E	N	1971	91564
8437	S	T	E	N	1971	91564
8438	S	D	E	N	1974	65212
8439	S	D	E	N	1974	65212
8440	S	D	E	N	1974	65212
8441	S	D	E	N	1974	65212
8448	S	D	E	N	1972	49784
8448	S	S	E	N	1972	49784
8449	S	D	E	N	1972	49784
8449	S	S	E	N	1972	49784
8450	S	D	E	N	1972	49784
8450	S	S	E	N	1972	49784
8451	S	D	E	N	1972	49784
8451	S	S	E	N	1972	49784
8452	S	D	E	N	1972	49784
8452	S	S	E	N	1972	49784
8453	S	D	E	N	1972	49784
8453	S	S	E	N	1972	49784
8454	S	D	E	N	1972	49784
8454	S	S	E	N	1972	49784
8455	S	D	E	N	1972	49784
8455	S	S	E	N	1972	49784
8460	S	T	E	N	1975	90444
8461	S	D	E	N	1975	90444
106-0004	S	S	E	N	1969	68271
0004	S	S	E	N	1967	98889
0018	L	D	E	N	1973	53878
0018	L	T	E	N	1973	53878
0018	S	D	E	L	1973	53712
0018	S	D	E	N	1973	53878
0018	S	T	E	L	1973	53878
0018	S	T	E	N	1973	53878
0018	S	S	E	N	1962	58977
0024	S	E	R	N	1971	61548
0024	S	E	E	N	1971	65901
0031	S	D	E	N	1973	49516
0031	S	D	E	N	1973	58740
0031	S	D	E	N	1961	62927
0031	S	E	E	N	1973	65676
0031	S	S	E	N	1967	98889
0033	S	D	E	L	1973	50894
0033	S	D	E	L	1973	56428
0035	S	D	R	N	1974	58130
0035	S	S	R	N	1974	58130
0035	S	D	E	N	1974	58131
0035	S	S	E	N	1974	58131
0035	S	S	E	N	1965	87702
0035	S	S	E	N	1968	87828
0035	S	S	E	N	1971	87887
0035	S	D	R	N	1974	90206
0035	S	D	E	N	1975	90207
0046	S	D	E	L	1974	60336
0052	S	D	E	N	1973	49546
0057	P	S	E	N	1966	68325
0057	S	S	E	N	1969	68271
0068	S	S	E	N	1962	58977
0081	D	S	E	N	1973	50739
0081	S	D	E	N	1973	52822
0081	S	D	E	N	1974	58048
0081	S	D	R	N	1974	60461
0081	S	S	R	N	1974	60461
0081	S	D	E	N	1974	60462
0081	S	S	E	N	1974	60462
0081	S	S	E	N	1967	98889
0090	S	D	E	L	1973	52442
0112	S	D	E	N	1972	49920
0112	S	D	E	N	1973	50996
0114	S	D	E	L	1973	55558
0114	S	D	E	N	1973	55558
0115	S	S	E	N	1962	58977
0117	S	D	E	N	1955	61305
0125	S	S	E	N	1964	93287
0131	S	D	E	L	1974	54314
0131	S	D	E	N	1974	54314
0131	S	D	E	L	1975	81367
0131	S	D	E	N	1975	81367
0131	S	S	E	L	1975	81367
0131	S	S	E	N	1975	81367
0138	S	D	R	N	1971	76503
0138	S	T	R	N	1971	76503
0138	S	D	E	N	1971	91564
0138	S	T	E	N	1971	91564
0152	L	S	E	N	1974	54304
0157	S	S	R	N	1973	87035
0157	S	S	E	N	1973	87036
0192	S	S	E	N	1967	98889
0205	S	D	R	H	1972	50653
0205	S	D	R	N	1972	50653
0205	S	S	E	N	1964	93287
0210	A	S	E	N	1973	53050
0210	D	D	E	N	1973	57107
0210	S	S	E	N	1973	55935
0225	L	D	E	N	1973	65678
0226	S	D	R	H	1972	50653
0226	S	D	R	N	1972	50653
0240	L	D	E	N	1973	53878
0240	L	T	E	N	1973	53878
0240	S	D	E	L	1973	53699
0240	S	D	E	N	1973	53878
0240	S	T	E	N	1973	53878
0240	S	S	E	L	1973	56441
0240	S	T	E	N	1974	61398
0286	S	D	E	L	1974	54326
0286	S	D	E	N	1974	54326
0286	S	S	E	N	1974	54326
0286	S	D	E	L	1972	55592
0286	S	D	E	N	1972	55592
0286	S	D	E	N	1951	75749
0286	S	T	E	N	1951	75749
0308	S	D	R	H	1972	50653
0308	S	D	R	N	1972	50653
0309	D	D	R	N	1973	50369
0309	D	D	E	N	1973	50370
0309	S	D	R	N	1973	50369
0309	S	D	E	N	1973	50370
0309	S	D	R	H	1972	50653
0309	S	D	R	N	1972	50653
0309	S	S	E	N	1964	93287
0327	D	D	R	N	1972	49840
0327	D	D	E	N	1973	55879
0327	S	D	R	N	1972	49840
0363	P	S	E	N	1967	66156
0363	S	S	E	N	1963	64232
0363	S	S	E	N	1969	68271
0497	D	D	E	L	1972	49912

Phys. State: A. Amorphous; C. Superconductive; D. Doped; F. Fibrous or Whisker; G. Gas; I. Ionized or Plasma; L. Liquid; P. Powder or Particle; S. Solid; T. Thin Film
Subject: D. Data; E. Experiment; S. Survey (Review, Compendium, etc.); T. Theory
Language: E. English; F. French; G. German; O. Other Languages; R. Russian
Temperature: L. Low (0 to 75K); N. Normal (75 to 1273K); H. High (above 1273K)

Substance Number	Phys. State	Subject	Language	Temperature	Year	EPIC Number
106-0497	S	D	R	L	1974	81222
0497	S	T	R	L	1974	81222
0497	S	D	E	L	1974	92382
0497	S	T	E	L	1974	92382
0508	D	D	E	N	1970	56062
0523	S	S	R	N	1974	93455
0523	S	S	E	N	1974	93456
0608	S	D	E	L	1973	51847
0612	S	D	E	L	1975	91864
0612	S	D	E	N	1975	91864
0612	S	S	E	L	1975	91864
0612	S	S	E	N	1975	91864
0612	S	T	E	L	1975	91864
0612	S	T	E	N	1975	91864
0621	S	D	E	L	1973	53700
0621	S	E	E	L	1973	53700
0622	S	D	R	L	1974	86618
0622	S	S	R	L	1974	86618
0622	S	T	R	L	1974	86618
0622	S	D	E	L	1975	94084
0622	S	S	E	L	1975	94084
0622	S	T	E	L	1975	94084
0623	S	D	R	L	1974	86618
0623	S	S	R	L	1974	86618
0623	S	T	R	L	1974	86618
0623	S	D	E	L	1975	94084
0623	S	S	E	L	1975	94084
0623	S	T	E	L	1975	94084
0628	S	D	E	L	1973	53700
0628	S	E	E	L	1973	53700
0872	S	D	E	L	1973	53701
0927	P	S	E	N	1969	75843
0927	S	D	E	N	1968	53358
0927	S	D	E	N	1973	57431
0927	S	S	E	N	1970	75833
0937	S	D	R	N	1971	76485
0937	S	S	R	N	1971	76485
0937	S	D	E	N	1971	91504
0937	S	S	E	N	1971	91504
0937	S	D	E	N	1964	93287
0937	S	S	E	N	1964	93287
0941	A	D	R	N	1973	83375
0941	A	D	E	N	1973	90273
0941	S	D	R	N	1973	83375
0941	S	D	E	N	1973	90273
1027	S	D	E	N	1964	93287
1027	S	S	E	N	1964	93287
1062	C	D	R	L	1972	63967
1062	C	T	R	L	1972	63967
1062	C	D	E	L	1972	68424
1062	C	T	E	L	1972	68424
1062	S	S	E	N	1972	87886
1062	S	D	E	N	1964	93287
1062	S	S	E	N	1964	93287
1079	S	T	E	N	1975	90470
1103	S	D	E	L	1973	51840
1103	S	D	O	L	1973	52667
1103	S	D	E	L	1973	57423
1103	S	D	E	N	1973	57423
1256	D	D	E	N	1972	49878
1256	S	D	E	N	1972	49878
1287	S	D	E	N	1964	93287
1287	S	S	E	N	1964	93287
1296	S	D	E	N	1973	51199
1299	S	D	E	N	1973	51151
1299	S	D	E	N	1975	65456
1299	S	D	R	N	1974	66730
1299	S	T	R	N	1974	66730
1299	S	D	E	N	1975	66731
1299	S	T	E	N	1975	66731
1299	S	S	E	N	1970	75905
1343	S	D	R	N	1971	76503
1343	S	T	R	N	1971	76503
1343	S	D	E	N	1971	91564
1343	S	T	E	N	1971	91564
1516	S	T	E	N	1973	52954
1517	S	D	E	L	1972	52964
1517	S	D	E	N	1972	52964
1522	S	D	E	L	1973	51146
1522	S	D	E	N	1973	51146
1522	S	D	E	N	1973	52190
1522	S	D	E	N	1968	53358
8014	S	S	R	N	1974	63165
8014	S	S	E	N	1975	63166
8014	S	D	E	N	1974	64327
8025	S	D	E	L	1974	53988
8040	S	S	R	N	1972	53547
8040	S	S	E	N	1973	53548
8040	S	S	E	N	1969	68271
8041	S	D	R	L	1972	58680
8041	S	D	R	N	1972	58680
8041	S	S	E	N	1969	68271
8041	S	S	E	N	1967	68371
8049	S	D	E	N	1972	49915
8081	S	D	E	N	1973	51883
8092	L	D	E	N	1974	54304
8095	S	D	E	L	1974	54326
8095	S	D	E	N	1974	54326
8095	S	D	E	L	1972	55592
8095	S	D	E	N	1972	55592
8115	S	D	E	L	1973	49513

Substance Number	Phys. State	Subject	Language	Temperature	Year	EPIC Number
106-8116	S	D	E	L	1973	49513
8117	S	D	E	N	1973	49522
8118	S	D	E	N	1973	49529
8119	S	D	E	N	1973	49529
8120	S	D	O	N	1973	49534
8120	S	S	E	L	1969	75843
8120	S	S	E	N	1969	75843
8121	S	D	O	L	1973	49534
8121	S	D	O	N	1973	49534
8121	S	S	E	L	1969	75843
8121	S	S	E	N	1969	75843
8122	S	D	O	L	1973	49534
8122	S	D	O	N	1973	49534
8123	S	D	E	H	1973	51137
8123	S	D	E	N	1973	51137
8123	S	D	E	N	1973	51249
8123	S	D	E	L	1973	55150
8123	S	D	E	N	1973	55150
8124	S	D	E	L	1971	49557
8124	S	D	E	N	1971	49557
8128	S	D	E	L	1972	49933
8128	S	D	E	N	1972	49933
8128	S	S	E	N	1967	68371
8128	S	S	E	N	1972	87823
8130	S	D	E	L	1973	49587
8131	S	D	E	L	1973	49611
8132	S	S	R	N	1973	87035
8132	S	S	E	N	1973	87036
8133	S	S	R	N	1973	87035
8133	S	S	E	N	1973	87036
8134	S	S	R	N	1973	87035
8134	S	S	E	N	1973	87036
8136	S	D	E	N	1973	49629
8136	S	T	E	N	1973	49629
8137	S	D	E	N	1973	49629
8137	S	T	E	N	1973	49629
8141	S	D	R	N	1972	49840
8144	S	D	E	N	1972	49878
8147	S	D	E	N	1973	49998
8148	S	D	E	N	1973	49998
8153	S	D	F	N	1973	50026
8157	S	D	R	N	1973	50195
8157	S	D	E	N	1973	50196
8157	S	S	R	N	1974	63165
8157	S	S	E	N	1975	63166
8158	S	D	R	L	1973	50255
8158	S	D	E	L	1973	50256
8159	S	D	R	L	1973	50255
8159	S	D	E	L	1973	50256
8160	S	D	R	L	1973	50255
8160	S	D	E	L	1973	50256
8166	S	D	E	L	1973	50404
8166	S	D	E	N	1973	50404
8167	S	D	E	L	1973	50404
8167	S	D	E	N	1973	50404
8168	S	D	E	L	1973	50404
8168	S	D	E	N	1973	50404
8169	S	D	E	L	1973	50404
8169	S	D	E	N	1973	50404
8170	S	D	E	L	1973	50404
8170	S	D	E	N	1973	50404
8171	S	D	E	L	1973	50404
8171	S	D	E	N	1973	50404
8172	S	D	E	L	1973	50404
8172	S	D	E	N	1973	50404
8173	S	D	E	L	1973	50404
8173	S	D	E	N	1973	50404
8174	S	D	E	L	1973	50404
8174	S	D	E	N	1973	50404
8175	S	D	E	L	1973	50404
8175	S	D	E	N	1973	50404
8176	S	D	E	L	1973	50404
8176	S	D	E	N	1973	50404
8177	S	D	E	L	1973	50404
8177	S	D	E	N	1973	50404
8178	S	D	E	L	1973	50404
8178	S	D	E	N	1973	50404
8179	S	D	E	L	1973	50404
8179	S	D	E	N	1973	50404
8181	S	D	E	L	1973	50437
8181	S	D	E	N	1973	50437
8182	S	D	E	L	1973	50437
8182	S	D	E	N	1973	50437
8182	S	D	E	L	1975	92154
8182	S	D	E	N	1975	92154
8183	S	D	E	N	1973	50097
8184	S	D	E	N	1973	50097
8185	S	D	E	N	1973	50097
8189	S	D	E	N	1973	50584
8190	P	D	E	N	1974	70390
8191	S	D	E	N	1973	50595
8192	S	D	F	N	1973	50618
8193	S	D	F	N	1973	50620
8201	S	D	R	N	1973	50727
8201	S	D	E	N	1973	53028
8204	S	D	E	L	1973	55279
8204	S	D	E	N	1973	55279
8206	S	D	E	H	1973	50780
8206	S	D	E	N	1973	50780
8207	S	D	E	L	1973	50814
8207	S	D	E	N	1973	50814

Substance Number	Phys. State	Subject	Language	Temperature	Year	EPIC Number
106-8210	S	D	E	L	1973	50909
8211	S	D	E	L	1973	50921
8212	S	D	E	N	1973	50940
8215	I	T	E	N	1973	51068
8216	I	T	E	N	1973	51068
8217	S	D	E	N	1973	56673
8217	S	S	E	N	1974	84003
8217	S	D	E	N	1974	90283
8218	S	D	E	L	1973	55150
8218	S	D	E	N	1973	55150
8222	S	D	E	L	1975	65472
8222	S	D	E	N	1975	65472
8223	S	S	E	L	1973	52649
8223	S	D	E	N	1973	56673
8223	S	D	E	N	1974	70072
8223	S	T	E	N	1974	70072
8224	S	D	E	N	1973	56673
8224	S	D	E	N	1974	70072
8224	S	T	E	N	1974	70072
8226	S	D	E	N	1973	51151
8227	S	D	E	N	1973	51151
8228	S	T	E	N	1973	51176
8228	S	T	E	L	1973	52441
8228	S	T	E	N	1973	52441
8228	S	D	E	N	1971	57180
8229	S	D	E	L	1973	51183
8229	S	D	E	N	1973	51183
8230	S	D	E	L	1973	51183
8230	S	D	E	N	1973	51183
8231	S	D	E	N	1973	51199
8232	S	D	E	N	1973	51199
8232	S	D	R	N	1974	52920
8232	S	D	E	N	1974	52921
8237	D	D	R	N	1973	51368
8237	D	D	E	N	1973	51369
8237	S	S	E	N	1972	53110
8237	S	D	E	L	1971	57198
8237	S	D	E	N	1971	57198
8237	S	D	R	H	1973	67370
8237	S	D	R	N	1973	67370
8242	S	D	R	N	1974	60471
8242	S	D	E	N	1974	60472
8244	S	D	R	N	1972	56904
8252	S	D	F	N	1973	51479
8256	S	D	E	N	1972	51585
8256	S	D	R	N	1973	52277
8257	S	D	E	N	1973	51659
8261	S	D	R	N	1973	51732
8261	S	D	E	N	1973	79136
8262	S	D	R	N	1973	51732
8262	S	D	R	N	1971	76478
8262	S	D	E	N	1973	79136
8262	S	D	E	N	1971	91502
8265	S	D	F	N	1973	51781
8266	S	D	F	N	1973	51781
8267	D	D	E	N	1973	51796
8268	S	D	F	L	1973	51806
8269	S	D	E	L	1973	51825
8269	S	D	E	L	1971	57177
8269	S	D	E	L	1975	90468
8270	S	D	E	L	1973	51826
8272	S	D	E	N	1973	50781
8273	S	D	E	N	1973	51659
8274	S	D	E	N	1973	51659
8275	S	D	E	N	1973	51659
8276	S	D	E	L	1973	49643
8277	S	D	E	L	1973	49643
8278	S	D	E	L	1973	49643
8279	S	D	E	L	1973	49643
8280	S	D	E	L	1973	49643
8281	S	D	E	L	1973	49643
8282	S	D	E	L	1973	49643
8282	S	D	E	N	1973	49643
8283	S	D	E	L	1973	49643
8284	S	D	E	L	1973	49643
8285	S	D	E	L	1973	49643
8285	S	D	E	N	1973	49643
8287	C	D	E	L	1972	49904
8288	S	T	E	N	1973	51863
8288	S	D	E	N	1958	75751
8288	S	T	E	N	1958	75751
8297	S	D	R	N	1973	52277
8298	S	D	R	N	1973	52281
8300	S	D	R	L	1974	81222
8300	S	T	R	L	1974	81222
8300	S	D	E	N	1975	90064
8300	S	D	E	L	1974	92382
8300	S	T	E	L	1974	92382
8302	S	T	E	L	1973	52441
8302	S	T	E	N	1973	52441
8302	S	D	E	N	1974	60340
8312	D	D	R	N	1974	66790
8312	D	D	E	N	1975	66791
8312	S	D	E	N	1968	53357
8312	S	D	E	L	1968	53358
8312	S	D	E	N	1968	53358
8312	S	D	R	N	1973	55072
8312	S	D	E	N	1974	55073
8312	S	D	E	N	1975	65456
8312	S	D	R	N	1974	66730
8312	S	T	R	N	1974	66730

Phys. State: **A.** Amorphous; **C.** Superconductive; **D.** Doped; **F.** Fibrous or Whisker; **G.** Gas; **I.** Ionized or Plasma; **L.** Liquid; **P.** Powder or Particle; **S.** Solid; **T.** Thin Film
Subject: **D.** Data; **E.** Experiment; **S.** Survey (Review, Compendium, etc.); **T.** Theory
Language: **E.** English; **F.** French; **G.** German; **O.** Other Languages; **R.** Russian
Temperature: **L.** Low (0 to 75K); **N.** Normal (75 to 1273K); **H.** High (above 1273K)

Substance Number	Phys. State	Subject	Language	Temperature	Year	EPIC Number
106-8312	S	D	E	N	1975	66731
8312	S	T	E	N	1975	66731
8312	S	D	R	N	1974	66790
8312	S	D	E	N	1975	66791
8312	S	S	E	N	1970	75905
8312	S	D	R	N	1975	86873
8312	S	D	E	N	1975	86874
8313	S	D	E	N	1970	52688
8316	S	D	E	L	1973	52786
8316	S	D	E	N	1973	52786
8317	S	D	E	L	1973	52786
8317	S	D	E	N	1973	52786
8318	S	T	R	N	1973	52840
8318	S	T	E	N	1973	52841
8319	S	T	R	N	1973	52840
8319	S	T	E	N	1973	52841
8320	S	T	R	N	1973	52840
8320	S	T	E	N	1973	52841
8321	S	T	R	N	1973	52840
8321	S	T	E	N	1973	52841
8322	S	D	E	N	1973	52943
8323	S	T	E	N	1973	52954
8324	S	D	E	L	1972	52964
8324	S	D	E	N	1972	52964
8325	S	D	E	N	1972	53250
8328	S	D	R	N	1973	50727
8328	S	D	E	N	1973	53028
8329	S	D	R	N	1973	50727
8329	S	D	E	N	1973	53028
8330	S	D	R	N	1973	50729
8330	S	D	E	N	1973	53030
8331	S	D	E	L	1974	60325
8331	S	D	E	N	1974	60325
8332	S	D	E	L	1972	53127
8333	S	D	R	N	1971	53129
8333	S	D	E	N	1972	53130
8334	S	D	R	N	1971	53129
8334	S	D	E	N	1972	53130
8349	S	S	E	N	1973	53420
8359	S	S	E	N	1972	53775
8360	S	D	E	L	1973	55279
8360	S	D	E	N	1973	55279
8363	S	D	E	L	1973	51821
8363	S	D	E	N	1973	51821
8363	S	E	E	L	1973	51821
8363	S	E	E	N	1973	51821
8364	S	D	E	N	1973	51890
8365	S	D	E	L	1973	51890
8365	S	D	E	N	1973	51890
8366	S	D	E	L	1973	51890
8366	S	D	E	N	1973	51890
8367	S	D	E	N	1973	51890
8368	S	D	E	N	1973	51883
8368	S	D	R	L	1973	55470
8368	S	D	R	N	1973	55470
8369	S	D	R	N	1973	50658
8370	S	D	R	N	1973	50658
8371	S	D	R	N	1973	50658
8372	S	D	R	N	1973	50658
8373	S	D	R	N	1973	50658
8374	S	S	E	N	1973	50715
8375	S	S	E	N	1973	50715
8375	S	D	E	N	1973	56673
8375	S	D	E	N	1974	70072
8375	S	T	E	N	1974	70072
8375	S	S	E	N	1968	75990
8376	S	S	E	N	1973	50715
8377	S	D	E	N	1973	51753
8378	S	D	E	N	1973	51753
8379	S	D	E	N	1973	51753
8380	S	D	E	N	1973	51753
8381	S	D	E	N	1973	51753
8384	S	D	E	L	1973	50817
8384	S	D	E	N	1973	50817
8384	S	E	E	L	1973	50817
8384	S	E	E	N	1973	50817
8386	S	D	E	L	1972	53698
8387	S	S	E	L	1972	53698
8391	S	D	E	N	1973	57108
8394	S	D	E	N	1975	68704
8394	S	T	E	N	1975	68704
8396	S	S	E	L	1973	52196
8397	S	D	E	L	1973	52649
8398	S	D	E	L	1973	52649
8399	S	D	E	L	1973	52649
8400	S	D	E	L	1973	52101
8401	S	D	E	N	1973	52101
8402	S	D	E	L	1973	52196
8403	S	T	E	N	1974	61161
8403	S	D	E	N	1974	70072
8403	S	T	E	N	1974	70072
8403	S	S	E	N	1968	75990
8404	S	D	E	L	1974	53988
8404	S	D	E	N	1974	53988
8406	S	D	E	L	1974	53988
8406	S	D	E	N	1974	53988
8407	S	D	E	L	1974	53988
8408	S	D	E	L	1974	53988
8409	S	D	E	L	1974	53988
8410	S	D	E	L	1974	53988
8410	S	D	E	N	1974	53988

Substance Number	Phys. State	Subject	Language	Temperature	Year	EPIC Number
106-8411	S	D	E	L	1974	53988
8411	S	D	E	N	1974	53988
8412	S	D	E	L	1974	53988
8413	S	D	E	L	1974	53988
8414	C	D	E	L	1974	53919
8417	S	D	E	L	1974	54327
8418	S	D	E	L	1974	54327
8419	S	D	E	L	1974	54327
8420	S	D	E	L	1974	54327
8420	S	D	E	N	1974	54327
8421	D	D	E	L	1974	54327
8422	S	D	E	L	1974	54326
8422	S	D	E	N	1974	54326
8422	S	D	E	L	1972	55592
8422	S	D	E	N	1972	55592
8426	S	S	E	N	1974	54319
8435	S	D	R	L	1973	55072
8435	S	D	E	L	1974	55073
8436	S	D	R	N	1973	55072
8436	S	D	E	N	1974	55073
8437	S	D	R	N	1973	55072
8437	S	D	E	N	1974	55073
8438	S	D	R	N	1973	55072
8438	S	D	E	N	1974	55073
8439	S	D	R	N	1973	55030
8439	S	D	E	N	1974	55031
8461	S	D	R	N	1974	60461
8461	S	S	R	N	1974	60461
8461	S	D	E	N	1974	60462
8461	S	S	E	N	1974	60462
8468	S	S	R	N	1973	57805
8468	S	S	E	N	1974	57806
8470	S	S	E	N	1974	59403
8472	S	D	E	L	1973	55150
8472	S	D	E	N	1973	55150
8483	S	D	E	L	1974	58058
8483	S	S	E	L	1974	58058
8483	S	T	E	L	1974	58058
8484	S	D	E	L	1974	58058
8484	S	S	E	L	1974	58058
8484	S	T	E	L	1974	58058
8486	T	D	E	N	1974	57998
8487	S	D	R	N	1973	55405
8492	S	D	E	L	1973	56441
8492	S	E	E	L	1973	56441
8492	S	S	E	L	1973	56441
8507	S	D	E	L	1973	52597
8509	P	D	E	N	1974	91407
8509	S	D	E	L	1973	52649
8509	S	D	E	N	1973	56673
8509	S	D	E	L	1975	90117
8509	S	D	E	N	1975	90117
8509	S	D	E	N	1974	91409
8510	S	D	E	N	1974	53865
8510	T	D	E	N	1973	62748
8538	S	D	E	L	1974	61159
8538	S	D	E	N	1974	61159
8539	S	D	E	L	1974	61159
8543	P	S	E	N	1969	75843
8543	S	S	E	N	1970	75833
8544	P	S	E	N	1969	75843
8544	S	S	E	L	1970	75833
8544	S	S	E	N	1970	75833
8546	S	D	R	L	1974	87292
8546	S	D	E	L	1975	87293
8547	S	D	E	N	1973	56673
8547	S	S	E	N	1974	84003
8549	S	D	R	N	1972	60737
8549	S	T	R	L	1972	60737
8549	S	D	E	N	1973	60738
8549	S	T	E	L	1973	60738
8549	S	D	R	N	1974	66730
8549	S	T	R	N	1974	66730
8549	S	D	E	N	1975	66731
8549	S	T	E	N	1975	66731
8549	S	D	R	N	1975	86867
8549	S	S	R	N	1975	86867
8549	S	D	E	N	1975	86868
8549	S	S	E	N	1975	86868
8549	S	D	O	N	1975	90101
8551	S	D	F	N	1973	54833
8553	S	D	E	N	1973	56856
8553	S	E	E	N	1973	56856
8553	S	D	R	N	1971	67825
8557	S	D	F	N	1973	56163
8558	S	D	E	N	1964	93287
8558	S	S	E	N	1964	93287
8559	C	D	R	L	1972	63967
8559	C	T	R	L	1972	63967
8559	C	D	E	L	1972	68424
8559	C	T	E	L	1972	68424
8559	S	D	E	N	1964	93287
8559	S	S	E	N	1964	93287
8560	S	D	E	N	1964	93287
8561	S	D	E	N	1964	93287
8561	S	S	E	N	1964	93287
8562	S	S	E	N	1964	93287
8565	S	D	R	N	1974	67753
8566	S	T	R	N	1972	60729
8566	S	T	E	N	1973	60730
8568	S	D	E	N	1973	54756

Substance Number	Phys. State	Subject	Language	Temperature	Year	EPIC Number
106-8569	S	D	E	N	1973	54764
8570	S	D	E	N	1973	54764
8571	S	D	E	N	1973	54764
8572	S	D	E	N	1973	55139
8573	S	D	E	N	1973	55139
8575	S	D	E	L	1973	55558
8575	S	D	E	N	1973	55558
8576	S	D	E	L	1972	55593
8582	S	D	E	L	1973	55963
8583	S	D	E	L	1973	55963
8584	S	D	E	N	1973	57108
8587	S	D	F	L	1973	55966
8590	S	D	R	N	1972	60737
8590	S	D	E	N	1973	60738
8591	S	D	R	N	1972	60737
8591	S	D	E	N	1973	60738
8591	S	D	R	N	1974	66730
8591	S	T	R	N	1974	66730
8591	S	D	E	N	1975	66731
8591	S	T	E	N	1975	66731
8592	S	D	R	N	1972	60737
8592	S	D	E	N	1973	60738
8593	S	D	R	N	1972	60737
8593	S	D	E	N	1973	60738
8594	S	D	R	N	1972	60737
8594	S	D	E	N	1973	60738
8595	S	D	E	L	1971	57502
8595	S	D	E	N	1971	57502
8597	S	D	E	N	1973	56673
8597	S	D	E	N	1974	70072
8597	S	T	E	N	1974	70072
8598	S	D	E	N	1973	56673
8598	S	D	E	N	1974	70072
8598	S	T	E	N	1974	70072
8599	S	D	E	N	1973	56673
8599	S	D	E	N	1974	70072
8599	S	T	E	N	1974	70072
8600	S	D	E	N	1973	56673
8600	S	D	E	N	1974	70072
8600	S	T	E	N	1974	70072
8601	S	D	E	N	1973	56673
8601	S	D	E	N	1974	70072
8601	S	T	E	N	1974	70072
8602	S	D	E	N	1973	56673
8602	S	D	E	N	1974	70072
8602	S	T	E	N	1974	70072
8603	S	D	E	N	1973	56673
8604	S	D	E	N	1973	56673
8604	S	S	E	N	1974	84003
8605	S	D	E	N	1973	56673
8605	S	S	E	N	1974	84003
8610	S	S	E	N	1974	84846
8620	S	D	G	N	1973	57056
8621	S	D	E	N	1973	57065
8624	S	D	E	N	1973	57108
8626	S	D	F	N	1971	57149
8629	S	D	E	L	1971	57190
8629	S	D	E	L	1971	66903
8630	S	D	E	L	1971	57190
8630	S	D	E	L	1971	66903
8631	S	D	E	L	1971	57190
8631	S	D	E	L	1971	66903
8632	S	D	R	L	1973	57216
8634	S	D	E	L	1971	57502
8634	S	D	E	N	1971	57502
8637	S	D	F	L	1973	57654
8637	S	D	F	N	1973	57654
8638	S	D	E	N	1974	57887
8639	S	D	F	L	1973	57940
8639	S	D	F	N	1973	57940
8642	S	D	R	N	1973	51724
8642	S	D	R	N	1971	66283
8642	S	D	R	N	1971	76478
8642	S	D	E	N	1971	91502
8643	S	D	R	N	1973	51724
8648	C	T	E	L	1974	63380
8649	S	D	E	L	1973	60606
8649	S	S	E	L	1973	60606
8655	S	D	E	L	1974	58505
8656	S	D	G	N	1973	58559
8657	S	D	R	N	1972	58756
8663	S	D	E	L	1975	63278
8663	S	D	E	N	1975	63278
8669	S	D	R	N	1971	66283
8672	S	D	E	N	1971	67020
8680	S	D	R	H	1973	67370
8680	S	D	R	N	1973	67370
8681	S	D	E	L	1973	67485
8681	S	D	E	N	1973	67485
8682	S	D	E	L	1975	90060
8683	S	D	E	L	1975	90060
8713	S	D	E	L	1975	90116
8713	S	D	E	N	1975	90116
8713	S	D	E	N	1974	92436
8714	P	D	E	N	1974	91407
8715	P	D	E	N	1974	91407
8716	P	D	E	N	1974	91407
8717	P	D	E	N	1974	91407
8718	S	D	E	L	1975	90117
8718	S	D	E	N	1975	90117
8718	S	S	E	N	1975	90117

Phys. State: **A.** Amorphous; **C.** Superconductive; **D.** Doped; **F.** Fibrous or Whisker; **G.** Gas; **I.** Ionized or Plasma; **L.** Liquid; **P.** Powder or Particle; **S.** Solid; **T.** Thin Film
Subject: **D.** Data; **E.** Experiment; **S.** Survey (Review, Compendium, etc.); **T.** Theory
Language: **E.** English; **F.** French; **G.** German; **O.** Other Languages; **R.** Russian
Temperature: **L.** Low (0 to 75K); **N.** Normal (75 to 1273K); **H.** High (above 1273K)

Substance Number	Phys. State	Subject	Language	Temperature	Year	EPIC Number
106-8718	S	D	E	N	1974	91409
8719	S	D	E	N	1975	90117
8719	S	D	E	N	1974	91409
8720	S	D	E	L	1975	90117
8720	S	D	E	N	1975	90117
8720	S	D	E	N	1974	91409
8721	S	D	E	L	1975	90117
8721	S	D	E	L	1974	91409
8722	S	D	E	L	1975	90117
8722	S	D	E	L	1974	91409
8735	S	D	R	N	1974	67753
8738	S	D	R	N	1971	67825
8741	S	D	E	N	1975	100033
8741	S	T	E	N	1975	100033
8750	S	D	R	N	1973	52665
8750	S	D	E	N	1974	63233
8753	S	D	R	N	1972	76545
8753	S	D	E	N	1972	91596
8754	C	D	R	L	1974	81228
8754	C	D	E	L	1974	92358
8754	S	D	R	L	1974	81228
8754	S	D	E	L	1974	92358
8755	C	D	R	L	1974	81228
8755	C	D	E	L	1974	92358
8755	S	D	R	L	1974	81228
8755	S	D	E	L	1974	92358
8759	S	D	R	N	1971	76478
8759	S	D	E	N	1971	91502
8760	S	D	R	N	1972	76522
8760	S	T	R	N	1972	76522
8760	S	D	E	N	1972	91508
8760	S	T	E	N	1972	91508
8761	S	D	R	N	1972	76522
8761	S	T	R	N	1972	76522
8761	S	D	E	N	1972	91508
8761	S	T	E	N	1972	91508
8769	S	D	E	L	1975	92154
8769	S	D	E	N	1975	92154
8771	S	D	E	L	1975	92154
8771	S	D	E	N	1975	92154
8779	S	S	E	N	1974	84003
8779	S	D	E	L	1975	91864
8779	S	D	E	N	1975	91864
8779	S	S	E	L	1975	91864
8779	S	S	E	N	1975	91864
8779	S	T	E	L	1975	91864
8779	S	T	E	N	1975	91864
8780	S	D	E	L	1975	91864
8780	S	D	E	N	1975	91864
8780	S	S	E	L	1975	91864
8780	S	S	E	N	1975	91864
8780	S	T	E	L	1975	91864
8780	S	T	E	N	1975	91864
8781	S	D	E	N	1974	70072
8781	S	T	E	N	1974	70072
8782	S	D	E	L	1967	100960
8782	S	E	E	L	1967	100960
8782	S	S	E	L	1967	100960
8782	S	T	E	L	1967	100960
8793	S	D	R	N	1970	76453
8793	S	T	R	N	1970	76453
8793	S	D	E	N	1970	91544
8793	S	T	E	N	1970	91544
8794	S	D	R	N	1970	76453
8794	S	T	R	N	1970	76453
8794	S	D	E	N	1970	91544
8794	S	T	E	N	1970	91544
8800	S	D	R	N	1974	93455
8800	S	T	R	N	1974	93455
8800	S	D	E	N	1974	93456
8800	S	T	E	N	1974	93456
8801	S	D	E	N	1973	56280
8801	S	T	E	L	1973	56280
8801	S	T	E	N	1973	56280
8802	S	D	E	N	1973	56280
8802	S	T	E	L	1973	56280
8803	S	D	E	N	1973	56280
8803	S	T	E	L	1973	56280
8803	S	T	E	N	1973	56280
8804	S	D	E	N	1973	56280
8804	S	T	E	L	1973	56280
8804	S	T	E	N	1973	56280
8805	S	D	E	N	1973	56280
8805	S	T	E	N	1973	56280
8810	S	D	E	N	1974	65213
8810	S	T	E	N	1974	65213
8811	S	D	R	N	1974	65411
8811	S	D	E	N	1975	65412
8812	S	D	E	N	1975	65456
8813	S	D	E	L	1975	65472
8813	S	D	E	N	1975	65472
8814	S	D	E	N	1975	65472
8815	S	D	E	N	1975	65472
8816	S	D	E	N	1975	65472
8818	S	D	R	N	1971	66283
8819	S	D	R	N	1971	66283
8820	S	D	R	N	1971	66283
8824	S	D	R	N	1972	68551
8824	S	T	R	N	1972	68551
8824	S	D	E	N	1972	68552
8824	S	T	E	N	1972	68552

Substance Number	Phys. State	Subject	Language	Temperature	Year	EPIC Number
106-8833	S	D	E	N	1973	65678
8834	S	D	E	N	1973	65678
8835	S	D	E	N	1973	65678
8839	S	D	E	N	1958	75751
8839	S	T	E	N	1958	75751
8840	S	D	E	N	1958	75751
8840	S	T	E	N	1958	75751
8841	S	S	E	N	1969	75903
8842	S	S	E	N	1969	75903
8843	S	S	E	N	1969	75903
8844	S	S	E	N	1969	75903
8845	S	S	E	N	1969	75903
8846	S	S	E	N	1969	75903
108-0005	L	S	E	N	1951	98663
0014	S	D	R	N	1974	63112
0014	S	S	R	N	1974	63112
0014	S	T	R	N	1974	63112
0014	S	D	E	N	1975	63113
0014	S	S	E	N	1975	63113
0014	S	T	E	N	1975	63113
0052	S	S	E	L	1975	92915
0087	D	D	R	N	1974	65375
0087	D	T	R	N	1974	65375
0087	D	D	E	N	1975	65376
0087	D	T	E	N	1975	65376
0087	S	T	E	N	1973	52954
8001	S	T	E	L	1973	51134
8001	S	D	E	L	1974	58010
8007	S	D	F	N	1973	50461
8007	S	D	R	N	1974	80756
8007	S	D	E	N	1974	95249
8008	S	D	E	L	1973	50874
8010	S	D	G	N	1973	52086
8010	S	D	R	N	1973	55474
8010	S	D	E	N	1975	90866
8012	S	S	E	N	1972	52983
8012	S	D	E	L	1974	61156
8013	S	D	R	N	1973	51313
8013	S	D	E	N	1974	60293
8013	S	S	E	N	1974	60293
8013	S	D	E	N	1973	62170
8018	S	D	G	N	1973	49864
8019	S	D	G	N	1973	49864
8020	S	D	G	N	1973	49864
8021	S	D	G	N	1973	49864
8022	S	D	G	N	1973	49864
8023	S	D	G	N	1973	49864
8024	S	D	G	N	1973	49864
8027	S	D	E	N	1973	51753
8029	S	D	E	L	1973	52658
8029	S	D	E	N	1973	52658
8030	S	D	E	L	1973	52597
8034	S	D	R	N	1974	58108
8034	S	D	E	N	1974	58109
8036	S	S	E	N	1973	54004
8037	S	S	E	N	1973	54004
8038	S	S	E	N	1973	54004
8041	S	D	E	L	1974	58909
8042	S	D	E	N	1973	54003
8048	S	D	E	L	1973	62753
8049	S	D	E	L	1974	60293
8049	S	S	E	N	1974	60293
8050	S	D	E	N	1974	60293
8050	S	S	E	N	1974	60293
8051	S	D	E	N	1974	60293
8051	S	S	E	N	1974	60293
8052	S	D	E	L	1974	60293
8052	S	D	E	N	1974	60293
8052	S	S	E	N	1974	60293
8053	S	D	E	L	1974	60387
8058	S	D	E	L	1975	90116
8058	S	D	E	L	1974	92436
8058	S	D	E	N	1974	92436
8061	S	D	E	N	1972	49784
8061	S	S	E	N	1972	49784
109-0025	A	S	E	N	1973	53052
0025	D	D	E	L	1973	50887
0025	D	S	E	N	1973	53052
0025	D	D	E	N	1974	54573
0025	D	D	R	N	1973	55406
0025	D	D	E	N	1974	57821
0025	S	D	E	N	1973	50608
0025	S	D	E	N	1973	50879
0025	S	D	E	L	1973	50887
0025	S	D	E	N	1973	50887
0025	S	T	E	N	1973	51158
0025	S	T	E	N	1973	51176
0025	S	S	E	N	1973	53052
0025	S	S	E	N	1974	53596
0025	S	D	E	L	1974	54122
0025	S	D	E	N	1974	54573
0025	S	D	R	N	1973	55406
0025	S	D	E	N	1974	57821
0025	S	D	E	N	1975	66530
0025	S	S	E	L	1970	75905
0036	S	D	R	N	1973	50357
0036	S	D	E	N	1973	50358
8001	S	D	E	L	1974	58010
8015	S	D	R	N	1973	50568

Substance Number	Phys. State	Subject	Language	Temperature	Year	EPIC Number
109-8015	S	D	E	N	1973	51153
8015	S	D	G	N	1973	52086
8015	S	D	R	N	1973	55474
8015	S	D	E	N	1974	70072
8015	S	T	E	N	1974	70072
8016	S	D	R	N	1973	50568
8016	S	D	R	N	1973	51313
8016	S	D	E	N	1973	62170
8016	S	D	E	N	1974	70072
8016	S	T	E	N	1974	70072
8017	D	D	E	N	1974	60291
8017	D	T	E	N	1974	60291
8017	T	D	E	N	1974	60291
8017	T	T	E	N	1974	60291
8019	S	D	E	L	1973	50879
8019	S	D	R	N	1973	52564
8019	S	D	E	N	1973	57789
8019	S	D	E	L	1974	62346
8019	S	S	E	L	1974	62346
8019	S	T	E	L	1974	62346
8020	D	D	E	L	1972	53158
8020	D	S	E	N	1973	56287
8020	S	D	E	L	1973	50879
8020	S	T	E	N	1973	51158
8020	S	D	E	L	1972	53158
8020	S	S	E	L	1970	75905
8020	S	D	R	L	1975	86839
8020	S	D	E	L	1975	86840
8020	T	S	E	N	1973	56287
8020	T	D	E	L	1974	58008
8021	S	D	E	L	1973	50879
8021	S	D	R	N	1973	52564
8021	S	S	R	N	1973	52564
8021	S	D	E	N	1973	57789
8021	S	S	E	N	1973	57789
8029	S	D	F	L	1973	51499
8029	S	D	F	N	1973	51499
8029	S	D	R	L	1973	67854
8029	S	D	R	N	1973	67854
8031	S	D	E	N	1973	51822
8031	S	D	E	L	1973	55943
8031	S	D	E	L	1974	58909
8033	S	D	E	L	1972	53158
8036	S	D	E	N	1973	51753
8036	S	D	E	L	1973	53293
8036	S	D	E	N	1973	53293
8039	S	D	E	L	1973	52597
8039	S	D	R	N	1973	55026
8039	S	D	E	N	1974	55027
8039	S	T	R	N	1974	58108
8039	S	T	E	N	1974	58109
8040	S	D	R	N	1973	52564
8040	S	D	E	N	1973	57789
8041	S	D	R	N	1973	52564
8041	S	D	E	N	1973	57789
8042	S	D	R	N	1973	52564
8042	S	D	E	N	1973	57789
8043	S	D	R	N	1973	52564
8043	S	D	E	N	1973	57789
8044	S	D	R	N	1973	52564
8044	S	D	E	N	1973	57789
8045	S	D	R	N	1973	52564
8045	S	D	E	N	1973	57789
8046	S	D	R	N	1973	52564
8046	S	D	E	N	1973	57789
8047	S	D	R	N	1973	52564
8047	S	D	E	N	1973	57789
8048	S	D	R	N	1973	52564
8048	S	D	E	N	1973	57789
8049	S	D	R	N	1973	52564
8049	S	D	E	N	1973	57789
8050	S	D	R	N	1974	58108
8050	S	D	E	N	1974	58109
8051	S	D	R	N	1973	55406
8051	S	D	E	N	1974	57821
8052	S	D	E	L	1974	58909
8053	S	S	E	L	1974	57305
8053	S	S	E	N	1974	57305
8054	S	S	E	L	1974	57305
8054	S	S	E	N	1974	57305
8056	S	D	E	L	1974	61159
8058	S	D	E	L	1974	61395
8059	S	D	E	L	1974	61395
8060	S	D	E	L	1974	61395
8061	S	D	E	L	1974	61159
8062	S	D	E	L	1974	61159
8064	S	D	R	L	1975	86839
8064	S	D	E	L	1975	86840
8067	S	D	E	N	1973	54003
8069	S	D	E	N	1973	56162
8070	S	S	E	N	1973	56342
8071	S	D	E	N	1973	56526
8072	S	D	E	L	1974	56610
8072	S	D	E	N	1974	70072
8072	S	T	E	N	1974	70072
8073	S	D	E	L	1974	56610
8074	S	D	E	L	1974	92437
8074	S	D	E	N	1974	92437
8081	S	D	E	L	1973	62753
8086	S	D	E	L	1975	90116
8086	S	D	E	N	1974	92436

Phys. State: **A.** Amorphous; **C.** Superconductive; **D.** Doped; **F.** Fibrous or Whisker; **G.** Gas; **I.** Ionized or Plasma; **L.** Liquid; **P.** Powder or Particle; **S.** Solid; **T.** Thin Film
Subject: **D.** Data; **E.** Experiment; **S.** Survey (Review, Compendium, etc.); **T.** Theory
Language: **E.** English; **F.** French; **G.** German; **O.** Other Languages; **R.** Russian
Temperature: **L.** Low (0 to 75K); **N.** Normal (75 to 1273K); **H.** High (above 1273K)

Substance Number	Phys. State	Subject	Language	Temperature	Year	EPIC Number
109-8087	S	D	E	L	1974	92437
8087	S	D	E	N	1974	92437
8088	S	D	E	L	1974	92437
8088	S	D	E	N	1974	92437
8089	S	D	E	L	1974	92437
8090	S	D	E	L	1974	92437
8090	S	D	E	N	1974	92437
8091	S	D	E	L	1974	92437
8091	S	D	E	N	1974	92437
8092	S	D	E	L	1974	92437
8092	S	D	E	N	1974	92437
8093	S	D	E	L	1974	92437
8093	S	D	E	N	1974	92437
8094	S	D	E	L	1974	92437
8095	S	D	R	L	1973	67854
8095	S	D	R	N	1973	67854
8098	S	D	E	N	1974	70072
8098	S	T	E	N	1974	70072
8102	S	D	E	N	1972	49784
8102	S	S	E	N	1972	49784
110-0007	S	D	E	N	1973	57680
0011	S	S	E	N	1973	53048
0011	S	S	E	N	1973	55935
0018	S	D	E	L	1973	49503
0018	S	D	E	L	1973	50957
0018	S	D	R	N	1973	52107
0018	S	D	E	N	1973	54543
0019	S	D	R	L	1973	57231
0019	S	D	E	L	1970	63653
0021	S	T	E	N	1976	101501
0025	A	S	E	N	1973	53050
0025	S	D	E	N	1976	102012
0028	S	S	E	N	1974	58007
0030	S	D	R	N	1974	60461
0030	S	S	R	N	1974	60461
0030	S	D	E	N	1974	60462
0030	S	S	E	N	1974	60462
0065	S	D	E	N	1973	49659
0065	S	D	R	N	1974	63165
0065	S	T	R	N	1974	63165
0065	S	D	E	N	1975	63166
0065	S	T	E	N	1975	63166
0173	S	D	E	N	1974	60390
0193	S	S	E	L	1973	53047
0193	S	S	E	N	1973	53047
0193	S	S	E	N	1973	53048
0194	D	D	F	N	1973	51479
0194	D	D	R	N	1973	55407
0194	D	D	E	N	1974	57824
0194	D	D	R	N	1974	58092
0194	D	D	E	N	1974	58093
0194	S	D	R	N	1973	50307
0194	S	D	E	N	1973	50308
0194	S	D	F	N	1973	50461
0194	S	D	E	N	1973	50811
0194	S	D	E	N	1972	56592
0194	S	D	E	N	1974	57974
0194	S	S	E	N	1974	57974
0194	S	D	E	N	1974	58003
0194	S	D	R	N	1973	58312
0194	S	T	R	N	1974	58662
0194	S	D	R	N	1974	60467
0194	S	D	E	N	1974	60468
0194	S	D	E	N	1974	61195
0194	S	D	R	N	1974	62018
0194	S	T	R	N	1974	62018
0194	S	D	E	N	1974	62019
0194	S	T	E	N	1974	62019
0194	S	D	R	N	1974	80756
0194	S	D	E	N	1974	95249
0199	S	D	F	N	1973	50461
0199	S	D	R	N	1974	80756
0199	S	D	E	N	1974	95249
0200	S	D	E	N	1974	58007
0202	S	D	E	N	1972	50530
0224	L	D	E	N	1973	57547
0245	S	D	F	N	1973	50461
0299	S	D	E	N	1973	50957
0299	S	D	E	L	1973	51145
0299	S	D	E	N	1973	51145
0299	S	D	E	N	1973	52952
0299	S	D	E	N	1974	60350
0299	S	D	E	L	1974	64713
0299	S	D	E	N	1974	64713
0299	S	T	E	L	1974	64713
0299	S	T	E	N	1974	64713
0369	D	D	E	N	1973	51199
0369	D	D	R	N	1974	52920
0369	D	D	E	N	1974	52921
0369	S	D	E	N	1973	51199
0369	S	D	R	N	1974	63084
0369	S	T	R	N	1974	63084
0369	S	T	E	N	1975	63085
0395	S	T	E	N	1973	51863
0395	S	D	E	N	1958	75751
0395	S	T	E	N	1958	75751
0411	S	D	E	N	1968	53357
0411	S	D	R	N	1968	66266
8013	S	D	E	N	1974	60390
8014	S	D	E	N	1973	51187

Substance Number	Phys. State	Subject	Language	Temperature	Year	EPIC Number
110-8029	S	D	E	N	1951	75749
8029	S	T	E	N	1951	75749
8036	T	S	E	N	1974	58000
8038	T	S	E	N	1974	58000
8039	S	D	E	N	1973	49659
8039	S	D	E	L	1973	50576
8039	S	D	E	N	1973	50576
8039	S	S	R	N	1973	57805
8039	S	S	E	N	1974	57806
8039	S	D	R	N	1974	60461
8039	S	S	R	N	1974	60461
8039	S	D	E	N	1974	60462
8039	S	S	E	N	1974	60462
8041	S	D	R	N	1974	60461
8041	S	S	R	N	1974	60461
8041	S	D	E	N	1974	60462
8041	S	S	E	N	1974	60462
8041	S	D	E	N	1975	90065
8041	S	T	E	N	1975	90065
8045	S	D	E	L	1973	49997
8045	S	D	E	N	1973	49997
8046	S	S	E	N	1971	59443
8049	S	D	E	N	1973	50038
8049	S	D	F	L	1969	75759
8049	S	T	F	L	1969	75759
8050	S	D	E	N	1973	50170
8051	S	D	E	N	1974	57974
8051	S	S	E	N	1974	57974
8051	S	D	E	N	1974	60302
8054	T	D	E	N	1973	51123
8057	S	D	F	N	1973	50461
8059	S	D	E	N	1972	50530
8060	S	D	R	N	1973	50568
8061	S	D	E	N	1973	50595
8062	S	D	E	N	1973	50595
8066	S	D	E	L	1973	50868
8066	S	D	E	N	1973	50868
8066	S	D	R	N	1974	60461
8066	S	S	R	N	1974	60461
8066	S	D	E	N	1974	60462
8066	S	S	E	N	1974	60462
8067	S	D	G	N	1973	52086
8067	S	D	E	N	1973	53819
8067	S	D	R	N	1973	55474
8068	S	D	G	N	1973	52086
8068	S	D	R	N	1973	55474
8068	S	D	E	N	1974	70072
8068	S	T	E	N	1974	70072
8069	S	D	G	N	1973	52086
8069	S	D	R	N	1973	55474
8070	S	T	O	N	1973	51531
8070	S	D	E	N	1973	65519
8071	S	D	E	L	1973	51175
8071	S	D	E	N	1973	51175
8072	S	D	E	N	1973	51175
8073	D	D	R	N	1973	52114
8073	D	D	G	N	1972	54629
8073	D	D	E	N	1973	54630
8073	D	D	E	N	1973	54921
8073	S	S	E	N	1973	51186
8073	S	T	O	N	1973	51531
8073	S	D	E	N	1973	51911
8074	S	D	R	N	1973	51313
8074	S	D	E	N	1973	62170
8074	S	D	R	L	1974	66770
8074	S	T	R	L	1974	66770
8074	S	D	E	L	1975	66771
8074	S	T	E	L	1975	66771
8074	S	S	E	N	1974	84003
8076	S	D	F	N	1973	51500
8077	S	D	R	N	1973	51540
8077	S	D	G	N	1950	53501
8077	S	D	E	N	1972	53502
8077	S	D	E	N	1973	63179
8078	S	D	E	L	1973	51652
8080	S	D	E	N	1973	51761
8081	S	D	F	N	1973	51781
8082	S	D	F	N	1973	51781
8082	S	D	E	N	1973	56343
8083	S	D	F	N	1973	51781
8085	S	D	E	L	1973	49643
8086	S	D	E	L	1973	49643
8087	S	D	E	L	1973	49643
8087	S	D	E	N	1973	49643
8088	S	T	E	N	1973	51863
8088	S	D	E	N	1958	75751
8088	S	T	E	N	1958	75751
8089	S	T	E	N	1973	51863
8089	S	D	E	N	1958	75751
8089	S	T	E	N	1958	75751
8090	D	D	O	N	1975	90682
8090	S	D	E	N	1973	51911
8090	S	D	R	N	1972	58201
8090	S	T	R	N	1972	58201
8092	S	D	G	N	1973	52086
8092	S	D	R	N	1973	55474
8092	S	D	E	N	1974	70072
8092	S	T	E	N	1974	70072
8092	S	S	E	N	1968	75990
8097	S	D	E	N	1973	52621
8098	S	D	E	N	1974	57999

Substance Number	Phys. State	Subject	Language	Temperature	Year	EPIC Number
110-8098	T	D	E	N	1974	53733
8099	S	D	E	L	1973	52789
8100	S	D	E	L	1973	52789
8102	S	D	E	N	1973	50944
8102	S	E	E	N	1973	50944
8102	S	D	E	N	1973	60604
8102	S	S	E	N	1973	60604
8102	S	T	E	N	1973	60604
8102	S	D	E	H	1973	101641
8103	S	T	R	N	1973	52840
8103	S	T	E	N	1973	52841
8103	S	D	R	N	1974	60467
8103	S	D	E	N	1974	60468
8104	S	T	R	N	1973	52840
8104	S	T	E	N	1973	52841
8105	S	D	R	N	1973	52862
8105	S	D	E	N	1973	52863
8105	S	D	F	N	1973	57670
8106	S	D	E	N	1972	52964
8107	S	D	E	N	1972	52964
8108	S	D	R	N	1973	50729
8108	S	D	E	N	1973	53030
8109	S	D	R	N	1973	50729
8109	S	D	E	N	1973	53030
8110	S	D	R	N	1973	50729
8110	S	D	E	N	1973	53030
8111	S	D	R	N	1973	50729
8111	S	D	E	N	1973	53030
8112	T	D	R	N	1973	55897
8117	S	D	G	N	1950	53501
8117	S	D	E	N	1972	53502
8121	S	D	E	N	1973	65524
8122	S	S	E	N	1962	58977
8123	S	D	F	L	1973	51110
8123	S	D	F	N	1973	51110
8123	S	D	E	L	1974	53624
8123	S	D	E	N	1974	53624
8124	S	D	E	L	1973	51821
8124	S	D	E	N	1973	51821
8124	S	E	E	L	1973	51821
8124	S	E	E	N	1973	51821
8126	S	D	E	N	1973	51891
8127	S	D	R	N	1973	50658
8128	S	S	E	N	1973	50715
8128	S	D	E	L	1974	56610
8128	S	S	E	N	1974	84003
8129	S	S	E	N	1973	50715
8130	S	S	E	N	1973	50715
8130	S	D	E	N	1974	70072
8130	S	T	E	N	1974	70072
8130	S	S	E	N	1974	84003
8131	S	S	E	N	1973	50715
8132	A	D	E	L	1974	62337
8132	A	D	E	N	1974	62337
8132	S	S	E	N	1973	50715
8132	S	D	F	H	1973	53869
8132	S	D	F	N	1973	53869
8132	S	D	R	N	1973	55474
8132	S	D	E	N	1974	70072
8132	S	T	E	N	1974	70072
8132	S	S	E	N	1974	84003
8133	S	S	E	N	1973	50715
8133	S	D	R	N	1973	55474
8134	S	D	E	L	1973	50817
8134	S	D	E	N	1973	50817
8134	S	E	E	L	1973	50817
8134	S	E	E	N	1973	50817
8138	S	S	E	L	1973	52196
8139	S	D	E	N	1973	52623
8140	S	D	E	N	1973	52623
8141	S	D	E	N	1973	52623
8142	S	D	E	N	1973	52623
8143	S	D	E	L	1973	52196
8144	S	D	E	L	1973	52196
8145	S	D	E	L	1973	52196
8146	S	D	E	N	1973	52689
8147	S	D	E	N	1973	52689
8148	S	T	E	N	1973	52689
8149	S	T	E	N	1973	52689
8150	S	T	E	N	1973	52689
8171	S	D	R	N	1974	58126
8171	S	D	E	N	1974	58127
8172	S	D	R	N	1974	58126
8172	S	D	E	N	1974	58127
8173	S	D	E	N	1974	58007
8174	S	D	E	N	1974	58007
8175	S	D	E	N	1974	58007
8176	S	D	E	N	1974	58003
8188	S	D	R	N	1974	60429
8188	S	D	E	N	1974	60430
8189	S	D	E	L	1974	61159
8189	S	D	E	N	1974	61159
8192	S	D	E	L	1974	61159
8193	S	D	E	L	1974	61159
8194	S	D	E	L	1974	61159
8194	S	D	E	N	1974	61159
8195	S	D	E	L	1974	61159
8195	S	D	E	N	1974	61159
8196	S	D	E	L	1974	61159
8198	S	D	E	N	1973	53882
8200	S	D	F	N	1973	54697

Phys. State: **A.** Amorphous; **C.** Superconductive; **D.** Doped; **F.** Fibrous or Whisker; **G.** Gas; **I.** Ionized or Plasma; **L.** Liquid; **P.** Powder or Particle; **S.** Solid; **T.** Thin Film
Subject: **D.** Data; **E.** Experiment; **S.** Survey (Review, Compendium, etc.); **T.** Theory
Language: **E.** English; **F.** French; **G.** German; **O.** Other Languages; **R.** Russian
Temperature: **L.** Low (0 to 75K); **N.** Normal (75 to 1273K); **H.** High (above 1273K)

Substance Number	Phys. State	Subject	Language	Temperature	Year	EPIC Number
110-8201	S	D	F	L	1973	54750
8202	S	D	E	N	1973	55663
8205	S	D	E	N	1973	57618
8207	S	D	E	L	1973	55963
8208	S	D	E	N	1973	56106
8216	S	D	E	N	1973	57124
8217	S	D	E	N	1973	57124
8219	S	D	E	N	1971	57057
8220	S	D	E	N	1971	57157
8222	D	D	O	N	1973	57898
8223	S	D	F	L	1973	57938
8223	S	D	F	N	1973	57938
8230	S	D	G	N	1973	58559
8231	S	D	E	L	1973	58633
8231	S	D	E	N	1973	58633
8234	C	D	E	L	1975	87154
8235	S	D	E	N	1974	60390
8236	S	D	E	N	1974	60390
8238	S	D	E	L	1975	63278
8245	S	D	R	N	1973	51289
8247	S	D	E	N	1971	67020
8248	S	D	E	N	1971	67020
8254	S	D	R	N	1974	67753
8260	S	D	E	N	1975	100033
8260	S	T	E	N	1975	100033
8262	S	D	E	N	1974	70072
8262	S	T	E	N	1974	70072
8265	S	D	R	N	1974	81234
8265	S	T	R	N	1974	81234
8265	S	D	E	N	1974	92364
8265	S	T	E	N	1974	92364
8268	S	D	E	N	1975	90801
8268	S	T	E	N	1975	90801
8269	S	D	E	N	1975	90801
8269	S	T	E	N	1975	90801
8270	S	D	E	N	1974	70072
8270	S	T	E	N	1974	70072
8271	S	D	E	N	1974	70072
8271	S	T	E	N	1974	70072
8276	S	D	R	N	1975	85350
8276	S	T	R	N	1975	85350
8276	S	D	E	N	1976	94077
8276	S	T	E	N	1976	94077
8278	S	D	R	L	1974	66770
8278	S	T	R	L	1974	66770
8278	S	D	E	L	1975	66771
8278	S	T	E	L	1975	66771
8281	L	D	E	N	1973	65678
8282	S	D	E	N	1973	65678
8283	S	D	E	L	1971	65747
8284	S	D	E	N	1958	75751
8284	S	T	E	N	1958	75751
8285	S	D	E	N	1958	75751
8285	S	T	E	N	1958	75751
8286	S	D	E	N	1958	75751
8286	S	T	E	N	1958	75751
8287	S	D	E	N	1958	75751
8287	S	T	E	N	1958	75751
8288	S	D	E	N	1958	75751
8288	S	T	E	N	1958	75751
8289	S	D	E	N	1958	75751
8289	S	T	E	N	1958	75751
111-0003	S	D	E	L	1975	63323
0003	S	S	E	L	1975	63323
0003	S	T	E	L	1975	63323
0003	S	S	E	L	1975	92915
0006	S	S	E	N	1969	68115
0008	S	S	E	N	1972	53227
0008	S	D	R	N	1974	58130
0008	S	S	R	N	1974	58130
0008	S	D	E	N	1974	58131
0008	S	S	E	N	1974	58131
0008	S	S	E	N	1965	87703
0008	S	S	E	N	1971	87884
0008	S	S	E	N	1972	87889
0008	S	D	R	N	1974	90206
0008	S	D	E	N	1975	90207
0008	S	D	E	N	1974	90545
0015	S	S	E	N	1969	68115
0021	S	S	E	N	1971	87884
0046	S	D	E	L	1973	53702
0046	S	D	E	N	1974	53898
0098	S	S	E	N	1969	68115
8002	S	S	E	N	1971	87884
8007	S	D	F	N	1970	49775
8007	S	E	F	N	1970	49775
8008	S	D	F	N	1970	49775
8008	S	E	F	N	1970	49775
8016	L	D	R	N	1973	49578
8016	S	D	R	N	1973	49578
8017	L	D	R	N	1973	49578
8017	S	D	R	N	1973	49578
8018	L	D	R	N	1973	49578
8018	S	D	R	N	1973	49578
8020	S	D	E	L	1973	52484
8021	L	S	E	H	1969	94149
8021	L	S	E	N	1969	94149
8021	S	S	E	N	1969	94149
8027	S	D	E	N	1973	50128
8029	S	D	R	L	1973	50353

Substance Number	Phys. State	Subject	Language	Temperature	Year	EPIC Number
111-8029	S	D	R	N	1973	50353
8029	S	D	E	L	1973	50354
8029	S	D	E	N	1973	50354
8031	S	S	E	N	1972	87889
8032	S	D	E	N	1973	50825
8033	S	D	E	N	1973	50825
8038	D	D	E	N	1973	51886
8038	S	D	E	N	1973	51886
8038	T	D	E	N	1973	51191
8038	T	D	E	N	1973	51192
8039	T	D	E	N	1973	51192
8041	D	D	E	L	1973	51203
8041	D	D	E	N	1973	51203
8041	S	D	E	L	1973	51202
8041	S	D	E	N	1973	51202
8043	S	D	E	N	1973	51822
8043	S	D	E	L	1974	58909
8043	S	D	E	N	1974	58909
8044	S	S	E	N	1973	50715
8044	S	D	E	L	1973	51162
8044	S	T	E	N	1973	52951
8044	S	D	E	N	1974	53596
8044	S	T	E	N	1974	53596
8044	S	S	E	N	1973	54004
8044	S	T	E	L	1971	60950
8044	S	T	E	N	1971	60950
8044	S	S	E	N	1968	75990
8045	S	D	G	N	1973	49864
8045	S	D	E	L	1971	57503
8046	S	D	G	N	1973	49864
8047	S	D	G	N	1973	49864
8048	S	D	G	N	1973	49864
8049	S	D	G	N	1973	49864
8050	S	D	G	N	1973	49864
8052	S	D	E	L	1973	51940
8053	S	D	E	L	1973	51940
8054	S	D	E	N	1973	52065
8055	S	D	F	L	1973	52198
8055	S	D	R	N	1971	66283
8058	S	S	E	L	1967	66157
8058	S	S	E	N	1967	66157
8058	S	D	E	N	1975	68710
8058	S	T	E	N	1975	68710
8059	S	D	E	L	1973	52486
8059	S	D	E	N	1973	52486
8060	S	D	E	L	1973	52486
8060	S	D	E	N	1973	52486
8061	S	D	R	N	1974	58094
8061	S	D	E	N	1974	58095
8061	S	D	R	N	1974	87294
8061	S	D	E	N	1975	87295
8062	S	T	E	N	1973	52951
8063	S	T	E	N	1973	52951
8064	S	T	E	N	1973	52951
8065	S	D	E	L	1972	52969
8065	S	D	E	N	1972	52969
8065	S	D	E	L	1972	53158
8065	S	D	E	N	1972	53158
8066	S	D	E	L	1972	52969
8066	S	D	E	L	1972	53010
8066	S	D	E	L	1972	53158
8067	S	D	E	L	1972	53010
8067	S	D	E	L	1972	53158
8071	S	D	E	L	1972	53158
8072	S	D	E	L	1972	53158
8074	S	D	E	N	1968	53358
8076	S	S	E	N	1973	50715
8083	S	S	E	N	1973	50715
8083	S	D	E	L	1975	90801
8083	S	D	E	N	1975	90801
8083	S	T	E	L	1975	90801
8083	S	T	E	N	1975	90801
8084	S	S	E	N	1973	50715
8085	S	S	E	N	1973	50715
8086	S	D	E	N	1973	51753
8089	S	D	E	L	1973	52597
8091	S	D	E	L	1938	60789
8092	S	D	E	L	1974	54572
8092	S	D	E	N	1974	54572
8094	S	D	E	L	1971	57146
8105	S	D	R	N	1974	58108
8105	S	D	E	N	1974	58109
8106	S	D	E	L	1974	58010
8107	S	D	R	N	1971	66283
8111	S	S	E	N	1973	54004
8117	S	D	E	L	1973	57111
8120	S	D	E	L	1974	58909
8120	S	D	E	N	1974	58909
8123	S	D	E	N	1975	68710
8123	S	T	E	N	1975	68710
8126	S	D	R	N	1971	66283
8130	S	D	E	N	1973	54003
8135	S	D	E	N	1974	57144
8136	S	D	R	N	1973	51724
8136	S	D	R	N	1971	66283
8137	L	D	E	H	1974	61375
8138	P	D	E	L	1973	60609
8138	P	T	E	L	1973	60609
8139	S	D	R	N	1971	66283
8140	S	D	R	N	1971	66283
8141	S	D	R	N	1971	66283

Substance Number	Phys. State	Subject	Language	Temperature	Year	EPIC Number
111-8142	S	D	R	N	1971	66283
8143	S	D	R	N	1971	66283
8144	S	D	R	N	1971	66283
8145	S	D	R	N	1971	66283
8146	S	D	R	N	1971	66283
8147	S	D	R	N	1971	66283
8149	S	D	R	N	1971	66283
8150	S	D	R	N	1971	66283
8159	A	D	E	L	1974	90538
8159	S	D	E	L	1974	90538
8178	S	D	E	L	1975	90116
8178	S	D	E	N	1975	90116
8178	S	D	E	N	1974	92436
8179	S	D	E	L	1975	90116
8179	S	D	E	N	1975	90116
8179	S	D	E	N	1974	92436
8180	S	D	E	L	1975	90116
8180	S	D	E	N	1975	90116
8180	S	D	E	N	1974	92436
8181	S	D	E	L	1975	90116
8181	S	D	E	N	1975	90116
8181	S	D	E	N	1974	92436
8182	S	D	E	L	1975	90116
8182	S	D	E	L	1974	92436
8182	S	D	E	N	1974	92436
8183	S	D	E	L	1975	90116
8183	S	D	E	L	1974	92436
8183	S	D	E	N	1974	92436
8184	S	D	E	L	1975	90116
8184	S	D	E	L	1974	92436
8184	S	D	E	N	1974	92436
8185	S	D	R	L	1973	67854
8185	S	D	R	N	1973	67854
8186	S	D	R	L	1973	67854
8186	S	D	R	N	1973	67854
8191	C	D	R	L	1974	81228
8191	C	D	R	L	1974	86222
8191	C	T	R	L	1974	86222
8191	C	D	E	L	1974	92358
8191	C	D	E	L	1974	92627
8191	C	T	E	L	1974	92627
8191	S	D	R	L	1974	81228
8191	S	D	R	L	1974	86222
8191	S	T	R	L	1974	86222
8191	S	D	E	L	1974	92358
8191	S	D	E	L	1974	92627
8191	S	T	E	L	1974	92627
8193	C	T	E	L	1974	63380
8199	S	D	F	L	1973	57624
8199	S	D	F	N	1973	57624
8199	S	T	F	L	1973	57624
8199	S	T	F	N	1973	57624
8200	S	D	R	N	1971	66283
8201	S	D	R	N	1971	66283
8202	S	D	R	N	1971	66283
8203	S	D	R	N	1971	66283
8204	S	D	R	N	1971	66283
8205	S	D	E	L	1975	68609
8205	S	D	E	N	1975	68609
8205	S	E	E	L	1975	68609
8205	S	E	E	N	1975	68609
8206	S	D	E	L	1975	68676
8206	S	D	E	N	1975	68676
8206	S	T	E	L	1975	68676
8206	S	T	E	N	1975	68676
8207	S	D	E	N	1972	49784
8207	S	S	E	N	1972	49784
8212	S	S	E	N	1969	75903
8213	S	S	E	N	1969	75903
112-0001	L	D	E	N	1973	50436
0001	L	S	E	N	1962	58977
0001	L	S	E	N	1951	98663
0010	D	S	E	N	1968	75835
0010	G	D	E	N	1973	50968
0010	L	S	E	N	1968	75835
0011	S	S	E	N	1969	68271
0021	S	S	E	N	1967	98889
0028	S	T	E	N	1974	54054
0028	S	S	E	N	1974	54577
0028	S	T	E	N	1974	57310
0035	S	S	E	N	1974	100965
0240	S	D	E	N	1973	49779
0240	T	D	E	N	1973	49779
0402	S	S	E	N	1969	68271
0406	S	D	E	N	1973	65678
0407	S	D	E	N	1973	65678
0577	S	D	E	N	1973	49779
0577	T	D	E	N	1973	49779
0583	S	D	E	L	1974	57310
0583	S	D	E	N	1974	57310
0583	S	S	E	H	1974	57310
0662	S	D	E	N	1973	49779
0662	T	D	E	N	1973	49779
8008	S	D	E	L	1974	58010
8020	S	S	R	N	1972	53547
8020	S	S	E	N	1973	53548
8020	S	D	R	N	1973	55010
8020	S	S	R	N	1973	55010
8020	S	D	E	N	1974	55011
8020	S	S	E	N	1974	55011

Phys. State: **A.** Amorphous; **C.** Superconductive; **D.** Doped; **F.** Fibrous or Whisker; **G.** Gas; **I.** Ionized or Plasma; **L.** Liquid; **P.** Powder or Particle; **S.** Solid; **T.** Thin Film
Subject: **D.** Data; **E.** Experiment; **S.** Survey (Review, Compendium, etc.); **T.** Theory
Language: **E.** English; **F.** French; **G.** German; **O.** Other Languages; **R.** Russian
Temperature: **L.** Low (0 to 75K); **N.** Normal (75 to 1273K); **H.** High (above 1273K)

Substance Number	Phys. State	Sub-ject	Lan-guage	Temper-ature	Year	EPIC Number
112-8025	D	D	E	N	1973	52077
8025	S	D	R	N	1972	50966
8025	S	S	E	N	1969	68271
8025	S	S	E	N	1967	68371
8026	S	D	E	L	1973	52435
8026	S	D	E	L	1974	54571
8026	S	D	E	N	1974	54571
8030	S	D	E	L	1973	50874
8033	S	D	R	N	1973	51349
8033	S	E	R	N	1973	51349
8033	S	D	E	N	1973	55170
8033	S	E	E	N	1973	55170
8035	S	D	G	N	1973	49864
8036	S	D	G	N	1973	49864
8037	S	D	G	N	1973	49864
8038	S	D	G	N	1973	49864
8039	S	D	G	N	1973	49864
8040	S	D	G	N	1973	49864
8041	S	D	G	N	1973	49864
8042	S	D	E	N	1973	52077
8045	S	D	R	N	1973	50954
8046	S	D	E	N	1973	51753
8048	S	D	E	L	1973	52597
8055	S	D	R	N	1973	58835
8057	S	D	R	N	1974	58108
8057	S	D	E	N	1974	58109
8058	S	S	E	N	1973	54004
8059	S	S	E	N	1973	54004
8060	S	D	E	L	1974	58909
8060	S	D	E	N	1974	58909
8062	S	D	F	L	1974	66369
8062	S	D	F	N	1974	66369
8064	P	D	E	L	1972	75996
8064	S	D	E	L	1972	75996
8066	S	D	E	N	1973	55890
8068	S	D	E	L	1974	56610
8076	S	D	G	N	1973	58559
8077	S	D	R	N	1973	58835
8079	S	D	G	N	1933	75814
8079	S	T	G	N	1933	75814
8098	S	D	E	N	1974	65213
8098	S	T	E	N	1974	65213
8099	S	D	E	N	1973	65678
114-0003	S	D	E	L	1974	54326
0003	S	D	E	N	1974	54326
0017	S	S	E	N	1971	87884
0045	L	D	E	N	1974	54304
0060	D	D	R	N	1974	58120
0060	D	D	E	N	1974	58121
0060	S	S	E	N	1974	54577
0060	S	D	R	N	1973	55012
0060	S	D	E	N	1974	55013
0060	S	D	R	N	1974	58120
0060	S	D	E	N	1974	58121
0060	S	D	R	N	1974	63128
0060	S	D	E	N	1975	63129
0060	S	D	E	N	1973	63666
0078	S	S	E	N	1971	87884
0111	S	D	R	N	1974	93455
0111	S	T	R	N	1974	93455
0111	S	D	E	N	1974	93456
0111	S	T	E	N	1974	93456
0112	S	D	R	N	1974	93455
0112	S	T	R	N	1974	93455
0112	S	D	E	N	1974	93456
0112	S	T	E	N	1974	93456
0113	S	D	R	N	1974	93455
0113	S	T	R	N	1974	93455
0113	S	D	E	N	1974	93456
0113	S	T	E	N	1974	93456
0114	S	D	R	N	1974	93455
0114	S	T	R	N	1974	93455
0114	S	D	E	N	1974	93456
0114	S	T	E	N	1974	93456
8001	D	D	R	L	1973	50209
8001	D	D	R	N	1973	50209
8001	D	D	E	L	1973	50210
8001	D	D	E	N	1973	50210
8001	D	S	E	L	1965	87781
8001	D	S	E	N	1965	87781
8001	L	S	E	N	1971	87884
8001	S	S	R	N	1973	87035
8001	S	S	E	N	1973	87036
8001	S	S	E	N	1963	87679
8001	S	S	E	L	1965	87781
8001	S	S	E	N	1965	87781
8001	S	S	E	N	1971	87884
8011	S	D	R	N	1973	62447
8021	S	D	E	L	1975	93528
8025	S	D	E	L	1974	54326
8033	S	D	E	L	1974	54326
8044	S	D	E	L	1973	50953
8052	S	T	E	N	1973	52951
8054	S	D	E	L	1973	50527
8054	S	D	E	N	1973	50527
8055	S	D	E	L	1973	50527
8055	S	D	E	N	1973	50527
8056	S	D	E	N	1973	51753
8057	S	D	E	L	1973	52658
8057	S	D	E	N	1973	52658

Substance Number	Phys. State	Sub-ject	Lan-guage	Temper-ature	Year	EPIC Number
114-8060	S	D	E	L	1973	56390
8061	S	D	E	L	1974	58053
8061	S	D	E	N	1974	58053
8071	S	D	E	L	1973	54003
8071	S	D	E	N	1973	54003
8071	S	D	E	L	1973	56352
8071	S	D	E	N	1973	56352
8072	S	D	E	N	1973	54003
8073	S	D	E	L	1973	55963
8074	S	D	E	L	1973	55963
8092	S	D	R	N	1974	93455
8092	S	T	R	N	1974	93455
8092	S	D	E	N	1974	93456
8092	S	T	E	N	1974	93456
8093	S	D	R	N	1974	93455
8093	S	T	R	N	1974	93455
8093	S	D	E	N	1974	93456
8093	S	T	E	N	1974	93456
8094	S	D	R	N	1974	93455
8094	S	T	R	N	1974	93455
8094	S	D	E	N	1974	93456
8094	S	T	E	N	1974	93456
8104	S	S	E	N	1969	75903
8105	S	S	E	N	1969	75903
116-8017	S	D	E	N	1975	63258
8032	S	D	R	L	1972	56906
8032	S	D	R	N	1972	56906
8034	S	D	G	N	1973	57056
8036	S	D	E	N	1973	65678
8039	S	D	R	N	1970	76453
8039	S	T	R	N	1970	76453
8039	S	D	E	N	1970	91544
8039	S	T	E	N	1970	91544
118-0003	S	S	E	N	1967	98889
0029	D	D	R	L	1971	49962
0029	D	D	R	N	1971	49962
0037	D	D	E	N	1973	52748
0041	S	S	E	N	1973	52168
0041	S	S	E	N	1974	54577
8005	C	S	E	L	1974	62805
8005	S	D	E	L	1973	50527
8005	S	D	E	N	1973	50527
8015	S	D	E	L	1973	50953
8017	S	T	E	N	1973	51176
8017	S	T	R	N	1972	60729
8017	S	T	E	N	1973	60730
8018	S	D	E	N	1973	51259
8018	S	D	E	N	1974	60252
8019	S	D	R	N	1973	51394
8019	S	D	E	N	1973	51395
8019	S	D	R	N	1973	52906
8019	S	D	E	N	1974	52907
8019	S	S	E	L	1972	53775
8019	S	S	E	N	1972	53775
8019	S	D	R	N	1974	58108
8019	S	D	E	N	1974	58109
8019	S	D	R	N	1974	58116
8019	S	D	E	N	1974	58117
8024	S	D	E	N	1972	52964
8024	S	S	E	N	1972	53775
8025	S	D	E	N	1973	50000
8025	S	D	E	L	1973	53293
8025	S	D	E	N	1973	53293
8025	S	D	E	L	1975	68676
8025	S	D	E	N	1975	68676
8025	S	T	E	L	1975	68676
8025	S	T	E	N	1975	68676
8026	S	S	E	N	1973	53420
8027	D	D	E	N	1972	53520
8028	S	S	E	L	1972	53775
8028	S	S	E	N	1972	53775
8039	S	D	E	L	1973	52597
8049	S	D	R	N	1974	58108
8049	S	D	E	N	1974	58109
8053	C	S	E	L	1974	62805
8054	C	S	E	L	1974	62805
8055	C	S	E	L	1974	62805
8056	C	S	E	L	1974	62805
8057	S	D	E	L	1974	58909
8069	S	D	R	N	1972	56905
8087	S	D	R	N	1970	76453
8087	S	T	R	N	1970	76453
8087	S	D	E	N	1970	91544
8087	S	T	E	N	1970	91544
8102	T	S	R	N	1974	66796
8102	T	S	E	N	1975	66797
119-0001	S	D	F	N	1973	51740
0001	S	D	E	N	1973	57666
0002	D	T	E	N	1973	50879
0002	S	D	E	N	1973	52822
0002	S	S	E	N	1969	68271
0002	S	S	E	N	1969	87723
0002	S	S	E	N	1967	98889
0008	S	D	E	N	1973	50879
0008	S	D	E	N	1973	50895
0008	S	D	E	N	1973	57916
0008	S	D	E	N	1974	58048
0008	S	D	R	N	1974	60461

Substance Number	Phys. State	Sub-ject	Lan-guage	Temper-ature	Year	EPIC Number
119-0008	S	S	R	N	1974	60461
0008	S	D	E	N	1974	60462
0008	S	S	E	N	1974	60462
0008	S	D	E	N	1967	98889
0040	S	D	R	L	1971	49962
0040	S	D	R	N	1971	49962
0041	S	D	E	N	1969	72658
0041	S	S	E	N	1969	72658
0041	S	D	E	N	1975	90471
0043	S	D	E	N	1973	50879
0043	S	D	E	N	1974	58048
0073	D	D	R	L	1971	49962
0073	D	D	R	N	1971	49962
8002	S	S	E	N	1962	87672
8003	S	S	R	N	1974	63165
8003	S	S	E	N	1975	63166
8003	S	D	E	N	1972	98783
8004	S	D	R	N	1974	65383
8004	S	T	R	N	1974	65383
8004	S	D	E	N	1975	65384
8004	S	T	E	N	1975	65384
8014	S	D	E	N	1972	49944
8014	S	D	E	N	1973	50879
8015	S	D	E	L	1973	51182
8015	S	D	E	N	1973	51182
8020	C	T	E	L	1974	79190
8024	S	D	E	N	1973	49642
8025	S	D	E	N	1972	49944
8029	S	D	O	L	1973	51947
8030	S	D	E	N	1973	51109
8035	S	S	R	N	1972	60735
8035	S	S	E	N	1973	60736
8038	S	D	R	N	1973	52277
8040	D	D	R	N	1973	55056
8040	D	D	E	N	1974	55057
8040	S	D	R	N	1973	55056
8040	S	D	E	N	1974	55057
8046	S	S	E	N	1973	53048
8046	S	D	E	L	1973	53319
8046	S	S	E	L	1974	57299
8047	S	D	E	N	1973	50944
8047	S	E	E	N	1973	50944
8047	S	D	E	N	1974	60297
8050	S	D	E	L	1973	51821
8050	S	D	E	N	1973	51821
8050	S	E	E	L	1973	51821
8050	S	E	E	N	1973	51821
8051	S	D	E	L	1973	51883
8051	S	D	E	N	1973	51883
8052	S	D	E	N	1973	51891
8058	S	T	E	N	1973	52689
8059	S	D	E	L	1973	52597
8060	S	D	E	N	1973	52597
8061	S	D	E	N	1973	52597
8062	S	D	E	L	1973	52597
8063	S	D	E	L	1973	52597
8080	S	D	E	L	1973	51184
8080	S	D	E	N	1973	51184
8080	S	D	E	L	1973	53293
8080	S	D	E	N	1973	53293
8080	S	D	E	N	1973	57666
8091	S	S	R	N	1974	63165
8091	S	S	E	N	1975	63166
8092	S	D	E	N	1973	56978
8096	S	D	E	L	1975	63278
8096	S	D	E	N	1975	63278
8100	S	D	E	N	1975	90060
8111	C	D	R	L	1974	81228
8111	C	D	E	L	1974	92358
8111	S	D	R	L	1974	81228
8111	S	D	E	L	1974	92358
8120	S	D	E	N	1972	49784
8120	S	S	E	N	1972	49784
8124	S	S	E	N	1969	75903
8125	S	S	E	N	1969	75903
8126	S	S	E	N	1969	75903
120-0001	D	D	E	N	1973	52640
0001	D	S	E	N	1970	75905
0001	S	T	E	N	1973	49696
0001	S	D	E	N	1973	52183
0001	S	D	E	N	1973	52640
0001	S	D	E	N	1974	58051
0001	S	D	R	N	1974	60461
0001	S	S	R	N	1974	60461
0001	S	D	E	N	1974	60462
0001	S	S	E	N	1974	60462
0001	S	D	E	N	1967	98889
0006	P	D	E	N	1973	56164
0006	S	D	E	N	1973	51017
0006	S	D	E	N	1973	56164
0010	S	D	F	N	1973	51103
0010	S	D	E	L	1973	55637
0010	S	D	E	N	1973	55637
0024	S	S	E	N	1974	54577
0025	S	D	E	N	1973	65678
0035	S	D	E	N	1972	54619
0035	S	D	R	N	1972	76549
0035	S	T	R	N	1972	76549
0035	S	D	E	N	1972	91599
0035	S	T	E	N	1972	91599

Phys. State: **A.** Amorphous; **C.** Superconductive; **D.** Doped; **F.** Fibrous or Whisker; **G.** Gas; **I.** Ionized or Plasma; **L.** Liquid; **P.** Powder or Particle; **S.** Solid; **T.** Thin Film
Subject: **D.** Data; **E.** Experiment; **S.** Survey (Review, Compendium, etc.); **T.** Theory
Language: **E.** English; **F.** French; **G.** German; **O.** Other Languages; **R.** Russian
Temperature: **L.** Low (0 to 75K); **N.** Normal (75 to 1273K); **H.** High (above 1273K)

Substance Number	Phys. State	Subject	Language	Temperature	Year	EPIC Number
120-0045	S	S	E	N	1972	87886
0057	S	D	E	L	1973	51800
0057	S	D	E	N	1973	51800
0057	S	T	E	L	1973	51800
0057	S	T	E	N	1973	51800
0057	S	D	E	L	1968	64268
0106	S	S	R	N	1974	93455
0106	S	S	E	N	1974	93456
0190	P	S	E	N	1969	75843
0190	S	D	E	L	1973	51789
0190	S	D	E	N	1973	51789
0190	S	D	E	N	1973	51936
0190	S	S	E	N	1973	51936
0190	S	D	E	L	1970	52686
0214	S	D	R	N	1973	50357
0214	S	D	E	N	1973	50358
8001	S	D	R	N	1972	100974
8001	S	T	R	N	1972	100974
8002	S	S	E	N	1966	87721
8002	S	S	E	N	1972	87886
8003	S	S	E	N	1966	87721
8003	S	S	E	N	1972	87886
8004	S	S	E	N	1966	87721
8004	S	S	E	N	1972	87886
8006	P	S	E	L	1968	68373
8006	S	S	E	L	1972	87886
8006	S	S	E	N	1972	87886
8021	S	D	E	L	1972	49502
8021	S	D	E	N	1972	49502
8021	S	D	E	L	1974	53593
8021	S	D	E	N	1974	53593
8021	S	T	E	L	1974	53593
8021	S	T	E	N	1974	53593
8021	S	D	E	N	1974	54963
8023	D	D	E	L	1973	49621
8023	D	D	E	N	1973	49621
8023	D	D	E	L	1975	92020
8023	S	D	E	L	1975	92020
8025	S	D	F	N	1972	49777
8026	S	D	F	N	1972	49777
8027	S	D	F	L	1972	49777
8027	S	D	F	N	1972	49777
8028	S	D	E	L	1972	49875
8028	S	D	E	N	1972	49875
8029	S	D	R	L	1971	49962
8029	S	D	R	N	1971	49962
8031	S	D	R	L	1973	50251
8031	S	D	E	L	1973	50252
8033	S	D	E	N	1973	50595
8034	S	D	E	L	1973	50606
8034	S	D	E	N	1973	50606
8034	S	D	E	N	1976	95560
8042	C	D	E	L	1974	62037
8042	S	S	E	L	1970	75833
8042	S	S	E	N	1970	75833
8042	S	S	E	N	1966	87721
8042	S	S	E	N	1972	87886
8046	S	T	E	N	1973	52951
8052	S	S	E	N	1973	50715
8052	S	D	E	N	1973	51891
8053	S	S	E	N	1973	50715
8053	S	S	E	N	1974	84003
8054	S	S	E	N	1973	50715
8054	S	S	E	N	1974	84003
8055	S	S	E	N	1973	50715
8056	S	S	E	N	1973	50715
8059	S	D	E	N	1973	51753
8060	S	D	E	N	1973	51753
8061	S	D	E	N	1973	51753
8062	S	D	E	N	1973	51753
8063	S	D	E	N	1973	51753
8064	S	D	E	L	1973	51936
8065	S	D	E	L	1973	52196
8066	S	D	E	L	1974	54963
8066	S	D	E	N	1974	54963
8066	S	D	E	N	1974	60340
8074	S	D	E	L	1973	62753
8075	S	D	E	L	1974	54963
8075	S	D	E	N	1974	54963
8076	S	D	R	N	1973	55026
8076	S	D	E	N	1974	55027
8076	S	T	R	N	1974	58108
8076	S	T	E	N	1974	58109
8077	S	D	R	N	1972	76549
8077	S	T	R	N	1972	76549
8077	S	D	E	N	1972	91599
8077	S	T	E	N	1972	91599
8078	S	D	E	L	1974	54055
8078	S	D	E	N	1974	54055
8078	S	S	E	N	1974	58053
8078	S	S	E	L	1971	59678
8082	S	D	E	L	1974	58053
8082	S	D	E	N	1974	58053
8082	S	D	E	L	1975	63305
8082	S	D	E	N	1975	63305
8083	S	D	E	L	1974	58053
8083	S	D	E	N	1974	58053
8083	S	D	E	L	1975	63305
8083	S	D	E	N	1975	63305
8096	S	S	E	N	1969	75843
8096	S	S	E	N	1966	87721
120-8098	S	D	E	N	1964	93287
8098	S	S	E	N	1964	93287
8110	S	D	E	N	1973	65678
8112	S	D	E	L	1973	57481
8112	S	D	E	N	1973	57481
8113	S	D	F	L	1973	57940
8113	S	D	F	N	1973	57940
8120	S	D	G	N	1973	58559
8126	S	D	E	N	1974	60252
8129	S	D	E	L	1975	63276
8130	S	D	E	L	1975	63278
8130	S	D	E	N	1975	63278
8131	S	D	E	L	1975	63305
8131	S	D	E	N	1975	63305
8134	S	D	R	N	1970	76453
8134	S	T	R	N	1970	76453
8134	S	D	E	N	1970	91544
8134	S	T	E	N	1970	91544
8135	S	D	E	L	1975	90060
8136	S	D	R	N	1971	90517
8146	S	S	E	L	1968	68373
8148	S	S	E	N	1972	87886
8149	S	S	E	N	1966	87721
8149	S	S	E	N	1972	87886
8153	S	S	E	N	1966	87721
8154	S	S	E	N	1966	87721
8155	S	S	E	N	1966	87721
8165	S	D	F	N	1971	75744
8165	S	T	F	N	1971	75744
8170	S	T	E	L	1975	90117
8170	S	T	E	N	1975	90117
8173	S	D	E	L	1975	92154
8173	S	D	E	N	1975	92154
8174	S	D	R	N	1972	100974
8174	S	T	R	N	1972	100974
8175	S	D	R	N	1972	100974
8175	S	T	R	N	1972	100974
8176	S	D	R	N	1972	100974
8176	S	T	R	N	1972	100974
122-0003	S	D	E	N	1968	64266
0004	S	S	E	N	1967	98889
0005	S	D	R	N	1973	53648
0005	S	D	E	N	1974	53649
0005	S	S	E	N	1967	98889
0013	D	D	O	N	1972	49897
0013	S	D	O	N	1972	49897
0013	S	D	E	N	1975	63306
0013	S	T	E	N	1975	63306
0013	S	D	R	N	1974	65391
0013	S	S	R	N	1974	65391
0013	S	T	R	N	1974	65391
0013	S	D	E	N	1975	65392
0013	S	S	E	N	1975	65392
0013	S	T	E	N	1975	65392
0014	D	T	E	N	1973	53809
0014	D	D	E	L	1973	60600
0014	D	D	E	N	1973	60600
0014	D	D	R	N	1973	67369
0014	P	D	E	N	1971	57195
0014	S	S	E	L	1973	51150
0014	S	S	E	N	1972	53110
0014	S	S	E	N	1972	53775
0014	S	S	E	L	1974	54064
0014	S	S	E	N	1974	54064
0014	S	D	O	N	1973	57053
0014	S	S	E	N	1971	57195
0014	S	D	E	L	1973	60600
0014	S	D	E	N	1973	60600
0014	S	D	R	N	1973	67368
0014	S	D	E	N	1970	68214
0014	S	D	E	N	1975	86761
0014	S	S	E	L	1974	94480
0014	S	S	E	N	1974	94480
0014	S	S	E	N	1967	98889
0016	S	D	E	N	1974	61166
0016	S	T	E	N	1974	61166
0016	S	S	E	N	1971	87881
0017	S	S	E	N	1967	98889
0023	D	T	R	N	1973	52384
0023	D	T	E	N	1973	57496
0023	S	S	E	N	1969	68271
0023	S	S	R	L	1973	87035
0023	S	S	E	L	1973	87036
0023	S	S	E	N	1967	98889
0026	S	D	R	N	1974	60461
0026	S	S	R	N	1974	60461
0026	S	D	E	N	1974	60462
0026	S	S	E	N	1974	60462
0026	S	D	R	N	1974	63060
0026	S	D	E	N	1975	63061
0026	S	S	E	L	1971	87881
0026	S	S	E	N	1971	87881
0026	S	S	E	L	1974	94480
0026	S	S	E	N	1974	94480
0030	S	D	R	L	1974	65391
0030	S	S	R	L	1974	65391
0030	S	T	R	L	1974	65391
0030	S	D	E	L	1975	65392
0030	S	S	E	L	1975	65392
0030	S	T	E	L	1975	65392
122-0030	S	T	E	L	1977	103589
0030	S	T	E	N	1977	103589
0031	S	S	E	N	1969	68271
0031	S	S	E	N	1967	98889
0037	S	S	E	N	1967	98889
0046	S	D	R	N	1974	63060
0046	S	D	E	N	1975	63061
0047	S	D	R	N	1973	67368
0050	S	S	E	N	1967	66368
0050	S	S	E	N	1969	68115
0053	S	S	E	N	1967	98889
0097	S	D	F	H	1972	49786
0097	S	D	F	N	1972	49786
0112	D	D	E	L	1974	60325
0112	D	D	E	N	1974	60325
0112	D	S	E	N	1970	75833
0112	S	T	E	N	1973	49685
0112	S	S	E	L	1973	51150
0112	S	S	E	N	1972	53110
0112	S	S	E	L	1974	54064
0112	S	S	E	N	1974	54064
0112	S	S	E	N	1970	75833
0112	S	S	E	N	1971	87881
0196	S	D	E	N	1974	57957
0196	S	T	E	N	1975	96226
0296	D	D	E	L	1974	57305
0296	D	D	E	N	1974	57305
0314	S	D	R	N	1974	63060
0314	S	D	E	N	1975	63061
0326	S	D	E	L	1973	55637
0326	S	D	E	N	1973	55637
0441	S	D	R	N	1973	50357
0441	S	D	E	N	1973	50358
0449	S	S	E	L	1975	92915
8027	S	D	E	L	1973	51046
8027	S	D	E	N	1973	51046
8028	S	S	E	L	1973	51150
8028	S	D	E	N	1974	61379
8028	S	S	E	N	1971	87881
8029	S	S	E	L	1973	51150
8029	S	D	E	L	1974	54064
8029	S	D	E	N	1974	54064
8029	S	S	E	L	1974	54064
8029	S	S	E	N	1974	54064
8029	S	D	E	N	1974	61379
8029	S	S	E	N	1971	87881
8030	S	S	E	L	1973	51150
8030	S	D	E	N	1974	61379
8030	S	S	E	N	1971	87881
8031	S	S	E	L	1973	51150
8031	S	D	E	N	1974	61379
8031	S	S	E	N	1971	87881
8032	S	S	E	L	1973	51150
8032	S	D	E	L	1974	54064
8032	S	D	E	N	1974	54064
8032	S	S	E	L	1974	54064
8032	S	S	E	N	1974	54064
8032	S	D	E	N	1974	61379
8032	S	S	E	N	1971	87881
8033	S	S	E	L	1973	51150
8035	S	D	R	L	1973	55404
8035	S	D	E	L	1974	57815
8036	S	D	E	L	1973	51209
8037	S	D	E	L	1973	51209
8038	D	D	E	L	1974	57305
8038	D	D	E	N	1974	57305
8043	S	D	R	N	1974	65391
8043	S	S	R	N	1974	65391
8043	S	T	R	N	1974	65391
8043	S	D	E	N	1975	65392
8043	S	S	E	N	1975	65392
8043	S	T	E	N	1975	65392
8045	S	S	E	N	1967	98889
8053	S	S	E	N	1972	53775
8053	S	D	E	L	1973	60600
8053	S	D	E	N	1973	60600
8068	S	D	F	L	1971	59041
8068	S	D	F	N	1971	59041
8078	S	D	R	N	1974	63060
8078	S	D	E	N	1975	63061
8079	D	D	E	N	1974	57957
8080	S	S	R	L	1974	58122
8080	S	S	R	N	1974	58122
8080	S	S	E	N	1974	58123
8081	S	D	R	N	1974	58108
8081	S	D	E	N	1974	58109
8082	S	D	R	N	1974	58108
8082	S	D	E	N	1974	58109
8083	S	D	R	N	1974	58108
8083	S	D	E	N	1974	58109
8084	S	D	R	N	1974	58108
8084	S	D	E	N	1974	58109
8085	S	D	R	N	1974	58108
8085	S	D	E	N	1974	58109
8088	S	S	E	N	1971	87881
8092	S	D	E	L	1974	61156
8093	S	D	E	L	1974	61379
8093	S	D	E	N	1974	61379
8093	S	S	E	N	1971	87881
8106	S	D	E	L	1973	55637
8106	S	D	E	N	1973	55637

Phys. State: **A.** Amorphous; **C.** Superconductive; **D.** Doped; **F.** Fibrous or Whisker; **G.** Gas; **I.** Ionized or Plasma; **L.** Liquid; **P.** Powder or Particle; **S.** Solid; **T.** Thin Film
Subject: **D.** Data; **E.** Experiment; **S.** Survey (Review, Compendium, etc.); **T.** Theory
Language: **E.** English; **F.** French; **G.** German; **O.** Other Languages; **R.** Russian
Temperature: **L.** Low (0 to 75K); **N.** Normal (75 to 1273K); **H.** High (above 1273K)

Substance Number	Phys. State	Subject	Language	Temperature	Year	EPIC Number
122-8112	P	D	E	N	1971	57195
8112	P	T	E	N	1971	57195
8112	S	D	O	N	1973	57053
8124	S	D	R	N	1972	76529
8124	S	S	E	L	1971	87881
8124	S	S	E	N	1971	87881
8124	S	D	E	N	1972	91534
8137	S	D	R	N	1970	76453
8137	S	T	R	N	1970	76453
8137	S	D	E	N	1970	91544
8137	S	T	E	N	1970	91544
123-0003	S	S	E	N	1969	68115
0003	S	S	E	N	1966	68361
0012	S	D	E	L	1975	63276
0014	S	S	E	N	1974	53593
0015	S	D	E	L	1975	63276
0015	S	S	R	N	1974	93455
0015	S	S	E	N	1974	93456
0025	S	T	E	N	1973	51176
0025	S	D	E	L	1973	51800
0025	S	D	E	N	1973	51800
0025	S	T	E	L	1973	51800
0025	S	T	E	N	1973	51800
0025	S	T	E	L	1973	52441
0025	S	T	E	N	1973	52441
0025	S	D	E	L	1974	53593
0025	S	D	E	N	1974	53593
0025	S	S	E	N	1974	53593
0025	S	D	E	L	1974	54113
0025	S	D	E	N	1974	54113
0025	S	S	E	L	1974	54113
0025	S	S	E	N	1974	54113
0025	S	D	E	L	1974	60334
0025	S	D	E	N	1974	60334
0025	S	D	E	L	1974	61167
0025	S	D	E	N	1974	61167
0025	S	S	E	L	1974	61168
0025	S	S	E	N	1974	61168
0026	S	D	E	N	1973	56347
0041	S	D	E	L	1973	51800
0041	S	D	E	N	1973	51800
0041	S	T	E	L	1973	51800
0041	S	T	E	N	1973	51800
8008	S	D	E	L	1973	52486
8008	S	D	E	N	1973	52486
8013	S	D	E	L	1974	58010
8013	S	D	E	N	1974	58010
8017	S	D	F	N	1970	49775
8017	S	E	F	N	1970	49775
8017	S	S	E	N	1969	68115
8018	L	S	E	N	1969	94149
8018	S	S	E	N	1970	68114
8018	S	S	E	N	1969	68115
8018	S	S	E	N	1969	94149
8018	S	D	E	L	1976	102173
8018	S	T	E	L	1976	102173
8039	S	D	R	N	1974	58102
8039	S	D	E	N	1974	58103
8043	S	D	E	L	1973	50606
8043	S	D	E	N	1973	50606
8044	S	D	E	L	1973	51177
8045	S	D	E	L	1973	51178
8045	S	D	E	N	1973	51178
8046	S	S	E	L	1973	51206
8046	S	D	E	L	1974	54965
8046	S	T	E	L	1974	54965
8047	S	D	E	L	1973	52486
8047	S	D	E	N	1973	52486
8048	S	D	E	L	1973	52486
8048	S	D	E	N	1973	52486
8049	S	D	E	N	1973	52951
8049	S	T	E	N	1973	52951
8051	S	D	R	N	1974	58102
8051	S	D	E	N	1974	58103
8051	S	D	R	L	1974	63131
8051	S	D	R	N	1974	63131
8051	S	D	E	L	1975	63132
8051	S	D	E	N	1975	63132
8052	S	D	E	N	1973	51753
8053	S	D	E	N	1973	51753
8054	S	D	E	N	1973	51753
8055	S	D	E	L	1974	60337
8057	S	D	E	L	1976	95560
8059	S	D	E	L	1974	54055
8059	S	D	E	N	1974	54055
8059	S	S	E	L	1971	59678
8060	S	S	E	L	1974	54055
8060	S	S	E	N	1974	54055
8061	S	D	E	L	1974	54072
8061	S	D	E	N	1974	54072
8061	S	D	E	L	1976	95560
8062	S	D	E	L	1974	54113
8062	S	D	E	N	1974	54113
8062	S	S	E	L	1974	54113
8062	S	S	E	N	1974	54113
8063	S	S	E	L	1971	59678
8064	S	S	E	L	1971	59678
8067	S	S	E	L	1974	61167
8072	S	D	E	L	1971	57503
8073	S	D	E	L	1975	68676

Substance Number	Phys. State	Subject	Language	Temperature	Year	EPIC Number
123-8073	S	D	E	N	1975	68676
8073	S	T	E	L	1975	68676
8073	S	T	E	N	1975	68676
8075	S	D	E	L	1975	63276
8076	S	D	E	L	1975	63276
8077	S	D	E	L	1975	63276
8078	S	D	E	L	1975	63276
8079	S	D	E	L	1975	63276
8080	S	D	E	L	1975	63276
8081	S	D	E	L	1975	63276
8082	S	D	E	L	1975	63276
8083	S	D	E	L	1975	63276
8084	S	D	E	L	1975	63276
8085	S	D	E	L	1975	63276
8086	S	D	E	L	1975	63276
8087	S	D	E	L	1975	63276
8088	S	D	E	L	1975	63276
8089	S	D	E	L	1975	63276
8090	S	D	E	L	1975	63276
8091	S	D	E	L	1975	63276
8092	S	D	E	L	1975	63276
8098	S	D	R	L	1973	67854
8098	S	D	R	N	1973	67854
8105	S	D	E	L	1975	65471
8105	S	D	E	N	1975	65471
8105	S	T	E	L	1975	65471
8105	S	T	E	N	1975	65471
125-8024	S	D	E	L	1973	50606
8024	S	D	E	N	1973	50606
8025	S	D	E	L	1973	50606
8025	S	D	E	N	1973	50606
8026	S	T	E	N	1973	52951
8027	S	D	E	N	1973	51753
8028	S	D	E	N	1973	51753
8034	S	D	R	N	1973	58835
8035	S	D	R	N	1973	58835
126-0002	S	S	E	N	1969	68115
0005	D	S	E	N	1963	87711
0005	D	S	E	N	1966	87712
0005	S	S	E	N	1969	68271
0005	S	S	E	N	1963	87711
0005	S	S	E	N	1966	87712
0011	S	D	E	L	1974	54113
0011	S	D	E	N	1974	54113
0011	S	S	E	L	1974	54113
0011	S	S	E	N	1974	54113
0025	D	D	E	N	1973	50000
0025	S	D	E	N	1973	50000
0025	S	D	E	L	1973	53293
0025	S	D	E	N	1973	53293
0025	S	D	E	L	1975	68676
0025	S	D	E	N	1975	68676
0025	S	T	E	L	1975	68676
0025	S	T	E	N	1975	68676
0038	S	D	E	N	1974	55229
0038	S	S	E	L	1974	70494
0038	S	S	E	N	1974	70494
0038	S	D	E	L	1972	70535
0038	S	D	E	N	1972	70535
0038	S	T	E	N	1971	75947
0039	S	S	R	N	1974	93455
0039	S	S	E	N	1974	93456
0046	S	D	E	L	1973	51889
0046	S	D	E	N	1973	51889
8001	S	D	E	L	1974	58010
8007	S	S	E	L	1973	51206
8007	S	S	E	L	1974	61394
8008	S	S	F	N	1973	52166
8010	S	D	R	N	1973	55687
8010	S	D	E	L	1973	60603
8010	S	D	E	N	1973	60603
8010	S	T	E	L	1973	60603
8010	S	T	E	N	1973	60603
8011	S	D	R	N	1973	55687
8012	S	D	E	L	1973	51800
8012	S	D	E	N	1973	51800
8012	S	T	E	L	1973	51800
8012	S	T	E	N	1973	51800
8012	S	D	R	N	1973	55687
8013	S	D	E	L	1973	51800
8013	S	D	E	N	1973	51800
8013	S	T	E	L	1973	51800
8013	S	T	E	N	1973	51800
8013	S	D	R	N	1973	55687
8014	S	D	R	N	1973	55687
8015	S	D	R	N	1973	55687
8016	S	D	R	N	1973	55687
8017	S	D	R	N	1973	55687
8020	S	D	E	N	1975	68710
8020	S	T	E	N	1975	68710
8032	L	D	R	N	1972	52223
8032	S	D	R	N	1972	52223
8032	S	S	E	N	1972	62298
8032	S	S	E	N	1973	62299
8037	L	S	E	H	1969	94149
8037	L	S	E	N	1969	94149
8037	S	D	R	N	1974	58102
8037	S	D	E	N	1974	58103
8037	S	S	E	N	1970	68114

Substance Number	Phys. State	Subject	Language	Temperature	Year	EPIC Number
126-8037	S	S	E	N	1969	68115
8037	S	S	E	N	1969	94149
8042	S	D	F	L	1973	52198
8043	S	D	E	N	1975	90480
8047	C	D	F	L	1975	63413
8047	C	S	F	L	1975	63413
8047	C	T	F	L	1975	63413
8047	P	S	E	L	1967	66157
8047	S	D	R	L	1973	50353
8047	S	D	R	N	1973	50353
8047	S	D	E	L	1973	50354
8047	S	D	E	N	1973	50354
8047	S	D	E	L	1973	51860
8047	S	T	E	L	1973	51860
8047	S	D	F	N	1973	57624
8047	S	T	F	N	1973	57624
8047	S	S	E	L	1967	66157
8047	S	S	E	N	1967	66157
8047	S	D	E	N	1975	68710
8047	S	T	E	N	1975	68710
8052	P	D	R	N	1973	56966
8052	S	S	R	N	1972	53547
8052	S	S	E	N	1973	53548
8052	S	S	E	L	1969	68271
8052	S	S	E	N	1969	68271
8052	S	D	R	N	1971	76480
8052	S	T	R	N	1971	76480
8052	S	D	E	N	1971	91500
8052	S	T	E	N	1971	91500
8053	S	D	E	L	1973	51195
8053	S	S	E	L	1973	51206
8057	S	D	F	N	1973	50026
8058	S	D	E	L	1973	50161
8058	S	D	E	N	1973	50161
8058	S	D	E	N	1973	51822
8058	S	D	E	L	1974	58909
8070	S	D	E	N	1972	53116
8071	C	D	E	L	1974	88597
8071	P	S	E	L	1974	70494
8071	P	S	E	N	1974	70494
8071	S	D	E	N	1974	55229
8071	S	S	E	L	1974	70494
8071	S	S	E	N	1974	70494
8071	S	D	E	L	1972	70535
8071	S	D	E	N	1972	70535
8077	S	D	E	L	1973	51889
8077	S	D	E	N	1973	51889
8091	S	D	E	L	1976	95560
8101	S	S	E	N	1969	75843
8108	S	D	R	N	1973	51732
8108	S	D	E	N	1973	79136
8120	S	D	E	L	1975	63276
8120	S	D	E	N	1975	63276
8121	S	D	E	L	1975	63276
8122	S	D	E	L	1975	63276
8123	S	D	E	L	1975	63276
8124	S	D	E	L	1975	63276
8124	S	D	E	N	1975	63276
8125	S	D	E	L	1975	63276
8126	S	D	E	L	1975	63276
8128	S	D	E	L	1975	63276
8129	S	D	E	L	1975	63276
8132	S	D	E	L	1974	65351
8133	S	D	R	L	1971	66125
8134	S	D	R	L	1971	66125
8135	S	D	R	N	1971	90517
8145	S	D	R	L	1973	67854
8145	S	D	R	N	1973	67854
8154	S	D	E	L	1974	61918
8154	S	D	E	N	1974	61918
8154	S	T	E	L	1974	61918
8154	S	T	E	N	1974	61918
8155	S	D	E	L	1974	61918
8155	S	D	E	N	1974	61918
8155	S	T	E	L	1974	61918
8155	S	T	E	N	1974	61918
8156	P	D	E	L	1975	68676
8156	P	D	E	N	1975	68676
8156	P	T	E	L	1975	68676
8156	P	T	E	N	1975	68676
8156	S	D	E	L	1975	68676
8156	S	D	E	N	1975	68676
8156	S	T	E	L	1975	68676
8156	S	T	E	N	1975	68676
127-8004	S	S	E	N	1969	68271
8005	S	D	E	N	1973	51822
8005	S	D	E	L	1974	58909
8005	S	D	E	N	1974	58909
8006	S	D	E	L	1973	51889
8006	S	D	E	N	1973	51889
8007	S	D	E	L	1973	51889
8007	S	D	E	N	1973	51889
8012	S	D	E	L	1974	58909
8012	S	D	E	N	1974	58909
8013	S	D	E	L	1974	58909
8014	S	D	E	L	1973	56390
8014	S	D	E	N	1973	56390
8016	S	D	E	N	1975	63276
8017	S	D	E	L	1975	63276
8018	S	D	E	L	1975	63276

Phys. State: **A.** Amorphous; **C.** Superconductive; **D.** Doped; **F.** Fibrous or Whisker; **G.** Gas; **I.** Ionized or Plasma; **L.** Liquid; **P.** Powder or Particle; **S.** Solid; **T.** Thin Film
Subject: **D.** Data; **E.** Experiment; **S.** Survey (Review, Compendium, etc.); **T.** Theory
Language: **E.** English; **F.** French; **G.** German; **O.** Other Languages; **R.** Russian
Temperature: **L.** Low (0 to 75K); **N.** Normal (75 to 1273K); **H.** High (above 1273K)

Substance Number	Phys. State	Subject	Language	Temperature	Year	EPIC Number
127-8019	S	D	E	L	1975	63276
128-8001	S	D	E	L	1973	50437
8001	S	D	E	N	1973	50437
129-8001	C	D	F	L	1975	63413
8001	C	S	F	L	1975	63413
8001	S	D	R	N	1973	58835
132-8002	S	D	E	L	1974	58909
8003	S	D	E	L	1974	58909
133-8001	S	T	E	N	1973	51132

Phys. State: **A.** Amorphous; **C.** Superconductive; **D.** Doped; **F.** Fibrous or Whisker; **G.** Gas; **I.** Ionized or Plasma; **L.** Liquid; **P.** Powder or Particle; **S.** Solid; **T.** Thin Film
Subject: **D.** Data; **E.** Experiment; **S.** Survey (Review, Compendium, etc.); **T.** Theory
Language: **E.** English; **F.** French; **G.** German; **O.** Other Languages; **R.** Russian
Temperature: **L.** Low (0 to 75K); **N.** Normal (75 to 1273K); **H.** High (above 1273K)

Chapter 18 Photoelectronic Properties

Substance Number	Phys. State	Subject	Language	Temperature	Year	EPIC Number
100-0045	S	S	G	N	1971	53540
0045	S	S	E	N	1972	59933
0045	S	S	O	N	1970	60098
0045	S	S	O	N	1971	60099
0045	S	S	E	N	1976	97315
0055	A	S	E	N	1973	53021
0055	A	E	E	N	1972	53276
0055	A	T	E	N	1972	53276
0055	A	S	E	N	1973	53426
0055	A	T	E	N	1973	57407
0055	A	S	E	N	1971	60961
0055	A	T	G	N	1972	62222
0055	A	T	E	N	1975	71361
0055	A	T	E	N	1975	86750
0055	A	T	E	N	1974	92433
0055	D	T	E	N	1973	59411
0055	D	T	R	N	1973	62165
0055	D	T	R	N	1973	66553
0055	D	T	E	N	1974	66554
0055	S	T	R	N	1972	50686
0055	S	T	E	N	1973	51065
0055	S	T	R	N	1973	51372
0055	S	T	E	N	1973	51373
0055	S	T	R	N	1973	51552
0055	S	T	R	N	1973	51696
0055	S	T	E	N	1973	52929
0055	S	T	E	N	1972	53086
0055	S	S	R	N	1971	53278
0055	S	S	E	N	1972	53279
0055	S	T	E	N	1973	53481
0055	S	T	E	N	1974	53600
0055	S	T	E	N	1973	53683
0055	S	S	E	N	1973	53782
0055	S	T	E	N	1973	53782
0055	S	S	R	N	1973	53794
0055	S	T	E	N	1974	54602
0055	S	S	E	N	1973	56284
0055	S	T	R	N	1973	57800
0055	S	T	E	N	1974	57801
0055	S	T	E	N	1974	57852
0055	S	S	E	N	1974	58810
0055	S	S	E	N	1970	59681
0055	S	T	E	N	1970	59681
0055	S	T	E	N	1971	60102
0055	S	T	E	N	1974	60528
0055	S	T	E	N	1963	60566
0055	S	T	R	N	1972	60717
0055	S	T	E	N	1973	60718
0055	S	T	R	N	1972	60729
0055	S	T	E	N	1973	60730
0055	S	E	E	N	1966	60796
0055	S	T	E	N	1966	60796
0055	S	T	E	N	1973	60976
0055	S	T	E	N	1970	61494
0055	S	E	R	N	1971	61550
0055	S	S	O	N	1972	61736
0055	S	T	R	N	1972	62715
0055	S	T	E	N	1975	63293
0055	S	T	E	N	1973	65311
0055	S	E	E	N	1971	65905
0055	S	T	R	N	1973	66549
0055	S	T	E	N	1974	66550
0055	S	T	R	N	1970	67419
0055	S	S	E	N	1968	67894
0055	S	T	E	N	1972	70542
0055	S	S	E	N	1970	70577
0055	S	T	E	N	1972	75889
0055	S	T	R	N	1973	86433
0055	S	T	E	N	1973	86434
0055	S	T	R	N	1974	88331
0055	S	T	E	N	1974	88332
0055	S	T	R	N	1974	94024
0055	S	T	E	N	1975	94025
0055	S	E	E	N	1975	96639
0055	S	T	E	N	1975	96639
0055	S	S	E	N	1976	97315
0055	S	T	E	N	1975	98207
0055	T	T	R	N	1972	50684
0055	T	T	E	N	1971	63890
0055	T	T	E	N	1970	70582
0055	T	T	E	N	1975	71361
0055	T	T	E	N	1974	89230
0055	T	T	E	N	1975	91631
0055	T	T	E	N	1975	94588
8003	S	T	E	N	1973	52472
8005	S	S	E	N	1973	58566
8007	S	T	O	N	1973	51729
8016	T	D	E	N	1973	53854
8019	S	T	R	N	1974	58590
8021	S	S	E	N	1973	58566
8021	T	D	R	N	1971	60225
8025	S	S	E	N	1973	58566
8037	A	T	E	N	1974	67203
8043	S	S	E	N	1973	58566
102-0005	L	D	E	N	1973	49672
0005	S	D	E	N	1974	58589
0005	S	D	E	N	1971	70591
0005	T	D	E	N	1973	54928
0009	D	D	R	N	1974	61996
0009	D	T	R	N	1974	61996
0009	D	D	E	N	1974	61997
0009	D	T	E	N	1974	61997
0009	D	D	R	N	1972	62856
0009	D	D	E	N	1973	65177
0009	D	D	E	N	1975	90105
0009	D	T	E	N	1975	90105
0009	L	D	E	N	1973	49672
0009	S	D	R	N	1974	61996
0009	S	T	R	N	1974	61996
0009	S	D	E	N	1974	61997
0009	S	T	E	N	1974	61997
0009	T	D	R	N	1972	62856
0009	T	D	E	N	1973	65177
0031	T	S	E	N	1967	87860
0038	S	D	E	N	1974	54305
0086	A	S	E	N	1964	75166
0086	D	D	E	N	1973	52191
0086	S	D	E	N	1974	55244
0086	S	S	E	N	1974	55244
0086	T	D	E	N	1973	52191
0105	S	D	E	N	1967	85339
0119	S	D	E	N	1974	54305
0120	T	D	O	N	1973	56806
0182	S	D	E	N	1974	54305
0382	S	D	R	N	1972	49823
8001	S	S	E	N	1962	87668
8001	T	D	E	N	1976	99553
8001	T	T	E	N	1976	99553
8018	T	D	E	N	1973	64100
8031	A	D	E	N	1973	51915
8031	A	S	E	N	1973	53021
8031	A	D	E	N	1972	53276
8031	A	D	E	N	1974	60536
8031	A	S	E	N	1974	61183
8031	A	D	E	N	1974	61387
8031	A	E	E	N	1974	61387
8031	A	S	E	N	1964	75166
8031	A	D	E	N	1974	92433
8031	D	D	E	N	1973	51915
8031	S	D	E	N	1974	54097
8031	S	S	E	N	1964	75166
8031	T	S	E	N	1974	61183
8031	T	D	E	N	1974	61387
8031	T	E	E	N	1974	61387
8041	D	D	E	N	1972	49783
8041	D	D	R	N	1973	50081
8041	D	D	E	L	1973	50753
8041	D	D	E	N	1973	50753
8041	D	D	E	L	1973	51042
8041	D	T	E	L	1973	51042
8041	D	D	E	N	1973	51427
8041	D	D	E	N	1973	52643
8041	D	D	E	N	1972	53068
8041	D	D	E	L	1972	53113
8041	D	D	E	N	1972	53138
8041	D	D	E	N	1972	53143
8041	D	D	E	N	1972	53220
8041	D	D	E	N	1972	53271
8041	D	D	E	L	1973	53440
8041	D	D	E	L	1973	53441
8041	D	D	E	N	1971	53515
8041	D	T	E	N	1971	53515
8041	D	D	E	N	1973	55085
8041	D	D	R	N	1973	55336
8041	D	D	R	N	1973	55342
8041	D	D	E	N	1973	56372
8041	D	D	E	N	1974	59274
8041	D	D	E	N	1974	59284
8041	D	D	E	N	1971	59711
8041	D	S	E	N	1970	61494
8041	D	D	R	N	1973	62726
8041	D	D	R	N	1970	63458
8041	D	T	R	N	1970	63458
8041	D	D	R	N	1973	63482
8041	D	D	E	N	1971	65048
8041	D	D	E	N	1970	65158
8041	D	T	E	N	1970	65158
8041	D	D	E	N	1970	65161
8041	D	D	E	N	1973	65322
8041	D	D	E	N	1975	66715
8041	D	E	E	N	1975	66715
8041	D	S	E	N	1975	66715
8041	D	T	E	N	1975	66715
8041	D	S	E	N	1964	87701
8041	D	D	E	N	1975	90007
8041	D	D	E	N	1975	90109
8041	D	T	E	N	1975	90109
8041	D	D	E	N	1975	95524
8041	D	T	E	N	1975	97860
102-8041	G	D	E	N	1973	56372
8041	G	E	E	N	1973	56372
8041	S	D	R	L	1973	50054
8041	S	D	R	N	1973	50054
8041	S	D	E	N	1973	50594
8041	S	D	E	N	1973	51065
8041	S	T	E	N	1973	51065
8041	S	D	E	N	1973	51790
8041	S	S	E	N	1970	52286
8041	S	D	E	L	1972	53184
8041	S	D	R	N	1972	53231
8041	S	D	E	N	1972	53232
8041	S	D	E	N	1972	53271
8041	S	D	R	N	1971	53300
8041	S	D	E	N	1973	53301
8041	S	D	E	N	1973	53481
8041	S	T	E	N	1973	53481
8041	S	S	E	N	1973	53782
8041	S	T	E	N	1973	53782
8041	S	D	R	L	1973	55167
8041	S	D	E	L	1974	55168
8041	S	D	E	L	1974	55243
8041	S	D	R	L	1973	55290
8041	S	D	R	N	1973	55308
8041	S	D	R	L	1973	55316
8041	S	D	E	N	1971	55377
8041	S	D	E	N	1973	56818
8041	S	D	E	N	1974	57852
8041	S	D	E	L	1974	58935
8041	S	D	E	N	1974	59233
8041	S	D	E	L	1974	59241
8041	S	D	E	L	1974	59249
8041	S	T	E	N	1971	60103
8041	S	D	E	N	1973	60177
8041	S	T	E	N	1973	60177
8041	S	D	E	N	1973	60976
8041	S	T	E	N	1973	60976
8041	S	S	E	N	1970	61494
8041	S	D	R	N	1971	61550
8041	S	E	R	N	1971	61550
8041	S	S	O	N	1972	61736
8041	S	D	E	N	1971	61764
8041	S	D	E	L	1973	62582
8041	S	D	R	N	1972	62691
8041	S	T	R	N	1970	63458
8041	S	D	E	N	1973	63515
8041	S	D	E	N	1972	63538
8041	S	D	E	N	1973	63838
8041	S	D	E	L	1975	65475
8041	S	T	E	L	1975	65475
8041	S	D	R	N	1971	67721
8041	S	D	R	N	1974	68636
8041	S	T	R	N	1974	68636
8041	S	D	E	N	1975	68637
8041	S	T	E	N	1975	68637
8041	S	T	E	L	1974	68690
8041	S	D	E	N	1975	73247
8041	S	S	E	N	1970	82820
8041	S	D	R	N	1975	86831
8041	S	D	E	N	1975	86832
8041	S	S	E	N	1962	87673
8041	S	S	E	L	1964	87701
8041	S	S	E	N	1964	87701
8041	S	D	R	N	1974	87755
8041	S	D	R	N	1974	90225
8041	S	D	E	N	1975	90226
8041	S	D	E	N	1974	92229
8041	S	D	E	N	1975	95524
8041	S	D	E	N	1975	97730
8041	S	D	E	N	1975	101024
8041	S	S	E	N	1975	101894
8041	T	D	E	N	1973	49528
8041	T	D	R	N	1972	50684
8041	T	D	E	L	1973	51410
8041	T	D	E	N	1973	51410
8041	T	D	R	L	1973	55330
8041	T	T	R	L	1973	55330
8041	T	D	E	L	1974	59266
8041	T	T	E	L	1974	59266
8041	T	D	R	N	1971	60225
8041	T	T	E	N	1971	63890
8041	T	S	E	N	1970	82820
8041	T	S	E	N	1964	87701
8041	T	S	E	N	1969	87821
8054	D	D	E	L	1972	51091
8054	D	D	E	N	1972	51091
8054	D	D	E	N	1966	60796
8054	S	D	R	L	1973	50225
8054	S	D	R	N	1973	50225
8054	S	D	E	L	1973	50226
8054	S	D	E	N	1973	50226
8054	S	D	E	L	1971	53516
8054	S	D	E	N	1971	53516
8054	S	D	E	N	1966	60796
8054	S	E	E	N	1966	60796

Phys. State: **A.** Amorphous; **C.** Superconductive; **D.** Doped; **F.** Fibrous or Whisker; **G.** Gas; **I.** Ionized or Plasma; **L.** Liquid; **P.** Powder or Particle; **S.** Solid; **T.** Thin Film
Subject: **D.** Data; **E.** Experiment; **S.** Survey (Review, Compendium, etc.); **T.** Theory
Language: **E.** English; **F.** French; **G.** German; **O.** Other Languages; **R.** Russian
Temperature: **L.** Low (0 to 75K); **N.** Normal (75 to 1273K); **H.** High (above 1273K)

Substance Number	Phys. State	Subject	Language	Temperature	Year	EPIC Number
102-8054	S	T	E	N	1966	60796
8054	S	D	R	N	1972	62693
8054	S	D	E	N	1972	64420
8054	S	S	E	N	1962	87667
8054	S	S	E	N	1966	87831
8069	A	D	R	N	1971	67725
8078	S	D	E	N	1971	49617
8078	S	D	R	N	1971	60230
8078	S	T	R	N	1971	60230
8079	L	D	E	N	1973	49672
8083	A	D	R	N	1971	67725
8083	S	D	R	N	1972	76530
8083	S	T	R	N	1972	76530
8083	S	D	E	N	1972	91535
8083	S	T	E	N	1972	91535
8084	D	D	R	N	1974	67749
8094	D	D	R	N	1973	62733
8094	D	D	E	N	1974	65329
8094	S	D	R	N	1973	55308
8094	S	D	E	N	1974	59233
8095	S	D	E	N	1972	63998
8095	S	E	E	N	1972	63998
8095	S	S	E	N	1965	87703
8106	A	S	E	N	1973	53021
8106	S	D	E	N	1974	54594
8106	T	D	E	N	1974	54594
8132	T	T	E	N	1976	99553
8133	A	D	E	N	1974	62603
8133	A	D	E	N	1973	67289
8133	A	S	E	N	1964	75166
8133	A	D	E	N	1974	84007
8133	T	D	E	N	1974	62603
8141	S	D	R	N	1973	55771
8163	A	D	E	N	1972	53376
8171	A	D	E	N	1972	53186
8171	T	D	E	N	1972	53186
8181	A	S	E	N	1973	53021
8182	A	S	E	N	1973	53021
8183	A	S	E	N	1973	53021
8333	S	D	F	N	1974	81628
8333	S	E	F	N	1974	81628
8339	S	D	R	N	1973	55771
8401	A	D	E	N	1974	92433
8434	A	D	R	N	1971	67725
8435	A	D	R	N	1971	67725
8437	S	D	E	N	1968	68207
8455	S	D	R	N	1972	76530
8455	S	T	R	N	1972	76530
8455	S	D	E	N	1972	91535
8455	S	T	E	N	1972	91535
8467	S	D	E	N	1970	63884
104-0006	D	D	R	N	1973	50213
0006	D	D	E	N	1973	50214
0006	D	D	E	N	1973	52629
0006	D	D	R	N	1972	62850
0006	D	D	E	N	1972	65169
0006	S	D	E	N	1973	49708
0006	S	D	R	N	1973	50213
0006	S	D	E	N	1973	50214
0006	S	D	E	L	1965	74575
0007	T	D	E	N	1976	100007
0007	T	T	E	N	1976	100007
0013	S	D	E	N	1973	62318
0013	S	E	E	N	1973	62318
0013	S	D	R	N	1974	63147
0013	S	T	R	N	1974	63147
0013	S	D	E	N	1975	63148
0013	S	T	E	N	1975	63148
0013	S	D	E	N	1973	65282
0013	S	D	E	N	1975	96170
0013	S	T	E	N	1975	96170
0013	T	D	E	N	1967	85905
0015	A	T	E	N	1974	92433
0021	T	D	E	N	1974	62566
0052	D	D	R	N	1973	57371
0094	S	D	E	N	1974	54305
0331	S	D	R	L	1973	50235
0331	S	D	E	L	1973	50236
8044	A	S	E	N	1973	53021
8045	T	S	E	N	1966	66068
8045	T	D	R	N	1974	94028
8045	T	T	R	N	1974	94028
8045	T	D	E	N	1975	94029
8045	T	T	E	N	1975	94029
8134	S	D	R	N	1973	50741
8134	S	D	E	N	1973	79428
8156	T	D	E	N	1973	57279
8156	T	T	E	N	1973	57279
8171	S	D	R	N	1973	55018
8171	S	D	E	N	1974	55019
8175	S	D	R	N	1973	51934
8175	S	D	E	N	1973	63232
8183	S	D	E	L	1975	87156
8183	S	D	E	N	1975	87156
8190	A	S	E	N	1973	53021
8198	S	D	G	N	1972	67868
8213	A	D	E	N	1974	53726
8213	T	D	E	N	1974	53726
8231	S	D	E	N	1974	54037
8294	S	D	R	N	1973	55817
104-8294	T	D	R	N	1973	55817
106-0002	S	T	G	N	1932	60155
0006	D	D	R	N	1973	50213
0006	D	D	E	N	1973	50214
0006	D	D	R	N	1973	54498
0006	D	D	E	N	1973	54499
0006	D	D	R	L	1973	56574
0006	D	D	R	N	1973	56574
0006	D	D	R	N	1972	62850
0006	D	D	E	N	1972	65169
0006	S	D	E	N	1973	49708
0006	S	D	R	N	1973	50213
0006	S	D	E	N	1973	50214
0006	S	E	E	N	1972	55357
0006	S	D	R	N	1974	62004
0006	S	T	R	N	1974	62004
0006	S	D	E	N	1974	62005
0006	S	T	E	N	1974	62005
0008	D	D	E	L	1973	50476
0024	D	D	R	N	1972	62850
0024	D	D	E	N	1972	65169
0035	D	D	R	N	1973	51733
0035	D	D	E	N	1973	79186
0035	D	S	E	L	1965	87702
0035	D	S	E	N	1965	87702
0035	D	S	E	N	1968	87828
0035	S	D	R	N	1969	52997
0035	S	D	E	N	1972	52998
0035	S	D	R	N	1972	63478
0035	S	D	E	N	1972	65927
0035	S	S	E	L	1965	87702
0035	S	S	E	N	1965	87702
0035	T	T	E	N	1971	63890
0035	T	D	E	N	1974	90647
0035	T	T	E	N	1974	90647
0104	D	T	E	N	1970	61741
0104	S	S	E	N	1971	87872
0104	T	D	E	N	1970	61741
0127	S	D	R	N	1973	50082
0127	S	D	E	N	1973	51428
0127	S	D	E	N	1975	63342
0127	S	T	E	N	1975	63342
0296	S	D	E	N	1974	54305
0327	T	D	E	N	1974	60654
0363	D	D	R	N	1973	50090
0363	D	D	R	N	1973	51550
0363	D	D	E	N	1971	53487
0363	D	D	E	N	1973	53681
0363	D	D	E	N	1974	53750
0363	D	T	E	N	1973	55163
0363	D	D	O	N	1972	59839
0363	D	T	O	N	1972	59839
0363	D	D	E	N	1972	60922
0363	D	S	E	N	1971	60964
0363	D	S	E	N	1970	61494
0363	D	D	E	N	1970	61742
0363	D	S	E	N	1963	64232
0363	D	D	E	N	1975	65427
0363	D	T	E	N	1975	65427
0363	D	S	E	N	1967	66156
0363	D	D	E	N	1973	66884
0363	D	D	O	N	1972	67610
0363	D	D	R	N	1974	67743
0363	D	D	E	N	1972	70404
0363	D	T	E	N	1972	70404
0363	D	D	E	N	1970	70573
0363	D	D	E	N	1957	89723
0363	D	E	E	N	1957	89723
0363	D	T	E	N	1957	89723
0363	D	D	E	N	1962	89724
0363	D	D	E	N	1962	89789
0363	D	D	O	N	1974	90631
0363	D	D	E	N	1975	92725
0363	D	E	E	N	1975	92725
0363	D	D	E	N	1975	94569
0363	D	E	E	N	1975	94569
0363	D	S	E	N	1975	95469
0363	D	D	R	N	1975	97671
0363	D	T	R	N	1975	97671
0363	D	D	E	N	1975	97672
0363	D	T	E	N	1975	97672
0363	P	S	E	N	1963	64232
0363	P	D	O	N	1972	67610
0363	P	D	O	N	1974	90476
0363	S	D	E	N	1972	49485
0363	S	D	R	L	1973	50074
0363	S	D	E	L	1973	50475
0363	S	D	E	N	1973	50638
0363	S	D	R	N	1972	51099
0363	S	D	E	L	1973	51425
0363	S	D	R	N	1973	51696
0363	S	T	R	N	1973	51696
0363	S	D	E	N	1973	52776
0363	S	D	E	N	1973	52929
0363	S	T	E	N	1973	52929
0363	S	D	E	N	1972	53183
0363	S	D	E	N	1972	53220
0363	S	D	R	N	1971	53304
0363	S	D	E	N	1972	53305
0363	S	D	E	N	1974	53615
106-0363	S	E	E	N	1974	53615
0363	S	D	E	N	1974	54097
0363	S	D	R	N	1973	54213
0363	S	D	R	N	1973	55289
0363	S	T	R	N	1973	55289
0363	S	D	R	N	1973	55993
0363	S	D	E	N	1973	56354
0363	S	D	O	N	1972	57001
0363	S	D	R	N	1973	57825
0363	S	D	E	N	1974	57826
0363	S	D	R	N	1973	58299
0363	S	D	E	N	1974	59248
0363	S	T	E	N	1974	59248
0363	S	T	E	N	1973	59409
0363	S	T	R	N	1972	60703
0363	S	T	E	L	1973	60704
0363	S	D	E	N	1972	60922
0363	S	D	E	N	1973	60976
0363	S	T	E	N	1973	60976
0363	S	S	E	N	1970	61494
0363	S	S	O	N	1972	61736
0363	S	D	E	N	1970	61742
0363	S	D	E	N	1971	61758
0363	S	D	E	N	1971	61760
0363	S	E	E	N	1971	61760
0363	S	T	E	N	1971	61760
0363	S	T	E	N	1971	61763
0363	S	T	R	N	1973	62163
0363	S	S	E	N	1973	63506
0363	S	D	E	N	1971	63879
0363	S	E	E	N	1971	63879
0363	S	S	E	N	1963	64232
0363	S	D	E	N	1965	64273
0363	S	T	E	N	1965	64273
0363	S	D	E	N	1974	64986
0363	S	S	E	L	1967	66156
0363	S	S	E	N	1967	66156
0363	S	D	R	L	1974	66742
0363	S	D	R	N	1974	66742
0363	S	T	R	L	1974	66742
0363	S	T	R	N	1974	66742
0363	S	D	E	L	1975	66743
0363	S	D	E	N	1975	66743
0363	S	T	E	L	1975	66743
0363	S	T	E	N	1975	66743
0363	S	D	O	N	1968	66798
0363	S	D	R	N	1973	67387
0363	S	D	R	N	1974	67743
0363	S	D	R	N	1970	67840
0363	S	D	G	N	1970	67881
0363	S	D	E	N	1970	70573
0363	S	D	E	N	1971	70600
0363	S	D	R	N	1974	71817
0363	S	D	E	N	1975	71966
0363	S	E	E	N	1975	75197
0363	S	D	E	N	1975	75197
0363	S	T	E	N	1972	75889
0363	S	T	E	N	1972	75889
0363	S	T	E	L	1968	75941
0363	S	D	R	N	1971	76475
0363	S	T	R	N	1971	76475
0363	S	D	R	N	1974	77923
0363	S	T	R	N	1974	77923
0363	S	S	E	N	1970	82820
0363	S	D	E	N	1975	88215
0363	S	T	E	N	1975	90653
0363	S	D	E	N	1971	91501
0363	S	T	E	N	1971	91501
0363	S	D	R	N	1974	92329
0363	S	D	E	N	1975	92330
0363	S	D	E	N	1975	92725
0363	S	E	E	N	1975	92725
0363	S	D	E	N	1975	93350
0363	S	E	E	N	1975	93350
0363	S	T	E	N	1975	93350
0363	S	D	E	N	1974	94513
0363	S	T	E	N	1974	94513
0363	S	T	E	N	1975	94644
0363	S	S	E	N	1976	97315
0363	T	D	R	N	1973	50090
0363	T	D	E	N	1973	50905
0363	T	D	R	N	1973	51555
0363	T	D	E	N	1972	53330
0363	T	D	E	N	1974	53750
0363	T	D	R	N	1972	55386
0363	T	T	R	N	1972	55386
0363	T	S	R	N	1969	59075
0363	T	S	E	N	1970	59076
0363	T	D	E	N	1973	59977
0363	T	E	E	N	1973	59977
0363	T	D	E	N	1970	61743
0363	T	T	E	N	1971	63890
0363	T	D	E	N	1972	64092
0363	T	D	E	N	1972	64094
0363	T	E	E	N	1972	64094
0363	T	S	E	N	1963	64232
0363	T	D	R	N	1973	65571
0363	T	D	E	N	1973	65572
0363	T	S	E	N	1967	66156
0363	T	D	E	N	1974	67104
0363	T	T	E	N	1974	67104

Phys. State: **A.** Amorphous; **C.** Superconductive; **D.** Doped; **F.** Fibrous or Whisker; **G.** Gas; **I.** Ionized or Plasma; **L.** Liquid; **P.** Powder or Particle; **S.** Solid; **T.** Thin Film
Subject: **D.** Data; **E.** Experiment; **S.** Survey (Review, Compendium, etc.); **T.** Theory
Language: **E.** English; **F.** French; **G.** German; **O.** Other Languages; **R.** Russian
Temperature: **L.** Low (0 to 75K); **N.** Normal (75 to 1273K); **H.** High (above 1273K)

Substance Number	Phys. State	Subject	Language	Temperature	Year	EPIC Number
106-0363	T	D	R	N	1972	67466
0363	T	D	R	N	1970	67769
0363	T	D	E	N	1972	75456
0363	T	T	E	N	1972	75456
0363	T	D	R	N	1971	76498
0363	T	T	R	N	1971	76498
0363	T	S	E	N	1970	82820
0363	T	D	E	N	1962	89724
0363	T	D	E	N	1962	89789
0363	T	D	R	N	1973	90437
0363	T	D	E	N	1971	91581
0363	T	T	E	N	1971	91581
0363	T	D	E	N	1975	94569
0363	T	E	E	N	1975	94569
0363	T	S	E	N	1975	94588
0363	T	D	E	N	1976	100152
0363	T	E	E	N	1976	100152
0363	T	T	E	N	1976	100152
0385	D	D	E	L	1972	53338
1019	S	D	E	N	1971	49617
1256	D	D	R	N	1973	53777
1256	D	D	E	N	1973	54546
1256	D	D	R	N	1972	58691
1256	S	D	R	N	1972	56996
1256	S	D	R	N	1972	58691
1519	D	D	R	N	1972	52258
1519	D	D	E	N	1971	63887
1519	D	T	E	N	1971	63887
1519	S	D	E	N	1974	53915
1519	S	D	E	N	1971	63887
1519	S	T	E	N	1971	63887
8001	S	D	R	N	1973	50075
8001	S	D	E	N	1973	51426
8001	S	D	O	N	1972	51453
8001	S	T	O	N	1972	51453
8001	S	D	R	N	1972	67464
8040	D	D	R	N	1973	55296
8040	D	D	E	N	1974	59280
8040	D	D	E	N	1971	64324
8040	D	S	E	N	1963	87710
8040	S	D	R	N	1972	49816
8040	S	D	R	N	1972	51100
8040	S	D	R	N	1973	51384
8040	S	D	E	N	1973	51385
8040	S	D	R	N	1973	51546
8040	S	D	R	N	1973	51696
8040	S	T	R	N	1973	51696
8040	S	D	R	N	1972	52267
8040	S	D	E	N	1973	52923
8040	S	D	E	N	1973	52929
8040	S	T	E	N	1973	52929
8040	S	D	R	N	1971	53304
8040	S	D	E	N	1972	53305
8040	S	S	R	N	1972	53547
8040	S	S	E	N	1973	53548
8040	S	D	E	N	1973	56398
8040	S	S	E	N	1972	59933
8040	S	D	R	N	1970	61027
8040	S	D	R	N	1971	67724
8040	S	D	E	N	1975	75197
8040	S	E	E	N	1975	75197
8040	S	S	E	N	1963	87710
8040	S	S	E	N	1974	99154
8040	T	D	E	N	1973	50749
8040	T	D	R	N	1971	53304
8040	T	D	E	N	1972	53305
8040	T	D	E	N	1973	53451
8040	T	T	E	N	1971	63890
8040	T	D	E	N	1971	63893
8040	T	E	E	N	1971	63893
8040	T	T	E	N	1971	63893
8040	T	D	R	N	1974	64516
8040	T	D	E	N	1975	91012
8040	T	E	E	N	1975	91012
8040	T	T	E	N	1975	91012
8041	D	D	E	N	1972	49494
8041	D	D	R	N	1973	51625
8041	D	D	E	N	1973	57645
8041	D	D	R	N	1970	61886
8041	D	D	E	N	1974	62323
8041	D	T	R	N	1972	62705
8041	D	T	E	N	1973	65301
8041	D	S	E	N	1967	68371
8041	D	D	G	N	1971	70363
8041	D	D	E	N	1973	79080
8041	D	S	E	N	1962	87659
8041	S	D	E	N	1972	49493
8041	S	D	E	N	1972	49494
8041	S	D	E	N	1973	54202
8041	S	E	E	N	1973	54202
8041	S	S	E	N	1972	59933
8041	S	D	E	N	1970	60042
8041	S	D	R	N	1969	61845
8041	S	D	E	N	1975	65477
8041	S	T	E	N	1975	65477
8041	S	D	E	N	1972	67637
8041	S	D	E	N	1972	67639
8041	S	S	E	N	1967	68371
8041	S	D	G	N	1971	70363
8041	S	D	E	N	1972	76043
8041	S	D	R	N	1971	77234
106-8041	S	S	E	N	1970	82820
8041	S	S	E	N	1962	87659
8041	S	D	E	N	1975	96664
8041	S	T	E	N	1975	96664
8041	S	S	E	N	1976	97315
8041	T	D	R	N	1973	50669
8041	T	D	R	N	1972	50684
8041	T	D	E	N	1973	51268
8041	T	D	R	N	1973	51625
8041	T	D	E	N	1973	52415
8041	T	D	E	N	1972	53183
8041	T	D	E	N	1973	53451
8041	T	D	E	N	1973	54928
8041	T	T	R	N	1972	56225
8041	T	D	E	N	1974	58002
8041	T	D	R	N	1971	60225
8041	T	D	R	N	1972	61035
8041	T	D	R	N	1973	61039
8041	T	D	E	N	1970	61743
8041	T	D	R	N	1969	61845
8041	T	D	R	N	1970	61886
8041	T	D	O	N	1970	62235
8041	T	T	O	N	1970	62235
8041	T	D	R	N	1974	62432
8041	T	D	R	N	1972	62620
8041	T	D	R	N	1973	62623
8041	T	E	R	N	1973	62623
8041	T	D	E	N	1972	64435
8041	T	D	E	N	1973	65120
8041	T	E	E	N	1973	65120
8041	T	D	E	N	1974	65334
8041	T	D	R	N	1974	66639
8041	T	T	R	N	1974	66639
8041	T	D	E	N	1974	66640
8041	T	T	E	N	1974	66640
8041	T	D	R	N	1972	67465
8041	T	S	E	N	1967	68371
8041	T	D	E	N	1970	70570
8041	T	T	E	N	1970	70570
8041	T	D	R	N	1973	71709
8041	T	S	E	N	1975	73152
8041	T	T	E	N	1975	73152
8041	T	D	R	N	1972	76519
8041	T	T	R	N	1972	76519
8041	T	D	E	N	1973	79080
8041	T	D	E	N	1973	82121
8041	T	S	E	N	1970	82820
8041	T	S	E	N	1962	87659
8041	T	D	R	N	1974	87962
8041	T	S	R	N	1974	87962
8041	T	D	E	N	1974	88072
8041	T	D	E	N	1972	91552
8041	T	T	E	N	1972	91552
8041	T	D	E	N	1975	91631
8041	T	S	E	N	1975	91631
8041	T	T	E	N	1975	91631
8041	T	D	R	N	1975	94567
8041	T	T	R	N	1975	94567
8041	T	D	E	N	1975	94613
8041	T	E	E	N	1975	94613
8041	T	T	E	N	1975	94613
8041	T	D	E	N	1976	95912
8041	T	T	E	N	1976	95912
8041	T	D	R	N	1975	100287
8041	T	T	R	N	1975	100287
8041	T	D	E	N	1975	100288
8041	T	T	E	N	1975	100288
8050	T	D	G	N	1970	66848
8127	S	D	E	N	1974	54033
8128	S	D	R	N	1972	49574
8128	S	D	E	N	1972	53401
8128	S	D	E	N	1973	53406
8128	S	D	E	L	1973	53852
8128	S	D	E	N	1974	54554
8128	S	E	E	N	1974	54554
8128	S	D	E	N	1973	55149
8128	S	D	E	N	1971	60102
8128	S	T	E	N	1974	61351
8128	S	S	E	N	1967	68371
8128	S	T	E	N	1975	76733
8128	S	S	E	N	1966	87831
8128	S	D	E	N	1974	96599
8128	S	E	E	N	1974	96599
8128	T	D	E	N	1973	51923
8132	S	D	E	N	1971	61077
8132	S	S	E	N	1970	61494
8134	D	D	R	N	1972	50956
8134	D	D	O	N	1972	57344
8134	D	D	R	N	1974	92329
8134	S	D	E	N	1975	92330
8134	T	D	R	N	1972	50956
8134	T	D	E	N	1972	64092
8134	T	D	E	N	1974	67104
8134	T	T	E	N	1974	67104
8135	S	D	E	N	1971	49617
8154	D	D	R	N	1973	51551
8154	D	T	E	N	1973	51551
8154	D	T	R	N	1973	51551
8154	D	D	E	N	1973	53682
8154	D	T	E	N	1973	53682
8154	T	D	R	N	1971	76494
106-8154	T	T	R	N	1971	76494
8154	T	D	E	N	1971	91578
8154	T	T	E	N	1971	91578
8209	S	D	E	N	1975	96147
8209	S	E	E	N	1975	96147
8209	S	T	E	N	1975	96147
8234	D	D	R	N	1973	51279
8234	S	D	R	N	1973	51561
8234	S	D	E	N	1974	53692
8271	D	D	E	N	1975	75629
8271	D	T	E	N	1975	75629
8271	T	D	E	N	1975	97322
8312	D	D	R	N	1974	63010
8312	D	E	R	N	1974	63010
8312	D	D	E	N	1974	63011
8312	D	E	E	N	1974	63011
8312	S	D	E	N	1971	57183
8312	S	D	R	N	1974	66774
8312	S	T	R	N	1974	66774
8312	S	D	E	N	1975	66775
8312	S	T	E	N	1975	66775
8312	S	D	R	N	1974	66790
8312	S	D	E	N	1975	66791
8312	S	D	G	N	1972	67868
8335	T	D	O	N	1971	61478
8342	D	D	R	N	1973	55292
8342	D	D	E	N	1974	59251
8469	S	D	E	N	1971	61077
8528	D	D	R	N	1973	55295
8528	D	D	E	N	1974	59271
8566	S	T	R	N	1972	60729
8566	S	T	E	N	1973	60730
8581	S	D	E	N	1973	55917
8742	S	D	E	N	1968	68207
8758	S	D	R	N	1971	76475
8758	S	T	R	N	1971	76475
8758	S	D	E	N	1971	91501
8758	S	T	E	N	1971	91501
8822	S	D	R	N	1974	66774
8822	S	T	R	N	1974	66774
8822	S	D	E	N	1975	66775
8822	S	T	E	N	1975	66775
8823	S	D	R	N	1974	65623
8823	S	T	R	N	1974	65623
8823	S	D	E	N	1974	68419
8823	S	T	E	N	1974	68419
109-0001	S	T	E	N	1974	61059
0025	S	T	E	N	1973	51219
110-0194	D	D	G	N	1972	67868
0194	S	D	R	N	1971	51252
8176	S	D	G	N	1972	67868
8233	S	D	E	N	1974	90378
111-0006	A	T	E	N	1974	92433
0008	A	T	E	N	1974	65585
0008	D	D	R	N	1973	50058
0008	D	D	R	N	1973	50071
0008	D	D	E	N	1973	51414
0008	D	D	R	N	1973	55321
0008	D	D	E	N	1974	59257
0008	D	D	E	N	1970	59690
0008	D	T	E	N	1970	59690
0008	D	D	E	N	1974	62030
0008	D	E	E	N	1974	62030
0008	D	T	E	N	1974	62030
0008	D	D	R	N	1974	66598
0008	D	D	E	N	1974	66599
0008	D	D	R	N	1974	76160
0008	D	D	E	N	1975	76161
0008	D	S	E	N	1962	87669
0008	D	S	E	L	1965	87703
0008	D	S	E	N	1965	87703
0008	D	D	R	N	1974	97464
0008	D	S	R	N	1974	97464
0008	D	D	E	N	1975	97465
0008	D	S	E	N	1975	97465
0008	F	S	E	N	1965	87703
0008	S	D	R	N	1973	50205
0008	S	D	E	N	1973	50206
0008	S	D	E	L	1973	50476
0008	S	T	E	N	1974	54040
0008	S	S	O	N	1972	61736
0008	S	D	E	N	1975	75197
0008	S	E	E	N	1975	75197
0008	S	S	E	N	1962	87669
0008	S	S	E	L	1965	87703
0008	S	S	E	N	1965	87703
0008	S	D	R	N	1972	50684
0008	T	T	E	N	1974	65585
0008	T	D	R	N	1971	67719
0021	D	D	E	N	1974	60371
0029	S	D	O	N	1971	53542
8002	D	S	E	N	1966	87831
8002	S	D	E	N	1972	51228
8002	S	D	E	L	1973	51869
8002	S	S	E	N	1970	52286
8002	S	D	R	N	1971	66986
8002	S	S	E	N	1962	87670
8002	S	S	E	N	1966	87831

Phys. State: **A.** Amorphous; **C.** Superconductive; **D.** Doped; **F.** Fibrous or Whisker; **G.** Gas; **I.** Ionized or Plasma; **L.** Liquid; **P.** Powder or Particle; **S.** Solid; **T.** Thin Film
Subject: **D.** Data; **E.** Experiment; **S.** Survey (Review, Compendium, etc.); **T.** Theory
Language: **E.** English; **F.** French; **G.** German; **O.** Other Languages; **R.** Russian
Temperature: **L.** Low (0 to 75K); **N.** Normal (75 to 1273K); **H.** High (above 1273K)

Substance Number	Phys. State	Subject	Language	Temperature	Year	EPIC Number
111-8007	S	D	E	L	1972	50851
8007	S	D	E	N	1972	50851
8007	S	D	E	N	1973	52046
8007	S	D	E	N	1973	56333
8007	S	E	E	N	1973	56333
8007	S	D	E	N	1974	61190
8007	S	D	E	L	1962	63880
8007	S	D	E	N	1962	63880
8009	S	D	E	N	1962	63880
8010	T	D	E	N	1970	70577
8019	S	D	R	N	1971	66986
8021	A	D	E	N	1972	53266
8021	T	D	E	N	1972	53266
8021	T	S	E	N	1974	57991
8068	S	D	R	N	1974	58526
8068	S	T	R	N	1974	58526
8068	S	D	E	N	1974	66302
8068	S	T	E	N	1974	66302
8075	A	S	E	N	1972	53376
8075	T	D	E	N	1971	53513
8075	T	S	E	N	1974	57991
8078	S	D	E	N	1974	54594
8078	T	D	E	N	1974	54594
8108	A	D	E	N	1974	57991
8108	A	S	E	N	1974	57991
8108	A	T	E	N	1974	57991
8108	T	D	E	N	1974	57991
8108	T	S	E	N	1974	57991
8108	T	T	E	N	1974	57991
8119	D	D	R	N	1973	55337
8119	D	D	E	N	1974	59275
8187	S	D	E	N	1968	68207
8190	S	D	R	N	1972	76507
8190	S	D	E	N	1972	91590
8192	S	D	R	N	1971	76488
8192	S	T	R	N	1971	76488
8192	S	D	E	N	1971	91569
8192	S	T	E	N	1971	91569
112-0001	L	D	E	N	1974	60354
0001	S	D	E	N	1973	52747
0040	S	D	E	N	1971	62074
0098	D	D	R	N	1974	58314
0402	S	S	E	N	1975	101023
8024	S	D	E	N	1971	49617
114-0001	S	D	E	L	1968	74624
0001	S	D	E	N	1968	74624
0002	S	D	E	L	1968	74624
0002	S	D	E	N	1968	74624
0006	S	D	E	N	1975	60963
0017	D	D	E	N	1973	50751
0017	S	D	R	L	1973	50205
0017	S	D	R	N	1973	50205
0017	S	D	E	L	1973	50206
0017	S	D	E	N	1973	50206
0017	S	S	E	N	1970	52286
0017	S	D	R	N	1971	60221
0017	S	S	E	N	1962	87660
0017	S	D	E	L	1975	91725
0017	S	E	E	L	1975	91725
0017	S	T	E	L	1975	91725
0017	S	D	E	N	1974	93257
0017	S	S	E	N	1963	98002
0017	T	S	E	N	1969	87821
0059	S	D	E	N	1974	54305
0060	S	D	R	N	1972	51532
0060	S	D	R	N	1970	52677
0060	S	T	R	N	1972	62845
0060	S	D	E	N	1973	63666
0060	S	E	E	N	1973	63666
0060	S	S	E	N	1973	63666
0060	S	T	E	N	1972	65172
0060	T	D	E	N	1973	55876
0060	T	S	E	N	1973	63666
8001	D	D	R	L	1973	54292
8001	D	T	R	N	1973	54292
8001	D	D	E	L	1973	54293
8001	D	T	E	N	1973	54293
8001	D	D	R	L	1974	60449
8001	D	D	R	N	1974	60449
8001	D	D	E	L	1974	60450
8001	D	D	E	N	1974	60450
8001	D	E	E	N	1973	61770
8001	D	T	E	N	1973	61770
8001	D	S	E	N	1963	87679
8001	S	D	E	N	1973	50509
8001	S	D	E	N	1973	51212
8001	S	D	E	N	1972	51228
8001	S	S	E	N	1970	52286
8001	S	D	E	N	1973	52464
8001	S	T	E	N	1973	52464
8001	S	D	R	L	1973	52890
8001	S	D	E	L	1974	52891
8001	S	D	E	N	1972	53103
8001	S	D	R	N	1973	55340
8001	S	D	E	N	1974	59278
8001	S	T	E	L	1963	60566
8001	S	D	R	L	1974	62427
8001	S	D	E	L	1974	65330
8001	S	D	R	L	1973	71670
114-8001	S	E	R	L	1973	71670
8001	S	D	E	L	1973	82405
8001	S	E	E	L	1973	82405
8001	S	T	R	N	1975	86863
8001	S	T	E	N	1975	86864
8001	S	S	E	N	1963	87679
8001	S	S	E	L	1965	87781
8001	S	S	E	N	1965	87781
8001	S	S	E	N	1966	87831
8001	S	D	R	L	1974	88331
8001	S	S	R	L	1974	88331
8001	S	T	R	L	1974	88331
8001	S	D	E	L	1974	88332
8001	S	S	E	L	1974	88332
8001	S	T	E	L	1974	88332
8001	T	D	E	N	1973	64100
8001	T	S	E	N	1965	87781
8011	T	D	E	N	1973	54928
8012	S	S	E	N	1962	87661
8018	T	D	E	N	1973	53451
8042	S	D	E	N	1973	50550
8043	S	D	E	N	1973	50550
8051	S	D	R	N	1970	52677
8066	S	D	R	N	1972	56997
116-8017	S	D	E	N	1975	96224
8017	S	T	E	N	1975	96224
118-0037	D	D	E	N	1974	62740
0037	D	D	E	N	1975	96224
0037	D	T	E	N	1975	96224
0037	S	D	R	N	1973	55018
0037	S	D	E	N	1974	55019
0037	S	S	R	N	1974	63147
0037	S	S	E	N	1975	63148
0037	S	T	E	N	1975	96224
8017	S	T	R	N	1972	60729
8017	S	T	E	N	1973	60730
8018	S	D	E	N	1973	65282
8018	S	D	E	N	1975	96224
8018	S	T	E	N	1975	96224
119-0001	S	E	E	N	1973	57480
0001	S	D	E	L	1975	63300
0001	S	D	E	N	1974	89519
0002	D	S	E	N	1969	87723
0002	S	S	E	N	1969	87723
0005	S	D	E	N	1974	60654
0008	D	D	E	N	1964	60562
0008	S	D	E	N	1964	60562
8002	D	S	E	N	1962	87672
8002	S	S	E	N	1962	87672
8084	S	S	E	N	1969	75843
120-0001	S	D	E	N	1971	49790
0001	S	D	E	N	1971	49791
0032	S	S	E	N	1974	66380
0036	S	D	E	N	1973	50556
0036	S	T	E	N	1973	50556
0233	D	D	R	N	1974	66643
0233	D	D	E	N	1974	66644
0233	D	D	R	N	1970	67037
0233	S	D	E	N	1971	49617
0233	S	D	R	N	1971	60230
0233	S	T	R	N	1971	60230
8022	D	D	R	N	1970	67037
8022	S	D	E	N	1971	49617
8022	S	D	R	N	1971	60230
8022	S	T	R	N	1971	60230
8078	D	D	R	N	1970	67037
8180	S	D	R	N	1976	99754
8180	S	T	R	N	1976	99754
8180	S	D	E	N	1976	101631
8180	S	T	E	N	1976	101631
122-0005	S	D	R	N	1973	50648
0005	S	S	E	N	1966	87831
0009	A	T	E	N	1974	92433
0009	T	T	E	N	1974	62293
0009	T	D	E	N	1975	86753
0012	S	D	E	N	1973	50556
0012	S	T	E	N	1973	50556
0016	S	D	R	N	1973	52535
0016	S	D	E	N	1974	53652
0016	S	D	E	N	1973	57885
0017	D	D	E	N	1974	62032
0017	D	E	E	N	1974	62032
0017	T	D	E	N	1974	53724
0017	T	E	E	N	1974	53724
0017	T	D	E	N	1974	62032
0017	T	E	E	N	1974	62032
0019	S	D	E	N	1972	53386
0023	D	D	R	N	1974	81407
0023	D	S	E	N	1963	87709
0023	D	D	E	N	1974	95806
0023	D	S	E	N	1974	99215
0023	P	S	E	N	1963	87709
0023	S	D	E	L	1973	51025
0023	S	D	E	N	1974	57588
0023	S	T	E	N	1974	57588
0023	S	D	E	N	1973	60976
122-0023	S	T	E	N	1973	60976
0023	S	D	E	N	1972	61767
0023	S	D	E	N	1975	63293
0023	S	S	E	N	1975	63293
0023	S	T	E	N	1975	63293
0023	S	D	R	N	1974	81407
0023	S	S	E	N	1963	87709
0023	S	D	E	N	1974	95806
0023	S	S	E	N	1974	99215
0023	T	D	G	N	1972	62222
0030	D	D	E	N	1973	51657
0030	S	D	E	L	1973	53578
0030	S	D	E	N	1973	53578
0050	D	D	R	N	1972	50687
0050	D	S	E	N	1967	68368
0050	P	S	E	N	1967	66368
0050	S	D	R	N	1972	50689
0050	T	D	E	N	1973	50424
0050	T	S	E	N	1967	68368
0053	T	S	E	N	1966	87833
0096	A	S	E	N	1971	60961
0096	A	S	E	N	1975	95324
0096	T	S	E	N	1971	60961
0105	T	D	O	N	1973	56266
0196	S	D	E	N	1973	65282
0196	S	T	E	N	1975	96226
8026	S	D	E	N	1973	50551
8044	T	D	E	N	1972	53416
123-0003	D	D	R	N	1972	51098
0003	D	T	R	N	1973	52531
0003	D	T	E	N	1974	57772
0003	D	D	R	N	1971	63462
0003	D	D	E	N	1971	65164
0003	S	D	E	N	1973	51070
0003	S	E	E	N	1973	51070
0003	S	D	E	N	1972	53183
0003	S	D	R	N	1971	67314
0003	S	S	E	N	1966	68361
0003	T	D	R	N	1972	50684
0003	T	T	R	N	1973	52531
0003	T	D	E	N	1972	53416
0003	T	T	E	N	1974	57772
0003	T	D	E	N	1970	59601
0003	T	T	R	N	1972	61906
0003	T	D	R	N	1971	63462
0003	T	D	E	N	1971	65164
0003	T	D	R	N	1971	67321
0003	T	D	R	N	1971	67323
0003	T	D	R	N	1970	67772
0003	T	S	E	N	1966	68361
0003	T	T	E	N	1970	70582
0003	T	D	E	N	1971	70599
0003	T	S	E	N	1966	87831
0003	T	S	E	N	1975	94588
0032	S	D	E	N	1974	59352
8017	S	D	E	N	1973	51070
8017	S	E	E	N	1973	51070
8017	S	D	E	N	1973	51642
8017	S	D	F	N	1970	59867
8017	S	S	E	N	1962	87674
8017	S	S	E	N	1966	87831
8017	T	D	R	N	1971	67321
8017	T	S	E	N	1966	87831
8018	S	D	E	N	1973	51070
8018	S	E	E	N	1973	51070
8018	S	S	E	N	1962	87671
8018	S	S	E	N	1966	87831
8018	S	T	E	N	1976	100173
8018	T	T	E	N	1974	58606
8018	T	D	F	N	1973	64583
8018	T	S	E	N	1970	68114
8018	T	S	E	N	1962	87671
8018	T	S	E	N	1966	87831
8025	T	D	R	N	1972	76540
8025	T	D	E	N	1972	91592
8039	S	D	R	N	1974	66592
8039	S	D	E	N	1974	66593
8039	T	D	E	N	1972	53321
8039	T	D	E	N	1972	53324
8039	T	D	E	N	1973	53434
8051	S	S	E	N	1972	53321
8051	S	S	E	N	1972	53324
8051	S	T	E	N	1975	76733
8051	S	S	E	N	1972	87824
8051	S	D	E	N	1974	88465
8051	T	S	E	N	1972	53321
8051	T	S	E	N	1972	53324
8051	T	D	E	N	1973	53434
8051	T	S	E	N	1972	87824
8051	T	D	E	N	1974	88465
8065	S	D	R	N	1973	52528
8065	S	D	R	N	1973	55298
8065	S	D	E	N	1974	57769
8065	S	D	E	N	1974	59283
8099	T	D	R	N	1972	76540
8099	T	D	E	N	1972	91592
8100	T	D	R	N	1972	76540
8100	T	D	E	N	1972	91592
126-0004	S	D	E	N	1974	58804

Phys. State: **A.** Amorphous; **C.** Superconductive; **D.** Doped; **F.** Fibrous or Whisker; **G.** Gas; **I.** Ionized or Plasma; **L.** Liquid; **P.** Powder or Particle; **S.** Solid; **T.** Thin Film
Subject: **D.** Data; **E.** Experiment; **S.** Survey (Review, Compendium, etc.); **T.** Theory
Language: **E.** English; **F.** French; **G.** German; **O.** Other Languages; **R.** Russian
Temperature: **L.** Low (0 to 75K); **N.** Normal (75 to 1273K); **H.** High (above 1273K)

Substance Number	Phys. State	Subject	Language	Temperature	Year	EPIC Number
126-0005	D	D	R	N	1971	56220
0005	D	S	E	N	1972	59933
0005	D	D	R	N	1974	60459
0005	D	D	E	N	1974	60460
0005	D	D	E	N	1972	63491
0005	D	E	E	N	1972	63491
0005	D	T	E	N	1972	63491
0005	D	S	E	N	1963	87711
0005	D	S	E	N	1966	87712
0005	P	S	E	N	1963	87711
0005	S	D	E	N	1973	50552
0005	S	D	E	N	1974	58032
0005	S	S	E	N	1974	58032
0005	S	D	R	N	1974	60459
0005	S	D	E	N	1974	60460
0005	S	D	R	L	1972	60699
0005	S	D	R	N	1972	60699
0005	S	T	R	L	1972	60699
0005	S	T	R	N	1972	60699
0005	S	D	E	L	1973	60700
0005	S	D	E	N	1973	60700
0005	S	T	E	L	1973	60700
0005	S	T	E	N	1973	60700
0005	S	D	E	N	1972	61023
0005	S	E	E	N	1972	61023
0005	S	D	E	N	1975	63293
0005	S	S	E	N	1975	63293
0005	S	T	E	N	1975	63293
0005	S	D	E	N	1972	63503
0005	S	T	E	N	1972	63759
0005	S	S	E	N	1963	87711
0005	S	S	E	N	1966	87712
0005	S	T	E	N	1975	93580
0005	T	D	E	N	1972	63491
0005	T	E	E	N	1972	63491
0005	T	D	E	N	1972	64092
0005	T	D	E	N	1970	70578
0005	T	D	F	N	1974	86060
0005	T	S	E	N	1966	87712
0005	T	D	E	N	1975	96126
0005	T	T	E	N	1975	96126
0014	A	S	E	N	1973	53021
0038	S	D	E	N	1975	65484
0043	T	T	E	N	1970	70582
8030	A	D	E	N	1972	49458
8030	A	D	E	N	1972	49467
8030	A	S	E	N	1973	53021
8030	A	D	E	N	1972	53386
8030	T	D	E	N	1972	49458
8030	T	D	E	N	1972	49467
8030	T	D	E	N	1972	53386
8030	T	D	R	N	1973	62623
8030	T	E	R	N	1973	62623
8030	T	D	E	N	1973	65120
8030	T	E	E	N	1973	65120
8032	A	D	E	N	1974	62603
8032	T	D	E	N	1974	62603
8046	A	D	E	N	1972	49467
8046	T	D	E	N	1972	49467
8052	D	D	E	N	1973	52087
8052	D	D	E	N	1974	53923
8052	D	D	E	N	1974	60751
8052	D	S	E	N	1963	68313
8052	S	D	R	N	1972	52267
8052	S	S	R	N	1972	53547
8052	S	S	E	N	1973	53548
8052	S	T	F	N	1974	56617
8052	S	D	R	N	1969	61845
8052	S	D	E	L	1975	88219
8052	S	D	E	N	1975	88219
8052	T	S	E	N	1963	68313
8092	S	D	E	N	1974	58804
8098	S	D	E	N	1975	65484
8100	A	D	E	N	1974	84459
8100	A	D	E	N	1974	86009
8100	T	D	E	N	1974	84459
8100	T	D	E	N	1974	86009
127-8004	D	S	E	N	1962	87666
8004	S	S	E	N	1970	52286
8004	S	D	R	N	1969	61845
8004	S	S	E	N	1962	87666
8004	T	D	F	N	1970	61670
8004	T	T	F	N	1970	61670
8004	T	D	R	N	1969	61845

Phys. State: **A.** Amorphous; **C.** Superconductive; **D.** Doped; **F.** Fibrous or Whisker; **G.** Gas; **I.** Ionized or Plasma; **L.** Liquid; **P.** Powder or Particle; **S.** Solid; **T.** Thin Film
Subject: **D.** Data; **E.** Experiment; **S.** Survey (Review, Compendium, etc.); **T.** Theory
Language: **E.** English; **F.** French; **G.** German; **O.** Other Languages; **R.** Russian
Temperature: **L.** Low (0 to 75K); **N.** Normal (75 to 1273K); **H.** High (above 1273K)

Chapter 19 Refractive Index

Substance Number	Phys. State	Subject	Language	Temperature	Year	EPIC Number
100-0045	L	S	E	N	1962	65935
0045	L	S	E	N	1972	87876
0045	L	S	E	N	1967	98664
0045	S	S	E	N	1973	56767
0045	S	S	E	N	1973	59376
0045	S	S	E	N	1974	62306
0045	S	S	E	N	1960	64411
0045	S	S	E	N	1974	64477
0045	S	S	E	N	1974	65104
0045	S	S	E	N	1962	65935
0045	S	S	E	N	1971	70398
0045	S	T	E	N	1971	70398
0045	S	S	E	N	1973	82686
0045	S	S	E	N	1967	98664
0045	S	S	E	N	1969	101680
0045	T	S	E	N	1973	82686
0045	T	S	E	N	1976	102567
0045	T	S	E	N	1975	103142
0045	T	S	E	N	1971	103208
0055	A	T	E	N	1974	92433
0055	D	D	E	N	1974	61432
0055	D	T	E	N	1974	61432
0055	S	D	G	N	1973	51927
0055	S	E	G	N	1973	51927
0055	S	S	G	N	1973	51927
0055	S	T	G	N	1973	51927
0055	S	T	E	N	1973	52084
0055	S	S	E	N	1973	56767
0055	S	S	E	N	1974	59353
0055	S	T	E	N	1974	59353
0055	S	T	E	N	1971	59614
0055	S	S	E	N	1974	60265
0055	S	T	E	N	1974	60265
0055	S	T	R	N	1970	61025
0055	S	E	R	L	1971	61558
0055	S	S	E	N	1974	62306
0055	S	S	O	N	1974	62496
0055	S	S	R	N	1973	62706
0055	S	S	E	N	1973	62815
0055	S	T	E	N	1973	62815
0055	S	S	E	N	1974	62816
0055	S	T	E	N	1970	63585
0055	S	T	E	N	1971	63593
0055	S	S	E	N	1974	64477
0055	S	S	E	N	1973	64495
0055	S	T	E	N	1973	64495
0055	S	S	E	N	1971	65080
0055	S	S	E	N	1974	65104
0055	S	S	E	N	1973	65302
0055	S	E	E	L	1971	65909
0055	S	S	E	N	1968	67894
0055	S	S	E	N	1971	70398
0055	S	T	E	N	1971	70398
0055	S	T	E	N	1971	70647
0055	S	T	E	N	1956	75076
0055	S	T	E	L	1973	86425
0055	T	E	E	N	1973	50093
0055	T	T	R	N	1973	54397
0055	T	T	E	N	1973	54398
0055	T	D	E	N	1973	55281
0055	T	S	E	N	1973	55281
0055	T	T	E	N	1973	55281
0055	T	T	E	N	1972	63961
0055	T	E	E	N	1975	87127
0055	T	S	E	N	1975	103142
0055	T	S	E	N	1971	103208
8003	S	S	E	N	1974	59353
8003	S	S	E	N	1973	62815
8003	S	S	E	N	1974	62816
8003	S	S	E	N	1974	64477
8003	S	S	E	N	1973	64495
8003	S	S	E	N	1974	65104
8003	S	S	E	N	1976	66532
8003	S	S	E	N	1973	68817
8003	S	D	E	N	1973	68861
8003	S	S	E	N	1971	70398
8003	S	T	E	N	1971	70398
8003	S	S	E	N	1975	93400
8003	S	E	E	N	1975	95407
8003	S	T	E	N	1975	95407
8003	S	T	E	N	1974	98283
8003	T	S	E	N	1976	66532
8006	S	E	E	N	1973	68860
8007	S	S	E	N	1973	60558
8007	S	S	O	N	1974	62496
8007	S	S	E	N	1974	62816
8007	S	S	E	N	1969	68271
8007	S	D	E	N	1973	68861
8007	S	S	E	N	1972	87823
8007	S	D	E	N	1975	91146
8008	S	S	E	N	1973	60558
8008	S	S	O	N	1974	62496
8008	S	S	E	N	1974	62816
8008	S	T	E	N	1972	63811
8008	S	T	G	N	1954	66199
100-8008	S	D	E	N	1973	68861
8008	S	D	R	N	1975	86845
8008	S	D	E	N	1975	86846
8008	S	S	E	N	1971	87884
8008	S	S	E	N	1972	87889
8008	S	T	E	N	1974	93385
8008	S	T	R	N	1975	101515
8008	S	T	E	N	1975	101516
8008	T	S	E	N	1969	87821
8010	S	S	E	N	1972	53175
8010	T	S	E	N	1972	53175
8015	S	S	E	N	1972	53175
8015	T	S	E	N	1972	53175
8016	S	D	E	N	1971	62600
8021	S	S	E	N	1972	60888
8031	S	D	R	N	1972	56989
8038	S	S	E	N	1969	68115
8038	S	S	E	N	1972	87824
8058	S	T	E	N	1974	57962
8059	S	S	E	N	1972	60888
8065	S	E	E	N	1975	91762
8065	S	T	E	N	1975	91762
8074	S	S	E	N	1973	60558
102-0002	A	T	E	N	1974	62549
0002	A	S	E	N	1970	65877
0002	L	D	R	H	1973	53997
0002	L	T	R	H	1973	53997
0002	L	D	E	H	1973	53998
0002	L	T	E	H	1973	53998
0002	S	S	E	N	1973	50526
0002	S	S	E	H	1972	53512
0002	S	S	E	N	1972	53512
0002	S	D	E	N	1974	54024
0002	S	D	E	N	1973	62386
0002	S	D	E	N	1975	65511
0002	S	E	E	N	1975	65511
0002	S	S	E	N	1975	65511
0002	S	T	E	N	1975	65511
0002	S	S	E	H	1970	65877
0002	S	S	E	N	1970	65877
0002	S	D	E	N	1972	66229
0002	S	D	E	N	1968	66313
0002	S	S	E	N	1965	68323
0002	S	D	E	N	1971	70398
0002	S	S	E	H	1964	75892
0002	S	S	E	N	1964	75892
0002	S	T	E	H	1964	75892
0002	S	T	E	N	1964	75892
0002	S	S	E	N	1971	87883
0002	S	S	E	H	1975	93181
0002	S	S	E	L	1975	93181
0002	S	S	E	N	1975	93181
0002	T	D	E	N	1973	50093
0002	T	D	E	N	1973	51254
0002	T	E	E	N	1973	51254
0002	T	D	E	N	1972	53252
0002	T	D	E	N	1971	62190
0002	T	S	E	N	1971	62190
0002	T	T	E	N	1974	62549
0002	T	S	E	N	1970	65877
0002	T	D	E	N	1966	66020
0002	T	S	E	N	1971	66197
0002	T	D	E	N	1969	66514
0002	T	T	E	N	1969	66514
0002	T	D	E	N	1975	66619
0002	T	D	E	N	1974	81418
0002	T	E	E	N	1975	87127
0002	T	S	E	N	1975	93181
0002	T	D	E	N	1975	96486
0002	T	T	E	N	1970	100000
0003	S	D	E	N	1962	64551
0005	S	D	E	N	1974	58589
0005	S	S	E	N	1975	96398
0009	S	D	E	N	1973	50924
0009	S	S	E	N	1973	62815
0009	S	S	E	N	1974	62816
0009	S	D	E	N	1973	65533
0009	S	S	E	N	1924	73267
0009	S	D	E	N	1961	75731
0009	S	T	E	N	1961	75731
0009	S	S	E	N	1971	87883
0009	S	S	E	N	1975	96398
0010	S	D	E	N	1973	50924
0010	S	S	E	N	1974	54065
0010	S	S	R	N	1973	56262
0010	S	S	E	N	1974	59353
0010	S	D	E	N	1972	60077
0010	S	D	E	N	1971	62600
0010	S	S	E	N	1973	62815
0010	S	S	E	N	1974	62816
0010	S	S	E	N	1949	63242
0010	S	S	E	N	1973	64495
0010	S	S	E	N	1970	65877
0010	S	D	E	N	1971	70398
102-0010	S	S	E	N	1924	73267
0010	S	D	E	N	1961	75731
0010	S	T	E	N	1961	75731
0010	S	S	E	N	1973	76721
0010	S	D	E	N	1974	80503
0010	S	S	E	N	1974	80503
0010	S	S	E	N	1971	87883
0010	S	S	E	N	1975	96398
0010	S	D	E	N	1976	101813
0010	S	E	E	N	1976	101813
0010	T	S	E	N	1976	102567
0013	S	S	E	N	1972	53073
0013	T	D	E	N	1969	95705
0016	T	D	E	N	1974	58226
0016	T	T	E	N	1974	58226
0016	T	D	E	N	1975	89528
0024	S	D	E	N	1958	75780
0024	S	T	E	N	1958	75780
0027	S	D	E	N	1966	66020
0041	S	S	E	N	1972	87889
0054	S	S	E	N	1970	87822
0054	S	S	E	N	1972	87890
0054	S	S	E	N	1976	101320
0086	A	D	E	N	1973	50526
0086	A	E	E	N	1973	50526
0086	A	D	E	N	1973	55107
0086	A	D	E	N	1972	63793
0086	A	S	E	N	1972	63793
0086	A	D	E	N	1972	63962
0086	S	D	E	N	1973	50526
0086	S	E	E	N	1973	50526
0086	S	S	E	N	1973	50526
0086	S	D	R	N	1972	54687
0086	S	S	E	N	1974	55244
0086	S	D	E	N	1974	60255
0086	S	D	E	N	1973	62386
0086	S	D	E	N	1971	62600
0086	S	D	E	N	1962	64551
0086	S	S	E	N	1962	64551
0086	S	S	E	N	1963	64748
0086	S	S	E	N	1970	65877
0086	S	T	E	N	1974	66230
0086	S	D	E	N	1975	66680
0086	S	T	E	N	1975	66680
0086	S	D	E	N	1971	70398
0086	S	S	E	N	1971	70398
0086	S	S	E	N	1971	87883
0086	S	D	E	N	1974	93375
0086	S	D	E	N	1975	93997
0086	S	D	E	N	1974	94581
0086	S	S	E	N	1976	101822
0086	T	D	E	N	1973	55107
0086	T	D	E	N	1974	60260
0086	T	D	E	N	1974	68831
0086	T	D	E	N	1975	93161
0086	T	D	E	N	1976	99986
0086	T	E	E	N	1976	99986
0086	T	D	E	N	1976	101813
0086	T	E	E	N	1976	101813
0086	T	D	E	N	1976	101822
0086	T	T	E	N	1976	101822
0086	T	D	E	N	1976	101825
0086	T	S	E	N	1976	102567
0105	S	D	R	N	1973	53779
0105	S	D	E	N	1973	55350
0105	S	D	R	N	1971	59379
0105	S	D	E	N	1967	85339
0105	S	S	E	N	1966	87830
0105	S	S	E	N	1971	87884
0105	T	D	E	N	1973	62595
0248	S	D	E	N	1971	61508
0248	S	S	E	N	1966	87830
0248	S	S	E	N	1971	87884
0250	D	D	E	N	1973	53727
0250	D	D	E	N	1974	60281
0250	D	D	E	N	1975	87179
0250	D	D	E	N	1976	99987
0250	D	E	E	N	1976	99987
0250	D	S	E	N	1976	99987
0250	S	D	E	N	1974	57289
0250	S	E	E	N	1974	57289
0250	S	S	E	N	1974	57289
0250	S	T	E	N	1974	57289
0250	S	D	E	N	1973	57902
0250	S	E	E	N	1973	57902
0250	S	S	E	N	1973	59376
0250	S	S	E	N	1973	60833
0250	S	E	E	N	1973	60841
0250	S	S	E	N	1973	60841
0250	S	D	E	N	1973	62386
0250	S	D	E	N	1973	66202
0250	S	T	E	N	1973	66202
0250	T	D	E	N	1974	60281
0281	S	S	E	N	1976	101320
0282	S	S	E	N	1976	101320

Phys. State: **A.** Amorphous; **C.** Superconductive; **D.** Doped; **F.** Fibrous or Whisker; **G.** Gas; **I.** Ionized or Plasma; **L.** Liquid; **P.** Powder or Particle; **S.** Solid; **T.** Thin Film
Subject: **D.** Data; **E.** Experiment; **S.** Survey (Review, Compendium, etc.); **T.** Theory
Language: **E.** English; **F.** French; **G.** German; **O.** Other Languages; **R.** Russian
Temperature: **L.** Low (0 to 75K); **N.** Normal (75 to 1273K); **H.** High (above 1273K)

Substance Number	Phys. State	Subject	Language	Temperature	Year	EPIC Number
102-0395	S	D	E	N	1958	75780
0395	S	T	E	N	1958	75780
8001	S	S	E	N	1973	53427
8001	S	D	E	N	1974	58808
8001	S	S	E	N	1974	58808
8001	S	T	E	N	1974	58808
8001	S	D	E	N	1974	60265
8001	S	T	E	N	1971	65080
8001	S	D	G	N	1954	66199
8001	S	T	G	N	1954	66199
8001	S	S	E	N	1962	87668
8001	S	S	E	N	1966	87830
8001	S	S	E	N	1971	87884
8001	S	D	E	N	1974	93385
8001	S	S	E	N	1972	97249
8001	S	D	R	N	1975	101515
8001	S	T	R	N	1975	101515
8001	S	D	E	N	1975	101516
8001	S	T	E	N	1975	101516
8027	S	S	E	N	1970	87822
8027	S	S	E	N	1976	101320
8028	S	S	E	N	1972	87890
8031	A	D	E	N	1973	50526
8031	A	E	E	N	1973	50526
8031	A	D	R	N	1972	51605
8031	A	D	E	N	1973	55107
8031	A	D	E	N	1972	63793
8031	A	S	E	N	1964	75166
8031	A	D	E	N	1974	92433
8031	S	D	R	N	1973	49763
8031	S	D	E	N	1973	50526
8031	S	E	E	N	1973	50526
8031	S	D	R	N	1974	87755
8031	S	E	R	N	1974	87755
8031	S	D	E	N	1974	92229
8031	S	E	E	N	1974	92229
8031	S	S	E	N	1972	98639
8031	T	D	R	N	1972	51605
8031	T	D	E	N	1973	55107
8031	T	S	E	N	1972	83589
8035	S	D	E	N	1974	60664
8035	S	D	E	N	1975	68777
8035	T	D	E	N	1967	75171
8041	A	D	E	N	1973	54224
8041	A	D	E	N	1974	60533
8041	A	D	E	N	1972	60905
8041	A	D	E	N	1972	63793
8041	D	S	E	N	1973	54221
8041	D	D	E	N	1974	57966
8041	D	E	E	N	1974	57966
8041	D	D	E	N	1973	60575
8041	D	D	E	N	1974	60692
8041	D	D	E	N	1974	61432
8041	D	T	E	N	1974	61432
8041	D	D	E	N	1974	62055
8041	D	S	E	N	1974	62055
8041	D	D	R	N	1974	62529
8041	D	S	R	N	1974	62529
8041	D	T	E	N	1974	63367
8041	D	D	E	N	1972	63761
8041	D	D	E	N	1974	64432
8041	D	S	E	N	1974	64432
8041	D	D	E	N	1972	66215
8041	D	D	E	N	1964	66316
8041	D	D	E	N	1974	80382
8041	D	S	E	N	1972	87889
8041	D	D	E	N	1975	93322
8041	D	S	E	N	1975	101890
8041	D	D	E	N	1976	102278
8041	S	D	R	N	1973	50233
8041	S	D	E	N	1973	50234
8041	S	S	E	N	1973	50526
8041	S	D	E	N	1973	50924
8041	S	D	E	N	1973	51650
8041	S	D	G	N	1973	51927
8041	S	E	G	N	1973	51927
8041	S	S	G	N	1973	51927
8041	S	T	G	N	1973	51927
8041	S	S	E	N	1973	52774
8041	S	D	E	N	1974	52800
8041	S	S	E	N	1972	53227
8041	S	S	E	N	1972	53244
8041	S	S	E	N	1972	53247
8041	S	E	E	N	1973	53405
8041	S	T	E	N	1973	53405
8041	S	S	E	N	1973	53939
8041	S	T	E	N	1973	53939
8041	S	D	E	N	1974	54024
8041	S	S	E	N	1973	54773
8041	S	S	R	N	1973	54986
8041	S	S	E	N	1974	54987
8041	S	S	E	N	1972	55728
8041	S	D	R	N	1972	56630
8041	S	S	R	N	1972	56630
8041	S	T	R	N	1972	56630
8041	S	D	E	N	1972	57756
8041	S	S	E	N	1972	57756
8041	S	T	E	N	1972	57756
8041	S	D	E	N	1974	57966
8041	S	E	E	N	1974	57966
8041	S	S	E	N	1974	57966

Substance Number	Phys. State	Subject	Language	Temperature	Year	EPIC Number
102-8041	S	D	E	N	1974	57977
8041	S	S	E	N	1974	57977
8041	S	D	E	N	1974	58808
8041	S	S	E	N	1974	58808
8041	S	T	E	N	1974	58808
8041	S	D	E	N	1970	59674
8041	S	S	E	N	1970	59674
8041	S	D	E	N	1974	60265
8041	S	D	E	N	1974	60533
8041	S	D	E	N	1974	60692
8041	S	T	E	N	1974	60692
8041	S	D	E	N	1972	60905
8041	S	D	E	N	1971	61508
8041	S	D	G	N	1971	62077
8041	S	D	E	N	1969	62248
8041	S	S	E	N	1971	62264
8041	S	D	E	N	1969	62273
8041	S	D	E	N	1973	62386
8041	S	S	O	N	1974	62496
8041	S	D	E	N	1971	62600
8041	S	D	R	N	1972	63700
8041	S	E	R	N	1972	63700
8041	S	S	R	N	1972	63700
8041	S	D	E	N	1972	63761
8041	S	D	E	N	1972	63962
8041	S	T	E	N	1971	65080
8041	S	D	E	N	1974	65242
8041	S	D	E	N	1972	65342
8041	S	E	E	N	1972	65342
8041	S	S	E	N	1972	65342
8041	S	D	E	N	1975	65438
8041	S	D	E	N	1975	65507
8041	S	E	E	N	1975	65507
8041	S	D	G	N	1954	66199
8041	S	T	G	N	1954	66199
8041	S	D	E	N	1972	66215
8041	S	D	E	N	1975	66716
8041	S	D	E	N	1971	70398
8041	S	D	E	L	1969	75248
8041	S	D	E	N	1969	75248
8041	S	D	E	N	1974	81547
8041	S	T	E	N	1974	81547
8041	S	S	E	N	1973	86380
8041	S	S	E	N	1962	87673
8041	S	S	E	N	1964	87701
8041	S	D	R	N	1974	87755
8041	S	E	R	N	1974	87755
8041	S	S	R	N	1974	87755
8041	S	S	E	N	1970	87822
8041	S	S	E	N	1970	87879
8041	S	S	E	N	1971	87883
8041	S	S	E	N	1971	87884
8041	S	S	R	N	1974	89991
8041	S	S	E	N	1975	89992
8041	S	D	E	N	1974	92229
8041	S	E	E	N	1974	92229
8041	S	S	E	N	1974	92229
8041	S	D	R	N	1974	92266
8041	S	S	R	N	1974	92266
8041	S	T	R	N	1974	92266
8041	S	D	E	N	1974	92267
8041	S	S	E	N	1974	92267
8041	S	T	E	N	1974	92267
8041	S	S	E	N	1975	93323
8041	S	T	E	N	1975	93357
8041	S	D	E	N	1974	93385
8041	S	D	E	N	1975	94150
8041	S	S	E	N	1975	97221
8041	S	S	E	N	1975	97223
8041	S	S	E	N	1972	97249
8041	S	S	E	N	1975	101032
8041	S	D	R	N	1975	101515
8041	S	T	R	N	1975	101515
8041	S	D	E	N	1975	101516
8041	S	T	E	N	1975	101516
8041	S	D	E	N	1976	101845
8041	S	T	E	N	1976	101845
8041	S	D	E	N	1976	101854
8041	S	E	E	N	1976	101854
8041	S	T	E	N	1976	101854
8041	S	D	E	N	1975	101890
8041	S	S	E	N	1975	101890
8041	S	T	E	N	1975	101890
8041	S	D	E	N	1976	102278
8041	T	D	E	N	1973	52588
8041	T	D	E	N	1973	54224
8041	T	D	E	N	1969	59773
8041	T	D	O	N	1972	59928
8041	T	D	E	N	1974	62550
8041	T	S	E	N	1964	87701
8041	T	S	E	N	1969	87821
8041	T	E	E	N	1975	89267
8041	T	T	E	N	1975	89267
8054	D	S	E	N	1973	53572
8054	S	D	E	N	1973	50924
8054	S	D	E	N	1973	53788
8054	S	E	E	N	1973	53788
8054	S	S	E	N	1973	53939
8054	S	T	E	N	1973	53939
8054	S	D	E	N	1974	58808
8054	S	S	E	N	1974	58808

Substance Number	Phys. State	Subject	Language	Temperature	Year	EPIC Number
102-8054	S	T	E	N	1974	58808
8054	S	D	E	N	1970	59674
8054	S	S	E	N	1970	59674
8054	S	T	E	N	1971	65080
8054	S	D	E	N	1963	65981
8054	S	D	G	N	1954	66199
8054	S	T	G	N	1954	66199
8054	S	S	E	N	1962	87667
8054	S	S	E	N	1971	87883
8054	S	S	E	N	1971	87884
8054	S	D	E	N	1974	93385
8054	S	S	E	N	1972	97249
8054	S	D	R	N	1975	101515
8054	S	T	R	N	1975	101515
8054	S	D	E	N	1975	101516
8054	S	T	E	N	1975	101516
8054	T	D	E	N	1974	58893
8054	T	S	E	N	1973	59311
8069	A	D	E	N	1968	75884
8069	A	D	R	N	1973	83375
8069	A	D	E	N	1973	90273
8069	S	D	E	N	1972	53335
8069	S	D	R	N	1972	56989
8069	S	D	E	N	1968	75884
8069	S	D	R	N	1973	83375
8069	S	D	E	N	1973	90273
8069	S	D	E	N	1976	99141
8069	S	S	E	N	1976	99141
8069	S	T	E	N	1976	99141
8074	D	D	E	N	1973	49526
8074	D	S	E	N	1974	80382
8074	D	D	E	N	1972	85903
8074	S	D	E	N	1973	49526
8074	S	S	E	N	1974	52799
8074	S	D	E	N	1972	53093
8074	S	E	R	N	1974	58949
8074	S	E	E	N	1974	65919
8074	S	S	E	N	1974	80382
8074	T	S	E	N	1973	62276
8078	S	D	E	N	1971	49617
8083	S	S	E	N	1972	53335
8084	S	S	E	N	1972	53335
8084	S	D	E	N	1976	99141
8084	S	S	E	N	1976	99141
8084	S	T	E	N	1976	99141
8090	S	D	E	N	1973	55151
8090	S	T	E	N	1973	55151
8090	S	D	E	N	1974	62023
8094	D	T	E	N	1975	101890
8094	S	S	E	N	1973	52774
8094	S	S	E	N	1972	53227
8094	S	D	E	N	1974	53918
8094	S	T	E	N	1974	53918
8094	S	S	E	N	1974	57977
8094	S	D	E	N	1975	65438
8094	S	D	E	N	1974	80382
8094	S	D	E	N	1974	81547
8094	S	S	E	N	1974	81547
8094	S	T	E	N	1974	81547
8094	S	S	E	N	1972	87889
8094	S	S	E	N	1975	93323
8094	S	D	E	N	1975	101890
8094	S	T	E	N	1975	101890
8095	D	S	E	N	1972	87889
8095	D	D	E	L	1974	88285
8095	S	S	E	N	1972	53227
8095	S	D	E	N	1974	57977
8095	S	S	E	N	1974	57977
8095	S	D	E	N	1975	86754
8095	S	S	E	N	1975	93323
8095	T	D	E	N	1974	93351
8096	S	S	E	N	1972	53335
8096	S	D	R	N	1970	55102
8096	S	D	E	N	1972	55103
8098	S	D	E	N	1973	52785
8112	T	D	E	N	1973	57902
8112	T	E	E	N	1973	57902
8132	S	S	E	N	1974	57977
8132	S	D	E	N	1971	61508
8132	S	S	E	N	1974	80382
8132	S	D	E	N	1974	81547
8132	S	T	E	N	1974	81547
8132	S	S	E	N	1971	87884
8133	A	D	O	N	1974	90527
8133	D	D	O	N	1974	90527
8134	S	S	E	N	1970	87822
8134	S	S	E	N	1972	87890
8137	S	S	E	N	1976	101320
8139	S	D	E	N	1976	99141
8139	S	S	E	N	1976	99141
8139	S	T	E	N	1976	99141
8142	S	S	E	N	1972	87889
8144	S	D	E	N	1973	55786
8153	T	D	E	N	1973	52214
8166	S	S	E	N	1976	101320
8171	A	D	E	N	1972	53186
8171	A	T	E	N	1972	53186
8171	T	D	E	N	1972	53186
8171	T	T	E	N	1972	53186
8179	S	S	E	N	1972	53335
8179	S	D	R	N	1970	55102

Phys. State: **A.** Amorphous; **C.** Superconductive; **D.** Doped; **F.** Fibrous or Whisker; **G.** Gas; **I.** Ionized or Plasma; **L.** Liquid; **P.** Powder or Particle; **S.** Solid; **T.** Thin Film
Subject: **D.** Data; **E.** Experiment; **S.** Survey (Review, Compendium, etc.); **T.** Theory
Language: **E.** English; **F.** French; **G.** German; **O.** Other Languages; **R.** Russian
Temperature: **L.** Low (0 to 75K); **N.** Normal (75 to 1273K); **H.** High (above 1273K)

Substance Number	Phys. State	Subject	Language	Temperature	Year	EPIC Number
102-8179	S	D	E	N	1972	55103
8180	S	S	E	N	1972	53335
8180	S	D	R	N	1970	55102
8180	S	D	E	N	1972	55103
8188	A	D	R	N	1973	83375
8188	A	D	E	N	1973	90273
8200	D	D	E	N	1973	53727
8228	S	D	R	N	1970	55102
8228	S	D	E	N	1972	55103
8228	S	D	E	N	1972	55511
8228	S	D	E	N	1976	99141
8228	S	S	E	N	1976	99141
8228	S	T	E	N	1976	99141
8229	S	D	R	N	1970	55102
8229	S	D	E	N	1972	55103
8230	S	D	R	N	1970	55102
8230	S	D	E	N	1972	55103
8230	S	D	E	N	1972	55511
8231	S	D	R	N	1970	55102
8231	S	D	E	N	1972	55103
8232	S	D	E	N	1974	60664
8238	S	D	E	N	1974	62023
8248	S	D	R	N	1970	55102
8248	S	D	E	N	1972	55103
8249	S	D	R	N	1970	55102
8249	S	D	E	N	1972	55103
8281	S	S	R	N	1973	56262
8281	S	S	E	N	1973	76721
8281	T	D	F	N	1973	54648
8299	S	D	E	N	1966	66020
8300	S	D	E	N	1966	66020
8301	S	D	E	N	1966	66020
8304	S	S	G	N	1959	65983
8304	S	S	E	N	1963	65984
8305	S	S	G	N	1959	65983
8305	S	S	E	N	1963	65984
8314	S	D	E	N	1975	91619
8331	S	D	O	N	1973	51964
8337	S	D	E	N	1972	55511
8340	S	D	R	N	1973	55828
8371	S	D	R	N	1973	49763
8401	A	D	E	N	1974	92433
8439	S	S	E	N	1976	101320
8443	S	D	E	N	1975	91619
8451	S	S	E	N	1975	96398
8452	S	S	E	N	1975	96398
8488	S	D	E	N	1973	66202
8488	S	T	E	N	1973	66202
8488	T	D	E	N	1973	66202
8488	T	T	E	N	1973	66202
8489	S	D	E	N	1973	66202
8489	S	T	E	N	1973	66202
8490	S	D	E	N	1973	66202
8490	S	T	E	N	1973	66202
104-0002	L	D	R	H	1973	53997
0002	L	T	R	H	1973	53997
0002	L	D	E	H	1973	53998
0002	L	T	E	H	1973	53998
0002	S	S	E	N	1969	68271
0002	S	S	E	N	1971	87883
0006	L	S	E	N	1976	66532
0006	S	D	E	N	1972	49483
0006	S	D	E	L	1973	50820
0006	S	D	E	N	1973	50820
0006	S	D	E	N	1973	50924
0006	S	D	E	N	1973	52605
0006	S	S	E	N	1972	53244
0006	S	S	E	N	1972	53247
0006	S	D	E	N	1973	54230
0006	S	S	E	N	1973	54773
0006	S	D	R	N	1973	58310
0006	S	D	R	N	1972	58487
0006	S	D	E	N	1972	60077
0006	S	D	E	N	1974	60265
0006	S	D	R	N	1974	60463
0006	S	D	E	N	1974	60464
0006	S	D	E	N	1969	62248
0006	S	D	R	N	1973	62520
0006	S	S	R	N	1973	62520
0006	S	D	E	N	1974	62521
0006	S	S	E	N	1974	62521
0006	S	D	E	N	1971	62600
0006	S	S	E	N	1949	63242
0006	S	S	E	N	1975	63327
0006	S	D	E	N	1975	63349
0006	S	E	E	N	1975	63349
0006	S	S	E	N	1973	63807
0006	S	T	E	N	1975	65508
0006	S	S	E	N	1970	65877
0006	S	D	E	N	1976	66532
0006	S	S	E	L	1976	66532
0006	S	S	E	N	1976	66532
0006	S	D	E	N	1973	68860
0006	S	D	E	N	1971	70398
0006	S	D	E	N	1972	70677
0006	S	E	E	N	1972	70677
0006	S	T	E	N	1972	70677
0006	S	D	E	L	1969	71197
0006	S	D	E	N	1969	71197
0006	S	S	G	N	1942	73252
104-0006	S	S	E	N	1924	73267
0006	S	D	E	N	1967	75203
0006	S	D	E	N	1968	75382
0006	S	E	E	N	1968	75382
0006	S	D	E	N	1958	75663
0006	S	E	E	N	1958	75663
0006	S	S	E	N	1958	75663
0006	S	D	E	N	1961	75731
0006	S	S	E	N	1961	75731
0006	S	T	E	N	1961	75731
0006	S	D	E	N	1966	75776
0006	S	E	E	N	1966	75776
0006	S	S	E	N	1966	75776
0006	S	D	E	N	1958	75780
0006	S	T	E	N	1958	75780
0006	S	S	E	N	1963	75839
0006	S	D	E	N	1969	85421
0006	S	S	E	N	1971	87883
0006	S	D	E	N	1975	89451
0006	S	S	E	N	1975	89451
0006	S	T	E	N	1975	89451
0006	S	D	E	N	1975	89452
0006	S	T	E	N	1975	93357
0006	S	D	E	N	1975	93400
0006	S	T	E	N	1975	97223
0006	S	S	E	N	1972	97249
0006	S	D	E	N	1976	99987
0006	S	E	E	N	1976	99987
0006	S	S	E	N	1976	99987
0006	S	D	E	N	1975	101022
0006	S	S	E	N	1976	101375
0006	S	E	E	N	1975	101658
0006	S	T	E	N	1975	101658
0006	S	D	R	N	1975	101804
0006	S	T	R	N	1975	101804
0006	S	D	E	N	1976	101805
0006	S	T	E	N	1976	101805
0006	S	D	E	N	1976	101845
0006	S	T	E	N	1976	101845
0006	S	D	E	N	1976	101853
0006	S	E	E	N	1976	101853
0006	S	T	E	N	1976	101853
0006	S	D	E	N	1974	102101
0006	S	E	E	N	1974	102101
0006	S	D	E	N	1976	102403
0006	S	T	E	N	1976	102403
0006	T	S	E	N	1971	100982
0007	A	S	E	N	1971	87884
0007	S	D	R	N	1971	59379
0007	S	D	E	N	1966	64254
0007	S	S	E	N	1967	68374
0007	S	S	E	N	1971	87884
0007	S	S	E	N	1972	102094
0007	T	D	E	N	1972	61068
0007	T	S	E	N	1972	61068
0007	T	S	E	N	1969	87821
0007	T	S	E	N	1971	87884
0008	G	D	E	N	1973	51502
0013	A	D	E	N	1974	53862
0013	S	T	E	N	1973	50380
0013	S	D	R	N	1974	58074
0013	S	D	E	N	1974	58075
0013	S	D	R	N	1972	60715
0013	S	D	E	N	1973	60716
0013	S	S	E	N	1967	85905
0013	T	D	E	N	1974	53862
0013	T	D	E	N	1967	85905
0015	S	D	E	N	1973	50127
0015	S	D	E	N	1974	62027
0015	S	D	E	N	1970	64545
0015	S	D	E	N	1973	75764
0015	S	T	E	N	1973	75764
0015	S	S	E	N	1964	101393
0021	A	D	E	N	1975	90859
0021	A	S	E	N	1975	90859
0021	T	D	E	N	1975	90859
0021	T	S	E	N	1975	90859
0022	S	D	E	N	1974	54337
0022	S	S	E	N	1970	87822
0022	S	D	E	N	1976	103162
0022	S	T	E	N	1976	103162
0027	A	D	E	N	1974	53862
0027	T	D	E	N	1974	53862
0031	S	D	E	N	1973	50924
0031	S	D	E	N	1974	60265
0031	S	T	E	N	1973	63782
0031	S	D	E	N	1976	66532
0031	S	S	E	N	1976	66532
0031	S	D	E	N	1972	70677
0031	S	E	E	N	1972	70677
0031	S	T	E	N	1972	70677
0031	S	D	E	N	1968	75382
0031	S	E	E	N	1968	75382
0031	S	S	E	N	1968	101416
0038	S	D	E	N	1958	75780
0038	S	T	E	N	1958	75780
0040	G	S	E	N	1973	98865
0049	S	D	E	N	1975	63361
0049	S	E	E	N	1975	63361
0049	S	S	E	N	1975	63361
0049	S	S	E	N	1969	68271
104-0053	L	S	E	N	1976	66532
0053	S	D	E	N	1973	50924
0053	S	D	E	N	1973	52605
0053	S	D	E	N	1974	60265
0053	S	S	E	N	1975	63327
0053	S	S	E	N	1970	65877
0053	S	D	E	N	1976	66532
0053	S	S	E	N	1976	66532
0053	S	D	E	N	1973	68860
0053	S	S	G	N	1942	73252
0053	S	D	E	N	1961	75731
0053	S	T	E	N	1961	75731
0053	S	D	E	N	1976	99987
0053	S	E	E	N	1976	99987
0053	S	S	E	N	1976	101374
0053	S	S	E	N	1976	101375
0053	S	D	R	N	1975	101804
0053	S	T	R	N	1975	101804
0053	S	D	E	N	1976	101805
0053	S	T	E	N	1976	101805
0053	S	D	E	N	1976	101853
0053	S	E	E	N	1976	101853
0053	S	T	E	N	1976	101853
0053	T	S	E	N	1976	66532
0056	G	S	E	N	1973	98865
0067	L	D	E	N	1929	73248
0095	S	D	E	L	1974	61157
0104	S	S	E	N	1973	50526
0104	S	D	R	N	1973	52216
0104	S	D	E	N	1974	54024
0104	S	S	R	N	1973	56262
0104	S	D	E	N	1974	60255
0104	S	D	E	N	1973	61830
0104	S	D	E	N	1971	62600
0104	S	S	E	N	1975	63327
0104	S	S	E	N	1962	64551
0104	S	S	E	N	1971	65015
0104	S	D	E	N	1963	65112
0104	S	S	E	N	1963	65112
0104	S	T	E	N	1963	65112
0104	S	D	E	N	1971	70398
0104	S	D	E	N	1972	70677
0104	S	E	E	N	1972	70677
0104	S	S	E	N	1972	70677
0104	S	T	E	N	1972	70677
0104	S	D	E	N	1964	73259
0104	S	T	E	N	1964	73259
0104	S	D	E	N	1963	73260
0104	S	E	E	N	1963	73260
0104	S	D	E	N	1967	74607
0104	S	D	E	N	1966	75114
0104	S	T	E	N	1966	75114
0104	S	S	E	N	1973	76721
0104	S	D	E	N	1974	84584
0104	S	D	R	L	1974	87288
0104	S	D	E	L	1975	87289
0104	S	S	E	N	1971	87883
0104	S	D	E	N	1975	93319
0104	S	E	E	N	1975	94151
0104	S	S	E	N	1976	95874
0104	S	D	G	N	1927	96122
0104	S	T	G	N	1927	96122
0104	S	S	R	N	1975	97090
0104	S	S	E	N	1975	97223
0104	S	S	E	N	1972	97249
0104	S	S	E	N	1976	101374
0104	S	S	E	N	1976	101375
0104	S	D	E	N	1976	101501
0104	S	D	E	N	1975	101659
0104	S	E	E	N	1975	101659
0104	S	D	E	N	1976	101796
0104	S	E	E	N	1976	101796
0104	S	S	E	N	1976	101796
0104	S	D	E	N	1976	101820
0104	S	E	E	N	1976	101820
0104	S	D	E	N	1976	101826
0104	S	D	E	N	1976	101839
0104	S	E	E	N	1976	101839
0104	S	S	E	N	1976	101839
0104	S	T	E	N	1976	101839
0104	S	D	E	N	1976	101845
0104	S	T	E	N	1976	101845
0104	S	D	E	N	1976	101853
0104	S	E	E	N	1976	101853
0104	S	T	E	N	1976	101853
0104	S	D	E	N	1976	103590
0104	S	T	E	N	1976	103590
0104	T	D	E	N	1974	52803
0104	T	E	E	N	1974	52803
0104	T	D	E	N	1974	68831
0104	T	D	E	N	1975	93161
0104	T	D	E	N	1976	101813
0104	T	E	E	N	1976	101813
0105	L	S	E	N	1976	66532
0105	S	D	E	N	1973	50924
0105	S	D	E	N	1974	60265
0105	S	D	E	N	1976	66532
0105	S	S	E	N	1976	66532
0106	S	D	E	N	1973	50924
0106	S	S	E	N	1972	53244
0106	S	S	E	N	1972	53247

Phys. State: **A.** Amorphous; **C.** Superconductive; **D.** Doped; **F.** Fibrous or Whisker; **G.** Gas; **I.** Ionized or Plasma; **L.** Liquid; **P.** Powder or Particle; **S.** Solid; **T.** Thin Film
Subject: **D.** Data; **E.** Experiment; **S.** Survey (Review, Compendium, etc.); **T.** Theory
Language: **E.** English; **F.** French; **G.** German; **O.** Other Languages; **R.** Russian
Temperature: **L.** Low (0 to 75K); **N.** Normal (75 to 1273K); **H.** High (above 1273K)

Substance Number	Phys. State	Subject	Language	Temperature	Year	EPIC Number
104-0106	S	S	E	N	1973	54773
0106	S	S	E	N	1970	65877
0106	S	D	E	N	1976	66532
0106	S	S	E	L	1976	66532
0106	S	S	E	N	1976	66532
0106	S	D	E	N	1971	70398
0106	S	S	E	N	1971	87883
0196	S	S	E	N	1969	68271
0196	S	T	R	N	1972	79283
0295	S	S	E	N	1971	87884
0302	S	D	E	N	1973	65000
0434	S	S	E	N	1972	53244
0434	S	S	E	N	1972	53247
0434	S	S	E	N	1966	87841
0533	S	D	E	N	1972	54618
0533	S	D	R	N	1973	54986
0533	S	D	E	N	1974	54987
0533	S	S	E	N	1970	87822
0533	S	S	E	N	1972	87890
8016	S	D	E	N	1974	60303
8032	S	S	E	N	1969	68271
8033	S	S	E	N	1969	68271
8036	S	S	E	N	1969	68271
8045	S	S	R	N	1972	62298
8045	S	S	E	N	1973	62299
8045	S	S	E	N	1966	66068
8069	T	D	E	N	1973	50382
8110	S	T	E	N	1973	50380
8110	S	S	E	N	1970	87822
8110	S	S	E	N	1972	87890
8123	S	D	R	N	1973	50233
8123	S	D	E	N	1973	50234
8123	S	D	R	N	1973	54986
8123	S	D	E	N	1974	54987
8156	T	D	E	N	1973	57279
8156	T	T	E	N	1973	57279
8162	S	D	R	N	1973	55068
8162	S	D	E	N	1974	55069
8164	S	D	E	N	1973	51802
8164	S	T	E	N	1973	51802
8166	S	D	E	N	1972	55832
8166	S	S	E	N	1972	87890
8171	S	D	R	N	1974	59397
8171	S	E	R	N	1974	59397
8171	S	D	E	N	1974	65920
8171	S	E	E	N	1974	65920
8171	S	D	R	N	1974	87019
8171	S	E	R	N	1974	87019
8171	S	D	E	N	1974	87020
8171	S	E	E	N	1974	87020
8180	S	D	E	N	1973	52779
8191	S	S	E	N	1972	53244
8191	S	S	E	N	1972	53247
8191	S	S	E	N	1973	54773
8191	S	D	E	N	1970	61482
8191	S	D	E	N	1971	62600
8191	S	S	E	N	1949	63242
8191	S	S	E	N	1974	64477
8191	S	S	E	N	1970	65877
8191	S	D	E	N	1971	70398
8191	S	S	E	N	1971	70398
8191	S	D	O	N	1974	87783
8191	S	T	O	N	1974	87783
8191	S	S	E	N	1966	87841
8191	S	S	E	N	1971	87883
8191	S	S	E	N	1971	100982
8191	T	S	E	N	1971	100982
8192	S	S	E	N	1972	53244
8192	S	S	E	N	1972	53247
8192	S	S	E	N	1970	65877
8192	S	S	E	N	1971	87883
8198	S	D	R	N	1973	54504
8198	S	D	E	N	1973	54505
8198	S	D	E	N	1974	56652
8231	S	D	R	N	1973	54986
8231	S	D	E	N	1974	54987
8295	S	D	E	N	1972	55832
8298	S	D	R	N	1973	56011
8298	S	D	E	N	1974	76600
8301	S	D	E	N	1974	56165
8302	S	D	E	N	1974	56165
8327	S	D	E	N	1961	60530
8366	S	S	E	N	1971	87884
8399	L	S	E	N	1973	98865
8400	L	S	E	N	1973	98865
8421	S	D	E	N	1974	88201
8421	S	D	E	N	1975	90104
8422	S	D	E	N	1975	90104
8423	A	D	E	N	1975	90859
8423	T	D	E	N	1975	90859
8445	T	T	R	N	1974	66752
8445	T	T	E	N	1975	66753
106-0001	G	D	E	N	1973	51502
0002	L	D	R	N	1973	54424
0002	L	S	R	N	1973	54424
0002	L	D	E	N	1973	54425
0002	L	S	E	N	1973	54425
0002	L	D	E	N	1971	67062
0002	L	S	E	N	1967	98664
0002	L	S	E	N	1973	98865
106-0002	L	D	E	N	1976	101704
0002	L	S	E	N	1976	101704
0002	L	T	E	N	1976	101704
0002	S	D	R	N	1974	90889
0002	S	E	R	N	1974	90889
0002	S	D	E	N	1974	93413
0002	S	E	E	N	1974	93413
0003	G	T	E	N	1973	50969
0003	G	D	E	N	1973	56259
0003	G	D	R	N	1973	57245
0003	G	D	E	N	1974	58694
0003	G	D	R	N	1974	87314
0003	G	D	E	N	1974	87315
0003	G	T	G	N	1893	89951
0003	G	D	R	N	1969	98250
0003	G	E	R	N	1969	98250
0003	L	E	R	N	1969	98250
0004	S	S	E	N	1973	62815
0004	S	S	E	N	1974	62816
0004	S	S	E	N	1969	68271
0005	S	D	R	N	1971	61549
0005	S	E	R	N	1971	61549
0005	S	S	E	N	1949	63242
0005	S	S	E	N	1970	65877
0005	S	D	E	N	1971	65902
0005	S	E	E	N	1971	65902
0005	S	D	F	N	1958	75815
0005	S	T	F	N	1958	75815
0005	S	S	E	N	1971	87883
0006	D	S	R	N	1970	61851
0006	D	D	E	N	1975	93312
0006	D	D	E	N	1976	97231
0006	D	D	E	N	1976	97743
0006	D	E	E	N	1976	97743
0006	D	D	E	N	1976	101442
0006	D	E	E	N	1976	101442
0006	D	T	E	N	1976	101442
0006	D	D	E	N	1976	101562
0006	D	D	E	N	1976	101819
0006	D	E	E	N	1976	101819
0006	L	S	R	N	1970	61851
0006	L	S	E	N	1976	66532
0006	L	D	E	N	1975	96222
0006	L	E	E	N	1975	96222
0006	S	D	E	N	1973	50924
0006	S	D	E	N	1973	52605
0006	S	S	E	N	1972	53244
0006	S	S	E	N	1972	53247
0006	S	D	E	N	1974	54024
0006	S	D	E	N	1973	54230
0006	S	S	E	N	1973	54773
0006	S	T	E	N	1972	55097
0006	S	D	R	N	1972	56630
0006	S	S	R	N	1972	56630
0006	S	T	R	N	1972	56630
0006	S	D	E	N	1972	57756
0006	S	S	E	N	1972	57756
0006	S	T	E	N	1972	57756
0006	S	D	R	N	1973	58310
0006	S	D	R	N	1972	58487
0006	S	T	E	N	1974	58821
0006	S	D	E	N	1972	60077
0006	S	D	E	N	1974	60255
0006	S	D	E	N	1974	60265
0006	S	D	E	N	1973	60866
0006	S	D	E	N	1973	60868
0006	S	D	E	N	1969	62248
0006	S	D	E	N	1973	62325
0006	S	D	R	N	1973	62520
0006	S	D	E	N	1974	62521
0006	S	S	E	N	1949	63242
0006	S	S	E	N	1975	63327
0006	S	D	E	N	1975	63349
0006	S	E	E	N	1975	63349
0006	S	D	R	N	1972	63700
0006	S	E	R	N	1972	63700
0006	S	S	R	N	1972	63700
0006	S	T	E	N	1973	63775
0006	S	S	E	N	1973	63807
0006	S	D	E	N	1972	65342
0006	S	E	E	N	1972	65342
0006	S	S	E	N	1972	65342
0006	S	S	E	N	1975	65507
0006	S	T	E	N	1975	65508
0006	S	D	E	N	1974	65616
0006	S	S	E	N	1970	65877
0006	S	D	E	N	1976	66532
0006	S	S	E	L	1976	66532
0006	S	S	E	N	1976	66532
0006	S	D	E	N	1973	68860
0006	S	D	E	N	1971	70398
0006	S	D	E	N	1972	70677
0006	S	E	E	N	1972	70677
0006	S	S	E	N	1972	70677
0006	S	T	E	N	1972	70677
0006	S	D	E	L	1969	71197
0006	S	D	E	N	1969	71197
0006	S	S	E	N	1924	73267
0006	S	D	E	N	1967	75203
0006	S	D	E	N	1958	75663
0006	S	E	E	N	1958	75663
106-0006	S	S	E	N	1958	75663
0006	S	D	E	N	1961	75731
0006	S	S	E	N	1961	75731
0006	S	T	E	N	1961	75731
0006	S	D	E	N	1966	75776
0006	S	E	E	N	1966	75776
0006	S	S	E	N	1966	75776
0006	S	D	E	N	1958	75780
0006	S	T	E	N	1958	75780
0006	S	D	F	N	1958	75815
0006	S	T	F	N	1958	75815
0006	S	D	E	N	1969	85421
0006	S	S	E	N	1971	87883
0006	S	D	E	N	1974	88462
0006	S	D	E	N	1975	89451
0006	S	S	E	N	1975	89451
0006	S	T	E	N	1975	89451
0006	S	D	E	N	1975	89452
0006	S	D	E	N	1975	93309
0006	S	D	E	N	1975	93312
0006	S	D	E	N	1975	93319
0006	S	T	E	N	1975	93357
0006	S	D	E	N	1974	93375
0006	S	D	E	N	1975	93400
0006	S	D	E	N	1975	94150
0006	S	D	E	N	1974	94581
0006	S	T	E	N	1975	97223
0006	S	D	E	N	1976	97231
0006	S	S	E	N	1972	97249
0006	S	D	E	N	1976	97743
0006	S	E	E	N	1976	97743
0006	S	S	E	N	1976	97743
0006	S	D	E	N	1976	99987
0006	S	E	E	N	1976	99987
0006	S	S	E	N	1976	99987
0006	S	D	E	N	1975	101022
0006	S	S	E	N	1976	101375
0006	S	D	E	N	1976	101442
0006	S	E	E	N	1976	101442
0006	S	S	E	N	1976	101442
0006	S	T	E	N	1976	101442
0006	S	D	E	N	1976	101562
0006	S	E	E	N	1976	101562
0006	S	E	E	N	1975	101658
0006	S	T	E	N	1975	101658
0006	S	D	E	N	1975	101659
0006	S	E	E	N	1975	101659
0006	S	T	E	N	1975	101659
0006	S	D	E	N	1976	101796
0006	S	E	E	N	1976	101796
0006	S	S	E	N	1976	101796
0006	S	D	R	N	1975	101804
0006	S	T	R	N	1975	101804
0006	S	D	E	N	1976	101805
0006	S	T	E	N	1976	101805
0006	S	D	E	N	1976	101813
0006	S	E	E	N	1976	101813
0006	S	D	E	N	1976	101819
0006	S	E	E	N	1976	101819
0006	S	D	E	N	1976	101820
0006	S	E	E	N	1976	101820
0006	S	E	E	N	1976	101834
0006	S	D	E	N	1976	101845
0006	S	T	E	N	1976	101845
0006	S	D	E	N	1976	101853
0006	S	E	E	N	1976	101853
0006	S	T	E	N	1976	101853
0006	S	D	E	N	1976	102403
0006	S	T	E	N	1976	102403
0006	S	D	E	N	1976	103590
0006	S	T	E	N	1976	103590
0006	T	D	E	N	1974	52803
0006	T	E	E	N	1974	52803
0006	T	S	E	N	1976	66532
0006	T	D	E	N	1974	68831
0006	T	D	E	N	1976	101808
0006	T	T	E	N	1976	101808
0006	T	S	E	N	1976	102567
0009	G	S	E	N	1973	98865
0009	G	S	E	N	1966	101379
0011	L	D	E	N	1972	49603
0011	L	D	F	N	1972	53801
0011	L	T	F	N	1972	53801
0011	L	S	E	N	1974	62735
0011	L	S	E	N	1972	83519
0011	L	S	E	N	1967	98664
0011	L	D	E	N	1976	101704
0011	L	T	E	N	1976	101704
0011	S	S	E	N	1920	73257
0021	G	D	E	N	1973	51502
0024	L	S	E	N	1976	66532
0024	S	D	E	N	1973	50924
0024	S	D	E	N	1973	52605
0024	S	S	E	N	1972	53244
0024	S	S	E	N	1972	53247
0024	S	D	E	N	1974	54024
0024	S	D	E	N	1973	54230
0024	S	S	E	N	1973	54773
0024	S	D	R	N	1972	56630
0024	S	S	R	N	1972	56630
0024	S	T	R	N	1972	56630

Phys. State: **A.** Amorphous; **C.** Superconductive; **D.** Doped; **F.** Fibrous or Whisker; **G.** Gas; **I.** Ionized or Plasma; **L.** Liquid; **P.** Powder or Particle; **S.** Solid; **T.** Thin Film
Subject: **D.** Data; **E.** Experiment; **S.** Survey (Review, Compendium, etc.); **T.** Theory
Language: **E.** English; **F.** French; **G.** German; **O.** Other Languages; **R.** Russian
Temperature: **L.** Low (0 to 75K); **N.** Normal (75 to 1273K); **H.** High (above 1273K)

Substance Number	Phys. State	Subject	Language	Temperature	Year	EPIC Number
106-0024	S	D	E	N	1972	57756
0024	S	S	E	N	1972	57756
0024	S	T	E	N	1972	57756
0024	S	D	R	N	1973	58310
0024	S	D	R	N	1972	58487
0024	S	S	E	N	1973	58898
0024	S	T	E	N	1973	58898
0024	S	T	R	N	1973	59726
0024	S	T	E	N	1973	59727
0024	S	D	E	N	1972	60077
0024	S	D	E	N	1974	60265
0024	S	S	E	N	1973	60840
0024	S	D	E	N	1970	61482
0024	S	E	R	N	1971	61548
0024	S	D	E	L	1971	61683
0024	S	D	E	N	1971	61683
0024	S	E	E	L	1971	61683
0024	S	E	E	N	1971	61683
0024	S	D	E	N	1969	62248
0024	S	D	R	N	1973	62520
0024	S	D	E	N	1974	62521
0024	S	D	E	N	1971	62600
0024	S	S	E	N	1974	62758
0024	S	S	E	N	1949	63242
0024	S	S	E	N	1975	63327
0024	S	D	R	N	1972	63700
0024	S	E	R	N	1972	63700
0024	S	S	R	N	1972	63700
0024	S	T	E	N	1973	63775
0024	S	S	E	N	1973	63807
0024	S	D	E	N	1972	65342
0024	S	E	E	N	1972	65342
0024	S	S	E	N	1972	65342
0024	S	T	E	N	1975	65508
0024	S	S	E	N	1970	65877
0024	S	E	E	N	1971	65901
0024	S	D	E	N	1976	66532
0024	S	S	E	L	1976	66532
0024	S	S	E	N	1976	66532
0024	S	D	E	N	1973	68860
0024	S	D	E	N	1971	70398
0024	S	D	E	N	1972	70677
0024	S	E	E	N	1972	70677
0024	S	S	E	N	1972	70677
0024	S	T	E	N	1972	70677
0024	S	D	E	L	1969	71197
0024	S	D	E	N	1969	71197
0024	S	S	G	N	1942	73252
0024	S	S	E	N	1924	73267
0024	S	D	E	N	1967	75203
0024	S	D	R	L	1974	75383
0024	S	D	R	N	1974	75383
0024	S	E	R	L	1974	75383
0024	S	E	R	N	1974	75383
0024	S	D	E	N	1958	75663
0024	S	E	E	N	1958	75663
0024	S	S	E	N	1958	75663
0024	S	D	E	N	1961	75731
0024	S	S	E	N	1961	75731
0024	S	T	E	N	1961	75731
0024	S	D	E	N	1966	75776
0024	S	E	E	N	1966	75776
0024	S	S	E	N	1966	75776
0024	S	D	F	N	1958	75815
0024	S	T	F	N	1958	75815
0024	S	T	O	N	1974	87783
0024	S	S	E	N	1971	87883
0024	S	D	E	N	1975	89452
0024	S	D	E	L	1974	93414
0024	S	D	E	N	1974	93414
0024	S	E	E	L	1974	93414
0024	S	E	E	N	1974	93414
0024	S	T	E	N	1975	97223
0024	S	S	E	N	1972	97249
0024	S	D	E	N	1976	99987
0024	S	E	E	N	1976	99987
0024	S	S	E	N	1976	99987
0024	S	S	E	N	1976	101374
0024	S	S	E	N	1976	101375
0024	S	D	R	N	1975	101804
0024	S	T	R	N	1975	101804
0024	S	D	E	N	1976	101805
0024	S	T	E	N	1976	101805
0024	S	D	E	N	1976	101845
0024	S	T	E	N	1976	101845
0024	S	D	E	N	1976	101853
0024	S	E	E	N	1976	101853
0024	S	T	E	N	1976	101853
0024	S	D	E	N	1976	102403
0024	S	T	E	N	1976	102403
0024	S	D	E	N	1976	103590
0024	S	T	E	N	1976	103590
0024	T	S	E	N	1973	62276
0024	T	S	E	N	1976	66532
0026	D	D	E	N	1975	62354
0026	D	D	F	N	1974	90680
0026	S	S	E	N	1973	50526
0026	S	D	R	N	1973	52216
0026	S	S	E	N	1972	53512
0026	S	D	E	N	1974	54024
0026	S	D	E	N	1973	61754
106-0026	S	S	E	N	1973	61754
0026	S	D	E	N	1973	61830
0026	S	D	E	N	1971	62186
0026	S	S	E	N	1949	63242
0026	S	S	E	N	1975	63327
0026	S	S	E	N	1962	64551
0026	S	S	E	N	1971	65015
0026	S	S	E	N	1970	65877
0026	S	D	E	N	1961	65970
0026	S	D	E	N	1971	70398
0026	S	D	E	N	1972	70677
0026	S	E	E	N	1972	70677
0026	S	S	E	N	1972	70677
0026	S	T	E	N	1972	70677
0026	S	S	G	N	1942	73252
0026	S	D	E	N	1963	73260
0026	S	E	E	N	1963	73260
0026	S	S	E	N	1963	73260
0026	S	S	E	N	1924	73267
0026	S	D	E	N	1967	74607
0026	S	T	E	N	1967	74607
0026	S	D	E	N	1966	75114
0026	S	T	E	N	1966	75114
0026	S	D	E	N	1958	75780
0026	S	T	E	N	1958	75780
0026	S	D	R	L	1974	87288
0026	S	D	E	L	1975	87289
0026	S	S	E	N	1971	87883
0026	S	D	F	N	1883	90237
0026	S	E	E	N	1975	94151
0026	S	D	E	N	1975	95407
0026	S	E	E	N	1975	95407
0026	S	S	E	N	1975	95407
0026	S	T	E	N	1975	95407
0026	S	S	E	N	1976	95874
0026	S	D	G	N	1927	96122
0026	S	T	G	N	1927	96122
0026	S	S	R	N	1975	97090
0026	S	S	E	N	1975	97223
0026	S	S	E	N	1972	97249
0026	S	D	E	N	1976	99987
0026	S	E	E	N	1976	99987
0026	S	S	E	N	1976	99987
0026	S	S	E	N	1976	101374
0026	S	S	E	N	1976	101375
0026	S	D	E	N	1976	101501
0026	S	D	E	N	1976	101650
0026	S	E	E	N	1976	101650
0026	S	D	E	N	1976	101796
0026	S	E	E	N	1976	101796
0026	S	S	E	N	1976	101796
0026	S	D	E	N	1976	101820
0026	S	E	E	N	1976	101820
0026	S	D	E	N	1976	101826
0026	S	D	E	N	1976	101839
0026	S	E	E	N	1976	101839
0026	S	S	E	N	1976	101839
0026	S	T	E	N	1976	101839
0026	S	D	E	N	1976	101845
0026	S	T	E	N	1976	101845
0026	S	D	E	N	1976	101853
0026	S	E	E	N	1976	101853
0026	S	T	E	N	1976	101853
0026	S	D	E	N	1976	103590
0026	S	T	E	N	1976	103590
0026	T	D	E	N	1974	52803
0026	T	E	E	N	1974	52803
0026	T	S	F	N	1973	54648
0026	T	D	F	N	1974	90680
0026	T	S	E	N	1957	95707
0026	T	T	E	N	1957	95707
0026	T	S	E	N	1971	100982
0034	G	D	E	N	1973	51502
0035	D	D	R	N	1976	103177
0035	D	T	R	N	1976	103177
0035	D	D	E	N	1976	103178
0035	D	T	E	N	1976	103178
0035	F	D	E	N	1971	65869
0035	S	D	R	N	1971	62098
0035	S	S	R	N	1971	62098
0035	S	D	E	N	1971	65869
0035	S	S	E	N	1971	65869
0035	S	D	E	N	1971	67085
0035	S	S	E	N	1971	67085
0035	S	S	E	N	1965	87702
0035	S	S	E	N	1968	87828
0035	S	S	E	N	1971	87883
0035	S	S	E	N	1971	87887
0035	S	D	R	N	1974	92266
0035	S	S	R	N	1974	92266
0035	S	T	R	N	1974	92266
0035	S	D	E	N	1974	92267
0035	S	S	E	N	1974	92267
0035	S	T	E	N	1974	92267
0035	T	D	E	N	1975	95534
0036	S	D	E	N	1976	103162
0036	S	T	E	N	1976	103162
0039	G	D	E	N	1973	51502
0045	S	D	E	N	1970	52695
0045	S	T	E	N	1967	75911
0050	S	D	R	N	1971	66990
106-0057	P	S	E	N	1966	68325
0057	S	S	E	N	1969	68271
0057	T	S	E	N	1966	68325
0060	T	S	E	N	1965	65978
0064	S	D	F	N	1971	83537
0066	G	D	E	N	1973	51502
0092	S	D	R	N	1973	57008
0093	S	D	R	N	1973	57008
0104	S	D	E	N	1973	52061
0104	S	D	E	N	1972	59903
0104	T	S	E	N	1971	87872
0128	L	S	E	N	1973	60748
0129	G	S	E	N	1973	98865
0156	S	D	E	N	1973	52510
0156	S	E	E	N	1973	52510
0157	L	D	E	N	1929	73248
0157	S	D	F	N	1958	75815
0157	S	T	F	N	1958	75815
0157	T	S	E	N	1971	100982
0158	S	S	E	N	1970	87822
0158	S	S	E	N	1971	87883
0158	S	S	E	N	1972	87890
0158	S	D	E	N	1976	103162
0158	S	T	E	N	1976	103162
0159	L	S	E	N	1976	66532
0159	S	D	E	N	1973	50924
0159	S	D	E	N	1974	60265
0159	S	D	E	N	1976	66532
0159	S	S	E	N	1976	66532
0165	L	D	R	N	1971	61853
0165	S	D	E	N	1973	50924
0165	S	D	E	N	1974	60265
0165	S	S	E	N	1975	63327
0165	S	T	E	N	1973	63782
0165	S	D	E	N	1976	66532
0165	S	S	E	N	1976	66532
0165	S	D	E	N	1973	68860
0165	S	S	G	N	1942	73252
0165	S	D	E	N	1975	89452
0165	S	D	R	N	1975	96822
0165	S	T	R	N	1975	96822
0165	S	D	E	N	1976	99237
0165	S	T	E	N	1976	99237
0165	S	S	E	N	1968	101416
0192	S	D	R	N	1972	79248
0192	S	D	E	N	1972	90275
0192	T	D	E	N	1974	53899
0192	T	S	E	N	1974	53899
0192	T	D	E	N	1973	55160
0192	T	S	E	N	1973	62276
0192	T	D	E	N	1975	65506
0192	T	S	E	N	1975	65506
0192	T	T	E	N	1975	65506
0192	T	D	E	N	1975	96486
0203	L	D	R	N	1971	61853
0203	P	S	E	N	1976	66532
0203	S	D	E	N	1973	50924
0203	S	D	E	N	1976	66532
0203	S	S	E	L	1976	66532
0203	S	S	E	N	1976	66532
0203	S	D	E	N	1968	75382
0203	S	E	E	N	1968	75382
0203	S	D	E	N	1976	99905
0203	S	S	E	N	1976	99905
0218	A	D	E	N	1974	53862
0218	T	D	E	N	1974	53862
0227	S	D	E	N	1974	101158
0227	S	T	E	N	1974	101158
0233	G	D	E	N	1973	51502
0234	S	D	E	N	1973	60868
0237	S	D	E	N	1976	66532
0237	S	S	E	N	1976	66532
0237	S	D	E	N	1975	98278
0237	S	E	E	N	1975	98278
0237	S	S	E	N	1975	98278
0237	S	T	E	N	1975	98278
0238	D	D	R	N	1971	54657
0238	S	D	E	N	1973	50924
0238	S	S	E	N	1972	53244
0238	S	S	E	N	1972	53247
0238	S	S	E	N	1973	54773
0238	S	D	E	L	1973	55351
0238	S	D	E	N	1973	55351
0238	S	S	E	L	1973	55351
0238	S	S	E	N	1973	55351
0238	S	S	R	N	1973	56262
0238	S	D	E	N	1972	60077
0238	S	D	E	N	1971	62600
0238	S	S	E	N	1970	65877
0238	S	D	E	N	1976	66532
0238	S	S	E	L	1976	66532
0238	S	S	E	N	1976	66532
0238	S	D	E	N	1971	70398
0238	S	D	E	N	1968	75382
0238	S	E	E	N	1968	75382
0238	S	S	E	N	1973	76721
0238	S	S	E	N	1971	87883
0238	S	D	R	N	1975	97183
0238	S	T	R	N	1975	97183
0238	S	D	E	N	1976	97184
0238	S	T	E	N	1976	97184

Phys. State: A. Amorphous; C. Superconductive; D. Doped; F. Fibrous or Whisker; G. Gas; I. Ionized or Plasma; L. Liquid; P. Powder or Particle; S. Solid; T. Thin Film
Subject: D. Data; E. Experiment; S. Survey (Review, Compendium, etc.); T. Theory
Language: E. English; F. French; G. German; O. Other Languages; R. Russian
Temperature: L. Low (0 to 75K); N. Normal (75 to 1273K); H. High (above 1273K)

Substance Number	Phys. State	Sub-ject	Lan-guage	Temper-ature	Year	EPIC Number
106-0238	T	S	E	N	1976	66532
0238	T	S	E	N	1971	100982
0363	A	D	E	N	1975	96894
0363	A	T	E	N	1975	96894
0363	A	D	E	N	1976	100416
0363	D	D	E	N	1972	62201
0363	D	S	E	N	1963	64232
0363	D	S	E	N	1967	66156
0363	S	D	R	N	1973	50215
0363	S	D	E	N	1973	50216
0363	S	D	R	N	1973	50233
0363	S	D	E	N	1973	50234
0363	S	T	R	L	1972	54233
0363	S	T	E	L	1973	54718
0363	S	D	E	N	1973	55872
0363	S	S	R	N	1973	56262
0363	S	D	R	N	1972	58597
0363	S	T	R	N	1972	58597
0363	S	D	E	N	1971	59436
0363	S	E	E	N	1971	59436
0363	S	D	E	N	1974	60691
0363	S	S	E	N	1974	60691
0363	S	D	E	L	1973	61472
0363	S	S	E	L	1973	61472
0363	S	D	E	N	1972	62201
0363	S	D	E	N	1969	62248
0363	S	D	E	N	1973	62386
0363	S	D	E	N	1971	62600
0363	S	D	R	N	1972	62695
0363	S	S	R	N	1972	62695
0363	S	D	R	N	1972	62713
0363	S	S	E	N	1963	64232
0363	S	D	E	N	1972	64422
0363	S	S	E	N	1972	64422
0363	S	D	E	N	1973	65309
0363	S	D	E	N	1975	65498
0363	S	S	E	N	1975	65498
0363	S	T	E	N	1975	65498
0363	S	S	E	N	1967	66156
0363	S	S	E	N	1969	68271
0363	S	T	E	N	1970	70645
0363	S	S	E	N	1973	76721
0363	S	D	R	L	1974	81216
0363	S	T	R	L	1974	81216
0363	S	S	E	N	1970	87822
0363	S	S	E	N	1971	87883
0363	S	D	R	N	1974	89254
0363	S	T	R	N	1974	89254
0363	S	D	E	N	1974	89255
0363	S	T	E	N	1974	89255
0363	S	S	R	L	1975	89630
0363	S	S	E	L	1975	89631
0363	S	D	E	N	1975	91671
0363	S	E	E	N	1975	91671
0363	S	D	E	L	1974	92375
0363	S	T	E	L	1974	92375
0363	S	D	R	L	1975	92860
0363	S	T	R	L	1975	92860
0363	S	D	E	L	1975	93520
0363	S	S	E	L	1975	93520
0363	S	D	R	N	1975	94599
0363	S	T	R	N	1975	94599
0363	S	D	E	N	1975	95584
0363	S	S	E	N	1975	95584
0363	S	T	E	N	1975	95584
0363	S	D	E	N	1976	95900
0363	S	T	E	N	1976	95900
0363	S	D	E	N	1975	96613
0363	S	D	E	L	1976	96883
0363	S	T	E	L	1976	96883
0363	S	D	E	N	1976	100416
0363	S	S	E	N	1976	100416
0363	S	S	E	N	1975	101890
0363	T	D	R	N	1974	57859
0363	T	T	R	N	1974	57859
0363	T	D	E	N	1974	59207
0363	T	T	E	N	1974	59207
0363	T	D	E	N	1974	60691
0363	T	E	E	N	1974	60691
0363	T	S	E	N	1974	60691
0363	T	D	E	N	1972	63961
0363	T	T	E	N	1972	63961
0363	T	S	E	N	1963	64232
0363	T	S	E	N	1967	66156
0363	T	D	E	N	1974	68253
0363	T	D	R	N	1966	75862
0363	T	D	E	N	1966	76050
0363	T	D	E	N	1975	96894
0363	T	T	E	N	1975	96894
0363	T	D	E	N	1976	99658
0363	T	D	E	N	1976	100416
0385	S	D	E	N	1973	55364
0385	S	D	E	N	1967	74607
0387	T	D	E	N	1975	96486
0387	T	D	E	N	1976	101813
0387	T	E	E	N	1976	101813
0387	T	D	E	N	1976	101815
0387	T	S	E	N	1976	101815
0387	T	S	E	N	1976	102567
0417	S	D	E	N	1972	64098
0495	S	D	E	N	1975	98278

Substance Number	Phys. State	Sub-ject	Lan-guage	Temper-ature	Year	EPIC Number
106-0495	S	E	E	N	1975	98278
0495	S	S	E	N	1975	98278
0495	S	T	E	N	1975	98278
0498	S	D	E	N	1973	50880
0508	S	S	E	N	1969	68271
0610	S	D	E	N	1963	73260
0610	S	E	E	N	1963	73260
0610	S	S	E	N	1963	73260
0628	S	D	F	N	1971	83537
0794	S	D	R	N	1971	66990
0940	S	D	R	N	1972	92408
0941	A	D	R	N	1973	83375
0941	A	D	E	N	1973	90273
0941	S	D	R	N	1973	52259
0941	S	D	E	N	1972	53335
0941	S	D	R	N	1973	83375
0941	S	D	E	N	1973	90273
1019	S	D	E	N	1971	49617
1070	S	D	E	N	1973	49987
1085	S	D	E	N	1974	60664
1256	S	D	E	N	1974	101330
1519	S	S	E	N	1972	53335
8001	S	D	R	N	1972	54155
8001	S	D	E	N	1972	54156
8014	S	S	E	N	1960	65977
8040	S	D	R	N	1973	50215
8040	S	D	E	N	1973	50216
8040	S	S	E	N	1972	53388
8040	S	D	E	N	1971	59436
8040	S	E	E	N	1971	59436
8040	S	D	E	N	1974	60691
8040	S	S	E	N	1974	60691
8040	S	D	R	N	1971	61029
8040	S	D	R	N	1974	61986
8040	S	S	R	N	1974	61986
8040	S	D	E	N	1974	61987
8040	S	S	E	N	1974	61987
8040	S	S	E	N	1963	87710
8040	S	D	R	N	1974	89254
8040	S	T	R	N	1974	89254
8040	S	D	E	N	1974	89255
8040	S	T	E	N	1974	89255
8040	S	D	R	N	1975	94599
8040	S	T	R	N	1975	94599
8040	S	D	E	N	1975	95584
8040	S	S	E	N	1975	95584
8040	S	T	E	N	1975	95584
8040	S	D	E	N	1976	95900
8040	S	T	E	N	1976	95900
8040	S	D	E	N	1976	99141
8040	S	S	E	N	1976	99141
8040	S	T	E	N	1976	99141
8040	T	D	E	N	1974	60691
8040	T	S	E	N	1974	60691
8040	T	D	R	N	1971	61029
8040	T	D	R	N	1970	61532
8040	T	D	R	N	1974	61952
8040	T	T	R	N	1974	61952
8040	T	D	E	N	1974	61953
8040	T	T	E	N	1974	61953
8040	T	D	E	N	1974	68253
8041	D	S	E	N	1973	58213
8041	D	D	E	N	1969	62248
8041	D	S	E	N	1970	65877
8041	D	S	E	N	1967	68371
8041	S	D	E	N	1973	50924
8041	S	D	R	N	1973	51272
8041	S	S	E	N	1972	53244
8041	S	S	E	N	1972	53247
8041	S	S	E	L	1972	53359
8041	S	S	E	N	1972	53359
8041	S	D	E	N	1974	54024
8041	S	D	E	N	1974	54310
8041	S	S	E	N	1973	54773
8041	S	D	E	N	1973	55872
8041	S	D	E	N	1974	58808
8041	S	S	E	N	1974	58808
8041	S	T	E	N	1974	58808
8041	S	D	E	N	1974	60255
8041	S	D	E	N	1974	60265
8041	S	D	E	N	1974	60691
8041	S	S	E	N	1974	60691
8041	S	D	R	L	1970	61009
8041	S	D	R	N	1970	61009
8041	S	D	E	L	1973	61472
8041	S	S	E	L	1973	61472
8041	S	D	E	N	1969	62273
8041	S	T	E	N	1969	62273
8041	S	D	E	N	1973	62325
8041	S	S	O	N	1974	62496
8041	S	D	E	N	1972	63899
8041	S	E	E	N	1972	63899
8041	S	T	E	N	1972	63899
8041	S	T	E	N	1971	65080
8041	S	E	E	N	1975	65507
8041	S	S	E	N	1975	65507
8041	S	S	E	L	1970	65877
8041	S	S	E	N	1967	68371
8041	S	D	E	N	1971	70398
8041	S	T	E	N	1970	70645
8041	S	D	E	L	1969	75248

Substance Number	Phys. State	Sub-ject	Lan-guage	Temper-ature	Year	EPIC Number
106-8041	S	D	E	N	1969	75248
8041	S	S	E	N	1962	87659
8041	S	D	R	N	1974	87755
8041	S	E	R	N	1974	87755
8041	S	S	R	N	1974	87755
8041	S	S	E	N	1971	87883
8041	S	D	E	N	1974	92229
8041	S	E	E	N	1974	92229
8041	S	S	E	N	1974	92229
8041	S	D	R	N	1974	92266
8041	S	S	R	N	1974	92266
8041	S	T	R	N	1974	92266
8041	S	D	E	N	1974	92267
8041	S	S	E	N	1974	92267
8041	S	T	E	N	1974	92267
8041	S	D	E	N	1959	92621
8041	S	D	E	N	1975	93319
8041	S	D	E	N	1974	93385
8041	S	D	E	N	1975	96613
8041	S	E	E	N	1975	97221
8041	S	S	E	N	1975	101032
8041	S	D	E	N	1976	101796
8041	S	E	E	N	1976	101796
8041	S	S	E	N	1976	101796
8041	S	D	E	N	1976	101854
8041	S	E	E	N	1976	101854
8041	S	T	E	N	1976	101854
8041	S	S	E	N	1975	101890
8041	T	S	F	N	1973	54648
8041	T	D	E	N	1974	60691
8041	T	S	E	N	1974	60691
8041	T	D	R	N	1970	61532
8041	T	D	R	N	1974	61988
8041	T	T	R	N	1974	61988
8041	T	D	E	N	1974	61989
8041	T	T	E	N	1974	61989
8041	T	D	E	N	1974	68253
8041	T	D	E	N	1974	68831
8041	T	D	E	N	1974	88488
8041	T	D	E	N	1974	89232
8041	T	D	E	N	1975	93161
8041	T	S	E	N	1971	100982
8045	S	S	E	N	1969	68271
8045	S	D	R	N	1975	97173
8045	S	T	R	N	1975	97173
8045	S	D	E	N	1975	98000
8045	S	T	E	N	1975	98000
8046	A	D	E	N	1974	53862
8046	S	D	R	N	1973	57008
8046	T	D	E	N	1974	53862
8046	T	D	E	N	1949	96118
8046	T	T	E	N	1949	96118
8048	S	S	E	N	1969	68271
8050	T	D	G	N	1970	66848
8087	S	D	F	N	1971	83537
8128	S	S	E	N	1967	68371
8128	S	S	E	N	1972	87823
8132	S	D	E	N	1971	59436
8132	S	E	E	N	1971	59436
8132	S	D	E	N	1971	61077
8132	S	D	E	N	1974	62029
8132	S	S	E	N	1974	62029
8132	S	T	E	N	1974	62029
8132	S	S	E	N	1972	87823
8134	S	S	E	N	1972	87823
8135	S	D	E	N	1971	49617
8154	T	D	R	N	1972	56995
8227	S	T	E	N	1975	65440
8236	S	D	F	N	1971	83537
8237	S	D	E	N	1972	53110
8241	S	S	E	N	1970	87822
8241	S	S	E	N	1972	87890
8253	S	D	F	N	1973	51480
8254	S	D	F	N	1973	51480
8300	S	D	E	N	1973	52314
8312	S	D	E	N	1973	52652
8330	S	D	R	N	1973	50729
8330	S	D	E	N	1973	53030
8338	S	D	R	N	1970	55102
8338	S	D	E	N	1972	55103
8340	S	D	R	N	1970	55102
8340	S	D	E	N	1972	55103
8342	S	S	E	N	1972	53335
8344	S	D	R	N	1970	55102
8344	S	D	E	N	1972	55103
8357	S	S	E	N	1972	53512
8357	S	S	R	N	1973	56262
8357	S	D	E	N	1971	62600
8357	S	S	E	N	1970	65877
8357	S	S	E	N	1973	76721
8357	S	D	E	N	1975	101659
8357	S	E	E	N	1975	101659
8358	S	S	E	N	1973	54773
8358	S	S	R	N	1973	56262
8358	S	D	E	N	1969	62248
8358	S	D	E	N	1971	62600
8358	S	S	E	N	1970	65877
8358	S	D	E	N	1968	75247
8358	S	S	E	N	1968	75247
8358	S	S	E	N	1973	76721
8358	S	D	E	L	1975	97147

Phys. State: **A.** Amorphous; **C.** Superconductive; **D.** Doped; **F.** Fibrous or Whisker; **G.** Gas; **I.** Ionized or Plasma; **L.** Liquid; **P.** Powder or Particle; **S.** Solid; **T.** Thin Film
Subject: **D.** Data; **E.** Experiment; **S.** Survey (Review, Compendium, etc.); **T.** Theory
Language: **E.** English; **F.** French; **G.** German; **O.** Other Languages; **R.** Russian
Temperature: **L.** Low (0 to 75K); **N.** Normal (75 to 1273K); **H.** High (above 1273K)

Substance Number	Phys. State	Subject	Language	Temperature	Year	EPIC Number
106-8358	S	D	E	N	1975	97147
8358	S	S	E	N	1971	100982
8358	S	D	E	N	1975	101659
8358	S	E	E	N	1975	101659
8432	S	D	R	N	1973	54440
8432	S	D	E	N	1973	54441
8452	S	D	R	N	1973	57016
8453	S	D	R	N	1970	55102
8453	S	D	E	N	1972	55103
8454	S	D	R	N	1970	55102
8454	S	D	E	N	1972	55103
8455	S	D	R	N	1970	55102
8455	S	D	E	N	1972	55103
8456	S	D	R	N	1970	55102
8456	S	D	E	N	1972	55103
8457	S	D	R	N	1970	55102
8457	S	D	E	N	1972	55103
8457	S	D	E	N	1972	55511
8458	S	D	R	N	1970	55102
8458	S	D	E	N	1972	55103
8459	S	D	R	N	1970	55102
8459	S	D	E	N	1972	55103
8462	S	T	E	N	1974	58816
8469	S	D	E	N	1971	61077
8489	L	D	R	N	1970	61851
8489	L	E	R	N	1970	61851
8489	L	T	R	N	1970	61851
8537	G	S	E	N	1973	98865
8540	D	S	E	N	1974	61187
8549	S	D	R	N	1974	66730
8549	S	T	R	N	1974	66730
8549	S	D	E	N	1975	66731
8549	S	T	E	N	1975	66731
8580	S	D	E	N	1973	55872
8580	S	D	E	N	1975	96613
8580	T	D	E	N	1975	96613
8581	S	D	E	N	1973	55917
8588	S	D	R	N	1973	56011
8588	S	D	E	N	1974	76600
8591	S	D	R	N	1974	66730
8591	S	T	R	N	1974	66730
8591	S	D	E	N	1975	66731
8591	S	T	E	N	1975	66731
8613	S	D	R	N	1973	57008
8614	S	D	R	N	1973	57016
8615	S	D	R	N	1973	57016
8616	S	D	R	N	1973	57016
8617	S	D	R	N	1973	57016
8618	S	D	R	N	1973	57016
8619	S	D	R	N	1973	57016
8685	S	D	R	N	1975	90487
8695	S	S	E	N	1970	65877
8732	G	S	E	N	1973	98865
8733	L	S	E	N	1973	98865
8830	S	S	E	N	1975	97799
108-0005	L	S	E	N	1974	62735
0005	L	T	E	N	1973	64819
0005	L	S	E	N	1972	83519
0005	L	S	E	N	1951	98663
0014	S	D	R	N	1973	54486
0014	S	E	R	N	1973	54486
0014	S	T	R	N	1973	54486
0014	S	D	E	N	1973	54487
0014	S	E	E	N	1973	54487
0014	S	T	E	N	1973	54487
0014	S	S	E	N	1970	87822
0014	S	S	E	N	1972	87890
0014	S	S	E	N	1976	101320
0052	S	D	R	N	1972	79248
0052	S	D	E	N	1972	90275
0114	S	D	R	N	1973	54486
0114	S	E	R	N	1973	54486
0114	S	T	R	N	1973	54486
0114	S	D	E	N	1973	54487
0114	S	E	E	N	1973	54487
0114	S	T	E	N	1973	54487
0114	S	S	E	N	1976	101320
8007	S	D	R	N	1975	86841
8007	S	D	E	N	1975	86842
8025	S	S	E	N	1972	87890
8026	G	S	E	N	1973	53954
8039	S	T	R	N	1973	62863
8039	S	T	E	N	1973	65166
8040	S	T	R	N	1973	62863
8040	S	T	E	N	1973	65166
109-0001	S	D	R	N	1972	79248
0001	S	D	E	N	1972	90275
0007	S	D	R	N	1972	79248
0007	S	D	E	N	1972	90275
0029	S	S	E	N	1972	53175
8011	S	D	R	N	1975	86841
8011	S	D	E	N	1975	86842
8013	S	S	E	N	1972	53175
8013	T	D	E	N	1973	57902
8013	T	E	E	N	1973	57902
8014	S	S	E	N	1972	53175
8065	S	D	R	N	1975	86841
8065	S	E	R	N	1975	86841
8065	S	D	E	N	1975	86842

Substance Number	Phys. State	Subject	Language	Temperature	Year	EPIC Number
109-8065	S	E	E	N	1975	86842
8099	S	D	E	N	1973	66202
8099	S	T	E	N	1973	66202
8099	T	D	E	N	1973	57902
8099	T	E	E	N	1973	57902
8099	T	D	E	N	1973	66202
8099	T	T	E	N	1973	66202
8100	T	D	E	N	1973	57902
8100	T	E	E	N	1973	57902
110-0002	S	D	E	N	1973	55086
0002	S	D	E	N	1974	60255
0002	S	D	E	N	1976	99911
0002	T	S	E	N	1973	62276
0002	T	D	E	N	1974	68831
0002	T	D	E	N	1975	93161
0002	T	D	E	N	1976	101813
0002	T	E	E	N	1976	101813
0002	T	D	E	N	1976	101825
0002	T	D	E	N	1976	102015
0002	T	S	E	N	1976	102567
0011	A	D	R	N	1973	54502
0011	A	D	E	N	1973	54503
0011	A	D	E	N	1973	56636
0011	S	D	R	N	1973	54502
0011	S	D	E	N	1973	54503
0011	S	D	E	N	1973	56636
0019	S	D	E	N	1961	65970
0021	S	S	E	N	1973	50526
0021	S	D	R	N	1973	52513
0021	S	S	E	N	1971	65015
0021	S	D	E	N	1966	75114
0021	S	T	E	N	1966	75114
0021	S	D	E	N	1976	101501
0021	S	D	E	N	1976	101813
0021	S	E	E	N	1976	101813
0021	T	S	E	N	1971	100982
0021	T	D	E	N	1976	101825
0021	T	S	E	N	1976	102567
0023	S	S	E	N	1972	53512
0023	S	D	E	N	1974	54024
0023	S	D	E	N	1969	60879
0023	S	E	E	N	1969	60879
0023	S	T	E	N	1969	60879
0023	S	D	E	N	1960	64749
0023	S	D	E	N	1975	65511
0023	S	E	E	N	1975	65511
0023	S	S	E	N	1975	65511
0023	S	T	E	N	1975	65511
0023	S	D	E	N	1961	65970
0023	S	D	E	N	1971	70398
0023	S	D	E	N	1974	81763
0023	S	E	E	N	1974	81763
0023	S	S	E	N	1974	81763
0023	S	S	E	N	1971	87883
0023	S	D	E	N	1976	95874
0023	S	T	E	N	1976	95874
0023	S	D	R	N	1975	97090
0023	S	T	R	N	1975	97090
0023	S	D	E	N	1959	99665
0023	S	S	E	N	1976	101374
0023	S	S	E	N	1976	101375
0023	S	D	E	N	1976	101853
0023	S	E	E	N	1976	101853
0023	S	T	E	N	1976	101853
0023	S	T	E	N	1976	103593
0023	T	D	E	N	1973	51076
0023	T	D	E	N	1973	52214
0023	T	D	E	N	1974	52803
0023	T	E	E	N	1974	52803
0023	T	D	F	N	1973	53787
0023	T	E	F	N	1973	53787
0023	T	D	E	N	1974	53899
0023	T	S	F	N	1973	54648
0023	T	D	E	N	1974	58961
0023	T	S	E	N	1973	62276
0023	T	D	E	N	1971	64338
0023	T	D	E	N	1968	64536
0023	T	T	E	N	1968	64536
0023	T	S	E	N	1970	65877
0023	T	S	E	N	1971	87883
0023	T	D	E	N	1975	89528
0023	T	D	E	N	1969	95705
0023	T	D	E	N	1950	95706
0023	T	T	E	N	1950	95706
0023	T	D	E	N	1957	95707
0023	T	S	E	N	1957	95707
0023	T	D	E	N	1949	96118
0023	T	T	E	N	1949	96118
0023	T	D	E	N	1975	96400
0023	T	E	E	N	1975	96400
0024	F	D	E	N	1973	50985
0024	L	D	R	N	1971	61852
0024	L	D	R	N	1970	62287
0024	L	D	E	N	1973	62288
0024	L	S	E	N	1976	66532
0024	S	D	E	N	1973	50924
0024	S	D	R	N	1973	52216
0024	S	S	R	N	1973	56262
0024	S	S	R	N	1973	59726
0024	S	S	E	N	1973	59727

Substance Number	Phys. State	Subject	Language	Temperature	Year	EPIC Number
110-0024	S	D	E	N	1974	60265
0024	S	D	E	N	1973	61830
0024	S	S	E	N	1949	63242
0024	S	S	E	N	1975	63327
0024	S	D	E	N	1975	63349
0024	S	E	E	N	1975	63349
0024	S	S	E	N	1973	63807
0024	S	D	E	L	1966	64256
0024	S	D	E	N	1966	64256
0024	S	S	E	N	1962	64551
0024	S	T	E	N	1975	65508
0024	S	S	E	N	1970	65877
0024	S	D	E	N	1976	66532
0024	S	S	E	L	1976	66532
0024	S	S	E	N	1976	66532
0024	S	D	E	N	1973	68860
0024	S	D	E	L	1973	70149
0024	S	D	E	N	1973	70149
0024	S	S	E	L	1973	70149
0024	S	S	E	N	1973	70149
0024	S	D	E	N	1971	70398
0024	S	D	E	N	1972	70677
0024	S	E	E	N	1972	70677
0024	S	S	E	N	1972	70677
0024	S	T	E	N	1972	70677
0024	S	D	E	L	1969	71197
0024	S	D	E	N	1969	71197
0024	S	S	G	N	1942	73252
0024	S	D	E	L	1966	74594
0024	S	D	E	N	1966	74594
0024	S	D	E	N	1961	75731
0024	S	S	E	N	1961	75731
0024	S	T	E	N	1961	75731
0024	S	D	E	N	1966	75776
0024	S	E	E	N	1966	75776
0024	S	S	E	N	1966	75776
0024	S	D	E	N	1958	75780
0024	S	T	E	N	1958	75780
0024	S	S	E	N	1973	76721
0024	S	S	E	N	1971	87883
0024	S	D	E	N	1974	87984
0024	S	S	E	N	1974	87984
0024	S	D	E	N	1975	95407
0024	S	E	E	N	1975	95407
0024	S	S	E	N	1975	95407
0024	S	T	E	N	1975	95407
0024	S	S	E	N	1976	95874
0024	S	D	R	N	1975	96822
0024	S	T	R	N	1975	96822
0024	S	S	R	N	1975	97090
0024	S	S	E	N	1975	97223
0024	S	S	E	N	1972	97249
0024	S	D	E	N	1976	99237
0024	S	T	E	N	1976	99237
0024	S	D	E	N	1976	99987
0024	S	E	E	N	1976	99987
0024	S	S	E	N	1976	99987
0024	S	S	E	N	1976	101304
0024	S	S	E	N	1976	101375
0024	S	E	E	N	1975	101658
0024	S	T	E	N	1975	101658
0024	S	E	E	N	1975	101662
0024	S	D	R	N	1975	101804
0024	S	T	R	N	1975	101804
0024	S	D	E	N	1976	101805
0024	S	T	E	N	1976	101805
0024	S	D	E	N	1976	101853
0024	S	E	E	N	1976	101853
0024	S	T	E	N	1976	101853
0024	S	T	E	N	1976	103593
0024	T	D	E	N	1973	50985
0024	T	S	E	N	1976	66532
0024	T	T	E	N	1957	95707
0036	L	D	R	N	1971	61852
0036	L	D	R	N	1970	62287
0036	L	D	E	N	1973	62288
0036	L	S	E	N	1976	66532
0036	P	D	E	N	1975	92949
0036	P	E	E	N	1975	92949
0036	P	S	E	N	1975	92949
0036	P	T	E	N	1975	92949
0036	S	D	E	N	1973	50924
0036	S	D	E	N	1973	52605
0036	S	D	E	N	1974	57862
0036	S	D	R	N	1974	58064
0036	S	S	R	N	1974	58064
0036	S	D	E	N	1974	58065
0036	S	S	E	N	1974	58065
0036	S	D	E	N	1974	60265
0036	S	S	E	N	1949	63242
0036	S	S	E	N	1975	63327
0036	S	E	E	N	1972	63568
0036	S	S	E	N	1972	63568
0036	S	T	E	N	1972	63568
0036	S	D	E	L	1973	63807
0036	S	D	E	N	1973	63807
0036	S	S	E	N	1970	65877
0036	S	D	E	L	1970	66152
0036	S	D	E	N	1970	66152
0036	S	D	E	N	1976	66532
0036	S	S	E	L	1976	66532

Phys. State: **A.** Amorphous; **C.** Superconductive; **D.** Doped; **F.** Fibrous or Whisker; **G.** Gas; **I.** Ionized or Plasma; **L.** Liquid; **P.** Powder or Particle; **S.** Solid; **T.** Thin Film
Subject: **D.** Data; **E.** Experiment; **S.** Survey (Review, Compendium, etc.); **T.** Theory
Language: **E.** English; **F.** French; **G.** German; **O.** Other Languages; **R.** Russian
Temperature: **L.** Low (0 to 75K); **N.** Normal (75 to 1273K); **H.** High (above 1273K)

Substance Number	Phys. State	Sub-ject	Lan-guage	Temper-ature	Year	EPIC Number
110-0036	S	S	E	N	1976	66532
0036	S	D	E	N	1971	70398
0036	S	D	E	L	1969	71197
0036	S	D	E	N	1969	71197
0036	S	S	G	N	1942	73252
0036	S	S	E	N	1971	87883
0036	S	D	E	N	1975	95407
0036	S	E	E	N	1975	95407
0036	S	S	E	N	1975	95407
0036	S	T	E	N	1975	95407
0036	S	D	R	N	1975	96822
0036	S	T	R	N	1975	96822
0036	S	D	E	N	1976	99237
0036	S	T	E	N	1976	99237
0036	S	D	E	N	1976	99987
0036	S	E	E	N	1976	99987
0036	S	S	E	N	1976	99987
0036	S	S	E	N	1976	102403
0036	S	T	E	N	1976	102403
0036	T	D	E	N	1974	52803
0036	T	E	E	N	1974	52803
0036	T	T	E	N	1972	70543
0036	T	D	E	N	1975	92949
0036	T	E	E	N	1975	92949
0036	T	S	E	N	1975	92949
0036	T	T	E	N	1975	92949
0037	L	D	R	N	1971	61852
0037	L	D	R	N	1970	62287
0037	L	D	E	N	1973	62288
0037	L	S	E	N	1976	66532
0037	S	D	E	L	1973	50820
0037	S	D	E	N	1973	50820
0037	S	D	E	N	1973	50924
0037	S	D	E	N	1973	52605
0037	S	D	E	N	1974	60265
0037	S	S	E	N	1975	63327
0037	S	D	E	N	1976	66532
0037	S	S	E	N	1976	66532
0040	G	D	E	N	1974	58694
0061	S	D	E	N	1974	60265
0061	S	D	E	N	1976	66532
0061	S	S	E	N	1976	66532
0083	S	S	R	N	1973	56262
0083	S	S	E	N	1973	76721
0083	T	D	E	N	1975	96486
0083	T	D	E	N	1976	101815
0083	T	S	E	N	1976	101815
0090	T	D	E	N	1975	96486
0090	T	D	E	N	1976	101815
0090	T	S	E	N	1976	101815
0107	T	D	E	N	1974	68831
0132	S	D	E	N	1974	54024
0132	S	S	E	N	1975	63327
0132	S	T	E	N	1975	65508
0132	S	D	E	N	1972	70677
0132	S	E	E	N	1972	70677
0132	S	T	E	N	1972	70677
0132	S	D	E	N	1967	74607
0132	S	D	E	N	1974	84584
0132	S	D	R	L	1974	87288
0132	S	D	E	L	1975	87289
0132	S	D	G	N	1927	96122
0132	S	T	G	N	1927	96122
0132	S	S	E	N	1976	101374
0132	S	S	E	N	1976	101375
0132	S	D	E	N	1976	101839
0132	S	E	E	N	1976	101839
0132	S	S	E	N	1976	101839
0132	S	T	E	N	1976	101839
0132	S	D	E	N	1976	101853
0132	S	E	E	N	1976	101853
0132	S	T	E	N	1976	101853
0132	S	D	E	N	1976	103590
0132	S	T	E	N	1976	103590
0132	T	D	E	N	1976	101825
0194	S	S	E	N	1972	53175
0194	S	D	R	N	1973	55068
0194	S	D	E	N	1974	55069
0194	S	D	E	N	1974	58050
0194	S	S	E	N	1974	58050
0194	S	D	E	N	1965	75938
0194	S	D	R	N	1975	86841
0194	S	S	R	N	1975	86841
0194	S	D	E	N	1975	86842
0194	S	S	E	N	1975	86842
0194	T	D	E	N	1974	54111
0194	T	D	E	N	1973	57902
0194	T	E	E	N	1973	57902
0195	S	S	E	N	1972	53175
0195	S	D	R	N	1975	86841
0195	S	D	E	N	1975	86842
0199	S	S	E	N	1972	53175
0199	S	D	R	N	1975	86841
0199	S	D	E	N	1975	86842
0245	S	D	R	N	1975	86841
0245	S	E	R	N	1975	86841
0245	S	D	E	N	1975	86842
0245	S	E	E	N	1975	86842
0269	G	D	E	N	1973	50421
0299	S	D	E	N	1973	52314
0351	T	D	E	N	1974	68831

Substance Number	Phys. State	Sub-ject	Lan-guage	Temper-ature	Year	EPIC Number
110-0352	S	D	E	N	1973	68839
8039	S	D	E	N	1973	52314
8044	T	D	E	N	1973	57902
8044	T	E	E	N	1973	57902
8051	S	D	R	N	1973	55068
8051	S	D	E	N	1974	55069
8051	T	D	E	N	1973	57902
8051	T	E	E	N	1973	57902
8051	T	T	R	N	1974	66752
8051	T	T	E	N	1975	66753
8053	S	S	E	N	1972	53175
8053	S	D	E	N	1974	54111
8053	S	D	E	N	1973	66202
8053	S	T	E	N	1973	66202
8053	T	D	E	N	1973	66202
8053	T	T	E	N	1973	66202
8057	S	D	R	N	1975	86841
8057	S	D	E	N	1975	86842
8093	S	D	E	N	1973	52314
8108	S	D	R	N	1973	50729
8108	S	D	E	N	1973	53030
8109	S	D	R	N	1973	50729
8109	S	D	E	N	1973	53030
8110	S	D	R	N	1973	50729
8110	S	D	E	N	1973	53030
8118	S	S	E	N	1972	53512
8118	S	S	R	N	1973	56262
8118	S	D	E	N	1971	62600
8118	S	D	E	N	1964	64248
8118	S	S	E	N	1964	64248
8118	S	T	E	N	1964	64248
8118	S	D	E	N	1962	64551
8118	S	S	E	N	1963	64748
8118	S	D	E	N	1960	64749
8118	S	S	E	N	1970	65877
8118	S	S	E	N	1973	76721
8153	T	D	E	N	1974	54308
8154	S	D	E	N	1974	54331
8161	S	D	R	N	1973	55068
8161	S	D	E	N	1974	55069
8162	S	D	R	N	1973	55068
8162	S	D	E	N	1974	55069
8214	T	D	E	N	1974	81418
8222	S	D	E	N	1965	75938
8277	T	D	E	N	1973	57902
8277	T	E	E	N	1973	57902
111-0003	S	D	R	N	1972	79248
0003	S	D	E	N	1972	90275
0006	A	D	E	N	1974	53862
0006	A	D	R	N	1973	54377
0006	A	D	E	N	1973	54378
0006	A	S	E	N	1969	68115
0006	S	D	R	N	1973	54377
0006	S	D	E	N	1973	54378
0006	S	D	E	N	1974	57297
0006	S	S	E	N	1974	57298
0006	S	D	E	N	1974	62027
0006	S	D	E	N	1974	63252
0006	S	D	E	N	1970	64545
0006	S	D	R	N	1969	65448
0006	S	D	E	N	1969	65449
0006	S	S	E	N	1970	65877
0006	S	S	E	N	1969	68115
0006	S	D	E	N	1964	75965
0006	T	D	E	N	1974	53862
0008	A	D	E	N	1974	60533
0008	A	D	E	N	1972	60905
0008	A	D	E	N	1972	63793
0008	D	D	E	N	1974	63393
0008	D	S	E	N	1972	87889
0008	S	S	E	N	1973	50526
0008	S	D	E	N	1973	50924
0008	S	S	E	N	1972	53227
0008	S	D	R	N	1973	54195
0008	S	D	E	N	1973	54196
0008	S	D	E	N	1974	54558
0008	S	S	E	N	1974	57977
0008	S	D	E	N	1974	58808
0008	S	S	E	N	1974	58808
0008	S	T	E	N	1974	58808
0008	S	D	E	N	1974	58958
0008	S	E	E	N	1974	58958
0008	S	S	E	N	1974	58958
0008	S	D	E	N	1970	59674
0008	S	S	E	N	1970	59674
0008	S	D	E	N	1974	60265
0008	S	D	E	N	1974	60533
0008	S	D	E	N	1972	60905
0008	S	D	E	N	1971	61508
0008	S	S	E	N	1971	62264
0008	S	D	E	N	1973	62386
0008	S	T	E	N	1971	65080
0008	S	S	E	N	1962	87669
0008	S	S	E	N	1965	87703
0008	S	S	E	N	1970	87822
0008	S	S	E	N	1971	87884
0008	S	S	E	N	1975	93323
0008	S	D	E	N	1974	93385
0008	S	S	E	N	1975	97223
0008	S	D	R	N	1975	101515

Substance Number	Phys. State	Sub-ject	Lan-guage	Temper-ature	Year	EPIC Number
111-0008	S	T	R	N	1975	101515
0008	S	D	E	N	1975	101516
0008	S	T	E	N	1975	101516
0008	S	D	E	N	1976	101845
0008	S	T	E	N	1976	101845
0008	T	D	R	N	1971	59188
0008	T	D	E	N	1971	59189
0015	A	S	E	N	1969	68115
0021	A	T	E	N	1974	62549
0021	S	S	R	N	1974	66446
0021	S	S	E	N	1974	66447
0021	S	S	E	N	1971	87884
0021	T	D	E	N	1974	58028
0021	T	S	E	N	1974	58028
0021	T	T	E	N	1974	62549
0046	S	D	R	N	1973	51356
0046	S	T	R	N	1973	51356
0046	S	D	E	N	1973	51357
0046	S	T	E	N	1973	51357
0046	S	D	E	N	1974	53898
0046	S	T	E	N	1974	53898
0050	S	S	E	N	1972	53335
0050	S	D	E	N	1976	99141
0050	S	S	E	N	1976	99141
0050	S	T	E	N	1976	99141
8002	D	D	R	N	1974	64959
8002	D	D	E	N	1975	68432
8002	S	D	E	N	1973	50924
8002	S	D	E	N	1974	58808
8002	S	S	E	N	1974	58808
8002	S	T	E	N	1974	58808
8002	S	D	E	N	1970	59674
8002	S	S	E	N	1970	59674
8002	S	D	E	N	1974	60265
8002	S	S	O	N	1974	62496
8002	S	D	F	N	1973	63636
8002	S	S	R	N	1974	64959
8002	S	T	E	N	1971	65080
8002	S	D	G	N	1954	66199
8002	S	T	G	N	1954	66199
8002	S	S	E	N	1975	68432
8002	S	S	E	N	1962	87670
8002	S	S	E	N	1971	87884
8002	S	D	E	N	1974	93385
8002	S	S	E	N	1972	97249
8002	S	D	R	N	1975	101515
8002	S	T	R	N	1975	101515
8002	S	D	E	N	1975	101516
8002	S	T	E	N	1975	101516
8002	T	S	E	N	1969	87821
8007	S	D	E	N	1973	49616
8007	S	S	E	N	1973	56247
8007	S	D	E	N	1972	63763
8007	S	D	R	N	1975	97173
8007	S	T	R	N	1975	97173
8007	S	D	E	N	1975	98000
8007	S	T	E	N	1975	98000
8007	S	D	E	N	1976	101746
8007	S	T	E	N	1976	101746
8008	T	D	R	N	1970	61533
8008	T	T	R	N	1970	61533
8009	S	D	E	N	1973	57453
8014	T	S	E	N	1972	60920
8014	T	D	E	N	1975	101768
8014	T	E	E	N	1975	101768
8014	T	D	R	N	1975	101769
8014	T	E	R	N	1975	101769
8015	A	D	E	N	1973	50526
8015	A	E	E	N	1973	50526
8015	A	D	E	N	1972	63793
8015	S	D	E	N	1973	50526
8015	S	E	E	N	1973	50526
8019	S	D	E	N	1964	59770
8019	S	T	E	N	1964	59770
8020	L	D	E	N	1973	49592
8020	S	D	E	N	1974	54308
8020	S	D	E	N	1973	57793
8020	S	E	E	N	1973	57902
8020	S	D	E	N	1973	66202
8020	S	T	E	N	1973	66202
8020	T	D	E	N	1973	49592
8021	S	S	E	N	1969	68115
8026	S	D	E	N	1974	81547
8026	S	S	E	N	1974	81547
8026	S	T	E	N	1974	81547
8026	T	S	E	N	1972	87889
8038	S	D	E	N	1973	52785
8078	A	D	E	N	1973	50526
8078	A	E	E	N	1973	50526
8078	S	D	E	N	1973	50526
8078	S	E	E	N	1973	50526
8079	A	D	E	N	1973	50526
8079	A	E	E	N	1973	50526
8079	S	D	E	N	1973	50526
8079	S	E	E	N	1973	50526
8080	A	S	E	N	1969	68115
8080	S	S	E	N	1973	50526
8087	D	D	E	N	1973	53727
8087	S	D	E	N	1974	58050
8113	A	D	E	N	1972	63793
8125	S	D	E	N	1974	61362

Phys. State: **A.** Amorphous; **C.** Superconductive; **D.** Doped; **F.** Fibrous or Whisker; **G.** Gas; **I.** Ionized or Plasma; **L.** Liquid; **P.** Powder or Particle; **S.** Solid; **T.** Thin Film
Subject: **D.** Data; **E.** Experiment; **S.** Survey (Review, Compendium, etc.); **T.** Theory
Language: **E.** English; **F.** French; **G.** German; **O.** Other Languages; **R.** Russian
Temperature: **L.** Low (0 to 75K); **N.** Normal (75 to 1273K); **H.** High (above 1273K)

Substance Number	Phys. State	Subject	Language	Temperature	Year	EPIC Number
111-8131	S	D	R	N	1973	56006
8132	S	D	E	N	1973	56122
8162	A	S	E	N	1972	87824
8162	S	S	E	N	1972	87824
8190	S	D	E	N	1974	62023
8195	S	D	E	N	1975	100607
8195	S	T	E	N	1975	100607
112-0001	G	D	E	N	1973	50969
0001	G	D	R	N	1974	87314
0001	G	D	E	N	1974	87315
0001	G	T	G	N	1893	89951
0001	L	D	E	N	1973	50969
0001	L	D	E	N	1973	51941
0001	L	S	G	N	1973	51981
0001	L	D	E	N	1972	53488
0001	L	E	E	N	1972	53488
0001	L	S	E	N	1972	53488
0001	L	T	E	N	1972	53488
0001	L	D	E	N	1973	53703
0001	L	D	E	N	1974	53741
0001	L	T	E	N	1974	53741
0001	L	D	E	N	1974	54549
0001	L	D	E	N	1973	56136
0001	L	E	E	N	1973	56136
0001	L	T	E	N	1973	56136
0001	L	D	E	N	1973	59134
0001	L	D	E	N	1974	60354
0001	L	S	E	N	1971	61220
0001	L	S	E	N	1974	62735
0001	L	T	E	N	1973	64819
0001	L	D	E	N	1971	67062
0001	L	S	R	N	1973	70985
0001	L	D	E	N	1911	75030
0001	L	S	E	N	1972	83519
0001	L	D	G	N	1894	89953
0001	L	S	G	N	1894	89953
0001	L	S	E	N	1974	94639
0001	L	S	E	N	1973	96050
0001	L	S	E	N	1951	98663
0001	L	D	E	N	1976	100174
0001	L	E	E	N	1976	100174
0001	L	T	E	N	1976	100174
0001	L	D	E	N	1976	101704
0001	L	S	E	N	1976	101704
0001	L	T	E	N	1976	101704
0001	L	D	E	N	1976	101746
0001	L	T	E	N	1976	101746
0001	S	D	E	N	1973	50146
0001	S	D	E	N	1973	50381
0001	S	D	E	N	1973	62386
0001	S	D	E	N	1976	101746
0001	S	T	E	N	1976	101746
0004	G	D	G	N	1894	89953
0004	G	S	G	N	1894	89953
0010	S	D	E	N	1973	55795
0011	S	S	E	N	1969	68271
0016	T	D	E	N	1976	99775
0016	T	E	E	N	1976	99775
0016	T	T	E	N	1976	99775
0021	D	D	R	N	1972	51966
0021	S	D	R	N	1972	51966
0021	T	D	E	N	1973	60933
0021	T	E	E	N	1973	60933
0021	T	D	E	N	1975	68613
0021	T	T	E	N	1975	68613
0028	S	D	R	N	1973	50233
0028	S	D	E	N	1973	50234
0028	S	D	E	N	1972	52225
0028	S	D	R	N	1973	54486
0028	S	E	R	N	1973	54486
0028	S	T	R	N	1973	54486
0028	S	D	E	N	1973	54487
0028	S	E	E	N	1973	54487
0028	S	T	E	N	1973	54487
0028	S	D	R	N	1971	61549
0028	S	E	R	N	1971	61549
0028	S	D	E	N	1971	65902
0028	S	E	E	N	1971	65902
0028	S	D	E	N	1975	87179
0028	S	S	E	N	1970	87822
0028	S	S	E	N	1972	87890
0028	S	D	R	N	1975	98033
0028	S	E	R	N	1975	98033
0028	S	T	R	N	1975	98033
0028	S	D	E	N	1975	98034
0028	S	E	E	N	1975	98034
0028	S	T	E	N	1975	98034
0028	S	D	E	N	1976	99987
0028	S	E	E	N	1976	99987
0028	S	S	E	N	1976	101320
0028	S	D	E	N	1976	102402
0028	S	E	E	N	1976	102402
0028	S	T	E	N	1976	102402
0035	S	D	E	N	1970	68244
0035	S	D	R	N	1975	90134
0035	S	D	E	N	1975	90135
0036	S	D	E	N	1973	56101
0038	S	D	R	N	1973	54486
0038	S	E	R	N	1973	54486
0038	S	T	R	N	1973	54486

Substance Number	Phys. State	Subject	Language	Temperature	Year	EPIC Number
112-0038	S	D	E	N	1973	54487
0038	S	E	E	N	1973	54487
0038	S	T	E	N	1973	54487
0038	S	S	E	N	1970	87822
0038	S	S	E	N	1971	87883
0038	S	S	E	N	1972	87890
0038	S	D	R	N	1975	98033
0038	S	E	R	N	1975	98033
0038	S	T	R	N	1975	98033
0038	S	D	E	N	1975	98034
0038	S	E	E	N	1975	98034
0038	S	T	E	N	1975	98034
0038	S	S	E	N	1976	101320
0096	S	D	R	N	1973	51319
0096	S	T	R	N	1973	51319
0096	S	D	R	N	1973	54486
0096	S	E	R	N	1973	54486
0096	S	T	R	N	1973	54486
0096	S	D	E	N	1973	54487
0096	S	E	E	N	1973	54487
0096	S	T	E	N	1973	54487
0096	S	D	R	N	1971	61549
0096	S	E	R	N	1971	61549
0096	S	D	E	N	1973	62386
0096	S	D	E	N	1971	65902
0096	S	E	E	N	1971	65902
0096	S	D	E	N	1973	89717
0096	S	T	E	N	1973	89717
0402	S	D	E	N	1973	62386
0402	S	S	E	N	1969	68271
0402	S	S	E	N	1975	90114
0402	S	D	E	N	1976	99141
0402	S	S	E	N	1976	99141
0402	S	T	E	N	1976	99141
0402	T	D	E	N	1975	90114
0402	T	T	E	N	1975	90114
0481	S	D	R	N	1972	79248
0481	S	D	E	N	1972	90275
0583	S	D	R	N	1973	54486
0583	S	E	R	N	1973	54486
0583	S	T	R	N	1973	54486
0583	S	D	E	N	1973	54487
0583	S	E	E	N	1973	54487
0583	S	T	E	N	1973	54487
0583	S	S	E	N	1976	101320
8024	S	D	E	N	1971	49617
8025	S	D	R	N	1973	51272
8025	S	S	E	N	1969	68271
8051	S	T	R	N	1973	62863
8051	S	T	E	N	1973	65166
8072	S	D	R	N	1973	57235
8073	S	D	R	N	1973	57235
114-0001	P	D	E	N	1975	92949
0001	P	E	E	N	1975	92949
0001	P	S	E	N	1975	92949
0001	P	T	E	N	1975	92949
0001	S	D	E	L	1973	50820
0001	S	D	E	N	1973	50820
0001	S	D	E	N	1973	50924
0001	S	D	E	N	1973	52605
0001	S	S	E	N	1972	53244
0001	S	S	E	N	1972	53247
0001	S	D	E	N	1973	54230
0001	S	S	E	N	1973	54773
0001	S	T	R	N	1974	58227
0001	S	D	R	N	1973	58310
0001	S	D	E	N	1972	60077
0001	S	D	E	N	1974	60265
0001	S	D	R	N	1973	62520
0001	S	S	R	N	1973	62520
0001	S	D	E	N	1974	62521
0001	S	S	E	N	1974	62521
0001	S	D	R	N	1973	62862
0001	S	S	E	N	1949	63242
0001	S	S	E	N	1975	63327
0001	S	D	E	N	1973	65167
0001	S	S	E	N	1970	65877
0001	S	D	E	N	1976	66532
0001	S	S	E	L	1976	66532
0001	S	S	E	N	1976	66532
0001	S	D	E	N	1971	70398
0001	S	D	E	N	1972	70677
0001	S	E	E	N	1972	70677
0001	S	T	E	N	1972	70677
0001	S	D	E	L	1969	71197
0001	S	D	E	N	1969	71197
0001	S	S	G	N	1942	73252
0001	S	S	E	N	1924	73267
0001	S	D	E	N	1967	75203
0001	S	D	E	N	1961	75731
0001	S	S	E	N	1961	75731
0001	S	T	E	N	1961	75731
0001	S	D	E	N	1966	75776
0001	S	E	E	N	1966	75776
0001	S	S	E	N	1966	75776
0001	S	D	E	N	1958	75780
0001	S	T	E	N	1958	75780
0001	S	D	E	N	1969	85421
0001	S	S	E	N	1971	87883
0001	S	D	E	N	1975	89452

Substance Number	Phys. State	Subject	Language	Temperature	Year	EPIC Number
114-0001	S	D	E	N	1975	93400
0001	S	S	E	N	1972	97249
0001	S	D	E	N	1976	99987
0001	S	E	E	N	1976	99987
0001	S	D	E	N	1975	101022
0001	S	S	E	N	1976	101375
0001	S	D	R	N	1975	101804
0001	S	T	R	N	1975	101804
0001	S	D	E	N	1976	101805
0001	S	T	E	N	1976	101805
0001	S	D	E	N	1976	101853
0001	S	E	E	N	1976	101853
0001	S	T	E	N	1976	101853
0001	T	S	E	N	1976	66532
0001	T	D	E	N	1975	92949
0001	T	E	E	N	1975	92949
0001	T	S	E	N	1975	92949
0001	T	T	E	N	1975	92949
0002	S	D	E	N	1974	60265
0002	S	D	E	N	1976	66532
0002	S	S	E	N	1976	66532
0002	S	D	E	N	1972	70677
0002	S	E	E	N	1972	70677
0002	S	T	E	N	1972	70677
0002	S	D	E	N	1968	75382
0002	S	E	E	N	1968	75382
0002	S	D	R	N	1975	96822
0002	S	T	R	N	1975	96822
0002	S	D	E	N	1976	99237
0002	S	T	E	N	1976	99237
0009	S	D	E	N	1973	50924
0009	S	D	R	N	1974	58064
0009	S	S	R	N	1974	58064
0009	S	D	E	N	1974	58065
0009	S	S	E	N	1974	58065
0009	S	D	E	N	1974	60265
0009	S	D	E	N	1976	66532
0009	S	S	E	N	1976	66532
0009	S	S	E	N	1963	75839
0009	T	D	E	L	1973	55193
0009	T	D	E	N	1973	55193
0009	T	D	E	L	1974	55194
0009	T	D	E	N	1974	55194
0010	S	D	E	N	1974	60265
0010	S	D	E	N	1976	66532
0010	S	S	E	N	1976	66532
0015	T	D	E	N	1975	90860
0017	S	D	E	N	1973	50924
0017	S	S	E	N	1973	53939
0017	S	T	E	N	1973	53939
0017	S	D	E	N	1974	58808
0017	S	S	E	N	1974	58808
0017	S	T	E	N	1974	58808
0017	S	D	E	N	1970	59674
0017	S	S	E	N	1970	59674
0017	S	D	E	N	1974	60265
0017	S	T	E	N	1971	65080
0017	S	D	G	N	1954	66199
0017	S	T	G	N	1954	66199
0017	S	S	E	N	1962	87660
0017	S	S	E	N	1971	87884
0017	S	D	E	N	1974	93385
0017	S	S	E	N	1963	98002
0017	S	D	R	N	1975	101515
0017	S	T	R	N	1975	101515
0017	S	D	E	N	1975	101516
0017	S	T	E	N	1975	101516
0017	T	S	E	N	1969	87821
0017	T	S	E	N	1971	87884
0046	D	D	E	N	1973	51742
0046	D	D	E	N	1973	55786
0055	T	D	E	N	1973	68874
0055	T	D	E	N	1976	101813
0055	T	E	E	N	1976	101813
0055	T	D	E	N	1976	101814
0055	T	T	E	N	1976	101814
0055	T	S	E	N	1976	102567
8001	D	S	E	N	1965	87781
8001	S	D	E	N	1973	50924
8001	S	D	R	N	1972	51263
8001	S	T	E	N	1973	52084
8001	S	S	E	N	1972	53244
8001	S	S	E	N	1972	53247
8001	S	D	E	N	1973	53564
8001	S	D	E	N	1973	53788
8001	S	E	E	N	1973	53788
8001	S	S	E	N	1973	53939
8001	S	T	E	N	1973	53939
8001	S	S	E	N	1973	54773
8001	S	D	E	N	1974	58808
8001	S	S	E	N	1974	58808
8001	S	T	E	N	1974	58808
8001	S	D	E	N	1970	59674
8001	S	S	E	N	1970	59674
8001	S	D	E	N	1974	60265
8001	S	D	E	N	1969	62248
8001	S	T	E	N	1971	65080
8001	S	S	E	N	1970	65877
8001	S	D	G	N	1954	66199
8001	S	T	G	N	1954	66199
8001	S	D	E	N	1975	66682

Phys. State: **A.** Amorphous; **C.** Superconductive; **D.** Doped; **F.** Fibrous or Whisker; **G.** Gas; **I.** Ionized or Plasma; **L.** Liquid; **P.** Powder or Particle; **S.** Solid; **T.** Thin Film
Subject: **D.** Data; **E.** Experiment; **S.** Survey (Review, Compendium, etc.); **T.** Theory
Language: **E.** English; **F.** French; **G.** German; **O.** Other Languages; **R.** Russian
Temperature: **L.** Low (0 to 75K); **N.** Normal (75 to 1273K); **H.** High (above 1273K)

Substance Number	Phys. State	Subject	Language	Temperature	Year	EPIC Number
114-8001	S	S	E	N	1963	87679
8001	S	S	E	N	1965	87781
8001	S	S	E	N	1971	87884
8001	S	D	R	N	1974	89991
8001	S	D	E	N	1975	89992
8001	S	D	E	N	1974	93385
8001	S	S	E	N	1972	97249
8001	S	D	R	N	1975	101515
8001	S	T	R	N	1975	101515
8001	S	D	E	N	1975	101516
8001	S	T	E	N	1975	101516
8001	T	S	E	N	1963	87679
8001	T	S	E	N	1965	87781
8001	T	S	E	N	1969	87821
8001	T	S	E	N	1971	87884
8001	T	S	E	N	1971	100982
8012	S	S	E	N	1962	87661
8048	S	D	E	N	1973	55786
8066	S	D	E	N	1974	57287
8066	S	E	E	N	1974	57287
8066	S	S	E	N	1974	57287
8077	S	D	E	N	1973	56154
116-0016	S	D	R	N	1973	57235
0017	S	T	E	N	1973	50380
0017	S	D	R	L	1972	60715
0017	S	D	E	N	1973	60716
0017	S	S	E	N	1967	75838
0031	S	T	E	N	1973	50380
8011	S	D	R	N	1973	57235
8017	S	T	E	N	1973	50380
8017	S	D	R	N	1972	60715
8017	S	D	E	N	1973	60716
8017	S	S	E	N	1975	63258
8017	S	S	E	N	1970	87822
8017	S	S	E	N	1972	87890
8030	S	D	F	N	1974	87699
8033	S	D	R	N	1973	57008
8035	S	D	R	N	1973	57235
8036	S	D	R	N	1973	57235
8044	S	D	E	N	1975	68590
8044	S	T	E	N	1975	68590
118-0020	S	D	R	N	1972	79248
0020	S	D	E	N	1972	90275
0037	A	D	E	N	1974	53862
0037	D	T	E	N	1974	53896
0037	D	D	E	N	1974	62740
0037	D	T	E	N	1974	62740
0037	S	D	R	N	1973	50233
0037	S	D	E	N	1973	50234
0037	S	T	E	N	1973	50380
0037	S	D	E	N	1972	51229
0037	S	D	R	N	1973	51366
0037	S	D	E	N	1973	51367
0037	S	D	E	N	1973	51924
0037	S	D	E	N	1974	53924
0037	S	T	E	N	1974	53924
0037	S	D	R	N	1973	54486
0037	S	E	R	N	1973	54486
0037	S	T	R	N	1973	54486
0037	S	D	E	N	1973	54487
0037	S	E	E	N	1973	54487
0037	S	T	E	N	1973	54487
0037	S	D	E	N	1973	55151
0037	S	D	E	H	1974	60261
0037	S	T	E	H	1974	60261
0037	S	D	E	N	1974	60307
0037	S	D	R	N	1971	61549
0037	S	E	R	N	1971	61549
0037	S	D	E	N	1973	62386
0037	S	D	E	N	1971	65902
0037	S	E	E	N	1971	65902
0037	S	S	E	N	1970	87822
0037	S	S	E	N	1971	87883
0037	S	S	E	N	1972	87890
0037	S	D	R	N	1974	92200
0037	S	T	R	N	1974	92200
0037	S	D	E	N	1974	92201
0037	S	T	E	N	1974	92201
0037	T	D	E	N	1974	53862
0037	T	D	E	N	1975	66717
0037	T	T	E	N	1975	66717
0037	T	D	E	N	1974	90072
0041	S	T	E	N	1973	50380
0041	S	D	E	N	1973	52168
0041	S	E	E	N	1973	52168
0041	S	S	E	N	1970	87822
0041	S	S	E	N	1972	87890
0042	S	D	R	N	1975	98033
0042	S	E	R	N	1975	98033
0042	S	T	R	N	1975	98033
0042	S	D	E	N	1975	98034
0042	S	E	E	N	1975	98034
0042	S	T	E	N	1975	98034
8018	S	D	E	N	1973	52123
8018	S	D	E	N	1973	52193
8018	S	D	E	N	1974	53895
8018	S	D	E	N	1974	60252
8018	S	D	E	N	1974	90311
8018	T	D	F	N	1973	54648

Substance Number	Phys. State	Subject	Language	Temperature	Year	EPIC Number
118-8050	S	D	E	N	1973	62386
8061	S	D	E	N	1974	61202
119-0002	A	D	E	N	1974	53862
0002	L	D	R	H	1973	53997
0002	L	T	R	H	1973	53997
0002	L	D	E	H	1973	53998
0002	L	T	E	H	1973	53998
0002	S	S	E	N	1973	50127
0002	S	D	E	N	1973	50924
0002	S	S	E	N	1972	53512
0002	S	D	E	N	1974	54024
0002	S	S	E	N	1974	59353
0002	S	D	E	N	1974	60265
0002	S	D	R	N	1974	60463
0002	S	D	E	N	1974	60464
0002	S	S	E	N	1973	62815
0002	S	S	E	N	1974	62816
0002	S	D	E	H	1966	64256
0002	S	D	E	L	1966	64256
0002	S	D	E	N	1966	64256
0002	S	S	E	N	1973	64495
0002	S	D	E	N	1962	64551
0002	S	S	E	N	1962	64551
0002	S	S	E	H	1970	65877
0002	S	S	E	L	1970	65877
0002	S	S	E	N	1970	65877
0002	S	D	E	N	1965	65978
0002	S	S	E	N	1965	65978
0002	S	S	E	N	1969	68271
0002	S	D	E	N	1971	70398
0002	S	D	E	H	1966	74594
0002	S	D	E	L	1966	74594
0002	S	D	E	N	1966	74594
0002	S	D	E	N	1961	75731
0002	S	S	E	N	1961	75731
0002	S	T	E	N	1961	75731
0002	S	D	E	N	1966	75776
0002	S	E	E	N	1966	75776
0002	S	S	E	N	1966	75776
0002	S	S	E	N	1969	87723
0002	S	S	E	N	1971	87883
0002	S	S	E	H	1975	93182
0002	S	S	E	N	1975	93182
0002	S	S	E	N	1975	97223
0002	S	D	E	N	1955	99794
0002	S	S	E	N	1955	99794
0002	S	T	E	N	1955	99794
0002	T	D	E	N	1974	53862
0002	T	S	F	N	1973	54648
0002	T	D	E	N	1971	64338
0002	T	D	E	N	1975	96486
0015	T	D	E	N	1974	56621
0064	S	S	E	N	1969	68271
0073	S	D	E	N	1973	62386
0073	S	S	E	N	1975	63336
8028	A	D	E	N	1974	53862
8028	T	D	E	N	1974	53862
8032	S	D	R	N	1973	51356
8032	S	T	R	N	1973	51356
8032	S	D	E	N	1973	51357
8032	S	T	E	N	1973	51357
8035	S	D	E	N	1973	52193
8035	S	D	R	N	1973	54500
8035	S	T	R	N	1973	54500
8035	S	D	E	N	1973	54501
8035	S	T	E	N	1973	54501
8035	S	D	R	N	1973	55048
8035	S	D	E	N	1974	55049
8035	S	D	R	N	1972	60715
8035	S	D	E	N	1973	60716
8048	S	S	E	N	1972	53512
8048	S	S	R	N	1973	56262
8048	S	D	E	N	1971	62600
8048	S	S	E	N	1970	65877
8048	S	S	E	N	1973	76721
8048	S	S	E	N	1975	93182
8088	S	D	R	N	1972	60715
8088	S	D	E	N	1973	60716
8089	S	S	E	N	1970	65877
8089	S	S	E	N	1975	93182
8090	S	D	R	N	1973	56011
8090	S	D	E	N	1974	76600
120-0001	T	D	E	N	1968	64270
0001	T	D	E	N	1975	66619
0004	T	D	E	N	1972	53252
0004	T	D	E	N	1973	60933
0004	T	E	E	N	1973	60933
0009	S	D	R	N	1972	64288
0009	S	T	R	N	1972	64288
0009	S	D	E	N	1972	68417
0009	S	T	E	N	1972	68417
0009	S	D	E	N	1976	101746
0009	S	T	E	N	1976	101746
0010	S	D	R	N	1972	79248
0010	S	D	E	N	1972	90275
0066	T	D	E	N	1973	50093
0080	S	D	E	N	1972	60077
0081	S	D	E	N	1958	75780
0081	S	T	E	N	1958	75780

Substance Number	Phys. State	Subject	Language	Temperature	Year	EPIC Number
120-0081	S	D	F	N	1958	75815
0081	S	T	F	N	1958	75815
0221	A	D	E	N	1974	52811
0221	A	S	E	N	1971	87885
0221	T	D	E	N	1974	52811
0221	T	D	E	N	1973	57598
0221	T	S	E	N	1973	57598
0233	S	D	E	N	1971	49617
0233	T	E	E	N	1974	62294
8022	S	D	E	N	1971	49617
8024	A	D	R	N	1971	59379
8024	A	T	E	N	1974	62549
8024	A	S	E	N	1971	87885
8024	S	S	E	N	1971	87885
8024	S	D	G	N	1974	91890
8024	S	E	G	N	1974	91890
8024	T	D	E	N	1973	57595
8024	T	D	E	N	1973	57598
8024	T	S	E	N	1973	57598
8024	T	D	E	N	1973	60933
8024	T	E	E	N	1973	60933
8024	T	T	E	N	1974	62549
8024	T	E	E	N	1975	87127
8024	T	S	E	N	1971	87885
8024	T	S	E	N	1972	87888
8024	T	D	E	N	1975	89267
8024	T	E	E	N	1975	89267
8024	T	T	E	N	1975	89267
8024	T	D	E	N	1976	97311
8030	S	D	R	N	1973	50233
8030	S	D	E	N	1973	50234
8042	S	S	E	N	1972	87886
8043	S	D	E	N	1973	52193
8043	S	D	R	N	1972	60715
8043	S	D	E	N	1973	60716
8107	T	D	E	N	1974	81418
8109	S	D	E	N	1973	57117
8110	S	D	R	N	1973	57235
8111	S	D	R	N	1973	57235
8126	S	D	E	N	1974	60252
8183	S	D	E	N	1976	102402
8183	S	E	E	N	1976	102402
8183	S	T	E	N	1976	102402
122-0003	T	D	E	N	1974	81418
0004	D	D	R	N	1972	51966
0004	S	D	R	N	1972	51966
0004	S	S	E	N	1975	93181
0004	T	D	E	N	1972	53252
0004	T	D	E	N	1974	53899
0004	T	S	E	N	1973	62276
0004	T	D	E	N	1975	96486
0004	T	D	E	N	1976	101825
0005	A	D	E	N	1974	53862
0005	S	T	E	N	1973	50380
0005	S	S	E	N	1972	53512
0005	S	D	E	N	1973	62386
0005	S	S	E	N	1970	65877
0005	S	D	F	N	1958	75815
0005	S	T	F	N	1958	75815
0005	S	S	E	N	1966	87831
0005	S	S	E	N	1971	87883
0005	T	D	E	N	1972	53252
0005	T	D	E	N	1974	53862
0005	T	D	E	N	1974	53899
0005	T	S	E	N	1974	53899
0005	T	D	E	N	1973	54809
0005	T	S	E	N	1973	62276
0008	T	D	E	N	1972	64098
0008	T	S	E	N	1972	64098
0009	A	D	R	L	1971	59379
0009	A	T	E	N	1974	62549
0009	A	D	E	N	1972	63793
0009	A	S	E	N	1970	65877
0009	A	S	E	N	1971	87885
0009	A	D	E	N	1976	99319
0009	D	D	E	N	1973	50093
0009	D	D	E	N	1973	60892
0009	D	D	E	N	1976	101526
0009	D	E	E	N	1976	101526
0009	D	S	E	N	1976	101526
0009	D	T	E	N	1976	101526
0009	L	D	G	H	1956	64941
0009	S	S	E	N	1973	50526
0009	S	D	E	N	1974	52796
0009	S	S	E	N	1974	52806
0009	S	S	E	N	1972	53512
0009	S	D	R	H	1971	59379
0009	S	D	E	N	1973	60634
0009	S	S	E	N	1973	60634
0009	S	D	R	N	1971	61549
0009	S	E	R	N	1971	61549
0009	S	T	R	N	1968	64541
0009	S	T	E	N	1968	64542
0009	S	D	R	N	1970	64846
0009	S	D	E	N	1970	64847
0009	S	D	G	H	1956	64941
0009	S	D	G	N	1956	64941
0009	S	D	R	N	1969	65448
0009	S	D	E	N	1969	65449
0009	S	D	E	N	1975	65511

Phys. State: **A.** Amorphous; **C.** Superconductive; **D.** Doped; **F.** Fibrous or Whisker; **G.** Gas; **I.** Ionized or Plasma; **L.** Liquid; **P.** Powder or Particle; **S.** Solid; **T.** Thin Film
Subject: **D.** Data; **E.** Experiment; **S.** Survey (Review, Compendium, etc.); **T.** Theory
Language: **E.** English; **F.** French; **G.** German; **O.** Other Languages; **R.** Russian
Temperature: **L.** Low (0 to 75K); **N.** Normal (75 to 1273K); **H.** High (above 1273K)

Substance Number	Phys. State	Subject	Language	Temperature	Year	EPIC Number
122-0009	S	E	E	N	1975	65511
0009	S	S	E	N	1975	65511
0009	S	T	E	N	1975	65511
0009	S	S	E	N	1970	65877
0009	S	D	E	N	1971	65902
0009	S	E	E	N	1971	65902
0009	S	D	E	N	1964	65967
0009	S	S	E	N	1971	66193
0009	S	S	G	N	1942	73252
0009	S	D	R	L	1974	75383
0009	S	D	R	N	1974	75383
0009	S	E	R	L	1974	75383
0009	S	E	R	N	1974	75383
0009	S	D	E	N	1973	75764
0009	S	T	E	N	1973	75764
0009	S	S	E	N	1971	87883
0009	S	D	E	N	1975	91762
0009	S	E	E	N	1975	91762
0009	S	T	E	N	1975	91762
0009	S	D	E	L	1974	93414
0009	S	D	E	N	1974	93414
0009	S	E	E	L	1974	93414
0009	S	E	E	N	1974	93414
0009	S	D	E	N	1976	99987
0009	S	E	E	N	1976	99987
0009	S	S	E	N	1976	99987
0009	T	D	E	N	1973	50093
0009	T	D	R	N	1973	52203
0009	T	D	R	N	1973	52317
0009	T	D	F	N	1973	52398
0009	T	D	E	N	1974	53899
0009	T	S	E	N	1974	53899
0009	T	D	E	N	1973	57729
0009	T	E	E	N	1973	57729
0009	T	D	R	L	1971	59379
0009	T	D	E	N	1973	60933
0009	T	E	E	N	1973	60933
0009	T	S	E	N	1973	62276
0009	T	T	E	N	1974	62549
0009	T	D	E	N	1972	63536
0009	T	D	E	N	1972	63537
0009	T	D	F	N	1973	65013
0009	T	D	R	N	1972	65446
0009	T	T	R	N	1972	65446
0009	T	D	E	N	1972	65447
0009	T	T	E	N	1972	65447
0009	T	D	E	N	1974	65625
0009	T	S	E	N	1974	65625
0009	T	E	E	H	1974	67106
0009	T	E	E	N	1974	67106
0009	T	D	G	N	1962	75921
0009	T	E	E	N	1975	87127
0009	T	D	E	N	1975	89267
0009	T	E	E	N	1975	89267
0009	T	T	E	N	1975	89267
0009	T	D	E	N	1974	92149
0009	T	E	E	N	1974	92149
0009	T	D	E	N	1975	92867
0009	T	D	E	N	1975	101768
0009	T	E	E	N	1975	101768
0009	T	D	R	N	1975	101769
0009	T	E	R	N	1975	101769
0009	T	D	O	N	1973	101913
0009	T	E	O	N	1973	101913
0009	T	T	O	N	1973	101913
0009	T	D	E	N	1973	101949
0009	T	T	E	N	1973	101949
0013	A	D	E	N	1974	53862
0013	S	T	E	N	1972	53221
0013	S	D	E	N	1956	75730
0013	S	T	E	N	1956	75730
0013	T	D	E	N	1974	53862
0014	D	D	E	N	1972	53110
0014	S	D	E	N	1972	53110
0016	A	D	E	N	1974	53862
0016	S	S	E	N	1971	87881
0016	S	D	E	N	1970	93295
0016	S	S	E	N	1970	93295
0016	T	D	E	N	1974	53862
0016	T	D	E	N	1975	66711
0016	T	T	E	N	1975	66711
0017	A	D	E	N	1974	53862
0017	T	D	E	N	1973	50764
0017	T	D	E	N	1974	53862
0017	T	D	E	N	1973	60933
0017	T	E	E	N	1973	60933
0017	T	D	R	N	1974	62804
0017	T	D	E	N	1974	65343
0017	T	S	E	N	1971	66197
0017	T	D	E	N	1976	101691
0017	T	T	E	N	1976	101691
0019	A	D	E	N	1972	53112
0019	S	D	E	N	1972	53112
0019	T	D	E	N	1972	53252
0019	T	D	E	N	1973	55135
0019	T	D	E	N	1973	57266
0023	A	D	E	N	1974	53862
0023	S	D	R	N	1973	50233
0023	S	D	E	N	1973	50234
0023	S	D	R	N	1973	54486
0023	S	E	R	N	1973	54486
122-0023	S	T	R	N	1973	54486
0023	S	D	E	N	1973	54487
0023	S	E	E	N	1973	54487
0023	S	T	E	N	1973	54487
0023	S	D	R	N	1974	59381
0023	S	D	E	N	1974	62041
0023	S	D	E	N	1973	62386
0023	S	D	E	N	1975	65498
0023	S	S	E	N	1975	65498
0023	S	T	E	N	1975	65498
0023	S	S	E	N	1969	68271
0023	S	T	E	N	1970	70645
0023	S	S	E	N	1963	87709
0023	S	S	E	N	1970	87822
0023	T	D	E	N	1974	53862
0030	A	D	E	N	1974	53862
0030	S	T	E	N	1973	50380
0030	S	D	R	N	1972	60715
0030	S	D	E	N	1973	60716
0030	S	D	E	N	1971	62600
0030	S	D	E	N	1962	64551
0030	S	S	E	N	1970	65877
0030	S	S	E	N	1971	87883
0030	T	D	E	N	1974	53862
0031	S	S	E	N	1969	68271
0037	S	D	R	N	1972	79248
0037	S	D	E	N	1972	90275
0037	T	D	E	N	1973	65532
0038	S	D	R	N	1972	79248
0038	S	D	E	N	1972	90275
0038	T	D	E	N	1975	90658
0046	T	D	E	N	1973	54809
0050	S	S	E	N	1969	68115
0050	T	D	E	N	1974	53626
0050	T	D	E	N	1974	53643
0050	T	D	E	N	1973	54774
0050	T	D	E	N	1972	59438
0050	T	T	E	N	1972	59438
0050	T	S	E	N	1967	68368
0050	T	D	E	N	1975	92802
0050	T	T	E	N	1975	92802
0053	A	D	E	N	1974	53862
0053	T	D	E	N	1974	53862
0053	T	S	E	N	1969	68115
0053	T	S	E	N	1966	87833
0067	S	S	E	N	1967	68368
0068	S	S	E	N	1969	68115
0068	T	S	E	N	1967	68368
0093	T	D	E	N	1973	65532
0096	S	S	E	N	1971	62264
0096	S	S	E	N	1970	65877
0096	T	D	E	N	1974	53899
0096	T	S	E	N	1974	53899
0096	T	D	E	N	1974	58226
0096	T	T	E	N	1974	58226
0096	T	D	G	N	1962	75921
0096	T	D	E	N	1975	89528
0096	T	D	E	N	1975	92867
0096	T	D	E	N	1976	99011
0096	T	E	E	N	1976	99011
0096	T	T	E	N	1976	99011
0096	T	D	E	N	1976	99966
0096	T	T	E	N	1976	99966
0096	T	S	E	N	1971	100982
0096	T	D	E	N	1975	101768
0096	T	E	E	N	1975	101768
0096	T	D	R	N	1975	101769
0096	T	E	R	N	1975	101769
0105	S	T	E	N	1973	50380
0105	S	D	E	N	1973	62386
0105	S	D	E	N	1972	93290
0105	T	D	O	N	1973	56266
0112	S	D	E	N	1972	53110
0112	T	S	E	N	1975	66711
0139	T	D	E	N	1971	63564
0139	T	S	E	N	1971	63564
0139	T	D	E	N	1974	81418
0208	S	D	R	N	1972	79248
0208	S	D	E	N	1972	90275
0340	S	D	R	N	1972	79248
0340	S	D	E	N	1972	90275
0367	A	D	E	N	1974	53862
0367	T	D	E	N	1974	53862
0449	S	D	R	N	1972	79248
0449	S	D	E	N	1972	90275
8012	T	D	E	N	1973	53458
8012	T	T	E	N	1976	101295
8045	A	D	E	N	1974	57286
8045	A	S	E	N	1970	65877
8045	A	D	E	N	1966	75534
8045	A	E	E	N	1966	75534
8045	A	S	E	N	1966	75534
8045	A	T	E	N	1966	75534
8045	A	E	E	N	1976	102402
8045	A	T	E	N	1976	102402
8045	D	E	E	N	1974	61928
8045	D	D	E	N	1975	65442
8045	D	D	E	N	1975	97891
8045	D	S	E	N	1975	97891
8045	D	T	E	N	1975	97891
8045	D	D	G	N	1976	99882
122-8045	D	E	G	N	1976	99882
8045	D	T	G	N	1976	99882
8045	D	D	E	N	1976	100620
8045	D	T	E	N	1976	100620
8045	F	D	E	N	1974	61928
8045	F	E	E	N	1974	61928
8045	P	D	F	N	1973	63457
8045	P	D	E	N	1975	92949
8045	P	E	E	N	1975	92949
8045	P	S	E	N	1975	92949
8045	P	T	E	N	1975	92949
8045	S	S	E	N	1974	52799
8045	S	D	E	L	1973	53709
8045	S	D	E	N	1973	53709
8045	S	D	E	N	1974	53738
8045	S	S	R	N	1973	56262
8045	S	D	E	N	1974	57289
8045	S	E	E	N	1974	57289
8045	S	S	E	N	1974	57289
8045	S	T	E	N	1974	57289
8045	S	D	E	N	1974	57797
8045	S	E	E	N	1973	60841
8045	S	S	E	N	1973	60841
8045	S	D	E	N	1973	62386
8045	S	D	E	N	1971	62600
8045	S	S	E	N	1975	63336
8045	S	D	E	N	1974	64539
8045	S	E	E	N	1974	64539
8045	S	S	E	N	1974	64539
8045	S	S	E	N	1973	64543
8045	S	S	E	N	1970	64545
8045	S	D	E	N	1971	64548
8045	S	S	E	N	1971	64548
8045	S	D	E	N	1962	64551
8045	S	D	E	N	1960	64749
8045	S	D	E	N	1975	65442
8045	S	D	E	N	1974	65625
8045	S	S	E	N	1970	65877
8045	S	S	E	N	1970	66180
8045	S	S	F	N	1974	66869
8045	S	D	E	N	1947	75773
8045	S	S	E	N	1947	75773
8045	S	T	E	N	1947	75773
8045	S	S	E	N	1973	76721
8045	S	D	E	N	1974	81696
8045	S	D	E	N	1975	87179
8045	S	S	E	N	1971	87883
8045	S	D	E	N	1974	88462
8045	S	D	E	N	1975	97891
8045	S	S	E	N	1975	97891
8045	S	T	E	N	1975	97891
8045	S	D	E	N	1976	99786
8045	S	E	E	N	1976	99786
8045	S	S	E	N	1976	99786
8045	S	D	E	H	1976	101304
8045	S	D	E	N	1976	101304
8045	S	T	E	N	1936	101914
8045	S	D	E	N	1976	102402
8045	T	S	E	N	1973	62276
8045	T	D	E	N	1965	64850
8045	T	D	E	N	1975	65442
8045	T	S	E	H	1970	65877
8045	T	S	E	N	1970	65877
8045	T	S	E	N	1971	87885
8045	T	D	E	N	1975	92949
8045	T	E	E	N	1975	92949
8045	T	S	E	N	1975	92949
8045	T	T	E	N	1975	92949
8046	S	S	E	N	1972	53512
8046	S	D	E	L	1973	53709
8046	S	D	E	N	1973	53709
8046	S	D	E	L	1971	64548
8046	S	D	E	N	1971	64548
8046	S	S	E	N	1970	65877
8046	S	S	E	N	1966	101404
8047	S	S	E	N	1963	64748
8048	S	S	E	N	1972	53512
8048	S	D	E	L	1973	53709
8048	S	D	E	N	1973	53709
8049	S	S	E	N	1972	53512
8049	S	S	E	N	1970	65877
8052	S	S	E	N	1972	53512
8052	S	D	E	N	1974	64539
8054	T	D	E	N	1974	58341
8067	S	D	E	N	1973	52576
8070	A	D	E	N	1974	53862
8070	T	D	E	N	1974	53862
8076	S	S	E	N	1970	65877
8076	T	S	E	N	1970	65877
8076	T	D	G	N	1962	75921
8076	T	D	E	N	1969	95705
8088	S	S	E	N	1971	87881
8103	F	D	E	N	1974	53738
8105	A	D	E	N	1975	97963
8105	S	D	E	N	1973	60634
8105	S	S	E	N	1973	60634
8105	T	D	E	N	1975	97963
8107	S	D	R	N	1973	56011
8107	S	D	E	N	1974	76600
8122	T	S	E	N	1969	68115
8125	S	D	E	N	1966	102229

Phys. State: **A.** Amorphous; **C.** Superconductive; **D.** Doped; **F.** Fibrous or Whisker; **G.** Gas; **I.** Ionized or Plasma; **L.** Liquid; **P.** Powder or Particle; **S.** Solid; **T.** Thin Film
Subject: **D.** Data; **E.** Experiment; **S.** Survey (Review, Compendium, etc.); **T.** Theory
Language: **E.** English; **F.** French; **G.** German; **O.** Other Languages; **R.** Russian
Temperature: **L.** Low (0 to 75K); **N.** Normal (75 to 1273K); **H.** High (above 1273K)

Substance Number	Phys. State	Subject	Language	Temperature	Year	EPIC Number
122-8126	S	D	E	N	1974	53738
8128	S	S	E	N	1972	53512
8132	S	S	E	N	1963	64748
8140	S	D	E	N	1976	102402
8140	S	E	E	N	1976	102402
8140	S	T	E	N	1976	102402
123-0003	S	S	E	N	1969	68115
0003	S	S	E	N	1966	68361
0003	S	S	E	N	1971	87883
0003	T	S	E	N	1966	68361
0032	S	S	E	N	1972	53335
0042	S	S	E	N	1972	53335
0051	S	D	E	N	1974	62023
8017	D	S	E	N	1975	63285
8017	S	D	E	N	1973	52463
8017	S	D	E	L	1975	63285
8017	S	S	E	N	1969	68115
8017	S	S	E	N	1962	87674
8017	S	D	E	N	1973	88343
8017	T	S	E	N	1972	87824
8018	D	S	E	N	1975	63285
8018	S	D	E	L	1975	63285
8018	S	S	E	N	1970	68114
8018	S	S	E	N	1969	68115
8018	S	S	E	L	1973	68901
8018	S	S	E	N	1973	68901
8018	S	S	E	N	1962	87671
8018	S	D	E	N	1973	88343
8018	T	D	E	N	1972	53263
8018	T	D	E	N	1974	61179
8018	T	S	E	N	1974	61179
8018	T	D	E	N	1974	88465
8018	T	S	E	N	1971	100982
8018	T	D	E	N	1973	102095
8018	T	T	E	N	1973	102095
8039	S	S	E	N	1972	87824
8039	S	D	E	N	1973	88343
8039	S	T	E	N	1973	88343
8051	S	D	E	N	1973	88343
8051	S	T	E	N	1973	88343
8051	S	D	E	N	1976	100173
8051	T	D	E	N	1972	53263
8051	T	D	E	N	1974	88465
8051	T	D	E	N	1973	102095
8051	T	T	E	N	1973	102095
8058	S	D	E	N	1973	88343
8058	S	T	E	N	1973	88343
126-0001	S	S	E	N	1969	68115
0002	S	S	E	N	1969	68115
0002	S	S	E	N	1972	87824
0004	S	S	E	N	1974	58804
0005	A	S	E	N	1970	65877
0005	S	D	R	N	1973	50233
0005	S	D	E	N	1973	50234
0005	S	D	E	N	1973	50924
0005	S	D	E	N	1974	58808
0005	S	S	E	N	1974	58808
0005	S	T	E	N	1974	58808
0005	S	D	G	N	1971	59423
0005	S	T	G	N	1971	59423
0005	S	D	E	N	1974	60255
0005	S	D	E	N	1974	60265
0005	S	D	E	N	1974	60691
0005	S	S	E	N	1974	60691
0005	S	D	E	L	1973	61472
0005	S	D	E	N	1973	61472
0005	S	D	E	N	1973	62325
0005	S	D	E	N	1973	62386
0005	S	S	E	N	1969	68271
0005	S	D	E	N	1971	70398
0005	S	S	E	N	1924	73267
0005	S	D	R	L	1974	75383
0005	S	D	R	N	1974	75383
0005	S	E	R	L	1974	75383
0005	S	E	R	N	1974	75383
0005	S	D	F	N	1958	75815
0005	S	T	F	N	1958	75815
0005	S	S	E	N	1963	87711
0005	S	S	E	N	1966	87712
0005	S	S	E	N	1970	87822
0005	S	S	E	N	1971	87883
0005	S	S	E	N	1974	89536
0005	S	D	E	N	1974	93385
0005	S	D	E	L	1974	93414
0005	S	D	E	N	1974	93414
0005	S	E	E	L	1974	93414
0005	S	E	E	N	1974	93414
0005	S	S	E	N	1975	97223
0005	S	S	E	N	1976	101374
0005	S	S	E	N	1976	101375
0005	S	D	E	N	1976	101796
0005	S	E	E	N	1976	101796
0005	S	S	E	N	1976	101796
0005	S	D	E	N	1976	101820
0005	S	E	E	N	1976	101820
0005	S	D	E	N	1976	101853
0005	S	E	E	N	1976	101853
0005	S	T	E	N	1976	101853
0005	S	S	E	N	1975	101890
126-0005	T	D	E	N	1973	51076
0005	T	D	E	N	1973	52214
0005	T	S	F	N	1973	54648
0005	T	D	E	N	1974	58226
0005	T	T	E	N	1974	58226
0005	T	D	E	N	1974	58961
0005	T	D	E	N	1974	60691
0005	T	S	E	N	1974	60691
0005	T	D	E	N	1974	61413
0005	T	T	E	N	1974	61413
0005	T	S	E	N	1973	62276
0005	T	S	E	N	1970	65877
0005	T	D	E	N	1974	68253
0005	T	D	E	N	1974	68831
0005	T	D	E	N	1971	70334
0005	T	T	E	N	1971	70334
0005	T	S	E	N	1963	87711
0005	T	S	E	N	1966	87712
0005	T	D	E	N	1975	89528
0005	T	D	E	N	1974	89536
0005	T	D	E	N	1975	93161
0005	T	D	E	N	1975	93485
0005	T	E	E	N	1975	93485
0005	T	D	E	N	1950	95706
0005	T	T	E	N	1950	95706
0005	T	T	E	N	1957	95707
0005	T	D	E	N	1975	96486
0005	T	D	E	N	1976	99658
0005	T	S	E	N	1971	100982
0005	T	D	E	N	1976	101825
0014	S	D	R	N	1974	86494
0014	S	T	R	N	1974	86494
0017	S	S	E	N	1969	68271
0017	S	T	R	N	1972	79283
0063	S	D	E	N	1974	62023
8026	S	D	E	N	1964	61307
8030	A	D	E	N	1972	53112
8030	A	D	E	N	1972	53386
8030	S	D	E	N	1972	53112
8030	T	D	E	N	1972	53386
8032	D	D	E	N	1972	100970
8032	D	T	E	N	1972	100970
8032	S	S	R	N	1972	62298
8032	S	S	E	N	1973	62299
8032	S	D	E	N	1972	100970
8032	S	T	E	N	1972	100970
8035	S	S	E	N	1969	68115
8037	S	S	E	L	1970	68114
8037	S	S	E	N	1970	68114
8037	S	S	E	N	1969	68115
8037	T	S	E	N	1970	68114
8037	T	D	E	N	1973	102095
8037	T	T	E	N	1973	102095
8048	T	D	E	N	1976	101298
8049	T	D	E	N	1976	101298
8050	T	D	E	N	1976	101298
8052	D	D	E	N	1974	60256
8052	D	E	E	N	1974	60256
8052	S	D	E	N	1973	50924
8052	S	S	E	N	1972	53244
8052	S	S	E	N	1972	53247
8052	S	D	E	N	1974	54024
8052	S	S	E	N	1973	54773
8052	S	D	R	N	1972	56630
8052	S	S	R	N	1972	56630
8052	S	T	R	N	1972	56630
8052	S	D	E	N	1972	57756
8052	S	S	E	N	1972	57756
8052	S	T	E	N	1972	57756
8052	S	D	E	N	1974	58808
8052	S	S	E	N	1974	58808
8052	S	T	E	N	1974	58808
8052	S	D	E	N	1974	60253
8052	S	E	E	N	1974	60253
8052	S	S	E	N	1974	60253
8052	S	D	E	N	1974	60255
8052	S	D	E	N	1974	60265
8052	S	D	E	N	1974	60691
8052	S	S	E	N	1974	60691
8052	S	D	E	L	1973	61472
8052	S	D	E	N	1973	61472
8052	S	S	E	N	1971	62264
8052	S	D	E	N	1974	62302
8052	S	E	E	N	1974	62302
8052	S	D	E	N	1973	62325
8052	S	D	E	N	1975	63349
8052	S	E	E	N	1975	63349
8052	S	D	R	N	1972	63700
8052	S	E	R	N	1972	63700
8052	S	S	R	N	1972	63700
8052	S	D	E	N	1965	64255
8052	S	S	E	N	1965	64255
8052	S	D	E	N	1972	65342
8052	S	E	E	N	1972	65342
8052	S	S	E	N	1972	65342
8052	S	E	E	N	1975	65507
8052	S	S	E	N	1975	65507
8052	S	S	E	N	1969	68271
8052	S	S	E	N	1963	68313
8052	S	D	E	N	1974	68823
8052	S	D	E	N	1971	70398
126-8052	S	T	E	N	1970	70645
8052	S	D	E	N	1974	87440
8052	S	S	E	N	1970	87822
8052	S	S	E	N	1971	87883
8052	S	D	E	N	1975	88455
8052	S	D	E	N	1975	93309
8052	S	D	E	N	1975	93312
8052	S	S	E	N	1975	93312
8052	S	D	E	N	1975	93344
8052	S	D	E	N	1974	93375
8052	S	D	E	N	1974	93385
8052	S	D	E	N	1975	94150
8052	S	E	E	N	1975	94151
8052	S	D	E	N	1974	94581
8052	S	D	E	N	1975	97511
8052	S	E	E	N	1975	97511
8052	S	T	E	N	1975	97511
8052	S	D	E	N	1976	99786
8052	S	E	E	N	1976	99786
8052	S	S	E	N	1976	99786
8052	S	D	E	N	1976	99989
8052	S	E	E	N	1976	99989
8052	S	S	E	N	1976	99989
8052	S	T	E	N	1976	99989
8052	S	D	E	N	1975	101042
8052	S	E	E	N	1975	101042
8052	S	D	E	N	1975	101043
8052	S	E	E	N	1975	101043
8052	S	T	E	N	1975	101043
8052	S	S	E	N	1976	101374
8052	S	S	E	N	1976	101375
8052	S	D	E	N	1975	101657
8052	S	E	E	N	1975	101657
8052	S	S	E	N	1975	101657
8052	S	T	E	N	1975	101657
8052	S	E	E	N	1975	101658
8052	S	T	E	N	1975	101658
8052	S	E	E	N	1975	101662
8052	S	D	E	N	1975	101672
8052	S	D	E	N	1975	101679
8052	S	E	E	N	1975	101679
8052	S	D	E	N	1976	101796
8052	S	E	E	N	1976	101796
8052	S	S	E	N	1976	101796
8052	S	D	E	N	1976	101820
8052	S	E	E	N	1976	101820
8052	S	S	E	N	1976	101838
8052	S	D	E	N	1976	101848
8052	S	E	E	N	1976	101848
8052	S	D	E	N	1976	101853
8052	S	E	E	N	1976	101853
8052	S	T	E	N	1976	101853
8052	S	E	E	N	1976	101854
8052	S	T	E	N	1976	101854
8052	S	D	E	N	1976	101860
8052	S	E	E	N	1976	101860
8052	S	D	E	N	1976	103590
8052	S	T	E	N	1976	103590
8052	T	S	F	N	1973	54648
8052	T	D	E	N	1973	55160
8052	T	D	E	N	1974	60691
8052	T	S	E	N	1974	60691
8052	T	D	R	N	1970	61532
8052	T	S	E	N	1970	65877
8052	T	D	E	N	1974	68253
8052	T	D	E	N	1975	93161
8052	T	D	E	N	1975	93354
8052	T	D	E	N	1975	94150
8052	T	D	E	N	1976	101813
8052	T	E	E	N	1976	101813
8052	T	D	E	N	1976	102015
8052	T	S	E	N	1976	102567
8055	S	S	E	N	1969	68115
8055	S	S	E	N	1972	87824
8073	S	S	R	N	1973	56262
8073	S	D	E	N	1971	62600
8073	S	D	E	N	1962	64551
8073	S	D	E	N	1960	64749
8073	S	S	E	N	1970	65877
8073	S	S	E	N	1973	76721
8073	S	S	E	N	1971	100982
8074	D	S	E	N	1970	65877
8074	S	S	E	N	1972	53244
8074	S	S	E	N	1972	53247
8074	S	S	E	N	1973	54773
8074	S	S	R	N	1973	56262
8074	S	D	E	N	1969	62248
8074	S	D	E	N	1971	62600
8074	S	E	E	N	1970	65877
8074	S	S	E	N	1973	76721
8074	S	S	E	N	1976	99989
8074	S	S	E	N	1971	100982
8074	S	E	E	N	1975	101662
8079	S	S	E	N	1969	68271
8080	S	S	E	N	1969	68271
8092	S	S	E	N	1974	58804
8137	S	S	E	N	1972	87824
127-8004	S	D	E	N	1973	50924
8004	S	D	E	N	1974	58808
8004	S	S	E	N	1974	58808

Phys. State: **A.** Amorphous; **C.** Superconductive; **D.** Doped; **F.** Fibrous or Whisker; **G.** Gas; **I.** Ionized or Plasma; **L.** Liquid; **P.** Powder or Particle; **S.** Solid; **T.** Thin Film
Subject: **D.** Data; **E.** Experiment; **S.** Survey (Review, Compendium, etc.); **T.** Theory
Language: **E.** English; **F.** French; **G.** German; **O.** Other Languages; **R.** Russian
Temperature: **L.** Low (0 to 75K); **N.** Normal (75 to 1273K); **H.** High (above 1273K)

Substance Number	Phys. State	Sub-ject	Lan-guage	Temper-ature	Year	EPIC Number
127-8004	S	T	E	N	1974	58808
8004	S	D	E	N	1971	59436
8004	S	E	E	N	1971	59436
8004	S	D	E	N	1974	60255
8004	S	D	E	N	1974	60265
8004	S	D	E	N	1974	60691
8004	S	S	E	N	1974	60691
8004	S	D	E	L	1973	61472
8004	S	D	E	N	1973	61472
8004	S	D	E	N	1972	63492
8004	S	S	E	N	1972	63492
8004	S	T	E	N	1971	65080
8004	S	S	E	N	1969	68271
8004	S	S	E	N	1970	87822
8004	S	D	E	N	1974	93385
8004	S	S	E	N	1975	101032
8004	S	S	E	N	1975	101890
8004	T	D	E	N	1974	60691
8004	T	E	E	N	1974	60691
8004	T	S	E	N	1974	60691
8004	T	D	R	N	1970	61532
8004	T	D	E	N	1974	68253
8004	T	D	E	N	1974	68831
8004	T	D	E	N	1975	93161
8004	T	D	R	N	1975	97638
8004	T	T	R	N	1975	97638
8004	T	D	E	N	1975	97639
8004	T	T	E	N	1975	97639

Phys. State: **A.** Amorphous; **C.** Superconductive; **D.** Doped; **F.** Fibrous or Whisker; **G.** Gas; **I.** Ionized or Plasma; **L.** Liquid; **P.** Powder or Particle; **S.** Solid; **T.** Thin Film
Subject: **D.** Data; **E.** Experiment; **S.** Survey (Review, Compendium, etc.); **T.** Theory
Language: **E.** English; **F.** French; **G.** German; **O.** Other Languages; **R.** Russian
Temperature: **L.** Low (0 to 75K); **N.** Normal (75 to 1273K); **H.** High (above 1273K)

Chapter 20 Thermoelectric Properties

Substance Number	Phys. State	Sub-ject	Lan-guage	Temper-ature	Year	EPIC Number
100-0045	L	E	E	N	1974	55733
0045	L	T	E	N	1974	55733
0045	S	E	E	N	1974	55733
0045	S	T	E	N	1974	55733
0045	S	S	E	H	1967	62829
0045	S	S	E	N	1967	62829
0045	S	S	O	N	1971	68939
0045	S	S	E	N	1972	68940
0045	S	S	E	N	1973	82686
0045	S	S	R	N	1971	87444
0045	S	S	E	N	1974	87445
0045	T	S	E	N	1973	82686
0055	A	D	E	N	1971	49794
0055	A	T	E	N	1973	51774
0055	A	S	E	N	1972	52414
0055	A	T	E	N	1974	86428
0055	A	T	E	N	1976	100646
0055	D	T	R	N	1974	72313
0055	D	T	E	N	1975	72358
0055	L	T	E	H	1975	88184
0055	L	T	E	N	1975	88184
0055	L	S	E	H	1969	94149
0055	L	S	E	N	1969	94149
0055	L	E	R	H	1975	95126
0055	L	E	R	N	1975	95126
0055	L	S	R	H	1966	95131
0055	L	S	R	N	1966	95131
0055	L	S	E	H	1966	96497
0055	L	S	E	N	1966	96497
0055	L	E	G	N	1976	99883
0055	S	E	R	N	1971	49756
0055	S	T	R	N	1973	50056
0055	S	T	R	N	1973	50063
0055	S	T	R	N	1973	51364
0055	S	T	E	N	1973	51365
0055	S	T	E	N	1973	51412
0055	S	T	E	N	1973	51419
0055	S	T	E	N	1973	51807
0055	S	E	R	N	1972	52222
0055	S	S	E	N	1972	53072
0055	S	E	E	N	1973	53714
0055	S	S	R	N	1973	53794
0055	S	S	E	N	1973	53986
0055	S	T	E	N	1973	54678
0055	S	T	E	N	1974	55246
0055	S	T	E	L	1974	55247
0055	S	T	E	N	1974	55247
0055	S	E	E	N	1973	55588
0055	S	T	E	N	1973	57483
0055	S	T	E	N	1974	58812
0055	S	T	E	N	1958	59568
0055	S	E	E	N	1974	59573
0055	S	T	E	N	1974	59573
0055	S	T	R	N	1972	60021
0055	S	T	R	N	1974	60433
0055	S	T	E	N	1974	60434
0055	S	E	R	N	1970	60752
0055	S	E	E	N	1974	60753
0055	S	E	E	N	1972	60929
0055	S	T	E	N	1972	60929
0055	S	E	O	L	1973	61079
0055	S	E	O	N	1973	61079
0055	S	E	R	N	1965	61106
0055	S	E	E	N	1965	61107
0055	S	T	R	N	1970	61243
0055	S	T	R	N	1970	61245
0055	S	T	E	N	1970	61493
0055	S	S	E	N	1970	61494
0055	S	E	E	N	1971	61678
0055	S	E	R	N	1973	61876
0055	S	T	R	N	1973	61876
0055	S	S	R	N	1972	62298
0055	S	S	E	N	1973	62299
0055	S	E	E	N	1974	62308
0055	S	S	G	H	1970	62356
0055	S	S	G	N	1970	62356
0055	S	T	R	N	1973	62731
0055	S	E	E	N	1974	62737
0055	S	E	E	N	1967	62829
0055	S	S	E	N	1967	62829
0055	S	T	R	N	1974	63078
0055	S	T	E	N	1975	63079
0055	S	T	E	N	1975	63321
0055	S	T	E	N	1973	63603
0055	S	T	E	N	1973	65327
0055	S	T	E	N	1962	65942
0055	S	T	R	N	1974	66452
0055	S	T	E	N	1974	66453
0055	S	T	R	N	1974	66454
0055	S	T	E	N	1974	66455
0055	S	D	E	N	1972	67891
0055	S	T	E	N	1961	74508
0055	S	T	E	N	1971	75288
0055	S	T	E	N	1962	75928
0055	S	T	R	N	1975	76851
100-0055	S	T	E	N	1975	76852
0055	S	T	E	N	1975	78758
0055	S	E	R	N	1974	80889
0055	S	T	R	N	1974	81141
0055	S	T	E	L	1974	86010
0055	S	T	E	N	1974	86010
0055	S	E	O	N	1974	86432
0055	S	S	R	N	1971	87444
0055	S	S	E	N	1974	87445
0055	S	T	R	N	1974	88156
0055	S	T	E	N	1974	88157
0055	S	E	R	L	1975	91273
0055	S	E	R	N	1975	91273
0055	S	E	E	N	1975	92037
0055	S	T	E	N	1975	92037
0055	S	E	E	N	1975	92166
0055	S	T	R	N	1974	92299
0055	S	T	E	N	1975	92300
0055	S	T	E	N	1975	92631
0055	S	E	E	N	1974	94093
0055	S	S	E	N	1969	94149
0055	S	T	R	L	1975	94941
0055	S	T	R	N	1975	94941
0055	S	E	E	L	1975	95910
0055	S	E	E	N	1975	95910
0055	S	T	E	L	1975	96880
0055	S	T	E	N	1975	96880
0055	S	T	E	N	1976	99749
0055	S	T	R	L	1975	100328
0055	S	T	E	L	1975	100329
0055	S	T	E	L	1976	100407
0055	S	T	E	N	1976	100407
0055	S	T	E	N	1976	101579
0055	T	T	R	N	1974	60397
0055	T	T	E	N	1974	60398
0055	T	D	R	N	1970	61000
0055	T	E	R	N	1970	61000
0055	T	T	R	N	1970	61245
0055	T	D	E	N	1974	62297
0055	T	E	E	N	1974	62297
0055	T	T	R	N	1973	62589
0055	T	T	E	N	1974	62590
8005	S	S	R	N	1973	55479
8007	S	S	E	N	1969	68271
8007	S	S	E	N	1972	87823
8008	S	S	E	N	1971	87884
8008	S	S	E	N	1972	87889
8009	S	T	E	N	1973	53420
8013	D	D	R	H	1973	52534
8013	D	D	R	N	1973	52534
8013	D	D	E	H	1974	53647
8013	D	D	E	N	1974	53647
8016	S	S	E	N	1972	59933
8021	S	S	O	N	1971	50466
8023	S	D	R	N	1970	61248
8023	S	E	R	N	1970	61248
8024	S	D	R	N	1970	61248
8024	S	E	R	N	1970	61248
8025	S	S	O	N	1971	50466
8035	S	S	O	N	1971	50466
8036	S	S	O	N	1971	50466
8038	S	S	E	N	1969	68115
8038	S	S	E	N	1972	87824
8040	S	S	E	N	1969	75843
8043	S	S	E	N	1969	75843
8057	S	T	R	N	1973	67856
8069	S	S	E	N	1972	87886
102-0002	S	D	E	N	1974	54024
0002	S	S	E	N	1974	54024
0002	S	T	E	N	1974	54024
0005	L	S	R	N	1973	55758
0005	L	D	E	N	1973	57072
0005	L	S	E	N	1973	57781
0005	S	D	E	N	1973	51746
0005	S	T	E	N	1973	51746
0005	S	S	E	N	1972	57870
0005	S	D	E	N	1971	87361
0005	S	T	E	N	1971	87361
0009	D	S	E	N	1972	61595
0009	S	S	E	N	1972	57870
0009	S	S	E	N	1972	61595
0010	D	S	E	N	1972	57870
0010	L	S	R	N	1973	55758
0010	L	S	E	N	1973	57781
0010	S	S	E	N	1972	57870
0041	S	S	E	N	1972	87889
0086	S	S	E	N	1972	59933
0120	L	D	R	N	1974	81330
0120	S	D	R	N	1973	50724
0120	S	D	E	N	1973	53025
0120	S	D	F	N	1970	59704
0120	S	E	F	N	1970	59704
0250	D	D	R	N	1971	91887
0250	D	T	R	N	1971	91887
102-0348	S	D	R	N	1974	63050
0348	S	D	E	N	1975	63051
8001	D	D	R	N	1966	59587
8001	D	E	R	N	1966	59587
8001	D	D	E	N	1966	63247
8001	D	E	E	N	1966	63247
8001	S	D	R	N	1966	59587
8001	S	E	R	N	1966	59587
8001	S	D	E	N	1966	63247
8001	S	E	E	N	1966	63247
8001	S	S	O	N	1966	66022
8001	S	S	E	N	1967	66023
8001	S	S	E	N	1962	87668
8001	S	S	E	N	1966	87830
8001	S	S	E	N	1971	87884
8012	S	D	R	H	1973	50321
8012	S	D	R	N	1973	50321
8012	S	D	E	H	1973	50322
8012	S	D	E	N	1973	50322
8012	S	D	R	N	1974	81141
8012	S	T	R	N	1974	81141
8012	S	D	E	N	1975	92631
8012	S	T	E	N	1975	92631
8012	S	D	R	H	1972	94899
8012	S	D	R	N	1972	94899
8012	S	D	E	H	1973	95896
8012	S	D	E	N	1973	95896
8012	S	D	E	N	1974	101642
8012	S	D	E	H	1976	102175
8012	S	D	E	N	1976	102175
8015	T	S	E	N	1974	94637
8018	S	S	E	N	1972	87889
8031	L	S	E	N	1970	59557
8031	S	D	E	N	1973	51769
8031	S	S	E	N	1972	59933
8035	S	D	E	N	1975	94550
8041	A	D	E	N	1972	49464
8041	A	S	E	N	1971	49794
8041	A	S	E	N	1970	75887
8041	A	S	E	N	1974	83952
8041	A	S	E	N	1974	86456
8041	D	D	R	N	1972	49888
8041	D	D	R	L	1973	50080
8041	D	D	E	L	1973	51433
8041	D	D	E	N	1973	51433
8041	D	D	R	N	1970	53088
8041	D	D	E	N	1972	53089
8041	D	D	E	L	1973	53414
8041	D	D	E	N	1973	53414
8041	D	D	R	N	1972	58203
8041	D	S	E	N	1964	87701
8041	S	D	E	N	1973	50701
8041	S	D	E	N	1974	54024
8041	S	S	E	N	1974	54024
8041	S	T	E	N	1974	54024
8041	S	D	E	N	1972	56330
8041	S	E	E	N	1971	61678
8041	S	S	O	N	1966	66022
8041	S	S	E	N	1967	66023
8041	S	D	R	N	1971	66998
8041	S	D	R	N	1975	81273
8041	S	S	E	N	1973	86380
8041	S	S	E	N	1962	87673
8041	S	S	E	N	1964	87701
8041	S	S	E	N	1971	87884
8041	S	D	E	L	1975	89446
8041	S	T	E	L	1975	89446
8041	S	D	E	N	1975	94088
8041	T	S	E	N	1974	83952
8041	T	S	E	N	1974	86456
8054	D	D	R	L	1973	50080
8054	D	D	R	N	1973	50080
8054	D	D	E	L	1973	51433
8054	D	D	E	N	1973	51433
8054	D	D	R	N	1973	58156
8054	D	S	E	N	1971	87884
8054	D	D	E	N	1963	98648
8054	S	S	E	N	1974	64457
8054	S	S	E	N	1962	87667
8054	S	S	E	N	1971	87884
8054	S	D	E	N	1963	98648
8065	D	D	R	N	1974	84840
8065	S	D	R	N	1974	84840
8065	S	D	R	N	1974	86779
8065	S	D	E	N	1974	90050
8066	L	D	E	H	1972	49461
8066	L	D	E	N	1972	49461
8066	L	D	R	N	1974	81330
8066	S	D	E	N	1972	49461
8066	S	D	R	N	1973	51553
8066	S	D	R	N	1973	52557
8066	S	D	E	N	1973	53684
8066	S	D	R	N	1973	58197
8066	S	D	R	N	1974	86779
8066	S	D	E	N	1974	90050

Phys. State: **A.** Amorphous; **C.** Superconductive; **D.** Doped; **F.** Fibrous or Whisker; **G.** Gas; **I.** Ionized or Plasma; **L.** Liquid; **P.** Powder or Particle; **S.** Solid; **T.** Thin Film
Subject: **D.** Data; **E.** Experiment; **S.** Survey (Review, Compendium, etc.); **T.** Theory
Language: **E.** English; **F.** French; **G.** German; **O.** Other Languages; **R.** Russian
Temperature: **L.** Low (0 to 75K); **N.** Normal (75 to 1273K); **H.** High (above 1273K)

Substance Number	Phys. State	Subject	Language	Temperature	Year	EPIC Number
102-8069	A	D	E	N	1968	75884
8069	L	D	E	N	1972	49463
8069	L	D	R	N	1973	64519
8069	S	D	R	N	1973	64519
8069	S	S	E	N	1975	94550
8071	S	D	E	L	1972	49487
8071	S	D	E	N	1972	49487
8072	S	D	E	N	1973	56172
8072	S	E	E	N	1973	56172
8072	S	S	E	N	1973	56172
8072	S	T	E	N	1973	56172
8072	S	D	E	N	1975	94661
8072	S	T	E	N	1975	94661
8078	A	S	E	N	1974	94637
8078	T	S	E	N	1974	94637
8083	S	D	R	N	1973	51606
8084	S	D	R	N	1973	55338
8084	S	D	E	N	1974	59276
8084	S	D	E	N	1975	94550
8087	S	D	E	N	1975	90396
8095	D	S	E	N	1965	87703
8095	S	D	R	N	1975	81273
8095	S	D	E	N	1975	94088
8096	L	D	R	N	1973	64519
8096	S	D	R	N	1970	55102
8096	S	D	E	N	1972	55103
8096	S	D	R	N	1973	64519
8096	S	D	E	N	1975	94550
8098	S	D	E	N	1974	53865
8106	A	T	E	N	1976	100646
8106	S	S	R	N	1970	53106
8106	S	S	E	N	1972	53107
8106	S	D	E	N	1974	54594
8108	S	D	R	N	1973	50724
8108	S	D	E	N	1973	53025
8133	A	D	E	N	1973	67289
8133	A	D	E	N	1972	75431
8133	A	T	E	N	1974	84007
8133	A	T	E	N	1976	100646
8133	D	D	E	N	1975	65858
8133	L	D	E	N	1975	65858
8133	S	S	R	N	1970	53106
8133	S	S	E	N	1972	53107
8133	T	D	E	N	1971	62269
8133	T	E	E	N	1971	62269
8133	T	D	E	N	1972	75431
8141	L	D	E	N	1973	51768
8141	L	D	E	N	1975	90018
8141	S	D	E	N	1971	59951
8157	S	D	E	L	1971	57502
8157	S	D	E	N	1971	57502
8169	S	S	E	N	1972	87886
8172	A	S	E	N	1972	53187
8175	L	D	R	N	1971	53312
8175	L	D	E	N	1973	53313
8175	S	D	R	N	1971	53312
8175	S	D	E	N	1973	53313
8176	L	D	R	N	1971	53312
8176	L	D	E	N	1973	53313
8176	S	D	R	N	1971	53312
8176	S	D	E	N	1973	53313
8177	L	D	R	N	1971	53312
8177	L	D	E	N	1973	53313
8177	S	D	R	N	1971	53312
8177	S	D	E	N	1973	53313
8178	L	D	R	N	1971	53312
8178	L	D	E	N	1973	53313
8178	S	D	R	N	1971	53312
8178	S	D	E	N	1973	53313
8179	S	D	R	N	1970	55102
8179	S	D	E	N	1972	55103
8179	S	S	E	N	1975	94550
8180	L	D	R	N	1973	64519
8180	S	D	R	N	1970	55102
8180	S	D	E	N	1972	55103
8180	S	D	R	N	1973	64519
8180	S	D	E	N	1975	94550
8187	S	T	E	N	1971	83795
8187	S	D	E	N	1975	94661
8187	S	T	E	N	1975	94661
8188	S	D	E	N	1970	63884
8189	D	D	E	L	1973	50538
8189	S	D	E	L	1973	50538
8189	S	E	E	L	1973	50538
8192	S	S	E	N	1974	61168
8214	S	D	E	N	1974	53865
8223	S	D	E	N	1973	56172
8223	S	E	E	N	1973	56172
8223	S	T	E	N	1973	56172
8223	S	D	E	N	1971	61726
8223	S	S	E	N	1971	61726
8223	S	D	E	N	1975	94661
8223	S	T	E	N	1975	94661
8228	L	D	R	N	1971	76499
8228	L	T	R	N	1971	76499
8228	L	D	E	N	1971	91563
8228	L	T	E	N	1971	91563
8228	S	D	R	N	1970	55102
8228	S	D	E	N	1972	55103
8228	S	D	R	N	1971	76499
8228	S	T	R	N	1971	76499

Substance Number	Phys. State	Subject	Language	Temperature	Year	EPIC Number
102-8228	S	D	E	N	1971	91563
8228	S	T	E	N	1971	91563
8229	S	D	R	N	1970	55102
8229	S	D	E	N	1972	55103
8230	S	D	R	N	1970	55102
8230	S	D	E	N	1972	55103
8231	S	D	R	N	1970	55102
8231	S	D	E	N	1972	55103
8241	S	D	E	N	1943	61285
8248	S	D	R	N	1970	55102
8248	S	D	E	N	1972	55103
8249	S	D	R	N	1970	55102
8249	S	D	E	N	1972	55103
8310	S	D	E	N	1975	94550
8335	L	D	R	N	1973	64519
8335	S	D	R	N	1973	64519
8374	S	D	E	N	1974	88681
8380	L	D	E	H	1975	90018
8381	L	D	E	N	1975	90018
8382	L	D	E	N	1975	90018
8383	A	T	E	N	1974	84007
8420	S	S	E	N	1972	87889
8437	S	D	E	N	1974	88681
8438	S	D	E	N	1974	88681
8466	S	D	E	N	1970	63884
8468	S	D	E	N	1970	63884
104-0006	L	S	E	N	1972	57870
0006	L	D	E	N	1975	80287
0006	L	T	E	N	1975	80287
0006	S	S	E	N	1972	57870
0006	S	D	E	N	1974	67107
0007	S	S	E	H	1967	68374
0007	S	S	E	N	1967	68374
0007	S	S	E	H	1971	87884
0013	S	D	R	N	1972	59071
0013	S	D	E	N	1972	59072
0013	S	D	E	N	1974	61339
0021	L	S	R	H	1966	95131
0021	L	S	E	H	1966	96497
0021	S	S	R	N	1966	95131
0021	S	S	E	N	1966	96497
0022	D	D	E	N	1971	59999
0022	L	D	E	N	1975	80287
0022	L	T	E	N	1975	80287
0031	L	D	E	N	1975	80287
0031	L	T	E	N	1975	80287
0049	S	D	R	H	1974	66744
0049	S	D	R	N	1974	66744
0049	S	T	R	H	1974	66744
0049	S	T	R	N	1974	66744
0049	S	D	E	H	1975	66745
0049	S	D	E	N	1975	66745
0049	S	T	E	H	1975	66745
0049	S	T	E	N	1975	66745
0049	S	S	E	N	1969	68271
0049	S	D	R	N	1972	76508
0049	S	E	R	N	1972	76508
0049	S	D	E	N	1972	91530
0049	S	E	E	N	1972	91530
0053	L	S	E	N	1972	57870
0053	L	D	E	N	1975	80287
0053	L	T	E	N	1975	80287
0053	S	S	E	N	1972	57870
0067	S	S	E	N	1972	57870
0069	L	D	R	N	1973	57010
0104	S	D	E	N	1974	54024
0104	S	S	E	N	1974	54024
0104	S	T	E	N	1974	54024
0105	L	S	E	N	1972	57870
0105	S	S	E	N	1972	57870
0106	L	S	E	N	1972	57870
0106	L	D	E	N	1975	80287
0106	L	T	E	N	1975	80287
0106	S	S	E	N	1972	57870
0196	S	S	E	N	1969	68271
0249	S	D	R	H	1972	94899
0249	S	D	R	N	1972	94899
0249	S	D	E	H	1973	95896
0249	S	D	E	N	1973	95896
0295	S	S	E	N	1971	87884
0409	S	D	R	N	1971	76503
0409	S	T	R	N	1971	76503
0409	S	D	E	N	1971	91564
0409	S	T	E	N	1971	91564
0471	S	D	E	N	1976	96888
0471	S	E	E	N	1976	96888
0572	S	D	R	N	1971	76503
0572	S	T	R	N	1971	76503
0572	S	D	E	N	1971	91564
0572	S	T	E	N	1971	91564
0573	S	D	R	N	1971	76503
0573	S	T	R	N	1971	76503
0573	S	D	E	N	1971	91564
0573	S	T	E	N	1971	91564
0574	S	D	R	N	1971	76503
0574	S	T	R	N	1971	76503
0574	S	D	E	N	1971	91564
0574	S	T	E	N	1971	91564
0575	S	D	R	N	1971	76503
0575	S	T	R	N	1971	76503

Substance Number	Phys. State	Subject	Language	Temperature	Year	EPIC Number
104-0575	S	D	E	N	1971	91564
0575	S	T	E	N	1971	91564
8010	L	D	E	N	1975	88234
8010	S	D	R	N	1967	72953
8010	S	S	E	N	1971	87884
8011	L	D	E	N	1975	88234
8015	S	S	E	N	1960	65977
8016	S	D	E	N	1974	53865
8042	D	D	R	N	1972	62716
8042	D	S	R	N	1972	62716
8042	D	D	E	N	1973	65312
8042	D	S	E	N	1973	65312
8042	L	D	R	H	1969	61867
8042	L	D	R	N	1969	61867
8042	S	D	R	N	1973	57802
8042	S	D	E	N	1974	57803
8042	S	D	E	L	1973	59900
8042	S	E	E	L	1973	59900
8042	S	T	E	L	1973	59900
8042	S	D	F	N	1971	61672
8042	S	E	F	N	1971	61672
8042	S	T	F	N	1971	61672
8042	S	S	E	N	1974	62277
8042	S	D	R	N	1966	62300
8042	S	D	E	N	1974	62301
8042	S	D	R	N	1972	62716
8042	S	D	E	N	1973	65312
8042	S	S	E	L	1966	66068
8042	S	S	E	N	1966	66068
8042	S	D	E	N	1962	75928
8042	S	T	E	N	1962	75928
8042	S	D	E	N	1975	96857
8042	S	T	E	N	1975	96857
8042	T	S	E	N	1966	66068
8045	D	D	E	L	1973	52709
8045	D	D	O	N	1972	61133
8045	D	D	R	L	1972	62298
8045	D	D	R	N	1972	62298
8045	D	D	E	L	1973	62299
8045	D	S	E	N	1966	66068
8045	D	D	E	N	1975	88288
8045	L	D	R	H	1969	61867
8045	L	D	R	N	1969	61867
8045	L	S	R	N	1972	62298
8045	L	S	E	N	1973	62299
8045	L	D	R	N	1972	63429
8045	L	D	E	N	1973	67081
8045	S	D	R	N	1971	49758
8045	S	D	R	N	1972	52221
8045	S	D	E	L	1973	52709
8045	S	S	E	N	1972	56769
8045	S	D	R	N	1972	59805
8045	S	D	E	N	1973	59806
8045	S	D	R	N	1971	61826
8045	S	D	E	N	1971	61827
8045	S	S	E	N	1974	62277
8045	S	D	R	N	1966	62300
8045	S	D	E	N	1974	62301
8045	S	D	R	N	1973	62728
8045	S	T	R	N	1973	62728
8045	S	S	E	N	1975	63321
8045	S	T	E	N	1975	63321
8045	S	D	E	N	1970	63587
8045	S	E	E	N	1970	63587
8045	S	D	E	L	1972	63966
8045	S	D	E	N	1973	65324
8045	S	T	E	N	1973	65324
8045	S	S	E	L	1966	66068
8045	S	S	E	N	1966	66068
8045	S	D	E	N	1962	75928
8045	S	T	E	N	1962	75928
8045	S	D	R	N	1972	76534
8045	S	D	E	N	1974	87918
8045	S	T	E	N	1974	87918
8045	S	D	E	N	1972	91537
8045	S	D	G	N	1975	91993
8045	S	E	E	N	1975	92037
8045	S	T	E	N	1975	92037
8045	S	D	E	N	1975	96857
8045	S	T	E	N	1975	96857
8045	S	D	E	N	1975	98084
8045	S	E	E	N	1975	98084
8045	S	D	E	N	1968	98762
8045	T	S	E	N	1966	66068
8068	S	D	R	H	1971	76476
8068	S	D	R	L	1971	76476
8068	S	D	R	N	1971	76476
8068	S	S	R	L	1971	76476
8068	S	S	R	N	1971	76476
8068	S	D	E	H	1971	91521
8068	S	D	E	L	1971	91521
8068	S	D	E	N	1971	91521
8068	S	S	E	L	1971	91521
8068	S	S	E	N	1971	91521
8083	S	S	E	N	1966	87721
8083	S	S	E	N	1972	87886
8099	S	D	R	H	1972	51232
8099	S	D	R	N	1972	51232
8099	S	D	O	H	1973	58144
8099	S	D	O	N	1973	58144
8106	S	D	E	N	1973	49520

Phys. State: **A.** Amorphous; **C.** Superconductive; **D.** Doped; **F.** Fibrous or Whisker; **G.** Gas; **I.** Ionized or Plasma; **L.** Liquid; **P.** Powder or Particle; **S.** Solid; **T.** Thin Film
Subject: **D.** Data; **E.** Experiment; **S.** Survey (Review, Compendium, etc.); **T.** Theory
Language: **E.** English; **F.** French; **G.** German; **O.** Other Languages; **R.** Russian
Temperature: **L.** Low (0 to 75K); **N.** Normal (75 to 1273K); **H.** High (above 1273K)

Substance Number	Phys. State	Subject	Language	Temperature	Year	EPIC Number
104-8108	D	D	R	N	1972	52222
8108	D	D	R	N	1973	54907
8108	D	T	O	N	1971	59997
8108	D	D	R	N	1972	62298
8108	D	D	E	N	1973	62299
8108	D	D	E	N	1968	98762
8108	S	D	R	N	1972	49727
8108	S	D	R	N	1973	54907
8108	S	S	E	N	1972	56769
8108	S	D	R	N	1971	58992
8108	S	D	E	N	1972	59135
8108	S	T	E	N	1972	59135
8108	S	D	E	N	1971	59999
8108	S	E	E	N	1971	59999
8108	S	S	R	N	1972	62298
8108	S	S	E	N	1973	62299
8108	S	S	E	L	1966	66068
8108	S	S	E	N	1966	66068
8108	S	D	O	N	1970	86322
8108	S	D	E	N	1973	86323
8108	S	D	E	N	1974	90003
8108	S	D	E	N	1968	98762
8108	T	D	R	N	1974	87931
8108	T	D	R	N	1974	89245
8108	T	D	E	N	1974	89246
8108	T	D	R	N	1975	93405
8108	T	D	E	N	1975	93406
8108	T	D	R	N	1975	93407
8108	T	D	E	N	1975	93408
8109	D	T	O	N	1971	59997
8109	S	D	R	N	1972	49727
8109	S	D	R	N	1973	52541
8109	S	D	E	N	1974	53676
8109	S	S	E	N	1972	56769
8109	S	D	E	N	1972	59135
8109	S	T	E	N	1972	59135
8109	S	D	R	N	1971	60192
8109	S	S	R	N	1972	62298
8109	S	S	E	N	1973	62299
8109	S	T	R	N	1972	85970
8109	S	T	E	N	1972	85971
8109	S	D	O	N	1970	86322
8109	S	D	E	N	1973	86323
8109	T	D	R	N	1973	52541
8109	T	D	E	N	1974	53676
8109	T	T	R	N	1973	62861
8109	T	T	E	N	1973	65168
8109	T	D	R	N	1975	101557
8109	T	T	R	N	1975	101557
8109	T	D	E	N	1975	101558
8109	T	T	E	N	1975	101558
8136	D	D	F	N	1974	55973
8136	S	D	F	N	1973	50942
8136	S	D	F	N	1974	55973
8136	S	T	F	N	1973	57939
8139	S	D	F	N	1973	50942
8139	S	T	F	N	1973	57939
8156	S	D	R	H	1972	51232
8156	S	D	R	N	1972	51232
8156	S	D	O	H	1973	58144
8156	S	D	O	N	1973	58144
8157	S	D	R	H	1972	51232
8157	S	D	R	N	1972	51232
8158	S	D	R	L	1972	51237
8159	S	D	R	N	1972	51237
8176	S	D	E	N	1973	52048
8194	D	S	E	N	1972	56769
8194	S	D	R	N	1971	60192
8194	S	S	R	N	1972	62298
8194	S	S	E	N	1973	62299
8194	S	D	E	N	1972	68995
8217	A	D	E	N	1971	60140
8217	S	D	E	N	1971	60140
8217	T	D	E	N	1971	60140
8218	A	D	R	N	1971	60139
8218	S	D	R	N	1971	60139
8218	T	D	R	N	1971	60139
8219	A	D	R	N	1971	60139
8219	A	D	E	N	1971	60140
8219	S	D	R	N	1971	60139
8219	S	D	E	N	1971	60140
8219	S	D	R	N	1970	61240
8219	T	D	R	N	1971	60139
8219	T	D	E	N	1971	60140
8220	A	D	R	N	1971	60139
8220	A	D	E	N	1971	60140
8220	S	D	R	N	1971	60139
8220	S	D	E	N	1971	60140
8220	T	D	R	N	1971	60139
8220	T	D	E	N	1971	60140
8254	S	D	F	N	1972	60959
8254	S	E	F	N	1972	60959
8269	D	D	R	H	1971	65450
8269	D	D	R	N	1971	65450
8269	D	D	E	H	1971	65451
8269	D	D	E	N	1971	65451
8269	S	D	R	H	1971	65450
8269	S	D	R	N	1971	65450
8269	S	D	E	H	1971	65451
8269	S	D	E	N	1971	65451
8272	S	D	R	N	1973	62447
104-8272	S	T	E	N	1975	99100
8315	S	D	E	L	1971	57502
8315	S	D	E	N	1971	57502
8320	L	D	E	H	1975	90018
8323	L	D	E	N	1975	90018
8366	S	S	E	N	1971	87884
8370	S	S	E	N	1966	66068
8411	S	D	E	N	1891	97023
8411	S	E	E	N	1891	97023
8412	S	D	E	N	1891	97023
8412	S	E	E	N	1891	97023
8413	S	D	E	N	1891	97023
8413	S	E	E	N	1891	97023
8414	S	D	E	N	1891	97023
8414	S	E	E	N	1891	97023
8415	S	D	E	N	1891	97023
8415	S	E	E	N	1891	97023
8416	S	D	E	N	1891	97023
8416	S	E	E	N	1891	97023
8418	S	D	R	N	1971	76486
8418	S	D	E	N	1971	91505
8419	S	D	R	N	1971	76486
8419	S	D	E	N	1971	91505
8420	S	D	R	H	1971	76476
8420	S	D	R	L	1971	76476
8420	S	D	R	N	1971	76476
8420	S	D	E	H	1971	91521
8420	S	D	E	L	1971	91521
8420	S	D	E	N	1971	91521
8446	S	D	E	H	1976	102175
8446	S	D	E	N	1976	102175
106-0004	S	D	R	H	1974	66744
0004	S	D	R	N	1974	66744
0004	S	T	R	H	1974	66744
0004	S	T	R	N	1974	66744
0004	S	D	E	H	1975	66745
0004	S	D	E	N	1975	66745
0004	S	T	E	H	1975	66745
0004	S	T	E	N	1975	66745
0004	S	S	E	H	1969	68271
0004	S	S	E	N	1969	68271
0006	L	S	E	N	1972	57870
0006	L	D	E	N	1975	80287
0006	L	T	E	N	1975	80287
0006	S	D	E	N	1974	54024
0006	S	S	E	N	1974	54024
0006	S	T	E	N	1974	54024
0006	S	S	E	N	1972	57870
0024	L	D	E	N	1975	80287
0024	L	T	E	N	1975	80287
0024	S	D	E	N	1974	54024
0024	S	S	E	N	1974	54024
0024	S	T	E	N	1974	54024
0024	S	S	E	N	1972	57870
0026	S	D	E	N	1974	54024
0026	S	S	E	N	1974	54024
0026	S	T	E	N	1974	54024
0035	D	S	E	N	1965	87702
0035	S	S	E	L	1965	87702
0035	S	S	E	N	1965	87702
0035	S	S	E	N	1968	87828
0035	S	S	E	N	1971	87887
0035	S	D	E	L	1975	91273
0035	S	D	E	N	1975	91273
0035	S	E	R	L	1975	91273
0035	S	E	R	N	1975	91273
0035	S	D	E	L	1975	95910
0035	S	D	E	N	1975	95910
0035	S	E	E	L	1975	95910
0035	S	E	E	N	1975	95910
0035	S	S	E	H	1962	99561
0035	S	S	E	N	1962	99561
0036	L	D	R	N	1973	55758
0036	L	D	E	N	1973	57072
0036	L	D	E	N	1973	57781
0036	T	D	R	N	1972	49937
0057	P	S	E	N	1966	68325
0057	S	S	E	N	1969	68271
0057	S	S	E	N	1966	68325
0060	L	D	R	N	1973	57010
0062	T	D	E	N	1974	58955
0062	T	T	E	N	1974	58955
0068	A	D	R	H	1972	76524
0068	S	D	R	N	1971	60135
0068	S	D	E	N	1971	60136
0068	S	D	R	N	1972	76524
0068	S	T	R	H	1972	76524
0068	S	T	R	N	1972	76524
0068	S	D	E	H	1972	91510
0068	S	D	E	N	1972	91510
0068	S	T	E	H	1972	91510
0068	S	T	E	N	1972	91510
0081	D	T	R	N	1975	90140
0081	D	T	E	N	1975	90141
0081	S	D	E	H	1971	49788
0081	S	S	E	N	1972	61595
0104	D	D	R	N	1973	51556
0104	D	D	E	N	1973	53687
0104	L	D	R	H	1970	53296
0104	L	D	E	H	1972	53297
106-0104	L	S	E	H	1971	87872
0104	L	D	R	H	1975	91346
0104	S	D	R	H	1970	53296
0104	S	D	R	N	1970	53296
0104	S	D	E	H	1972	53297
0104	S	D	E	N	1972	53297
0104	S	D	R	N	1972	59068
0104	S	D	E	N	1972	59069
0104	S	D	F	N	1970	59704
0104	S	E	F	N	1970	59704
0104	S	S	E	H	1971	87872
0104	S	S	E	N	1971	87872
0104	T	D	R	N	1973	51556
0104	T	D	E	N	1973	53687
0125	S	D	E	N	1973	50707
0125	S	D	O	H	1973	58144
0125	S	D	O	N	1973	58144
0125	S	D	E	N	1964	93287
0125	S	S	E	N	1964	93287
0127	S	S	R	N	1971	60135
0127	S	S	E	N	1971	60136
0127	S	S	R	H	1972	76524
0127	S	S	R	N	1972	76524
0127	S	S	E	H	1972	91510
0127	S	S	E	N	1972	91510
0138	T	D	E	N	1974	58955
0138	T	T	E	N	1974	58955
0157	D	S	E	N	1972	57870
0157	S	S	E	N	1972	57870
0158	D	D	E	N	1975	80287
0158	D	T	E	N	1975	80287
0158	L	D	R	N	1973	55758
0158	L	S	R	N	1973	55758
0158	L	D	E	N	1973	57781
0158	L	S	E	N	1973	57781
0158	L	D	E	N	1975	80287
0158	L	T	E	N	1975	80287
0158	S	S	E	N	1972	57870
0158	S	S	E	N	1972	87890
0165	L	D	E	N	1975	80287
0165	L	T	E	N	1975	80287
0203	L	D	E	N	1975	80287
0203	L	T	E	N	1975	80287
0205	S	D	O	H	1973	58144
0205	S	D	O	N	1973	58144
0205	S	D	E	N	1964	93287
0205	S	S	E	N	1964	93287
0226	S	D	E	N	1964	93287
0226	S	S	E	N	1964	93287
0308	S	D	E	N	1973	50707
0308	S	D	O	H	1973	58144
0308	S	D	O	N	1973	58144
0308	S	D	E	N	1964	93287
0308	S	S	E	N	1964	93287
0309	P	S	E	N	1966	87721
0309	S	S	E	N	1966	87721
0309	S	S	E	N	1972	87886
0309	S	D	E	N	1964	93287
0309	S	S	E	N	1964	93287
0363	D	D	R	N	1973	51550
0363	D	D	E	N	1973	53681
0363	D	S	E	N	1963	64232
0363	D	S	E	N	1967	66156
0363	S	D	E	N	1973	57563
0363	S	T	E	N	1973	57563
0363	S	S	E	N	1969	68271
0363	T	D	E	N	1974	53750
0363	T	S	E	N	1974	53750
0363	T	S	E	N	1967	66156
0423	S	D	O	H	1973	58144
0423	S	D	O	N	1973	58144
0452	S	S	E	N	1964	93287
0505	L	D	R	N	1971	76462
0505	L	D	E	N	1971	91582
0523	S	D	E	N	1972	53078
0639	S	D	E	N	1964	93287
0639	S	S	E	N	1964	93287
0640	S	D	O	H	1973	58144
0640	S	D	O	N	1973	58144
0797	T	D	E	N	1974	58955
0797	T	T	E	N	1974	58955
0937	D	D	R	N	1971	76469
0937	D	D	E	N	1971	91495
0937	S	D	R	N	1971	76469
0937	S	D	R	N	1971	76485
0937	S	S	R	N	1971	76485
0937	S	D	E	N	1971	91495
0937	S	D	E	N	1971	91504
0937	S	S	E	N	1971	91504
0941	S	D	E	N	1975	94550
1027	S	D	R	N	1973	56473
1027	S	D	E	N	1964	93287
1027	S	S	E	N	1964	93287
1062	S	S	E	N	1966	87721
1062	S	S	E	H	1972	87886
1062	S	S	E	N	1972	87886
1079	S	D	R	N	1967	53069
1079	S	D	E	N	1972	53070
1083	S	D	R	N	1973	50037
1085	S	D	E	N	1973	56345
1085	S	D	E	N	1975	94550

Phys. State: **A.** Amorphous; **C.** Superconductive; **D.** Doped; **F.** Fibrous or Whisker; **G.** Gas; **I.** Ionized or Plasma; **L.** Liquid; **P.** Powder or Particle; **S.** Solid; **T.** Thin Film
Subject: **D.** Data; **E.** Experiment; **S.** Survey (Review, Compendium, etc.); **T.** Theory
Language: **E.** English; **F.** French; **G.** German; **O.** Other Languages; **R.** Russian
Temperature: **L.** Low (0 to 75K); **N.** Normal (75 to 1273K); **H.** High (above 1273K)

Substance Number	Phys. State	Subject	Language	Temperature	Year	EPIC Number
106-1287	S	D	R	N	1965	76400
1287	S	T	R	N	1965	76400
1287	S	D	E	N	1965	91743
1287	S	T	E	N	1965	91743
1287	S	S	E	N	1964	93287
8001	D	D	E	N	1972	53071
8001	D	T	E	N	1972	53071
8001	D	D	R	N	1973	54954
8001	D	D	R	N	1972	76512
8001	D	D	E	N	1972	91556
8001	S	T	R	N	1973	50063
8001	S	T	E	N	1973	51419
8001	S	D	R	N	1973	55288
8001	S	T	R	N	1973	55288
8001	S	D	E	N	1974	59247
8001	S	T	E	N	1974	59247
8001	S	D	R	N	1971	61477
8001	S	D	E	N	1971	65921
8001	S	D	R	N	1972	76505
8001	S	T	R	N	1972	76505
8001	S	D	E	N	1972	91528
8001	S	T	E	N	1972	91528
8014	S	S	E	N	1960	65977
8018	S	D	R	N	1966	62300
8018	S	D	E	N	1974	62301
8033	D	D	R	N	1971	67327
8033	S	D	R	N	1971	67327
8040	D	S	E	N	1963	87710
8040	S	D	R	N	1973	55300
8040	S	T	E	N	1973	57563
8040	S	D	E	N	1974	59225
8040	S	D	E	N	1972	59904
8040	S	E	E	N	1972	59904
8040	S	T	E	N	1972	59904
8040	S	S	E	N	1972	59933
8040	S	S	E	N	1969	68271
8040	S	S	E	N	1963	87710
8041	D	S	E	N	1967	68371
8041	P	S	E	N	1967	68371
8041	S	D	E	N	1974	54024
8041	S	S	E	N	1974	54024
8041	S	T	E	N	1974	54024
8041	S	S	E	N	1969	68271
8041	S	S	E	N	1967	68371
8041	S	D	R	L	1973	71674
8041	S	D	R	N	1973	71674
8041	S	T	R	L	1973	71674
8041	S	T	R	N	1973	71674
8041	S	D	E	L	1973	82272
8041	S	D	E	N	1973	82272
8041	S	T	E	L	1973	82272
8041	S	T	E	N	1973	82272
8041	S	S	E	N	1962	87659
8041	S	S	E	N	1972	87823
8041	T	T	R	N	1972	62620
8041	T	T	E	N	1972	64435
8049	S	D	E	N	1972	49915
8074	D	D	R	N	1973	50355
8074	D	D	E	N	1973	50356
8074	S	D	R	N	1973	50355
8074	S	D	E	N	1973	50356
8074	S	D	R	N	1971	64585
8074	S	T	R	N	1971	64585
8074	S	D	E	N	1971	68414
8074	S	T	E	N	1971	68414
8075	S	D	R	N	1971	64585
8075	S	T	R	N	1971	64585
8075	S	D	R	L	1970	67624
8075	S	D	R	N	1970	67624
8075	S	D	E	N	1971	68414
8075	S	T	E	N	1971	68414
8081	D	D	R	N	1973	52556
8081	L	D	R	H	1970	53296
8081	L	D	E	H	1972	53297
8081	L	D	R	H	1975	91346
8081	S	D	R	H	1970	53296
8081	S	D	R	N	1970	53296
8081	S	D	E	H	1972	53297
8081	S	D	E	N	1972	53297
8081	S	D	R	N	1973	55711
8081	S	D	R	N	1974	93465
8081	S	D	E	N	1974	93466
8084	L	D	R	H	1970	53296
8084	L	D	E	H	1972	53297
8084	L	D	R	H	1975	91346
8084	S	D	R	N	1972	49759
8084	S	D	R	H	1970	53296
8084	S	D	R	N	1970	53296
8084	S	D	E	H	1972	53297
8084	S	D	E	N	1972	53297
8084	S	D	R	N	1972	59068
8084	S	D	E	N	1972	59069
8084	S	D	R	L	1972	60544
8084	S	D	R	N	1972	60544
8084	S	D	E	L	1972	60545
8084	S	D	E	N	1972	60545
8084	S	E	R	N	1975	94018
8084	S	E	E	N	1975	94019
8118	S	D	E	N	1973	49529
8119	S	D	E	N	1973	49529
8125	S	D	R	N	1972	49559

Substance Number	Phys. State	Subject	Language	Temperature	Year	EPIC Number
106-8126	S	D	R	N	1972	49559
8127	S	D	R	N	1972	58679
8127	S	S	E	N	1972	87823
8128	D	S	E	N	1967	68371
8128	S	D	R	N	1971	52298
8128	S	D	E	N	1971	52299
8128	S	S	E	N	1967	68371
8128	S	D	R	L	1973	71674
8128	S	D	R	N	1973	71674
8128	S	T	R	L	1973	71674
8128	S	T	R	N	1973	71674
8128	S	D	E	L	1973	82272
8128	S	D	E	N	1973	82272
8128	S	T	E	L	1973	82272
8128	S	T	E	N	1973	82272
8128	S	S	E	N	1972	87823
8143	D	D	R	N	1973	50355
8143	D	D	E	N	1973	50356
8143	S	D	E	N	1972	49865
8143	S	D	R	N	1973	50355
8143	S	D	E	N	1973	50356
8143	S	D	R	N	1971	64585
8143	S	T	R	N	1971	64585
8143	S	D	E	N	1971	68414
8143	S	T	E	N	1971	68414
8143	T	D	R	N	1973	58553
8149	S	D	E	L	1973	50004
8149	S	D	E	N	1973	50004
8149	S	D	E	N	1973	50815
8153	S	D	F	N	1973	50026
8164	S	D	R	N	1973	50355
8164	S	D	E	N	1973	50356
8165	S	D	R	N	1973	50355
8165	S	D	E	N	1973	50356
8182	S	D	E	L	1975	92154
8182	S	D	E	N	1975	92154
8194	S	D	R	N	1973	50652
8195	S	D	R	N	1973	50652
8196	S	D	R	N	1973	50652
8197	S	D	R	N	1973	50652
8208	S	D	E	N	1973	50815
8234	S	S	E	N	1972	87823
8237	S	D	E	N	1974	57860
8261	S	D	R	N	1973	51732
8261	S	D	E	N	1973	79136
8262	S	D	R	N	1973	51732
8262	S	D	R	N	1971	76478
8262	S	D	E	N	1973	79136
8262	S	D	E	N	1971	91502
8270	S	D	R	N	1973	58519
8295	S	D	E	N	1973	52233
8312	S	D	E	N	1968	53358
8312	S	D	R	N	1973	58519
8322	S	D	E	N	1973	52943
8325	S	D	E	N	1972	52993
8333	S	D	R	N	1971	53129
8333	S	D	E	N	1972	53130
8334	S	D	R	N	1971	53129
8334	S	D	E	N	1972	53130
8335	S	D	F	N	1970	84029
8335	S	D	R	N	1974	93465
8335	S	T	R	N	1974	93465
8335	S	D	E	N	1974	93466
8335	S	T	E	N	1974	93466
8338	L	D	R	N	1971	53312
8338	L	D	E	N	1973	53313
8338	S	D	R	N	1971	53312
8338	S	D	E	N	1973	53313
8338	S	D	R	N	1970	55102
8338	S	D	E	N	1972	55103
8339	L	D	R	N	1971	53312
8339	L	D	E	N	1973	53313
8339	S	D	R	N	1971	53312
8339	S	D	E	N	1973	53313
8340	L	D	R	N	1971	53312
8340	L	D	E	N	1973	53313
8340	S	D	R	N	1971	53312
8340	S	D	E	N	1973	53313
8340	S	D	R	N	1970	55102
8340	S	D	E	N	1972	55103
8341	L	D	R	N	1971	53312
8341	L	D	E	N	1973	53313
8341	S	D	R	N	1971	53312
8341	S	D	E	N	1973	53313
8344	S	D	R	N	1970	55102
8344	S	D	E	N	1972	55103
8347	S	S	E	N	1973	53420
8347	S	D	E	H	1973	65651
8347	S	D	E	N	1973	65651
8347	S	T	E	H	1973	65651
8347	S	T	E	N	1973	65651
8348	S	S	E	N	1973	53420
8348	S	D	E	H	1973	65651
8348	S	D	E	N	1973	65651
8348	S	T	E	H	1973	65651
8348	S	T	E	N	1973	65651
8349	S	S	E	N	1973	53420
8349	S	D	E	H	1973	65651
8349	S	D	E	N	1973	65651
8349	S	T	E	H	1973	65651
8349	S	T	E	N	1973	65651

Substance Number	Phys. State	Subject	Language	Temperature	Year	EPIC Number
106-8392	S	D	E	N	1967	75175
8393	S	D	E	N	1967	75175
8394	S	D	R	N	1973	58519
8394	S	D	E	N	1967	75175
8453	S	D	R	N	1970	55102
8453	S	D	E	N	1972	55103
8454	S	D	R	N	1970	55102
8454	S	D	E	N	1972	55103
8455	L	D	R	N	1972	76551
8455	L	T	R	N	1972	76551
8455	L	D	E	N	1972	91546
8455	L	T	E	N	1972	91546
8455	S	D	R	N	1970	55102
8455	S	D	E	N	1972	55103
8455	S	D	R	N	1972	76551
8455	S	T	R	N	1972	76551
8455	S	D	E	N	1972	91546
8455	S	T	E	N	1972	91546
8456	S	D	R	N	1970	55102
8456	S	D	E	N	1972	55103
8457	S	D	R	N	1970	55102
8457	S	D	E	N	1972	55103
8458	L	D	R	N	1972	76551
8458	L	T	R	N	1972	76551
8458	L	D	E	N	1972	91546
8458	L	T	E	N	1972	91546
8458	S	D	R	N	1970	55102
8458	S	D	E	N	1972	55103
8458	S	D	R	N	1972	76551
8458	S	T	R	N	1972	76551
8458	S	D	E	N	1972	91546
8458	S	T	E	N	1972	91546
8459	S	D	R	N	1970	55102
8459	S	D	E	N	1972	55103
8467	S	D	R	N	1973	55288
8467	S	T	R	N	1973	55288
8467	S	D	E	N	1974	59247
8467	S	T	E	N	1974	59247
8467	S	D	R	N	1968	61308
8467	S	D	E	N	1968	61309
8510	S	D	E	N	1974	53865
8511	S	D	E	N	1974	53865
8515	L	D	E	N	1972	52135
8515	S	D	E	N	1972	52135
8516	L	D	E	N	1972	52135
8516	S	D	E	N	1972	52135
8521	S	D	R	N	1971	64585
8521	S	T	R	N	1971	64585
8521	S	D	E	N	1971	68414
8521	S	T	E	N	1971	68414
8523	S	S	E	N	1960	65977
8524	S	S	E	N	1960	65977
8527	T	D	R	N	1973	56329
8529	S	D	R	N	1973	56861
8529	S	D	E	N	1973	57295
8529	S	D	R	N	1974	58280
8529	S	D	E	N	1974	77075
8531	S	S	E	N	1972	87823
8535	S	T	E	N	1974	66363
8545	S	D	R	N	1972	68551
8545	S	T	R	N	1972	68551
8545	S	D	E	N	1972	68552
8545	S	T	E	N	1972	68552
8549	S	D	R	N	1973	58519
8561	S	D	E	N	1964	93287
8562	S	D	E	N	1964	93287
8562	S	S	E	N	1964	93287
8564	D	S	E	N	1974	87606
8564	S	S	E	N	1974	87606
8567	S	D	R	N	1973	54689
8589	T	D	R	N	1973	56055
8595	S	D	E	L	1971	57502
8595	S	D	E	N	1971	57502
8611	S	D	E	N	1966	85403
8634	S	D	E	L	1971	57502
8634	S	D	E	N	1971	57502
8641	S	D	R	N	1973	51609
8642	S	D	R	N	1973	51724
8642	S	D	R	N	1971	66283
8642	S	D	R	N	1971	76478
8642	S	D	E	N	1971	91502
8643	S	D	R	N	1973	51724
8644	D	D	E	N	1973	53834
8644	S	D	E	H	1973	65651
8644	S	D	E	N	1973	65651
8644	S	T	E	H	1973	65651
8644	S	T	E	N	1973	65651
8646	D	D	R	N	1974	58280
8646	D	D	E	N	1974	77075
8646	S	D	R	N	1974	58280
8646	S	D	E	N	1974	77075
8650	L	D	R	N	1971	76462
8650	L	D	E	H	1975	90018
8650	L	D	E	N	1971	91582
8651	L	D	E	N	1975	90018
8652	L	D	E	N	1975	90018
8653	L	D	R	N	1971	76462
8653	L	D	E	N	1975	90018
8653	L	D	E	N	1971	91582
8658	S	D	R	N	1973	58870
8669	S	D	R	N	1971	66283

Phys. State: **A.** Amorphous; **C.** Superconductive; **D.** Doped; **F.** Fibrous or Whisker; **G.** Gas; **I.** Ionized or Plasma; **L.** Liquid; **P.** Powder or Particle; **S.** Solid; **T.** Thin Film
Subject: **D.** Data; **E.** Experiment; **S.** Survey (Review, Compendium, etc.); **T.** Theory
Language: **E.** English; **F.** French; **G.** German; **O.** Other Languages; **R.** Russian
Temperature: **L.** Low (0 to 75K); **N.** Normal (75 to 1273K); **H.** High (above 1273K)

Substance Number	Phys. State	Subject	Language	Temperature	Year	EPIC Number
106-8752	S	S	E	N	1975	63321
8752	S	T	E	N	1975	63321
8759	S	D	R	N	1971	76478
8759	S	D	E	N	1971	91502
8765	S	D	F	N	1975	98079
8765	S	E	F	N	1975	98079
8769	S	D	E	L	1975	92154
8769	S	D	E	N	1975	92154
8770	S	D	E	L	1975	92154
8770	S	D	E	N	1975	92154
8771	S	D	E	L	1975	92154
8771	S	D	E	N	1975	92154
8811	S	D	R	N	1974	65411
8811	S	T	R	N	1974	65411
8811	S	D	E	N	1975	65412
8811	S	T	E	N	1975	65412
8818	S	D	R	N	1971	66283
8819	S	D	R	N	1971	66283
8820	S	D	R	N	1971	66283
8824	S	D	R	N	1972	68551
8824	S	T	R	N	1972	68551
8824	S	D	E	N	1972	68552
8824	S	T	E	N	1972	68552
8825	S	D	R	N	1972	68551
8825	S	T	R	N	1972	68551
8825	S	D	E	N	1972	68552
8825	S	T	E	N	1972	68552
8832	S	D	E	H	1973	65651
8832	S	D	E	N	1973	65651
8832	S	T	E	H	1973	65651
8832	S	T	E	N	1973	65651
108-0079	S	D	E	N	1974	54324
109-8019	S	D	R	N	1973	52564
8019	S	D	E	N	1973	57789
8020	S	T	R	N	1975	86839
8020	S	T	E	N	1975	86840
8021	S	D	R	N	1973	52564
8021	S	D	E	N	1973	57789
8040	S	D	R	N	1973	52564
8040	S	D	E	N	1973	57789
8041	S	D	R	N	1973	52564
8041	S	D	E	N	1973	57789
8042	S	D	R	N	1973	52564
8042	S	D	E	N	1973	57789
8051	S	D	R	L	1974	60439
8051	S	D	R	N	1974	60439
8051	S	D	E	L	1974	60440
8051	S	D	E	N	1974	60440
8064	S	T	R	N	1975	86839
8064	S	T	E	N	1975	86840
110-0007	S	D	R	N	1967	53069
0007	S	D	E	N	1972	53070
0010	S	D	R	N	1966	59587
0010	S	E	R	N	1966	59587
0010	S	D	E	N	1966	63247
0010	S	E	E	N	1966	63247
0011	D	D	R	N	1973	55830
0011	D	D	E	N	1960	60561
0011	D	E	E	N	1960	60561
0011	D	T	E	N	1960	60561
0011	S	D	R	N	1973	55830
0023	S	D	E	N	1974	54024
0023	S	S	E	N	1974	54024
0023	S	T	E	N	1974	54024
0025	S	D	E	L	1973	50004
0025	S	D	E	N	1973	50004
0025	S	D	R	N	1974	88553
0025	S	D	E	N	1974	94190
0028	D	T	R	N	1975	90140
0028	D	T	E	N	1975	90141
0132	S	D	E	N	1974	54024
0132	S	S	E	N	1974	54024
0132	S	T	E	N	1974	54024
0194	D	T	R	N	1975	90140
0194	D	T	E	N	1975	90141
8015	S	D	R	N	1971	64585
8015	S	T	R	N	1971	64585
8015	S	D	E	N	1971	68414
8015	S	T	E	N	1971	68414
8036	S	D	E	N	1973	49520
8037	S	D	E	N	1973	49520
8038	S	T	E	N	1973	51807
8046	S	D	E	L	1973	50004
8046	S	D	E	N	1973	50004
8046	S	S	E	N	1970	75905
8046	S	D	E	N	1975	91913
8046	S	T	E	N	1975	91913
8047	S	D	E	L	1973	50004
8047	S	D	E	N	1973	50004
8064	S	D	R	N	1971	64585
8064	S	T	R	N	1971	64585
8064	S	D	E	N	1971	68414
8064	S	T	E	N	1971	68414
8082	S	D	R	N	1973	55807
8082	S	D	E	N	1973	56370
8083	S	D	E	N	1973	56370
8112	D	T	R	N	1975	90140
8112	D	T	E	N	1975	90141
110-8112	S	D	F	N	1973	51110
8112	S	S	E	N	1970	75905
8119	D	T	R	N	1975	90140
8119	D	T	E	N	1975	90141
8121	D	T	R	N	1975	90140
8121	D	T	E	N	1975	90141
8123	S	D	F	N	1973	51110
8135	S	D	F	N	1975	98079
8135	S	E	F	N	1975	98079
8181	L	D	E	N	1972	52135
8181	S	D	E	N	1972	52135
8203	S	D	R	N	1973	55807
8204	S	D	R	N	1973	55807
8205	S	D	R	N	1973	55807
8205	S	D	E	N	1973	56370
8215	S	D	G	N	1973	57058
111-0001	S	D	E	N	1973	53044
0008	S	E	E	N	1971	61678
0008	S	D	E	N	1974	62277
0008	S	S	E	L	1971	87884
0008	S	S	E	N	1971	87884
0008	T	D	R	N	1971	59188
0008	T	D	E	N	1971	59189
0015	S	S	E	N	1969	68115
0029	S	D	R	N	1965	76401
0029	S	D	E	N	1965	91742
0050	S	D	E	N	1975	94550
8002	A	S	E	N	1971	49794
8002	A	S	E	N	1970	75887
8002	D	D	R	L	1973	50080
8002	D	D	R	N	1973	50080
8002	D	D	R	N	1972	51113
8002	D	D	E	L	1973	51433
8002	D	D	E	N	1973	51433
8002	D	D	R	N	1972	76506
8002	D	D	E	N	1972	91529
8002	S	D	R	N	1972	76506
8002	S	D	R	N	1972	76521
8002	S	S	R	N	1972	76521
8002	S	T	R	N	1972	76521
8002	S	S	E	N	1962	87670
8002	S	S	E	N	1971	87884
8002	S	S	E	N	1972	87889
8002	S	D	E	N	1972	91507
8002	S	S	E	N	1972	91507
8002	S	T	E	N	1972	91507
8002	S	D	E	N	1972	91529
8007	S	D	R	N	1965	76401
8007	S	D	E	N	1965	91742
8010	L	S	E	N	1974	79184
8015	A	D	E	N	1973	51901
8015	T	D	E	N	1973	51901
8016	L	D	R	N	1973	49578
8016	S	D	R	N	1973	49578
8017	L	D	R	N	1973	49578
8017	S	D	R	N	1973	49578
8018	L	D	R	N	1973	49578
8018	S	D	R	N	1973	49578
8021	A	D	E	N	1973	51901
8021	A	D	E	N	1976	99925
8021	A	T	E	N	1976	99925
8021	L	S	E	N	1969	68115
8021	L	S	E	N	1974	79184
8021	P	S	E	N	1969	68115
8021	S	D	G	L	1971	59513
8021	S	D	G	N	1971	59513
8021	S	E	G	N	1971	59513
8021	S	S	G	L	1971	59513
8021	S	S	G	N	1971	59513
8021	S	D	E	N	1971	59951
8021	S	S	E	N	1969	68115
8021	S	D	R	N	1975	75092
8021	S	D	E	N	1975	91748
8021	T	D	E	N	1973	51901
8021	T	D	E	N	1976	99925
8021	T	T	E	N	1976	99925
8025	S	D	E	N	1973	49999
8031	D	S	E	N	1972	87889
8031	S	S	E	N	1972	87889
8038	S	D	E	N	1974	53865
8041	S	D	R	H	1972	55387
8041	S	D	R	N	1972	55387
8041	S	D	E	H	1974	88429
8041	S	D	E	N	1974	88429
8044	S	D	E	N	1973	65773
8044	S	T	E	N	1973	65773
8055	S	S	E	L	1967	66157
8055	S	S	E	N	1967	66157
8055	S	D	R	N	1971	66283
8057	S	D	R	N	1972	52209
8058	S	S	E	L	1967	66157
8058	S	S	E	N	1967	66157
8065	S	D	E	L	1972	52969
8065	S	D	E	N	1972	52969
8065	S	D	E	L	1972	53158
8065	S	D	E	N	1972	53158
8065	S	D	E	L	1973	53293
8065	S	D	E	N	1973	53293
8071	S	D	E	N	1974	54324
8075	A	D	E	N	1973	51901
111-8075	A	D	E	N	1972	75431
8075	T	D	E	N	1973	51901
8075	T	D	E	N	1973	55106
8075	T	D	E	N	1971	62269
8075	T	E	E	N	1971	62269
8075	T	D	E	N	1972	75431
8077	D	T	E	L	1972	53500
8078	T	D	E	N	1971	53513
8078	T	D	E	N	1971	62269
8079	A	D	E	N	1973	51901
8079	D	D	E	N	1972	49462
8079	L	D	E	N	1972	49462
8079	T	D	E	N	1973	51901
8107	S	D	R	N	1971	66283
8108	A	D	E	N	1975	96723
8108	S	S	E	N	1969	68115
8108	S	D	R	N	1976	101176
8108	S	D	E	N	1976	101886
8108	T	D	E	N	1975	96723
8108	T	D	R	N	1976	101176
8108	T	S	R	N	1976	101176
8108	T	D	E	N	1976	101886
8108	T	S	E	N	1976	101886
8114	A	D	E	N	1973	51901
8114	T	D	E	N	1973	51901
8117	S	D	E	N	1972	63827
8126	S	D	R	N	1971	66283
8127	D	S	E	N	1972	87824
8127	D	D	R	N	1974	90221
8127	D	D	E	N	1975	90222
8127	S	S	E	N	1972	87824
8127	S	S	R	N	1974	90221
8127	S	S	E	N	1975	90222
8136	S	D	R	N	1973	51724
8136	S	D	R	N	1971	66283
8139	S	D	R	N	1971	66283
8140	S	D	R	N	1971	66283
8141	S	D	R	N	1971	66283
8142	S	D	R	N	1971	66283
8143	S	D	R	N	1971	66283
8144	S	D	R	N	1971	66283
8145	S	D	R	N	1971	66283
8145	S	S	E	N	1966	87721
8146	S	D	R	N	1971	66283
8147	S	D	R	N	1971	66283
8149	S	D	R	N	1971	66283
8150	S	D	R	N	1971	66283
8151	S	T	E	N	1975	99100
8153	S	D	R	N	1970	67414
8154	S	D	R	N	1970	67423
8162	A	D	E	N	1972	75431
8162	T	D	E	N	1972	75431
8168	S	S	E	N	1966	87721
8187	S	D	R	N	1972	55387
8187	S	D	E	N	1974	88429
8188	S	D	R	H	1972	55387
8188	S	D	R	N	1972	55387
8188	S	D	E	H	1974	88429
8188	S	D	E	N	1974	88429
8189	S	D	R	N	1972	55387
8189	S	D	E	N	1974	88429
8192	S	D	R	N	1971	76488
8192	S	T	R	N	1971	76488
8192	S	D	E	N	1971	91569
8192	S	T	E	N	1971	91569
8200	S	D	R	N	1971	66283
8201	S	D	R	N	1971	66283
8202	S	D	R	N	1971	66283
8203	S	D	R	N	1971	66283
8204	S	D	R	N	1971	66283
112-0001	G	D	R	N	1975	91000
0001	G	E	R	N	1975	91000
0001	G	T	R	N	1975	91000
0001	G	D	E	N	1975	97077
0001	G	E	E	N	1975	97077
0001	G	T	E	N	1975	97077
0001	L	D	R	N	1975	91000
0001	L	E	R	N	1975	91000
0001	L	T	R	N	1975	91000
0001	L	D	E	N	1975	97077
0001	L	E	E	N	1975	97077
0001	L	T	E	N	1975	97077
0010	D	S	E	N	1968	75835
0010	L	S	E	N	1968	75835
0247	S	D	E	N	1964	93287
0247	S	S	E	N	1964	93287
0481	S	D	F	H	1973	50619
8020	S	S	E	N	1974	64457
8020	S	S	E	N	1969	68271
8025	D	D	R	N	1971	52298
8025	D	D	E	N	1971	52299
8025	D	D	R	N	1972	60021
8025	D	D	E	L	1976	101450
8025	D	D	E	N	1976	101450
8025	D	T	E	L	1976	101450
8025	D	T	E	N	1976	101450
8025	S	D	R	N	1971	52298
8025	S	D	E	N	1971	52299
8025	S	S	E	N	1974	64457
8025	S	D	R	N	1969	67411

Phys. State: **A.** Amorphous; **C.** Superconductive; **D.** Doped; **F.** Fibrous or Whisker; **G.** Gas; **I.** Ionized or Plasma; **L.** Liquid; **P.** Powder or Particle; **S.** Solid; **T.** Thin Film
Subject: **D.** Data; **E.** Experiment; **S.** Survey (Review, Compendium, etc.); **T.** Theory
Language: **E.** English; **F.** French; **G.** German; **O.** Other Languages; **R.** Russian
Temperature: **L.** Low (0 to 75K); **N.** Normal (75 to 1273K); **H.** High (above 1273K)

Substance Number	Phys. State	Subject	Language	Temperature	Year	EPIC Number
112-8025	S	S	E	N	1969	68271
8025	S	S	E	N	1967	68371
8032	S	S	E	N	1972	87823
8083	S	S	E	N	1972	87823
8084	S	S	E	L	1972	87823
8084	S	S	E	N	1972	87823
8087	S	S	E	N	1972	87823
114-0006	L	D	R	N	1973	57010
0017	D	D	R	N	1971	66936
0017	D	S	E	N	1971	87884
0017	S	D	R	N	1971	66936
0017	S	S	E	N	1962	87660
0017	S	S	E	N	1971	87884
0017	S	S	E	N	1963	98002
0046	D	D	E	N	1973	51742
0112	S	D	R	N	1974	93455
0112	S	T	R	N	1974	93455
0112	S	D	E	N	1974	93456
0112	S	T	E	N	1974	93456
0113	S	D	R	N	1974	93455
0113	S	T	R	N	1974	93455
0113	S	D	E	N	1974	93456
0113	S	T	E	N	1974	93456
8001	A	S	E	N	1970	59557
8001	A	S	E	N	1970	75887
8001	D	D	R	N	1972	51113
8001	D	D	R	L	1973	55343
8001	D	D	R	N	1973	55343
8001	D	D	E	L	1974	59285
8001	D	D	E	N	1974	59285
8001	D	D	R	N	1965	61106
8001	D	D	E	N	1965	61107
8001	D	S	E	N	1970	75887
8001	D	D	R	N	1972	76546
8001	D	S	R	N	1972	76546
8001	D	S	E	N	1975	87741
8001	D	S	E	L	1965	87781
8001	D	D	E	N	1972	91593
8001	D	S	E	N	1972	91593
8001	S	T	R	N	1973	52523
8001	S	T	E	N	1974	57764
8001	S	S	E	N	1970	59557
8001	S	E	R	N	1965	61106
8001	S	E	E	N	1965	61107
8001	S	S	E	N	1974	64457
8001	S	D	R	N	1972	76517
8001	S	T	R	N	1972	76517
8001	S	S	E	N	1963	87679
8001	S	S	E	L	1965	87781
8001	S	S	E	N	1965	87781
8001	S	S	E	L	1971	87884
8001	S	S	E	N	1971	87884
8001	S	S	E	N	1972	87889
8001	S	D	E	N	1972	91561
8001	S	T	E	N	1972	91561
8001	T	S	E	N	1965	87781
8010	D	D	R	N	1971	67054
8010	S	D	R	N	1972	76548
8010	S	D	E	N	1972	91598
8011	S	D	R	N	1973	62447
8012	S	S	E	N	1962	87661
8058	S	D	G	N	1971	59640
8065	S	D	E	N	1972	63827
8067	L	D	E	N	1972	101939
8067	L	T	E	N	1972	101939
8067	S	D	E	N	1972	101939
8067	S	T	E	N	1972	101939
8069	T	D	E	N	1974	83981
116-8037	S	D	R	N	1973	58870
8038	S	D	R	N	1973	58870
118-8005	C	S	E	L	1974	62805
8026	S	S	E	N	1973	53420
8053	C	S	E	L	1974	62805
8054	C	S	E	L	1974	62805
8055	C	S	E	L	1974	62805
8056	C	S	E	L	1974	62805
8072	S	D	R	N	1973	58870
8073	S	D	R	N	1973	58870
119-0001	S	D	R	N	1967	53069
0001	S	D	E	N	1972	53070
0002	D	S	E	N	1969	87723
0002	P	S	E	H	1969	87723
0002	S	D	E	N	1974	54024
0002	S	S	E	N	1974	54024
0002	S	T	E	N	1974	54024
0002	S	D	E	N	1970	68210
0002	S	S	E	N	1969	68271
0002	S	S	E	H	1963	87682
0002	S	S	E	N	1963	87682
0002	S	S	E	H	1969	87723
0002	S	S	E	N	1969	87723
0008	D	E	E	H	1964	60562
0008	D	E	E	N	1964	60562
0008	D	T	R	H	1975	90140
0008	D	T	R	N	1975	90140
0008	D	T	E	H	1975	90141
0008	D	T	E	N	1975	90141
119-0008	S	D	E	H	1971	49788
0008	S	S	E	H	1974	54022
0008	S	S	E	N	1974	54022
0008	S	S	E	N	1974	87606
0010	S	D	E	N	1972	67192
8001	S	S	E	N	1960	65977
8002	S	S	E	N	1962	87672
8015	S	D	R	N	1971	64585
8015	S	T	R	N	1971	64585
8015	S	D	E	N	1971	68414
8015	S	T	E	N	1971	68414
8019	S	D	E	N	1972	56855
8026	S	D	R	N	1971	64585
8026	S	T	R	N	1971	64585
8040	D	D	R	N	1973	55056
8040	D	D	E	N	1974	55057
8040	S	D	R	N	1973	55056
8040	S	D	E	N	1974	55057
8084	D	D	R	N	1973	56469
8084	D	D	E	N	1973	76678
8093	S	D	G	N	1973	57057
8094	S	D	G	N	1973	57057
120-0001	D	E	F	N	1974	68558
0001	D	T	R	N	1975	90140
0001	D	T	E	N	1975	90141
0001	S	D	E	H	1971	49788
0001	S	D	R	N	1971	49983
0001	S	D	E	N	1960	60561
0001	S	D	E	N	1970	68210
0001	S	E	F	N	1974	68558
0001	S	D	E	N	1975	91134
0001	S	E	E	N	1975	91134
0004	D	S	E	N	1966	87721
0017	S	D	E	N	1964	93287
0017	S	S	E	N	1964	93287
0023	S	D	O	H	1973	58144
0023	S	D	O	N	1973	58144
0023	S	D	E	N	1964	93287
0023	S	S	E	N	1964	93287
0035	S	D	E	N	1972	54619
0035	S	D	E	N	1964	93287
0035	S	S	E	N	1964	93287
0036	S	D	E	N	1972	53013
0045	S	D	O	H	1973	58144
0045	S	D	O	N	1973	58144
0045	S	S	E	N	1972	87886
0045	S	D	E	N	1964	93287
0045	S	S	E	N	1964	93287
0051	S	D	O	H	1973	58144
0051	S	D	O	N	1973	58144
0051	S	D	E	N	1964	93287
0051	S	S	E	N	1964	93287
0057	S	D	E	L	1968	64268
0057	S	D	E	N	1968	64268
0073	T	D	E	N	1975	91956
0073	T	E	E	N	1975	91956
0106	S	D	E	N	1974	54324
0140	S	D	R	N	1967	53069
0140	S	D	E	N	1972	53070
0199	S	S	E	N	1966	87721
8001	S	D	R	L	1972	100974
8001	S	D	R	N	1972	100974
8003	S	S	E	N	1972	87886
8013	S	D	R	N	1971	66935
8023	D	D	E	L	1973	49621
8023	D	D	E	N	1973	49621
8042	D	D	R	N	1974	93453
8042	D	T	R	N	1974	93453
8042	D	D	E	N	1974	93454
8042	D	T	E	N	1974	93454
8042	S	D	E	N	1972	56855
8042	S	S	E	N	1966	87721
8042	S	D	R	N	1974	93453
8042	S	T	R	N	1974	93453
8042	S	D	E	N	1974	93454
8042	S	T	E	N	1974	93454
8050	S	S	E	N	1973	53420
8077	S	D	R	H	1973	53995
8077	S	D	R	L	1973	53995
8077	S	D	R	N	1973	53995
8077	S	D	E	H	1973	53996
8077	S	D	E	L	1973	53996
8077	S	D	E	N	1973	53996
8079	S	D	R	N	1973	52563
8079	S	D	E	N	1973	57788
8089	S	D	R	N	1971	64585
8089	S	T	R	N	1971	64585
8089	S	D	E	N	1971	68414
8089	S	T	E	N	1971	68414
8090	S	D	R	N	1971	64585
8090	S	T	R	N	1971	64585
8090	S	D	E	N	1971	68414
8090	S	T	E	N	1971	68414
8121	S	D	R	N	1973	58870
8122	S	D	R	N	1973	58870
8132	S	D	R	N	1971	66935
8133	S	D	R	N	1971	66935
8136	S	D	R	N	1971	90517
8147	S	S	E	N	1966	87721
8149	S	S	E	L	1966	87721
120-8149	S	S	E	N	1966	87721
8151	S	S	E	N	1966	87721
8152	S	S	E	N	1966	87721
8153	S	S	E	N	1966	87721
8154	S	S	E	N	1966	87721
8156	S	S	E	N	1966	87721
8158	S	S	E	N	1966	87721
8173	S	D	E	L	1975	92154
8173	S	D	E	N	1975	92154
8174	S	D	R	N	1972	100974
8175	S	D	R	N	1972	100974
8176	S	D	R	N	1972	100974
8179	S	D	E	N	1974	62056
8179	S	T	E	N	1974	62056
122-0004	D	S	E	N	1972	61595
0004	S	D	G	H	1973	50015
0005	D	D	E	H	1964	60562
0005	D	D	E	N	1964	60562
0005	D	S	E	H	1974	87606
0005	D	S	E	N	1974	87606
0005	S	D	E	H	1964	60562
0005	S	D	E	N	1964	60562
0005	S	E	E	H	1964	60562
0005	S	E	E	N	1964	60562
0005	S	S	E	N	1964	60562
0005	S	D	O	N	1973	64997
0008	S	D	F	N	1971	59552
0013	S	D	R	N	1972	49829
0014	D	D	E	N	1974	57860
0014	S	D	E	N	1975	91134
0014	S	E	E	N	1975	91134
0016	D	D	R	N	1971	76496
0016	D	D	E	N	1971	91580
0016	L	S	R	H	1966	95131
0016	L	S	E	H	1966	96497
0016	S	S	E	N	1971	87881
0016	S	S	R	N	1966	95131
0016	S	S	E	N	1966	96497
0017	S	D	E	H	1974	55261
0017	S	D	E	N	1974	55261
0023	S	D	E	N	1973	57563
0023	S	T	E	N	1973	57563
0023	S	D	E	N	1972	60929
0023	S	E	E	N	1972	60929
0023	S	S	E	L	1963	87709
0023	S	S	E	N	1963	87709
0026	S	D	R	N	1974	63060
0026	S	D	E	N	1975	63061
0026	S	S	E	N	1970	75833
0026	S	S	E	N	1971	87881
0031	S	D	R	H	1974	66744
0031	S	D	R	N	1974	66744
0031	S	T	R	H	1974	66744
0031	S	T	R	N	1974	66744
0031	S	D	E	H	1975	66745
0031	S	D	E	N	1975	66745
0031	S	T	E	H	1975	66745
0031	S	T	E	N	1975	66745
0031	S	S	E	N	1969	68271
0031	S	D	R	N	1972	76508
0031	S	E	R	N	1972	76508
0031	S	D	E	N	1972	91530
0031	S	E	E	N	1972	91530
0037	S	D	E	N	1970	58979
0046	S	S	E	N	1970	75833
0047	D	D	E	L	1973	52020
0047	D	D	E	N	1973	52020
0047	D	D	E	N	1974	62056
0047	D	T	E	N	1974	62056
0047	S	D	E	L	1973	52020
0047	S	D	E	N	1973	52020
0047	S	D	E	N	1974	62056
0047	S	T	E	N	1974	62056
0050	S	S	E	N	1969	68115
0053	D	S	E	N	1969	68115
0053	D	S	E	N	1966	87833
0053	S	S	E	N	1969	68115
0053	T	S	E	N	1966	87833
0068	S	S	E	N	1969	68115
0068	S	S	E	N	1967	68368
0093	S	D	O	N	1973	51459
0098	S	D	R	N	1974	67757
0112	S	S	E	N	1971	87881
0112	T	S	E	N	1971	87881
0196	S	D	E	N	1975	96226
0196	S	T	E	N	1975	96226
0201	S	D	E	N	1965	64246
0314	S	D	R	N	1974	63060
0314	S	D	E	N	1975	63061
0450	S	D	E	N	1965	64246
8028	S	S	E	N	1973	51150
8028	S	S	E	N	1971	87881
8029	S	S	E	N	1973	51150
8029	S	S	E	N	1971	87881
8030	S	S	E	N	1973	51150
8030	S	S	E	N	1971	87881
8031	S	S	E	N	1973	51150
8031	S	S	E	N	1971	87881
8032	S	S	E	N	1973	51150
8032	S	S	E	N	1971	87881

Phys. State: **A.** Amorphous; **C.** Superconductive; **D.** Doped; **F.** Fibrous or Whisker; **G.** Gas; **I.** Ionized or Plasma; **L.** Liquid; **P.** Powder or Particle; **S.** Solid; **T.** Thin Film
Subject: **D.** Data; **E.** Experiment; **S.** Survey (Review, Compendium, etc.); **T.** Theory
Language: **E.** English; **F.** French; **G.** German; **O.** Other Languages; **R.** Russian
Temperature: **L.** Low (0 to 75K); **N.** Normal (75 to 1273K); **H.** High (above 1273K)

Substance Number	Phys. State	Subject	Language	Temperature	Year	EPIC Number
122-8033	S	S	E	L	1973	51150
8033	S	S	E	N	1973	51150
8054	T	D	E	N	1972	64079
8078	S	D	R	N	1974	63060
8078	S	D	E	N	1975	63061
8078	S	S	E	N	1970	75833
8088	S	S	E	N	1971	87881
8113	S	D	G	N	1973	57059
8124	S	S	E	N	1970	75833
8124	S	D	R	H	1972	76529
8124	S	D	R	N	1972	76529
8124	S	S	E	N	1971	87881
8124	S	D	E	H	1972	91534
8124	S	D	E	N	1972	91534
123-0003	D	S	E	N	1966	68361
0003	L	S	E	H	1969	68115
0003	S	D	R	N	1966	62300
0003	S	D	E	N	1974	62301
0003	S	S	E	N	1969	68115
0003	S	S	E	N	1966	68361
0003	S	D	R	N	1975	94600
0003	S	T	R	N	1975	94600
0003	S	D	E	N	1975	100283
0003	S	T	E	N	1975	100283
0003	T	S	E	N	1966	68361
0025	S	S	E	N	1974	61168
0026	S	D	E	L	1972	49487
0026	S	D	E	N	1972	49487
0048	S	D	R	N	1972	49646
8004	S	D	E	N	1973	52053
8017	S	D	R	N	1974	58895
8017	S	D	R	N	1966	62300
8017	S	D	E	N	1974	62301
8017	S	D	E	N	1974	64884
8017	S	S	E	N	1969	68115
8017	S	D	R	N	1971	76500
8017	S	T	R	N	1971	76500
8017	S	S	E	N	1962	87674
8017	S	D	E	N	1971	91566
8017	S	T	E	N	1971	91566
8017	S	D	R	N	1974	97481
8017	S	D	E	N	1974	97482
8018	D	D	E	N	1972	49874
8018	D	T	E	L	1972	53500
8018	D	D	R	N	1973	58209
8018	D	D	E	N	1972	59135
8018	D	T	E	N	1972	59135
8018	D	D	E	N	1974	59204
8018	D	D	R	N	1973	59370
8018	D	D	R	N	1972	62320
8018	D	D	E	N	1974	62321
8018	D	D	R	N	1972	62719
8018	D	D	R	N	1973	65315
8018	D	D	E	N	1962	73285
8018	D	E	E	N	1962	73285
8018	D	D	E	N	1972	83516
8018	D	S	E	N	1962	87671
8018	D	D	R	N	1975	99646
8018	D	D	E	N	1975	103293
8018	L	S	E	N	1974	79184
8018	S	T	E	N	1973	57483
8018	S	D	R	N	1974	57869
8018	S	D	R	N	1973	58209
8018	S	D	E	N	1972	59070
8018	S	S	E	N	1972	59070
8018	S	T	E	N	1972	59070
8018	S	D	E	N	1974	59204
8018	S	D	R	N	1973	59370
8018	S	D	E	N	1971	60173
8018	S	D	R	N	1968	60749
8018	S	D	E	N	1974	60750
8018	S	D	R	N	1966	62300
8018	S	D	E	N	1974	62301
8018	S	D	R	N	1973	62729
8018	S	T	E	N	1975	63321
8018	S	S	E	N	1974	64457
8018	S	D	E	N	1974	64881
8018	S	D	E	N	1973	65325
8018	S	S	E	N	1960	65977
8018	S	S	E	L	1970	68114
8018	S	S	E	N	1970	68114
8018	S	S	E	N	1969	68115
8018	S	D	E	N	1966	75147
8018	S	T	R	N	1972	85970
8018	S	S	E	N	1962	87671
8018	S	D	R	N	1966	91929
8018	S	D	R	N	1974	93120
8018	S	D	E	N	1975	93121
8018	S	D	E	N	1961	97244
8018	S	E	E	N	1961	97244
8018	S	T	E	N	1961	97244
8018	S	D	E	N	1961	97245
8018	S	E	E	N	1961	97245
8018	S	T	E	N	1961	97245
8018	S	T	E	N	1975	99100
8018	S	T	E	N	1976	101579
8018	T	D	R	N	1974	58894
8018	T	D	E	N	1968	59520
8018	T	D	E	N	1972	61768
8018	T	D	R	N	1973	62729
123-8018	T	D	E	N	1974	64883
8018	T	D	E	N	1973	65325
8018	T	S	E	N	1962	87671
8018	T	D	R	N	1974	93120
8018	T	D	E	N	1975	93121
8039	S	D	R	N	1973	50066
8039	S	D	E	N	1973	51420
8039	S	D	R	N	1974	58895
8039	S	D	E	N	1974	64884
8039	S	S	E	N	1972	87824
8039	S	D	R	N	1974	97468
8039	S	D	E	N	1975	97469
8050	S	D	R	N	1973	50725
8050	S	D	E	N	1973	53026
8051	D	S	E	N	1970	68114
8051	S	D	R	N	1973	50725
8051	S	D	E	N	1973	53026
8051	S	D	F	N	1972	61662
8051	S	D	R	L	1974	63131
8051	S	D	R	N	1974	63131
8051	S	D	E	L	1975	63132
8051	S	D	E	N	1975	63132
8051	S	S	E	N	1970	68114
8051	S	S	E	N	1972	87824
8051	S	D	R	N	1975	94942
8051	S	D	E	N	1975	95895
8065	S	D	R	N	1973	52528
8065	S	D	E	N	1974	57769
8066	S	D	E	N	1972	63827
8074	D	S	E	N	1972	87824
8094	S	S	E	N	1972	87824
125-8036	S	D	R	N	1973	58870
126-0001	S	S	E	N	1969	68115
0001	S	S	E	N	1972	87824
0001	T	D	E	N	1969	59589
0005	D	D	E	N	1973	51938
0022	S	D	R	N	1967	53069
0022	S	D	E	N	1972	53070
0036	S	D	R	N	1967	53069
0036	S	D	E	N	1972	53070
0037	S	D	R	N	1967	53069
0037	S	D	E	N	1972	53070
0038	S	D	R	N	1967	53069
0038	S	D	E	N	1972	53070
0038	S	D	E	N	1972	70535
0038	S	T	E	L	1976	103263
0043	L	D	R	N	1971	59646
0043	L	D	E	N	1971	59647
0043	L	S	E	N	1970	59699
0043	S	D	R	N	1972	66992
0059	S	D	R	N	1972	76557
0059	S	T	R	N	1972	76557
0059	S	D	E	N	1972	91550
0059	S	T	E	N	1972	91550
8010	S	D	R	N	1973	55687
8011	S	D	R	N	1973	55687
8012	S	D	R	N	1973	55687
8013	S	D	R	N	1973	55687
8014	S	D	R	N	1973	55687
8015	S	D	R	N	1973	55687
8016	S	D	R	N	1973	55687
8017	S	D	R	N	1973	55687
8020	S	S	E	L	1967	66157
8020	S	S	E	N	1967	66157
8026	S	D	R	N	1971	58851
8026	S	D	E	N	1964	61307
8026	S	D	R	N	1966	62300
8026	S	D	E	N	1974	62301
8030	A	D	E	N	1973	51901
8030	A	D	E	N	1972	53386
8030	D	D	E	N	1972	49462
8030	D	S	R	N	1972	59001
8030	D	S	E	N	1972	59002
8030	D	S	E	N	1970	59699
8030	D	D	R	N	1974	87318
8030	D	D	E	N	1974	87319
8030	L	D	E	N	1972	49462
8030	L	D	R	H	1973	56862
8030	L	D	R	N	1973	56862
8030	L	D	E	H	1973	57296
8030	L	D	R	N	1973	57296
8030	L	S	R	N	1972	59001
8030	L	S	E	N	1972	59002
8030	L	S	E	N	1970	59699
8030	L	D	R	H	1969	61867
8030	L	D	R	N	1969	61867
8030	L	D	R	N	1974	87318
8030	L	D	E	N	1974	87319
8030	T	D	E	N	1973	51901
8030	T	D	E	N	1972	53386
8032	D	D	R	N	1972	50174
8032	D	D	E	N	1973	54934
8032	D	D	R	N	1970	55104
8032	D	D	E	N	1972	55105
8032	D	D	R	N	1973	55822
8032	D	D	E	N	1975	88288
8032	D	D	E	N	1972	100970
8032	D	D	G	N	1976	101451
8032	L	D	R	H	1969	61867
126-8032	L	D	R	N	1969	61867
8032	S	D	G	N	1973	52363
8032	S	S	R	N	1970	55104
8032	S	S	E	N	1972	55105
8032	S	D	F	N	1971	61672
8032	S	E	F	N	1971	61672
8032	S	T	F	N	1971	61672
8032	S	S	E	N	1974	62277
8032	S	D	R	N	1972	62298
8032	S	D	E	N	1973	62299
8032	S	D	R	N	1966	62300
8032	S	D	E	N	1974	62301
8032	S	D	R	N	1972	76548
8032	S	D	E	N	1975	88288
8032	S	D	E	N	1972	91598
8032	S	D	E	N	1975	96857
8032	S	T	E	N	1975	96857
8032	S	D	E	N	1972	100970
8032	T	D	R	N	1972	50174
8034	D	D	R	N	1973	51515
8034	D	D	R	N	1974	66637
8034	D	D	E	N	1974	66638
8034	L	D	R	N	1973	51515
8034	L	D	R	N	1971	59646
8034	L	D	E	N	1971	59647
8034	L	S	E	N	1970	59699
8034	L	D	R	N	1974	66637
8034	L	D	E	N	1974	66638
8034	S	D	R	N	1972	66992
8035	L	D	R	H	1973	50726
8035	L	D	R	N	1973	50726
8035	L	D	E	H	1973	53027
8035	L	D	E	N	1973	53027
8035	S	S	E	N	1969	68115
8035	S	S	E	N	1972	87824
8037	L	S	E	H	1970	68114
8037	L	S	E	N	1970	68114
8037	S	S	E	L	1970	68114
8037	S	S	E	N	1970	68114
8037	S	S	E	N	1969	68115
8037	S	D	R	N	1974	86780
8037	S	S	E	N	1972	87824
8037	S	D	E	N	1974	90054
8037	S	D	R	N	1974	97481
8037	S	D	E	N	1974	97482
8037	T	D	R	N	1972	49570
8037	T	D	E	N	1969	59589
8038	S	D	E	N	1972	56855
8046	A	D	E	N	1973	51901
8046	T	D	E	N	1973	51901
8047	S	S	E	L	1967	66157
8047	S	S	E	N	1967	66157
8051	S	D	R	N	1972	66992
8052	D	E	E	N	1974	60751
8052	D	T	E	N	1974	60751
8052	S	D	E	N	1974	54024
8052	S	S	E	N	1974	54024
8052	S	T	E	N	1974	54024
8052	S	T	E	N	1973	57563
8055	L	D	R	N	1973	50726
8055	L	D	E	N	1973	53027
8055	S	S	E	N	1969	68115
8055	S	D	R	N	1971	76500
8055	S	T	R	N	1971	76500
8055	S	D	E	N	1971	91566
8055	S	T	E	N	1971	91566
8057	S	D	F	N	1973	50026
8059	D	D	R	N	1972	50654
8059	D	D	R	N	1973	52563
8059	D	D	E	N	1973	57788
8059	D	S	E	N	1969	75843
8059	S	D	R	N	1973	52563
8059	S	D	E	N	1973	57788
8061	S	D	E	N	1972	56855
8067	S	D	R	N	1973	51601
8067	S	S	E	N	1972	87824
8068	S	D	R	N	1973	51601
8068	S	S	E	N	1972	87824
8071	S	D	E	N	1972	70535
8075	L	D	E	N	1972	49462
8083	S	D	R	N	1975	91201
8083	S	D	E	N	1975	94197
8085	T	D	E	N	1969	59589
8094	A	D	O	N	1970	60019
8094	S	D	R	N	1973	55285
8094	S	D	E	N	1974	59242
8094	S	D	O	N	1970	60019
8094	S	D	R	N	1970	61240
8094	T	D	O	N	1970	60019
8095	D	D	R	N	1973	61824
8095	D	D	E	N	1973	61825
8095	S	D	R	N	1973	61824
8095	S	D	E	N	1973	61825
8098	D	D	R	N	1974	93453
8098	D	T	R	N	1974	93453
8098	D	D	E	N	1974	93454
8098	D	T	E	N	1974	93454
8098	S	D	R	N	1974	93453
8098	S	T	R	N	1974	93453
8098	S	D	E	N	1974	93454
8098	S	T	E	N	1974	93454

Phys. State: **A.** Amorphous; **C.** Superconductive; **D.** Doped; **F.** Fibrous or Whisker; **G.** Gas; **I.** Ionized or Plasma; **L.** Liquid; **P.** Powder or Particle; **S.** Solid; **T.** Thin Film
Subject: **D.** Data; **E.** Experiment; **S.** Survey (Review, Compendium, etc.); **T.** Theory
Language: **E.** English; **F.** French; **G.** German; **O.** Other Languages; **R.** Russian
Temperature: **L.** Low (0 to 75K); **N.** Normal (75 to 1273K); **H.** High (above 1273K)

Substance Number	Phys. State	Sub-ject	Lan-guage	Temper-ature	Year	EPIC Number
126-8099	S	S	E	N	1960	65977
8100	A	D	E	N	1974	84459
8100	A	D	E	N	1974	86009
8100	T	D	E	N	1974	84459
8100	T	D	E	N	1974	86009
8101	S	S	E	N	1969	75843
8104	T	D	R	N	1973	56300
8107	L	S	E	N	1974	84453
8108	S	D	R	N	1973	51732
8108	S	D	E	N	1973	79136
8119	L	D	E	N	1974	84454
8135	S	D	R	N	1971	90517
127-8002	D	D	R	N	1973	51346
8002	D	D	R	N	1973	52745
8002	D	D	E	N	1974	52746
8002	D	D	E	N	1973	59208
8002	D	D	R	N	1972	67958
8002	D	D	E	N	1972	67959
8002	L	D	E	N	1972	49460
8002	L	D	R	N	1973	51346
8002	L	D	R	N	1973	52745
8002	L	D	E	N	1974	52746
8002	L	S	E	N	1974	54095
8002	L	S	R	N	1972	59001
8002	L	S	E	N	1972	59002
8002	L	D	E	N	1973	59208
8002	L	D	R	N	1971	59646
8002	L	D	E	N	1971	59647
8002	L	S	E	N	1970	59699
8002	L	D	R	N	1972	67958
8002	S	D	R	N	1972	66992
8002	S	D	E	N	1972	67959
8004	S	S	E	N	1969	68271
8004	S	D	R	N	1974	86780
8004	S	S	E	N	1972	87823
8004	S	D	E	N	1974	90054
8004	T	D	E	N	1968	59520
8008	S	D	G	N	1971	59640

Phys. State: **A.** Amorphous; **C.** Superconductive; **D.** Doped; **F.** Fibrous or Whisker; **G.** Gas; **I.** Ionized or Plasma; **L.** Liquid; **P.** Powder or Particle; **S.** Solid; **T.** Thin Film
Subject: **D.** Data; **E.** Experiment; **S.** Survey (Review, Compendium, etc.); **T.** Theory
Language: **E.** English; **F.** French; **G.** German; **O.** Other Languages; **R.** Russian
Temperature: **L.** Low (0 to 75K); **N.** Normal (75 to 1273K); **H.** High (above 1273K)

Chapter 21 Work Function

Substance Number	Phys. State	Sub-ject	Lan-guage	Temper-ature	Year	EPIC Number
100-0045	D	S	E	N	1975	95469
0045	G	D	E	N	1973	51491
0045	G	S	E	N	1973	51491
0045	G	T	E	N	1973	51491
0045	G	S	E	H	1964	87578
0045	L	D	E	N	1973	51491
0045	L	S	E	N	1973	51491
0045	L	T	E	N	1973	51491
0045	S	S	R	N	1966	53120
0045	S	S	E	N	1972	53121
0045	S	S	R	N	1974	83872
0045	S	S	E	N	1974	91448
0045	S	S	E	N	1976	97315
0055	D	T	R	N	1974	77934
0055	D	T	E	N	1974	94494
0055	D	S	E	N	1975	95469
0055	P	E	F	N	1973	55913
0055	S	T	E	N	1973	53754
0055	S	S	E	N	1970	59681
0055	S	T	E	N	1947	61287
0055	S	S	R	N	1974	83872
0055	S	S	E	N	1974	91448
0055	S	S	E	N	1976	97315
0055	T	D	O	N	1974	88134
8003	S	S	E	N	1975	86763
8007	S	S	E	N	1969	68271
8008	S	S	E	N	1971	87884
8038	S	S	E	N	1969	68115
8059	S	S	E	N	1974	54348
102-0002	S	D	E	H	1973	49433
0002	S	T	E	N	1973	52794
0002	S	S	E	N	1947	66510
0002	T	D	E	N	1973	65547
0002	T	D	O	N	1974	67787
0002	T	S	E	N	1975	91987
0002	T	D	R	H	1975	95124
0002	T	D	R	N	1975	95124
0002	T	S	R	H	1975	95124
0002	T	S	R	N	1975	95124
0002	T	D	E	H	1976	95907
0002	T	D	E	N	1976	95907
0002	T	S	E	H	1976	95907
0002	T	S	E	N	1976	95907
0317	G	D	E	N	1973	52751
8001	S	S	E	N	1971	87884
8041	D	D	R	N	1972	50696
8041	D	D	E	N	1971	59711
8041	D	T	E	N	1971	59711
8041	D	D	R	N	1975	86877
8041	D	D	E	N	1975	86878
8041	D	S	E	N	1964	87701
8041	D	D	E	N	1975	97860
8041	D	T	E	N	1975	97860
8041	P	D	R	N	1969	67767
8041	S	D	R	N	1973	52892
8041	S	D	E	N	1974	52893
8041	S	D	E	N	1972	53477
8041	S	D	E	N	1971	62264
8041	S	D	R	N	1969	67767
8041	S	T	R	N	1974	68636
8041	S	T	E	N	1975	68637
8041	S	D	E	N	1974	80374
8041	S	S	E	N	1973	86380
8041	S	D	R	N	1975	86877
8041	S	D	E	N	1975	86878
8041	S	S	E	N	1962	87673
8041	S	S	E	N	1964	87701
8041	S	S	E	N	1971	87884
8054	S	S	E	L	1971	87884
8054	S	S	E	N	1971	87884
8142	S	S	E	N	1972	87889
8170	T	D	E	N	1972	53183
8170	T	E	E	N	1972	53183
8170	T	D	R	H	1970	67315
8170	T	D	R	N	1970	67315
104-0002	S	D	E	N	1973	52322
0002	S	T	E	N	1973	52794
0002	S	S	E	H	1969	68271
0002	S	D	R	N	1974	80408
0002	S	S	R	N	1974	80408
0002	S	D	E	N	1974	95255
0002	S	S	E	N	1974	95255
0007	S	T	E	N	1974	58431
0021	S	D	E	N	1973	65641
0049	D	D	O	N	1974	88134
0049	S	D	R	N	1973	51370
0049	S	T	R	N	1973	51370
0049	S	D	E	N	1973	51371
0049	S	T	E	N	1973	51371
0049	S	D	E	N	1974	53627
0049	S	S	E	N	1969	68271
0049	S	D	R	N	1972	76508
0049	S	D	E	N	1972	91530

Substance Number	Phys. State	Sub-ject	Lan-guage	Temper-ature	Year	EPIC Number
104-0049	S	S	E	N	1975	96477
0049	S	D	E	N	1976	100580
0049	T	D	R	N	1971	76365
0049	T	D	E	N	1971	85671
0049	T	D	O	N	1974	88134
0049	T	D	E	N	1975	101649
0053	S	D	E	N	1975	86763
0105	S	D	E	N	1975	86763
0196	S	D	E	N	1974	53627
0196	S	S	E	N	1969	68271
8032	S	D	E	N	1974	53627
8032	S	S	E	N	1969	68271
8033	S	D	E	N	1974	53627
8033	S	S	E	N	1969	68271
8045	S	S	E	N	1966	66068
8053	S	D	R	H	1974	75323
8053	S	D	G	H	1973	82255
8053	S	T	G	H	1973	82255
8053	S	D	G	N	1974	93012
8053	S	D	E	H	1974	93218
8069	S	S	R	N	1970	53179
8069	S	S	E	N	1972	53180
8069	S	D	R	H	1972	58305
8069	S	D	R	N	1974	67946
8069	S	D	E	N	1974	67947
8069	S	D	R	N	1973	71959
8069	S	D	E	N	1973	82778
8069	S	D	E	H	1974	89508
8069	T	D	E	N	1974	90583
8083	S	D	R	H	1974	66614
8083	S	D	E	H	1974	66615
8083	S	D	R	H	1974	75323
8083	S	D	G	H	1973	82255
8083	S	T	G	H	1973	82255
8083	S	S	E	N	1966	87721
8083	S	D	G	N	1974	93012
8083	S	D	E	H	1974	93218
8083	S	D	G	H	1973	82255
8090	S	T	G	H	1973	82255
8099	S	D	R	H	1974	66614
8099	S	D	E	H	1974	66615
8099	S	D	G	H	1973	82255
8099	S	T	G	H	1973	82255
8099	S	S	E	N	1974	93387
8105	S	D	G	H	1973	82255
8105	S	T	G	H	1973	82255
8108	S	S	E	N	1966	66068
8114	S	D	R	H	1974	66614
8114	S	D	E	H	1974	66615
8115	S	D	G	H	1973	82255
8115	S	T	G	H	1973	82255
8140	S	D	R	H	1974	87071
8140	S	D	E	H	1974	87072
8141	S	D	R	H	1974	87071
8141	S	D	E	H	1974	87072
8142	S	D	R	H	1974	87071
8142	S	D	E	H	1974	87072
8143	S	D	R	H	1974	87071
8143	S	D	E	H	1974	87072
8144	S	D	R	H	1974	87071
8144	S	D	E	H	1974	87072
8145	S	D	R	H	1974	87071
8145	S	D	E	H	1974	87072
8146	S	D	R	H	1974	87071
8147	S	D	R	H	1974	87071
8147	S	D	E	H	1974	87072
8156	S	D	R	H	1974	66614
8156	S	D	E	H	1974	66615
8156	S	D	G	H	1973	82255
8156	S	T	G	H	1973	82255
8157	S	D	G	H	1973	82255
8157	S	T	G	H	1973	82255
8159	S	D	R	H	1974	75323
8159	S	D	G	H	1973	82255
8159	S	T	G	H	1973	82255
8159	S	D	G	N	1974	93012
8159	S	D	E	H	1974	93218
8185	S	D	R	H	1974	87071
8185	S	D	E	H	1974	87072
8230	S	D	R	H	1974	75323
8230	S	D	G	H	1973	82255
8230	S	T	G	H	1973	82255
8230	S	D	G	N	1974	93012
8230	S	D	E	H	1974	93218
8265	G	S	E	N	1973	53059
8270	T	T	O	N	1974	88134
8271	T	T	O	N	1974	88134
8279	S	D	R	H	1974	75323
8279	S	D	E	H	1974	93218
8280	S	D	R	H	1974	75323
8280	S	D	G	H	1973	82255
8280	S	T	G	H	1973	82255
8280	S	D	G	N	1974	93012
8280	S	D	E	H	1974	93218
8281	S	D	R	H	1974	75323

Substance Number	Phys. State	Sub-ject	Lan-guage	Temper-ature	Year	EPIC Number
104-8281	S	D	G	H	1973	82255
8281	S	T	G	H	1973	82255
8281	S	D	G	N	1974	93012
8281	S	D	E	H	1974	93218
8282	S	D	R	H	1974	75323
8282	S	D	G	H	1973	82255
8282	S	T	G	H	1973	82255
8282	S	D	G	N	1974	93012
8282	S	D	E	H	1974	93218
8283	S	D	R	H	1974	75323
8283	S	D	G	H	1973	82255
8283	S	T	G	H	1973	82255
8283	S	D	G	N	1974	93012
8283	S	D	E	H	1974	93218
8284	S	S	E	N	1974	93387
8301	S	D	E	N	1973	65641
8302	S	D	E	N	1973	65641
8303	S	D	G	H	1969	86378
8303	S	D	G	N	1969	86378
8303	S	D	E	H	1972	86379
8303	S	D	E	N	1972	86379
8305	S	S	E	H	1972	87656
8344	S	D	G	H	1973	82255
8344	S	T	G	H	1973	82255
8344	S	D	G	N	1974	93012
8346	S	D	E	N	1973	65641
8347	S	D	E	N	1973	65641
8401	S	D	O	N	1974	67789
8434	S	D	G	H	1973	82255
8434	S	T	G	H	1973	82255
8435	S	D	G	H	1973	82255
8435	S	T	G	H	1973	82255
106-0004	S	D	E	N	1974	53627
0004	S	S	E	N	1969	68271
0004	S	S	E	N	1975	96477
0006	S	D	E	N	1975	86763
0008	T	D	E	N	1974	54061
0008	T	D	E	N	1974	67124
0008	T	T	E	N	1974	67124
0024	S	D	E	N	1971	83801
0024	S	D	E	N	1975	86763
0035	S	D	E	N	1973	53037
0035	S	S	E	H	1965	87702
0035	S	S	E	N	1965	87702
0035	S	S	E	N	1968	87828
0035	S	S	E	N	1971	87887
0057	S	S	E	N	1969	68271
0057	S	S	E	N	1966	68325
0081	S	D	E	N	1973	52826
0095	S	D	E	N	1973	52826
0104	S	D	R	N	1973	51556
0104	S	D	E	N	1973	53687
0125	S	D	R	H	1972	49817
0125	S	D	R	H	1972	50044
0125	S	D	R	H	1973	52392
0125	S	D	E	H	1973	54539
0125	S	D	R	H	1973	71960
0125	S	D	R	H	1974	75323
0125	S	D	E	H	1973	82779
0125	S	D	R	H	1974	86075
0125	S	D	E	H	1975	86076
0125	S	D	G	H	1974	93012
0125	S	D	E	H	1974	93218
0127	S	S	E	N	1947	66510
0159	S	D	E	N	1975	86763
0168	G	S	E	N	1973	53059
0203	T	D	R	N	1974	62567
0205	S	D	R	H	1972	50044
0226	S	D	R	H	1972	50044
0237	S	S	E	N	1975	86763
0237	T	S	E	N	1972	87889
0308	D	D	R	H	1973	71775
0308	D	D	R	N	1973	71775
0308	D	D	E	H	1974	81483
0308	D	D	E	N	1974	81483
0308	S	D	R	H	1972	50044
0308	S	S	R	N	1970	53179
0308	S	S	E	N	1972	53180
0308	S	D	R	H	1973	71775
0308	S	S	R	N	1973	71775
0308	S	D	R	H	1974	75323
0308	S	D	E	H	1974	81483
0308	S	S	E	H	1974	81483
0308	S	S	E	N	1974	81483
0308	S	D	G	H	1974	93012
0308	S	D	E	H	1974	93218
0308	S	D	R	H	1976	99762
0308	S	S	R	H	1976	99762
0308	S	D	E	H	1976	101355
0308	S	S	E	H	1976	101355
0309	S	D	R	H	1972	50044
0309	S	S	E	H	1966	87721
0309	S	S	E	N	1966	87721

Phys. State: A. Amorphous; C. Superconductive; D. Doped; F. Fibrous or Whisker; G. Gas; I. Ionized or Plasma; L. Liquid; P. Powder or Particle; S. Solid; T. Thin Film
Subject: D. Data; E. Experiment; S. Survey (Review, Compendium, etc.); T. Theory
Language: E. English; F. French; G. German; O. Other Languages; R. Russian
Temperature: L. Low (0 to 75K); N. Normal (75 to 1273K); H. High (above 1273K)

Substance Number	Phys. State	Subject	Language	Temperature	Year	EPIC Number
106-0310	S	D	R	H	1972	49817
0353	S	S	E	N	1967	62829
0363	S	D	E	N	1973	57560
0363	S	D	E	N	1971	62312
0363	S	S	E	N	1969	68271
0363	S	D	E	N	1974	80374
0363	S	S	E	N	1975	92725
0363	S	S	E	N	1975	96148
0363	T	S	E	N	1967	66156
0417	S	S	R	N	1970	53179
0417	S	S	E	N	1972	53180
0508	S	D	E	N	1974	53627
0508	S	S	E	N	1969	68271
0639	S	D	R	H	1972	50044
0744	S	S	R	N	1970	53179
0744	S	S	E	N	1972	53180
0937	S	S	R	N	1970	53179
0937	S	S	E	N	1972	53180
0937	S	D	R	H	1974	75323
0937	S	D	G	H	1974	93012
0937	S	D	E	H	1974	93218
1001	S	D	R	H	1972	51450
1001	S	D	E	H	1972	53035
1027	S	D	R	H	1972	49817
1027	S	D	R	H	1972	51450
1027	S	D	E	H	1972	53035
1027	S	D	R	H	1974	75323
1027	S	D	G	H	1974	93012
1027	S	D	E	H	1974	93218
1062	S	D	R	H	1972	51450
1062	S	D	E	H	1972	53035
1062	S	D	R	H	1974	75323
1062	S	D	G	H	1974	93012
1062	S	D	E	H	1974	93218
1287	S	D	R	H	1974	75323
1287	S	D	G	H	1974	93012
1287	S	D	E	H	1974	93218
8008	D	D	O	N	1974	67789
8008	S	T	O	N	1971	67029
8040	S	D	E	N	1971	62312
8040	S	S	E	N	1969	68271
8040	S	S	E	N	1976	97315
8041	S	D	E	N	1971	62312
8041	S	S	E	N	1969	68271
8041	S	S	E	N	1967	68371
8041	S	D	E	N	1975	94613
8041	S	S	E	N	1976	97315
8041	T	S	E	N	1967	68371
8045	S	D	E	N	1974	53627
8045	S	S	E	N	1969	68271
8048	S	D	E	N	1974	53627
8050	T	D	E	N	1972	53477
8050	T	S	E	N	1972	87889
8063	S	D	R	N	1973	51370
8063	S	T	R	N	1973	51370
8063	S	D	E	N	1973	51371
8063	S	T	E	N	1973	51371
8084	S	D	E	H	1974	93218
8086	S	D	E	H	1974	93218
8087	S	D	E	H	1974	93218
8088	S	D	E	H	1974	93218
8089	S	D	E	H	1974	93218
8090	S	D	E	H	1974	93218
8091	S	D	E	H	1974	93218
8262	S	D	O	N	1973	58160
8262	S	D	R	H	1974	75323
8262	S	D	E	H	1974	93218
8271	S	S	E	N	1975	96148
8355	T	D	E	N	1972	53475
8388	S	D	E	N	1972	80067
8530	S	D	R	N	1973	51528
8530	S	D	E	N	1973	53680
8537	G	S	E	N	1973	53059
8542	S	S	E	N	1972	80067
8548	S	D	R	H	1974	86075
8548	S	D	E	H	1975	86076
8558	S	D	R	H	1974	75323
8558	S	D	G	H	1974	93012
8558	S	D	E	H	1974	93218
8559	S	D	R	H	1974	75323
8559	S	D	G	H	1974	93012
8559	S	D	E	H	1974	93218
109-0025	S	S	E	N	1973	53587
110-0024	S	D	E	N	1974	66105
0024	S	T	E	N	1974	66105
0024	S	S	E	N	1975	86763
0025	S	S	E	N	1947	66510
0030	S	S	E	N	1947	66510
0036	S	S	E	N	1975	86763
0037	S	S	E	N	1975	86763
0061	S	S	E	N	1975	86763
0156	S	S	E	N	1967	62829
8199	S	D	O	N	1973	58160
8199	S	D	R	H	1974	75323
8199	S	D	E	H	1974	93218
111-0008	S	D	R	N	1973	52892
0008	S	D	E	N	1974	52893
0008	S	D	E	N	1971	62264
111-0008	S	D	E	N	1974	80374
0008	S	S	E	N	1971	87884
8002	S	S	E	N	1971	87884
8002	S	S	E	N	1975	100607
8006	S	T	R	N	1974	60425
8006	S	T	E	N	1974	60426
8014	S	T	R	N	1974	60425
8014	S	T	E	N	1974	60426
8021	S	S	E	N	1969	68115
112-0001	S	S	R	N	1973	51370
0001	S	S	E	N	1973	51371
0011	S	S	E	N	1969	68271
0247	S	D	R	H	1974	93037
0247	S	D	R	N	1974	93037
0247	S	D	E	H	1975	93038
0247	S	D	E	N	1975	93038
0402	S	D	E	N	1973	57560
8025	S	S	E	N	1969	68271
114-0009	T	D	E	N	1973	52659
0017	S	S	E	N	1971	87884
0060	S	D	R	N	1970	52677
8001	S	D	E	N	1972	49929
8001	S	S	E	N	1963	87679
8001	S	S	E	N	1965	87781
8001	S	S	E	N	1971	87884
8001	T	S	E	N	1965	87781
8051	S	D	R	N	1970	52677
119-0001	S	T	E	N	1973	57480
0001	S	D	E	N	1974	89519
0002	P	S	E	H	1966	63913
0002	P	S	E	N	1966	63913
0002	S	T	E	N	1973	52794
0002	S	D	E	N	1974	53627
0002	S	S	E	H	1966	63913
0002	S	S	E	N	1966	63913
0002	S	S	E	N	1969	68271
0002	S	S	E	H	1963	87682
0002	S	S	E	N	1963	87682
0002	S	S	E	N	1969	87723
0002	T	S	E	N	1966	63913
0005	S	D	R	N	1975	86859
0005	S	D	E	N	1975	86860
0015	S	D	E	N	1973	65641
0015	S	D	R	N	1975	86859
0015	S	D	E	N	1975	86860
0064	S	D	E	N	1974	53627
8008	S	D	E	N	1974	53627
8018	S	D	G	H	1973	82255
8018	S	T	G	H	1973	82255
8058	S	D	R	H	1974	75323
8058	S	D	G	N	1974	93012
8058	S	D	E	H	1974	93218
8079	S	D	R	N	1973	58734
8079	S	D	E	N	1974	68941
120-0001	D	D	E	N	1973	50019
0001	D	D	E	N	1973	52825
0001	D	D	E	N	1971	52970
0001	D	D	R	N	1973	58292
0001	S	D	E	N	1973	50019
0001	S	D	E	N	1973	50438
0001	S	D	R	N	1973	50634
0001	S	D	E	N	1973	52823
0001	S	D	E	N	1973	52824
0001	S	D	E	N	1973	53032
0001	S	D	E	N	1973	53754
0001	S	D	E	N	1975	90821
0001	T	D	E	N	1974	67124
0001	T	T	E	N	1974	67124
0010	S	D	R	N	1973	52568
0017	S	D	R	H	1974	93037
0017	S	D	R	N	1974	93037
0017	S	D	E	H	1975	93038
0017	S	D	E	N	1975	93038
0023	S	D	R	H	1974	93037
0023	S	D	R	N	1974	93037
0023	S	D	E	H	1975	93038
0023	S	D	E	N	1975	93038
8024	T	S	E	N	1971	87885
122-0003	S	S	R	N	1970	53179
0003	S	S	E	N	1972	53180
0003	T	D	E	H	1972	86959
0004	S	S	E	N	1974	93387
0005	P	D	F	N	1973	55913
0005	P	D	F	N	1973	55914
0005	S	D	R	N	1973	50634
0005	S	D	E	N	1973	52173
0005	S	E	E	N	1973	52173
0005	S	T	E	N	1973	52794
0005	S	D	E	N	1973	53032
0023	D	T	R	N	1974	80752
0023	D	T	E	N	1974	95261
0023	S	S	E	N	1974	53916
0023	S	S	E	N	1969	68271
0023	S	S	E	N	1963	87709
0031	S	D	R	N	1973	51370
0031	S	T	R	N	1973	51370
122-0031	S	D	E	N	1973	51371
0031	S	T	E	N	1973	51371
0031	S	D	E	N	1974	53627
0031	S	S	E	N	1969	68271
0031	S	D	R	N	1972	76508
0031	S	S	R	N	1972	76508
0031	S	D	E	N	1972	91530
0031	S	S	E	N	1972	91530
0031	S	S	E	N	1975	96477
0031	T	S	R	N	1970	53179
0031	T	S	E	N	1972	53180
0037	S	D	R	N	1973	52568
0050	S	S	E	N	1947	66510
0050	S	S	E	N	1969	68115
0050	T	S	E	N	1967	66368
0050	T	S	E	N	1967	68368
0096	T	D	O	N	1974	67787
0208	S	D	R	N	1973	52568
8004	T	D	E	N	1972	53475
8041	S	D	R	N	1973	52568
123-0003	S	S	E	N	1969	68115
8017	S	S	E	N	1969	68115
8018	S	S	E	N	1970	68114
8018	S	S	E	N	1969	68115
126-0005	S	S	E	N	1969	68271
0017	S	D	E	N	1974	53627
0017	S	S	E	N	1969	68271
8037	S	S	E	N	1970	68114
8037	S	S	E	N	1969	68115
8052	S	D	E	N	1973	57560
8052	S	D	E	N	1971	62264
8052	S	S	E	N	1969	68271
8061	S	D	R	H	1974	75323
8061	S	D	G	N	1974	93012
8061	S	D	E	H	1974	93218
8062	S	D	O	N	1973	58160
8062	S	D	R	H	1974	75323
8062	S	D	G	N	1974	93012
8062	S	D	E	H	1974	93218
8079	S	D	E	N	1974	53627
8079	S	S	E	N	1969	68271
8080	S	D	E	N	1974	53627
8108	S	D	O	N	1973	58160
8108	S	D	R	H	1974	75323
8108	S	D	G	N	1974	93012
8108	S	D	E	H	1974	93218
8109	S	D	R	H	1974	75323
8109	S	D	G	N	1974	93012
8109	S	D	E	H	1974	93218
127-8004	S	S	E	N	1969	68271
8004	S	S	E	N	1976	97315

Phys. State: **A.** Amorphous; **C.** Superconductive; **D.** Doped; **F.** Fibrous or Whisker; **G.** Gas; **I.** Ionized or Plasma; **L.** Liquid; **P.** Powder or Particle; **S.** Solid; **T.** Thin Film
Subject: **D.** Data; **E.** Experiment; **S.** Survey (Review, Compendium, etc.); **T.** Theory
Language: **E.** English; **F.** French; **G.** German; **O.** Other Languages; **R.** Russian
Temperature: **L.** Low (0 to 75K); **N.** Normal (75 to 1273K); **H.** High (above 1273K)

Chapter 22 Piezoelectric Properties

Substance Number	Phys. State	Sub-ject	Lan-guage	Temper-ature	Year	EPIC Number
100-0045	S	S	E	N	1974	58043
0055	S	T	E	N	1974	54341
0055	S	E	E	N	1973	54838
0055	S	T	E	N	1974	58810
0055	S	T	E	N	1972	75889
0055	S	T	E	N	1975	91784
8003	S	D	E	N	1973	57710
8003	S	T	R	N	1974	58064
8003	S	T	E	N	1974	58065
8003	S	E	R	N	1972	66855
8007	S	S	E	N	1974	54346
8007	S	S	E	N	1969	68271
8007	S	S	E	N	1972	87823
8008	S	S	E	N	1971	87884
8038	S	S	E	N	1969	68115
102-0005	S	D	E	N	1974	58043
0005	S	D	E	N	1974	61365
0054	S	S	E	N	1975	68617
0054	S	S	E	N	1970	87822
0054	S	S	E	N	1972	87890
0054	S	S	E	N	1976	101320
0105	S	D	E	N	1974	58043
0105	S	S	E	N	1971	87884
0105	T	D	E	N	1974	57903
0248	S	D	E	N	1974	58043
0248	S	S	E	N	1971	87884
0250	S	S	E	N	1973	60833
0281	S	S	E	N	1976	101320
0282	S	D	E	N	1975	68617
0282	S	S	E	N	1976	101320
0342	S	D	E	N	1974	90344
8001	D	S	E	N	1971	87884
8001	S	D	E	N	1974	58043
8001	S	S	R	N	1970	66024
8001	S	S	E	N	1970	66025
8001	S	S	E	N	1966	87830
8001	S	S	E	N	1971	87884
8027	S	S	E	N	1975	68617
8027	S	S	E	N	1970	87822
8027	S	S	E	N	1976	101320
8028	S	S	E	N	1972	87890
8041	D	S	E	N	1964	87701
8041	S	S	E	N	1973	55127
8041	S	D	E	N	1973	56818
8041	S	D	E	N	1974	58043
8041	S	S	R	N	1970	66024
8041	S	S	E	N	1970	66025
8041	S	D	E	N	1966	75395
8041	S	S	E	N	1966	75395
8041	S	S	E	N	1973	86380
8041	S	S	E	N	1962	87673
8041	S	S	E	N	1964	87701
8041	S	S	E	N	1971	87884
8054	S	S	E	L	1974	53913
8054	S	D	E	N	1974	58043
8054	S	S	R	N	1970	66024
8054	S	S	E	N	1970	66025
8054	S	S	E	N	1962	87667
8054	S	S	E	N	1971	87884
8090	S	D	E	N	1973	50008
8090	S	D	E	N	1973	55151
8090	S	T	E	N	1973	55151
8132	S	D	E	N	1974	58043
8132	S	S	E	N	1971	87884
8134	S	S	E	N	1972	87890
8137	S	D	E	N	1975	68617
8137	S	S	E	N	1976	101320
8166	S	S	E	N	1976	101320
8439	S	S	E	N	1976	101320
104-0002	S	D	E	N	1974	58043
0002	S	S	E	N	1969	68271
0007	S	D	E	N	1974	58043
0007	S	S	E	N	1971	87884
0007	S	S	E	N	1972	102094
0013	D	D	E	N	1972	49836
0013	D	D	R	N	1973	51280
0013	D	E	R	N	1973	51280
0013	D	D	O	N	1973	52219
0013	D	D	F	N	1973	53868
0013	S	S	E	N	1972	53208
0013	S	T	R	N	1973	54982
0013	S	T	E	N	1974	54983
0013	S	T	R	N	1973	56885
0013	S	S	R	N	1973	58749
0013	S	T	E	N	1975	64577
0013	S	D	G	N	1974	90255
0013	S	D	E	N	1974	90345
0013	S	T	E	N	1974	90345
0013	S	D	E	N	1974	90351
0013	S	T	E	N	1974	90351
0013	T	D	E	N	1973	53451
0013	T	D	E	N	1967	85905
0022	S	D	E	N	1974	58043
104-0104	S	D	R	N	1974	60399
0104	S	D	E	N	1974	60400
0295	S	S	E	N	1971	87884
0533	S	S	E	N	1973	55127
0533	S	S	E	N	1970	87822
0533	S	S	E	N	1972	87890
8042	S	S	E	N	1966	66068
8045	S	S	E	N	1966	66068
8110	S	S	E	N	1973	55127
8110	S	S	E	N	1970	87822
8110	S	S	E	N	1972	87890
8160	S	T	R	N	1973	51360
8160	S	T	E	N	1973	51361
8161	D	D	R	N	1973	52500
8161	D	D	E	N	1974	63246
8161	S	T	R	N	1973	51360
8161	S	T	E	N	1973	51361
8161	S	D	R	N	1973	52500
8161	S	D	E	N	1974	63246
8169	S	D	E	N	1973	56344
8169	S	D	E	N	1974	68409
8171	D	D	E	N	1973	66096
8171	S	D	O	L	1973	54850
8171	S	D	O	N	1973	54850
8171	S	D	O	L	1973	65654
8171	S	D	O	N	1973	65654
8285	S	D	E	N	1973	53958
8421	S	D	E	N	1974	88201
8421	S	T	E	N	1974	88201
106-0006	D	D	E	N	1976	97743
0006	D	E	E	N	1976	97743
0006	D	S	E	N	1976	97743
0006	S	D	R	N	1972	66855
0006	S	D	E	N	1976	97743
0006	S	E	E	N	1976	97743
0006	S	S	E	N	1976	97743
0024	S	S	E	N	1973	60840
0024	S	D	R	N	1972	66855
0026	S	D	R	N	1974	60399
0026	S	D	E	N	1974	60400
0035	S	D	R	N	1973	51618
0035	S	D	E	N	1974	58043
0035	S	S	E	N	1968	87828
0035	S	S	E	N	1971	87887
0036	S	D	E	N	1974	58043
0158	S	D	E	N	1974	54346
0158	S	D	E	N	1974	58043
0363	D	D	R	N	1971	51987
0363	D	S	E	N	1967	66156
0363	S	D	G	N	1973	52664
0363	S	S	E	N	1974	54075
0363	S	E	E	N	1973	54838
0363	S	D	R	N	1973	55058
0363	S	D	E	N	1974	55059
0363	S	S	E	N	1973	55127
0363	S	T	R	N	1973	55300
0363	S	T	E	N	1973	57563
0363	S	D	E	N	1974	58043
0363	S	T	E	N	1974	59225
0363	S	T	E	N	1974	61182
0363	S	S	E	N	1963	64232
0363	S	D	E	N	1974	64986
0363	S	T	E	N	1974	64986
0363	S	S	R	N	1970	66024
0363	S	S	E	N	1970	66025
0363	S	S	E	N	1967	66156
0363	S	S	E	N	1969	68271
0363	S	S	E	N	1972	87823
8040	D	S	E	N	1963	87710
8040	S	D	E	N	1973	50040
8040	S	D	R	N	1973	51384
8040	S	D	E	N	1973	51385
8040	S	D	G	N	1973	52664
8040	S	T	R	N	1973	55300
8040	S	T	E	N	1973	57563
8040	S	D	E	N	1974	58043
8040	S	D	R	N	1972	58690
8040	S	T	E	N	1974	59225
8040	S	S	R	N	1970	66024
8040	S	S	E	N	1970	66025
8040	S	S	E	N	1969	68271
8040	S	S	E	N	1972	87823
8041	S	D	G	N	1973	52664
8041	S	S	E	N	1972	53359
8041	S	D	E	N	1974	58043
8041	S	S	E	N	1969	68271
8041	S	S	E	N	1967	68371
8132	S	S	E	N	1972	87823
8209	S	D	E	N	1974	53603
8209	S	T	E	N	1974	53603
8241	S	S	E	N	1970	87822
8241	S	S	E	N	1972	87890
8253	S	D	F	N	1973	51480
8254	S	D	F	N	1973	51480
106-8473	S	D	E	N	1974	55119
108-0014	S	S	E	N	1970	87822
0014	S	S	E	N	1972	87890
0014	S	S	E	N	1976	101320
0114	S	S	E	N	1976	101320
110-0024	S	D	R	N	1974	58086
0024	S	T	R	N	1974	58086
0024	S	D	E	N	1974	58087
0024	S	T	E	N	1974	58087
0024	S	D	R	N	1972	66855
0036	S	D	R	N	1974	58064
0036	S	S	R	N	1974	58064
0036	S	D	E	N	1974	58065
0036	S	S	E	N	1974	58065
0132	S	D	R	N	1974	60399
0132	S	D	E	N	1974	60400
111-0008	S	D	O	N	1973	57210
0008	S	D	E	N	1974	58043
0008	S	S	R	N	1970	66024
0008	S	S	E	N	1970	66025
0008	S	S	E	N	1971	87884
0021	S	D	E	N	1974	58043
0046	S	D	G	N	1973	51929
0046	S	D	E	N	1972	53169
0046	S	D	E	N	1972	53240
0046	S	D	E	N	1974	90306
0050	S	D	E	N	1974	53603
0050	S	T	E	N	1974	53603
8002	D	S	E	N	1962	87670
8002	S	D	E	N	1974	58043
8002	S	S	R	N	1970	66024
8002	S	S	E	N	1970	66025
8002	S	S	E	N	1962	87670
8002	S	S	E	N	1971	87884
8031	S	S	E	N	1972	87889
8042	S	D	E	N	1972	93293
8042	S	E	E	N	1972	93293
8042	S	S	E	N	1972	93293
8042	S	T	E	N	1972	93293
8061	S	D	R	L	1974	58094
8061	S	D	R	N	1974	58094
8061	S	D	E	L	1974	58095
8061	S	D	E	N	1974	58095
8125	S	D	E	N	1974	58322
112-0028	S	D	R	N	1973	55034
0028	S	E	R	N	1973	55034
0028	S	D	E	N	1974	55035
0028	S	E	E	N	1974	55035
0028	S	S	E	N	1975	68617
0028	S	S	E	N	1970	87822
0028	S	S	E	N	1972	87890
0028	S	S	E	N	1976	101320
0035	S	D	R	N	1973	55034
0035	S	E	R	N	1973	55034
0035	S	D	E	N	1974	55035
0035	S	E	E	N	1974	55035
0035	S	D	E	N	1975	91944
0038	S	D	R	N	1973	55034
0038	S	E	R	N	1973	55034
0038	S	D	E	N	1974	55035
0038	S	E	E	N	1974	55035
0038	S	S	E	N	1975	68617
0038	S	S	E	N	1970	87822
0038	S	S	E	N	1972	87890
0038	S	S	E	N	1976	101320
0402	S	D	E	N	1973	50571
0402	S	S	E	N	1969	68271
0583	S	D	E	N	1975	68617
0583	S	S	E	N	1976	101320
8025	S	D	E	N	1974	58043
114-0001	D	E	E	N	1963	64750
0001	S	E	E	N	1963	64750
0009	S	D	R	N	1974	58064
0009	S	S	R	N	1974	58064
0009	S	D	E	N	1974	58065
0009	S	S	E	N	1974	58065
0017	D	D	E	N	1975	63562
0017	D	T	E	N	1975	63562
0017	S	D	E	N	1974	58043
0017	S	S	R	N	1970	66024
0017	S	S	E	N	1970	66025
0017	S	S	E	N	1962	87660
0017	S	S	E	N	1971	87884
0017	S	S	E	N	1963	98002
0060	S	D	R	N	1974	60437
0060	S	D	E	N	1974	60438
8001	A	S	E	N	1970	59557
8001	D	S	E	N	1963	87679
8001	D	S	E	N	1965	87781
8001	D	S	E	N	1971	87884

Phys. State: **A.** Amorphous; **C.** Superconductive; **D.** Doped; **F.** Fibrous or Whisker; **G.** Gas; **I.** Ionized or Plasma; **L.** Liquid; **P.** Powder or Particle; **S.** Solid; **T.** Thin Film
Subject: **D.** Data; **E.** Experiment; **S.** Survey (Review, Compendium, etc.); **T.** Theory
Language: **E.** English; **F.** French; **G.** German; **O.** Other Languages; **R.** Russian
Temperature: **L.** Low (0 to 75K); **N.** Normal (75 to 1273K); **H.** High (above 1273K)

Substance Number	Phys. State	Subject	Language	Temperature	Year	EPIC Number
114-8001	S	D	E	N	1973	51833
8001	S	D	E	N	1974	58043
8001	S	S	E	N	1970	59557
8001	S	S	R	N	1970	66024
8001	S	S	E	N	1970	66025
8001	S	D	R	N	1972	67057
8001	S	S	E	N	1963	87679
8001	S	S	E	N	1965	87781
8001	S	S	E	N	1971	87884
8045	S	D	E	N	1973	50939
8046	S	D	E	N	1973	50939
116-0017	S	D	E	L	1973	57638
0017	S	T	E	N	1975	64577
0031	S	T	E	N	1975	64577
0031	S	D	E	N	1974	90342
0031	S	T	E	N	1974	90342
8017	S	T	E	N	1975	64577
8025	D	D	E	N	1975	91963
8025	S	D	E	N	1975	91963
118-0037	S	D	R	N	1973	50203
0037	S	D	E	N	1973	50204
0037	S	D	R	N	1972	54942
0037	S	S	E	N	1973	55127
0037	S	D	E	N	1973	55151
0037	S	S	R	N	1973	56887
0037	S	D	R	N	1973	56888
0037	S	D	R	N	1974	58094
0037	S	D	E	N	1974	58095
0037	S	D	R	N	1974	58132
0037	S	E	R	N	1974	58132
0037	S	D	E	N	1974	58133
0037	S	E	E	N	1974	58133
0037	S	D	E	N	1974	60503
0037	S	S	E	N	1970	87822
0037	S	S	E	N	1972	87890
0037	S	D	R	N	1975	90144
0037	S	E	R	N	1975	90144
0037	S	T	R	N	1975	90144
0037	S	D	E	N	1975	90145
0037	S	E	E	N	1975	90145
0037	S	T	E	N	1975	90145
0041	S	S	R	N	1973	56887
0041	S	D	R	N	1973	56888
0041	S	D	E	N	1973	57719
0041	S	S	E	N	1970	87822
0041	S	S	E	N	1972	87890
0042	S	S	E	N	1972	53208
0042	S	T	R	L	1974	68626
0042	S	T	R	N	1974	68626
0042	S	T	E	L	1975	68627
0042	S	T	E	N	1975	68627
8018	S	D	E	N	1973	51258
8018	S	D	E	N	1973	52123
8018	S	E	E	N	1973	52123
8075	S	D	E	N	1974	63253
8076	S	D	E	N	1974	63253
120-0235	S	T	R	N	1973	51360
0235	S	T	E	N	1973	51361
0235	S	S	E	N	1972	53208
122-0012	S	D	E	N	1975	90692
0013	D	D	O	N	1972	49897
0013	S	D	O	N	1972	49897
0013	S	S	R	N	1974	86817
0013	S	S	E	N	1975	92635
0023	D	S	E	N	1963	87709
0023	S	D	E	N	1973	51525
0023	S	D	G	N	1973	52664
0023	S	T	R	N	1973	55300
0023	S	D	R	N	1973	55706
0023	S	T	E	N	1973	57563
0023	S	D	E	N	1974	58043
0023	S	D	R	N	1972	58690
0023	S	T	E	N	1974	59225
0023	S	S	R	N	1970	66024
0023	S	S	E	N	1970	66025
0023	S	S	E	N	1969	68271
0023	T	D	E	N	1973	53352
0023	T	D	E	N	1973	57273
0030	S	T	E	N	1975	64577
0030	S	T	E	N	1974	90343
0105	S	D	E	N	1972	93290
0196	D	D	E	N	1972	49820
0196	D	D	E	N	1972	53292
0196	D	E	E	N	1972	53292
0196	S	D	E	N	1972	53076
0196	S	S	E	N	1972	53208
0196	S	D	E	N	1974	55119
0196	S	D	R	N	1972	58713
0196	S	T	E	N	1975	63345
0196	S	D	G	N	1974	90255
8067	S	D	E	N	1973	52576
123-0003	S	S	E	L	1969	68115
0003	S	S	E	N	1969	68115
0003	S	S	E	L	1966	68361
0003	S	S	E	N	1966	68361
8017	S	S	E	N	1969	68115
123-8018	S	S	E	N	1970	68114
8018	S	S	E	N	1969	68115
8018	S	S	E	N	1962	87671
126-0005	S	D	G	N	1973	52664
0005	S	T	R	N	1973	55300
0005	S	D	E	N	1974	58043
0005	S	T	E	N	1974	59225
0005	S	D	R	N	1974	60427
0005	S	D	E	N	1974	60428
0005	S	S	E	N	1969	68271
0005	S	S	E	N	1963	87711
0005	S	S	E	N	1966	87712
0005	T	T	E	N	1970	70578
0014	S	D	R	N	1974	58098
0014	S	D	E	N	1974	58099
8052	S	D	G	N	1973	52664
8052	S	T	E	N	1973	57563
8052	S	D	E	N	1974	58043
8052	S	S	E	N	1969	68271
8052	S	S	E	N	1963	68313
127-8004	S	D	G	N	1973	52664
8004	S	D	E	N	1974	58043
8004	S	S	E	N	1969	68271

Phys. State: A. Amorphous; C. Superconductive; D. Doped; F. Fibrous or Whisker; G. Gas; I. Ionized or Plasma; L. Liquid; P. Powder or Particle; S. Solid; T. Thin Film
Subject: D. Data; E. Experiment; S. Survey (Review, Compendium, etc.); T. Theory
Language: E. English; F. French; G. German; O. Other Languages; R. Russian
Temperature: L. Low (0 to 75K); N. Normal (75 to 1273K); H. High (above 1273K)

Part C
BIBLIOGRAPHY

PART C

USE OF THE BIBLIOGRAPHY

A. GENERAL CONSIDERATIONS

Because of the wide variety of literature sources cited (i.e., serial publications, dissertations, government and industrial reports, books, etc.), three specific formats for bibliographic citations are used in the *Bibliography*. In connection with the establishment of bibliographic format, a number of problems of general character are encountered in reporting bibliographic information on a broad scope, CINDAS procedures in coping with these problems are fully described below:

1. Titles reported in the *Bibliography* are taken either from an abstract or from the original work. In the case of translated titles, wide discrepancies often exist between various sources. In general, CINDAS makes no special effort to check the accuracy of titles.
2. The names of authors reported in abstracts, and even in original publications, are at times misspelled and/or incomplete. CINDAS attempts to report the correct names of authors.
3. The names of scientific and technical journals are normally abbreviated according to the notations used by the abstracting journals. In those cases where a journal name is not applicable, the name of the publisher, symposium, or disseminating agency is entered in place of the journal name, depending upon the reference work.
4. Keypunching format limitations necessitated the adoption of substitute representations for some of the symbols and alphabetic and numeric arrangements. The following are examples of substitute representations used in the *Bibliography:*
   a. Subscripts are either spelled out or written on the line. Examples:
      $C_P \equiv$ specific heat at constant pressure; $C_{12}H_{26} \equiv$ C12H26; etc.
   b. Superscripts are spelled out. Examples:
      $V^2 \equiv$ V squared; $\sqrt{2} \equiv$ square root of two; etc.
   c. Diacritical marks used with proper names or words have been omitted, and no attempt has been made to insert vowels or other speech sounds.

B. ABBREVIATIONS AND ACRONYMS USED IN BIBLIOGRAPHIC CITATIONS

AAAS.........American Association for the Advancement of Science
AAIE..........American Association of Industrial Engineers
AD............Prefix Catalog Codes for Defense Documentation Center (DDC) (Formerly ASTIA)
AEC...........Atomic Energy Commission
AEDC.........Arnold Engineering and Development Center
AF............Air Force
AFB...........Air Force Base
AFML.........Air Force Materials Laboratory
AFWL.........Air Force Weapons Laboratory
AGARD.......Advisory Group for Aeronautical Research and Development
AIAA.........American Institute of Aeronautics and Astronautics
AIAE..........Associate Institute of Automobile Engineering
AICE..........American Institute of Chemical Engineering
AIEE..........American Institute of Electrical Engineers (Now IEEE)
AIIE..........American Institute of Industrial Engineers
AIME.........American Institute of Mining and Metallurgical Engineers
AIP...........American Institute of Physics
AISI...........American Iron and Steel Institute
AM............Applied Mechanics Reviews
AMRA........Army Materials Research Agency
ANL..........Argonne National Laboratory
AOA..........American Ordnance Association
APDA.........Atomic Power Development Association, Inc.
API...........American Petroleum Institute
ARB...........ASTIA Report Bibliography
ARC..........Aeronautical Research Council
ARDE.........Armament Research and Development Establishment
ARF...........Armour Research Foundation
ARL...........Aeronautical Research Laboratories
ARS...........American Rocket Society (Now AIAA)
ASHRAE......American Society of Heating, Refrigeration, Air Conditioning Engineers
ASM..........American Society for Metals
ASME.........American Society for Mechanical Engineers
ASR...........American Society of Rocketry
ASSE..........American Society of Safety Engineers
ASTE..........American Society of Tool Engineers
ASTIA.........Armed Services Technical Information Agency (Now DDC)

ASTM.........American Society for Testing and Materials
ASTME....... American Society of Tool and Manufacturing Engineers
BC............ British Ceramic Society
BISI...........British Iron and Steel Industry
BR............ Battelle Technical Review
BTJ...........ASTIA Bibliographies
BU ORD.......Bureau of Ordnance
BU WEPS.....Bureau of Weapons
CFSTI.........Clearinghouse for Federal Scientific and Technical Information (Now NTIS)
CNEN.........Comitato Nazionale per L'Energia Nucleare (National Nuclear Energy Committee)
CNDR.........Consiglio Nazionale Delle Ricerche (National Research Council of Italy)
CNES......... Centre National D'Etudes Spatiales (National Center for Space Studies)
COSATI.......Committee on Scientific and Technical Information (Formerly COSI)
COSI.......... Committee on Scientific Information (Now COSATI)
CPIA..........Chemical Propulsion Information Agency
CRREL........Cold Regions Research and Engineering Laboratory
CSTAR........Confidential Scientific and Technical Aerospace Reports (Now STAR)
DASA......... Defense Atomic Support Agency
DDC.......... Defense Documentation Center
DDR&E........Directorate of Defense Research and Engineering
DMIC......... Defense Metals Information Center
DOD.......... U. S. Department of Defense
DOFL......... Diamond Ordnance Fuze Laboratory (HDL)
DPGR.........Dugway Proving Ground
ECOM.........Electronics Command, U. S. Army
EPIC.......... Electronic Properties Information Center
EURATOM.....European Atomic Energy Community
FAI........... Federation Aeronautique Internationale
FID........... International Federation of Documentation
FPL........... Forest Production Laboratory
FTD...........Foreign Technology Division
HDL.......... Harry Diamond Laboratory
IAA........... International Academy of Astronautics
IAS............Institute of Aero/Space Science (Now AIAA)
IEE............Institute of Electrical and Electronic Engineers (Formerly AIEE & IRE)
IEEE..........Institute of Electrical and Electronic Engineers
IIT............ Illinois Institute of Technology Research Institute
IPST...........Israel Program for Scientific Translation, Ltd.
IRE........... Institute of Radio Engineers (Now IEEE)
ISA............Instrument Society of America
JAERI.........Japan Atomic Energy Research Institute
JANAF........Joint Army–Navy–Air Force
JPL............Jet Propulsion Laboratory
KAPL.........Knolls Atomic Power Plant
MA............Metallurgical Abstracts, Series II
MR............ASM Review of Current Metal Literature (in Metals Review)
NADC.........Naval Air Development Center
NAS...........National Academy of Science
NASA.........National Aeronautics and Space Administration
NASC.........National Aeronautics and Space Council
NAS/NRC.....National Academy of Science—National Research Council
NATO.........North Atlantic Treaty Organization
NBS...........National Bureau of Standards
NDAC.........National Defense Advisory Committee
NDRC.........National Defense Research Council
NOTS......... Naval Ordnance Test Station
NPL...........National Physical Laboratory (England)
NRC.......... National Research Council (Canada)
NRD.......... Naval Research and Development (Now ONR)
NRL...........Naval Research Laboratory
NS............ Nuclear Science Abstracts
NSF...........National Science Foundation
NTIS..........National Technical Information Service (Formerly CFSTI)
OAR.......... Office Aerospace Research
ONERA....... Office National D'Etudes et de Recherches Aerospatiales (France)
ONR.......... Office of Naval Research
ORNL.........Oak Ridge National Laboratory
OSI............Office of Scientific Information
OSR...........Office of Scientific Research
OTS...........Office of Technological Service
RA............Refrigeration Abstracts
REIC..........Radiation Effects Information Center
RIA...........Rock Island Arsenal
RM............ASM Review of Metal Literature
RPL...........Rocket Propulsion Laboratory
RR............ U. S. Government Research Reports (OTS)
SIPRE.........Snow, Ice and Permafrost Research Establishment
STAR......... Scientific and Technical Aerospace Reports (Formerly CSTAR)
TA............Technical Abstracts Bulletin (AD)
TML.......... Titanium Metallurgical Laboratory
TPRC......... Thermophysical Properties Research Center
TT............ Technical Translations (OTS)
UCRL.........University of California Radiation Laboratory
UGAR.........United States Government Announcements Reports (Now GRA)
USAEC........U. S. Atomic Energy Commission
USBM.........U. S. Bureau of Mines
USDA.........U. S. Department of Agriculture
USJPRS....... U. S. Joint Publication Research Service
USL...........Underwater Sound Laboratory
WADC........Wright Air Development Center
WADD........Wright Air Development Division
WRAC........ Willow Run Aeronautical Center

BIBLIOGRAPHY

EPIC Number *Bibliographic Citation*

49416 PREPARATION AND SOME PHYSICAL PROPERTIES OF SILVER(I) OXIDE AND SILVER(II) OXIDE THIN FILMS.
FARHAT, E. ROBIN-KANDARE, S.
C. R. ACAD. SCI.
276 B (3), 127-30, 1973.

49419 MICROWAVE CONDUCTIVITY AND PERMITTIVITY IN GERMANIUM, SILICON, AND GALLIUM ARSENIDE.
KUMAR, A. KOTHARI, P. C.
J. PURE APPL. PHYS.
10 (10), 740-1, 1972.

49433 RESISTIVITY MEASUREMENTS OF INSULATORS AT HIGH TEMPERATURES USING THE FOUR-POINT PROBE TECHNIQUE.
SCHEMMEL, R. R. PHILIPP, L. D.
GORDON, R. L. BATES, J. L.
HANFORD ENGINEERING DEVELOPMENT LAB., RICHLAND, WASH.
42PP., 1972.
(HEDL-TME-72-73 N73-21243 AVAIL. NTIS)

49455 RADIATION EFFECTS IN IONIC CRYSTALS.
VOROB'EV, A. A. ZAVADOVSKAYA, E. K.
RADIATS. FIZ. KRIST. P-N-PEREKHODOV
28-32, 1972.
(FROM: NAUKA I TEKHNIKA: MINSK, USSR; EDITED BY N. N. SIROTA)

49458 OPTICAL AND TRANSPORT PROPERTIES OF AMORPHOUS ANTIMONY SELENIDE.
WOOD, C. HURYEH, Z. SHAFFER, J. C.
J. NON-CRYST. SOLIDS
8-10, 209-14, 1972.

49460 HALL COEFFICIENT OF LIQUID SEMICONDUCTORS.
DONALLY, J. M. CUTLER, M.
J. NON-CRYST. SOLIDS
8-10, 280, 1972.

49461 TRANSPORT PROPERTIES OF SILVER TELLURIDE AT THE MELTING POINT AND IN THE LIQUID STATE.
VAN DONG, N.
J. NON-CRYST. SOLIDS
8-10, 281-6, 1972.

49462 HALL EFFECT IN SEMICONDUCTING ELECTRONIC LIQUIDS.
ANDREEV, A. A. MAMADALIEV, M.
J. NON-CRYST. SOLIDS
8-10, 287-92, 1972.

49463 ELECTRICAL CONDUCTIVITY AND THERMOPOWER OF LIQUID CADMIUM GERMANIUM ARSENIDE.
HURST, C. H. DAVIS, E. A.
J. NON-CRYST. SOLIDS
8-10, 316-20, 1972.

49464 THERMOELECTRIC POWER OF AMORPHOUS SEMICONDUCTORS.
BEYER, W. STUKE, J.
J. NON-CRYST. SOLIDS
8-10, 321-5, 1972.

49465 ELECTRICAL PROPERTIES OF BISTABLE NIOBIUM PENTOXIDE FILMS.
HERRELL, D. J. PARK, K. C.
J. NON-CRYST. SOLIDS
8-10, 449-54, 1972.

49466 TEMPERATURE DEPENDENCE OF A.C. CONDUCTIVITY OF THIN EVAPORATED FILMS OF ARSENIC SULFIDES, ARSENIC SELENIDE, AND SELENIUM.
STREET, R. A. YOFFE, A. D.
J. NON-CRYST. SOLIDS
8-10, 745-51, 1972.

49467 PHOTOCONDUCTIVITY IN AMORPHOUS ANTIMONY-SELENIUM LAYERS.
HURYCH, Z. MUELLER, R. WANG, C. C.
WOOD, C.
J. NON-CRYST. SOLIDS
11 (2), 153-60, 1972.

49470 DEMONSTRATION OF A DOUBLE ELECTRICAL CONDUCTIVITY IN POTASSIUM NITRATE.
SIOUFLI, J. C.
C. R. ACAD. SCI.
275 (1), 37-40, 1972.

49471 THERMOLUMINESCENCE MECHANISM IN DOSIMETRY-TYPE LITHIUM FLUORIDE.
CHRISTY, R. W. MAYHUGH, M. R.
J. APPL. PHYS.
43 (7), 3216, 1972.

49474 EFFECT OF PRESSURE ON ELECTRICAL CONDUCTIVITIES OF FUSED ALKALI METAL HALIDES AND SILVER HALIDES.
CLEAVER, B. SMEDLEY, S. I. SPENCER, P. N.
J. CHEM. SOC., FARADAY TRANS. 1
68 (9), 1720-34, 1972.

49479 DIELECTRIC CONSTANT OF POTASSIUM NIOBATE SINGLE CRYSTALS UNDER BIASING CONDITIONS.
KULKARNI, R. H. INGLE, S. G.
J. PHYS.
5 (8), 1474-7, 1972.

49480 FERROELECTRIC HYSTERESIS LOOP OF SILVER SODIUM NITRITE BY QUASISTATIC ELECTRIC FIELD.
GESI, K.
J. PHYS. SOC. JAP.
32 (6), 1679, 1972.

49481 F(SUBSCRIPT B) CENTERS IN ALKALI HALIDES.
NISHIMAKI, N. MATSUSAKA, Y. DOI, Y.
J. PHYS. SOC. JAP.
33 (2), 424-9, 1972.

49483 ERROR IN THE POTASSIUM BROMIDE DISPERSION EQUATION.
JUNE, K. R.
APPL. OPT.
11 (7), 1655, 1972.

49485 PHOTOCONDUCTIVITY OF CADMIUM SULFIDE CRYSTALS IRRADIATED WITH FAST ELECTRONS.
YOSHIDA, T. OKA, T. KITAGAWA, M.
APPL. PHYS. LETT.
21 (1), 1-2, 1972.

49487 GALVANOMAGNETIC AND THERMOELECTRIC PROPERTIES OF URANIUM PHOSPHIDE AND URANIUM ARSENIDE.
HENKIE, Z.
BULL. ACAD. POL. SCI., SER. SCI. CHIM.
20 (6), 531-8, 1972.

49490 DEBYE TEMPERATURES AND ENERGY BAND GAP OF CUBIC SEMICONDUCTORS.
AGGARWAL, M. D. VERMA, J. K. D.
CZECH. J. PHYS.
22 (7), 621-3, 1972.

49493 INFLUENCE OF DEFORMATION ON THE CONDUCTIVITY AND PHOTOCONDUCTIVITY OF P-TYPE CADMIUM TELLURIDE.
SVOBODA, M. KLIER, E.
CZECH. J. PHYS.
22 (8), 725-56, 1972.

49494 INFLUENCE OF ANNEALING ON THE CONDUCTIVITY AND PHOTOCONDUCTIVITY OF P-TYPE CADMIUM TELLURIDE.
SVOBODA, M. KLIER, E.
CZECH. J. PHYS.
22 (8), 711-24, 1972.

49495 ELECTRICAL RESISTIVITY IN GOLD-COPPER ALLOY.
SRIVASTAVA, A. K. JOSHI, M. M.
INDIAN J. PURE APPL. PHYS.
10 (4), 260-2, 1972.

49502 MAGNETIC PROPERTIES OF ANTIFERROMAGNETIC NEPTUNIUM PHOSPHIDE.
LANDER, G. H. DUNLAP, B. D. LAM, D. J.
HARVEY, A. NOWIK, I. MUELLER, M. H.
ALDRED, A. T.
AIP (AMER. INST. PHYS.) CONF. PROC.
(10) (PT. 1), 88-92, 1973.

49503 ABSOLUTE MEASUREMENT OF THE TRANSVERSE K-DEPENDENT SUSCEPTIBILITY IN ANTIFERROMAGNETIC MANGANESE (II)-FLUORIDE.
LURIE, N. A. SHIRANE, G. HELLER, P.
LINZ, A.
AIP (AMER. INST. PHYS.) CONF. PROC.
(10) (PT. 1), 93-7, 1973.

49504 HYSTERETIC PROPERTIES OF SMALL, SOFT MAGNETIC BARS.
DOYLE, W. D. CASEY, M.
AIP (AMER. INST. PHYS.) CONF. PROC.
(10) (PT. 1), 227-31, 1973.

49505 DEPENDENCE OF THE UNIAXIAL MAGNETIC ANISOTROPY ON THE MISFIT STRAIN IN GADOLINIUM GALLIUM: YTTRIUM IRON GARNET LPE (LIQUID-PHASE EPITAXIAL) FILMS.
STACY, W. T. JANSSEN, M. M.
ROBERTSON, J. M. VAN HOUT, M. J. G.
AIP (AMER. INST. PHYS.) CONF. PROC.
(10) (PT. 1), 314-18, 1973.

49509 MAGNETIC PROPERTIES OF MANGANESE BORIDE.
NERESON, N. BOWMAN, A. ARNOLD, G.
AIP (AMER. INST. PHYS.) CONF. PROC.
(10) (PT. 1), 658, 1973.

49510 MAGNETIC PROPERTIES OF HOLMIUM-SILVER.
NERESON, N.
AIP (AMER. INST. PHYS.) CONF. PROC.
(10) (PT. 1), 669-73, 1973.

EPIC Number	Bibliographic Citation
49512	MOESSBAUER EFFECT STUDIES OF THE MAGNETIC PROPERTIES OF THE BISMUTH LANTHANUM IRON OXIDE SYSTEM. SHAUGHNESSY, T. P. CHEN, J. H. AIP (AMER. INST. PHYS.) CONF. PROC. (10) (PT. 2), 1143–7, 1973.
49513	MAGNETIC PROPERTIES OF THE SPINEL SYSTEM CHROMIUM MANGANESE SELENIDE SULFIDE. ROBBINS, M. GIBART, P. HOLMES, L. M. SHERWOOD, R. C. HULL, G. W. AIP (AMER. INST. PHYS.) CONF. PROC. (10) (PT. 2), 1153–7, 1973.
49516	STRONG MAGNETIC FIELD EFFECT ON MAGNETOELECTRIC PROPERTIES OF CHROMIUM (III) OXIDE SINGLE CRYSTAL. DAIDO, K. HOSHIKAWA, K. UEMURA, C. AIP (AMER. INST. PHYS.) CONF. PROC. (10) (PT. 2), 1416, 1973.
49517	MAGNETIC FIELD EFFECT IN THERMOMAGNETIC RECORDING. MINNAJA, N. BOSCHETTI, P. L. CHEN, D. AIP (AMER. INST. PHYS.) CONF. PROC. (10) (PT. 2), 1435–9, 1973.
49520	ELECTRIC CONDUCTIVITY AND THERMOELECTRIC POWER OF FERRIMAGNETICS WITH MAGNETOPLUMBITE STRUCTURE. BASZYNSKI, J. ACTA PHYS. POL. 43 A (4), 499–505, 1973.
49522	PARAMAGNETISM OF LITHIUM FERRITE–CHROMITES. OBUSZKO, Z. KOLODZIEJCZYK, A. PSZCZOLA, J. ACTA PHYS. POL. 43 A (4), 611–19, 1973.
49525	MAGNETIC, ELECTRICAL, AND PHYSICAL PROPERTIES OF LITHIUM OXIDE–IRON (III) OXIDE–SILICON DIOXIDE COMPOSITIONS. WEAVER, E. A. FIELD, M. B. AMER. CERAM. SOC., BULL. 52 (5), 467–72, 1973.
49526	INDICES OF REFRACTION OF THE BIAXIAL CRYSTAL YTTRIUM ORTHOALUMINATE. MARTIN, K. W. DE SHAZER, L. G. APPL. OPT. 12 (5), 941–3, 1973.
49528	PROPERTIES OF A HIGH–RESISTIVITY LAYER IN EPITAXIALLY GROWN GALLIUM ARSENIDE FILM. OKAMOTO, H. SAKATA, S. APPL. PHYS. LETT. 22 (9), 446–7, 1973.
49529	ANOMALOUSLY LARGE THERMOELECTRIC COOLING FIGURE OF MERIT IN THE KONDO SYSTEMS CERIUM–PALLADIUM AND CERIUM–INDIUM. GAMBINO, R. J. GROBMAN, W. D. TOXEN, A. M. APPL. PHYS. LETT. 22 (10), 506–7, 1973.
49530	GREEN LIGHT EMISSION FROM ZINC–DOPED ALUMINUM GALLIUM PHOSPHIDE ALLOYS. SONOMURA, H. NANMORI, T. MIYAUCHI, T. APPL. PHYS. LETT. 22 (10), 532–3, 1973.
49532	MAGNETIC ANISOTROPY OF EUROPIUM YTTRIUM IRON GALLIUM GARNET FILMS GROWN ON GARNET SUBSTRATES WITH DIFFERENT LATTICE PARAMETERS. GIESS, E. A. CRONEMEYER, D. C. APPL. PHYS. LETT. 22 (11), 601–2, 1973.
49533	OPTICAL AND ELECTRICAL PROPERTIES OF METAL PHOTODOPED CHALCOGENIDE GLASSES. SHIMIZU, I. SAKUMA, H. KOKADO, H. INOUE, E. BULL. CHEM. SOC. JAP. 46 (4), 1291–5, 1973.
49534	MAGNETISM AND ELECTRIC CONDUCTIVITY OF PYRITE–TYPE 3D TRANSITION METAL DISULFIDES. NARROW D BAND METALS. OGAWA, S. BUSSEI 14 (3), 155–65, 1973.
49538	PHOTOELECTRON SPECTRUM OF HYPOFLUOROUS ACID. BERKOWITZ, J. DEHMER, J. L. APPELMAN, E. H. CHEM. PHYS. LETT. 19 (3), 334–6, 1973.
49540	PRESENT UNDERSTANDING OF THE MAGNETIC PROPERTIES OF SAMARIUM COBALTIDE. MC CURRIE, R. A. COBALT (ENGL. ED.) (1), 23–4, 28, 1973.
49541	THERMOELECTRONIC EMISSION METHOD FOR INVESTIGATION OF POINT DEFECTS RESPONSIBLE FOR NONSTOICHIOMETRIC PHASES AT HIGH TEMPERATURE. LOUP, J. P. ODIER, PH. ANTHONY, A. M. COLLOG. INT. CENT. NAT. RECH. SCI. (205), 235–9, 1972.
49543	INFRARED, EPR AND PHOTOELECTRON SPECTROSCOPIC STUDY OF THE INTERACTION OF GASEOUS PROPYLENE AND OXYGEN WITH VANADIUM PENTOXIDE. VALDELIEVRE, M. DECHY, G. LEROY, J. M. C. R. ACAD. SCI. 276 C (14), 1179–82, 1973.
49544	CONDUCTIVITY OF ANTIMONY SESQUIOXIDE MELTS. ZENAIDI, N. RENAUD, R. JOSIEN, F. A. C. R. ACAD. SCI. 276 C (15), 1297–1300, 1973.
49545	ELECTRICAL PROPERTIES OF SODIUM CHLORIDE CRYSTALS DOPED WITH BISMUTH (3+) ION COORDINATELY BOUND ON OXYGEN. HARTMANOVA, M. MARIANA, E. LEBL, M. CZECH. J. PHYS. 22 (7), 623–7, 1972.
49546	MAGNETIC PROPERTIES OF CRYSTALLINE BORON. MATYAS, M. CZECH. J. PHYS. 23 (4), 473–8, 1973.
49547	FAR–INFRARED MEASUREMENT OF THE ENERGY GAP OF VANADIUM–SILICON. TANNER, D. B. SIEVERS, A. J. COO–3151–11 13PP., 1972. (AVAIL. DEP. NTIS)
49551	DEPENDENCE OF ZINC OXIDE LUMINESCENCE ON ADSORBED GASES. BLIZNAKOV, G. M. KUNEV, K. D. DAFINOVA, R. DOKL. BOLG. AKAD. NAUK 25 (6), 755–8, 1972.
49552	PREPARATION AND ELECTRIC PROPERTIES OF DOPED AND UNDOPED CADMIUM TELLURIDE SINGLE CRYSTALS. POLIVKA, P. ELEKTROTECH. CAS. 24 (1), 36–41, 1973.
49555	EPITAXIAL GALLIUM ARSENIDE CRYSTALS. II. ELECTRICAL PROPERTIES OF GALLIUM ARSENIDE EPITAXIAL LAYER. RYUZAN, O. KOTANI, T. AKITA, K. FUJITSU SCI. TECH. J. 8 (2), 131–47, 1972.
49557	MAGNETIC PROPERTIES OF HEXAAMMINECHROMIUM (III) PENTACHLOROCADMATE (II). HATFIELD, W. E. ESTES, W. E. JETER, D. Y. HEMPEL, J. C. INORG. CHEM. 10 (9), 2074–6, 1971.
49558	SHARP–LINE LUMINESCENCE AND ABSORPTION FOR THE HEXABROMOOSMATE (IV) ION IN SINGLE CRYSTALS OF CESIUM HEXABROMOZIRCONATE (IV) AT 20 K. NIMS, J. L. PATTERSON, H. H. KHAN, S. M. VALENCIA, C. M. INORG. CHEM. 12 (7), 1602–8, 1973.
49559	TERNARY COMPOUNDS IN A ZINC–CADMIUM–ANTIMONY SYSTEM. KAZITSYN, N. V. YURKOV, V. A. IZV. VYSSH. UCHEB. ZAVED., TSVET. MET. 15 (6), 65–70, 1972.
49561	ENERGY TRANSFER FROM GADOLINIUM (3+) TO PRASEODYMIUM (3+) AND YTTERBIUM (3+) IONS IN A FLUORITE CRYSTAL. ORLOV, M. S. SAITKULOV, I. G. IZV. AKAD. NAUK SSSR, SER. FIZ. 37 (3), 458–60, 1973. (FOR ENGLISH TRANSLATION SEE E54510)
49562	APPARATUS FOR MEASURING MAGNETIC SUSCEPTIBILITY. MEL'NIK, V. M. FIZ. ELEKTRON. (LVOV) (2), 97–9, 1970.
49563	STRUCTURE AND PHYSICAL PROPERTIES OF LEAD TELLURIDE THIN AND SUPERTHIN SINGLE–CRYSTAL LAYERS. BILEN'KII, B. F. SHRIBALO, YU. M. BILEN'SKII, B. F. SHRIBALO, YU. M. FIZ. ELEKTRON. (LVOV) (4), 52–7, 1971.
49564	EFFECT OF HIGH–DENSITY COLOR CENTERS ON THE COEFFICIENT OF SECONDARY ELECTRON EMISSION OF POTASSIUM CHLORIDE THIN FILMS. TRAVINA, V. N. MILIYANCHUK, M. V. PASHOVSKII, M. V. SAVITSKII, V. G. TSAL, M. O. FIZ. ELEKTRON. (LVOV) (4), 62–5, 1971.
49567	CATHODOLUMINESCENCE OF YTTRIUM ALUMINUM GARNET CRYSTALS WITH A CHROMIUM IMPURITY. ZAKHARKO, M. M. FIZ. ELEKTRON. (LVOV) (5), 69–71, 1972.

EPIC Number	Bibliographic Citation
49568	ELECTRON EMISSION OF INDIUM SELENIDE CRYSTALS IN STRONG ELECTRIC FIELDS. MILIYANCHUK, A. V. STAKHIRA, I. M. KUSHNIR, R. M. FIZ. ELEKTRON. (LVOV) (5), 78–81, 1972.
49569	EFFECT OF THE STRUCTURE OF LOW-DENSITY POTASSIUM CHLORIDE AND MAGNESIUM OXIDE THIN FILMS ON THEIR SECONDARY EMISSION. TRAVINA, V. N. FIZ. ELEKTRON. (LVOV) (5), 82–5, 1972.
49570	PREPARATION, STRUCTURE, AND ELECTRIC PROPERTIES OF TIN TELLURIDE THIN FILMS. GAIDUCHOK, G. M. VOITKIV, V. V. BRODIN, I. I. FREIK, D. M. FIZ. ELEKTRON. (LVOV) (5), 89–92, 1972.
49571	ELECTRIC PROPERTIES OF P-TYPE LEAD TELLURIDE SINGLE-CRYSTAL FILMS. NABITOVICH, I. D. BUDZHAK, YA. S. OSIPOVA, V. V. SHKRYBALO, YU. M. FIZ. ELEKTRON. (LVOV) (5), 93–6, 1972.
49573	PROCEDURE FOR CATHODOLUMINESCENCE STUDIES OF SOLIDS IN THE ENERGY REGION OF 100 EV–10 KEV. ZAKHARKO, M. M. FIZ. ELEKTRON. (LVOV) (5), 118–20, 1972.
49574	APPARATUS FOR STUDYING PHOTOCONDUCTIVITY AND OPTICAL CHARACTERISTICS OF CRYSTALS IN THE INFRARED SPECTRAL REGION. BILEN'KII, B. F. GRECHUKH, Z. G. LUK'YANETS, V. M. PASHKOVSKII, M. V. FIZ. ELEKTRON. (LVOV) (5), 134–5, 1972.
49575	LUMINESCENCE OF OXYGEN CENTERS IN ALUMINUM NITRIDE. PASTRNAK, J. PACESOVA, S. SANDA, J. ROSA, J. IZV. AKAD. NAUK SSSR, SER. FIZ. 37 (3), 599–602, 1973. (FOR ENGLISH TRANSLATION SEE E54513)
49578	ELECTRICAL AND PHYSICAL PROPERTIES OF A III(2)-B IV-C-VI(3) COMPOUNDS IN SOLID AND LIQUID STATES. GLAZOV, V. M. DOVLETOV, K. ATAEV, K. TASHLIEV, K. IZV. AKAD. NAUK TURKM. SSR, SER. FIZ.-TEKH., KHIM. GEOL. NAUK (2), 101–4, 1973.
49580	AFTERGLOW OF CALCIUM FLUORIDE-NEODYMIUM FLUORIDE CRYSTALS IRRADIATED BY COBALT-60 GAMMA-RAYS. TAVSHUNSKII, G. A. KAIPOV, B. IZV. AKAD. NAUK UZB. SSR, SER. FIZ.-MAT. NAUK (1), 82–4, 1973.
49581	MOLYBDENUM FLUOROBROMIDE. KHALDOYANIDI, K. A. OPALOVSKII, A. A. IZV. SIB. OTD. AKAD. NAUK SSSR, SER. KHIM. NAUK (2), 142–5, 1973.
49582	CONTINUOUS MODEL FOR TL (THERMOLUMINESCENCE) TRAPS. WATANABE, S. MORATO, S. P. INST. ENERG. AT., SAO PAULO, BRAZIL 18PP., 1971. (IEA-256, AVAIL. NTIS)
49583	MEASUREMENT OF MAGNETOSTRICTION CONSTANTS BY MEANS OF FERRIMAGNETIC RESONANCE. ARAI, K. JAP. J. APPL. PHYS. 11 (9), 1303–7, 1972.
49584	LUMINESCENCE OF BOUND EXCITONS IN TELLURIUM-DOPED ZINC SULFIDE CRYSTALS. FUKUSHIMA, T. SHIONOYA, S. JAP. J. APPL. PHYS. 12 (4), 549–56, 1973.
49585	COMPOSITION DEPENDENCE OF BAND GAPS OF COPPER GALLIUM INDIUM SULFIDE. MIYAUCHI, T. YAMAMOTO, N. HAMAKAWA, Y. NISHINO, T. JAP. J. APPL. PHYS. 12 (4), 606–7, 1973.
49587	MAGNETIC AND THERMAL STUDIES ON ERBIUM COBALT-ERBIUM ALUMINUM. OESTERREICHER, H. J. APPL. PHYS. 44 (5), 2350–4, 1973.
49591	RESIDUAL ACCEPTORS IN NATURAL GALLIUM ANTIMONIDE AND GALLIUM INDIUM ANTIMONIDE. THEIR CONTRIBUTION TO TRANSPORT BETWEEN 4.7 AND 32 K. CAMPOS, M. D. GOUSKOV, A. GOUSKOV, L. PONS, J. C. J. APPL. PHYS. 44 (6), 2642–6, 1973.
49592	DETERMINATION OF THE LOCAL VARIATION OF THE MAGNETIC PROPERTIES OF LIQUID-PHASE EPITAXIAL IRON GARNET FILMS. HANSEN, P. KRUMME, J. P. J. APPL. PHYS. 44 (6), 2847–52, 1973.
49594	SELF-EXCITED LUMINESCENCE IN GALLIUM ARSENIDE. KAMEDA, S. CARR, W. N. J. APPL. PHYS. 44 (6), 2910–12, 1973.
49598	FLUORESCENT CROSS SECTIONS AND YIELDS OF CARBON DIOXIDE CATION FROM THRESHOLD TO 185 ANGSTROM. SAMSON, J. A. R. GARDNER, J. L. J. CHEM. PHYS. 58 (9), 3771–4, 1973.
49600	PHOTOELECTRON EMISSION BY SOLVATED ELECTRONS IN LIQUID AMMONIA. AULICH, H. BARON, B. DELAHAY, P. LUGO, R. J. CHEM. PHYS. 58 (10), 4439–43, 1973.
49603	DISPERSION OF THE MOLECULAR OPTICAL ANISOTROPY BY DEPOLARIZED RAYLEIGH SCATTERING AND BIREFRINGENCE INDUCED BY HIGH ENERGY LASER WAVES. LALANNE, J. R. MARTIN, F. B. BOTHOREL, P. J. COLLOID INTERFACE SCI. 39 (3), 601–10, 1972.
49606	LUMINESCENT PROPERTIES OF MAGNESIUM-DIFFUSED GALLIUM PHOSPHIDE. MICHEL, C. BHARGAVA, R. N. J. ELECTRON. MATER. 2 (2), 283–95, 1973.
49611	MAGNETIC SUSCEPTIBILITIES OF CESIUM MANGANESE TRICHLORIDE DIHYDRATE AND CESIUM MANGANESE TRICHLORIDE DIDEUTERATE. KOBAYASHI, H. TSUJIKAWA, K. FRIEDBERG, S. A. J. LOW TEM. PHYS. 10 (5–6), 621–33, 1973.
49613	PHOTOLUMINESCENCE DUE TO ISOELECTRONIC OXYGEN AND TELLURIUM TRAPS IN II-VI ALLOYS. ISELER, G. W. STRAUSS, A. J. J. LUMIN 3 (1), 1–17, 1970.
49614	DETERMINATION OF DEPTHS AND FREQUENCY FACTORS OF TRAPS BY UV AMPLITUDE MODULATED EXCITATION. BLANC, G. CEVA, T. J. LUMIN 6 (3), 147–66, 1973.
49615	PROCESSES OCCURRING IN THE SURFACE REGION OF CADMIUM SULFIDE SINGLE CRYSTALS UNDER ELECTRON BOMBARDMENT, PHOTOEXCITATION, AND GAS ADSORPTION AND THEIR ROLE IN THE 80 K-EXCITON PHOTOLUMINESCENCE. CHEREDNICHENKO, A. E. NOVIKOV, B. V. BENEMANSKAYA, G. V. J. LUMIN. 6 (3), 193–205, 1973.
49616	ELLIPSOMETRIC DETERMINATION OF THE OPTICAL ANISOTROPY OF GALLIUM SELENIDE. MEYER, F. DE KLUIZENAAR, E. E. DEN ENGELSEN, D. J. OPT. SOC. AMER. 63 (5), 529–32, 1973.
49617	USE OF CERTAIN METALLIC AZIDES FOR THE DEVELOPMENT OF A FIELD CONTROLLED DRY PHOTOGRAPHIC PROCESS. ROBILLARD, J. J. J. PHOTOGR. SCI. 19 (2), 25–37, 1971.
49620	SCREENED EXCHANGE IN SEMICONDUCTORS. INKSON, J. C. J. PHYS. 6 C (9), L181–L185, 1973.
49621	MOESSBAUER INVESTIGATION OF THE METAL-NONMETAL TRANSITION IN HEXAGONAL NICKEL(II) SULFIDE DOPED WITH A 2 ATOMIC PERCENT IRON-57. GOSSELIN, J. R. TOWNSEND, M. G. TREMBLAY, R. J. RIPLEY, L. G. CARSON, D. W. J. PHYS. 6 C (9), 1661–72, 1973.
49629	MAGNETIC PROPERTIES OF DYSPROSIUM - IRON - COBALT AND HOLMIUM - IRON - COBALT. NARASIMHAN, K. S. V. L. BUTERA, R. A. CRAIG, R. S. J. PHYS. CHEM. SOLIDS 34 (6), 1075–7, 1973.
49630	K BETA EMISSION AND K ABSORPTION SPECTRA OF CHLORINE IN COPPER(I) CHLORIDE. SUGIURA, C. J. PHYS. SOC. JAP. 33 (2), 571, 1972.

EPIC Number	Bibliographic Citation
49632	THE L(2,3) VALENCE BAND EMISSION SPECTRUM OF THALLOUS CHLORIDE. AITA, O. NAGAKURA, I. SAGAWA, T. J. PHYS. SOC. JAP. 33 (3), 750–3, 1972.
49637	MEASUREMENTS OF PHOTOLUMINESCENCE OF INDIUM DOPED CADMIUM CHROMIUM SULFIDE SINGLE CRYSTALS. OSAKA, S. OKA, T. FUJITA, H. J. PHYS. SOC. JAP. 34 (3), 836, 1973.
49642	MAGNETIC AND OPTICAL INVESTIGATION OF MAGNESIUM MANGANESE OXIDE. PORTA, P. VALIGI, M. J. SOLID STATE CHEM. 6 (3), 344–7, 1973.
49643	PREPARATION, MAGNETIC PROPERTIES, AND MOESSBAUER STUDY OF THE MODIFIED PYROCHLORES M–II M–III F(6) A. BANKS, E. DELUCA, J. A. BERKOOZ, O. J. SOLID STATE CHEM. 6 (4), 569–73, 1973.
49646	SEMICONDUCTING CHARACTERISTICS OF THE MONOCLINIC POLYPHOSPHIDE ZINC PHOSPHIDE. ZDANOWICZ, W. WOJAKOWSKI, A. KHIM. SVYAZ POLUPROV. POLUMETALLAKH 253–6, 1972.
49647	DEEP LEVELS IN GALLIUM ARSENIDE CONTAINING OXYGEN AND IRON. MOLDOVANOVA, M. A. KAKANAKOV, R. D. KHIM. SVYAZ POLUPROV. POLUMETALLAKH 257–62, 1972.
49652	TEMPERATURE DEPENDENCE OF THE REDUCED FERMI LEVEL IN THALLIUM SELENIDE. SHIN, K. HASHIMOTO, K. KYUSHU DAIGAKU KOGAKU SHUHO 45 (6), 820–6, 1972.
49654	ENERGY TRANSFER FROM EXCITONS TO ACTIVATOR IN THALLIUM–DOPED POTASSIUM IODIDE CRYSTAL. BERZINA, B. OBRAZTSOVA, YU. N. LATV. PSR ZINAT. AKAD. VESTIS, FIZ. TEH. ZINAT. SER. (3), 69–73, 1972.
49658	PREPARATION AND ELECTRICAL PROPERTIES OF NICKEL SELENIDE SULFIDE PYRITES. BOUCHARD, R. J. GILLSON, J. L. JARRETT, H. S. MATER. RES. BULL. 8 (5), 489–96, 1973.
49659	MAGNETIC AND CRYSTALLOGRAPHIC PROPERTIES OF THE MIXED SYSTEM IRON (III) FLUORIDE–POTASSIUM TRIFLUOROMANGANATE (II). DARCY, L. WOJTOWICZ, P. J. RAYL, M. MATER. RES. BULL. 8 (5), 515–22, 1973.
49660	EFFECT OF ASYMMETRICAL CONDUCTIVITY ON CURRENT DISTRIBUTION IN POROUS ELECTRODES. EULER, K. J. METALLOBERFLAECHE–ANGEW. ELECTROCHEM. 27 (3), 87–9, 1973.
49664	DEVICE FOR THE STUDY OF SINGLE CRYSTAL THERMOLUMINESCENCE. APPLICATION TO THE EMISSION OF CALCIUM OXIDE. SCHWARTZ, M. KANE, M. FALGON, R. JANIN, J. NOUV. REV. OPT. 4 (1), 43–9, 1973.
49665	ENERGY BAND STRUCTURE OF RUBIDIUM CHLORIDE AND CESIUM CHLORIDE. DONATO, E. GIULIANO, E. S. RUGGERI, R. NUOVO CIMENTO SOC. ITAL. FIS. 15 B (1), 77–93, 1973.
49667	ABSORPTION SPECTRUM AND ELECTRONIC PARAMAGNETIC RESONANCE OF POINT DEFECTS ASSOCIATED TO IMPURITIES IN CUPROUS CHLORIDE. GOLTZENE, A. SCHWAB, C. MEYER, B. NIKITINE, S. OPT. COMMUN. 5 (4), 248–51, 1972.
49669	MULTIPHOTON IMPURITY LUMINESCENCE IN ZINC SULFIDE. CATALANO, I. M. CINGOLANI, A. MINAFRA, A. OPT. COMMUN. 7 (3), 270–1, 1973.
49670	OPTICAL PROPERTIES OF SOME MAGNETIC MATERIALS FOR COHERENT MAGNETIC VIBRATIONS. OLIVEI, A. OPT. COMMUN. 7 (4), 357–62, 1973.
49671	STUDY BH LUMINESCENCE TECHNIQUES OF TRAPS IN SILVER HALIDES. FATUZZO, E. OGGIONI, R. PHOTOGR. SCI. ENG. 17 (3), 319–25, 1973.

EPIC Number	Bibliographic Citation
49672	PHOTOVOLTAIC EFFECT IN PHOTOGRAPHIC COATINGS. VLASOV, V. G. MEIKLYAR, P. V. PHOTOGR. SCI. ENG. 17 (3), 343–7, 1973.
49678	TRAPPED HOLES AND TRAPPED–HOLE DIFFUSION IN DOPED CALCIUM FLUORIDE CRYSTALS IRRADIATED BY CATHODE RAYS. BANERJEE, H. D. RATNAM, V. V. PHYSICA (UTRECHT) 65 (1), 97–108, 1973.
49679	ELECTRICAL CONDUCTION IN LOW–MOBILITY MATERIALS. BRANSKY, I. TALLAN, N. M. PHYS. ELECTRON. CERAM., PROC. ELECTRON. PHENOMENA CERAM. CONF. PT. A, 67–98, 1971.
49684	RELATION BETWEEN PHOTOEMISSION–DETERMINED VALENCE BAND GAPS IN SEMICONDUCTORS AND INSULATORS AND IONICITY PARAMETERS. GROBMAN, W. D. EASTMAN, D. E. COHEN, M. L. PHYS. LETT. 43 A (1), 49–50, 1973.
49685	COULOMB INTERACTIONS IN METALLIC VANADIUM DIOXIDE. HEARN, C. J. HYLAND, G. J. PHYS. LETT. 43 A (1), 87–8, 1973.
49687	ENERGY LEVELS OF TETRAGONALLY SITED PRASEODYMIUM (3+) IONS IN CALCIUM FLUORIDE CRYSTALS. HARGREAVES, W. A. PHYS. REV. 6 B (9), 3417–22, 1972.
49696	ANALYSIS OF THE EXCHANGE PARAMETERS AND MAGNETIC PROPERTIES OF NICKEL (II) OXIDE. SHANKER, R. SINGH, R. A. PHYS. REV. 7 B (11), 5000–5, 1973.
49700	FINAL–STATE STRUCTURE IN PHOTOEMISSION FROM TRANSITION–METAL COMPOUNDS. WERTHEIM, G. K. GUGGENHEIM, H. J. HUEFNER, S. PHYS. REV. LETT 30 (21), 1050–3, 1973.
49705	FIELD EFFECT ON THE EXCITONIC LUMINESCENCE IN CESIUM IODIDE. GRIGOREV, V. A. POLLINI, I. PHYS. STATUS SOLIDI 56 B (2), 507–12, 1973.
49708	PHOTOCONDUCTIVITY OF POTASSIUM CHLORIDE AND POTASSIUM BROMIDE WITH F–CENTERS. HOFFMAN, H. J. PHYS. STATUS SOLIDI 57 B (1), 123–34, 1973.
49709	ENERGY BANDS OF COPPER CHLORIDE. II. CALCULATION AND RESULTS. CALABRESE, E. FOWLER, W. B. PHYS. STATUS SOLIDI 57 B (1), 135–44, 1973.
49710	VALENCE BANDS OF AMORPHOUS AND CRYSTALLINE GERMANIUM TELLURIDE DETERMINED BY X–RAY AND UV PHOTOEMISSION. SHEVCHIK, N. J. TEJADA, J. LANGER, D. W. CARDONA, M. PHYS. STATUS SOLIDI 57 B (1), 245–56, 1973.
49711	COLOR CENTERS IN TRIVALENT RARE EARTH ION–DOPED YTTRIUM ORTHOALUMINATE CRYSTALS. ARSEN'EV, P. A. VAKHIDOV, SH. A. IBRAGIMOVA, E. M. PHYS. STATUS SOLIDI 17 A (1), K45–K47, 1973.
49712	DIELECTRIC PROPERTIES OF BARIUM CHLORATE MONOHYDRATE SINGLE CRYSTAL. KHANNA, R. K. SOBHANADRI, J. PHYS. STATUS SOLIDI 17 A (1), 65–70, 1973.
49714	MAGNETIC PROPERTIES OF LIQUID–PHASE EPITAXIAL FILMS OF GADOLINIUM GALLIUM IRON YTTRIUM GARNET FOR OPTICAL MEMORY APPLICATIONS. KRUMME, J. P. BARTELS, G. TOLKSDORF, W. PHYS. STATUS SOLIDI 17 A (1), 175–9, 1973.
49715	SURFACE LUMINESCENCE IN GALLIUM ARSENIDE AT LASER EXCITATION. ZUEV, V. A. LITOVCHENKO, V. G. SUKACH, G. A. KORBUTYAK, D. V. PHYS. STATUS SOLIDI 17 A (1), 353–8, 1973.
49717	PROPERTIES OF CADMIUM MERCURY TELLURIDE FILMS. KOLEZHUK, K. V. FEDORUS, G. A. POLUPROV. TEKH. MIKROELEKTRON. (9), 18–20, 1972.

EPIC Number	Bibliographic Citation
49721	**ELECTROLUMINESCENCE OF CALCIUM SULFIDE PALLADIUM DOPED PHOSPHORS.** LAWANGAR, R. D. NARLIKAR, A. V. PROC. NUCL. PHYS. SOLID STATE PHYS. SYMP. C (16), 103–6, 1972.
49727	**EFFECT OF HIGH-HYDROSTATIC-PRESSURE TREATMENT OF TETRADYMITE-LATTICE MATERIALS ON THEIR STRUCTURE AND PROPERTIES.** GORELIK, S. S. KRUPIN, A. V. DUDKIN, L. D. DUBROVINA, A. N. BETUGANOV, M. A. SOLOV'EV, V. YA. VEKSHIN, B. S. NIKITIN, YU. N. ZIMICHEVA, G. M. CHERNYSHEVA, T. F. SB., MOSK. INST. STALI SPLAVOV (68), 87–95, 1972.
49732	**THE 7-LINE LUMINESCENCE SPECTRUM OF (NEEH) (NITROGEN-ELECTRON-ELECTRON-HOLE) IN NITROGEN-DOPED GALLIUM PHOSPHIDE. CORRECTION.** CZAJA, W. KRAUBAUER, L. CURTIS, B. J. DEAN, P. J. SOLID STATE COMMUN. 12 (8), 807–10, 1973.
49734	**WAVELENGTH-MODULATED SPECTRUM OF STRONTIUM TITANATE(IV) AND POTASSIUM TANTALATE(V).** BLAZEY, K. W. SURFACE SCI. 37 (1), 251–7, 1973.
49735	**DIRECT AND MODULATED REFLECTANCE SPECTRA OF MANGANESE(II) OXIDE, COBALT(II) OXIDE, AND NICKEL(II) OXIDE.** MESSICK, L. WALKER, W. C. GLOSSER, R. SURFACE SCI. 37 (1), 267–79, 1973.
49738	**INFRARED-MODULATED REFLECTANCE SPECTRA OF N- AND P-TYPE GALLIUM ANTIMONIDE AND N-TYPE INDIUM ANTIMONIDE.** PILLER, H. SO, C. K. WHITED, R. C. PARSONS, B. J. SURFACE SCI. 37 (2), 639–49, 1973.
49739	**REFLECTANCE MODULATION IN MERCURY TELLURIDE.** MORITANI, A. HAMAGUCHI, C. NAKAI, J. SURFACE SCI. 37 (3), 769–76, 1973.
49754	**SPECTRAL TRANSFORMERS MADE FROM CALCIUM ORTHO-PHOSPHATE ACTIVATED BY MERCURYLIKE IONS.** LUSHCHIK, N. E. MERILOO, I. TR. INST. FIZ. ASTRON., AKAD. NAUK EST. SSR (40), 83–110, 1972.
49755	**MEASURMENT OF THE LUMINESCENT PROPERTIES OF SOLIDS IRRADIATED BY ULTRASOFT X-RAYS.** SAAR, A. GRISHAKOV, F. P. ELANGO, M. TR. INST. FIZ. ASTRON., AKAD. NAUK EST. SSR (40), 111–18, 1972.
49756	**APPARATUS FOR THE HIGH-SPEED MEASUREMENTS OF THERMOELECTRIC PARAMETERS OF EMICONDUCTOR MATERIALS IN THE 150–500 K RANGE.** ERASOVA, N. A. KAIDANOV, V. I. NOVICHKOV, A. I. NUROMSKII, A. B. TR. LENINGRAD. POLITEKH. INST. (325), 10–16, 1971. (FOR ENGLISH TRANSLATION SEE E62308)
49757	**COMPUTATION OF THE FORBIDDEN BAND WIDTH IN SLAG-FORMING OXIDES.** PAVLOV, V. V. TR. URAL. POLITEKH. INST. (204), 105–9, 1972.
49758	**KINETIC EFFECTS IN MANY-VALLEY SEMICONDUCTORS IN A STRONG MAGNETIC FIELD.** ASKEROV, B. M. KULIEV, B. I. ISMAILOV, I. A. ABDULKADYROV, V. A. UCH. ZAP., AZERB. UNIV., SER. FIZ.-MAT. NAUK (3), 71–6, 1971.
49759	**PRODUCTION AND STUDY OF ELECTRICAL PROPERTIES OF P-TYPE COPPER TELLURIDE SINGLE CRYSTALS.** MUSAEV, A. M. MAMEDOV, M. SH. KERIMOV, I. G. UCH. ZAP., AZERB. UNIV., SER. FIZ.-MAT. NAUK (1), 101–4, 1972.
49762	**NONPARABOLICITY OF THE N-INDIUM ARSENIDE CONDUCTANCE BAND IN THE LIGHT ABSORPTION SPECTRUM OF FREE CARRIERS.** LISITSA, M. P. DEMIDENKO, Z. A. MALINKO, V. N. PIDLISNYI, E. V. UKR. FIZ. ZH. (RUSS. ED.) 18 (3), 512–14, 1973.
49763	**OPTICAL PROPERTIES OF ARSENIC-SELENIUM-THALLIUM SYSTEM GLASSES.** FUNTIKOV, V. A. BAIDAKOV, L. A. VESTN. LENINGRAD. UNIV., FIZ., KHIM. (1), 139–43, 1973.

EPIC Number	Bibliographic Citation
49768	**ELECTRICAL RESISTIVITY AND MAGNETIC SUSCEPTIBILITY MEASUREMENTS ON COPPER ARSENIDES.** PAUMELS, L. J. MAEROVET, F. VERVAEKE, R. Z. ANORG. ALLG. CHEM. 397 (3), 307–13, 1973.
49769	**TEMPERATURE AND CONCENTRATION. DEPENDENCE OF ELECTRIC RESISTIVITY OF SOLID ALLOYS IN THE MAGNESIUM-CADMIUM SYSTEM.** FISCHER, G. GODEL, D. STEEB, S. Z. METALLK. 64 (3), 200–3, 1973.
49774	**RESISTIVITY OF CALCIUM OXIDE-NICKEL OXIDE-IRON OXIDE COMPOUNDS.** VASILIU, A. REZLESCU, N. LUCA, E. AN. STINT. UNIV. AL. I. CUZA IASI, SECT. 18 18 (2), 149–53, 1972.
49775	**EXPERIMENTAL MAGNETIC SUSCEPTIBILITY OF TERNARY COMPOUNDS CONSISTING OF LEAD, GALLIUM, AND SELENIUM.** ADOU, J. J. EHOLIE, R. BAUDET, J. ANN. UNIV. ABIDJAN C (6), 105–9, 1970.
49777	**INFLUENCE OF TANTALUM-NIOBIUM SUBSTITUTION ON THE CRYSTALLOGRAPHIC AND DIELECTRIC PROPERTIES OF THE SODIUM STRONTIUM NIOBIUM OXIDE AND SODIUM BARIUM NIOBIUM OXIDE PHASES.** CHAMINADE, J. P. PERRON, A. RAVEZ, J. HAGENMULLER, P. BULL. SOC. CHIM. FR. (10), 3751–2, 1972.
49778	**ELECTRIC CONDUCTIVITY OF MOLTEN ALKALI METAL NITRATES AT HIGH PRESSURES. III. PRESSURE RANGE UP TO 55 KBAR.** PILZ, V. TOEDHEIDE, K. BER. BUNSENGES. PHYS. CHEM. 77 (1), 29–36, 1973.
49779	**MAGNETIC SUSCEPTIBILITY AND EQUIILIBRIUM DIAGRAM OF PALLADIUM HYDRIDE.** FRIESKE, H. WICKE, E. BER. BUNSENGES. PHYS. CHEM. 77 (1), 48–52, 1973.
49780	**DIELECTRIC LOSS MEASUREMENTS ON NONPOLAR LIQUIDS IN THE MICROWAVE REGION FROM 18 TO 37 GHZ.** DAGG, I. R. REESOR, G. E. CAN. J. PHYS. 50 (20), 2397–401, 1972.
49782	**STRUCTURE AND ELECTRICAL CONDUCTIVITY OF AMORPHOUS ZINC TELLURIDE AND CADMIUM TELLURIDE.** BROWN, H. M. BRODIE, D. E. CAN. J. PHYS. 50 (20), 2512–19, 1972.
49783	**EXTRINSIC PHOTOCONDUCTIVITY IN GALLIUM ARSENIDE.** PRAT, F. FORTIN, E. CAN. J. PHYS. 50 (20), 2551–4, 1972.
49784	**SYNTHESIS AND PROPERTIES OF ORDERED PEROVSKITES BARIUM, STRONTIUM, (YTTRIUM, GADOLINIUM, DYSPROSIUM, ERBIUM, MOLYBDENUM, TUNGSTEN) OXIDE.** KAMATA, K. YOSHIMURA, M. NAKAMURA, T. SATA, T. CHEM. LETT. (12), 1201–6, 1972.
49786	**STRUCTURE AND MAGNETIC PROPERTIES OF SAMARIUM AS THE SESQUIOXIDE AND THE METAL.** PERAKIS, N. KERN, F. C. R. ACAD. SCI. 275 (19), 677–80, 1972.
49788	**MEASUREMENTS OF THE HOLE DRIFT MOBILITY IN SEVERAL MONOXIDES AT HIGH TEMPERATURES.** BRANSKY, I. TALLAN, N. M. CONDUCTION LOW-MOBILITY MATER., PROC. INT. CONF., 2ND 31–9, 1971.
49789	**ELECTRON HOLE MOBILITY IN HAFNIUM OXIDE, ZIRCONIUM OXIDE, AND THORIUM OXIDE.** WIMMER, J. M. TALLAN, N. M. CONDUCTION LOW-MOBILITY MATER., PROC. INT. CONF., 2ND 41–7, 1971.
49790	**PHOTOCONDUCTIVITY OF SINGLE CRYSTALS OF NICKEL OXIDE IN THE VISIBLE AND NEAR UV REGION.** ROSENBLUM, E. TANNHAUSER, D. S. CONDUCTION LOW-MOBILITY MATER., PROC. INT. CONF., 2ND 49–57, 1971.
49791	**DRIFT MOBILITY OF HOLES IN NICKEL OXIDE.** BENGUIGUI, L. TANNHAUSER, D. S. CONDUCTION LOW-MOBILITY MATER., PROC. INT. CONF., 2ND 59–62, 1971.

EPIC Number	Bibliographic Citation
49792	**RELAXATION OF THE CONDUCTIVITY IN SOME SPINEL FERRITES.** REZLESCU, N. CUCIUREANU, E. CONDUCTION LOW-MOBILITY MATER., PROC. INT. CONF., 2ND 71-5, 1971. (EDITED BY N. KLEIN)
49793	**ELECTRICAL PROPERTIES OF VANADIUM PENTOXIDE.** SCOTT, A. B. MC CULLOCH, J. C. MAR, K. M. CONDUCTION LOW-MOBILITY MATER., PROC. INT. CONF., 2ND 107-13, 1971.
49794	**ELECTRICAL PROPERTIES OF AMORPHOUS SEMICONDUCTORS.** STUKE, J. CONDUCTION LOW-MOBILITY MATER., PROC. INT. CONF., 2ND 193-206, 1971.
49800	**ANALYSIS OF THERMOLUMINESCENCE KINETICS OF MANGANESE DOPED CALCIUM FLUORIDE DOSIMETERS.** ADAM, G. KATRIEL, J. THIRD INT. CONF. LUMIN. DOSIM., PROC. 9-15, 1971.
49801	**INFLUENCE OF HYDROXIDE IMPURITIES ON THERMOLUMINESCENCE IN LITHIUM FLUORIDE.** DE WERD, L. A. STOEBE, T. G. THIRD INT. CONF. LUMIN. DOSIM., PROC. 78-89, 1971.
49802	**EFFECT OF DEEP TRAPS ON SUPRALINEARITY, SENSITIZATION, AND OPTICAL THERMOLUMINESCENCE IN LITHIUM FLUORIDE TLD (THERMOLUMINESCENCE DOSIMETRY).** SUNTA, C. M. BAPAT, V. N. KATHURIA, S. P. THIRD INT. CONF. LUMIN. DOSIM., PROC. 146-55, 1971.
49803	**EMISSION SPECTRA OF VARIOUS THERMOLUMINESCENCE PHOSPHORS.** KONSCHAK, K. PULZER, R. HUEBNER, K. THIRD INT. CONF. LUMIN. DOSIM., PROC. 249-54, 1971.
49804	**STUDY OF SILVER, IRON, COBALT, AND MOLYBDENUM AS LITHIUM BORATE ACTIVATORS FOR ITS USE IN THERMOLUMINESCENT DOSIMETRY.** MORENO Y MORENO, A. ARCHUNDIA, C. SALSBERG, L. THIRD INT. CONF. LUMIN. DOSIM., PROC. 305-31, 1971.
49806	**JAHN-TELLER EFFECT AND THALLIUM ION-TYPE CENTERS IN ALKALI HALIDES.** FUKUDA, A. PHYS. IMPURITY CENT. CRYST., PROC. INT. SEMIN. 505-27, 1972.
49808	**LUMINESCENCE OF ALKALI HALIDE CRYSTALS IN AN ELECTRICAL FIELD.** KUCHIN, V. D. DIELEKTRIKI (2), 7-9, 1972.
49809	**DETERMINATION OF THE CURIE POINT OF FERROELECTRICS BY MEASURING THE ELECTRICAL CONDUCTIVITY OF SEMICONDUCTOR FILMS ON A SURFACE.** KLIMENKO, A. P. TKHORIK, YU. A. KHRASHCHEVSKII, V. A. CHERNAYA, N. S. DIELEKTRIKI (2), 38-40, 1972.
49811	**EFFECT OF DEVIATIONS FROM STOCHIOMETRY ON THE PROPERTIES OF ZINC SILICON ARSENIDE SEMICONDUCTOR.** AVERKIEVA, G. K. PROCHUKHAN, V. D. TASHTANOVA, M. DOKL. AKAD. NAUK SSSR 206 (3), 638-40, 1972. (FOR ENGLISH TRANSLATION SEE E58866)
49812	**TEMPERATURE DEPENDENCE OF THE ELECTROPHYSICAL PROPERTIES IN MOLYBDENUM PENTABORIDE AND TUNGSTEN PENTABORIDE.** SAMSONOV, G. V. GORYACHEV, YU. M. KOVENSKAYA, B. A. DOPOV. AKAD. NAUK UKR. RSR 34 A (10), 943- , 1972.
49814	**MICROWAVE MEASUREMENT OF SURFACE CONDUCTIVITY AND PERMITTIVITY OF THIN LAYERS IN AN E010 RESONATOR.** FREY, W. ELECTRON. LETT. 8 (19), 486-8, 1972.
49815	**GALLIUM ARSENIDE-ALUMINUM ARSENIDE SOLID SOLUTIONS.** AMIRANIDZE, M. D. BERDZENISHVILI, A. I. DZHAKHUTASHVILI, T. V. MATINOVA, M. S. MIRTSKHULAVA, A. A. SAKVARELIDZE, L. G. CHIKOVANI, R. I. SHKOL'NIK, A. L. ELEKTRON. TEKH. NAUCH.-TEKH. SB. MATER. (1), 65-70, 1972.
49816	**CRYSTAL STRUCTURE AND ELECTRICAL PROPERTIES OF CADMIUM SELENIDE LAYERS OBTAINED BY DEPOSITION IN A QUASICLOSED OBJECT.** SHALIMOVA, K. V. STAROSTIN, V. V. MUKHIN, YU. A. ELEKTRON. TEKH. NAUCH.-TEKH. SB. MATER. (1), 129-9, 1972.
49817	**THERMAL EMISSION PROPERTIES OF COMPLEX TITANIUM CARBIDE-TUNGSTEN CARBIDE IN THE HOMOGENEITY REGION.** PODCHERNYAEVA, I. A. SIMAN, N. I. FOMENKO, V. S. CHAPLYGIN, F. I. ELEKTRON. STR. FIZ. SVOISTVA TVERD. TELA, DOKL. VSES. SIMP. FIZ. SVOISTVAM ELEKTRON. STR. PEREKHODNYKH METAL., IKH SPLAVOV SOEDIN., 7TH 2, 156-60, 1972.
49819	**EFFECT OF TECHNOLOGICAL PARMETERS ON THE HALL ELECTRON MOBILITY IN INDIUM ANTIMONIDE THIN FILMS PREPARED BY THE FLASH VAPOR DEPOSITION METHOD.** BETKO, T. ELEKTROTECH. CAS. 23 (6), 331-7, 1972.
49820	**STABILIZATION EFFECTS IN PIEZOELECTRIC LEAD TITANATE ZIRCONATE CERAMICS.** THOMANN, H. FERROELECTRICS 4 (3), 141-6, 1972.
49822	**HALL EFFECT AND MAGNETIC SUSCEPTIBILITY IN BISMUTH SULFIDE SINGLE CRYSTALS GROWN FROM THE GAS PHASE.** STEFANISHIN, E. D. BILYI, M. N. PIDORYA, M. M. FIZ. ELEKTRON. (LVOV) (5), 3-5, 1972.
49823	**ELECTRIC AND OPTICAL PROPERTIES OF SYNTHETIC DIAPHORITE.** ANDRIEVSKII, A. I. PRYAMUKHIN, V. E. FIZ. ELEKTRON. (LVOV) (5), 6-7, 1972.
49824	**ELECTRIC AND MAGNETIC PROPERTIES OF ARGYRODITE AND CONFIELDITE IN THE PHASE TRANSITION REGION.** OSIPISHIN, I. S. BUTSKO, N. I. PIDORYA, M. M. FIZ. ELEKTRON. (LVOV) (5), 8-11, 1972.
49828	**EFFECT OF COOLING CONDITIONS ON ELECTRICAL CONDUCTIVITY OF BARIUM TITANATE WITH SOME NONISOVALENT ADDITIVES.** SINYAKOV, E. V. KOLESNICHENKO, K. A. KRYZHANOVSKAYA, N. A. FIZ. KHIM. TVERD. TELA (2), 86-90, 1972.
49829	**ELECTRICAL CONDUCTIVITY OF POLYCRYSTALLINE LEAD TITANATE AND CHANGES IN IT FOLLOWING DOPING.** PROKOPALO, O. I. GOL'TSOV, YU. I. BOGATIN, A. S. SERVULI, V. A. BOGATINA, V. N. SUZDALEV, V. YA. BELOVA, L. A. FIZ. KHIM. TVERD. TELA (2), 91-5, 1972.
49830	**MAGNETIC PROPERTIES OF NICKEL-GADOLINIUM FILMS.** SHELKOVNIKOV, V. N. KAMENEVA, G. A. MANAKOV, N. A. FIZ. MAGN. PLENOK (4), 40-5, 1971.
49833	**ANISOTROPY OF HOLE MOBILITY IN GALLIUM SELENIDE.** SCHMID, PH. MOOSER, E. HELV. PHYS. ACTA 45 (6), 870-2, 1972.
49834	**ELECTROLUMINESCENCE IN GALLIUM SELENIDE.** VOITCHOVSKY, J. P. MOOSER, E. HELV. PHYS. ACTA 45 (6), 877-80, 1972.
49835	**LIGHT-EMITTING DIODES FOR DISPLAY AND TERMINAL APPLICATIONS.** LORENZ, M. R. IEEE INT. CONV. DIG. 192-3, 1972.
49836	**PIEZOELECTRIC EFFECT IN ALUMINUM-DOPED BARIUM TITANATE CERAMIC.** AMIN, M. TAWFIK, A. INDIAN J. PHYS. 46 (5), 227-32, 1972.
49838	**THERMOLUMINESCENCE STUDY OF MANGANESE, ZIRCONIUM-DOPED STRONTIUM SULFIDE PHOSPHORS.** PATHAK, G. R. KAMRA, P. C. INDIAN J. PURE APPL. PHYS. 10 (7), 567-9, 1972.

EPIC Number	Bibliographic Citation

49840 **MODIFICATION OF MAGNETIC PROPERTIES OF CHROMIUM DIOXIDE.**
ARIYA, S. M. VASILEVSKII, YU. A.
VOLODINA, A. P. MOROZOVA, M. P.
OSMOLOVSKII, M. G.
ISSLED. OBL. NEORG. TEKHNOL.
332-4, 1972.

49842 **VIBRONIC STRUCTURE OF LUMINESCENCE SPECTRA OF IONS IN A CRYSTAL.**
MIYAKAWA, T.
IZV. AKAD. NAUK SSSR, SER. FIZ.
37 (3), 528-31, 1973.
(FOR ENGLISH TRANSLATION SEE E54512)

49843 **ELECTROLUMINESCENCE OF ALKALI HALIDE CRYSTALS.**
PARACCHINI, C.
IZV. AKAD. NAUK SSSR, SER. FIZ.
37 (4), 700-4, 1973.
(FOR ENGLISH TRANSLATION SEE E54515)

49844 **RESONANCE LUMINESCENCE OF FREE EXCITONS IN CRYSTALS.**
PERMOGOROV, S. A. TRAVNIKOV, V. V.
SEL'KIN, A. V.
IZV. AKAD. NAUK SSSR, SER. FIZ.
37 (4), 711-13, 1973.
(FOR ENGLISH TRANSLATION SEE E54516)

49845 **RESONANCE INTERACTION BETWEEN ORTHO- AND PARA-EXCITONS IN A COPPER (I) OXIDE DURING PHONON PARTICIPATION.**
KREINGOL'D, F. I. MAKAROV, V. L.
IZV. AKAD. NAUK SSSR, SER. FIZ.
37 (4), 714-17, 1973.
(FOR ENGLISH TRANSLATION SEE E54517)

49846 **MULTISTEP TWO-PHOTON RADIATION DURING THE INTERACTION OF ONE ELECTRON-HOLE PAIR WITH ACTIVATOR CENTERS IN ALKALI HALIDE CRYSTALS.**
ZAZUBOVICH, S. G. KINK, M. JAEK, I.
OSMININ, V. S.
IZV. AKAD. NAUK SSSR, SER. FIZ.
37 (4), 732-5, 1973.
(FOR ENGLISH TRANSLATION SEE E54518)

49847 **LUMINESCENCE OF THE TUNGSTATE(VI) GROUP IN ORDERED PEROVSKITES.**
BLASSE, G. CORSMIT, A. F. VAN DER PAS, M.
IZV. AKAD. NAUK SSSR, SER. FIZ.
37 (4), 736-7, 1973.
(FOR ENGLISH TRANSLATION SEE E54520)

49848 **SPECTROSCOPIC STUDY OF BIELECTRON OR BIHOLE ENERGY LEVELS IN A BISMUTH IODIDE CRYSTAL.**
GROSS, E. F. STAROSTIN, N. V.
SHEPILOV, M. P. SHEKHMAMET'EV, R. I.
IZV. AKAD. NAUK SSSR, SER. FIZ.
37 (4), 885-90, 1973.
(FOR ENGLISH TRANSLATION SEE E54526)

49852 **CHANGES IN THE VALUES OF SPECIFIC ELECTRICAL CONDUCTIVITY, CONSTANTS OF THE IONIC PRODUCT OF WATER, AND CROSSLINKING AT THE ABSOLUTE BOILING POINT OF WATER AND AQUEOUS SOLUTIONS.**
FOKEEV, V. M.
ISV. VYSSH. UCHEB. ZAVED., GEOL. RAZVED.
15 (10), 83-8, 1972.

49856 **OPTICAL SPECTRA AND ENERGY LEVELS OF ERBIUM-DOPED YTTRIUM ORTHOALUMINATE.**
DONLAN, V. L. SANTIAGO, A. A., JR.
J. CHEM. PHYS.
57 (11), 4717-23, 1972.

49857 **ENERGY LEVELS OF ERBIUM (3+) IONS IN THREE RARE EARTH HYDROXIDES.**
CONE, R. L.
J. CHEM. PHYS.
57 (11), 4893-903, 1972.

49858 **ELECTRICAL CONDUCTION IN AMMONIUM PERCHLORATE.**
OWEN, G. P. THOMAS, J. M. WILLIAMS, J. O.
J. CHEM. SOC., FARADAY TRANS.
68 (12), 2356-66, 1972.

49859 **LUMINESCENT PROPERTIES OF THIOGALLATE PHOSPHORS. II. CERIUM TRIPOSITIVE ION-ACTIVATED PHOSPHORS FOR FLYING SPOT SCANNER APPLICATIONS.**
PETERS, T. E.
J. ELECTROCHEM. SOC.
119 (12), 1720-3, 1972.

49860 **SOLID-STATE IONICS. NEW HIGH IONIC CONDUCTIVITY SOLID ELECTROLYTE SILVER IODIDE TUNGSTATE(VI) AND USE OF THIS COMPOUND IN A SOLID-ELECTROLYTE CELL.**
TAKAHASHI, T. IKEDA, S. YAMAMOTO, O.
J. ELECTROCHEM. SOC.
120 (5), 647-51, 1973.

49862 **SUPERCONDUCTING TERNARY SULFIDE SILVER PALLADIUM SULFIDE.**
KHAN, H. R. TRUNK, H. RAUB, CH. J.
FERTIG, W. A. LAWSON, A. C.
J. LESS-COMMON METALS
30 (1), 167-8, 1973.

49864 **MAGNETIC PROPERTIES OF PALLADIUM ALLOYS WITH GADOLINIUM, DYSPROSIUM, AND HOLMIUM.**
LOEBICH, O., JR. RAUB, E.
J. LESS-COMMON METALS
31 (1), 111-18, 1973.

49865 **CRYSTAL GROWTH AND THERMOELECTRIC PROPERTIES OF CHROMIUM DISILICIDE.**
NISHIDA, I.
J. MATER. SCI.
7 (10), 1119-24, 1972.

49866 **MEASUREMENT OF THE RESISTIVITY AND OXIDATION KINETICS OF PLUTONOUM OXIDE.**
CHEREAU, P. WADIER, J. F.
J. NUCL. MATER.
46 (1), 1-8, 1973.

49867 **HALL MOBILITY MEASUREMENTS ON IRON-RICH NICKEL FERRITES FROM ROOM TEMPERATURE TO 600.**
TURNER, C. E.
J. PHYS.
5 C (20), 2859-66, 1972.

49874 **PHYSICAL PROPERTIES OF THE LEAD TELLURIDE-MAGNESIUM TELLURIDE ALLOY SYSTEM.**
CROCKER, A. J. SEALY, B. J.
J. PHYS. CHEM. SOLIDS
33 (12) 2183-90, 1972.

49875 **THERMAL, MAGNETIC, AND ELECTRICAL CHARACTERISTICS OF PRASEODYMIUM-NICKEL.**
CRAIG, R. S. SANKAR, S. G. MARZOUK, N.
RAO, V. U. S. WALLACE, W. E. SEGAL, E.
J. PHYS. CHEM. SOLIDS
33 (12), 2267-74, 1972.
(AD 761 923)

49876 **EFFECT OF THE HYDROSTATIC PRESSURE ON THE ELECTRICAL CONDUCTIVITY OF SILVER IODIDE.**
HOSHINO, H. SHIMOJI, M.
J. PHYS. CHEM. SOLIDS
33 (12), 2303-9, 1972.

49877 **SEVERAL OPTICAL PROPERTIES OF SINGLE-CRYSTAL CALCIUM TUNGSTATE DOPED WITH 0.1-1.8 ATOM PER CENT AMERICIUM TRIPOSITIVE.**
FINCH, C. B. CLARK, G. W.
J. PHYS. CHEM. SOLIDS
34 (5), 922-4, 1973.

49878 **ELECTRICAL AND MAGNETIC PROPERTIES OF CHROMIUM CADMIUM INDIUM SULFIDE.**
KIRIHATA, H. ENDO, S. IRIE, T.
J. PHYS. SOC. JAP.
33 (3), 848, 1972.

49879 **MEASUREMENT OF MAGNETOSTRICTION CONSTANTS OF LITHIUM FERRITE BY FERRIMAGNETIC RESONANCE.**
ARAI, K. TSUYA, N.
J. PHYS. SOC. JAP.
33 (6), 1581-3, 1972.

49883 **LUMINESCENCE OF LEAD(II) CHLORIDE AND LEAD(II) BROMIDE SINGLE CRYSTALS. II. LUMINESCENCE AND EPR OF ULTRAVIOLET-IRRADIATED CRYSTALS.**
DE GRUIJTER, W. C. KERSSEN, J.
J. SOLID STATE CHEM.
5 (3), 467-6, 1972.

49884 **SHAPE OF A PARAMETRIC LUMINESCENCE LINE IN LITHIUM NIOBATE CRYSTALS.**
KRINDACH, D. P. KHOLODNYKH, A. I.
CHURIN, A. A.
KVANTOVAYA ELEKTRON. (MOSCOW)
(7), 71-3, 1972.

49888 **FARADAY EFFECT IN N-GALLIUM ARSENIDE IN THE RANGE OF INTERMEDIATE DOPING.**
DREIMANIS, E. KLOTINS, E. PETROV, V. K.
LATV. PSR ZINAT. AKAD. VESTIS, FIZ. TEH. ZINAT. SER.
(5), 25-31, 1972.

49889 **MAGNETIC PROPERTIES OF MANGANESE BORIDE.**
NERESON, N. BOWMAN, A. ARNOLD, G.
REPORT LA-DC-72-1282
5PP., 1972.
(AVAIL. DEP. NTIS.)

49891 **QUASISTATIC AND DYNAMIC MAGNETIC REVERSAL OF SINGLE-CRYSTAL MAGNESIUM MANGANESE FERRITE FILMS AND PREREQUISITES FOR THEIR USE AS MEMORY ELEMENTS.**
CHERVINSKII, M. M. SHVALEV, YU. V.
MAGN. ELEM. PAMYATI, TR. VSES. SOVESHCH. MAGN. ELEM. AVTOMAT. VYCHISL. TEKH., 12TH
141-9, 1972.
(FROM: NAUKA: MOSCOW, USSR; EDITED BY M. A. ROZENBLAT)

49895 **IMPROVEMENT OF THE CHARACTERISTICS OF ZINC SELENIDE SULFIDE ELECTROLUMINESCENT PHOSPHORS.**
AWAZU, K. MATSUNAGA, K. TSUBOI, S.
MITSUBISHI DENKI GIHO
46 (12), 1400-7, 1972.

EPIC Number	Bibliographic Citation
49896	**X-RAY LUMINESCENCE OF ERBIUM TRIPOSITIVE ION-DOPED LANTHANUM FLUORIDE SINGLE CRYSTALS.** AZAROV, V. V. SHCHERBINA, E. V. MONOKRIST. TEKH. (5), 39–43, 1971.
49897	**ELECTROMECHANICAL PROPERTIES AND APPLICATIONS OF LEAD TITANATE CERAMICS.** UEDA, I. KOBAYASHI, S. IKEGAMI, S. NAT. TECH. REP. 18 (4), 413–25, 1972.
49904	**ANOMALOUS DEPENDENCE OF THE SUPERCONDUCTING TRANSITION TEMPERATURE OF CERIUM-RUTHENIUM ON MAGNETIC ION CONCENTRATION.** HILLENBRAND, B. WILHELM, M. PHYS. LETT. 41 A (5), 419–20, 1972.
49905	**ZIRCONIUM SULFIDE. NEW SUPERCONDUCTING BINARY SULFIDE.** JOHNSTON, D. C. MOODENBAUGH, A. PHYS. LETT. 41 A (K), 447–8, 1972. (AD 760 839)
49906	**DEPENDENCE OF THE INSULATOR-METAL TRANSITION IN EUROPIUM OXIDE ON MAGNETIC ORDER.** SHAPIRA, Y. FONER, S. REED, T. B. BIRECKI, H. STANLEY, H. E. PHYS. LETT. 41 A (5), 471–2, 1972.
49907	**APW (AUGMENTED PLANE WAVE) BAND STRUCTURE OF METALLIC VANADIUM DIOXIDE.** CHATTERJEE, S. MITRA, T. K. HYLAND, G. J. PHYS. LETT. 42 A (1), 56–8, 1972.
49910	**CONVERGENCE OF RECEIPROCAL-LATTICE EXPANSIONS AND SELF-CONSISTENT ENERGY BANDS OF SODIUM FLUORIDE.** BRENER, N. E. FRY, J. L. PHYS. REV. 6 B (10), 4016–25, 1972
49912	**MAGNETIC PROPERTIES OF IRON (2+) ION-DOPED MANGANESE CARBONATE.** MAARTENSE, I. PHYS. REV. 6 B (11), 4324–31, 1972.
49915	**TEMPERATURE-DEPENDENT ELECTRONIC TRANSITION IN CERIUM HYDRIDE.** LIBOWITZ, G. G. PACK, J. G. BINNIE, W. P. PHYS. REV. 6 B (12), 4540–6, 1972.
49917	**MAGNETIC SUSCEPTIBILITY OF AMORPHOUS SEMICONDUCTORS.** DI SALVO, F. J. MENTH, A. WASZCZAK, J. V. TAUC, J. PHYS. REV. 6 B (12), 4574–81, 1972.
49918	**LUMINESCENCE EXCITATION SPECTRA OF ZINC SILICON PHOSPHIDE AT 2 K.** SHAH, J. PHYS. REV. 6 B (12), 4592–6, 1972.
49919	**TRANSPORT PROPERTIES OF SEMICONDUCTING PHOSPHATE GLASSES.** SAYER, M. MANSINGH, A. PHYS. REV. 6 B (12), 4629–43, 1972.
49920	**MAGNETIC FIELD DEPENDENCE OF THE ADIABATIC SUSCEPTIBILITY TENSOR OF POWDERED CERIUM MAGNESIUM NITRATE.** ABRAHAM, B. M. KETTERSON, J. B. ROACH, P. R. PHYS. REV. 6 B (12), 4675–9, 1973.
49921	**ENERGY BANDS FOR POTASSIUM TRIFLUORONICKOLLATE, STRONTIUM TITANATE (IV), POTASSIUM MOLYBDATE (V), AND POTASSIUM TANTALATE (V).** MATTHEISS, L. F. PHYS. REV. 6 B (12), 4718–40, 1972.
49925	**LUMINESCENCE OF COPPER (I) OXIDE. EXCITONIC MOLECULES OR NOT.** PETROFF, Y. YU, P. Y. SHEN, Y. R. PHYS. REV. LETT. 29 (23), 1558–62, 1972.
49928	**EFFECT OF A MAGNETIC FIELD ON THE IMPURITY CONDUCTION IN P-GALLIUM ARSENIDE.** JANSAK, L. LAGUNOVA, T. S. PHYS. STATUS SOLIDI 13 A (2), K151–K154, 1972.
49929	**WORK FUNCTION CHANGES OF INDIUM ANTIMONIDE BY IRRADIATION.** LEHR, S. MANTKE, W. PAGNIA, H. PHYS. STATUS SOLIDI 13 A (2), K159–K161, 1972.
49933	**MAGNETIC SUSCEPTIBILITY OF MERCURY CADMIUM TELLURIDE.** IVANOV-OMSKII, V. I. KOLOMIETS, B. T. OGORODNIKOV, V. K. SMEKALOVA, K. P. TSMOTS, V. M. PHYS. STATUS SOLIDI 14 A (1), 51–8, 1972.
49934	**CONDUCTIVITY AND STIMULATED EMISSION IN CADMIUM SULFIDE UNDER INTENSE ELECTRON BEAM EXCITATION.** BILLE, J. VON BOJNICIC-KNINSKI, S. RUPPEL, W. PHYS. STATUS SOLIDI 14 A (1), 141–5, 1972.
49935	**ELECTRICAL PROPERTIES OF TIN DISELENIDE UNDER PRESSURE.** LIKHTER, A. I. PEL, E. G. PRISYAZHNYUK, S. I. PHYS. STATUS SOLIDI 14 A (1), 265–70, 1972.
49936	**PHOTOEMISSION STUDIES OF ELECTRONIC COLOR CENTERS IN ADDITIVELY COLORED POTASSIUM CHLORIDE AND POTASSIUM BROMIDE CRYSTALS.** KASHKAI, A. D. BEREZIN, A. A. ARSENEVA-GEIL, A. N. MATVEEV, M. S. PHYS. STATUS SOLIDI 54 B (1), 113–19, 1972.
49937	**PROPERTIES OF CUPROUS IODIDE FILMS.** FLASENKO, N. A. KONONETS, YA. F. POLUPROV. TEKH. MIKROELEKTRON. (7), 73–8, 1972.
49942	**QUADRUPOLE SPLITTING AND MAGNETIC SUSCEPTIBILITIES OF PSEUDOTETRAHEDRAL FERROUS COMPOUNDS.** PAL, A. K. PAL, D. GHOSHAL, A. K. PROC. NUCL. PHYS. SOLID STATE PHYS. SYMP., (16) C, 555–8, 1972.
49944	**MAGNETIC SUSCEPTIBILITY OF MANGANESE SELENIDE-MANGANESE TELLURIDE SYSTEM AT LOW TEMPERATURES.** DELAL, V. N. K. KEER, H. V. BISWAS, A. B. PROC. NUCL. PHYS. SOLID STATE PHYS. SYMP., (16) C, 633–7, 1972.
49950	**TEMPERATURE DEPENDENCE OF ELECTRICAL CONDUCTIVITY OF NONSTABILIZED ZIRCONIUM DIOXIDE.** KUTZENDORFER, J. SRAMEK, J. SILIKATY 16 (4), 311–17, 1972.
49953	**HOT ELECTRON MOBILITY IN CADMIUM SULFIDE.** NAG, B. R. SOLID STATE COMMUN. 11 (8), 987–90, 1972.
49956	**BOSE CONDENSATION OF EXCITONIC MOLECULES IN CADMIUM SELENIDE.** KURODA, H. SHIONOYA, S. SAITO, H. HANAMURA, E. SOLID STATE COMMUN. 12 (6), 533–6, 1973.
49958	**STRUCTURE, COMPOSITION, AND DIELECTRIC PROPERTIES OF LANTHANUM-CONTAINING PHASES OF CRYSTALLIZATION PRODUCTS OF SILICA-ALUMINA-LANTHANUM OXIDE-TITANIUM(IV) OXIDE SYSTEM GLASSES.** BOGDANOVA, G. S. KOZEL'SKAYA, E. S. ZEVIN, L. S. STEKLO, TR. NAUCH.-ISSLED. INST. (3), 96–9, 1971.
49960	**MEASUREMENT OF THE DIELECTRIC CONSTANT OF A SOLID BY AN IMMERSION METHOD. III. DIELECTRIC CONSTANT OF LIF.** OMINO, A. NIGARA, Y. KAMIYOSHI, K. TOHOKU DAIGAKU KAGAKU KEISOKU KENKYUSHO HOKOKU 21 (1), 45–50, 1972.
49962	**MAGNETIC PROPERTIES OF NEODYMIUM TRIPOSITIVE ION-CONTAINING COMPOUNDS WITH SCHEELITE STRUCTURE.** KHATS'KO, E. N. KALININ, P. S. ZVYAGIN, A. I. PELIKH, L. N. KOBETS, M. I. TR. FIZ.-TEKH. INST. NIZK. TEMP., AKAD. NAUK UKR. (15), 34–43, 1971. (8E1226).
49963	**MIXED CONDUCTIVITY OF THE LANTHANUM OXIDE-STRONTIUM OXIDE SYSTEM.** VOLCHENKOVA, Z. S. TR. INST. ELEKTROKHIM., URAL. NAUCH. TSENTR. AKAD. NAUK (17), 137–45, 1971.
49968	**ELECTROLUMINESCENCE BRIGHTNESS WAVES OF ZINC SULFIDE LUMINOPHORS OPERATING ON ALTERNATING VOLTAGE.** CHUGUNOV, A. P. TR. MOSK. ENERG. INST. (94), 110–16, 1971.
49969	**ELECTROLUMINESCENCE OF GALLIUM ARSENIDE.** SPIVAK, V. S. TR. MOSK. ENERG. INST. (94), 117–19, 1971.

EPIC Number	Bibliographic Citation
49971	**SECONDARY ELECTRON EMISSION OF SOME CERAMICS AND SUPPRESSOR COATINGS.** MALYNIN, YU. G. TR. MOSK. ENERG. INST. (108), 85–7, 1972.
49972	**DEVELOPMENT OF A METHOD OF MEASURING ELECTRICAL CONDUCTIVITY OF MAGNETITE FILMS ON CARBON STEEL.** KRASIKOV, E. A. TR. MOSK. ENERG. INST. (126), 59–64, 1972.
49973	**ELECTRICAL PROPERTIES OF EPITAXIAL GALLIUM ARSENIDE FILMS IN WEAK AND STRONG ELECTRIC FIELDS.** BELOVA, N. A. KEMARSKII, V. A. LYUBCHENKO, V. E. SKVORTSOVA, N. E. TR. SIMP. FIZ. PLAZMY ELEK NEUSTOICHIVOSTYAM TVERD. TELAKH 220–30, 1972. (12E994).
49977	**THEORY OF PERPENDICULAR MAGNETIC REVERSAL AND MICROBAND STRUCTURE OF SINGLE CRYSTAL FERRITE FILMS.** ANTONOV, L. I. TELESNIN, R. V. UCH. ZAP., KUIBYSHEV. GOS. PEDAGOG. INST. 104 (4), 70–81, 1972.
49978	**RESONANCE PROPERTIES AND CRYSTALLOGRAPHIC MAGNETIC ANISOTROPY OF FILMS OF MAGNESIUM–MANGANESE–COBALT FERRITE.** DUNAEVA–MITLINA, T. A. UCH. ZAP., KUIBYSHEV. GOS. PEDAGOG. INST. 104 (4), 82–91, 1972.
49979	**ROTATION HYSTERESIS IN FILMS OF MAGNESIUM–MANGANESE FERRITE.** KOSHKIN, L. I. DUNAEVA–MITLINA, T. A. GAVRILIN, V. P. UCH. ZAP., KUIBYSHEV. GOS. PEDAGOG. INST. 104 (4), 103–7, 1972.
49980	**COMPLEX DIELECTRIC CONSTANT OF EPITAXIAL SINGLE–CRYSTAL FILMS OF MAGNESIUM–MANGANESE FERRITE.** VEDENEV, A. P. UCH. ZAP., KUIBYSHEV. GOS. PEDAGOG. INST. 104 (4), 108–13, 1972.
49981	**HALL EFFECT ON SINGLE–CRYSTAL FILMS OF MAGNESIUM–MANGANESE FERRITES.** MITLINA, L. A. VEDENEV, A. P. KHARLAMOV, A. D. UCH. ZAP., KUIBYSHEV. GOS. PEDAGOG. INST. 104 (4), 114–19, 1972.
49982	**ELECTRICAL CONDUCTIVITY OF NICKEL MONOXIDE IN ATMOSPHERES OF COMPLEX COMPOSITION.** SUNTSOV, N. V. UCH. ZAP. URAL. GOS. UNIV. (119), 91–3, 1971.
49983	**CORRELATION OF ELECTRICAL AND DIFFUSION PROPERTIES OF NICKEL MONOXIDE IN THERMODYNAMIC EQUILIBRIUM WITH A GAS PHASE OF COMPLEX COMPOSITION.** SUNTSOV, N. V. UCH. ZAP. URAL. GOS. UNIV. (119), 94–7, 1971.
49986	**DEPENDENCE OF TRANSITION PROPERTIES OF THE UNIVALENT NITRATES UPON STRUCTURAL ENTITIES.** FERMOR, J. H. KJEKSHUS, A. ACTA CHEM. SCAND. 27 (3), 915–23, 1973.
49987	**CRYSTAL STRUCTURE, LINEAR AND NONLINEAR OPTICAL PROPERTIES OF CALCIUM IODATE HEXAHYDRATE.** MOROSIN, B. BERGMAN, J. G. CRANE, G. R. ACTA CRYSTALLOGR., SECT. B 29 (5), 1067–72, 1973.
49989	**ANNEALING OF MAGNETIC PROPERTIES OF ION–IMPLANTED GARNET EPITAXIAL FILMS.** SMITH, D. H. NORTH, J. C. AIP (AMER. INST. PHYS.) CONF. PROC. (10), (PT. 1), 334–8, 1973.
49991	**QUADRUPOLAR COUPLING AND ITS CONTRIBUTION TO ELECTRICAL RESISTIVITY.** SABLIK, M. J. TEITELBAUM, H. H. LEVY, P. M. AIP (AMER. INST. PHYS.) CONF. PROC. (10), (PT. 1), 548–52, 1973.
49997	**MAGNETIC PROPERTIES OF STRONTIUM IRON OXYFLUORIDE A HIGHLY ANISOTROPIC OXYFLUORIDE.** SCHELLENG, J. H. AIP (AMER. INST. PHYS.) CONF. PROC. (10), (PT. 2), 1054–88 1973.
49998	**MAGNETIC AND ELECTRIC PROPERTIES OF MATERIALS IN THE SYSTEM COPPER CHROMIUM IRON SELENIDE SULFIDE.** GYORGY, E. M. ROBBINS, M. GILBART, P. REED, W. A. SCHNETTLER, F. J. AIP (AMER. INST. PHYS.) CONF. PROC. (10), (PT. 2), 1148–52, 1973.
49999	**EFFECT OF COULOMBIC AND MAGNETIC DISORDER ON TRANSPORT IN MAGNETIC SEMICONDUCTORS.** VON MOLNAR, S. HOLTZBERG, F. AIP (AMER. INST. PHYS.) CONF. PROC. (10), (PT. 2), 1259–73, 1973.
50000	**MAGNETIC SUSCEPTIBILITY OF EXCHANGE–COUPLED VAN VLECK IONS. LANTHANUM SAMARIUM SULFIDE.** TORRANCE, J. B. HOLTZBERG, F. MCGUIRE, T. R. AIP (AMER. INST. PHYS.) CONF. PROC. (10), (PT. 2), 1279–83, 1973.
50003	**SPIN–DEPENDENT TRANSPORT PROPERTIES OF TIN TELLURIDE–MANGANESE TELLURIDE SYSTEMS.** GHAZALI, A. ESCORNE, M. RODOT, H. LEROUX–HUGON, P. AIP CONF. PROC. (10), (PT. 2), 1374–8, 1973.
50004	**ELECTRICAL PROPERTIES OF PURE AND SUBSTITUTED MAGNETITE FROM 4.2 TO 300 K.** CONSTANTIN, C. ROSENBERG, M. AIP CONF. PROC. (10), (PT. 2), 1389–92, 1973.
50005	**ELECTRICAL CONDUCTIVITY AND HYPERFINE INTERACTIONS IN METAL IRON OXIDE NEEL TEMPERATURE ABOVE AND BELOW (TN).** EVANS, B. J. AIP CONF. PROC. (10), (PT. 2), 1398–402, 1973.
50008	**PYROELECTRIC EFFECT IN THALLIUM ARSENIC SELENIDE ERRATUM.** DEIS, D. W. ROLAND, G. W. APPL. PHYS. LETT. 22 (10), 554, 1973.
50009	**RADIATION EFFECTS ON DIELECTRIC MATERIALS.** CONRAD, E. E. ANNU. REP., CONF. ELEC. INSUL. DIELEC. PHENOMENA 320–3, 1972.
50014	**CONDUCTIVITY MEASUREMENTS WITH THE CONDUCTIVITY MEASURING APPARATUS, MODEL LF 39.** PUELLEN, C. APOTHEKERPRAKT. PHARM.–TECH. ASSISTENT 19 (4), 25–32, 1973.
50015	**ELECTRIC CONDUCTIVITY AND THERMOELECTRIC POWER OF PURE AND CALCIUM OXIDE–STABILIZED ZIRCONIUM OXIDE AT TEMPERATURES BETWEEN 1000 AND 1700 DEGREES AND OXYGEN PARTIAL PRESSURES BETWEEN 1 AND 10 SUPERSCRIPT(–16) ATM.** FISHCHER, W. A. PIEPER, C. ARCH. EISENHUETTENW. 44 (4), 251–9, 1973.
50019	**RELATION BETWEEN THE WORK FUNCTION AND CATALYTIC ACTIVITY OF LITHIUM–DOPED NICKEL OXIDE SINGLE CRYSTALS.** DEREN, J. NOWOTNY, J. OBLAKOWSKI, J. SADOWSKI, A. BULL. ACAD. POL. SCI., SER. SCI. CHIM. 21 (4), 307–10, 1973.
50020	**SPECTRAL RESPONSE OF PHOSPHORS TO FAST IONS.** HASTINGS, L. GOH, E. H. SPENCELEY, B. J. CAN. J. PHYS. 51 (11), 1143–7, 1973.
50022	**PHTOELECTRON SPECTRA AND MOLECULAR PROPERTIES. ,IX. DIFLUORODISULFANE AND THIOTHIONYL FLUORIDE.** WAGNER, G. BOCK, H. BUDENZ, R. SEEL, F. CHEM. BER. 106 (4), 1285–9, 1973.
50023	**PRESSURE EFFECT ON OPTICAL SPECTRA AND ELECTRICAL RESISTIVITY OF SOME PLATINUM COMPLEXES.** HARA, Y. SHIROTANI, I. MINOMURA, S. CHEM. LETT. (6), 579–82, 1973.
50025	**ALTERNATING CURRENT POTENTIOMETRIC METHOD FOR HIGH TEMPERATURE RESISTIVITY AND PHASE BOUNDARY DETERMINATIONS.** CHIOTTI, P. COLLOQ. INT. CENT. NAT. RECH. SCI. (205), 33–8, 1972.
50026	**COPPER VANADIUM SULFIDE AND THALLIUM VANADIUM SULFIDE, NEW VANADIUM TERNARIES, HOMOLOGS OF LAUTITE.** KAMSU KOM, J. FOURNES, L. C. R. ACAD. SCI. 276 C (19), 1521–4, 1973.
50027	**VIBRATIONAL LUMINESCENCE OF NITROUS OXIDE EXCITED BY AN ELECTRIC DISCHARGE.** FARRENQ, R. GAULTIER, D. C. R. ACAD. SCI. 276 B (23), 859–62, 1973.

EPIC Number	Bibliographic Citation

50030 **LUMINESCENT PROPERTIES OF ALUMINUM NITRIDE ACTIVATED BY EUROPIUM.**
KAREL, F. MARES, J.
CZECH. J. PHYS.
23 (6), 652–9, 1973.

50032 **ROLE OF NICKEL IN STIMULATED PROCESSES IN SODIUM CHLORIDE.**
VOSZKA, R. WATTERICH, A. FOLDVARI, I.
BOHUN, A. POLAK, K.
CZECH. J. PHYS.
23 (6), 670–80, 19739

50034 **OPTICAL ABSORPTION SPECTRA IN INFRARED AND VISIBLE REGIONS AND DIELECTRIC CONSTANTS OF THE GLASSY STATE OF THE LEAD OXIDE-BORON OXIDE BINARY SYSTEM.**
OYAMADA, R. HAGIWARA, H. KUROSAWA, T.
DENKI KAGAKU
41 (1), 13–6, 1973.

50037 **CHANGE IN ELECTRICAL CONDUCTIVITY DURING THE SOLID-PHASE FORMATION OF LANTHANUM CHROMITE AND ITS ELECTROPHYSICAL PROPERTIES.**
RUBINCHIK, YA. S. REZNIKOV, M. YA.
DOKL. AKAD. NAUK BELORUSS. SSR
17 (5), 434–6, 1973.

50038 **TYPE OF TRANSITION IN THE REORIENTATION RANGE FOR FERRITE PEROVSKITES.**
APOSTOL'V, A. V. ILIEV, L. T.
DOKL. BOLG. AKAD. NAUK
26 (3), 315–8, 1973.

50040 **PIEZOELECTRIC COUPLING PARAMETER FOR ACOUSTIC SURFACE WAVES IN A LAYERED CADMIUM-SELENIDE ON-YZ-CUT-LITHIUM-NIOBATE STRUCTURE.**
VOGES, E. ANGERSTEIN, J.
ELECTRON. LETT.
9 (11), 241–2, 1973.

50044 **THERMAL EMISSION PROPERTIES OF GROUP IV-V TRANSITION METAL CARBIDES IN THEIR HOMOGENEITY REGIONS.**
SAMSONOV, G. V. NAUMENKO, V. YA.
OKHREMCHUK, L. N. PODCHERNYAEVA, I. A.
FOMENKO, V. S.
ELEKTRON. STR. FIZ. SVOISTVA TVERD. TELA, DOKL. VSES. SIMP. FIZ. SVOISTVAM ELEKTRON. STR. PEREKHODNYKH METAL., IKH. SPLAVON SOEDIN., 7TH
2, 147–56, 1972.

50045 **OPTICAL AND LUMINESCENCE PROPERTIES OF CADMIUM BROMIDE-TIN AND CADMIUM CHLORIDE-TIN SINGLE CRYSTALS.**
ZHEREBETSKII, S. K. LYSKOVICH, A. B.
CHORNII, Z. P. PENTSAK, G. M.
FIZ. ELECTRON. (LVOV)
(5), 55–7, 1972.

50046 **SELF-TRAPPED ELECTRONIC EXCITATION IN BARIUM BROMIDE CRYSTALS.**
CHORNII, Z. P. MAKSIMOVICH, KH. K.
VAIDANICH, V. I.
FIZ. ELEKTRON. (LVOV)
(5), 58–60, 1972.

50052 **MAGNETIC SUSCEPTIBILITY OF COPPER-ALUMINUM ALLOYS IN SOLID AND LIQUID STATES.**
STAKHOV, D. A. BATALIN, G. I.
KOSTYUK, L. YA
FIZ. METAL. METALLOVED.
35 (4), 715–18, 1973.

50054 **RECOMBINATION PROCESSES IN THE SUBSURFACE REGION OF GALLIUM ARSENIDE.**
VALIEV, K. A. GRITCHENKO, V. N.
PASHINTSEV, YU. I.
FIZ. TEKH. POLUPROV.
7 (3), 505–12, 1973.
(FOR ENGLISH TRANSLATION SEE E51410)

50055 **BAND STRUCTURE OF INDIUM ARSENIDE.**
KARYMSHAKOV, R. K.
FIZ. TEKH. POLUPROV.
7 (3), 513–18, 1973.
(FOR ENGLISH TRANSLATION SEE E51411)

50056 **THERMOGALVANOMAGNETIC PHENOMENA IN SEMICONDUCTORS AT LOW TEMPERATURES.**
JASEVICUITE, J.
FIZ. TEKH. POLUPROV.
7 (3), 525–30, 1973.
(FOR ENGLISH TRANSLATION SEE E51412)

50057 **ELECTRICAL CONDUCTIVITY OF ALUMINUM GALLIUM ARSENIDE VARIABLE-GAP CRYSTALS.**
MATULENIS, A. POZELA, J. TSARENKOV, B. V.
JUCIENE, V. YAKOVLEV, YU. P.
FIZ. TEKH. POLUPROV.
7 (3), 591–3, 1973.
(FOR ENGLISH TRANSLATION SEE E51413)

50058 **YELLOW ELECTROLUMINESCENCE OF GALLIUM PHOSPHIDE.**
ABAGYAN, S. A. IZERGIN, A. P.
KUZNETSOV, YU. N. PERSHINA, T. E.
PERSHIN, YU. I.
FIZ. TEKH. POLUPROV.
7 (3), 596–8, 1973.
(FOR ENGLISH TRANSLATION SEE E51414)

50059 **PHOTOLUMINESCENCE OF EPITIAZIAL LAYERS OF INDIUM GALLIUM PHOSPHIDE SOLID SOLUTIONS IN THE RANGE OF COMPOSITIONS 0.3.**
ALFEROV, ZH. I. GARBUZOV, D. Z.
KONNIKOV, S. G. KOP'EV, P. S.
MISHURNYI, V. A. RUMYANTSEV, V. D.
TRET'YAKOV, D. N.
FIZ. TEKH. POLUPROV.
7 (3), 624–7, 1973.
(FOR ENGLISH TRANSLATION SEE E51415)

50061 **RADIATIVE RECOMBINATION IN PURE INDIUM ANTIMONIDE CRYSTALS AT LOW TEMPERATURES.**
GRISHECHKINA, S. P. SHOTOV, A. P.
FIZ. TEKH. POLUPROV.
7 (J), 707–10, 1973.
(FOR ENGLISH TRANSLATION SEE E51417)

50062 **QUANTUM OSCILLATIONS OF N-MERCURY TELLURIDE GALVANOMAGNETIC COEFFICIENTS AT LOW TEMPERATURES.**
IVANOV-OMSKII, V. I. KONSTANTINOVA, N. N.
PERFEN'EV, R. V. SOLOGUB, V. V.
TAGIEV, I. G.
FIZ. TEKH. POLUPROV.
7 (4), 715–24, 1973.
(FOR ENGLISH TRANSLATION SEE E51418)

50063 **ANISOTROPIC THERMOELEMENTS.**
KOROLYUK, S. L. PILAT, I. M.
SAMOILOVICH, A. G. SLIPCHENKO, V. N.
SNARSKII, A. A. TSAR'KOV, E. F.
FIZ. TEKH. POLUPROV.
7 (4), 725–34, 1973.
(FOR ENGLISH TRANSLATION SEE E51419)

50064 **QUANTUM SIZE EFFECTS IN SEMICONDUCTOR FILMS WITH SURFACE STATES.**
KONSTANTINOV, O. V. FILATOV, O. N.
SHIK, A. YA.
7 (4), 786–9, 1973.

50065 **FINE STRUCTURE OF THE EMISSION LINE OF THE GROUND EXCITON STATE N O IN GALLIUM SELENIDE.**
ABDULLAEV, G. B. BELEN'KII, G. L.
KHALILOV, V. KH. SALAEV, E. YU.
FIZ. TEKH. POLUPROV.
7 (4), 818–20, 1973.

50066 **DETERMINATION OF THE HOLE EFFECTIVE MASS IN LEAD TIN SELENIDE CRYSTALS FROM THE MEASUREMENTS OF THE NERNST-ETTINGSHAUSEN EFFECT.**
KUCHERENKO, I. V. TAKTAKISHVILI, M. S.
SHOTOV, A. P.
FIZ. TEKH. POLUPROV.
7 (4), 822–4, 1973.
(FOR ENGLISH TRANSLATION SEE E51420)

50067 **DISPERSION LAW OF THE SILVER SELENIDE CONDUCTIVITY REGION.**
GORBACHEV, V. V. PUTILIN, I. M.
FIZ. TECH. POLUPROV.
7 (4), 833–4, 1973.
(FOR ENGLISH TRANSLATION SEE E51421)

50068 **OPTICAL PROPERTIES OF CADMIUM GALLIUM SULFIDE AND CADMIUM GALLIUM SELENIDE AT 200–600 NM.**
ABDULLAEV, G. B. GUSEINOVA, D. A.
KERIMOVA, T. G. NANI, R. KH.
FIZ. TEKH. POLUPROV.
7 (4), 840–2, 1973.
(FOR ENGLISH TRANSLATION SEE E51422)

50069 **TEMPERATURE DEPENDENCE OF THE EFFECTIVE MASS OF ELECTRONS IN SILVER SELENIDE.**
GORBACHEV, V. V. PUTILIN, I. M.
FIZ. TEKH. POLUPROV.
7 (4), 844–5, 1973.
(FOR ENGLISH TRANSLATION SEE E51423)

50070 **DETERMINATION OF EFFECTIVE HOLE MOBILITY USING IR ABSORPTION AND FIELD-EFFECT MEASUREMENTS.**
NEIZVESTNYI, I. G. MIRONOV, F. S.
SINYUKOV, M. P.
FIZ. TEKH. POLUPROV.
7 (4), 822–7, 1973.
(FOR ENGLISH TRANSLATION SEE E51424)

50071 **PHOTOELECTRIC PROPERTIES OF SEMIINSULATED GALLIUM PHOSPHIDE AND GALLIUM PHOSPHIDE-BASED DIODE STRUCTURES.**
MURYGIN, V. I. ORLOV, B. M.
SOKOL'NIKOV, A. V.
FIZ. TEKH. POLUPROV.
7 (4), 858–9, 1973.

EPIC Number	Bibliographic Citation
50072	**DETERMINATION OF THE ACTIVATION ENERGY OF A PARTIALLY COMPENSATED IMPURITY LEVEL. I.** KLOTINS, E. FIZ. TEKH. POLUPROV. 7 (4), 859–60, 1973.
50073	**DETERMINATION OF THE ACTIVATION ENERGY OF A PARTIALLY COMPENSATED IMPURITY LEVEL. II.** KLOTINS, E. FIZ. TEKH. POLUPROV. 7 (4), 860, 1973.
50074	**HOT EXCITONS IN THE PHOTOCONDUCTIVITY SPECTRUM OF CADMIUM SULFIDE CRYSTALS AT 4.2 K.** GASTEV, S. V. LIDER, K. F. NOVIKOV, B. V. FIZ. TEKH. POLUPROV. 7 (5), 901–4, 1973. (FOR ENGLISH TRANSLATION SEE E51425)
50075	**TEMPERATURE DEPENDENCE OF ANISOTROPY OF ELECTRON MOBILITY IN P-CADMIUM ANTIMONIDE.** GERTOVICH, T. S. ZHAD'KO, I. P. RARENKO, I. M. ROMANOV, V. A. YUROV, YU. G. FIZ. TEKH. POLUPROV. 7 (5), 946–50, 1973. (FOR ENGLISH TRANSLATION SEE E51426)
50077	**PIEZOELECTROABSORPTION IN GALLIUM ARSENIDE.** BEROZASHVILI, YU. N. GOGOLIN, O. V. LORDKIPANIDZE, D. SH. FIZ. TEKH. POLUPROV. 7 (5), 975–6, 1973. (FOR ENGLISH TRANSLATION SEE E51430)
50079	**ELECTRICAL PROPERTIES OF EPITAXIAL TIN-DOPED GALLIUM ARSENIDE.** EMEL'YANENKO, O. V. LAGUNOVA, T. S. RADU, R. K. TALALAKIN, G. N. TELEGIN, A. A. FIZ. TEKH. POLUPROV. 7 (5), 979–80, 1973. (FOR ENGLISH TRANSLATION SEE E51432)
50080	**THERMOELECTROMOTIVE FORCE AND PHONON DRAG IN HEAVILY DOPED III - V CRYSTALS.** EMELYANENKO, O. V. SKRIPKIN, V. A. POPOVA, V. A. FIZ. TEKH. POLUPROV. 7 (5), 981–3, 1973. (FOR ENGLISH TRANSLATION SEE E51433)
50081	**FIELD STIMULATION OF QUENCHING OF IMPURITY PHOTOCONDUCTIVITY IN CHROMIUM-DOPED GALLIUM ARSENIDE.** PEKA, G. P. MIRETS, L. Z. FIZ. TEKH. POLUPROV. 7 (5), 951–4, 1973. (FOR ENGLISH TRANSLATION SEE E51427)
50082	**CONTACT PHOTOELECTROMOTIVE FORCE AND NEGATIVE PHOTOCONDUCTIVITY IN HIGH-RESISTANCE COPPER(I) OXID CRYSTALS IN THE EXCITON ABSORPTION REGION.** TAZENKOV, B. A. MERZLYAKOV, V. P. FIZ. TEKH. POLUPROV. 7 (5), 955–7, 1973. (FOR ENGLISH TRANSLATION SEE E51428)
50083	**PHOTOLUMINESCENCE OF EPITAXIAL LAYERS OF TELLURIUM DOPED N-ALUMINUM GALLIUM ARSENIDE.** ROGULIN, V. YU. SHLENSKII, A. A. FIZ. TEKH. POLUPROV. 7 (5), 988–90, 19739 (FOR ENGLISH TRANSLATION SEE E51434)
50084	**DEFECT ASSOCIATION IN ZINC TELLURIDE.** BRODIN, M. S. GOER, D. B. MATSKO, M. G. FIZ. TEKH. POLUPROV. 7 (5), 997–9, 1973. (FOR ENGLISH TRANSLATION SEE E51435)
50087	**INFLUENCE OF GAS-PHASE STOICHIOMETRY ON THE PROPERTIES OF VAPOR-GROWN GALLIUM INDIUM PHOSPHIDE ALLOYS.** ENSTROM, R. E. NUESE, C. J. BAN, V. S. APPERT, J. R. GALLIUM ARSENIDE RELAT. COMPOUNDS, PROC. INT. SYMP., 4TH 37–47, 1973.
50088	**OPTICAL CHARACTERIZATION OF GALLIUM ARSENIDE PHOSPHIDE.** LORENZ, M. R. BLAKESLEE, A. E. GALLIUM ARSENIDE RELAT. COMPOUNDS, PROC. INT. SYMP., 4TH 106–17, 1973.
50089	**ELECTRICAL AND PHOTOLUMINESCENCE BEHAVIOR OF IMPURITIES IN INDIUM PHOSPHIDE.** MULLIN, J. B. ROYLE, A. STRAUGHAN, B. W. TUFTON, P. J. WILLIAMS, E. W. GALLIUM ARSENIDE RELAT. COMPOUNDS, PROC. INT. SYMP., 4TH 118–29, 1973.
50090	**ELECTRICAL PROPERTIES AND PHOTOCONDUCTIVITY OF CADMIUM SULFIDE THIN FILMS OBTAINED IN A HYDROGEN ATMOSPHERE.** AKRAMOV, KH. T. YULDASHEV, B. D. SAIDKHANOV, A. GELIOTEKHNIKA (2), 3–5, 1973.
50091	**HIGH-PRESSURE PROPERTIES OF FERROUS SULFIDE AND THEIR GEOPHYSICAL INTERPRETATION.** STILLER, H. VOLLSTAEDT, H. FROELICH, F. HEINRICH, R. WAESCH, R. SEIPOLD, U. GEOFIZ. SB. (KIEV) (49), 3–8, 1972.
50093	**REFRACTIVE INDEX DISPERSION IN SEMICONDUCTOR-RELATED THIN FILMS.** WARNECKE, A. J. LOPRESTI, P. J. IBM J. RES. DEVELOP. 17 (3), 256–62, 1973.
50095	**APPARATUS FOR MEASURING THE HALL CONSTANT FOR SEMICONDUCTORS UP TO 1000.** ASTAKHOV, O. P. SGIBNEV, I. V. IZMER. TEKH. (4), 61, 1973.
50097	**ELECTRICAL AND MAGNETIC PROPERTIES OF SOME COPPER-MANGANESE SPINELS.** SUSEELA, S. SINHA, A. P. B. INDIAN J. PURE APPL. PHYS. 11 (2), 112–15, 1973.
50100	**CONTROLLABLE SECONDARY ELECTRON EMISSION AT HIGH ENERGIES.** LORIKYAN, M. P. KAVALOV, R. L. TROFIMCHUK, N. N. IZV. AKAD. NAUK ARM. SSR, FIZ. 8 (1), 33–6, 1973.
50102	**HOPPING CONDUCTIVITY IN GRANULAR METALS. CADMIUM SULFIDE SINGLE CRYSTALS.** SHENG, PING, ABELES, B. ARIE, Y. DUBOVOI, V. K. KONOZENKO, I. D. PHYS. REV. LETT. 31 (1), 44–7, 1973.
50104	**REACTION OF TELLURIUM VAPOR WITH A COPPER PLATE.** YURLOVA, G. A. KASATKINA, T. M. TSALLAGOV, S. G. IZV. AKAD. NAUK SSR, NEORG. MATER. J (5), 764–7, 1973.
50105	**PREPARATION AND STUDY OF THE ELECTRICAL PROPERTIES OF CADMIUM TIN ARSENIDE SINGLE CRYSTALS WITH SMALL ADDITIONS OF III - V COMPOUNDS.** ALLANAZAROV, A. DOVLETMURADOV, CH. SERGINOV, M. IZV. AKAD. NAUK TURKM. SSR, SER. FIZ.-TEKH., KHIM. GEOL. NAUK (6), 45–52, 1972.
50107	**RADIATION-STIMULATED THERMOLUMINESCENCE OF ALUMINUM YTTRIUM GARNET CRYSTALS ACTIVATED BY RARE EARTH IONS.** VAKHIDOV, SH. A. YUSUPOV, A. A. IZV. AKAD. NAUK UZB. SSR, SER. FIZ.-MAT. NAUK 17 (2), 65–6, 1973.
50109	**IONIZATION OF LUMINESCENCE CENTERS IN ALKALI HALIDE PHOSPHORS BY UNRELAXED HOLES.** ALUKERS, E. KALININS, J. CHERNOV, S. A. SVARCS, K. IZV. AKAD. NAUK SSSR, SER. FIZ. 37 (4), 738–40, 1973. (FOR ENGLISH TRANSLATION SEE E54519)
50111	**CONFIGURATION INTERACTION AND CORRELATION EFFECTS IN DONOR-ACCEPTOR PAIR SPECTRA.** MARKHAM, L. WILLIAMS, F. IZV. AKAD. NAUK SSSR, SER. FIZ. 37 (4), 803–9, 1973. (FOR ENGLISH TRANSLATION SEE E54522)
50112	**DONOR-ACCEPTOR PAIRS IN IONIC CRYSTALS.** SCHWOTZER, G. KOETITZ, G. GOERLICH, P. IZV. AKAD. NAUK SSSR, SER. FIZ. 37 (4), 810–17, 1973. (FOR ENGLISH TRANSLATION SEE E54523)
50113	**HOT LUMINESCENCE OF IMPURITY MOLECULAR IONS IN ALKALI HALIDE CRYSTALS.** REBANE, K. SAARI, P. MAURING, T. IZV. AKAD. NAUK SSSR, SER. FIZ. 37 (4), 848–54, 1973. (FOR ENGLISH TRANSLATION SEE E54524)
50114	**ACTIVATORS OF SILICON CARBIDE LUMINESCENCE.** VAHNER, H. VIOLIN, E. E. KALNINS, A. TAIROV, YU. M. TSVETKOV, V. F. IZV. LENINGRAD. ELEKTROTEKH. INST. (101), 20–7, 1972.

EPIC Number	Bibliographic Citation

50115 ELECTROLUMINESCENCE OF GALLIUM PHOSPHIDE IN THE VISIBLE SPECTRAL REGION.
SAMORUKOV, B. E.
IZV. VYSSH. UCHEB. ZAVED., FIZ.
16 (4), 12–16, 1973.
(FOR ENGLISH TRANSLATION SEE E79418)

50121 PHOTOLUMINESCENT OF SODIUM AND POTASSIUM NITRIDES.
GAVRISHCHENKO, YU. V. IVANOV, G. F.
IZV. VYSSH. UCHEB. ZAVED., FIZ.
16 (4), 150–1, 1973.
(FOR ENGLISH TRANSLATION SEE E79433)

50122 TEMPERATURE DEPENDENCE OF THE STEADY-STATE INTENSITY OF RADICAL-RECOMBINATION LUMINESCENCE.
KHORUZHII, V. D. SIVOV, YU. A.
NASLEDNIKOV, YU. M.
IZV. VYSSH. UCHEB. ZAVED., FIZ.
16 (4), 151–4, 1973.
(FOR ENGLISH TRANSLATION SEE E79432)

50125 ELECTRICAL CONDUCTION OF RARE-EARTH-DOPED BARIUM TITANATE SINGLE CRYSTALS.
MURAKAMI, T. NAKAHARA, M. MIYASHITA, T.
UEDA, S.
J. AMER. CERAM. SOC.
56 (6), 291–3, 1973.

50126 EFFECT OF RARE-EARTH IONS ON ELECTRICAL CONDUCTIVITY OF BARIUM TITANATE CERAMICS.
MURAKAMI, T. MIYASHITA, T. NAKAHARA, M.
SEKINA, E.
J. AMER. CERAM. SOC.
56 (6), 294–7, 1973.

50127 RELAXATION OF VOLUME AND INDEX OF REFRACTION IN PRESSURE-COMPACTED BORON OXIDE GLASS.
MIZOUCHI, N. COPPER, A. R., JR.
J. AMER. CERAM. SOC.
56 (6), 320–3, 1973.

50128 NEUTRON DIFFRACTION, MAGNETIC, AND SUPERCONDUCTING MEASUREMENTS ON VANADIUM-MANGANESE-GALLIUM ALLOYS.
KITCHINGHAM, W. J. NORMAN, P. L.
J. APPL. CRYSTALLOGR.
6 (PT. 3), 240–3, 1973.

50131 DEPTH-RESOLVED CATHODOLUMINESCENCE IN UNDAMAGED AND ION-IMPLANTED GALLIUM ARSENIDE, ZINC SULFIDE, AND CADMIUM SULFIDE.
NORRIS, C. B. BARNES, C. E. BEEZHOLD, W.
J. APPL. PHYS.
44 (7), 3209–21, 1973.

50133 X-RAY K BETA EMISSION AND ABSORPTION SPECTRA OF CHLORINE IN RUBIDIUM CHLORIDE.
SUGIURA, C.
J. CHEM. PHYS.
58 (8), 3527–8, 1973.

50135 OPTICAL STUDY OF THE CHEMISTRY OF MANGANESE DIPOSITIVE ION DURING THE FORMATION OF CALCIUM FLUOROPHOSPHATE PHOSPHORS.
WACHTEL, A. RYAN, F. M.
J. ELECTROCHEM. SOC.
120 (5), 693–5, 1973.

50136 EMISSION COLOR OF EUROPIUM-DOPED YTTRIUM OXIDE SULFUR PHOSPHOR.
FOREST, H.
J. ELECTROCHEM. SOC.
120 (5), 695–7, 1973.

50137 PHOTOLUMINESCENCE OF GEL-GROWN LEAD (II) HYDROXIDE IODIDE SINGLE CRYSTALS.
SCHWARTZ, A. O'CONNELL, J. C.
J. ELECTROCHEM. SOC.
120 (5), 697–8, 1973.

50138 CHEMICAL COMPOSITION AND ELECTRICAL PROPERTIES OF TIN OXIDE FILMS PREPARED BY VAPOR DEPOSITION.
ABOAF, J. A. MARCOTTE, V. C. CHOU, N. J.
J. ELECTROCHEM. SOC.
120 (5), 701–2, 1973.

50140 FLUORESCENCE EXCITATION AND PHOTOELECTRON SPECTRA OF CARBON DIOXIDE INDUCED BY VACUUM ULTRAVIOLET RADIATION BETWEEN 185 AND 716 ANGSTROM.
SAMSON, J. A. R. GARDNER, J. L.
J. GEOPHYS. RES.
78 (19), 3663–7, 1973.

50142 LUMINESCENCE AND ENERGY LEVELS OF SAMARIUM (2+) IN ALKALI HALIDES.
GUZZI, M. BALDINI, G.
J. LUMIN.
6 (4), 270–84, 1973.

50143 THERMOLUMINESCENCE (TL), PHOSPHORESCENCE, AND CRYOLUMINESCENCE OF N-TYPE HEXAGONAL (6H) SILICON CARBIDE CRYSTALS.
HALPERIN, A. ZAKS, E. SILBERG, E.
J. LUMIN.
6 (4), 304–19, 1973.

50144 LUMINESCENCE OF MAGNESIUM IONS IN ORDERED AND DISORDERED LITHIUM ALUMINUM OXIDE.
MC NICOL, B. D. POTT, G. T.
J. LUMIN.
6 (4), 320–34, 1973.

50146 OPTICAL CONSTANTS OF ICE IN THE INFRARED.
SCHAAF, J. W. WILLIAMS, D.
J. OPT. SOC. AMER.
63 (6), 726–32, 1973.

50148 APPARATUS FOR THE MEASUREMENT OF THE HALL EFFECT IN SEMICONDUCTORS AT HIGH TEMPERATURES.
HALES, M. C. KNIGHT, J. R.
J. PHYS.
6 E (6), 520–1, 1973.

50150 BAND STRUCTURE AND OPTICAL PROPERTIES OF TETRAGONAL BARIUM TITANATE.
MICHEL-CALENDINI, F. M. MESNARD, G.
J. PHYS.
6 C (10), 1709–22, 1973.

50151 ENERGY BANDS IN LITHIUM FLUORIDE AND SOLID ARGON.
MICKISH, D. J. KUNZ, A. B.
J. PHYS.
6 C (10), 1723–33, 1973.

50152 HALL EFFECT IN AN ACOUSTOELECTRIC DOMAIN IN P-TYPE GALLIUM ANTIMONIDE.
LEPETRE, T. P. DUSSEAU, J. M. ROBERT, J. L.
PISTOULET, B.
J. PHYS.
6 C (10), 1794–9, 1973.

50154 ACCEPTOR LEVELS IN GALLIUM ARSENIDE.
WHITE, A. M. DEAN, P. J. ASHEN, D. J.
MULLIN, J. B. WEBB, M. DAY, B.
GREENE, P. D.
J. PHYS.
6 C (11), L243–L246, 1973.

50155 PHONON DISPERSION CURVES, INFRARED, AND RAMAN SPECTRA OF STRONTIUM (II) CHLORIDE.
DENHAM, P. A. MORSE, P. L. R.
WILKINSON, G. R.
J. PHYS.
6 C (12), 2366–75, 1973.

50161 PARAMAGNETIC SUSCEPTIBILITY OF SAMARIUM-ZINC.
STEWART, A. M.
J. PHYS.
3 F (5), 1024–30, 1973.

50165 HALOGEN DOUBLETS IN THE PHOTOEMISSION SPECTRA OF THE ALKALI IODIDES.
ONUKI, H. KANBE, J. ONAKA, R.
J. PHYS. SOC. JAP.
34 (2), 560, 1973.

50167 LUMINESCENCE FROM X-RAY IRRADIATED CADMIUM FLUORIDE AND BARIUM FLUORIDE.
TZALMONA, A.
J. PHYS. SOC. JAP.
34 (4), 1108, 1973.

50168 PHOTOLUMINESCENCE INDUCED IN ZINC SULFIDE BY ELECTRON IRRADIATION.
SHONO, Y. YOSHIDA, T.
J. PHYS. SOC. JAP.
34 (4), 1109, 1973.

50169 IONIC CONDUCTIVITY OF LEAD BROMIDE CRYSTALS.
HOSHINO, H. YOKOSE, S. SHIMOJI, M.
J. SOLID STATE CHEM.
7 (1), 1–6, 1973.

50170 CRYSTALLOGRAPHIC AND MAGNETIC PROPERTIES OF THE CADMIUM HYDROXIDE LAYER STRUCTURE COMPOUND TITANIUM (IV) SULFIDE CONTAINING EXTRA IRON.
TAKAHASHI, T. YAMADA, O.
J. SOLID STATE CHEM.
7 (1), 25–30, 1973.

50173 CHEMICAL BOND CHARACTER AND SHORT-RANGE ORDER STRUCTURE IN VITREOUS SEMICONDUCTORS FROM ELECTRIC AND MAGNETIC PROPERTY DATA.
BORISOVA, Z. U. BAIDAKOV, L. A.
KHIM. SVYAZ POLUPROV. POLUMETALLAKH
281–8, 1972.

50174 EFFECT OF THE CONDENSATION RATE ON THE THERMOELECTRIC PROPERTIES OF ANTIMONY AND BISMUTH TELLURIDE FILMS.
KRAVCHUK, V. V.
KHOLOD. TEKH. TEKHNOL.
(15), 78–81, 1972.

50179 EFFECTS OF THE LAYERED STRUCTURE AND THE ABSORPTION EDGE OF BISMUTH OXIDE IODIDE SINGLE CRYSTALS.
BORETS, A. N. SHTILIKHA, M. V. PUGA, G. D.
FIZ. TVERD. TELA
15 (1), 42–7, 1973.
(FOR ENGLISH TRANSLATION SEE EPIC NO. 50180)

EPIC Number	Bibliographic Citation

50180 **EFFECTS OF THE LAYERED STRUCTURE AND THE ABSORPTION EDGE OF BISMUTH OXIDE IODIDE SINGLE CRYSTALS.**
BORETS, A. N. SHTILIKHA, M. V. PUGA, G. D.
SOV. PHYS. - SOLID STATE
15 (1), 28-31, 1973.
(ENGLISH TRANSLATION OF FIZ. TVERD. TELA, 15 (1), 42-7, 1973; FOR ORIGINAL SEE E50179)

50183 **BEHAVIOR OF COMPLEX HONEYCOMB DOMAIN STRUCTURE OF MANGANESE-ALUMINUM-GERMANIUM CRYSTALS IN MAGNETIC FIELDS.**
KANDAUROVA, G. S. DERYAGIN, A. V.
LAGUTIN, A. E.
FIZ. TVERD. TELA
15 (1), 56-60, 1973.
(FOR ENGLISH TRANSLATION SEE EPIC NO. 50184)

50184 **BEHAVIOR OF COMPLEX HONEYCOMB DOMAIN STRUCTURE OF MANGANESE-ALUMINUM-GERMANIUM CRYSTALS IN MAGNETIC FIELDS.**
KANDAUROVA, G. S. DERYAGIN, A. V.
LAGUTIN, A. E.
SOV. PHYS. - SOLID STATE
15 (1), 38-40, 1973.
(FOR ENGLISH TRANSLATION OF FIZ. TVERD. TELA, 15 (1), 56-60, 1973; FOR ORIGINAL SEE E50183)

50187 **COMPARATIVE INVESTIGATION OF THE ANISOTROPY OF ELECTRICAL CONDUCTIVITY IN VARIOUS SILICON CARBIDE POLYTYPES.**
LOMAKINA, G. A. VODAKOV, YU. A.
FIZ. TVERD. TELA
15 (1), 123-7, 1973.
(FOR ENGLISH TRANSLATION SEE EPIC NO. 50188)

50188 **COMPARATIVE INVESTIGATION OF THE ANISOTROPY OF ELECTRICAL CONDUCTIVITY IN VARIOUS SILICON CARBIDE POLYTYPES.**
LOMAKINA, G. A. VODAKOV, YU. A.
SOV. PHYS. - SOLID STATE
15 (1), 83-6, 1973.
(FOR ENGLISH TRANSLATION OF FIZ. TVERD. TELA, 15 (1), 123-7, 1973; FOR ORIGINAL SEE EPIC NO. 50187)

50189 **INFLUENCE OF HYDROSTATIC PRESSURE ON THE IONIC CONDUCTIVITY OF SILVER CHLORIDE AND SILVER CHLORIDE PLUS MANGANESE CHLORIDE SINGLE CRYSTALS.**
MURIN, A. N. MURIN, I. V. SIVKOV, V. P.
FIZ. TVERD. TELA
15 (1), 142-7, 1973.
(FOR ENGLISH TRANSLATION SEE EPIC NO. 50190)

50190 **INFLUENCE OF HYDROSTATIC PRESSURE ON THE IONIC CONDUCTIVITY OF SILVER CHLORIDE AND SILVER CHLORIDE PLUS MANGANESE CHLORIDE SINGLE CRYSTALS.**
MURIN, A. N. MURIN, I. V. SIVKOV, V. P.
SOV. PHYS. - SOLID STATE
15 (1), 98-101, 1973.
(FOR ENGLISH TRANSLATION OF FIZ. TVERD. TELA, 15 (1), 142-7, 1973; FOR ORIGINAL SEE EPIC NO. 50189)

50191 **HYSTERESIS OF MAGNETIZATION REVERSAL IN ORTHOFERRITE CRYSTALS.**
KHRABROV, V. I.
FIZ. TVERD. TELA
15 (1), 148-54, 1973.
(FOR ENGLISH TRANSLATION SEE E50192)

50192 **HYSTERESIS OF MAGNETIZATION REVERSAL IN ORTHOFERRITE CRYSTALS.**
KHRABROV, V. I.
SOV. PHYS. - SOLID STATE
15 (1), 102-6, 1973.
(FOR ENGLISH TRANSLATION OF FIZ. TVERD. TELA, 15 (1), 148-54, 1973; FOR ORIGINAL SEE E50191)

50195 **ESR INVESTIGATION OF CHROMIUM TELLURIDE AT PRESSURES UP TO 50 KBARS.**
SHANDITSEV, V. A. VERESHCHAGIN, L. F.
YAKOVLEV, E. N. GRAZHDANKINA, N. P.
ALAEVA, T. I.
FIZ. TVERD. TELA
15 (1), 212-5, 1973.
(FOR ENGLISH TRANSLATION SEE EPIC NO. 50196)

50196 **ISR INVESTIGATION OF CHROMIUM TELLURIDE AT PRESSURES UP TO 50 KBARS.**
SHANDITSEV, V. A. VERESHCHAGIN, L. F.
YAKOVLEV, E. N. GRAZHDANKINA, N. P.
ALAEVA, T. I.
SOV. PHYS. - SOLID STATE
15 (1), 146-8, 1973.
(ENGLISH TRANSLATION OF FIZ. TVERD. TELA, 15 (1), 212-5, 1973; FOR ORIGINAL SEE E20195)

50197 **SYMMETRY OF TITANIUM ION ACTIVATOR CENTERS IN GLASSY SILICA.**
AMOSOV, A. V. ZAKHAROV, V. K. YUDIN, D. M.
FIZ. TVERD. TELA
15 (1), 241-7, 1973.
(FOR ENGLISH TRANSLATION SEE E50198)

50198 **SYMMETRY OF TITANIUM ION ACTIVATOR CENTERS IN GLASSY SILICA.**
AMOSOV, A. V. ZAKHAROV, V. K. YUDIN, D. M.
SOV. PHYS. - SOLID STATE
15 (1), 167-71, 1973.
(FOR ENGLISH TRANSLATION OF FIZ. TVERD. TELA, 15 (1), 241-7, 1973; FOR ORIGINAL SEE E50197)

50201 **THERMAL CONDUCTIVITY OF CADMIUM TIN ARSENIDE SELENIDE SOLID SOLUTIONS IN MAGNETIC FIELDS.**
AMIRKHANOVA, D. KH. KHOKHLACHEV, P. P.
FIZ. TVERD. TELA
15 (1), 277-9, 1973.
(FOR ENGLISH TRANSLATION SEE E50202)

50202 **THERMAL CONDUCTIVITY OF CADMIUM TIN ARSENIDE SELENIDE SOLID SOLUTIONS IN MAGNETIC FIELDS.**
AMIRKHANOVA, D. KH. KHOKHLACHEV, P. P.
SOV. PHYS. - SOLID STATE
15 (1), 196-7, 1973.
(FOR ENGLISH TRANSLATION OF FIZ. TVERD. TELA, 15 (1), 277-9, 1973; FOR ORIGINAL SEE E50201)

50203 **MEASUREMENTS OF THE PIEZOELECTRIC COEFFICIENTS OF LITHIUM NIOBATE BY THE INTERFERENCE DILATOMETER METHOD.**
KISELEV, D. F. FIRSOVA, M. M.
FIZ. TVERD. TELA
15 (1), 279-81, 1973.
(FOR ENGLISH TRANSLATION SEE EPIC NO. 50204)

50204 **MEASUREMENTS OF THE PIEZOELECTRIC COEFFICIENTS OF LITHIUM NIOBATE BY THE INTERFERENCE DILATOMETER METHOD.**
KISELEV, D. F. FIRSOVA, M. M.
SOV. PHYS. - SOLID STATE
15 (1), 198-9, 1973.
(FOR ENGLISH TRANSLATION OF FIZ. TVERD. TELA, 15 (1), 279-81, 1973; FOR ORIGINAL SEE EPIC NO. 50203)

50205 **DETECTION OF DEEP LEVELS IN SEMICONDUCTORS.**
IVASHCHENKO, A. I. KOVALEVSKAYA, G. G.
ALYUSHINA, V. I. NASLEDOV, D. N.
SLOBODCHIKOV, S. V.
FIZ. TVERD. TELA
15 (1), 284-6, 1973.
(FOR ENGLISH TRANSLATION SEE EPIC NO. 50206)

50206 **DETECTION OF DEEP LEVELS IN SEMICONDUCTORS.**
IVASHCHENKO, A. I. KOVALEVSKAYA, G. G.
ALYUSHINA, V. I. NASLEDOV, D. N.
SLOBODCHIKOV, S. V.
SOV. PHYS. - SOLID STATE
15 (1), 202-3, 1973.
(FOR ENGLISH TRANSLATION OF FIZ. TVERD. TELA, 15 (1), 284-6, 1973; FOR ORIGINAL SEE EPIC NO. 50205)

50209 **INFLUENCE OF COBALT IMPURITIES ON GALVANOMAGNETIC PROPERTIES OF INDIUM ANTIMONIDE.**
VINOGRADOVA, K. I. NASLEDOV, D. N.
SMETANNIKOVA, YU. S. TASHKHODZHAEV, T. K.
FIZ. TVERD. TELA
15 (1), 295-7, 1973.
(FOR ENGLISH TRANSLATION SEE EPIC NO. 50210)

50210 **INFLUENCE OF COBALT IMPURITIES ON GALVANOMAGNETIC PROPERTIES OF INDIUM ANTIMONIDE.**
VINOGRADOVA, K. I. NASLEDOV, D. N.
SMETANNIKOVA, YU. S. TASHKHODZHAEV, T. K.
SOV. PHYS. - SOLID STATE
15 (1), 212-3, 1973.
(FOR ENGLISH TRANSLATION OF FIZ. TVERD. TELA, 15 (1), 295-7, 1973; FOR ORIGINAL SEE EPIC NO. 50209)

50211 **MAGNETIC PROPERTIES AND MOSSBAUER EFFECT IN FERROELECTRIC BISMUTH TITANIUM IRON OXIDE.**
KIZHAEV, S. A. SULTANOV, G. D.
MIRISHLI, F. A.
FIZ. TVERD. TELA
15 (1), 297-300, 1973.
(FOR ENGLISH TRANSLATION SEE E50212)

50212 **MAGNETIC PROPERTIES AND MOSSBAUER EFFECT IN FERROELECTRIC BISMUTH TITANIUM IRON OXIDE.**
KIZHAEV, S. A. SULTANOV, G. D.
MIRISHLI, F. A.
SOV. PHYS. - SOLID STATE
15 (1), 214-6, 1973.
(FOR ENGLISH TRANSLATION OF FIZ. TVERD. TELA, 15 (1), 297-300, 1973; FOR ORIGINAL SEE EPIC NO. 50211)

50213 **INFLUENCE OF OXYGEN IONS ON THE PHOTOCONDUCTIVITY OF POTASSIUM CHLORIDE AND POTASSIUM BROMIDE SINGLE CRYSTALS.**
KATS, M. L. GYUNSBURG, K. E.
GOLUBENTSEVA, L. I. ZVEZDOVA, N. P.
FIZ. TVERD. TELA
15 (1), 303-5, 1973.
(FOR ENGLISH TRANSLATION SEE EPIC NO. 50214)

EPIC Number	Bibliographic Citation
50214	**INFLUENCE OF OXYGEN IONS ON THE PHOTOCONDUCTIVITY OF POTASSIUM CHLORIDE AND POTASSIUM BROMIDE SINGLE CRYSTALS.** KATS, M. L. GYUNSBURG, K. E. GOLUBENTSEVA, L. I. ZVEZDOVA, N. P. SOV. PHYS. - SOLID STATE 15 (1), 221-2, 1973. (FOR ENGLISH TRANSLATION OF FIZ. TVERD. TELA, 15 (1), 303-5, 1973; FOR ORIGINAL SEE EPIC NO. 50213)
50215	**EXTERNAL-PUMPING-INDUCED CHANGE IN THE ELECTRON COMPONENT OF THE PERMITTIVITY OF PHOTOCONDUCTING SEMICONDUCTORS.** MAEV, R. G. POLUEKTOV, I. A. PUSTOVOIT, V. I. FIZ. TVERD. TELA 15 (1), 1821, 1973. (FOR ENGLISH TRANSLATION SEE EPIC NO. 50216)
50216	**EXTERNAL-PUMPING-INDUCED CHANGE IN THE ELECTRON COMPONENT OF THE PERMITTIVITY OF PHOTOCONDUCTING SEMICONDUCTORS.** MAEV, R. G. POLUEKTOV, I. A. PUSTOVOIT, V. I SOV. PHYS. - SOLID STATE 15 (1), 12-4, 1973. (FOR ENGLISH TRANSLATION OF FIZ. TVERD. TELA, 15 (1), 1821, 1973; FOR ORIGINAL SEE E50215)
50217	**STRUCTURE OF THE EDGE LUMINESCENCE SPECTRA OF CADMIUM SELENIDE AT HIGH EXCITATION DENSITIES.** BALTRAMEYUNAS, R. A. VAITKUS, YU. YU. VISHCHAKAS, YU. K. NYUNKA, V. V. FIZ. TVERD. TELA 15 (1), 319-21, 1973. (FOR ENGLISH TRANSLATION SEE E50218)
50218	**STRUCTURE OF THE EDGE LUMINESCENCE SPECTRA OF CADMIUM SELENIDE AT HIGH EXCITATION DENSITIES.** BALTRAMEYUNAS, R. R. VAITKUS, YU. YU. VISHCHAKAS, YU. K. NYUNKA, V. V. SOV. PHYS. - SOLID STATE 15 (1), 236-7, 1973. (FOR ENGLISH TRANSLATION OF FIZ. TVERD. TELA, 15 (1), 319-21, 1973; FOR ORIGINAL SEE E50217)
50219	**EFFECTS OF AN ELECTRIC FIELD ON ELECTRONIC STRUCTURE IN SINGLE CRYSTALS OF VANADIUM PENTOXIDE.** VALIEV, K. A. MOKEROV, V. G. RAKOV, A. V. FIZ. TVERD. TELA 15 (2), 361-7, 1973. (FOR ENGLISH TRANSLATION SEE E50220)
50220	**EFFECTS OF AN ELECTRIC FIELD ON ELECTRONIC STRUCTURE IN SINGLE CRYSTALS OF VANADIUM PENTOXIDE.** VALIEV, K. A. MOKEROV, V. G. RAKOV, A. V. SOV. PHYS. - SOLID STATE 15 (2), 265-8, 1973. (ENGLISH TRANSLATION OF FIZ. TVERD. TELA, 15 (2), 361-7, 1973; FOR ORIGINAL SEE E50219)
50221	**ACOUSTIC PARAMAGNETIC RESONANCE OF DOUBLY IONIZED IRON AND TRIPLY IONIZED IRON IN GALLIUM ARSENIDE.** GANAPOL'SKII, E. M. FIZ. TVERD. TELA 15 (2), 368-75, 1973. (FOR ENGLISH TRANSLATION SEE E50222)
50222	**ACOUSTIC PARAMAGNETIC RESONANCE OF DOUBLY IONIZED IRON AND TRIPLY IONIZED IRON IN GALLIUM ARSENIDE.** GANAPOL'SKII, E. M. SOV. PHYS. - SOLID STATE 15 (2), 269-73, 1973. (ENGLISH TRANSLATION OF FIZ. TVERD. TELA, 15 (2), 368-75, 1973; FOR ORIGINAL SEE E50221)
50223	**HIGH-TEMPERATURE TRANSITION TO METALLIC CONDUCTION IN SELENIUM-TELLURIUM MELTS.** ANDREEV, A. A. ALEKSEEV, V. A. MANUKYAN, A. L. SHUMILOVA, L. N. FIZ. TVERD. TELA 15 (2), 382-4, 1973. (FOR ENGLISH TRANSLATION SEE E50224)
50224	**HIGH-TEMPERATURE TRANSITION TO METALLIC CONDUCTION IN SELENIUM-TELLURIUM MELTS.** ANDREEV, A. A. ALEKSEEV, V. A. MANUKYAN, A. L. SHUMILOVA, L. N. SOV. PHYS. - SOLID STATE 15 (2), 277-8, 1973. (ENGLISH TRANSLATION OF FIZ. TVERD. TELA, 15 (2), 382-4, 1973; FOR ORIGINAL SEE E50223)
50225	**HEATING OF ELECTRONS WITH LIGHT IN N INDIUM ARSENIDE.** MIKHAILOVA, M. P. NASLEDOV, D. M. SLOBODCHIKOV, S. V. KHAMROKULOV, M. FIZ. TVERD. TELA 15 (2), 390-4, 1973. (FOR ENGLISH TRANSLATION SEE E50226)
50226	**HEATING OF ELECTRONS WITH LIGHT IN N INDIUM ARSENIDE.** MIKHAILOVA, M. P. NASLEDOV, D. N. SLOBODCHIKOV, S. V. KHAMROKULOV, M. SOV. PHYS. - SOLID STATE 15 (2), 282-4, 1973. (ENGLISH TRANSLATION OF FIZ. TVERD. TELA, 15 (2), 390-4, 1973; FOR ORIGINAL SEE E50225)
50227	**EFFECT OF ELECTRIC FIELDS ON THE ABSORPTION OF LIGHT BY DEEP IMPURITY CENTERS.** VINOGRADOV, V. S. FIZ. TVERD. TELA 15 (2), 395-403, 1973. (FOR ENGLISH TRANSLATION SEE E50228)
50228	**EFFECT OF ELECTRIC FIELDS ON THE ABSORPTION OF LIGHT BY DEEP IMPURITY CENTERS.** VINOGRADOV, V. S. SOV. PHYS. - SOLID STATE 15 (2), 285-9, 1973. (ENGLISH TRANSLATION OF FIZ. TVERD. TELA, 15 (2), 395-403, 1973; FOR ORIGINAL SEE E50227)
50229	**SPIN WAVES IN YTTRIUM IRON GARNET WITH A PERIODIC DOMAIN STRUCTURE.** SOLOMKO, A. A. MYKITYUK, V. I. FIZ. TVERD. TELA 15 (2), 449-51, 1973. (FOR ENGLISH TRANSLATION SEE E50230)
50230	**SPIN WAVES IN YTTRIUM IRON GARNET WITH A PERIODIC DOMAIN STRUCTURE.** SOLOMKO, A. A. MYKITYUK, V. I. SOV. PHYS. - SOLID STATE 15 (2), 320-1, 1973. (ENGLISH TRANSLATION OF FIZ. TVERD. TELA, 15 (2), 449-51, 1973; FOR ORIGINAL SEE E50229)
50233	**DISPERSION OF THE NONLINEAR REFRACTIVE INDEX IN NONCENTROSYMMETRIC CRYSTALS.** SHALDIN, YU. V. BELOGUROV, D. A. FIZ. TVERD. TELA 15 (2), 483-5, 1973. (FOR ENGLISH TRANSLATION SEE E50234)
50234	**DISPERSION OF THE NONLINEAR REFRACTIVE INDEX IN NONCENTROSYMMETRIC CRYSTALS.** SHALDIN, YU. V. BELOGUROV, D. A. SOV. PHYS. - SOLID STATE 15 (2), 339-40, 1973. (ENGLISH TRANSLATION OF FIZ. TVERD. TELA, 15 (2), 483-5, 1973; FOR ORIGINAL SEE E50233)
50235	**LOW-TEMPERATURE PHOTOCONDUCTIVITY AND ABSORPTION SPECTRA OF BUSMUTH TRIIODIDE SINGLE CRYSTALS.** VAINRUB, A. M. ILL'INSKII, A. V. NOVIKOV, B. V. FIZ. TVERD. TELA 15 (2), 490-2, 1973. (FOR ENGLISH TRANSLATION SEE E50236)
50236	**LOW-TEMPERATURE PHOTOCONDUCTIVITY AND ABSORPTION SPECTRA OF BISMUTH TRIIODIDE SINGLE CRYSTALS.** VAINRUB, A. M. ILL'INSKII, A. V. NOVIKOV, B. V. SOV. PHYS. - SOLID STATE 15 (2), 343-4, 1973. (ENGLISH TRANSLATION OF FIZ. TVERD. TELA, 15 (2), 490-2, 1973; FOR ORIGINAL SEE E50235)
50237	**MICROSTRUCTURE AND MAGNETIZATION DETAILS OF FILMS WITH STRIPE DOMAINS.** BEREZIN, D. G. DUNAEVA-MITLINA, T. A. KHRAMOV, B. V. FIZ. TVERD. TELA 15 (2), 493-7, 1973. (FOR ENGLISH TRANSLATION SEE E50238)
50238	**MICROSTRUCTURE AND MAGNETIZATION DETAILS OF FILMS WITH STRIPE DOMAINS.** BEREZIN, D. G. DUNAEVA-MITLINA, T. A. KHRAMOV, B. V. SOV. PHYS. - SOLID STATE 15 (2), 345-7, 1973. (ENGLISH TRANSLATION OF FIZ. TVERD. TELA, 15 (2), 493-7 1973; FOR ORIGINAL SEE E50237)
50239	**MONOMOLECULAR AND BIMOLECULAR THERMALLY STIMULATED LUMINESCENCE PEAKS OF IONIC CRYSTALS CONTAINING ELECTRON TRAPS OF A SINGLE TYPE.** LEIMAN, V. I. FIZ. TVERD. TELA 15 (2), 503-8, 1973. (FOR ENGLISH TRANSLATION SEE E50240)
50240	**MONOMOLECULAR AND BIMOLECULAR THERMALLY STIMULATED LUMINESCENCE PEAKS OF IONIC CRYSTALS CONTAINING ELECTRON TRAPS OF A SINGLE TYPE.** LEIMAN, V. I. SOV. PHYS. - SOLID STATE 15 (2), 351-3, 1973. (ENGLISH TRANSLATION OF FIZ. TVERD. TELA, 15 (2), 503-8, 1973; FOR ORIGINAL SEE E50239)

EPIC Number	Bibliographic Citation
50243	**BETHE AND DAVYDOV MAGNETIC SPLITTINGS IN WEAKLY FERROMAGNETIC POTASSIUM MANGANESE TRIFLUORIDE.** KHARKYANEN, V. N. PETROV, E. G. FIZ. TVERD. TELA 15 (2), 531–6, 1973. (FOR ENGLISH TRANSLATION SEE E50244)
50244	**BETHE AND DAVYDOV MAGNETIC SPLITTINGS IN WEAKLY FERROMAGNETIC POTASSIUM MANGANESE TRIFLUORIDE.** KHARKYANEN, V. N. PETROV, E. G. SOV. PHYS. - SOLID STATE 15 (2), 368–71, 1973. (ENGLISH TRANSLATION OF FIZ. TVERD. TELA, 15 (2), 531–6, 1973; FOR ORIGINAL SEE E50243)
50247	**MAGNETIZATION AND MAGNETIZATION PROCESSES IN YTTRIUM IRON GARNETS WITH A LAMINAR DOMAIN STRUCTURE.** SOLOMKO, A. A. MYKITYUK, V. I. GAIDAI, YU. A. FIZ. TVERD. TELA 15 (2), 554–6, 1973. (FOR ENGLISH TRANSLATION SEE E50248)
50248	**MAGNETIZATION AND MAGNETIZATION PROCESSES IN YTTRIUM IRON GARNETS WITH A LAMINAR DOMAIN STRUCTURE.** SOLOMKO, A. A. MYKITYUK, V. I. GAIDAI, YU. A. SOV. PHYS. - SOLID STATE 15 (2), 383–4, 1973. (ENGLISH TRANSLATION OF FIZ. TVERD. TELA, 15 (2), 554–6, 1973; FOR ORIGINAL SEE E50247)
50249	**EFFECT OF PLASTIC DEFORMATION ON THE OPTICAL PROPERTIES OF POTASSIUM CHLORIDE–EUROPIUM CRYSTAL PHOSPHORS.** KALABUKHOV, N. P. KOVALEV, V. K. FIZ. TVERD. TELA 15 (2), 557–8, 1973. (FOR ENGLISH TRANSLATION SEE E50250)
50250	**EFFECT OF PLASTIC DEFORMATION ON THE OPTICAL PROPERTIES OF POTASSIUM CHLORIDE–EUROPIUM CRYSTAL PHOSPHORS.** KALABUKHOV, N. P. KOVALEV, V. K. SOV. PHYS. - SOLID STATE 15 (2), 385, 1973. (ENGLISH TRANSLATION OF FIZ. TVERD. TELA, 15 (2), 557–8, 1973; FOR ORIGINAL SEE E50249)
50251	**NATURE OF MAGNETIC ORDERING IN NEODYMIUM SULFIDE NEAR 45 K.** NOVIKOV, V. I. POGARSKII, A. M. SHALYT, S. S. FIZ. TVERD. TELA 15 (2), 561–2, 1973. (FOR ENGLISH TRANSLATION SEE E50252)
50252	**NATURE OF MAGNETIC ORDERING IN NEODYMIUM SULFIDE NEAR 45 K.** NOVIKOV, V. I. POGARSKII, A. M. SHALYT, S. S. SOV. PHYS. - SOLID STATE 15 (2), 388, 1973. (ENGLISH TRANSLATION OF FIZ. TVERD. TELA, 15 (2), 561–2, 1973; FOR ORIGINAL SEE E50251)
50255	**COLLAPSE OF THE MAGNETIC SUBLATTICES IN ANTIFERROMAGNETIC ORDERED PEROVSKITES CONTAINING COBALT.** BOKOV, V. A. STAROVOITOV, A. T. PARFENOVA, N. N. FIZ. TVERD. TELA 15 (2), 577–9, 1973. (FOR ENGLISH TRANSLATION SEE E50256)
50256	**COLLAPSE OF THE MAGNETIC SUBLATTICES IN ANTIFERROMAGNETIC ORDERED PEROVSKITES CONTAINING COBALT.** BOKOV, V. A. STAROVOITOV, A. T. PARFENOVA, N. N. SOV. PHYS. - SOLID STATE 15 (2), 400–1, 1973. (ENGLISH TRANSLATION OF FIZ. TVERD. TELA, 15 (2), 577–9, 1973; FOR ORIGINAL SEE E50255)
50257	**CHANGES IN THE MAGNETIC AND MAGNETOSTRICTIVE PROPERTIES OF THE FERRITE NICKEL CHROMIUM FERRITE ON TRANSITION FROM THE CUBIC TO THE TETRAGONALLY DISTORTED PHASE.** BELOV, K. P. GORYAGA, A. N. ANTOSHINA, L. G. POPOV, YU. F. FIZ. TVERD. TELA 15 (2), 580–2, 1973. (FOR ENGLISH TRANSLATION SEE E50258)
50258	**CHANGES IN THE MAGNETIC AND MAGNETOSTRICTIVE PROPERTIES OF THE FERRITE NICKEL CHROMIUM FERRITE ON TRANSITION FROM THE CUBIC TO THE TETRAGONALLY DISTORTED PHASE.** BELOV, K. P. GORYAGA, A. N. ANTOSHINA, L. G. POPOV, YU. F. SOV. PHYS. - SOLID STATE 15 (2), 403–4, 1973. (ENGLISH TRANSLATION OF FIZ. TVERD. TELA, 15 (2), 580–28 1973; FOR ORIGINAL SEE E50257)
50259	**OPTICAL PROPERTIES OF YTTRIUM IRON GARNET.** GALUZA, A. E. EREMENKO, V. V. KIRICHENKO, A. P. FIZ. TVERD. TELA 15 (2), 585–7, 1973. (FOR ENGLISH TRANSLATION SEE E50260)
50260	**OPTICAL PROPERTIES OF YTTRIUM IRON GARNET.** GALUZA, A. I. EREMENKO, V. V. KIRICHENKO, A. P. SOV. PHYS. - SOLID STATE 15 (2), 407–8, 1973. (ENGLISH TRANSLATION OF FIZ. TVERD. TELA, 15 (2), 585–7, 1973; FOR ORIGINAL SEE E50259)
50261	**EFFECT OF UNIAXIAL COMPRESSION ON THE SHAPE OF THE INTRINSIC ABSORPTION EDGE IN CADMIUM TELLURIDE.** ANDRIYASHIK, M. V. KURIK, M. V. MANZHARA, V. S. MATLAK, V. V. SKITSKO, I. F. FIZ. TVERD. TELA 15 (2), 591–4, 1973. (FOR ENGLISH TRANSLATION SEE E50262)
50262	**EFFECT OF UNIAXIAL COMPRESSION ON THE SHAPE OF THE INTRINSIC ABSORPTION EDGE IN CADMIUM TELLURIDE.** ANDRIYASHIK, M. V. KURIK, M. V. MANZHARA, V. S. MATLAK, V. V. SKITSKO, I. F. SOV. PHYS. - SOLID STATE 15 (2), 413–4, 1973. (ENGLISH TRANSLATION OF FIZ. TVERD. TELA, 15 (2), 591–4, 1973; FOR ORIGINAL SEE E50261)
50273	**CALCULATION OF THE COEFFICIENT OF ABSORPTION OF STRONG LIGHT BY CARRIERS IN SEMICONDUCTORS.** DZHAKSIMOV, E. FIZ. TVERD. TELA 15 (2), 644–5, 1973. (FOR ENGLISH TRANSLATION SEE E50274)
50274	**CALCULATION OF THE COEFFICIENT OF ABSORPTION OF STRONG LIGHT BY CARRIERS IN SEMICONDUCTORS.** DZHAKSIMOV, E. SOV. PHYS. - SOLID STATE 15 (2), 456, 1973. (ENGLISH TRANSLATION OF FIZ. TVERD. TELA, 15 (2), 644–5, 1973; FOR ORIGINAL SEE E50273)
50275	**PARALLEL PUMPING OF THE SPIN–WAVE INSTABILITY IN FERRITES WITH VARIOUS SATURATION MAGNETIZATIONS.** GRANKIN, V. L. MELKOV, G. A. RUBAN, V. A. FIZ. TVERD. TELA 15 (2), 632–4, 1973. (FOR ENGLISH TRANSLATION SEE E50276)
50276	**PARALLEL PUMPING OF THE SPIN–WAVE INSTABILITY IN FERRITES WITH VARIOUS SATURATION MAGNETIZATIONS.** GRANKIN, V. L. MELKOV, G. A. RUBAN, V. A. SOV. PHYS. - SOLID STATE 15 (2), 447–8, 1673. (ENGLISH TRANSLATION OF FIZ. TVERD. TELA, 15 (2), 632–4, 1973; FOR ORIGINAL SEE E50275)
50277	**ELECTRON SPIN RESONANCE OF COBALT IONS IN LITHIUM–GALLIUM SPINEL.** KOZHUKAR, A. YU. SELEZNEV, V. N. TSINTSADZE, G. A. SHAPOVALOV, V. A. FIZ. TVERD. TELA 15 (3), 706–9, 1973. (FOR ENGLISH TRANSLATION SEE E50278)
50278	**ELECTRON SPIN RESONANCE OF COBALT IONS IN LITHIUM–GALLIUM SPINEL.** KOZHUKAR, A. YU. SELEZNEV, V. N. TSINTSADZE, G. A. SHAPOVALOV, V. A. SOV. PHYS. - SOLID STATE 15 (3), 496–8, 1973. (ENGLISH TRANSLATION OF FIZ. TVERD. TELA, 15 (3), 706–9, 1973; FOR ORIGINAL SEE E50277)
50283	**EFFECT OF PARAMAGNETIC RESONANCE ON ELECTRICAL CONDUCTIVITY OF SEMICONDUCTORS IN STRONG ELECTRIC FIELDS.** ZAITSEV, A. N. FIZ. TVERD. TELA 15 (3), 733–9, 1973. (FOR ENGLISH TRANSLATION SEE E50284)
50284	**EFFECT OF PARAMAGNETIC RESONANCE ON ELECTRICAL CONDUCTIVITY OF SEMICONDUCTORS IN STRONG ELECTRIC FIELDS.** ZAITSEV, A. N. SOV. PHYS. - SOLID STATE 15 (3), 513–6, 1973. (ENGLISH TRANSLATION OF FIZ. TVERD. TELA, 15 (3), 733–9, 1973; FOR ORIGINAL SEE E50283)
50285	**DISTRIBUTION OF THE MAGNETIZATION IN FERRITE FILMS WITH STRIPE DOMAINS.** BEREZIN, D. G. DUNAEVA–MITLINA, T. A. KHRAMOV, B. V. FIZ. TVERD. TELA 15 (3), 762–5, 1973. (FOR ENGLISH TRANSLATION SEE E50286)

EPIC Number	Bibliographic Citation

50286 **DISTRIBUTION OF THE MAGNETIZATION IN FERRITE FILMS WITH STRIPE DOMAINS.**
BEREZIN, D. G. DUNAEVA-MITLINA, T. A.
KHRAMOV, B. V.
SOV. PHYS. - SOLID STATE
15 (3), 531-3, 1973.
(ENGLISH TRANSLATION OF FIZ. TVERD. TELA, 15 (3), 762-5, 1973; FOR ORIGINAL SEE E50285)

50289 **LUMINESCENCE OF EXCITONS LOCALIZED AT DONORACCEPTOR DIPOLES IN ALPHA SILICON CARBIDE (6H).**
GORBAN', I. S. SLOBODYANYUK, A. V.
FIZ. TVERD. TELA
15 (3), 789-92, 1973.
(FOR ENGLISH TRANSLATION SEE E50290)

50290 **LUMINESCENCE OF EXCITONS LOCALIZED AT DONOR-ACCEPTOR DIPOLES IN ALPHA SILICON CARBIDE (6H).**
GORBAN', I. S. SLOBODYANYUK, A. V.
SOV. PHYS. - SOLID STATE
15 (3), 548-9, 1973.
(ENGLISH TRANSLATION OF FIZ. TVERD. TELA, 15 (3), 789-92, 1973; FOR ORIGINAL SEE E50289).

50295 **GALVANOMAGNETIC EFFECTS IN P-TYPE BISMUTH SESQUITELLURIDE AND THE MODEL OF TWO VALENCE SUBBANDS.**
SOLOGUB, V. V. GOLETSKAYA, A. D.
PAVLOV, S. T.
FIZ. TVERD. TELA
15 (3), 850-5, 1973.
(FOR ENGLISH TRANSLATION SEE E50296)

50296 **GALVANOMAGNETIC EFFECTS IN P-TYPE BISMUTH SESQUITELLURIDE AND THE MODEL OF TWO VALENCE SUBBANDS.**
SOLOGUB, V. V. GOLETSKAYA, A. D.
PAVLOV, S. T.
SOV. PHYS. SOLID STATE
15 (3), 585-8, U.MO.
(ENGLISH TRANSLATION OF FIZ. TVERD. TELA, 15 (3), 850-5, 1973; FOR ORIGINAL SEE E50295)

50297 **STARK EFFECT IN FREE AND BOUND EXCITONS IN A CADMIUM SELENIDE CRYSTAL.**
RAZBIRIN, B. S. URAL'TSEV, I. N.
BOGDANOV, A. A.
FIZ. TVERD. TELA
15 (3), 878-83, 1973.
(FOR ENGLISH TRANSLATION SEE E50298)

50298 **STARK EFFECT IN FREE AND BOUND EXCITONS IN A CADMIUM SELENIDE CRYSTAL.**
RAZBIRIN, B. S. URAL'TSEV, I. N.
BOGDANOV, A. A.
SOV. PHYS. - SOLID STATE
15 (3), 604-7, 1973.
(ENGLISH TRANSLATION OF FIZ. TVERD. TELA, 15 (3), 878-83, 1973; FOR ORIGINAL SEE E50297)

50301 **MAGNETIC ANISOTROPY OF CERIUM-SUBSTITUTED YTTRIUM IRON GARNET.**
BELOV, K. P. VOLKOVA, N. V. RAITSIS, V. I.
FIZ. TVERD. TELA
15 (3), 890-2, 1973.
(FOR ENGLISH TRANSLATION SEE E50302)

50302 **MAGNETIC ANISOTROPY OF CERIUM-SUBSTITUTED YTTRIUM IRON GARNET.**
BELOV, K. P. VOLKOVA, N. V. RAITSIS, V. I.
SOV. PHYS. - SOLID STATE
15 (3), 612-3, 1973.
(ENGLISH TRANSLATION OF FIZ. TVERD. TELA, 15 (3), 890-2, 1973; FOR ORIGINAL SEE E50301)

50307 **EXISTENCE OF THE CURIE POINT IN THE PRESENCE OF A STATIC MAGNETIC FIELD.**
SHEBALDIN, N. V.
FIZ. TVERD. TELA
15 (3), 916-8, 1973.
(FOR ENGLISH TRANSLATION SEE E50308)

50308 **EXISTENCE OF THE CURIE POINT IN THE PRESENCE OF A STATIC MAGNETIC FIELD.**
SHEBALDIN, N. V.
SOV. PHYS. - SOLID STATE
15 (3), 634-5, 1973.
(ENGLISH TRANSLATION OF FIZ. TVERD. TELA, 15 (3), 916-8, 1973; FOR ORIGINAL SEE E50307)

50309 **MECHANISM OF THE ABSORPTION OF LIGHT IN INTRINSIC III-V SEMICONDUCTORS.**
SINYAVSKII, E. P. ZENCHENKO, V. P.
FIZ. TVERD. TELA
15 (3), 918-21, 1973.
(FOR ENGLISH TRANSLATION SEE E50310)

50310 **MECHANISM OF THE ABSORPTION OF LIGHT IN INTRINSIC III-V SEMICONDUCTORS.**
SINYAVSKII, E. P. ZENCHENKO, V. P.
SOV. PHYS. - SOLID STATE
15 (3), 636-7, 1973.
(ENGLISH TRANSLATION OF FIZ. TVERD. TELA, 15 (3), 918-21, 1973; FOR ORIGINAL SEE E50309)

50321 **ELECTRICAL PROPERTIES, REFLECTION SPECTRUM, AND CONDUCTION MECHANISM OF ALUMINUM DODECABORIDE (ALPHA ALUMINUM 12 BORIDE).**
BEREZIN, A. A. GOLIKOVA, O. A.
ZAITSEV, V. K. KAZANIN, M. M. ORLOV, V. M.
STIL'BANS, L. S. TKALENKO, E. N.
FIZ. TVERD. TELA
15 (3), 952-5, 1973.
(FOR ENGLISH TRANSLATION SEE E50322)

50322 **ELECTRICAL PROPERTIES, REFLECTION SPECTRUM, AND CONDUCTION MECHANISM OF ALUMINUM DODECABORIDE (ALPHA ALUMINUM 12 BORIDE).**
BEREZIN, A. A. GOLIKOVA, O. A.
ZAITSEV, V. K. KAZANIN, M. M. ORLOV, V. M.
STIL'BANS, L. S. TKALENKO, E. N.
SOV. PHYS. - SOLID STATE
15 (3), 664-5, 1973.
(ENGLISH TRANSLATION OF FIZ. TVERD. TELA, 15 (3), 952-5, 1973; FOR ORIGINAL SEE E50321)

50325 **INFLUENCE OF THE MAGNETIC ANISOTROPY ON THE CONDUCTIVITY OF THE FERRITE COPPER COBALT FERRITE.**
IVANNIKOV, V. L. MIRYASOV, N. Z.
SEMKINA, V. A. TASKAEV, V. P.
FIZ. TVERD. TELA
15 (3), 959-60, 1973.
(FOR ENGLISH TRANSLATION SEE E50326)

50326 **INFLUENCE OF THE MAGNETIC ANISOTROPY ON THE CONDUCTIVITY OF THE FERRITE COPPER COBALT FERRITE.**
IVANNIKOV, V. L. MIRYASOV, N. Z.
SEMKINA, V. A. TASKAEV, V. P.
SOV. PHYS. - SOLID STATE
15 (3), 670, 1973.
(ENGLISH TRANSLATION OF FIZ. TVERD. TELA, 15 (3), 959-60, 1973; FOR ORIGINAL SEE E50325)

50327 **LAYERED DOMAIN STRUCTURES IN THIN ORTHOFERRITE PLATES.**
LL'YASHENKO, E. I. KLEPARSKII, V. G.
FIZ. TVERD. TELA
15 (4), 989-95, 1973.
(FOR ENGLISH TRANSLATION SEE E50328)

50328 **LAYERED DOMAIN STRUCTURES IN THIN ORTHOFERRITE PLATES.**
LL'YASHENKO, E. I. KLEPARSKII, V. G.
SOV. PHYS. - SOLID STATE
15 (4), 684-7, 1973.
(ENGLISH TRANSLATION OF FIZ. TVERD. TELA, 15 (2), 989-95, 1973; FOR ORIGINAL SEE E50327)

50335 **CERTAIN ASPECTS OF LIGHT DIFFRACTION BY A DOMAIN STRUCTURE.**
SHCHEGLOV, V. I.
FIZ. TVERD. TELA
15 (4), 1046-9, 1973.
(FOR ENGLISH TRANSLATION SEE E50336)

50336 **CERTAIN ASPECTS OF LIGHT DIFFRACTION BY A DOMAIN STRUCTURE.**
SHCHEGLOV, V. I.
SOV. PHYS. - SOLID STATE
15 (4), 718-20, 1973.
(ENGLISH TRANSLATION OF FIZ. TVERD. TELA, 15 (4), 1046-9, 1973; FOR ORIGINAL SEE E50335)

50343 **PARAMAGNETIC RESONANCE AND SPIN-LATTICE RELAXATION OF CHROMIUM IONS IN CALCIUM TUNGSTATE SINGLE CRYSTALS.**
ABDULSABIROV, R. YU. ZARIPOV, M. M.
KURKIN, I. N. TSVETKOV, E. A.
SHLENKIN, V. I.
FIZ. TVERD. TELA
15 (4), 1152-6, 1973.
(FOR ENGLISH TRANSLATION SEE E50344)

50344 **PARAMAGNETIC RESONANCE AND SPIN-LATTICE RELAXATION OF CHROMIUM IONS IN CALCIUM TUNGSTATE SINGLE CRYSTALS.**
ABDULSABIROV, R. YU. ZARIPOV, M. M.
KURKIN, I. N. TSVETKOV, E. A. SHLENKIN, V. I
SOV. PHYS. - SOLID STATE
15 (4), 779-81, 1973.
(ENGLISH TRANSLATION OF FIZ. TVERD. TELA, 15 (4), 1152-6, 1973; FOR ORIGINAL SEE E50343)

50347 **EFFECT OF UNIAXIAL MECHANICAL STRESS ON THE DOMAIN STRUCTURE OF ORTHORHOMBIC BARIUM TITANATE SINGLE CRYSTALS.**
SINYAKOV, E. V. FLEROVA, S. A.
ARKHIPOV, V. N.
FIZ. TVERD. TELA
15 (4), 1237-9, 1973.
(FOR ENGLISH TRANSLATION SEE E50348)

50348 **EFFECT OF UNIAXIAL MECHANICAL STRESS ON THE DOMAIN STRUCTURE OF ORTHORHOMBIC BARIUM TITANATE SINGLE CRYSTALS.**
SINYAKOV, E. V. FLEROVA, S. A.
ARKHIPOV, V. N.
SOV. PHYS. - SOLID STATE
15 (4), 832, 1973.
(ENGLISH TRANSLATION OF FIZ. TVERD. TELA, 15 (4), 1237-9, 1973; FOR ORIGINAL SEE E50347)

EPIC Number	Bibliographic Citation

50349 **STRIPE STRUCTURE AND MAGNETOOPTICAL DIFFRACTION IN THE ORTHOFERRITES.**
CHETKIN, M. V. DIDOSYAN, YU. S.
FIZ. TVERD. TELA
15 (4), 1247–9, 1973.
(FOR ENGLISH TRANSLATION SEE E50350)

50350 **STRIPE STRUCTURE AND MAGNETOOPTICAL DIFFRACTION IN THE ORTHOFERRITES.**
CHETKIN, M. V. DIDOSYAN, YU. S.
SOV. PHYS. – SOLID STATE
15 (4), 840–1, 1973.
(ENGLISH TRANSLATION OF FIZ. TVERD. TELA, 15 (4), 1247–9, 1973; FOR ORIGINAL SEE E50349)

50353 **ANOMALOUS TEMPERATURE DEPENDENCE OF THE SUSCEPTIBILITY AND STRUCTURAL TRANSITIONS IN COMPOUNDS WITH HIGH SUPERCONDUCTING TRANSITION TEMPERATURES T. C.**
KODESS, B. N.
FIZ. TVERD. TELA
15 (4), 1252–4, 1973.
(FOR ENGLISH TRANSLATION SEE E50354)

50354 **ANOMALOUS TEMPERATURE DEPENDENCE OF THE SUSCEPTIBILITY AND STRUCTURAL TRANSITIONS IN COMPOUNDS WITH HIGH SUPERCONDUCTING TRANSITION TEMPERATURES T C.**
KODESS, B. N.
SOV. PHYS. – SOLID STATE
15 (4), 844–5, 1973.
(ENGLISH TRANSLATION OF FIZ. TVERD. TELA, 15 (4), 1252–4, 1973; FOR ORIGINAL SEE E50353)

50355 **ELECTRICAL PROPERTIES OF SOME SOLID SOLUTIONS OF 3C TRANSITION METAL SILICIDES.**
NIKITIN, E. N. TARASOV, V. I. ZAITSEV, V. K.
FIZ. TVERD. TELA
15 (4), 1254–6, 1973.
(FOR ENGLISH TRANSLATION SEE E50356)

50356 **ELECTRICAL PROPERTIES OF SOME SOLID SOLUTIONS OF 3C TRANSITION METAL SILICIDES.**
NIKITIN, E. N. TARASOV, V. I. ZAITSEV, V. K.
SOV. PHYS. – SOLID STATE
15 (4), 846–7, 1973.
(ENGLISH TRANSLATION OF FIZ. TVERD. TELA, 15 (4), 1254–6, 1973; FOR ORIGINAL SEE E50355)

50357 **PARAMAGNETISM OF NEODYMIUM, SAMARIUM, AND EUROPIUM.**
SMIRNOV, S. V. ROZHDESTVENSKII, F. A.
MAKURIN, YU. N. KRYLOV, E. I.
FIZ. TVERD. TELA
15 (4), 1256–7, 1973.
(FOR ENGLISH TRANSLATION SEE E50358)

50358 **PARAMAGNETISM OF NEWODYMIUM, SAMARIUM, AND EUROPIUM.**
SMIRNOV, S. V. ROZHDESTVENSKII, F. A.
MAKURIN, YU. N. KRYLOV, E. I.
SOV. PHYS. – SOLID STATE
15 (4), 848, 1973.
(ENGLISH TRANSLATION OF FIZ. TVERD. TELA, 15 (4), 1256–7, 1973; FOR ORIGINAL SEE E50357)

50361 **INTERACTION BETWEEN F ELECTRONS AND IMPURITY COMPLEXES IN POTASSIUM CHLORIDE CRYSTALS.**
PERSHITS, YA. N. SHONIN, V. N.
FIZ. TVERD. TELA
15 (4), 1272–4, 1973.
(FOR ENGLISH TRANSLATION SEE E50362)

50362 **INTERACTION BETWEEN F ELECTRONS AND IMPURITY COMPLEXES IN POTASSIUM CHLORIDE CRYSTALS.**
PERSHITS, YA. N. SHONIN, V. N.
SOV. PHYS. – SOLID STATE
15 (4), 862–3, 1973.
(ENGLISH TRANSLATION OF FIZ. TVERD. TELA, 15 (4), 1272–4, 1973; FOR ORIGINAL SEE E50361)

50367 **X-RAY SPECTRUM AND BAND STRUCTURE OF BORON PHOSPHIDE CRYSTALS.**
FOMICHEV, V. A.
FIZ. TVERD. TELA
15 (4), 1286–8, 1973.
(FOR ENGLISH TRANSLATION SEE E50368)

50368 **X-RAY SPECTRUM AND BAND STRUCTURE OF BORON PHOSPHIDE CRYSTALS.**
FOMICHEV, V. A.
SOV. PHYS. – SOLID STATE
15 (4), 873–4, 1973.
(ENGLISH TRANSLATION OF FIZ. TVERD. TELA, 15 (4), 1286–8, 1973; FOR ORIGINAL SEE E50367)

50369 **MAGNETIC SUSCEPTIBILITY AND SUPERCONDUCTIVITY OF SOLID SOLUTIONS OF NIOBIUM AND TUNGSTEN MONOCARBIDES.**
DUBROVSKAYA, L. B. RABIN'KIN, A. G.
FIZ. TVERD. TELA
15 (4), 1289–91, 1973.
(FOR ENGLISH TRANSLATION SEE E50370)

50370 **MAGNETIC SUSCEPTIBILITY AND SUPERCONDUCTIVITY OF SOLID SOLUTIONS OF NIOBIUM AND TUNGSTEN MONOCARBIDES.**
DUBROVSKAYA, L. B. RABIN'KIN, A. G.
SOV. PHYS. – SOLID STATE
15 (4), 875–6, 1973.
(ENGLISH TRANSLATION OF FIZ. TVERD. TELA, 15 (4), 1289–91, 1973; FOR ORIGINAL SEE E50369)

50371 **EFFECT OF A PARAEXCITON LEVEL ON THE TEMPERATURE DEPENDENCE OF EXCITON LUMINESCENCE IN A CUPROUS OXIDE CRYSTAL.**
KREINGOL'D, F. I. MAKAROV, V. L.
FIZ. TVERD. TELA
15 (4), 1307–9, 1973.
(FOR ENGLISH TRANSLATION SEE E50372)

50372 **EFFECT OF A PARAEXCITON LEVEL ON THE TEMPERATURE DEPENDENCE OF EXCITON LUMINESCENCE IN A CUPROUS OXIDE CRYSTAL.**
KREINGOL'D, F. I. MAKAROV, V. L.
SOV. PHYS. – SOLID STATE
15 (4), 890, 1973.
(ENGLISH TRANSLATION OF FIZ. TVERD. TELA, 15 (4), 1307–9, 1973; FOR ORIGINAL SEE E50371)

50380 **TWO-OSCILLATOR DESCRIPTION OF OPTICAL PROPERTIES OF OXYGEN-OXTAHEDRA FERROELECTRICS.**
UCHIDA, N.
J. APPL. PHYS.
44 (5), 2072–80, 1973.

50381 **MEASUREMENT OF REFRACTIVE INDEX OF WATER UNDER HIGH DYNAMIC PRESSURES.**
YADAV, H. S. MURTY, D. S. VERMA, S. N.
SINHA, K. H. C. GUPTA, B. M. CHAND, D.
J. APPL. PHYS.
44 (5), 2197–2200, 1973.

50382 **DIAGNOSIS OF THE OPTICAL PROPERTIES AND STRUCTURE OF LANTHANUM HEXABORIDE THIN FILMS.**
PESCHMANN, K. R. CALOW, J. T. KNAUFF, K. G.
J. APPL. PHYS.
44 (5), 2252–6, 1973.

50385 **DETERMINATION OF MAGNETIC BUBBLE FILM PARAMETERS FROM STRIP DOMAIN MEASUREMENTS.**
SHAW, R. W. HILL, D. E. SANDFORT, R. M.
MOODY, J. W.
J. APPL. PHYS.
44 (5), 2346–9, 1973.

50386 **ANALYSIS OF A METHOD FOR MEASURING THE MAGNETOCRYSTALLINE ANISOTHROPY OF BUBBLE MATERIALS.**
DRUYVESTEYN, W. F. DORLEIJN, J. W. F.
RIJNIERSE, P. J.
J. APPL. PHYS.
44 (5), 2397–2400, 1973.

50393 **LUMINESCENCE CHARACTERISTICS OF EPITAXIALLY GROWN CUBIC ZINC SULFIDE.**
GHOSH, A. K. ADDISS, R. R., JR.
J. APPL. PHYS.
44 (10), 4431–6, 1973.

50396 **POLYCRYSTALLINE CERAMIC LASERS.**
GRESKOVICH, C. CHERNOCH, J. P.
J. APPL. PHYS.
44 (10), 4599–4606, 1973.

50398 **DEFECT STRUCTURE AND ELECTRONIC DONOR LEVELS IN STANNIC OXIDE CRYSTALS.**
SAMSON, S. FONSTAD, C. G.
J. APPL. PHYS.
44 (10), 4618–21, 1973.

50400 **PHOTOLUMINESCENCE OF ION-IMPLANTATION-DAMAGED N-TYPE GALLIUM ARSENIDE.**
SUMMERS, C. J. MIKLOSZ, J. C.
J. APPL. PHYS.
44 (10), 4653–6, 1973.

50404 **MAGNETIC PROPERTIES OF RARE EARTH COBALT GERMANIUM COMPOUNDS.**
MCCALL, W. M. NARASIMHAN, K. S. V. L.
BUTERA, R. A.
J. APPL PHYS.
44 (10), 4724–6, 1973.

50405 **MAGNETIC PROPERTIES OF ERBIUM-SILVER.**
NERESON, N.
J. APPL. PHYS.
44 (10), 4727–31, 1973.

50407 **FARADAY ROTATION AND OPTICAL ABSORPTION OF A SINGLE CRYSTAL OF BISMUTH-SUBSTITUTED GADOLINIUM IRON GARNET.**
TAKEUCHI, H. ITO, S-I. MIKAMI, I.
TANIGUCHI, S.
J. APPL. PHYS.
44 (10), 4789–90, 1973.

EPIC Number	Bibliographic Citation
50410	**ANHARMONIC FORCE FIELD OF THE METABORATE ION IN ALKALI HALIDES.** SMITH, D. F., JR. J. CHEM. PHYS. 58 (11), 4776–8, 1973.
50411	**MAGNETIC QUENCHING OF FLUORESCENCE IN NITROGEN DIOXIDE.** SOLARZ, R. BUTLER, S. LEVY, D. H. J. CHEM. PHYS. 58 (11), 5172–3, 1973.
50415	**ON THE VIBROELECTRONIC RAMAN EFFECT.** KANE-MAGUIRE, C. KONINGSTEIN, J. A. J. CHEM. PHYS. 59 (4), 1899–1904, 1973.
50417	**OPTICAL AND MAGNETIC RESONANCE SPECTRA OF INORGANIC MOLECULAR CRYSTALS–URANIUM BOROHYDRIDE IN HAFNIUM BOROHYDRIDE.** BERNSTEIN, E. R. KEIDERLING, T. A. J. CHEM. PHYS. 59 (4), 2105–22, 1973.
50418	**RADIATIVE AND RADIATIONLESS DECAY PROCESSES IN RHODIUM (III) AMMINE COMPLEXES.** THOMAS, T. R. WATTS, R. J. CROSBY, G. A. J. CHEM. PHYS. 59 (4), 2123–31, 1973.
50419	**DIELECTRIC PROPERTIES OF HYDROGEN HALIDES. IV. FERROELECTRIC BEHAVIOR IN HYDROGEN BROMIDE.** CICHANOWSKI, S. W. COLE, R. H. J. CHEM. PHYS. 59 (5), 2420–5, 1973.
50421	**INDICES OF REFRACTION OF HYDROGEN FLUORIDE AND MOLECULAR FLUORINE. II.** PENNING, D. F. WEIMER, D. RUMPEL, W. F. J. CHEM. PHYS. 59 (5), 2496–7, 1973.
50424	**PHOTOPROPERTIES OF ANODIZED LEAD MONOXIDE.** SHEA, M. J. MICHELS, W. C. J. CHEM. PHYS. 59 (5), 2764–5, 1973.
50433	**LUMINESCENT RISE TIMES OF INORGANIC PHOSPHORS EXCITED BY HIGH INTENSITY ULTRAVIOLET LIGHT.** ANDERSON, R. J. RICCHIO, S. G. APPL. OPT. 12 (11), 2751–8, 1973.
50436	**UCHF STUDY OF MAGNETIC PROPERTIES OF WATER. A COMPARISON OF THE DALGARNO AND THE KARPLUS–KOLKER METHODS.** JASZUNSKI, M. SADLEJ, A. J. BULL. ACAD. POLON. SCI., SER. SCI. CHIM. 21 (6), 433–7, 1973.
50437	**MAGNETIC PROPERTIES OF URANIUM COMPOUNDS OF LOW URANIUM CONTENTS: URANIUM COPPER, ZINC AND CADMIUM INTERMETALLICS.** MISIUK, A. MULAK, J. CZOPNIK, A. BULL. ACAD. POLON. SCI., SER. SCI. CHIM. 21 (6), 487–93, 1973.
50438	**EFFECT OF OXYGEN CHEMISORPTION ON THE WORK FUNCTION OF SINGLECRYSTALLINE NICKEL OXIDE.** DEREN, J. NOWOTNY, J. SADOWSKI, A. BULL. ACAD. POLON. SCI., SER. SCI. CHIM. 21 (6), 503–8, 1973.
50439	**DOMAIN STRUCTURE OF MANGANESE BORIDE.** WRZECIONO, A. BULL. ACAD. POL. SCI., SER. SCI., MATH. ASTRON. PHYS. 21 (6), 585–7, 1973.
50441	**ELECTRICAL CONDUCTIVITY OF NICKEL OXIDE–MAGNESIUM OXIDE SINGLE CRYSTALS.** CHOI, J. S. LEE, H. Y. KIM, K. H. J. PHYS. CHEM. 77 (20), 2430–3, 1973.
50443	**ELECTRICAL CHARGE TRANSPORT IN SINGLE–CRYSTAL CALCIUM TUNGSTATE.** RIGDON, M. A. GRACE, R. E. J. AM. CERAM. SOC. 56 (9), 475–8, 1973.
50445	**DEFORMATION TEXTURE AND MAGNETIC PROPERTIES OF BARIUM FERRITE.** HODGE, M. H. BITLER, W. R. BRADT, R. C. J. AMER. CERAM. SOC. 56 (10), 497–501, 1973.
50446	**THERMAL DECOMPOSITION OF SODALITES.** SCHIPPER, D. J. LATHOUWERS, T. W. VAN DOORN, C. Z. J. AMER. CERAM. SOC. 56 (10), 523–5, 1973.
50460	**THERMOPHYSICAL PROPERTIES AND ELECTRONIC STRUCTURE OF RARE EARTH CHALCOGENIDES.** GORYACHEV, YU. M. KUTSENOK, T. G. HIGH TEMP. – HIGH PRESSURES 4 (6), 663–9, 1972.
50461	**INFLUENCE OF THE PRESSURE ON THE CURIE TEMPERATURE OF RARE EARTH GARNETS UP TILL 60 K BAR.** BOCQUILLON, G. LORIERS–SUSSE, C. LORIERS, J. HIGH TEMP. – HIGH PRESSURES 5 (2), 161–8, 1973.
50462	**THE EFFECT OF TEMPERATURE AND PRESSURE ON THE ELECTRICAL CONDUCTANCE OF MOLTEN MERCURY (II) IODIDE.** BANNARD, J. E. TREIBER, G. HIGH TEMP. – HIGH PRESSURES 5 (2), 177–82, 1973.
50466	**THERMOELECTRIC PROPERTIES OF CERAMIC REFRACTORY SEMICONDUCTORS.** GORYACHEV, YU. M. YARMOLA, T. M. KONF. KERAM. ELEKTRON., 4TH XVI, 1–10, 1971.
50467	**EFFECT OF ALUMINUM OXIDE ON DIELECTRIC PROPERTIES AND DENSIFICATION OF BARIUM TITANATE.** BUH, M. KOLAR, D. GUHA, J. P. KONF. KERAM. ELEKTRON., 4TH XX, 1–7, 1971.
50468	**CONDUCTIVITY OF BARIUM TITANATE CERAMICS.** GODEFROY, L. KONF. KERAM. ELEKTRON. XXII, 4, 1–6, 1971.
50470	**BAND STRUCTURE OF OPTICAL INTERBAND CONDUCTION OF METALLIC COMPOUNDS WITH LATTICE A 15.** MASH, I. D. KRATK. SOOBSHCH. FIZ. (9), 3–10, 1972.
50471	**KINETICS OF RESTORATION OF THE LUMINESCENCE OF GALLIUM ARSENIDE SINGLE CRYSTALS IRRADIATED BY AN INTENSE ELECTRON BEAM.** BOGDANKEVICH, O. V. BORISOV, N. A. KALENDIN, V. V. KOVSH, I. B. KRYUKOVA, I. V. KVANTOVAYA ELEKTRON. (5), 108–11, 1972. (FOR ENGLISH TRANSLATION SEE E53015)
50475	**EXCITON LUMINESCENCE AND PHOTOCONDUCTIVITY OF CADMIUM SULFIDE UNDER HIGH INTENSITY EXCITATION.** SAITO, H. SHIONOYA, S. LUMIN. CRYST., MOL., SOLUTIONS, PROC. INT. CONF. 104–14, 1973.
50476	**EXCITON LUMINESCENCE AND PHOTOCONDUCTIVITY IN HIGHLY EXCITED GALLIUM PHOSPHIDE.** NAKAMURA, A. MORIGAKI, K. LUMIN. CRYST., MOL., SOLUTIONS, PROC. INT. CONF. 144–8, 1973.
50477	**ANTI–STOKES EXCITON EMISSION IN CADMIUM SULFIDE CRYSTALS.** BECKMANN, E. BROSER, I. BROSER, R. LUMIN. CRYST., MOL., SOLUTIONS, PROC. INT. CONF. 155–61, 1973.
50478	**MAGNETOOPTIC EFFECTS IN RECOMBINATION LUMINESCENCE FROM SELFTRAPPED EXCITONS.** KABLER, M. N. MARRONE, M. J. FOWLER, W. B. LUMIN. CRYST., MOL., SOLUTIONS, PROC. INT. CONF. 171–80, 1973.
50479	**LUMINESCENCE OF SIMPLE POLYATOMIC ANIONS.** MCGLYNN, S. P. LUMIN. CRYST., MOL., SOLUTIONS, PROC. INT. CONF. 399–407, 1972.
50480	**STIMULATION OF NONRADIATIVE DECAY UNDER INTENSIVE LIGHT EXCITATION.** TKACHUK, A. M. FEDOROV, A. A. LUMIN. CRYST., MOL., SOLUTIONS, PROC. INT. CONF. 413–18, 1973.
50481	**ELECTROLUMINESCENCE IN GALLIUM NITRIDE.** PANKOVE, J. I. MILLER, E. A. BERKEYHEISER, J. E. LUMIN. CRYST., MOL., SOLUTIONS, PROC. INT. CONF. 426–30, 1973.
50482	**LUMINESCENCE STUDY OF THE ELECTRONIC BAND STRUCTURE OF INDIUM GALLIUM PHOSPHORUS ARSENIDE.** ONTON, A. CHICOTKA, R. J. LUMIN. CRYST., MOL., SOLUTIONS, PROC. INT. CONF. 431–8, 1973.
50483	**RADIATIVE RECOMBINATION INVOLVING ACCEPTORS IN GALLIUM ANTIMONIDE.** RUEHLE, W. JAKOWETZ, W. PILKUHN, M. LUMIN. CRYST., MOL., SOLUTIONS, PROC. INT. CONF. 444–8, 1973.

EPIC Number	Bibliographic Citation
50484	**RESONANT LUMINESCENCE OF FREE EXCITONS IN CRYSTALS.** GROSS, E. PERMOGROV, S. A. TRAVNIKOV, V. V. SELKIN, A. V. LUMIN. CRYST., MOL., SOLUTIONS, PROC. INT. CONF. 455-60, 1973.
50485	**EFFECT OF DISLOCATIONS ON THE LUMINESCENCE SPECTRA OF CADIUM SULFIDE AND CADMIUM SELENIDE SINGLE CRYSTALS.** OSIPYAN, YU, A. SHTEINMAN, E. A. LUMIN. CRYST., MOL., SOLUTIONS, PROC. INT. CONF. 467-72, 1973.
50486	**PHOTOLUMINESCENCE OF T-CENTERS IN POTASSIUM HALIDE CRYSTALS.** TOPA, V. VELICESCU, B. MATEESCU, I. LUMIN. CRYST., MOL., SOLUTIONS, PROC. INT. CONF. 497-501, 1973. (FROM: PLENUM: NEW YORK, N. Y.; EDITED BY F. WILLIAMS)
50487	**PHOTOLUMINESCENCE OF COLOR CENTERS IN ALKALINE EARTH FLUORIDE CRYSTALS.** RAUCH, R. LUMIN. CRYST., MOL., SOLUTIONS, PROC. INT. CONF. 502-7, 1973.
50488	**LUMINESCENCE OF OXYGEN CENTERS IN ALUMINUM NITRIDE.** PASTRNAK, J. PACESOVA, S. SCHANDA, J. ROSA, J. LUMIN. CRYST., MOL., SOLUTIONS, PROC. INT. CONF. 508-13, 1973.
50489	**LUMINESCENCE OF II-VI COMPOUNDS DOPED WITH TRANSITION METAL IONS.** KAZANSKII, S. A. KHILKO, G. I. NATADZE, A. L. RYSKIN, A. I. LUMIN. CRYST., MOL., SOLUTIONS, PROC. INT. CONF. 553-63, 1973.
50490	**ELECTRON TRANSFER BY THE TUNNEL EFFECT AND ITS INFLUENCE ON THE F CENTER LUMINESCENCE IN ALKALI HALIDES.** ECABERT, M. SCHNEGG, P. A. RUEDIN, Y. AEGERTER, M. A. JACCARD, C. LUMIN. CRYST., MOL., SOLUTIONS, PROC. INT. CONF. 582-9, 1973.
50491	**ELECTROLUMINESCENCE IN ALKALI HALIDE CRYSTALS.** PARACCHINI, C. LUMIN. CRYST., MOL., SOLUTIONS, PROC. INT. CONF. 590-7, 1973. (FROM: PLENUM: NEW YORK, N. Y.; EDITED BY F. WILLIAMS)
50492	**PHOTOLUMINESCENCE SPECTRA OF SINGLE CRYSTALS OF YTTERBIUM (2+)-DOPED STRONTIUM CHLORIDE.** WITZKE, H. MCCLURE, D. S. MITCHELL, B. LUMIN. CRYST., MOL., SOLUTIONS, PROC. INT. CONF. 598-605, 1973.
50493	**TUNNEL LUMINESCENCE OF PURE AND THALLIUM AND SILVER-DOPED ALKALI HALIDE CRYSTALS.** BOGANS, J. KANDERS, U. LEINERTE-NEILANDE, I. MILLERS, D. NAGORNYI, A. TALE, I. VALBIS, J. LUMIN. CRYST., MOL., SOLUTIONS, PROC. INT. CONF. 621-7, 1973.
50496	**PREPARATION OF HIGH RESISTIVITY ANTIMONY SELENIDE BY ZONE REFINING.** BALMER, B. BAUMGARTNER, W. BOHAC, P. MATER. RES. BULL. 8 (5), 481-8, 1973.
50499	**MEASURING THE ELECTRICAL RESISTIVITY OF A BINARY ALLOY.** BERNABAI, U. GAUZZI, F. MET. ITAL. 65 (3), 129-32, 1973.
50504	**ROLE OF IMPURITY MICRODEFECTS IN THE LOW-TEMPERATURE AFTERFLOW OF CESIUM IODIDE CRYSTALS.** PANOVA, A. N. SHIRAN, N. V. MONOKRIST. TEKH. (3), 86-93, 1970.
50506	**PHOTOELECTROLUMINESCENCE IN ZINC SULFIDE.** MAXIA, V. MUNTONI, C. MURGIA, M. CORTESE, C. NUOVO CIMENTO SOC. ITAL. FIS. 15 B (2), 121-35, 1973.
50507	**BAND STRUCTURE CALCULATION OF SEMICONDUCTORS AND ALLOYS WITH DIAMOND- AND ZINC BLENDE-CRYSTAL LATTICES.** ANDA, E. V. MAJLIS, N. NUOVO CIMENTO SOC. ITAL. FIZ. 15 B (2), 225-44, 1973.
50509	**NONLINEAR PHOTOCONDUCTIVE RESPONSE OF ROOM TEMPERATURE INDIUM ANTIMONIDE TO HIGH INTENSITY 5.3 MICRON RADIATION.** HAMMOND, C. R. STANLEY, C. R. OPTO-ELECTRONICS 5 (3), 249-54, 1973.
50511	**OPTICAL SPECTRA OF IRON GROUP IONS IN ALUMINUM OXIDE SINGLE CRYSTALS.** BARANOV, M. N. KUSTOV, E. F. OPT. SPEKTROSK. 34 (4), 726-8, 1973.
50513	**ISOCHORIC TEMPERATURE DEPENDENCE OF THE STATIC DIELECTRIC CONSTANT OF THALLIUM BROMIDE.** LOWNDES, R. P. PHONONS, PROC. INT. CONF. 353-7, 1971.
50516	**EMPIRICAL BAND SCHEME FOR RHOMBOHEDRAL VANADIUM- (III) OXIDE.** BALBERG, I. PHYS. LETT. 43 A (6), 497-8, 1973.
50522	**ENERGY BANDS OF SEMICONDUCTING VANADIUM DIOXIDE.** CARUTHERS, E. KLEINMAN, L. PHYS. REV. 7 B (8), 3760-6, 1973.
50526	**COMPOSITIONAL TRENDS IN THE OPTICAL PROPTERTIES OF AMORPHOUS LONE-PAIR SEMICONDUCTORS.** KASTNER, M. PHYS. REV. 7 B (12), 5237-52, 1973.
50527	**MICROSCOPIC AND MACROSCOPIC ELECTRONIC PROPERTIES OF THE GOLD-COPPER-TYPE ALLOYS. LANTHANUM-TIN-LANTHANUM-INDIUM PSEUDOBINARY ALLOY SYSTEM.** TOXEN, A. M. GAMBINO, R. J. WELSH, L. B. PHYS. REV. 8 (1), 90-7, 1973.
50528	**MAGNETOSTRICTION OF RUTHENIUM-SUBSTITUTED YTTRIUM IRON GARNET.** HANSEN, P. PHYS. REV. 8 B (1), 246-53, 1973.
50530	**MAGNETIC PROPERTIES OF DIAMAGNETIC-SUBSTITUTED YTTERBIUM IRON GARNET EXPLAINED BY THE STATISTICAL MODEL OF THE MOLECULAR FIELD. III. CURIE TEMPERATURES, MAGNETIC SUSCEPTIBILITIES, AND ANISOTROPY OF SILICON-CALCIUM- AND GALLIUM-SUBSTITUTED YTTERBIUM IRON GARNET.** GRILL, A. SCHIEBER, M. PHYS. REV. 8 B (1), 373-7, 1972.
50531	**ENHANCEMENT OF IMPURITY-ION ABSORPTION DUE TO RADIATION-PRODUCED DEFECTS.** YUN, S. I. KAPPERS, L. A. SIBLEY, W. A. PHYS. REV. 8 B (2), 773-9, 1973.
50532	**CHLORINE-K-X-RAY SPECTRA AND ELECTRONIC BAND STRUCTURE OF COPPER (I) CHLORIDE.** SUGIURA, C. PHYS. REV. 8 B (2), 823-6, 1973.
50533	**OPTICAL PROPERTIES OF MAGNESIUM DIPOSITIVE ION IN PURE AND FAULTED CUBIC ZINC SULFIDE SINGLE CRYSTALS.** LAMBERT, B. BUCH, T. GEOFFROY, A. PHYS. REV. 8 (2), 863-9, 1973.
50535	**ENERGY TRANSFER BETWEEN THE LOW-LYING ENERGY LEVELS OF PRASEODYMIUM (3+) IONS AND NEODYMIUM (3+) IONS IN LANTHANUM TRICHLORIDE.** KRASUTSKY, N. MOOS, H. W. PHYS. REV. 8 B (0), 1010-20, 1973.
50537	**OPTICAL REFLECTIVITY AND BAND STRUCTURE OF ZINC SULFIDE SELENIDE MIXED CRYSTALS.** KIRSCHFELD, K. E. NELKOWSKI, N. WAGNER, T. S. PHYS. REV. LETT. 29 (1), 66-8, 1973.
50538	**ANOMALY IN THE THERMOELECTRIC POWER DUE TO CRYSTAL-FIELD-SPLIT IMPURITIES.** UMLAUF, E. PEPPERL, G. MEYER, A. PHYS. REV. LETT. 30 (23), 1173-5, 1973.
50539	**BAND STRUCTURE OF MOLYBDENUM (IV) SULFIDE AND NIOBIUM (IV) SULFIDE.** KASOWSKI, R. V. PHYS. REV. LETT. 30 (23), 1175-8, 1973.
50541	**DIRECT EVIDENCE FOR A BOTTLENECK OF EXCITON-POLARITON RELAXATION IN CADMIUM SULFIDE.** HELM, U. WIESNER, P. PHYS. REV. LETT. 30 (24), 1205-7, 1973.

EPIC Number	Bibliographic Citation
50542	**MAGNETOPHONON EFFECT IN N-TYPE MERCURY CADMIUM TELLURIDE.** KAHLERT, H. BAUER, G. PHYS. REV. LETT. 30 (24), 1211–14, 1973.
50543	**EFFECTS OF INHOMOGENEOUS BROADENING ON COOPERATIVE SPONTANEOUS EMISSION OF RADIATION.** RESSAYRE, E. TALLET, A. PHYS. REV. LETT. 30 (25), 1239–41, 1973.
50544	**OPTICAL QUENCHING OF PHOTOLUMINESCENCE IN CHALCOGENIDE GLASSES. EVIDENCE FOR STATES IN MIDGAP.** BISHOP, S. G. GUENZER, C. S. PHYS. REV. LETT. 30 (26), 1309–12, 1973.
50545	**OPTICAL DIELECTRIC FUNCTION OF THE LITHIUM-FLUORIDE CRYSTAL.** MENZEL, W. P. LIN, C. C. FOUQUET, D. F. LAFON, E. E. CHANEY, R. C. PHYS. REV. LETT. 30 (26), 1313–15, 1973.
50548	**SYMMETRY CHARACTER OF THE E1 EDGE IN INDIUM ANTIMONID** SARI, S. O. PHYS. REV. LETT. 30 (26), 1323–5, 1973. (AD 767466)
50550	**PHOTOCONDUCTIVITY OF ZINC INDIUM SELENIDE AND ZINC INDIUM TELLURIDE.** MANCA, P. RAGA, F. SPIGA, A. PHYS. STATUS SOLIDI 16 A (2), K105–K108, 1973.
50551	**PHOTOCONDUCTIVITY IN CRYSTALLINE AND AMORPHOUS ANTIMONY TRIOXIDE.** WOLFFING, B. HURYCH, Z. PHYS. STATUS SOLIDI 16 A (2), K161–K163, 1973.
50552	**PHOTOVOLTAIC PROPERTIES OF ZINC SULFIDE CRYSTALS.** JACOBSEN, G. MAENHOUT-VAN DER VORST W. PHYS. STATUS SOLIDI 17 A (1), K15–K18, 1973.
50554	**ROLE OF F- AND F PRIME-CENTERS IN THE EXOEMISSION OF BERYLLIUM OXIDE.** KORTOV, V. S. SHALYAPIN, A. L. GAPRINDOSHVILI, A. Y. PHYS. STATUS SOLIDI 17 A (1), K33–K36, 1973.
50555	**SPECTROSCOPIC PROPERTIESOF LANTHANUM BERYLLIUM OXIDE SINGLE CRYSTALS.** VORONKO, YU. K. MAKSIMOVA, G. V. OSIKO, V. V. SOBOL, A. A. STARIKOV, B. P. TIMOSHECHKIN, M. I. PHYS. STATUS SOLIDI 17 A (1), K41–K43, 1973.
50556	**DEPENDENCE OF RAMAN SCATTERING CROSS SECTION ON LASER INTENSITY FOR SEMICONDUCTING SODIUM TUNGSTEN CRYSTALS.** SALJE, E. HOPPMANN, G. PHYS. STATUS SOLIDI 17 A (1), K57–60, 1973.
50557	**ELECTRICAL CONDUCTION PROCESSES IN LITHIUM NIOBATE SINGLE CRYSTALS.** ANTONOV, V. A. ARSEN'EV, P. A. BARANOV, B. A. MAYER, A. A. FARSHTENDIKER, V. L. PHYS. STATUS SOLIDI 17 A (1), K61–K64, 1973.
50558	**ELECTRICAL PROPERTIES OF HIGH-RESISTANCE ZINC GERMANIUM PHOSPHIDE SINGLE CRYSTALS.** GRIGOR'EVA, V. S. PROCHUKHAN, V. D. RUD, YU. V. YAKOVENKO, A. A. PHYS. STATUS SOLIDI 17 A (1), K69–K74, 1973.
50559	**VALENCE BAND STRUCTURE OF CADMIUM GERMANIUM DIARSENIDE FROM ELECTROREFLECTANCE SPECTRA.** KRIVAITE, G. BORSHCHEVSKII, A. S. SILEIKA, A. PHYS. STATUS SOLIDI 57 B (1), K39–K41, 1973.
50565	**OPTICAL ABSORPTION AND LUMINESCENCE OF I-CENTERS IN POTASSIUM BROMIDE.** TAKAHASHI, M. SAIDOH, M. ITOH, N. PHYS. STATUS SOLIDI 57 B (2), 749–56, 1973.
50566	**STRAIN DERIVATIVES OF THE STATIC AND HIGH-FREQUENCY DIELECTRIC CONSTANTS OF RUBIDIUM AND CESIUM HALIDES.** SRINIVASAN, R. SRINIVASAN, K. PHYS. STATUS SOLIDI 57 (2), 757–66, 1973.
50567	**OPTICAL PROPERTIES OF SILICON DITELLURIDE.** LAMBROS, A. P. ECONOMOU, N. A. PHYS. STATUS SOLIDI 57 B (2), 793–9, 1973.
50568	**ANOMALOUS BEHAVIOR OF MAGNETIC SUSCEPTIBILITY NEAR THE MAGNETIC COMPENSATION TEMPERATURE IN COMPOUNDS OF RARE EARTH METALS WITH IRON.** BISLIEV, A. M. ZVEZDIN, A. K. KIM, D. NIKITIN, S. A. POPKOV, A. F. PIS'MA. ZH. EKSP. TEOR. FIZ. 17 (9), 484–8, 1973.
50571	**ELASTIC AND PIEZOELECTRIC PROPERTIES OF ALPHA-MERCURY SULFIDE.** SAPRIEL, J. LANCON, R. PROC. 61 (5), 678–9, 1973.
50572	**MOLYBDENUM DISULFIDE-BASED EXTENSOMETRIC GAGE.** VARDANYAN, V. R. OGANESYAN, V. KH. MANUKYAN, A. G. SB. NAUCH. TR., EREVAN. POLITEKH. INST. 36 (4), 148–51, 1972.
50573	**IONIC CONDUCTIVITY OF YTTRIUM FLUORIDE AND LUTETIUM FLUORIDE.** O'KEEFFE, M. SCIENCE 180 (4092), 1276–7, 1973.
50574	**GIANT MAGNETOREFLECTANCE OF COBALT DICHROMIUM TETRASULFIDE.** AHRENKIEL, R. K. LEE, T. H. LYU, S. L. MOSER, F. SOLID STATE COMMUN. 12 (11), 1113–15, 1973.
50576	**MAGNETIC SUSCEPTIBILITY OF POTASSIUM TRIFLUOROMANGANATE (II) BELOW 80 K.** MAARTENSE, I. SOLID STATE COMMUN. 12 (11), 1133–6, 1973.
50577	**CYCLOTRON RESONANCE OF POSITIVE HOLES IN SILVER BROMIDE.** TAMURA, H. MASUMI, T. SOLID STATE COMMUN. 12 (11), 1183–6, 1973.
50578	**EVIDENCE FOR STRESS-INDUCED DECOUPLING OF VALENCE BANDS IN GALLIUM ANTIMONIDE FROM GALVANOMAGNETIC MEASUREMENTS.** METZLER, R. A. BECKER, W. M. SOLID STATE COMMUN. 12 (11), 1209–12, 1973.
50579	**ENERGY OF FREE AND BOUND EXCITONS IN GALLIUM ARSENIDE IN A MAGNETIC FIELD.** DREYBODT, W. WILLMANN, F. BETTINI, M. BAUSER, E. SOLID STATE COMMUN. 12 (11), 1217–20, 1973.
50581	**ELECTRICAL PROPERTIES OF COPPER-INDIUM DISELENIDE SINGLE CRYSTALS.** PARKES, J. TOMLINSON, R. D. HAMPSHIRE, M. J. SOLID-STATE ELECTRON. 16 (7), 773–7, 1973.
50583	**ELECTRICAL CONDUCTIVITY OF ANISOTROPIC SEMICONDUCTORS.** RADULESCU, D. N. TATARU-MIHAI, P. I. STUD. UNIV. BABES-BOLYAI, SERV. PHYS. 18 (1), 49–52, 1973.
50584	**HYDROXY-BRIDGED METAL COMPOUNDS. I. CRYSTALLOGRAPHIC, MAGNETIC, AND THERMAL PROPERTIES OF COPPER (II) PERIODATES.** UGGLA, R. ORAMA, O. KLINGA, M. HARJULIN, C. PUSA, P. SUOM. KEMISTILEHTI 46 B (5–6), 148–50, 1973.
50586	**UNIAXIAL MAGNETIC ANISOTROPY IN ERBIUM-EUROPIUM, YTTRIUM-EUROPIUM, AND YTTRIUM-GADOLINIUM-THULIUM GARNET FILMS FOR BUBBLE-DOMAIN DEVICES.** SMITH, A. B. KESTIGIAN, M. BEKEBREDE, W. R. AIP CONF. PROC. (10), (PT. 1), 309–13, 1973.
50587	**EXPERIMENTS IN THE LIQUID-PHASE SINTERING OF SAMARIUM-COBALT.** CARRIKER, R. C. RASHIDI, A. S. AIP AMER. PROC. INST. PHYS. CONF. (10), (PT. 1), 608–12, 1973.
50590	**ELECTRICAL PROPERTIES OF 17-PALLADIUM 15-SELENIDE, PENTAPLATINUM TETRASELENIDE, AND PLATINUM TELLURIDE.** KJEKSHUS, A. ACTA CHEM. SCAND. 27 (4), 1452–4, 1973.

EPIC Number	Bibliographic Citation
50594	**MEASUREMENTS OF PHOTOELECTRIC VOLTAGE AND PHOTOCONDUCTIVITY IN GALLIUM ARSENIDE SINGLE CRYSTALS.** WOJAS, J. WOJAS, B. ACTA PHYS. POL. 43 A (6), 851-5, 1973.
50595	**CRYSTAL STRUCTURE AND MAGNETIC PROPERTIES OF HEUSLER-TYPE ALLOYS M-TITANIUM-ANTIMONY (M NICKEL, COBALT, IRON) AND IRON-TITANIUM-TIN.** SZYTULA, A. TOMKOWICZ, Z. TUROWSKI, M. ACTA PHYS. POL. 44 A (1), 147-9, 1973.
50602	**EXOELECTRON EMISSION DURING PHASE CHANGES AND REACTIONS IN SOLIDS.** SUJAK, B. GORECKI, T. WIAD. CHEM. 27 (6), 361-84, 1973.
50604	**EFFECT OF STRUCTURAL IMPERFECTIONS ON MAGNETIC PROPERTIES OF EPITAXIAL GARNET BUBBLE FILMS.** MILNE, A. D. OWENS, J. M. SOLOMONS, B. THORNLEY, S. J. AIP AMER. PROC. INST. PHYS. CONF. (10), (PT. 1), 414-18, 1973.
50605	**EFFECT OF THE ORDER-DISORDER TRANSITION ON THE ELECTRICAL AND MAGNETIC PROPERTIES OF TRI-IRON ALUMINIDE.** THOMAS, G. A. LAWRENCE, J. M. HORN, P. M. PARKS, R. D. AIP AMER. PROC. INST. PHYS. CONF. (10), (PT. 2), 910-14, 1973.
50606	**STABILIZATION OF THE ACTINIDE-TRIRHODIUM ENERGY BAND IN ACTINIDE-RHODIUM INTERMETALLIC COMPOUNDS.** NELLIS, W. J. HARVEY, A. R. BRODSKY, M. B. AIP AMER. PROC. INST. PHYS. CONF. (10), (PT. 2), 1076-80, 1973.
50607	**POLARIZED PHOTOELECTRONS FROM PURE AND DOPED EUROPIUM OXIDE SINGLE CRYSTALS.** SATTLER, K. SIEGMANN, H. C. AIP AMER. PROC. INST. PHYS. CONF. (10), (PT. 2), 1274-8, 1973.
50608	**BOUND MAGNETIC POLARONS AND THE SUSCEPTIBILITY OF EUROPIUM OXIDE.** MCGUIRE, T. R. TORRANCE, J. B. SHAFER, M. W. AIP AMER. PROC. INST. PHYS. CONF. (10), (PT. 2), 1289-93, 1973.
50612	**ELECTROLUMINESCENCE IN ZINC SELENIDE-ZINC TELLURIDE HETEROJUNCTIONS.** LOZYKOWSKI, H. J. OCZKOWSKI, H. L. FIRSZT, F. BULL. ACAD. POL. SCI., SER. SCI., MATH., ASTRON. PHYS. 21 (5), 485-9, 1973.
50614	**RAMAN SPECTRUM OF TETRAGONAL EUROPIUM (3+) CALCIUM DIFLUORIDE.** KONINGSTEIN, J. A. LUCAZEAU, G. CHEM. PHYS. 1 (2), 112-19, 1973.
50617	**INFLUENCE OF THE CONCENTRATION OF METALLIC IMPURITIES ON THE ELECTRICAL PROPERTIES OF SILICON MONOXIDE THIN FILMS.** PINGUET, J. MINN, S. S. C. R. ACAD. SCI., SER. 276 B (22), 841-4, 1973.
50618	**NEW EUROPIUM (II) COMPOUND, EUROPIUM CHLORIDE FLUORIDE.** TANGUY, B. PEZAT, M. FONTENIT, C. FOUASSIER, C. C. R. ACAD. SCI., SER. 277 C (1), 25-7, 1973.
50619	**ELECTRICAL PROPERTIES AND STRUCTURAL DEFECTS OF HOLMIUM SESQUIOXIDE AT HIGH TEMPERATURE.** WILBERT, Y. BREUIL, H. DHERBOMEZ, N. C. R. ACAD. SCI., SER. 276 C (24), 1723-6, 1973.
50620	**STRUCTURE AND PROPERTIES OF LANTHANUM COBALT OXIDE.** LEHUEDE, P. DAIRE, M. C. R. ACAD. SCI., SER. 276 C (26), 1783-5, 1973.
50624	**INTERPRETATION OF THE LIGHT SCATTERING SPECTRUM OF PARAMAGNETIC IRON (II) FLUORIDE.** HOFF, J. T. KONINGSTEIN, J. A. CHEM. PHYS. 1 (3), 232-7, 1973.
50626	**X-RAY PHOTOELECTRON, X-RAY EMISSION, AND UV SPECTRA OF SILICON DIOXIDE CALCULATED BY THE SCF X ALPHA SCATTERED WAVE METHOD.** TOSSELL, J. A. VAUGHAN, D. J. JOHNSON, K. H. CHEM. PHYS. LETT. 20 (4), 329-34, 1973.

EPIC Number	Bibliographic Citation
50627	**NONRADIATIVE DECAY PROCESSES IN ISOLATED SULFUR DIOXIDE MOLECULES EXCITED WITHIN THE FIRST ALLOWED ABSORPTION BAND (2500-3200 A).** CALVERT, J. G. CHEM. PHYS. LETT. 20 (5), 484-8, 1973.
50631	**SIMPLE DEVICE FOR CRYSTAL CLEAVAGE IN LIQUID HELIUM.** BECKMANN, E. RASS, R. CRYOGENICS 13 (7), 437, 1973.
50633	**EMISSION BANDS OF NINE ALKALI HALIDES WITH THALLIUM.** BOHUN, A. PETRU, J. DOLEJSI, J. CZECH. J. PHYS. 23 (6), 683-4, 1973.
50634	**ELECTRICAL PROPERTIES AND PHASE-STRUCTURAL STATE OF NICKEL(II) OXIDE-TITANIUM(IV) OXIDE SYSTEM CATALYSTS.** DULOV, A. A. ABRAMOVA, L. A. GERSHENZON, I. SH. RUBINSHTEIN, A. M. DOKL. AKAD. NAUK SSSR 210 (2), 345-8, 1973. (FOR ENGLISH TRANSLATION SEE E53032)
50638	**THERMOMODULATED PHOTOCONDUCTIVITY (TMPH) OF CADMIUM SULFIDE.** BORISOV, M. BALEVA, M. I. ILIEV, M. N. DOKL. BOLG. AKAD. NAUK 26 (3), 319-22, 1973.
50641	**FLUX GROWN POTASSIUM TANTALATE NIOBATE SINGLE CRYSTALS AND THEIR ELECTRICAL PROPERTIES.** HIGASHI, N. TANIGUCHI, I. DOSHISHA DAIGAKU RIKOGAKU KENKYU HOKOKU 13 (3), 152-63, 1972.
50643	**TEMPERATURE DEPENDENCE OF A FORBIDDEN BAND IN WIDEGAP FERROELECTRICS.** KONSIN, P. I. KRISTOFEL, N. N. EESTI NSV TEAD. AKAD. TOIM., FUUS., MAT. 22 (2), 173-8, 1973.
50644	**MEASUREMENT AND CONTROL OF THE DIELECTRIC PROPERTIES OF LIQUIDS, SUBJECTED TO ELECTROPHYSICAL TREATMENT, USING SUPERHIGH FREQUENCY RESONANCE SYSTEMS.** GOS'KOV, P. I. SIL'NYAGIN, O. V. SALIKHOV, V. A. ELECKTRON. OBRAB. MATER. (1), 56-9, 1973.
50645	**CHANGES IN THE ELECTRONIC STRUCTURE OF NICKEL-MANGANESE ALLOY ALLOYED WITH D TRANSITION ELEMENTS.** FADIN, V. P. ZHUKOVA, V. M. PANIN, V. E. RYABYSHKINA, G. A. ELECTRON. STR. FIZ. SVOISTVA TVERD. TELA (1), 61-6, 1972.
50646	**BAND STRUCTURE CONSTANTS AND THE GALVANOMAGNETIC PROPERTIES OF P-INDIUM ANTIMONIDE.** ERMOLOVICH, YU. B. ELEKTRON. STR. FIZ. SVOISTVA TVERD. TELA (2), 53-6, 1972.
50647	**ELECTROLUMINESCENCE IN A CONSTANT FIELD OF ZINC SULFIDE-COPPER, MANGANESE, CHLORINE FILMS OBTAINED BY SUBLIMATION IN VACUO.** KONONENKO, V. I. LUR'E, V. I. ELEKTRON. TEKH. NAUCH.-TEKH. SB., MIKROELEKTRON. (2), 85-8, 1972.
50648	**ELECTROCHEMICAL AND PHOTOELECTROCHEMICAL PROCESSES ON TITANIUM OXIDES. I. TITANIUM DIOXIDE SINGLE CRYSTALS.** SHUB, D. M. REMNEV, A. A. VESELOVSKII, V. I. ELEKTROKHIMIYA 9 (5), 676-9, 1973.
50650	**PHYSICOCHEMICAL PROPERTIES OF THERMALLY STABLE FERRITES WITH ADDITIONS OF TRANSITION METAL OXIDES.** GLOTOV, V. G. ZINOV'YEVA, I. G. PRONIN, L. A. ELEKTRON. STR. FIZ. SVOISTVA TVERD. TELA (1), 119-24, 1972. (FROM: REF. ZH., FIZ., E 1973, ABSTR. NO. 2E1370)
50651	**DIELECTRIC PROPERTIES OF DENSE LANTHANUM SULFIDE SAMPLES.** GUBKIN, A. N. GRIZIK, A. A. ZAKHAROV, A. K. PONAMAREV, N. M. ELEKTRON. STR. FIZ. SVOISTVA TVERD. TELA (1), 149-56, 1972.
50652	**THERMOELECTRIC PROPERTIES OF CERIUM TELLURIDES.** TYURIN, E. G. YAREMBASH, E. I. CHUKALIN, V. I. ELEKTRON. STR. FIZ. SVOISTVA TVERD. TELA (1), 156-61, 1972.

EPIC Number	Bibliographic Citation
50653	**MAGNETIC PROPERTIES OF CUBIC MONOCARBIDES OF GROUP IVB-VB TRANSITION METALS.** BORUKHOVICH, A. S. DUBROVSKAYA, L. B. MATVEENKO, I. I. GEL'D, P. V. ELEKTRON. STR. FIZ. SVOISTVA TVERD. TELA (2), 76-82, 1972.
50654	**ELECTROPHYSICAL CHARACTERISTICS OF TUNGSTEN DISELENIDEBASED MATERIALS.** VORONOV, B. K. DUDKIN, L. D. LYUSKIN, S. N. TRUSOVA, N. N. ELEKTRON. STR. FIZ. SVOISTVA TVERD. TELA (2), 119-26, 1972.
50655	**ELECTRICAL CONDUCTIVITY OF ANODIC OXIDE FILMS ON TANTALUM.** ODYNETS, L. L. RAIKERUS, P. A. ELEKTRON. TEKH., NAUCH.-TEKH. SB., RADIODETALI (2), 23-8, 1972.
50656	**MAGNETIC SUSCEPTIBILITY MEASUREMENTS.** GREGSON, A. K. ELECTRON. STRUCT. MAGN. INORG. COMPOUNDS 2, 247-91, 1973.
50657	**EFFECT OF MICROIMPURITIES ON THE THERMOLUMINESCENCE OF LITHIUM FLUORIDE SINGLE CRYSTALS.** NEPOMNYASHCHIKH, A. I. BOBR-SERGEEV, A. A. EZHEG., INST. GEOKHIM., SIB. OTD., AKAD. NAUK SSSR 360-4, 1972.
50658	**MAGNETIC AND MAGNETOSTRICTION PROPERTIES OF COBALT-SUBSTITUTED RARE EARTH GARNET FERRITES.** SOKOLOV, V. I. MILL, B. V. FIZ. KHIM. FERRITOV 50-68 1973.
50660	**MAGNETOCRYSTALLINE ANISOTROPY OF SOME FERRITES OF SPINEL STRUCTURE.** IVANNIKOV, V. L. MIRAYASOV, N. Z. FIZ. KHIM. FERRITOV 195-216, 1973.
50662	**COMPOSITION ON THE NUMBER OF BARKHAUSEN JUMPS IN ELECTROLYTIC SUPERCRITICAL FILMS.** ZOLOTKOVSKII, B. S. FIZ. PLENOK (1) 44-50, 1972. (FROM: REF. ZH., FIZ., E. ABSTR. NO. 1E1591, 1973)
50663	**ORDERING OF AN ALLOY IN SINGLE-CRYSTAL IRON-ALUMINUM AND IRON-SILICON FILMS AND MAGNETIC ANISOTROPY OF THE FILM.** KORCHMAR, V. S. PYN'KO, V. G. KVEGLIS, L. I. FIZ. MAGN. PLENOK (4), 189-96, 1971.
50664	**ELECTRICAL PROPERTIES OF LITHIUM-CHROMIUM FERRITES AFTER HEAT TREATMENT IN AN ELECTRICAL FIELD.** MAKIENKO, N. V. KARPENKO, V. F. KOSHKIN, L. I. FIZ. MAGN. PLENOK (4), 218-25, 1971.
50668	**CRYSTAL STRUCTURE AND MAGNETIC PROPERTIES OF SAMARIUM-COBALT ALLOY POWDERS.** UL'YANOV, A. I. DERYAGIN, A. V. MISHIN, D. D. FIZ. METAL. METALLOVED. 35 (5), 1094-6, 1973.
50669	**ANOMALOUS DEMBER EFFECT IN CADMIUM TELLURIDE FILMS WITH ANOMALOUSLY LARGE PHOTOVOLTAGE.** KORSUNSKII, M. I. SOMINSKII, M. M. FIZ. TEKH. POLUPROV. 7 (3), 480-7, 1973. (FOR ENGLISH TRANSLATION SEE E52415)
50671	**TEMPERATURE DEPENDENCE OF INDIUM ANTIMONIDE SURFACE-LAYER RESISTANCE IN THE REGION OF TRANSFORMATION INTO A SUPERCONDUCTING STATE.** ABDULLAEV, A. VITOVSKII, N. A. KRYMOVA, E. D. MASHOVETS, T. V. RYVKIN, S. M. SHIK, A. YA. FIZ. TEKH. POLUPROV. 7 (5), 925-7, 1973. (FOR ENGLISH TRANSLATION SEE E52417)
50672	**IMPURITY STATES OF GALLIUM IN LEAD TELLURIDE.** VEIS, A. N. KAIDANOV, V. I. KOSTYLEVA, N. A. MEL'NIK, R. B. UKHANOV, YU. I. FIZ. TEKH. POLUPROV. 7 (5), 928-30, 1973. (FOR ENGLISH TRANSLATION SEE E52418)
50674	**MAGNETORESISTANCE OF FINITE SEMICONDUCTOR SAMPLES IN THE HIGH-ELECTRIC FIELD REGION.** VAKSER, A. I. FIZ. TEKH. POLUPROV. 7 (5), 1001-4, 1973. (FOR ENGLISH TRANSLATION SEE E52420)
50676	**TRANSVERSE MAGNETORESISTANCE OF EPITAXIAL LAYERS OF N-TYPE GALLIUM ARSENIDE.** GORODNICHII, O. P. SEITOV, E. P. SHAVRIN, A. G. FIZ. TEKH. POLUPROV. 7 (5), 1015-17, 1973. (FOR ENGLISH TRANSLATION SEE E52422)
50677	**THEORY OF LUMINESCENCE OF STRONGLY DOPED SEMICONDUCTORS.** LEVANYUK, A. P. OSIPOV, V. V. FIZ. TEKH. POLUPROV. 7 (6), 1058-68, 1973. (FOR ENGLISH TRANSLATION SEE E52423)
50678	**THEORY OF LUMINESCENCE OF STRONGLY-DOPED COMPENSATED NONDEGENERATE SEMICONDUCTORS.** LEVANYUK, A. P. OSIPOV, V. V. FIZ. TEKH. POLUPROV. 7 (6), 1069-80, 1973. (FOR ENGLISH TRANSLATION SEE E52424)
50679	**INDIRECT EXCITON AND PHONON-FREE TRANSITIONS IN GALLIUM SULFIDE.** RAZBIRIN, B. S. KARAMAN, M. I. MUSHINSKII, V. P. STARUKHIN, A. N. FIZ. TEKH. POLUPROV. 7 (6), 1112-16, 1973. (FOR ENGLISH TRANSLATION SEE E52425)
50680	**RADIATIVE RECOMBINATION WITH AN ENERGY DEFICIT IN INDIUM ANTIMONIDE.** KASTAL'SKII, A. A. RYVKIN, S. M. FILATOVA, E. S. YAGODKIN, V. M. FIZ. TEKH. POLUPROV. 7 (6), 1117-23, 1973. (FOR ENGLISH TRANSLATION SEE E52426)
50681	**RED BAND OF CADMIUM DIPHOSPHIDE RECOMBINATION EMISSION.** VAVILOV, V. S. NEGRII, V. D. KOVAL, V. S. POTYKEVICH I. V. POTYKEVICH, YU. V. CHUKICHEV, M. V. FIZ. TEKH. POLUPROV. 7 (6), 1148-54, 1973. (FOR ENGLISH TRANSLATION SEE E52427)
50682	**MAGNETOOPTICAL ABSORPTION IN SEMICONDUCTORS WITH NONSPHERICAL BANDS.** ZHILICH, A. G. MONOZON, B. S. FIZ. TEKH. POLUPROV. 7 (6), 1164-71, 1973. (FOR ENGLISH TRANSLATION SEE E52428)
50683	**MAGNETORESISTANCE IN STRONGLY COMPENSATED N-INDIUM ANTIMONIDE.** CHUSOV, I. I. YAREMENKO, N. G. FIZ. TEKH. POLUPROV. 7 (6), 1233-6, 1973. (FOR ENGLISH TRANSLATION SEE E52928)
50684	**ANOMALOUSLY LARGE PHOTOELECTRIC AND PHOTOMAGNETO-ELECTRIC EFFECTS IN SEMICONDUCTOR FILMS.** ADIROVICH, E. I. MASTOV, E. M. MIRZAMAKHMUDOV, T. NAIMANBAEV, R. RUBINOV, V. M. SHAKIROV, N. YUABOV, YU. M. FOLOELEK. YAVLENIYA POLUPROV. OPTOELEKTRON. 143-229, 1972.
50686	**PHOTOCONDUCTIVITY AND PHOTOMAGNETOELECTRIC EFFECT IN SEMICONDUCTORS AT HIGH CONCENTRATIONS OF NONEQUILIBRIUM CARRIERS.** ARONOV, D. A. ZAITOVA, V. KOTOV, E. P. SHAMASOV, R. G. FOTOELEK. YAVLENIYA POLUPROV. OPTOELEKTRON. 241-82, 1972.
50687	**PHOTOCONDUCTIVITY OF THIN FILMS OF LEAD(II) OXIDE IN STRONG ELECTRIC FIELDS.** GASANOV, O. K. GERTSENOVSK. CHTENIYA., FIZ. POLUPROV. ELEKTRON. KRATKOE SODERZH. DOKL., 25TH 5-9, 1972.
50688	**EVALUATION OF THE DENSITY-OF-STATES EFFECTIVE MASS IN LEAD MONOXIDE.** IZVOZCHIKOV, V. A. GERTSENOVSKI. CHTENIYZ, FIZ. POLUPROV. ELEKTRON., KRATKOE SODERZH. DOKL., 25TH 26-8, 1972.
50689	**CURRENT INSTABILITY AND RELOCATION OF REGIONS OF PHOTOELECTRIC SENSITIVITY OF LEAD(II) OXIDE SPECIMENS.** IZVOZCHIKOV, V. A. IVANDIKOVA, N. A. POTACHEV, S. A. GERTSENOVSK. CHTENIYA, FIZ. POLUPROV. ELEKTRON., KRATKOE SODERZH. DOKL., 25TH 28-32, 1972.
50690	**HALL MOBILITY OF CHARGE CARRIERS IN POLYCRYSTALLINE POLYMORPHOUS LEAD OXIDE AT 400-500 K.** ANUFRIEV, YU. P. IZVOZCHIKOV, V. A. GERTSENOVSK. CHTENIYA, FIZ. POLUPROV. ELEKTRON., KRATKOE SODERZH. DOKL., 25TH 32-6, 197I.

EPIC Number	Bibliographic Citation
50692	**HALL EFFECT IN COPPER(I) OXIDE.** TAZENKOV, B. A. GRUZDEV, F. A. GERSENOVSK. CHTENIYA, FIZ. POLUPROV. ELEKTRON., KRATKOE SODERZH. DOKL., 25TH 87-90, 1972.
50693	**EXPERIMENTAL APPARATUS FOR COMPLEX STUDIES OF OPTICAL AND PHOTOELECTRIC CHARACTERISTICS OF SEMICONDUCTORS.** TAZENKOV, B. A. KHALTURIN, A. S. GERTZENOVSK. CHTENIKA, FIZ. POLUPROV. KRATK. SODERZH. DOKL., 25TH 91-5, 1972.
50694	**SECONDARY ELECTRON EMISSION OF LITHIUM AND LITHIUM OXIDE.** BRONSHTEIN, I. M. BROZDNICHENKO, A. N. KUDRYASH, A. P. GERTSENOVSKIE CHTENIYA, FIZ. POLUPROV. ELEKTRON., KRATK. SODERZH. DOKL., 25TH 99-101, 1972.
50696	**SECONDARY ELECTRON EMISSION OF A GALLIUM ARSENIDE SINGLE CRYSTAL WITH NEGATIVE ELECTRON AFFINITY.** AFONINA, L. F. STUCHINSKII, G. B. GERTSENOVSKIE CHTENIYA, FIZ. POLUPROV. ELEKTRON., KRATK. SODERZH. DOKL., 25TH 103-5, 1972.
50700	**ELECTRICAL CONDUCTION OWING TO DEFECT CENTERS PRODUCED BY ION IMPLANTATION IN GALLIUM ARSENIDE.** KATO, Y. SHIRAKI, Y. SHIMADA, T. RADIAT. DAMAGE DEFECTS SEMICOND., PROC. INT. CONF. 348-54, 1973.
50701	**POINT DEFECTS IN GALLIUM ARSENIDE USING PRECISION LATTICE PARAMETER MEASUREMENTS.** DRISCOLL, C. M. H. WILLOUGHBY, A. F. W. RADIAT. DAMAGE DEFECTS SEMICOND., PROC. INT. CONF. 377-86, 1973.
50703	**BEHAVIOR OF DEFECTS IN IRRADIATED CADMIUM TELLURIDE.** TAGUCHI, T. SHIRAFUJI, J. INUISHI, Y. RADIAT. DAMAGE DEFECTS SEMICOND., PROC. INT. CONF. 407-15, 1973.
50704	**STRUCTURE AND SECONDARY EMISSION OF MAGNESIUM OXIDE LAYERS APPLIED ON A MOLYBDENUM SINGLE CRYSTAL.** BORISOV, V. L. DOSYAGAEV, A. V. RADIOTEKH. ELEKTRON. 18 (5), 1084-5, 1973.
50705	**EFFECT OF ELECTRON BOMBARDMENT ON THE THERMOELECTRONIC EMISSION OF AN YTTRIUM OXIDE CATHODE.** SORONKINA, V. M. KOSTIN, V. N. KREPAK, V. N. RADIOTEKHNIKA (KHARKOV) (22), 88-91, 1972.
50706	**DETERMINATION OF THE EFFECTIVE MASS OF ELECTRONS IN GALLIUM ARSENIDE BY MEASURING THE FARADAY EFFECT IN THE INFRARED REGION.** CONSTANTINESCU, C. NAN, S. REV. ROUM. PHYS. 18 (3), 335-41, 1973.
50707	**ELECTRICAL PROPERTIES OF CARBIDES OF TRANSITION METALS OF GROUP IV IN THE 20-2000 TEMPERATURE RANGE.** GOLIKOVA, O. A. DZHAFAROV, E. O. AVGUSTINIK, A. I. KLIMASHIN, G. M. HEAT TRANSFER-SOV. RES. 5 (2), 11-14, 1973.
50709	**ELECTRODE BEHAVIOR AND THE DETERMINATION OF DEFECT ENERGIES FROM MEASUREMENTS OF IONIC CONDUCTIVITY IN SODIUM CHLORIDE CRYSTALS.** WHITHAM, W. CALDERWOOD, J. H. IEEE TRANS. ELEC. INSUL. 8 (2), 60-8, 1973.
50712	**FREQUENCY DEPENDENCE OF DOUBLE-BAND ELECTROLUMINOPHORS.** PRAKASH, S. G. INDIAN J. PHYS. 47 (5), 301-5, 1973.
50713	**SYNTHESIS OF DOUBLE BAND COPPER AND HYDROGEN-ACTIVATED ZINC SULFIDE ELECTROLUMINESCENT PHOSPHORS.** PRAKASH, S. G. INDIAN J. PURE APPL. PHYS. 11 (3), 224-5, 1973.
50714	**PHOTOLUMINESCENCE IN SILVER- AND CHLORINE-ACTIVATED ZINC OXIDE PHOSPHORS.** PANDEY, K. N. BALAKRISHNA, S. KANARI, P. S. INDIAN J. PURE APPL. PHYS. 11 (3), 227-8, 1973.
50715	**MAGNETIC PROPERTIES OF RARE EARTH INTERMETALLIC COMPOUNDS.** BARBARA, B. GIGNOUX, D. GIVORD, D. GIVORD, F. LEMAIRE, R. INT. J. MAGN. 4 (1), 77-83, 1973.
50716	**NEW MEASUREMENTS OF ABSORPTION COEFFICIENT AND FARADAY ROTATION ON MANGANESE-BISMUTH THIN FILMS.** PAPP, A. HARMS, H. INT. J. MAGN. 4 (1), 85-8, 1973.
50718	**DIELECTRIC PROPERTIES OF CALCIUM TITANATE IN THE RADIO-FREQUENCY RANGE.** KUZNETSOV, A. A. ISSLED. FIZ. VOP. METOD. DEMON, EKSP. (2), 8-11, 1971.
50720	**ROLE OF THE SURFACE IN LUMINESCENCE AND RADICAL-RECOMBINATION LUMINESCENCE PHENOMENA IN SEMICONDUCTORS.** VOL'KENSHTEIN, F. F. SOKOLOV, V. A. PEKA, G. P. STYROV, V. V. MALAKHOV, V. V. IZV. AKAD. NAUK SSSR, SER. FIZ. 37 (4), 855-9, 1973.
50721	**SPECTRAL-LUMINESCENT STUDY OF URANYL COMPOUNDS.** VOLOD'KO, L. V. KOMYAK, A. I. SEVCHENKO, A. N. UMREIKO, D. S. IZV. AKAD. NAUK SSSR, SER. FIZ. 37 (4), 865-9, 1973. (FOR ENGLISH TRANSLATION SEE E54525)
50723	**EFFECT OF SUBSIDIARY EXTREMA OF THE CONDUCTION BAND ON THE MAXIUMUM VALUE OF ELECTRON CONCENTRATION IN AIII - BV COMPOUNDS.** MIRGALOVSKAYA, M. S. ILCHENKO, L. N. IZV. AKAD. NAUK SSSR, NEORG. MATER. 9 (5), 834-6, 1973. (FOR ENGLISH TRANSLATION SEE E53024)
50724	**MOBILITY AND EFFECTIVE MASS OF ELECTRONS IN SILVER (I) SULFIDE AND SILVER SULFIDE TELLURIDE.** ASTAKHOV, O. P. GOLYSHEV, V. D. SGIBNEV, I. V. IZV. AKAD. NAUK SSSR, NEORG. MATER. 9 (5), 841-2, 1973. (FOR ENGLISH TRANSLATION SEE E53025)
50725	**LOCAL ENVIRONMENT OF TIN AND TELLURIUM ATOMS WHEN SELENIUM IS INTRODUCED INTO THE LEAD TIN TELLURIDE SYSTEM.** BEKKER, A. A. KAUKIS, A. TSYPIN, M. I. OSTROVSKAYA, L. M. NESMEYANOV, A. N. IZV. AKAD. NAUK SSSR, NEORG. MATER. 9 (5), 845-6, 1973. (FOR ENGLISH TRANSLATION SEE E53026)
50726	**ELECTRIC CONDUCTIVITY AND THERMOEMF. OF TIN-SELENIUM ALLOYS IN THE LIQUID STATE.** KAZANDZHAN, B. I. MISHUTKINA, T. I. IZV. AKAD. NAUK SSSR, NEORG. MATER. 9 (6), 911-14, 1973. (FOR ENGLISH TRANSLATION SEE E53027)
50727	**MAGNETIC PROPERTIES OF CHROMIUM TELLUROCHALCOGENIDES.** IKORSKII, V. N. IZV. AKAD. NAUK SSSR, NEORG. MATER. 9 (6), 938-43, 1973. (FOR ENGLISH TRANSLATION SEE E53028)
50728	**MAGNETIC SUSCEPTIBILITY OF METAL DODECARBORIDES WITH URANIUM DODECABORIDE-TYPE STRUCTURE.** ODINTSOV, V. V. KOSTETSKII, I. I. L'VOV, S. N. IZV. AKAD. NAUK SSSR, NEORG. MATER. 9 (6), 944-7, 1973. (FOR ENGLISH TRANSLATION SEE E53029)
50729	**PROPERTIES OF ALKALI METAL MONOFLUOROPHOSPHATES.** MARDIROSOVA, I. V. BUKHALOVA, G. A. SHPAKOVA, V. M. TOKMAN, I. A. IZV. AKAD. NAUK SSSR, NEORG. MATER. 9 (6), 970-4, 1973. (FOR ENGLISH TRANSLATION SEE E53030)
50730	**EFFECT OF CHEMICAL HOMOGENEITY ON THE MAGNETIC PROPERTIES OF NICKEL CHROMITE FERRITE.** ANASTOSYUK, N. V. KOVALEVA, Z. I. NIKOLAEV, V. I. OLEINIKOV, N. N. RUSAKOV, V. S. TRET'YAKOV, YU. D. IZV. AKAD. NAUK SSSR, NEORG. MATER. 9 (6), 1079-81, 1973. (FOR ENGLISH TRANSLATION SEE E53031)
50731	**OPTICAL PROPERTIES OF GALLIUM ARSENIDE-GALLIUM PHOSPHIDE SOLID SOLUTIONS PREPARED BY A ZONE MELTING METHOD.** OVCHINNIKOV, S. YU. RAZBEGAEV, V. N. IZV. LENINGRAD. ELEKTROTEKH. INST. (108), 19-31, 1972.

EPIC Number	Bibliographic Citation
50732	**ELECTROOPTICAL ABSORPTION ON NONCROSSOVER TRANSITIONS IN GALLIUM PHOSPHIDE.** GLINSKII, G. F. PIKHTIN, A. N. YAS'KOV, D. A. IZV. LENINGRAD. ELEKTROTEKH. INST. (108), 32–45, 1972.
50733	**EFFECT OF ALUMINUM ON THE PHOTOLUMINESCENCE OF GALLIUM PHOSPHIDE.** BASETSKII, V. YA. PESKOV, O. G. IZV. LENINGRAD. ELEKTROTEKH. INST. (110), 99–104, 1972.
50734	**ELECTROLUMINESCENT DIODES BASED ON GALLIUM PHOSPHIDE DEOXIDIZED BY ALUMINUM.** BASETSKII, V. YA. PESKOV, O. G. IZV. LENINGRAD. ELEKTROTEKH. INST. (110), 104–10, 1972.
50739	**PHYSICOCHEMICAL AND CATALYTIC PROPERTIES OF THE LITHIUM OXIDE–COBALT(II) OXIDE SYSTEM.** BIELANSKI, A. KLUZ, Z. IZV. OTD. KHIM. NAUKI, BULG. AKAD. NAUK 6 (1), 21–33, 1973.
50740	**MAGNETIC PROPERTIES OF INTERMETALLIC COMPOUNDS WITH RARE EARTH ELEMENTS.** VOL'SKII, A. A. KRAPOSHIN, V. S. LIVSHITS, B. G. LINETSKII, YA. L. SAVICH, A. N. IZV. VYSSH. UCHEB. ZAVED., CHERN. MET. (4), 139–41, 1973.
50741	**PHOTOCONDUCTIVITY AND PHOTOLUMINESCENCE OF BISMUTH OXYCHLORIDE SINGLE CRYSTALS.** BLETSKAN, D. I. KOPINETS, I. F. RUBISH, I. D. TURGANITSA, I. I. SHTILIKHA, M. V. IZV. VYSSH. UCHEB. ZAVED., FIZ. 16 (5), 65–8, 1973. (FOR ENGLISH TRANSLATION SEE E79428)
50742	**CRYSTAL LATTICE DISTORTION EFFECT ON THE MAGNETIC ANISOTROPY OF LITHIUM–ALUMINUM FERRITES.** STEL'MASHENKO, M. A. RUBAL'SKAYA, E. V. PERVEEVA, A. I. SHLYAKHINA, L. P. NEKHOROSHEV, G. V. IZV. VYSSH. UCHEB. ZAVED., FIZ. 16 (5), 113–16, 1973. (FOR ENGLISH TRANSLATION SEE E79081)
50743	**GALVANOMAGNETIC PROPERTIES OF MONOCARBIDES OF IVA AND VA–GROUP TRANSITION METALS.** BORUKHOVICH, A. S. GEL'D, P. V. STARTSEV, V. E. IZV. VYSSH. UCHEB. ZAVED., FIZ. 16 (5), 142–5, 1973. (FOR ENGLISH TRANSLATION SEE E79073)
50744	**BAND STRUCTURE OF A III B V–A II B VI SOLID SOLUTIONS. I. OPTICAL PROPERTIES OF INDIUM ARSENIDE–CADMIUM TELLURIDE SOLID SOLUTIONS DETERMINED BY THE INTERACTION OF LIGHT WITH FREE CHARGE CARRIERS.** SEMIKOLENOVA, N. A. KHABAROV, E. N. IZV. VYSSH. UCHEB. ZAVED., FIZ. 16 (6), 76–82, 1973. (FOR ENGLISH TRANSLATION SEE E78977)
50747	**ELECTRICAL PROPERTIES OF ZINC OXIDE–BISMUTH OXIDE CERAMICS.** MORRIS, W. G. J. AMER. CERAM. SOC. 56 (7), 360–4, 1973.
50748	**MEASUREMENT OF DIPOLE RELAXATION TIME AND DIELECTRIC LOSS FACTOR AT VERY LOW FREQUENCY BY THERMALLY STIMULATED CURRENT.** HINO, T. SUZUKI, K. YAMASHITA, K. JAP. J. APPL. PHYS. 12 (5), 651–6, 1973.
50749	**FIELD QUENCHING IN PHOTOCONDUCTIVE CADMIUM SELENIDE FILMS.** YODOGAWA, Y. SHIMIZU, K. KANAMORI, H. JAP. J. APPL. PHYS. 12 (5), 711–14, 1973.
50751	**STATIC N–TYPE NEGATIVE DIFFERENTIAL CONDUCTIVITY IN SEMICONDUCTORS INDUCED BY THERMAL QUENCHING OF PHOTOCONDUCTIVITY.** TOKUMARU, Y. MIKOSHIBA, N. JAP. J. APPL. PHYS. 12 (6), 876–80, 1973.
50752	**VELOCITY–FIELD CHARACTERISTICS IN III–V MIXED CRYSTALS, GALLIUM ANTIMONIDE ARSENIDE AND INDIUM GALLIUM ARSENIDE.** INOUE, M. ASHIDA, K. SUGINO, T. SHIRAFUJI, J. INUISHI, Y. JAP. J. APPL. PHYS. 12 (6), 932–3, 1973.
50753	**PHOTOCONDUCTIVITY ASSOCIATED WITH CHROMIUM IN GALLIUM ARSENIDE.** BOIS, D. PINARD, P. JAP. J. APPL. PHYS. 12 (6), 936–7, 1973.
50754	**THREE–STEP POSITIVE TEMPERATURE COEFFICIENT OF RESISTIVITY ON ANTIMONY–CONTAINING BARIUM TITANATE ZIRCONATE COMPOSITE CERAMICS WITH A SURFACE BARRIER LAYER.** KUWABARA, M. SAWAMURA, K. YANAGIDA, H. JAP. J. APPL. PHYS. 12 (6), 950–1, 1973.
50756	**DEFECT AND IMPURITY THERMODYNAMICS IN RUTILE–LIKE SYSTEMS.** DE FORD, J. W. JOHNSON, O. W. J. APPL. PHYS. 44 (7), 3001–7, 1973.
50757	**LUMINESCENCE OF GALLIUM PHOSPHIDE AT HIGH EXCITATION.** TSU, R. J. APPL. PHYS. 44 (7), 3176–9, 1973.
50758	**LUMINESCENCE FROM INDIUM GALLIUM PHOSPHIDE PREPARED BY VAPOR–PHASE EPITAXY.** KRESSEL, H. NUESE, C. J. LADANY, I. J. APPL. PHYS. 44 (7), 3266–72, 1973.
50764	**SELECTED PROPERTIES OF PYROLYTIC TANTALUM (V) OXIDE FILMS.** KNAUSENBERGER, W. H. TAUBER, R. N. J. ELECTROCHEM. SOC. 120 (7), 927–31, 1973.
50765	**RESISTIVITY AND PHOTOLUMINESCENCE OF IODINE ACTIVATED ZINC (SULFIDE, SELENIDE) ANNEALED IN LIQUID ZINC.** OZAWA, L. HERSH, H. N. J. ELECTROCHEM. SOC. 120 (7), 938–42, 1973.
50766	**VAPOR GROWTH OF INDIUM GALLIUM PHOSPHIDE FOR P–N JUNCTION ELECTROLUMINESCENCE. II. LUMINESCENCE CHARACTERISTICS.** NUESE, C. J. SIGAI, A. G. ABRAHAMS, M. S. GANNON, J. J. J. ELECTROCHEM. SOC. 120 (7), 956–65, 1973.
50769	**VALENCE STATES OF NITROSYL ION.** FIELD, R. W. J. MOL. SPECTROSC. 47 (2), 194–203, 1973.
50770	**RECOMBINATION LUMINESCENCE LIFETIMES AND THE SELF–TRAPPED EXCITON IN ALKALI HALIDES.** FISCHBACH, J. U. FROCHLIEH, D. KABLER, M. N. LUMIN, J. J. LUMIN. 6 (1), 29–43, 1973.
50771	**ELECTRIC FIELD EFFECT ON THE LUMINESCENCE OF POTASSIUM IODIDE THALLIUM.** NAUAILHAT, A. PERRENOUD, R. AEGERTER, M. A. ROSSEL, J. J. LUMIN. 6 (4), 245–55, 1973.
50772	**OPTICAL PROPERTIES AND BAND STRUCTURE OF GROUP III–V COMPOUNDS AND ALLOYS.** ONTON, A. J. LUMIN. 7, 95–113, 1973.
50773	**LUMINESCENCE IN GALLIUM NITRIDE.** PANKOVE, J. I. J. LUMIN. 7, 114–26, 1973.
50774	**ADVANCES IN INJECTION LUMINESCENCE OF GROUP II–VI COMPOUNDS.** AVEN, M. DEVINE, J. Z. J. LUMIN. 7, 195–212, 1973.
50775	**THE D.C. ELECTROLUMINESCENCE IN ZINC SULFIDE AND RELATED COMPOUNDS.** VECHT, A. J. LUMIN. 7, 213–27, 1973.
50776	**NEAR EDGE OPTICAL ABSORPTION AND LUMINESCENCE OF GALLIUM SELENIDE, GALLIUM SULFIDE, AND OF MIXED CRYSTALS.** MERCIER, A. MOOSER, E. VOITCHOVSKY, J. P. J. LUMIN. 7, 241–66, 1973.
50777	**BAND STRUCTURE AND OPTICAL PROPERTIES OF SMALL GAP SEMICONDUCTORS AND ALLOYS.** BALKANSKI, M. J. LUMIN. 7, 451–70, 1973.

EPIC Number	Bibliographic Citation
50780	**MAGNETIC SUSCEPTIBILITY AND ELECTRIC RESISTIVITY OF TITANIUM-COBALT.** ARAJS, S. STELMACH, A. A. MARTIN, M. C. J. LESS-COMMON METALS 32 (1), 173-5, 1973.
50781	**HYDROGEN ABSORPTION AND MAGNETIC PROPERTIES OF LANTHANUM-COBALT-NICKEL COMPOUNDS.** VAN MAL, H. H. BUSCHOW, K. H. J. KUIJPERS, F. A. J. LESS-COMMON METALS 32 (2), 289-96 1973.
50782	**EFFECTS OF DOMAINS ON CRYSTAL-OPTICS PROPERTIES AND INTENSITY OF RAMAN SCATTERING IN A 45 Y-CUT POTASSIUM DIHYDROGEN PHOSPHATE CRYSTAL.** TAKAGI, Y. SHIGENARI, T. J. OPT. SOC. AMER. 63 (8), 995-1002, 1973.
50785	**MEASUREMENT OF THE TRIGONAL SPLITTING OF IRON (2+) IONS IN ALUMINUM OXIDE BY A FREQUENCY CROSSING TECHNIQUE USING THERMAL PHONONS.** ANDERSON, B. R. CHALLIS, L. J. J. PHYS. 6 C (13), L266-L270, 1973.
50787	**BAND STRUCTURE OF SOLID HYDROGEN FLUORIDE.** BASSANI, F. PIETRONERO, L. RESTA, R. J. PHYS. 6 C (13), 2133-46, 1973.
50789	**OPTICAL ABSORPTION EDGES OF COMPOUND SEMICONDUCTORS IN THE ZINC SILICON PHOSPHIDE-ZINC SILICON ARSENIDE RANGE.** CLARK, W. C. STROUD, R. F. J. PHYS. 6 C (13), 2184-90, 1973.
50790	**MOESSBAUER STUDY AND BAND STRUCTURE OF IRON DISILICIDE.** BLAAUW, C. VAN DER WOUDE, F. SAWATZKY, G. A. J. PHYS. 6 C (14), 2371-81, 1973.
50791	**VARIATIONS IN THE RESISTIVITY OF EVAPORATED FILMS OF CADMIUM SULFIDE.** BUCKLEY, R. W. WOODS, J. J. PHYS. 6 D (9), 1084-9, 1973.
50794	**LOW TEMPERATURE HALL MEASUREMENTS IN A CRYOSTAT WITH A BUILT-IN MAGNET.** ALTWEIN, M. FINKENRATH, H. STOECKEL, T. J. PHYS. 6 E (7), 623-7, 1973.
50803	**ANOMALOUS BEHAVIOR OF CARRIER HALL MOBILITY IN ELECTRON-IRRADIATED GALLIUM ARSENIDE.** KRIVOV, M. A. MALYANOV, S. V. MELEV, V. G. RADIATS. DEFEKTY POLUPROV. 268-9, 1972.
50804	**LOW-TEMPERATURE ELECTRONIC TRANSPORT PROPERTIES OF THALLIUM TELLURIDE.** CRUCEANU, E. LUECK, R. REV. ROUM. PHYS. 18 (3), 343-6, 1973.
50805	**ELECTRICAL CONDUCTIVITY OF B-GALLIUM (III) OXIDE.** COJOCARU, L. N. REV. ROUM. PHYS. 18 (3), 409-11, 1973.
50806	**MEASUREMENT OF HIGH RESISTIVITY SEMICONDUCTORS USING THE VAN DER PAUW METHOD.** HEMENGER, P. M. REV. STI. INSTRUM. 44 (6), 698-700, 1973.
50808	**COMPILATION OF ENERGY BAND GAP IN ELEMENTAL AND BINARY COMPOUND SEMICONDUCTORS AND INSULATORS.** STREHLOW, W. H. COOK, E. L. J. PHYS. CHEM. REF. DATA 2 (1), 163-99, 1973.
50811	**NONLINEAR MAGNETIC SUSCEPTIBILITY OF YIG (YTTRIUM IRON GARNET) IN THE HIGH FREQUENCY MAGNETIC FIELD NEAR THE CURIE TEMPERATURE.** HASHIMOTO, T. SATO, A. FUJIWARA, Y. J. PHYS. SOC. JAP. 35 (1), 81-4, 1973.
50814	**MAGNETIC PROPERTIES OF FCC. GAMMA-PHASE IN THE TERNARY COBALT-MANGANESE-IRON SYSTEM.** MATSUI, M. SATO, K. ADACHI, K. J. PHYS. SOC. JAP. 35 (2), 419-25, 1973.
50815	**ELECTRICAL CONDUCTION IN COBALT IRON TITANIUM OXIDE AND COBALT IRON OXIDE SINGLE CRYSTALS.** YAMADA, T. J. PHYS. SOC. JAP. 35 (1), 130-3, 1973.
50816	**HYDROSTATIC-PRESSURE EFFECTS ON THE DIELECTRIC PROPERTIES OF FERROELECTRIC SILVER SODIUM NITRITE.** GESI, K. OZAWA, K. J. PHYS. SOC. JAP. 35 (1), 199-203, 1973.
50817	**MAGNETIC PROPERTIES OF FACE-CENTERED CUBIC GAMMA-PHASE IN THE TERNARY COBALT - MANGANESE - IRON SYSTEM.** MATSUI, M. SATO, K. ADACHI, K. J. PHYS. SOC. JAP. 35 (2), 419-25, 1973.
50818	**TEMPERATURE DEPENDENCE OF MAGNETIC ANISOTROPY IN MANGANESE-ALUMINUM-GERMANIUM.** SHIBATA, K. WATANABE, H. YAMAUCHI, K. SHINOHARA, T. J. PHYS. SOC. JAP. 35 (2), 448-51, 1973.
50820	**TEMPERATURE DEPENDENCE OF THE FUNDAMENTAL SPECTRA OF POTASSIUM HALIDES IN THE SCHUMANN ULTRAVIOLET REGION.** TOMIKI, T. MIYATA, T. TSUKAMOTO, H. J. PHYS. SOC. JAP. 35 (2), 495-507, 1973.
50822	**BOSE CONDENSATION OF EXCITONIC MOLECULES IN CADMIUM SELENIDE.** KURODA, H. SHIONOYA, S. SAITO, H. HANAMURA, E. J. PHYS. SOC. JAP. 35 (2), 534-42, 1973.
50825	**CRYSTAL STRUCTURES AND MAGNETIC PROPERTIES OF STOICHIOMETRIC INTERMETALLIC COMPOUNDS PALLADIUM-MANGANESE-GERMANIUM AND RHODIUM-MANGANESE-GERMANIUM.** MASUMOTO, H. WATANABE, K. MITERA, M. J. PHYS. SOC. JAP. 34 (5), 1414, 1973.
50826	**MAGNETIC PROPERTIES OF ORDERED IRON (PALLADIUM-PLATINUM) ALLOY.** KADOMATSU, H. FUJII, H. OKAMOTO, T. J. PHYS. SOC. JAP. 34 (5), 1417, 1973.
50829	**FARADAY EFFECT MEASUREMENT OF THE CONDUCTION ELECTRON EFFECTIVE MASS IN CADMIUM DIINDIUM TETRASULFIDE.** GAGLARDI, K. SCHWERDTFEGER, C. F. J. PHYS. CHEM. SOLIDS 34 (7), 1281-3, 1973.
50830	**IODINE AS A DONOR IN CADMIUM SULFIDE.** VYDYANATH, H. R. CHERN, S. S. KROGER, F. A. J. PHYS. CHEM. SOLIDS 34 (8), 1317-21, 1973.
50831	**DIELECTRIC LOSS IN SODIUM CHLORIDE SINGLE CRYSTALS UNDER THE SIMULTANEOUS ACTION OF A.C. AND D.C. VOLTAGES.** RAPOS, M. CALDERWOOD, J. H. J. PHYS. CHEM. SOLIDS 34 (8), 1455-7, 1973.
50832	**RELATIVE SPECTRAL ABSORPTION COEFFICIENTS FOR THE FUNDAMENTAL VIBRATIONAL-ROTATIONAL BANDS OF ALUMINUM OXIDE.** SULZMANN, K. G. P. J. QUANT. SPECTROSC. RADIAT. TRANSFER 13 (9), 931-5, 1973.
50834	**LUMINESCENCE OF COPPER (I) OXIDE SINGLE CRYSTALS.** KUZ'MINA, I. P. LOBACHEV, A. N. PREDTECHENSKII, B. S. STAROSTINA, L. S. STOPACHINSKII, V. B. KHAIDUKOV, N. M. KRISTALLOGRAFIYA 18 (3), 635-7, 1973.
50835	**PREPARATION AND PHYSICAL FUNDAMENTAL CHARACTERIZATION OF ALUMINUM GALLIUM ARSENIDE CRYSTALS.** FISCHER, P. KUEHN, G. BINDEMANN, R. RHEINLAENDER, B. HOERIG, W. KRIST. TECH. 8 (1-3), 167-76, 1973.
50836	**EXPERIMENT WHICH CONFLICTS WITH THE FISCHER MODEL FOR ELECTROLUMINESCENCE.** CORTESE, C. MAXIA, V. MURGIA, M. LETT. NUOVO CIMENTO SOC. ITAL. FIS. 7 (5), 167-70, 1973.
50837	**DEPTH OF ELECTRON TRAPS IN SILVER CHLORIDE CRYSTALS BY THE THERMOLUMINESCENCE METHOD.** ARAMU, F. MAXIA, V. SPANO, G. LETT. NUOVO CIMENTO SOC. ITAL. FIS. 7 (9), 353-7, 1973.

EPIC Number	Bibliographic Citation

50838 **CALCULATION OF THE PLASMA OSCILLATION FREQUENCY OF VALANCE ELECTRONS AND THE OPTICAL DIELECTRIC CONSTANT OF ANTIMONY TRISULFIDE SINGLE CRYSTALS.**
AUDZIONIS, A. I. KARPUS, A. S.
LIET. FIZ. RINKINYS
13 (1), 89–99, 1973.

50842 **EXPERIMENTAL INVESTIGATIONS ON LUMINESCENCE AT HIGH CONCENTRATIONS OF CARRIERS AND EXCITONS.**
LEVY, R. BIVAS, A. GRUN, J. B.
LUMIN. CRYST., MOL., SOLUTIONS, PROC. INT. CONF.
136–43, 1973.

50843 **SPECTRAL INVESTIGATION OF LUMINESCENCE CENTERS WITH THE GENERALIZED METHOD OF ALENTSEV.**
ANTIPOVA-KARATAEVA, I. I. GOLUBEVA, N. P.
FOK, M. V.
LUMIN. CRYST., MOL., SOLUTIONS, PROC. INT. CONF.
232–8, 1973.

50844 **COMPLEX STRUCTURE OF THE IMPURITY LUMINESCENCE SPECTRA OF ZINC SULFIDE SINGLE CRYSTALS.**
GEORGOBIANI, A. N. BLAZHEVICH, A. I.
OZEROV, YU. V. PANASJUK, E. I. TODUA, P. A.
FRIEDRICH, H.
LUMIN. CRYST., MOL., SOLUTIONS, PROC. INT. CONF.
239–44, 1973.

50845 **DONOR-DOUBLE ACCEPTOR LUMINESCENCE OF ZINC TELLURIDE.**
BRYANT, F. J. BAKER, A. T. J.
LUMIN. CRYST., MOL., SOLUTIONS, PROC. INT. CONF.
250–7, 1973.

50846 **PHOTOLUMINESCENCE STUDY OF LATTICE DEFECTS IN CADMIUM TELLURIDE BY MEANS OF HEAT TREATMENT AND ELECTRON IRRADIATION.**
TAGUCHI, T. SHIRAFUJI, J. INUISHI, Y.
LUMIN. CRYST., MOL., SOLUTIONS, PROC. INT. CONF.
258–61, 1973.

50847 **LUMINESCENCE OF ZINC TELLURIDE AND ITS MODULATION BY INFRARED RADIATION.**
MARUANI, A. NOBLAC, J. P. DURAFFOURG, G.
LUMIN. CRYST., MOL., SOLUTIONS, PROC. INT. CONF.
262–8, 1973.

50848 **ELECTRONIC STRUCTURE AND LUMINESCENCE OF PHOSPHORS BASED ON IIA-VIB COMPOUNDS.**
MIKHAILIN, V. V.
LUMIN. CRYST., MOL., SOLUTIONS, PROC. INT. CONF.
269–74, 1973.
(FROM: PLENUM: NEW YORK, N. Y., EDITED BY FERD. WILLIAMS)

50849 **ENERGY SHIFT OF DONOR-ACCPTOR EMISSION ON VARYING THE EXCITATION INTENSITY.**
ZACKS, E. HALPERIN, A.
LUMIN. CRYST., MOL., SOLUTIONS, PROC. INT. CONF.
419–25, 1973.

50850 **CHARACTERIZATION OF DEFECTS IN GALLIUM ARSENIDE BY PHOTOLUMINESCENCE MEASUREMENTS.**
FABRE, E.
LUMIN. CRYST., MOL., SOLUTIONS, PROC. INT. CONF.
439–43, 1973.

50851 **PHOTOLUMINESCENCE OF GALLIUM SELENIDE.**
CINGOLANI, A. EVANGELISTI, F.
MINAFRA, A. RIZZO, A.
LUMIN. CRYST., MOL., SOLUTIONS, PROC. INT. CONF.
449–54, 1973.
(FROM: PLENUM: NEW YORK, N. Y., EDITED BY FERD. WILLIAMS)

50854 **LUMINESCENCE OF ISOELECTRONIC MANGANESE (4+) AND CHROMIUM (3+) IONS IN MAGNESIUM ORTHOTITANATE.**
DITTMANN, R. HAHN, D. STADE, J.
LUMIN. CRYST., MOL., SOLUTIONS, PROC. INT. CONF.
518–23, 1973.

50856 **LUMINESCENCE PROCESSES IN BISMUTH(3+) CENTERS.**
BOULON, G. GAUME-MAHN, F. PEDRINI, C.
JACQUIER, B. JANIN, J. CURIE, D.
LUMIN. CRYST., MOL., SOLUTIONS, PROC. INT. CONF.
530–7, 1973.
(FROM: PLENUM: NEW YORK, N. Y., EDITED BY FERD. WILLIAMS)

50857 **POLARIZED LUMINESCENCE OF SEMICONDUCTORS DUE TO OPTICAL ORIENTATION OF ELECTRONS.**
GIOEV, R. I. ZAKHARCHENYA, B. P.
FLEISHER, V. G.
LUMIN. CRYST., MOL., SOLUTIONS, PROC. INT. CONF.
564–74, 1973.

50858 **TUNGSTEN HEXAOXIDE LUMINESCENCE IN ORDERED PEROVSKITES.**
BLASSE, G. CORSMIT, A. F. VAN DER PAS, M.
LUMIN. CRYST., MOL., SOLUTIONS, PROC. INT. CONF.
612–15, 1973.
(FROM: PLENUM: NEW YORK, N. Y., EDITED BY FERD. WILLIAMS)

EPIC Number	Bibliographic Citation

50859 **CONFIGURATION INTERACTION AND CORRELATION EFFECTS IN DONOR-ACCEPTOR PAIR SPECTRA.**
MEHRKAM, L. WILLIAMS, F.
LUMIN. CRYST., MOL., SOLUTIONS, PROC. INT. CONF.
628–37, 1973.

50860 **DONOR-ACCEPTOR PAIRS IN IONIC CRYSTALS.**
SCHWOTREV, G. KOETITZ, G. GOERLICH, P.
LUMIN. CRYST., MOL., SOLUTIONS, PROC. INT. CONF.
638–48, 1973.
(FROM: PLENUM: NEW YORK, N. Y., EDITED BY FERD. WILLIAMS)

50861 **COMPOSITION DEPENDENCY OF THERMOLUMINESCENCE OF NEW PHOSPHORS FOR RADIATION DOSIMETRY.**
TORYU, T. SAKAMOTO, H. HITOMI, T.
KOTERA, N. YAMADA, H.
LUMIN. CRYST., MOL., SOLUTIONS, PROC. INT. CONF.
685–9, 1973.

50862 **HOT LUMINESCENCE OF MOLECULAR IMPURITY IONS IN IN ALKALI HALIDE CRYSTALS.**
REBANE, K. SAARI, P. MAURING, T.
LUMIN. CRYST., MOL., SOLUTIONS, PROC. INT. CONF.
690–9, 1973.

50863 **VIBRATIONAL EMISSION FROM HYDROXIDE IONS IN POTASSIUM BROMIDE, INDUCED BY EXCITATION OF THE ELECTRONIC STATES.**
CAPELLETTI, R. FERMI, F. FIESCHI, R.
LUMIN. CRYST., MOL., SOLUTIONS, PROC. INT. CONF.
700–6, 1973.

50864 **EFFECT OF PRESSURE AND TEMPERATURE ON THE MAGNETIC HYPERFINE INTERACTION OF IRON IN COBALT OXIDE.**
SYASSEN, K. HOLZAPFEL, W. B.
PHYS. REV.
8 (5), 1799– 805, 1973.

50865 **DOUBLY EXCITED CHROMIUM ION PAIRS IN ZINC GALLATE.**
VAN GORKOM, G. G. P.
PHYS. REV.
8 B (5), 1827–34, 1973.

50866 **ANTIRESONANCE IN THE OPTICAL SPECTRUM OF EUROPIUM IONS IN PLATINUM DOPED EUROPEIUM GALLIUM OXIDE.**
VAN DER ZIEL, J. P. UITERT, L. G.
PHYS. REV.
8 B (5), 1835–45, 1973.

50867 **RADIATIVE AND NONRADIATIVE TRANSITIONS IN PRASEODYMIUM DOPED LANTHANUM CHLORIDE AND PRASEODYMIUM CHLORIDE.**
GERMAN, K. R. KIEL, A.
PHYS. REV.
8 B (5), 1846–53, 1973.

50868 **MOSSBAUER STUDY OF MAGNETIC STATES OF POTASSIUM IRON FLUORIDE AND IMPLICATIONS FOR RUBDIUM IRON FLUORIDE.**
DAVIDSON, G. R. EIBSCHUTZ, M.
GUGGENHEIM, H. J.
PHYS. REV.
8 B (5), 1864–79, 1973.

50869 **COOPERATIVE ABSORPTION AND LUMINESCENCE IN CHROMIUM DOPED EUROPIUM ALUMINUM OXIDE.**
VAN DER ZIEL, J. P. VAN UITERT, L. G.
PHYS. REV.
8 B (5), 1889–93, 1973.

50870 **FAR-INFRARED MEASUREMENT OF THE ENERGY GAP OF TRIVANADIUM SILICIDE.**
TANNER, D. B. SIEVERS, A. J.
PHYS. REV.
8 B (5), 1978–81, 1973.

50872 **ELECTRIC AND DIELECTRIC PROPERTIES OF POLYCRYSTALLINE YTTRIUM IRON GARNET: SPACE-CHARGE-LIMITED CURRENTS IN AN INHOMOGENEOUS SOLID.**
LARSEN, P. K. METSELAAR, R.
PHYS. REV.
8 B (5), 2016–25, 1973.

50873 **PRESSURE AND TEMPERATURE DEPENDENCES OF THE DIELECTRIC PROPERTIES AND RAMAN SPECTRA OF RUBIDIUM DIHYDROGEN PHOSPHATE.**
PEERCY, P. S. SAMARA, G. A.
PHYS. REV.
8 B (5), 2033–48, 1973.

50874 **MAGNETIC ORDERING IN DYSPROSIUM HYDROXIDE AND HOLMIUM HYDROXIDE.**
CATANESE, C. A. MEISSNER, H. E.
PHYS. REV.
8 B (5), 2060–74, 1973.

50879 **EXHANGE-PERTURBATION TREATMENT OF MAGNETIC ORDERING IN NONCONDUCTING SOLIDS.**
RITTER, R. JANSEN, L. LOMBARDI, E.
PHYS. REV.
8 B (5), 2139–54, 1973.

EPIC Number	Bibliographic Citation
50880	**ANALYSIS OF FAR-INFRARED SPECTRA OF ANTIFERROMAGNETIC IRON CARBONATE.** PRINZ, G. A. FORESTER, D. W. LEWIS, J. L. PHYS. REV. 8 B (5), 2155-65, 1973.
50882	**GYROMAGNETIC RATIOS OF METALLIC SAMARIUM COMPOUNDS.** STEWART, A. M. PHYS. REV. 8 B (5), 2214-21, 1973.
50884	**STATISTICAL MECHANICS AND CRITICAL BEHAVIOR OF THE MAGNETOELECTRIC EFFECT IN GADOLINIUM VANADATE.** GORODETSKY, G. HORNREICH, R. M. WANKLYN, B. M. PHYS. REV. 8 B (5), 2263-7, 1973.
50887	**EUROPIUM OXIDE. I. RESISTIVITY AND HALL EFFECT IN FIELDS UP TO 150 KOE.** SHAPIRA, Y. FONER, S. REED, T. B. PHYS. REV. 8 B (5), 2299-2315, 1973.
50888	**EUROPIUM OXIDE. II. DEPENDENCE OF THE INSULATOR-METAL TRANSITION ON MAGNETIC ORDER.** SHAPIRA, Y. FONER, S. AGGARWAL, R. L. REED, T. B. PHYS. REV. 8 B (5), 2316-26, 1973.
50889	**IDENTIFICATION OF ENERGY LEVELS OF PRASEODYMIUM IONS IN LANTHANUM CHLORIDE.** KIEL, A. GERMAN, K. R. PHYS. REV. 8 B (5), 2353-4, 1973.
50890	**IDENTIFICATION OF ENERGY LEVELS OF PRASEODYMIUM IONS IN LANTHANUM CHLORIDE-A REPLY.** HARGREAVES, W. A. PHYS. REV. 8 B (5), 2355-7, 1973.
50894	**AN A.C. MAGNETIC SUSCEPTIBILITY DETERMINATION OF OF MAGNETIC PHASE TRANSITION IN NICKEL (II) CHLORIDE HEXAHYDRATE.** BECERRA, C. C. PADUAN FILHO, A. PHYS. LETT. 44 A (1), 13-14, 1973.
50895	**MAGNETIC SUSCPTIBILITY OF MANGANESE (II) OXIDE ASSOCIATED WITH THE FIRST-ORDER PHASE TRANSITION.** SEINO, D. MIYAHARA, S. NORO, Y. PHYS. LETT. 44 A (1), 35-6, 1973.
50897	**PHOTOLUMINESCENCE EXCITATION SPECTRA AND CARRIER DIFFUSION LENGTHS IN GLASSY ARSENIC SELENIDE TELLURIDE.** BISHOP, S. G. PHYS. LETT. 44 A (2), 107-8, 1973.
50898	**ELECTRONIC STRUCTURE AND PROPERTIES OF TITANIUM DISULFIDE.** MYRON, H. W. FREEMAN, A. J. PHYS. LETT. 44 A (3), 167-8, 1973. (AD 768 539)
50903	**ELECTRICAL PROPERTIES OF COPPER GALLIUM SULFIDE.** TELL, B. KASPER, H. M. J. APPL. PHYS. 44 (11), 4988-90, 1973.
50904	**TEMPERATURE DEPENDENCE OF PHOTOLUMINESCENCE FROM GERMANIUM-DOPED AND UNDOPED GALLIUM ARSENIDE.** DINGLE, R. J. APPL PHYS. 44 (11), 5001-4, 1973.
50905	**ELECTRICAL PROPERTIES OF CADMIUM SULFIDE THIN FILMS IN THE THICKNESS DIRECTION.** LEIGHTON, W. H. J. APPL. PHYS. 44 (11), 5011-20, 1973.
50906	**ELECTROLUMINESCENCE OF GADOLINIUM-DOPED CADMIUM FLUORIDE IN A LIGHT-EMITTING DIODE.** YANEY, P. P. BAFICO, M. A. J. APPL. PHYS. 44 (11), 5029-30, 1973.
50907	**CRYSTAL AND LUMINESCENCE PROPERTIES OF CONSTANT-TEMPERATURE LIQUID-PHASE-EXPITAXIAL INDIUM GALLIUM PHOSPHIDE GROWN ON (100) GALLIUM ARSENIC PHOSPHIDE.** MACKSEY, H. M. LEE, M. H. HOLONYAK, N., JR. HITCHENS, W. R. DUPUIS, R. D. CAMPBELL, J. C. J. APPL. PHYS. 44 (11), 5035-40, 1973.
50908	**DOMAIN-WALL ENERGY IN MAGNETIC GARNET BUBBLE MATERIALS.** SHUMATE, P. W., JR. J. APPL. PHYS. 44 (11), 5075-7, 1973.
50909	**FARADAY ROTATION IN CEROUS METAPHOSPHATE GLASS AT LIQUID-HELIUM TEMPERATURES.** WERTHEIMER, M. R. J. APPL. PHYS. 44 (11), 5078-9, 1973.
50910	**PREPARATION AND SOME PROPERTIES OF ZINC TIN ANTIMONIDE.** SCOTT, W. J. APPL. PNYS. 44 (11), 5165-6, 1973.
50911	**SHORT-WAVELENGTH EDGE EMISSION BANDS IN UNDOPED CADMIUM SULFIDE.** GREENE, L. C. WILSON, H. A. J. APPL. PHYS. 44 (11), 5173-4, 1973.
50912	**REVISION OF THE DIELECTRIC CONSTANT OF ICE IN THE MILLIMETER-WAVE SPECTRUM.** PERRY, J. W. STRAITON, A. W. J. APPL. PHYS. 44 (11), 5180, 1973.
50921	**EXPERIMENTAL INVESTIGATION OF THE COOPERATIVE JAHN-TELLER EFFECT IN THULIUM CADMIUM COMPOUNDS.** LUTHI, B. MULLEN, M. E. ANDRES, K. BUCHER, E. MAITA, J. P. PHYS. REV. 8 B (6), 2639-48, 1973.
50922	**ELECTRICAL PROPERTIES OF AMORPHOUS INDIUM ANTIMONIDE.** HAUSER, J. J. PHYS. REV. 8 B (6), 2678-84, 1973.
50923	**VALENCE-BAND DENSITY OF STATES OF INDIUM PHOSPHIDE AND GALLIUM ANTIMONIDE AS DETERMINED BY X-RAY PHOTOEMISSION.** VESELY, C. J. KINGSTON, D. L. PHYS. REV. 8 B (6), 2685-7, 1973.
50924	**THEORY OF THE TEMPERATURE DERIVATIVE OF THE REFRACTIVE INDEX IN TRANSPARENT CRYSTALS.** TSAY, Y-F. BENDOW, B. MITRA, S. S. PHYS. REV. 8 B (6), 2688-96, 1973. (AD-776035, AFCRL-TR-0116) (N76-12355)
50925	**SPHERICAL MODEL OF SHALLOW ACCEPTOR STATES IN SEMICONDUCTORS.** BALDERESCHI, A. LIPARI, N. O. PHYS. REV. 8 B (6), 2697-2709, 1973.
50928	**CALCULATED VALENCE-BAND DENSITIES OF STATES AND PHOTOEMISSION SPECTRA OF DIAMOND AND ZINC-BLENDE SEMICONDUCTORS.** CHELIKOWSKY, J. CHADI, D. J. COHEN, M. L. PHYS. REV. 8 B (6), 2786-94, 1973.
50931	**MAGNETIC-FIELD-INDUCED ENERGY SHIFTS OF THE GROUND STATE OF BOUND EXCITONS IN GALLIUM ARSENIDE.** WILLMANN, F. DREYBRODT, W. BETTINI, M. PHYS. REV. 8 B (6), 2891-5, 1973.
50934	**ELECTRONIC STATES AND OPTICAL PROPERTIES IN CUBIC ICE.** PARRAVICINI, G. P. RESCA, L. PHYS. REV. 8 B (6), 3009-23, 1973.
50936	**THEORY OF MULTIPHONON ABSORPTION IN INSULATING CRYSTALS.** SPARKS, M. SHAM, L. J. PHYS. REV. 8 B (6), 3037-48, 1973.
50939	**PYROELECTRIC AND ELECTOOPTIC EFFECTS IN LITHIUM INDIUM DISULFIDE AND LITHIUM INDIUM DISELENIDE.** NEGRAN, T. J. KASPER, H. M. GLASS, A. M. MATER. RES. BULL. 8 (6), 743-8, 1973.
50940	**HIGH PRESSURE SYNTHESIS OF ILMENITE TYPE MANGANESE CHROMIUM OXIDE AND ITS MAGNETIC PROPERTIES.** SAWAMOTO, H. MATER. RES. BULL. 8 (7), 767-75, 1973.
50941	**CADMIUM SELENIDE SINGLE CRYSTALS WITH N- AND P-TYPE OF CONDUCTIVITY APPROACHING INTRINSIC.** BAUBINAS, R. JANUSKEVICIUS, Z. SAKALAS, A. MATER. RES. BULL. 8 (7), 817-23, 1973.

EPIC Number	Bibliographic Citation
50942	**COMPARISON OF ELECTRICAL PROPERTIES OF EUROPIUM AND YTTERBIUM HEXABORIDES.** MERCURIO, J. P. ETOURNEAU, J. NASLAIN, R. HAGENMULLER, P. MATER. RES. BULL. 8 (7), 837–43, 1973.
50943	**ABSORPTION AND EMISSION OF THE FA–CENTER IN SODIUM–DOPED–POTASSIUM CHLORIDE.** HONDA, S. TOMURA, M. MEM. FAC. ENG., HIROSHIMA UNIV. 4 (3), 129–38, 1972.
50944	**CORRELATION OF MAGNETIC PERMEABILITY AND MICROSTRUCTURE IN CUPRONICKEL ALLOYS.** VOWLES, M. BILLINGHAM, J. CULPAN, E. A. METAL SCI. J. 7 (5), 77–81, 1973.
50946	**MAGNETIC SUSCEPTIBILITY OF INDIUM–BISMUTH SYSTEM ALLOYS.** KUZ'MENKO, P. P. SUPRUNENKO, P. A. KOTIKOVA, T. D. NIKITENKO, V. G. METALLOFIZIKA (44), 77–80, 1973.
50948	**CAPTURE CENTERS IN RARE EARTH (3+) ION–ACTIVATED LANTHANUM FLUORIDE SINGLE CRYSTALS.** AZAROV, V. V. SHCHERBINA, E. V. MONOKRIST, TEKH. (3), 66–71, 1970.
50949	**NATURE OF THERMOLUMINESCENCE ARISING IN MAGNESIUM FLUORIDE–DOPED LITHIUM FLUORIDE COLORED CRYSTALS.** PANOVA, A. N. UGLANOVA, V. V. CHARKINA, T. A. MONOKRIST. TEKH. (3), 78–85, 1970.
50950	**CENTERS OF ADDITIONAL LUMINESCENCE IN SODIUM IODIDE, THALLIUM–DOPED SODIUM IODIDE, AND INDIUM–DOPED SODIUM IODIDE CRYSTALS CONTAINING OXYGEN IMPURITIES.** ASTOPIEVA, A. M. MUSTAFINA, R. KH. PANOVA, A. N. MONOKRIST. TEKH. (3), 94–101, 1970.
50951	**TEMPERATURE BROADENING OF LUMINESCENCE LINES OF THE GROUP OF NEODYMIUM (3+) ION IN ALUMINUM YTTRIUM GARNET CRYSTALS.** OSTROVSKAYA, E. M. SAZONOVA, S. A. SKOROBOGATOV, B. S. MONOKRIST. TEKH. (3), 135–9, 1970.
50953	**SUPERCONUCTING AND OTHER ELECTRONIC PROPERTIES OF LANTHANUM–INDIUM, LANTHANUM–THALLIUM, AND SOME RELATED PHASES.** HEINIGER, F. BUCHER, E. MAITA, J. P. DESCOUTS, P. PHYS. REV. 8 B (7), 3194–3205, 1973.
50954	**MAGNETOCHEMICAL PROPERTIES OF POLYPHOSPHORIC ACIDS.** ZDUKOS, A. T. SVISTUNOV, V. A. KAMALOV, Z. K. UZB. KHIM. ZH. 17 (3), 8–10, 1973.
50956	**INFRARED AND TEMPERATURE QUENCHING OF LUMINESCENCE AND PHOTOCONDUCTIVITY OF COPPER– AND CHLORINE–DOPED ZINC CADMIUM SULFIDE.** VLASENKO, N. A. KONOVETS, N. K. UKR. FIZ. ZH. (RUSS. ED.) 17 (10), 1590–9, 1972.
50957	**THERMAL CONDUCTIVITY IN TWO SIMPLE ANTIFERROMAGNETS: RUBIDIUM MANGANESE FLUORIDE AND MANGANESE FLUORIDE.** GUSTAFSON, J. WALKER, C. T. PHYS. REV. 8 B (7), 3309–22, 1973.
50958	**TEMPERATURE AND POLARIZATION DEPENDENCE OF THE OPTICAL ABSORPTION EDGE OF GADOLINIUM MOLYBDATE.** ZEIDLER, J. R. ULLMAN, F. G. PHYS. REV. 8 B (7), 3371–7, 1973.
50961	**RECOMBINATION INTERACTIONS OF LUMINESCENCE CENTERS IN LEAD– AND MANGANESE–ACTIVATED CADMIUM CHLORIDE AND BROMIDE.** LYSKOVICH, A. B. CHORNII, Z. P. LAKHOTSKII, T. V. KUSHNIR, O. B. UKR. FIZ. ZH. (RUSS. ED.) 17 (10), 1625–32, 1972.
50965	**THERMOCHROMISM AND ELECTRICAL CONDUCTIVITY IN DOPED STRONTIUM TITANATE.** WILD, R. L. ROCKAR, E. M. SMITH, J. C. PHYS. REV. 8 B (8), 3828–35, 1973.
50966	**MAGNETIC PROPERTIES OF MERCURY TELLURIDE WITH A TRIPLET–HOLE COUPLING.** BAGINSKII, V. M. TOVSTYUK, K. D. UKR. FIZ. ZH. (RUSS. ED.) 17 (10), 1737–9, 1972.
50967	**ELECTRICAL CONDUCTIVITY OF ALUMINUM–COPPER ALLOYS IN A LIQUID STATE.** ROMANOVA, A. V. PERSION, Z. V. UKR. FIZ. ZH. (RUSS. ED.) 17 (10), 1747–9, 1972.
50968	**CALCULATION OF THE MAGNETIC SUSCEPTIBILITY OF THE AMMONIA MOLECULE.** CHANG, S. S. HAMEKA, H. F. J. CHEM. PHYS. 59 (6), 3297–3300, 1973.
50969	**POLARIZABILITY CALCULATIONS ON WATER, HYDROGEN, OXYGEN, AND CARBON DIOXIDE.** NIR, S. ADAMS, S. REIN, R. J. CHEM. PHYS. 59 (6), 3341–55, 1973.
50972	**IMPROVEMENT OF SERVICE PROPERTIES OF STEEL E12 BY CHROMIZING.** DUBININ, G. N. RYBKIN, V. F. PETROVA, M. P. ARTEM'EVA, L. I. NADEZHNOST DOLGOVECHNOST METAL. MATER. MACHINOSTR. PRIBOROSTR. 93–8, 1972.
50975	**TOTAL EMISSIVE POWER OF ALLOYS OF SILICON WITH IRON, COBALT, AND NICKEL IN THE TEMPERATURE RANGE FROM 900 TO 1750 C.** SHVAREV, K. M. BAUM, B. A. GEL'D, P. V. TEPLOFIZ. VYS. TEMP. 11 (1), 78–83, 1973. (FOR ENGLISH TRANSLATION SEE E50976)
50976	**TOTAL EMISSIVE POWER OF ALLOYS OF SILICON WITH IRON, COBALT, AND NICKEL IN THE TEMPERATURE RANGE FROM 900 TO 1750 C.** SHVAREV, K. M. BAUM, B. A. GEL'D, P. V. HIGH TEMP. 11 (1), 66–70, 1973. (ENGLISH TRANSLATION OF TEPLOFIZ. VYS. TEMP., 11 (1), 78–83, 1973; FOR ORIGINAL SEE E50975)
50979	**OPTICAL PROPERTIES OF U CENTERS IN ALKALI HALIDES AND ALKALINE EARTH FLUORIDES.** BENNETT, H. S. J. RES. NAT. BUR STAND. 77 A (5), 659–65, 1973.
50981	**ELECTRICAL CONDUCTIVITY OF ALPHA–FERRIC OXIDES.** KANEKO, K. INOUYE, K. NIPPON KAGAKU KAISHI (6), 1075–81, 1973.
50983	**RAPID SCANNING SPECTROMETER AND TIME AVERAGING METHOD FOR CATHODOLUMINESCENCE.** AICARDI, J. P. LEYRIS, J. P. MASSE, G. NOUV. REV. OPT. 4 (2), 97–104, 1973.
50985	**LIGHT MODES IN THIN POLYURETHANE AND LITHIUM FLUORIDE FILMS.** HORNAUER, D. RAETHER, H. OPT. COMMUN. 7 (4), 297–301, 1973.
50986	**ACTION OF X–RAYS ON EUROPIUM(3+) ION–DOPED SODIUM FLUORIDE SINGLE CRYSTALS.** POTAPENKO, G. D. PISARENKO, V. F. OPT. SPEKTROSK 34 (4), 800–1, 1973. (FOR ENGLISH TRANSLATION SEE E52820)
50988	**TEMPERATURE DEPOLARIZATION OF LUMINESCENCE OF TIN DIPOSITIVE ION–ACTIVATED POTASSIUM CHLORIDE–TYPE CENTERS.** KRISTOFEL, N. N. KHIZHNYAKOV, V. V. OPT. SPEKTROSK. 34 (6), 1236–7, 1973. (FOR ENGLISH TRANSLATION SEE E53708)
50995	**SECONDARY EMISSION OF RADIATION BY EXCITONS IN CADMIUM SULFIDE CRYSTALS.** GROSS, E. F. PERMOGOROV, S. A. TRAVNIKOV, V. V. SEL'KIN, A. V. PHYS. IMPURITY CENT. CRYST., PROC. INT. SEMIN. SELEC. PROBL. THEORY IMPURITY CENT. CRYST. 627–42, 1972.
50996	**MAGNETIC ANISOTROPY IN DEMAGNETIZED SAMPLES OF POWDERED CMN (CERIUM MAGNESIUM NITRATE).** BEDUZ, C. MEIJER, H. C. BOTS, G. J. C. PHYS. LETT. 44 A (3), 185–6, 1973.
50999	**ELECTRONIC STRUCTURE OF VANADIUM CARBIDE.** ZBASNIK, J. TOTH, L. E. PHYS. REV. 8 B (2), 452–9, 1973.

EPIC Number	Bibliographic Citation
51005	LOW-FREQUENCY IMPURITY-PAIR CONDUCTIVITY IN DOPED SEMICONDUCTORS. LYO, S. K. HOLSTEIN, T. PHYS. REV. 8 B (2), 682-92, 1973. (AD 771 510)
51007	X-RAY PHOTOELECTRON STUDY OF THE VALENCE BANDS IN CUPROUS HALIDES. KONO, S. ISHII, T. SAGAWA, T. KOBAYASI, T. PHYS. REV. 8 B (2), 795-803, 1973.
51010	OPTICAL SPECTRA OF CHROMIUM(3+) ION PAIRS IN THE SPINEL ZINC GALLIUM OXIDE. VAN GORKOM, G. G. P. HENNING, J. C. M. VAN STAPELE, R. P. PHYS. REV. 8 B (3), 955-73, 1973.
51016	MAGNETIC PROPERTIES OF THREE-DIMENSIONALLY QUANTIZED SEMIMETALS. CHU, H. T. PHYS. REV. 8 B (4), 1296-302, 1973.
51017	BAND STRUCTURE OF NICKEL SULFIDE AS CALCULATED USING A SIMPLIFIED LINEAR-COMBINATION-OF-MUFFIN-TIN-ORBITALS METHOD. KASOWSKI, R. V. PHYS. REV. 8 B (4), 1378-82, 1973.
51020	PAIR SPECTRA AND THE SHALLOW ACCEPTORS IN ZINC SELENIDE. MERZ, J. L. NASSAU, K. SHIEVER, J. W. PHYS. REV. 8 B (4), 1444-52, 1973.
51021	SPONTANEOUS AND STIMULATED LUMINESCENCE IN CADMIUM SULFIDE AND ZINC SULFIDE EXCITED BY MULTIPHOTON OPTICAL PUMPING. CATALANO, I. M. CINGOLANI, A. MINAFRA, A. PHYS. REV. 8 B (4), 1488-92, 1973.
51024	PHONON DRAG AND THE LOW-TEMPERATURE ELECTRICAL RESISTIVITY OF THE ALKALI METALS. POTASSIUM. KAVEH, M. WISER, N. PHYS. REV. LETT. 29 (20), 1374-7, 1972.
51025	SURFACE PHONONS IN THE OSCILLATORY PHOTOCONDUCTIVITY OF ZINC OXIDE. LUETH, H. PHYS. REV. LETT. 29 (20), 1377-9, 1972.
51026	CHARGE-CARRIER TRANSPORT PHENOMENA IN AMORPHOUS SILICAON DIOXIDE. DIRECT MEASUREMENT OF THE DRAFT MOBILITY AND LIFETIME. HUGHES, R. C. PHYS. REV. LETT. 30 (26), 1333-6, 1973.
51030	ABSENCE OF A HALL EFFECT IN ICE CRYSTALS. SOKOLOFF, J. B. PHYS. REV. LETT. 31 (2), 90-2, 1973.
51032	ELECTRONIC STRUCTURE AND SCATTERING PROPERTIES OF POTASSIUM IODIDE. PHOTOEMISSION. BAER, A. D. LAPEYRE, G. J. PHYS. REV. LETT. 31 (5), 304-7, 1973.
51033	LUMINESCENCE OF MANGANESE IN ZINC SELENIDE. ALLEN, J. W. RYALL, M. D. WRAY, E. M. PHYS. STATUS SOLIDI 17 A (2), K101-K105, 1973.
51034	STIMULATED EMISSION FROM NEODYMIUM(3+) ACTIVATED LITHIUM LANTHANUM MOLYBDATE(VI) CRYSTAL LASER. KAMINSKII, A. A. MAYER, A. A. SARKISOV, S. E. PROVOTOROV, M. V. PHYS. STATUS SOLIDI 17 A (2), K115-K117, 1973.
51035	MAGNETOCRYSTALLINE ANISOTROPY OF EQUIATOMIC RARE EARTH-ZINC COMPOUNDS. DYSPROSIUM-ZINC AND ERBIUM-ZINC. MORIN, P. PIERRE, J. PHYS. STATUS SOLIDI 17 A (2), 479-82, 1973.
51037	PHOTOLUMINESCENCE OF GALLIUM SELENIDE. CINGOLANI, A. EVANGELISTI, F. MINAFRA, A. RIZZO, A. PHYS. STATUS SOLIDI 17 A (2), 541-6, 1973.
51041	ELECTRICAL PROPERTIES OF UNDOPED P-CADMIUM ANTIMONIDE UNDER HIGH ELECTRIC FIELD AT LOW TEMPERATURES. MATSUNAMI, H. KUHARA, Y. TANAKA, T. PHYS. STATUS SOLIDI 17 A (2), 621-9, 1973.
51042	RADIATIVE RECOMBINATION IN MOLECULAR OXYGEN DOPED N-TYPE GALLIUM ARSENIDE AT LOW TEMPERATURES. LI, S. S. HUANG, C. I. PHYS. STATUS SOLIDI 17 A (2), 659-63, 1973.
51043	METHOD OF DIRECT MEASUREMENT OF NONLINEARITY IN THE DEPENDENCE OF PHOTOLUMINESCENCE ON EXCITATION INTENSITY. GAJ, J. A. PHYS. STATUS SOLIDI 17 A (2), 685-90, 1973.
51046	MAGNETIC PROPERTIES OF ZINC VANADIUM OXIDE SPINEL. NIZIOL, S. PHYS. STATUS SOLIDI 18 A (1), K11-K13, 1973.
51047	STIMULATED EMISSION FROM LUTETIUM ALUMINUM OXIDE CRYSTALS WITH HOLMIUM (3+), ERBIUM (3+), AND THULIUM (3+) IONS. KAMINSKII, A. A. BAGDASAROV, KH. S. PETROSYAN, A. G. SARKISOV, S. E. PHYS. STATUS SOLIDI 1, A (1), K31-K34, 1973.
51048	MAGNETIC FIELD DEPENDENCE OF KINETIC COEFFICIENTS OF CADMIUM ARSENIDE SINGLE CRYSTALS. ARUSHANOV, E. K. CHUIKO, G. P. PHYS. STATUS SOLIDI 17 A (2), K135-K138, 1973.
51049	DIELECTRIC BEHAVIOR OF COPPER ZINC FERRITES. REZLESCU, E. PHYS. STATUS SOLIDI 17 A (2), K139-K141, 1973.
51050	ADDITIONAL METHOD FOR THE ESTIMATION OF THE EFFECTIVE MASS BAND GAP IN NONPARABOLIC SEMICONDUCTORS. PHADKE, U. P. PHYS. STATUS SOLIDI 17 A (2), K149-52, 1973.
51051	CONDUCTIVITY OF P-TYPE ZINC SILICON ARSENIDE CRYSTALS IN THE REGION OF HIGH TEMPERATURES. AVERKIEVA, G. K. PROCHUKHAN, V. D. RUD, YU. V. TASHTANOVA, M. PHYS. STATUS SOLIDI 17 A (2), K153-K156, 1973.
51054	MAGNETOCRYSTALLINE ANISOTROPY AND EFFECT OF APPLIED FIELD ON THE SINUSOIDAL MAGNETIC STRUCTURES OF TERBIUM-ZINC AND HOLMIUM-ZINC. DEBRAY, D. PHYS. STATUS SOLIDI 18 A (1), 227-34, 1973.
51055	FARADAY EFFECT INVESTIGATION ON CONCENTRATION AND TEMPERATURE DEPENDENCE OF EFFECTIVE ELECTRON MASS IN N-TYPE GALLIUM ARSENIDE. CONSTANTINESCU, C. NAN, S. PHYS. STATUS SOLIDI 18 A (1), 277-82, 1973.
51057	IONIC CONDUCTIVITY OF PURE AND DOPED BARIUM FLUORIDE CRYSTALS. BOLLMANN, W. PHYS. STATUS SOLIDI 18 A (1), 313-21, 1973.
51058	PHOTOLUMINESCENCE OF LITHIUM-DOPED CADMIUM SULFIDE. PLOIX, J. L. DUGUE, M. PHYS. STATUS SOLIDI 18 A (1), 323-7, 1973.
51060	OPTICAL AND THERMAL DEPTH OF SHALLOW TRAPS IN ZINC SULFIDE. BAUR, G. WENGERT, R. WITTWER, V. PHYS. STATUS SOLIDI 18 A (1), 337-45, 1973.
51065	INFLUENCE OF INTERBAND RECOMBINATION ON THE PHOTOCONDUCTIVITY AND THE PHOTOELECTROMAGNETIC EFFECT IN SEMICONDUCTORS WITH DEEP TRAPS. ARONOV, D. A. SAITOVA, V. PHYS. STATUS SOLIDI 58 B (1), K39-K43, 1973.
51068	JAHN-TELLER MANIFESTATION IN AN ORBITAL TRIPLET COUPLED TO E SUB G AND T SUB 2G MODES. BHATTACHARYYA, B. D. PHYS. STATUS SOLIDI 57 B (2), K149-K153, 1973.
51069	CONDUCTION BAND PARAMETERS OF BISMUTH (III) SELENIDE FROM SHUBNIKOV-DE HAAS INVESTIGATIONS. KOEHLER, H. PHYS. STATUS SOLIDI 58 B (1), 91-100, 1973.

EPIC Number	Bibliographic Citation

51070 **PHOTOELECTRIC PROPERTIES OF THE LEAD CHALCOGENIDES.**
CARDONA, M. LANGER, D. W.
SHEVCHIK, N. J. TEJEDA, J.
PHYS. STATUS SOLIDI
58 B (1), 127–37, 1973.

51072 **PHOTOELECTRIC PROPERTIES OF MAGNESIUM–SILICON, MAGNESIUM–GERMANIUM, AND MAGNESIUM–TIN. 1. X–RAY EXCITATION.**
TEJEDA, J. CARDONA, M. SHEVCHIK, N. J.
LANGER, D. W. SCHOENHERR, E.
PHYS. STATUS SOLIDI
58 B (1), 189–200, 1973.

51075 **EXCITATION SPECTRA OF LUMINESCENCE IN CADMIUM SULFIDE.**
PLANEL, R. BONNOT, A.
BENOIT A LA GUILLAUME, C.
PHYS. STATUS SOLIDI
58 B (1), 251–66, 1973.

51076 **KONDO–TYPE RESISTIVITY ANOMALY IN NOBLE METAL ALLOYS WITH 3D METALS.**
INOUE, K. NAKAMURA, Y.
PHYS. STATUS SOLIDI
58 B (1), 355–69, 1973.

51078 **ANISOTROPY OF ELECTRICAL CONDUCTIVITY IN ORIENTED SAMPLES OF GLASSLIKE SEMICONDUCTORS.**
KOLOMIETS, B. T. LYUBIN, V. M. SHILO, V. P.
PISMA ZH. EKSP. TEOR. FIZ.
17 (10), 577–80, 1973.
(FOR ENGLISH TRANSLATION SEE E52821)

51082 **PREPARATION AND PROPERTIES OF CADMIUM ARSENIDE FILMS ON DIELECTRIC SUBSTRATES.**
VLASENKO, N. A. KOSHEVSKAYA, S. V.
KRULIKOVSKII, B. K. CHERNAYA, N. S.
POLUPROV. TEKH. MIKROELECTRON.
(11), 110–11, 1973.

51084 **USE OF A PHOTOELECTRON MULTIPLIER IN A LOGARITHMIC REGIME FOR STUDYING THE KINETICS OF LUMINESCENCE QUENCHING.**
BACHERIKOV, V. V. KAGAIN, V. E.
MAKAROV, YU. A. NIKOLAEV, YU. N.
TARASOV, V. M.
PRIB. TEKH. EKSP.
(3), 206–7, 1973.
(FOR ENGLISH TRANSLATION SEE E65916)

51085 **MEASUREMENT OF THE DIELECTRIC CONSTANT OF LIQUIDS IN STRONG ELECTRICAL FIELDS.**
GARBER, R. I. SLINCHENKO, V. I.
PRIB. TEKH. EKSP.
(3), 227–9, 1973.
(FOR ENGLISH TRANSLATION SEE E65917)

51086 **LIQUID–PHASE EPITAXIAL GROWTH OF GALLIUM ARSENIDE.**
BAPAT, D. R. GUHA, S. RAVI, H. N.
ROY, S. K.
PROC. SYMP. ELECTRON. (ELECTRON TUBE SEMICOND. DEVICES)
2, 21–30, 1972.

51091 **ELECTRON IRRADIATION DAMAGE STUDIES IN INDIUM ARSENIDE.**
LINDSAY, D. J. C. BANBURY, P. C.
RADIAT. DAMAGE DEFECTS SEMICOND., PROC. INT. CONF.
34–41, 1973.
(FROM: INST. PHYS.: LONDON, ENGLAND)

51098 **ELECTRICAL AND PHOTOELECTRIC PROPERTIES OF SEMICONDUCTING LEAD SULFIDE FILMS CONTAINING RADIATION STRUCTURE DEFECTS.**
BORTNIK, M. V. GONOV, A. N. ZAITOV, F. A.
LISOVSKII, G. A.
RADIATS. DEFEKTY POLUPROV.
167–8, 1972.

51099 **CADMIUM SULFIDE PHOTOELECTRIC AND OPTICAL PROPERTY INSTABILITY ASSOCIATED WITH FREE–COMPONENT FORMATION AND MIGRATION PROCESSES.**
KANEEV, M. K. MANNANOVA, KH. KH.
NIYAZOV, KH. R. NIYAZOVA, O. R.
RADIATS. DEFEKTY POLUPROV.
181–3, 1972.

51100 **PHOTOCONDUCTIVITY SPECTRUM IN IRRADIATED CADMIUM SELENIDE.**
USTYANOV, V. I.
RADIATS. DEFEKTY POLUPROV.
197–9, 1972.

51102 **EFFECT OF IRRADIATION TEMPERATURE ON GALLIUM ARSENIDE ELECTRICAL PROPERTIES.**
KURILOVICH, N. F.
RADIATS. DEFEKTY POLUPROV.
264–5, 1972.

51103 **PROPERTIES OF NEODYMIUM OXIDE SINGLE CRYSTALS CONNECTED WITH STRUCTURAL ANISOTROPY.**
TUETA, R. LEJUS, A. M.
REV. CHIM. MINER.
10 (1–2), 105–13, 1973.

51107 **DIELECTRIC PROPERTIES OF THE CALCIUM NICKEL FERRITE SYSTEM.**
VASILIU, A. CUCIUREANU, E. REZLESCU, N.
LUCA, E.
REV. ROUM. PHYS.
18 (1), 49–55, 1973.

51109 **INFLUENCE OF THE CATION DISTRIBUTUON ON THE MAGNETIC SUSCEPTIBILITY OF MAGNESIUM MANGANESE OXIDE.**
BUNGET, I. LEONOVICI, M. R.
REV. ROUM. PHYS.
18 (3), 319–22, 1973.

51110 **PHYSICAL PROPERTIES OF THE LITHIUM–ZINC FERRITES.**
REZLESCU, N. CONDURACHE, D.
NAUM, C. LUCA, E.
REV. ROUM. PHYS.
18 (6), 727–34, 1973.

51113 **MORPHOLOGICAL CHARACTERISTICS OF INDIUM AND GALLIUM ANTIMONIDE SINGLE CRYSTALS WITH THE FACE EFFECT.**
MIRGALOVSKAYA, M. S. RAUKHMAN, M. R.
STRELNIKOVA, I. A.
ROST KRIST.
9, 142–5, 1972.

51114 **RADICAL–RECOMBINATION LUMINESCENCE OF CALCIUM OXIDE–BASED PHOSPHORS EXCITED BY ATOMIC OXYGEN.**
POPOV, D. P. KROTOV, YU. V.
SB. NAUCH. TR., NORILSK. VECH. IND. INST.
(11), 56–60, 1971.

51115 **ABSOLUTE ENERGY YIELD MEASUREMENT OF RADIOLUMINESCENCE OF ALKALI HALIDE CRYSTALS.**
KARPOV, I. K. MATYUSHKOV, V. V.
MIKHALCHENKO, G. A.
ST. TR., KAFEDRA YAD. FIZ. KAFEDRA RADIATS. KHIM., LENINGRAD. TEKHNOL. INST.
(1), 26–35, 1971.

51120 **LOW TEMPERATURE MAGNETIC PROPERTIES IN BARIUM IRON ZINC TITANIUM MANGANESE OXIDE.**
MAHONEY, J. P. TAUBER, A. SAVAGE, R. O.
AIP (AMER. INST. PHYS.) CONF. PROC.
(10), (PT. 1), 159–63, 1973.

51121 **HIGH REMANENT MAGNESIUM MANGANESE INTERMETALLIC FERRITE FOR MICROWAVE APPLICATIONS BY ARCPLASMA SPRAYING.**
HARRIS, D. H.
AIP (AMER. INST. PHYS.) CONF. PROC.
(10), (PT. 1), 164–8, 1973.

51123 **PROPERTIES OF RARE EARTH IRON GARNETS GROWN IN BARIUM OXIDE–BASED AND LEAD OXIDE–BASED SOLVENTS.**
HISKES, R. BURMEISTER, R. A.
AIP (AMER. INST. PHYS.) CONF. PROC.
(10), (PT. 1), 304–8, 1973.

51124 **MAGNETIC BUBBLE DOMAINS IN EUROPIUM YTTRIUM IRON OXIDE FILMS ON SAMARIUM GALLIUM OXIDE SUBSTRATES.**
PLASKETT, T. S. KLOKHOLM, E. HU, H. L.
OKANE, D. F.
AIP (AMER. INST. PHYS.) CONF. PROC.
(10), (PT. 1), 319–23, 1973.

51125 **EXPERIMENTAL STUDY OF DOMAIN WALL RESPONSE TO SINUSOIDAL AND PULSED FIELDS.**
ARGYLE, B. E. MALOZEMOFF, A. P.
AIP (AMER. INST. PHYS.) CONF. PROC.
(10), (PT. 1), 344–8, 1973.

51127 **TWO TYPES OF BUBBLES IN GARNET FILMS.**
BRAGINSKI, A. I. OEFFINGER, T. R.
PATTERSON, R. W. CHARAP, S. H.
AIP (AMER. INST. PHYS.) CONF. PROC.
(10), (PT. 1), 354–8, 1973.

51128 **PULSED LASER THERMAL NUCLEATION OF BUBBLES IN GARNET FILMS.**
ROSSOL, F. C.
AIP (AMER. INST. PHYS.) CONF. PROC.
(10), (PT. 1), 359–63, 1973.

51130 **COERCIVITY MEASUREMENT IN MAGNETIC BUBBLE GARNETS.**
CLOVER, R. B. CUTLER, L. S. LACEY, R. F.
AIP (AMER. INST. PHYS.) CONF. PROC.
(10), (PT. 1), 388–92, 1973.

51131 **BUBBLE MOBILITY IN THE SYSTEM YTTRIUM GADOLINIUM YTTERBIUM EUROPIUM ALUMINUM GALLIUM IRON OXIDE.**
BORRELLI, N. F. CHEN, S. L. MURPHY, J. A.
FEHLNER, F. P.
AIP (AMER. INST. PHYS.) CONF. PROC.
(10), (PT. 1), 398–402, 1973.

51132 **MODEL CALCULATIONS OF THE PARAMAGNETIC SUSCEPTIBILITY FOR THE MODIFIED ZENER MODEL OF FERROMAGNETISM.**
BARTEL, L. C.
AIP (AMER. INST. PHYS.) CONF. PROC.
(10), (PT. 1), 530–4, 1973.

EPIC Number	Bibliographic Citation

51134 COOPERATIVE JAHN–TELLER EFFECT IN DYSPROSIUM ANTIMONIDE.
UFFER, L. F. LEVY, P. M. CHEN, H. H.
AIP (AMER. INST. PHYS.) CONF. PROC.
(10), (PT. 1), 553–7, 1973.

51136 A WALL PINNING MODEL FOR THE COERCIVE FORCE IN MULTIDOMAIN SINGLE CRYSTAL (RARE EARTH) COBALT ALLOYS.
SEARLE, C. W. FREDERICK, W. G. D.
GARRETT, H. J.
AIP (AMER. INST. PHYS.) CONF. PROC.
(10), (PT. 1), 573–7, 1973.

51137 MAGNETIC PHASE ANALYSIS OF RHENIUM COBALT INTERMETALLIC PERMANENT MAGNETIC MATERIALS.
MENTH, A. BACHMANN, K.
AIP (AMER. INST. PHYS.) CONF. PROC.
(10), (PT. 1), 578–81, 1973.

51138 MAGNETIC PROPERTIES OF SPUTTER DEPOSITED RARE EARTH–COBALT PERMANENT MAGNETS.
GARRETT, H. J. FREDERICK, W. G. D.
ALLEN, R. P.
AIP (AMER. INST. PHYS.) CONF. PROC.
(10), (PT. 1), 582, 1973.

51139 COBALT–SAMARIUM PERMANENT MAGNET ALLOYS: VARIATION OF LATTICE PARAMETERS WITH COMPOSITION AND TEMPERATURE.
MARTIN, D. L. BENZ, M. G. ROCKWOOD, A. C.
AIP (AMER. INST. PHYS.) CONF. PROC.
(10), (PT. 1), 583–7, 1973.

51140 DOMAIN WALL PINNING CENTERS, PARTICLE SIZE AND COERCIVITY DISTRIBUTIONS IN SAMARIUM COBALT INTERMETALLIC.
MCCURRIE, R. A.
AIP (AMER. INST. PHYS.) CONF. PROC.
(10), (PT. 1), 588–92, 1973.

51141 INTRINSIC MAGNETIC PROPERTIES AND MECHANISM OF MAGNETIZATION OF COBALT–IRON–COPPER–RARE EARTH PERMANENT MAGNETS.
NESBITT, E. A. CHIN, G. Y. HULL, G. W.
SHERWOOD, R. C. GREEN, M. L. WERNICK, J. H.
AIP (AMER. INST. PHYS.) CONF. PROC.
(10), (PT. 1), 593–7, 1973.

51143 MANUFACTURE OF RARE EARTH–COBALT MAGNETS.
WEIHRAUCH, P. F. PALADINO, A. E. DAS, D. K.
REID, W. R. LESENSKY, L. WETTSTEIN, E. C.
GALE, A. A.
AIP (AMER. INST. PHYS.) CONF. PROC.
(10), (PT. 1), 638–42, 1973.

51144 PRESENT UNDERSTANDING OF COERCIVITY IN COBALT–RARE EARTHS.
LIVINGSTON, J. D.
AIP (AMER. INST. PHYS.) CONF. PROC.
(10), (PT. 1), 643–57, 1973.

51145 THE MAGNETIC STRUCTURE OF RUBIDIUM MANGANESE BROMIDE.
GLINKA, C. J. MINKIEWICZ, V. J. COX, D. E.
KHATTAK, C. P.
AIP (AMER. INST. PHYS.) CONF. PROC.
(10), (PT. 1), 659–63, 1973.

51146 THE THREE DIMENSIONAL MAGNETIC STRUCTURE OF CESIUM NICKEL FLUORIDE.
STEINER, M. DACHS, H. BABEL, D.
AIP (AMER. INST. PHYS.) CONF. PROC.
(10), (PT. 1), 664–8, 1973.

51147 SPIRAL STRUCTURE OF BARIUM COBALT RHENIUM OXIDE.
KHATTAK, C. P. COX, D. E. WANG, F. F. Y.
AIP (AMER. INST. PHYS.) CONF. PROC.
(10), (PT. 1), 674–8, 1973.

51148 MAGNETIC ORDERING OF THE LINEAR CHAIN ANTIFERROMAGNET CESIUM MANGANESE BROMIDE.
EIBSCHUTZ, M. SHERWOOD, R. C. HSU, F. S. L.
COX, D. E.
AIP (AMER. INST. PHYS.) CONF. PROC .
(10), (PT. 1), 684–8, 1973.

51150 THE MAGNETIC AND METAL–INSULATOR TRANSITION IN THE MAGNELI PHASE VANADIUM OXIDE.
KACHI, S.
AIP (AMER. INST. PHYS.) CONF. PROC.
(10), (PT. 1), 714–22, 1973.

51151 THE PREPARATION AND MAGNETO–OPTICAL PROPERTIES OF HOT–PRESSINGS OF THE MAGNETIC SEMICONDUCTORS NONSTOICHIOMETRIC CADMIUM COBALT CHROMIUM SULFIDES.
COBURN, T. J. PEARLMAN, D. CARNALL, E., JR.
MOSER, F. LEE, T. H. LYU, S. L.
MARTIN, T. W.
AIP (AMER. INST. PHYS.) CONF. PROC.
(10), (PT. 1), 740–4, 1973.

51153 MAGNETOCRYSTALLINE ANISOTROPY IN CUBIC RARE EARTH–IRON INTERMETALLIC COMPOUNDS.
CLARK, A. E. BELSON, H. S. TAMAGAWA, N.
AIP (AMER. INST. PHYS.) CONF. PROC.
(10), (PT. 1), 749–53, 1973.

51158 THE ROLE OF DIPOLE–DIPOLE INTERACTIONS IN THE CRITICAL BEHAVIOR OF FERROMAGNETIC MATERIALS.
ARROTT, A. S. HEINRICH, B. NOAKES, J. E.
AIP (AMER. INST. PHYS.) CONF. PROC.
(10), (PT. 1), 822–6, 1973.

51159 METAMAGNETISM OF IRON CHLORIDE NEAR THE TRICRITICAL POINT.
KENAN, R. P. MILLS, R. E.
AIP (AMER. INST. PHYS.) CONF. PROC.
(10), (PT. 2), 875–9, 1973.

51162 SUSCEPTIBILITY OF THE FERROMAGNET GADOLINIUM NICKEL INTERMETALLIC.
HORN, P. M. PARKS, R. D.
AIP (AMER. INST. PHYS.) CONF. PROC.
(10), (PT. 2), 915, 1973.

51166 SUPERPARAMAGNETIC FERRITE PARTICLES PRODUCED BY MILLING.
BERKOWITZ, A. E. LAHUT, J. A.
AIP (AMER. INST. PHYS.) CONF. PROC.
(10), (PT. 2), 966–70, 1973.

51169 SINGLE CRYSTAL MANGANESE BISMUTH PLATELET BY VACUUM DEPOSITION.
HONDA, S. KONISHI, S. KUSUDA, T.
AIP (AMER. INST. PHYS.) CONF. PROC.
(10), (PT. 2), 986–9, 1973.

51172 ANISOTROPIC EXCHANGE EFFECTS IN THE OPTICAL SPECTRUM OF FERROMAGNETIC ERBIUM TRIPOSITIVE ION DOPED TERBIUM HYDROXIDE.
CONE, R. L. WOLF, W. P.
AIP (AMER. INST. PHYS.) CONF. PROC.
(10), (PT. 2), 1039–43, 1973.

51173 WEAK FERROMAGNETISM IN BISMUTH IRON OXIDE–NEODYMIUM IRON OXIDE SOLID SOLUTIONS.
WOOD, V. E. AUSTIN, A. E.
AIP (AMER. INST. PHYS.) CONF. PROC.
(10), (PT. 2), 1049–53, 1973.

51174 MAGNETIC PROPERTIES OF SOME RARE–EARTH GOLD COMPOUNDS.
SILL, L. R. SNOW, S. R. FEDRO, A. J.
AIP (AMER. INST. PHYS.) CONF. PROC.
(10), (PT. 2), 1060–4, 1973.

51175 MAGNETIC PROPERTIES OF YTTRIUM–THORIUM–IRON AND LUTETIUM–THORIUM–IRON ALLOYS.
KUNESH, C. J. NARASIMHAN, K. S. V. L.
BUTERA, R. A.
AIP (AMER. INST. PHYS.) CONF. PROC.
(10), (PT. 2), 1065–9, 1973.

51176 THEORY OF MAGNETIC PHASE TRANSITIONS IN METALLIC ACTINIDE COMPOUNDS.
ERDOS, P. ROBINSON, J. M.
AIP (AMER. INST. PHYS.) CONF. PROC.
(10), (PT. 2), 1070–4, 1973.

51177 PRESSURE INDUCED LOSS OF FERROMAGNETISM IN URAXIUM–PLATINUM.
HUBER, J. G. MAPLE, M. B. WOHLLEBEN, D.
AIP (AMER. INST. PHYS.) CONF. PROC.
(10), (PT. 2), 1075, 1973.

51178 LOW TEMPERATURE SPECIFIC HEAT AND MAGNETIC PROPERTIES OF RARE EARTH (LANTHANUM, CERIUM, PRASEODYMIUM, NEODYMIUM) INTERMETALLIC COMPOUNDS.
NARASIMHAN, K. S. V. L. RAO, V. U. S.
BUTERA, R. A.
AIP (AMER. INST. PHYS.) CONF. PROC.
(10), (PT. 2), 1081–5, 1973.

51182 ANOMALOUS MAGNETIC BEHAVIOR OF MANGANESE SILICIDE.
LEVINSON, L. M. LANDER, G. H.
STEINITZ, M. O.
AIP (AMER. INST. PHYS.) CONF. PROC.
(10), (PT. 2), 1138–42, 1973.

51183 MAGNETIC ORDERING IN NONSTOICHIOMETRIC LITHIUM CHROMIUM NICKEL OXIDE.
TAUBER, A. BANKS, E.
AIP (AMER. INST. PHYS.) CONF. PROC.
(10), (PT. 2), 1158–62, 1973.

51184 RARE EARTH INTERCALATION AND MAGNETIC PROPERTIES OF LAYER TYPE COMPOUNDS.
SUBBA RAO, G. V. SHAFER, M. W. TAO, L.
AIP (AMER. INST. PHYS.) CONF. PROC.
(10), (PT. 2), 1173–7, 1973.

51185 KRAMERS–KRONIG ANALYSIS AND MAGNETOREFLECTANCE OF EUROPIUM CHALCOGENIDES.
GUNTHERODT, G. WACHTER, P.
AIP (AMER. INST. PHYS.) CONF. PROC.
(10), (PT. 2), 1284–8, 1973.

51186 RECENT ADVANCEMENT IN THE FIELD OF HIGH FREQUENCY FERRITES.
SUGIMOTO, M.
AIP (AMER. INST. PHYS.) CONF. PROC.
(10), (PT. 2), 1335–49, 1973.

EPIC Number	Bibliographic Citation
51187	PRESSURE VARIATION OF THE CURIE TEMPERATURE AND SPONTANEOUS MAGNETIZATION IN IRON PHOSPHIDE AND NONSTOICHIOMETRIC IRON PHOSPHIDE ARSENIDE. GOODENOUGH, J. B. KAFALAS, J. A. DWIGHT, K. MENYUK, N. CATALANO, A. AIP (AMER. INST. PHYS.) CONF. PROC. (10), (PT. 2), 1355-9, 1973.
51189	FARADAY ROTATION AND OPTICAL ABSORPTION OF EPITAXIAL FILMS OF NONSTOICHIOMETRIC YTTRIUM BISMUTH IRON OXIDE. WITTEKOEK, S. ROBERTSON, J. M. POPMA, T. J. A. BONGERS, P. F. AIP (AMER. INST. PHYS.) CONF. PROC. (10), (PT. 2), 1418-22, 1973.
51190	MAGNETIC PROPERTIES AND CURIE-POINT WRITING IN EVAPORATED MANGANESE ALUMINUM GERMANIUM FILMS. AHN, K. Y. SAWATZKY, E. BROWN, B. R. AIP (AMER. INST. PHYS.) CONF. PROC. (10), (PT. 2), 1423-7, 1973.
51191	MAGNETIC AND MAGNETO-OPTICAL PROPERTIES OF SPUTTERED MANGANESE GALLIUM GERMANIUM FILMS. SAWATZKY, E. STREET, G. B. AIP (AMER. INST. PHYS.) CONF. PROC. (10), (PT. 2), 1428, 1973.
51192	MAGNETIC PROPERTIES OF THIN FILMS IN THE MANGANESE-GALLIUM-GERMANIUM SYSTEM. LEE, K. SUITS, J. C. AIP (AMER. INST. PHYS.) CONF. PROC. (10), (PT. 2), 1429-33, 1973.
51194	DIRECT MEASUREMENT OF CRYSTAL-FIELD SPLITTINGS IN PRASEODYMIUM NITROGEN. DAVIS, H. L. MOOK, H. A. AIP (AMER. INST. PHYS.) CONF. PROC. (10), (PT. 2), 1548-53, 1973.
51195	SUBLATTICE MAGNETIZATION AND THE EXCHANGE INTERACTION IN NONSTOICHIOMETRIC TERBIUM YTTRIUM ANTIMONIDE. CABLE, J. W. COMLY, J. B. COOPER, B. R. JACOBS, I. S. KOEHLER, W. C. VOGT, O. AIP (AMER. INST. PHYS.) CONF. PROC. (10), (PT. 2), 1554-8, 1973.
51196	CONTRIBUTIONS TO THE ANISOTROPY OF NICKEL DIPOSITIVE IONS IN TETRAHEDRAL SITES. POINTON, A. J. WETTON, G. A. AIP (AMER. INST. PHYS.) CONF. PROC. (10), (PT. 2), 1573-7, 1973.
51197	ANNEALING OF COBALT-FERROUS FERRITE FILMS ON GLASS SUBSTRATES IN THE REMANENT STATE. BORRELLI, N. F. CHEN, S. L. MURPHY, J. A. AIP (AMER. INST. PHYS.) CONF. PROC. (10), (PT. 2), 1588-92, 1973.
51198	CHARACTERIZATION OF THE GROWTH INDUCED ANISOTROPY IN A MIXED RARE EARTH IRON GARNET. DILLON, J. F., JR. BLOUNT, E. I. GYORGY, E. M. AIP (AMER. INST. PHYS.) CONF. PROC. (10), (PT. 2), 1593-7, 1973.
51199	STUDY OF THE SPIN REORIENTATION IN COBALT - AND CHROMIUM - SUBSTITUTED YTTRIUM IRON OXIDE. KREN, E. PARDAVI, M. POKO, Z. SVAB, E. ZSOLDOS, E. AIP (AMER. INST. PHYS.) CONF. PROC. (10), (PT. 2), 1603-6, 1973.
51200	MEASURING MAGNETOSTRICTION WITH ROTATING SAMPLE MAGNETOMETER AND ROTATING FIELD MAGNETOMETER. FLANDERS, P. J. AIP (AMER. INST. PHYS.) CONF. PROC. (10), (PT. 2), 1607-11, 1973.
51202	ANOMALIES IN THE MAGNETIC PROPERTIES OF NICKEL GALLIUM INTERMETALLIC ALLOYS. SCHINKEL, C. J. DE BOER, F. R. DE HON, B. AIP (AMER. INST. PHYS.) CONF. PROC. (10), (PT. 2), 1613-7, 1973.
51203	THE SPATIAL DISTRIBUTION OF THE MAGNETIZATION AROUND IRON IMPURITIES IN NICKEL GALLIUM INTERMETALLIC. CABLE, J. W. CHILD, H. R. AIP (AMER. INST. PHYS.) CONF. PROC. (10), (PT. 2), 1623-6, 1973.
51205	COOPERATIVE JAHN-TELLER EFFECTS IN MAGNETIC MATERIALS. GEHRING, K. A. AIP (AMER. INST. PHYS.) CONF. PROC. (10), (PT. 2), 1648-63, 1973.
51206	SINGLET-GROUND-STATE DYNAMICS. BIRGENEAU, R. J. AIP (AMER. INST. PHYS.) CONF. PROC. (10), (PT. 2), 1664-88, 1973.

EPIC Number	Bibliographic Citation
51208	ELECTRONIC BAND STRUCTURE OF POTASSIUM TANTALATE. EDMONDSON, D. R. SOLID STATE COMMUN. 12 (10), 981-4, 1973.
51209	MAGNETIC STRUCTURES AND MAGNETIC SUSCEPTIBILITIES OF TERBIUM OXYSULFIDE AND OXYSELENIDE. ABBAS, Y. ROSSAT-MIGNOD, J. QUEZEL, G. SOLID STATE COMMUN. 12 (10), 985-91, 1973.
51211	NEW METHOD OF CAUSING SENSITIZED LUMINESCENCE IN MANGANESE-ACTIVATED, CERIUM-SENSITIZED CALCIUM FLUORIDE PHOSPHORS. BANERJEE, H. D. RATNAM, V. V. SOLID STATE COMMUN. 12 (10), 1049-52, 1973.
51212	TWO-PHOTON INTERBAND MAGNETOABSORPTION IN INDIUM ANTIMONIDE. MANLIEF, S. K. PALIK, E. D. SOLID STATE COMMUN. 12 (10), 1071-5, 1973.
51213	RESISTIVITIES OF CERIUM-ALUMINUM AND LANTHANUM-ALUMINUM COMPOUNDS UNDER PRESSURE. PERCHERON, A. ACHARD, J. C. GOROCHOV, O. CORNUT, B. JEROME, D. COQBLIN, B. SOLID STATE COMMUN. 12 (12), 1289-94, 1973.
51216	TEMPERATURE DEPENDENCE OF THE FUNDAMENTAL ABSORPTION EDGE IN CADMIUM TELLURIDE. CAMASSEL, J. AUVERGNE, D. MATHIEU, H. TRIBOULET, R. MARFAING, Y. SOLID STATE COMMUN. 13 (1), 63-8, 1973.
51218	NEW STRUCTURES IN PHOTOELECTRIC SPECTRA OF LEAD TELLURIDE. ABBATI, I. BRAICOVICH, L. DE MICHELIS, B. SOLID STATE COMMUN. 13 (2), 137-40, 1973.
51219	MAGNETIC ORDER EFFECT ON OPTICAL ABSORPTION AND PHOTOCONDUCTIVITY IN EUROPIUM(II) OXIDE THIN FILMS. LLINARES, C. MONTEIL, E. BORDURE, G. PAPARODITIS SOLID STATE COMMUN. 13 (2), 205-8, 1973.
51220	ELECTROLUMINESCENCE FROM CADMIUM SULFIDE METAL-SEMICONDUCTOR, METAL-INSULATOR-SEMCONDUCTOR AND SEMICONDUCTOR-INSULATOR-SEMICONDUCTOR DEVICES. WHEELER, D. J. HANEMAN, D. SOLID-STATE ELECTRON. 16 (8), 875-82, 1973.
51221	AUTODOPING EFFECTS OF GERMANIUM IN VAPOR-GROWN GALLIUM ARSENIDE PHOSPHIDE LAYERS ON GERMANIUM SUBSTRATES. KASANO, H. SOLID-STATE ELECTRON. 16 (8), 913-20, 1973.
51224	MAGNETIC PROPERTIES OF PSEUDOBINARY INTERMETALLIC COMPOUNDS, CERIUM-METAL-ALUMINUM WHERE R IS GADOLINIUM, ERBIUM, OR TERBIUM. NICULESCU, V. POP, I. STUD. UNIV. BABES-BOLYAI, SER. PHYS. 18 (1), 35-9, 1973.
51225	ELECTRON EMISSION FROM ALUMINUM OXIDE IN CESIUM VAPOR. WILSON, R. G. SURFACE SCI. 38 (1), 261-4, 1973.
51228	PHOTOELECTRIC E M F (ELECTROMOTIVE FORCE) INDUCED BY Q-SWITCHED CARBON DIOXIDE LASER IN SEMICONDUCTORS. PANYAKEOW, S. MORISAKI, H. SHIRAFUJI, J. INUISHI, Y. TECHNOL. REP. OSAKA UNIV. 22 (1053-1089), 563-74, 1972.
51229	NATURE OF INTERNAL ELECTRIC FIELD DURING OPTICAL DAMAGE PROCESS IN LITHIUM NIOBATE(V). YASOJIMA, Y. OHMORI, Y. INUISHI, Y. TECHNOL. REP. OSAKA UNIV. 22 (1053-1089), 575-83, 1972.
51230	DIELECTRIC DISPERSION OF POTASSIUM CHLORIDE ICE. IV. DIELECTRIC DISPERSION OF LOW-CONCENTRATION ICE. MAENO, N. TEION KAGAKU, BUTSURI-HEN (30), 1-8, 1972.
51231	DIELECTRIC PROPERTIES OF SINGLE CRYSTALS OF ICE CONTAINING CHLORINE. MAENO, N. TEION KAGAKU, BUTSURI-HEN (30), 9-21, 1972.

EPIC Number	Bibliographic Citation

51232 **ELECTRON TRANSFER IN GROUP IV TRANSITION METAL DIBORIDES.**
KOVENSKAYA, B. A.
TEKHNOL. POLUCH. NOVYKH. MATER.
3-6, 1972.

51234 **EFFECT OF HEAT TREATMENT ON ELECTRICAL RESISTIVITY AND OPTICAL PROPERTIES OF INDIUM NITRIDE FILMS.**
ANDREEVA, A. F. ELISEEVA, O. I.
TEKHNOL. POLUCH. NOVYKH MATER.
251-4, 1972.

51237 **ELECTRICAL AND MAGNETIC PROPERTIES OF SAMARIUM HEXABORIDE.**
PADERNO, YU. B. KONOVALOVA, E. S.
NOVIKOV, V. I.
TEPLOFIZ. SVOISTVA VESHCHESTV PRI NIZH. TEMP.
130-4, 1972.

51249 **VARIATION OF THE MAGNETIC PROPERTIES OF SAMARIUM ALLOYS WITH TEMPERATURE.**
KAMINO, K. KIMURA, Y. SUZUKI, T.
ITAYAMA, Y.
TRANS. JAP. INST. METALS
14 (2), 135-9, 1973.

51252 **PHOTOCONDUCTIVITY MECHANISM IN MAGNETICALLY CONCENTRATED CRYSTALS.**
EREMENKO, V. V. KIRICHENKO, A. P.
RUBTSOV, V. N. SMIRNOV, V. S.
TR. FIZ.-TEKH. INST. NIZK. TEMP., AKAD. NAUK UKR. SSR
(16), 50-8, 1971.

51253 **MEASUREMENT OF A TRANSITION LINE WIDTH OF N O WITH AN H F LASER.**
NACHSHON, Y. COLEMAN, P. D.
APPL. OPT.
12 (12), 2810-11, 1973.

51254 **MEASUREMENT OF THIN FILM PARAMETERS WITH A PRISM COUPLER.**
ULRICH, R. TORGE, R.
APPL. OPT.
12 (12), 2901-8, 1973.

51258 **PHASE RELATIONS IN LEAD LANTHANUM ZIRCONIUM TITANATE.**
OBRYAN, H. M., JR.
J. AMER. CERAM. SOC.
56 (7), 385-8, 1973.

51259 **DISCUSSION OF EFFECTS OF GRAIN SIZE AND POROSITY ON ELECTRICAL AND OPTICAL PROPERTIES OF P L Z T CERAMICS.**
BRADLEY, F. N.
J. AMER. CERAM. SOC.
56 (7), 404, 1973.

51263 **OPTICAL PHENOMENA IN SEMICONDUCTORS DURING HEATING OF ELECTRON GAS.**
VOROBEV, L. E. KOMISSAROV, V. S.
STAFEEV, V. I. USHAKOV, A. YU.
SHTURBIN, A. V.
TR. SIMP. FIZ. PLAZMY ELEK. NEUSTOICHIVOSTYAM TVERD. TELAKH
200-6, 1972.

51265 **THERMAL CONDUCTIVITY OF SOME REFRACTORY CARBIDES AND BORIDES.**
LVOV, S. N. LESNAYA, M. I.
VINITSKII, I. M. NAUMENKO, V. YA.
TEPLOFIZ. VYS. TEMP.
10 (6), 1327-9, 1972.
(FOR ENGLISH TRANSLATION SEE E51266)

51266 **THERMAL CONDUCTIVITY OF SOME REFRACTORY CARBIDES AND BORIDES.**
LVOV, S. N. LESNAYA, M. I.
VINITSKII, I. M. NAUMENKO, V. YA.
HIGH TEMP.
10 (6), 1196-8, 1972.
(ENGLISH TRANSLATION OF TEPLOFIZ. VYS. TEMP., 10 (6), 1327-9, 1972; FOR ORIGINAL SEE E51265)

51267 **DIELECTRIC AND ELECTRIC PROPERTIES OF CALCIUM METATITANATE WITH A CHROMIUM ION IMPURITY.**
TOCHENAYA, A. G.
TR. MOSK. INST. ELEKTRON. MASHINOSTR.
(21), 75-9, 1972.

51268 **CRYSTAL STRUCTURE AND ELECTRICAL RESISTIVITY OF VACUUM-DEPOSITED CADMIUM TELLURIDE FILMS.**
HUNG, M. P. CHANG, Y. Y.
TSAI,LIAO KO HSUEH
4 (3), 163-76, 1973.

51269 **DIELECTRIC PROPERTIES OF AMORPHOUS FILMS OF ANTIMONY TRISELENIDE.**
FEDOSEEVA, N. V.
UCH. ZAP., GORK. UNIV.
(148), 83-7, 1972.

51271 **HIGH-TEMPERATURE STUDIES OF STEADY-STATE AND NON-EQUILIBRIUM ELECTRICAL CONDUCTIVITY OF CADMIUM SULFIDE CRYSTALS.**
RUD, YU. V. SANIN, K. V.
UKR. FIZ. ZH. (RUSS. ED.)
18 (4), 615-20, 1973.

51272 **OPTICAL CONSTANTS OF CADMIUM AND MERCURY TELLURIDES IN THE INTRINSIC ABSORPTION RANGE.**
ODARICH, V. A.
UKR. FIZ. ZH. (RUSS. ED.)
18 (4), 656-8, 1973.

51273 **SUPERCONDUCTIVITY OF SOME TRANSITION METAL-BERYLLIUM COMPOUNDS.**
MATYUSHENKO, N. N. MATSAKOVA, A. A.
PUGACHEV, N. S.
UKR. FIZ. ZH. (RUSS. ED.)
18 (4), 672-5, 1973.

51275 **LUMINESCENCE OF CADMIUM SULFIDE SINGLE CRYSTALS DOPED WITH DIFFERENT DONORS AND ACCEPTORS.**
ERMOLOVICH, I. B. MATVIEVSKAYA, G. I.
PEKAR, G. S. SHEINKMAN, M. K.
UKR. FIZ. ZH. (RUSS. ED.)
18 (5), 732-41, 1973.

51276 **EFFECT OF RADIATION DEFECTS ON RADICAL-RECOMBINATION LUMINESCENCE.**
BAZHIN, A. I. BRIK, O. G.
UKR. FIZ. ZH. (RUSS. ED.)
18 (5), 793-6, 1973.

51278 **EFFECT OF A SURFACE STATE ON REFLECTION AND LUMINESCENCE SPECTRA OF CADMIUM SULFIDE CRYSTALS.**
BRODIN, M. S. KRITSKII, A. V.
MYASNIKOV, E. N. STRASHNIKOVA, M. I.
SHLYAKHOVA, L. A.
UKR. FIZ. ZH. (RUSS. ED.)
18 (5), 828-34, 1973.

51279 **EFFECT OF A COPPER IMPURITY ON PHOTOCONDUCTIVITY AND PHOTOLUMINESCENCE OF CADMIUM SELENIDE TELLURIDE SOLID SOLUTIONS.**
DANIYAROV, O. OLEINIK, G. S.
UKR. FIZ. ZH. (RUSS. ED.)
18 (5), 852-4, 1973.

51280 **MEASUREMENT OF SMALL COEFFICIENTS OF ELECTROMECHANICAL COUPLING.**
ZHABITENKO, N. K. KUCHEROV, I. YA.
UKR. FIZ. ZH. (RUSS. ED.)
18 (5), 864-6, 1973.

51281 **CONDUCTION-BAND STRUCTURE IN MERCURY SELENIDE AND MERCURY SELENIDE-MERCURY SULFIDE SOLID SOLUTIONS.**
VOLZHENSKAYA, L. G. KREVS, V. E.
PASHKOVSKII, M. V.
UKR. FIZ. ZH. (RUSS. ED.)
18 (5), 935-9, 1973.

51283 **DEFECTS GENERATED BY X-RAY EMISSION IN POTASSIUM CHLORIDE CRYSTALS.**
GORBENKO, P. K. KOVTUN, A. A. EZHOV, N. M.
TELYATNIK, A. I.
UKR. FIZ. ZH. (RUSS. ED.)
18 (7), 1069-74, 1973.

51284 **PARAMETERS AFFECTING THE RESISTIVITY OF VAPOR DEPOSITED CADMIUM SULFIDE FILMS.**
DOUCAS, G.
VACUUM
22 (12), 651-2, 1972.

51286 **RELATION BETWEEN THE DIELECTRIC CONSTANT AND SPONTANEOUS MAGNETIZATION IN COBALT CHROMITE FERRITES.**
DAMILKEVICH, M. I. LITVINOVICH, G. V.
VESTN. BELORUSS. UNIV.
1 (3), 56-9, 1973.

51289 **PULSED PERMEABILITY OF SOME FERRITES IN THE REGION OF STRONG FIELDS.**
SUKHAREVSKII, V. G. GRISHIN, V. K.
VORONOV, V. A.
VESTN. MOSK. UNIV., FIZ., ASTRON.
14 (2), 237-9, 1973.

51291 **DIELECTRIC PROPERTIES OF LEAD ZIRCONATE DOPED WITH BISMUTH OZIDE.**
LEVINA, M. E. KOLBENOVA, G. I.
TRETYAKOV, YU. D.
VESTN. MOSK. UNIV., KHIM.
14 (2), 187-90, 1973.

51292 **IMPURITY RECOMBINATION RADIATION IN ALUMINUM ANTIMONIDE.**
SIROTA, N. N. LUKOMSKII, A. I.
VESTSI. AKAD. NAVUK BELARUS. SSR, SER. FIZ.-MAT. NAVUK
(2), 122-4, 1973.

51294 **APPLICATION OF SILICIDES AS ANTIEMISSION MATERIALS.**
SCHNEIDER, P.
VIDE
27 (162), 254-9, 1973.

EPIC Number | Bibliographic Citation

51295 CHEMICAL-THERMOLUMINESCENCE OF CALCIUM CARBONATES.
MOROZOV, G. V.
VOP. GEOL. OSAD. OTLOZH. UKR.
220-3, 1972.

51297 LUMINESCENCE EXCITATION SPECTRA OF EUROPIUM ACTIVATED ALKALINE EARTH SULFATES AT 6-40 EV.
IVANOV, L. N. MIKHAILIN, V. V.
OREKHANOV, P. A.
VSES. KONF. SPEKTROSK. VAKUUM. ULTRAFIOLETA VZAIMODEISTVIYU IZLUCH. VESHCHESTVOM 3RD
123-5, 1972.

51298 OPTICAL PROPERTIES OF POLYCRYSTALLINE SILICON DIOXIDE LAYERS IN THE 30-200 NM SPECTRAL REGION AND QUARTZ BAND STRUCTURE.
SOROKIN, O. M. BLANK, V. A. LEBEDEVA, G. A.
VSES. KONF. SPEKTROSK. VAKUUM. ULTRAFIOLETA VZAIMODEISTVIYU IZLUCH. VESHCHESTVOM, 3RD
181-3, 1972.

51304 DIELECTRIC PROPERTIES.
POTTEL, R.
WATER: COMPR. TREATISE
3, 401-55, 1973.

51305 TWO TYPES OF LUMINESCENCE CENTERS IN ALKALI HALIDE PHOSPHORS AND FEATURES IN THEIR EXCITATION PROCESES.
SHAMOVSKII, L. M.
ZAKONOMER. RASPREDEL. PRIMESNYKH TSENTROV IONNYKH KRIST.
(2), 7-21, 1971.

51306 LUMINESCENCE OF A THALLIUM-ACTIVATED CESIUM IODIDE PHOSPHOR AS A FUNCTION OF ACTIVATOR CONCENTRATION AND THE EXCITATION PROCESS.
GUTAN, V. B. SHAMOVSKII, L. M.
ZAKONOMER. RASPREDEL. PRIMESNYKH TSENTROV IONNYKH KRIST.
(2), 43-50, 1971.

51307 ELECTRICAL CONDUCTIVITY OF NIOBIUM OXIDE AND NIOBIUM TITANIUM OXIDE.
SAKATA, T. FROMM, E.
Z. ANORG. ALLG. CHEM.
398 (2), 129-35, 1973.

51313 MAGNETIC PROPERTIES OF COMPOUNDS OF RARE EARTH METALS AND IRON OF THE R FE(3) TYPE, WHERE R IS YTTRIUM, DYSPROSIUM, HOLMIUM, AND ERBIUM.
BELOV, K. P. NIKITIN, S. A. BISLIEV, A. M.
SAVITSKII, E. M. TEREKHOVA, V. F.
KOLESNICHENKO, V. E.
ZH. EKSP. TEOR. FIZ.
64 (6), 2154-9, 1973.
(FOR ENGLISH TRANSLATION SEE E62170)

51314 OPTICAL ORIENTATION OF EXCITONS IN UNIAXIAL CRYSTALS. LARGE EXCHANGE SPLITTING.
BIR, G. L. PIKUS, G. E.
ZH. EKSP. TEOR. FIZ.
64 (6), 2210-21, 1973.
(FOR ENGLISH TRANSLATION SEE E62171)

51315 CHANGE IN THE EFFECTIVE MOBILITY OF CURRENT CARRIERS IN LAYERS OF POLYCRYSTALLINE ZINC OXIDE UNDER AN ELECTRICAL POTENTIAL.
POVKHAN, T. I.
ZH. NAUCH. PRIKL. FOTOGR. KINEMATOGR.
18 (3), 207-8, 1973.

51316 X-RAY-ELECTRON SPECTRA OF COBALT(II) COMPOUNDS.
NEFEDOV, V. I. BARANOVSKII, I. B.
MOLODKIN, A. K. OMURALIEVA, U. O.
ZH. NEORG. KHIM.
18 (5), 1295-7, 1973.
(FOR ENGLISH TRANSLATION SEE E55171)

51317 ELECTRICAL CONDUCTIVITY OF URANIUM BETA-DIOXIDE MODIFIED BY MAGNESIUM OXIDE, STRONTIUM OXIDE, AND NIOBIUM PENTOXIDE ADDITIVES.
VLASOV, V. G. PIS'MENKO, V. T.
ULYASHEV, S. P. SHALAGINOV, V. N.
BEKETOV, A. R.
ZH. PRIKL. KHIM. (LENINGRAD)
46 (1), 36-40, 1973.
(FOR ENGLISH TRANSLATION SEE E55347)

51319 CALCULATION OF THE PRINCIPAL VALUE OF THE REFRACTIVE INDEX OF AN IODIC ACID CRYSTAL.
POLKOVNIKOV, B. F.
ZH. PRIKL. SPEKTROSK.
18 (4), 741-2, 1973.
(FOR ENGLISH TRANSLATION SEE E89717)

51320 EFFECT OF CERIUM ON THE LUMINESCENCE OF LANTHANIDES IN MATRIXES ACTIVATED BY THE PRESENCE OF OXYGEN.
BREGEDA, I. D.
ZH. PRIKL. SPEKTROSK.
18 (5), 839-42, 1973.

51322 PHOTOLUMINESCENCE SPECTRA OF ZIRCONIUM DIOXIDE POWDERS.
MOCHNIAK, J.
ZH. PRIKL. SPEKTROSK.
18 (5), 917-19, 1973.

51324 EXCITATION OF DIVALENT RARE-EARTH ION LUMINESCENCE IN CALCIUM FLUORIDE CRYSTALS BY RUBY AND NEODYMIUM LASERS.
GINTOFT, R. I.
ZH. PRIKL. SPEKTROSK.
18 (6), 1060-2, 1973.

51325 POSITION OF THE SELF-ABSORPTION EDGE OF SOLUTIONS OF FERROELECTRIC CRYSTALS.
NETESOVA, N. P. RUBLEV, V. V.
ZH. PRIKL. SPEKTROSK.
18 (6), 1074-6, 1973.

51326 LUMINESCENCE SPECTRA AND STRUCTURE OF EUROPIUM NITRATE CRYSTAL HYDRATES.
ZOLIN, V. F. POPOV, A. P. SAMOKHINA, M. A.
TSARYUK, V. I.
ZH. PRIKL. SPEKTROSK.
19 (1), 74-7, 1973.

51327 RADIATION SPECTRA OF COPPER-ACTIVATED ZINC SULFIDE SINGLE CRYSTALS.
NEMCHENKO, A. M.
ZH. PRIKL. SPEKTROSK.
19 (1), 134-9, 1973.

51329 INTERPRETATION OF INFRARED AND LUMINESCENCE SPECTRA OF EUROPIUM AND URANYL NITRATES.
BABICH, YA. I. GUREV, K. I. ZOLIN, V. F.
KOVNER, M. A. FISHER, P. S. TSARYUK, V. I.
ZH. PRIKL. SPEKTROSK.
19 (1), 158, 1973.

51330 CHEMICAL SHIFT IN THE K-LEVEL IN PHOTOELECTRONIC SPECTRA.
MAZALOV, L. N. SADOVSKII, A. P.
MURAKHTANOV, V. V. GUZHAVINA, T. I.
ZH. STRUKT. KHIM.
13 (3), 477-82, 1973.
(FOR ENGLISH TRANSLATION SEE E64877)

51333 THERMOELECTRONIC EMISSION OF SOME CATHODIC MATERIALS.
GORDON, V. G. KULVARSKAYA, B. S.
LEVINOV, B. M. REKOV, A. I.
SPIRIDONOV, E. G.
ZH. TEKH. FIZ.
43 (5), 1000-3, 1973.
(FOR ENGLISH TRANSLATION SEE E54126)

51338 HALL EFFECT OF PURE AND COPPER-DOPED ZINC OXIDE CRYSTALS.
HAUSMANN, A. TEUERLE, W.
Z. PHYS.
259 (2), 189-94, 1973.

51345 USE OF THE HALL EFFECT FOR STUDYING THE CHEMISORPTION OF ATOMIC AND MOLECULAR OXYGEN ON OXIDE SEMICONDUCTORS.
AGAYAN, B. S. MYASNIKOV, I. A.
TSIVENKO, V. I.
ZH. FIZ. KHIM.
47 (4), 980-3, 1973.
(FOR ENGLISH TRANSLATION SEE E53848)

51346 EFFECT OF CADMIUM IMPURITIES ON THE ELECTRICAL CONDUCTIVITY AND THERMOELECTROMOTIVE FORCE OF THALLIUM TELLURIDE IN A LIQUID STATE.
KAZANDZHAN, B. I. TSURIKOV, A. A.
ZH. FIZ. KHIM.
47 (4), 1002-4, 1973.
(FOR ENGLISH TRANSLATION SEE E59208)

51347 ELECTRICAL CONDUCTANCE OF MELTS IN SODIUM HEXAFLUOROALUMINATE-SODIUM CHLORIDE AND SODIUM HEXAFLUOROALUMINATE-BARIUM CHLORIDE SYSTEMS.
KUVAKIN, M. A. EVSTIFEEV, E. N.
ISPOLIN, V. A. TALANOVA, L. P.
ZH. FIZ. KHIM.
47 (4), 1036, 1973.
(FOR ENGLISH TRANSLATION SEE E55345)

51348 AMMONIA CONDUCTIVITY NEAR THE TRIPLE POINT.
LEONIDOVA, G. G. POLANDOV, I. N.
ZH. FIZ. KHIM.
47 (5), 1261, 1973.
(FOR ENGLISH TRANSLATION SEE E57487)

51349 MAGNETIC BALANCE FOR MEASURING THE MAGNETIC SUSCEPTIBILITY OF WEAKLY MAGNETIC SUBSTANCES.
OZERETSKOVSKII, I. N. PCHELKIN, V. A.
LUKYANOV, V. F.
ZH. FIZ. KHIM.
47 (5), 1324-6, 1973.
(FOR ENGLISH TRANSLATION SEE E55170)

51350 TRIGONAL FLUORINE CENTERS FORMED BY ERBIUM IONS IN FLUORITE-TYPE SINGLE CRYSTALS.
AIZENBERG, I. B. DAVYDOVA, M. P.
MALKIN, B. Z. SMIRNOV, A. I. STOLOV, A. L.
FIZ. TVERD. TELA, (LENINGRAD)
15 (5), 1345-52, 1973.
(FOR ENGLISH TRANSLATION SEE E51351)

EPIC Number | Bibliographic Citation

51351 TRIGONAL FLUORINE CENTERS FORMED BY ERBIUM IONS IN FLUORITE-TYPE SINGLE CRYSTALS.
AIZENBERG, I. B. DAVYDOVA, M. P.
MALKIN, B. Z. SMIRNOV, A. I. STOLOV, A. L.
SOV. PHYS. - SOLID STATE
15 (5), 914–8, 1973.
(ENGLISH TRANSLATION OF FIZ. TVERD. TELA, (LENINGRAD) 15 (5), 1345–52, 1973; FOR ORIGINAL SEE E51350)

51356 ANISOTROPY OF A NONLINEAR REFRACTIVE INDEX IN GADOLINIUM AND TERBIUM MOLYBDATE SINGLE CRYSTALS.
SHALDIN, YU. V. BELOGUROV, D. A.
PROKHORTSEVA, T. M.
FIZ. TVERD. TELA (LENINGRAD)
15 (5), 1383–7, 1973.
(FOR ENGLISH TRANSLATION SEE E51357)

51357 ANISOTROPY OF THE NONLINEAR REFRACTIVE INDEX OF OF SINGLE CRYSTALS OF GADOLINIUM AND TERBIUM MOLYBDATES.
SHALDIN, YU. V. BELOGUROV, D. A.
PROKHORTSEVA, T. M.
SOV. PHYS. - SOLID STATE
15 (5), 936–8, 1973.
(ENGLISH TRANSLATION OF FIZ. TVERD. TELA, (LENINGRAD) 15 (5), 1383–7, 1973; FOR ORIGINAL SEE E51356)

51358 ISOTOPIC EFFECT IN RUBIDIUM HYDROGEN PHOSPHATE CRYSTALS.
STRUKOV, B. A. BADDUR, A. ZINENKO, V. N.
MISHCHENKO, A. V. KOPTSIK, V. A.
FIZ. TVERD. TELA (LENINGRAD)
15 (5), 1388–94, 1973.
(FOR ENGLISH TRANSLATION SEE E51359)

51359 ISOTOPIC EFFECT IN RUBIDIUM HYDROGEN PHOSPHATE CRYSTALS.
STRUKOV, B. A. BADDUR, A. ZINENKO, V. N.
MISHCHENKO, A. V. KOPTSIK, V. A.
SOV. PHYS. - SOLID STATE
15 (5), 939–42, 1973.
(ENGLISH TRANSLATION OF FIZ. TVERD. TELA (LENINGRAD) 15 (5), 1388–94, 1973; FOR ORIGINAL SEE E 51358)

51360 THERMODYNAMIC EXAMINATION OF THE PROPERTIES OF FERROELECTRICS WITH A TETRAGONAL POTASSIUM-TUNGSTEN BRONZE-TYPE STRUCTURE.
ISUPOV, V. A.
FIZ. TVERD. TELA (LENINGRAD)
15 (5), 1404–9, 1973.
(FOR ENGLISH TRANSLATION SEE E51361)

51361 THERMODYNAMIC PROPERTIES OF FERROELECTRICS HAVING A POTASSIUM-TUNGSTEN-BRONZE-TYPE TETRAGONAL STRUCTURE.
ISUPOV, V. A.
SOV. PHYS. - SOLID STATE
15 (5), 949–52, 1973.
(ENGLISH TRANSLATION OF FIZ. TVERD. TELA (LENINGRAD) 15 (5), 1404–9, 1973; FOR ORIGINAL SE E51360)

51364 TWO-STATE DRAG OF ELECTRONS BY PHONONS AND EXPONENTIALLY HIGH THERMOELECTRIC POWER.
KOZLOV, V. A. LIDORENKO, N. S.
NAGAEV, E. L.
FIZ. TVERD. TELA (LENINGRAD)
15 (5), 1458–67, 1973.
(FOR ENGLISH TRANSLATION SEE E51365)

51365 TWO-STATE DRAG OF ELECTRONS BY PHONONS AND EXPONENTIALLY HIGH THERMOELECTRIC POWER.
KOZLOV, V. A. LIDORENKO, N. S.
NAGAEV, E. L.
SOV. PHYS. - SOLID STATE
15 (5), 982–7, 1973.
(ENGLISH TRANSLATION OF FIZ. TVERD. TELA (LENINGRAD) 15 (5), 1458–67, 1973; FOR ORIGINAL SEE E51364)

51366 DIELECTRIC SPECTRUM OF LITHIUM NIOBATE.
POPLAVKO, YU. M. MERIAKRI, V. V.
ALESHECHKIN, V. N. TSYKALOV, V. G.
USHATKIN, E. F. KNYAZEV, A. S.
FIZ. TVERD. TELA (LENINGRAD)
15 (5), 1473–6, 1973.
(FOR ENGLISH TRANSLATION SEE E51367)

51367 PERMITTIVITY SPECTRUM OF LITHIUM NIOBATE.
POPLAVKO, YU. M. MERIAKRI, V. V.
ALESHECHKIN, V. N. TSYKALOV, V. G.
USHATKIN, E. F. KNYAZEV, A. S.
SOV. PHYS. - SOLID STATE
15 (5), 991–2, 1973.
(ENGLISH TRANSLATION OF FIZ. TVERD. TELA (LENINGRAD) 15 (5), 1473–6, 1973; FOR ORIGINAL SEE E51366)

51368 MAGNETIC PHASE DIAGRAM OF SOLID SOLUTIONS IN THE (VANADIUM CHROMIUM) DIOXIDE SYSTEM.
NOVIKOV, V. N. TALLERCHIK, B. A.
SHUSTROV, B. A.
FIZ. TVERD. TELA (LENINGRAD)
15 (5), 1477–80, 1973.
(FOR ENGLISH TRANSLATION SEE E51369)

51369 MAGNETIC PHASE DIAGRAM OF SOLID SOLUTIONS IN THE (VANADIUM CHROMIUM) DIOXIDE SYSTEM.
NOVIKOV, V. N. TALLERCHIK, B. A.
SHUSTROV, B. A.
SOV. PHYS. - SOLID STATE
15 (5), 993–5, 1973.
(ENGLISH TRANSLATION OF FIZ. TVERD. TELA (LENINGRAD) 15 (5), 1477–80, 1973; FOR ORIGINAL SEE E51368)

51370 THERMIONIC EMISSION OF ALKALINE EARTH METAL OXIDES WITH HIGH DENSITY OF LOCAL STATES ON THE CRYSTAL SURFACE.
NIKONOV, B. P.
FIZ. TVERD. TELA (LENINGRAD)
15 (5), 1481–8, 1973.
(FOR ENGLISH TRANSLATION SEE E51371)

51371 THERMIONIC EMISSION OF ALKALINE-EARTH METAL OXIDES WITH HIGH DENSITIES OF LOCALIZED STATES AT THE CRYSTAL SURFACE.
NIKONOV, B. P.
SOV. PHYS. - SOLID STATE
15 (5), 996–1000, 1973.
(ENGLISH TRANSLATION OF FIZ. TVERD. TELA (LENINGRAD) 15 (5), 1481–8, 1973; FOR ORIGINAL SEE E51370)

51372 CREATION OF ELECTRONS AND HOLES BY MICROWAVE FIELDS IN SEMIMETALS SIMILAR TO BISMUTH.
BEINIKHES, I. L. KOGAN, SH. M.
FIZ. TVERD. TELA (LENINGRAD)
15 (5), 1489–93, 1973.
(FSOR ENGLISH TRANSLATION SEE E51373)

51373 CREATION OF ELECTRONS AND HOLES BY MICROWAVE FIELDS IN SEMIMETALS SIMILAR TO BISMUTH.
BEINIKHES, I. L. KOGAN, SH. M.
SOV. PHYS. - SOLID STATE
15 (5), 1001–3, 1973.
(ENGLISH TRANSLATION OF FIZ. TVERD. TELA (LENINGRAD) 15 (5), 1489–93, 1973; FOR ORIGINAL SEE E51372)

51376 BINDING ENERGY OF INDIRECT EXCITONS IN CRYSTALS OF THE DIAMOND AND SPHALERITE TYPES.
ZUBKOVA, S. M. TOLPYGO, K. B.
FIZ. TVERD. TELA (LENINGRAD)
15 (5), 1516–9, 1973.
(FOR ENGLISH TRANSLATION SEE E51377)

51377 BINDING ENERGY OF INDIRECT EXCITONS IN CRYSTALS OF THE DIAMOND AND SPHALERITE TYPES.
SUBKOVA, S. M. TOLPYGO, K. .B.
SOV. PHYS. - SOLID STATE
15 (5), 1017–8, 1973.
(ENGLISH TRANSLATION OF FIZ. TVERD. TELA (LENINGRAD) 15 (5), 1516–9, 1973; FOR ORIGINAL SEE E51376)

51378 TRANSITION RADIATION AND OPTICAL PROPERTIES OF SUBSTANCES IN THE VACUUM ULTRAVIOLET REGION.
ISPIRYAN, K. A. KAZANDZHYAN, S. T.
FIZ. TVERD. TELA (LENINGRAD)
15 (5), 1551–5, 1973.
(FOR ENGLISH TRANSLATION SEE E51379)

51379 TRANSITION RADIATION AND OPTICAL PROPERTIES OF SUBSTANCES IN THE VACUUM ULTRAVIOLET REGION.
ISPIRYAN, K. A. KAZANDZHYAN, S. T.
SOV. PHYS. - SOLID STATE
15 (5), 1039–41, 1973.
(ENGLISH TRANSLATION OF FIZ. TVERD. TELA (LENINGRAD) 15 (5), 1551–5, 1973; FOR ORIGINAL SEE E51378)

51380 PHOTON MULTIPLICATION IN POTASSIUM CHLORIDE AND SODIUM CHLORIDE CRYSTALS.
IVANOV, S. N. ILMAS, E. R.
LUSHCHIK, CH. B. MIKHAILIN, V. V.
FIZ. TVERD. TELA (LENINGRAD)
15 (5), 1574–8, 1973.
(FOR ENGLISH TRANSLATION SEE E51381)

51381 PHOTON MULTIPLICATION IN POTASSIUM CHLORIDE AND SODIUM CHLORIDE CRYSTALS.
IVANOV, S. N. ILMAS, E. R.
LUSHCHIK, CH. B. MIKHAILIN, V. V.
SOV. PHYS. - SOLID STATE
15 (5), 1053–5, 1973.
(ENGLISH TRANSLATION OF FIZ. TVERD. TELA (LENINGRAD) 15 (5), 1574–8, 1973; FOR ORIGINAL SEE E51380)

EPIC Number | Bibliographic Citation

51384 **EFFECT OF TEMPERATURE AND CONDUCTIVITY ON THE ELASTIC AND PIEZOELECTRIC PROPERTIES OF CADMIUM SELENIDE WITH WURTZITE STRUCTURE.**
TOKAREV, E. F. PADO, G. S.
CHERNOZATONSKII, L. A. DRACHEV, V. V.
FIZ. TVERD. TELA (LENINGRAD)
15 (5), 1593–5, 1973.
(FOR ENGLISH TRANSLATION SEE E51385)

51385 **INFLUENCE OF TEMPERATURE AND CONDUCTIVITY ON THE ELASTIC AND PIEZOELECTRIC PROPERTIES OF CADMIUM SELENIDE WITH THE WURTZITE STRUCTURE.**
TOKAREV, E. F. PADO, G. S.
CHERNOZATONSKII, L. A. DRACHEV, V. V.
SOV. PHYS. - SOLID STATE
15 (5), 1064–5, 1973.
(ENGLISH TRANSLATION OF FIZ. TVERD. TELA (LENINGRAD) 15 (5), 1593–5, 1973; FOR ORIGINAL SEE E51384)

51386 **INFLUENCE OF THE DEGREE OF IMPERFECTION OF SUBSTRATES ON THE STRUCTURE OF EPITAXIAL FILMS OF GALLIUM ARSENIDE.**
KUZNETSOV, YU. N. MARKOVA, T. I.
OLKHOVIKOVA, T. I. KHASHIMOV, F. R.
FIZ. TVERD. TELA (LENINGRAD)
15 (5), 1597–9, 1973.
(FOR ENGLISH TRANSLATION SEE E51387)

51387 **INFLUENCE OF THE DEGREE OF IMPERFECTION OF SUBSTRATES ON THE STRUCTURE OF EPITAXIAL FILMS OF GALLIUM ARSENIDE.**
KUZNETSOV, YU. N. MARKOVA, T. I.
OLKHOVIKOVA, T. I. KHASHIMOV, F. R.
SOV. PHYS. - SOLID STATE
15 (5), 1067–8, 1973.
(ENGLISH TRANSLATION OF FIZ. TVERD. TELA (LENINGRAD) 15 (5), 1597–9, 1973; FOR ORIGINAL SE E51386)

51390 **CHANGE IN THE HALL CONSTANT SIGN IN A HIGH ELECTRICAL FIELD.**
MAZUR, M. M. MUKHORTOV, YU. P.
PUSTOVOIT, V. I.
FIZ. TVERD. TELA (LENINGRAD)
15 (5), 1601–3, 1973.
(FOR ENGLISH TRANSLATION SEE E51391)

51391 **CHANGE IN THE SIGN OF THE HALL COEFFICIENT IN STRONG ELECTRIC FIELDS.**
MAZUR, M. M. MUKHORTOV, YU. P.
PUSTOVOIT, V. I.
SOV. PHYS. - SOLID STATE
15 (5), 1071–2, 1973.
(ENGLISH TRANSLATION OF FIZ. TVERD. TELA (LENINGRAD) 15 (5), 1601–3, 1973; FOR ORIGINAL SE E51390)

51392 **CYLINDRICAL MAGNETIC DOMAINS IN SINGLE CRYSTALS OF NONCUBIC BISMUTH–CALCIUM–VANADIUM IRON GARNETS.**
YAKOVLEV, YU. M. FILONICH, V. S.
KLYUCHNIKOV, M. M. SAPOZHNIKOV, YU. L.
FIZ. TVERD. TELA (LENINGRAD)
15 (5), 1607–9, 1973.
(FOR ENGLISH TRANSLATION SEE E51393)

51393 **CYLINDRICAL MAGNETIC DOMAINS IN SINGLE CRYSTALS OF NONCUBIC BISMUTH–CALCIUM–VANADIUM IRON GARNETS.**
YAKOVLEV, YU. M. FILONICH, V. S.
KLYUCHNIKOV, M. M. SAPOZHNIKOV, YU. L.
SOV. PHYS. - SOLID STATE
15 (5), 1077–8, 1973.
(ENGLISH TRANSLATION OF FIZ. TVERD. TELA (LENINGRAD) 15 (5), 1607–9, 1973; FOR ORIGINAL SEE E51392)

51394 **MAGNETIC STRUCTURE OF LANTHANUM ORTHOVANADATE.**
ZUBKOV, V. G. BAZUEV, G. V.
PERELYAEV, V. A. SHVEIKIN, G. P.
FIZ. TVERD. TELA (LENINGRAD)
15 (5), 1610–12, 1973.
(FOR ENGLISH TRANSLATION SEE E51395)

51395 **MAGNETIC STRUCTURE OF LANTHANUM ORTHOVANADATE.**
ZUBKOV, V. G. BAZUEV, G. V.
PERELYAEV, V. A. SHVEIKIN, G. P.
SOV. PHYS. - SOLID STATE
15 (5), 1079–80, 1973.
(ENGLISH TRANSLATION OF FIZ. TVERD. TELA (LENINGRAD) 15 (5), 1610–12, 1973; FOR ORIGINAL SEE E51394)

51398 **DIFFERENTIAL LUMINESCENCE SPECTRUM.**
BUDYANSKII, V. I. LEPSVERIDZE, D. S.
SALKOV, E. A. SHEPELSKII, G. A.
FIZ. TVERD. TELA (LENINGRAD)
15 (5), 1620–1, 1973.
(FOR ENGLISH TRANSLATION SEE E51399)

51399 **DIFFERENTIAL LUMINESCENCE SPECTRA.**
BUDYANSKII, V. I. LEPSVERIDZE, D. S.
SALKOV, E. A. SHEPELSKII, G. A.
SOV. PHYS. - SOLID STATE
15 (5), 1088–9, 1973.
(ENGLISH TRANSLATION OF FIZ. TVERD. TELA (LENINGRAD) 15 (5), 1620–1, 1973; FOR ORIGINAL SEE E51398)

51400 **STRUCTURE OF THE IMPURITY ABSORPTION IN N–TYPE ALPHA SILICON CARBIDE.**
KOLESNIKOV, A. A. MAKAROV, E. A. GUK, G. N.
FIZ. TVERD. TELA (LENINGRAD)
15 (5), 1640, 1973.
(FOR ENGLISH TRANSLATION SEE E51401)

51401 **STRUCTURE OF THE IMPURITY ABSORPTION IN N–TYPE ALPHA SILICON CARBIDE.**
KOLESNIKOV, A. A. MAKAROV, E. A. GUK, G. N.
SOV. PHYS. - SOLID STATE
15 (5), 1105, 1973.
(ENGLISH TRANSLATION OF FIZ. TVERD. TELA (LENINGRAD) 15 (5), 1640, 1973; FOR ORIGINAL SEE E51400)

51406 **HALL EFFECT IN TELLURIUM–SELENIUM, ARSENIC TELLURIDE–ARSENIC SELENIDE, AND INDIUM–TELLURIUM MELTS.**
ANDREEV, A. A. TURGUNOV, T.
FIZ. TVERD. TELA (LENINGRAD)
15 (5), 1645–6, 1973.
(FOR ENGLISH TRANSLATION SEE EPIC E51407)

51407 **HALL EFFECT IN MOLTEN TELLURIUM–SELENIUM, ARSENIC TELLURIDE–ARSENIC SELENIDE, AND INDIUM–TELLURIUM SYSTEMS.**
ANDREEV, A. A. TURGUNOV, T.
SOV. PHYS. - SOLID STATE
15 (5), 1109, 1973.
(ENGLISH TRANSLATION OF FIZ. TVERD. TELA (LENINGRAD) 15 (5), 1645–6, 1973; FOR ORIGINAL SEE E51406)

51408 **ELECTRICAL CONDUCTIVITY AND DIELECTRIC PROPERTIES OF FINE–GRAINED FILMS COMPOSED OF OXIDIZED ALUMINUM PARTICLES.**
PETROV, YU. I. KOTELNIKOV, V. A.
FIZ. TVERD. TELA (LENINGRAD)
15 (5), 1646–8, 1973.
(FOR ENGLISH TRANSLATION SEE E51409)

51409 **ELECTRICAL CONDUCTIVITY AND DIELECTRIC PROPERTIES OF FINE–GRAINED FILMS COMPOSED OF OXIDIZED ALUMINUM PARTICLES.**
PETROV, YU. I. KOTELNIKOV, V. A.
SOV. PHYS. - SOLID STATE
15 (5), 1110–11, 1973.
(ENGLISH TRANSLATION OF FIZ. TVERD. TELA (LENINGRAD) 15 (5), 1646–8, 1973; FOR ORIGINAL SE E51408)

51410 **RECOMBINATION PROCESSES NEAR THE SURFACE OF GALLIUM ARSENIDE.**
VALIEV, K. A. GRITCHENKO, V. N.
PASHINTSEV, YU. I.
SOV. PHYS. - SEMICOND.
7 (3), 357–60, 1973.
(ENGLISH TRANSLATION OF FIZ. TEKH. POLUPROV., 7 (3), 505–12, 1973; FOR ORIGINAL SEE E50054)

51411 **ENERGY–BAND STRUCTURE OF INDIUM ARSENIDE.**
KARYMSHAKOV, R. K.
SOV. PHYS. - SEMICOND.
7 (3), 361–4, 1973.
(ENGLISH TRANSLATION OF FIZ. TEKH. POLUPROV., 7 (3), 513–8, 1973; FOR ORIGINAL SEE E50055)

51412 **THEORY OF THERMOGALVANOMAGNETIC EFFECTS IN SEMICONDUCTORS AT LOW TEMPERATURES.**
YASEVICHYUTE, YA.
SOV. PHYS. - SEMICOND.
7 (3), 369–72, 1973.
(ENGLISH TRANSLATION OF FIZ. TEKH. POLUPROV., 7 (3), 525–30, 1973; FOR ORIGINAL SEE E50056)

51413 **ELECTRICAL CONDUCTIVITY OF VARIABLE–GAP GALLIUM, ALUMINUM, ARSENIDE CRYSTALS.**
MATULENIS, A. YU. POZHELA, YU. K.
TSARENKOV, B. V. YUTSENE, V. YU.
YAKOVLEV, YU. P.
SOV. PHYS. - SEMICOND.
7 (3), 409–10, 1973.
(ENGLISH TRANSLATION OF FIZ. TEKH. POLUPROV., 7 (3), 591–3, 1973; FOR ORIGINAL SEE E50057)

51414 **YELLOW ELECTROLUMINESCENCE OF GALLIUM PHOSPHORUS.**
ABAGYAN, S. A. IZERGIN, A. P.
KUZNETSOV, YU. N. PERSHINA, T. E.
PERSHIN, YU. I.
SOV. PHYS. - SEMICOND.
7 (3), 412–3, 1973.
(ENGLISH TRANSLATION OF FIZ. TEKH. POLUPROV., 7 (3), 596–8, 1973; FOR ORIGINAL SEE E50058)

EPIC Number	Bibliographic Citation

51415 **PHOTOLUMINESCENCE OF EPITAXIAL GALLIUM-INDIUM PHOSPHIDE SOLID SOLUTION FILMS OF COMPOSITIONS.**
ALFEROV, ZH. I. GARBUZOV, D. Z.
KONNIKOV, S. G. KOPEV, P. S. MISHURNYI, V. A
RUMYANTSEV, V. D. TRETYAKOV, D. N.
SOV. PHYS. - SEMICOND.
7 (3), 435-6, 1973.
(ENGLISH TRANSLATION OF FIZ. TEKH. POLUPROV., 7 (3), 624-7, 1973; FOR ORIGINAL SEE E50059)

51417 **FEATURES OF RADIATIVE RECOMBINATION IN PURE INDIUM ANTIMONY CRYSTALS AT LOW TEMPERATURE.**
GRISHECHKINA, S. P. SHOTOV, A. P.
SOV. PHYS. - SEMICOND.
7 (4), 491-3, 1973.
(ENGLISH TRANSLATION OF FIZ. TEKH. POLUPROV. 7 (4), 707-10, 1973; FOR ORIGINAL SEE E50061)

51418 **LOW-TEMPERATURE QUANTUM OSCILLATIONS OF GALVANOMAGNETIC COEFFECIENTS OF N-TYPE MERCURY TELLURIUM.**
IVANOV-OMSKII, V. I. KONSTANTINOVA, N. N.
PARFEN'EV, R. V. SOLOGUB, V. V.
TAGIEV, I. G.
SOV. PHYS. - SEMICOND.
7 (4), 496-501, 1973.
(ENGLISH TRANSLATION OF FIZ. TEKH. POLUPROV., 7 (4), 715-24, 1973; FOR ORIGINAL SEE E50062)

51419 **ANISOTROPIC THERMOELEMENTS.**
KOROLYUK, S. L. PILAT, I. M.
SAMOILOVICH, A. G. SLIPCHENKO, V. N.
SNARSKII, A. A. TSARKOV, E. F.
SOV. PHYS. - SEMICOND.
7 (4), 502-7, 1973.
(ENGLISH TRANSLATION OF FIZ. TEKH. POLUPROV., 7 (4), 725-33, 1973; FOR ORIGINAL SEE E50063)

51420 **DETERMINATION OF THE EFFECTIVE MASS OF HOLES IN LEAD TIN SELENIUM CRYSTALS FROM THE NERNST-ETTINGSHAUSEN EFFECT.**
KUCHERENKO, I. V. TAKTAKISHVILI, M.S.
SOV. PHYS. - SEMICOND.
7 (4), 562-3, 1973.
(ENGLISH TRANSLATION OF FIZ. TEKH. POLUPROV., 7 (4), 822-4, 1973; FOR ORIGINAL SEE E50066)

51421 **DISPERSION LAW OF THE CONDUCTION BAND OF SILVER SELENIDE.**
GORBACHEV, V. V. PUTILIN, I. M.
SOV. PHYS. - SEMICOND.
7 (4), 571, 1973.
(ENGLISH TRANSLATION OF FIZ. TEKH. POLUPROV., 7 (4), 833-4, 1973; FOR ORIGINAL SEE E50067)

51422 **OPTICAL PROPERTIES OF CADMIUM GALLIUM SULFUR AND CADMIUM GALLIUM SELENIUM IN THE 200-600 NM REGION.**
ABDULLAEV, G. B. GUSEINOVA, D. A.
SOV. PHYS. - SEMICOND.
7 (4), 575-6, 1973.
(ENGLISH TRANSLATION OF FIZ. TEKH POLUPROV., 7 (4), 840-2, 1973; FOR ORIGINAL SEE E50068)

51423 **TEMPERATURE DEPENDENCE OF THE EFFECTIVE MASS OF ELECTRONS IN SILVER SELENIDE.**
GORBACHEV, V. V. PUTILIN, I. M.
SOV. PHYS. - SEMICOND.
7 (4), 578, 1973.
(ENGLISH TRANSLATION OF FIZ. TEKH. POLUPROV., 7 (4), 844-5, 1973; FOR ORIGINAL SEE E50069)

51424 **DETERMINATION OF THE EFFECTIVE MOBILITY OF HOLES FROM THE INFRARED ABSORPTION AND THE FIELD EFFECT.**
NEIZVESTNYI, I. G. MIRONOV, F. S.
SINYUKOV, M. P.
SOV. PHYS. - SEMICOND.
7 (4), 586-7, 1973.
(ENGLISH TRANSLATION OF FIZ. TEKH. POLUPROV., 7 (4), 855-7, 1973; FOR ORIGINAL SEE E50070)

51425 **HOT EXCITONS IN THE PHOTOCONDUCTIVITY SPECTRUM OF CADMIUM SULFUR CRYSTALS AT 4.2 K.**
GASTEV, S. V. LIDER, K. F. NOVIKOV, B. V.
SOV. PHYS. - SEMICOND.
7 (5), 613-5, 1973.
(ENGLISH TRANSLATION OF FIZ. TEKH. POLUPROV., 7 (5), 901-4, 1973; FOR ORIGINAL SEE E50074)

51426 **TEMPERATURE DEPENDENCE OF THE ANTISOTROPY OF THE ELECTRON MOBILITY IN P-TYPE CADMIUM ANTIMONY.**
GERTOVICH, T. S. ZHADKO, I. P.
ROMANOV, V. A. YUROV, YU. G.
SOV. PHYS. - SEMICOND.
7 (5), 642-4, 1973.
(ENGLISH TRANSLATION OF FIZ. TEKH. POLUPROV., 7 (5), 946-50, 1973; FOR ORIGINAL SEE E50075)

51427 **FIELD ENHANCEMENT OF THE QUENCHING OF THE IMPURITY PHOTOCONDUCTIVITY OF CHROMIUM DOPED GALLIUM ARSENIDE.**
PEKA, G. P. MIRETS, L. Z.
SOV. PHYS. - SEMICOND.
7 (5), 645-6, 1973.
(ENGLISH TRANSLATION OF FIZ. TEKH. POLUPROV., 7 (5), 951-4, 1973; FOR ORIGINAL SEE E50081)

51428 **CONTACT PHOTO-EMF AND NEGATIVE PHOTOCONDUCTIVITY OF HIGH-RESISTIVITY CUPROUS OXIDE CRYSTALS IN THE EXCITON ABSORPTION REGION.**
TAZENKOV, B. A. MERZLYAKOV, V. P.
SOV. PHYS. - SEMICOND.
7 (5), 647-8, 1973.
(ENGLISH TRANSLATION OF FIZ. TEKH. POLUPROV., 7 (5), 955-7, 1973; FOR ORIGINAL SEE E50082)

51430 **PIEZOELECTROABSORPTION IN GALLIUM ARSENIDE.**
BEROZASHVILI, YU. N. GOGOLIN, O. V.
LORDKIPANIDZE, D. SH.
SOV. PHYS. - SEMICOND.
7 (5), 661-2, 1973.
(ENGLISH TRANSLATION OF FIZ. TEKH. POLUPROV., 7 (5), 975-6, 1973; FOR ORIGINAL SEE E50077)

51432 **SOME FEATURES OF THE ELECTRICAL PROPERTIES OF EPITAXIAL TIN-DOPED GALLIUM ARSENIDE.**
EMELYANENKO, O. V. LAGUNOVA, T. S.
RADU, R. K. TALALAKIN, G. N. TELEGIN, A. A.
SOV. PHYS. - SEMICOND.
7 (5), 665-6, 1973.
(ENGLISH TRANSLATION OF FIZ. TEKH. POLUPROV., 7 (5), 979-80, 1973; FOR ORIGINAL SEE E50079)

51433 **THERMOELECTRIC POWER AND PHONON DRAG IN HEAVILY DOPED III-V CRYSTALS.**
EMELYANENKO, O. V. SKRIPKIN, V. A.
POPOVA, V. A.
SOV. PHYS. - SEMICOND.
7 (5), 667-8, 1973.
(ENGLISH TRANSLATION OF FIZ. TEKH. POLUPROV., 7 (5), 981-3, 1973; FOR ORIGINAL SEE E50080)

51434 **SOME FEATURES OF THE PHOTOLUMINESCENCE OF EPITAXIAL TELLURIUM-DOPED N-TYPE ALUMINUM GALLIUM ARSENIDE FILMS.**
ROGULIN, V. YU. SHLENSKII, A. A.
SOV. PHYS. - SEMICOND.
7 (5), 673-4, 1973.
(ENGLISH TRANSLATION OF FIZ. TEKH. POLUPROV., 7 (5), 988-90, 1973; FOR ORIGINAL SEE E50083)

51435 **DEFECT COMPLEXES IN ZINC TELLURIDE.**
BRODIN, M. S. GOER, D. B. MATSKO, M. G.
SOV. PHYS. - SEMICOND.
7 (5), 681-2, 1973.
(ENGLISH TRANSLATION OF FIZ. TEKH. POLUPROV., 7 (5), 997-9, 1973; FOR ORIGINAL SEE E50084)

51438 **MOLTEN SALTS: VOLUME 3, NITRATES, NITRITES, AND MIXTURES. ELECTRICAL CONDUCTANCE, DENSITY, VISCOSITY, AND SURFACE TENSION DATA.**
JANZ, G. J. KREBS, U. SIEGENTHALER, H. F.
TOMKINS, R. P. T.
J. PHYS. CHEM. REF. DATA
1 (3), 581-746, 1972.
(ERRATUM: TITLE IBID, AUTHORS IBID, J. IBID, 3 (2), 607, 1974.)

51439 **MICROWAVE SPECTRA OF MOLECULES OF ASTROPHYSICAL INTEREST. IV. HYDROGEN SULFIDE.**
HELMINGER, P. DE LUCIA, F. C.
KIRCHHOFF, W. H.
J. PHYS. CHEM. REF. DATA
2 (2), 215-23, 1973.

51441 **SURVEY OF PHOTOCHEMICAL AND RATE DATA FOR TWENTY-EIGHT REACTIONS OF INTEREST IN ATMOSPHERIC CHEMISTRY.**
HAMPSON, R. F. BRAUN, W. BROWN, R. L.
GARVIN, D. HERRON, J. T. HUIE, R. E.
KURYLO, M. J. LAUFER, A. H. MCKINLEY, J. D.
OKABE, H. SCHEER, M. D. TSANG, W.
J. PHYS. CHEM. REF. DATA
2 (2), 267-311, 1973.

51442 **COMPILATION OF THE STATIC DIELECTRIC CONSTANT OF INORGANIC SOLIDS.**
YOUNG, K. F. FREDERIKSE, H. P. R.
J. PHYS. CHEM. REF. DATA
2 (2), 313-409, 1973.

51445 **INFLUENCE OF THE ELECTRIC FIELD STRENGTH ON EFFECTIVE MOBILITY OF CARRIERS IN POLYCRYSTALLINE THIN FILMS OF CADMIUM SELENIDE.**
JAKUBOWSKI, A. KUZNICKI, Z. T.
ELEKTRONIKA
14 (6), 230-3, 1973.

51448 **ELECTRICAL CONDUCTIVITY OF TUNGSTEN TRIOXIDE.**
HIROSE, T. KAWANO, I. NIINO, M.
PHYSICAL SOCIETY OF JAPAN, JOURNAL
33, 272PP., 1972.

51450 **CORRELATION BETWEEN THE WORK FUNCTION OF TRANSITION METAL CARBIDES AND THE SURFACE RECOMBINATION OF HYDROGEN ATOMS IN THE REGION OF HOMOGENEITY.**
SAMSONOV, G. V. PODCHERNIAEVA, I. A.
FOMENKO, V. S. LAVRENKO, V. A.
OKHREMCHUK, L. N. PROTSENKO, T. G.
POROSH. MET.
11, 62-66, 1972.
(FOR ENGLISH TRANSLATION SEE E53035)

EPIC Number	Bibliographic Citation
51453	CERTAIN PHOTOELECTRICAL PROPERTIES OF CADMIUM ANTIMONIDE RELATED TO ELECTROCONDUCTIVITY ANISOTROPY. GERTOVICH, T. S. ZHADKO, I. P. RARENKO, I. M. ROMANOV, V. O. UKR. FIZ. ZH. 17, 948–953, 1972.
51457	ELECTRICAL PROPERTIES OF HYDRATED AND PARTIALLY HYDRATED ZEOLITES X AND Y. JANSEN, F. J. SCHOONHEYDT, R. A. ADVAN. CHEM. SER. 121, 96–105, 1973. (FROM: MOL. SIEVES, INT. CONF., 3RD)
51458	SURGE VOLTAGE TESTING OF ALUMINUM OXIDE FILMS. MOSSER, I. ALUMINIUM (DUESSELDORF) 49 (7), 475–6, 1973.
51459	ELECTRIC CONDUCTIVITY OF SCANDIUM(III) OXIDE. ALBELLA, J. M. PAJARES, J. A. SORIA, J. A. AN. FIS. 69 (4–6), 129–34, 1973.
51461	VALENCE BAND DENSITY OF STATES AND CORE LEVEL SHIFTS OF SILVER THIOGALLATE AS DETERMINED BY X-RAY PHOTOEMISSION. LUCIANO, M. J. VESELY, C. J. APPL. PHYS. LETT. 23 (2), 60–1, 1973.
51462	FIELD AND TIME THRESHOLDS FOR THE ELECTRICAL FIXATION OF HOLOGRAMS RECORDED IN STRONTIUM BARIUM NIOBATE CRYSTALS. MICHERON, F. BISMUTH, G. APPL. PHYS. LETT. 23 (2), 71–2, 1973.
51464	ELECTRIC FIELD ENHANCEMENT OF ESCAPE PROBABILITY ON NEGATIVE-ELECTRON-AFFINITY SURFACES. HOWORTH, J. R. HARMER, A. L. TRAWNY, E. W. L. HOLTOM, R. SHEPPARD, C. J. R. APPL. PHYS. LETT. 23 (3), 123–4, 1973.
51465	DETERMINATION OF DEEP-LEVEL ENERGY AND DENSITY PROFILES IN INHOMOGENEOUS SEMICONDUCTORS. GOTO, G. YANAGISAWA, S. WADA, O. TAKANASHI, H. APPL. PHYS. LETT. 23 (3), 150–1, 1973.
51467	BAND ASSIGNMENT IN ULTRAVIOLET PHOTOELECTRON SPECTROSCOPY. BALLARD, R. E. APPL. SPECTROSC. REV. 7 (2), 183–213, 1973.
51470	SOLUTION OF SECULAR DETERMINANTS FOR GROUP UV AND III-V SEMICONDUCTORS BY SYMMETRY ANALYSIS. JOSHUA, S. J. MORGAN, D. AUST. J. PHYS. 26 (4), 501–11, 1973.
51477	EMISSION SPECTRA OF HEXAAMMINECHROMIUM(III) HEXACYANOCOBALTATE(III). KATAOKA, H. BULL. CHEM. SOC. JAP. 46 (7), 2078–86, 1973.
51479	CRYSTAL GROWTH AND CHARACTERIZATION OF CHROMIUM-DOPED Y I G SINGLE CRYSTALS BY VAPOR-PHASE TRANSFER. LAUNAY, J. C. MORELL, A. POUCHARD, M. BULL. SOC. SCI. BRETAGNE 48, 125–34, 1973.
51480	TEST OF SYNTHESIS AND GROWTH OF RARE EARTH HYDROXYCARBONATES AND CHLOROCARBONATES BY THE HYDROTHERMAL METHOD. BOTHOREL, M. M. P. BULL. SOC. SCI. BRETAGNE 48, 173–82, 1973.
51484	FREQUENCY DEPENDENCE OF CONDUCTIVITY IN AMORPHOUS ZINC TELLURIDE. WEBB, J. B. BRODIE, D. E. CAN. J. PHYS. 51 (15), 1593–6, 1973.
51486	MAGNETOELASTIC INTERACTIONS IN THE RARE EARTH-IRON CUBIC LAVES PHASE COMPOUNDS. SOUTHERN, B. W. CAN. J. PHYS. 51 (15), 1646–52, 1973.
51491	CNDO [COMPLETE NEGLECT OF DIFFERENTIAL OVERLAP] TREATMENTS ON ELECTRONIC SPECTRA OF SMALL MOLECULES. ZAHRADNIK, R. CARSKY, P. COLLECT. CZECH. CHEM. COMMUN. 38 (7), 1876–85, 1973.
51497	DEVICE FOR MEASURING THE PERMITTIVITIES OF LIQUIDS WITH VERY HEAVY LOSSES AT ULTRA HIGH FREQUENCIES. APPLICATION TO MOLTEN SALTS. DOUCET, Y. SANTINI, R. TETE, A. C. R. ACAD. SCI. 277 B (1), 9–12, 1973.
51499	MAGNETIC SUSCEPTIBILITY AND ELECTRICAL RESISTIVITY OF THE COMPOUND EUROPIUM-TIN. PERCHERON, A. GOROCHOV, O. ACHARD, J. C. C. R. ACAD. SCI. 277 C (2), 81–3, 1973.
51500	CRYSTALLOGRAPHIC AND DIELECTRIC PROPERTIES OF FLUORINE SUBSTITUTED POTASSIUM NIOBATE PHASES. MALABRY, G. RAYEZ, J. FOURQUET, J. L. DE PAPE, R. C. R. ACAD. SCI. 277 C (2), 105–8, 1973.
51502	DISPERSION AND REFRACTIVITY OF GASES FOR INTERFEROMETRIC PRESSURE-SCANNING. GAULT, W. A. SHEPHERD, G. G. APPL. OPT. 12 (8), 1739–40, 1973.
51503	MEASUREMENT OF LOW ABSORPTION COEFFICIENTS IN CRYSTALS. JOHNSON, D. C. APPL. OPT. 12 (9), 2192–7, 1973.
51507	EMISSION BAND SPECTRUM OF HAFNIUM IODIDE IN THE RED. SAVITHRY, T. RAO, D. V. K. RAO, P. T. CURR. SCI. 42 (15), 533–4, 1973.
51511	CONCENTRATION PROFILE OF DEEP-LEVEL IMPURITIES IN VAPOR PHASE EPITAXIAL GALLIUM ARSENIDE GROWN UNDER VARIOUS ARSENIC VAPOR PRESSURES. OKAMOTO, H. SAKATA, S. SAKAI, K. DENKI TSUSHIN KENKYUJO KENKYU JITSUYOKA HOKOKU 22 (3), 749–65, 1973.
51515	POSSIBLE REGULATION OF THE CONCENTRATION OF ONE-SIGN CARRIERS IN A THALLIUM(I) SELENIDE MELT. KAZANDZHAN, B. I. TSURIKOV, A. A. DOKL. AKAD. NAUK SSSR 210 (3), 633–6, 1973.
51516	MAGNETIZATION REVERSAL OF MANGANESE-BISMUTH THIN FILMS. SHUR, YA. S. GLAZER, A. A. TAGIROV, R. I. POTAPOV, A. P. GASS, V. G. DOKL. AKAD. NAUK SSSR 210 (4), 822–5, 1973. (FOR ENGLISH TRANSLATION SEE E53241)
51518	CONTROL OF THE COERCIVE FORCE LEVEL OF FERROMAGNETS BY INTRODUCING ACTIVATOR IONS. BONDAREV, D. E. KIRICHOK, P. P. ZINOVEVA, I. G. SHAMANOV, M. A. DOKL. AKAD. NAUK SSSR 210 (5), 1063–6, 1973. (FOR ENGLISH TRANSLATION SEE E53242)
51520	SELF-REVERSAL OF THERMORESIDUAL MAGNETIZATION IN NATURAL SPINELS OF THE ISOMORPHOUS SERIES IRON OXIDE-ALUMINUM MAGNESIUM OXIDE SERIES. KUDRYAVTSEVA, G. P. ZHILYAEVA, V. A. DOKL. AKAD. NAUK SSSR 211 (1), 189–92, 1973.
51522	ENERGY GAP WIDTH OF THE COMPOUND SILVER ANTIMONY TELLURIDE. GOCHEV, D. K. DECHEVA, S. K. DIMITROVA, S. K. DOKL. BOLG. AKAD. NAUK 26 (5), 619–22, 1973.
51523	CHANGES IN THE TEMPERATURE DEPENDENCE OF THE CONDUCTIVITY OF NONLINEAR SEMICONDUCTOR RESISTORS OF BLACK SILICON CARBIDE DUE TO REACTOR NEUTRON RADIATION. RIBAROV, S. R. DOKL. BOLG. AKAD. NAUK 26 (5), 627–30, 1973.
51524	HIGH-FIELD TRANSPORT IN INDIUM PHOSPHIDE. FAWCETT, W. HERBERT, D. C. ELECTRON. LETT. 9 (14), 308–9, 1973.
51525	PREFERENTIAL EXCITATION OF SECOND-MODE PIEZOELECTRIC SURFACE WAVES IN ZINC OXIDE-LAYERED SUBSTRATES. ARMSTRONG, G. A. CARMPIN, S. ELECTRON. LETT. 9 (14), 322–3, 1973.
51526	SEMICONDUCTOR PROPERTIES OF SOLID SOLUTIONS OF ZINC PHOSPHIDE-CADMIUM ARSENIDE TYPE. ZDANOWICZ, W. KROLICKI, F. PLENKIEWICZ, P. ELECTRON TECHNOL. 5 (2), 81–6, 1972.

EPIC Number	Bibliographic Citation
51527	GALVANOLUMINESCENCE IN METAL (SEMICONDUCTOR)- OXIDE-ELECTROLYTE SYSTEMS. GARDIN, YU. E. KULABUKHOV, V. M. LEGOSTAEV, V. A. ELEKTRON. TEKH., NAUCH.-TEKH. SB., RADIODETALI (2), 83-8, 1972.
51528	PHOTOEMISSION OF SODIUM-RUBIDIUM, SODIUM-CESIUM, RUBIDIUM-POTASSIUM, AND POTASSIUM-CESIUM BINARY ALLOYS. MALOV, YU. I. SHEBZUKHOV, M. D. ELEKTROKHIMIYA 9 (6), 815-17, 1973. (FOR ENGLISH TRANSLATION SEE E53680)
51530	ELECTRICAL CONDUCTIVITY OF LITHIUM SODIUM SULFATE IN MOLTEN AND IN SOLID STATES. POLISHCHUK, A. F. SHURKHAL, T. M. ELEKTROKHIMIYA 9 (6), 838-41, 1973. (FOR ENGLISH TRANSLATION SEE E53679)
51531	FERRITES FOR MAGNETIC HEADS. KULIKOWSKI, J. LESNIEWSKI, A. MAKOLAGWA, S. ELEKTRONIKA 14 (6), 246-51, 1973.
51532	LUX-AMPERE CHARACTERISTICS OF ANTIMONY IODIDE SULFIDE SINGLE CRYSTALS. SAVCHENKO, E. A. FIZ.-MAT. ISSLED. 19-22, 1972.
51540	NEUTRON-DIFFRACTION STUDY OF THE MAGNETIC AND ATOMIC STRUCTURES OF AN ORDERED IRON-PLATINUM ALLOY OF EQUIATOMIC COMPOSITION. KELAREV, V. V. VOKHMYANIN, A. P. DOROFEEV, YU. A. SIDOROV, S. K. FIZ. METAL. METALLOVED. 35 (6), 1302-3, 1973. (FOR ENGLISH TRANSLATION SEE E63179)
51543	CRYSTAL GROWTH AND ELECTRICAL PROPERTIES OF MANGANESE-DOPED TIN TELLURIDE. I. INOUE, M. YAGI, H. MORISHITA, S. FUKUI DAIGAKU KOGAKUBU KENKYU HOKOKU 21 (1), 25-34, 1973.
51544	DIELECTRIC CONSTANT AND LOSS TANGENT OF SOME ALKALI HALIDE CRYSTALS. INOMATA, H. FUKUOKA KYOIKU DAIGAKU KIYO, DAI-3-BU, RIKA-HEN 22, 105-9, 1972.
51546	LOW-FREQUENCY INSTABILITY OF VOLTAGE AT THE POTENTIAL PROBE IN CADMIUM SELENIDE. RYBIN, V. N. FIZ. TEKH. POLUPROV. 7 (3), 499-504, 1973. (FOR ENGLISH TRANSLATION SEE E52923)
51547	DIFFUSION OF LUMINESCENCE CENTERS IN GALLIUM ARSENIDE. VOROBKALO, F. M. GLINCHUK, K. D. PROKHOROVICH, A. V. FIZ. TEKH. POLUPROV. 7 (5), 896-900, 1973. (FOR ENGLISH TRANSLATION SEE E52924)
51550	TEMPERATURE DEPENDENCE OF CADMIUM SULFIDE CONDUCTIVITY WITH DONOR AND ACCEPTOR IMPURITIES. KONSTANTINOVA, E. KUNEV, S. FIZ. TEKH. POLUPROV. 7 (6), 1033-7, 1973. (FOR ENGLISH TRANSLATION SEE E53681)
51551	PHOTOCONDUCTIVITY AND PROCESSES OF ADHESION AND RECOMBINATION IN GOLD-DOPED CADMIUM GALLIUM SELENIDE SINGLE CRYSTALS. ABDULLAEV, G. B. AGAEV, V. G. ANTONOV, V. B. MAMEDOV, A. A. NANI, R. KH. SADAEV, E. YU. FIZ. TEKH. POLUPROV. 7 (6), 1051-7, 1973. (FOR ENGLISH TRANSLATION SEE E53682)
51552	PHOTOELECTRIC METHOD FOR MEASURING THE ENERGY DEPENDENCE OF IMPACT IONIZATION PROBABILITY IN SEMICONDUCTORS. KUMEKOV, S. E. YASSIEVICH, I. N. FIZ. TEKH. POLUPROV. 7 (6), 1081-5, 1973. (FOR ENGLISH TRANSLATION SEE E53683)
51553	INELASTICITY OF ELECTRON SCATTERING IN SILVER TELLURIDE. ALIEV, S. A. SUYUNOV, U. KH. ARASLY, D. G. ALIEV, M. I. FIZ. TEKH. POLUPROV. 7 (6), 1086-91, 1973. (FOR ENGLISH TRANSLATION SEE E53684)
51555	SPACE-CHARGE-LIMITED CURRENTS IN CADMIUM SULFIDE FILMS. MARAKHONOV, V. M. SEISYAN, R. P. FIZ. TEKH. POLUPROV. 7 (6), 1141-7, 1973. (FOR ENGLISH TRANSLATION SEE E53686)
51556	PHOTOSENSITIVITY OF A P-COPPER(I) SULFIDE-N-SILICON HETEROJUNCTION. DROZDOV, V. A. MEL'NIKOV, M. M. FIZ. TEKH. POLUPROV. 7 (6), 1194-6, 1973. (FOR ENGLISH TRANSLATION SEE E53687)
51557	ELECTROOPTICAL ABSORPTION IN SEMICONDUCTORS WITH LARGE FLUCTUATIONS IN IMPURITY CONCENTRATION. MERKULOV, I. A. PEREL, V. I. FIZ. TEKH. POLUPROV. 7 (6), 1197-202, 1973. (FOR ENGLISH TRANSLATION SEE E53688)
51558	SHIFT CONSTANTS OF THE DEFORMATION POTENTIAL IN INDIUM ANTIMONIDE. VOLKOV, A. S. GALAVANOV, V. V. MILORAVA, V. A. FIZ. TEKH. POLUPROV. 7 (6), 1220-2, 1973. (FOR ENGLISH TRANSLATION SEE E53689)
51559	EXCITON SPECTRA OF HEAVILY DOPED CADMIUM SULFIDE SINGLE CRYSTALS. GROSS, E. F. PERMOGOROV, S. A. REZNITSKII, A. N. USAROV, E. N. FIZ. TEKH. POLUPROV. 7 (7), 1255-62, 1973. (FOR ENGLISH TRANSLATION SEE E53690)
51561	IMPURITY ELECTROABSORPTION IN CADMIUM SELENIDE TELLURIDE SINGLE CRYSTALS. BUDYANSKII, V. I. DANIYAROV, O. SAL'KOV, E. A. SHEINKMAN, M. K. SHEPEL'SKII, G. A. FIZ. TEKH. POLUPROV. 7 (7), 1296-300, 1973. (FOR ENGLISH TRANSLATION SEE E53692)
51562	NATURE OF THE TEMPERATURE DEPENDENCE OF ELECTRIC CONDUCTIVITY IN COPPER CHALCOGENIDES AT HIGH TEMPERATURES IN SOLID AND LIQUID STATES. GLAZOV, V. M. BURKHANOV, A. S. FIZ. TEKH. POLUPROV. 7 (7), 1401-5, 1973. (FOR ENGLISH TRANSLATION SEE E53693)
51563	THEORY OF THE ELECTRICAL CONDUCTIVITY OF MULTIVALLEY SEMICONDUCTORS WITH CHARGED POINT DEFECTS. KORNYUSHIN, YU. V. FIZ. TEKH. POLUPROV. 7 (7), 1417-19, 1973. (FOR ENGLISH TRANSLATION SEE E53694)
51564	SHAPE OF THE NATURAL ABSORPTION EDGE IN A CADMIUM MERCURY SELENIDE SOLID SOLUTION. KIREEV, P. S. VOLKOV, V. V. FIZ. TEKH. POLUPROV. 7 (7), 1419-23, 1973. (FOR ENGLISH TRANSLATION SEE E53695)
51572	INFRARED SPECTRA OF INDIUM ARSENIDE HEAVILY DOPED WITH TELLURIUM AND SELENIUM. LANGE, V. N. KOTRUBENKO, B. P. GERTSENOVSKIE CHTENIYA, OBSHCH. EKSP. FIZ., KRATK. 26-31, 1971.
51579	RESISTIVE MEASUREMENTS ON AN IMPROVED NIOBIUM-ALUMINUM-GERMANIUM SUPERCONDUCTING RIBBON. EAGAR, T. W. ROSE, R. M. IEEE TRANS. NUCL. SCI. 20 (3), 742-3, 1973.
51580	MICROWAVE MEASUREMENTS OF THE DIELECTRIC CONSTANT OF SULFATES USING LOOYENGAS FORMULA. KHANNA, R. K. SOBHANADRI, J. INDIAN J. PURE APPL. PHYS. 11 (4), 250-1, 1973.
51581	EFFECT OF ANIONIC COPING ON THE OPTICAL AND THERMAL BLEACHING CHARACTERISTICS OF THE POTASSIUM CHLORIDE CRYSTAL. MUKHERJEE, M. L. INDIAN J. PURE APPL. PHYS. 11 (4), 252-6, 1973.
51583	EMISSION SPECTRUM OF CALCIUM MONOIODIDE. KHANNA, L. K. DUBEY, V. S. INDIAN J. PURE APPL. PHYS. 11 (4), 286-8, 1973.
51585	ATOMIC AND MAGNETIC STRUCTURE OF NICKEL COPPER MANGANESE ANTIMONIDE ALLOYS. SZYTULA, A. INST. NUCL. PHYS., CRACOW, REP. (816/PS), 20, 1972.

EPIC Number	Bibliographic Citation

51586 **COMPARISON OF MAGNETIC STURCUTRES WITH THE SUPER-EXCHANGE THEORY.**
LUCZYNSKA, K. OLES, A.
INST. TECH. JAD., AGH REP.
(23/PS), 8 PP., 1972.

51588 **SURFACE FLASHOVER IN COMPRESSED SULFUR HEXAFLUORIDE.**
GREENWOOD, P. WHITTINGTON, H. W.
INT. CONF. GAS DISCHARGES, (PROC.), 2ND
233-5, 1972.

51589 **ELECTRIC BREAKDOWN OF NITROUS OXIDE AT HIGH VOLTAGES.**
DUTTON, J. HARRIS, F. M. HUGHES, D. B.
INT. CONF. GAS DISCHARGES, (PROC.), 2ND
273-5, 1972.

51593 **ELECTRICAL BREAKDOWN AND PREBREAKDOWN DARK CURRENT IN COMPRESSED SULFUR HEXAFLUORIDE.**
SHIBUYA, Y. YAMADA, N. NITTA, T.
INT. CONF. GAS DISCHARGES, (PROC.), 2ND
320-2, 1972.

51594 **EDGE BREAKDOWN BETWEEN UNIFORM-FIELD ELECTRODES IN SULFUR HEXAFLUORIDE.**
MUNK NIELSEN, T. PEDERSEN, A.
INT. CONF. GAS DISCHARGES, (PROC.), 2ND
323-5, 1972.

51595 **VOLTAGE-TIME CHARACTERISTICS OF COMPRESSED SULFUR HEXAFLUORIDE DISCHARGE.**
BORIN, V. N.
INT. CONF. GAS DISCHARGES, (PROC.), 2ND
329-31, 1972.

51596 **IONIZATION AND BREAKDOWN IN SULFUR HEXAFLUORIDE.**
CRICHTON, B. H. CRICHTON, G. C.
TEDFORD, D. J.
INT. CONF. GAS DISCHARGES, (PROC.), 2ND
385-7, 1972.

51601 **THERMOELECTRIC PROPERTIES OF TIN(II) TELLURIDE-TIN (II) SULFIDE AND TIN(II) TELLURIDE-TIN(II) SELENIDE ALLOYS WITH LOW SULFUR AND SELENIUM CONTENT.**
NASIROV, YA. N. OSMANOV, T. G.
PIRIZADE, M. M.
IZV. AKAD. NAUK AZERB. SSR, SER. FIZ.-TEKH. MAT. NAUK
(1), 3-7, 1973.

51605 **CHANGE IN THE REFRACTIVE INDEX OF AMORPHOUS ARSENIC SELENIDE IN AN ELECTRICAL FIELD.**
KOLOMIETS, B. T. MAZETS, T. F.
MAMEDOV, A. M. EFENDIEV, SH. M.
IZV. AKAD. NAUK AZERB. SSR, SER. FIZ.-TEKH. MAT. NAUK
(2), 127-30, 1972.

51606 **THERMOELECTRIC POWER AND EFFECTIVE MASS OF HOLES IN CADMIUM SILICON ARSENIDE.**
SERGINOV, M. RUD, YU. V.
PROCHUKHAN, V. D. SKRIPKIN, V. A.
IZV. AKAD. NAUK TURKM. SSR, SER. FIZ.- TEKH., KHIM. GEOL. NAUK
(3), 105-7, 1973.

51609 **PROPERTIES OF COPPER GERMANIUM SELENIDE DURING DEVIATIONS FROM STOICHIOMETRY.**
ROGACHEVA, E. I. MELIKHOVA, A. N.
PANASENKO, N. M.
IZV. AKAD. NAUK SSSR, NEORG. MATER.
9 (6), 915-18, 1973.

51614 **ELECTROPHYSICAL PROPERTIES OF BARIUM TITANATE THIN FILMS PREPARED BY A CATHODIC SPUTTERING TECHNIQUE.**
DUDKEVICH, V. P. MARGOLIN, A. M.
GAVRILYACHENKO, V. G. BONDARENKO, V. S.
FESENKO, E. G.
IZV. AKAD. NAUK SSSR, NEORG. MATER.
9 (6), 1069-70, 1973.

51615 **ELECTRIC CONDUCTIVITY OF SCANDIUM OXIDE.**
VOLCHENKOVA, Z. S. NEDOPEKIN, V. M.
IZV. AKAD. NAUK SSSR, NEORG. MATER.
9 (6), 1073-4, 1973.

51616 **SYNTHESIS OF EPITAXIAL TELLURIDE FILMS.**
EZHOVSKII, YU. K. KALINKIN, I. P.
MURAV'EVA, K. K. ALESKOVSKII, V. B.
IZV. AKAD. NAUK SSSR, NEORG. MATER.
9 (7), 1115-20, 1973.

51618 **EFFECT OF UNIAXIAL DEFORMATION ON THE SPECIFIC RESISTANCE OF HEXAGONAL SILICON CARBIDE.**
AZIMOV, S. A. LUTFULLAEV, A. MIRZABAEV, M.
KHAIRULLAEV, SH.
IZV. AKAD. NAUK UZB. SSR, SER. FIZ.-MAT. NAUK
17 (3), 52-4, 1973.

51621 **DISPERSION OF TOTAL CONDUCTIVITY IN DOPED POLYCRYSTALLINE BARIUM TITANATE.**
BOGATINA, V. N. BOGATIN, A. S.
PROKOPALO, O. I.
IZV. VYSSH. UCHEB. ZAVED., FIZ.
16 (6), 52-6, 1973.
(FOR ENGLISH TRANSLATION SEE E79050)

EPIC Number	Bibliographic Citation

51623 **SHORT-TERM ELECTRIC RELAXATIONS IN ALKALI HALIDE CRYSTALS.**
DYACHENKO, N. G. TYURIN, A. V.
SHEVELEVA, A. S.
IZV. VYSSH. UCHEB. ZAVED., FIZ.
16 (6), 101-6, 1973.
(FOR ENGLISH TRANSLATION SEE E78997)

51624 **EFFECT OF BASE LAYER ORIENTATION IN THE (111)-(100) RANGE ON THE GROWTH RATE AND PARAMETERS OF GALLIUM ARSENIDE AND GALLIUM INDIUM ARSENIDE AS FILMS.**
KULISH, U. M.
IZV. VYSSH. UCHEB. ZAVED., FIZ.
16 (6), 121-3, 1973.
(FOR ENGLISH TRANSLATION SEE E78992)

51625 **TRAPPING OF ELECTRONS IN SELENIUM-DOPED CADMIUM TELLURIDE RECRYSTALLIZED FILMS.**
GAVRILENKO, N. V. KATERENYUK, D. M.
IZV. VYSSH. UCHEB. ZAVED., FIZ.
16 (5), 126-8, 1973.
(FOR ENGLISH TRANSLATION SEE E79080)

51626 **PROPERTIES OF ALUMINUM NITRIDE FILMS PREPARED BY REACTIVE VAPORIZATION.**
SLAVNIKOV, V. S. USYNINA, N. A.
SLAVNIKOVA, M. M. TRUBITSYN, A. M.
IZV. VYSSH. UCHEB. ZAVED., FIZ.
16 (6), 149-51, 1973.
(FOR ENGLISH TRANSLATION SEE E91486)

51628 **ANODIC OXIDATION OF SOME METALS IN A FLOW DISCHARGE PLASMA.**
FAIZULLIN, F. F. AVERYANOV, E. E.
IZV. VYSSH. UCHEB. ZAVED., KHIM. KHIM. TEKNOL.
16 (7), 1023-5, 1973.

51629 **RESISTANCE MATERIALS MADE OF LANTHANUM HEXABORIDE AND GLASS.**
SMIRNOV, M. A. MAKHMUDBEKOV, I. B.
IZV. VYSSH. UCHEB. ZAVED., NEFT GAZ
16 (6), 99-102, 1973.

51631 **SUPERHIGH-FREQUENCY BREAKDOWN OF N-INDIUM ANTIMONIDE.**
PISKAREV, V. I.
IZV. VYSSH. UCHEB. ZAVED., RADIOFIZ.
16 (6), 957-60, 1973.

51632 **REEQUILIBRATION KINETICS FOR UNDOPED AND LITHIUM-DOPED SINGLE CRYSTAL NICKEL OXIDE.**
NOWOTNY, J. WAGNER, J. B., JR.
J. AMER. CERAM. SOC.
56 (7), 397-8, 1973.

51633 **FERROELECTRIC-PARAELECTRIC PHASE TRANSITION IN LEAD TITANATE CONTAINING LATTICE DEFECTS.**
SHIRASAKI, S. TAKAHASHI, K. KAKEGAWA, K.
J. AMER. CERAM. SOC.
56 (8), 430-5, 1973.

51634 **LUMINESCENCE EFFECT IN DEFORMED CALCIUM OXIDE.**
CHEN, Y. UNRUH, W. P. ABRAHAM, M. M.
TURNER, T. J. NELSON, C. M.
J. AMER. CERAM. SOC.
56 (8), 438-9, 1973.

51635 **HIGH OXIDE ION CONDUCTION IN SINTERED OXIDES OF THE SYSTEM BISMUTH(III) OXIDE-TUNGSTEN(VI) OXIDE.**
TAKAHASHI, T. IWAHARA, H.
J. APPL. ELECTROCHEM.
3 (1), 65-72, 1973.

51636 **PHOTOELECTRON SPECTRA OF OSMIUM AND RUTHENIUM TETROXIDES.**
FOSTER, S. FELPS, S. CUSACHS, L. C.
MCGLYNN, S. P.
J. AMER. CHEM. SOC.
95 (17), 5521-4, 1973.

51637 **X-RAY PHOTOELECTRON SPECTROSCOPY OF CHLORINE TRIFLUORIDE, SULFUR TETRAFLUORIDE, AND PHOSPHORUS PENTAFLUORIDE.**
SHAW, R. W., JR. CARROLL, T. X.
THOMAS, T. D.
J. AMER. CHEM. SOC.
95 (18), 5870-5, 1973.

51640 **PULSED MICROWAVE BREAKDOWN IN GASES WITH A LOW DEGREE OF PREIONIZATION.**
DAWSON, E. F. LEDERMAN, S.
J. APPL. PHYS.
44 (7), 3066-73, 1973.

51641 **PULSE RESPONSE OF D.C. ELECTROLUMINESCENT MANGANOSE-DOPED ZINC SULFIDE POWDERED PHOSPHOR.**
YAMAMOTO, R. YAMAZOE, H.
J. APPL. PHYS.
44 (7), 3191-2, 1973.

51642 **PHOTOVOLTAIC EFFECT IN LEAD SELENIDE P-N JUNCTIONS.**
CHAMBOULEYRON, I. BESSON, J. M.
BALKANSKI, M.
J. APPL. PHYS.
44 (7), 3222-7, 1973.

EPIC Number	Bibliographic Citation
51643	**THERMAL ACTIVATION ENERGY OF MANGANESE ACCEPTORS IN GALLIUM ARSENIDE AS A FUNCTION OF IMPURITY SPACING.** BLAKEMORE, J. S. BROWN, W. J., JR. STASS, M. L. WOODBURY, D. A. J. APPL. PHYS. 44 (7), 3352–4, 1973.
51646	**K X-RAY SPECTRA AND ELECTRONIC BAND STRUCTURE OF MANGANESE PHOSPHIDE.** NAKAMORI, H. TSUTSUMI, K. SUGIURA, C. J. APPL. PHYS. 44 (8), 3473–5, 1973.
51648	**CRYSTAL GROWTH OF ZINC CADMIUM TELLURIDE SOLID SOLUTIONS AND THEIR OPTICAL PROPERTIES AT THE PHOTON ENERGIES OF THE LOWEST BAND-GAP REGION.** EBINA, A. SAITO, K. TAKAHASHI, T. J. APPL. PHYS. 44 (8), 3659–62, 1973.
51649	**TEMPERATURE DEPENDENCE OF THE MICROWAVE BEHAVIOR OF POLAR SEMICONDUCTORS.** LOESCHNER, H. KRANZER, D. J. APPL. PHYS. 44 (8), 3663–8, 1973.
51650	**REFRACTIVE INDEX OF N-TYPE GALLIUM ARSENIDE.** ZOROOFCHI, J. BUTLER, J. K. J. APPL. PHYS. 44 (8), 3697–9, 1973.
51651	**MONTE-CARLO CALCULATION OF THE ELECTRON DRIFT VELOCITY IN GALLIUM ARSENIDE WITH A SUPERLATTICE.** ANDERSEN, D. L. AAS, E. J. J. APPL. PHYS. 44 (8), 3721–5, 1973.
51652	**MAGNETIC PHASE TRANSITION IN THULIUM-IRON.** GUBBENS, P. C. M. BUSCHOW, K. H. J. J. APPL. PHYS. 44 (8), 3739–41, 1973.
51653	**THERMAL HYSTERESIS OF MAGNETIZATION CURVE IN MANGANESE BISMUTH FILMS BELOW ROOM TEMPERATURE.** EGASHIRA, K. YOSHII, S. J. APPL. PHYS. 44 (8), 3742–5, 1973.
51654	**LONGITUDINAL IMAGINARY SUSCEPTIBILITY OF POLYCRYSTALLINE AND IMPURITY-DOPED YIG (YTTRIUM-IRON GARNET) IN STRONG RF (RESONANCE FREQUENCY) FIELDS.** BORGHESE, C. J. APPL. PHYS. 44 (8), 3746–51, 1973.
51655	**MAGNETIZATION REVERSAL PROCESS IN CHEMICALLY PRECIPITATED AND ORDINARY PREPARED BARIUM IRON OXIDE.** HANEDA, K. KOJIMA, H. J. APPL. PHYS. 44 (8), 3760–2, 1973.
51656	**X-RAY DIFFRACTION TOPOGRAPHY OF MAGNETIC DOMAINS IN ORTHOFERRITES.** PATEL, J. R. VAN UITERT, L. G. MATHIOT, A. J. APPL. PHYS. 44 (8), 3763–5, 1973.
51657	**EXCITATION MECHANISM OF THE CHROMIUM(3+) LUMINESCENCE CENTER IN STRONTIUM TITANATE(IV).** GHOSH, A. K. ADDISS, R. R., JR. LAUER, R. B. J. APPL. PHYS. 44 (8), 3798–800, 1973.
51658	**COMPENSATION BUBBLE. NEW TYPE OF MAGNETIC BUBBLE.** KRUMME, J. P. HANSEN, P. J. APPL. PHYS. 44 (8), 3805–7, 1973.
51659	**HYDROTHERMAL PREPARATION AND MAGNETIC PROPERTIES OF DYSPROSIUM OXIDE CARBONATE, HOLMIUM OXIDE CARBONATE, ERBIUM OXIDE CARBONATE, AND YTTERBIUM OXIDE CARBONATE.** NORLUND CHRISTENSEN, A. ACTA CHEM. SCAND. 27 (5), 1835–7, 1973.
51669	**FLUORESCENCE OF CARBON DISULFIDE VAPOR.** LAMBERT, C. KIMBELL, G. H. CAN. J. CHEM. 51 (16), 2601–8, 1973.
51672	**ELECTRIC FIELD DEPENDENCE OF CURIE TEMPERATURE IN FERROELECTRIC CRYSTALS.** SEMWAL, B. S. SHARMA, P. K. CAN. J. PHYS. 51 (17), 1874–81, 1973.
51681	**STIMULATED RADIATION OF NEODYMIUM TRIPOSITIVE IONS IN CRYSTALS AT THE FLUORINE-4(3/2) TO IODINE-4(13/2) TRANSITION.** ALKESANDROV, V. I. KAMINSKII, A. A. MAKSIMOVA, G. V. PROKHOROV, A. M. SARKISOV, S. E. SOBOL, A. A. TATARINTSEV, V. M. DOKL. AKAD. NAUK SSSR 211 (3), 567–70, 1973.
51683	**MEASUREMENT OF THE HALL EFFECT AND THE CONDUCTIVITY OF HIGH-RESISTANCE SEMICONDUCTORS AT HIGH TEMPERATURES.** ZIEGLER, E. SIEGEL, W. KUEHNEL, G. EXP. TECH. PHYS. 21 (4), 369–73, 1973.
51686	**CHANGES IN THE ELECTRICAL RESISTANCE OF A NICKEL-MANGANESE ORDERED ALLOY DURING IRRADIATION BY FISSION FRAGMENTS.** RAESKII, V. M. NAUMINIKOV, V. I. KISELEV, L. M. SVIRIDOV, A. F. FIZ. METAL. METALLOVED. 35 (5), 932–6, 1973. (FOR ENGLISH TRANSLATION SEE E63173)
51688	**X-RAY PHOTOELECTRON SPECTROSCOPY AND BAND STRUCTURE OF SOLIDS.** SOKOLOV, O. B. FINASHKIN, V. K. FIZ. METAL. METALLOVED. 36 (1), 7–17, 1973. (FOR ENGLISH TRANSLATION SEE E63180)
51689	**MAGNETIC HYSTERESIS IN SINGLE CRYSTALS OF RARE EARTH METAL-COBALT OR YTTRIUM-COBALT COMPOUNDS.** ERMOLENKO, A. S. KOROLEV, A. V. FIZ. METAL. METALLOVED. 36 (1), 52–9, 1973. (FOR ENGLISH TRANSLATION SEE E63182)
51696	**MECHANISM OF FROZEN (RESIDUAL) CONDUCTIVITY OF SEMICONDUCTORS.** SANDOMIRSKII, V. B. ZHDAN, A. G. MESSERER, M. A. GULYAEV, I. B. FIZ. TEKH. POLUPROV. 7 (7), 1314–23, 1973. (FOR ENGLISH TRANSLATION SEE E52929)
51700	**ELECTRICAL CONDUCTIVITY OF P-INDIUM ANTIMONIDE DURING UNIAXIAL COMPRESSION.** VALYASHKO, E. G. KOSHELEV, O. G. PLESKACHEVA, T. B. FIZ. TEKH. POLUPROV. 7 (7), 1360–3, 1973. (FOR ENGLISH TRANSLATION SEE E52933)
51702	**MAGNETORESISTANCE AND ELECTRON SCATTERING ON POLAR OPTICAL VIBRATIONS IN PURE GALLIUM ARSENIDE AND INDIUM PHOSPHIDE CRYSTALS.** VORONINA, T. I. EMELYANENKO, O. V. NASLEDOV, D. N. NEDEOGLO, D. D. FIZ. TEKH. POLUPROV. 7 (7), 1382–8, 1973. (FOR ENGLISH TRANSLATION SEE E52935)
51704	**PROPERTIES OF GALLIUM ARSENIDE CONTAINING A CHROMIUM IMPURITY.** BRODOVOI, V. A. DERIKOT, N. Z. FIZ. TEKH. POLUPROV. 7 (7), 1431–3, 1973. (FOR ENGLISH TRANSLATION SEE E52937)
51710	**STRUCTURAL PARAMETERS AND ELECTRICAL CONDUCTIVITY OF SOLID SPINEL SOLUTIONS OF VANADITES WITH FERRITES.** VARSKOI, B. N. VOROBEV, YU. P. BOGDANOVICH, M. P. VAKHRAMEEV, A. V. MEN, A. N. CHUFAROV, G. N. GETEROGENNYE PROTSESSY UCHASTIEM TVERD. FAZ 107–27, 1970.
51714	**ELECTROOPTICAL ABSORPTION IN ANTIMONY IODIDE SULFIDE.** ZEINALLY, A. KH. MAMEDOV, A. M. EFENDIEV, SH. M. IZV. AKAD. NAUK AZERB. SSR, SER. FIZ.-TEKH. MAT. NAUK (1), 106–10, 1973.
51721	**STRUCTURE AND PROPERTIES OF MERCURY(II) TELLURIDE CRYSTALS.** ALEKSEENKO, L. I. ANTONIV, I. P. SAVITSKII, V. G. FILATOVA, A. K. CHEDZHEMOVA, I. L. IZV. AKAD. NAUK SSSR, NEORG. MATER. 9 (7), 1249–51, 1973.
51723	**OPTICAL PROPERTIES OF TIN ZINC ANTIMONIDE.** VERGER, L. I. KRADINOVA, L. V. PETROV, V. M. PROCHUKHAN, V. D. IZV. AKAD. NAUK SSSR, NEORG. MATER. 9 (7), 1258–9, 1973.
51724	**PHYSICAL PROPERTIES OF CHROMIUM-VANADIUM-GERMANIUM SOLID SOLUTIONS.** RYKOVA, M. A. SABIRZYANOV, A. V. GEL'D, P. V. IZV. AKAD. NAUK SSSR, NEORG. MATER. 9 (7), 1260–1, 1973.

EPIC Number | Bibliographic Citation

51725 DIELECTRIC CONSTANT OF CALCIUM METATITANATE-STRONTIUM METANIOBATE-SYSTEM MATERIALS.
PLINER, T. A. VOVKOTRUB, E. G.
KASIMOV, G. G.
IZV. AKAD. NAUK SSSR, NEORG. MATER.
9 (7), 1272, 1973.

51729 INTENSITY DEPENDENCE OF PHOTOCONDUCTIVITY AND PARAMETERS OF RECOMBINATION CENTERS.
VATEVA, E.
IZV. FIZ. INST. ANEB (AT. NAUCHNOEKSP. BAZA), BULG. AKAD. NAUK.
23, 77-93, 1973.

51730 BEHAVIOR OF A COPPER IMPURITY IN A CADMIUM TIN ARSENIDE COMPOUND.
VOEVODINA, O. T. VYATKIN, A. P.
VOEVODIN, V. G. OTMAN, YA. I. OTTS, V. L.
IZV. VYSSH. UCHEB. ZAVED., FIZ.
16 (7), 39-44, 1973.
(FOR ENGLISH TRANSLATION SEE E79154)

51732 PHYSICAL PROPERTIES OF SOLID SOLUTIONS AT LOW TEMPERATURES.
RYKOVA, M. A. SABIRZYANOV, A. V.
GELD, P. V.
IZV. VYSSH. UCHEB. ZAVED., FIZ.
16 (7), 134-6, 1973.
(FOR ENGLISH TRANSLATION SEE E79136)

51733 IMPURITY PHOTOCONDUCTIVITY OF N-TYPE BETA-SILICON CARBIDE CRYSTALS.
ALTAISKII, YU. M. KALABUKHOV, N. P.
KISELEV, V. S.
IZV. VYSSH. UCHEB. ZAVED., FIZ.
16 (7), 139-40, 1973.
(FOR ENGLISH TRANSLATION SEE E79186)

51734 STRUCTURE AND THERMAL STABILITY OF SPUTTERED GOLD-TANTALUM FILMS.
CHRISTOU, A. DAY, H.
J. APPL. PHYS.
44 (8), 3386-93, 1973.

51735 INFRARED STIMULABLE GREEN EMISSION AND RED EMISSION UP-CONVERSION PHOSPHORS.
LOW, N. M. P.
J. CAN. CERAM. SOC.
41, 7-12, 1972.

51736 PREPARATION AND CHARACTERIZATION OF INFRARED STIMULABLE RARE EARTH TRIFLUORIDE PHOSPHORS.
LOW, N. M. P. MAJOR, A. L.
J. CAN. CERAM. SOC.
41, 13-18, 1972.

51737 ENERGY TRANSFER UPCONVERSION IN LANTHANUM(III) FLUORIDE DOPED WITH PRASEODYMIUM(3+).
ZALUCHA, D. J. WRIGHT, J. C. FONG, F. K.
J. CHEM. PHYS.
59 (3), 997-1001, 1973.

51738 ENERGY TRANSFER IN MONOCHROMATICALLY EXCITED NITRIC OXIDE.
MELTON, L. A. KLEMPERER, W.
J. CHEM. PHYS.
59 (3), 1099-115, 1973.

51739 PHOTOELECTRON SPECTRUM OF PENTABORANE.
JONES, R. W. KOSKI, W. S.
J. CHEM. PHYS.
59 (3), 1228-31, 1973.

51740 MAGNETIC PROPERTIES OF POLYCRYSTALLINE MOLYBDENUM DISULFIDES.
BELOUGNE, P. ZANCHETTA, J. V.
ROUILLON, J. C.
J. CHIM. PHYS. PHYSICOCHIM. BIOL.
70 (4), 682-3, 1973.

51741 ELECTRIC CONDUCTIVITY AND PROTON DIFFUSION IN OXONIUM PERCHLORATE.
POTIER, A. ROUSSELET, D.
J. CHIM. PHYS. PHYSICOCHIM. BIOL.
70 (6), 873-8, 1973.

51742 VAPOR AND FLUX GROWTH OF GAMMA-INDIUM SULFIDE, A NEW MODIFICATION OF INDIUM SESQUISULFIDE.
DIEHL, R. NITSCHE, R.
J. CRYST. GROWTH
20 (1), 38-46, 1973.

51743 FACTORS INFLUENCING THE LUMINOUS DECAY CHARACTERISTICS OF CERIUM(3+) ACTIVATED YTTRIUM ALUMINUM OXIDE.
GIBBONS, E. F. TIEN, T. Y. DELOSH, R. G.
ZACMANIDIS, P. J. STADLER, H. L.
J. ELECTROCHEM. SOC.
120 (6), 835-7, 1973.

51744 ELECTRICAL CONDUCTANCE OF MOLTEN ALKALI CARBONATE BINARY MIXTURES.
SPEDDING, P. L.
J. ELECTROCHEM. SOC.
120 (8), 1049-52, 1973.

51746 SILVER/SILVER IODIDE/SILVER THERMOCELL.
HUNGER, H. F.
J. ELECTROCHEM. SOC.
120 (9), 1157-61, 1973.

51747 ELECTRICAL CONDUCTIVITY OF CALCIUM OXIDE-DOPED NONSTOICHIOMETRIC CERIUM DIOXIDE FROM 700 TO 1500.
BLUMENTHAL, R. N. BRUGNER, F. S.
GARNIER, J. E.
J. ELECTROCHEM. SOC.
120 (9), 1230-7, 1973.

51748 D.C. CONDUCTION AND ELECTROLUMINESCENCE IN DIELECTRIC-EMBEDDED ZINC SULFIDE: MANGANESE, COPPER, OR CHLORINE.
FIKIET, J. M. PLUMB, J. L.
J. ELECTROCHEM. SOC.
120 (9), 1238-41, 1973.

51749 GALLIUM ALUMINUM ARSENIDE-GALLIUM ARSENIDE P-P-N HETEROJUNCTION SOLAR CELLS.
HOVEL, H. J. WOODALL, J. M.
J. ELECTROCHEM. SOC.
120 (9), 1246-52, 1973.

51750 EVALUATION OF PROCESSES USED TO FABRICATE LIGHT-EMITTING DIODES.
SUMMERS, C. J. BLACK, J. F. REID, F. J.
J. ELECTRON. MATER.
2 (3), 387-402, 1973.

51752 ELECTRON TRANSFER SPECTRA OF TETRAVALENT LANTHANIDE IONS IN ZIRCONIUM DIOXIDE.
VAN VUGT, N. WIGMANS, T. BLASSE, G.
J. INORG. NUCL. CHEM.
35 (7), 2601-2, 1973.

51753 CRYSTAL STRUCTURE AND MAGNETIC PROPERTIES OF SOME 7:3 BINARY PHASES BETWEEN LANTHANIDES AND METALS OF THE 8TH GROUP.
OLCESE, G. L.
J. LESS-COMMON METALS
33 (1), 71-81, 1973.

51754 CORRELATION BETWEEN COERCIVE FIELD AND STRUCTURE OF SAMARIUM-COBALT.
KHAN, Y. QURESHI, A. H.
J. LESS-COMMON METALS
32 (2), 307-10, 1973.

51758 PHOTOCAPACITANCE IN THE STUDY OF NONRADIATIVE CENTERS.
HENRY, C. H.
J. LUMIN.
7, 127-45, 1973.

51759 FUNDAMENTALS OF STIMULATED EMISSION IN SEMICONDUCTORS.
PILKUHN, M. H.
J. LUMIN.
7, 269-83, 1973.

51760 ISOELECTRONIC TRAPS IN SEMICONDUCTORS (EXPERIMENTAL).
DEAN, P. J.
J. LUMIN.
7, 51-78, 1973.

51761 STUDY OF LANTHANUM FERRITE FROM MOESSBAUER SPECTRA.
DROFENIK, M. HANZEL, D. MOLJK, A.
J. MATER. SCI.
8 (7), 924-7, 1973.

51762 PLASMA SPRAYING OF FERRITES.
PREECE, I. ANDREWS, C. W. D.
J. MATER. SCI.
8 (7), 964-7, 1973.

51764 USE OF STRIP-LINE CONFIGURATION IN MICROWAVE MOISTURE MEASUREMENTS. II.
KENT, M.
J. MICROWAVE POWER
8 (2), 189-94, 1973.

51765 SPECTRUM OF WATER VAPOR IN THE 1.9 AND 2.7 MU-REGIONS.
PUGH, L. A. RAO, N. K.
J. MOL. SPECTROSC.
47 (3), 403-8, 1973.

51767 FLUORESCENCE SPECTRUM OF CHLORINE DIOXIDE INDUCED BY THE 4765 A ARGON-ION LASER LINE.
CURL, R. F., JR. ABE, K. BISSINGER, J.
BENNETT, C. TITTEL, F. K.
J. MOL. SPECTROSC.
48 (1), 72-85, 1973.

51768 ELECTRICAL CONDUCTIVITY AND THERMOELECTRIC POWER OF LIQUID SILVER ANTIMONY DITELLURIDE.
NGUYEN, V. D.
J. NON-CRYST. SOLIDS
12 (2), 161-7, 1973.

EPIC Number	Bibliographic Citation
51769	**ELECTRICAL CONDUCTIVITY AND THERMOELECTRIC POWER IN AMORPHOUS ARSENIC–SELENIUM–THALLIUM SEMICONDUCTORS.** STRUNK, R. J. NON-CRYST. SOLIDS 12 (2), 168–76, 1973.
51772	**ABSORPTION AND FLUORESCENCE OF LEAD IN GERMANATE, BORATE AND PHOSPHATE GLASSES.** REISFELD, R. LEIBLICH, N. J. NON-CRYST. SOLIDS 12 (2), 207–12, 1973.
51774	**PRINCIPLES OF ELECTRICAL BEHAVIOR OF AMORPHOUS SEMICONDUCTOR ALLOYS.** VAN ROOSBROECK, W. J. NON-CRYST. SOLIDS 12 (2), 232–62, 1973.
51775	**ELECTRICAL CONDUCTIVITY AND X-RAY STUDY OF A HIGH–TEMPERATURE TRANSITION IN URANIUM OXIDE.** NAITO, K. TSUJI, T. MATSUI, T. J. NUCL. MATER. 48 (1), 58–66, 1973.
51779	**BAND STRUCTURE OF COPPER(I) BROMIDE.** KHAN, M. A. J. PHYS. (PARIS) 34 (7), 597–602, 1973.
51780	**STRESS–DEPENDENT EPR OF RUTHENIUM(3+) IN YTTRIUM GALLIUM GARNET AND THE MAGNETOSTRICTION OF RUTHENIUM IN GARNETS.** HODGES, J. A. CHANTEREAU, F. J. PHYS. (PARIS) 34 (7), 623–8, 1973.
51781	**3D–ELECTRON DELOCALIZATION IN THE SEMIMETALLIC COMPOUNDS M SELENOFERRATE WITH M = TITANIUM, CHROMIUM, IRON, COBALT, NICKEL.** REGNARD, J. R. CHAPPERT, J. J. PHYS. (PARIS) 34 (8–9), 721–31, 1973.
51782	**NEW APPROACH TO BAND GAPS IN ORDERED AND DISORDERED MATERIALS.** JONES, R. J. PHYS. 6 C (14), 2318–28, 1973.
51783	**NARROW–BAND CHARGE TRANSPORT IN TIN TETRAIODIDE.** WHALL, T. E. JUZOVA, V. J. PHYS. 6 C (14), 2329–36, 1973.
51787	**THERMAL CONDUCTIVITY OF NICKEL(II) OXIDE AND COBALT(II) OXIDE AT THE NEEL TEMPERATURE.** LEWIS, F. B. SAUNDERS, N. H. J. PHYS. C 6 C (15), 2525–32, 1973.
51789	**EFFECT OF NONSTOICHIOMETRY ON THE MAGNETIC PROPERTIES OF NICKEL(II) SULFIDE.** GAUTIER, F. KRILL, G. LAPIERRE, M. F. ROBERT, C. J. PHYS. 6 C (16), L320–L323, 1973.
51790	**INFRARED STUDIES OF THE ACCEPTOR STATES IN EPITAXIAL FILMS OF GALLIUM ARSENIDE.** KIRKMAN, R. F. STRADLING, R. A. J. PHYS. 6 C (16), L324–L328, 1973.
51791	**IMPACT IONIZATION THRESHOLDS IN SEMICONDUCTORS.** BALLINGER, R. A. MAJOR, K. G. MALLINSON, J. R. J. PHYS. 6 C (16), 2573–85, 1973.
51792	**LARGE SATELLITE SEPARATIONS IN CORE ELECTRON PHOTOEMISSION LINES FROM TITANIUM TRIFLUORIDE.** WALLBANK, B. JOHNSON, C. E. MAIN, I. G. J. PHYS. 6 C (17), L340–L342, 1973.
51793	**THERMOLUMINESCENCE SPECTRUM OF HEAVILY IRRADIATED LITHIUM FLUORIDE.** JAIN, K. BAPAT, V. N. KATHURIA, S. P. J. PHYS. 6 C (17), L343–L344, 1973.
51795	**EFFECTIVE IONIC CHARGES AND CHEMICAL BONDING IN GALLIUM SELENIDE AND GALLIUM TELLURIDE FROM CHEMICAL SHIFTS OF X–RAY K ABSORPTION DISCONTINUITIES.** SAPRE, V. B. MANDE, C. J. PHYS. CHEM. SOLIDS 34 (8), 1351–6, 1973.
51796	**MAGNETIC PROPERTIES OF VAPOR GROWN CRYSTALS OF HEXAGONAL CHROMIUM TELLURIDE.** STREET, G. B. SAWATZKY, E. LEE, K. J. PHYS. CHEM. SOLIDS 34 (8), 1453–5, 1973.
51799	**DEFECT CENTERS IN ANTIMONY DOPED SODIUM CHLORIDE CRYSTALS.** RADHAKRISHNA, S. KARGUPPIKAR, A. M. J. PHYS. CHEM. SOLIDS 34 (9), 1497–505, 1973.
51800	**THEORY OF MAGNETISM FOR SEMIMETALLIC URANIUM COMPOUNDS.** ADACHI, H. IMOTO, S. J. PHYS. CHEM. SOLIDS 34 (9), 1537–42, 1973.
51802	**FERROELECTRIC AND OPTICAL PROPERTIES OF BARIUM TITANIUM NIOBIUM OXIDE SINGLE CRYSTALS.** ITOH, Y. IWASAKI, H. J. PHYS. CHEM. SOLIDS 34 (10), 1639–45, 1973.
51805	**PAIR SCATTERING AND THE PHOTOEMISSION EFFECT IN GALLIUM ARSENIDE.** SARAVIA, L. R. DUOMARCO, J. L. J. PHYS. CHEM. SOLIDS 34 (10), 1661–73, 1973.
51806	**MOESSBAUER EFFECT STUDY OF BRIARTITE.** IMBERT, P. VARRET, F. WINTENBERGER, M. J. PHYS. CHEM. SOLIDS 34 (10), 1675–82, 1973.
51807	**THERMOELECTRIC POWER OF ANTIFERROMAGNETIC SEMICONDUCTORS NEAR THE NEEL TEMPERATURE.** SUGIHARA, K. J. PHYS. CHEM. SOLIDS 34 (10), 1727–36, 1973.
51809	**MICROWAVE DIELECTRIC CONSTANT AND ITS TEMPERATURE DEPENDENCE IN CADMIUM INDIUM SULFIDE.** SLAGSVOLD, B. J. J. PHYS. CHEM. SOLIDS 34 (10), 1752–4, 1973.
51813	**LUMINESCENCE OF MANGANESE–DOPED ZINC SELENIDE.** JONES, G. WOODS, J. J. PHYS. 6 D (13), 1640–51, 1973.
51821	**DILUTE INTERMETALLIC COMPOUNDS. PROPERTIES OF ZINC TRANSITION METAL ZETA PHASES.** CAPLIN, A. D. DUNLOP, J. B. J. PHYS. 3 F (8), 1621–47, 1973.
51822	**PARAMAGNETIC SUSCEPTIBILITY OF SAMARIUM–ZINC INTERMETALLIC.** STEWART, A. M. J. PHYS. METAL PHYS. 3 F (5), 1024–1030, 1973.
51824	**DOMAIN WALL MOTION IN FERROELECTRIC SWITCHING.** HAYASHI, M. J. PHYS. SOC. JAP. 34 (6), 1686, 1973.
51825	**MAGNETIZATION OF TWO–DIMENSIONAL FERROMAGNET POTASSIUM TETRAFLUOROCUPRATE(II).** KUBO, H. SHIMOHIGASHI, K. YAMADA, I. J. PHYS. SOC. JAP. 34 (6), 1687, 1973.
51826	**EFFECT OF PRESSURE ON NEEL TEMPERATURE OF ZINC CHROMIUM SELENIDE.** FUJII, H. KAMIGAICHI, T. OKAMOTO, T. J. PHYS. SOC. JAP. 34 (6), 1689, 1973.
51828	**ANISOTROPY OF MAGNETORESISTANCE OF IRON CHROMIUM SULFIDE SINGLE CRYSTALS.** WATANABE, T. J. PHYS. SOC. JAP. 34 (6), 1695, 1973.
51829	**FINE STRUCTURE IN THE ABSORPTION SPECTRA OF WEAK FERROMAGNETIC IRON BORATE.** HIRANO, M. YOSHINO, I. OKUDA, T. TSUSHIMA, T. J. PHYS. SOC. JAP. 35 (1), 299, 1973.
51831	**ELECTRICAL PROPERTIES OF INDIUM SELENIDE.** MORI, S. J. PHYS. SOC. JAP. 35 (1), 310, 1973.
51833	**CALCULATION OF THE STRENGTH OF THE IMPURITY CYCLOTRON–RESONANCE HARMONICS.** MIYAKE, S. J. J. PHYS. SOC. JAP. 35 (2), 551–7, 1973.
51834	**DIELECTRIC AND ELECTROOPTIC PROPERTIES OF (POTASSIUM LEAD) (ZINC NIOBIUM) OXIDE.** KOJIMA, F. NOMURA, S. J. PHYS. SOC. JAP. 35 (2), 624, 1973.

EPIC Number	Bibliographic Citation

51835 **OPTICAL PROPERTIES OF LEAD IODIDE SINGLE CRYSTALS.**
KATO, Y. GOTO, T. UETA, M.
J. PHYS. SOC. JAP.
35 (2), 625, 1973.

51836 **EFFECT OF PHASE TRANSITION ON AN OPTICAL SPECTRUM IN AMMONIUM BROMIDE-COPPER(2+) ION, PHASE III-IV.**
TAKAGI, R. NAKAYAMA, S. KAWAMORI, A.
SUZUKI, K.
J. PHYS. SOC. JAP.
35 (2), 626, 1973.

51839 **MICROWAVE RESONANCE AND RELAXATION OF EXCESS IRON-MANGANESE FERRITES.**
WATANABE, Y.
J. PHYS. SOC. JAP.
35 (3), 716-21, 1973.

51840 **NEUTRON DIFFRACTION STUDY IN THE ONE-DIMENSIONAL ANTIFERROMAGNET POTASSIUM TRIFLUOROCUPRATE(I).**
IKEDA, H. HIRAKAWA, K.
J. PHYS. SOC. JAP.
35 (3), 722-8, 1973.

51847 **CHLORINE-NUCLEAR-MAGNETIC-RESONANCE STUDY OF THE FERROMAGNET GADOLINIUM TRICHLORIDE.**
HESSLER, J. P.
PHYS. REV.
8 B (7), 3151-60, 1973.

51848 **ABSORPTION AND MAGNETIC-CIRCULAR-DICHROISM SPECTRA OF OCTAHEDRAL CERIUM IONS IN CESIUM SODIUM YTTRIUM CHLORIDE.**
SCHWARTZ, R. W. SCHATZ, P. N.
PHYS. REV.
8 B (7), 3229-36, 1973.

51852 **ELECTRICAL CONDUCTIVITY OF POTASSIUM DIHYDROGEN ARSENATE AND POTASSIUM DIDEUTERIUM ARSENATE.**
FAIRALL, C. W. REESE, W.
PHYS. REV.
8 B (7), 3475-8, 1973.

51856 **X-RAY BAND SPECTRA AND ELECTRONIC STRUCTURE OF TITANIUM DISULFIDE.**
FISCHER, D. W.
PHYS. REV.
8 B (8), 3576-82, 1973.

51858 **PERCOLATION VIEW OF TRANSPORT PROPERTIES IN SODIUM TUNGSTEN OXIDE.**
LIGHTSEY, P. A.
PHYS. REV.
8 B (8), 3586-9, 1973.

51859 **DE HAAS-VAN ALPHEN EFFECT AND FERMI SURFACE OF THE ORDERED ALLOY YTTRIUM ZINC.**
JAN, J.-P.
PHYS. REV.
8 B (8), 3590-4, 1973.

51860 **INFLUENCE OF A STRONG MAGNETIC FIELD ON THE TETRAGONAL PHASE OF VANADIUM SILICON-TYPE COMPOUNDS.**
TING, C. S. GANGULY, A. K.
ZEYHER, R. BIRMAN, J. L.
PHYS. REV.
8 B (8), 3665-74, 1973.
(ERRATUM: 9 B (6), 2784, 1974)

51861 **CONDUCTION IN RANDOM SYSTEMS.**
AMBEGAOKAR, V. COCHRAN, S. KURKIJARVI, J.
PHYS. REV.
8 B (8), 3682-8, 1973.
(AD 776 479)

51862 **BAND STRUCTURES OF TRANSITION-METAL-DICHALCOGENIDE LAYER COMPOUNDS.**
MATTHEISS, L. F.
PHYS. REV.
8 B (8), 3719-40, 1973.

51863 **MAGNETIC PROPERTIES OF SOME COMPLEXES OF MOLYBDENUM IONS.**
DE, I. DESAI, V. P. CHAKRAVARTY, A. S.
PHYS. REV.
8 B (8), 3769-72, 1973.

51864 **BAND STRUCTURE AND FERMI-SURFACE PROPERTIES OF ORDERED BETA-BRASS.**
SKRIVER, H. L. CHRISTENSEN, N. E.
PHYS. REV.
8 B (8), 3778-93, 1973.

51865 **EFFECT OF DISORDER ON THE CONDUCTION-BAND EFFECTIVE MASS, VALENCE-BAND SPIN-ORBIT SPLITTING, AND THE DIRECT BAND GAP IN III-V ALLOYS.**
BEROLO, O. WOOLLEY, J. C. VAN VECHTEN, J. A.
PHYS. REV.
8 B (8), 3794-8, 1973.

51866 **IMPURITY CONDUCTION AND THE METAL-NONMETAL TRANSITION IN MANGANESE-DOPED GALLIUM ARSENIDE.**
WOODBURY, D. A. BLAKEMORE, J. S.
PHYS. REV.
8 B (8), 3803-10, 1973.

51869 **PHOTOCONDUCTIVITY ASSOCIATED WITH LANDAU STRUCTURE IN GALLIUM ANTIMONIDE.**
FILION, A. FORTIN, E.
PHYS. REV.
8 B (8), 3852-60, 1973.

51870 **INTERBAND GAMMA SUB SIX TO GAMMA SUB EIGHT TRANSITION MAGNETOABSORPTION IN MERCURY TELLURIDE.**
GULDNER, Y. RIGAUX, C.
GRYNBERG, M. MYCIELSKI, A.
PHYS. REV.
8 B (8), 3875-83, 1973.

51871 **SUBMILLIMETER CYCLOTRON RESONANCE AND RELATED PHENOMENA IN MERCURY TELLURIDE.**
TUCHENDLER, J. GRYNBERG, M. COUDER, Y.
THOME, H. LE TOULLEC, R.
PHYS. REV.
8 B (8), 3884-94, 1973.

51874 **ULTRASONIC-WAVE DISPERSION IN CADMIUM SULFIDE.**
KRISCHER, C.
PHYS. REV.
8 B (8), 3908-13, 1973.

51875 **TEMPERATURE DEPENDENCE OF THE EPR SPECTRA OF NIOBIUM-DOPED TITANIUM DIOXIDE.**
ZIMMERMANN, P. H.
PHYS. REV.
8 B (8), 3917-27, 1973.

51876 **PHOTOEMISSION STUDIES OF CESIUM TELLURIDE.**
POWELL, R. A. SPICER, W. E.
FISHER, G. B. GREGORY, P.
PHYS. REV.
8 B (8), 3987-95, 1973.

51877 **COMMENT ON AC CONDUCTIVITY OF SCANDIUM OXIDE AND A NEW HOPPING MODEL FOR CONDUCTIVITY.**
ROCKSTAD, H. K. PIKE, G. E.
PHYS. REV.
8 B (8), 4026-7, 1973.

51878 **THERMOLUMINESCENCE OF POTASSIUM BROMIDE CRYSTALS.**
LEVINSON, J. HALPERIN, A. ROTH, M.
PHYS. REV.
8 B (8), 4041-2, 1973.

51879 **APPROXIMATE MEAN ABSORPTION COEFFICIENT FOR WATER.**
COAKLEY, J. A., JR.
J. QUANT. SPECTROSC. RADIAT. TRANSFER
13 (10), 937-52, 1973.

51882 **ANISOTROPIC CONDUCTIVITY OF LEAD CHLORIDE FLUORIDE.**
SCHOONMAN, J. DIRKSEN, G. J. BLASSE, G.
J. SOLID STATE CHEM.
7 (3), 245-9, 1973.

51883 **MAGNETIC PROPERTIES OF THE COMPOUNDS (MANGANESE, CHROMIUM) ANTIMONIDE, VANADIUM ANTIMONIDE AND (MANGANESE, VANADIUM)ANTIMONIDE WITH B8-TYPE STRUCTURES.**
BOUWMAN, J. VAN BRUGGEN, C. F. HAAS, C.
J. SOLID STATE CHEM.
7 (3), 255-61, 1973.

51884 **COMPUTER SIMULATION OF DEFECTS IN AMMONIUM PERCHLORATE.**
GOLDSTEIN, M. KEENAN, A. G.
J. SOLID STATE CHEM.
7 (3), 286-91, 1973.

51885 **MOESSBAUER STUDY OF THE THERMAL DECOMPOSITION PRODUCTS OF BARIUM FERRATE(VI).**
ICHIDA, T.
J. SOLID STATE CHEM.
7 (3), 308-15, 1973.

51886 **MAGNETIC PROPERTIES OF THE MANGANESE-GALLIUM-ALUMINUM-GERMANIUM SYSTEM.**
STREET, G. B.
J. SOLID STATE CHEM.
7 (3), 316-20, 1973.

51888 **MAGNETIC SUSCEPTIBILITY OF COBALT(4+) IN OCTAHEDRAL AND TETRAHEDRAL ENVIRONMENTS.**
CANDELA, G. A. KAHN, A. H. NEGAS, T.
J. SOLID STATE CHEM.
7 (4), 360-9, 1973.

51889 **MAGNETIC PROPERTIES OF URANIUM CHALCOGENIDES WITH COMPOSITION CLOSE TO UY(2).**
SUSKI, W.
J. SOLID STATE CHEM.
7 (4), 385-99, 1973.

51890 **MAGNETIC AND ELECTRICAL PROPERTIES OF RARE EARTH CHROMIUM SELENIDE.**
GOROCHOV, O. MC KINZIE, H.
J. SOLID STATE CHEM.
7 (4), 400-7, 1973.

EPIC Number	Bibliographic Citation
51891	**PREPARATION AND PROPERTIES OF SOME TRANSITION METAL PHOSPHORUS TRISULFIDE COMPOUNDS.** TAYLOR, B. E. STEGER, J. WOLD, A. J. SOLID STATE CHEM. 7 (4), 461-7, 1973.
51892	**LUMINESCENCE OF MANGANESE(2+) ION IN STRONTIUM GALLIUM OXIDE LANTHANUM MAGNESIUM GALLIUM OXIDE AND BARIUM GALLIUM OXIDE.** VERSTEGEN, J. M. P. J. J. SOLID STATE CHEM. 7 (4), 468-73, 1973.
51895	**TUNNELING STUDIES OF THE FORMATION OF INTERMETALLIC COMPOUNDS IN GOLD-LEAF FILMS.** HEBARD, A. F. J. VAC. SCI. TECHNOL. 10 (5), 606-10, 1973.
51896	**RADIO FREQUENCY SPUTTERED LUMINESCENT RARE EARTH OXYSULFIDE FILMS.** MAPLE, T. G. BUCHANAN, R. A. J. VAC. SCI. TECHNOL. 10 (5), 616-20, 1973.
51900	**FIELD EFFECTS IN EXTREMELY THIN CRYSTALS OF BISMUTH TELLURIUM SULFIDE.** GROTE, U. H. SOONPAA, H. H. J. VAC. SCI. TECHNOL. 10 (5), 723-4, 1973.
51901	**AMORPHOUS THIN FILMS.** WOOD, C. GILBERT, L. R. MUELLER, R. GARNER, C. M. J. VAC. SCI. TECHNOL. 10 (5), 739-43, 1973.
51902	**SUBSTRATE EFFECTS IN THE THEORY OF NEGATIVE DIFFERENTIAL RESISTANCE.** HAYES, T. M. THORNBURG, D. D. J. VAC. SCI. TECHNOL. 10 (5), 744-7, 1973.
51905	**MAGNETOCRYSTALLINE ANISOTROPY CONSTANT IN SAMARIUM(COBALT-COPPER) BASE ALLOY.** KATAYAMA, T. SHIBATA, T. JAP. J. APPL. PHYS. 12 (5), 762-4, 1973.
51907	**SYNTHESIS AND SOME PROPERTIES OF SOLID SOLUTIONS IN THE GALLIUM PHOSPHIDE-ZINC SULFIDE AND GALLIUM PHOSPHIDE-ZINC SELENIDE PSEUDOBINARY SYSTEMS.** SONOMURA, H. URAGAKI, T. MIYAUCHI, T. JAP. J. APPL. PHYS. 12 (7), 968-73, 1973.
51909	**HIGH-FREQUENCY CONDUCTIVITY IN COBALT-IRON FERRITE.** YAMAZAKI, Y. SATOU, M. JAP. J. APPL. PHYS. 12 (7), 998-1000, 1973.
51910	**DETERMINATION OF HOLE AND ELECTRON TRAPS FROM CAPACITANCE MEASUREMENTS.** IKOMA, T. JEPPSSON, B. JAP. J. APPL. PHYS. 12 (7), 1011-19, 1973.
51911	**LOW-FREQUENCY MAGNETIC RESONANCE OBSERVED IN THE THERMAL CHANGE OF THE PERMEABILITY OF FERRITES.** HISATAKE, K. OHTA, K. JAP. J. APPL. PHYS. 12 (7), 1024-7, 1973.
51912	**MAGNETIC PROPERTIES OF SINGLE CRYSTAL MANGANESE-BISMUTH PLATELET.** HONDA, S. HOSOKAWA, Y. KONISHI, S. KUSUDA, T. JAP. J. APPL. PHYS. 12 (7), 1028-35, 1973.
51913	**PHOTOLUMINESCENCE OF 4H-SILICON CARBIDE SINGLE CRYSTALS GROWN FROM THE SILICON MELT.** SUZUKI, A. MATSUNAMI, H. TANAKA, T. JAP. J. APPL. PHYS. 12 (7), 1083-4, 1973.
51914	**EPITAXIAL CADMIUM SULFIDE FILMS FOR TRANSPARENT ELECTRODE.** YOSHIKAWA, A. KONDO, R. SAKAI, Y. JAP. J. APPL. PHYS. 12 (7), 1069-7, 1973.
51915	**VARIATION OF PHOTOCONDUCTIVITY SPECTRA OF AMORPHOUS ARSENIC(III) SELENIDE WITH LIGHT CHOPPING FREQUENCY.** KITAO, M. MOCHIZUKI, T. YAMADA, S JAP. J. APPL. PHYS. 12 (7), 1077-8, 1973.
51916	**DOSE DEPENDENCE OF PHOTOLUMINESCENCE DEGRADATION IN TELLURIUM ION-IMPLANTED GALLIUM ARSENIDE.** LIN, M-S. GAMO, K. MASUDA, K. NAMBA, S. JAP. J. APPL. PHYS. 12 (7), 1092-3, 1973.
51917	**FERROELECTRIC PROPERTIES OF TUNGSTEN-BRONZE TYPE LANTHANUM-LITHIUM SODIUM BARIUM NIOBIUM OXIDE SINGLE CRYSTALS.** MASUDA, Y. WADA, M. JAP. J. APPL. PHYS. 12 (7), 1101-2, 1973.
51918	**LUMINESCENCE OF YTTRIUM OXIDE FILMS DURING ANODIZATION OF YTTRIUM.** MIZUKI, I. BABA, N. TAJIMA, S. JAP. J. APPL. PHYS. 12 (7), 1109-10, 1973.
51920	**ELECTRIC BREAK-DOWN PHENOMENON.** HISATAKE, K. NAKAYAMA, K. OHTA, K. JAP. J. APPL. PHYS. 12 (7), 1116-17, 1973.
51921	**ELECTRICAL CONDUCTION AND PHASE TRANSITION OF COPPER SULFIDES.** OKAMOTO, K. KAWAI, S. JAP. J. APPL. PHYS. 12 (8), 1130-8, 1973.
51922	**MODULATION OF MICROWAVE TRANSMISSION BY ACOUSTOELECTRIC DOMAINS IN CADIUM SULFIDE.** YAMAMOTO, K. WADA, O. ABE, K. JAP. J. APPL. PHYS. 12 (8), 1215-21, 1973.
51923	**EPITAXIAL GROWTH OF CADMIUM MERCURY TELLURIDE.** SARAIE, J. FURUKAWA, S. SAWA, B. TANAKA, T. JAP. J. APPL. PHYS. 12 (8), 1259-60, 1973.
51924	**MEASUREMENT OF OPTICALLY INDUCED REFRACTIVE-INDEX CHANGES WITH SHARP-EDGED ILLUMINATION PATTERN.** YAMAZAKI, Y. SATOU, M. JAP. J. APPL. PHYS. 12 (8), 1269-70, 1973.
51925	**INFRARED OPTICAL ABSORPTION IN CADMIUM ARESNIDE.** IWAMI, M. YOSHIDA, M. KAWABE, K. JAP. J. APPL. PHYS. 12 (8), 1276-7, 1973.
51927	**INFRARED STUDY OF PHOTOELASTICITY IN SEMICONDUCTOR SINGLE CRYSTALS.** BRAUER, K. H. FEUERSTAKE, J. FROEHLICH, F. MOHR, U. KRIST. TECH. 8 (1-3), 253-69, 1973.
51928	**PROPERTIES OF POLAR GADOLINIUM MOLYBDATE. I. OPTICAL STUDIES FOR SWITCHING BEHAVIOR.** KUERSTEN, H. D. BOHM, J. SCHEIDING, C. BLUMBERG, H. KRIST. TECH. 8 (1-3), 303-9, 1973.
51929	**PROPERTIES OF POLAR GADOLINIUM MOLYBDATE. II. MORPHIC PIEZOELECTRIC AND ELASTIC COEFFICIENTS.** SCHEIDING, C. SCHMIDT, G. KUERSTEN, H. D. KRIST. TECH. 8 (1-3), 311-21, 1973.
51930	**PREPARATION AND SOME PHYSICAL-CHEMICAL PROPERTIES OF SYNTHETIC PYRARGYRITE SINGLE CRYSTALS.** GOLOVEI, M. I. GURZAN, M. I. OLEKSEYUK, I. D. REZ, I. S. VOROSHILOV, YU. V. ROMAN, I. YU. KRIST. TECH. 8 (4), 453-6, 1973.
51932	**MORPHOLOGY OF THE DOMAIN STRUCTURE OF ANTIMONY IODIDE SULFIDE CRYSTALS.** ZADOROZHNAYA, L. A. LYAKHOVITSKAYA, V. A. BELYAEV, L. M. KRISTALLOGR1FIYA 18 (3), 579-83, 1973. (FOR ENGLISH TRANSLATION SEE E63230)
51934	**ELECTRON MECHANISM OF THE EFFECT OF RADIATION ON REPOLARIZATION OF FERROELECTRICS.** GREKOV, A. A. MALITSKAYA, M. A. FRIDKIN, V. M. KRISTALLOGRAFIYA 18 (4), 788-95, 1973. (FOR ENGLISH TRANSLATION SEE E63232)
51936	**METAL-SEMICONDUCTOR PHASE DIAGRAM FOR NICKEL SULFIDE SELENIDE.** JARRETT, H. S. BOUCHARD, R. J. GILLSON, J. L. JONES, G. A. MARCUS, S. M. WEIHER, J. F. MATER. RES. BULL. 8 (8), 877-82, 1973.
51937	**NONOHMIC CURRENTS IN INHOMOGENEOUS POLYCRYSTALINE YTTRIUM IRON GARNET.** LARSEN, P. K. METSELAAR, R. MATER. RES. BULL. 8 (8), 882-92, 1973.

EPIC Number	Bibliographic Citation

51938 **ION IMPLANTATION OF ZINC SULFIDE.**
GEORGOBIANI, A. N. KOTLYAREVSKII, M. B.
ZLOBIN, V. N. TODUA, P. A. GENERALOV, YU. P.
DEMENT'EV, B. P.
MATER. RES. BULL.
8 (8), 893–7, 1973.

51939 **ELECTRICAL CONDUCTIVITY OF PURE AND CALCIUM OXIDE-DOPED THORIUM OXIDE CERAMICS.**
MEHROTRA, A. K. MAITI, H. S.
SUBBARAO, E. C.
MATER. RES. BULL.
8 (8), 899–907, 1973.
(AD–780 177)

51940 **NEW FERROMAGNETIC MOLYBDENUM SPINELS.**
BARZ, H.
MATER. RES. BULL.
8 (8), 983–8, 1973.

51941 **INFRARED SPECTRUM OF WATER.**
ROBERTSON, C. W. CURNUTTE, B. WILLIAMS, D.
MOL. PHYS.
26 (1), 183–91, 1973.

51942 **ASSIGNMENT OF THE PHOTOELECTRON SPECTRUM OF SULFUR DIOXIDE.**
LLOYD, D. R. ROBERTS, P. J.
MOL. PHYS.
26 (1), 225–30, 1973.

51947 **CL SUB B-TYPE INTERMETALLIC COMPOUND PALLADIUM MANGANESE TELLURIDE AND ITS MAGNETIC PROPERTIES.**
MASUMOTO, H. WATANABE, K. OHNUMA, S.
NIPPON KINZOKU GAKKAISHI
37 (8), 872–5, 1973.

51949 **TEMPERATURE DEPENDENCE OF IR ABSORPTION IN FUSED QUARTZ AT HIGH TEMPERATURES.**
PRIKHADKO, L. V. BAGDASAROV, KH. S.
OPT. SPEKTROSK.
34 (6), 1210–11, 1973.
(FOR ENGLISH TRANSLATION SEE E54432)

51950 **OPTICAL ABSORPTION SPECTRA OF EXCITED CHROMIUM(3+) IONS IN MAGNESIUM SPINEL AT ROOM AND LIQUID-NITROGEN TEMPERATURES.**
SVIRIDOV, D. T. SEVAST'YANOV, B. K.
OREKHOVA, V. P. SVIRIDOVA, R. K.
VEREMEICHIK, T. F.
OPT. SPEKTROSK.
35 (1), 102–7, 1973.
(FOR ENGLISH TRANSLATION SEE E54435)

51951 **ENERGY SPECTRA OF THE LAMINATED ANTIFERROMAGNETICS LITHIUM TETRAFLUORONICKELATE(II), POTASSIUM TETRAFLUORONICKELATE(II), AND RUBIDIUM TETRAFLUORONICKELATE(II).**
PISAREV, R. V. KARAMYAN, A. A.
NESTEROVA, N. N. SYRNIKOV, P. P.
OPT. SPEKTROSK.
35 (1), 156–8, 1973.
(FOR ENGLISH TRANSLATION SEE E54436)

51952 **LUMINESCENCE AND EXCITATION SPECTRA OF LITHIUM HYDRIDE AND LITHIUM HYDRIDE-D SINGLE CRYSTALS AT LOW TEMPERATURES.**
REBANE, L. VLASOV, B. V. GAVRILOV, F. F.
CHOLAKH, S. O. PIROGOV, V. D.
OPT. SPEKTROSK.
35 (1), 160–2, 1973.
(FOR ENGLISH TRANSLATION SEE E54437)

51954 **EFFECT OF SOME TRACE ADDITIVES ON THE MAGNETIC PARAMETERS OF MANGANESE-MAGNESIUM-ZINC FERRITES FOR MAGNETIC MEMORY. II.**
DZHOGLEV, D. ILIEV, I.
KHIM. IND. (SOFIA)
45 (2), 63–5, 1973.

51960 **STATIC AND MICROWAVE PROPERTIES OF N-GALLIUM ARSENIDE IN THE HOT ELECTRON REGION.**
SAITO, S. OHSUKA, T.
KOGAKUIN DAIGAKU KENKYU HOKOKU
(33), 142–53, 1973.

51962 **PROPERTIES AND FORMATION CONDITIONS FOR ELECTRICALLY CONDUCTING POLYMERIC COATINGS WITH TWO-DIMENSIONALLY ORIENTED FILLER STRUCTURES.**
SHCHIBRYA, N. G. GUL, V. E.
KOLLOID. ZH.
35 (3), 511–16, 1973.
(FOR ENGLISH TRANSLATION SEE E55346)

51964 **SINGLE CRYSTALS OF SILICON ARSENIDE.**
KUNIOKA, A.
KOTAI BUTSURI
8 (6), 337–41, 1973.

51966 **PHYSICAL PROPERTIES OF ZIRCONIUM DIOXIDE AND HAFNIUM DIOXIDE SINGLE CRYSTALS.**
ALEKSANDROV, V. I. LOMONOVA, E. E.
MAIER, A. A. OSIKO, V. V. TATARINTSEV, V. M.
KRATK. SOOBSHCH. FIZ.
(11), 3–7, 1972.

51968 **BAND STRUCTURE OF THE GROUP II-V COMPOUND SEMICONDUCTOR, CADMIUM ANTIMONIDE. I. SYMMETRY PROPERTIES OF CRYSTALS AND THE SPACE GROUP D.**
YAMADA, Y. HASHIMOTO, K.
KYUSHU DAIGAKU KOGAKU SHUHO
46 (3), 363–70, 1973.

51969 **GREEN LUMINESCENCE OF ZINC OXIDE.**
PANDEY, K. N. KANARI, P. S. SINGH, V. B.
LABDEV
9 A (3–4), 220–1, 1971.

51973 **EFFECT OF ELECTRON-PHONON INTERACTION ON OPTICAL AND ELECTRIC PROPERTIES OF ANTIMONY TRISULFIDE SINGLE CRYSTALS.**
AUDZIONIS, A. I. KARPUS, A. S.
LIET. FIZ. RINKINYS
13 (2), 241–9, 1973.

51976 **FINE STRUCTURES IN THE ABSORPTION SPECTRUM OF ALPHA-MANGANESE SULFIDE.**
KOMURA, H.
MEM. FAC. SCI., KYOTO UNIV., SER. PHYS., ASTROPHYS., GEOPHYS. CHEM.
34 (1), 41–59, 1972.

51979 **ANODIZING OF AN ALUMINUM TAPE WITH ALTERNATING CURRENT FOR THE PRODUCTION OF AN ELECTRIC INSULATION LAYER.**
KOROTKOVA, T. S. MARTYNOVA, N. I.
METAL. NEMETAL. POKRYTIYA LEGK. MET. SPLAVOV
89–92, 1972.

51980 **RESISTIVITY OF ALUMINUM-COPPER-LITHIUM ALLOYS DURING TRITIUM(1) ALUMINUM-COPPER-LITHIUM PRECIPITATION.**
THOMPSON, G. E. NOBLE, B.
METAL. SCI. J.
7 (1), 32–5, 1973.

51981 **REFRACTIVE INDEXES OF LIQUIDS AND SOLUTIONS.**
BOGUTH, W.
MICROSC. ACTA
74 (3), 217–21, 1973.

51983 **EFFECT OF ION BOMBARDMENT ON THE ELECTRICAL CONDUCTIVITY OF SILICON DIOXIDE FILMS.**
SHITOVA, E. V. ZORIN, E. I.
PAVLOV, P. V. MUREL, A. V.
MIKROELEKTRONIKA
1 (3), 273–4, 1972.

51984 **TANTALUM THIN FILM ELEMENTS.**
INOUE, Y. HAMANAKA, K.
FUJIWARA, T. HAYAMA, M.
MITSUBISHI DENKI GIHO
46 (6), 701–5, 1972.

51985 **IONIC DISSOCIATION ENERGY IN ELECTRICAL CONDUCTIVITY BEHAVIOR OF POLYMERS.**
MIYAMOTO, T. SHIBAYAMA, K.
MITSUBISHI DENKI LAB. REP.
13 (1-2-3-4), 55–62, 1972.

51987 **DOPING OF CADMIUM SULFIDE SINGLE CRYSTALS WITH LITHIUM DURING THE PRODUCTION OF DIFFUSION ACOUSTOELECTRICAL TRANSDUCERS.**
FAINER, M. SH. SYSOEV, L. A.
ATROSHCHENKO, L. V. OBUKHOVSKII, YA. A.
MONOKRIST. TEKH.
(4), 144–8, 1971.

51988 **DOPING INDIUM TELLURIDE-TYPE SEMICONDUCTORS BY THE ZONE COMPENSATING METHOD.**
ADAMOV, L. S. GALCHINETSKII, L. P.
KORIN, A. I.
MONOKRIST. TEKH.
(6), 38–45, 1972.

51989 **DEPENDENCE OF LUMINESCENCE IN ZINC SULFIDE: MANGANESE PHOSPHOR ON THE CONCENTRATION OF MANGANESE(2+) IONS.**
ATO, Y. MIYAGAWA, S. HUZIMURA, R.
OZAWA, L.
NAGOYA KOGYO. GIJUTSU SHIKENSHO HOKOKU
22 (1), 18–22, 1973.

52004 **X-RAY PHOTOEMISSION MEASUREMENTS OF RUBIDIUM CHLORIDE.**
VESELY, C. J. KINGSTON, D. L. LANGER, D. W.
PHYS. LETT.
44 A (2), 137–8, 1973.

52006 **ANGULAR DEPENDENCE OF INTENSITY, CHEMICAL SHIFT, AND FINE STRUCTURE OF THE DISCONTINUOUS COMPTON SCATTERING.**
MUEHLE, P.
PHYS. LETT.
44 A (5), 315–16, 1973.

52014 **OPTICAL AND SPIN RESONANCE SPECTRA IN OCTAHEDRALLY COORDINATED YTTERBIUM(3+) IONS.**
LOW, W. MOSKOWITZ, H.
PHYS. LETT.
44 A (7), 451–2, 1973.

EPIC Number	Bibliographic Citation
52020	**THERMOELECTRIC EFFECTS IN PURE AND VANADIUM-DOPED TITANIUM(III) OXIDE SINGLE CRYSTALS.** SHIN, S. H. CHANDRASHEKHAR, G. V. LOEHMAN, R. E. HONIG, J. M. PHYS. REV. 8 B (4), 1364-72, 1973.
52024	**SELF-ACTION OF LASER BEAMS IN SEMICONDUCTORS.** DUBEY, P. K. PARANJAPE, V. V. PHYS. REV. 8 B (4), 1514-22, 1973.
52025	**EFFECT OF DEFORMATION ON THE CONDUCTION BAND OF INDIUM ANTIMONIDE.** HOWLETT, W. ZUKOTYNSKI, S. PHYS. REV. 8 B (4), 1523-30, 1973.
52026	**THEORY OF PHONON-ASSISTED HOPPING CONDUCTION IN A PIEZOELECTRIC SEMICONDUCTOR.** TOYABE, T. ASAI, S. PHYS. REV. 8 B (4), 1531-8, 1973.
52028	**PHONON PROPERTIES AND ELECTRON-PHONON INTERACTION IN THALLIUM-DOPED POTASSIUM HALIDES.** BENEDEK, G. TERZI, N. PHYS. REV. 8 B (4), 1746-63, 1973.
52030	**COULOMB EFFECTS ON THE GAIN SPECTRUM OF SEMICONDUCTORS.** BRINKMAN, W. F. LEE, P. A. PHYS. REV. LETT. 31 (4), 237-40, 1973.
52031	**CRITICAL RESISTIVITY NEAR AN ORDER-DISORDER TRANSITION.** THOMAS, G. A. GIRAY, A. B. PARKS, R. D. PHYS. REV. LETT. 31 (4), 241-4, 1973.
52035	**MAGNETIC SUSCEPTIBILITY AS A PROBE OF THE ATOMIC ORDERING IN IRON-ALUMINUM.** HORN, P. M. LAWRENCE, J. PARKS, R. D. THOMAS, G. A. PHYS. REV. LETT. 31 (7), 471-4, 1973.
52040	**TEMPERATURE DEPENDENCE OF THE ABSORPTION COEFFICIENT OF ALKALI HALIDES IN THE MULTIPHONON REGIME.** MARADUDIN, A. A. MILLS, D. L. PHYS. REV. LETT. 31 (11), 718-21, 1973.
52044	**THE 0.94, 1.01, AND 1.29 EV LUMINESCENCE BANDS IN LASER-EXCITED N-GALLIUM ARSENIDE.** GLINCHUK, K. D. LINNIK, L. F. RODIONOV, V. E. PHYS. STATUS SOLIDI 18 A (1), K23-K26, 1973.
52046	**PHOTOVOLTAIC INVESTIGATION OF THE HOMOGENEITY OF GALLIUM SELENIDE SINGLE CRYSTALS.** ADDUCI, F. FERRARA, M. TANTALO, P. PHYS. STATUS SOLIDI 18 A (1), K35-8, 1973.
52048	**GALVANOMAGNETIC PROPERTIES OF COPPER CHROMIUM SELENIDE BROMIDE.** VALIEV, L. M. KERIMOV, I. G. NAMAZOV, Z. M. PHYS. STATUS SOLIDI 18 A (2), K117-K120, 1973.
52050	**INFRARED LUMINESCENCE OF GALLIUM ARSENIDE PHOSPHIDE.** HEINE, G. MORGENSTERN, M. PHYS. STATUS SOLIDI 18 A (2), K139-K141, 1973.
52051	**INFLUENCE OF HYDROSTATIC PRESSURE ON THE FERROELECTRIC PHASE TRANSITION OF CADMIUM TITANATE(IV) CERAMICS.** MARTIN, G. HEGENBARTH, E. PHYS. STATUS SOLIDI 18 A (2), K151-K152, 1973.
52053	**GALVANO- AND THERMOMAGNETIC PROPERTIES OF PLATINUM ANTIMONIDE.** ABDULLAEV, A. A. ANGELOVA, L. A. KUZNETSOV, V. K. ORMONT, A. B. PASHINTSEV, YU. I. PHYS. STATUS SOLIDI 18 A (2), 459-63, 1973.
52054	**SEMIINSULATING SILICON ZINC PHOSPHIDE.** ZIEGLER, E. SIEGEL, W. KUEHNEL, G. K. PHYS. STATUS SOLIDI 18 A (2), 483-7, 1973.
52055	**SPONTANEOUS AND STIMULATED EMISSION IN GRADED CADMIUM SULFIDE SELENIDE CRYSTALS.** HUBER, G. BILLE, J. BRAUN, W. FISCHER, T. PHYS. STATUS SOLIDI 18 A (2), 489-94, 1973.

EPIC Number	Bibliographic Citation
52057	**LONG-LIFETIME PHOTOLUMINESCENCE IN GALLIUM SELENIDE.** VOITCHOVSKY, J. P. MERCIER, A. PHYS. STATUS SOLIDI 18 A (2), 545-51, 1973.
52058	**DOMAINS IN SINTERED COBALT-SAMARIUM MAGNETS.** LIVINGSTON, J. D. PHYS. STATUS SOLIDI 18 A (2), 579-88, 1973.
52061	**OPTICAL PROPERTIES AND ENERGY BAND SCHEME OF CUPROUS SULFIDES WITH ORDERED AND DISORDERED COPPER IONS.** MULDER, B. J. PHYS. STATUS SOLIDI 18 A (2), 633-8, 1973.
52064	**MEASUREMENT AND INTERPRETATION OF THE IONIC CONDUCTION IN ALKALI HALIDES.** NADLER, C. ROSSEL, J. PHYS. STATUS SOLIDI 18 A (2), 711-22, 1973.
52065	**MAGNETIC PROPERTIES OF THE COMPOUND URANIUM PHOSPHORUS TELLURIUM.** ZYGMUNT, A. CZOPNIK, A. PHYS. STATUS SOLIDI 18 A (2), 731-4, 1973.
52072	**VALENCE-BAND PROPERTIES OF BISMUTH(III) TELLURIDE FROM GALVANOMAGNETIC MEASUREMENTS.** SOLOGUB, V. V. GOLETSKAYA, A. D. LANG, I. G. PAVLOV, S. T. PHYS. STATUS SOLIDI 58 B (2), 457-70, 1973.
52073	**PHOTOELECTRIC PROPERTIES OF MAGNESIUM-SILCON, MAGNESIUM-GERMANIUM AND MAGNESIUM-TIN. II. ULTRAVIOLET EXCITATION.** CARDONA, M. TEJEDA, J. SHEVCHIK, N. J. LANGER, D. W. PHYS. STATUS SOLIDI 58 B (2), 483-91, 1973.
52075	**PSEUDOPOTENTIAL BAND STRUCTURE OF ZINC(II) OXIDE.** BLOOM, S. ORTENBURGER, I. PHYS. STATUS SOLIDI 58 B (2), 561-6, 1973.
52076	**OPTICAL PROPERTIES AND COLLECTIVE EXCITATIONS IN MOLYBDENUM SULFIDE AND NIOBIUM SELENIDE IN THE 1.7 TO 30 EV RANGE.** MARTIN, L. MAMY, R. COUGET, A. RAISIN, C. PHYS. STATUS SOLIDI 58 B (2), 623-7, 1973.
52077	**MAGNETIC PROPERTIES OF MANGANESE-DOPED MERCURY TELLURIDE.** SAVAGE, H. RHYNE, J. J. HOLM, R. CULLEN, J. R. CARROLL, C. E. WOHLFARTH, E. P. PHYS. STATUS SOLIDI 58 B (2), 685-9, 1973.
52078	**MEAN SQUARE VIBRATIONAL AMPLITUDES IN LEAD TELLURIDE.** GHEZZI, C. PHYS. STATUS SOLIDI 58 B (2), 737-44, 1973.
52079	**TWO-PHOTON EXCITATION SPECTRA OF TRIVALENT RARE EARTH ION LUMINESCENCE IN CRYSTALS.** APANASEVICH, P. A. GINTOFT, R. I. KOROL'KOV, V. S. MAKHANEK, A. G. SKRIPKO, G. A. PHYS. STATUS SOLIDI 58 B (2), 745-57, 1973.
52080	**LASER EMISSION IN CADMIUM SELENIDE DUE TO EXCITON-EXCITON AND EXCITON-ELECTRON INTERACTION.** BRAUN, W. BILLE, J. FISCHER, T. HUBER, G. PHYS. STATUS SOLIDI 58 B (2), 759-65, 1973.
52083	**SIZE DEPENDENCE OF MAGNETORESISTANCE OF MANY-VALLEY SEMICONDUCTORS.** MITIN, V. V. PRIMA, N. A. PHYS. STATUS SOLIDI 58 B (2), 809-19, 1973.
52084	**HOT ELECTRON FARADAY ROTATION AND BIREFRINGENCE IN SEMICONDUCTORS WITH NONPARABOLIC ENERGY BANDS.** ALMAZOV, L. A. PHYS. STATUS SOLIDI 58 B (2), 821-30, 1973.
52085	**EFFECT OF DEFORMATION ON OPTICAL ABSORPTION OF MAGNESIUM(II) OXIDE SINGLE CRYSTALS.** TURNER, T. J. MURPHY, C. SCHULTHEISS, T. PHYS. STATUS SOLIDI 58 B (2), 843-7, 1973.

EPIC Number	Bibliographic Citation

52086 **ANALYSIS OF SUSCEPTIBILITY AND MAGNETIZATION OF (GADOLINIUM, TERBIUM, DYSPROSIUM, HOLMIUM, ERBIUM, OR THULIUM)-DIIRON COMPOUNDS BY MOLECULAR FIELD THEORY.**
HILSCHER, G. RAIS, H. KIRCHMAYR, H. R.
PHYS. STATUS SOLIDI
59 B (1), K5–K9, 1973.

52087 **AUTOIONIZATION OF THE T-3(1)(P-3) STATE OF TITANIUM IMPURITIES IN ZINC SELENIDE.**
KOCOT, K. BARANOWSKI, J. M.
PHYS. STATUS SOLIDI
59 B (1), K11–12, 1973.

52088 **REDETERMINATION OF THE EFFECTIVE MASS IN HEAVILY-DOPED N-TYPE INDIUM ARSENIDE.**
SENECHAL, R. R. WOOLLEY, J. C.
PHYS. STATUS SOLIDI
59 B (1), K35–K37, 1973.

52089 **THERMAL RECOVERY OF RADIATION HARDENING ACCOMPANIED BY TL (THERMOLUMINESCENCE) AND THERMAL DECAY OF THE V SUB 1 BAND IN SODIUM-DOPED POTASSIUM BROMIDE.**
OKADA, T. TANIMURA, K. SUITA, T.
PHYS. STATUS SOLIDI
59 B (1), K39–K42, 1973.

52090 **NON-GAMMA DONOR LEVELS IN GALLIUM ARSENIDE.**
BAZHENOV, V. K.
PHYS. STATUS SOLIDI
59 B (1), K51–K53, 1973.

52092 **PHOTOEMISSION AND DENSITY OF VALENCE STATES OF THE II-VI COMPOUNDS. I. ZINC TELLURIDE, CADMIUM SELENIDE, CADMIUM TELLURIDE, MERCURY SELENIDE, AND MERCURY TELLURIDE.**
SHEVCHIK, N. J. TEJEDA, J.
CARDONA, M. LANGER, D. W.
PHYS. STATUS SOLIDI
59 B (1), 87–100, 1973.
(AD-782 811)

52098 **MINORITY CARRIER MAGNETOPHONON RESONANCE IN P-INDIUM ANTIMONIDE AND IN P-GALLIUM ANTIMONIDE-INDIUM ANTIMONIDE SOLID SOLUTIONS.**
BYSZEWSKI, P. WALUKIEWICZ, W.
PHYS. STATUS SOLIDI
59 B (1), 321–7, 1973.

52099 **SUPERCONDUCTIVITY IN THE PALLADIUM-HYDROGEN SYSTEM.**
SKOSKIEWICZ, T.
PHYS. STATUS SOLIDI
59 B (1), 329–34, 1973.

52101 **MAGNETIC INTERACTIONS IN 3-DIEMENSIONAL BODY-CENTERED CUBIC. HEISENBERG FERROMAGNETS. III. DIAQUATETRACHLORODIPOTASSIUM (OR DIAMMONIUM) CUPRATE.**
KLAASSEN, T. O. LOOYESTIJN, W. J.
POULIS, N. J.
PHYSICA (UTRECHT)
66 (3), 567–80, 1973.

52103 **NEW EMISSION SPECTRUM OF HAFNIUM BROMIDE IN THE VISIBLE.**
SAVITHRY, T. RAO, D. V. K. RAO, P. T.
PHYSICA (UTRECHT)
67 (2), 400–4, 1973.

52107 **SPECTROSCOPIC STUDY OF THE INTERMEDIATE STATE IN ANTIFERROMAGNETIC MANGANESE(II) FLUORIDE.**
MILNER, A. A. POPKOV, YU. A. EREMENKO, V. V.
PISMA ZH. EKSP. TEOR. FIZ.
18 (1), 39–42, 1973.
(FOR ENGLISH TRANSLATION SEE E54543)

52114 **EFFECT OF INDIUM(III) OXIDE ADDITIVES ON THE PROPERTIES OF A MANGANESE-ZINC FERRITE.**
VLADIMIRTSEVA, L. A. SAMSONOV, G. V.
GORBATYUK, V. A.
POROSH. MET.
13 (8), 80–3, 1973.
(FOR ENGLISH TRANSLATION SEE E54921)

52118 **LUMINESCENCE SPECTRA IN CADMIUM SELENIDE SINGLE CRYSTALS AT HIGH EXCITATION DENSITIES.**
BAUBINAS, R. BALTRAMIEJUNAS, R. VAITKUS, J.
NARKEVICIUS, V. NIUNKA, V.
PROBL. FIZ. SOEDIN. II - IV
1, 136–40, 1972.

52120 **ELECTROLUMINESCENT PHOSPHORS.**
SCHLAM, E.
PROC. IEEEE
61 (7), 894–901, 1973.

52121 **DIRECT-CURRENT ELECTROLUMINESCENCE IN ZINC SULFIDE. STATE OF THE ART.**
VECHT, A. WERRING, N. J. ELLIS, R.
SMITH, P. J. F.
61 (7), 902–7, 1973.

52123 **DIELECTRIC AND OPTICAL PROPERTIES OF A QUASIFERROELECTRIC PLZT CERAMIC.**
CARL, K. GEISEN, K.
PROC. IEEE
61 (7), 967–74, 1973.

52127 **POINT DEFECTS IN SODIUM CHLORATE CRYSTALS.**
RAMASASTRY, C. REDDY, K. V.
PROC. ROY. SOC. LONDON
335 A (1), 1–14, 1973.

52128 **ELLIPSOMETRIC INVESTIGATION OF THE ELECTROOPTIC AND ELECTROSTRICTIVE EFFECTS IN ANODIC TANTALUM (V) OXIDE FILMS.**
CORNISH, W. D. YOUNG, L.
PROC. ROY SOC. LONDON
335 A (1), 39–50, 1973.

52135 **THERMOELECTRIC POWER OF LIQUID METALS AND ALLOYS.**
ENDERBY, J. E. HOWE, R. A.
PROP. LIQUID METALS. PROC. INT. CONF., 2ND
283–7, 1973.
(EDITED BY SAKAE TAKEUCHI. TAYLOR AND FRANCIS: LONDON, ENGLAND)

52151 **BLUE-GREEN NUMERIC DISPLAY USING ELECTROLUMINESCENT GALLIUM NITRIDE.**
PANKOVE, J. I.
RCA REV.
34 (2), 336–43, 1973.

52152 **ZINC DISPLACEMENT THRESHOLD AND ZINC VACANCY LUMINESCENCE IN ELECTRON-IRRADIATED ZINC-TELLURIUM.**
MEESE, J. M. PARK, Y. S.
RADIAT. DAMAGE DEFECTS SEMICOND., PROC. INT. CONF.
51–9, 1973.

52153 **TRAPPING LEVELS IN HEAVY ION IMPLANTED CADMIUM TELLURIDE.**
GETTINGS, M. STEPHENS, K. G.
RADIAT. EFF.
18 (3–4), 275–7, 1973.

52160 **CALCULATION OF THE SECONDARY ELECTRONIC EMISSION OF SEMICONDUCTOR SYSTEMS WITH NEGATIVE AFFINITY TAKING INTO ACCOUNT CURRENT TAKE-OFF.**
YASNOPOLSKII, N. L. INDRISHENOK, V. I.
RADIOTEKH. ELEKTRON.
18 (6), 1237–42, 1973.
(FOR ENGLISH TRANSLATION SEE E66038)

52162 **NONRECIPROCAL HELICON WAVE PROPAGATION IN N-INDIUM ANTIMONIDE AT SUPERHIGH FREQUENCIES.**
KONONENKO, V. K. KULESHOV, E. M.
RADIOTEKH. ELEKTRON.
18 (7), 1429–33, 1973.

52164 **CRYSTAL CHEMISTRY AND RARE EARTH LUMINESCENCE OF MIXED METAL OXIDES.**
BLASSE, G.
REV. CHIM. MINER.
10 (1–2), 39–46, 1973.

52166 **MAGNETISM OF THE RARE EARTH METALS.**
LEMAIRE, R. PIERRE, J.
REV. CHIM. MINER.
10 (1–2), 273–90, 1973.

52167 **RARE EARTHS LUMINESCENCE.**
LAVEANT, P.
REV. CHIM. MINER.
10 (1–2), 329–45, 1973.

52168 **STOICHIOMETRY AND OPTICAL QUALITY OF LITHIUM TANTALATE(V) SINGLE CRYSTALS.**
MIYAZAWA, S. IWASAKI, H.
REV. ELEC. COMMUN. LAB.
21 (5–6), 374–83, 1973.

52169 **NERNST-EINSTEIN RELATION. ELECTROTRANSPORT IN IRON MONOXIDE.**
MORIN, F. BERANGER, G. LACOMBE, P.
REV. INT. HAUTES TEMP. REFRACT.
10 (2), 91–101, 1973.

52172 **INFLUENCE OF THE SMALL ADDITIONS OF CALCIUM OXIDE ON THE DIELECTRIC BEHAVIOR OF NICKEL FERRITE.**
REZLESCU, E. REZLESCU, N. VASILIU, A.
LUCA, E.
REV. ROUM. PHYS.
18 (5), 647–54, 1973.

52173 **ANALYSIS AND IMPROVEMENT OF THE KELVIN METHOD FOR MEASURING DIFFERENCES IN WORK FUNCTION.**
DE BOER, J. S. W. KRUSEMEYER, H. J.
BURHOVEN JASPERS, N. C.
REV. SCI. INSTRUM.
44 (8), 1003–8, 1973.

52180 **DETERMINATION OF ELECTRONIC PROPERTIES OF DEEP-LEVEL IMPURITIES IN SEMICONDUCTORS.**
SAKAI, K. IKOMA, T.
SEISAN-KENKYU
20 (7), 278–87, 1973.

EPIC Number	Bibliographic Citation

52183 **CRITICAL BEHAVIOR OF SPONTANEOUS MAGNETIZATION IN THE ANTIFERROMAGNETIC NICKEL(II) OXIDE.**
NEGOVETIC, I. KONSTANTINOVIC, J.
SOLID STATE COMMUN.
13 (3), 249-52, 1973.

52184 **SHUBNIKOV-DE HAAS EFFECTS IN BISMUTH SELENIDE WITH HIGH CARRIER CONCENTRATIONS.**
HYDE, G. R. DILLON, R. O. BEALE, H. A.
SPAIN, I. L. WOOLLAM, J. A. SELLYMER, D. J.
SOLID STATE COMMUN.
13 (3), 257-63, 1973.

52186 **NORMAL STATE RESISTANCE BEHAVIOR AND SUPERCONDUCTIVITY.**
FISK, Z. LAWSON, A. C.
SOLID STATE COMMUN.
13 (3), 277-9, 1973.
(AD-771 565)

52187 **SPONTANEOUS AND STIMULATED EMISSION OF ZINC(II) OXIDE BY TWO QUANTUM EXCITATION.**
KLINGSHIRN, C.
SOLID STATE COMMUN.
13 (3), 297-301, 1973.

52188 **FUNDAMENTAL ABSORPTION SPECTRA OF TRANSITION METAL CHLORIDES.**
ISHII, T. SAKISAKA, Y. MATSUKAWA, T.
SATO, S. SAGAWA, T.
SOLID STATE COMMUN.
13 (3), 281-4, 1973.

52190 **CESIUM TRIFLUORONICKELATE(II). FERROMAGNETIC CHAINS WITH X-Y LIKE ANISOTROPY.**
LEBESQUE, J. V. SNEL, J. SMIT, J. J.
SOLID STATE COMMUN.
13 (3), 371-6, 1973.

52191 **PHOTOVOLTAGE IN SILVER PHOTODOPING OF AMORPHOUS ARSENIC SULFIDE FILMS.**
MATSUDA, A. KIKUCHI, M.
SOLID STATE COMMUN.
13 (3), 401-3, 1973.

52192 **DIRTY DISPLACIVE FERROELECTRICS.**
BURNS, G. SCOTT, B. A.
SOLID STATE COMMUN.
13 (3), 417-21, 1973.

52193 **INDEX OF REFRACTION IN DIRTY DISPLACIVE FERROELECTRICS.**
BURNS, G. SCOTT, B. A.
SOLID STATE COMMUN.
13 (3), 423-6, 1973.

52195 **SHUBNIKOV-DE HAAS EFFECTS IN P-TYPE ANTIMONY TELLURIDE.**
VON MIDDENDORFF, A. DIETRICH, K.
LANDWEHR, G.
SOLID STATE COMMUN.
13 (4), 443-6, 1973.

52196 **FERROMAGNETIC RARE EARTH AND DIAMAGNETIC IRON SUB-LATTICES IN TERNARY R FE(0.67) GE(1.33) TYPE COMPOUNDS.**
FELNER, I. SCHIEBER, M.
SOLID STATE COMMUN.
13 (4), 457-61, 1973.

52197 **THEORY OF HOT ELECTRON MAGNETOPHONON RESONANCE IN LONGITUDINAL MAGNETIC FIELDS.**
YAMADA, E.
SOLID STATE COMMUN.
13 (4), 503-5, 1973.

52198 **PARAMAGNETIC SUSCEPTIBILITY AND TRANSITION AT A LOW TEMPERATURE. I. EFFECT OF SECOND INTRANSITIVE COMPONENT ON VANADIUM COMPOUNDS.**
KODESS, B. N.
SOLID STATE COMMUN.
13 (5), 523-5, 1973.

52199 **MAGNETIC ANISOTROPY OF RARE EARTH-ZINC EQUIATOMIC COMPOUNDS TERBIUM-ZINC AND HOLMIUM-ZINC.**
MORIN, P. PIERRE, J.
SOLID STATE COMMUN.
13 (5), 537-40, 1973.

52201 **SPECTROSCOPIC STUDIES OF THE EMISSION FROM PLASMAS GENERATED BY AN INTENSE ELECTRON BEAM.**
CARLSON, G. A.
REC. SYMP. ELECTRON, ION, LASER BEAM TECHNOL., 11TH
121-30, 1971.
(EDITED BY R. F. M. THORNLEY, SAN FRANCISCO PRESS, INC.: SAN FRANCISCO, CALIF.)

52203 **OPTICAL PROPERTIES OF GLASS COATED WITH THIN FILM OF SILICA.**
KUCIREK, J. SLADKOVA, J.
SCR. FAC. SCI. NATUR. UNIV. PURKYNIANAE BRUN.
2 (3), 101-5, 1973.

52205 **POSSIBLE EXISTENCE OF A CONTINUOUS SERIES OF SOLID SOLUTIONS IN THE GALLIUM SULFIDE-GALLIUM SELENIDE SYSTEM.**
MUSHINSKII, V. P. PALAKI, L. I.
PRILEPOV, V. D.
NEKOT. VOP. KHIM. FIZ. POLUPROV. SLOZHNOGO SOSTAVA, MATER. VSES. SIMP., 3RD
211-13, 1970.

52206 **CRYSTAL-CHEMICAL FEATURES OF SEMICONDUCTOR ALLOYS OF THE CADMIUM SULFIDE-INDIUM SULFIDE SECTION.**
RADAUTSAN, S. I. DONIKA, F. G.
TEZLEVAN, V. E. DAMASKIN, I. A.
NEKOT. VOP. KHIM. FIZ. POLUPROV. SLOZHNOGO SOSTAVA, MATER. VSES. SIMP., 3RD
221-4, 1970.

52207 **PREPARATION AND STUDY OF SOME PROPERTIES OF THIN FILMS OF ALKALI METAL META-SELENOARSENITES.**
GOLOVEI, M. I. LADA, A. V. SEMRAD, E. E.
NEKOT. VOP. KHIM. FIZ. POLUPROV. SLOZHNOGO SOSTAVA, MATER. VSES. SIMP., 3RD
267-71, 1970.

52208 **PIEZOREFLECTANCE OF GALLIUM PHOSPHIDE.**
TAKIZAWA, T.
NIHON DAIGAKU BUNRIGAKUBU SHIZENKAGAKU KENKYUSHO KENKYU KIYO
(8), 1-16, 1973.

52209 **PROPERTIES OF YTTERBIUM SELENOGERMANATE.**
KAREAV, Z. SH. FEDORCHENKO, V. P.
ABDULLAEV, M. YU. KULIEVA, S. I.
NOV. POLUPROV. MATER.
121-3, 1972.

52214 **OPTICAL CONSTANTS DETERMINATION IN THIN FILMS WITH THE HELP OF A PHOTOMETRIC METHOD.**
MUCHA, B. MACKIEWICZ, J. KOWALEZYK, R.
OPT. APPL.
3 (1), 74-6, 1973.

52216 **OPTICAL CHARACTERISTICS OF LARGE SINGLE CRYSTALS OF FLUORIDES.**
CHERNEVSKAYA, E. G. ALEKSEEVA, T. A.
BAKHSHIEVA, G. F. LOVKOV, A. N.
TIKHMIROV, A. I. SHELUD'KO, R. N.
KALININA, M. V.
OPT.-MEKH. PROM.
40 (6), 47-8, 1973.
(FOR ENGLISH TRANSLATION SEE E61830)

52219 **EFFECT OF AGING ON SOME PROPERTIES OF BARIUM TITANATE PIEZOELECTRIC CERAMICS.**
JOSIMOVIC, M. TIMCENKO, R.
TEHNIKA (BELGRADE)
28 (6), 1153-6, 1973.

52220 **MAGNETORESISTIVE EFFECTS IN MOLTEN SEMICONDUCTORS.**
KUTVITSKII, V. A. SHURYGIN, P. M.
TEKHNOL. MATER. ELEKTRON. TEKH.
(2), 169-74, 1972.

52221 **THERMOELECTRIC PHENOMENA ON THE BOUNDARY OF A SEMICONDUCTOR WITH ITS MELT.**
ORLOV, A. M. SHURYGIN, P. M.
TEKHNOL. MATER. ELEKTRON. TEKH.
(2), 96-101, 1972.

52222 **MEASUREMENT OF THE THERMOELECTRIC PARAMETERS OF SEMICONDUCTING MATERIALS.**
GREKHOV, YU. N. SHURYGIN, P. M.
LEONOV, V. V.
TEKHNOL. MATER. ELEKTRON. TEKH.
(2), 146-52, 1972.

52223 **TEMPERATSURE DEPENDENCE OF MAGNETIC SUSCEPTIBILITY OF TELLURIDES.**
KUTVITSKII, V. A. SHURGIN, P. M.
KISELEV, V. B.
TEKHNOL. MATER. ELEKTRON. TEKH.
(2), 153-8, 1972.

52224 **MAGNETIC SUSCEPTIBILITY OF SEMICONDUCTORS IN SOLID AND LIQUID STATES.**
KUTVITSKII, V. A. SHURYGIN, P. M.
KISELEV, V. B.
TEKHNOL. MATER. ELEKTRON. TEKH.
(2), 164-8, 1972.

52225 **EFFECT OF IONIC MOTION ON THE REFRACTIVE INDEX OF PARAELECTRIC POTASSIUM DIHYDROGEN PHOSPHATE IN THE VICINITY OF CURIE POINT.**
KAWABE, K. KAMIURA, Y.
TECHNOL. REP. OSAKA UNIV.
22 (1053-89), 391-9, 1972.

52229 **LUMINESCENCE, HOT LUMINESCENCE, AND SCATTERING AS COMPONENTS OF SECONDARY LUMINESCENCE.**
REBANE, K.
SPEKTROSK. KRIST., MATER. SIMP. SPEKTROSK. KRIST., AKTIV. IONAMI REDKOZEMEL. PEREKHODNYKH METAL., 3RD
42-58, 1973.
(EDITED BY P. P. FEOFILOV, 'NAUKA,' LENINGRAD. OTD.: LENINGRAD, USSR.)

EPIC Number	Bibliographic Citation

52231 **SILICIDES AS ANTIEMISSION MATERIALS FOR HIGH POWER TUBES.**
SCHNEIDER, P.
TESLA ELECTRON.
6 (2), 35–40, 1973.

52233 **PROPERTIES OF CADMIUM LEAD TELLURIDE THIN FILMS.**
HARRIS, J. J. CROCKER, A. J.
THIN SOLID FILMS
17 (2), 129–37, 1973.

52240 **RESIDUAL POLARIZATION IN ALKALI METAL HALIDE CRYSTALS.**
NEKRASOV, M. M. RODIONOV, M. K.
BELYAKOV, B. M. KIRILENKO, M. I.
TR. MOSK. INST. ELEKTRON. MASHINOSTR.
(27), 47–53, 1972.

52242 **ELECTRIC CONDUCTIVITY OF ALKALI METAL FLUORIDE MELTS.**
SMIRNOV, M. V. SHUMOV, YU. A.
KHOKHLOV, V. A.
TR. INST. ELEKTROKHIM., URAL. NAUCH. TSENTR. AKAD. NAUK SSSR
(18), 3–9, 1972.

52246 **THERMAL CONDUCTIVITY OF LIQUID THALLIUM CHALCOGENIDES.**
FEDOROV, V. I.
TR. MOSK. ENERG. INST.
(115), 41–51, 1972.

52247 **PROPERTIES OF IRON GROUP IONS IN OXIDE SINGLE CRYSTALS.**
KUSTOV, E. F. FURSIKOV, M. A. BARANOV, M. N.
TR. MOSK. ENERG. INST.
(143), 70–5, 1972.

52251 **CHANGES IN DEFECT STRUCTURE AS A RESULT OF COMPRESSION AND SUBSEQUENT ANNEALING OF TABLETS OF CADMIUM OR ZINC CHALCOGENIDES.**
LOTT, K.
TR. TALLIN. POLITEKH. INST.
(323), 11–22, 1972.

52252 **HIGH-TEMPERATURE DYNAMIC EQUILIBRIUM IN CADMIUM SULFIDE.**
AARNA, H. LANGOVITS, A. V. KUKK, P.
TR. TALLIN. POLITEKH. INST.
(323), 45–51, 1972.

52253 **PARTIAL EQUILIBRIUM IN CADMIUM SULFIDE.**
AARNA, H. FREIBERG, A. M. KUKK, P.
TR. TALLIN. POLITEKH. INST.
(323), 53–8, 1972.

52254 **GROWING CADMIUM SELENIDE SINGLE CRYSTALS FROM THE VAPOR PHASE.**
VARVAS, J. NIRK, T.
TR. TALLIN. POLITEKH. INST.
(323), 59–64, 1972.

52255 **EQUIPMENT FOR THE MEASUREMENT OF HIGH-TEMPERATURE CONDUCTIVITY IN GROUP II CHALCOGENIDES IN AN ATMOSPHERE OF COMPONENT VAPORS.**
NIRK, T. NOGES, M.
TR. TALLIN. POLITEKH. INST.
A (323), 65–70, 1972.

52256 **HIGH-TEMPERATURE EQUILIBRIUM OF DEFECTS IN CADMIUM SELENIDE SINGLE CRYSTALS.**
VARVAS, J. NIRK, T. KALLASTE, T.
TR. TALLIN. POLITEKH. INST.
(323), 71–7, 1972.

52257 **FROZEN STATE OF DEFECTS IN CADMIUM SELENIDE.**
NIRK, T.
TR. TALLIN. POLITEKH. INST.
(323), 79–84, 1972.

52258 **PHOTOCONDUCTIVITY OF CADMIUM TIN PHOSPHIDE SINGLE CRYSTALS AT HIGH LEVELS OF OPTICAL EXCITATION.**
GORYUNOVA, N. A. KOVALSKAYA, V. A.
LEONOV, E. I. PYSHKIN, S. L.
RADAUTSAN, S. I. FERDMAN, N. A.
TROINYE POLUPROV.
115–17, 1972.

52259 **OPTICAL PROPERTIES OF CADMIUM GERMANIUM PHOSPHIDE.**
POTYKEVICH, I. V. BELYAEV, O. N.
VLADIMIROVA, A. A. KIRILENKO, M. M.
SEREDUII, V. P. SERYI, V. I.
TROIN. POLUPROV. II – IV – V(2) – II – III(2) – VI(4)
127–32, 1972.

52260 **ABSORPTION SPECTRA OF CADMIUM GERMANIUM ARSENIDE PHOSPHIDE SOLID SOLUTIONS.**
VOITSEKHOVSKII, A. V. PETRUSENKO, S. K.
TROIN. POLUPROV. II – IV – V(2) – II – III(2) – VI(4)
195–8PP., 1972.

52261 **INFRARED ABSORPTION AND REFLECTION IN SILICON ZINC ARSENIDE-GALLIUM ARSENIDE SOLID SOLUTIONS.**
NAZAROV, A. MAMAEV, S. KARYMSHAKOV, R. V.
TROIN. POLUPROV. II – IV – V(2) – II – III(2) – VI(4)
198–201PP., 1972.

52262 **OPTICAL ABSORPTION IN THE COMPOUNDS GERMANIUM ZINC NITRIDE, GERMANIUM MAGNESIUM NITRIDE, AND MAGNESIUM SILICON NITRIDE.**
VOLGIN, YU. N. GREKOV, F. F.
DUBROVSKII, G. P. ZYKOV, A. M.
UKHANOV, YU. I.
TROIN. POLUPROV. II – IV – V(2) – II – III(2) – IV(4)
206–10PP., 1972.

52263 **OPTICAL ABSORPTION OF CADMIUM INDIUM SULFIDE AND CADMIUM GALLIUM SULFIDE SINGLE CRYSTALS.**
GUSEINOV, D. T. DZHURAEV, N. D. NANI, R. KH.
TROIN. POLUPROV.
228–30, 1972.

52264 **ELECTRICAL PROPERTIES OF CADMIUM GERMANIUM PHOSPHIDE SEMICONDUCTOR COMPOUND IN CRYSTALLINE AND GLASSY STATES.**
KIRILENKO, M. M. FEDOTOV, V. G.
FEDOTOVSKII, A. V.
TROINYE POLUPROV.
146–9, 1972.

52265 **RELATION OF THE DIELECTRIC CONSTANT OF WATER TO ITS MINERALIZATION.**
KLUGMAN, I. YU.
TR. METROL. INST. SSSR
(136), 103–11, 1972.

52267 **GROWTH OF SOME A2B6-TYPE COMPOUND SINGLE CRYSTALS BY A MODIFIED PIPER-POLICH METHOD.**
KYVERIK, K. A. NYGES, M. T.
TT. TALLIN. POLITEKH. INST.
(323), 85–8, 1972.

52275 **X-RAY SPECTRAL DATA ON THE VALENCE BAND AND CONDUCTION BAND STRUCTURES IN VANADIUM COMPOUNDS OF V(3) X TYPE.**
BONDARENKO, T. N. DZEGANOVSKII, V. P.
ZHURAKOVSKII, E. A.
UKR. FIZ. ZH. (RUSS. ED.)
18 (7), 1121–30, 1973.

52277 **EFFECT OF S-D HYBRIDIZATION IN ALLOYS ON THE VALUE OF THE CORE-POLARIZATION CONTRIBUTION TO AN EFFECTIVE FIELD ON THE NUCLEUS OF A DIAMAGNETIC ATOM.**
TAMAEV, S. T. VALIEV, KH. KH. IRKAEV, S. M.
KUZMIN, R. N.
VESTN. AKAD. NAUK KAZ. SSR
29 (6), 54–6, 1973.

52278 **NONEQUILIBRIUM DEPLETION AND SURFACE-BARRIER PHOTO EFFECT IN GALLIUM ARSENIDE AT THE BOUNDARY WITH ELECTROLYTES.**
KONOROV, P. P. TARANTOV, YU. A. GUREV, A. I.
VESTN. LENINGRAD. UNIV., FIZ., KHIM.
(2), 47–52, 1973.

52281 **CHANGE IN THE SUSCEPTIBILITY OF FERRITES AT HIGH PRESSURES.**
KHACHATRYAN, YU. M.
VESTSI AKAD. NAVUK BELARUS. SSR, SER. FIZ.-MAT. NAVUK
(4), 85–99, 1973.

52283 **OPTICAL SPECTROSCOPY IN SEMICONDUCTORS IN HIGH MAGNETIC FIELDS USING POLARIZATION MODULATION.**
SARI, S. O. SCHNATTERLY, S. E.
SURFACE SCI.
37, 328–39, 1973.
(AD-767 510, AFOSR-TR-73-1748, AVAIL. NTIS)

52286 **ELECTRO-OPTICAL STUDIES.**
BOEER, K. W.
DEPT. OF PHYSICS, UNIV. OF DELAWARE, NEWARD
105PP., 1970.
(AD-767 370, AVAIL. NTIS)

52289 **PHOTOLUMINESCENCE AT HIGH EXCITON DENSITIES IN CADMIUM SULFIDE.**
FIGUERIRA, J. F. MAHR, H.
PHYS. REV.
7 B (10), 4520–7, 1973.
(AD-767 159, AVAIL. NTIS)

52290 **DEFECT LEVELS IN NEUTRON-IRRADIATED GALLIUM ARSENIDE SCHOTTKY DIODES AND LASER DIODE DEGRADATION.**
LUDMAN, J. E.
NORTHEASTERN UNIVERSITY, PH.D. THESIS
81PP., 1973.
(AD-766 245, AFCRL-TR-73-0344, AVAIL. NTIS)

52291 **OBSERVATION OF FERROELECTRIC DOMAINS WITH A SCANNING ELECTRON MICROSCOPE.**
CHASE, A. B. HARTWICK, T. S.
THE AEROSPACE CORP., EL SEGUNDO, CALIF.
14PP., 1973.
(AS-766 258, SAMSO-TR-73-239, N74-12440, AVAIL. NTIS)

52298 **ZONE STRUCTURE AND ELECTRON SCATTERING MECHANISM IN THE SOLID SOLUTIONS MERCURY, CADMIUM TELLURIDE.**
ALIYEV, S. A. ALIYEV, E. M. GADZHIYEV, T. G.
ALIYEV, M. I.
UKR. FIZ. ZH.
16 (10), 1685–9, 1971.
(FOR ENGLISH TRANSLATION SEE E52299)

EPIC Number	Bibliographic Citation

52299 **ZONE STRUCTURE AND ELECTRON SCATTERING MECHANISM IN THE SOLID SOLUTIONS MERCURY, CADMIUM TELLURIDE.**
ALIYEV, S. A. ALIYEV, E. M. GADZHIYEV, T. G.
ALIYEV, M. I.
FOREIGN TECHNOLOGY DIV., AIR FORCE SYSTEMS COMMAND
11PP., 1971.
(ENGLISH TRANSLATION OF UKR. FIZ. ZH., 16 (10), 1685-9, 1971; FOR ORIGINAL SEE E52298)
(AD-766 564, FTD-HT-23-25-74, AVAIL. NTIS)

52300 **MAGNETIC PROPERTIES OF PLUTONIUM MONOARSENIDE.**
BLAISE, A. FOURNIER, J. M. SALMON, P.
SOLID STATE COMMUN.
13 (5), 555-7, 1973.

52302 **REFLECTION MEASUREMENTS WITH POLARIZATION MODULATION. METHOD TO INVESTIGATE BANDGAPS IN BIREFRINGENT MATERIALS LIKE I-III-VI SUB 2 CHALCOPYRITE COMPOUNDS.**
BETTINI, M.
SOLID STATE COMMUN.
13 (5), 599-602, 1973.

52303 **AMBIVALENCE OF YTTERBIUM IN YTTERBIUM-ALUMINUM.**
HAVINGA, E. E. BUSCHOW, K. H. J.
VAN DAAL, H. J.
SOLID STATE COMMUN.
13 (5), 621-7, 1973.

52304 **FROZEN (METASTABLE) CONDUCTIVITY IN SEMICONDUCTORS.**
SANDOMIRSKII, V. B. ZHDAN, A. G.
MESSERER, M. A. GULYAEV, I. B.
PYASTA, YA. A. DAREVSKII, A. S.
SOLID-STATE ELECTRON.
16 (10), 1097-102, 1973.

52306 **DIELECTRIC PROPERTIES OF RF [RADIO FREQUENCY]-SPUTTERED SILICON DIOXIDE FILMS.**
MEAUDRE, M. MEAUDRE, R.
SOLID-STATE ELECTRON.
16 (10), 1205-7, 1973.

52307 **THICK-FILM PASTES FOR MULTILAYER USE.**
KURZWEIL, K. LOUGHRAN, J.
SOLID STATE TECHNOL.
16 (5), 36-42, 1973.

52309 **SECONDARY ELECTRON EMISSION FROM INSULATORS BY ION BOMBARDMENT.**
UCHIIKE, H. SHINODA, T. FUKUSHIMA, Y.
AISHIMA, A.
SHINKU
16 (5), 180-5, 1973.

52313 **MEASUREMENT OF ELECTRIC CONDUCTIVITY OF MAGNESIUM OXIDE SINGLE CRYSTAL AT HIGH TEMPERATURE USING A SOLAR FURNACE.**
AFZAL, F. A. GIUTRONICH, J. E.
SOL. ENERGY
15 (2), 125-31, 1973.

52314 **TRANSVERSE AND LONGITUDINAL LATTICE FREQUENCIES AND INTERIONIC POTENTIAL IN SOME AMF SUB 3 PEROVSKITE FLUORIDE CRYSTALS.**
NAKAGAWA, I.
SPECTROCHEM. ACTA
29 (7), (PART A), 1451-61, 1973.

52315 **FLUORESCENCE ENHANCEMENT OF EUROPIUM TRIPOSITIVE ION IN PHOSPHORYL(V) CHLIRIDE-TIN(IV) CHLORIDE AND OF SAMARIUM TRIPOSITIVE ION IN PHOSPHORYL(V) CHLORIDE-ZIRCONIUM(IV)CHLORIDE.**
CHRYSOCHOOS, J. TOKOUSBALIDES, P.
SPECTROSC. LETT.
6 (7), 435-45, 1973.

52316 **POLARIZATION DIAGRAMS OF A RUBIDIUM URANYL NITRATE CRYSTAL.**
VOLODKO, L. V. KOMYAK, A. I.
POSLEDOVICH, M. R.
SPEKTROSK., TR. SIB. SOVESHCH., 6TH
262-5, 1973.

52317 **SPECTROSCOPIC STUDY OF A SILICON DIOXIDE FILM FORMATION PROCESS.**
SULIMIN, A. D. SHIPILOVA, D. P.
YAKOVLEV, O. I.
SPEKTROSK., TR. SIB. SOVESHCH., 6TH
260-2, 1973.

52318 **ENERGY SPECTRUM OF ELECTRONS IN ISOELECTRONIC INDIUM ANTIMONIDE-CADMIUM TELLURIDE-SILVER IODIDE COMPOUNDS.**
GUZHOV, A. A. TULVINSKII, V. B.
SHUBA, YU. A.
SPEKTROSK., TR. SIB. SOVESHCH., 6TH
265-7PP., 1973.
(EDITED BY N. A. PRILEZHAEVA, NAUKA: MOSCOW, USSR)

52319 **NMR IN INTERMETALLIC COMPOUNDS OF ALUMINUM WITH RARE EARTHS.**
NICULESCU, V.
STUD. CERCET. FIZ.
25 (5), 517-45, 1973.

52322 **ELECTRON-BEAM INDUCED REDUCTION OF CARBON CONCENTRATION ON BERYLLIUM OXIDE AND ITS EFFECTS ON BERYLLIUM OXIDE AND ITS EFFECTS ON SECONDARY ELECTRON EMISSION.**
GOLDSTEIN, B.
SURFACE SCI.
39 (2), 261-71, 1973.

52323 **PROPERTIES OF MATERIALS OF THE BARIUM METAITITANATE-CALCIUM ZIRCONATE SYSTEM.**
STEMPKOWSKI, J.
SZKLO CERAM.
24 (5), 141-3, 1973.

52325 **THEORY OF THE 4F(14)-4F(13)5D SPECTRUM OF A YTTERBIUM(2+) ION IN CUBIC CRYSTALS.**
EREMIN, M. V. LEUSHIN, A. M.
SPEKTROSK. KRIST., MATER. SIMP. SPEKTROSK. KRIST., AKTIV. IONAMI REDKOZEMEL. PEREKHODNYKH METAL., 3RD
100-5, 1973.

52326 **ENERGY STRUCTURE OF A 5D1 CONFIGURATION OF CERIUM IMPURITY CENTERS IN CRYSTALS.**
ZAKHAROV, V. K. STAROSTIN, N. V.
SPEKTROSK. KRIST. MATER. SIMP. SPEKTROSK. KRIST., AKTIV. IONAMI REDKOZEMEL. PEREKHODNYKH METAL., 3RD
113-15, 1972.

52327 **CONFIGURATION OF D ELECTRONS IN LOW-SYMMETRY FIELDS.**
SVIRIDOV, D. T. VEREMEICHIK, T. F.
SPEKTROSK. KRIST., MATER. SIMP. SPEKTROSK. KRIST., AKTIV. IONAMI REDKOZEMEL. PEREKHODNYKH METAL., 3RD
115-17, 1973.

52328 **MAGNETIC AND ACOUSTIC EXCITATION OF FINE AND NUCLEAR HYPERFINE SUBLEVELS OF RARE EARTH IONS IN GARNET FERRITES.**
SABUROVA, R. V. KOPVILLEM, U. KH.
SPEKTROSK. KRIST., MATER. SIMP. SPEKTROSK. KRIST., AKTIV, IONAMI REDKOZEMEL. PEREKHODNYKH METAL., 3RD
154-5, 1973.

52329 **X-RAY LUMINESCENCE AND THERMAL DEEXCITATION SPECTRA FOR RARE EARTH IONS IN FLUORITE-TYPE CRYSTALS AND ANALYSIS OF MULTI-CENTER SYSTEMS.**
LUKS, R. K. STOLOV, A. L.
SPEKTROSK. KRIST., MATER. SIMP. SPEKTROSK. KRIST., AKTIV. IONAMI REDKOZEMEL. PEREKHODNYKH METAL., 3RD
159-61, 1973.

52330 **STRUCTURE OF LUMINESCENCE CENTERS IN NEODYMIUM-(3+)-DOPED GADOLINIUM ALUMINATE CRYSTALS.**
TKACHUK, A. M. NATADZE, A. L. MORDSON, M. A.
ZONN, Z. N.
SPEKTROSK. KRIST., MATER. SIMP. SPEKTROSK. KRIST., AKTIV. IONAMI REDKOZEMEL. PEREKHODNYKH METAL., 3RD
165-8, 1973.

52331 **COMPARISON OF EUROPIUM(3+) ION SPECTRA IN OXIDES AND OXYSULFIDES OF RARE EARTH ELEMENTS.**
AMIRYAN, A. M. BABICH, YA. M. BABKINA, T. V.
ZORINA, L. N. MURAVEV, Z. N.
NARYSHKINA, S. I. SOSHCHIN, N. P.
SPEKTROSK. KRIST., MATER. SIMP. SPEKTROSK. KRIST., AKTIV. IONAMI REDKOZEMEL. PEREKHODNYKH METAL., 3RD
168-72, 1973.

52332 **FLUORESCENCE OF DYSPROSIUM(3+) ION IN YTTRIUM OXIDE.**
LEVSHIN, V. L. LYUBAVSKAYA, I. K.
MAKSIMOVA, N. D.
SPEKTROSK. KRIST., MATER. SIMP. SPEKTROSK. KRIST., AKTIV. IONAMI REDKOZEMEL. PEREKHODNYKH METAL., 3RD
173-6, 1973.

52333 **LUMINESCENCE SPECTRA AND KINETICS OF RARE EARTH ORTHOPHOSPHATES.**
KRASILOV, YU. I. ORLOVSKII, V. P.
REPKO, V. P. SAFRONOV, G. M.
TANANAEV, I. V. ELLERT, G. V.
SPEKTROSK. KRIST., MATER. SIMP. SPEKTROSK. KRIST., AKTIV. IONAMI REDKOZEMEL. PEREKHODNYKH METAL., 3RD
180-4, 1973.

52334 **LUMINESCENCE OF RARE EARTH IONS IN ZIRCONIUM SILICATE PHOSPHORS.**
SHALYAPIN, A. L. SHUL'GIN, B. V.
GAVRILOV, F. F. FEDOROVSKIKH, YU. A.
CHUKHLANTSEV, V. G.
SPEKTROSK. KRIST., MATER. SIMP. SPEKTROSK, KRIST., AKTIV. IONAMI REDKOZEMEL. PEREKHODNYKH METAL., 3RD
184-7PP., 1973.
(EDITED BY P. P. FEOFILOV, NAUKA, LENINGRAD. OTD.: LENINGRAD, USSR)

52335 **ABSORPTION AND LUMINESCENCE SPECTRA OF NEODYMIUM-(3+) IONS IN BARIUM SODIUM NIOBATE SINGLE CRYSTALS.**
VALYASHKO, E. G. KUKINA, A. M.
RASHKOVICH, L. N.
SPEKTROSK. KRIST., MATER. SIMP. SPEKTROSK. KRIST., AKTIV. IONAMI REDKOZEMEL. PEREKHODNYKH METAL., 3RD
187-90, 1973.

EPIC Number	Bibliographic Citation

52336 **LUMINESCENCE OF RARE EARTH IONS IN SULFATES.**
BYKOVSKII, P. I.
SPEKTROSK. KRIST., MATER. SIMP. SPEKTROSK. KRIST., AKTIV. IONAMI REDKOZEMEL. PEREKHODNYKH METAL., 3RD
190–3, 1973.

52337 **LUMINESCENCE OF LANTHANIDE IONS IN SODIUM FLUORIDE SINGLE CRYSTALS.**
POTAPENKO, G. D. PISARENKO, V. F.
SPEKTROSK. KRIST., MATER. SIMP. SPEKTROSK. KRIST., AKTIV. IONAMI REDKOZEMEL. PEREKHODNYKH METAL., 3RD
193–5PP., 1973.
(EDITED BY P. P. FEOFILOV, NAUKA, LENINGRAD, OTD.: LENINGRAD, USSR)

52338 **RADIATION SPECTRA OF ERBIUM(3+) ION IN ZINC SULFIDE–CADMIUM SULFIDE MIXED LUMINOPHORS.**
LEVSHIN, V. L. SENASHENKO, M. V.
SPEKTROSK. KRIST., MATER. SIMP. SPEKTROSK. KRIST., AKTIV. IONAMI REDKOZEMEL. PEREKHODNYKH METAL., 3RD
195–8, 1973.

52339 **SPECTROLUMINESCENCE PROPERTIES OF EUROPIUM(2+) IONS WITH DIFFERENT COORDINATION ENVIRONMENTS IN IONIC CRYSTALS.**
LAPSHIN, A. I.
SPEKTROSK. KRIST., MATER. SIMP. SPEKTROSK. KRIST., AKTIV. IONAMI REDKOZEMEL. PEREKHODNYKH METAL., 3RD
199–201, 1973.

52340 **SPECTRA OF MAGNESIUM POTASSIUM FLUORIDE AND MAGNESIUM SODIUM FLUORIDE CRYSTALS CONTAINING EUROPIUM(2+) IONS.**
BODRUG, S. N. VALYASHKO, E. G.
MEDNIKOVA, V. N. SVIRIDOV, D. T.
SVIRIDOVA, R. K.
SPEKTROSK. KRIST., MATER. SIMP. SPEKTROSK. KRIST., AKTIV. IONAMI REDKOZEMEL. PEREKHODNYKH METAL., 3RD
201–5, 1973.

52341 **RECOMBINATION LUMINESCENCE SPECTRA OF EUROPIUM(2+) ION–ACTIVATED ALKALI HALIDE CRYSTALS.**
SHURALEVA, E. I. PARFIANOVICH, I. A.
IVAKHNENKO, P. S.
SPEKTROSK. KRIST., MATER. SIMP. SPEKTROSK. KRIST., AKTIV. IONAMI REDKOZEMEL. PEREKHODNYKH METAL., 3RD
206–8, 1973.

52342 **SENSITIZATION OF HOLMIUM(3+) EMISSION BY EUROPIUM(2+) IONS IN CALCIUM FLUORIDE CRYSTALS.**
GILMAN, I. YA. KIRILYUK, L. V. SKIBA, N. E.
SORIN, L. A. CHUMACHKOVA, M. M.
SPEKTROSK. KRIST., MATER. SIMP. SPEKTROSK. KRIST., AKTIV. IONAMI REDKOZEMEL. PEREKHODNYKH METAL., 3RD
209–11, 1973.

52343 **SENSITIZATION OF HOLMIUM(3+) LUMINESCENCE IN HOLMIUM(3+) AND EUROPIUM(2+) ION–DOPED SODIUM BROMIDE CRYSTALS.**
AKULININA, A. V. PISARENKO, V. F.
SPEKTROSK. KRIST., MATER. SIMP. SPEKTROSK. KRIST., AKTIV. IONAMI REDKOZEMEL. PEREKHODNYKH METAL., 3RD
211–13, 1973.

52344 **MECHANISM OF LUMINESCENCE EXCITATION AND ENERGY TRANSFER IN VANADATES.**
SHULGIN, B. V. FOTIEV, A. A. KHODOS, M. YA.
KORDYUKOV, N. I. SHALYAPIN, A. L.
SPEKTROSK. KRIST., MATER. SIMP. SPEKTROSK. KRIST., AKTIV. IONAMI REDKOZEMEL. PEREKHODNYKH METAL., 3RD
216–20, 1973.

52345 **MECHANISM OF THE EXCITATION OF PHOTOLUMINESCENCE IN ERBIUM–ACTIVATED II–VI SINGLE CRYSTALS.**
GUDYMENKO, L. F. LISITSA, M. P.
VITRIKHOVSKII, N. I.
SPEKTROSK. KRIST., MATER. SIMP. SPEKTROSK. KRIST., AKTIV. IONAMI REDKOZEMEL. PEREKHODNYKH METAL., 3RD
220–3, 1973.

52351 **ABSORPTION SPECTRA OF MAGNESIUM TUNGSTATE CRYSTALS CONTAINING IRON GROUP IONS.**
VARINA, T. M. BOKSHA, O. N.
SPEKTROSK. KRIST., MATER. SIMP. SPEKTROSK. KRIST., AKTIV. IONAMI REDKOZEMEL. PEREKHODNYKH METAL., 3RD
279–82PP., 1973.
(EDITED BY P. P. FEOFILOV, NAUKA, LENINGRAD. OTD.: LENINGRAD, USSR)

52352 **ABSORPTION SPECTRUM OF EXCITED CRYSTALS OF CHROMIUM(3+) ION–ACTIVATED MAGNESIUM SPINEL MAGNESIUM ALUMINATE.**
SEVASTYANOV, B. K. OREKHOVA, V. P.
SPEKTROSK. KRIST., MATER. SIMP. SPEKTROSK. KRIST., AKTIV. IONAMI REDKOZEMEL. PEREKHODNYKH METAL., 3RD
297–301, 1973.

52354 **LUMINESCENCE PHENOMENA ACCOMPANYING SOME ADSORPTIONS.**
BREYSSE, M. FAURE, L. CLAUDEL, B.
VERON, J.
VIDE
28 (164), 72–3, 1973.

52357 **ION DOPING OF P–INDIUM ANTIMONIDE WITH SULFUR. POLYMERS ON THEIR ELECTRICAL CONDUCTIVITY, ION MOBILITY, AND DIPOLE–SEGMENTAL RELAXATION.**
BRILLIANTOV, E. I. GUSEVA, M. I.
KOROLEVA, N. V. KORSHUNOV, A. B.
MAKAROV, A. G. STARININ, K. V.
VSES. SIMP. VZAIMODEISTIYU AT. CHASTITS TVERD. TELOM, 2ND
397–400, 1972.

52362 **DIFFUSION AND ION CONDUCTIVITY OF ALKALI HALIDES.**
BERG, G.
WISS. Z. MARTIN–LUTHER–UNIV., HALLE–WITTENBERG, MATH.–NATURWISS. REIHE
22 (2), 59–77, 1973.

52363 **ELECTROMOTIVE FORCE AND VALENCE–BAND MODEL OF ANTIMONY TRITELLURIDE.**
SUESSMANN, H.
WISS. Z. MARTIN–LUTHER–UNIV., HALLE–WITTENBERG, MATH.–NATURWISS. REIHE
22 (2), 105–12, 1973.

52369 **POLARIZATION–OPTICAL INVESTIGATION OF MAGNETIZATION PROCESSES NEAR DISLOCATIONS IN YTTRIUM IRON GARNET SINGLE CRYSTALS.**
VLASKO–VLASOV, V. K. DEDUKH, L. M.
NIKITENKO, V. I.
ZH. EKSP. TEOR. FIZ.
65 (1), 377–95, 1973.
(FOR ENGLISH TRANSLATION SEE E63207)

52370 **MAGNETIC ANISOTROPY AND THE MAGNETOSTRICTION OF NEODYMIUM–SUBSTITUTED YTTRIUM GARNET FERRITES.**
VOLKOVA, N. V. RAITSIS, V. I.
ZH. EKSP. TEOR. FIZ.
65 (2), 688–92, 1973.
(FOR ENGLISH TRANSLATION SEE E63208)

52372 **THEORY OF IMPURITY FERROMAGNETISM OF SEMICONDUCTORS.**
ABRIKOSOV, A. A.
ZH. EKSP. TEOR. FIZ.
65 (2), 814–22, 1973.
(FOR ENGLISH TRANSLATION SEE E63212)

52373 **EFFECT OF DISLOCATIONS ON THE ELECTRICAL PROPERTIES OF P–GERMANIUM.**
OSIP'YAN, YU. A. SHEVCHENKO, S. A.
ZH. EKSP. TEOR. FIZ.
65 (2), 698–704, 1973.
(FOR ENGLISH TRANSLATION SEE E63209)

52377 **ELECTRICAL CONDUCTIVITY OF ZIRCONIUM AND HAFNIUM TETRACHLORIDES.**
ALEKSEEVA, L. V. BYSTROVA, O. N.
DENISOVA, N. D. KUTSEVA, V. S.
ZH. FIZ. KHIM.
47 (5), 1338, 1973.
(FOR ENGLISH TRANSLATION SEE E57490)

52380 **NATURE OF EXOELECTRONIC EMISSION FROM CRYSTAL PHOSPHORS. I. SULFIDES.**
KRYLOVA, I. V. KONYUSHKINA, N. I.
ZH. FIZ. KHIM.
47 (6), 1475–8, 1973.
(FOR ENGLISH TRANSLATION SEE E57493)

52384 **MAGNETIC PROPERTIES OF COBALT(II) OXIDE – ZINC OXIDE SOLID SOLUTIONS.**
KEROVA, L. S. LOGINOV, G. M. MOROZOVA, M. P.
ZH. FIZ. KHIM.
47 (6), 1620, 1973.
(FOR ENGLISH TRANSLATION SEE E57496)

52386 **EFFECT OF THERMAL DECOMPOSITION ON THE ELECTRICAL CONDUCTIVITY OF AMMONIUM SULFATE.**
KHAIRETDINOV, E. F. MEERSON, E. E.
BOLDYREV, V. V.
ZH. FIZ. KHIM.
47 (7), 1763–5, 1973.
(FOR ENGLISH TRANSLATION SEE E58579)

52387 **DIELECTRIC MEASUREMENTS IN THE EARLY STAGES OF HARDENING OF MONOMINERAL BINDERS.**
SVATOVSKAYA, L. B. SHIBALLO, V. G.
ZH. PRIKL. KHIM. (LENINGRAD)
46 (6), 1219–23, 1973.
(FOR ENGLISH TRANSLATION SEE E55648)

52392 **CARBIDE EMITTERS WITH INCREASED THERMIONIC EFFECIENCY.**
KAN, KH. S. KUL'VARSKAYA, B. S.
ZH. TEKH. FIZ.
43 (6), 1269–74, 1973.
(FOR ENGLISH TRANSLATION SEE E54539)

52393 **NUMERICAL RESULTS FOR THE CALCULATION OF THE STATIC DIELECTRIC CONSTANT OF HYDROGEN CHLORIDE.**
JANSOONE, V. M.
ACTA PHYS. AUSTR.
37 (4), 326–34, 1973.

EPIC Number	Bibliographic Citation

52398 **OPTICAL PROPERTIES OF SILICON DIOXIDE FILMS ON SILICON SUBSTRATE.**
PHUC, D. V.
ACTA TECH. (BUDAPEST)
74 (3-4), 263-74, 1973.

52400 **ELECTRICAL CONDUCTIVITY OF SALT MELTS IN A LITHIUM CHLORIDE-BARIUM CHLORIDE SYSTEM.**
SMIRNOV, M. V.
TR. INST. ELEKTROKHIM., AKAD. NAUK SSSR, URAL. FILIAL
33-6, 1969.
(FOR ENGLISH TRANSLATION SEE E52401)

52401 **ELECTRICAL CONDUCTIVITY OF SALT MELTS IN A LITHIUM CHLORIDE-BARIUM CHLORIDE SYSTEM.**
SMIRNOV, M. V.
ARMY FOREIGN SCIENCE AND TECHNOLOGY CENTER, CHARLOTTESVILLE, VIRGINIA
6PP., 1973.
(ENGLISH TRANSLATION OF TR. INST. ELEKTROKHIM., AKAD. NAUK SSSR, URAL. FILIAL, 33-6, 1969; FOR ORIGINAL SEE E52400)
(AD-766 573, FSTC-HT-23-2006-72, AVAIL. NTIS)

52403 **HOT-ELECTRON CONCEPT FOR POOLE-FRENKELCONDUCTION IN AMORPHOUS DIELECTRIC SOLIDS.**
ANTULA, J.
J. APPL. PHYS.
43 (11), 4663-7, 1972.
(AD-766 631, AFOSR-TR-73-1574, AVAIL. NTIS)

52405 **HIGH RESOLUTION LOW TEMPERATURE SPECTRA OF TERBIUM TRIPOSITIVE ION IN YTTRIUM ALUMINATE.**
BERG, J. L.
AIR FORCE INSTITUTE OF TECHNOLOGY, M. S. THESIS
94PP., 1973.
(AD-766 881, GEP-PH-73-3, N74-10999, AVAIL. NTIS)

52408 **PREDICTION OF NEW MULTIPLET STRUCTURE IN PHOTO-EMISSION EXPERIMENTS.**
BAGUS, P. S. FREEMAN, A. J. SASAKI, F.
PHYS. REV. LETT.
30 (18), 850-3, 1973.
(AD-767 088, AFOSR-TR-73-1604, AVAIL NTIS)

52412 **FAR-ULTRAVIOLET REFLECTANCE OF II-VI COMPOUNDS AND CORRELATION WITH THE PENN-PHILLIPS GAP.**
FREEOUF, J. L.
PHYS. REV.
7 B (8), 3810-30, 1973.
(AD-767 151, AFOSR-TR-73-1584, AVAIL. NTIS)

52414 **ELECTRONIC PHENOMENA IN AMORPHOUS SEMICONDUCTORS.**
FRITZSCHE, H.
J. ANN. REV. MAT. SCI.
2, 697-744, 1972.
(AD-767 157, AFOSR-TR-73-1608, AVAIL. NTIS)

52415 **ANOMALOUS DEMBER EFFECT IN CADMIUM TELLURIDE FILMS EXHIBITING ANOMALOUSLY LARGE PHOTOVOLTAGE.**
KORSUNSKII, M. I. SOMINSKII, M. M.
SOV. PHYS. SEMICOND.
7 (3), 342-68 1973.
(ENGLISH TRANSLATION OF FIZ. TEKH. POLUPROV., 7 (3), 480-7, 1973; FOR ORIGINAL SEE E50669)

52417 **TEMPERATURE DEPENDENCE OF THE RESISTANCE OF A SURFACE LAYER IN INDIUM ANTIMONIDE IN THE SUPERCONDUCTIVITY TRANSITION REGION.**
ABDULLAEV, A. VITOVSKII, N. A.
KRYMOVA, E. D. MASHOVETS, T. V.
RYVKIN, S. M. SHIK, A. YA.
SOV. PHYS. SEMICOND.
7 (5), 628-9, 1973.
(ENGLISH TRANSLATION OF FIZ. TEKH. POLUPROV., 7 (5), 925-7, 1973; FOR ORIGINAL SEE E50671)

52418 **IMPURITY STATES OF GALLIUM IN LEAD TELLURIDE.**
VEIS, A. N. KAIDANOV, V. I.
KOSTYLEVA, N. A. MELNIK, R. B.
UKHANOV, YU. I.
SOV. PHYS. SEMICOND.
7 (5), 630-1, 1973.
(ENGLISH TRANSLATION OF FIZ. TEKH. POLUPROV., 7 (5), 928-30, 1973; FOR ORIGINAL SEE E50672)

52420 **MAGNETORESTISTANCE OF FINITE SEMICONDUCTOR SAMPLES IN STRONG ELECTRIC FIELDS.**
VAKSER, A. I.
SOV. PHYS. SEMICOND.,
7 (5), 684-5, 1973.
(ENGLISH TRANSLATION OF FIZ. TEKH. POLUPROV., 7 (5), 1001-4, 1973; FOR ORIGINAL SEE E50674)

52422 **TRANSVERSE MAGNETORESTISTANCE OF EPITAXIAL FILMS OF N-TYPE GALLIUM ARSENIDE.**
GORODNICHII, O. P. SEITOV, E. P.
SHAVRIN, A. G.
SOV. PHYS. SEMICOND.
7 (5), 694-5, 1973.
(ENGLISH TRANSLATION OF FIZ. TEKH. POLUPROV., 7 (5), 1015-7, 1973; FOR ORIGINAL SEE E50676)

EPIC Number	Bibliographic Citation

52423 **THEORY OF THE LUMINESCENCE OF HEAVILY DOPED SEMICONDUCTORS.**
LEVANYUK, A. P. OSIPOV, V. V.
SOV. PHYS. SEMICOND.
7 (6), 721-6, 1973.
(ENGLISH TRANSLATION OF FIZ. TEKH. POLUPROV., 7 (6), 1058-68, 1973; FOR ORIGINAL SEE E50677)

52424 **THEORY OF THE LUMINESCENCE OF HEAVILY DOPED COMPENSATED NONDEGENERATE SEMICONDUCTORS.**
LEVANYUK, A. P. OSIPOV, V. V.
SOV. PHYS. SEMICOND.
7 (6), 727-33, 1973.
(ENGLISH TRANSLATION OF FIZ. TEKH. POLUPROV., 7 (6), 1069-80, 1973; FOR ORIGINAL SEE E50678)

52425 **INDIRECT EXCITONS AND PHONONLESS TRANSITIONS IN GALLIUM SULFIDE.**
RAZBIRIN, B. S. KARAMAN, M. I.
MUSHINSKII, V. P. STARUKHIN, A. N.
SOV. PHYS. SEMICOND.
7 (6), 753-5, 1973.
(ENGLISH TRANSLATION OF FIZ. TEKH. POLUPROV., 7 (6), 1112-6, 1973; FOR ORIGINAL SEE E50679)

52426 **RADIATIVE RECOMBINATION WITH AN ENERGY DEFICT IN INDIUM ANTIMONIDE.**
KASTALSKII, A. A. RYVKIN, S. M.
FILATOVA, E. S. YAGODKIN, V. M.
SOV. PHYS. SEMICOND.
7 (6), 756-9, 1973.
(ENGLISH TRANSLATION OF FIZ. TEKH. POLUPROV., 7 (6), 1117-23, 1973; FOR ORIGINAL SEE E50680)

52427 **INVESTIGATION OF THE RED RECOMBINATION RADIATION BAND OF CADMIUM DISPHOSPHIDE.**
VAVILOV, V. S. NEGRII, V. D. KOVAL, V. S.
POTYKEVICH, I. V. POTYKEVICH, YU. V.
CHUKICHEV, M. V.
SOV. PHYS. SEMICOND.
7 (6), 773-6, 1973.
(ENGLISH TRANSLATION OF FIZ. TEKH. POLUPROV., 7 (6), 1148-54, 1973; FOR ORIGINAL SEE E50681)

52428 **MAGNETOOPTIC ABSORPTION IN SEMICONDUCTORS WITH NONSPHERICAL BANDS.**
ZHILICH, A. G. MONOZON, B. S.
SOV. PHYS. SEMICOND.
7 (6), 783-7, 1973.
(ENGLISH TRANSLATION OF FIZ. TEKH. POLUPROV., 7 (6), 1164-71, 1973; FOR ORIGINAL SEE E50682)

52429 **CRYSTAL FIELD AND SITE SYMMETRY OF TRIVALENT CERIUM IONS IN CALCIUM FLUORIDE: THE C4V AND C3V CENTERS WITH INTERSITIAL-FLUORIDE CHARGE COMPENSATOR.**
MANTHEY, W. J.
PHYS. REV.
8 B (9), 4086-98, 1973.

52430 **MAGNETIC, TRANSPORT, AND NUCLEAR-MAGNETIC-RESONANCE PROPERTIES OF NONSTOICHRIOMETRIC URANIUM PLUTONIUM ALUMINIDE.**
ARKO, A. J. FRADIN, F. Y. BRODSKY, M. B.
PHYS. REV.
8 B (9), 4104-18, 1973.

52435 **MAGNETIC AND THERMAL PROPERTIES OF TERBIUM HYDROXIDE.**
CATANESE, C. A. SKJELTORP, A. T.
MEISSNER, H. E. WOLF, W. P.
PHYS. REV.
8 B (9), 4223-46, 1973.

52437 **EXCHANGE SCATTERING IN A FERROMAGNETIC SEMICONDUCTOR.**
COCHRANE, R. W. HEDGCOCK, F. T.
STROM-OLSEN, J. O.
PHYS. REV.
8 B (9), 4262-6, 1973.

52438 **ANISOTROPY AND MAGNETOSTRICTION OF IRIDIUM SUBSTITUTED YTTRIUM IRON GARNET.**
HANSEN, P. SCHULDT, J. TOLKSDORF, W.
PHYS. REV.
8 B (9), 4274-87, 1973.

52441 **THEORY OF MAGNETIC PROPERTIES OF ACTINIDE COMPOUNDS. I.**
ROBINSON, J. M. ERDOS, P.
PHYS. REV.
8 B (9), 4333-47, 1973.

52442 **MOSSBAUER-EFFECT MEASUREMENTS IN ANTIFERROMAGNETIC IRON CHLORIDE.**
STAMPFEL, J. P. OOSTERHUIS, W. T.
WINDOW, B. BARROS, F. D.
PHYS. REV.
8 B (9), 4371-82, 1973.

52449 **BOND-ORBITAL MODEL AND THE PROPERTIES OF TETRAHEDRALLY COORDINATED SOLIDS.**
HARRISON, W. A.
PHYS. REV.
8 B (10), 4487-98, 1973.

EPIC Number	Bibliographic Citation

52451 **CUBIC-TO-TETRAGONAL TRANSFORMATION AND SUSCEPTIBILITY IN LANTHANUM SILVER INDIUM ALLOYS.**
IHRIG, H. VIGREN, D. T. KUBLER, J.
METHFESSEL, S.
PHYS. REV.
8 B (10), 4525-33, 1973.

52457 **ACCEPTOR-TO-BAND TRANSITIONS IN SEMICONDUCTORS: PHOTOLUMINESCENCE, EXPONENTIAL ABSORPTION EDGES, AND FINAL-STATE INTERACTIONS.**
DOW, J. D. SMITH, D. L. LEDERMAN, F. L.
PHYS. REV.
8 B (10), 4612-26, 1973.

52459 **TEMPERATURE DEPENDENCE OF THE MERCURY TELLURIDE BAND GAP.**
GUNENZER, C. S. BIENENSTOCK, A.
PHYS. REV.
8 (10), 4655-67, 1973.

52460 **THERMAL CONDUCTIVITY OF GALLIUM ARSENIDE AT LOW TEMPERATURES.**
CHAUDHURI, N. WADHWA, R. S. TIKU, P.
SREEDHAR, A. K.
PHYS. REV.
8 B (10), 4668-70, 1973.

52461 **BAND INVERSION OF LEAD TIN SELENIUM ALLOYS UNDER HYDROSTATIC PRESSURE. I. THEORETICAL BAND STRUCTURE ANALYSIS.**
MARTINEZ, G.
PHYS. REV.
8 B (10), 4678-85, 1973.

52462 **BAND INVERSION OF LEAD TIN SELENIUM ALLOYS UNDER HYDROSTATIC PRESSURE. II. GALVANOMAGNETIC PROPERTIES.**
MARTINEZ, G.
PHYS. REV.
8 B (10), 4686-92, 1973.

52463 **BAND INVERSION IN LEAD TIN SELENIUM ALLOYS UNDER HYDROSTATIC PRESSURE. III. LASER EMISSION.**
MARTINEZ, G.
PHYS. REV.
8 B (10), 4693-707, 1973.

52464 **GENERALIZED PHOTOELECTROMAGNETIC EFFECT IN SEMICONDUCTORS.**
LILE, D. L.
PHYS. REV.
8 B (10), 4708-22, 1973.

52468 **SIMPLIFIED ANALYSIS OF ELECTRON-HOLE RECOMBINATION IN ZINC- AND O-DOPED GALLIUM PHOSPHIDE.**
HENRY, C. H. BACHRACH, R. Z.
SCHUMAKER, N. E.
PHYS. REV.
8 B (10), 4761-7, 1973.

52469 **IONIC CONDUCTION IN LANTHANUM FLUORIDE THIN FILMS.**
TILLER, C. O. LILLY, A. C. LAROY, B. C.
PHYS. REV.
8 B (10), 4787-94, 1973.

52472 **MULTIPHOTON ABSORPTION IN THE F CENTER.**
CHOUDHURY, B. J.
PHYS. REV.
8 B (10), 4849-56, 1973.

52473 **X-RAY PHOTOELECTRON BAND STRUCTURE OF SOME TRANSITION-METAL COMPOUNDS.**
HUFNER, S. WERTHEIM, G. K.
PHYS. REV.
8 B (10), 4857-67, 1973.

52474 **INDUCED FAR-INFRARED ABSORPTION IN MIXED ALKALI HALIDE CRYSTALS.**
DE JONG C WEGDAM, G. H. VAN DER ELSKEN, J.
PHYS. REV.
8 B (10), 4868-74, 1973.

52475 **HOPPING CONDUCTIVITY IN ONE DIMENSIONAL DISORDERED COMPOUNDS.**
SHANTE, V. K. S. VARMA, C. M.
PHYS. REV.
8 B (10), 4885-9, 1973.
(AD 778 976)

52477 **MOLECULAR ELECTRON AFFINITIES FROM COLLISIONAL IONIZATION OF CESIUM. I. NITRIC OXIDE, NITROGEN DIOXIDE, AND NITROUS OXIDE.**
NALLEY, S. J. COMPTON, R. N.
SCHWEINLER, H. C. ANDERSON, V. E.
J. CHEM. PHYS.
59 (8), 4125-39, 1973.

52478 **MOLECULAR ELECTRON AFFINITIES FROM COLLISIONAL IONIZATION OF CESIUM. II. SULFUR HEXAFLUORIDE AND TELLURIUM HEXAFLUORIDE.**
COMPTON, R. N. COOPER, C. D.
J. CHEM. PHYS.
59 (8), 4140-4, 1973.

EPIC Number	Bibliographic Citation

52479 **MULTIPLET SPLITTING IN LS HOLE STATES OF MOLECULES.**
DAVIS, D. W. MARTIN, R. L. BANNA, M. S.
SHIRLEY, D. A.
J. CHEM. PHYS.
59 (8), 4235-45, 1973.

52480 **PHOTOIONIZATION OF CARBON DIOXIDE.**
MC CULLOH, K. E.
J. CHEM. PHYS.
59 (8), 4250-9, 1973.
(AD 776 450)

52481 **ROTATIONAL BAND SHAPES IN PHOTOELECTRON SPECTROSCOPY: HYDROGEN FLUORIDE AND DEUTERATED HYDROGEN FLUORIDE.**
WALKER, T. E. H. DEHMER, P. M. BERKOWITZ, J.
J. CHEM. PHYS.
59 (8), 4292-8, 1973.

52482 **ABSORPTION AND PHOTOIONIZATION CROSS SECTIONS FOR WATER AND DEUTERIUM OXIDE IN THE VACUUM ULTRAVIOLET.**
KATAYAMA, D. H. HUFFMAN, R. E.
O BRYAN, C. L.
J. CHEM. PHYS.
59 (8), 4309-19, 1973.

52484 **MAGNETOTHERMODYNAMICS OF GADOLINIUM GALLIUM GARNET. I. HEAT CAPACITY, ENTROPY, MAGNETIC MOMENT FROM 0.5 TO 4.2 K, WITH FIELDS TO 90 K G ALONG THE (100) AXIS.**
FISHER, R. A. BRODALE, G. E. HORNUNG, E. W.
GIAUQUE, W. F.
J. CHEM. PHYS.
59 (9), 4652-63, 1973.

52485 **ELECTRON TRANSFER BAND IN THE CHLORINE K-X-RAY ABSORPTION SPECTRA OF SOME TRANSITION METAL CHLORIDES.**
SUGIURA, C.
J. CHEM. PHYS.
59 (9), 4907-108 1973.

52486 **NUCLEAR RESONANCE AND MAGNETIC SUSCEPTIBILITY STUDY OF PLATINUM-GROUP IV A COMPOUNDS.**
WEAVER, H. T. QUINN, R. K. BAUGHMAN, R. J.
KNAUER, R. C.
J. CHEM. PHYS.
59 (9), 4961-5, 1973.

52489 **SPECTRA OF MANGANESE HEXAFLUORIDE ION IN ENVIRONMENTS OF O(H) AND D(3D) SYMMETRY.**
HELMHOLZ, L. RUSSO, M. E.
J. CHEM. PHYS.
59 (10), 5455-708 1973.

52491 **PHOTOELECTRON SPECTRA OF CARBONYL SELENIDE, THIOCARBONYL SELENIDE, AND CARBON DISELENIDE.**
FROST, D. C. LEE, S. T. MC DOWELL, C. A.
J. CHEM. PHYS.
59 (10), 5484-93, 1973.

52493 **OPTICAL STUDY OF ION-DEFECT CLUSTERING IN ERBIUM TRIPOSITIVE ION DOPED CALCIUM FLUORIDE.**
FENN, J. B., JR. WRIGHT, J. C. FONG, F. K.
J. CHEM. PHYS.
59 (10), 5591-9, 1973.

52496 **PRESSURE DEPENDENCE OF THE NEAR-INFRARED ABSORPTION IN CHROMIUM DOPED ZINC SULFIDE.**
KELLEY, C. S.
J. CHEM. PHYS.
59 (10), 5737-9, 1973.

52500 **INFLUENCE OF EXTERNAL FACTORS ON THE ELECTROPHYSICAL PROPERTIES OF PIEZOELECTRIC CERAMICS MADE FROM SOLID SOLUTIONS OF LEAD BARIUM NIOBATE.**
ANAN'EVA, A. A. UGRYUMOVA, M. A.
SHAEVICH, T. A.
AKUST. ZH.
19 (4), 494-7, 1973.
(FOR ENGLISH TRANSLATION SEE E63246)

52501 **MEASUREMENT OF CHEMICAL SHIFTS BY THE SOFT X-RAY APPEARANCE POTENTIAL TECHNIQUE.**
PARK, R. L. HOUSTON, J. E.
AMER. CHEM. SOC., DIV. PETROL. CHEM., PREPR.
17 (2), C83-C90, 1972.

52505 **OPTICAL ABSORPTION IN FUSED SILICA AND FUSED QUARTZ AT 1.06 MU.**
RICH, T. C. PINNOW, D. A.
APP. OPT.
12 (10), 2234, 1973.

52506 **DIELECTRIC PROPERTIES OF ALUMINA CALCINED AT DIFFERENT TEMPERATURES.**
KLUG, O. KONYA, J. RIEDL, I.
BANYASZ. KOHASZ. LAPOK, KOHASZ.
106 (6), 277-81, 1973.

52507 **CONTINUOUS TRANSTION FROM INSULATOR TO IONIC CONDUCTOR AS DEMONSTRATED ON BISMUTH CHLORIDE.**
TREIBER, G. TOEDHEIDE, K.
BER. BUNSENGES. PHYS. CHEM.
77 (7), 540-8, 1973.

EPIC Number	Bibliographic Citation
52510	**REFLECTION SPECTROSCOPY OF OPTICALLY ACTIVE MATERIALS.** EINHORN, A. J. PHELPS, F. W., JR. PAO, Y. H. CHEM. PHYS. 1 (4), 277–96, 1973.
52512	**SEARCH FOR ACTIVE MEDIA FOR LASERS.** KAMINSKII, A. A. DOKL. AKAD. NAUK SSSR 211 (4), 811–13, 1973. (FOR ENGLISH TRANSLATION SEE E54875)
52513	**OPTICAL CONSTANTS AND EXCITON STATES IN LEAD(II) FLUORIDE.** MALYSHEVA, A. F. PLEKHANOV, V. G. EESTI NSV TEAD. AKAD. TOIM., FUUS., MAT. 22 (3), 286–95, 1973.
52515	**EFFECT OF THE DOMAIN STRUCTURE CONFIGURATION ON ELECTRICAL PROPERTIES OF FERROELECTRIC CERAMICS.** VERBITSKAYA, T. N. PROVOTOROVA, E. V. RAEVSKAYA, E. B. ELEKTRON. TEKH. NAUCH.-TEKH. SB., RADIODETALI (1), 37–41, 1972.
52520	**EFFECT OF A HIGH MAGNETIC FIELD ON THE PHOTOLUMINESCENCE SPECTRUM OF N-GALLIUM ARSENIDE.** ZVEREV, L. P. MIN'KOV, G. M. NEGASHEV, S. A. FIZ. TEKH. POLUPROV. 7 (8), 1585–8, 1973. (FOR ENGLISH TRANSLATION SEE E57761)
52521	**OPTICAL ABSORPTION IN NICKEL-DOPED GALLIUM ARSENIDE.** BAZHENOV, V. K. RASHEVSKAYA, E. P. SOLOV'EV, N. N. TOIGEL, M. G. FIZ. TEKH. POLUPROV. 7 (8), 1601–4, 1973. (FOR ENGLISH TRANSLATION SEE E57762)
52522	**EXCITON INTERACTION AND LASER RADIATION OF CADMIUM TELLURIDE.** GOLUBEV, G. P. SYSUN, V. V. YAKOVLEV, V. A. FIZ. TEKH. POLUPROV. 7 (8), 1606–7, 1973. (FOR ENGLISH TRANSLATION SEE E57763)
52523	**DIFFUSION THERMOEMF. IN N-INDIUM ANTIMONIDE.** KOSAREV, V. V. TAMARIN, P. V. FIZ. TEKH. POLUPROV. 7 (8), 1617–20, 1973. (FOR ENGLISH TRANSLATION SEE E57764)
52525	**EFFECT OF A MAGNETIC FIELD ON THE HEATING OF ELECTRONS IN N-INDIUM ANTIMONIDE.** IL'IN, V. A. LITVAK-GORSKAYA, L. B. RABINOVICH, R. I. SHAPIRO, E. Z. FIZ. TEKH. POLUPROV. 7 (8), 1631–3, 1973. (FOR ENGLISH TRANSLATION SEE E57766)
52528	**PHOTOELECTRIC PROPERTIES OF ZINKENITE.** DMYTRIV, A. YU. KOVAL'SKII, P. N. MAKARENKO, V. V. FIZ. TEKH. POLUPROV. 7 (8), 1641–3, 1973. (FOR ENGLISH TRANSLATION SEE E57769)
52529	**MECHANISM OF COMPENSATION IN SEMIINSULATING ARSENIDE CONTAINING AN IRON IMPURITY.** GANAPOL'SKII, E. M. OMEL'YANOVSKII, E. M. PEROVA, L. YA. FISTUL, V. I. FIZ. TEKH. POLUPROV. 7 (8), 1643–5, 1973. (FOR ENGLISH TRANSLATION SEE E57770)
52530	**DETERMINATION OF TRAP PARAMETERS IN CADMIUM SELENIDE FROM THE CURVES OF THE TEMPERATURE DEPENDENCE OF SOUND AMPLIFICATION.** KOCHNEVA, N. S. VASIL'EV, B. P. FIZ. TEKH. POLUPROV. 7 (8), 1650–2, 1973. (FOR ENGLISH TRANSLATION SEE E57771)
52531	**PHOTOCONDUCTIVITY OF LEAD SULFIDE.** ZUBKOVA, T. I. IL'IN, V. I. FIZ. TEKH. POLUPROV. 7 (8), 1653–5, 1973. (FOR ENGLISH TRANSLATION SEE E57772)
52532	**EFFECT OF IMPURITY IONS ON BAND STRUCTURE DURING INTERMEDIATE DOPING.** KLOTINS, E. PETROV, V. K. FIZ. TEKH. POLUPROV. 7 (8), 1655–7, 1973. (FOR ENGLISH TRANSLATION SEE E57773)
52534	**CARRIER MOBILITY IN N-TYPE YTTRIUM IRON GARNET.** KSENDZOV, YA. M. KOTEL'NIKOVA, A. M. MAKAROV, V. V. FIZ. TVERD. TELA 15 (8), 2343–6, 1973. (FOR ENGLISH TRANSLATION SEE E53647)
52535	**PHOTOELECTRIC PROPERTIES OF VANADIUM PENTOXIDE SINGLE CRYSTALS.** MOKEROV, V. G. FIZ. TVERD. TELA 15 (8), 2393–6, 1973. (FOR ENGLISH TRANSLATION SEE E53652)
52537	**BISTABLE STATE OF MICROPLASMAS IN ELECTRIC BREAKDOWN OF SEMICONDUCTOR FIELD-EMISSION CATHODES.** SHLYAKHTENKO, P. G. MILESHKINA, N. V. DOROTYNSKII, M. G. FIZ. TVERD. TELA 15 (8), 2494–6, 1973. (FOR ENGLISH TRANSLATION SEE E53664)
52538	**TEMPERATURE DEPENDENCE OF THE ACTIVATION ENERGY OF ELECTRICAL CONDUCTION IN ARSENIC SELENIDE.** ANDREEV, A. A. LEBEDEV, E. A. SHMURATOV, E. A. SHPUNT, V. KH. FIZ. TVERD. TELA 15 (8), 2500–1, 1973. (FOR ENGLISH TRANSLATION SEE E53667)
52539	**BRIGHTNESS WAVES OF X-RAY RADIOELECTROLUMINESCENCE OF THALLIUM DOPED POTASSIUM IODIDE.** POLOGRUDOV, V. V. KARNAUKHOV, E. N. EGOROV, V. N. FIZ. TVERD. TELA 15 (8), 2523–24, 1973. (FOR ENGLISH TRANSLATION SEE E53672)
52540	**HALL COEFFICIENT OF METAL-LIKE SEMICONDUCTOR MELTS.** ANDREEV, A. A. TURGUNOV, T. FIZ. TVERD. TELA 15 (8), 2531–2, 1973. (FOR ENGLISH TRANSLATION SEE E53675)
52541	**INFLUENCE OF THE NATURE OF DEFORMATION ON THE ELECTRICAL PROPERTIES OF BISMUTH ANTIMONIDE-TELLURIDE SOLID SOLUTIONS.** AVERKIN, A. A. GOL'TSMAN, E. M. ZHAPAROV, ZH. ZH. ZHEMCHUZHINA, E. A. KOMISSARCHIK, M. G. POLISTANSKII, YU. G. FIZ. TVERD. TELA 15 (8), 2543–5, 1973. (FOR ENGLISH TRANSLATION SEE E53676)
52543	**MASS OF THE HOLE DENSITY OF STATES IN P-TYPE INDIUM ANTIMONY DEDUCED FROM GALVANOMAGNETIC MEASUREMENTS.** TAMARIN, P. V. LANG, I. G. PAVLOV, S. T. FIZ. TVERD. TELA 15 (8), 2557–9, 1973. (FOR ENGLISH TRANSLATION SEE E53677)
52548	**PROPERTIES OF MANGANESE-ZINC FERRITES IN RELATION TO OXYGEN CONTENT OF SOLIDS.** BEYER, P. HERMSDORFER TECH. MITT. 12 (34), 1059–80, 1972.
52549	**ELECTRON SPECTROSCOPY OF MOLYBDENUM SULFIDES.** RATNASAMY, P. INDIAN J. CHEM. 11 (7), 695, 1973.
52556	**EFFECT OF AN ALUMINUM IMPURITY ON THE ELECTROPHYSICAL PROPERTIES OF COPPER SELENIDE.** ABDULLAEV, G. B. ALIYAROVA, Z. A. ISKENDEROV, S. O. AKHUNDOVA, E. A. IZV. AKAD. NAUK AZERB. SSR, SER. FIZ.-TEKH. MAT. NAUK (1), 59–62, 1973.
52557	**STRUCTURE OF THE CONDUCTION BAND OF SILVER TELLURIDE.** ALIEV, S. A. SUYUNOV, U. KH. ALIEV, M. I. IZV. AKAD. NAUK AZERB. SSR, SER. FIZ.-TEKH. MAT. NAUK (1), 63–6, 1973.
52560	**LUMINESCENCE AND ABSORPTION SPECTRA OF RARE EARTH ORTHOPHOSPHATES ACTIVATED BY NEODYMIUM, EUROPIUM, AND TERBIUM IONS.** IONKINA, E. A. MOROZOV, N. N. MURAV'EV, E. N. ORLOVSKII, V. P. REPKO, V. P. IZV. AKAD. NAUK SSSR, NEORG. MATER. 9 (7), 1270–1, 1973. (FOR ENGLISH TRANSLATION SEE E57785)
52561	**PROPERTIES OF GALLIUM ARSENIDE DOPED BY TELLURIUM IONS.** ZELEVINSKAYA, V. M. KACHURIN, G. A. SMIRNOV, L. S. IZV. AKAD. NAUK SSSR, NEORG. MATER. 9 (8), 1316–19, 1973. (FOR ENGLISH TRANSLATION SEE E57786)
52562	**AMORPHOUS STATE-POLYCRYSTAL PHASE TRANSITION IN CARBON, SILICON, GERMANIUM, GERMANIUM SELENIDE, AND GERMANIUM TELLURIDE THIN FILMS AND ITS EFFECT ON ELECTRICAL CONDUCTIVITY AND OPTICAL DENSITY.** ZAKHAROV, V. P. ZALIVA, V. I. IZV. AKAD. NAUK SSSR, NEORG. MATER. 9 (8), 1325–9, 1973. (FOR ENGLISH TRANSLATION SEE E57787)

EPIC Number	Bibliographic Citation
52563	**MECHANISM OF ELECTRICAL CONDUCTIVITY AND BAND MODEL OF TUNGSTEN DISELENIDE-NIOBIUM SELENIDE QUASIBINARY ALLOYS.** KALIKHMAN, V. L. KASIYAN, I. M. PECHENNIKOV, A. V. YAREMBASH, E. I. SADOVSKAYA, O. A. TYURIN, E. G. IZV. AKAD. NAUK SSSR, NEORG. MATER. 9 (8), 1333–8, 1973. (FOR ENGLISH TRANSLATION SEE 57788)
52564	**MAGNETIC AND ELECTRIC PROPERTIES OF EUROPIUM TELLURIDES AND SELENIDES.** BUTASOV, O. B. CHECHERNIKOV, V. I. PECHENNIKOV, A. V. YAREMBASH, E. L. SADOVSKAYA, O. A. TYURIN, E. G. IZV. AKAD. NAUK SSSR, NEORG. MATER. 9 (8), 1339–41, 1973. (FOR ENGLISH TRANSLATION SEE E57789)
52566	**MAGNETIC SUSCEPTIBILITY AND ELECTRIC RESISTANCE OF IRON, COBALT, AND NICKEL MONOBORIDES.** BUDOZHAPOV, V. D. ZELENIN, L. P. CHEMERINSKAYA, L. S. SIDORENKO, F. A. GEL'D, P. V. IZV. AKAD. NAUK SSSR, NEORG. MATER. 9 (8), 1447–8, 1973. (FSOR ENGLISH TRANSLATION SEE E57791)
52567	**FORMATION OF HEMATITE FROM AMORPHOUS IRON HYDROXIDE STUDIES BY A MOESSBAUER SPECTROSCOPIC METHOD.** LOSEVA, G. V. MURASHKO, N. V. IZV. AKAD. NAUK SSSR, NEORG. MATER. 9 (8) 1456–7, 1973. (FSOR ENGLISH TRANSLATION SEE E57792)
52568	**ELECTROPHYSICAL PROPERTIES OF THE SURFACE OF IRRADIATED CATALYSTS.** SPITSYN, V. I. PIROGOVA, G. N. SOPINA, A. A. IZV. OTD. KHIM. NAUKI, BULG, AKAD. NAUK. 6 (1), 77–83, 1973.
52569	**VISCOSITY AND ELECTRICAL RESISTIVITY OF CHROMIUM - NICKEL ALLOYS.** TYAGUNOV, G. V. BAUM, B. A. KUSHNIR, M. N. IZV. VYSSH. UCHEB. ZAVED., FIZ. 16 (5), 149–51, 1973. (FOR ENGLISH TRANSLATION SEE E78966)
52570	**STRUCTURE AND ELECTRIC PROPERTIES OF COPPER SELENIDE THIN FILMS.** KOGUT, A. N. MELNIK, A. I. MIKOLAICHUK, A. G. ROMANISHIN, B. M. IZV. VYSSH. UCHEB. ZAVED., FIZ. 16 (8), 90–4, 1973. (FOR ENGLISH TRANSLATION SEE E79103)
52576	**FERROELECTRIC, PIEZOELECTRIC, AND OPTICAL PROPERTIES OF STRONTIUM TELLURATE (IV) SINGLE CRYSTALS AND PHASE-TRANSITION POINTS IN THE SOLID-SOLUTION** YAMADA, T. IWASAKI, I. J. APPL. PHYS. 44 (9), 3934–9, 1973.
52579	**DIELECTRIC CONSTANT AND ASSOCIATION IN LIQUID HYDROGEN FLUORIDE.** COLE, R. H. J. CHEM. PHYS. 59 (3), 1545–6, 1973.
52580	**TEMPERATURE AND FREQUENCY DEPENDENCES OF DIELECTRIC PROPERTIES OF SODIUM SULFATE SINGLE CRYSTAL.** KHANNA, R. K. SOBHANADRI, J. J. CHEM. PHYS. 59 (3), 1547–8, 1973.
52583	**NONRADIATIVE AND FLUORESCENCE LIFETIMES IN SAMARIUM(2+)-DOPED CALCIUM FLUORIDE.** ANSON, M. MC GEOCH, M. W. SMITH, R. C. J. CHEM. PHYS. 59 (4), 2143–4, 1973.
52584	**X-RAY PHOTOELECTRON SPECTROSCOPY OF CHROMIUM-OXYGEN SYSTEMS.** ALLEN, G. C. CURTIS, M. T. HOOPER, A. J. TUCKER, P. M. J. CHEM. SOC., DALTON TRANS. (16), 1675–83, 1973.
52587	**ACCELERATED DIELCTRIC BREAKDOWN OF SILICON DIOXIDE FILMS.** OSBURN, C. M. CHOU, N. J. J. ELECTROCHEM. SOC. 120 (10), 1377–8, 1973.
52588	**ANODIC OXIDATION OF GALLIUM ARSENIDE IN AQUEOUS HYDROGEN PEROXIDE SOLUTION.** LOGAN, R. A. SCHWARTZ, B. SUNDBURG, W. J. J. ELECTROCHEM. SOC. 120 (10), 1385–90, 1973.

EPIC Number	Bibliographic Citation
52589	**PROPERTIES OF EPITAXIAL GALLIUM ARSENIDE FROM TRIMETHYLGALLIUM AND ARSINE.** ITO, S. SHINOHARA, T. SEKI, Y. J. ELECTROCHEM. SOC. 120 (10), 1419–23, 1973.
52591	**THEORY AND APPLICATIONS OF PHOTOELECTRON SPECTROSCOPY. 32. PHOTOIONIZATION CROSS SECTIONS. HELIUM (HE I) AND HELIUM (HE II) PHOTOELECTRON SPECTRA OF FLUORINE COMPOUNDS.** SCHWEIG, A. THIEL, W. J. ELECTRON SPECTROSC. RELAT. PHENOMENA 2 (2), 199–200, 1973.
52593	**THE 304 A PHOTOELECTRON SPECTRA OF CARBON MONOXIDE, NITROGEN, OXYGEN, AND CARBON DIOXIDE.** GARDNER, J. L. SAMSON, J. A. R. J. ELECTRON SPECTROSC. RELAT. PHENOMENA 2 (3), 259–66, 1973.
52595	**HIGH-TEMPERATURE PHOTOELECTRON SPECTROMETERS.** ALLEN, J. D. JR. BOGGESS, G. W. GOODMAN, T. D. WACHTEL, A. S., JR. SCHWEITZER, G. K. J. ELECTRON SPECTROSC. RELAT. PHENOMENA 2 (3), 289–94, 1973.
52596	**LOW-TEMPERATURE PROPERTIES OF CERIUM-ALUMINUM AND COMPARISON TO LANTHANUM-ALUMINUM.** WALKER, E. PURWINS, H. G. LANDOLT, M. HULLIGER, F. J. LESS-COMMON METALS 33 (2), 203–8, 1973.
52597	**MAGNETIC PROPERTIES OF CESIUM CHLORIDE-TYPE RARE EARTH-MAGNESIUM COMPOUNDS.** BUSCHOW, K. H. J. J. LESS-COMMON METALS 33 (2), 239–44, 1973.
52605	**RATIOS OF STRAIN-OPTICAL CONSTANTS OF ALKALI HALIDES BY AN ULTRASONIC TECHNIQUE.** PETTERSEN, H. E. J. OPT. SOC. AMER. 63 (10), 1243–5, 1973.
52619	**RADIATIVE AND NONRADIATIVE DECAY OF EUROPIUM (3+) IONS IN LANTHANUM ALUMINATE.** DELSART, CH. J. PHYS. (PARIS) 34 (8–9), 711–19, 1973.
52621	**MAGNETIC PROPERTIES OF IRON TITANIUM SULFIDE.** MURANAKA, S. J. PHYS. SOC. JAP. 35 (2), 616, 1973.
52623	**PHYSICAL PROPERTIES OF LEAD IRON URANIUM OXIDE AND ITS SOLID SOLUTIONS.** NOMURA, S. KAWACHI, M. KOJIMA, F. J. PHYS. SOC. JAP. 35 (4), 1008–15, 1973.
52624	**DIELECTRIC BEHAVIOR OF POTASSIUM DIHYDROGEN PHOSPHATE AND ROCHELLE SALT POWDERS.** MANSINGH, A. BAWA, S. S. J. PHYS. SOC. JAP. 35 (4), 1036–41, 1973.
52627	**LUMINESCENCE CENTERS OF CALCIUM (SULFIDE, SELENIDE) PHOSPHORS ACTIVATED WITH IMPURITY IONS HAVING S2 CONFIGURATION. I. ANTIMONY(3+)-ACTIVATED CALCIUM(SULFIDE SELENIDE) PHOSPHORS.** YAMASHITA, N. J. PHYS. SOC. JAP. 35 (4), 1089–97, 1973.
52628	**MAGNETOPHONON RESONANCE OF HOT ELECTRONS IN N-INDIUM ANTIMONIDE AT 77 K.** SHIRAKAWA, T. HAMAGUCHI, C. NAKAI, J. J. PHYS. SOC. JAP. 35 (4), 1098–105, 1973.
52629	**EXCITED STATES OF NEUTRAL SILVER CENTER IN ALKALI HALIDES EMBEDDED IN CONTINUUM.** SAIDOH, M. ITOH, N. J. PHYS. SOC. JAP. 35 (4), 1122–6, 1973.
52630	**LUMINESCENCE OF RF-SPUTTERED OXIDE FILMS DURING SPUTTERING.** RATINEN, H. J. APPL. PHYS. 44 (9), 3817–20, 1973.
52631	**VAPOR-PHASE GROWTH AND ELECTRICAL CONDUCTIVITY OF PURE AND IMPURITY-DOPED AMMONIUM HALIDE CRYSTALS.** RADHAKRISHNA, S. SHARMA, B. D. J. APPL. PHYS. 44 (9), 3848–50, 1973.
52632	**THE RF SPUTTERING OF ZINC OXIDE SHEAR-WAVE TRANSDUCERS.** LEHMANN, H. W. WIDMER, R. J. APPL. PHYS. 44 (9), 3868–79, 1973.

EPIC Number	Bibliographic Citation
52635	CHROMIUM-RARE EARTH ENERGY TRANSFER IN YTTRIUM ORTHOALUMINATE. WEBER, M. J. J. APPL. PHYS. 44 (9), 4058-64, 1973.
52636	ADSORPTION OF CARBON DIOXIDE LASER RADIATION BY CARBONYL FLUORIDE. DOUGHTY, J. R. JACK, J. L. O PRAY, J. E. J. APPL. PHYS. 44 (9), 4065-6, 1973.
52637	ELECTROLUMINESCENCE SATURATION AND I-V (CURRENT-VOLTAGE) MEASUREMENTS OF ZINC-DIFFUSED GALLIUM PHOSPHIDE DIODES. LUTHER, L. C. HARRISON, D. A. DERICK, L. J. APPL. PHYS. 44 (9), 4072-8, 1973.
52640	ELASTIC, MAGNETIC, AND ELECTRICAL PROPERTIES OF PURE AND LITHIUM-DOPED NICKEL OXIDE. NOTIS, M. R. SPRIGGS, R. M. HAHN, W. C., JR. J. APPL. PHYS. 44 (9), 4165-71, 1973.
52641	CONTROLLED ADJUSTMENT OF BUBBLE DOMAIN PARAMETERS IN EPITAXIAL GARNET FILMS BY THERMAL ANNEALING. SMITH, D. H. HAGEDORN, F. B. HEWITT, B. S. J. APPL. PHYS. 44 (9), 4177-80, 1973.
52642	POLARIZED NEUTRON TECHNIQUES FOR THE OBSERVATION OF FERROMAGNETIC DOMAINS. SCHLENKER, M. SHULL, C. G. J. APPL. PHYS. 44 (9), 4181-4, 1973.
52643	INJECTION DEPENDENCE OF THE EXCESS CARRIER LIFETIMES IN CHROMIUM-DOPED N-TYPE GALLIUM ARSENIDE. HUANG, C. I. LI, S. S. J. APPL. PHYS. 44 (9), 4214-15, 1973.
52644	LUMINESCENCE OF BERYLLIUM- AND MAGNESIUM-DOPED GALLIUM NITRIDE. HEGEMS, M. DINGLE, R. J. APPL. PHYS. 44 (9), 4234-5, 1973.
52649	MAGNETIC CHARACTERISTICS OF LANTHANIDE-COBALT THORIUM-COBALT PSEUDOBINARY SYSTEMS. WALLACE, W. E. SWEARINGEN, J. T. J. SOLID STATE CHEM. 8 (1), 37-8, 1973.
52650	A.C. CONDUCTIVITY OF AMORPHOUS ARSENIC-SELENIUM-GERMANIUM FILMS. ZEMBUTSU, S. IGO, T. JAP. J. APPL. PHYS. 12 (8), 1261-2, 1973.
52651	DOPING AND ENERGY LEVELS OF SILICON AND GERMANIUM IN GALLIUM ARSENIDE GROWN FROM THE VAPOR PHASE. NAKANISI, T. JAP. J. APPL. PHYS. 12 (8), 1263-6, 1973.
52652	REFLECTIVITY OF CADMIUM CHROMIUM SELENIDE NEAR THE CURIE POINT. ITOH, T. MIYATA, N. NARITA, S. JAP. J. APPL. PHYS. 12 (8), 1265-6, 1973.
52653	NEGATIVE DIFFERENTIAL CONDUCTIVITY AND CURRENT OSCILLATION IN P-CADMIUM TELLURIDE. TOKUMARU, Y. MIKOSHIBA, N. JAP. J. APPL. PHYS. 12 (8), 1270-2, 1973.
52654	D.C. CONDUCTIVITY OF COMPRESSED CADMIUM SELENIDE POWDERS. SATO, K. NISHIMURA, M. YOSHIZAWA, M. JAP. J. APPL. PHYS. 12 (8), 1274-6, 1973.
52655	STRUCTURAL AND ELECTRICAL PROPERTIES OF MANGANESE MAGNESIUM TELLURIDE. ANZAI, S. WATANABE, K. IWAMA, M. MORITA, A. YANAGISAWA, S. JAP. J. APPL. PHYS. 12 (8), 1289-90, 1973.
52656	ELECTRICAL CONDUCTIVITY OF CADMIUM SULFIDE POWDERS WITH THE WIDE VARIATION OF CONCENTRATIONS OF BOTH COPPER IMPURITIES AND HALIDE IMPURITIES. OTOTAKE, M. SATO, K. YOSHIZAWA, M. JAP. J. APPL. PHYS. 12 (8), 1290-1, 1973.
52657	DOUBLE A.C. METHOD FOR SENSITIVE MEASUREMENT OF THE HALL EFFECT. KANEDA, T. KOBAYASHI, S. SHIMODA, K. JAP. J. APPL. PHYS. 12 (9), 1335-7, 1973.

EPIC Number	Bibliographic Citation
52658	HIGH-PRESSURE SYNTHESIS OF PEROVSKITE TYPE RARE EARTH INDIUM OXIDE. SAWAMOTO, H. JAP. J. APPL. PHYS. 12 (9), 1432-8, 1973.
52659	FIELD EMISSION STUDIES OF SODIUM IODIDE AND MERCURY IN TUNGSTEN. WASHIMI, H. JAP. J. APPL. PHYS. 12 (9), 1446-54, 1973.
52664	DETERMINATION OF THE RELATIVE STABILITY OF THE ZINC BLENDE AND WURTZITE STRUCTURE BY THE PIEZOELECTRIC EFFECT. HUEBNER, K. KRIST. TECH. 8 (7), 847-51, 1973.
52665	GROWTH AND STUDY OF CRYSTALS OF DOUBLE CADMIUM OXIDES WITH PEROVSKITE-TYPE STRUCTURE. SPINKO, R. I. LEBEDEV, V. N. KOLESOVA, R. V. FESENKO, E. G. KRISTALLOGRAFIYA 18 (4), 849-51, 1973. (ENGLISH TRANSLATION SEE E63233)
52666	GALVANOMAGNETIC EFFECT AND OPTICAL ABSORPTION IN THALLIUM SELENIDE. SHIN, K. HASHIMOTO, K. KYUSHU DAIGAKU KOGAKU SHUHO 46 (3), 357-62, 1973.
52667	MAGNETIC PROPERTIES OF POTASSIUM TRIFLUOROCUPRATE(II). MIIKE, H. HIRAKAWA, K. KYUSHU DAIGAKU KOGAKU SHUHO 46 (3), 402-5, 1973.
52672	DETERMINATION OF IONIZATION POTENTIALS FROM PHOTOELECTRON SPECTRA. SMITH, W. L. MOL. PHYS. 26 (2), 361-7, 1973.
52675	CHEMICAL BOND NATURE AND ENERGY BAND STRUCTURE IN DIAMONDLIKE SEMICONDUCTORS. LEVIN, A. A. NEKOT. VOP. KHIM. FIZ. POLUPROV. SLOZHNOGO SOSTAVA, MATER, VSES. SIMP., 3RD 19-25PP., 1970.
52677	EFFECT OF THE SURFACE STATE OF V - VI - VII -TYPE CRYSTALS ON SOME OF THEIR PHYSICAL PROPERTIES. KOPINETS, I. F. MIKULANINETS, S. V. RUBISH, I. D. TURYANITSA, I. D. CHEPUR, D. V. NEKOT. VOP. KHIM. FIZ. POLUPROV. SLOZHNOGO SOSTAVA, MATER. VSES. SIMP., 3RD 164-8, 1970.
52679	OPTICAL PROPERTIES OF SILICON DIOXIDE IN THE 5-40 E V SPECTRAL REGION. SOROKIN, O. M. BLANK, V. A. LEBEDEVA, G. A. OPT. SPEKTROSK. 35 (3), 501-7, 1973. (FOR ENGLISH TRANSLATION SEE E54454)
52681	EFFECTS OF ETCHING ON MAGNETIZATION REVERSAL IN SAMARIUM-COBALT PARTICLES. MC CURRIE, R. A. CARSWELL, G. P. PHIL. MAG. 28 (3), 611-21, 1973.
52686	MAGNETIC PROPERTIES OF PYRITE-TYPE NICKEL SULFIDE. MIYADAI, T. MIYAHARA, S. TAKIZAWA, K. UCHINO, K. PHYS. LETT. 44 A (7), 529-30, 1973.
52688	EXPERIMENTAL STUDY OF THE TWO-DIMENSIONAL ISING ANTIFERROMAGNET RUBIDIUM COBALT FLUORIDE. SAMUELSEN, E. J. PHYS. REV. LETT. 31 (15), 936-8, 1973.
52689	ATOMIC AND MAGNETIC STRUCTURE OF MANGANESE IRON SILICIDE. BINCZYCKA, H. DIMITRIJEVIC, Z. GAJIC, B. SZYTULA, A. PHYS. STATUS SOLIDI 19 A (1), K13-17, 1973.
52690	ENERGY SPECTRUM OF THERMALLY STIMULATED EXOELECTRONS FROM BERYLLIUM OXIDE. PETERSON, D. D. PHYS. STATUS SOLIDI 19 A (1), K47-50, 1973.
52691	VARIATION OF THE ENERGY AND INTENSITY OF BERYLLIUM OXIDE EXOELECTRONS. KORTOV, V. S. PHYS. STATUS SOLIDI 19 A (1), 59-66, 1973.

EPIC Number	Bibliographic Citation
52692	**OPTICAL PROPERTIES OF TANTALUM BORATE, A COMPOUND WITH UNUSUAL COORDINATIONS.** BLASSE, G. VAN DEN HEUVEL, G. P. M. PHYS. STATUS SOLIDI 19 A (1), 111–17, 1973.
52693	**LOW-TEMPERATURE FIELD-EFFECT OF GALLIUM-ARSENIDE WITH AN IMPURITY BAND.** SITENKO, T. N. LYASHENKO, V. I. PHYS. STATUS SOLIDI 19 A (1), 147–58, 1973.
52694	**DOMAINS. II. TYPES IN FERROLECTROCHEMICAL GADOLINIUM MOLYBDATE.** BOHM, J. KUERSTEIN, H. D. PHYS. STATUS SOLIDI 19 A (1), 179–83, 1973.
52695	**OPTICAL STUDIES OF AMMONIUM CHLORIDE NEAR -30.** ADAM, M. SEARBY, G. M. PHYS. STATUS SOLIDI 19 A (1), 185–92, 1973.
52696	**INITIATION OF EXOELECTRON EMISSION BY THERMALLY RELEASED HOLES IN SINGLE CRYSTAL MAGNESIUM OXIDE.** MOLLENKOPF, H. C. HALLIBURTON, L. E. KOHNKE, E. E. PHYS. STATUS SOLIDI 19 A (1), 243–50, 1973.
52697	**FORMULAS RELATED TO THE APPLICATION OF THE KANE CONDUCTION BAND TO MEASUREMENTS ON III-V SEMICONDUCTORS.** SENECHAL, R. R. WOOLLEY, J. C. PHYS. STATUS SOLIDI 19 A (1), 251–7, 1973.
52699	**SPECTRAL PROPERTIES OF RARE EARTH IONS IN YTTRIUM ALUMINATE CRYSTALS.** ANTONOV, V. A. ARSENEV, P. A. BIENERT, K. E. POTEMKIN, A. V. PHYS. STATUS SOLIDI 19 A (1), 289–99, 1973.
52700	**MAGNETIZATION PROCESSES IN IRON-SILICON SINGLE CRYSTALS AT HIGH FREQUENCIES.** GAEHRS, H. J. KRANZ, J. PASSON, B. PHYS. STATUS SOLIDI 19 A (1), 301–5, 1973.
52702	**EINSTEIN RELATION FOR ELECTRON PLASMA OF SOLIDS IN A QUANTIZING MAGNETIC FIELD.** ARONZON, B. A. MEILIKHOV, E. Z. PHYS. STATUS SOLIDI 19 A (1), 313–17, 1973.
52703	**THERMALLY AND PHOTON-STIMULATED DEPOLARIZATION CURRENTS IN KRS-5 CRYSTALS POLARIZED BY LIGHT.** BOTILA, T. CROITORIU, N. PHYS. STATUS SOLIDI 19 A (1), 357–63, 1973.
52704	**EFFECT OF THE INELASTICITY OF SCATTERING AND NONPARABOLICITY OF BAND ON TRANSVERSE MAGNETORESISTANCE OF THE DEGENERATE N-INDIUM ANTIMONIDE TYPE SEMICONDUCTORS IN A QUANTIZING MAGNETIC FIELD.** AGAEVA, R. G. ASKEROV, B. M. GASHIMZADE, F. M. PHYS. STATUS SOLIDI 59 B (1), K43–K46, 1973.
52705	**TWO-STEP EXCITATION OF PHOTOLUMINESCENCE IN GALLIUM PHOSPHIDE.** SCHINDLER, A. BINDEMANN, R. KREHER, K. PHYS. STATUS SOLIDI 59 B (2), 439–45, 1973.
52706	**DETERMINATION OF THE DOMAIN WALL ENERGY FROM HYSTERESIS LOOPS IN YIG (YTTRIUM IRON GARNET).** GUYOT, M. GLOBUS, A. PHYS. STATUS SOLIDI 59 B (2), 447–54, 1973.
52708	**HOT-EXCITON LUMINESCENCE IN CADMIUM SELENIDE CRYSTALS.** GROSS, E. F. PERMOGOROV, S. A. MOROZENKO, YA. KHARLAMOV, B. PHYS. STATUS SOLIDI 59 B (2), 551–60, 1973.
52709	**MAGNETO-SEEBECK EFFECT AND SHUBNIKOV-DE HAAS EFFECT IN N-TYPE BISMUTH TELLURIDE.** SCHROEDER, B. VON MIDDENDORFF, A. KOEHLER, H. LANDWEHR, G. PHYS. STATUS SOLIDI 59 B (2), 561–8, 1973.
52724	**THERMOPHYSICAL PROPERTIES OF ZIRCONIUM CARBIDE IN THE HIGH-TEMPERATURE REGION.** MEBED, M. M. YURCHAK, R. P. KOROLEV, L. A. TEPLOFIZ. VYS. TEMP. 11 (2), 427–9, 1973. (FOR ENGLISH TRANSLATION SEE E52725)
52725	**THERMOPHYSICAL PROPERTIES OF ZIRCONIUM CARBIDE IN THE HIGH-TEMPERATURE REGION.** MEBED, M. M. YURCHAK, R. P. KOROLEV, L. A. HIGH TEMP. 11 (2), 380–1, 1973. (ENGLISH TRANSLATION OF TEPLOFIZ. VYS. TEMP., 11 (2), 427–9, 1973; FOR ORIGINAL SEE E52724)
52745	**THERMOELECTRIC PROPERTIES OF A THALLIUM TELLURIUM MELT DOPED WITH SELENIUM AND THALIUM.** KAZANDZHAN, B. I. TSURIKOV, A. A. TEPLOFIZ. VYS. TEMP. 11 (3), 675–7, 1973. (FOR ENGLISH TRANSLATION SEE E52746)
52746	**THERMOELECTRIC PROPERTIES OF A THALLIUM TELLURIUM MELT DOPED WITH SELENIUM AND THALIUM.** KAZANDZHAN, B. I. TSURIKOV, A. A. HIGH TEMP. 11 (3), 610–2, 1974. (ENGLISH TRANSLATION OF TEPLOFIZ. VYS. TEMP., 11 (3), 675–7, 1973; FOR ORIGINAL SEE E52745)
52747	**BOUND-FREE TRANSITION OF TRAPPED ELECTRONS IN POLAR MATRICES.** FUEKI, K. FENG, D-F. KEVAN, L. J. CHEM. PHYS. 59 (12), 6201–8, 1973.
52748	**ELECTRONIC STRUCTURE AND OPTICAL INDEX DAMAGE OF IRON-DOPED LITHIUM NIOBATE.** CLARK, M. G. DISLAVO, F. J. GLASS, A. M. PETERSON, G. E. J. CHEM. PHYS. 59 (12), 6209–19, 1973.
52751	**ARSENIC MONOFLUORIDE: DISSOCIATION ENTHALPY, IONIZATION POTENTIAL, ELECTRON AFFINITY, DIPOLE MOMENT, SPECTROSCOPIC CONSTANTS, AND IDEAL GAS THERMODYNAMIC FUNCTIONS FROM A HARTREE-FOCK MOLECULAR ORBITAL INVESTIGATION.** OHARE, P. A. G. BATANA, A. WAHL, A. C. J. CHEM. PHYS. 59 (12), 6495–6501, 1973.
52754	**HALL COEFFICIENT OF VANADIUM CARBIDE AS A FUNCTION OF TEMPERATURE AND CARBON CONCENTRATION.** SHACKLETTE, L. W. ASHWORTH, H. J. APPL. PHYS. 44 (12), 5254–8, 1973.
52756	**DIRECT OBSERVATION OF FERROELECTRIC DOMAINS IN MODIFIED LEAD ZIRCONATE TITANATE CERAMICS BY TRANSMISSION ELECTRON MICROSCOPY.** HARDIMAN, B. ZEYFANG, R. REEVES, C. J. APPL. PHYS. 44 (12), 5266–7, 1973.
52758	**BACKSCATTERED ELECTRONS FROM SEMICONDUCTORS AND THEIR EFFECT ON THE RESOLUTION OF TRANSMISSION SECONDARY EMISSION RATIOS.** KENNEDY, A. J. KALWEIT, H. W. J. APPL. PHYS. 44 (12), 5301–8, 1973.
52759	**CALCULATED ENERGY DISTRIBUTIONS OF ELECTRONS EMITTED FROM NEGATIVE ELECTRON AFFINITY GALLIUM ARSENIDE: CESIUM-OXIDE SURFACES.** ESCHER, J. S. SCHADE, H. J. APPL. PHYS. 44 (12), 5309–13, 1973.
52768	**NORMAL SPECTRAL EMISSIVITY OF NEAR-STOICHIOMETRIC SINGLE-CRYSTAL NICKEL OXIDE IN THE RED AND IN THE GREEN.** MADJID, A. H. MARTINEZ, J. M. J. APPL. PHYS. 44 (12), 5419–22, 1973.
52769	**INFLUENCE OF PRESSURE AND TEMPERATURE ON SWITCHING IN VANADIUM PENTOXIDE.** VEZZOLI, G. C. NAPIER, A. J. APPL. PHYS. 44 (12), 5426–31, 1973.
52771	**TWO-CARRIER MODEL FOR HIGH FIELD CONDUCTION IN SILICON DIOXIDE.** O DWYER, J. J. J. APPL. PHYS. 44 (12), 5438–40, 1973.
52772	**OPTICAL-COUPLING EFFICIENCY OF GALLIUM PHOSPHIDE: NITROGEN GREEN-LIGHT-EMITTING DIODES.** BACHRACH, R. Z. JOYCE, W. B. DIXON, R. W. J. APPL. PHYS. 44 (12), 5458–62, 1973.
52773	**ELECTRON TRAPPING LEVELS IN CADMIUM SELENIDE SINGLE CRYSTALS.** MANFREDOTTI, C. RIZZO, A. VASANELLI, L. GALASSINI, S. RUGGIERO, L. J. APPL. PHYS. 44 (12), 5463–9, 1973.

EPIC Number	Bibliographic Citation
52774	BEAM DIVERGENCE OF THE EMISSION FROM DOUBLE-HETEROSTRUCTURE INJECTION LASERS. CASEY, H. C., JR. PANISH, M. B. MERZ, J. L. J. APPL. PHYS. 44 (12), 5470–5, 1973.
52776	OBSERVATION OF THREE-PHOTON CONDUCTIVITY IN CADMIUM SULFIDE WITH MODE-LOCKED NEODYMIUM: GLASS LASER PULSES. JAYARAMAN, S. LEE, C. H. J. APPL. PHYS. 44 (12), 5480–2, 1973.
52778	DETERMINATION OF MOBILITY BY 8-MM MICROWAVE MAGNETOREFLECTIVITY IN SEMICONDUCTORS. FORTINI, A. MADELON, R. LANDE, R. HAIRIE, A. J. APPL. PHYS. 44 (12), 5489–94, 1973.
52779	LUMINESCENCE OF BISMUTH GERMANATE: SPECTRAL AND DECAY PROPERTIES. WEBER, M. J. MONCHAMP, R. R. J. APPL. PHYS. 44 (12), 5495–9, 1973.
52780	TEST FOR OHMIC CONDUCTIVITY AT TURNOVER IN AN AMORPHOUS CHALCOGENIDE SANDWICH STRUCTURE. THORNBURG, D. D. JOHNSON, R. I. J. APPL. PHYS. 44 (12), 5500–3, 1973.
52781	INFECTION AND REMOVAL OF IONIC CHARGE AT ROOM TEMPERATURE THROUGH THE INTERFACE OF AIR WITH SILICON OXIDE. WOODS, M. H. WILLIAMS, R. J. APPL. PHYS. 44 (12), 5506–10, 1973.
52782	PUMPING OF NITROGEN DOPED NONSTOICHIOMETRIC GALLIUM ARSENIDE PHOSPHIDE (AT 77 DEGREES K) BY AN ELECTRON BEAM FROM A GAS PLASMA. HOLONYAK, N., JR. CAMPBELL, J. C. LEE, M. H. VERDEYEN, J. T. JOHNSON, W. L. CRAFORD, M. G. FINN, D. J. APPL. PHYS. 44 (12), 5517–21, 1973.
52783	PHOTOLUMINESCENCE PROBING OF HETEROJUNCTIONS. DANIELS, E. STEINVALL, O. J. APPL. PHYS. 44 (12), 5526–30, 1973.
52784	SUPERCONDUCTING PROPERTIES, ELECTRICAL RESISTIVITIES, AND STRUCTURE OF NIOBIUM NITROGEN THIN FILMS. SHY, Y. M. TOTH, L. E. SOMASUNDARAM, R. J. APPL. PHYS. 44 (12), 5539–45, 1973.
52785	OPTICAL ANISOTROPY EFFECTS IN MAGNETO-OPTIC MEMORY MATERIALS. JACOBS, J. T. TREVES, D. J. APPL. PHYS. 44 (12), 5546–52, 1973.
52786	STRUCTURE AND PROPERTIES OF REDUCED LANTHANUM COBALT OXIDE. SIS, L. B. WIRTZ, G. P. SORENSON, S. C. J. APPL. PHYS. 44 (12), 5553–9, 1973.
52787	MAGNETO-OPTIC KERR ROTATION OF BISMUTH-SUBSTITUTED IRON GARNETS IN THE 2–5.2-E V SPECTRAL RANGE. WITTEKOEK, S. POPMA, T. J. A. J. APPL. PHYS. 44 (12), 5560–6, 1973.
52789	MAGNETIC INVESTIGATIONS ON PSEUDOBINARY ALLOYS OF TERBIUM IRON AND ALUMINUM. OESTERREICHER, H. PITTS, R. J. APPL. PHYS. 44 (12), 5570–4, 1973.
52790	COMPOSITION AND IRRADIATION-TEMPERATURE DEPENDENCE OF THE UNIAXIAL ANISOTROPY ENERGY OF LARGE-GRAIN IRON-NICKEL ALLOY THIN FILMS. WILLIAMS, C. M. SCHINDLER, A. I. J. APPL. PHYS. 44 (12), 5575–9, 1973.
52793	SUBMICRON THICKNESS CALIBRATION OF VAPOR-DEPOSITED SILICON OXIDE FILMS BY INFRARED SPECTROSCOPY. WONG, J. J. APPL. PHYS. 44 (12), 5629–30, 1973.
52794	IMAGE FORCE WORK FUNCTION OF DIELECTRIC LAYERS. DIONNE, G. F. J. APPL. PHYS. 44 (12), 5637–8, 1973. (AD-778 410, ESD-TR-74-126)
52795	PHOTOLUMINESCENCE DETERMINATION OF CADMIUM DIFFUSION IN ZINC SELENIDE. MARTIN, W. E. J. APPL. PHYS. 44 (12), 5639–41, 1973.
52796	POLYMER-CLAD FUSED-SILICA OPTICAL FIBER. SUZUKI, Y. KASHIWAGI, H. APPL. OPT. 13 (1), 1–2, 1974.
52799	LASER INDUCED DAMAGE TO OPTICAL MATERIALS, 1973: A CONFERENCE REPORT. GLASS, A. J. GUENTHER, A. H. APPL. OPT. 13 (1), 74–88, 1974.
52800	MICROLENSES FOR COUPLING JUNCTION LASERS TO OPTICAL FIBERS. COHEN, L. G. SCHNEIDER, M. V. APPL. OPT. 13 (1), 89–94, 1974.
52803	MEASURING THE REFRACTIVE INDEX AND THICKNESS OF THIN TRANSPARENT FILMS: METHOD. DANEU, V. SANCHEZ, A. APPL. OPT. 13 (1), 122–8, 1974.
52806	OPTICAL FIBERS FOR COMMUNICATION. GLOGE, D. APPL. OPT. 13 (2), 249–54, 1974.
52808	LASER-INDUCED CHEMICAL REACTIONS. KARLOV, N. V. APPL. OPT. 13 (2), 301–9, 1974.
52811	THIN-FILM LASER-TO-FIBER COUPLER. BOIVIN, L. P. APPL. OPT. 13 (2), 391–5, 1974.
52820	EFFECT OF X-RAYS ON EUROPIUM (3+) ION-DOPED SODIUM FLUORIDE SINGLE CRYSTALS. POTAPENKO, G. D. PISARENKO, V. F. OPT. SPECTROS., USSR 34 (4), 461–2, 1973. (ENGLISH TRANSLATION OF OPT. SPEKTROSK., 34 (4), 800–1, 1973; FOR ORIGINAL SEE E50986)
52821	ANISOTROPY OF ELECTRICAL CONDUCTIVITY IN ORIENTED SAMPLES OF GLASSLIKE SEMICONDUCTORS. KOLOMIETS, B. T. LYUBIN, V. M. SHILO, V. P. JETP LETTERS 17 (10), 412–4, 1973. (ENGLISH TRANSLATION OF PISMA ZH. EKSP. TEOR. FIZ., 17 (10), 577–80, 1973; FOR ORIGINAL SEE E51078)
52822	INVESTIGATION OF THE MAGNETIC AND ADSORPTIVE PROPERTIES OF THE COBALT OXIDE-MAGNESIUM OXIDE SOLID SOLUTIONS. DYREK, K. BULL. ACAD. POL. SCI., SER. SCI. CHIM. 21 (9), 675–84, 1973.
52823	STUDIES ON THE SURFACE ELECTRICAL PHENOMENA ACCOMPANYING SORPTION OF OXYGEN ON TRANSITION METAL OXIDES. I. GENERAL CONSIDERATIONS FOR NICKEL OXIDE. NOWOTNY, J. BULL. ACAD. POL. SCI., SER. SCI. CHIM. 21 (10), 743–50, 1973.
52824	STUDIES ON THE SURFACE ELECTRICAL PHENOMENA ACCOMPANYING SORPTION OF OXYGEN ON TRANSITION METAL OXIDES. II. KINETIC DATA FOR UNDOPED NICKEL OXIDE. NOWOTNY, J. BULL. ACAD. POL. SCI., SER. SCI. CHIM. 21 (10), 751–6, 1973.
52825	STUDIES ON THE SURFACE ELECTRICAL PHENOMENA ACCOMPANYING SORPTION OF OXGYGEN ON TRANSITION METAL OXIDES. III. KINETIC DATA FOR LITHIUM-DOPED NICKEL OXIDE. NOWOTNY, J. BULL. ACAD. POL. SCI., SER. SCI. CHIM. 21 (11), 815–28, 1973.
52826	STUDIES ON THE SURFACE ELECTRICAL PHENOMENA ACCOMPANYING SORPTION OF OXYGEN ON TRANSITION METAL OXIDES. IV. KINETIC DATA FOR COBALT OXIDE AND COBALT DIOXIDE. NOWOTNY, J. BULL. ACAD. POL. SCI., SER. SCI. CHIM. 21 (11), 821–8, 1973.
52827	ELECTRICAL CONDUCTIVITY OF CHROMIUM-DOPED NICKEL OXIDE. MROWEC, S. NOWOTNY, J. WALEC, T. BULL. ACAD. POL. SCI., SER. SCI. CHIM. 21 (11), 829–37, 1973.

EPIC Number	Bibliographic Citation

52830 **QUANTUM THEORY OF THE PERMITTIVITY OF HOT ELECTRONS.**
VASKO, F. T.
FIZ. TVERD. TELA (LENINGRAD)
15 (6), 1693–6, 1973.
(FOR ENGLISH TRANSLATION SEE E52831)

52831 **QUANTUM THEORY OF THE PERMITTIVITY OF HOT ELECTRONS.**
VASKO, F. T.
SOV. PHYS. SOLID STATE
15 (6), 1136–7, 1973.
(ENGLISH TRANSLATION OF FIZ. TVERD. TELA, 15 (6), 1693–6, 1973; FOR ORIGINAL SEE E52830)

52832 **HEATING OF ELECTRONS IN GALLIUM ARSENIDE AND INDIUM PHOSPHIDE AT LOW TEMPERATURES.**
EMELYANENKO, O. V. NASLEDOV, D. N.
NEDEOGLO, D. D.
FIZ. TVERD. TELA
15 (6), 1712–7, 1973.
(FOR ENGLISH TRANSLATION SEE E52833)

52833 **HEATING OF ELECTRONS IN GALLIUM ARSENIDE AND INDIUM PHOSPHIDE AT LOW TEMPERATURES.**
EMELYANENKO, O. V. NASLEDOV, D. N.
NEDEOGLO, D. D.
SOV. PHYS. SOLID STATE
15 (6), 1147–50, 1973.
(ENGLISH TRANSLATION OF FIZ. TVERD. TELA, 15 (6), 1712–7, 1973; FOR ORIGINAL SEE E52832)

52836 **STUDY OF THE PHOTOPLASTIC EFFECT AT ALPHA AND BETA DISLOCATIONS IN CADMIUM SULFIDE.**
OSIPYAN, YU. A. PETRENKO, V. F.
STRUKOVA, G. K.
FIZ. TVERD. TELA
15 (6), 1752–6, 1973.
(FOR ENGLISH TRANSLATION SEE E52837)

52837 **STUDY OF THE PHOTOPLASTIC EFFECT AT ALPHA AND BETA DISLOCATIONS IN CADMIUM SULFIDE.**
OSIPYAN, YU. A. PETRENKO, V. F.
STRUKOVA, G. K.
SOV. PHYS. SOLID STATE
15 (6), 1172–4, 1973.
(ENGLISH TRANSLATION OF FIZ. TVERD. TELA, 15 (6), 1752–6, 1973; FOR ORIGINAL SEE E52836)

52838 **TEMPERATURE DEPENDENCES OF THE ELASTIC CONSTANTS OF GALLIUM ARSENIDE.**
BURENKOV, YU. A. BURDUKOV, YU. M.
DAVYDOV, S. YU. NIKANOROV, S. P.
FIZ. TVERD. TELA
15 (6), 1757–61, 1973.
(FOR ENGLISH TRANSLATION SEE E52839)

52839 **TEMPERATURE DEPENDENCES OF THE ELASTIC CONSTANTS OF GALLIUM ARSENIDE.**
BURENKOV, YU. A. BURDUKOV, YU. M.
DAVYDOV, S. YU. NIKANOROV, S. P.
SOV. PHYS. SOLID STATE
15 (6), 1175–7, 1973.
(ENGLISH TRANSLATION OF FIZ. TVERD. TELA, 15 (6), 1757–61, 1973; FOR ORIGINAL SEE E52838)

52840 **CONCENTRATION DEPENDENCE OF THE MAGNETIC MOMENT AND CURIE POINT OF MIXED FERRITES WITH GARNET STRUCTURE.**
DUBININ, S. F. SIDOROV, S. K.
FIZ. TVERD. TELA (LENINGRAD)
15 (6), 1798–803, 1973.
(FOR ENGLISH TRANSLATION SEE E52841)

52841 **DEPENDENCES OF THE MAGNETIC MOMENT AND CURIE TEMPERATURE ON THE COMPOSITION OF MIXED IRON GARNETS.**
DUBININ, S. F. SIDOROV, S. K.
SOV. PHYS. SOLID STATE
15 (6), 1200–3, 1973.
(ENGLISH TRANSLATION OF FIZ. TVERD. TELA, 15 (6), 1798–1803, 1973; FOR ORIGINAL SEE E52840)

52842 **ABSORPTION SPECTRA OF ACCEPTOR–EXCITON COMPLEXES IN ALPHA SILICON CARBIDE (6H).**
GORBAN, I. S. KROKHMAL, A. P.
FIZ. TVERD. TELA
15 (6), 1820–1, 1973.
(FOR ENGLISH TRANSLATION SEE E52843)

52843 **ABSORPTION SPECTRA OF ACCEPTOR–EXCITON COMPLEXES IN ALPHA SILICON CARBIDE (6H).**
GORBAN, I. S. KROKHMAL, A. P.
SOV. PHYS. SOLID STATE
15 (6), 1213–4, 1973.
(ENGLISH TRANSLATION OF FIZ. TVERD. TELA, 15 (6), 1820–1, 1973; FOR ORIGINAL SEE E52842)

52848 **IMPURITY CENTERS IN FLUORITE–TYPE CRYSTALS WITH LARGE ERBIUM(3+) ION CONCENTRATIONS.**
AIZENBERG, I. B. ORLOV, M. S. STOLOV, A. L.
FIZ. TVERD. TELA (LENINGRAD)
15 (6), 1860–2, 1973.
(FOR ENGLISH TRANSLATION SEE E52849)

52849 **IMPURITY CENTERS IN FLUORITE–TYPE CRYSTALS AT HIGH ERBIUM (3+) CONCENTRATIONS.**
AIZENBERG, I. B. ORLOV, M. S. STOLOV, A. L.
SOV. PHYS. SOLID STATE
15 (6), 1240–1, 1973.
(ENGLISH TRANSLATION OF FIZ. TVERD. TELA, 15 (6), 1860–2, 1973; FOR ORIGINAL SEE E52848)

52852 **NONLINEAR ROTATION OF THE PLANE OF POLARIZATION OF LIGHT IN DODECABISMUTH GERMANATE CRYSTALS.**
BAIRAMOV, B. KH. ZAKHARCHENYA, B. P.
TOPOROV, V. V. KHASHKHOZHEV, Z. M.
FIZ. TVERD. TELA
15 (6), 1868–73, 1973.
(FOR ENGLISH TRANSLATION SEE E52853)

52853 **NONLINEAR ROTATION OF THE PLANE OF POLARIZATION OF LIGHT IN DODECABISMUTH GERMANATE CRYSTALS.**
BAIRAMOV, B. KH. ZAKHARCHENYA, B. P.
TOPOROV, V. V. KHASHKHOZHEV, Z. M.
SOV. PHYS. SOLID STATE
15 (6), 1245–8, 1973.
(ENGLISH TRANSLATION OF FIZ. TVERD. TELA, 15 (6), 1868–73, 1973; FOR ORIGINAL SEE E52852)

52854 **PHASE TRANSITIONS IN FERROELECTRIC SOLID SOLUTIONS.**
ZAITSEV, R. O.
FIZ. TVERD. TELA
15 (6), 1874–82, 1973.
(FOR ENGLISH TRANSLATION SEE E52855)

52855 **PHASE TRANSITIONS IN FERROELECTRIC SOLID SOLUTIONS.**
ZAITSEV, R. O.
SOV. PHYS. SOLID STATE
15 (6), 1249–53, 1973.
(ENGLISH TRANSLATION OF FIZ. TVERD. TELA, 15 (6), 1874–82, 1973; FOR ORIGINAL SEE E52854)

52856 **INFRARED ABSORPTION AND FEATURES OF THE ENERGY STRUCTURE OF BISMUTH BROMIDE TELLURIDE LAMINATED CRYSTALS.**
BORETS, A. N. PUGA, G. D. CHEPUR, D. V.
FIZ. TVERD. TELA (LENINGRAD)
15 (6), 1884–8, 1973.
(FOR ENGLISH TRANSLATION SEE E52857)

52857 **INFRARED ABSORPTION AND SOME FEATURES OF THE ENERGY STRUCTURE OF LAYERED BISMUTH BROMIDE TELLURIDE CRYSTALS.**
BORETS, A. N. PUGA, G. D. CHEPUR, D. V.
SOV. PHYS. SOLID STATE
15 (6), 1255–6, 1973.
(ENGLISH TRANSLATION OF FIZ. TVERD. TELA, 15 (6), 1884–8, 1973; FOR ORIGINAL SEE E52856)

52860 **TEMPERATURE DEPENDENCE OF VANADIUM SILICIDE ELECTRIC RESISTANCE.**
MARCHENKO, V. A.
FIZ. TVERD. TELA (LENINGRAD)
15 (6), 1893–5, 1973.
(FOR ENGLISH TRANSLATION SEE E52861)

52861 **TEMPERATURE DEPENDENCE OF THE ELECTRICAL RESISTIVITY OF VANADIUM SILICIDE.**
MARCHENKO, V. A.
SOV. PHYS. SOLID STATE
15 (6), 1261–2, 1973.
(ENGLISH TRANSLATION OF FIZ. TVERD. TELA, 15 (6), 1893–5, 1973; FOR ORIGINAL SEE E52860)

52862 **MAGNETIC STRUCTURE OF EXTREMELY SMALL ANTIFERROMAGNETIC PARTICLES OF BETA IRON HYDROPEROXIDE.**
VOZNYUK, P. O. DUBININ, V. N.
FIZ. TVERD. TELA
15 (6), 1897–9, 1973.
(FOR ENGLISH TRANSLATION SEE E52863)

52863 **MAGNETIC STRUCTURE OF EXTREMELY SMALL ANTIFERROMAGNETIC PARTICLES OF BETA IRON HYDROPEROXIDE.**
VOZNYUK, P. O. DUBININ, V. N.
SOV. PHYS. SOLID STATE
15 (6), 1265–6, 1973.
(ENGLISH TRANSLATION OF FIZ. TVERD. TELA, 15 (6), 1897–9, 1973; FOR ORIGINAL SEE E52862)

52866 **EFFECT OF AN ANION IMPURITY ON A RADIATION CHANGE IN POTASSIUM CHLORIDE CONDUCTIVITY.**
PERSHITS, YA. N. ANDRUSICH, V. A.
FIZ. TVERD. TELA (LENINGRAD)
15 (6), 1919–21, 1973.
(FOR ENGLISH TRANSLATION SEE E52867)

52867 **INFLUENCE OF ANION IMPURITIES ON THE RADIATION–INDUCED CHANGE IN THE CONDUCTIVITY OF POTASSIUM CHLORIDE.**
PERSHITS, YA. N. ANDRUSICH, V. A.
SOV. PHYS. SOLID STATE
15 (6), 1284–5, 1973.
(ENGLISH TRANSLATION OF FIZ. TVERD. TELA, 15 (6), 1919–21, 1973; FOR ORIGINAL SEE E52866)

EPIC Number	Bibliographic Citation

52868 **EXOELECTRON EMISSION FROM SODIUM CHLORIDE.**
KONYUSHKINA, N. I. KRYLOVA, I. V.
FIZ. TVERD. TELA (LENINGRAD)
15 (6), 1925–7, 1973.
(FOR ENGLISH TRANSLATION SEE E52869)

52869 **EXOEMISSION OF ELECTRONS FROM SODIUM CHLORIDE.**
KONYUSHKINA, N. I. KRYLOVA, I. V.
SOV. PHYS. SOLID STATE
15 (6), 1289–90, 1973.
(ENGLISH TRANSLATION OF FIZ. TVERD. TELA, 15 (6), 1925–7, 1973; FOR ORIGINAL SEE E52868)

52870 **FERROELECTRIC BEHAVIOR OF VACUUM CONDENSATES OF LEAD GERMANATE.**
TOMASHPOLSKII, YU. YA. PENTEGOVA, M. V.
FIZ. TVERD. TELA
15 (6), 1943–4, 1973.
(FOR ENGLISH TRANSLATION SEE E52871)

52871 **FERROELECTRIC BEHAVIOR OF VACUUM CONDENSATES OF LEAD GERMANATE.**
TOMASHPOLSKII, YU. YA. PENTEGOVA, M. V.
SOV. PHYS. SOLID STATE
15 (6), 1304, 1973.
(ENGLISH TRANSLATION OF FIZ. TVERD. TELA, 15 (6), 1943–4, 1973; FOR ORIGINAL SEE E52870)

52874 **EFFECT OF GAMMA RADIATION ON ERBIUM AND YTTERBIUM CENTERS IN FLUORITE.**
KORNIENKO, L. S. RYBALTOVSKII, A. O.
FIZ. TVERD. TELA
15 (7), 1975–83, 1973.
(FOR ENGLISH TRANSLATION SEE E52875)

52875 **EFFECT OF GAMMA RADIATION ON ERBIUM AND YTTERBIUM CENTERS IN FLUORITE.**
KORNIENKO, L. S. RYBALTOVSKII, A. O.
SOV. PHYS. SOLID STATE
15 (7), 1322–6, 1974.
(ENGLISH TRANSLATION OF FIZ. TVERD. TELA, 15 (7), 1975–83, 1973; FOR ORIGINAL SEE E52874)

52876 **PHASE TRANSITIONS IN CESIUM DIHYDROGEN ARSENATE AND DIDEUTERATED CESIUM DIHYDROGEN ARSENATE CRYSTALS.**
STRUKOV, B. A. BADDUR, A. ZINENKO, V. I.
MIKHAILOV, V. K. KOPTSIK, V. A.
FIZ. TVERD. TELA
15 (7), 2018–23, 1973.
(FOR ENGLISH TRANSLATION SEE E52877)

52877 **PHASE TRANSITIONS IN CESIUM DIHYDROGEN ARSENATE AND DIDEUTERATED CESIUM DIHYDROGEN ARSENATE CRYSTALS.**
STRUKOV, B. A. BADDUR, A. ZINENKO, V. I.
MIKHAILOV, V. K. KOPTSIK, V. A.
SOV. PHYS. SOLID STATE
15 (7), 1347–50, 1974.
(ENGLISH TRANSLATION OF FIZ. TVERD. TELA, 15 (7), 2018–23, 1973; FOR ORIGINAL SEE E52876)

52880 **FLUCTUATIONS AND DIFFERENTIAL CONDUCTIVITY OF HOT ELECTRONS NEAR THE CYCLOTRON RESONANCE.**
USTINOV, N. G.
FIZ. TVERD. TELA
15 (7), 2088–91, 1973.
(FOR ENGLISH TRANSLATION SEE E52881)

52881 **FLUCTUATIONS AND DIFFERENTIAL CONDUCTIVITY OF HOT ELECTRONS NEAR THE CYCLOTRON RESONANCE.**
USTINOV, N. G.
SOV. PHYS. SOLID STATE
15 (7), 1389–91, 1974.
(ENGLISH TRANSLATION OF FIZ. TVERD. TELA, 15 (7), 2088–91, 1973; FOR ORIGINAL SEE E52880)

52882 **INFLUENCE OF ILLUMINATION ON THE KINETICS OF THERMAL DECOMPOSITION AND THE COMPOSITION OF CADMIUM SULFIDE CRYSTALS IN VACUO.**
PIKUS, G. YA. TETERYA, V. P.
FIZ. TVERD. TELA
15 (7), 2098–2103, 1973.
(FOR ENGLISH TRANSLATION SEE E52883)

52883 **INFLUENCE OF ILLUMINATION ON THE KINETICS OF THERMAL DECOMPOSITION AND THE COMPOSITION OF CADMIUM SULFIDE CRYSTALS IN VACUO.**
PIKUS, G. YA. TETERYA, V. P.
SOV. PHYS. SOLID STATE
15 (7), 1396–9, 1974.
(ENGLISH TRANSLATION OF FIZ. TVERD. TELA, 15 (7), 2098–2103, 1973; FOR ORIGINAL SEE E52882)

52884 **MAGNETOSTRICTION OF MANGANESE ARSENIDE AND CHROMIUM TELLURIDE.**
BURKHANOV, A. M. FAKIDOV, I. G.
FIZ. TVERD. TELA (LENINGRAD)
15 (7), 2110–13, 1973.
(FOR ENGLISH TRANSLATION SEE E52885)

52885 **MAGNETOSTRICTION OF MANGANESE ARSENIDE AND CHROMIUM TELLURIDE.**
BURKHANOV, A. M. FAKIDOV, I. G.
SOV. PHYS. SOLID STATE
15 (7), 1404–6, 1974.
(ENGLISH TRANSLATION OF FIZ. TVERD. TELA, 15 (7), 2110–3, 1973; FOR ORIGINAL SEE E52884)

52888 **THEORY OF INFRARED ABSORPTION BY FREE CARRIERS.**
LANG, I. G.
FIZ. TVERD. TELA
15 (7), 2136–42, 1973.
(FOR ENGLISH TRANSLATION SEE E52889)

52889 **THEORY OF INFRARED ABSORPTION BY FREE CARRIERS.**
LANG, I. G.
SOV. PHYS. SOLID STATE
15 (7), 1420–3, 1974.
(ENGLISH TRANSLATION OF FIZ. TVERD. TELA, 15 (7), 2136–42, 1973; FOR ORIGINAL SEE E52888)

52890 **OSCILLATIONS OF THE PHOTOMAGNETOELECTRIC EFFECT AND PHOTOCONDUCTIVITY OF INDIUM ANTIMONIDE IN A MAGNETIC FIELD DUE TO INTERBAND OPTICAL TRANSITIONS.**
KAMENEV, YU. E. KULESHOV, E. M.
PARFENEV, R. V.
FIZ. TVERD. TELA (LENINGRAD)
15 (7), 2175–7, 1973.
(FOR ENGLISH TRANSLATION SEE E52891)

52891 **OSCILLATIONS OF THE INTERBAND PHOTOMAGNETIC EFFECT AND PHOTOCONDUCTIVITY OF INDIUM ANTIMONIDE IN A MAGNETIC FIELD.**
KAMENEV, YU. E. KULESHOV, E. M.
PARFENEV, R. V.
SOV. PHYS. SOLID STATE
15 (7), 1445–6, 1974.
(ENGLISH TRANSLATION OF FIZ. TVERD. TELA, 15 (7), 2175–7, 1973; FOR ORIGINAL SEE E52890)

52892 **RELATION OF SECONDARY ELECTRON EMISSION OF GALLIUM ARSENIDE AND GALLIUM PHOSPHIDE CRYSTALS WITH A CHANGE IN ELECTRON AFFINITY VALUE DURING CESIUM ADSORPTION.**
AFONINA, L. F. STUCHINSKII, G. B.
FIZ. TVERD. TELA (LENINGRAD)
15 (7), 2179–81, 1973.
(FOR ENGLISH TRANSLATION SEE E52893)

52893 **RELATIONSHIP BETWEEN THE SECONDARY EMISSION OF ELECTRONS FROM GALLIUM ARSENIDE AND GALLIUM PHOSPHIDE CRYSTALS AND THE CHANGE IN THE ELECTRON AFFINITY IN THE ADSORPTION OF CESIUM.**
AFONINA, L. F. STUCHINSKII, G. B.
SOV. PHYS. SOLID STATE
15 (7), 1448–9, 1974.
(ENGLISH TRANSLATION OF FIZ. TVERD. TELA, 15 (7), 2179–81, 1973; FOR ORIGINAL SEE E52892)

52896 **INFLUENCE OF CHEMISORPTION ON ELECTRONIC PHASE TRANSITIONS.**
GUDZ, A. D. IVANKIV, L. I.
PENTSAK, A. M. CHOPKO, S. N.
FIZ. TVERD. TELA
15 (7), 2187, 1973.
(FOR ENGLISH TRANSLATION SEE E52897)

52897 **INFLUENCE OF CHEMISORPTION ON ELECTRONIC PHASE TRANSITIONS.**
GUDZ, A. D. IVANKIV, L. I.
PENTSAK, A. M. CHOPKO, S. N.
SOV. PHYS. SOLID STATE
15 (7), 1454, 1974.
(ENGLISH TRANSLATION OF FIZ. TVERD. TELA 15 (7), 2187, 1973; FOR ORIGINAL SEE E52896)

52898 **NUCLEAR GAMMA RESONANCE OF DYSPROSIUM-DOPED SEMICONDUCTING BARIUM TITANATE.**
MURIN, A. N. MOTORNYI, A. V.
FIZ. TVERD. TELA
15 (7), 2190–1, 1973.
(FOR ENGLISH TRANSLATION SEE E52899)

52899 **NUCLEAR GAMMA RESONANCE OF DYSPROSIUM-DOPED SEMICONDUCTING BARIUM TITANATE.**
MURIN, A. N. MOTORNYI, A. V.
SOV. PHYS. SOLID STATE
15 (7), 1457, 1974.
(ENGLISH TRANSLATION OF FIZ. TVERD. TELA, 15 (7), 2190–1, 1973; FOR ORIGINAL SEE E52898)

52902 **TRANSFORMATION OF COLOR CENTERS IN X-RAY-TREATED THALLIUM-DOPED POTASSIUM CHLORIDE CRYSTALS.**
LOBANOV, B. D. PARFIANOVICH, I. A.
FIZ. TVERD. TELA (LENINGRAD)
15 (7), 2194–5, 1973.
(FOR ENGLISH TRANSLATION SEE E52903)

52903 **CONVERSION OF COLOR CENTERS IN X-IRRADIATED THALLIUM-DOPED POTASSIUM CHLORIDE CRYSTALS.**
BOBANOV, B. D. PARFIANOVICH, I. A.
SOV. PHYS. SOLID STATE
15 (7), 1460, 1974.
(ENGLISH TRANSLATION OF FIZ. TVERD. TELA, 15 (7), 2194–5, 1973; FOR ORIGINAL SEE E52902)

EPIC Number | Bibliographic Citation

52904 **ELECTRIC AND ELECTROOPTICAL PROPERTIES OF STOICHIOMETRIC BARIUM STRONTIUM NIOBATE SINGLE CRYSTALS.**
VORONOV, V. V. DESYATKOVA, S. M.
IVLEVA, L. I. KUZMINOV, YU. S.
FIZ. TVERD. TELA (LENINGRAD)
15 (7), 2198–200, 1973.
(FOR ENGLISH TRANSLATION SEE E52905)

52905 **ELECTRICAL AND ELECTROOPTIC PROPERTIES OF STOICHIOMETRIC BARIUM-STRONTIUM NIOBATE SINGLE CRYSTALS.**
VORONOV, V. V. DESYATKOVA, S. M.
IVLEVA, L. I. KUZMINOV, YU. S.
LYAPUNOVA, L. G. OSIKO, V. V.
SOV. PHYS. SOLID STATE
15 (7), 1463–4, 1974.
(ENGLISH TRANSLATION OF FIZ. TVERD. TELA, 15 (7), 2198–200, 1973; FOR ORIGINAL SEE E52904)

52906 **HEAT CAPACITY AND MAGNETIC PHASE TRANSITION IN LANTHANUM ORTHOVANADATE.**
BORUKHOVICH, A. S. BAZUEV, G. V.
SHVEIKIN, G. P.
FIZ. TVERD. TELA (LENINGRAD)
15 (7), 2203–5, 1973.
(FOR ENGLISH TRANSLATION SEE E52907)

52907 **SPECIFIC HEAT AND MAGNETIC PHASE TRANSITION IN LANTHANUM ORTHOVANADATE.**
BORUKHOVICH, A. S. BAZUEV, G. V.
SHVEIKIN, G. P.
SOV. PHYS. SOLID STATE
15 (7), 1467–8, 1974.
(ENGLISH TRANSLATION OF FIZ. TVERD. TELA, 15 (7), 2203–5, 1973; FOR ORIGINAL SEE E52906)

52908 **DOMAIN STRUCTURE OF A LARGE YTTRIUM ORTHOFERRITE SINGLE CRYSTAL.**
BENIDZE, O. M. ZALESSKII, A. V.
FIZ. TVERD. TELA (LENINGRAD)
15 (7), 2207–9, 1973.
(FOR ENGLISH TRANSLATION SEE E52909)

52909 **DOMAIN STRUCTURE OF A LARGE YTTRIUM IRON GARNET SINGLE CRYSTAL.**
BENIDZE, O. M. ZALESSKII, A. V.
SOV. PHYS. SOLID STATE
15 (7), 1471–2, 1974.
(ENGLISH TRANSLATION OF FIZ. TVERD. TELA, 15 (7), 2207–9, 1973; FOR ORIGINAL SEE E52908)

52914 **VIBRONIC SPECTRA OF SILVER SODIUM NITRITE FERROELECTRIC.**
MYASNIKOVA, T. P. RABKIN, L. M.
MARISOVA, S. V.
FIZ. TVERD. TELA (LENINGRAD)
15 (7), 2234–6, 1973.
(FOR ENGLISH TRANSLATION SEE E52915)

52915 **VIBRONIC SPECTRA OF THE FERROELECTRIC SILVER SODIUM NITRITE.**
MYASNIKOVA, T. P. RABKIN, L. M.
MARISOVA, S. V.
SOV. PHYS. SOLID STATE
15 (7), 1493–4, 1974.
(ENGLISH TRANSLATION OF FIZ. TVERD. TELA, 15 (7), 2234–6, 1973; FOR ORIGINAL SEE E52914)

52916 **STRUCTURE OF THE LONG-WAVE ABSORPTION EDGE OF CADMIUM GERMANIUM PHOSPHIDE CRYSTALS.**
GORBAN, I. S. ZHARKOV, I. P.
LUGOVSKII, V. V. TYCHINA, I. I.
SERYI, V. I.
FIZ. TVERD. TELA (LENINGRAD)
15 (7), 2238–9, 1973.
(FOR ENGLISH TRANSLATION SEE E52917)

52917 **STRUCTURE OF THE LONG-WAVELENGTH ABSORPTION EDGE OF CADMIUM GERMANIUM PHOSPHIDE CRYSTALS.**
GORBAN, I. S. ZHARKOV, I. P.
LUGOVSKII, V. V. TYCHINA, I. I.
SERYI, V. I.
SOV. PHYS. SOLID STATE
15 (7), 1497, 1974.
(ENGLISH TRANSLATION OF FIZ. TVERD. TELA, 15 (7), 2238–9, 1973; FOR ORIGINAL SEE E52916)

52920 **SOME FEATURES OF THE SPIN REORIENTATION IN YTTRIUM ORTHOFERRITE AT LOW DEGREES OF SUBSTITUTION OF IRON WITH COBALT IONS.**
BELOV, K. P. GAPEEV, A. K. KADOMTSEVA, A. M.
LEDNEVA, T. M. LUKINA, M. M.
OVCHINNIKOVA, T. L. KHAFIZOVA, N. A.
FIZ. TVERD. TELA
15 (7), 2244–7, 1973.
(FOR ENGLISH TRANSLATION SEE E52921)

52921 **SOME FEATURES OF THE SPIN REORIENTATION IN YTTRIUM ORTHOFERRITE AT LOW DEGREES OF SUBSTITUTION OF IRON WITH COBALT IONS.**
BELOV, K. P. GAPEEV, A. K. KADOMTSEVA, A. M.
LEDNEVA, T. M. LUKINA, M. M.
OVCHINNIKOVA, T. L. KHAFIZOVA, N. A.
SOV. PHYS. SOLID STATE
15 (7), 1501–2, 1974.
(ENGLISH TRANSLATION OF FIZ. TVERD. TELA, 15 (7), 2244–7, 1973; FOR ORIGINAL SEE E52920)

52923 **LOW-FREQUENCY VOLTAGE INSTABILITY AT A POTENTIAL PROBE APPLIED TO CADMIUM SELENIDE.**
RYBIN, V. N.
SOV. PHYS. SEMICOND.
7 (3), 353–6, 1973.
(ENGLISH TRANSLATION OF FIZ. TEKH. POLUPROV., 7 (3), 499–504, 1973; FOR ORIGINAL SEE E51546)

52924 **DIFFUSION OF RADIATIVE RECOMBINATION CENTERS IN GALLIUM ARSENIDE.**
VOROBKALO, F. M. GLINCHUK, K. D.
PROKHOROVICH, A. V.
SOV. PHYS. SEMICOND.
7 (5), 610–2, 1973.
(ENGLISH TRANSLATION OF FIZ. TEKH. POLUPROV., 7 (5), 896–900, 1973; FOR ORIGINAL SEE E51547)

52928 **MAGNETORESISTANCE OF STRONGLY COMPENSATED N-TYPE INDIUM ANTIMONIDE.**
CHUSOV, I. I. YAREMENKO, N. G.
SOV. PHYS. SEMICOND.
7 (6), 830–1, 1973.
(ENGLISH TRANSLATION OF FIZ. TEKH. POLUPROV., 7 (6), 1233–6, 1973; FOR ORIGINAL SEE E50683)

52929 **MECHANISM OF RESIDUAL (FROZEN-IN) CONDUCTIVITY OF SEMICONDUCTORS.**
SANDOMIRSKII, V. B. ZHDAN, A. G.
MESSERER, M. A. GYLYAEV, I. B.
SOV. PHYS. SEMICOND.
7 (7), 881–6, 1973.
(ENGLISH TRANSLATION OF FIZ. TEKH. POLUPROV., 7 (7), 1314–23, 1973; FOR ORIGINAL SEE E51696)

52933 **ELECTRICAL CONDUCTIVITY OF UNIAXIALLY COMPRESSED P-TYPE INDIUM ANTIMONIDE.**
VALYASHKO, E. G. KOSHELEV, O. G.
PLESKACHEV, T. B.
SOV. PHYS. SEMICOND.
7 (7), 912–3, 1973.
(ENGLISH TRANSLATION OF FIZ. TEKH. POLUPROV., 7 (7), 1360–3, 1973; FOR ORIGINAL SEE E51700)

52935 **MAGNETORESISTANCE AND SCATTERING OF ELECTRONS BY POLAR OPTICAL PHONONS IN PURE GALLIUM ARSENIDE AND INDIUM PHOSPHIDE CRYSTALS.**
VORONINA, T. I. EMELYANENKO, O. V.
NASLEDOV, D. N. NEDEOGLO, D. D.
SOV. PHYS. SEMICOND.
7 (7), 925–8, 1973.
(ENGLISH TRANSLATION OF FIZ. TEKH. POLUPROV., 7 (7), 1382–8, 1973; FOR ORIGINAL SEE E51702)

52937 **SOME PROPERTIES OF CHROMIUM-DOPED GALLIUM ARSENIDE.**
BRODOVOI, V. A. DERIKOT, N. Z.
SOV. PHYS. SEMICOND.
7 (7), 958–9, 1973.
(ENGLISH TRANSLATION OF FIZ. TEKH. POLUPROV., 7 (7), 1431–3, 1973; FOR ORIGINAL SEE E51704)

52941 **NEAR-INFRARED ABSORPTION OF COBALT DIPOSITIVE ION IN ZINC SULFIDE: WEAK JAHN-TELLER COUPLING IN THE 4T2 AND 4T1 STATES.**
KOIDL, P. SCHIRMER, O. F. KAUFMANN, U.
PHYS. REV.
8 B (11), 4926–34, 1973.

52942 **EXCITATION OF UV FLUORESCENCE IN LANTHANUM FLUORIDE DOPED WITH TRIVALENT CERIUM AND PRASEODYMIUM.**
ELIAS, L. R. HEAPS, W. S. YEN, W. M.
PHYS. REV.
8 B (11), 4989–95, 1973.
(AD 776 483)

52943 **SPIN-STATE EQUILIBRIA IN HOLMIUM COBALTATE.**
BHIDE, V. G. RAJORIA, D. S. REDDY, Y. S.
RAO, G. R. RAO, C. N. R.
PHYS. REV.
8 B (11), 5028–34, 1973.

52951 **MOMENT REDUCTION IN MAGNETICALLY ORDERED SAMARIUM INTERMETALLICS.**
BUSCHOW, K. H. J. VAN DIEPEN, A. M.
WIJN, H. W.
PHYS. REV.
8 B (11), 5134–8, 1973.

52952 **HEAT CAPACITY OF RUDIDIUM MANGANESE FLUORIDE NEAR THE ANTIFERROMAGNETIC TRANSITION TEMPERATURE.**
KORNBLIT, A. AHLERS, G.
PHYS. REV.
8 B (11), 5163–74, 1973.

EPIC Number	Bibliographic Citation
52954	**MAGNETIC SYMMETRY OF RARE-EARTH ORTHOCHROMITES AND ORTHOFERRITES.** YAMAGUCHI, T. TSUSHIMA, K. PHYS. REV. 8 B (11), 5187-98, 1973.
52956	**ENERGY BAND STRUCTURE OF COBALT PHOSPHIDE.** DRAKE, J. SCHLESINGER, M. PHYS. REV. 8 B (11), 5221-5, 1973.
52957	**FLUORESCENCE STUDIES OF THE ENERGY TRANSFER MANGANESE DIPOSITIVE ION TO ERBIUM TRIPOSITIVE ION IN MANGANESE FLUORIDE.** FLAHERTY, J. M. DI BARTOLO, B. PHYS. REV. 8 B (11), 5232-8, 1973.
52962	**ORIGIN OF THE MAGNETIC ANISOTROPY ENERGY OF THE EUROPIUM MONOCHALCOGENIDES.** KASUYA, A. TACHIKI, M. PHYS. REV. 8 B (11), 5298-310, 1973. (AD-782 435)
52964	**PREPARATION AND PROPERTIES OF RARE-EARTH COMPOUNDS.** WOOD, V. E. BROG, K. C. AUSTIN, A. E. MILLER, J. F. JONES, W. H., JR. COLLINGS, E. W. BAXTER, R. D. BATTELLE, COLUMBUS LABORATORIES, OHIO 39PP., 1972. (AD-735 120, AVAIL. DDC)
52965	**DC-ELECTROLUMINESCENT FLAT PANEL DISPLAY.** HANAK, J. J. YOCOM, P. N. DAVY, J. G. RCA LABORATORIES, PRINCETON, NEW JERSEY 38PP., 1972. (AD-73P 342, ECOM-0290-9, AVAIL. DDC)
52968	**LATTICE DYNAMICAL PROPERTIES OF NARROW GAP SEMICONDUCTORS.** BURSTEIN, E. PINCZUK, A. WALLIS, R. F. DEPT. OF PHYSICS, UNIV. OF PENNSYLVANIA 22PP., 1972.
52969	**SYNTHESIS OF RARE EARTH COMPOUNDS AND STUDY OF THEIR MAGNETIC OPTICAL AND SEMICONDUCTING PROPERTIES.** HOLTZBERG, F. MC GUIRE, T. R. PENNEY, T. SHAFER, M. W. VON MOLNAR, S. THOMAS J. WATSON RESEARCH CENTER, YORKTOWN HEIGHTS, NEW YORK 31PP., 1972. (AD-736 374, ARPA-1588, AVAIL. DDC)
52970	**SOLID STATE RESEARCH, 1971.** MC WHORTER, A. L. LEXINGTON LINCOLN LAB., MASSACHUSETTS INST. OF TECHNOLOGY 78PP., 1971. (AD-736 501, ESD-TR-71-300, AVAIL. DDC)
52973	**ZERO-BIAS CONTACT RESISTANCES OF GOLD-GALLIUM ARSENIDE.** MCCOLL, M. MILLEA, M. F. MEAD, C. A. THE AEROSPACE CORP. 33PP., 1972. (AD-737 112, SAMSO-TR-72-17, AVAIL. DDC)
52974	**CONDUCTION MECHANISMS IN THICK FILM MICROCIRCUITS.** VEST, R. W. ADVANCED RESEARCH PROJECTS AGENCY 46PP., 1972. (AD-737 382, ARPA-1642, AVAIL. DDC)
52975	**LUMINESCENCE OF CADMIUM SELENIDE AND SULFIDE AND THE INFLUENCE OF DEFECTS.** ARORA, B. M. COORDINATED SCIENCE LAB., URBANA, ILLINOIS 173PP., 1972. (AD-737 910, AVAIL. DDC)
52976	**STRUCTURAL EFFECTS ON ELECTRICAL PROPERTIES IN AMORPHOUS SEMICONDUCTORS.** KINSER, D. L. WILSON, L. K. ADVANCED RESEARCH PROJECTS AGENCY 46PP., 1972. (AD-737 916, ARPA-1562, AVAIL. DDC)
52977	**DIELECTRIC RELAXATION IN CRYSTALLINE VANADIUM OXIDE.** MAR, K. M. SCOTT, A. B. OREGON STATE UNIVERSITY 12PP., 1972. (AD-738 474, AVAIL. DDC)
52979	**FABRICATION AND PROPERTIES OF SILICON COMPOUNDS.** LANGE, F. F. TERWILLIGER, G. R. WESTINGHOUSE ELECTRIC CORP., PITTSBURGH, PA. 104PP., 1972. (AD-738 865, AVAIL. DDC)
52981	**PHOTOEMISSION PROPERTIES OF ALUMINUM OXIDE AND EVAPORATED ALUMINUM FILMS.** KOYAMA, R. Y. AIR FORCE CAMBRIDGE RES. LAB. 23PP., 1972. (AD-739 198, AFCRL-72-0037, AVAIL. DDC)
52982	**NEW METHODS FOR GROWTH AND CHARACTERIZATION OF GALLIUM ARSENIDE AND MIXED III-V SEMICONDUCTOR CRYSTALS.** WILCOX, W. R. ADVANCED RESEARCH PROJECTS AGENCY 45PP., 1972. (AD-739 374, ARPA-1623, AVAIL. DDC)
52983	**UMIST, THE SOLID STATE PHYSICS CONFERENCE.** CONDELL, W. J. OFFICE OF NAVAL RESEARCH, LONDON 22PP., 1972. (AD-739 691, ONRL-C-4-72, AVAIL. DDC)
52988	**CHARACTERIZATION OF IR WINDOWS.** HAGGERTY, J. S. PETERS, E. T. ARTHUR D LITTLE, INC. 32PP., 1972. (AD-740 144, ADL-74010, AVAIL. DDC)
52989	**HIGH-BRIGHTNESS ELECTROLUMINESCENT DIODES.** NUESE, C. J. SIGAI, A. G. KUDMAN, I. RCA LABS., PRINCETON, N. J. 62PP., 1972. (AD-740 183, PRRL-72-CR-5, AVAIL. DDC)
52990	**DC-ELECTROLUMINESCENT FLAT PANEL DISPLAY.** HANAK, J. J. YOCOM, P. N. DAVY, J. G. RCA LABS., PRINCETON, N. J. 19PP., 1972. (AD-740 231, PRRL-72-CR-4, AVAIL. DDC)
52993	**NEW SUPERCONDUCTORS-THIRD SEMI-ANNUAL TECHNICAL REPORT.** COLLMAN, J. P. LITTLE, W. A. LELAND STANFORD JUNIOR UNIV., STANFORD, CALIF. 122PP., 1972. (AD-740 698, AVAIL. DDC)
52995	**SOLID STATE RESEARCH, 1972.** MC WHORTER, A. L. LEXINGTON LINCOLN LAB., MASSACHUSETTS INST. OF TECHNOLOGY 72PP., 1972. (AD-740 874, ESD-TR-72-53, AVAIL. DDC)
52996	**CONSOLIDATED SEMIANNUAL PROGRESS REPORT NO. 14: COVERING RESEARCH ACTIVITY DURING THE PERIOD 31 MARCH 1971 THROUGH OCTOBER 1971.** KAPRIELIAN, Z. A. UNIVERSITY OF SOUTHERN CALIFORNIA, LOS ANGELES 172PP., 1972. (AD-740 880, AFOSR-TR-72-0919, AVAIL. DDC)
52997	**CERTAIN TECHNICAL POSSIBILITIES OF PHOTOCELLS BASED ON BETA-SILICON.** ALTAISKII, YU. M. VESTN. KIEV. POLITEKH. INST. (6), 124-9, 1969. (FOR ENGLISH TRANSLATION SEE E52998)
52998	**CERTAIN TECHNICAL POSSIBILITIES OF PHOTOCELLS BASED ON BETA-SILICON.** ALTAISKII, YU. M. FOREIGN TECHNOLOGY DIV., WRIGHT-PATTERSON AFB, OHIO 8PP., 1972. (ENGLISH TRANSLATION OF VESTN. KIEV. POLITEKH. INST. (6), 124-9, 1969; FOR ORIGINAL SEE E52997) (AD-739 223, FTD-HT-23-1240-71, AVAIL. DDC)
52999	**RESEARCH AND DEVELOPMENT OF RARE EARTH-TRANSITION METAL ALLOYS AS PERMANENT MAGNET MATERIALS.** RAY, A. E. STRNAT, K. J. RES. INST., UNIV. DAYTON, DAYTON, OHIO 34PP., 1973. (AFML-TR-112, AVAIL. NTIS)
53000	**CORRELATED THERMALLY ACTIVATED POLARIZATION, CONDUCTION, AND LUMINESCENCE EFFECTS IN LITHIUM FLUORIDE AS FUNCTIONS OF IRRADIATION, DOPING, AND THERMAL HISTORY.** FIELDS, D. E. MORAN, P. R. OAK RIDGE NATL. LAB., OAK RIDGE, TENN. 87PP., 1973. (ORNL-4850, AVAIL. NTIS)
53001	**COBALT-SAMARIUM PERMANENT MAGNET ALLOYS. VARIATION OF LATTICE PARAMETERS WITH COMPOSITION AND TEMPERATURE.** MARTIN, D. L. BENZ, M. G. ROCKWOOD, A. C. METALL, CERAM. LAB., GEN. ELECTRIC CO., SCHENECTADY, N. Y. V, 1-4, 1973. (AFML-TR-73-50, AVAIL. NTIS)

EPIC Number	Bibliographic Citation
53005	**MAGNETIZATION MEASUREMENTS OF SUPERCONDUCTING NIOBIUM-TITANIUM, NIOBIUM-ZIRCONIUM, NIOBIUM-TIN, AND VANADIUM-GALLIUM MATERIALS AT 4.2 DEGREES K.** KREBS, K. R. PYTLIK, J. SEIBT, E. INST. EXP. KERNPHYS., KERNFORSCHUNGSZENT., KARLSRUHE, GER. 39PP., 1972. (KFK-1683, AVAIL. NTIS)
53008	**VISIBLE FLUORESCENCE AND THERMOLUMINESCENCE OF YTTRIUM ALUMINATE CRYSTALS CONTAINING ERBIUM, EUROPIUM, NEODYMIUM, TERBIUM, YTTERBIUM, AND OTHER OPTICALLY ACTIVE CENTERS.** LAND, P. L. AEROSPACE RES. LAB., WRIGHT-PATTERSON AIR FORCE BASE, OHIO 54PP., 1973. (AD-759 161, AVAIL. NTIS)
53010	**SOLID SOLUBILITY IN THE FACE CENTERED CUBIC GADOLINIUM SELENIDE.** HOLTZBERG, F. CRONEMEYER, D. C. MC GUIRE, T. R. VON MOLNAR, S. IBM WATSON RESEARCH CENTER, YORKTOWN HEIGHTS, N. Y. 637-44, 1972. (N72-30727, AVAIL. NTIS)
53013	**CRYSTAL STURCTURE AND PHYSICAL PROPERTIES OF A TRICLINIC SODIUM TUNGSTEN OXIDE.** FRAZEN, H. F. SHANKS, H. R. DE JONG, B. H. W. S. IOWA STATE UNIV., OF SCIENCE AND TECHN., AMES 41-50, 1972. (N72-30684, AVAIL. NTIS)
53015	**KINETICS OF RECOVERY OF LUMINESCENCE PROPERTIES OF GALLIUM ARSENIDE SINGLE CRYSTALS IRRADIATED WITH HIGH-ENERGY ELECTRONS.** BOGDANKEVICH, O. V. BORISOV, N. A. KALENDIN, V. V. KOVSH, I. B. KRIUKOVA, I. V. SOV. J. QUANTUM ELECTRONICS 2, 479-81, 1973. (ENGLISH TRANSLATION OF KVANTOVAIA ELEKTRONIKA MOSCOW, (5), 108-11, 1972; FOR ORIGINAL SEE E50471)
53019	**GALLIUM PHOSPHIDE WITH NITROGEN DOPING FROM THE GAS PHASE.** METTLER, K. SIEMENS FORSCHUNGS UND ENTWICKLUNGSBERICHTE 2 (4), 222-6, 1973.
53021	**PHOTOELECTRIC PHENOMENA IN AMORPHOUS CHALCOGENIDE SEMICONDUCTORS.** KOLOMIETS, B. T. LIUBIN, V. M. PHYSICA STATUS SOLIDI - APPLIED RESEARCH 17 A 11-46, 1973.
53024	**INFLUENCE OF SUBSIDIARY EXTREMA IN THE CONDUCTIVITY ZONE ON THE LIMITING ELECTRON CONCENTRATION IN A (III) B (V) COMPOUNDS.** MIRGALOVSKAYA, M. S. ILCHENKO, L. N. INORG. MAT., USSR 9 (5), 746-8, 1973. (ENGLISH TRANSLATION OF IZV. AKAD. NAUK SSSR, NEORG. MATER., 9 (5), 834-6, 1973; FOR ORIGINAL SEE E50723)
53025	**ELECTRON MOBILITY AND EFFECTIVE MASS IN SILVER SULFIDE AND SILVER SULFIDE TELLURIDE.** ASTAKHOV, O. P. GOLYSHEV, V. D. SGIBNEV, I. V. INORG. MAT., USSR 9 (5), 753-4, 1973. (ENGLISH TRANSLATION OF IZV. AKAD. NAUK SSSR, NEORG. MATER., 9 (5), 841-2, 1973; FOR ORIGINAL SEE E50724)
53026	**CHARACTERISTICS OF THE LOCAL ENVIRONMENT OF TIN AND TELLURIUM ATOMS WHEN SELENIUM IS INCORPORATED INTO THE SYSTEM LEAD TIN TELLURIDE.** BEKKER, A. A. KAUKIS, A. A. TSYPIN, M. I. OSTROVSKAYA, L. M. NESMEYANOV, A. N. INORG. MAT., USSR 9 (5), 757-8, 1973. (ENGLISH TRANSLATION OF IZV. AKAD. NAUK SSSR, NEORG. MATER., 9 (5), 845-6, 1973; FOR ORIGINAL SEE E50725)
53027	**ELECTRICAL CONDUCTIVITY AND THERMO-EMF OF LIQUID ALLOYS OF THE SYSTEM TIN-SELENIUM.** KAZANDZHAN, B. I. MISHUTKINA, T. I. INORG. MAT., USSR 9 (6), 816-8, 1973. (ENGLISH TRANSLATION OF IZV. AKAD. NAUK SSSR, NEORG. MATER., 9 (6), 911-14, 1973; FOR ORIGINAL SE E50726)
53028	**MAGNETIC PROPERTIES OF CHROMIUM TELLUROCHALCOGENIDES.** IKORSKII, V. N. INORG. MAT., USSR 9 (6), 839-43, 1973. (ENGLISH TRANSLATION OF IZV. AKAD. NAUK SSSR, NEORG. MATER., 9 (6), 938-43, 1973; FOR ORIGINAL SEE E50727)
53029	**MAGNETIC SUSCEPTIBILITIES OF DODECABORIDES OF METALS WITH THE URANIUM DODECABORIDE-TYPE STRUCTURE.** ODINTSOV, V. V. KOSTETSKII, I. I. LVOV, S. N. INORG. MAT., USSR 9 (6), 844-7, 1973. (ENGLISH TRANSLATION OF IZV. AKAD. NAUK SSSR, NEORG. MATER., 9 (6), 944-7, 1973; FOR ORIGINAL SEE E50728)
53030	**SOME PROPERTIES OF ALKALI METAL MONOFLUOROPHOSPHATES.** MARDIROSOVA, I. V. BUKHALOVA, G. A. SHPAKOVA, V. M. TOKMAN, I. A. INORG. MAT., USSR 9 (6), 868-71, 1973. (ENGLISH TRANSLATION OF IZV. AKAD. NAUK SSSR, NEORG. MATER., 9 (6), 970-4, 1973; FOR ORIGINAL SEE E50729)
53031	**EFFECT OF CHEMICAL UNIFORMITY ON THE MAGNETIC PROPERTIES OF NICKEL FERRITE-CHROMITE.** ANASTASYUK, N. V. KOVALEVA, Z. I. NIKOLAEV, V. I. OLEINIKOV, N. N. RUSAKOV, V. S. TRETYAKOV, YU. D. INORG. MAT., USSR 9 (6), 966-7, 1973. (ENGLISH TRANSLATION OF IZV. AKAD. NAUK SSSR, NEORG. MATER., 9 (6), 1079-81, 1973; FOR ORIGINAL SEE E50730)
53032	**ELECTRICAL PROPERTIES AND PHASE-STRUCTURAL COMPOSITION OF CATALYSTS OF THE NICKEL OXIDE-TITANIUM OXIDE SYSTEM.** DULOV, A. A. ABRAMOVA, L. A. GERSHENZON, I. SH. RUBINSHTEIN, A. M. PROC. ACAD. SCI., USSR, CHEM. SECT. 210 (2), 387-9, 1973. (ENGLISH TRANSLATION OF DOKL. AKAD. NAUK SSSR, 210 (2), 345-8, 1973; FOR ORIGINAL SEE E50634)
53035	**CORRELATION BETWEEN THE WORK FUNCTIONS OF TRANSITION METAL CARBIDES IN THEIR HOMOGENEITY REGIONS AND SURFACE RECOMBINATION OF HYDROGEN ATOMS.** SAMSONOV, G. V. PODCHERNYAEVA, I. A. FOMENKO, V. S. LOVRENKO, V. A. OKHREMCHUK, L. N. PROTSENKO, T. G. SOV. POWDER MET. METAL CERAM. 11 (5), 389-92, 1972. (ENGLISH TRANSLATION OF POROSH. MET., 11 (5), 62-6, 1972; FOR ORIGINAL SEE E51450)
53037	**WORK FUNCTION OF SILICON CARBIDE.** OKHREMCHUK, L. N. IN ITS TECHNOL. OF PRODUCING NEW MATER. 23, 4-7, 1973.
53042	**Z-LIKE CENTERS IN VANADIUM-DOPED SODIUM CHLORIDE CRYSTALS.** POLAK, K. BOHUN, A. LEBL, M. Z. PHYS. 261 (3), 269-72, 1973.
53044	**ELECTRICAL PROPERTIES OF BETA-GALLIUM OXIDE.** COJOCARU, L. N. ALECU, I. D. Z. PHYS. CHEM. (FRANKFURT AM MAIN) 84 (5-6), 325-31, 1973.
53046	**STRUCTURE CHANGE OF NICKEL OXIDE AT THE NEEL TEMPERATURE AND ITS INFLUENCE ON ELECTRICAL CONDUCTIVITY.** DEREN, J. STOCH, L. ZIOLKOWSKI, J. ZESZ. NAUK. AKAD. GORN.-HUTN., CRACOW, MAT., FIZ., CHEM. 6, 59-64, 1971.
53047	**AMORPHOUS ANTIFERROMAGNETISM IN SOME TRANSITION ELEMENT-PHOSPHORUS PENTOXIDE GLASSES.** EGAMI, T. SACLI, O. A. SIMPSON, A. W. TERRY, A. L. WEDGWOOD, F. A. AMORPHOUS MAGN., PROC. INT. SYMP. 27-45, 1973. (EDITED BY H. O. HOOPER, PLENUM: NEW YORK, N. Y.)
53048	**ANTIFERROMAGNETISM IN THE VANADIUM, MANGANESE, AND IRON PHOSPHATE GLASS SYSTEMS.** WILSON, L. K. FRIEBELE, E. J. KINSER, D. L. AMORPHOUS MAGN., PROC. INT. SYMP. 65-76, 1973. (EDITED BY H. O. HOOPER, PLENUM: NEW YORK, N.Y.)
53050	**NOVEL DISPERSIONS OF IRON IN AMORPHOUS GLASS-LIKE CARBONS. EXPLORATORY MAGNETIC STUDIES.** THOMPSON, A. W. WALKER, P. L., JR. MULAY, L. N. AMORPHOUS MAGN., PROC. INT. SYMP. 111-17, 1973. (EDITED BY H. O. HOOPER, PLENUM: NEW YORK, N. Y.)
53051	**MAGNETIC SUSCEPTIBILITY OF CHALCOGENIDE GLASSES.** TAUC, J. DI SALVO, F. J. PETERSON, G. E. WOOD, D. L. AMORPHOUS MAGN., PROC. INT. SYMP. 119-32, 1973. (EDITED BY H. O. HOOPER, PLENUM: NEW YORK, N. Y.)

EPIC Number	Bibliographic Citation

53052 **LONG AND SHORT RANGE MAGNETIC INTERACTIONS AND ELECTRIC SWITCHING IN HIGHLY DOPED, AMORPHOUS FERROMAGNETIC SEMICONDUCTORS.**
WACHTER, P.
AMORPHOUS MAGN., PROC. INT. SYMP.
133-40, 1973.
(EDITED BY HENRY O. HOOPER, PLENUM: NEW YORK, N. Y.)

53053 **DIELECTRIC PROPERTIES OF ICE GROWN FROM POTASSIUM CHLORIDE SOLUTION.**
MAENO, N.
CONTRIB. INST. LOW TEMP. SCI., HOKKAIDO UNIV.
A (25), 47PP., 1973.

53055 **GAS BREAKDOWN MECHANISMS IN ELECTRONEGATIVE GASES (SULFUR HEXAFLUORIDE) AND IN GAS MIXTURES.**
WIELAND, A.
ELEKTROTECH. Z., AUSG.
94 A (7), 370-3, 1973.

53058 **MEASUREMENT OF THE ELECTRIC CONDUCTIVITY OF POROUS NITRIDE MATERIALS BY FOUR-PROBE METHOD.**
SUBBOTINA, T. S.   KAMYSHOV, V. M.
GETEROGENNYE PROTSESSY UCHASTICM TVERD. FAZ
75-88, 1970.

53059 **LOW-LYING ELECTRONIC STATES OF DIATOMIC HALOGEN MOLECULES.**
COXON, J. A.
MOL. SPECTROSC.
1, 177-228, 1973.

53061 **EFFECT OF LITHIUM FLUORIDE ON THE ELECTRICAL CONDUCTIVITY OF POLYCRYSTALLINE MAGNESIUM OXIDE.**
VOLYNETZ, F. K.   DRONOVA, G. I.
UDALOVA, L. V.
IZV. AKAD. NAUK, SSR, NEORG. MATER.
8 (2), 391-2, 1972.
(FOR ENGLISH TRANSLATION SEE E53062)

53062 **EFFECT OF LITHIUM FLUORIDE ON THE ELECTRICAL CONDUCTIVITY OF POLYCRYSTALLINE MAGNESIUM OXIDE.**
VOLYNETZ, F. K.   DRONOVA, G. I.
UDALOVA, L. V.
NATIONAL LENDING LIBRARY FOR SCIENCE AND TECHNOLOGY, BOSTON SPA (ENGLAND)
6PP., 1973.
(ENGLISH TRANSLATION OF IZV. AKAD. NAUK SSR, NEORG. MATER., 8 (2), 391-2, 1972; FOR ORIGINAL SEE E53061)
(N73-30711, NLL-M-23040-(5828.4F), AVAIL. NLL)

53063 **FERROELECTRONICS AND ANTIFERROELECTRICS.**
SMOLENSKII, G. A.
NAUKA PUBLISHING HOUSE, LENINGRAD BRANCH
476PP., 1971.
(FOR ENGLISH TRANSLATION SEE E53064)

53064 **FERROELECTRICS AND ANTIFERROELECTRICS.**
SMOLENSKII, G. A.
ARMY FOREIGN SCIENCE AND TECHNOLOGY CENTER, CHARLOTTESVILLE, VIRGINIA
628PP., 1972.
(ENGLISH TRANSLATION OF RUSSIAN BOOK, NAUKA PUBLISHING HOUSE, LENINGRAD BRANCH, 476PP., 1971; FOR ORIGINAL SEE E53063)
(AD-741 037, FST-HT-23-456-72, AVAIL. DDC)

53065 **INVESTIGATION OF ELECTRONIC CERAMIC FIBERS FOR NONDESTRUCTIVE EVALUATION OF ADVANCED COMPOSITES.**
HENRY, E. C.
MISSILE AND SPACE DIV., GENERAL ELECTRIC CO. PHILADELPHIA, PA.
42PP., 1972.
(AD-741 236, N72-29609, AVAIL. DDC)

53066 **INFRARED PHOTOCATHODE.**
SONNENBERG, H.
GTE SYLVANIA INC., MOUNTAIN VIEW, CALIF.
20PP., 1972.
(AD-741 260, AVAIL. DDC)

53068 **THE STUDY OF THE INTERACTION OF INTENSE PICOSECOND LIGHT PULSE WITH MATERIALS: OBSERVATION OF TWO PHOTON CONDUCTIVITY IN GALLIUM ARSENIDE WITH NANOSECOND AND PICOSECOND LIGHT PULSES.**
JAYARAMAN, S.   LEE, C. H.
DEPT. OF ELECTRICAL ENGINEERING, MARYLAND UNIV., COLLEGE PARK
18PP., 1972.
(AD-741 391, N72-29756, AVAIL. DDC)

53069 **ELECTRON STRUCTURE AND PHYSICAL PROPERTIES OF SOME SULFIDES OF D-TRANSITION METALS.**
OGANESYAN, V. KH.
IZV. AKAD. NAUK ARM. SSR, FIZ.
2 (1), 55-64, 1967.
(FOR ENGLISH TRANSLATION SEE E53070)

53070 **ELECTRON STRUCTURE AND PHYSICAL PROPERTES OF SOME SULFIDES OF D-TRANITION METALS.**
OGANESYAN, V. K.
FOREIGN TECHNOLOGY DIV., WRIGHT-PATTERSON AIR FORCE BASE, OHIO
18PP., 1972.
(ENGLISH TRANSLATION OF IZV. AKAD. NAUK ARM. SSR, FIZ., 2 (1), 55-64, 1967; FOR ORIGINAL SEE E53069)
(AD-741 498, FTD-MT-24-1383-71, N72-30761)

53071 **THE EFFECT OF IMPURITIES ON THE THERMAL EFFICIENCY OF A SHORT CIRCUITED GENERATOR.**
ANATYCHUK, L. I.   DIMITRASHCHUK, V. T.
ARMY FOREIGN SCIENCE AND TECHNOLOGY CENTER, CHARLOTTESVILLE, VIRGINIA
7PP., 1972.
(AD-741 727, FSTC-HT-23-1575-71, AVAIL. DDC)

53072 **THERMOELECTRIC GENERATORS.**
OKHOTIN, A. S.   YEFREMOV, A. A.
OKHOTIN, V. S.   PUSHKARSKIY, A. S.
ARMY FOREIGN SCIENCE AND TECHNOLOGY CENTER, CHARLOTTEVILLE, VIRGINIA
363PP., 1972.
(AD-741 858, FSTC-HT-23-1023-72, AVAIL. DDC)

53073 **POLARISCOPIC CHARACTERIZATION OF SAPPHIRE AND SPINEL.**
MC CAULEY, J. W.
ARMY MATERIALS AND MECHANICS RESEARCH CENTER, WATERTOWN, MASS.
20PP., 1972.
(AD-741 810, AMMRC-TR-72-1, N72-29769, AVAIL. DDC)

53074 **MANUAL FOR THE STUDY OF THE PROPERTIES OF ICE.**
SAVELEV, B. A.
ARCTIC INST. OF NORTH AMERICA, WASHINGTON, D. C.
280PP., 1972.
(AD-741 870, CRREL-TL-343, AVAIL. DDC)

53075 **PROPERTIES OF NIOBIUM ALUMINUM IN HIGH MAGNETIC FIELDS.**
FONER, S.   MC NIFF, E. J., JR.   GEBALLE, T. H.
WILLIAMS, R. H.   BUEHLER, E.
PHYSICA
55, 534-9, 1971.
(AD-741 968, AFOSR-TR-72-1047, AVAIL. DDC)

53076 **WHISKER REINFORCEMENT OF PIEZOELECTRIC TRANSDUCER CERAMIC FOR NAVAL APPLICATIONS.**
FEITH, K. E.   KERR, G. S.
INTERAND CORP., ROCKVILLE, MD.
123PP., 1972.
(AD-742 118, AVAIL. DDC)

53078 **ELECTRONICS STRUCTURE AND THERMOELECTRIC PROPERTIES OF TRANSITION METAL COMPOUNDS.**
GORYACHEV, YU. M.   KUTSENOK, T. G.
ZADVORNYI, L. I.
ARMY FOREIGN SCIENCE AND TECHNOLOGY CENTER, CHARLOTTESVILLE, VA.
11PP., 1972.
(AD-742 511, FSTC-HT-23-216-72, N72-31762)

53081 **RADIATIVE RECOMBINATION IN SEMICONDUCTORS.**
GERSHENZON, M.
ELECTRONIC SCIENCES LAB., UNIVERSITY OF SOUTHERN CALIF., LOS ANGELES
18PP., 1972.
(AD-742 729, AROD-7403-1-E, N72-31764, AVAIL. DDC)

53086 **SEMICONDUCTOR SOLAR ENERGY CONVERTERS AND THE PHENOMENON OF PHOTO CONDUCTIVITY QUENCHING.**
ISAMUKHAMEDORA, M. S.
KARAGEORGIY-ALKALAYEV, P. M.
ARMY FOREIGN SCIENCE AND TECHNOLOGY CENTER, CHARLOTTESVILLE, VA.
8PP., 1972.
(AD-743 031, FSTC-HT-23-1577-71, N72-31083, AVAIL. DDC)

53088 **SOME ELECTRICAL AND THERMAL ELECTRICAL PROPERTIES OF GALLIUM ARSENIDE-CADMIUM SULFIDE SOLID SOLUTIONS.**
VOITSEKHOVSKII, A. V.   PASHUN, A. D.
IZV. VYSSH. UCHEB. ZAVED., FIZ.
(5), 153-5, 1970.
(FOR ENGLISH TRANSLATION SEE E53089)

53089 **SOME ELECTRICAL AND THERMAL ELECTRICAL PROPERTIES OF GALLIUM ARSENIDE-CADMIUM SULFIDE SOLID SOLUTIONS.**
VOITSEKHOVSKII, A. V.   PASHUN, A. D.
ARMY FOREIGN SCIENCE AND TECHNOLOGY CENTER CHARLOTTESVILLE, VA.
8PP., 1972.
(ENGLISH TRANSLATION OF IZV. VYSSH. UCHEB. ZAVED., FIZ., (5), 153-5, 1970; FOR ORIGINAL SEE E53088)
(AD-742 894, FSTC-HT-23-1583-71, N72-31760)

53090 **TRIATOMIC CENTROSYMMETRIC CRYSTALS.**
ROLAND, G. W.   ISAACS, T. J.
STEINBRUEGGE, K. B.   MAZELSKY, R.
RUBENSTEIN, M.   PRICE, A.
WESTINGHOUSE ELECTRIC CORP., PITTSBURGH, PA.
27PP., 1972.
(AD-743 115, 72-9J8-WIMAT-R1, AVIAL. DDC)

EPIC Number	Bibliographic Citation

53093 **INFRARED LASER MATERIALS.**
MORRISON, A. D. MONCHAMP, R. R. BASS, M.
WEBER, M. J.
RESEARCH DIVISION, RAYTHEON CO., WALTHAM, MASS.
81PP., 1972.
(AD-743 223, ECOM-0150-F, AVAIL. DDC)

53094 **PIEZOELECTRIC-PIEZORESISTIVE COUPLED STRAIN TRANSDUCER.**
CLINE, G. L.
AIR FORCE INSTITUTE OF TECHNOLOGY, M. S. THESIS
106PP., 1972.
(AD-743 318, GE/EE/72-8, AVAIL. DDC)

53095 **THE STUDY OF THE INTERACTION OF INTENSE PICOSECOND LIGHT PULSE WITH MATERIALS.**
LEE, C. H. PARK, Y. H.
DEPT. OF ELECTRICAL ENGINEERING, MARYLAND UNIV., COLLEGE PARK
64PP., 1972.
(AD-743 517, AVAIL. DDC)

53097 **HIGH RESOLUTION LOW TEMPERATURE SPECTRA OF ERBIUM TRIPOSITIVE ION IN YTTRIUM ALUMINATE.**
SANTIAGO, A. A.
AIR FORCE INSTITUTE OF TECHNOLOGY, M. S. THESIS
109PP., 1972.
(AD-743 568, GEP/PH/72-20, AVAIL. DDC)

53099 **THEORETICAL ELECTRON DENSITY OF STATES STUDY OF TETRAHEDRALLY BONDED SEMICONDUCTORS.**
STUKEL, D. J. COLLING, T. C. EUWEMA, R. N.
PROC. MATERIALS RES. SYMP., ELECTRONIC DENSITY OF STATES, CONF.
93-103, 1972.
(AD-743 731, ARL-72-0044, AVAIL. DDC)

53102 **FUNDAMENTAL RESEARCH IN CERAMICS.**
HIRTHE, W. M. SEITZ, M. A.
MARQUETTE UNIV., MILWAUKEE, WIS.
86PP., 1972.
(AD-744 004, ARL-72-0048, AVAIL. DDC)

53103 **NON-LINEAR PHENOMENA IN SEMICONDUCTORS THROUGH MULTIPHOTON ABSORPTION.**
ANCKER-JOHNSON, B. FOSSUM, H. J. CHEN, W. S.
AEROSPACE GROUP, BOEING CO., SEATTLE, WASH.
26PP., 1972.
(AD-744 131, AFOSR-TR-72-1211, AVAIL. DDC)

53106 **CHALCOGENIDE GLASS SEMICONDUCTORS. II.**
VASKO, A. SRB, I. LEZAL, D.
ELEKTROTECH. CAS.
21 (7), 524-30, 1970.
(FOR ENGLISH TRANSLATION SEE E53107)

53107 **CHALCOGENIDE GLASS SEMICONDUCTORS.**
VASKO, A. SRB, I. LEZAL, D.
FOREIGN TECHNOLOGY DIVISION, WRIGHT-PATTERSON AIR FORCE BASE, OHIO
13PP., 1972.
(ENGLISH TRANSLATION OF ELEKTROTECH. CAS., 21 (7), 524-30, 1970; FOR ORIGINAL SEE E53106)
(AD-744 249, FTD-HC-23-1786-71, N72-32736, AVAIL. DDC)

53110 **PREPARATION AND POTICAL PROPERTIES OF CRYSTALS AND FILMS OF VANADIUM OXIDES.**
FAN, J. C. C.
DIV. OF ENGINEERING AND APPLIED PHYSICS, HARVARD UNIV., CAMBRIDGE, MASS.
96PP., 1972.
(AD-744 319, ARPA-TR-43, AVAIL. DDC)

53111 **POSITRON ANNIHILATION EXPERIMENTS AND THE BAND STRUCTURE OF VANADIUM SILICIDE.**
BERKO, S. WEGER, M.
BRANDEIS UNIV., WALTHAM, MASS.
20PP., 1972.
(AD-744 499, AROD-3389:19-P, AVAIL. DDC)

53112 **ELECTRICAL AND OPTICAL PROPERTIES OF AMORPHOUS MATERIALS.**
WOOD, C.
DEPT. OF PHYSICS, NORTHERN ILLINOIS UNIV., DE KALB
103PP., 1972.
(AD-744 698, AVAIL. DDC)

53113 **CONDUCTION MECHANISMS FOR ELECTRONIC DEVICES.**
REDFIELD, D. BALBERG, I.
RADIO CORP. OF AMERICA LABS., PRINCETON, N. J.
87PP., 1972.
(AD-744 708, N72-33718, PRRL-72-CR-26, AVAIL DDC)

53114 **FERROELECTRICITY AND CONDUCTION IN FERROELECTRIC CRYSTALS.**
CROSS, L. E.
MATERIALS RESEARCH LAB., PENNSYLVANIA STATE UNIVERSITY, UNIVERSITY PARK, PA.
128PP., 1972.
(AD-744 834, AFAL-TR-72-146, AVAIL. DDC)

EPIC Number	Bibliographic Citation

53115 **THE LYDDANE-SACHS-TELLER RELATION OF FINITE WAVE VECTOR.**
BURSTEIN, E. MARADUDIN, A. A. MINNICK, R.
DEPT. OF PHYSICS, CALIFORNIA UNIV.
8PP., 1972.
(AD-744 906, AVAIL. DDC)

53116 **PREPARATION AND PROPERTIES OF RARE-EARTH COMPOUNDS.**
WOOD, V. E. BROG, K. C. AUSTIN, A. E.
MILLER, J. F. JONES, W. H.
BATTELLE COLUMBUS LABS., OHIO
54PP., 1972.
(AD-744 980, N73-10726, AVAIL. DDC)

53120 **ELECTRICAL BREAKDOWN AND DISCHARGE IN A VACUUM.**
SLIVKOV, I. N. MIKHAILOV, V. I.
SIDOROV, N. I. NASTYUKHA, A. I.
ELEKTRICHESKII PROBOI RAZRYAD VACUUME, MOSCOW, ATOMIZDAT
1-298, 1966.
(FOR ENGLISH TRANSLATION SEE E53121)

53121 **ELECTRICAL BREAKDOWN AND DISCHARGE IN A VACUUM.**
SLIVKOV, I. N. MIKHAILOV, V. I.
SIDOROV, N. I. NASTYUKHA, A. I.
FOREIGN TECHNOLOGY DIV., WRIGHT-PATTERSON AIR FORCE BASE, OHIO
354PP., 1972.
(ENGLISH TRANSLATION OF ELEKTRICHESKII PROBOI RAZRYAD VACUUME, MOSCOW, ATOMIZDAT, 1-298, 1966; FOR ORIGINAL SEE E53120)
(AD-745 471, N72-33676, FTD-MT-24-123-71)

53126 **RESEARCH AND DEVELOPMENT OF YTTRIUM ALUMINATE LASERS.**
WEBER, M. J. BASS, M.
RESEARCH DIVISION, RAYTHEON CO., WALTHAM, MASS.
117PP., 1972.
(AD-746 032, AFML-TR-72-32, AVAIL. DDC)

53127 **LOW TEMPERATURE MAGNETIC AND THERMAL PROPERTIES OF NICKEL TIN HEXACHLORIDE HEXAHYDRATE.**
MYERS, B. E. POLGAR, L. G. FRIEDBERG, S. A.
DEPT. OF PHYSICS, CARNEGIE-MELLON UNIV. PITTSBURGH, PA.
30PP., 1972.
(AD-746 114, AVAIL. DDC)

53128 **ELECTRICAL HIGH-PRESSURE MOLECULAR GAS LASERS.**
SEPPI, E. J.
INSTITUTE FOR DEFENSE ANALYSES, ARLINGTON, VA.
50PP., 1972.
(AD-746 148, N73-11478, AVAIL. DDC)

53129 **PROPERTIES OF ALLOYS OF ZIRCONIUM AND NIOBIUM CARBIDES IN THEIR HOMOGENEITY DOMAIN.**
SAMSONOV, G. V.
POROSH. MET.
(2), 85-8, 1971.
(FOR ENGLISH TRANSLATION SEE E53130)

53130 **PROPERTIES OF ALLOYS OF ZIRCONIUM AND NIOBIUM CARBIDES IN THEIR HOMOGENEITY DOMAIN.**
SAMSONOV, G. V.
ARMY FOREIGN SCIENCE AND TECHNOLOGY CENTER, CHARLOTTESVILLE, VIRGINIA
7PP., 1972.
(ENGLISH TRANSLATION OF POROSH. MET., (2), 85-8, 1971; FOR ORIGINAL SEE E50129)
(AD-746 217, FSTC-HT-23-1558-72, AVAIL. DDC)

53131 **NEW NEODYMIUM DOPED YTTRIUM ALUMINUM GARNET 4 F 3-2 TO 4 I 9-2 LASER TRANSITIONS.**
POMPHREY, P. J.
AIR FORCE INSTITUTE OF TECHNOLOGY, M. S. THESIS
67PP., 1972.
(AD-746 218, GEP/PH/72-15, AVAIL. DDC)

53132 **SPIN-FLIP RAMAN SCATTERING IN CADMIUM SULFIDE.**
WALKER, T. W.
AIR FORCE INSTITUTE OF TECHNOLOGY, M. S. THESIS
74PP., 1972.
(AD-746 219, GEP/PH/72-23, AVAIL. DDC)

53133 **PHOTOEMISSION STUDIES WITH SEVERAL INDEPENDENT PARAMETERS.**
KOYAMA, R. Y.
NATIONAL BUREAU OF STANDARDS, WASHINGTON, D.C.
37PP., 1972.
(AD-746 319, AFCRL-72-0367, AVAIL. DDC)

53134 **PHOTOIONIZATION MASS SPECTROMETRIC STUDY OF NO. A CLOSER LOOK AT THE THRESHOLD REGION.**
KILLGOAR, P. C. LEROI, G. E.
BERKOWITZ, J. CHUPKA, W. A.
DEPT. OF CHEMISTRY, MICHIGAN STATE UNIVERSITY, EAST LANSING
16PP., 1972.
(AD-746 463, AVAIL. DDC)

EPIC Number | Bibliographic Citation

53135 ULTRASOFT-X-RAY REFLECTION, REFRACTION, AND PRODUCTION OF PHOTOELECTRONS (100–1000–E V REGION).
HENKI, B. L.
PHYS. REV.
6 A (1), 94–104, 1972.
(AD–746 535, AFOSR–TR–72–1393, AVAIL. DDC)

53138 TRANSPORT AND PHOTOELECTRICAL PROPERTIES OF GALLIUM ARSENIDE CONTAINING DEEP ACCEPTORS.
BROWN, W. J. BLAKEMORE, J. S.
J. APPL. PHYS.
43 (5), 2242–6, 1972.
(AD–746 554, AFOSR,TR–72–1434, AVAIL. DDC)

53142 DIELECTRIC REPORT.
WESTPHAL, W. B. SILS, A.
MASSACHUSETTS INST. OF TECHNOLOGY, CAMBRIDGE, MASS.
243PP., 1972.
(AD–746 686, AFML–TR–72–39, AVAIL. DDC)

53143 SYNTHESIS OF COMPOUND SEMICONDUCTING MATERIALS AND DEVICE APPLICATIONS.
STEVENSON, D. A.
CENTER FOR MATERIALS RESEARCH, STANFORD UNIVERSITY, CALIFORNIA
186PP., 1972.
(AD–746 882, N73–11783, CMR–72–10, AVAIL. DDC)

53144 PROGRESS REPORT FOR JULY 1, 1971 THROUGH JUNE 30, 1972.
COORDINATED SCIENCE LAB.
COORDINATED SCIENCE LAB., ILLINOIS UNIV., URBANA
317PP., 1972.
(AD–747 132, AVAIL. DDC)

53146 ABSORPTION SPECTRUM OF HD IN THE VACUUM–UV REGION. RYDBERG STATES AND IONIZATION ENERGY.
TAKEZAWA, S. TANAKA, Y.
J. CHEM. PHYS.
56 (12), 6125–30, 1972.
(AD–747 143, AFCRL–72–0463, AVAIL. DDC)

53158 SYNTHESIS OF RARE EARTH COMPOUNDS AND A STUDY OF THEIR MAGNETIC OPTICAL AND SEMICONDUCTING PROPERTIES.
HOLTZBERG, F. MC GUIRE, T. R. PENNEY, T.
SHAFER, M. W. VON MOLNAR, S.
IBM WATSON RESEARCH CENTER, YORKTOWN HEIGHTS, N. Y.
88PP., 1972.
(AD–747 839, N73–12835, ARPA–1588, AVAIL. DDC)

53159 THEORY OF SURFACE MAGNETOPLASMONS IN SEMICONDUCTORS.
BRION, J. J. WALLIS, R. F. HARTSTEIN, A.
BURSTEIN, E.
PHYS. REV. LETT.
28 (22), 1455–8, 1972.
(AD–747 892, AVAIL. DDC)

53162 NONLINEAR BEHAVIOR OF TRANSDUCER CERAMICS.
LEBLANC, C. L.
NAVAL UNDERWATER SYSTEMS CENTER, NEWPORT, RHODE ISLAND
52PP., 1972.
(AD–748 198, NUSC–TR–4295, AVAIL. DDC)

53163 ELECTRONIC AND RADIATION DAMAGE PROPERTIES OF RUTILE.
DE FORD, J. W. JOHNSON, O. W. ROSENBERGER, F
DEPT. OF PHYSICS, UTAH UNIVERSITY, SALT LAKE CITY, UTAH
1–19, 1972.
(AD–748 298, AVAIL. DDC)

53164 DEFECT AND IMPURITY THERMODYNAMICS IN RUTILE–LIKE SYSTEMS.
DE FORD, J. W. JOHNSON, O. W.
DEPT. OF PHYSICS, UTAH UNIVERSITY, SALT LAKE CITY, UTAH
20–47, 1972.
(AD–748 298, AVAIL. DDC)

53165 AN EXPERIMENTAL TECHNIQUE FOR THE PRECISE DETERMINATION OF H AND D CONCENTRATION IN RUTILE TITANIUM DIOXIDE.
JOHNSON, O. W. DE FORD, J.
DEPT. OF PHYSICS, UTAH UNIVERSITY, SALT LAKE CITY, UTAH
49–66, 1972.
(AD–748 298, AVAIL. DDC)

53166 THE BAND GAP ABSORPTION OF RUTILE TITANIUM DIOXIDE.
SHANER, J. W.
DEPT. OF PHYSICS, UTAH UNIVERSITY, SALT LAKE CITY, UTAH
68–76, 1972.
(AD–748 298, AVAIL. DDC)

53167 VACUUM REDUCTION OF RUTILE.
OHLSEN, W. D. JOHNSON, O. W.
DEPT. OF PHYSICS, UTAH UNIVERSITY, SALT LAKE CITY, UTAH
78–86, 1972.
(AD–748 298, AVAIL. DDC)

53169 PRODUCTION OF SPONTANEOUS POLARIZATION BY ELASTIC INSTABILITIES IN PIEZOELECTRIC MATERIALS.
HARDY, J. R. ULLMAN, F. G. BOYER, L. L.
BEHLEN PHYSICS LAB., UNIVERSITY OF NEBRASKA, LINCOLN
157PP., 1972.
(AD–748 294, AFOSR–TR–72–1283, AVAIL. DDC)

53171 NEW METHODS FOR GROWTH AND CHARACTERIZATION OF GALLIUM ARSENIDE AND MIXED III–V SEMICONDUCTOR CRYSTALS.
WILCOX, W. R.
ELECTRONIC SCIENCE LAB., UNIVERSITY OF SOUTHERN CALIF., LOS ANGELES
129PP., 1972.
(AD–748 344, AVAIL. DDC)

53173 HIGH TEMPERATURE DEPENDENCE OF THE ELECTRON HALL MOBILITY IN GAMMA–IRRADIATED POTASSIUM CHLORIDE.
EISELE, I. KEVAN, L.
J. CHEM. PHYS.
56 (11), 5738–9, 1972.
(AD–748 374, AFOSR–TR–72–1746, AVAIL. DDC)

53175 MAGNETIC BUBBLE MATERIALS.
SHAW, R. W. SANDFORT, R. M. MOODY, J. W.
MONSANTO RESEARCH CORP., ST. LOUIS, MO.
177PP., 1972.
(AD–748 426, MRC–SL–339, AVAIL. DDC)

53176 PERTURBED BANDS IN REAL SEMICONDUCTING GLASSES.
BOER, K. W.
J. NON–CRYST. SOLIDS
8 (10), 586–91, 1972.
(AD–748 489, AVAIL. DDC)

53177 THE INFLUENCE OF DOPING ON FIELD QUENCHING IN CADMIUM SULFIDE.
HADLEY, H. C. VOSS, P. BOER, K. W.
PHYS. STATUS SOLIDI
11 A, K145–K148, 1972.
(AD–748 490, AVAIL. DDC)

53178 STRUCTURAL EFFECTS ON ELECTRICAL PROPERTIES IN AMORPHOUS SEMICONDUCTORS.
KINSER, D. L. WILSON, L. K.
SCHOOL OF ENGINEERING, VANDERBILT UNIVERSITY, NASHVILLE, TENNESSEE
248PP., 1972.
(AD–748 661, N73–13751, AVAIL. DDC)

53179 PRINCIPLES OF THERMOELECTRONIC AND MAGNETO–HYDRODYNAMIC CONVERSION OF ENERGY.
AREFYEV, K. M. PAKYEV, I. I.
OSNOVY TERMOELEKTRONNOGO I MAGNITOGIDRODINAMICHESKOGO PREOBRAZOVANIYA ENERGII, ATOMIZDAT MOSCOW
215PP., 1970.
(FOR ENGLISH TRANSLATION SEE E53180)

53180 PRINCIPLES OF THERMOELECTRONIC AND MAGNETO–HYDRODYNAMIC CONVERSION OF ENERGY.
AREFYEV, K. M. PAKYEV, I. I.
FOREIGN TECHNOLOGY DIVISION, WRIGHT–PATTERSON AIR FORCE BASE, OHIO
293PP., 1972.
(ENGLISH TRANSLATION OF OSNOVY TERMOELEKTRONNOGO I MAGNITOGIDRODINAMICHESKOGO PREOBRAZOVANIYA ENERGII, ATOMIZDAT MOSCOW, 215PP., 1970; FOR ORIGINAL SEE E53179)
(AD–748 707, FTD–MT–24–1464–71, AVAIL. DDC)

53183 PROBLEMS OF SOLID STATE ELECTRONICS.
ZUBENKO, YU. W.
ARMY FOREIGN SCIENCE AND TECHNOLOGY CENTER, CHARLOTTESVILLE, VA.
138PP., 1972.
(AD–748 739, FSTC–HT–23–1500–72, N73–12262, AVAIL. DDC)

53184 SOLID STATE RESEARCH.
MC WHORTER, A. L.
LINCOLN LABORATORY, MASSACHUSETTS INSTITUTE OF TECHNOLOGY, LEXINGTON
76PP., 1972.
(AD–748 836, ESD–TR–72–109, AVAIL. DDC)

53186 A CENTER OF COMPETENCE IN SOLID STATE MATERIALS AND DEVICES.
LINDHOLM, F. A. CHENETTE, E. R.
GOULD, R. W. HENCH, L. L.
LI, S. S. VAN DER ZIEL, A.
ENGINEERING AND INDUSTRIAL EXPERIMENT STATION, UNIVERSITY OF FLORIDA, GAINESVILLE
197PP., 1972.
(AD–748 862, AFCRL–72–0336, N73–13746)

53187 HALL COEFFICIENT AND MAGNETORESISTANCE OF AMORPHOUS THALLIUM SELENIDE–ARSENIC TELLURIDE.
CARVER, G. P. ALLGAIER, R. S.
J. NON–CRYST. SOLIDS
8 (10), 347–52, 1972.
(AD–748 981, ARPA–1573, AVAIL. DDC)

EPIC Number	Bibliographic Citation

53189 **SUPERCONDUCTIVITY OF DOUBLE CHALCOGENIDES: LITHIUM TITANIUM SULFIDES.**
BARZ, H. E. COOPER, A. S. CORENZWIT, E.
MAREZIO, M. MATTHIAS, B. T. SCHMIDT, P. H.
SCIENCE
175, 884-5, 1972.
(AD-749 085, AFOSR-TR-72-1807, AVAIL. DDC)

53192 **THERMALLY INDUCED NEGATIVE RESISTANCE IN SILICON-DOPED YTTRIUM IRON GARNET.**
KAPLAN, T. BULLOCK, D. C.
ADLER, D. EPSTEIN, D. J.
APPL. PHYS. LETT.
20 (11), 439-41, 1972.
(AD-749 203, AVAIL. DDC)

53195 **BAND STRUCTURE AND ELECTRICAL PROPERTIES OF AMORPHOUS SEMICONDUCTORS.**
ADLER, D.
MASSACHUSETTS INSTITUTE OF TECHNOLOGY, CAMBRIDGE
12PP., 1972.
(AD-749 379, N73-13761, AVAIL. DDC)

53199 **PHOTOMULTIPLIER TUBE FOR EFFICIENT INFRARED DETECTION.**
FISHER, D. G. HUGHES, F. R.
RCA ELECTRONIC COMPONENTS, LANCASTER, PA.
31PP., 1972.
(AD-749 645, ECOM-0273-6, AVAIL. DDC)

53200 **NEUTRON INDUCED DAMAGE IN P- AND N-TYPE LEAD SULFIDE SINGLE CRYSTAL FILMS.**
CULPEPPER, R. M.
NAVAL ORDANCE LAB., WHITE OAK, SILVER SPRING, MD.
193PP., 1972.
(AD-749 689, NOLTR-72-119, AVAIL. DDC)

53201 **OPTICAL ABSORPTION OF GALLIUM SELENIDE AND GALLIUM TELLURIDE SINGLE CRYSTALS AND SOLID SOLUTIONS BASED ON THEM.**
MUSHINSKIY, V. P. KARAMAN, M. I.
SB. NAUCH. STATEY YESTESTVENNYYE MAT NAUK
71-84, 1969.
(FOR ENGLISH TRANSLATION SEE E53202)

53202 **OPTICAL ABSORPTION OF GALLIUM SELENIDE AND GALLIUM TELLURIDE SINGLE CRYSTALS AND SOLID SOLUTIONS BASED ON THEM.**
MUSHINSKIY, V. P. KARAMAN, M. I.
FOREIGN TECHNOLOGY DIVISION, WRIGHT-PATTERSON AIR FORCE BASE, OHIO
14PP., 1972.
(ENGLISH TRANSLATION OF SB. NAUCH. STATEY YESTESTVENNYYE MAT. NAUK, 71-84, 1969; FOR ORIGINAL SEE E53201)
(AD-749 750, FTD-HT-23-551-72, AVAIL. DDC)

53207 **INFRARED ABSORPTION BANDS OF NITROUS OXIDE.**
BURCH, D. E. GRYVNAK, D. A. PEMBROOK, J. D.
AERONUTRONIV DIVISION, PHILCO-FORD CORP., NEWPORT BEACH, CALIFORNIA
85PP., 1972.
(AD-749 879, AFCRL-72-0387, AVAIL. DDC)

53208 **SEISMIC DETERMINATION OF GEOLOGICAL DISCONTINUITIES AHEAD OF RAPID EXCAVATION.**
GUPTA, R. R.
BENDIX RESEARCH LAB., SOUTHFIELD, MICHIGAN
82PP., 1972.
(AD-749 977, AVAIL. DDC)

53210 **SECOND HARMONIC GENERATION AND TWO-PHOTON LUMINESCENCE IN THE EXCITON REGION OF COPPER CHLORIDE.**
HAUEISEN, D. C.
SOLID STATE COMMUN.
10 (12), 1313-5, 1972.
(AD-750 065, AVAIL. DDC)

53212 **THE DIELECTRIC RELAXATION SPECTRA OF ICE 1-H SINGLE CRYSTALS.**
WESTPHAL, W. B. MYKOLAJEWYCZ, R.
RUNCK, A. H. VON HIPPEL, A.
LAB. FOR INSULATION RESEARCH, MASSACHUSETTS INSTITUTE OF TECHNOLOGY
6PP., 1972.
(AD-750 125, AVAIL. DDC)

53213 **ICE CHEMISTRY: IS ICE 1-H A PROTON SEMICONDUCTOR.**
VON HIPPEL, A. R. RUNCK, A. H.
WESTPHAL, W. B.
LAB. FOR INSULATION RESEARCH, MASSACHUSETTS INSTITUTE OF TECHNOLOGY
9PP., 1972.
(AD-750 125, AVAIL. DDC)

53215 **DEPENDENCE OF SILVER HALIDE ENERGY BANDS ON LATTICE CONSTANT AND HALOGEN.**
FOWLER, W. B.
PHYS. STATUS SOLIDI
52 B 591-9, 1972.
(AD-750 233, AFOSR-TR-72-1933, AVAIL. DDC)

EPIC Number	Bibliographic Citation

53217 **MEASUREMENT OF THE ANGULAR DISTRIBUTION OF PHOTOELECTRONS FROM THIRD GENERATION PHOTOCATHODE MATERIALS.**
POLLARD, J. H.
ARMY ELECTRONICS COMMAND, NIGHT VISION LAB., FORT BELVOIR, VA.
15PP., 1972.
(AD-750 364, N73-15239, AVAIL. DDC)

53219 **EXCITATION AT ELECTRODES.**
HAUGSJAA, P. O. FRENCH, K. W. HELLER, A.
GTE LAB., WALTHAM, MASS.
15PP., 1972.
(AD-750 401, AVAIL. DDC)

53220 **THE STUDY OF THE INTERACTION OF INTENSE PICOSECOND LIGHT PULSE WITH MATERIALS(1) MEASUREMENT OF PICOSECOND PULSE WIDTH USING TWO-PHOTON CONDUCTIVITY IN GALLIUM ARSENIDE.(2) THREE PHOTON CONDUCTIVITY IN CADMIUM SULFIDE.**
LEE, C. H. JAYARAMAN, S.
DEPT. OF ELECTRICAL ENGINEERING, UNIVERSITY OF MARYLAND, COLLEGE PARK
8PP., 1972.
(AD-750 414, AVAIL. DDC)

53221 **TESTING A POINT-DIPOLE ELECTRO-OPTIC MODEL BY AN APPLICATION TO LEAD TITANATE.**
SANCHEZ, A. S.
AIR FORCE INST. OF TECHNOLOGY, WRIGHT-PATTERSON AIR FORCE BASE, OHIO, M. S. THESIS
72PP., 1972.
(AD-753 467, N73-18773, GEP/PH/72-19, AVAIL. DDC)

53223 **STUDY OF THE NATURE OF A P-N HETEROGENEOUS JUNCTION IN A CADMIUM SELENIDE MONOCRYSTAL OBTAINED BY THE GAS TRANSPORT METHOD.**
MAMEDOVA, G. A. BAKIROV, M. YA.
IZV. AKAD. NAUK AZERB. SSR, SER. FIZ.-TEKHN. MAT. NAUK
(6), 6-8, 1969.
(FOR ENGLISH TRANSLATION SEE E53224)

53224 **STUDY OF THE NATURE OF A P-N HETEROGENEOUS JUNCTION IN A CADMIUM SELENIDE MONOCRYSTAL OBTAINED BY THE GAS TRANSPORT METHOD.**
MAMEDOVA, G. A. BAKIROV, M. YA.
FOREIGN TECHNOLOGY DIV., WRIGHT-PATTERSON AIR FORCE BASE, OHIO
10PP., 1972.
(ENGLISH TRANSLATION OF IZV. AKAD. NAUK AZERB. SSR, SER. FIZ.-TEKHN. MAT. NAUK, (6), 6-8, 1969; FOR ORIGINAL SEE E53223)
(AD-750 506, FTD-HT-23-262-72, AVAIL. DDC)

53227 **LIGHT-EMITTING DIODES FOR LASER PUMPING.**
WINSTON, H. V. NEUBERGER, M.
ELECTRONIC PROPERTIES INFORMATION CENTER, HUGHES AIRCRAFT COMP., CULVER CITY, CALIF.
30PP., 1972.
(AD-750 576, EPIC-IR-80, N73-15545, AVAIL. DDC)

53228 **OPTOELECTRONIC ELECTRON EMITTER.**
SCHADE, H. E. KRESSEL, H. LOCKWOOD, H. F.
RADIO CORP. OF AMERICA, PRINCETON, N. J.
28PP., 1972.
(AD-750 611, N73-15247, ECOM-0059-3, PRRL-72-CR-40, AVAIL. DDC)

53229 **THEORY OF THE INFRARED ABSORPTION SPECTRUM OF A COBALT FLUORIDE SINGLE CRYSTAL.**
PERESADA, V. I. SYRKIN, E. S.
SPEKTROSK. KRIST., MATER. SIMP., 2ND
88-89, 1970.
(FOR ENGLISH TRANSLATION SEE E53230)

53230 **THEORY OF THE INFRARED ABSORPTION SPECTRUM OF A COBALT FLUORIDE SINGLE CRYSTAL.**
PERESADA, V. I. SYRKIN, E. S.
FOREIGN TECHNOLOGY DIVISION, WRIGHT-PATTERSON AIR FORCE BASE, OHIO
4PP., 1972.
(ENGLISH TRANSLATION OF SPEKTROSK. KRIST., MATER. SIMP., 2ND, 88-90, 1970; FOR ORIGINAL SEE E52230)
(AD-750 647, FTD-HT-23-324-72, AVAIL. DDC)

53231 **SURFACE SPACE-CHARGE EFFECT ON CERTAIN PHOTOELECTRIC PROPERTIES OF GALLIUM ARSENIDE(P-TYPE).**
BORKOVSKAYA, O. YU.
UKR. FIZ. ZH.
17 (5), 835-8, 1972.
(FOR ENGLISH TRANSLATION SEE E53232)

53232 **SURFACE SPACE-CHARGE EFFECT ON CERTAIN PHOTOELECTRIC PROPERTIES OF GALLIUM ARSENIDE(P-TYPE).**
BORKOVSKAYA, O. YU.
DEFENCE RESEARCH INFORMATION CENTRE ORPINGTON, ENGLAND
5PP., 1972.
(ENGLISH TRANSLATION OF UKR. FIZ. ZH., 17 (5), 835-8, 1972; FOR ORIGINAL SEE E53231)
(AD-750 696, N73-20787, DRIC-TRANS-2913, AVAIL. DDC)

EPIC Number	Bibliographic Citation
53233	**ELECTRICAL BREAKDOWN OF DIELECTRICS WITH A DIPOLE STRUCTURE.** PRIKHODKO, N. TOMSK. SIBIR. FIZ.-TEKH. INST., TRUDY 6 (2), 114-9, 1945. (FOR ENGLISH TRANSLATION SEE E53234)
53234	**ELECTRICAL BREAKDOWM OF DIELECTRICS WITH A DIPOLE STRUCTURE.** PRIKHOD'KO, N. FOREIGN TECHNOLOGY DIVISION, WRIGHT-PATTERSON AIR FORCE BASE, OHIO 9PP., 1972. (ENGLISH TRANSLATION OF TOMSK. SIBIR. FIZ. TEKH. INST., TRUDY, 6 (2), 114-9, 1945; FOR ORIGINAL SEE E53233) (AD-750 699, FTD-HC-23-1176-72, AVAIL. DDC)
53238	**A PRELIMINARY STUDY OF THE ELECTRICAL PROPERTIES OF SEMICONDUCTING CADMIUM FLUORIDE WITH CERIUM 3+ AND GADOLINIUM 3+ CODOPANTS.** BAFICO, M. A. YANEY, P. P. RESEARCH INSTITUTE, UNIVERSITY OF DAYTON, OHIO 99PP., 1972. (AD-750 937, AFML-TR-72-140, UDRI-TR-72-37, AVAIL. DDC)
53239	**RESONANT INTERACTIONS BETWEEN LOCALIZED LONGITUDINAL-OPTICAL PHONONS AND CONTINUUM STATES OF DONORS IN CADMIUM SULFIDE AND CADMIUM SELENIDE.** HENRY, C. H. HOPFIELD, J. J. PHYS. REV. 6 (6), 2233-8, 1972. (AD-750 980, AFOSR-TR-72-2042, AVAIL. DDC)
53240	**PYROELECTRIC DETECTION PROPERTIES OF GADOLINIUM MOLYBDATE.** ULLMAN, F. G. GANGULY, B. N. ZEIDLER, J. R. J. ELECTRON. MATER. 1 (3), 425-34, 1972. (AD-751 008, AFOSR-TR-72-2073, AVAIL. DDC)
53241	**STUDY OF THE MAGNETIC REVERSAL PROCESS IN MANGANESE-BISMUTH THIN FILMS.** SHUR, YA. S. GLAZER, A. A. TAGIROV, R. I. POTAPOV, A. P. GASS, V. G. SOV. PHYS. DOKL. 18 (6), 416-8, 1973. (ENGLISH TRANSLATION OF DOKL. AKAD. NAUK SSSR, 210 (4), 822-5, 1973; FOR ORIGINAL SEE E51516)
53242	**CONTROL OF THE LEVEL OF COERCIVE FORCE IN FERRIMAGNETS BY THE INTRODUCTION OF ACTIVATOR IONS.** BONDAREV, D. E. KIRICHOK, P. P. ZINOVEVA, I. G. SHAMANOV, M. A. SOV. PHYS. DOKL. 18 (6), 424-5, 1973. (ENGLISH TRANSLATION OF DOKL. AKAD. NAUK SSSR, 210 (5), 1063-6, 1973; FOR ORIGINAL SEE E51518)
53243	**RESEARCH ON II-VI COMPOUNDS AT VERY LOW TEMPERATURES.** KREITMAN, M. M. DEPT. OF PHYSICS, DAYTON UNIV., OHIO 179PP., 1971. AD-739 867, ARL-71-0290,
53244	**SOME ASPECTS OF OPTICAL EVALUATION OF CARBON DIOXIDE LASER WINDOW MATERIALS AT AFCRL.** BENDOW, B. HORDNIK, LIPSON, H. SKOLNIK, L. AIR FORCE CAMBRIDGE RESEARCH LAB. 31PP., 1972. (AFCRL-72-0404, AD-749 864, AVAIL. DDC)
53245	**R AND D ON THE APPLICATION OF POLYCRYSTALLINE ZINC SELENIDE AND CADMIUM TELLURIDE TO HIGH ENERGY IR LASER WINDOWS.** BENECKE, M. W. PORTER, C. R. ROY, D. W. COORS PORCELAIN CO., GOLDEN, COLO. 143PP., 1972. (AD-753 068, AFML-TR-72-177, N73-18512, AVAIL. DDC)
53246	**THEORETICAL STUDIES OF HIGH-POWER INFRARED WINDOW MATERIALS.** SPARKS, M. S. ZONICS, INC., VAN NUYS, CALIF. 174PP., 1972. (AD-756 080, N73-22453, AVAIL. DDC)
53247	**OPTICAL PERFORMANCE EVALUATION OF INFRARED TRANSMITTING MATERIALS.** BERNARD, B. GIANINO, P. D. AIR FORCE CAMBRIDGE RESEARCH LAB. 29PP., 1972. (AD-756 825, AFCRL-72-565, AVAIL. DDC)
53248	**STUDY OF WINDOWS FOR PULSED CARBON DIOXIDE LASERS.** CORNELL, G. J. ITT COMPONENTS GROUP EUROPE 17PP., 1972. (AD-906 574, AVAIL. DDC)
53249	**COBALT LASER RADIATION ABSORPTION IN SULFUR HEXAFLUORIDE AIR BOUNDARY LAYERS.** ANDERSON, J. D., JR. WAGNER, J. L. KNOTT, J. NAVAL ORDNANCE LAB., SILVER SPRING, MARYLAND 59PP., 1972. (AD-751 016, NOLTR-72-172, AVAIL. DDC)
53250	**NEW SUPERCONDUCTORS.** COLLMAN, J. P. LITTLE, W. A. LELAND STANFORD JUNIOR UNIVERSITY, STANFORD, CALIF. 126PP., 1972. (AD-751 038, AVAIL. DDC)
53251	**CURRENT STATUS OF SOME BASIC PROBLEMS IN AMORPHOUS SEMICONDUCTORS.** PAUL, W. DIVISION OF ENGINEERING AND APPL. PHYS., HARVARD UNIVERSITY, CAMBRIDGE, MASS. 36PP., 1972. (AD-751 084, AVAIL. DDC)
53252	**LOW TEMPERATURE METAL OXIDE DEPOSITION BY ALKOXIDE HYDROLYSIS.** SLADEK, K. J. GIBERT, W. W. PROC. INT. CONF. CHEMICAL VAPOR DEPOSITION, 3RD 215-31, 1972. (AD-751- 203, AFOSR-TR-72-2091, AVAIL. DDC)
53253	**INFRARED LINE SHAPE STUDY USING A TUNABLE 2.0-MICRON HELIUM-XENON LASER.** LONG, R. K. MILLS, F. S. ELECTROSCIENCE LAB., OHIO STATE UNIVERSITY, COLUMBUS 26PP., 1972. (AD-751 230, AVAIL. DDC)
53254	**LUMINESCENCE IN ZINC SULFIDE.** BROVETTO, P. CORTESE, C. MAXIA, V. ISTITUTO ELETTROTECNICO NAZIONALE, GALILEO FERRARIS, TURIN, ITALY 40PP., 1972. (AD-751 302, AFOSR-TR-72-2077, AVAIL. DDC)
53255	**FAR INFRARED ISOLATOR.** PAO, Y-H. BOORD, W. T. CASE WESTERN RESERVE UNIVERSITY, CLEVELAND, OHIO 46PP., 1972. (AD-751 319, AFCRL-72-0444, AVAIL. DDC)
53256	**ELECTRONIC STRUCTURE AND KINETICS OF THE OXIDATION OF BARIUM AND STRONTIUM.** KRESS, K. A. LAPEYRE, G. J. PHYS. REV. LETT. 28 (25), 1639-43, 1972. (AD-751 347, AFOSR-TR-72-2118, AVAIL. DDC)
53257	**CH AND CD BOND-STRETCHING MODES IN THE LUMINESCENCE OF H- AND D- IMPLANTED SILICON CARBIDE.** CHOYKE, W. J. PATRICK, L. PHYS. REV. LETT. 29 (6), 355-6, 1972. (AD-751 370, AFOSR-TR-72-2123, AVAIL. DDC)
53259	**THE TEMPERATURE VARIATION OF THE ELECTRON DIFFUSION LENGTH AND THE INTERNAL QUANTUM EFFICIENCY IN GALLIUM ARSENIC ELECTROLUMINESCENT DIODES.** BAHRAMAN, A. OLDHAM, W. G. SOLID STATE ELECTRON. 15, 907-17, 1972. (AD-751 385, AFOSR-TR-72-2136, AVAIL. DDC)
53260	**DIPOLAR CONTRIBUTION TO THE ANISOTROPY ENERGY OF THE EUROPIUM MONOCHALCOGENIDES.** KASUYA, A. TACHIKI, M. AIP (AMER. INST. PHYS.) CONF. PROC. (5), 845-9, 1972. (AD-751 409, AFOSR-TR-72-2117, AVAIL. DDC)
53261	**ELECTRICAL TRANSPORT PROPERTIES OFS VANADIUM DIOXIDE NEAR ITS SEMICONDUCTOR-TO-METAL TRANSITION.** RESEVEAR, W. H. DIV. OF ENGINEERING AND APPL. PHYS., HARVARD UNIVERSITY, CAMBRIDGE, MASS. 214PP., 1972. (AD-751 524, HP-31, N73-16759, AVAIL. DDC)
53262	**THE TRAP STRUCTURE OF PYROLYTIC ALUMINUM OXIDE IN MOS CAPACITORS.** HARARI, E. ROYCE, B. S. H. SOLID STATE AND MATERIALS LAB., SCHOOL OF ENGINEERING AND APPLIED SCIENCE, PRINCETON, N. J. 9PP., 1972. (AD-751 629, PSSL-141172, AVAIL. DDC)
53263	**THE DETERMINATION OF OPTICAL PROPERTIES AND ENERGY GAP OF LEAD (1-X) TIN (X) TELLURIUM THIN FILMS IN THE FUNDAMENTAL ABSORPTION EDGE REGION.** WALZ, V. M., JR. NAVAL POSTGRADUATE SCHOOL, MONEREY, CALIF., M. S. THESIS 76PP., 1972. (AD-751 650, N73-16747, AVAIL. DDC)

EPIC Number *Bibliographic Citation*

53266 **EFFECTS OF ANNEALING IN THE ELECTRO-OPTICAL PROPERTIES OF AMORPHOUS GERMANIUM (.5) TELLURIUM (.5) FILMS.**
SCHARNHORST, K. P. RIEDL, H. R.
NAVAL ORDANCE LAB., WHITE OAK, SILVER SPRING, MD.
39PP., 1972.
(AD-752 024, N73-17787, NOLTR-72-196, AVAIL. DDC)

53270 **CONDUCTION MECHANISMS FOR ELECTRONIC DEVICES.**
REDFIELD, D.
RCA LABORATORIES, PRINCETON, N. J.
17PP., 1972.
(AD-752 100, N73-17790, PRRL-72-CR-28, AVAIL. DDC)

53271 **SOLID STATE RESEARCH.**
MCWHORTER, A. L.
LINCOLN LABORATORY, MASSACHUSETTS INSTITUTE OF TECHNOLOGY
92PP., 1972.
(AD-752 556, ESD-TR-72-211, AVAIL. DDC)

53272 **LATTICE INSTABILITIES IN SUPERCONDUCTING TERNARY MOLYBDENUM SULFIDES.**
LAWSON, A. C.
MATER. RES. BULL.
7, 773-6, 1972.
(AD-752 635, AFOSR-TR-72-2243, AVAIL. DDC)

53274 **CHARACTERIZATION OF IRIDIUM WINDOWS.**
HAGGERTY, J. S. PETERS, E. T.
LITTLE (ARTHUR D) INC., CAMBRIDGE, MASS.
27PP., 1972.
(AD 740 144 AD-752 783, ADL-74010, AVAIL. DDC)

53275 **RADAR CROSS-SECTION MEASUREMENTS OF SNOW AND ICE.**
HOEKSTRA, P. SPANOGLE, D.
COLD REGIONS RESEARCH AND ENGINEERING LAB., HANOVER, N. H.
43PP., 1972.
(AD-752 900, CRREL-TR-235, AVAIL. DDC)

53276 **CHARACTERIZATION OF CONDUCTION PROCESSES IN AMORPHOUS SEMICONDUCTORS.**
STONE, J. L.
TEXAS A AND M RESEARCH FOUNDATION, COLLEGE STATION,
111PP., 1972.
(AD-753 053, N73-18762, AVAIL. DDC)

53278 **SEMICONDUCTOR PHOTOCONVERTORS.**
VASILYEV, A. M. LANDSMAN, A. P.
POLUPROVODNIKOVYYE FOTOPREOBRAZOVATELI, IZDVO, SOVETSKOYE RADIO, MOSCOW
1-225, 1971.
(FOR ENGLISH TRANSLATION SEE E53279)

53279 **SEMICONDUCTOR PHOTOCONVERTORS.**
VASILYEV, A. M. LANDSMAN, A. P.
FOREIGN TECHNOLOGY DIV., WRIGHT-PATTERSON AIR FORCE BASE, OHIO
283PP., 1972.
(ENGLISH TRANSLATION OF POLUPROVODNIKOVYYE FOTOPREOBRAZOVATELI, IZD-VO, SOVETSKOYE RADIO, MOSCOW, 1-2258 1971; FOR ORIGINAL SEE E53278)
(AD-753 063, FTD-HT-23-317-72, AVAIL. DDC)

53282 **STRUCTURAL AND MAGNETIC PROPERTIES OF THE BISMUTH-MANGANESE BISMUTH CONTROLLED EUTECTIC.**
BOULBES, J. C. KRAFT, R. W.
NOTIS, M. R. GRAHAM, C. D., JR.
PROC. CONF. ON IN SITU COMPOSITES
27, 1972.
(AD-754 779, N73-20625, AVA2L. DDC)

53287 **NERNST LAMP FOR LASER PUMPING.**
POLLACK, S. A. CALDWELL, J. J., JR.
OPTITRON, INC., TORRANCE, CALIF.
48PP., 1973.
(AD-755 207, AVAIL. DDC)

53290 **LUMINESCENCE OF SILVER CHLORIDE CRYSTALS.**
VACEK, K.
CZECH. J. PHYS.
10, 66-73, 1960.
(FOR ENGLISH TRANSLATION SEE E53291)

53291 **LUMINESCENCE OF SILVER CHLORIDE CRYSTALS.**
VACEK, K.
NAVAL RESEARCH LAB., WASHINGTON, D. C.
13PP., 1973.
(ENGLISH TRANSLATION OF CZECH. J. PHYS., 10, 66-73, 1960; FOR ORIGINAL SEE E53290)
(AD-755 430, NRL-TRANS-1262, N73-21677, AVAIL. DDC)

53292 **MEASUREMENT OF THE PYROELECTRIC COEFFICIENT OF LEAD ZIRCONATE TITANATE.**
MC GEVNA, V. SACCENTI, J. MC NEILLY, J.
U. S. ARMY BALLISTIC RESEARCH LAB., ABERDEEN PROVING GROUND, MARYLAND
45PP., 1972.
(AD-755 520, BRL-1614, AVAIL. DDC)

EPIC Number *Bibliographic Citation*

53293 **RESEARCH IN THE SYNTHESIS OF RARE EARTH COMPOUNDS AND A STUDY OF THEIR MAGNETIC OPTICAL AND SEMICONDUCTING PROPERTIES.**
HOLTZBERG, F. TAO, L. J. PENNEY, T.
SHAFER, M. W. VON MOLNAR, S.
INT. BUSINESS MACHINES CORP., THOMAS J. WATSON RESEARCH CENTER, YORKTOWN HEIGHTS, N. Y.
53PP., 1973.
(AD-755 925, N73-21164, AVAIL. DDC)

53295 **RELATIVISTIC ELECTRONIC BAND STRUCTURE OF THE HEAVY METALS AND THEIR INTERMETALLIC COMPOUNDS.**
FREEMAN, A. J. KOELLING, D. D.
J. PHYS. (PARIS), COLLOQ.
33 (5-6), C3-57-C3-72, 1972.
(AD-756 021, AFOSR-TR-73-0333, AVAIL. DDC)

53296 **VARIATION OF ELECTRIC CONDUCTIVITY AND THERMAL EMF AT FUSION OF COPPER CHALCOGENIDES.**
GLAZOV, V. M.
IZV. VYSSH. UCHEB. ZAVED. TSVET. MET.
27-31, 1970.
(FOR ENGLISH TRANSLATION SEE E53297)

53297 **VARIATION OF ELECTRIC CONDUCTIVITY AND THERMAL EMF AT FUSION OF COPPER CHALCOGENIDES.**
GLAZOV, V. M.
ARMY FOREIGN SCIENCE AND TECHNOLOGY CENTER, CHARLOTTE, VIRGINIA
8PP., 1972.
(ENGLISH TRANSLATION OF IZV. VYSSH. UCHEB. ZAVED. TSVET. MET., 27-31, 1970; FOR ORIGINAL SEE E53296)
(AD-756 088, FSTC-HT-23-1273-72, N73-22694 AVAIL. DDC)

53299 **DEVICE FABRICATION AND RADIATION EFFECTS STUDIES OF VARIOUS SEMICONDUCTORS.**
KIM, T. W. GRANNEMANN, W. W.
BUREAU OF ENGINEERING, NEW MEXICO UNIV. ALBUQUERQUE
133PP., 1972.
(AD-756 249, AVAIL. DDC)

53300 **INVESTIGATION OF PHOTOELECTRIC CHARACTERISTICS OF GALLIUM ARSENIDE SOLAR CELLS OVER A WIDE RANGE OF CHANGE IN LIGHT FLUX.**
KAGAN, M. B. LYUBASHEVSKAYA, T. L.
GELIOTEKHNIKA
(2), 12-21, 1971.
(FOR ENGLISH TRANSLATION SEE E53301)

53301 **INVESTIGATION OF PHOTOELECTRIC CHARACTERISTICS OF GALLIUM ARSENIDE SOLAR CELLS OVER A WIDE RANGF OF CHANGE IN LIGHT FLUX.**
KAGAN, M. B. LYUBASHEVSKAYA, T. L.
FOREIGN SCIENCE AND TECHNOLOGY CENTER, CHARLOTTESVILLE, N. C.
12PP., 1973.
(ENGLISH TRANSLATION OF GELIOTEKHNIKA, (2), 12-21, 1971; FOR ORIGINAL SEE E53300)
(AD-756 228, FSTC-HT-23-2027-72, N73-21962)

53302 **NEW METHODS FOR GROWTH AND CHARACTERIZATION OF GALLIUM ARSENIDE AND MIXED III-V SEMICONDUCTOR CRYSTALS.**
WILCOX, W. R.
ELECTRONIC SCIENCES LAB., UNIVERSITY OF SOUTHERN CALIF., LOS ANGELES
106PP., 1972.
(AD-756 259, N73-23777, AVAIL. DDC)

53303 **THE EFFECTS OF PROTON BOMBARDMENT ON LEAD TIN TELLURIDE.**
ANDERSON, D. G.
NAVAL POSTGRADUATE SCHOOL, MONTEREY, CALIF., M. S. THESIS
85PP., 1972.
(AD-756 542, N73-22696, AVAIL. DDC)

53304 **HETEROGENEOUS SOLAR CONVERTORS BASED ON POLYCRYSTALLINE CADMIUM SULFIDE AND CADMIUM SELENIDE.**
KOMASHCHENKO, V. A. MARCHENKO, A. I.
FEDORUS, G. A.
POLUPROV. TEKH. MIKROELEKTRON.
(4), 112-21, 1971.
(FOR ENGLISH TRANSLATION SEE E53305)

53305 **HETEROGENEOUS SOLAR CONVERTORS BASED ON POLYCRYSTALLINE CADMIUM SULFIDE AND CADMIUM SELENIDE.**
KOMASHCHENKO, V. A. MARCHENKO, A. I.
FEDORUS, G. A.
FOREIGN SCIENCE AND TECHNOLOGY CENTER, CHARLOTTESVILLE, VIRGINIA
10PP., 1972.
(ENGLISH TRANSLATION OF POLUPROV. TEKH. MIKROELEKTRON., (4), 112-21, 1971; FOR ORIGINAL SEE E53304)
(AD-756 594, FSTC-HT-23-113-72, N73-21960)

53311 **COMMENTS ON DC CONDUCTIVITY IN AMORPHOUS SEMICONDUCTORS.**
POLLAK, M.
DEPT. PHYS., UNIVERSITY OF CALIFORNIA, RIVERSIDE,
10PP., 1972.
(AD-756 783, AVAIL. DDC)

EPIC Number	Bibliographic Citation

53312 **THERMOELECTRIC EFFECTS ON THE BOUNDARY OF SOLID AND LIQUID PHASES OF TERNARY SEMICONDUCTORS AND ALLOYS OF THE A-12B-IVC-V13 TYPE.**
DOVLETOV, K. ASTAKHOV, O. P. BERGER, L. I.
IZV. AKAD. NAUK TURKM. SSR, SER. FIZ. TEKH. KHIM. GEOL. NAUK
(2), 94-6, 1971.
(FOR ENGLISH TRANSLATION SEE E53313)

53313 **THERMOELECTRIC EFFECTS ON THE BOUNDARY OF SOLID AND LIQUID PHASES OF TERNARY SEMICONDUCTORS AND ALLOYS OF THE A-12B-IVC-V13 TYPE.**
DOVLETOV, K. ASTAKHOV, O. P. BERGER, L. I.
FOREIGN SCIENCE AND TECHNOLOGY CENTER, CHARLOTTESVILLE, VIRGINIA
6PP., 1973.
(ENGLISH TRANSLATION OF IZV. AKAD. NAUK TURKM. SSR, SER. FIZ. TEKH. KHIM. GEOL. NAUK, (2), 94-6, 1971; FOR ORIGINAL SEE E53312)
(AD-756 899, FSTC-HT-23-2029-72, N73-21972)

53314 **ON THE INTERPRETATION OF AC CONDUCTIVITY IN AMORPHOUS SEMICONDUCTORS.**
POLLAK, M.
DEPT. PHYS., UNIVERSITY OF CALIF., RIVERSIDE
47PP., 1973.
(AD-757 097, N73-23780, AVAIL. DDC)

53316 **EFFECTS OF NEUTRON IRRADIATION ON THE ELECTRICAL PROPERTIES OF INDIUM ARSENIDE.**
BOLTAKS, B. I. SAVIN, E. P.
RADIATS. FIZ. NEMETAL. KRIST., TR. SOVESHCH.
116-23, 1970.
(FOR ENGLISH TRANSLATION SEE E53317)

53317 **EFFECTS OF NEUTRON IRRADIATION ON THE ELECTRICAL PROPERTIES OF INDIUM ARSENIDE.**
BOLTAKS, B. I. SAVIN, E. P.
ARMY FOREIGN SCIENCE AND TECHNOLOGY CENTER, CHARLOTTESVILLE, VIRGINIA
11PP., 1973.
(ENGLISH TRANSLATION OF RADIATS. FIZ. NEMETAL. KRIST., TR. SOVESHCH., 116-23, 1970; FOR ORIGINAL SEE E53316)
(AD-757 468, FSTC-HT-23-1435-72, N73-23792)

53318 **ELECTRIC FIELD INDUCED INSTABILITY IN TRANSITION METAL COMPOUNDS.**
FREUD, P. J.
BATTELLE, COLUMBUS LABS., OHIO
31PP., 1973.
(AD-758 270, AFOSR-TR-73-0528, N73-24771, AVAIL. DDC)

53319 **MAGNETIC PROPERTIES OF AN AMORPHOUS ANTIFERROMAGNET: MANGANESE PHOSPHATE GLASS.**
FRIEBELE, E. J.
VANDERBILT UNIVERSITY, NASHVILLE, TENNESSEE, PH. D. THESIS
97PP., 1973.
(AD-758 373, AVAIL. DDC)

53320 **CONDUCTIVITY PROFILE OF CADMIUM SULFIDE AFTER SULFUR DIFFUSION.**
RIESSLER, W. A.
HARRY DIAMOND LABS., WASHINGTON, D. C.
20PP., 1973.
(AD-758 450, HDL-TM-73-1, N73-24773, AVAIL. DDC)

53321 **THIN FILM LEAD (0.9) TIN (0.1) SELENIUM PHOTOCONDUCTIVE INFRARED DETECTORS, METALLURGICAL AND ELECTRICAL MEASUREMENTS.**
MC BRIDE, W. G., JR.
NAVAL POSTGRADUATE SCHOOL, MONTEREY, CALIF., M. S. THESIS
89PP., 1972.
(AD-758 519, N73-26693, AVAIL. DDC)

53324 **THIN-FILM LEAD TIN SELENIDE PHOTOCONDUCTIVE INFRARED DETECTORS. PHOTOCONDUCTIVITY MEASUREMENTS.**
HOLMQUIST, K. E.
NAVAL POSTGRADUATE SCHOOL, MONTEREY, CALIF., M. S. THESIS
129PP., 1972.
(AD-758 685, AVAIL. DDC)

53325 **RESEARCH TO INVESTIGATE THE AGING CHARACTERISTICS OF SAMARIUM COBALT MAGNETS.**
MILDRUM, H. F.
RESEARCH INSTITUTE, UNIV. OF DAYTON, OHIO
52PP., 1973.
(AD-758 806, AFML-TR-73-46, UDRI-TR-73-11, AVAIL. DDC)

53330 **THE EFFECTS OF GAMMA RADIATION ON PHOTOCURRENT-VOLTAGE CHARACTERISTICS OF CADMIUM SULFIDE FILMS.**
KAO, K. C. SADHU, A.
RADIAT. EFF.
14, 279-80, 1972.
(AD-761 714)

53333 **ON THE CALCULATION OF THE MONOCHROMATIC ABSORPTION COEFFICIENT IN THE NARROW REGIONS OF THE OSCILLATORY-ROTATIONAL SPECTRUM OF WATER.**
IPPOLITOV, I. I. MAKUSHKIN, YU. S. ORLOV, A. A.
TRUDY MEZHVUZOVSKOGO NAUCH. SOVESHCHANIYA PO SPEKTRALNOY PROZRACHNOSTI ATMOSFERY V VIDIMOY I INFRAKRASNOY OBLASTYAKH SPEKTRA
30-46, 1968.
(FOR ENGLISH TRANSLATION SEE E53334)

53334 **ON THE CALCULATION OF THE MONOCHROMATIC ABSORPTION COEFFICIENT IN THE NARROW REGIONS OF THE OSCILLATORY-ROTATIONAL SPECTRUM OF WATER.**
IPPOLITOV, I. I. MAKUSHKIN, YU. S. ORLOV, A. A.
FOREIGN TECH. DIV., WPAFB, OHIO
15PP., 1973.
(ENGLISH TRANSLATION OF TR. MEZHVUZOVSKOGO NAUCH. SOVESHCHANIYA PO SPEKTRALNOY PROZRACHNOSTI ATMOSFERY V VIDIMOY IN INFRAKRASNOY OBLASTYAKH NPEKTRA, 30-46, 1968; FOR ORIGINAL SEE E53333)
(AD-759 238, FTD-MT-24-1605-72, N73-25743)

53335 **CADMIUM GERMANIUM ARSENIDE AND CADMIUM GERMANIUM PHOSPHIDE CHALCOPYRITE MATERIALS FOR INFRARED NONLINEAR OPTICS.**
KILDAL, H.
MICROWAVE LAB., STANFORD UNIV., STANFORD, CALIF.
184PP., 1972.
(AD-759 556, AFML-TR-72-277, AVAIL. DDC)

53338 **PHOTOCONDUCTIVITY IN HIGH PURITY, SEMICONDUCTING CADMIUM FLUORIDE.**
FELDMAN, B. J. PERSHAN, P. S.
SOLID STATE COMMUN.
11 (9), 1131-4, 1972.
(AD-760 101, AVAIL. DDC)

53344 **OPTICAL ABSORPTION INDUCED BY STRONG EXCITATION.**
LANGER, D. W. GOTO, T.
PROC. INT. CONF. PHYS. SEMICOND., 11TH
705-10, 1972.
(AD-760 261, ARL-73-0097, AVAIL. DDC)

53346 **P-TYPE CONDUCTION IN UNDOPED ZINC SELENIUM.**
YU, P. W. PARK, Y. S.
APPL. PHYS. LETT.
22 (7), 345-6, 1973.
(AD-760 663, ARL-73-0101, AVAIL. DDC)

53352 **SPUTTERED THIN FILM RESEARCH.**
SHUSKUS, A. J. QUINN, D. J. PARADIS, E. L. BERAK, J. M. REEDER, T. M.
RESEARCH LAB., UNITED AIRCRAFT CORP., EAST HARTFORD, CONN.
68PP., 1973.
(AD-760 715, UARL-M951337-6, AVAIL. DDC)

53355 **SUPERCONDUCTIVITY IN THE MAGNESIUM-CADMIUM SYSTEM: EXTRAPOLATED CRITICAL TRANSITION TEMPERATURE FOR PURE MAGNESIUM.**
MOTA, A. C. BREWSTER, P. WANG, R.
PHYS. LETT.
41 A (2), 99-101, 1972.
(AD-760 984, AFOSR-TR-73-0898, AVAIL. DDC)

53356 **BAND STRUCTURE AND DISPERSION RELATIONS IN II-VI COMPOUNDS.**
BALKANSKI, M.
UNIVERSITE DE PARIS, ECOLE NORMALE SUPERIEURE LABORATOIRE DE PHYSIQUE
9PP., 1965.
(AD-629 201, ARL-66-0036, AVAIL. DDC)

53357 **SOLID STATE RESEARCH.**
MC WHORTER, A. L.
LINCOLN LAB., MASSACHUSETTS INSTITUTE OF TECHNOLOGY
64PP., 1968.
(AD-678 534, ESD-TR-68-241, AVAIL. DDC)

53358 **SOLID STATE RESEARCH.**
MC WHORTER, A. L.
LINCOLN LAB., MASSACHUSETTS INSTITUTE OF TECHNOLOGY
64PP., 1968.
(AD-681 141, ESD-TR-68-353, AVAIL. DDC)

53359 **ELECTRO-OPTIC PROPERTIES AND MODULATOR APPLICATIONS OF CADMIUM TELLURIDE.**
NEUBERGER, M.
ELECTRONIC PROPERTIES INFORMATION CTR., HUGHES AIRCRAFT CO., CULVER CITY, CALIF.
27PP., 1972.
(AD-740 207, EPIC-IR-75-REV, N72-29742, AVAIL. DDC)

53360 **CRYSTALLINE AND AMORPHOUS SILICON-TELLURIUM ALLOYS.**
PETERSEN, K. E. ADLER, D.
MASSACHUSETTS INSTITUTE OF TECHNOLOGY, CAMBRIDGE
3-4, 1971.
(AD-740 838, N72-29760, AVAIL. DDC)

EPIC Number *Bibliographic Citation*

53361 **INFRARED ABSORPTIVITY OF ICE IH AND ITS ATMOSPHERIC EMISSION.**
CARLON, H. R.
DEPT. OF THE ARMY, EDGEWOOD ARSENAL, MD.
17PP., 1972.
(AD-743 445, AVAIL. DDC)

53368 **OPEN-TUBE ZINC DIFFUSED GALLIUM ARSENIDE (1-X) PHOSPHORUS (X) LIGHT-EMITTING DIODES.**
PANCHOLY, R. K. KUKLMANN, G. J.
GRANNEMANN, W. W.
BUREAU OF ENGINEERING RESEARCH, NEW MEXICO UNIVERSITY, ALBUQUERQUE
79-88, 1972.
(AD-752 561, N73-17791, AVAIL. DDC)

53369 **ELECTRON AND NEUTRON RADIATION EFFECTS ON ELECTRON-BEAM EVAPORATED HIGH-MOBILITY THIN FILMS OF INDIUM ANTIMONIDE.**
KIM, T. W. DEOKAR, V. D. GRANNEMANN, W. W.
BUREAU OF ENGINEERING RESEARCH, NEW MEXICO UNIVERSITY, ALBUQUERQUE
93-4, 1972.
(AD-752 561, N73-17791, AVAIL. DDC)

53370 **METAL-INSULATOR-SEMICONDUCTOR STRUCTURES CREATED BY ION IMPLANTATION.**
FITE, C. B. KOPP, R. J. GRANNEMANN, W. W.
BUREAU OF ENGINEERING RESEARCH, NEW MEXICO UNIVERSITY, ALBUQUERQUE
102-5, 1972.
(AD-752 561, N73-17791, AVAIL. DDC)

53371 **METAL-TITANIUM OXIDE-SILICON STRUCTURES.**
KOPP, R. J. GRANNEMANN, W. W.
BUREAU OF ENGINEERING RESEARCH, NEW MEXICO UNIVERSITY, ALBUQUERQUE
106-7, 1972.
(AD-752 561, N73-17791, AVAIL. DDC)

53373 **STUDIES OF TELLURIUM AND ARSENIC SELENIDE.**
POWELL, R. A. GREGORY, P. SPICER, W. E.
CENTER FOR MATERIALS RESEARCH, STANFORD UNIVERSITY, STANFORD, CALIFORNIA
11-17, 1972.
(AD-752 798, CMR-72-17, AVAIL. DDC)

53374 **STUDIES OF THE GERMANIUM TELLURIDE SYSTEM.**
FISHER, G. SPICER, W. E.
CENTER FOR MATERIALS RESEARCH, STANFORD UNIVERSITY, STANFORD, CALIFORNIA
18-20, 1972.
(AD-752 798, CMR-72-17, AVAIL. DDC)

53375 **THE STRUCTURE OF CHALCOGENIDE GLASSES.**
BIENENSTOCK, A.
CENTER FOR MATERIALS RESEARCH, STANFORD UNIVERSITY, STANFORD, CALIFORNIA
55-67, 1972.
(AD-752 798, CMR-72-17, AVAIL. DDC)

53376 **PHOTOCONDUCTIVITY IN AMORPHOUS CHALCOGENIDES.**
ARNOLDUSSEN, T. C. BUBE, R. H.
CENTER FOR MATERIALS RESEARCH, STANFORD UNIVERSITY, STANFORD, CALIF.
72-87, 1972.
(AD-752 798, CMR-72-17, AVAIL. DDC)

53377 **ELECTRICAL BREAKDOWN OF LIQUID DIELECTRICS (A REVIEW).**
BALYGIN, I. E.
ELEKTRICHESTVO, USSR
(1), 89-92, 1954.
(FOR ENGLISH TRANSLATION SEE E53378)

53378 **ELECTRICAL BREAKDOWN OF LIQUID DIELECTRICS (A REVIEW).**
BALYGIN, I. E.
FOREIGN TECHNOLOGY DIVISION, WRIGHT-PATTERSON AIR FORCE BASE, OHIO
13PP., 1972.
(ENGLISH TRANSLATION OF ELEKTRICHESTVO, USSR, (1), 89-92, 1954; FOR ORIGINAL SEE E53377)
(AD-752 819, FTD-HT-23-772-72, AVAIL. DDC)

53379 **INVESTIGATION OF INTRINSIC DEFECTS IN ZINC SELENIDE SINGLE CRYSTALS THROUGH HIGH-TEMPERATURE EQUILIBRIUM CONDUCTIVITY MEASUREMENTS.**
JAHN, J-U.
INTERN. WISS. KOLLOQUIM, TECH. HOCHSHULE ILMENAU, 15TH
211-8, 1970.
(FOR ENGLISH TRANSLATION SEE E53380)

53380 **INVESTIGATION OF INTRINSIC DEFECTS IN ZINC SELENIDE SINGLE CRYSTALS THROUGH HIGH-TEMPERATURE EQUILIBRIUM CONDUCTIVITY MEASUREMENTS.**
JAHN, J-U.
FOREIGN TECHNOLOGY DIV., WRIGHT-PATTERSON AIR FORCE BASE, OHIO
14PP., 1972.
(ENGLISH TRANSLATION OF INTERN. WISS. KOLLOQUIM, TECH. HOCHSHULE ILMENAU, 15TH, 211-8, 1970; FOR ORIGINAL SEE E53379)
(AD-753 043, FTD-HT-23-1583-72, N73-18764)

53386 **ELECTRICAL AND OPTICAL PROPERTIES OF AMORPHOUS MATERIALS.**
WOOD, C.
NORTHERN ILLINOIS UNIVERSITY, DEKALB, ILLINOIS
72PP., 1972.
(AD-753 903, AVAIL. DDC)

53388 **RADIATION EFFECTS IN SEMICONDUCTING LASER MATERIALS.**
ARORA, B. M.
COORDINATED SCIENCE LAB., ILLINOIS UNIV., URBANA
135PP., 1972.
(AD-754 217, ARL-72-0087, N73-19516, AVAIL. DDC)

53389 **SOLID SOLUTION STRENGTHENING AND FUNDAMENTAL DESIGN OF TITANIUM ALLOYS.**
COLLINGS, E. W. GEGEL, H. L. HO, J. C.
AIR FORCE MATERIALS LAB., WRIGHT-PATTERSON AIR FORCE BASE, OHIO
54PP., 1972.
(AD-754 240, AFML-TR-72-171, N73-19551, AVAIL. DDC)

53390 **MECHANICAL BEHAVIOR OF III-V AND II-VI COMPOUNDS.**
COPLEY, S. M.
ELECTRONIC SCIENCES LAB., UNIVERSITY OF SOUTHERN CALIF., LOS ANGELES
19PP., 1972.
(AD-754 280, USCEE-431, AVAIL. DDC)

53391 **STUDY OF DEFECTS IN II-VI COMPOUNDS.**
KROGER, F. A. GERSHENZON, M.
CHERN, S. S. VYDYANATH, H. R.
ELECTRONIC SCIENCES LAB., UNIVERSITY OF SOUTHERN CALIFORNIA, LOS ANGELES
23-6PP., 1972.
(AD-754 280, USCEE-431, AVAIL. DDC)

53392 **TECHNIQUES FOR INDIRECT MEASUREMENTS OF SMALL ABSORPTIVE LOSSES.**
STEIER, W. H.
ELECTRONIC SCIENCES LAB., UNIVERSITY OF SOUTHERN CALIFORNIA, LOS ANGELES
30-1, 1972.
(AD-754 280, USCEE-431, AVAIL. DDC)

53394 **LOW TEMPERATURE GROWTH OF CUBIC GALLIUM NITRIDE.**
LITTLEJOHN, M. A. HAUSER, J. R.
ANDREWS, J. E.
DEPT. OF ELECTRICAL ENGINEERING, NORTH CAROLINA STATE UNIV., RALEIGH
9PP., 1973.
(AD-755 237, N73-22704, AVAIL. DDC)

53395 **ELECTRIC STRENGTH OF LIQUID DIELECTRICS.**
BALYGIN, I.
ELEKTRICHESKAYA PROCHNOST ZHIDKIKH DIELEKTRIKOV
1-227, 1964.
(FOR ENGLISH TRANSLATION SEE E53396)

53396 **ELECTRIC STRENGTH OF LIQUID DIELECTRICS.**
BAYLGIN, I.
FOREIGN TECHNOLOGY DIV., WRIGHT-PATTERSON AIR FORCE BASE, OHIO
321PP., 1972.
(ENGLISH TRANSLATION OF ELEKTRICHESKAYA PROCHNOST ZHIDKIKH DIELEKTRIKOV, 1-227, 1964; FOR ORIGINAL SEE E53395)
(AD-755 756, FTD-HC-23-732-72, N73-22546)

53400 **THE ELECTRICAL CONDUCTIVITY BEHAVIOR OF A MIXED VALENCE PLATINUM COMPLEX AT HIGH PRESSURES.**
INTERRANTE, L. V. BUNDY, F. P.
SOLID STATE COMMUN.
11 (12), 1641-5, 1972.
(AD-761 263, AFOSR-TR-73-0923, AVAIL. DDC)

53401 **STUDY OF THE EFFECTS OF RADIATION ON THE ELECTRICAL AND OPTICAL PROPERTIES OF MERCURY CADMIUM TELLURIUM.**
COLWELL, J. F. LEADON, R. E.
MALLON, C. E. NABER, J. E.
GULF RADIATION TECHNOLOGY, SAN DIEGO, CALIF.
64PP., 1972.
(AD-761 488, AFCRL-TR-73-0170, GULF-RT-A12410 AVAIL. DDC)

53402 **EXCITON SCREENING IN AMORPHOUS MAGNESIUM-BISMUTH AND MAGNESIUM-ANTIMONY ALLOYS.**
SLOWIK, J. H. BROWN, F. C.
PHYS. REV. LETT.
29 (14), 934-7, 1972.
(AD-761 841, AROD-4928:30P, AVAIL. DDC)

53403 **EFFECT OF OXIDE DEFECT STRUCTURE ON THE ELECTRICAL PROPERTIES OF ZIRCONIUM OXIDE.**
KUMAR, A. RAJDEV, D. DOUGLASS, D. L.
J. AMER. CERAM. SOC.
55 (9), 439-45, 1972.
(AD-761 875, AROD-8268:2MC, AVAIL. DDC)

EPIC Number	Bibliographic Citation

53404 **HEAT CAPACITY AND ELECTRICAL RESISTIVITY OF SOME LANTHANIDE-NICKEL COMPOUNDS BETWEEN 5 AND 300 K.**
MARZOUK, N. CRAIG, R. S. WALLACE, W. E.
J. PHYS. CHEM. SOLIDS
34, 15-21, 1973.
(AD-761 932, AROD-5375:13MC, AVAIL. DDC)

53405 **FREE-CARRIER OPTICAL EFFECTS IN GALLIUM ARSENIDE.**
KAHAN, A.
AIR FORCE CAMBRIDGE RESEARCH LABS., L. G. HANSCOM FIELD, MASS.
41PP., 1973.
(AD-762 273, AFCRL-TR-73-0122, N73-29791, AVAIL. DDC)

53406 **DEVELOPMENT OF MERCURY, CADMIUM TELLURIUM ELEVATED TEMPERATURE PHOTOVOLTAIC DETECTORS.**
MC NALLY, P. J.
HONEYWELL RADIATION CENTER, LEXINGTON, MASS.
42PP., 1973.
(AD-762 352, AVAIL. DDC)

53408 **PHOTOELECTRON AND OPTICAL SPECTRA OF TITANIUM CHLORIDE AND VANADIUM CHLORIDE.**
PARAMESWARAN, T. ELLIS, D. E.
J. CHEM. PHYS.
58 (5), 2088-95, 1973.
(AD-762 675, AFOSR-TR-73-1096, AVAIL. DDC)

53409 **OPTICAL AND MAGNETOOPTICAL ABSORPTION IN PURE MERCURY TELLURIUM.**
SALEH, A. S. FAN, H. Y.
PHYS. STATUS SOLIDI
53 B 163-8, 1972.
(AD-762 705, AROD-10090:4-P, AVAIL. DDC)

53413 **PRESSURE DEPEDNDENCE OF MAGNESIUM TIN ELECTRICAL RESISTANCE.**
THRASHER, P. H. KEARNEY, R. J.
PHYS. STATUS SOLIDI
B, 53, 623-33, 1972.
(AD-762 873, AROD-7985:11-P, AVAIL. DDC)

53414 **CONDUCTION MECHANISMS FOR ELECTRONIC DEVICES.**
REDFIELD, D.
RADIO CORP. OF AMERICA, PRINCETON, N. J.
32PP., 1973.
(AD-763 426, N73-30729, PRRL-73-CR-35, AVAIL. DDC)

53415 **RESEARCH ON TERNARY COMPOUND SEMICONDUCTORS FOR LONG-WAVELENGTH INFRARED DETECTION.**
SCOTT, M. W.
CORPORATE RESEARCH CENTER, HONEYWELL INC. BLOOMINGTON, MINN.
49PP., 1973.
(AD-763 466, AVAIL. DDC)

53416 **EPITAXIC SUBLIMATION METHODS FOR THE STUDY OF PSEUDO-BINARY SEMICONDUCTOR ALLOYS.**
ZEMEL, J. N.
LAB. FOR RESEARCH ON THE STRUCTURE OF MATTER, UNIV. PENNSYLVANIA, PHILADELPHIA
45PP., 1972.
(AD-763 488, AVAIL. DDC)

53420 **INTERPRETATION OF THE TRANSPORT PROPERTIES OF RARE EARTH-NICKEL OXIDES AND COPPER OXIDES COMPOUNDS.**
GOODENOUGH, J. B.
MATER. RES. BULL.
8 (4), 423-32, 1973.
(AD-763 576, ESD-TR-73-97, AVAIL. DDC)

53423 **IRRADIATION EFFECTS IN LEAD TIN TELLURIUM.**
COLWELL, J. F. GREEN, B. A. HARPER, H. W.
LEADON, R. E. NABER, J. A.
INTELCOM RAD TECH., SAN DIEGO, CALIF.
74PP., 1973.
(AD-768 073, AVAIL. DDC)

53426 **RESEARCH ON AMORPHOUS MATERIALS.**
SPICER, W. E. BIENENSTOCK, A. BUBE, R. H.
CENTER FOR MATERIALS REAEARCH, STANFORD UNIV., CALIF.
9PP., 1973.
(AD-768 805, CMR-73-10, AVAIL. DDC)

53427 **RESEARCH ON THE PREPARATION AND PROPERTIES OF SEMICONDUCTOR COMPOUNDS AS ALUMINUM ANTIMONIDE.**
MIDDLETON, A. E. COLLIS, W. J.
HARPSTER, J. W. DAVE, H. K.
ELECTRONIC MATERIALS AND DEVICES LAB., OHIO STATE UNIV. RESEARCH FOUNDATION, COLUMBUS
98PP., 1973.
(AD-769 242, OSURF-3411-2, AVAIL. DDC)

53429 **INTERPRETATION OF AC CONDUCTIVITY IN AMORPHOUS SEMICONDUCTORS.**
POLLAK, M.
DEPT. OF PHYSICS, CALIFORNIA UNIV., RIVERSIDE
56PP., 1973.
(AD-769 550, AVAIL. DDC)

53430 **LASER RELATED STUDY OF TIPLY IONIZED PROMETHIUM IN LITHIUM YTTRIUM TETRAFLUORIDE.**
WORTMAN, D. E. MORRISON, C. A.
HARRY DIAMOND LABS., WASHINGTON, D. C.
27PP., 1973.
(AD-769 589, HDL-TR-1641, N74-16197, AVAIL. DDC)

53431 **REVIEW OF SILICON NITRIDE.**
CROFT, W. J. CUTLER, I. B.
EUROPEAN RESEARCH OFFICE, LONDON, ENGLAND
44PP., 1973.
(AD-769 680, ONRL-R-16-73, AVAIL. DDC)

53432 **THE RELATIONSHIP BETWEEN THERMAL AND ELECTRICAL PROPERTIES OF ICE.**
KORENNOV, B. I. CHEREPANOV, V. G.
EKSP. ISSLED. PROTSESSOV TEPLOOBMENA MERZLYKH GORNYKH PORODAKH
65-8, 1972.
(FOR ENGLISH TRANSLATION SEE E53433)

53433 **THE RELATIONSHIP BETWEEN THERMAL AND ELECTRICAL PROPERTIES OF ICE.**
KORENNOV, B. I. CHEREPANOV, V. G.
U. S. ARMY COLD REGIONS RESEACH AND ENGR. LAB., HANOVER, NEW HAMPSHIRE
17PP., 1973.
(ENGLISH TRANSLATION OF EKSP. ISSLED. PROTSSOV TEPLOOBMENA MERZLYKH GORNYKH PORODAKH, 65-8, 1972; FOR ORIGINAL SEE E53432)
(AD-769 725, CRREL-TL-402, AVAIL. DDC)

53434 **STUDY OF LEAD TIN TELLURIDE AND LEAD TIN SELENIDE.**
ROMSOS, A. E.
NAVAL POSTGRADUATE SCHOOL, MONTEREY, CALIF., M. S. THESIS
69PP., 1973.
(AD-769 756, N74-15931, AVAIL. DDC)

53435 **ON THE PRESSURE DEPENDENCE OF THE ELECTRICAL CONDUCTIVITY OF NICKEL OXIDE AT HIGH TEMPERATURES.**
STROUD, J. E. BRANSKY, I. TALLAN, N. M.
J. CHEM. PHYS.
58 (3), 1263-4, 1973.
(AD-769 782, ARL-73-0199, AVAIL. DDC)

53439 **MAGNETIC AND OPTICAL PROPERTIES OF TRANSITION METAL IONS IN SINGLE CRYSTALS.**
DORAIN, P. B.
DEPT. OF CHEMISTRY, BRANDEIS UNIV., WALTHAM, MASS
55PP., 1973.
(AD-769 870, ARL-73-0139, AVAIL. DDC)

53440 **RADIATIVE RECOMBINATION IN OXIDE-DOPED N-TYPE GALLIUM ARSENIDE AT LOW TEMPERATURES.**
LI, S. S. HUANG, C. I.
DEPT. OF ELECTRICAL ENGRS., FLORIDA UNIV. GAINESVILLE
7-15, 1973.
(AD-769 962, AFCRL-TR-73-0529, AVAIL. DDC)

53441 **INJECTION DEPENDENCE OF THE EXCESS CARRIER LIFETIMES IN CHROMIUM-DOPED N-TYPE GALLIUM ARSENIDE.**
HUANG, C. I. LI, S. S.
DEPT. OF ELECTRICAL ENGRS., FLORIDA UNIV., GAINESVILLE
16-20, 1973.
(AD-769 962, AFCRL-TR-73-0529, AVAIL. DDC)

53442 **MECHANICAL BEHAVIOR OF III-V AND II-VI COMPOUNDS.**
COPLEY, S. M. SWAMINATHAN, V.
ELECTRONIC SCIENCES LAB., UNIV. OF SOUTHERN CALIF., LOS ANGELES
15-24, 1973.
(AD-770 009, AFCRL-TR-73-0414, AVAIL. DDC)

53443 **DIELECTRIC CONSTANT MEASUREMENT.**
CROWELL, C. R. JOSHI, S.
ELECTRONIC SCIENCES LAB., UNIV. OF SOUTHERN CALIF., LOS ANGELES
26-9, 1973.
(AD-770 009, AFCRL-TR-0414, AVAIL. DDC)

53446 **WAVELENGTH DEPENDENT CALORIMETRY.**
STEIER, W. H. NIEH, S. T. K. JOINER, R.
ELECTRONIC SCIENCES LAB., UNIV. OF SOUTHERN CALIF., LOS ANGELES
35-7, 1973.
(AD-770 009, AFCRL-TR-0414, AVAIL. DDC)

53448 **COMMENTS ON DC CONDUCTIVITY IN AMORPHOUS SEMICONDUCTORS.**
POLLAK, M. HALPERIN, B. I.
DEPT. OF PHYSICS, CALIFORNIA UNIV., RIVERSIDE
11PP., 1973.
(AD-770 054, AVAIL. DDC)

53451 **SOVIET RESEARCH ON SEMICONDUCTOR THIN FILMS: A SURVEY.**
RUDINS, G.
RAND CORP., SANTA MONICA, CALIF.
129PP., 1973.
(AD-770 606, R-1181-ARPA, AVAIL. DDC)

EPIC Number	Bibliographic Citation
53452	**RADIATION EFFECTS IN FIBER OPTIC WAVEGUIDES.** SIGEL, G. H., JR. NAVAL RESEARCH LAB., WASHINGTON, D. C. 42PP., 1973. (AD-770 850, NRL-MR-2704, AVAIL. DDC)
53457	**PROTON-CONDUCTING GLASSES.** ANGELL, C. A. SCHOOL OF ELECTRICAL ENGR., PURDUE UNIV., LAFAYETTE, IND. 19-32, 1973. (AD-771 336, AVAIL. DDC)
53458	**SCANNING ELLIPSOMETRIC SPECTROSCOPY: STUDY OF THE FORMATION OF THE ANODIC OXIDE FILM ON NOBLE METALS.** HORKANS, J. CAHAN, B. D. YEAGER, E. CASE WESTERN RESERVE UNIV., CLEVELAND, OHIO 42PP., 1973. (AD-771 466, AVAIL. DDC)
53461	**LOW-FREQUENCY IMPURITY HOPPING HALL CONDUCTIVITY.** LYO, S. K. J. PHYS., SOLID STATE PHYS. 6 C 2158-68, 1973. (AD-771 553, AVAIL. DDC)
53462	**ELECTROLUMINESCENCE IN II-VI COMPOUNDS.** YEE, S. MC CARTHY, S. MACOMBER, G. WEI, C. H. DEPT. OF ELECTRICAL ENGINEERING, WASHINGTON UNIV., SEATTLE 66PP., 1973. (AD-771 583, ARL-73-0130, AVAIL. DDC)
53463	**INDIUM PHOSPHIDE STUDY.** PAXMAN, D. H. MULLARD RESEARCH LABORATORIES 46PP., 1972. (AD-901 976, AVAIL. DDC)
53465	**HIGH RESOLUTION PHOTOLUMINESCENCE SPECTROSCOPY IN III-V MATERIALS.** WHITE, A. M. DEAN, P. J. PROCUREMENT EXECUTIVE, ROYAL RADAR ESTABLISHMENT, MALVERN, WORCS. 5.1-5.3, 1972. (AD-903 520, AVAIL. DDC)
53466	**THE ELECTRONIC BAND STRUCTURE OF THE WIDE BAND GAP SEMICONDUCTORS GA N AND AL N.** JONES, D. LETTINGTON, A. H. PROCUREMENT EXECUTIVE, ROYAL RADAR ESTABLISHMENT, MALVERN, WORCS. 7.1-7.5, 1972. (AD-903 520, AVAIL. DDC)
53467	**TWO-PHOTON PHOSPHOR INDIUM PHOSPHIDE LIGHT EMITTING DIODES.** PORTEOUS, P. WEBB, M. WILLIAMS, E. W. PROCUREMENT EXECUTIVE, ROYAL RADAR ESTABLISHMENT, MALVERN, WORCS. 9.1-9.3, 1972. (AD-903 520, AVAIL. DDC)
53470	**AN IMPROVED GALLIUM ARSENIDE TRANSMISSION PHOTOCATHODE.** ALLENSON, M. B. KING, P. G. R. ROWLAND, M. C. STEWARD, G. J. SYMS, C. H. A. SERL TECH. J. 22 (3), 11.1-11.5, 1972. (AD-904 893)
53471	**LUMINESCENCE DUE TO DIFFUSED COPPER IN GALLIUM PHOSPHIDE.** WIGHT, D. R. TRUSSLER, J. W. A. HARDING, W. SERL TECH. J. 22 (3), 12.1-12.6, 1972. (AD-904 893)
53473	**PYROLYTIC BORON NITRIDE.** AIREY, A. C. SWINDELLS, R. BRITISH CERAMIC RESEARCH ASSOCIATION 5PP., 1972. (AD-906 521, AVAIL. DDC)
53475	**LOW WORK FUNCTION DISPENSER CATHODES.** CAMP, G. H. TUCK, R. A. EMI-VARIAN LIMITED, HAYES, MIDDLESEX, ENGLAND 36PP., 1972. (AD-906 892, AVAIL. DDC)
53476	**EVALUATION OF BERYLLIA CERAMICS FOR ELECTRONIC APPLICATIONS.** GEORGE, W. BRITISH CERAMIC RESEARCH ASSOCIATION 5PP., 1972. (AD-906 941)
53477	**PHOTOEMISSION FROM GALLIUM ARSENIDE.** ALLEN, G. A. MULLARD RESEARCH LABORATORIES 30PP., 1972. (AD-906 957, AVAIL. DDC)
53478	**RESEARCH ON GALLIUM NITRIDE ELECTROLUMINESCENT LIGHT SOURCES.** WICKENDEN, D. K. HIRST RESEARCH CENTRE, WEMBLEY 18PP., 1972. (AD-907 762, AVAIL. DDC)
53481	**THE MEASUREMENT OF ELECTRON DIFFUSION LENGTH IN IPITAXIAL GALLIUM ARSENIDE USING THE PHOTOVOLTAIC EFFECT.** ALLENSON, M. B. SERVICES ELECTRONICS RESEARCH LAB., BALDOCK, ENGLAND 11.1-11.9, 1973. (AD-915 992, AVAIL. DDC)
53484	**THE ELECTRICAL PROPERTIES OF 60 KE V ZINC IONS IMPLANTED INTO SEMI-INSULATING GALLIUM ARSENIDE.** LITTLEJOHN, M. A. ANIKARA, R. SOLID STATE DEVICE LAB., NORTH CAROLINA STATE UNIV., RALEIGH 66PP., 1972. (NASA-CR-112199, N73-10716, SDL-15, AVAIL. NASA)
53487	**PHOTOEMF IN CADMIUM SULFIDE.** BOER, K. W. DEPT. OF PHYSICS, DELAWARE UNIV., NEWARK 55PP., 1971. (N73-13730, NASA-CR-129675, AVAIL. NASA)
53488	**REFLECTANCE OF AQUEOUS SOLUTIONS.** QUERRY, M. R. OPTICAL PHYSICS LAB., MISSOURI UNIV., KANSAS CITY 176PP., 1972. (NASA-CR-130136, N73-15700, AVAIL. NASA)
53498	**OPTICAL ABSORPTION IN FUSED SILICA AT ELEVATED TEMPERATURES DURING 1.5-ME V ELECTRON IRRADIATION.** SMITH, A. B. LEWIS RESEARCH CENTER, CLEVELAND, OHIO 36PP., 1972. (NASA-TN-D-6840, N72-26551, AVAIL. NASA)
53500	**THERMOELECTRIC MATERIALS EVALUATION PROGRAM.** HAMPLE, E. F., JR. ELECTRICAL PRODUCTS GROUP, MINNESOTA MINING AND AND MFG. CO., ST. PAUL 81PP., 1972. (N73-26585, MMM-2473-342, AVAIL. NASA)
53501	**STUDY OF CONVERSIONS IN THE PLATINUM-IRON SYSTEM.** KUSSMAN, A. VON RITTBERG, G. Z. METALLK. 41, 470-7, 1950. (FOR ENGLISH TRANSLATION SEE E53502)
53502	**STUDY OF CONVERSIONS IN THE PLATINUM-IRON SYSTEM.** KUSSMAN, A. VON RITTBERG, G. TECHTRAN CORP., GLEN BURNIE, MD. 21PP., 1972. (ENGLISH TRANSLATION OF Z. METALLK., 41, 470-7, 1950; FOR ORIGINAL SEE E53501) (NASA-TT-F-14320, N72-27576, AVAIL. NASA)
53503	**PROPERTIES OF SELECTED SUPERCONDUCTIVE MATERIALS.** ROBERTS, B. W. SUPERCONDUCTIVE MATERIALS DATA CENTER, GENERAL ELECTRIC CO., SCHENECTADY, N. Y. 100PP., 1972. (NBS-TN-724, NBS-TN-482, N72-27790, AVAIL. NASA)
53506	**ELECTRICAL SCREENING PROCEDURE FOR SOLID IONIC CONDUCTORS.** KAUTZ, H. E. SINGER, J. FIELDER, W. L. FORDYCE, J. S. LEWIS RESEARCH CENTER, CLEVELAND, OHIO 11PP., 1973. (NASA-TN-D-7146, N73-18758, AVAIL. NASA)
53512	**HANDBOOK OF THE OPTICAL, THERMAL AND MECHANICAL PROPERTIES OF SIX POLYCRYSTALLINE DIELECTRIC MATERIALS.** DEWITT, D. P. THERMOPHYSICAL PROPERTIES RES. CTR., PURDUE UNIV. 247PP., 1972. (N72-33713, NASA-CR-114500, TPRC-19, AVAIL. NASA)
53513	**RESEARCH ON THE PROPERTIES OF AMORPHOUS SEMICONDUCTORS AT HIGH TEMPERATURES.** DE NEUFVILLE, J. P. ENERGY CONVERSION DEVICES, INC., TROY, MICH. 109PP., 1971. (AD-742 833, N72-31758, ECD-516-3, ARPA-1570, AVAIL. NASA)

EPIC Number	Bibliographic Citation
53515	**INVESTIGATION OF THE RECOMBINATION AND TRAPPING PROCESSES OF PHOTO-INJECTED CARRIERS IN SEMI-INSULATING CHROMIUM-DOPED GALLIUM ARSENIDE USING PME AND PC METHODS.** LI, S. S. HUNAG, C. I. DEPT. OF ELECTRICAL ENGINEERING, FLORIDA UNIV., GAINESVILLE, FLORIDA 9-24, 1971. (AD-743 834, N72-32724, AFCRL-72-0075 AVAIL. NASA)
53516	**LOW TEMPERATURE PHOTOMAGNETOELECTRIC AND PHOTOCONDUCTIVE EFFECTS IN N-TYPE INDIUM ARSENIDE.** LI, S. S. HUANG, C. I. DEPT. OF ELECTRICAL ENGINEERING, FLORIDA UNIV., GAINESVILLE, FLORIDA 25-34PP., 1971. (AD-743 834, N72-32724, AFCRL-72-0075, AVAIL. NASA)
53519	**DEVELOPMENT OF GALLIUM ARSENIDE INFRARED WINDOW MATERIAL.** THOMPSON, A. G. BELL AND HOWELL CO., PASSADENA, CALIF. 64PP., 1972. (N73-11473, AD-746 500, ARPA-306, AVAIL. NASA)
53520	**OPTICAL AND MAGNETIC PROPERTIES OF SOME TRANSITION METAL IONS IN LITHIUM PHOSPHATE GLASS.** BERRETZ, M. HOLT, S. L. DEPT. OF PHYSICS AND ASTRONOMY, WYOMING UNIV., LARAMIE 8-23, 1972. (AD-746 516, N73-11777, AVAIL. NASA)
53529	**EVALUATION OF GALLIUM NITRIDE FOR ACTIVE MICROWAVE DEVICES.** GERSHENZON, M. WING, H. S. ELECTRONIC SCIENCES LAB., UNIV. OF SOUTHERN CALIF., LOS ANGELES 11PP., 1973. (AD-763 413, N73-30726, AVAIL. NASA)
53532	**SPACE ELECTRIC POWER R AND D PROGRAM.** LOS ALAMOS SCIENTIFIC LABORATORY LOS ALAMOS SCIENTIFIC LAB., N. MEX. 28PP., 1972. (N73-24092, LA-5113, AVAIL. NASA)
53535	**STUDY OF THE DEFECT STRUCTURE OF NONSTOICHIOMETRIC CERIUM DIOXIDE.** BLUMENTHAL, R. N. MARQUETTE UNIV., MILWAUKEE, WIS., COLLEGE OF ENGINEERING 34PP., 1972. (N73-19759, COO-1441-19, AVAIL. NASA)
53540	**RADIATION DETECTION IN THE FAR INFRARED USING QUANTUM PHOTOCONDUCTORS.** VOBIAN, J. FERNMELDETECHNISCHES ZENTRALAMT, DARMSTADT, WEST GERMANY 146PP., 1971. (N73-11144, FTZ-A-14-TBR-4, AVAIL. NASA)
53541	**STUDY OF THE INFLUENCE OF HYDROSTATIC PRESSURE ON THE HIGH TEMPERATURE ELECTRICAL CONDUCTIVITY OF CRYSTALS OF LITHIUM FLUORIDE AND FLUORIDES OF ALKALINE EARTH METALS.** LALLEMAND, M. FACULTE DES SCIENCES, UNIVERSITY OF PARIS, FRANCE, PH. D. THESIS 123PP., 1972. (N73-10719, AVAIL. NASA)
53542	**PHOTOCONDUCTIVE AND PHOTOVOLTAIC EFFECTS IN THE INDIRECT GAP REGION OF GALLIUM SULFIDE.** GRANDOLFO, M. MARIUTTI, G. ISTITUTO SUPERIORE DI SANITA, ROME, ITALY 19PP., 1971. (N72-31737, ISS-71/33, AVAIL. NASA)
53543	**ABSORPTION OF BARIUM SODIUM NIOBIUM OXIDE CRYSTALS IN THE EXCITED STATE.** TIMOSHENKOV, V. A. ZH. PRIKL. SPEKTROSK. 18 (4), 739-40, 1973. (FOR ENGLISH TRANSLATION SEE E53544)
53544	**ABSORPTION OF BARIUM SODIUM NIOBIUM OXIDE CRYSTALS IN THE EXCITED STATE.** TIMOSHENKOV, V. A. LOCKHEED MISSILES AND SPACE CO., PALO ALTO, CALIF. 2PP., 1973. (ENGLISH TRANSLATION OF ZH. PRIKL. SPEKTROSK., 18 (4), 739-40, 1973; FOR ORIGINAL SEE E53543) (N73-30714, AVAIL. NASA)
53547	**SELENIDES.** OBOLONCHIK, V. A. SELENIDY 117-31 AND 273-80, 1972. (FOR ENGLISH TRANSLATION SEE E53548)
53548	**SELENIDES.** OBOLONCHIK, V. A. JOINT PUBLICATIONS RES. SERVICE, ARLINGTON, VA. 20PP., 1973. (ENGLISH TRANSLATION OF SELENIDY, 117-31 AND 273-80, 1972; FOR ORIGINAL SEE E53547) (N73-19752, JPRS-58293, AVAIL. NASA)
53558	**HIGH-RESOLUTION X-RAY PHOTOEMISSION FROM SODIUM METAL AND ITS HYDROXIDE.** CITRIN, P. H. PHYS. REV. 8 B (12), 5545-56, 1973.
53560	**ATOMIC PSEUDOPOTENTIALS AND THE IONICITY PARAMETER OF PHILLIPS AND VAN VECHTEN.** CHADI, D. J. COHEN, M. L. GROBMAN, W. D. PHYS. REV. 8 B (12), 5587-91, 1973.
53561	**ANALYSIS OF HIGH-FIELD HALL-COEFFICIENT BEHAVIOR IN UNIAXIALLY STRESSED P-GALLIUM ANTIMONIDE.** METZLER, R. A. BECKER, W. M. PHYS. REV. 8 B (12), 5604-12, 1973.
53562	**COHERENT-POTENTIAL APPROXIMATION IN A TWO-BAND MODEL: ELECTRONIC AND TRANSPORT PROPERTIES OF SEMICONDUCTING BINARY ALLOYS.** SEN, P. N. PHYS. REV. 8 B (12), 5613-23, 1973. (AD 779 103)
53564	**TWO-PHONON DEFORMATION POTENTIAL COUPLING: FREE CARRIER ABSORPTION IN INDIUM ANTIMONIDE.** GANGULY, A. K. NAGAI, K. L. PHYS. REV. 8 B (12), 5654-63, 1973.
53565	**PHOTOIONIZATION CROSS SECTION FOR MANGANESE ACCEPTORS IN GALLIUM ARSENIDE.** BROWN, W. J., JR. WOODBURY, D. A. BLAKEMORE, J. S. PHYS. REV. 8 B (12), 5664-70, 1973.
53568	**PHOTOLUMINESCENCE EXCITATION SPECTRA IN CHALCOGENIDE GLASSES.** BISHOP, S. G. MITCHELL, D. L. PHYS. REV. 8 B (12), 5696-5703, 1973.
53569	**FUNDAMENTAL ENERGY GAPS OF ALUMINUM ARSENIC AND ALUMINUM PHOSPHIDE FROM PHOTOLUMINESCENCE EXCITATION SPECTRA.** MONEMAR, B. PHYS. REV. 8 B (12), 5711-8, 1973.
53570	**ENERGY RELAXATION OF PHOTOEXCITED HOT ELECTRONS IN GALLIUM ARSENIDE.** ULBRICH, R. PHYS. REV. 8 B (1.), 5719-27, 1973.
53572	**THERMOREFLECTANCE AT THE FUNDAMENTAL GAP OF HEAVILY DOPED N-TYPE INDIUM ARSENIDE.** SENECHAL, R. R. WOOLEY, J. C. PHYS. REV. 8 B (12), 5738-46, 1973. (ERRATUM: TITLE IBID, AUTHOR IBID, J. IBID, 10 (4), 1768, 1974.)
53573	**PHONON-CORRELATION EFFECTS IN THE OPTICAL-ABSORPTION SPECTRA OF FREE POLARONS.** HUYBRECHTS, W. DEVREESE, J. PHYS. REV. 8 B (12), 5754-8, 1973.
53574	**ELECTRONIC BAND STRUCTURES OF ANTIMONY SILICON IN THE PARA- AND FERROELECTRIC PHASES.** NAKO, K. BALKANSKI, M. PHYS. REV. 8 B (12), 5759-80, 1973.
53578	**ENERGY LEVELS OF IRON AND ALUMINUM IN STRONTIUM TITANIUM OXIDE.** MORIN, F. J. OLIVER, J. R. PHYS. REV. 8 B (12), 5847-54, 1973.
53579	**POSITION OF A D-LIKE STATE OF THE F CENTER IN POTASSIUM CHLORIDE.** BONCIANI, M. GRASSANO, U. M. ROSEI, R. PHYS. REV. 8 B (12), 5855-9, 1973.
53580	**INFRARED ABSORPTION OF PAIRS OF COUPLED LOCAL-MODE OSCILLATORS IN POTASSIUM CHLORIDE.** DE SOUZA, M. LUTY, F. PHYS. REV. 8 B (12), 5866-74, 1973.

EPIC Number	Bibliographic Citation

53581 KINETICS OF SELF-TRAPPED HOLES IN ALKALI-HALIDE CRYSTALS: EXPERIMENTS IN THALLIUM DOPED SODIUM IODIDE AND POTASSIUM IODIDE.
DIETRICH, H. B. PURDY, A. E. MURRAY, R. B.
WILLIAMS, R. T.
PHYS. REV.
8 B (12), 5894-901, 1973.

53582 THEORY OF SELF-TRAPPED EXCITON LUMINESCENCE IN HALIDE CRYSTALS.
FOWLER, W. B. MARRONE, M. J. KABLER, M. N.
PHYS. REV.
8 B (12), 5909-19, 1973.

53583 ONE-ELECTRON INTERPRETATION OF OPTICAL ABSORPTION AND SOFT-X-RAY DATA IN MAGNESIUM OXIDE.
WALCH, P. F. ELLIS, D. E.
PHYS. REV.
8 B (12), 5920-33, 1973.

53584 OPTICAL-ABSORPTION EDGE AND RAMAN SCATTERING IN GERMANIUM SELENIUM GLASSES.
TRONC, P. BENSOUSSAN, M. BRENAC, A.
SEBENNE, C.
PHYS. REV.
8 B (12), 5947-56, 1973.

53585 CHEMICAL BONDING EFFECTS IN THE OXYGEN K-ALPHA X-RAY EMISSION BANDS OF SILICA.
GILBERT, T. L. STEVENS, W. J. SCHRENK, H.
YOSHIMINE, M. BAGUS, P. S.
PHYS. REV.
8 B (12), 5977-98, 1973.

53586 DYNAMIC JAHN-TELLER EFFECT OF CHROMIUM IN MAGNESIUM OXIDE: HYPERSONIC ATTENUATION.
LANGE, J. N.
PHYS. REV.
8 B (12), 5999-6009, 1973.

53587 QUASIELASTIC ELECTRON SCATTERING IN EUROPIUM OXIDE: A POSSIBLE EXPLANATION FOR THE OBSERVED PARAMAGNETIC SPIN-POLARIZED PHOTOEMISSION.
EASTMAN, D. E.
PHYS. REV.
8 B (12), 6027-9, 1973.

53588 EMPIRICAL RELATION BETWEEN ENERGY GAP AND LATTICE CONSTANT IN CUBIC SEMICONDUCTORS.
DALVEN, R.
PHYS. REV.
8 B (12), 6033-4, 1973.

53589 ELECTROSTATICALLY CORRELATED CRYSTAL-FIELD INTERACTION THROUGH THE B(0,0) TERM OF GADOLINIUM TRIPOSITIVE ION IN CALCIUM FLUORIDE, STRONTIUM FLUORIDE AND BARIUM FLUORIDE.
YANEY, P. P.
PHYS. REV.
9 B (1), 73-86, 1974.

53590 SURFACE SUPERCONDUCTIVITY IN NIOBIUM AND NIOBIUM-TANTALUM ALLOYS.
HOPKINS, J. R. FINNEMORE, D. K.
PHYS. REV.
9 B (1), 108-14, 1974.

53593 STRONG CRYSTALLINE ELECTRIC FIELDS AND THE MAGNETIC AND NUCLEAR-MAGNETIC-RESONANCE PROPERTIES OF THE ACTINIDE MONOPHOSPHIDES: NEPTUNIUM PHOSPHIDE.
LAM, D. J. FRADIN, F. Y.
PHYS. REV.
9 B (1), 238-47, 1974.

53594 MAGNETOELASTICITY IN SAMARIUM IRON.
ROSEN, M. KLIMKER, H. ATZMONY, U.
DARIEL, M. P.
PHYS. REV.
9 B (1), 254-8, 1974.

53596 CRITICAL MAGNETIC SUSCEPTIBILITY IN THE PRESENCE OF LONG-RANGE FORCES.
HORN, P. M. PARKS, R. D. LAMBETH, D. N.
STANLEY, H. E.
PHYS. REV.
9 B (1), 316-22, 1974.
(AD 777 232)

53598 ELECTRONIC STRUCTURE AND OPTICAL PROPERTIES OF LAYERED DICHALCOGENIDES: TITANIUM SULFIDE AND TITANIUM SELENIDE.
MYRON, H. W. FREEMAN, A. J.
PHYS. REV.
9 B (2), 481-6, 1974.
(AD 778 267)

53599 DIELECTRIC FUNCTION IN MERCURY TELLURIUM BETWEEN 8 AND 300 DEGREES K.
GRYNBERG, M. LE TOULLEC, R. BALKANSKI, M.
PHYS. REV.
9 B (2), 517-26, 1974.

EPIC Number	Bibliographic Citation

53600 TRANSIENT PHOTOVOLTAIC EFFECTS IN ANISOTROPIC SEMICONDUCTORS.
SUBRAMANIAN, A. GORDON, S. J.
SCHETZINA, J. F.
PHYS. REV.
9 (2), 536-44, 1974.

53601 FAR-INFRARED STUDY OF FREE CARRIERS AND THE PLASMON-PHONON INTERACTION IN CADMIUM TELLURIDE.
PERKOWITZ, S. THORLAND, R. H.
PHYS. REV.
9 B (2), 545-50, 1974.

53602 LOW-TEMPERATURE OPTICAL ABSORPTION AND MAGNETIC CIRCULAR DICHROISM OF YTTERBIUM TELLURIDE THIN FILMS.
SURYANARAYANAN, R. FERRE, J. BRIAT, B.
PHYS. REV.
9 B (2), 554-7, 1974.

53603 ELECTRO-OPTIC BEHAVIOR AND DIELECTRIC CONSTANTS OF ZINC GERMANIUM PHOSPHIDE AND COPPER GALLIUM SULFIDE.
TURNER, E. H. BUEHLER, E. KASPER, H.
PHYS. REV.
9 B (2), 558-61, 1974.

53604 PHOTOEXCITED HOT ELECTRONS AND EXCITONS IN CADMIUM SELENIDE AT 2 DEGREES K.
SHAH, J.
PHYS. REV.
9 B (2), 562-7, 1974.

53605 TEMPERATURE DEPENDENCE OF THE ELECTRON EFFECTIVE MASS IN INDIUM ANTIMONY.
KOTELES, E. S. DATARS, W. R.
PHYS. REV.
9 B (2), 568-71, 1974.

53606 FAR-INFRARED PHONON ABSORPTION IN INDIUM ANTIMONY.
KOTELES, E. S. DATARS, W. R. DOLLING, G.
PHYS. REV.
9 B (2), 572-82, 1974.

53607 TOTAL VALENCE-BAND DENSITIES OF STATES OF III-V AND II-VI COMPOUNDS FROM X-RAY PHOTOEMISSION SPECTROSCOPY.
LEY, L. POLLAK, R. A. MC FEELY, F. R.
KOWALCZYK, S. P. SHIRLEY, D. A.
PHYS. REV.
9 B (2), 600-21, 1974.

53609 DIELECTRIC CONSTANT AND ANOMALOUS MAGNETORESISTANCE OF ZERO-GAP SEMICONDUCTORS.
LIU, L. TAN, M.
PHYS. REV.
9 B (2), 632-5, 1974.

53610 THERMOREFLECTANCE SPECTRA OF DIAMOND AND ZINC-BLENDE SEMICONDUCTORS IN THE VACUUM-ULTRAVIOLET REGION.
GUIZZETTI, G. NOSENZO, L. REGUZZONI, E.
SAMOGGIA, G.
PHYS. REV.
9 B (2), 640-7, 1974.

53611 EFFECT OF UNIAXIAL STRESS ON SHUBNIKOV-DE HAAS OSCILLATIONS IN MERCURY SELENIDE.
SEILER, D. G. HATHCOX, K. L.
PHYS. REV.
9 B (2), 648-57, 1974.

53614 OPTICAL ORIENTATION OF EXCITONS IN CADMIUM SULFIDE.
BONNOT, A. PLANEL, R.
DENOIT A LA GUILLAUME, C.
PHYS. REV.
9 B (2), 690-702, 1974.

53615 TRANSMITTANCE, LUMINESCENCE, AND PHOTOCURRENT IN CADMIUM SULFIDE UNDER TWO-PHOTON EXCITATION.
CATALANO, I. M. CINGOLANI, A. MINAFRA, A.
PHYS. REV.
9 B (2), 707-10, 1974.

53619 INFRARED ABSORPTION DUE TO MULTIPHONON PROCESSES IN THE TRANSPARENT REGIME OF SOLIDS.
NAMJOSHI, K. V. MITRA, S. S.
PHYS. REV.
9 B (2), 815-22, 1974.
(AD-A012 553, N76-12355)

53620 EXPLICIT EXPONENTIAL FREQUENCY DEPENDENCE OF MULTIPHONON INFRARED ABSORPTION.
SHAM, L. J. SPARKS, M.
PHYS. REV.
9 B (2), 827-9, 1974.

53621 QUASISELECTION RULE FOR INFRARED ABSORPTION BY SODIUM CHLORIDE STRUCTURE CRYSTALS.
DUTHLER, C. J. SPARKS, M.
PHYS. REV.
9 B (2), 830-2, 1974.

EPIC Number	Bibliographic Citation
53622	**COMMENT ON TEMPERATURE DEPENDENCE OF THE OPTICAL TRANSMISSION EDGE IN CADMIUM ARSENIDE PHOSPHIDE ALLOYS.** AUBIN, M. J. PHYS. REV. 9 (2), 833–5, 1974.
53624	**RESISTIVITY AND CURIE POINT OF LITHIUM ZINC FERRITES.** REZLESCU, N. CONDURACHE, D. PETRARIU, P. LUCA, E. J. AMER. CERAM. SOC. 57 (1), 40–1, 1974.
53625	**ELECTRONIC CONDUCTIVITY IN THE PRESENCE OF ACOUSTOELECTRIC DOMAINS.** MACOMBER, G. NEUDORFER, M. YEE, S. J. APPL. PHYS. 45 (1), 17–22, 1974. (AD 778 969)
53626	**OXIDATION OF LEAD FILMS BY RF SPUTTER ETCHING IN AN OXYGEN PLASMA.** GREINER, J. H. J. APPL. PHYS. 45 (1), 32–7, 1974.
53627	**ELECTRON AFFINITIES OF THE ALKALINE EARTH CHALCOGENIDES.** TSOU, K. Y. HENSLEY, E. B. J. APPL. PHYS. 45 (1), 47–9, 1974.
53628	**EFFECTS OF DC SUBSTRATE BIAS ON THE PROPERTIES OF RF-SPUTTERED AMORPHOUS GERMANIUM DITELLURIDE FILMS.** FAGEN, E. A. NOWICKI, R. S. SEGUIN, R. W. J. APPL. PHYS. 45 (1), 50–9, 1974.
53634	**TUNNELING IN SILICON CARBIDE ELECTROLUMINESCENT DIODES.** BARNES, C. E. J. APPL. PHYS. 45 (1), 193–200, 1974.
53635	**PREPARATION AND PROPERTIES OF GREEN-LIGHT-EMITTING CADMIUM SULFIDE-COPPER GALLIUM SULFIDE HETERODIODES.** WAGNER, S. J. APPL. PHYS. 45 (1), 246–51, 1974.
53638	**OPTICAL PROPERTIES OF VAPOR-GROWN INDIUM GALLIUM 1-X ARSENIC EPITAXIAL FILMS ON GALLIUM ARSENIDE AND INDIUM GALLIUM 1-X PHOSPHORUS SUBSTRATES.** ENSTROM, R. E. ZANZUCCHI, P. J. J. APPL. PHYS. 45 (1), 300–6, 1974.
53641	**PREPARATION AND HIGH-FIELD SUPERCONDUCTING PROPERTIES OF VAPOR-DEPOSITED NIOBIUM TIN ALLOYS.** ENSTROM, R. E. APPERT, J. R. J. APPL. PHYS. 45 (1), 421–8, 1974.
53643	**TUNNELING IN LEAD-LEAD OXIDE-LEAD JUNCTIONS.** BASAVAIAH, S. ELDRIDGE, J. M. MATISOO, J. J. APPL. PHYS. 45 (1), 457–64, 1974.
53644	**BAND-BENDING EFFECTS IN SODIUM POTASSIUM ANTIMONIDE AND POTASSIUM CESIUM ANTIMONY PHOTOCATHODES.** FISHER, D. G. MC DONIE, A. F. SOMMER, A. H. J. APPL. PHYS. 45 (1), 487–8, 1974.
53647	**CARRIER MOBILITY IN N-TYPE YTTRIUM IRON GARNET.** KSENDZOV, YA. M. KOTEL'NIKOVA, A. M. MAKAROV, V. V. SOV. PHYS. SOLID STATE 15 (8), 1563–4, 1974. (ENGLISH TRANSLATION OF FIZ. TVERD. TELA, 15 (8), 2343–6, 1973; FOR ORIGINAL SEE E52534)
53648	**VIBRATIONAL SPECTRA OF RUTILE.** KNYAZEV, A. S. ZAKHAROV, V. P. MITYUREVA, I. A. POPLAVKO, YU. M. FIZ. TVERD. TELA 15 (8), 2371–7, 1973. (FOR ENGLISH TRANSLATION SEE E53649)
53649	**VIBRATIONAL SPECTRA OF RUTILE.** KNYAZEV, A. S. ZAKHAROV, V. P. MITYUREVA, I. A. POPLAVKO, YU. M. SOV. PHYS. SOLID STATE 15 (8), 1579–82, 1974. (ENGLISH TRANSLATION OF FIZ. TVERD. TELA, 15 (8), 2371–7, 1973; FOR ORIGINAL SEE E53648)
53650	**PHOTOIONIZATION OF SILVER(0) CENTERS IN SILVER-ACTIVATED POTASSIUM CHLORIDE.** OSMININ, V. S. FIZ. TVERD. TELA (LENINGRAD) 15 (8), 2386–92, 1973. (FOR ENGLISH TRANSLATION SEE E53651)
53651	**PHOTOIONIZATION OF SILVER (0) CENTERS IN SILVER-ACTIVATED POTASSIUM CHLORIDE.** OSMININ, V. S. SOV. PHYS. SOLID STATE 15 (8), 1588–91, 1974. (ENGLISH TRANSLATION OF FIZ. TVERD. TELA, 15 (8), 2386–92, 1973; FOR ORIGINAL SEE E53650)
53652	**PHOTOELECTRIC PROPERTIES OF VANADIUM PENTOXIDE SINGLE CRYSTALS.** MOKEROV, V. G. SOV. PHYS. SOLID STATE 15 (8), 1592–4, 1974. (ENGLISH TRANSLATION OF FIZ. TVERD. TELA, 15 (8), 2393–6, 1973; FOR ORIGINAL SEE E52535)
53657	**CUBIC TRIPOSITIVE EUROPIUM DOPED CENTERS IN PEROVSKITE-TYPE CRYSTALS.** AL'TSHULER, N. S. IVOILOVA, E. KH. STOLOV, A. L. FIZ. TVERD. TELA 15 (8), 2407–11, 1973. (FOR ENGLISH TRANSLATION SEE E53658)
53658	**CUBIC TRIPOSITIVE EUROPIUM DOPED CENTERS IN PEROVSKITY-TYPE CRYSTALS.** AL'TSHULER, N. S. IVOILOVA, E. KH. STOLOV, A. L. SOV. PHYS. SOLID STATE 15 (8), 1602–4, 1974. (ENGLISH TRANSLATION OF FIZ. TVERD. TELA, 15 (8), 2407–11, 1973; FOR ORIGINAL SEE E53657)
53661	**THERMAL FIELD IONIZATION OF ELECTRON TRAPS IN INDIUM AND SODIUM-DOPED POTASSIUM CHLORIDE LUMINESCENT CRYSTALS.** LEIMAN, V. I. DENKS, V. DUDEL'ZAK, A. E. FIZ. TVERD. TELA (LENINGRAD) 15 (8), 2454–9, 1973. (FOR ENGLISH TRANSLATION SEE E53662)
53662	**THERMAL-FIELD IONIZATION OF ELECTRON TRAPS IN LUMINESCENT POTASSIUM CHLORIDE-INDIUM-SODIUM CRYSTALS.** LEIMAN, V. I. DENKS, V. P. DUDEL'ZAK, A. E. SOV. PHYS. SOLID STATE 15 (8), 1630–3, 1974. (ENGLISH TRANSLATION OF FIZ. TVERD. TELA, 15 (8), 2454–9, 1973; FOR ORIGINAL SEE E53661)
53664	**BISTABLE STATE OF MICROPLASMAS IN ELECTRIC BREAKDOWN OF SEMICONDUCTOR FIELD-EMISSION CATHODES.** SHLYAKHTENKO, P. F. MILESHKINA, N. V. KOROTYNSKII, M. G. SOV. PHYS. SOLID STATE 15 (8), 1654–5, 1974. (ENGLISH TRANSLATION OF FIZ. TVERD. TELA, 15 (8), 2494–6, 1973; FOR ORIGINAL SEE E52537)
53665	**THERMAL CONDUCTIVITY OF THALLIUM ARSENIC SULFIDE AND THALLIUM ARSENIC TELLURIDE IN SOLID AND LIQUID STATES.** AMIRKHANOV, KH. I. GADZHIEV, G. G. ISMAILOV, SH. M. MAGOMEDOV, YA. B. FIZ. TVERD. TELA 15 (8), 2497–9, 1973. (FOR ENGLISH TRANSLATION SEE E53666)
53666	**THERMAL CONDUCTIVITY OF THALLIUM ARSENIC SULFIDE AND THALLIUM ARSENIC TELLURIDE IN SOLID AND LIQUID STATES.** AMIRKHANOV, KH. I. GADZHIEV, G. G. ISMAILOV, SH. M. MAGOMEDOV, YA. B. SOV. PHYS. SOLID STATE 15 (8), 1657–8, 1974. (ENGLISH TRANSLATION OF FIZ. TVERD. TELA, 15 (8), 2497–9, 1973; FOR ORIGINAL SEE E53665)
53667	**TEMPERATURE DEPENDENCE OF THE ACTIVATION ENERGY OF ELECTRICAL CONDUCTION IN ARSENIC SELENIDE.** ANDREEV, A. A. LEBEDEV, E. A. SHMURATOV, E. A. SHPUNT, V. KH. SOV. PHYS. SOLID STATE 15 (8), 1659, 1974. (ENGLISH TRANSLATION OF FIZ. TVERD. TELA, 15 (8), 2500–1, 1973; FOR ORIGINAL SEE E52538)
53668	**ANISOTROPY OF THE ELECTRIC POLARIZATION OF THE CUBIC PARAELECTRIC PHASE OF PEROVSKITE FERROELECTRICS.** KIRILLOV, V. V. ISUPOV, V. A. FIZ. TVERD. TELA 15 (8), 2502–4, 1973. (FOR ENGLISH TRANSLATION SEE E53669)
53669	**ANISOTROPY OF THE ELECTRIC POLARIZATION OF THE CUBIC PARAELECTRIC PHASE OF PEROVSKITE FERROELECTRICS.** KIRILLOV, V. V. ISUPOV, V. A. SOV. PHYS. SOLID STATE 15 (8), 1660–1, 1974. (ENGLISH TRANSLATION OF FIZ. TVERD. TELA, 15 (8), 2502–4, 1973; FOR ORIGINAL SEE E53668)

EPIC Number	Bibliographic Citation

53670 **ELECTRON SPIN RESONANCE SPECTRA OF FERRIC IONS IN VANADIUM OXIDE.**
IOFFE, V. A. GRUNIN, V. S. PATRINA, I. B.
KRYMSKII, SH. Z.
FIZ. TVERD. TELA
15 (8), 2510–3, 1973.
(FOR ENGLISH TRANSLATION SEE E53671)

53671 **ELECTRON SPIN RESONANCE SPECTRA OF FERRIC IONS IN VANADIUM OXIDE.**
IOFFE, V. A. GRUNIN, V. S. PATRINA, I. B.
KRYSMKII, SH. Z.
SOV. PHYS. SOLID STATE
15 (8), 1668–9, 1974.
(ENGLISH TRANSLATION OF FIZ. TVERD. TELA, 15 (8), 2510–3, 1973; FOR ORIGINAL SEE E53670)

53672 **BRIGHTNESS WAVES OF X-RAY RADIOELECTROLUMINESCENCE OF THALLIUM DOPED POTASSIUM IODIDE.**
POLOGRUDOV, V. V. KARNAUKHOV, E. N.
EGOROV, V. N.
SOV. PHYS. SOLID STATE
15 (8), 1678, 1974.
(ENGLISH TRANSLATION OF FIZ. TVERD. TELA, 15 (8), 2523–4, 1973; FOR ORIGINAL SEE E52539)

53673 **TRANSVERSE ANHARMONICITY OF CHAIN-LIKE CRYSTALS.**
BERCHA, D. M. ZAYACHKOVSKII, M. P.
BALETSKII, D. YU.
FIZ. TVERD. TELA
15 (8), 2527–8, 1973.
(FOR ENGLISH TRANSLATION SEE E53674)

53674 **TRANSVERSE ANHARMONICITY OF CHAIN-LIKE CRYSTALS.**
BERCHA, D. M. ZAYACHKOVSKII, M. P.
BALETSKII, D. YU.
SOV. PHYS. SOLID STATE
15 (8), 1681, 1974.
(ENGLISH TRANSLATION OF FIZ. TVERD. TELA, 15 (8), 2527–8, 1973; FOR ORIGINAL SEE E53673)

53675 **HALL COEFFICIENT OF METAL-LIKE SEMICONDUCTOR MELTS.**
ANDREEV, A. A. TURGUNOV, T.
SOV. PHYS. SO.ID STATE
15 (8), 1684, 1974.
(ENGLISH TRANSLATION OF FIZ. TVERD. TELA, 15 (8), 2531–2, 1973; FOR ORIGINAL SEE E52540)

53676 **INFLUENCE OF THE NATURE OF DEFORMATION ON THE ELECTRICAL PROPERTIES OF BISMUTH ANTIMONIDE-TELLURIDE SOLID SOLUTIONS.**
AVERKIN, A. A. GOL'TSMAN, B. M.
ZHAPAROV, ZH. ZH. ZHEMOHUZHINA, E. A.
KOMISSARCHIK, M. G. POLISTANSKII, YU. G.
SOV. PHYS. SOLID STATE
15 (8), 1694, 1974.
(ENGLISH TRANSLATION OF FIZ. TVERD. TELA, 15 (8), 2543–5, 1973; FOR ORIGINAL SEE E52541)

53677 **MASS OF THE HOLE DENSITY OF STATES IN P-TYPE INDIUM ANTIMONY DEDUCED FROM GALVANOMAGNETIC MEASUREMENTS.**
TAMARIN, P. V. LANG, I. G. PAVLOV, S. T.
SOV. PHYS. SOLID STATE
15 (8), 1704–5, 1974.
(ENGLISH TRANSLATION OF FIZ. TVERD. TELA, 15 (8), 2557–9, 1973; FOR ORIGINAL SEE E52543)

53679 **ELECTRICAL CONDUCTIVITY OF LITHIUM SODIUM SULFATE IN THE MOLTEN AND SOLID STATES.**
POLISHCHUK, A. F. SHURZHAL, T. M.
SOV. ELECTROCHEM.
9 (6), 802–5, 1973.
(ENGLISH TRANSLATION OF ELEKTROKHIMIYA, 9 (6), 838–41, 1973; FOR ORIGINAL SEE E51530)

53680 **STUDY OF THE PHOTOEMISSION OF BINARY SODIUM-RUBIDIUM, SODIUM - CESIUM, RUBIDIUM - POTASSIUM, AND POTASSIUM-CESIUM ALLOYS.**
MALOV, YU. I. SHEBZUKHOV, M. D.
SOV. ELECTROCHEM.
9 (6), 780–2, 1973.
(ENGLISH TRANSLATION OF ELEKTROKHIMIYA, 9 (6), 815–7, 1973; FOR ORIGINAL SEE E51528)

53681 **SOME FEATURES OF THE TEMPERATURE DEPENDENCE OF THE CONDUCTIVITY OF CADMIUM SULFIDE DOPED WITH DONOR AND ACCEPTOR IMPURITIES.**
KONSTANTINOVA, E. KYNEV, S.
SOV. PHYS. SEMICOND.
7 (6), 705–7, 1973.
(ENGLISH TRANSLATION OF FIZ. TEKH. POLUPROV., 7 (6), 1033–7, 1973; FOR ORIGINAL SEE E51550)

53682 **PHOTOCONDUCTIVITY, TRAPPING PROCESSES, AND RECOMBINATION IN GOLD-DOPED CADMIUM GALLIUM SELENIDE SINGLE CRYSTALS.**
ABDULLAEV, G. B. AGAEV, V. G.
ANTONOV, V. B. MAMEDOV, A. A. NANI, R. KH.
SALAEV, E. YU.
SOV. PHYS. SEMICOND.
7 (6), 717–20, 1973.
(ENGLISH TRANSLATION OF FIZ. TEKH. POLUPROV., 7 (6), 1051–7, 1973; FOR ORIGINAL SEE E51551)

53683 **PHOTOELECTRIC METHOD OF MEASUREMENT OF THE ENERGY DEPENDENCE OF THE IMPACT IONIZATION PROBABILITY IN SEMICONDUCTORS.**
KUMEKOV, S. E. YASSIEVICH, I. N.
SOV. PHYS. SEMICOND.
7 (6), 734–6, 1973.
(ENGLISH TRANSLATION OF FIZ. TEKH. POLUPROV., 7 (6), 1081–5, 1973; FOR ORIGINAL SEE E51552)

53684 **INELASTICITY OF THE SCATTERING OF ELECTRONS IN SILVER TELLURIDE.**
ALIEV, S. A. SUYUNOV, U. KH. ARASLY, D. G.
ALIEV, M. I.
SOV. PHYS. SEMICOND.
7 (6), 737–40, 1973.
(ENGLISH TRANSLATION OF FIZ. TEKH. POLUPROV., 7 (6), 1086–91, 1973; FOR ORIGINAL SEE E51553)

53686 **SPACE-CHARGE-LIMITED CURRENT IN CADMIUM SULFIDE FILMS.**
MARAKHONOV, V. M. SEISYAN, R. P.
SOV. PHYS. SEMICOND.
7 (6), 769–72, 1973.
(ENGLISH TRANSLATION OF FIZ. TEKH. POLUPROV., 7 (6), 1141–7, 1973; FOR ORIGINAL SEE E51555)

53687 **PHOTOSENSITIVITY OF P-COPPER SULFIDE-N-SILICON HETEROJUNCTIONS.**
DROZDOV, V. A. MEL'NIKOV, M. M.
SOV. PHYS. SEMICOND.
7 (6), 801–2, 1973.
(ENGLISH TRANSLATION OF FIZ. TEKH. POLUPROV., 7 (6), 1194–6, 1973; FOR ORIGINAL SEE E51556)

53688 **ELECTROABSORPTION IN SEMICONDUCTORS WITH LARGE-SCALE FLUCTUATIONS OF IMPURITY CONCENTRATION.**
MERKULOV, I. A. PEREL, V. I.
SOV. PHYS. SEMICOND.
7 (6), 803–6, 1973.
(ENGLISH TRANSLATION OF FIZ. TEKH. POLUPROV., 7 (6), 1197–1202, 1973; FOR ORIGINAL SEE E51557)

53689 **SHEAR DEFORMATION POTENTIAL CONSTANTS OF INDIUM ANTIMONIDE.**
VOLKOV, A. S. GALAVANOV, V. V.
MILORAVA, V. A.
SOV. PHYS. SEMICOND.
7 (6), 819–20, 1973.
(ENGLISH TRANSLATION OF FIZ. TEKH. POLUPROV., 7 (6), 1220–2, 1973; FOR ORIGINAL SEE E51558)

53690 **EXCITON SPECTRA OF HEAVILY DOPED CADMIUM SULFIDE SINGLE CRYSTALS.**
GROSS, E. F. PERMOGOROV, S. A.
REZNITSKII, A. N. USAROV, E. N.
SOV. PHYS. SEMICOND.
7 (7), 844–8, 1974.
(ENGLISH TRANSLATION OF FIZ. TEKH. POLUPROV., 7 (7), 1255–62, 1973; FOR ORIGINAL SEE E51559)

53692 **IMPURITY ELECTROABSORPTION IN CADMIUM SELENIDE TELLURIDE CRYSTALS.**
BUDYANSKII, V. I. DANIYAROV, O.
SAL'KOV, E. A. SHEINKMAN, M. K.
SHEPEL'SKII, G. A.
SOV. PHYS. SEMICOND.
7 (7), 869–71, 1974.
(ENGLISH TRANSLATION OF FIZ. TEKH. POLUPROV., 7 (7), 1296–1300, 1973; FOR ORIGINAL SEE E51561)

53693 **NATURE OF THE TEMPERATURE DEPENDENCES OF THE ELECTRICAL CONDUCTIVITY OF CUPROUS CHALCOGENIDES AT HIGH TEMPERATURES IN SOLID AND LIQUID STATES.**
GLAZOV, V. M. BURKHANOV, A. S.
SOV. PHYS. SEMICOND.
7 (7), 936–8, 1974.
(ENGLISH TRANSLATION OF FIZ. TEKH. POLUPROV., 7 (7), 1401–5, 1973; FOR ORIGINAL SEE E51562)

53694 **THEORY OF THE ELECTRICAL CONDUCTIVITY OF MANY-VALLEY SEMICONDUCTORS WITH CHARGED POINT DEFECTS.**
KORNYUSHIN, YU. V.
SOV. PHYS. SEMICOND.
7 (7), 947–8, 1974.
(ENGLISH TRANSLATION OF FIZ. TEKH. POLUPROV., 7 (7), 1417–19, 1973; FOR ORIGINAL SEE E51563)

53695 **PROFILE OF THE FUNDAMENTAL ABSORPTION EDGE OF CADMIUM MERCURY SELENIDE SOLID SOLUTIONS.**
KIREEV, P. S. VOLKOV, V. V.
SOV. PHYS. SEMICOND.
7 (7), 949–51, 1974.
(ENGLISH TRANSLATION OF FIZ. TEKH. POLUPROV., 7 (7), 1419–23, 1973; FOR ORIGINAL SEE E51564)

53698 **CALORIMETRIC STUDY OF A RANDOM ISING SPIN SYSTEM: COBALT ZINC, CESIUM CHLORIDE.**
LAGENDIJK, E. HUISKAMP, W. J.
PHYSICA
62, 444–60, 1972.
(COMMUN. KAMERLINGH ONNES LAB., UNIV. LEIDEN, NO. 396)

EPIC Number	Bibliographic Citation
53699	**THE MAGNETIC DIAGRAM OF STATE OF COBALT CHLORIDE HEXAHYDRATE.** METSELAAR, J. W. DE KLERK, D. PHYSICA 63, 191–6, 1973. (COMMUN. KAMERLINGH ONNES LAB., UNIV. LEIDEN, NO. 697)
53700	**CALORIC AND MAGNETIC PROPERTIES OF TWO COMPOUNDS HAVING PREDOMINANTLY MAGNETIC DIPOLE-DIPOLE INTERACTIONS: DYSPROSIUM TRICHLORIDE HEXAHYDRATE AND ERBIUM TRICHLORIDE HEXAHYDRATE.** LAGENDIJK, E. HUISKAMP, W. J. PHYSICA 65, 118–55, 1973. (COMMUN. KAMERLINGH ONNES LAB., UNIV. LEIDEN NO. 396.)
53701	**SPECIFIC HEAT AND NMR OF COPPER NITRATE TRIHYDRATE AT THE HIGH-FIELD PHASE TRANSITION.** VAN TOL, M. W. DIEDERIX, K. M. POULIS, N. J. PHYSICA 64, (2), 363–86, 1973. (COMMUN. KAMERLINGH ONNES LAB., UNIV. LEIDEN, NO. 397.)
53702	**MAGNETOTHERMODYNAMICS OF ANTIFERROMAGNETIC, FERROELECTRIC, FERROELASTIC BETA-GADOLINIUM MOLYBDATE. IV. THERMODYNAMIC TEMPERATURE AND OTHER PROPERTIES WITHOUT HEAT INTRODUCTION BELOW 0.5 K. FIELDS TO 10 KILOGAUSS ALONG THE C-PLUS CRYSTAL AXIS.** FISHER, R. A. HORNUNG, E. W. BRODALE, G. E. GIAUQUE, W. F. J. CHEM. PHYS. 59 (11), 5796–5809, 1973.
53703	**HIGH FREQUENCY DIELECTRIC RESPONSE OF DIPOLAR LIQUIDS.** LOBO, R. ROBINSON, J. E. RODRIGUEZ, S. J. CHEM. PHYS. 59 (11), 5992–6008, 1973.
53706	**A REINVESTIGATION OF THE SYMMETRIC STRETCHING MODE OF MATRIX-ISOLATED ALUMINUM OXIDE.** LYNCH D. A., JR. ZEHE, M. J. CARLSON, K. D. J. PHYS. CHEM. 78 (3), 236–8, 1974.
53708	**TEMPERATURE DEPOLARIZATION OF THE LUMINESCENCE OF TIN ION-ACTIVATED POTASSIUM CHLORIDE-TYPE CENTERS.** KRISTOFEL, N. N. KHIZHNYAKOV, V. V. OPT. SPECTROS., USSR 34 (6), 721–2, 1973. (ENGLISH TRANSLATION OF OPT. SPEKTROSK., 34 (6), 1236–7, 1973; FOR ORIGINAL SEE E50988)
53709	**THE EFFECT OF TEMPERATURE AND PRESSURE ON THE REFRACTIVE INDEX OF SOME OXIDE GLASSES.** WAXLER, R. M. CLEEK, G. W. J. RES. NAT. BUR. STAND. 77 A (6), 755–63, 1973.
53712	**RELAXATION MEASUREMENTS ON SINGLE CRYSTALS OF MANGANESE DICHLORIDE TETRAHYDRATE AND MANGANESE DIBROMIDE TETRAHYDRATE NEAR THE MAGNETIC PHASE TRANSITION.** VAN DUYNEVELDT, A. J. SOETEMAN, J. GORTER, C. J. COOPERATIVE PHENOMENA 281–, 1973. (COMMUN. KAMERLINGH ONNES LAB., UNIV. LEIDEN, NO. 397)
53714	**MEASUREMENT OF THE THERMOELECTRIC PROPERTIES OF METALS AND SEMICONDUCTORS AT QUASI-HYDROSTATIC PRESSURES UP TO 60 KBAR. 1. BISMUTH.** KHVOSTANTSEV, L. G. VERESHCHAGIN, L. F. ULIYANITSKAYA, N. M. HIGH TEMP. - HIGH PRESSURES 5 (3), 261–4, 1973.
53715	**CONDUCTIVITY MEASUREMENTS ON THORIA AND THORIA-YTTRIA SOLID SOLUTIONS AT HIGH OXYGEN PRESSURES.** IQBAL, M. BAKER, E. H. HIGH TEMP. - HIGH PRESSURES 5 (3), 265–71, 1973.
53717	**RECOMBINATION TRANSITIONS IN ZINC-NITROGEN-DOPED GALLIUM ARSENIDE 1-X PHOSPHIDE X IN THE DIRECT AND INDIRECT COMPOSITION REGIONS.** CAMPBELL, J. C. HOLONYAK, N., JR. LEE, M. H. LUDOWISE, M. J. CRAFORD, M. G. FINN, D. GROVES, W. O. J. APPL. PHYS. 45 (2), 795–9, 1974.
53720	**OPTICAL SPECTRA AND RELAXATION OF CHROMIUM TRIPOSITIVE IONS IN YTTRIUM ALUMINATE.** WEBER, M. J. VARITIMOS, T. E. J. APPL. PHYS. 45 (2), 810–6, 1974.
53721	**EFFECTS OF UNIAXIAL STRESS ON GALLIUM ARSENIDE PHOSPHORUS RED-LIGHT-EMITTING DIODES.** SHARE, S. J. APPL. PHYS. 45 (2), 817–22, 1974.
53722	**SHARP-LINE AND BROAD-BAND EMISSION IN SILVER GALLIUM SULFIDE CRYSTALS.** YU, P. W. PARK, Y. S. J. APPL. PHYS. 45 (2), 823–7, 1974. (AD 786 280)
53724	**UV-STIMULATED PHOTOCURRENT SPECTROSCOPY AND TRAPPING KINETICS OF A 2.1 - E V TRAP IN ANODIC TANTALUM OXIDE FILMS.** THOMAS, J. H., III J. APPL. PHYS. 45 (2), 835–42, 1974.
53726	**AMORPHOUS BISMUTH-GERMANIUM THIN FILMS. II. OPTICAL AND PHOTOELECTRICAL PROPERTIES.** VASS, R. W. ANDERSON, R. M. J. APPL. PHYS. 45 (2), 855–66, 1974.
53727	**NEW INTERMEDIATE GAIN LASER MATERIAL: DOPED YTTRIUM GARNETS.** WATTS, R. K. HOLTON, W. C. J. APPL. PHYS. 45 (2), 873–81, 1974.
53729	**EPITAXIAL LEAD SELENIDE AND LEAD TIN SELENIDE: GROWTH AND ELECTRICAL PROPERTIES.** HOHNKE, D. K. KAISER, S. W. J. APPL. PHYS. 45 (2), 892–7, 1974.
53730	**EFFECTS OF DISLOCATION DENSITY ON THE PROPERTIES OF LIQUID PHASE EPITAXIAL GALLIUM ARSENIDE.** ETTENBERG, M. J. APPL. PHYS. 45 (2), 901–6, 1974.
53733	**GROWTH-INDUCED MAGNETIC ANISOTROPY IN VARIOUSLY ORIENTED EPITAXIAL FILMS OF SAMARIUM-DOPED YTTRIUM IRON GALLIUM GARNET.** HAGEDORN, F. B. HEWITT, B. S. J. APPL. PHYS. 45 (2), 925–8, 1974.
53735	**DETERMINATION OF CARRIER MOBILITIES IN SEMIINSULATING GALLIUM ARSENIDE.** PHILADELPHEUS, A. TH. EUTHYMIOU, P. C. J. APPL. PHYS. 45 (2), 955–7, 1974.
53736	**LEAD TULLURIDE-GERMANIUM HETEROJUNCTION PROPERTIES.** PERFETTI, P. CERRINA, F. COLUZZA, C. MARGARITONDO, G. J. APPL. PHYS. 45 (2), 972–3, 1974.
53737	**PHOTOLUMINESCENCE OF NITROGEN-IMPLANTED GALLIUM ARSENIDE DOPED PHOSPHIDE.** STREETMAN, B. G. ANDERSON, R. E. WOLFORD, D. J. J. APPL. PHYS. 45 (2), 974–6, 1974.
53738	**OPTICAL DISPERSION OF UNCLAD FIBERS OVER LIMITED WAVELENGTHS.** PRESBY, H. M. APPL. OPT. 13 (3), 465–7, 1974.
53741	**KRAMERS-KRONIG ANALYSIS OF RATIO REFLECTANCE SPECTRA MEASURED AT AN OBLIQUE ANGLE.** QUERRY, M. R. HOLLAND, W. E. APPL. OPT. 13 (3), 595–8, 1974.
53743	**THEORY OF SOLUTION STRENGTHENING OF ALKALI HALIDE CRYSTALS.** GILMAN, J. J. J. APPL. PHYS. 45 (2), 508–9, 1974.
53745	**VAPOR-PHASE EPITAXIAL GROWTH OF GALLIUM ARSENIDE IN A NITROGEN ATMOSPHERE.** IHARA, M. DAZAI, K. RYUZAN, O. J. APPL. PHYS. 45 (2), 528–31, 1974.
53747	**LUMINESCENCE FROM ACOUSTOELECTRIC DOMAINS IN CADMIUM SELENIDE.** MACOMBER, G. NEUDORFER, M. YEE, S. S. J. APPL. PHYS. 45 (2), 553–5, 1974. (AD-786 363)
53748	**SPECIFIC HEATS OF ZINC TELLURIDE, ZINC SELENIDE, AND GALLIUM PHOSPHIDE.** IRWIN, J. C. LA COMBE, J. J. APPL. PHYS. 45 (2), 567–73, 1974.

EPIC Number	Bibliographic Citation
53749	ELECTRICAL AND OPTICAL PROPERTIES OF SINGLE CRYSTALS IN THE IRON OXIDE-MANGANESE OXIDE SYSTEMS. GOODWIN, C. A. BOWEN, H. K. ADLER, D. J. APPL. PHYS. 45 (2), 626-32, 1974.
53750	THERMOELECTRIC AND PHOTOTHERMOELECTRIC EFFECTS IN SEMICONDUCTORS: CADMIUM SULFIDE FILMS. WU, C.-H. BUBE, R. H. J. APPL. PHYS. 45 (2), 648-60, 1974.
53752	SWITCHING IN COPPER OXIDE. ZARABI, M. J. SATYAM, M. J. APPL. PHYS. 45 (2), 775-80, 1974.
53754	NUMERICAL ANALYSIS OF THE KINETIC EQUATION FOR THE WORK FUNCTION CHANGES OF SEMICONDUCTING OXIDES. BIALAS, S. NOWOTNY, J. BULL. ACAD. POLON. SCI., SER. SCI. CHIM. 21 (12), 923-9, 1973.
53755	ELECTRICAL CONDUCTIVITY OF UNDOPED, LITHIUM AND CHROMIUM DOPED NICKEL OXIDE SINGLE CRYSTALS. NOWOTNY, J. WAGNER, J. B., JR. BULL. ACAD. POLON. SCI., SER. SCI. CHIM. 21 (12), 931-6, 1973.
53756	SYTHESIS, CHARACTERIZATION, AND CONSOLIDATION OF SILICON NITROGEN OBTAINED FROM AMMONOLYSIS OF SILICON CHLORIDE. MAZDIYASNI, K. S. COOKE, C. M. J. AMER. CERAM. SOC. 56 (11), 628-33, 1973.
53758	POLYCRYSTALLINE BISMUTH TITANATE THIN FILMS FOR MICROELECTRONIC APPLICATIONS. SZEDON, J. R. WU, S. Y. AIR FORCE AVIONICS LAB., WRIGHT-PATTERSON AIR FORCE BASE, OHIO 50PP., 1973. (AFAL-TR-72-303, AVAIL. WPAFB)
53775	METAL-INSULATOR TRANSITION IN EXTRINSIC SEMICONDUCTORS. MOTT, N. F. ADVAN. PHYS. 21 (94), 785-823, 1972.
53777	EFFECTS OF LIGHT STORAGE IN CADMIUM INDIUM SULFIDE CRYSTALS. ABDULAEV, G. B. BELEN'KII, G. L. LARIONKINA, L. S. NANI, R. KH. SALAEV, E. YU. FIZ. TEKH. POLUPROV. 7 (4), 821-2, 1973. (FOR ENGLISH TRANSLATION SEE E54546)
53779	MEASUREMENT OF OPTICAL PROPERTIES OF POLYCRYSTALLINE ALUMINUM NITRIDE IN THE 0.10-25 MU-REGION. KUTOLIN, S. A. LUKINA, L. L. SAMOILOVA, R. N. IZV. AKAD. NAUK SSSR, NEORG. MATER. 9 (6), 964-6, 1973. (FOR ENGLISH TRANSLATION SEE E55350)
53782	PHOTOEFFECTS IN SEMICONDUCTORS. MOSS, T. S. J. LUMIN. 7, 359-89, 1973.
53785	LEAD CENTERS IN ALKALI HALIDES. SODIUM CHLORIDE, POTASSIUM CHLORIDE, AND POTASSIUM BROMIDE. SASTRY, S. B. S. VISWANATHAN, V. RAMASASTRY, C. J. PHYS. SOC. JAP. 35 (2), 508-13, 1973.
53786	ELECTRONIC BAND STRUCTURE AND OPTICAL PROPERTIES OF LEAD TELLURIDE, LEAD SELENIDE AND LEAD SULFIDE. KOHN, S. E. YU, P. Y. PETROFF, Y. SHEN, Y. R. TSANG, Y. COHEN, M. L. PHYS. REV. 8 B (4), 1477-88 1973.
53787	DETERMINATION OF THE OPTICAL CONSTANTS OF THIN FILMS OF LOW ABSORBANCE. APPLICATION TO MAGNESIUM FLUORIDE IN THE 1000-2000 A REGION. DAUDE, A. SAVARY, A. SEIGNAE, A. ROBIN, S. OPT. ACTA 20 (5), 353-7, 1973.
53788	AN AMPLITUDE FOURIER SPECTROMETER FOR INFRARED SOLID STATE SPECTROSCOPY. GAST, J. GENZEL, L. OPT. COMMUN. 8 (1), 26-30, 1973.
53789	THEORY OF INFRARED ABSORPTION BY CRYSTALS IN THE HIGH FREQUENCY WING OF THEIR FUNDAMENTAL LATTICE ABSORPTION. MILLS, D. L. MARADUDIN, A. A. PHYS. REV. 8 B (4), 1617-30, 1973.
53790	VIBRATION-INDUCED ABSORPTION (B BAND) OF S-2-CONFIGURATIONS IONS IN ALKALI-HALIDE CRYSTALS. TSUBOI, T. NAKAI, Y. OYAMA, K. JACOBS, P. W. M. PHYS. REV. 8 B (4), 1698-707, 1973.
53794	HOT ELECTRONS. POZELA, J. PROM. ARM. (5), 76-8, 1973.
53796	LOW-TEMPERATURE PHASE TRANSITION OF SODIUM NIOBATE AND THE STRUCTURE OF THE LOW-TEMPERATURE PHASE, N. DARLINGTON, C. N. W. MEGAW, H. D. ACTA CRYSTALLOGR. 29 B (PT. 10), 2171-85, 1973.
53798	STRUCTURE AND MAGNETIC PROPERTIES OF PHASES OCCURRING IN A COBALT-SILICON ALLOY OF EUTECTIC COMPOSITION. JOHNSON, R. E. RAYSON, H. W. WRIGHT, W. ACTA MET. 21 (10), 1471-7, 1973.
53799	PREPARATION AND SEMICONDUCTING PROPERTIES OF PSEUDOBINARY SOLID SOLUTIONS ZINC ARSENIDE - ZINC PHOSPHIDE. ZDANOWICZ, W. KROLICKI, F. PLENKIEWICZ, P. ACTA PHYS. POL. 44 A (3), 447-54, 1973.
53801	POLARIZATION STATE OF A VERY INTENSE LIGHT BEAM AFTER TRAVERSING A NONLINEAR MEDIUM. NGUYEN PHU, X. DESBLANCS, R. G. ADVAN. RAMAN SPECTROSC. 1, 43-56, 1972.
53802	RAMAN SPECTRUM OF SINGLE CRYSTAL LEAD(II) TITANATE. FREY, R. A. ADVAN. RAMAN SPECTROSC. 1, 181-7, 1972.
53804	RAMAN SCATTERING OF LIGHT BY MOLECULAR IMPURITIES IN ALKALI HALIDES. REBANE, K. REBANE, L. HALDRE, T. GOROKHOVSKII, A. A. ADVAN. RAMAN SPECTROSC. 1, 379-84, 1972.
53809	OCCURRENCE OF LOCAL MAGNETIC MOMENTS IN DISORDERED MATERIALS. CYROT, M. AMORPHOUS MAGN., PROC. INT. SYMP. 161-7, 1973. (EDITED BY HENRY O. HOOPER, PLENUM: NEW YORK)
53819	AMORPHOUS SPIN POLARIZATION IN A TERBIUM-IRON COMPOUND. RHYNE, J. J. PICKART, S. J. ALPERIN, H. A. AMORPHOUS MAGN., PROC. INT. SYMP. 373-81, 1973. (EDITED BY HENRY O. HOOPER, PLENUM: NEW YORK)
53822	X-RAY PHOTOELECTRON SPECTRA OF LEAD OXIDES. KIM, K. S. O'LEARY, T. J. WINOGRAD, N. ANAL. CHEM. 45 (13), 2214-18, 1973.
53823	LUMINESCENCE OF UNDOPED MAGNESIUM OXIDE UNDER IRRADIATION WITH 500-KEV PROTONS. SEIYAMA, T. YOSHIDA, T. HIRAOKA, E. ANNU. REP. RADIAT. CENT. OSAKA PREFECT. 13, 73-5, 1972.
53824	EFFECTS OF ROOM-TEMPERATURE ANNEALING ON THE LUMINESCENCE OF ELECTRON-IRRADIATED ZINC SULFIDE. SHONO, Y. YOSHIDA, T. ANNU. REP. RADIAT. CENT. OSAKA PREFECT. 13, 76-8, 1972.
53826	MEASUREMENT OF ELECTRIC CONDUCTIVITY OF MOLTEN FLUORIDES. PTAK, W. BOTOR, J. ARCH. HUTN. 18 (2), 101-14, 1973.
53834	DOPING EFFECTS ON THE SEMICONDUCTING PROPERTIES OF GADOLINIUM COPPER OXIDE. KENJO, T. YAJIMA, S. BULL. CHEM. SOC. JAP. 46 (9), 2619-25, 1973.
53835	EMISSION PROCESSES IN CADMIUM PHOTOSENSITIZATION. TSUNASHIMA, S. TOYONO, T. SATO, S. BULL. CHEM. SOC. JAP. 46 (9), 2654-9, 1973.
53838	DIELECTRIC ANOMALY OF POTASSIUM SULFATE NEAR THE PHASE TRANSITION POINT. WATANABE, T. SAKAI, K. IWAI, S. BULL. TOKYO INST. TECHNOL. (117), 13-15, 1973.

EPIC Number	Bibliographic Citation
53840	HIGHER PERMANENT MAGNET ENERGY PRODUCTS. NEW OUTLOOKS AND ADVANCES WITH RESPECT TO INTERMETALLIC COMPOUNDS OF RARE EARTHS. FAHLENBRACH, H. CHEM.-ANLAGEN VERFAHREN (5), 105-6, 1973.
53844	ELECTROLUMINESCENCE OF ZINC TELLURIDE DIODES. BALA, W. LOZYKOWSKI, H. SEKULSKI, J. BULL. ACAD. POL. SCI., SER. SCI., MATH., ASTRON. PHYS. 21 (11), 1047-53, 1973.
53848	USE OF THE HALL EFFECT TO STUDY THE CHEMISORPTION OF ATOMIC AND MOLECULAR OXYGEN ON OXIDE SEMICONDUCTORS. AGAYAN, B. S. MYASNIKOV, I. A. TSIVENKO, V. I. RUSS. J. PHYS. CHEM. 47 (4), 553-5, 1973. (ENGLISH TRANSLATION OF ZH. FIZ. KHIM., 47 (4), 980-3, 1973; FOR ORIGINAL SEE E51345)
53851	THE CHEMISTRY OF LEAD SULFIDE PHOTODETECTORS, VOLUME I: THE CHEMISTRY OF SENSITIZATION. WOLTEN, G. M. THE AEROSPACE CORP., EL SEGUNDO, CALIF. 20PP., 1973. (AD-771 770, SAMSO-TR-73-391, VOL. 1, AVAIL. NTIS)
53852	ELECTRON RADIATION DAMAGE AND ANNEALING OF MERCURY(1-X) CADMIUM(X) TELLURIDE AT LOW TEMPERATURES. MELNGAILIS, J. RYAN, J. L. HARMAN, T. C. J. APPL. PHYS. 44 (6), 2647-51, 1973. (AD-771 844, ESD-TR-73-314, AVAIL. NTIS)
53853	FREE-CARRIER ABSORPTION IN N-TYPE LEAD TELLURIDE. STRAUSS, A. J. J. NONMETALS 1, 133-6, 1973. (AD-772 149, ESD-TR-73-149, AVAIL. NTIS)
53854	FIELD-DEPENDENT CONDUCTIVITY OF CHALCOGENIDE GLASSES. REINHARD, D. K. ARNTZ, V. O. ADLER, D. APPL. PHYS. LETT. 23 (9), 521-3, 1973. (AD-772 264, AVAIL. NTIS)
53855	PROPERTIES OF CRYSTALLINE AND AMORPHOUS SILICON TELLURIDE. PETERSEN, K. E. BIRKHOLZ, U. ADLER, D. PHYS. REV. 8 (4), 1453-61, 1973. (AD-772 305, AVAIL. NTIS)
53860	EFFECT OF MILLING ON THE INTRINSIC COERCIVITY OF BARIUM FERRITE POWDERS. HANEDA, K. KOJIMA, H. J. AMER. CERAM. SOC. 57 (2), 68-71, 1974.
53861	TRANSITION FROM IONIC TO ELECTRONIC CONDUCTION IN PURE THORIUM OXIDE UNDER REDUCING CONDITIONS. CHOUDHURY, N. S. PATTERSON, J. W. J. AMER. CERAM. SOC. 57 (2), 90-4, 1974.
53862	SPUTTERED THIN FILMS FOR INTEGRATED OPTICS. DEITCH, R. H. WEST, E. J. GIALLORENZI, T. G. WELLER, J. F. APPL. OPT. 13 (4), 712-15, 1974.
53863	INVESTIGATIONS OF LASER-INDUCED THERMAL LENSING AND INTERFERENCE FROM INFRARED TRANSMITTING MATERIALS. BENDOW, B. SKOLNIK, L. H. CROSS, E. F. APPL. OPT. 13 (4), 729-31, 1974. (AD 780 888)
53864	LOW LOSS FUSED SILICA MADE BY THE PLASMA TORCH. NASSAU, K. RICH, T. C. SHIEVER, J. W. APPL. OPT. 13 (4), 744-5, 1974.
53865	OPTICAL DATA STORAGE POTENTIAL OF SIX MATERIALS. BROWN, B. R. APPL. OPT. 13 (4), 761-6, 1974.
53867	MAGNETIC PROPERTIES OF COBALT PEROXYTITANATE. DE STROOPER, K. HENRIET-ISERENTANT, C. ROBBRECHT, G. BRABERS, V. C. R. ACAD. SCI. 277 B (3), 75-8, 1973.
53868	PYROELECTRIC BEHAVIOR NEAR THE CURIE POINT OF BARIUM TITANATES DOPED WITH IRON. THIEBAUD, C. CHANUSSOT, G. C. R. ACAD. SCI. 277 B (3), 95-8, 1973.
53869	VARIATION WITH TEMPERATURE OF THE MOESSBAUER PARAMETERS AND MAGNETIC PROPERTIES OF AN YTTRIUM - IRON COMPOUND. BARB, D. BURZO, E. MORARIU, M. C. R. ACAD. SCI. 277 B (6), 131-4, 1973.
53871	EXPERIMENTAL RESULTS CONCERNING THE DISTRIBUTION OF GROUPS OF TRAPS DUE TO COBALT IN A ZINC SULFIDE ACTIVATED WITH COPPER AND WITH COBALT AT DIFFERENT NEAR-AMBIENT TEMPERATURES. LE MOAL-DAIRE, M. F. SEVERIN-ROLLAND, F. C. R. ACAD. SCI. 277 B (7), 159-62, 1973.
53873	NEW THEORY OF THE ELECTRICAL CONDUCTIVITY OF ALKALI METAL HALIDES DOPED WITH BIVALENT IMPURITIES. BIZOUARD, M. C. R. ACAD. SCI., SER. 277 B (9), 211-13, 1973.
53874	COLLISION-FREE, TIME-RESOLVED FLUORESCENCE OF SULFUR DIOXIDE EXCITED NEAR 2900 A. BRUS, L. E. MC DONALD, J. R. CHEM. PHYS. LETT. 21 (2), 283-8, 1973.
53877	CHEMILUMINESCENCE AND LASER PHOTOLUMINESCENCE OF SOME DIATOMIC METAL HALIDES. CAPELLE, G. A. BRADFORD, R. S. BROIDA, H. P. CHEM. PHYS. LETT. 21 (2), 418-20, 1973.
53878	MAGNETIC PROPERTIES OF MOLTEN CHLORIDE SYSTEMS: MANGANESE(II) CHLORIDE - POTASSIUM CHLORIDE, COBALT(II) CHLORIDE - POTASSIUM CHLORIDE, AND NICKEL(II) CHLORIDE - POTASSIUM CHLORIDE. TANEMOTO, K. NAKAMURA, T. SATA, T. CHEM. LETT. (8), 911-14, 1973.
53882	SYNTHESIS AND CRYSTALLOGRAPHIC AND MAGNETIC PROPERTIES OF BORIDE OXIDE, IRON OXIDE, MAGNESIUM AND BORIDE OXIDE, IRON OXIDE NICKEL OXIDE. MIKHOV, V. T. APOSTOLOV, A. TARALESHKOVA, V. S. ANDREEVSKA, V. G. DOKL. BOLG. AKAD. NAUK 26 (7), 859-62, 1973.
53884	INFLUENCE OF HEAT TREATMENT ON THE POSISTOR EFFECT OF SEMICONDUCTIVE BARIUM TITANATE CERAMIC. SIMEONOV, K. DOKL. BOLG. AKAD. NAUK 26 (7), 887-90, 1973.
53888	LOW-COERCIVITY COPPER-MANGANESE FERRITES WITH RECTANGULAR HYSTERESIS LOOPS CONTAINING ZINC AND CALCIUM. KHOMYAKOV, YU. M. ELEKTRON. STR. FIZ. SVOISTVA TVERD. TELA, DOKL. VSES. SIMP. FIZ. SVOISTVAM ELEKTRON. STR. PEREKHODNYKH METAL., IKH SPLAVOV SOEDIN., 7TH 1, 125-31, 1972. (EDITED BY G. V. SAMSONOV, NAUKOVA DUMKA: KIEV, USSR)
53893	MAGNETIC MATERIALS FOR OPTICAL RECORDING. CHEN, D. APPL. OPT. 13 (4), 767-78, 1974.
53894	OPTIMUM THICKNESS OF MANGANESE BISMUTH FILMS FOR MAGNETOOPTICAL MEMORY. ESHO, S. NOGUCHI, S. ONO, Y. NAGAO, M. APPL. OPT. 13 (4), 779-83, 1974.
53895	ELECTRICAL CONTROL IN PHOTOFERROELECTRIC MATERIALS FOR OPTICAL STORAGE. MICHERON, F. MAYEUX, C. TROTIER, J. C. APPL. OPT. 13 (4), 784-7, 1974.
53896	IRON-DOPED LITHIUM NIOBIUM OXIDE FOR READ-WRITE APPLICATIONS. STAEBLER, D. L. PHILLIPS, W. APPL. OPT. 13 (4), 788-94, 1974.
53898	DIGITAL SPATIAL MODULATORS. TAKEDA, Y. APPL. OPT. 13 (4), 825-31, 1974.
53899	EVOLUTION OF OPTICAL THIN FILMS BY SPUTTERING. COLEMAN, W. J. APPL. OPT. 13 (4), 946-51, 1974.
53901	INFRARED ABSORPTION OF MIXED SILICON ISOTOPE PAIRS IN GALLIUM ARSENIDE. LEUNG, P. C. FREDRICKSON, J. SPITZER, W. G. KAHAN, A. BOUTHILLETTE, L. J. APPL. PHYS. 45 (3), 1009-12, 1974. (AD-781 450)

EPIC Number *Bibliographic Citation*

53902 **ELECTRICAL CONDUCTIVITY OF DISORDERED LAYERS IN GALLIUM ARSENIDE CRYSTAL PRODUCED BY ION IMPLANTATION.**
KATO, Y. SHIMADA, T. SHIRAKI, Y.
KOMATSUBARA, K. F.
J. APPL. PHYS.
45 (3), 1044–9, 1974.

53903 **DEFECT CENTERS IN OXYGEN-DEFICIENT RE-SPUTTERED SILICON OXIDE FILMS. II. THERMOLUMINESCENCE.**
HICKMOTT, T. W.
J. APPL. PHYS.
45 (3), 1060–70, 1974.

53904 **EFFECT OF HYDROXIDE ION ON THE LOW-FREQUENCY DIELECTRIC CONSTANT OF VITREOUS SILICA.**
ANDEEN, C. SCHUELE, D. JONTANELLA, J.
J. APPL. PHYS.
45 (3), 1071–4, 1974.

53908 **CONTACT-FREE CONDUCTIVITY IN A INHOMOGENEOUS MEDIUM: VITREOUS SEMICONDUCTORS.**
STROM, U. TAYLOR, P. C.
J. APPL. PHYS.
45 (3), 1246–53, 1974.

53910 **PROPERTIES OF SCHOTTKY BARRIERS AND P–N JUNCTIONS PREPARED WITH GALLIUM ARSENIDE AND ALUMINUM GALLIUM ARSENIDE MOLECULAR BEAM EPITAXIAL LAYERS.**
CHO, A. Y. CASEY, H. C., JR.
J. APPL. PHYS.
45 (3), 1258–63, 1974.

53912 **PROPERTIES OF ZINC-DOPED GALLIUM NITRIDE. I. PHOTOLUMINESCENCE.**
PANKOVE, J. I. BERKEYHEISER, J. E.
MILLER, E. A.
J. APPL. PHYS.
45 (3), 1280–6, 1974.

53913 **HOT-ELECTRON MAGNETIC SUSCEPTIBILITY OF DEGENERATE SEMICONDUCTORS AT LOW TEMPERATURES.**
PAL, B. P. SHARMA, S. K.
J. APPL. PHYS.
45 (3), 1287–90, 19 7.

53914 **EVIDENCE OF A PRECIPITATELIKE ZONE IN A S-GROWN GALLIUM ARSENIDE AND ITS INFLUENCE ON OPTICAL ABSORPTIVITY.**
VANDER SANDE, J. B. PETERS, E. T.
J. APPL. PHYS.
45 (3), 1298–1301, 1974.

53915 **PREPARATION AND PROPERTIES OF CADMIUM TIN PHOSPHIDE, INDIUM PHOSPHIDE HETEROJUNCTIONS GROWN BY LPE FROM TIN SOLUTION.**
SHAY, J. L. BACHMAN, K. J. BUEHLER, E.
J. APPL. PHYS.
45 (3), 1302–10, 1974.

53916 **LOW-ENERGY CATHODOLUMINESCENCE OF ZINC OXIDE: THE ZINC OXIDE-PLASMA DISPLAY.**
PENNEBAKER, W. B. O'HANLON, J. F.
J. APPL. PHYS.
45 (3), 1315–22, 1974.

53917 **CALCULATION OF THE MINORITY-CARRIER CONFINEMENT PROPERTIES OF III–V SEMICONDUCTOR HETEROJUNCTIONS (APPLIED TO TRANSMISSION-MODE PHOTOCATHODES).**
JAMES, L. W.
J. APPL. PHYS.
45 (3), 1326–35, 1974.

53918 **LOW-CURRENT-DENSITY LIGHT-EMITTING-DIODE PUMPED NEODYMIUM: YTTRIUM ARGON GARNET LASER USING A SOLID CYLINDRICAL REFLECTOR.**
FARMER, G. I. KIANG, Y. C.
J. APPL. PHYS.
45 (3), 1356–71, 1974.

53919 **SOME SUPERCONDUCTING PROPERTIES OF MULTIFILAMENTARY NIOBIUM CARBONITRIDE.**
OHMER, M. C. FREDERICK, W. G. D.
J. APPL. PHYS.
45 (3), 1382–4, 1974.

53921 **TRANSITION TEMPERATURES AND CRYSTAL STRUCTURES OF SINGLE-CRYSTAL AND POLYCRYSTALLINE NIOBIUM NITRIDE FILMS.**
OYA, G–I. ONODERA, Y.
J. APPL. PHYS.
45 (3), 1389–97, 1974.

53923 **INJECTION ELECTROLUMINESCENCE IN PHOSPHOROUS-ION-IMPLANTED ZINC SELENIDE P–N JUNCTION DIODES.**
PARK, Y. S. SHIN, B. K.
J. APPL. PHYS.
45 (3), 1444–6, 1974.
(AD–786 279, ARL–74–0053)

53924 **CHARACTERISTICS OF EFFUSED SLAB WAVEGUIDES IN LITHIUM NIOBIUM OXIDE.**
WOOD, V. E. HARTMAN, N. F. VERBER, C. M.
J. APPL. PHYS.
45 (3), 1449–51, 1974.

53925 **MOBILITY OF ELECTRONS IN MERCURY CADMIUM TELLURIDE.**
CHATTOPADHYAY, D. NAG, B. R.
J. APPL. PHYS.
45 (3), 1463–5, 1974.

53927 **DETERMINATION OF RELEVANT PARAMETERS OF THE DOPANTS ZINC AND TELLURIUM FROM C–T MEASUREMENTS IN GALLIUM PHOSPHIDE (ZINC, OXIDE) P–N JUNCTIONS.**
FERENCZI, G.
J. APPL. PHYS.
45 (3), 1480–1, 1974.

53928 **THERMAL EXPANSION AND ELECTRICAL CONDUCTIVITY OF COPPER IRON SULFIDE SEMICONDUCTOR FILMS AT LOW TEMPERATURES.**
ALIEV, F. YU. KASUMOVA, E. G.
PIS'MA ZH. EKSP. TEOR. FIZ.
18 (1), 3–7, 1973.

53939 **QUANTUM THEORY OF FREE CARRIER ABSORPTION IN POLAR SEMICONDUCTORS.**
JENSEN, B.
ANN. PHYS. (N. Y.)
80 (2), 284–360, 1973.

53943 **TWO-PHOTON ABSORPTION OF NEODYMIUM LASER RADIATION IN GALLIUM ARSENIDE.**
KLEINMAN, D. A. MILLER, R. C.
NORDLAND, W. A., JR.
APPL. PHYS. LETT.
23 (5), 243–4, 1973.

53954 **EXPERIMENTAL INFORMATION ON THE ANGLE DEPENDENT INTERACTION BETWEEN POLYATOMIC MOLECULES.**
BEENAKKER, J. J. M. KNAAP, H. F. P.
SANCTUARY, B. C.
AIP (AMER. INST. PHYS.) CONF. PROC.
(11), 21–50, 1973.

53958 **NEW PIEZOELECTRIC CRYSTAL. BARIUM GERMANIUM TITANIUM OXIDE.**
KIMURA, M. DOI, K. NANAMATSU, S.
KAWAMURA, T.
APPL. PHYS. LETT.
23 (10), 531–2, 1973.

53960 **HIGH-FIELD MAGNETIZATION AND COERCIVITY OF AMORPHOUS RARE EARTH IRON ALLOYS.**
CLARK, A. E.
APPL. PHYS. LETT.
23 (11), 642–4, 1973.

53982 **CLUSTER MODEL CALCULATIONS OF SILICON DEFECTS.**
SCHAAKE, H. F. HENCH, L. L.
DEPT. OF ELECTRICAL ENGINEERING, FLORIDA UNIV., GAINESVILLE
73–174, 1972.
(AD–766 406, AFCRL–TR–73–0164, AVAIL. NTIS)

53986 **TRANSPORT PROCESSES IN SOLIDS.**
GLICKSMAN, M.
AIP (AMER. INST. PHYS.), CONF. PROC.
(11), 99–129, 1973.

53988 **MAGNETIC SUSCEPTIBILITIES OF TRIVALENT LANTHANIDE IONS IN AN OCTAHEDRAL ENVIRONMENT.**
HOEHN, M. V. KARRAKER, D. G.
J. CHEM. PHYS.
60 (2), 393–7, 1974.

53989 **ELECTRONIC SPECTRUM AND MAGNETIC PROPERTIES OF CESIUM MANGANESE BROMIDE.**
MC PHERSON, G. L. ALDRICH, H. S.
CHANG, J. R.
J. CHEM. PHYS.
60 (2), 534–7, 1974.

53990 **OPTICAL STUDY OF THE SITE SYMMETRY DISTRIBUTION IN POTASSIUM BROMIDE: SAMARIUM.**
SUNDBERG, M. N. LAUER, H. V. CHILVER, C. R.
FONG, F. K.
J. CHEM. PHYS.
60 (2), 561–71, 1974.

53995 **THERMAL CONDUCTIVITY OF VANADIUM AND CHROMIUM MONONITRIDES.**
AIVAZOV, M. I. MURANEVICH, A. KH.
DOMASHNEV, I. A.
TEPLOFIZ. VYS. TEMP.
11 (4), 768–71, 1973.
(FOR ENGLISH TRANSLATION SEE E53996)

53996 **THERMAL CONDUCTIVITY OF VANADIUM AND CHROMIUM MONONITRIDES.**
AIVAZOV, M. I. MURANEVICH, A. KH.
DOMASHNEV, I. A.
HIGH TEMP.
11 (4), 690–2, 1973.
(ENGLISH TRANSLATION OF TEPLOFIZ. VYS. TEMP., 11 (4), 768–71, 1973; FOR ORIGINAL SEE E53995)

EPIC Number	Bibliographic Citation
53997	**RADIATION OF A HOMOGENEOUS PLANE-PARALLEL BED OF SPHERICAL PARTICLES.** DOMBROVSKII, L. A. IVENSKIKH, N. N. TEPLOFIZ. VYS. TEMP. 11 (4), 818-22, 1973. (FOR ENGLISH TRANSLATION SEE E53998)
53998	**RADIATION OF A HOMOGENEOUS PLANE-PARALLEL BED OF SPHERICAL PARTICLES.** DOMBROVSKII, L. A. IVENSKIKH, N. N. HIGH TEMP. 11 (4), 731-4, 1973. (ENGLISH TRANSLATION OF TEPLOFIZ. VYS. TEMP., 11 (4), 818-22, 1973; FOR ORIGINAL SEE E53997)
54003	**MAGNETIC PROPERTIES OF RARE EARTH-INDIUM INTERMETALLIC COMPOUNDS.** HUTCHENS, R. D. WALLACE, W. E. NERESON, N. DEPT. CHEM. UNIV. PITTSBURGH, PITTSBURGH, PA. 12PP., 1973. (COO-3429-10, AVAIL. NTIS)
54004	**MAGNETIC AND ELECTRICAL CHARACTERISTICS OF TERNARY SYSTEMS INVOLVING RARE EARTHS AND D-TRANSITION METALS.** WALLACE, W. E. CRAIG, R. S. RAO, V. U. S. BUTERA, R. A. DEPT. CHEM., UNIV. PITTSBURGH, PITTSBURGH, PA. 19PP., 1973. (COO-3429-17, AVAIL. NTIS)
54007	**PHASE DIAGRAMS AND OTHER DATA FOR LIQUID METAL AND INORGANIC MOLTEN SALT SYSTEMS. ALKALI METAL TETRAFLUOROBORATES.** OHNO, H. FURUKAWA, K. JAPAN AT. ENERGY RES. INST., TOKYO, JAPAN 57PP., 1972. (JAERI-M-5023, AVAIL. NTIS)
54020	**LOW TEMPERATURE COEFFAICIENTS OF RESISTANCE IN MANGANESE OXIDE FILMS.** FRANKSON, R. W. SLACK, L. H. AMER. CERAM. SOC. BULL. 53 (2), 153-5, 1974.
54022	**DEFECTS IN OXIDES.** WAGNER, J. B., JR. AMER. CERAM. SOC. BULL. 53 (3), 224-31, 1974.
54023	**REACTION SINTERED SILICON NITRIDE FOR HIGH TEMPERATURE RADOME APPLICATIONS.** WALTON, J. D., JR. AMER. CERAM. SOC. BULL. 53 (3), 255-8, 1974.
54024	**HIGH-POWER 2- TO 6- MU M WINDOW MATERIAL FIGURES OF MERIT WITH EDGE COOLING AND SURFACE ABSORPTION INCLUDED.** SPARKS, M. CHOW, H. C. J. APPL. PHYS. 45 (4), 1510-7, 1974. (ERRATUM: TITLE IBID, AUTHORS IBID, J. IBID, 45 (8), 3697, 1974.)
54026	**OPTICAL AND CHANNELING STUDIES OF ION-BOMBARDED GALLIUM PHOSPHIDE.** WEMPLE, S. H. NORTH, J. C. DISHMAN, J. M. J. APPL. PHYS. 45 (4), 1578-89, 1974.
54027	**IMPURITY CONTROL OF DOMAIN SWITCHING IN FERROELECTRIC BISMUTH TITANATE.** LUKE, T. E. J. APPL. PHYS. 45 (4), 1605-10, 1974.
54028	**DIFFERENTIAL THERMAL ANALYSIS OF FERROELECTRIC AND FERROELASTIC TRANSITIONS IN BARIUM SODIUM NIOBATE.** TOLEDANO, J. C. PATEAU, L. J. APPL. PHYS. 45 (4), 1611-4, 1974.
54033	**LIGHT-EMITTING MECHANISM OF ZINC TELLURIDE-CADMIUM SULFIDE HETEROJUNCTION DIODES.** OTA, T. KOBAYASHI K. TAKAHASHI, K. J. APPL. PHYS. 45 (4), 1750-5, 1974.
54034	**INFLUENCE OF DISLOCATIONS ON ELECTRICAL CONDUCTIVITY OF CADMIUM TELLURIDE.** BUCH, F. AHLQUIST, C. N. J. APPL. PHYS. 45 (4), 1756-61, 1974. (AD-782 830)
54035	**BEHAVIOR OF ABOVE-GAP NN PAIR STATES IN RADIATIVE RECOMBINATION IN NITROGEN MONOPOSITIVE ION DOPED GALLIUM ARSENIDE PHOSPHIDE.** LEE, M. H. HOLONYAK, N., JR. CAMPBELL, J. C. GROVES, W. O. CRAFORD, M. G. J. APPL. PHYS. 45 (4), 1775-8, 1974.
54036	**SPONTANEOUS POWER AND THE COHERENT STATE OF INJECTION LASERS.** SOMMERS, H. S., JR. NORTH, D. O. J. APPL. PHYS. 45 (4), 1787-93, 1974.
54037	**ELECTRON EFFECTIVE MASS AND CONDUCTION-BAND EFFECTIVE DENSITY OF STATES IN BISMUTH SILICON OXIDE.** LAUER, R. B. J. APPL. PHYS. 45 (4), 1794-7, 1974.
54038	**OPERATION OF A SMALL SINGLE-MODE STABLE CW HYDROGEN FLUORIDE LASER.** HINCHEN, J. J. J. APPL. PHYS. 45 (4), 1818-21, 1974.
54040	**INFLUENCE OF DEEP TRAPS ON THE MEASUREMENT OF FREE-CARRIER DISTRIBUTIONS IN SEMICONDUCTORS BY JUNCTION CAPACITANCE TECHNIQUES.** KIMERLING, L. C. J. APPL. PHYS. 45 (4), 1839-45, 1974.
54045	**CONDUCTANCE SWITCHING OF THERMALLY GROWN SILICON OXIDE.** WILMSEN, C. W. ALLENDER, M. C. J. APPL. PHYS. 45 (4), 1912-4, 1974.
54054	**TRANSVERSE SUSCEPTIBILITY IN POTASSIUM DIHYDROGEN PHOSPHATE TYPE CRYSTALS.** HAVLIN, S. LITOV, E. UEHLING, E. A. PHYS. REV. 9 B (3), 1024-8, 1974.
54055	**MAGNETIC PROPERTIES OF NEPTUNIUM PALLADIUM AND PLUTONIUM PALLADIUM INTERMETALLIC COMPOUNDS.** NELLIS, W. J. HARVEY, A. R. LANDER, G. H. DUNLAP, B. D. BRODSKY, M. B. MUELLER, M. H. REDDY, J. F. DAVIDSON, G. R. PHYS. REV. 9 B (3), 1041-51, 1974.
54057	**PHONON BEHAVIOR AND DISORDER MECHANISM IN SODIUM CHLORATE.** RAO, A. D. P. ANDRADE, P. R. PORTO, S. P. S. PHYS. REV. 9 B (3), 1077-84, 1974.
54059	**OPTICAL PROPERTIES AND ELECTRONIC STRUCTURE OF ORDERED AND DISORDERED COPPER GOLD.** SCOTT, W. MULDAWER, L. PHYS. REV. 9 B (4), 1115-25, 1974.
54061	**MODEL CALCULATION FOR FIELD EMISSION FROM ADSORBATE-COVERED 100 FACE OF TUNGSTEN.** BAGCHI, A. YOUNG, P. L. PHYS. REV. 9 B (4), 1194-9, 1974.
54064	**MICROSCOPIC MAGNETIC PROPERTIES OF METALLIC AND INSULATING VANADIUM OXIDES.** GOSSARD, A. C. REMEIKA, J. P. RICE, T. M. YASUOKA, H. PHYS. REV. 9 B (4), 1230-9, 1974.
54065	**SUPERCONVERGENCE AND SUM RULES FOR THE OPTICAL CONSTANTS: PHYSICAL MEANING, COMPARISON WITH EXPERIMENT, AND GENERALIZATION.** ALTARELLI, M. SMITH, D. Y. PHYS. REV. 9 B (4), 1290-8, 1974.
54071	**SIGN REVERSAL IN THE FIELD DEPENDENCE OF THE HALL EFFECT IN YTTRIUM ZINC AT LIQUID-HELIUM TEMPERATURES.** JAN, J. P. MARTIN, N. L. WENGER, A. PHYS. REV. 9 B (4), 1377-80, 1974.
54072	**SPIN FLUCTUATIONS IN ACTINIDE INTERMETALLIC COMPOUNDS.** BRODSKY, M. B. PHYS. REV. 9 B (4), 1381-7, 1974.
54075	**ANISOTROPIC PIEZOELECTRIC POLARON.** LICARI, J. J. WHITFIELD, G. PHYS. REV. 9 B (4), 1432-40, 1974.
54076	**RESISTIVITY OF NEARLY MAGNETIC METALS AT HIGH TEMPERATURES: APPLICATION TO NEPTUNIUM AND PLUTONIUM.** JULLIEN, R. BEAL-MONOD, M. T. COQBLIN, B. PHYS. REV. 9 B (4), 1441-57, 1974.

EPIC Number	Bibliographic Citation
54079	PHOTOEMISSION STUDY OF THE EFFECT OF BULK DOPING AND OXYGEN OXPOSURE ON SILICON SURFACE STATES. WAGNER, L. F. SPICER, W. E. PHYS. REV. 9 B (4), 1512–5, 1974.
54080	DEPENDENCE OF EXCITON REFLECTANCE ON FIELD AND OTHER SURFACE CHARACTERISTICS: THE CASE OF INDIUM PHOSPHIDE. EVANGELISTI, F. FISCHBACH, J. U. FROVA, A. PHYS. REV. 9 B (4), 1516–24, 1974.
54081	CUBIC CONTRIBUTIONS TO THE SPHERICAL MODEL OF SHALLOW ACCEPTOR STATES. BALDERESCHI, A. LIPARI, N. O. PHYS. REV. 9 B (4), 1525–39, 1974.
54082	NONLOCAL PSEUDOPOTENTIALS FOR GERMANIUM AND GALLIUM ARSENIDE. PANDEY, K. C. PHILLIPS, J. C. PHYS. REV. 9 B (4), 1552–9, 1974.
54083	FINE STRUCTURE OF E–1 PEAK IN GERMANIUM AND GALLIUM ARSENIDE. PANDEY, K. C. PHILLIPS, J. C. PHYS. REV. 9 B (4), 1560–3, 1974.
54084	KINETICS OF LONG–WAVELENGTH INFRARED STIMULATION OF DONOR–ACCEPTOR PAIR LUMINESCENCE IN ZINC SULFIDE. ALLEN, J. W. PHYS. REV. 9 B (4), 1564–77, 1974.
54085	STUDY OF LOCALIZED LEVELS. II. THE MEANING OF TEMPERATURE–INDUCED CHANGES IN ACTIVATION ON ENERGIES FOR ELECTRICAL CONDUCTION. SCHMIDLIN, F. W. ROBERTS, G. G. PHYS. REV. 9 B (4), 1578–90, 1974.
54086	TEMPERATURE–DEPENDENT ELECTRICAL PROPERTIES OF MERCURY SELENIDE. LEHOCZKY, S. L. BROERMAN, J. G. NELSON, D. A. WHITSETT, C. R. PHYS. REV. 9 B (4), 1598–1620, 1974.
54087	ELECTRON MOBILITY IN INDIUM GALLIUM ARSENIDE ALLOYS. GLICKSMAN, M. ENSTROM, R. E. MITTLEMAN, S. A. APPERT, J. R. PHYS. REV. 9 B (4), 1621–6, 1974.
54089	ELECTRONIC STRUCTURE AND OPTICAL PROPERTIES OF LEAD IODIDE. SCHLUTER, I. CH. SCHLUTER, M. PHYS. REV. 9 B (4), 1652–63, 1974.
54091	THEORY OF ELECTRICAL INSTABILITIES OF MIXED ELECTRONIC AND THERMAL ORIGIN. KROLL, D. M. PHYS. REV. 9 B (4), 1669–1706, 1974.
54092	ENERGY BANDS OF SILVER INDIUM SULFIDE IN THE CHALCOPYRITE AND ORTHORHOMBIC STRUCTURES. SHAY, J. L. TELL, B. SCHIAVONE, L. M. KASPER, H. M. THIEL, F. PHYS. REV. 9 B (4), 1719–23, 1974.
54094	EXCITON STATES OF SEMICONDUCTORS IN A HIGH MAGNETIC FIELD. ALTARELLI, M. LIPARI, N. O. PHYS. REV. 9 B (4), 1733–50, 1974.
54095	PSEUDOGAP OF LIQUID THALLIUM TELLURIDE. CUTLER, M. PHYS. REV. 9 B (4), 1762–76, 1974.
54096	CALCULATED PROPERTIES OF THE N–2 DEFECT IN SODIUM AZIDE. BARTRAM, R. H. FISCHER, C. R. KEMMEY, P. J. PHYS. REV. 9 B (4), 1777–82, 1974.
54097	AC CONDUCTIVITY AND AC PHOTOCONDUCTIVITY IN AMORPHOUS AND CRYSTALLINE INSULATORS. ABKOWITZ, M. LAKATOS, A. SCHER, H. PHYS. REV. 9 B (4), 1813–22, 1974.
54098	ANALYTICAL AND EXPERIMENTAL CHECK OF A MODEL FOR CORRELATED THERMOLUMINESCENCE AND THERMALLY STIMULATED CONDUCTIVITY. FIELDS, D. E. MORAN, P. R. PHYS. REV. 9 B (4), 1836–41, 1974.
54099	CONDUCTIVITY AND DIELECTRIC CONSTANTS OF LITHIUM DEUTERIUM. VAROTSOS, P. PHYS. REV. 9 B (4), 1866–9, 1974.
54101	ELECTRONIC TRANSITIONS OF OXYGEN ADSORBED ON CLEAN SILICON (111) AND (100) SURFACES. IBACH, H. ROWE, J. E. PHYS. REV. 9 B (4), 1951–7, 1974.
54106	LUMINESCENCE CENTERS IN H– AND D–IMPLANTED 6H SILICON CARBIDE. PATRICK, L. CHOYKE, W. J. PHYS. REV. 9 B (4), 1997, 1974.
54108	DYNAMICAL JAHN–TELLER EFFECTS IN THE GROUND 4 T 1G AND THE EXCITED 4 T 2G ORBITAL TRIPLETS OF COBALT TRIPOSITIVE ION IN A MAGNESIUM OXIDE CRYSTAL. RAY, T. REGNARD, J. R. PHYS. REV. 9 B (5), 2110–21, 1974.
54109	DISPERSION OF THE SOFT E–MODE POLARITON IN BARIUM TITANIUM OXIDE. HEIMAN, D. USHIODA, S. PHYS. REV. 9 B (5), 2122–8, 1974. (AD–782 961)
54110	RUDERMAN–KITTEL–KASUYA–YOSIDA INTERACTION AND THE PARAMAGNETIC PROPERTIES OF RARE EARTH ZINC INTERMETALLIC COMPOUNDS. DEBRAY, D. SAKURAI, J. PHYS. REV. 9 B (5), 2129–33, 1974.
54111	OPTICAL PROPERTIES OF EPITAXIAL IRON GARNET THIN FILMS. WEMPLE, S. H. BLANK, S. L. SEMAN, J. A. BIOLSI, W. A. PHYS. REV. 9 B (5), 2134–44, 1974.
54113	THEORY OF MAGNETIC PROPERTIES OF ACTINIDE COMPOUNDS. II. ROBINSON, J. M. ERDOS, P. PHYS. REV. 9 B (5), 2187–93, 1974.
54116	ELECTRONIC STRUCTURE OF CUBIC LAVES–PHASE ZIRCONIUM ZINC: COMBINED INTERPOLATION SCHEME. JOHNSON, D. L. PHYS. REV. 9 B (5), 2273–87, 1974.
54122	TEMPERATURE DEPENDENCE OF THE FIRST– AND SECOND– ORDER CUBIC ANISOTROPY CONSTANTS IN EUROPIUM OXIDE. HUGHES, R. S. EVERETT, G. E. LAWSON, A. W. PHYS. REV. 9 B (5), 2394–8, 1974.
54126	THERMIONIC EMISSION OF CERTAIN CATHODE MATERIALS. GORDON, V. G. KUL'VARSKAYA, B. S. LEVINOV, B. M. REKOV, A. I. SPIRIDONOV, E. G. SOV. PHYS. TECH. PHYS. 18 (5), 632–4, 1973. (ENGLISH TRANSLATION OF ZH. TEKH. FIZ., 43 (5), 1000–3, 1973; FOR ORIGINAL SEE E51333)
54149	MASS SPECTROMETRY AND LUMINESCENT PROPERTIES OF ZINC SULFIDE:IODIDE SINGLE CRYSTALS. GUTAN, V. B. KUTSEV, V. S. LAVROV, A. V. SMAGINA, E. I. OPT. AND SPEKTROSK. 33 (6), 1116–20, 1972. (FOR ENGLISH TRANSLATION SEE E54150)
54150	MASS SPECTROMETRY AND LUMINESCENT PROPERTIES OF ZINC SULFIDE:IODIDE SINGLE CRYSTALS. GUTAN, V. B. KUTSEV, V. S. LAVROV, A. V. SMAGINA, E. I. OPT. SPECTROS., USSR 33 (6), 611–3, 1972. (ENGLISH TRANSLATION OF OPT. SPEKTROSK., 33 (6), 1116–20, 1972; FOR ORIGINAL SEE E54149)
54155	CADMIUM ANTIMONIDE AS A FILTER FOR IR RADIATION. BOGOMOLOV, P. A. BORETS, A. N. GERTOVICH, T. S. GOROBETS, N. V. RARENKO, I. M. TOVSTYUK, K. V. OPT.–MEKH. PROM.–ST. (USSR) 39 (10), 64, 1972. (FOR ENGLISH TRANSLATION SEE E54156)

EPIC Number	Bibliographic Citation
54156	**CADMIUM ANTIMONIDE AS A FILTER FOR IR RADIATION.** BOGOMOLOV, P. A. BORETS, A. N. GERTOVICH, T. S. GOROBETS, N. V. RARENKO, I. M. TOVSTYUK, K. V. SOV. J. OPT. TECHNOL. 39 (10), 645–6, 1972. (ENGLISH TRANSLATION OF OPT. MEKH. PROM., 39 (10), 64, 1972; FOR ORIGINAL SEE E54155)
54159	**OPTICAL AND ELECTRICAL PROPERTIES OF THIN FILMS OF GROUP V METAL NITRIDES.** CHEREZOVA, L. A. KRYZHANOVSKII, B. P. OPT.–MEKH. PROM.–ST. 39 (11), 65–6, 1972. (FOR ENGLISH TRANSLATION SEE E54160)
54160	**OPTICAL AND ELECTRICAL PROPERTIES OF THIN FILMS OF GROUP V METAL NITRIDES.** CHEREZOVA, L. A. KRYZHANOVSKII, B. P. SOV. J. OPT. TECHNOL. 39 (11), 717–8, 1972. (ENGLISH TRANSLATION OF OPT. MEKH. PROM., 39 (11) 65–6, 1972; FOR ORIGINAL SEE E54159)
54173	**NEGATIVE LONGITUDINAL MAGNETORESISTANCE OF N–TYPE INDIUM ANTIMONY AT 30 K.** IL'IN, V. A. SHAPIRO, E. Z. FIZ. TEKH. POLUPROVODN. 7 (2), 393–5, 1973. (FOR ENGLISH TRANSLATION SEE E54174)
54174	**NEGATIVE LONGITUDINAL MAGNETORESISTANCE OF N–TYPE INDIUM ANTIMONY AT 30 K.** IL'IN, V. A. SHAPIRO, E. Z. SOV. PHYS. – SEMICOND. 7 (2). 281–2, 1973. (ENGLISH TRANSLATION OF FIZ. TEKH. POLUPROV., 7 (2), 393–5, 1973; FOR ORIGINAL SEE E54173)
54179	**INFLUENCE OF UNIAXIAL COMPRESSION ON THE IMPURITY–BAND CONDUCTION IN P–TYPE INDIUM ANTIMONY.** GALAVANOV, V. V. OBUKHOV, S. A. FIZ. TEKH. POLUPROVODN. 7 (2), 400–2, 1973. (FOR ENGLISH TRANSLATION SEE E54180)
54180	**INFLUENCE OF UNIAXIAL COMPRESSION ON THE IMPURITY–BAND CONDUCTION IN P–TYPE INDIUM ANTIMONY.** GALAVANOV, V. V. OBUKHOV, S. A. SOV. PHYS. – SEMICOND. 7 (2), 287–8, 1973. (ENGLISH TRANSLATION OF FIZ. TEKH. POLUPROV., 7 (2), 400–2, 1973; FOR ORIGINAL SEE E54179)
54183	**ABSORPTION COEFFICIENT OF THE IS–2P LINE OF DEEP IMPURITY CENTERS.** YAKOVIEV, V. A. BIRYUKOVA, V. V. FIZ. AND TEKH. POLUPROVODN., USSR 7 (2), 407–9, 1973. (FOR ENGLISH TRANSLATION SEE E54184)
54184	**ABSORPTION COEFFICIENT OF THE 1S–2P LINE OF DEEP IMPURITY CENTERS.** YAKOVLEV, V. A. BIRYUKOVA, V. V. SOV. PHYS. – SEMICOND. 7 (2), 293–4, 1973. (ENGLISH TRANSLATION OF FIZ. TEKH. POLUPROV., 7 (2), 407–9, 1973; FOR ORIGINAL SEE E54183)
54193	**INVESTIGATION OF THE ABSORPTION EDGE OF ARSENIC SESQUISNLFIDE – GERMANIUM GLASSES.** ANDRIESH, A. M. TSIULYANU, D. I. FIZ. TEKH. POLUPROVODN. USSR 7 (2), 417–20, 1973. (FOR ENGLISH TRANSLATION SEE E54194)
54194	**INVESTIGATION OF THE ABSORPTION EDGE OF ARSENIC SULFIDE–GERMANIUM GLASSES.** ANDRIESH, A. M. TSIULYANU, D. I. FIZ. TEKH. POLUPROVODN. (USSR) 7 (2), 417–20, 1973. (ENGLISH TRANSLATION OF FIZ. TEKH. POLUPROV., 7 (2), 417–20, 1973; FOR ORIGINAL SEE E54193)
54195	**INDUCED BIREFRINGENCE IN GALLIUM PHOSPHIDE.** GLURDZHIDZE, L. N. IZERGIN, A. P. REMENYUK, A. D. KOPYLOVA, Z. N. FIZ. AND TEKH. POLUPROVODN., USSR 7 (2), 420–2, 1973. (FOR ENGLISH TRANSLATION SEE E54196)
54196	**INDUCED BIREFRINGENCE IN GALLIUM PHOSPHIDE.** GLURDZHIDZE, L. N. IZERGIN, A. P. REMENYUK, A. D. KOPYLOVA, Z. N. SOV. PHYS. – SEMICOND. 7 (2), 305–6, 1973. (ENGLISH TRANSLATION OF FIZ. TEKH. POLUPROV., 7 (2), 420–2, 1973; FOR ORIGINAL SEE E54195)

EPIC Number	Bibliographic Citation
54197	**TEMPERATURE DEPENDENCE OF THE MAXIMUM IN THE LUMINESCENCE SPECTRUM OF INDIUM ARSENIDE P–N JUNCTIONS.** ANISIMOVA, I. D. DRUGOVA, A. A. KURBATOV, L. N. KUZNETSOVA, E. M. YUNGERMAN, V. M. FIZ. TEKH. POLUPROVODN. 7 (2), 423–5, 1973. (FOR ENGLISH TRANSLATION SEE E54198)
54198	**TEMPERATURE DEPENDENCE OF THE MAXIMUM IN THE LUMINESCENCE SPECTRUM OF INDIUM ARSENIDE P–N JUNCTIONS.** ANISIMOVA, I. D. DRUGOVA, A. A. KURBATOV, L. N. KUZNETSOVA, E. M. YUNGERMAN, V. M. SOV. PHYS. – SEMICOND. 7 (2), 307–8, 1973. (ENGLISH TRANSLATION OF FIZ. TEKH. POLUPROV., 7 (2), 423–5, 1973; FOR ORIGINAL SEE E54197)
54199	**ELECTRORELECTION SPECTRA OF CRYSTALLINE AND GLASSY CADMIUM GERMANIUM ARSENIDE.** AKIMCHENKO, I. P. IVANOV, V. S. BORSHCHEVSKII, A. S. FIZ. TEKH. POLUPROVODN. 7 (2), 425–6, 1973. (FOR ENGLISH TRANSLATION SEE E54200)
54200	**ELECTROREFLECTION SPECTRA OF CRYSTALLINE AND GLASSY CADMIUM GERMANIUM ARSENIDE.** AKIMCHENKO, I. P. IVANOV, V. S. BORSHCHEVSKII, A. S. SOV. PHYS. – SEMICOND. 7 (2), 309–10, 1973. (ENGLISH TRANSLATION OF FIZ. TEKH. POLUPROV., 7 (2), 425–6, 1973; FOR ORIGINAL SEE E54199)
54202	**THE GENERATION OF FREE CARRIERS IN CD TE BY RADIATION.** TOUSEK, J. CZECH. J. PJYS. 23 B (12), 1403–6, 1973.
54204	**ANOMALOUSLY HIGH VALUES OF TRANSPARENCY OF GALLIUM ARSENIDE UNDER THE INTERACTION OF PICOSECOND LIGHT PULSES.** ZUBAREV, I. G. MATVEETS, YU. A. MIRONOV, A. B. SHATBERASHVILI, O. B. IZV. AKAD. NAUK SSSR SER. FIZ. 37 (10), 2099–103, 1973.
54206	**OPTICAL ABSORPTION COEFFICIENT IN GALLIUM NITRIDE GROWN BY VAPOUR PHASE EPITAXY USING GALLIUM BROMIDE AND AMMONIA.** MORIMOTO, Y. USHIO, S. JAP. J. APPL. PHYS. 12 (11), 1820, 1973.
54213	**THE PHOTOELECTRONICS ELEMENTS FROM DIFFERENT HETEROJUNCTIONS WITH CADMIUM SULFIDE.** KYNEV, S. T. KONSTANTINOVA, E. STOYANOV, V. STEFANOV, R. LITOV. FIZ. SB. (USSR) 13 (4), 587–98, 1973.
54214	**THEORETICAL LOWER BOUND ON THE ABSORPTION COEFFICIENT OF INFRARED TRANSMITTING MATERIALS.** BENDOW, B. GIANINO, P. D. OPT. COMMUN. 9 (3), 306–10, 1973.
54221	**ELECTRICAL CONDUCTION IN N–TYPE GERMANIUM AT VERY LOW TEMPERATURES.** GONDA, S. RES. ELECTROTECH. LAB. (JAPAN) (738), 1–67PP., 1973.
54224	**FAR INFRARED ABSORPTION OF AMORPHOUS BA AS AND FE.** STIMETS, R. W. WALDMAN, J. LIN, J. CHANG, T. S. SOLID STATE COMMUN. 13 (9), 1485–9, 1973.
54225	**OPTICAL ABSORPTION AND LUMINESCENCE OF N–IRRADIATED KBR.** CHOUDRY, A. MITRA, S. S. SOLID STATE COMMUN. (USA) 13 (10), 1689–91, 1973.
54230	**EFFECT OF TEMPERATURE ON THE PIEZOOPTIC DISPERSION IN SOME ALKALI HALIDE CRYSTALS.** RAO, K. V. K. MURTY, V. G. K. CURR. SCI. 42 (9), 310–11, 1973.
54233	**PIEZOOPTICAL STUDIES OF THE EXCITON SPECTRUM OF CADMIUM SULFIDE.** BRODIN, M. S. BLONSKII, I. V. DAVYDOVA, N. A. STRASHNIKOVA, M. I. FIZ. TVERD. TELA (LENINGRAD) 14 (11), 3356–61, 1972. (FOR ENGLISH TRANSLATION SEE E54718)

EPIC Number | Bibliographic Citation

54238 **SUPERCONDUCTIVITY AND PHONON SOFTENING.**
ALLEN, P. B. COHEN, M. L.
PHYS. REV. LETT.
29 (24), 1593–6, 1972.

54260 **TRANSITION FROM METALLIC TO ACTIVATION CONDUCTIVITY IN COMPENSATED SEMICONDUCTORS.**
SHKLOVSKII, B. I. EFROS, A. L.
ZH. EKSP. TEOR. FIZ.
61 (2), 816–25, 1971.
(FOR ENGLISH TRANSLATION SEE E54261)

54261 **TRANSITION FROM METALLIC TO ACTIVATION CONDUCTIVITY IN COMPENSATED SEMICONDUCTORS.**
SHKLOVSKII, B. I. EFROS, A. L.
SOV. PHYS. JETP
34 (2), 435–9, 1972.
(ENGLISH TRANSLATION OF ZH. EKSP. TEOR. FIZ., 61 (2), 816–25, 1971; FOR ORIGINAL SEE E54260)

54264 **INTERBAND BREAKDOWN AND THE PINCH EFFECT IN BISMUTH-ANTIMONY ALLOYS.**
BRANDT, N. B. SVISTOV, E. A. SVISTOVA, E. A.
YAKOVLEV, G. D.
ZH. EKSP. TEOR. FIZ.
61 (3), 1078–86, 1971.
(FOR ENGLISH TRANSLATION SEE E54265)

54265 **INTERBAND BREAKDOWN AND THE PINCH EFFECT IN BISMUTH-ANTIMONY ALLOYS.**
BRANDT, N. B. SVISTOV, E. A. SVISTOVA, E. A.
YAKOVLEV, G. D.
SOV. PHYS. JETP
34 (3), 575–9, 1972.
(ENGLISH TRANSLATION OF ZH. EKSP. TEOR. FIZ., 61 (3), 1078–86, 1971; FOR ORIGINAL SEE E54264)

54268 **DISCRETE LEVELS IN THE FORBIDDEN BAND OF A DISORDERED SEMICONDUCTOR.**
BONCH-BRUEVICH, V. L.
ZH. EKSP. TEOR. FIZ.
61 (3), 1168–76, 1971.
(FOR ENGLISH TRANSLATION SEE E54269)

54269 **DISCRETE LEVELS IN THE FORBIDDEN BAND OF A DISORDERED SEMICONDUCTOR.**
BONCH-BRUEVICH, V. L.
SOV. PHYS. JETP
34 (3), 623–7, 1972.
(ENGLISH TRANSLATION OF ZH. EKSP. TEOR. FIZ., 61 (3), 1168–76, 1971; FOR ORIGINAL SEE E54268)

54274 **MAGNETOSTRICTUON OF A URANIUM PHOSPHIDE SINGLE CRYSTAL.**
TRZEBIATOWSKI, W. HENKE, Z. BELOV, K. P.
DMITRIEVSKII, A. S. LEVITIN, R. Z.
POPOV, YU. F.
ZH. EKSP. TEOR. FIZ.
61 (4), 1522–5, 1971.
(FOR ENGLISH TRANSLATION SEE E54275)

54275 **MAGNETOSTRICTION OF A URANIUM PHOSPHIDE SINGLE CRYSTAL.**
TRZEBIATOWSKI, W. HENKE, Z. BELOV, K. P.
DMITRIEVSKII, A. S. LEVITIN, R. Z.
POPOV, YU. F.
SOV. PHYS. JETP
34 (4), 811–2, 1972.
(ENGLISH TRANSLATION OF ZH. EKSP. TEOR. FIZ., 61 (4), 1522–5, 1971; FOR ORIGINAL SEE E54274)

54276 **HOPPING CONDUCTIVITY OF SEMICONDUCTORS IN STRONG MAGNETIC FIELDS.**
SHKLOVSKII, B. I.
ZH. EKSP. TEOR. FIZ.
61 (5), 2033–40, 1971.
(FOR ENGLISH TRANSLATION SEE E54277)

54277 **HOPPING CONDUCTIVITY OF SEMICONDUCTORS IN STRONG MAGNETIC FIELDS.**
SHKLOVSKII, B. I.
SOV. PHYS. JETP
34 (5), 1084–8, 1972.
(ENGLISH TRANSLATION OF ZH. EKSP. TEOR. FIZ., 61 (5), 2033–40, 1971; FOR ORIGINAL SEE E54276)

54280 **ELECTRON MOBILITY IN DENSE GASES.**
PALKINA, L. A. SMIRNOV, B. M. FIRSOV, O. B.
ZH. SKSP. TEOR. FIZ.
61 (6), 2319–25, 1971.
(FOR ENGLISH TRANSLATION SEE E54281)

54281 **ELECTRON MOBILITY IN DENSE GASES.**
PALKINA, L. A. SMIRNOV, B. M. FIRSOV, O. B.
SOV. PHYS. JETP
34 (6), 1242–5, 1972.
(ENGLISH TRANSLATION OF ZH. EKSP. TEOR. FIZ., 61 (6), 2319–25, 1971; FOR ORIGINAL SEE E54280)

54286 **ANOMALOUS HALL EFFECT FOR POLARIZED ELECTRONS IN SEMICONDUCTORS.**
ABAKUMOV, V. N. YASSIEVICH, I. N.
ZH. EKSP. TEOR. FIZ.
61 (6), 2571–9, 1972.
(FOR ENGLISH TRANSLATION SEE E54287)

54287 **ANOMALOUS HALL EFFECT FOR POLARIZED ELECTRONS IN SEMICONDUCTORS.**
ABAKUMOV, V. N. YASSIEVICH, I. N.
SOV. PHYS. JETP
34 (6), 1375–8, 1972.
(ENGLISH TRANSLATION OF ZH. EKSP. TEOR. FIZ., 61 (6), 2571–9, 1972; FOR ORIGINAL SEE E54286)

54292 **ALTERNATING OSCILLATIONS IN THE PHOTOCURRENT SPECTRA OF NONEQUILIBRIUM PHOTOELECTRONS IN P-TYPE INDIUM ANTIMONY SUBJECTED TO QUANTIZING MAGNETIC FIELDS.**
ALEKSANDROV, A. S. BYKOVSKII, YU. A.
ELESIN, V. F. PROTASOV, E. A.
RODINOV, A. G.
ZH. EKSP. TEOR. FIZ.
64 (1), 231–44, 1973.
(FOR ENGLISH TRANSLATION SEE E54293)

54293 **ALTERNATING OSCILLATIONS IN THE PHOTOCURRENT SPECTRA NONEQUILIBRIUM PHOTOELECTRONS IN P-TYPE INDIUM ANTIMONY SUBJECTED TO QUANTIZING MAGNETIC FIELDS.**
ALEKSANDROV, A. S. BYKOVSKII, YU. A.
ELESIN, V. F. PROTASOV, E. A.
RODIONOV, A. G.
SOV. PHYS. JETP
37 (1), 120–6, 1973.
(ENGLISH TRANSLATION OF ZH. EKSP. TEOR. FIZ., 64 (1), 231–44, 1973; FOR ORIGINAL SEE E54292)

54294 **SPATIAL DISPERSION OF TWO-PHOTON ABSORPTION.**
KLYSHKO, D. N. POLKOVNIKOV, B. V.
ZH. EKSP. TEOR. FIZ.
64 (1), 297–300, 1973.
(FOR ENGLISH TRANSLATION SEE E54295)

54295 **SPATIAL DISPERSION OF TWO-PHOTON ABSORPTION.**
KLYSHKO, D. N. POLKOVNIKOV, B. V.
SOV. PHYS. JETP
37 (1), 154–5, 1973.
(ENGLISH TRANSLATION OF ZH. EKSP. TEOR. FIZ., 64 (1), 297–300, 1973; FOR ORIGINAL SEE E54294)

54298 **THEORY OF SPONTANEOUS AND STIMULATED ELECTROLUMINESCENCE OF ZINC SULFIDE: MANGANESE FILMS.**
VLASENKO, N. A. PEKAR, S. I. PEKAR, V. S.
ZH. EKSP. TEOR. FIZ.
64 (1), 371–9, 1973.
(FOR ENGLISH TRANSLATION SEE E54299)

54299 **THEORY OF SPONTANEOUS AND STIMULATED ELECTROLUMINESCENCE OF ZINC SULFIDE: MANGANESE FILMS.**
VLASENKO, N. A. PEKAR, S. I. PEKAR, V. S.
SOV. PHYS. JETP
37 (1), 190–4, 1973.
(ENGLISH TRANSLATION OF ZH. EKSP. TEOR. FIZ., 64 (1), 371–9, 1973; FOR ORIGINAL SEE E54298)

54304 **FIELD DEPENDENCE OF NUCLEAR MAGNETIC RELAXATION OF TIN IN TIN CHLORIDE, TIN BROMIDE, AND TIN IODIDE.**
SHARP, R. R.
J. CHEM. PHYS.
60 (3), 1149–57, 1974.

54305 **MODEL FOR SPIN-ORBIT INTERACTIONS WITH INCLUSION OF D ELECTRONS: APPLICATIONS TO PHOTOELECTRON SPECTROSCOPY.**
LEE, T. H. RABALAIS, J. W.
J. CHEM. PHYS.
60 (3), 1172–6, 1974.

54306 **FLUORESCENCE OF THE POTASSIUM HYDRIDE MOLECULE.**
CRUSE, J. A. ZARE, R. N.
J. CHEM. PHYS.
60 (3), 1182, 1974.

54308 **EXCITATION OF HYBRID MODES IN MAGNETOOPTIC WAVEGUIDES.**
WARNER, J.
APPL. OPT.
13 (5), 1001–4, 1974.

54309 **CHROMATIC DELAY IN LIGHT EMITTING DIODES.**
HOLDEN, W. S. HUBBARD, W. M.
PERSONICK, S. D.
APPL. OPT.
13 (5), 1050–2, 1974.

54310 **FAR INFRARED OPTICAL PROPERTIES OF SELENIUM AND CADMIUM TELLURIDE.**
DANIELEWICZ, E. J. COLEMAN, P. D.
APPL. OPT.
13 (5), 1164–70, 1974.

54311 **SOME LIMITATIONS ON THE INTERPRETATION OF SPECULAR REFLECTION SPECTRA WITH AN APPLICATION TO SOLID CARBON OXIDE.**
BUXTON, R. A. H. DULEY, W. W.
APPL. OPT.
13 (5), 1184–92, 1974.

EPIC Number *Bibliographic Citation*

54312 QUANTITATIVE STUDIES OF HYDROGEN NITRATE VAPOR ABSORPTION IN THE 1700-2636-A WAVELENGTH REGION.
SCHMIDT, S. C. GOLDMAN, A. BONOMO, F. S.
MURCRAY, D. G. AMME, R. C.
APPL. OPT.
13 (5), 1202-8, 1974.

54313 INTERFERENCE FILTERS FOR THE ULTRAVIOLET AND THE SURFACE PLASMON OF ALUMINUM.
SPILLER, E.
APPL. OPT.
13 (5), 1209-15, 1974.

54314 LOW TEMPERATURE MAGNETIC SUSCEPTIBILITY OF URANIUM CHLORIDE.
GRUBER, J. B. HECHT, H. G.
J. CHEM. PHYS.
60 (4), 1352-4, 1974.

54315 FIRST IONIZATION POTENTIALS OF SOME REFRACTORY OXIDE VAPORS.
RAUH, E. G. ACKERMANN, R. J.
J. CHEM. PHYS.
60 (4), 1396-1400, 1974.

54316 MEASUREMENT OF VIBRATIONAL-VIBRATIONAL EXCHANGE RATES FOR EXCITED VIBRATIONAL LEVELS ($2 \leq V \leq 4$) IN HYDROGEN FLUORIDE GAS.
OSGOOD, R. M., JR. SACKETT, P. B. JAVAN, A.
J. CHEM. PHYS.
60 (4), 1464-80, 1974.

54319 MOLECULAR ZEEMAN EFFECT, ELECTRIC DIPOLE MOMENT, AND BORON NUCLEAR HYPERFINE COUPLING CONSTANTS IN HYDROGEN BORON SULFIDE.
PEARSON, E. F. NORRIS, C. L. FLYGARE, W. H.
J. CHEM. PHYS.
60 (5), 1761-4, 1974.

54320 DIELECTRIC RELAXATION IN WATER IN THE NEIGHBORHOOD OF 4 C.
GRANT, E. H. SHEPPARD, R. J.
J. CHEM. PHYS.
60 (5), 1792-6, 1974.

54321 MANGANESE DIBORATE: CRYSTAL STRUCTURE, MAGNETIZATION, AND THERMAL EXTINCTION DEPENDENCE.
ABRAHAMS, S. C. BERNSTEIN, J. L. GIBART, P.
ROBBINS, M. SHERWOOD, R. C.
J. CHEM. PHYS.
60 (5), 1899-1905, 1974.

54323 ZERO PHONON TRANSITIONS AND INTERACTING JAHN-TELLER PHONON ENERGIES FROM THE FLUORESCENCE SPECTRUM OF ALPHA-ALUMINUM OXIDE: TITANIUM TRIPOSITIVE.
GACHTER, B. F. KONINGSTEIN, J. A.
J. CHEM. PHYS.
60 (5), 2003-6, 1974.

54324 ELECTRICAL TRANSPORT PROPERTIES OF SINGLE CRYSTAL RARE-EARTH SESQUISULFIDES.
TAHER, S. M. A. GRUBER, J. B.
J. CHEM. PHYS.
60 (5), 2050-6, 1974.

54326 MAGNETIC PROPERTIES OF THE TRICHLORIDES, TRIBROMIDES, AND TRIIODIDES OF URANIUM, PLUTONIUM, AND NEPTUNIUM.
JONES, E. R., JR. HENDRICKS, M. E.
STONE, J. A. KARRAKER, D. G.
J. CHEM. PHYS.
60 (5), 2088-94, 1974.

54327 MAGNETIC PROPERTIES OF TRIVALENT ACTINIDES IN THE OCTAHEDRAL COMPOUNDS OF CESIUM SODIUM TRANSURANIUM HEXACHLORIDE.
HENDRICKS, M. E. JONES, E. R., JR.
STONE, J. A. KARRAKER, D. G.
J. CHEM. PHYS.
60 (5), 2095-2103, 1974.

54328 ENTHALPY OF FORMATION OF GERMANIUM TRIFLUORIDE.
WANG, J. L. F. MARGRAVE, J. L.
FRANKLIN, J. L.
J. CHEM. PHYS.
60 (5), 2158-62, 1974.

54329 NUCLEAR MAGNETIC RESONANCE STUDY OF THE TRANSITION METAL MONOBORIDES. II. NUCLEAR ELECTRIC QUADRUPOLE AND MAGNETIC SHIFT PARAMETERS OF THE METAL NUCLEI IN VANADIUM BORIDE, COBALT BORIDE, AND NIOBIUM BORIDE.
CREEL, R. B. SEGEL, S. L. BARNES, R. G.
SCHOENBERGER, R. J. TORGESON, D. R.
J. CHEM. PHYS.
60 (6), 2310-22, 1974.

54330 COMPLEX MOLECULES IN CESIUM-RARE EARTH IODIDE VAPORS.
LIU, C. S. ZOLLWEG, R. J.
J. CHEM. PHYS.
60 (6), 2384-90, 1974.

54331 STRUCTURAL ASPECTS OF NONLINEAR OPICS: OPTICAL PROPERTIES OF POTASSIUM IODIDE OXIDE FLUORIDE AND ITS RELATED IODATES.
BERGMAN, J. G. CRANE, G. R.
J. CHEM. PHYS.
60 (6), 2470-4, 1974.

54336 OPTICAL ABSORPTION IN YTTERBIUM MONOCHALCOGENIDES UNDER PRESSURE.
NARAYANAMURTI, V. JAYARAMAN, A. BUCHER, E.
PHYS. REV.
9 B (6), 2521-3, 1974.

54337 TEMPERATURE DEPENDENCE OF RAMAN SCATTERING, ELECTRO-OPTIC, AND DIELECTRIC PROPERTIES OF COPPER BROMIDE.
TURNER, E. H. KAMINOW, I. P. SCHWAB, C.
PHYS. REV.
9 B (6), 2524-9, 1974.

54339 EFFECT OF NONPARABOLICITY ON THE DAMPING OF HELICONS IN SEMICONDUCTORS IN THE EXTREME QUANTUM LIMIT.
PAL, B. P. SHARMA, S. K.
PHYS. REV.
9 B (6), 2558-63, 1974.

54341 MICROSCOPIC THEORY OF DIELECTRIC SCREENING AND LATTICE DYNAMICS. II. PHONON SPECTRA AND EFFECTIVE CHARGES.
PRICE, D. L. SINHA, S. K. GUPTA, R. P.
PHYS. REV.
9 B (6), 2573-89, 1974.

54343 TRANSVERSE MAGNETORESISTANCE OF NONDEGENERATE SEMICONDUCTORS IN STRONG MAGNETIC FIELDS.
CASSIDAY, D. R. SPECTOR, H. N.
PHYS. REV.
9 B (6), 2618-22, 1974.

54345 DENSITIES OF VALENCE STATES OF AMORPHOUS AND CRYSTALLINE III-V AND II-VI SEMICONDUCTORS.
SHEVCHIK, N. J. TEJEDA, J. CARDONA, M.
PHYS. REV.
9 (6), 2627-48, 1974.

54346 ANHARMONICITY IN COPPER CHLORIDE-ELASTIC, DIELECTRIC, AND PIEZOELECTRIC CONSTANTS.
HANSON, R. C. HELLIWELL, K. SCHWAB, C.
PHYS. REV.
9 B (6), 2649-54, 1974.

54347 PHOTOEMISSION STUDIES OF LITHIUM CHLORIDE, SODIUM CHLORIDE, AND POTASSIUM CHLORIDE.
PONG, W. SMITH, J. A.
PHYS. REV.
9 B (6), 2674-8, 1974.

54348 CHLORINE-K - X-RAY SPECTRA AND ELECTRONIC BAND STRUCTURES OF MAGNESIUM CHLORIDE, CALCIUM CHLORIDE, STRONTIUM CHLORIDE, AND BARIUM CHLORIDE.
SUGIURA, C.
PHYS. REV.
9 B (6), 2679-83, 1974.

54350 POLAR ISOTOPE MODES IN CRYSTALS: APPLICATION TO RUBIDIUM CHLORATE.
HWANG, D. M.
PHYS. REV.
9 B (6), 2717-22, 1974.

54351 VIBRATIONAL PROPERTIES OF POTASSIUM TANTALUM OXIDE AT CRITICAL POINTS IN THE BRILLOUIN ZONE.
YACOBY, Y. LINZ, A.
PHYS. REV.
9 B (6), 2723-42, 1974.

54352 MACROSCOPIC LENGTH CHANGES DUE TO THE ALIGNMENT OF ELASTIC DIPOLES IN POTASSIUM CHLORIDE.
BALZER, R. PETERS, H. WAIDELICH, W.
PEISL, H.
PHYS. REV.
9 B (6), 2746-53, 1974.

54353 EVIDENCE FOR A MOBILITY EDGE IN INVERSION LAYERS.
STERN, F.
PHYS. REV.
9 B (6), 2762-5, 1974.

54354 ELECTRICAL RESISTIVITY OF AN EINSTEIN SOLID.
COOPER, J. R.
PHYS. REV.
9 B (6), 2778-80, 1974.

54357 TEMPERATURE VARIATIONS OF THE ELECTRONIC-VIBRATIONAL SPECTRUM OF LANTHANUM ALUMINUM OXIDE-CHROMIUM CRYSTALS.
TKACHUK, A. M. FEDOROV, A. A.
OPT. SPEKTROSK.
34 (1), 113-16, 1973.
(FOR ENGLISH TRANSLATION SEE E54358)

EPIC Number	Bibliographic Citation

54358 **TEMPERATURE VARIATIONS OF THE ELECTRONIC-VIBRATIONAL SPECTRUM OF LANTHANUM ALUMINUM OXIDE-CHROMIUM CRYSTALS.**
TKACHUK, A. M. FEDOROV, A. A.
OPT. SPECTROS., USSR
34 (1), 61-2, 1973.
(ENGLISH TRANSLATION OF OPT. SPEKTROSK., 34 (1), 113-16, 1973; FOR ORIGINAL SEE E54357)

54359 **LUMINESCENCE CENTRE IN POTASSIUM BROMIDE-THALLIUM BROMIDE SINGLE CRYSTALS WITH THALLIUM BROMIDE CONCENTRATIONS UP TO 20 MOL..**
GINDINA, R. I. ELANGO, A. A. KHAAV, A. A.
MAAROOS, A. A. TSIRK, A. A.
OPT. SPEKTROSK.
34 (1), 117-23, 1973.
(FOR ENGLISH TRANSLATION SEE E54360)

54360 **LUMINESCENCE CENTERS IN POTASSIUM BROMIDE-THALLIUM BROMIDE SINGLE CRYSTALS WITH THALLIUM BROMIDE CONCENTRATIONS UP TO 20 MOL..**
GINDINA, R. I. ELANGO, A. A. KHAAV, A. A.
MAAROOS, A. A. TSIRK, A. A.
OPT. SPECTROS., USSR
34 (1), 63-6, 1973.
(ENGLISH TRANSLATION OF OPT. SPEKTROSK., 34 (1), 117-23, 1973; FOR ORIGINAL SEE E54359)

54361 **METHOD OF CALCULATING THE ENERGY OF OPTICAL TRANSITIONS FROM THE VALENCE BAND TO THE CONDUCTION BAND IN THE FRAMEWORK OF A SIMPLIFIED MODEL OF A CONDENSED MEDIUM.**
KUTOLIN, S. A. SAMOILOVA, R. N.
OPT. SPEKTROSK.
34 (1), 124-7, 1973.
(FOR ENGLISH TRANSLATION SEE E54362)

54362 **METHOD OF CALCULATING THE ENERGY OF OPTICAL TRANSITIONS FROM THE VALENCE BAND TO THE CONDUCTION BAND IN THE FRAMEWORK OF A SIMPLIFIED MODEL OF A CONDENSED MEDIUM.**
KUTOLIN, S. A. SAMOILOVA, R. N.
OPT. SPECTROS., USSR
34 (1), 67-8, 1973.
(ENGLISH TRANSLATION OF OPT. SPEKTROSK., 34 (1), 124-7, 1973; FOR ORIGINAL SEE E54361)

54369 **INTERPRETATION OF THE EXPONENTIAL DECREASE OF THE ABSORPTION COEFFICIENT BEYOND THE HEAD OF THE 4.3 MU BAND OF CARBON DIOXIDE GAS.**
FOMIN, V. V.
OPT. SPEKTROSK.
34 (2), 243-6, 1973.
(FOR ENGLISH TRANSLATION SEE E54370)

54370 **INTERPRETATION OF THE EXPONENTIAL DECREASE OF THE ABSORPTION COEFFICIENT BEYOND THE HEAD OF THE 4.3 MU BAND OF CARBON DIOXIDE GAS.**
FOMIN, V. V.
OPT. SPECTROS., USSR
34 (2), 136-8, 1973.
(ENGLISH TRANSLATION OF OPT. SPEKTROSK., 34 (2), 243-6, 1973; FOR ORIGINAL SEE E54369)

54371 **THE MECHANISM OF AUTOIONIZATION PROCESSES IN CARBON SULFIDE.**
KLEIMENOV, V. I. CHIZHOV, YU. V.
VILESOV, F. I.
OPT. SPEKTROSK.
34 (2), 256-60, 1973.
(FOR ENGLISH TRANSLATION SEE E54372)

54372 **THE MECHANISM OF AUTOIONIZATION PROCESS IN CARBON SULFIDE.**
KLEIMENOV, V. I. CHIZHOV, YU. V.
VILESOV, F. I.
OPT. SPECTROS., USSR
34 (2), 144-6, 1973.
(ENGLISH TRANSLATION OF OPT. SPEKTROSK., 34 (2), 256-60, 1973; FOR ORIGINAL SEE E54371)

54373 **F-F TRANSISITONS IN THE SPECTRA OF POTASSIUM MAGNESIUM FLUORIDE AND SODIUM MAGNESIUM FLUORIDE CRYSTALS ACTIVATED WITH EUROPIUM.**
BODRUG, S. N. VALYASHKO, E. G.
MEDNIKOVA, V. N. SVIRIDOV, D. T.
SVIRIDOV, R. K.
OPT. SPEKTROSK.
34 (2), 312-14, 1973.
(FOR ENGLISH TRANSLATION SEE E54374)

54374 **F-F TRANSITIONS IN THE SPECTRA OF POTASSIUM MAGNESIUM FLUORIDE AND SODIUM MAGNESIUM FLUORIDE CRYSTALS ACTIVATED WITH EUROPIUM.**
BODRUG, S. N. VALYASHKO, E. G.
MEDNIKOVA, V. N. SVIRIDOV, D. T.
SVIRIDOV, R. K.
OPT. SPECTROS., USSR
34 (2), 176-7, 1973.
(ENGLISH TRANSLATION OF OPT. SPEKTROSK., 34 (2), 312-14, 1973; FOR ORIGINAL SEE E54373)

54375 **TEMPERATURE SHIFT OF THE ENERGY LEVELS OF THE NEODYMIUM TRIPOSITIVE ION IN YTTRIUM - ALUMINUM - GARNET SINGLE CRYSTALS.**
OSTROVSKAYA, E. M. SAZONOVA, S. A.
SKOROBOGATOV, B. S.
OPT. SPEKTROSK.
34 (2), 315-18, 1973.
(FOR ENGLISH TRANSLATION SEE E54376)

54376 **TEMPERATURE SHIFT OF THE ENERGY LEVELS OF THE NEODYMIUM TRIPOSITIVE ION IN YTTRIUM - ALUMINUM - GARNET SINGLE CRYSTALS.**
OSTROVSKAYA, E. M. SAZONOVA, S. A.
SKOROBOGATOV, B. S.
OPT. SPECTROS., USSR
34 (2), 178-80, 1973.
(ENGLISH TRANSLATION OF OPT. SPEKTROSK., 34 (2), 315-18, 1973; FOR ORIGINAL SEE E54375)

54377 **OPTICAL CONSTANTS OF GERMANIUM DIOXIDES IN THE 4000-200 CM-1 REGION.**
ZOLOTAREV, V. M. MOROZOV, V. N.
OPT. SPEKTROSK.
34 (2), 319-22, 1973.
(FOR ENGLISH TRANSLATION SEE E54378)

54378 **OPTICAL CONSTANTS OF GERMANIUM DIOXIDES IN THE 4000-200 CM-1 REGION.**
ZOLOTAREV, V. M. MOROZOV, V. N.
OPT. SPECTROS., USSR
34 (2), 181-2, 1973.
(ENGLISH TRNSLATION OF OPT. SPEKTROSK., 34 (2), 319-22, 1973; FOR ORIGINAL SEE E54377)

54381 **SOME ELECTRICAL AND OPTICAL PROPERTIES OF CHROMIUM-, MOLYBDENUM- AND TUNGSTEN-NITRIDE LAYERS.**
CHEREZOVA, L. A. KRYZHANOVSKII, B. P.
OPT. SPEKTROSK.
34 (2), 414-17, 1973.
(FOR ENGLISH TRANSLATION SEE E54382)

54382 **SOME ELECTRICAL AND OPTICAL PROPERTIES OF CHROMIUM-, MOLYBDENUM- AND TUNGSTEN-NITRIDE LAYERS.**
CHEREZOVA, L. A. KRYZHANOVSKII, B. P.
OPT. SPECTROS., USSR
34 (2), 234-6, 1973.
(ENGLISH TRANSLATION OF OPT. SPEKTROSK., 34 (2), 414-7, 1973; FOR ORIGINAL SEE E54381)

54383 **POLARIZED PHOSPHORESCENCE AND ABSORPTION OF CRYSTALLINE SILVER NITRITE.**
REZNIK, L. E. GARBER, P. R.
OPT. SPEKTROSK.
34 (2), 418-20, 1973.
(FOR ENGLISH TRANSLATION SEE E54384)

54384 **POLARIZED PHOSPHORESCENCE AND ABSORPTION OF CRYSTALLINE SILVER NITRITE.**
REZNIK, L. E. GARBER, P. R.
OPT. SPECTROS., USSR
34 (2), 237-8, 1973.
(ENGLISH TRANSLATION OF OPT. SPEKTROSK., 34 (2), 418-20, 1973; FOR ORIGINAL SEE E54383)

54389 **OPTICAL ABSORPTION AND LUMINESCENCE SPECTRA OF ZINC- AND CADMIUM- TUNGSTATE SINGLE CRYSTALS ACTIVATED WITH CHROMIUM.**
NOSENKO, A. E. FUTORSKII, D. L. L.
OPT. SPEKTROSK.
34 (3), 501-4, 1973.
(FOR ENGLISH TRANSLATION SEE E54890)

54390 **OPTICAL ABSORPTION AND LUMINESCENCE SPECTRA OF ZINC- AND CADMIUM- TUNGSTATE SINGLE CRYSTALS ACTIVATED WITH CHROMIUM.**
NOSENKO, A. E. FUTORSKII, D. L. L.
OPT. SPECTROS., USSR
34 (3), 286-7, 1973.
(ENGLISH TRANSLATION OF OPT. SPEKTROSK., 34 (3), 501-4, 1973; FOR ORIGINAL SEE E54389)

54393 **COLOR CENTERS AND RECOMBINATION LUMINESCENCE IN POTASSIUM IODIDE-SILVER CRYSTALS.**
PENZINA, E. E. PARFIANOVICH, I. A.
LOBANOV, B. D.
OPT. SPEKTROSK.
34 (3), 515-20, 1973.
(FOR ENGLISH TRANSLATION SEE E54394)

54394 **COLOR CENTERS AND RECOMBINATION LUMINESCENCE IN POTASSIUM IODIDE-SILVER CRYSTALS.**
PENZINA, E. E. PARFIANOVICH, I. A.
LOBANOV, B. D.
OPT. SPECTROS., USSR
34 (3), 294-7, 1973.
(ENGLISH TRANSLATION OF OPT. SPEKTROSK., 34 (3), 515-20, 1973; FOR ORIGINAL SEE E54393)

54395 **INVESTIGATION OF THE OPTICAL CONSTANTS OF LEAD CHLORIDE AND LEAD BROMIDE AT 78 K IN THE ENERGY RANGE 3.5-11.0 EV.**
MALYSHEVA, A. F. PLEKHANOV, V. G.
OPT. SPEKTROSK.
34 (3), 527-31, 1973.
(FOR ENGLISH TRANSLATION SEE E54396)

EPIC Number	Bibliographic Citation
54396	**INVESTIGATION OF THE OPTICAL CONSTANTS OF LEAD CHLORIDE AND LEAD BROMIDE AT 78 K IN THE ENERGY RANGE 3.5–11.0 EV.** MALYSHEVA, A. F. PLEKHANOV, V. G. OPT. SPECTROS., USSR 34 (3), 302–4, 1973. (ENGLISH TRANSLATION OF OPT. SPEKTROSK., 34 (3), 527–31, FOR ORIGINAL SEE E54395)
54397	**DETERMINATION OF THE OPTICAL DENSITY OF SEMICONDUCTOR LAYERS ON TRANSPARENT SUBSTRATES.** KURIK, M. W. ROZHKO, A. KH. OPT. SPEKTROSK. 34 (3), 532–4, 1973. (FOR ENGLISH TRANSLATION SEE E54398)
54398	**DETERMINATION OF THE OPTICAL DENSITY OF SEMICONDUCTOR LAYERS ON TRANSPARENT SUBSTRATES.** KURIK, M. W. ROZHKO, A. KH. OPT. SPECTROS., USSR 34 (3), 305–6, 1973. (ENGLISH TRANSLATION OF OPT. SPEKTROSK., 34 (3), 532–4, 1973; FOR ORIGINAL SEE E54397)
54401	**DEPENDENCE ON THE POSITION OF LUMINESCENCE BANDS DUE TO THALLIUM CENTERS ON IONIC RADII OF CATIONS AND ANIONS IN THE HOST LATTICE OF SOME ALKALI-HALIDE CRYSTALS.** VISHNEVSKII, V. N. PIDZYRAILO, N. S. OPT. SPEKTROSK. 34 (3), 592–3, 1973. (FOR ENGLISH TRANSLATION SEE E54402)
54402	**DEPENDENCE ON THE POSITION OF LUMINESCENCE BANDS DUE TO THALLIUM CENTERS ON IONIC RADII OF CATIONS AND ANIONS IN THE HOST LATTICE OF SOME ALKALI-HALIDE CRYSTALS.** VISHNEVSKII, V. N. PIDZYRAILO, N. S. OPT. SPECTROS., USSR 34 (3), 338–9, 1973. (ENGLISH TRANSLATION OF OPT. SPEKTROSK., 34 (3), 592–3, 1973; FOR ORIGINAL SEE E54401)
54403	**POLARIZED LUMINESCENCE OF YTTERBIUM DIPOSITIVE ION DOPED CALCIUM FLUORIDE CRYSTALS.** KAPLYANSKII, A. A. SMOLYANSKII, P. L. OPT. SPEKTROSK. 34 (3), 624–5, 1973. (FOR ENGLISH TRANSLATION SEE E54404)
54404	**POLARIZED LUMINESCENCE OF YTTERBIUM DIPOSITIVE ION DOPED CALCIUM FLUORIDE CRYSTALS.** KAPLYANSKII, A. A. SMOLYANSKII, P. L. OPT. SPECTROS., USSR 34 (3), 361–2, 1973. (ENGLISH TRANSLATION OF OPT. SPEKTROSK., 34 (3), 624–5, 1973; FOR ORIGINAL SEE E54403)
54411	**LUMINESCENCE MECHANISM OF PAIR CENTERS IN POTASSIUM IODIDE-THALLIUM PHOSPHOR.** SMOLSKAYA, L. P. PARFIANOVICH, I. A. SHURALEVA, E. I. MOROZHNIKOVA, L. V. OPT. SPEKTROSK., USSR 34 (4), 722–5, 1973. (FOR ENGLISH TRANSLATION SEE E54412)
54412	**LUMINESCENCE MECHANISM OF PAIR CENTERS IN POTASSIUM IODIDE-THALLIUM PHOSPHOR.** SMOLSKAYA, L. P. PARFIANOVICH, I. A. SHURALEVA, E. I. MOROZHNIKOVA, L. V. OPT. SPECTROS., USSR 34 (4), 416–8, 1973. (ENGLISH TRANSLATION OF OPT. SPEKTROSK., 34 (4), 722–5, 1973; FOR ORIGINAL SEE E54411)
54417	**PHOTOELECTRON SPECTRA OF THIOPHOSPHORYLCHLORIDE AND SOME OF ITS AMINOSUBSTITUTED DERIVATIVES.** VOVNA, V. I. LOPATIN, S. N. PETTSODL, R. VILESOV, F. I. AKOPYAN, M. E. OPT. SPEKTROSK., 34 (5), 868–71, 1973. (FSOR ENGLISH TRANSLATION SEE E54418)
54418	**PHOTOELECTRON SPECTRA OF THIOPHOSPHORYLCHLORIDE AND SOME OF ITS AMINOSUBSTITUTED DERIVATIVES.** VOVNA, V. I. LOPATIN, S. N. PETTSODL, R. VILESOV, F. I. AKOPYAN, M. E. OPT. SPECTROS., USSR 34 (5), 501–2, 1973. (ENGLISH TRANSLATION OF OPT. SPEKTROSK., 34 (5), 868–71, 1973; FOR ORIGINAL SEE E54417)
54419	**DETERMINATION OF OSCILLATOR STRENGTHS FOR TRANSITIONS IN TIN DIPOSITIVE ION DOPED HYDROGEN CHLORIDE SOLUTION.** BELYI, M. U. ZAKHARCHENKO, I. V. OKHRIMENKO, B. A. OPT. SPECKTROS. 34 (5), 907–12, 1973. (FOR ENGLISH TRANSLATION SEE E54420)

EPIC Number	Bibliographic Citation
54420	**DETERMINATION OF OSCILLATOR STRENGTHS FOR TRANSITIONS IN TIN DIPOSITIVE ION DOPED HYDROGEN CHLORIDE SOLUTION.** BELYI, M. U. ZAKHARCHENKO, I. V. OKHRIMENKO, B. A. OPT. SPECTROS., USSR 34 (5), 521–4, 1973. (ENGLISH TRANSLATION OF OPT. SPEKTROSK., 34 (5), 907–12, 1973; FOR ORIGINAL SEE E54419)
54424	**UNIVERSAL INTERMOLECULAR INTERACTIONS AND TEMPERATURE DEPENDENCE OF THE REFRACTIVE INDEX OF NONPOLAR LIQUIDS.** BOKOV, O. G. OPT. SPEKSTROSK. 34 (5), 1000–1002, 1973. (FOR ENGLISH TRANSLATION SEE E54425)
54425	**UNIVERSAL INTERMOLECULAR INTERACTIONS AND TEMPERATURE DEPENDENCE OF THE REFRACTIVE INDEX OF NONPOLAR LIQUIDS.** BOKOV, O. G. OPT. SPECTROS., USSR 34 (5), 577–9, 1973. (ENGLISH TRANSLATION OF OPT. SPEKTROSK., 34 (5), 1000–1002, 1973; FOR ORIGINAL SEE E54424)
54428	**TOTAL EMISSION OF THE FUNDAMENTAL NITROGEN OXIDE BAND AT HIGH TEMPERATURES.** KONKOV, A. A. VORONTSOV, A. V. OPT. SPEKTROSK. 34 (5), 1026–7, 1973. (FOR ENGLISH TRANSLATION SEE E54429)
54429	**TOTAL EMISSION OF THE FUNDAMENTAL NITROGEN OXIDE BAND AT HIGH TEMPERATURES.** KONKOV, A. A. VORONTSOV, A. V. OPT. SPECTROS., USSR 34 (5), 595–6, 1973. (ENGLISH TRANSLATION OF OPT. SPEKTROSK., 34 (5), 1026–7, 1973; FOR ORIGINAL SEE E54428)
54432	**TEMPERATURE DEPENDENCE OF INFRARED ABSORPTION IN FUSED QUARTZ AT HIGH TEMPERATURES.** PRIKHODKO, L. V. BAGDASAROV, KH. S. OPT. SPECTROS., USSR 34 (6), 702, 1973. (ENGLISH TRANSLATION OF OPT. SPEKTROSK., 34 (6), 1210–11, 1973; FOR ORIGINAL SEE E51949)
54435	**OPTICAL ABSORPTION SPECTRA OF EXCITED CHROMIUM TRIPOSITIVE IONS IN MAGNESIUM SPINEL AT ROOM AND LIQUID NITROGEN TEMPERATURES.** SVIRIDOV, D. T. SEVASTYANOV, B. K. OREKHOVA, V. P. SVIRIDOVA, R. K. VEREMEICHIK, T. F. OPT. SPECTROS., USSR 35 (1), 59–61, 1973. (ENGLISH TRANSLATION OF OPT. SPEKTROSK., 35 (1), 102–7, 1973; FOR ORIGINAL SEE E51950)
54436	**ENERGY SPECTRA OF THE LAYERED ANTIFERROMAGNETS LITHIUM TETRAFLUORONICKELATE, POTASSIUM TETRAFLUORONICKELATE, AND RUBIDIUM TETRAFLUORONICKELATE.** PISAREV, R. V. KARAMYAN, A. A. NESTEROVA, N. N. SYRNIKOV, P. P. OPT. SPECTROS., USSR 35 (1), 88–9, 1973. (ENGLISH TRANSLATION OF OPT. SPEKTROSK., 35 (1), 156–8, 1973; FOR ORIGINAL SEE E51951)
54437	**LUMINESCENCE AND EXCITATION SPECTRA OF LITHIUM HYDRIDE AND LITHIUM HYDRIDE-D SINGLE CRYSTALS AT LOW TEMPERATURES.** REBANE, L. A. VLASOV, B. V. GAVRILOV, F. F. CHOLAKH, S. O. PIROGOV, V. D. OPT. SPECTROS., USSR 35 (1), 91–2, 1973. (ENGLISH TRANSLATION OF OPT. SPEKTROSK., 35 (1), 160–2, 1973; FOR ORIGINAL SEE E51952)
54440	**OPTICAL CHARACTERISTICS OF A FLUOROAPATITE SINGLE CRYSTAL IN THE INFRARED.** SHAGANOV, I. I. LIBOV, V. S. OPT. SPEKTROSK. 35 (1), 181–3, 1973. (FOR ENGLISH TRANSLATION SEE E54441)
54441	**OPTICAL CHARACTERISTICS OF A FLUOROAPATITE SINGLE CRYSTAL IN THE INFRARED.** SHAGANOV, I. I. LIBOV, V. S. OPT. SPECTROS., USSR 35 (1), 106–7, 1973. (ENGLISH TRANSLATION OF OPT. SPEKTROSK., 35 (1), 181–3, 1973; FOR ORIGINAL SEE E54440)
54444	**SPIN MEMORY OF EUROPIUM DIPOSITIVE ION IN CALCIUM FLUORIDE.** KOMAROV, A. V. RYABCHENKO, S. M. OPT. SPEKTROSK. 35 (2), 173–5, 1973. (FOR ENGLISH TRANSLATION SEE E54445)

EPIC Number	Bibliographic Citation
54445	**SPIN MEMORY OF EUROPIUM DIPOSITIVE ION IN CALCIUM FLUORIDE.** KOMAROV, A. V. RYABCHENKO, S. M. OPT. SPECTROS., USSR 35 (2), 100–1, 1973. (ENGLISH TRANSLATION OF OPT. SPEKTROSK., 35 (2), 173–5, 1973; FOR ORIGINAL SEE E54444)
54446	**MEASUREMENT OF THE PARAMETERS OF THE ABSORPTION LINE GAMMA = MU M IN THE ROTATIONAL SPECTRUM OF WATER VAPOR.** RYADOV, V. YA. FURASHOV, N. I. OPT. SPEKTROSK. 35 (3), 433–8, 1973. (FOR ENGLISH TRANSLATION SEE E54447)
54447	**MEASUREMENT OF THE PARAMETERS OF THE ABSORPTION LINE GAMMA = MU M IN THE ROTATIONAL SPECTRUM OF WATER VAPOR.** RYADOV, V. YA. FURASHOV, N. I. OPT. SPECTROS., USSR 35 (3), 255–7, 1973. (ENGLISH TRANSLATION OF OPT. SPEKTROSK., 35 (3), 433–8, 1973; FOR ORIGINAL SEE E54446)
54448	**CALCULATION OF THE STATES OF A CERIUM TRIPOSITIVE ION IN FLUORITE-TYPE CRYSTALS.** STAROSTIN, N. V. GRUZDEV, P. F. GANIN, V. A. CHEBOTAREVA, T. E. OPT. SPEKTROSK. 35 (3), 476–81, 1973. (FOR ENGLISH TRANSLATION SEE E54449)
54449	**CALCULATION OF THE STATES OF A CERIUM TRIPOSITIVE ION IN FLUORITE-TYPE CRYSTALS.** STAROSTIN, N. V. GRUZDEV, P. F. GANIN, V. A. CHEBOTAREVA, T. E. OPT. SPECTROS., USSR 35 (3), 277–80, 1973. (ENGLISH TRANSLATION OF OPT. SPEKTROSK., 35 (3), 476–81, 1973; FOR ORIGINAL SEE E54448)
54450	**TEMPERATURE SHIFT OF NEODYMIUM TRIPOSITIVE ENERGY LEVELS IN CALCIUM TUNGSTATE CRYSTALS.** BONCHKOVSKII, V. I. KOBZAR-ZLENKO, V. A. SAZONOVA, S. A. SKOROBOGATOV, B. S. OPT. SPEKTROSK. 35 (3), 482–5, 1973. (FOR ENGLISH TRANSLATION SEE E54451)
54451	**TEMPERATURE SHIFT OF NEODYMIUM TRIPOSITIVE ENERGY LEVELS IN CALCIUM TUNGSTATE CRYSTALS.** BONCHKOVSKII, V. I. KOBZAR-ZLENKO, V. A. SAZONOVA, S. A. SKOROBOGATOV, B. S. OPT. SPECTROS., USSR 35 (3), 281–2, 1973. (ENGLISH TRANSLATION OF OPT. SPEKTROSK., 35 (3), 482–5, 1973; FOR ORIGINAL SEE E54450)
54452	**MECHANISM OF RADIATION-INDUCED AND PHOTOEXCITED SCINTILLATIONS IN THALLIUM DOPED CESIUM IODIDE.** GULAKOV, I. R. PERTSEV, A. N. OPT. SPEKTROSK. 35 (3), 492–6, 1973. (FOR ENGLISH TRANSLATION SEE E54453)
54453	**MECHANISM OF RADIATION-INDUCED AND PHOTOEXCITED SCINTILLATIONS IN THALLIUM DOPED CESIUM IODIDE.** GULAKOV, I. R. PERTSEV, A. N. OPT. SPECTROS., USSR 35 (3), 286–8, 1973. (ENGLISH TRANSLATION OF OPT. SPEKTROSK., 35 (3), 492–6, 1973; FOR ORIGINAL SEE E54452)
54454	**OPTICAL PROPERTIES OF SILICON OXIDE IN THE SPECTRAL REGION 5–40 E V.** SOROKIN, O. M. BLANK, V. A. LEBEDEVA, G. A. OPT. SPECTROS., USSR 35 (3), 291–4, 1973. (ENGLISH TRANSLATION OF OPT. SPEKTROSK., 35 (3), 501–7, 1973; FOR ORIGINAL SEE E52679)
54464	**INTERPRETATION OF LUMINESCENCE SPECTRA OF URANYL MOLYBDATE AND URANYL TUNGSTATE.** ZOLIN, V. F. ROZMAN S. P. FISHER, P. S. OPT. SPEKTROSK. 35 (3), 589–90, 1973. (FOR ENGLISH TRANSLATION SEE E54465)
54465	**INTERPRETATION OF LUMINESCENCE SPECTRA OF URANYL MOLYBDATE AND URANYL TUNGSTATE.** ZOLIN, V. F. ROZMAN S. P. FISHER, P. S. OPT. SPECTROS., USSR 35 (3), 345–6, 1973. (ENGLISH TRANSLATION OF OPT. SPEKTROSK., 35 (3), 589–90, 1973; FOR ORIGINAL SEE E54464)
54466	**MULTIQUANTUM ABSORPTION OF LIGHT BY CONDUCTION ELECTRONS IN EXTRINSIC SEMICONDUCTORS.** MALEVICH, V. L. EPSHTEIN, E. M. OPT. SPEKTROSK. 35 (3), 591–2, 1973. (FOR ENGLISH TRANSLATION SEE E54467)
54467	**MULTIQUANTUM ABSORPTION OF LIGHT BY CONDUCTION ELECTRONS IN EXTRINSIC SEMICONDUCTORS.** MALEVICH, V. L. EPSHTEIN, E. M. OPT. SPECTROS., USSR 35 (3), 346–7, 1973. (ENGLISH TRANSLATION OF OPT. SPEKTROSK., 35 (3), 591–2, 1973; FOR ORIGINAL SEE E54466)
54472	**SODIUM COLOR CENTERS IN POTASSIUM BROMIDE CRYSTALS.** AVDONIN, V. P. NECHAEV, A. F. PLACHENOV, B. T. OPT. SPEKTROSK. 35 (4), 650–4, 1973. (FOR ENGLISH TRANSLATION SEE E54473)
54473	**SODIUM COLOR CENTERS IN POTASSIUM BROMIDE CRYSTALS.** AVDONIN, V. P. NECHAEV, A. F. PLACHENOV, B. T. OPT. SPECTROS., USSR 35 (4), 379–81, 1973. (ENGLISH TRANSLATION OF OPT. SPEKTROSKK., 35 (4), 650–4, 1973; FOR ORIGINAL SEE E54472)
54474	**THERMALLY STIMULATED LUMINESCENCE IN POTASSIUM IODIDE PHOSPHORS.** SMOLSKAYA, L. P. PARFIANOVICH, I. A. SHURALEVA, E. I. OPT. SPEKTROSK. 35 (4), 661–6, 1973. (FOR ENGLISH TRANSLATION SEE E54475)
54475	**THERMALLY STIMULATED LUMINESCENCE IN POTASSIUM IODIDE PHOSPHORS.** SMOLSKAYA, L. P. PARFIANOVICH, I. A. SHURALEVA, E. I. OPT. SPECTROS., USSR 35 (4), 385–7, 1973. (ENGLISH TRANSLATION OF OPT. SPEKTROSK., 35 (4), 661–6, 1973; FOR ORIGINAL SEE E54474)
54476	**MAGNETOOPTICAL STUDY OF EUROPIUM DIPOSITIVE IN CALCIUM FLUORIDE.** KOMAROV, A. V. RYABCHENKO, S. M. OPT. SPEKTROSK. 35 (4), 667–71, 1973. (FOR ENGLISH TRANSLATION SEE E54477)
54477	**MAGNETOOPTICAL STUDY OF EUROPIUM DIPOSITIVE IN CALCIUM FLUORIDE.** KOMAROV, A. V. RYABCHENKO, S. M. OPT. SPECTROS., USSR 35 (4), 388–90, 1973. (ENGLISH TRANSLATION OF OPT. SPEKTROSK., 35 (4), 667–71, 1973; FOR ORIGINAL SEE E54476)
54478	**SPECIAL FEATURES OF LUMINESCENCE OF A PRASEODYMIUM TRIPOSITIVE ION IN A SCHEELITE-TYPE CRYSTALS UNDER EXCITATION INTO THE CHARGE TRANSFER BAND.** REUT, E. G. RYSKIN, A. I. OPT. SPEKTROSK. 35 (4), 672–6, 1973. (FOR ENGLISH TRANSLATION SEE E54479)
54479	**SPECIAL FEATURES OF LUMINESCENCE OF A PRASEODYMIUM TRIPOSITIVE ION IN A SCHEELITE-TYPE CRYSTALS UNDER EXCITATION INTO THE CHARGE TRANSFER BAND.** REUT, E. G. RYSKIN, A. I. OPT. SPECTROS., USSR 35 (4), 391–3, 1973. (ENGLISH TRANSLATION OF OPT. SPEKTROSK., 35 (4), 672–6, 1973; FOR ORIGINAL SEE E54478)
54486	**ANISOTROPY OF A NONLINEAR REFRACTIVE INDEX IN ACENTRIC CRYSTALS: LINEAR ELECTROOPTIC EFFECT.** SHALDIN, YU. V. BELOGUROV, D. A. OPT. SPEKTROSK. 35 (4), 693–701, 1973. (FOR ENGLISH TRANSLATION SEE E54487)
54487	**ANISOTROPY OF A NONLINEAR REFRACTIVE INDEX IN ACENTRIC CRYSTALS: LINEAR ELECTROOPTIC EFFECT.** SHALDIN, YU. V. BELOGUROV, D. A. OPT. SPECTROS. 35 (4), 400–7, 1973. (ENGLISH TRANSLATION OF OPT. SPEKTROSK., 35 (4), 693–701, 1973; FOR ORIGINAL SEE E54486)
54490	**USE OF MOLECULAR-ORBITAL METHOD FOR THE CALCULATION OF IMPURITY ELECTRONIC LEVELS IN IONIC CRYSTALS. I: MOLECULAR MODEL FOR THE POTASSIUM CHLORIDE CENTER.** ERMOSHKIN, A. N. EVARESTOV, R. A. OPT. SPEKTROSK. 35 (4), 786–9, 1973. (FOR ENGLISH TRANSLATION SEE E54491)
54491	**USE OF MOLECULAR-ORBITAL METHOD FOR THE CALCULATION OF IMPURITY ELECTRONIC LEVELS IN IONIC CRYSTALS. I: MOLECULAR MODEL FOR THE POTASSIUM CHLORIDE CENTER.** ERMOSHKIN, A. N. EVARESTOV, R. A. OPT. SPECTROS., USSR 35 (4), 456–8, 1973. (ENGLISH TRANSLATION OF OPT. SPEKTROSK., 35 (4), 786–9, 1973; FOR ORIGINAL SEE E54490)

EPIC Number	Bibliographic Citation
54492	**TEMPERATURE QUENCHING OF URANIUM LUMINESCENCE IN SCHEELITE-TYPE SINGLE CRYSTALS.** MOROZOVA, L. G. FEOFILOV, P. P. OPT. SPEKTROSK. 35 (4), 789-90, 1973. (FOR ENGLISH TRANSLATION SEE E54493)
54493	**TEMPERATURE QUENCHING OF URANIUM LUMINESCENCE IN SCHEELITE-TYPE SINGLE CRYSTALS.** MOROZOVA, L. G. FEOFILOV, P. P. OPT. SPECTROS., USSR 35 (4), 458-9, 1973. (ENGLISH TRANSLATION OF OPT. SPEKTROSK., 35 (4), 789-90, 1973; FOR ORIGINAL SEE E54492)
54494	**VIRTUAL CHARGE EXCHANGE AS A MECHANISM OF NON-RADIATIVE TRANSITION BETWEEN TERMS OF RARE-EARTH IONS IN SCHEELITE AND FERGUSONITE TYPE CRYSTALS.** REUT, E. G. RYSKIN, A. I. OPT. SPEKTROSK. 35 (5), 862-7, 1973. (FOR ENGLISH TRANSLATION SEE E54495)
54495	**VIRTUAL CHARGE EXCHANGE AS A MECHANISM OF NON-RADIATIVE TRANSITION BETWEEN TERMS OF RARE-EARTH IONS IN SCHEELITE AND FERGUSONITE TYPE CRYSTALS.** REUT, E. G. RYSKIN, A. I. OPT. SPECTROS., USSR 35 (5), 501-4, 1973. (ENGLISH TRANSLATION OF OPT. SPEKTROSK., 35 (5), 862-7, 1973; FOR ORIGINAL SEE E54494)
54496	**OPTICAL SPECTRA AND INTERACTION OF RARE EARTH IONS IN DOUBLY ACTIVATED FLUORITE CRYSTALS.** BATYGOV, S. KH. VORONKO, YU. K. GAIGEROVA, L. S. FEDEROV, V. S. OPT. SPEKTROSK. 35 (P), 868-7K, 1973. (FOR ENGLISH TRANSLATION SEE E54497)
54497	**OPTICAL SPECTRA AND INTERACTION OF RARE EARTH IONS IN DOUBLY ACTIVATED FLUORITE CRYSTALS.** BATYGOV, S. KH. VORONKO, YU. K. GAIGEROVA, L. S. FEDEROV, V. S. OPT. SPECTROS., USSR 35 (5), 505-8, 1973. (ENGLISH TRANSLATION OF OPT. SPEKTROSK., 35 (5), 868-75, 1973; FOR ORIGINAL SEE E54496)
54498	**THEORETICAL AND EXPERIMENTAL STUDY OF LOCALIZED LEVELS IN EUROPIUM DIPOSITIVE ION DOPED POTASSIUM CHLORIDE.** PARFIANOVICH, I. A. METSIK, V. M. SALOMATOV, V. N. SHURALEVA, E. I. OPT. SPEKTROSK. 35 (5), 876-9, 1973. (FOR ENGLISH TRANSLATION SEE E54499)
54499	**THEORETICAL AND EXPERIMENTAL STUDY OF LOCALIZED LEVELS IN EUROPIUM DIPOSITIVE ION DOPED POTASSIUM CHLORIDE.** PARFIANOVICH, I. A. METSIK, V. M. SALOMATOV, V. N. SHURALEVA, E. I. OPT. SPECTROS., USSR 35 (5), 509-10, 1973. (ENGLISH TRANSLATION OF OPT. SPEKTROSK., 35 (5), 876-9, 1973; FOR ORIGINAL SEE E54498)
54500	**CONTROL OF OPTICAL RADIATION BY MEANS OF LEAD MAGNONIOBATE CRYSTALS.** ADRIANOVA, I. I. BEREZHNOI, A. A. NEFEDOVA, E. V. PISMENNYI, V. A. SKORNYAKOVA, K. P. OPT. SPEKTROSK. 35 (5), 888-93, 1973. (FOR ENGLISH TRANSLATION SEE E54501)
54501	**CONTROL OF OPTICAL RADIATION BY MEANS OF LEAD MAGNONIOBATE CRYSTALS.** ADRIANOVA, I. I. BEREZHNOI, A. A. NEFEDOVA, E. V. PISMENNYI, V. A. POPOV, YU. V. SKORNYAKOVA, K. P. OPT. SPECTROS., USSR 35 (5), 515-7, 1973. (ENGLISH TRANSLATION OF OPT. SPEKTROSK., 35 (5), 888-93, 1973; FOR ORIGINAL SEE E54500)
54502	**OPTICAL CONSTANTS OF IRON OXIDE IN THE INFRARED RANGE OF THE SPECTRUM.** POPOVA, S. I. TOLSTYKH, T. S. IVLEV, L. S. OPT. SPEKTROSK. 35 (5), 945-55, 1973. (FOR ENGLISH TRANSLATION SEE E54503)
54503	**OPTICAL CONSTANTS OF IRON OXIDE IN THE INFRARED RANGE OF THE SPECTRUM.** POPOVA, S. I. TOLSTYKH, T. S. IVLEV, L. S. OPT. SPECTROS., USSR 35 (5), 551-2, 1973. (ENGLISH TRANSLATION OF OPT. SPEKTROSK., 35 (5), 945-55, 1973; FOR ORIGINAL SEE E54502)

EPIC Number	Bibliographic Citation
54504	**OPTICAL AND MAGNETOOPTICAL PROPERTIES OF IRON BORATE IN THE VISIBLE AND NEAR ULTRAVIOLET SPECTRAL REGIONS.** EDELMAN, I. S. MALAKHOVSKII, A. V. OPT. SPEKTROSK. 35 (5), 959-61, 1973. (FOR ENGLISH TRANSLATION SEE E54505)
54505	**OPTICAL AND MAGNETOOPTICAL PROPERTIES OF IRON BORATE IN THE VISIBLE AND NEAR ULTRAVIOLET SPECTRAL REGIONS.** EDELMAN, I. S. MALAKHOVSKII, A. V. OPT. SPECTROS., USSR 35 (5), 554-5, 1973. (ENGLISH TRANSLATION OF OPT. SPEKTROSK., 35 (5), 959-61, 1973; FOR ORIGINAL SEE E54504)
54506	**EFFECT OF MATRIX DISORDER ON ANTI-STOKES LUMINESCENCE OF ERBIUM TRIPOSITIVE.** ORLOV, M. S. SAITKULOV, I. G. STOLOV, A. L. OPT. SPEKTROSK. 35 (5), 979-82, 1973. (FOR ENGLISH TRANSLATION SEE E54507)
54507	**EFFECT OF MATRIX DISORDER ON ANTI-STOKES LUMINESCENCE OF ERBIUM TRIPOSITIVE.** ORLOV, M. S. SAITKULOV, I. G. STOLOV, A. L. OPT. SPECTROS., USSR 35 (5), 568-70, 1973. (ENGLISH TRANSLATION OF OPT. SPEKTROSK., 35 (5), 979-82, 1973; FOR ORIGINAL SEE E54506)
54508	**TEMPERATURE BROADENING AND SHIFT OF PHONONLESS LINES LINES IN THE SPECTRA OF CRYSTALLINE URANYL COMPOUND WITH A POLYMER-TYPE STRUCTURE.** SHCHELOKOV, R. N. ELLERT, G. V. KARASEV, V. E. KRASILOV, YU. I. GAEVOI, G. M. OPT. SPEKTROSK. 35 (5), 982-3, 1973. (FOR ENGLISH TRANSLATION SEE E54509)
54509	**TEMPERATURE BROADENING AND SHIFT OF PHONONLESS LINES IN THE SPECTRA OF CRYSTALLINE URANYL COMPOUND WITH A POLYMER-TYPE STRUCTURE.** SHCHELOKOV, R. N. ELLERT, G. V. KARASEV, V. E. KRASILOV, YU. I. GAEVOI, G. M. OPT. SPECTROS., USSR 35 (5), 570-1, 1973. (ENGLISH TRANSLATION OF OPT. SPEKTROSK., 35 (5), 982-3, 1973; FOR ORIGINAL SEE E54508)
54510	**ENERGY TRANSFER FROM GADOLINIUM TO PRASEODYMIUM AND YTTERBIUM IONS IN A FLUORITE CRYSTAL.** ORLOV, M. S. SAITKULOV, I. G. BULL. ACAD. SCI., USSR, PHYS. SER. 37 (3), 1-2, 1973. (ENGLISH TRANSLATION OF IZV. AKAD. NAUK SSSR, SER. FIZ., 37 (3), 458-60, 1973; FOR ORIGINAL SEE E49561)
54512	**VIBRONIC STRUCTURE OF THE LUMINESCENT SPECTRA OF IONS IN A CRYSTAL.** MIYAKAWA, T. BULL. ACAD. SCI., USSR, PHYS. SER. 37 (3), 63-6, 1973. (ENGLISH TRANSLATION OF IZV. AKAD. NAUK SSSR, SER. FIZ., 37 (3), 528-31, 1973; FOR ORIGINAL SEE E49842)
54513	**LUMINESCENCE OF OXYGEN CENTERS IN ALUMINUM NITRIDE.** PASTRNAK, J. PACESOVA, S. SANDA, J. ROSE, J. BULL. ACAD. SCI., USSR, PHYS. SER. 37 (3), 123-5, 1973. (ENGLISH TRANSLATION OF IZV. AKAD. NAUK SSSR, SER. FIZ., 37 (3), 599-602, 1973; FOR ORIGINAL SEE E49575)
54515	**ELECTROLUMINESCENCE OF ALKALI HALIDE CRYSTALS.** PARACCHINI, C. BULL. ACAD. SCI., USSR, PHYS. SER. 37 (4), 10-3, 1973. (ENGLISH TRANSLATION OF IZV. AKAD. NAUK SSSR, SER. FIZ., 37 (4), 700-4, 1973; FOR ORIGINAL SEE E49843)
54516	**RESONANCE LUMINESCENCE OF FREE EXCITONS IN CRYSTALS.** PERMOGOROV, S. A. TRAVNIKOV, V. V. SEL'KIN, A. V. BULL. ACAD. SCI., USSR, PHYS. SER. 37 (4), 19-21, 1973. (ENGLISH TRANSLATION OF IZV. AKAD. NAUK SSSR, SER. FIZ., 37 (4), 711-13, 1973; FOR ORIGINAL SEE E49844)
54517	**RESONANT INTERACTION BETWEEN ORTHO- AND PARA-EXCITONS INVOLVING PHONONS IN A CUPROUS OXIDE CRYSTAL.** KREINGOL'D, F. I. MAKAROV, V. L. BULL. ACAD. SCI., USSR, PHYS. SER. 37 (4), 22-5, 1973. (ENGLISH TRANSLATION OF IZV. AKAD. NAUK SSSR, SER. FIZ., 37 (4), 714-7, 1973; FOR ORIGINAL SEE E49845)

EPIC Number	Bibliographic Citation
54518	MULTISTAGE EMISSION OF TWO PHOTONS DURING THE INTERACTION OF ONE ELECTRON–HOLE PAIR WITH ACTIVATOR CENTERS IN ALKALI HALIDE CRYSTALS. ZAZUBOVICH, S. G. KINK, M. F. YAEK, I. V. OSMININ, V. S. BULL. ACAD. SCI., USSR, PHYS. SER. 37 (4), 40–3, 1973. (ENGLISH TRANSLATION OF IZV. AKAD. NAUK SSSR, SER. FIZ., 37 (4), 732–5, 1973; FOR ORIGINAL SEE E49846)
54519	IONIZATION OF LUMINESCENCE CENTERS IN ALKALI HALIDE PHOSPHORS BY UNRELAXED HOLES. ALUKER, E. D. KALNIN, YU. KH. CHERNOV, S. A. SHVARTS, K. K. BULL. ACAD. SCI., USSR, PHYS. SER. 37 (4), 46–8, 1973. (ENGLISH TRANSLATION OF IZV. AKAD. NAUK SSSR, SER. FIZ., 37 (4), 738–40, 1973; FOR ORIGINAL SEE E50109)
54520	LUMINESCENCE OF TUNGSTATE IN ORDERED PEROVSKITES. BLASSE, G. CORSMIT, A. F. VAN DER PAS, M. BULL. ACAD. SCI., USSR, PHYS. SER. 37 (4), 44–5, 1973. (ENGLISH TRANSLATION OF IZV. AKAD. NAUK SSSR, SER. FIZ., 37 (4), 736–7, 1973; FOR ORIGINAL SEE E49847)
54522	CONFIGURATIONAL INTERACTION AND CORRELATION EFFECTS IN THE SPECTRA OF DONOR–ACCEPTOR PAIRS. MERKAM, L. WILLIAMS, F. E. BULL. ACAD. SCI., USSR, PHYS. SER. 37 (4), 104–9, 1973. (ENGLISH TRANSLATION OF IZV. AKAD. NAUK SSSR, SER. FIZ., 37 (4), 803–9, 1973; FOR ORIGINAL SEE E50111)
54523	DONOR–ACCEPTOR PAIRS IN IONIC CRYSTALS. SCHWOTZER, H. KOTITZ, G. GORLICH, P. BULL. ACAD. SCI., USSR, PHYS. SER. 37 (4), 110–5, 1973. (ENGLISH TRANSLATION OF IZV. AKAD. NAUK SSSR, SER. FIZ., 37 (4), 810–7, 1973; FOR ORIGINAL SEE E50112)
54524	HOT LUMINESCENCE OF IMPURITY MOLECULAR IONS IN ALKALI HALIDE CRYSTALS. REBANE, K. K. SAARI, P. M. MAURING, T. KH. BULL. ACAD. SCI., USSR, PHYS. SER. 37 (4), 142–7, 1973. (ENGLISH TRANSLATION OF IZV. AKAD. NAUK SSSR, SER. FIZ., 37 (4), 848–54, 1973; FOR ORIGINAL SEE E50113)
54525	LUMINESCENCE–SPECTRUM STUDY OF CRYSTALS OF URANYL COMPOUNDS. VOLOD'KO, L. V. KOMYAK, A. I. SEVCHENKO, A. N. UMREIKO, D. S. BULL. ACAD. SCI., USSR, PHYS. SER. 37 (4), 158–61, 1973. (ENGLISH TRANSLATION OF IZV. AKAD. NAUK SSSR, SER. FIZ., 37 (4), 865–9, 1973; FOR ORIGINAL SEE E50721)
54526	SPECTROSCOPIC STUDY OF BIELECTRON OR BIHOLE ENERGY LEVELS IN A BISMUTH IODIDE CRYSTAL. GROSS, E. F. STAROSTIN, N. V. SHEPILOV, M. P. SHEKHMAMET'EV, R. I. BULL. ACAD. SCI., USSR, PHYS. SER. 37 (4), 174–8, 1973. (ENGLISH TRANSLATION OF IZV. AKAD. NAUK SSSR, SER. FIZ., 37 (4), 885–90, 1973; FOR ORIGINAL SEE E49848)
54539	IMPROVED CARBIDE THERMIONIC EMITTERS. KAN, KH. S. KUL'VARSKAYA, B. S. SOV. PHYS. TECH. PHYS. 18 (6), 803–6, 1973. (ENGLISH TRANSLATION OF ZH. TEKH. FIZ., 43 (6), 1269–74, 1973; FOR ORIGINAL SEE E52392)
54543	SPECTROSCOPIC INVESTIGATION OF THE INTERMEDIATE STATE IN ANTIFERROMAGNETIC MANGANESE FLUORIDE. MIL'NER, A. A. POPKOV, YU. A. EREMENKO, V. V. JETP LETTERS 18 (1), 20–2, 1973. (ENGLISH TRANSLATION OF PIS'MA ZH. EKSP. TEOR. FIZ., 18 (1), 39–42, 1973; FOR ORIGINAL SEE E52107)
54546	EFFECTS OF LIGHT STORAGE IN CADMIUM INDIUM SULFIDE CRYSTALS. ABDULLAEV, G. B. BELEN'KII, G. L. LARIONKINA, L. S. NANI, R. KH. SALAEV, E. YU. SOV. PHYS. SEMICOND. 7 (4), 561, 1973. (ENGLISH TRANSLATION OF FIZ. TEKH. POLUPROV., 7 (4), 821–2, 1973; FOR ORIGINAL SEE E53777)
54547	THICKNESS OF 90 FERROELECTRIC DOMAIN WALLS IN (BARIUM, LEAD) TITANIUM OXIDE SINGLE CRYSTALS. DENNIS, M. D. BRADT, R. C. J. APPL. PHYS. 45 (5), 1931–3, 1974.
54549	MICROWAVE DIELECTRIC CONSTANT MEASUREMNTS ON LOSSY STATIC AND FLOWING LIQUIDS: B X V EFFECTS. FOLEN, V. J. KREBS, J. J. GINGERICH, M. E. J. APPL. PHYS. 45 (5), 1962–4, 1974.
54551	VIBRATIONAL MODES IN LEAD–LANTHANUM–ZIRCONATE–TITANATE CERAMICS. LURIO, A. BURNS, G. J. APPL. PHYS. 45 (5), 1986–92, 1974.
54552	ON THE NATURE OF CONDUCTION AND SWITCHING IN SILICON OXIDE. SHATZKES, M. AV–RON, M. ANDERSON, R. M. J. APPL. PHYS. 45 (5), 2065–77, 1974.
54554	AUGER–LIMITED CARRIER LIFETIMES IN MERCURY CADMIUM TELLURIDE AT HIGH EXCESS CARRIER CONCENTRATIONS. BARTOLI, F. ALLEN, R. ESTEROWITZ, L. KRUER, M. J. APPL. PHYS. 45 (5), 2150–4, 1974.
54555	NITROGEN CONCENTRATION IN GALLIUM PHOSPHIDE MEASURED BY OPTICAL ABSORPTION AND BY PROTON–INDUCED NUCLEAR REACTIONS. LIGHTOWLERS, E. C. NORTH, J. C. LORIMOR, O. G. J. APPL. PHYS. 45 (5), 2191–2200, 1974.
54556	INFLUENCE OF STOICHIOMETRY ON THE METAL–SEMICONDUCTOR TRANSITION IN VANADIUM DIOXIDE. GRIFFITHS, C. H. EASTWOOD, H. K. J. APPL. PHYS. 45 (5), 2201–6, 1974.
54558	GEOMETRICAL PROPERTIES OF RANDOM PARTICLES AND THE EXTRACTION OF PHOTONS FROM ELECTROLUMINESCENT DIODES. JOYCE, W. B. BACHRACH, R. Z. DIXON, R. W. SEALER, D. A. J. APPL. PHYS. 45 (5), 2229–53, 1974.
54559	DETERMINATION OF FERMI–LEVEL EFFECT ON SI–SITE DISTRIBUTION IN GALLIUM ARSENIDE: SILICON. KUNG, J. K. SPITZER, W. G. J. APPL. PHYS. 45 (5), 2254–7, 1974.
54560	LUMINESCENCE IN EPITAXIAL GALLIUM NITRIDE: CADMIUM. LAGERSTEDT, O. MONEMAR, B. J. APPL. PHYS. 45 (5), 2266–72, 1974.
54561	FIELD MODULATION TECHNIQUE WITH SYNCHRONOUS DETECTION FOR MEASURING MAGNETIC PROPERTIES IN TIME–DEPENDENT FIELDS. FEU, A. TRUEBA, A. J. APPL. PHYS. 45 (5), 2286–92, 1974.
54564	ELECTRON MIXROSCOPE STUDY OF SILVER COLLOIDS IN POTASSIUM CHLORIDE: SILVER. JAIN, S. C. ARORA, N. D. CHAUDHARY, K. L. J. APPL. PHYS. 45 (5), 2368–9, 1974.
54565	SPECTRUM OF FIRST–NEAREST–NEIGHBOR CHROMIUM TRIPOSITIVE PAIRS IN RUBY. VAN DER ZIEL, J. P. PHYS. REV. 9 B (7), 2846–62, 1974.
54571	MAGNETIC FORM FACTOR OF TERBIUM IN TERBIUM HYDROXIDE. BRUN, T. O. LANDER, G. H. PHYS. REV. 9 B (7), 3003–12, 1974.
54572	MAGNETIZATION STUDIES OF GERMANIUM TELLURIDE MANGANESE TELLURIDE PSEUDOBINARY ALLOYS. COCHRANE, R. W. PLISCHKE, M. STROM–OLSEN, J. O. PHYS. REV. 9 B (7), 3013–21, 1974.
54573	EXCHANGE OPTICS IN GADOLINIUM–DOPED EUROPIUM OXIDE. SCHOENES, J. WACHTER, P. PHYS. REV. 9 B (7), 3097–3105, 1974.
54576	NONLINEARITY OF THE MAGNETIZATION IN WEAK FERROMAGNETS: ORTHOFERRITES. TENENBAUM, Y. PHYS. REV. 9 B (7), 3141–6, 1974.
54577	DIPOLAR THEORY OF FERROELECTRICS REVISITED. GONZALO, J. A. PHYS. REV. 9 B (7), 3149–52, 1974.

EPIC Number | Bibliographic Citation

54578 **VACUUM-ULTRAVIOLET OPTICAL PROPERTIES OF SINGLE-CRYSTAL CADMIUM.**
OLSON, C. G. LYNCH, D. W.
PHYS. REV.
9 B (8), 3159–68, 1974.

54582 **PHOTOLUMINESCENCE OF H- AND D-IMPLANTED 4H SILICON CARBIDE.**
CHOYKE, W. J. PATRICK, L.
PHYS. REV.
9 B (8), 3214–19, 1974.
(AD-782 749)

54587 **SELF-CONSISTENT BAND STRUCTURE OF ORDERED BETA-BRASS.**
MORUZZI, V. L. WILLIAMS, A. R. JANAK, J. F.
SOFES, C.
PHYS. REV.
9 B (8), 3316–20, 1974.

54592 **DIELECTRIC FUNCTION FOR A MODEL, TWO-BAND SEMIMETAL.**
CZACHOR, A.
PHYS. REV.
9 B (8), 3357–68, 1974.

54593 **CHARACTERISTIC-ENERGY-LOSS SPECTRA OF VANADIUM AND OF VANADIUM OXIDE.**
SZALKOWSKI, F. J. BERTRAND, P. A.
SOMORJAI, G. A.
PHYS. REV.
9 B (8), 3369–76, 1974.

54594 **LOCALIZED STATES AND CARRIER TRANSPORT IN AMORPHOUS CHALCOGENIDE SEMICONDUCTORS.**
ARNOLDUSSEN, T. C. MENEZES, C. A.
NAKAGAWA, Y. BUBE, R. H.
PHYS. REV.
9 B (8), 3377–93, 1974.
(AD-786 290)

54595 **STRONTIUM TITANIUM OXIDE ELECTROREFLECTANCE: FLATBAND-ELECTROLYTE AND SCHOTTKY-BARRIER MEASUREMENTS.**
MACK, S. A. HANDLER, P.
PHYS. REV.
9 B (8), 3415–23, 1974.

54596 **THEORY OF SURFACE POLARITONS IN ANISOTROPIC DIELECTRIC MEDIA WITH APPLICATION TO SURFACE MAGNETOPLASMONS IN SEMICONDUCTORS.**
WALLIS, R. F. BRION, J. J. BURSTEIN, E.
HARTSTEIN, A.
PHYS. REV.
9 B (8), 3424–37, 1974.
(AD-782 115)

54600 **PHOTOEMISSION SPECTROSCOPY USING SYNCHROTRON RADIATION. I. OVERVIEWS OF VALENCE-BAND STRUCTURE FOR GERMANIUM, GALLIUM ARSENIDE, GALLIUM PHOSPHIDE, INDIUM ANTIMONY, ZINC SELENIDE, CADMIUM TELLURIDE, AND SILVER IODIDE.**
EASTMAN, D. E. GROBMAN, W. D. FREEOUF, J. L.
ERBUDAK, M.
PHYS. REV.
9 B (8), 3473–88, 1974.

54601 **TWO-PHOTON ABSORPTION WITH EXCITON EFFECT FOR DEGENERATE VALENCE BANDS.**
LEE, C. C. FAN, H. Y.
PHYS. REV.
9 B (8), 3502–16, 1974.
(AD 778 979)

54602 **CARRIER DISTRIBUTION IN GRADED-BAND-GAP SEMICONDUCTORS UNDER ASYMMETRIC BAND-EDGE GRADIENTS.**
CHATTOPADHYAYA, S. K. MATHUR, V. K.
PHYS. REV.
9 B (8), 3517–23, 1974.

54603 **EXCITON AND IMPURITY STATES IN ALKALI HALIDES.**
O'BRIEN, W. P., JR. HERNANDEZ, J. P.
PHYS. REV.
9 B (8), 3560–72, 1974.

54604 **X-RAY PHOTOEMISSION STUDIES OF THE ALKALI HALIDES.**
KOWALCZYK, S. P. MC FEELY, F. R. LEY, L.
POLLAK, R. A. SHIRLEY, D. A.
PHYS. REV.
9 B (8), 3573–81, 1974.

54605 **HALL EFFECT IN POTASSIUM BROMIDE CONTAINING F-CENTERS AT LOW TEMPERATURES.**
DURAN, A. T. MEJIA, C. R.
PHYS. REV.
9 B (8), 3582–6, 1974.

54606 **OBSERVATIONS OF FORBIDDEN SOFT-X-RAY TRANSITIONS: LITHIUM K ABSORPTION IN LITHIUM FLUORIDE.**
SONNTAG, B. F.
PHYS. REV.
9 B (8), 3601–2, 1974.

54608 **SURFACE-STATE DENSITIES ON CLEAN SEMICONDUCTOR SURFACES MEASURED BY ELLIPSOMETRY.**
MEYER, F.
PHYS. REV.
9 B (8), 3622–6, 1974.

54618 **PIEZO- AND THERMO- OPTICAL PROPERTIES OF BISMUTH GERMANIUM OXIDE.**
HENNESSEY, P.
PENNSYLVANIA STATE UNIV., UNIVERSITY PARK, PH. D. THESIS
140PP., 1972.
(UNIV. MICORFILMS NO. 72-33172, N73-26754)

54619 **ELECTRONIC PROPERTIES OF VANADIUM NITRIDES.**
AJAMI, F. I.
PENNSYLVANIA UNIVERSITY, PHILADELPHIA, PH. D. THESIS
106PP., 1972.
(UNIV. MICROFILMS NO. 72-25356, N73-22473)

54629 **THE INFLUENCE OF TITANIUM IONS ON THE MAGNETIC PROPERTIES OF MANGANESE-ZINC FERRITES.**
HANKE, I.
BER. DEUT. KERAM. GES.
49 (9), 295–300, 1972.
(FOR ENGLISH TRANSLATION SEE E54630)

54630 **THE INFLUENCE OF TITANIUM IONS ON THE MAGNETIC PROPERTIES OF MANGANESE-ZINC FERRITES.**
HANKE, I.
NATIONAL LENDING LIBRARY FOR SCIENCE AND TECHNOLOGY
13PP., 1973.
(ENGLISH TRANSLATION OF BER. DEUT. KERAM. GES., 49 (9), 295–300, 1972; FOR ORIGINAL SEE E54629)
(NLL-TRANS-862-(9022.64), N73-25626)

54640 **FORMATION OF F-CENTERS IN POTASSIUM IODIDE CRYSTALS AT LIQUID NITROGEN TEMPERATURES.**
BUIKO, V. M. ZHUSUPOV, T.
ELEKTRON. IONNYE PROTSESSY NEMETAL. KRIST.
57–60PP., 1972.
(EDITED BY A. A. ALYBAKOV, IZD. ILIM: FRUNZE, USSR)

54645 **EFFECT OF A SURFACE ELCTRIC FIELD ON GALLIUM ARSENIDE ABSORPTION.**
KRAVCHENKO, A. F. TEREKHOV, A. S.
FIZ. TEKH. POLUPROV.
7 (11), 2234–5, 1973.
(FOR ENGLISH TRANSLATION SEE E59281)

54646 **SPECTRAL PROPERTIES OF CADMIUM SELENIDE SINGLE CRYSTALS DUE TO THEIR SURFACE.**
DAVYDOVA, N. A. MYASNIKOV, E. N.
STRASHNIKOVA, M. I.
FIZ. TVERD. TELA (LENINGRAD)
15 (11), 3332–7, 1973.
(FOR ENGLISH TRANSLATION SEE E55190)

54648 **PURE OXIDE AND MONOXIDE CERAMICS. PRODUCTS FOR OPTICS. THIN LAYERS.**
PEYSSOU, J.
IND. CERAM.
(664), 517–26, 1973.

54653 **FABRICATION AND PROPERTIES OF POLYCRYSTALLINE ALKALI HALIDES.**
BOWEN, H. K. SINGH, R. N.
POSEN, H. ARMINGTON, A. KULIN, S. A.
MATER. RES. BULL.
8 (12), 1389–99, 1973.

54657 **DETERMINATION OF THE REFRACTIVE INDEX OF SINGLE CRYSTALS OF THALLIUM- OR SODIUM-ACTIVATED CESIUM IODIDE.**
NOSULENKO, N. A. NAUMENKO, N. M.
TSIRLIN, YU. A.
MONOKRIST. TEKH.
(5), 93–6, 1971.

54661 **SULFUR IMPURITY LEVEL DEPENDENCE ON BAND STRUCTURE VARIATION WITH PRESSURE IN GALLIUM INDIUM ANTIMONDIE.**
D'OLNE CAMPOS, M. GOUSKOV, A. GOUSKOV, L.
PHYS. STATUS SOLIDI
61 B (1), 77–85, 1974.

54662 **CALCULATED INFRARED ABSORPTION DUE TO IMPURITIES IN CESIUM HALIDES.**
RAM, P. N. AGRAWAL, B. K.
PHYS. STATUS SOLIDI
61 B (1), 341–51, 1974.

54669 **ANNEALING AND PHASE STABILITY OF TANTALUM FILMS SPUTTERED IN ARGON-OXYGEN. THIN SOLID FILMS**
FEINSTEIN, L. G. HUTTEMANN, R. D.
THIN SOLID FILMS
20 (1), 103–14, 1973.

54670 **INTERVALLEY ELECTRON TRANSFER IN INDIUM ANTIMONIDE FILMS.**
WIEDER, H. H. COLLINS, D. A.
THIN SOLID FILMS
20 (1), 201–8, 1973.

EPIC Number | Bibliographic Citation

54678 **SEVERAL KINETIC COEFFICIENTS AND THE RELATIONS BETWEEN THEM FOR ONE TYPE OF THE CHARGE CARRIER.**
KONIG, B.
ACTA PHYS. SLOVACA
23 (3), 173–80, 1973.

54683 **INTERACTION BETWEEN THE NICKEL ALUMINUM PHASE AND NICKEL TANTALUM.**
MINTS, R. S. D'IAKONOVA, N. P.
UMANSKII, YA. S. BONDARENKO, YU. A.
BONDARENKO, T. A.
AKAD. NAUK SSSR, DOKL.
206, 87,88, 1972.

54687 **THE INTRINSIC-ABSORPTION EDGE IN BULK AND THIN-FILM ARSENIC SULFIDE CRYSTALS.**
TSVELYKH, N. G.
AKAD. NAUK SSSR, IZV., NEORG. MATER.
8, 1379–83, 1972.

54689 **KINETIC CHARACTERISTICS OF TITANIUM CARBIDE NITRIDE AND ZIRCONIUM NIOBIUM CARBIDE SOLID SOLUTIONS.**
BORUKHOVICH, A. S. DUBROVSKAYA, L. B.
MATVEENKO, I. I. ORDAN'IAN, S. S.
AKAD. NAUK SSSR, IXV., NEORG. MATER.
9, 791–5, 1973.

54697 **MAGNETIC AND CRYSTALLOGRAPHIC STUDIES OF IRON-GERMANIUM SOLID SOLUTION.**
TURBIL, J. P. MICHEL, A.
ANN. CHIM.
8 (4), 225–8, 1973.

54704 **ELECTRICAL PROPERTIES OF INSULATING MATERIALS UNDER THE SIMULTANEOUS ACTION OF A.C. AND D.C. VOLTAGE.**
RAPOS, M.
ANNU. REP., CONF. ELEC. INSUL. DIELEC. PHENOMENA
98–104, 1972.

54718 **PIEZOOPTIC INVESTIGATIONS OF THE EXCITON SPECTRUM OF CADMIUM SULFIDE.**
BRODIN, M. S. BLONSKII, I. V.
DAVYDOVA, N. A. STRASHNIKOVA, M. I.
SOV. PHYS. SOLID STATE
14 (11), 2841–4, 1973.
(ENGLISH TRANSLATION OF FIZ. TVERD. TELA, 14 (11), 3356–61, 1972; FOR ORIGINAL SEE E54233)

54727 **AMMONIA ABSORPTION RELEVANT TO THE ALBEDO OF JUPITER. I - EXPERIMENTAL RESULTS.**
DICK, K. A. ZIKO, A. O.
ASTROPHYSICAL JOURNAL
182 (1), 609–613, 1973.

54728 **RADIATION EFFECTS IN THALLIUM-ACTIVATED CESIUM IODIDE SINGLE CRYSTALS DURING GAMMA-RADIATION.**
BEREZIN, I. A. GORBACHEV, V. M.
KUZYANOV, V. V. STEN'GACH, I. N.
UVAROV, N. A.
AT. ENERG.
35 (5), 364–6, 1973.

54750 **NEW OXYFLUORIDES OF RUTILE AND TRIRUTILE STRUCTURE.**
SENEGAS, J. GALY, J.
C. R. ACAD. SCI., SER.
277 C (22), 1243–6, 1973.

54756 **WEAK FERROMAGNETISM OF ORTHORHOMBIC COPPER IRON SULFIDE.**
TOWNSEND, M. G. HORWOOD, J. L.
GOSELIN, J. R.
CAN. J. PHYS.
51 (20), 2162–5, 1973.

54758 **NERNST-ETTINGSHAUSEN EFFECTS IN GALLIUM INDIUM ARSENIDE.**
DEMARS, D. J. E. WOOLLEY, J. C.
CAN. J. PHYS.
51 (22), 2369–75, 1973.

54762 **AN APPARATUS FOR MEASURING THE HALL EFFECT OF HIGH-RESISTIVITY MATERIALS IN ALTERNATING ELECTRIC AND MAGNETIC FIELDS.**
THURZO, I.
CESK. CAS. FYS.
22 A (5), 451–7, 1972.

54764 **MEASUREMENT OF ANISOTROPIC MAGNETIC SUSCEPTIBILITIES USING THE FARADAY METHOD.**
MARSHALL, R. C. JAMES, D. W.
BRETHERTON, L.
CHEM. INSTRUM.
5 (2), 127–39, 1973.

54768 **EVAPORATED CARBON FILMS.**
MC LINTOCK, I. S. ORR, J. C.
CHEM. PHYS. CARBON
11, 243–312, 1973.

54769 **MEMORY SWITCHING IN A TYPE I AMORPHOUS CHALCOGENIDE.**
THORNBURG, D. D.
J. ELECTRON. MATER.
2 (1), 3–15, 1973.

54770 **OPTICAL PROPERTIES OF PHOTOCHROMATIC SULFUR-DOPED CHLOROSODALITE.**
CHANG, I. F. ONTON, A.
J. ELECTRON. MATER.
2 (1), 17–46, 1973.

54771 **GALLIUM ARSENIDE FOR LASER WINDOW APPLICATIONS.**
THOMPSON, A. G.
J. ELECTRON. MATER.
2 (1), 47–70, 1973.

54772 **PSEUDOBINARY PHASE DIAGRAM AND EXISTENCE REGIONS FOR LEAD SULFIDE 1-X SELENIDE.**
STRAUSS, A. J. HARMAN, T. C.
J. ELECTRON. MATER.
2 (1), 71–85, 1973.

54773 **OPTICAL PERFORMANCE EVALUATION OF INFRARED TRANSMITTING MATERIALS.**
BENDOW, B. GIANINO, P. D.
J. ELECTRON. MATER.
2 (1), 87–114, 1973.

54774 **AUGER AND ELLIPSOMETRIC STUDIES OF ULTRA-THIN LEAD OXIDE GROWTH ON LEAD.**
CHOU, N. J. ELDRIDGE, J. M. HAMMER, R.
DONG, D.
J. ELECTRON. MATER.
2 (1), 115–26, 1973.

54775 **STRENGTHENING OF HALIDES FOR INFRARED WINDOWS.**
ARMINGTON, A. F. POSEN, H. LIPSON, H.
J. ELECTRON. MATER.
2 (1), 127–36, 1973.

54776 **THE LUMINESCENT PROPERTIES OF NITROGEN DOPED GALLIUM ARSENIDE LIGHT EMITTING DIODES.**
CRAFORD, M. G. KEUNE, D. L. GROVES, W. O.
HERZOG, A. H.
J. ELECTRON. MATER.
2 (1), 137–58, 1973.

54807 **FINE STRUCTURE OF THE IMPURITY A-ABSORPTION BANDS IN ALKALI METAL HALIDES.**
BOHUN, A. PRACKA, M. JERABEK, J.
CZECH. J. PHYS.
23 (10), 1147–8, 1973.

54809 **OPTICAL CONSTANTS OF THIN OXIDE FILMS ON TITANIUM.**
KUCIREK, J.
CZECH. J. PHYS.
23 (12), 1382–94, 1973.

54820 **LOW-TEMPERATURE ASSOCIATION OF SODIUM CHLORIDE + BISMUTH CHLORIDE CRYSTALS.**
HARTMANOVA, M. MARIANI, E.
PHYS. SLOVACA
23 (4), 217–23, 1973.

54828 **ELECTRICAL CONDUCTIVITY OF THORIUM DIOXIDE.**
BATES, J. L. SCHEMMEL, R. R.
BATTELLE-NORTHWEST, RICHLAND, WASH.
56PP., 1972.
(BNWL-1671, N73-21475, AVAIL. NTIS)

54829 **EFFECT OF TEMPERATURE ON THE ELECTRICAL CONDUCTIVITY OF MOLTEN POTASSIUM THIOCYANATE.**
DULIEU, P. CLAES, P.
BULL. SOC. CHIM. BELG.
82 (9–10), 639–43, 1973.

54832 **ELECTRICAL RESISTIVITY AT HIGH TEMPERATURES OF THE SYSTEMS (CHROMIUM-MANGANESE)-BERYLLIUM AND (VANADIUM-CHROMIUM)-BERYLLIUM.**
KAPPLER, J. WUCHER, J.
C. R. ACAD. SCI.
277 B (13), 337–40, 1973.

54833 **MAGNETIC INTERACTIONS IN THE INVERSE SPINEL COBALT TITANIUM OXIDE.**
DE STROOPER, K. ROBBRECHT, G. BRABERS, V.
C. R. ACAD. SCI.
277 B (13), 395–7, 1973.

54836 **ELECTRICAL PROPERTIES OF ERBIUM, THULIUM(III), YTTERBIUM(III), AND LUTETIUM OXIDES AT HIGH TEMPERATURE AS A FUNCTION OF THE OXYGEN PRESSURE.**
BREUIL, H. DHERBOMEZ, N. WILBERT, Y.
C. R. ACAD. SCI.
277 C (18), 871–3, 1973.

54838 **ULTRASONIC MODULATION OF MICROWAVES IN PIEZOELECTRIC SEMICONDUCTORS.**
MATHUR, S. S. SAGOO, M. S.
CAN. J. PHYS.
51 (23), 2459–63, 1973.

54850 **CRYSTAL GROWTH AND DIELECTRIC PROPERTIES OF THE FERROELECTRIC STRONTIUM BARIUM NIOBATE.**
SAKAMOTO, K. UNOKI, H. SAKUDO, T.
DENSHI GIJUTSU SOGO KENKYUJO IHO
37 (4), 429–36, 1973.

EPIC Number	Bibliographic Citation

54861 **ELECTRICAL PROPERTIES AND STRUCTURAL TRANSFORMATIONS IN SILVER SULFIDE THIN FILMS.**
ISKENDEROV, R. N. NURIEV, I. R.
SULTANOV, R. M. SHAFI-ZADE, R. B.
DOKL. AKAD. NAUK AZERB. SSR
29 (5), 16-19, 1973.

54869 **EFFECT OF RADIATION ON THE ELECTRICAL CONDUCTIVITY OF SOME RARE EARTH AND YTTRIUM OXIDES.**
SPITSYN, V. I. PIROGOVA, G. N.
STEL'MAKH, N. S.
DOKL. AKAD. NAUK SSSR
212 (6), 1389-92, 1973.

54871 **REGULARITIES IN SPECTRA OF SILVER IODIDE CRYSTAL EDGE RADIATION.**
BARSHCHEVSKII, B. U. FOK, M. V.
SAFRONOV, G. M. SADOVSKAYA, O. A.
DOKL. AKAD. NAUK SSSR
213 (3), 614-17, 1973.

54873 **ION-ELECTRON EMISSION FROM SODIUM CHLORIDE AND POTASSIUM BROMIDE COLORED CRYSTALS.**
ARIFOV, U. A. RAKHIMOV, R. R. GAIPOV, S.
ABDULKHAKOV, I.
DOKL. AKAD. NAUK UZB. SSR
29 (9), 21-3, 1972.

54875 **EXPLORATION OF ACTIVE MEDIA FOR LASERS.**
KAMINSKII, A. A.
SOV. PHYS. DOKL.
18 (8), 529-30, 1974.
(ENGLISH TRANSLATION OF DOKL. AKAD. NAUK SSSR, 211 (4), 811-3, 1973; FOR ORIGINAL SEE E52512)

54881 **TRANSPORT PROPERTIES OF FERROMAGNETIC SYSTEMS NEAR THE CRITICAL POINT. ELECTRICAL RESISTIVITY.**
KAWATRA, M. P. BUDNICK, J. I.
DYN. ASPECTS CRIT. PHENOMENA, PROC. CONF.
257-91, 1972.

54886 **SIMPLE THEORETICAL APPROACH TO PHASE TRANSITIONS. CERIUM, METAL-INSULATORS, AND ANTIFERROMAGNETIC CHROMIUM.**
FALICOV, L. M.
DYN. ASPECTS CRIT. PHENOMENA, (PROC.) CONF.
454-90PP., 1972.
(EDITED BY J. I. BUDNICK, GORDON AND BREACH: NEW YORK, N. Y.)

54890 **PROPERTIES OF FUSED POLYSULFIDES. I. ELECTRICAL CONDUCTIVITY OF FUSED SODIUM AND POTASSIUM POLYSULFIDES.**
CLEAVER, B. DAVIES, A. J. HAMES, M. D.
ELECTROCHIM. ACTA
18 (10), 719-26, 1973.

54894 **SPECTRAL COMPOSITION OF THERMOLUMINESCENCE OF ACTIVATED CRYSTALS OF LITHIUM AND SODIUM FLUORIDES.**
ALYBAKOV, A. A. GUBANOVA, V. A.
ELEKTRON. IONNYE PROTSESSY NEMETAL. KRIST.
45-9, 1972.

54895 **APPARATUS FOR REGISTRATION OF EXOELECTRONIC EMISSIONS AND CONDUCTIVITY OF EXCITED CRYSTALS.**
RESNYANSKII, V. F.
ELEKTRON. IONNYE PROTSESSY NEMETAL. KRIST.
50-6, 1972.

54901 **MICROWAVE HALL-MOBILITY MEASUREMENTS ON 1-DIMENSIONAL CONDUCTING SYSTEMS BROMINE-CONTAINING POTASSIUM TETRACYANOPLATINUM HYDRATE AND QUINOLINIUM.**
SAYED, M. M. WESTGATE, C. R.
ELECTRON. LETT.
9 (22), 529, 1973.

54903 **ELECTRICAL PROPERTIES OF EVAPORATED MERCURY TELLURIDE FILMS.**
SIEKIERSKA, K.
ELECTRON TECHNOLOGY
4 (4), 73-103, 1971.

54906 **MAGNETIC ANISOTROPY IN MANGANESE IRON SPINELS ABOVE 300 K.**
JAGUSZTYN-BUZE, M.
ELECTRON TECHNOL.
6 (1-2), 165-84, 1973.

54907 **DETERMINATION OF THE OPTIMUM CONCENTRATION OF A DOPING ADDITIVE INTRODUCED INTO SEMICONDUCTOR MATERIALS.**
BERCHENKO, M. A. MALEVSKII, YU. N.
MAMEDOV, M. R. ALATYRTSEV, G. A.
ELEKTRON. OBRAB. MATER.
(2), 88-9, 1973.

54917 **EFFECT OF HIGH FIELDS ON THE ELECTRICAL CONDUCTIVITY OF MOLTEN ALKALI METAL CHLORIDES.**
SHABANOV, O. M. GADZHIEV, S. M.
TAGIROV, S. M.
ELEKTROKHIMIYA
9 (11), 1742, 1973.

54921 **EFFECT OF INDIUM OXIDE ADDITIONS ON THE PROPERTIES OF MANGANESE-ZINC FERRITE.**
VLADIMIRTSEVA, L. A. SAMSONOV, G. V.
GORBATYUK, V. A.
SOV. POWDER MET. METAL CERAM.
12 (8), 669-71, 1973.
(ENGLISH TRANSLATION OF POROSH. MET., 12 (8), 80-3, 1973; FOR ORIGINAL SEE E52114)

54928 **ANOMALOUS PHOTOVOLTAGE IN VACUUM-DEPOSITED INDIUM TELLURIDE AND SILVER IODIDE FILMS.**
BENDA, M.
ELEKTROTECH. CAS.
24 (6), 417-19, 1973.

54934 **ELECTRIC PROPERTIES OF GERMANIUM-DOPED ANTIMONY TELLURIDE CRYSTALS.**
TICHY, L. HORAK, J. VASKO, A.
FRUMAR, M.
PHYS. STATUS SOLDI
20 A (2), 717-24, 1973.

54938 **MEASUREMENT OF THE PIEZORESISTANCE COEFFICIENT OF N-TYPE SILICON CARBIDE AT 20-600 K.**
LYUBIMSKII, V. M. USOL'TSEVA, N. YA.
FIZ. TEKH. POLUPROV.
49-52, 1972.

54942 **TEMPERATURE DEPENDENCE OF THE PIEZOELECTRIC SIGNAL OF FERROELECTRIC LITHIUM NIOBATE.**
REZNICHENKO, S. A.
FIZ. TEKH. POLUPROV.
63-6, 1972.

54947 **PIEZORESISTANCE IN N-GALLIUM ARSENIDE.**
DRAGUNOV, V. P. KOZEEV, E. V.
KRAVCHENKO, A. F. KHOLYAVKO, V. N.
FIZ. TEKH. POLUPROV.
7 (8), 1466-9, 1973.

54950 **METAL-DIELECTRIC TRANSITION IN A MAGNETIC FIELD IN COMPENSATED GALLIUM ARSENIDE.**
ZAVARITSKAYA, E. I. VORONOVA, I. D.
ROZHDESTVENSKAYA, N. V.
FIZ. TEKH. POLUPROV.
7 (8), 1479-84, 1973.

54952 **ELECTRON MOBILITY IN PURE N-INDIUM ANTIMONIDE IN THE 20-75 K RANGE.**
GERSHENZON, E. M. KURILENKO, I. N.
LITVAK-GORSKAYA, L. B. RABINOVICH, R. I.
FIZ. TEKH. POLUPROV.
7 (8), 1501-6, 1973.

54953 **ENERGY SPECTRUM AND MOBILITY OF CHARGE CARRIERS IN UNDOPED CADMIUM GERMANIUM PHOSPHIDE CRYSTALS.**
BORSHCHEVSKII, A. S. RUD, YU. V.
UNDALOV, YU. K.
FIZ. TEKH. POLUPROV.
7 (8), 1570-4, 1973.

54954 **ANOMALOUS PROPERTIES OF N-CADMIUM ANTIMONIDE.**
RARENKO, I. M. SEMIZOROV, A. F.
GERTOVICH, T. S. GRITSYUK, B. N.
FIZ. TEKH. POLUPROV.
7 (8), 1595-8, 1973.

54955 **MAGNETIC SUSCEPTIBILITY OF IRON-DOPED GALLIUM ARSENIDE.**
ANDRIANOV, D. G. MURAVLEV, YU. B.
SAVEL'EV, A. S. SOLOV'EV, N. N.
FISTUL, V. I.
FIZ. TEKH. POLUPROV.
7 (8), 1622-5, 1973.

54956 **EFFECT OF SCATTERING INELASTICITY AND NONPARABOLICITY OF A BAND ON THE LONGITUDINAL MAGNETORESISTANCE OF N-INDIUM ANTIMONIDE DEGENERATE SEMICONDUCTORS IN A QUANTUM MAGNETIC FIELD.**
AGAEVA, R. G. ASKEROV, B. M.
GASHIMZADE, F. M.
FIZ. TEKH. POLUPROV.
7 (8), 1625-7, 1973.

54957 **FIELD DEFORMATION OF THE IMPURITY EMISSION SPECTRUM OF COPPER-DOPED GALLIUM ARSENIDE.**
PEKA, G. P. BRODOVOI, V. A.
FIZ. TEKH. POLUPROV.
7 (8), 1645-8, 1973.

54963 **MAGNETIC PROPERTIES OF THE NEPTUNIUM MONOPNICTIDES.**
ALDRED, A. T. DUNLAP, B. D. HARVEY, A. R.
LAM, D. J. LANDER, G. H. MUELLER, M. H.
PHYS. REV.
9 B (9), 3766-79, 1974.

54965 **TEMPERATURE DEPENDENCE OF THE MAGNETIC EXCITATIONS IN SINGLET-GROUND-STATE SYSTEMS: PARAMAGNETIC AND ZERO-TEMPERATURE BEHAVIOR OF PRASEODYMIUM THALLIUM AND (PRASEODYMIUM LANTHANUM) THALLIUM.**
HOLDEN, T. M. BUYERS, W. J. L.
PHYS. REV.
9 B (9), 3797-3805, 1974.

EPIC Number	Bibliographic Citation
54968	ALLOWANCE FOR RELAXATION EFFECTS IN SURFACE LAYERS OF SEMICONDUCTORS IN INVESTIGATIONS OF ELECTRON EMISSION RESULTING FROM ION BOMBARDMENT. OMEL'YANOVSKAYA, N. M. LEBEDEV, S. YA. FIZ. TVERD. TELA 15 (9), 2612–4, 1973. (FOR ENGLISH TRANSLATION SEE E54969)
54969	ALLOWANCE FOR RELAXATION EFFECTS IN SURFACE LAYERS OF SEMICONDUCTORS IN INVESTIGATIONS OF ELECTRON EMISSION RESULTING FROM ION BOMBARDMENT. OMEL'YANOVSKAYA, N M. LEBEDEV, S. YA. SOV. PHYS. SOLID STATE 15 (9), 1738–9, 1974. (ENGLISH TRANSLATION OF FIZ. TVERD. TELA, 15 (9), 2612–4, 1973; FOR ORIGINAL SEE E54968)
54970	DRAG OF CONDUCTION ELECTRONS BY PHOTONS DUE TO DIRECT TRANSITIONS BETWEEN SPIN BRANCHES. ARIFZHANOV, S. B. DANISHEVSKII, A. M. FIZ. TVERD. TELA 15 (9), 2626–8, 1973. (FOR ENGLISH TRANSLATION SEE E54971)
54971	DRAG OF CONDUCTION ELECTRONS BY PHOTONS DUE TO DIRECT TRANSITIONS BETWEEN SPIN BRANCHES. ARIFZHANOV, S. B. DANISHEVSKII, A. M. SOV. PHYS. SOLID STATE 15 (9), 1747–8, 1974. (ENGLISH TRANSLATION OF FIZ. TVERD. TELA, 15 (9), 2626–8, 1973; FOR ORIGINAL SEE E54970)
54974	EFFECT OF PHONON HEATING ON THE PROPAGATION OF HIGH–FREQUENCY ELECTROMAGNETIC WAVES. GASYMOV, T. M. KATANOV, A. A. FIZ. TVERD. TELA 15 (9), 2644–6, 1973. (FOR ENGLISH TRANSLATION SEE E54975)
54975	EFFECT OF PHONON HEATING ON THE PROPAGATION OF HIGH–FREQUENCY ELECTROMAGNETIC WAVES. GASYMOV, T. M. KATANOV, A. A. SOV. PHYS. SOLID STATE 15 (9), 1759–60, 1974. (ENGLISH TRANSLATION OF FIZ. TVERD. TELA, 15 (9), 2644–6, 1973; FOR ORIGINAL SEE E54974)
54976	ANALYSIS OF THE TEMPERATURE DEPENDENCE OF THE INTENSITY OF THE EXCITON LUMINESCENCE OF CADMIUM SULFIDE SINGLE CRYSTALS. GRIN', V. F. SAL'KOV, E. A. KHVOSTOV, V. A. FIZ. TVERD. TELA 15 (9), 2694–2700, 1973. (FOR ENGLISH TRANSLATION SEE E54977)
54977	ANALYSIS OF THE TEMPERATURE DEPENDENCE OF THE INTENSITY OF THE EXCITON LUMINESCENCE OF CADMIUM SULFIDE SINGLE CRYSTALS. GRIN', V. F. SAL'KOV, E. A. KHVOSTOV, V. A. SOV. PHYS. SOLID STATE 15 (9), 1792–5, 1974. (ENGLISH TRANSLATION OF FIZ. TVERD. TELA, 15 (9), 2694–2700, 1973; FOR ORIGINAL SEE E54976)
54978	INFLUENCE OF BIEXCITONS ON EDGE ABSORPTION AND LUMINESCENCE. GOGOLIN, A. A. FIZ. TVERD. TELA 15 (9), 2746–56, 1973. (FOR ENGLISH TRANSLATION SEE E54979)
54979	INFLUENCE OF BIEXCITONS ON EDGE ABSORPTION AND LUMINESCENCE. GOGOLIN, A. A. SOV. PHYS. SOLID STATE 15 (9), 1824–30, 1974. (ENGLISH TRANSLATION OF FIZ. TVERD. TELA, 15 (9), 2745–56, 1973; FOR ORIGINAL SEE E54978)
54982	NEW STRUCTURE–SENSITIVE PHOTOELECTRIC EFFECT IN BARIUM TITANATE CRYSTALS. DUDKEVICH, V. P. ZAKHARCHENKO, I. N. FESENKO, E. G. FIZ. TVERD. TELA 15 (9), 2766–8, 1973. (FOR ENGLISH TRANSLATION SEE E54983)
54983	NEW STRUCTURE–SENSITIVE PHOTOELECTRIC EFFECT IN BARIUM TITANATE CRYSTALS. DUDKEVICH, V. P. ZAKHARCHENKO, I. N. FESENKO, E. G. SOV. PHYS. SOLID STATE 15 (9), 1838–9, 1974. (ENGLISH TRANSLATION OF FIZ. TVERD. TELA, 15 (9), 2766–8, 1973; FOR ORIGINAL SEE E54982)
54984	THERMAL CONDUCTIVITY OF LITHIUM FLUORIDE IN THE 300–1100 K TEMPERATURE RANGE. MEN', A. A. CHECHEL'NITSKII, A. Z. SOKOLOV, V. A. SIMUN, E. N. FIZ. TVERD. TELA 15 (9), 2773–5, 1973. (FOR ENGLISH TRANSLATION SEE E54985)
54985	THERMAL CONDUCTIVITY OF LITHIUM FLUORIDE IN THE 300–1100 K TEMPERATURE RANGE. MEN', A. A. CHECHEL'NITSKII, A. Z. SOKOLOV, V. A. SIMUN, E. N. SOV. PHYS. SOLID STATE 15 (9), 1844–5, 1974. (ENGLISH TRANSLATION OF FIZ. TVERD. TELA, 15 (9), 2773–5, 1973; FOR ORIGINAL SEE E54984)
54986	DISPERSION OF THE NONLINEAR REFRACTIVE INDEX OF GYROTROPIC SILLENITE–TYPE CRYSTALS. SHALDIN, YU. V. BELOGUROV, D. A. FIZ. TVERD. TELA 15 (9), 2776–8, 1973. (FOR ENGLISH TRANSLATION SEE E54987)
54987	DISPERSION OF THE NONLINEAR REFRACTIVE INDEX OF GYROTROPIC SILLENITE–TYPE CRYSTALS. SHALDIN, YU. V. BELOGUROV, D. A. SOV. PHYS. SOLID STATE 15 (9), 1846–7, 1974. (ENGLISH TRANSLATION OF FIZ. TVERD. TELA, 15 (9), 2776–8, 1973; FOR ORIGINAL SEE E54986)
54990	POLARIZATION PROPERTIES OF MANY–PHOTON INTERBAND ABSORPTION OF LIGHT IN CUBIC CRYSTALS. IVCHENKO, E. L. PERLIN, E. YU. FIZ. TVERD. TELA 15 (9), 2781–3, 1973. (FOR ENGLISH TRANSLATION SEE E54991)
54991	POLARIZATION PROPERTIES OF MANY–PHOTON INTERBAND ABSORPTION OF LIGHT IN CUBIC CRYSTALS. IVCHENKO, E. L. PERLIN, E. YU. SOV. PHYS. SOLID STATE 15 (9), 1850–1, 1974. (ENGLISH TRANSLATION OF FIZ. TVERD. TELA, 15 (9), 2781–3, 1973; FOR ORIGINAL SEE E54990)
54992	PROBABILITY OF RECOMBINATION OF A HOLE AND AN IMPURITY ELECTRON IN THE FLUORITE LATTICE. KASK, N. E. KORNIENKO, L. S. FEDOROV, G. M. CHERNOV, P. V. FIZ. TVERD. TELA 15 (9), 2789–90, 1973. (FOR ENGLISH TRANSLATION SEE E54993)
54993	PROBABILITY OF RECOMBINATION OF A HOLE AND AN IMPURITY ELECTRON IN THE FLUORITE LATTICE. KASK, N. E. KORNIENKO, L. S. FEDOROV, G. M. CHERNOV, P. V. SOV. PHYS. SOLID STATE 15 (9), 1856–7, 1974. (ENGLISH TRANSLATION OF FIZ. TVERD. TELA, 15 (9), 2789–90, 1973; FOR ORIGINAL SEE E54992)
54996	QUANTUM SIZE EFFECT IN THIN LAYERED COPPER IODIDE FILMS. AGEEV, L. A. MILOSLAVSKII, V. K. SHKLYAREVSKII, I. N. FIZ. TVERD. TELA 15 (9), 2794–6, 1973. (FOR ENGLISH TRANSLATION SEE E54997)
54997	QUANTUM SIZE EFFECT IN THIN LAYERED COPPER IODIDE FILMS. AGEEV, L. A. MILOSLAVSKII, V. K. SHKLYAREVSKII, I. N. SOV. PHYS. SOLID STATE 15 (9), 1861–2, 1974. (ENGLISH TRANSLATION OF FIZ. TVERD. TELA, 15 (9), 2794–6, 1973; FOR ORIGINAL SEE E54996)
55008	THERMAL CONDUCTIVITY OF NEODYMIUM MONOSULFIDE. OSKOTSKII, V. S. SMIRNOV, I. A. KHUSNUTDINOVA, V. YA. FIZ. TVERD. TELA 15 (9), 2811–3, 1973. (FOR ENGLISH TRANSLATION SEE E55009)
55009	THERMAL CONDUCTIVITY OF NEODYMIUM MONOSULFIDE. OSKOTSKII, V. S. SMIRNOV, I. A. KHUSNUTDINOVA, V. YA. SOV. PHYS. SOLID STATE 15 (9), 1875–6, 1974. (ENGLISH TRANSLATION OF FIZ. TVERD. TELA, 15 (9), 2811–3, 1973; FOR ORIGINAL SEE E55008)
55010	NATURE OF LATTICE DEFECTS IN MERCURY SELENIDE. KREVS, V. E. FIZ. TVERD. TELA 15 (9), 2815–6, 1973. (FOR ENGLISH TRANSLATION SEE E55011)
55011	NATURE OF LATTICE DEFECTS IN MERCURY SELENIDE. KREVS, V. E. SOV. PHYS. SOLID STATE 15 (9), 1879, 1974. (ENGLISH TRANSLATION OF FIZ. TVERD. TELA, 15 (9), 2815–6, 1973; FOR ORIGINAL SEE E55010)

EPIC Number	Bibliographic Citation

55012 **INFLUENCE OF ILLUMINATION ON AN INDUCED PHASE TRANSITION IN ANTIMONY SULFIDE IODIDE CRYSTALS.**
VOLNYANSKII, M. D. KUDZIN, A. YU.
SUKHINSKII, A. N.
FIZ. TVERD. TELA
15 (9), 2819–20, 1973.
(FOR ENGLISH TRANSLATION SEE E55013)

55013 **INFLUENCE OF ILLUMINATION ON AN INDUCED PHASE TRANSITION IN ANTIMONY SULFIDE IODIDE CYRSTALS.**
VOLNYANSKII, M. D. KUDZIN, A. YU.
SUKHINSKII, A. N.
SOV. PHYS. SOLID STATE
15 (9), 1882, 1974.
(ENGLISH TRANSLATION OF FIZ. TVERD. TELA, 15 (9), 2819–20, 1973; FOR ORIGINAL SEE E55012)

55014 **MAGNETOPHONON OSCILLATIONS OF THE TRANSVERSE MAGNETORESISTANCE OF CADMIUM MERCURY TELLURIDE.**
BERCHENKO, N. N. PASHKOVSKII, M. V.
FIZ. TVERD. TELA
15 (9), 2820–2, 1973.
(FOR ENGLISH TRANSLATION SEE E55015)

55015 **MAGNETOPHONON OSCILLATIONS OF THE TRANSVERSE MAGNETORESISTANCE OF CADMIUM MERCURY TELLURIDE.**
BERCHENKO, N. N. PASHKOVSKII, M. V.
SOV. PHYS. SOLID STATE
15 (9), 1883, 1974.
(ENGLISH TRANSLATION OF FIZ. TVERD. TELA, 15 (9), 2820–2, 1973; FOR ORIGINAL SEE E55014)

55018 **PHOTOSENSITIVITY OF FERROELECTRIC NIOBATES.**
IONOV, P. V.
FIZ. TVERD. TELA
15 (9), 2827–8, 1973.
(FOR ENGLISH TRANSLATION SEE E55019)

55019 **PHOTOSENSITIVITY OF FERROELECTRIC NIOBATES.**
IONOV, P. V.
SOV. PHYS. SOLID STATE
15 (9), 1888–9, 1974.
(ENGLISH TRANSLATION OF FIZ. TVERD. TELA, 15 (9), 2827–8, 1973; FOR ORIGINAL SEE E55018)

55020 **PULSED POLARIZATION SWITCHING IN THE FERROELECTRIC SODIUM AMMONIUM SELENATE DIHYDRATE.**
ZAITSEVA, M. P. KRUMIN, A. E.
ZHEREBTSOVA, L. I. VLASOV, V. G.
FIZ. TVERD. TELA
15 (9), 2829–31, 1973.
(FOR ENGLISH TRANSLATION SEE E55021)

55021 **PULSED POLARIZATION SWITCHING IN THE FERROELECTRIC SODIUM AMMONIUM SELENATE DIHYDRATE.**
ZAITSEVA, M. P. KRUMIN, A. E.
ZHEREBTSOVA, L. I. VLASOV, V. G.
SOV. PHYS. SOLID STATE
15 (9), 1890–1, 1974.
(ENGLISH TRANSLATION OF FIZ. TVERD. TELA, 15 (9), 2829–31, 1973; FOR ORIGINAL SEE E55020)

55022 **NATURE OF THE SPONTANEOUS DEFORMATION OF VACUUM CONDENSATES OF BARIUM TITANATE.**
TOMASHPOL'SKII, YU. YA. SEVOST'YANOV, M. A.
FIZ. TVERD. TELA
15 (9), 2840–2, 1973.
(FOR ENGLISH TRANSLATION SEE E55023)

55023 **NATURE OF THE SPONTANEOUS DEFORMATION OF VACUUM CONDENSATES OF BARIUM TITANATE.**
TOMASHPOL'SKII, YU. YA. SEVOST'YANOV, M. A.
SOV. PHYS. SOLID STATE
15 (9), 1900–1, 1974.
(ENGLISH TRANSLATION OF FIZ. TVERD. TELA, 15 (9), 2840–2, 1973; FOR ORIGINAL SEE E55022)

55026 **WEAK FERROMAGNETISM OF NEODYMIUM AND EUROPIUM ORTHOVANADITES.**
BAZUEV, G. V. MATVEENKO, I. I.
ZUBKOV, V. G. SHVEIKIN, G. P.
FIZ. TVERD. TELA
15 (9), 2849–51, 1973.
(FOR ENGLISH TRANSLATION SEE E55027)

55027 **WEAK FERROMAGNETISM OF NEODYMIUM AND EUROPIUM ORTHOVANADITES.**
BAZUEV, G. V. MATVEENKO, I. I.
ZUBKOV, V. G. SHVEIKIN, G. P.
SOV. PHYS. SOLID STATE
15 (9), 1908–9, 1974.
(ENGLISH TRANSLATION OF FIZ. TVERD. TELA, 15 (9), 2849–51, 1973; FOR ORIGINAL SEE E55026)

55028 **INFRARED LINE LUMINESCENCE OF ALPHA–SILICON CARBIDE (15R) CRYSTALS.**
GORBAN, I. S. SLOBODYANYUK, A. V.
FIZ. TVERD. TELA
15 (10), 2877–9, 1973.
(FOR ENGLISH TRANSLATION SEE E55029)

EPIC Number	Bibliographic Citation

55029 **INFRARED LINE LUMINESCENCE OF ALPHA–SILICON CARBIDE (15R) CRYSTALS.**
GORBAN, I. S. SLOBODYANYUK, A. V.
SOV. PHYS. SOLID STATE
15 (10), 1925–6, 1974.
(ENGLISH TRANSLATION OF FIZ. TVERD. TELA, 15 (10), 2877–9, 1973; FOR ORIGINAL SEE E55028)

55030 **MAGNETIC ORDERING OF TETRAGONALLY DISTORTED FERRITE COPPER IRON OXIDE.**
BELOV, K. P. GORYAGA, A. N.
ANTOSHINA, L. G.
FIZ. TVERD. TELA
15 (10), 2895–8, 1973.
(FOR ENGLISH TRANSLATION SEE E55031)

55031 **MAGNETIC ORDERING OF TETRAGONALLY DISTORTED FERRITE COPPER IRON OXIDE.**
BELOV, K. P. GORYAGA, A. N. ANTOSHINA, L. G.
SOV. PHYS. SOLID STATE
15 (10), 1935–6, 1974.
(ENGLISH TRANSLATION OF FIZ. TVERD. TELA, 15 (10), 2895–8, 1973; FOR ORIGINAL SEE E55030)

55034 **INVESTIGATION OF THE PHOTOELASTICITY OF FERROELECTRICS BY THE DIFFRACTION OF LIGHT ON ULTRASOUND.**
MARTYNOV, V. G. ALEKSANDROV, K. S.
ANISTRATOV, A. T.
FIZ. TVERD. TELA
15 (10), 2922–6, 1973.
(FOR ENGLISH TRANSLATION SEE E55035)

55035 **INVESTIGATION OF THE PHOTOELASTICITY OF FERROELECTRICS BY THE DIFFRACTION OF LIGHT ON ULTRASOUND.**
MARTYNOV, V. G. ALEKSANDROV, K. S.
ANISTRATOV, A. T.
SOV. PHYS. SOLID STATE
15 (10), 1950–2, 1974.
(ENGLISH TRANSLATION OF FIZ. TVERD. TELA, 15 (10), 2922–6, 1973; FOR ORIGINAL SEE E55034)

55038 **MANY–CENTER STRUCTURE OF THE ESR SPECTRA OF POTASSIUM MAGNESIUM FLUORIDE AND POTASSIUM ZINC FLUORIDE CRYSTALS ACTIVATED WITH EUROPIUM DIPOSITIVE AND GADOLINIUM TRIPOSITIVE IONS.**
AL'TSHULER, N. S. IVOILOVA, E. KH.
LIVANOVA, L. D. STEPANOV, V. G.
STOLOV, A. L.
FIZ. TVERD. TELA
15 (10), 2958–62, 1973.
(FOR ENGLISH TRANSLATION SEE E55039)

55039 **MANY–CENTER STRUCTURE OF THE ESR SPECTRA OF POTASSIUM MAGNESIUM FLUORIDE AND POTASSIUM ZINC FLUORIDE CRYSTALS ACTIVATED WITH EUROPIUM DIPOSITIVE AND GADOLINIUM TRIPOSITIVE IONS.**
AL'TSHULER, N. S. IVOILOVA, E. KH.
LIVANOVA, L. D. STEPANOV, V. G.
STOLOV, A. L.
SOV. PHYS. SOLID STATE
15 (10), 1973–5, 1974.
(ENGLISH TRANSLATION OF FIZ. TVERD. TELA, 15 (10), 2958–62, 1973; FOR ORIGINAL SEE E55038)

55040 **CRYSTAL FIELD AND MAGNETIC ANISOTROPY OF RARE EARTH COBALT COMPOUNDS.**
IRKHIN, YU. P. ZABOLOTSKII, E. I.
FIZ. TVERD. TELA
15 (10), 2963–6, 1973.
(FOR ENGLISH TRANSLATION SEE E55041)

55041 **CRYSTAL FIELD AND MAGNETIC ANISOTROPY OF RARE EARTH COBALT COMPOUNDS.**
IRKHIN, YU. P. ZABOLOTSKII, E. I.
ROZENFEL'D, E. V. KARPENKO, V. P.
SOV. PHYS. SOLID STATE
15 (10), 1976–8, 1974.
(ENGLISH TRANSLATION OF FIZ. TVERD. TELA, 15 (10), 2963–6, 1973; FOR ORIGINAL SEE E55040)

55042 **INTERACTION OF DISLOCATIONS WITH ELECTRON AND HOLE CENTERS IN ALKALI HALIDE CRYSTALS.**
SHMURAK, S. Z. SENCHUKOV, F. D.
FIZ. TVERD. TELA
15 (10), 2976–9, 1973.
(FOR ENGLISH TRANSLATION SEE E55043)

55043 **INTERACTION OF DISLOCATIONS WITH ELECTRON AND HOLE CENTERS IN ALKALI HALIDE CRYSTALS.**
SHMURAK, S. Z. SENCHUKOV, F. D.
SOV. PHYS. SOLID STATE
15 (10), 1985–6, 1974.
(ENGLISH TRANSLATION OF FIZ. TVERD. TELA, 1P (10), 2976–9, 1973; FOR ORIGINAL SEE E55042)

55044 **RATE OF BAND–EDGE MOTION AT THE TRANSITION OF BISMUTH ANTIMONY ALLOYS TO THE GAPLESS STATE IN A MAGNETIC FIELD.**
BRANDT, N. B. CHUDINOV, S. M.
KARAVAEV, V. G. KORCHAK, B. A.
FIZ. TVERD. TELA
15 (10), 2992–5, 1973.
(FOR ENGLISH TRANSLATION SEE E55045)

EPIC Number *Bibliographic Citation*

55045 **RATE OF BAND-EDGE MOTION AT THE TRANSITION OF BISMUTH ANTIMONY ALLOYS TO THE GAPLESS STATE IN A MAGNETIC FIELD.**
BRANDT, N. B. CHUDINOV, S. M.
KARAVAEV, V. G. KORCHAK, B. A.
SOV. PHYS. SOLID STATE
15 (10), 1995–6, 1974.
(ENGLISH TRANSLATION OF FIZ. TVERD. TELA, 15 (10), 2992–5, 1973; FOR ORIGINAL SEE E55044)

55046 **SOFT MODE IN THE VIBRATIONAL SPECTRUM OF CALCIUM METATITANATE.**
KNYAZEV, A. S. POPLAVKO, YU. M.
ZAKHAROV, V. P. ALEKSEEV, V. V.
FIZ. TVERD. TELA
15 (10), 3006–10, 1973.
(FOR ENGLISH TRANSLATION SEE E55047)

55047 **SOFT MODE IN THE VIBRATIONAL SPECTRUM OF CALCIUM METATITANATE.**
KNYAZEV, A. S. POPLAVKO, YU. M.
ZAKHAROV, V. P. ALEKSEEV, V. V.
SOV. PHYS. SOLID STATE
15 (10), 2003–5, 1974.
(ENGLISH TRANSLATION OF FIZ. TVERD, TELA, 15 (10), 3006–10, 1973; FOR ORIGINAL SEE E55046)

55048 **DISPERSION OF THE ELECTROOPTIC EFFECT IN LEAD MAGNONIOBATE IN THE VISIBLE PART OF THE SPECTRUM.**
KAMZINA, L. S. KRAINIK, N. N.
BEREZHNOI, A. A.
FIZ. TVERD. TELA
15 (10), 3011–3, 1973.
(FOR ENGLISH TRANSLATION SEE E55049)

55049 **DISPERSION OF THE ELECTROOPTIC EFFECT IN LEAD MAGNONIOBATE IN THE VISIBLE PART OF THE SPECTRUM.**
KAMZINA, L. S. KRAINIK, N. N.
BEREZHNOI, A. A.
SOV. PHYS. SOLID STATE
15 (10), 2006–7, 1974.
(ENGLISH TRANSLATION OF FIZ. TVERD. TELA, 15 (10), 3011–3, 1973; FOR ORIGINAL SEE E55048)

55052 **TRANSMISSION OF LUMINESCENCE BY A BOUNDARY OF A CRYSTAL IN THE VICINITY OF EXCITON RESONANCES IN THE PRESENCE OF SPATIAL DISPERSION.**
PERMOGOROV, S. A. SEL'KIN, A. V.
FIZ. TVERD. TELA
15 (10), 3025–8, 1973.
(FOR ENGLISH TRANSLATION SEE E55053)

55053 **TRANSMISSION OF LUMINESCENCE BY A BOUNDARY OF A CRYSTAL IN THE VICINITY OF EXCITON RESONANCES IN THE PRESENCE OF SPATIAL DISPERSION.**
PERMOGOROV, S. A. SEL'KIN, A. V.
SOV. PHYS. SOLID STATE
15 (10), 2015–7, 1974.
(ENGLISH TRANSLATION OF FIZ. TVERD. TELA, 15 (10), 3025–8, 1973; FOR ORIGINAL SEE E55052)

55054 **MECHANISM OF CHARGE TRANSFER IN THE LATTICES OF AMMONIUM SALTS.**
KHAIRETDINOV, E. F. BURSHTEIN, A. I.
BOLDYREV, V. V.
FIZ. TVERD. TELA
15 (10), 3029–34, 1973.
(FOR ENGLISH TRANSLATION SEE E55055)

55055 **MECHANISM OF CHARGE TRANSFER IN THE LATTICES OF AMMONIUM SALTS.**
KHAIRETDINOV, E. F. BURSHTEIN, A. I.
BOLDYREV, V. V.
SOV. PHYS. SOLID STATE
15 (10), 2018–21, 1974.
(ENGLISH TRANSLATION OF FIZ. TVERD. TELA, 15 (10), 3029–34, 1973; FOR ORIGINAL SEE E55054)

55056 **ANOMALIES OF THE TRANSPORT COEFFICIENTS OF MANGANESE TELLURIDE NEAR THE NEEL POINT.**
AVDEEV, B. V. KRASHENININ, YU. P.
FIZ. TVERD. TELA
15 (10), 3044–7, 1973.
(FOR ENGLISH TRANSLATION SEE E55057)

55057 **ANOMALIES OF THE TRANSPORT COEFFICIENTS OF MANGANESE TELLURIDE NEAR THE NEEL POINT.**
AVDEEV, B. V. KRASHENININ, YU. P.
SOV. PHYS. SOLID STATE
15 (10), 2028–9, 1974.
(ENGLISH TRANSLATION OF FIZ. TVERD. TELA, 15 (10), 3044–7, 1973; FOR ORIGINAL SEE E55056)

55058 **AMPLIFICATION OF ULTRASOUND IN CADMIUM SULFIDE IN THE PRESENCE OF ELECTRON INJECTION FROM CONTACTS.**
GAEVSKII, V. S. KUCHEROV, I. YA.
PERGA, V. M.
FIZ. TVERD. TELA
15 (10), 3071–3, 1973.
(FOR ENGLISH TRANSLATION SEE E55059)

EPIC Number *Bibliographic Citation*

55059 **AMPLIFICATION OF ULTRASOUND IN CADMIUM SULFIDE IN THE PRESENCE OF ELECTRON INJECTION FROM CONTACTS.**
GAEVSKII, V. S. KUCHEROV, I. YA.
PERGA, V. M.
SOV. PHYS. SOLID STATE
15 (10), 2045–6, 1974.
(ENGLISH TRANSLATION OF FIZ. TVERD. TELA, 15 (10), 3071–3, 1973; FOR ORIGINAL SEE E55058)

55064 **INVESTIGATION OF BARIUM TITANATE AT SUBMILLIMETER WAVELENGTHS.**
MERIAKRI, V. V. POPLAVKO, YU. M.
USHATKIN, E. F. PASHKOV, V. M.
FIZ. TVERD. TELA
15 (10), 3082–3, 1973.
(FOR ENGLISH TRANSLATION SEE E55065)

55065 **INVESTIGATION OF BARIUM TITANATE AT SUBMILLIMETER WAVELENGTHS.**
MERIAKRI, V. V. POPLAVKO, YU. M.
USHATKIN, E. F. PASHKOV, V. M.
SOV. PHYS. SOLID STATE
15 (10), 2054–5, 1974.
(ENGLISH TRANSLATION OF FIZ. TVERD. TELA, 15 (10), 3082–3, 1973; FOR ORIGINAL SEE E55064)

55066 **INVESTIGATION OF DEFECTS IN TITANIUM DIOXIDE BY THE METHOD OF THERMALLY STIMULATED DEPOLARIZATION CURRENTS.**
AVDEEV, A. L. DANILYUK, YU. L.
ROZENBERG, L. A.
FIZ. TVERD. TELA
15 (10), 3090–1, 1973.
(FOR ENGLISH TRANSLATION SEE E55067)

55067 **INVESTIGATION OF DEFECTS IN TITANIUM DIOXIDE BY THE METHOD OF THERMALLY STIMULATED DEPOLARIZATION CURRENTS.**
AVDEEV, A. L. DANILYUK, YU. L.
ROZENBERG, L. A.
SOV. PHYS. SOLID STATE
15 (10), 2061, 1974.
(ENGLISH TRANSLATION OF FIZ. TVERD. TELA, 15 (10), 3090–1, 1973; FOR ORIGINAL SEE E55066)

55068 **MAGNETOOPTIC PROPERTIES OF MATERIALS WITH A CYLINDRICAL DOMAIN STRUCTURE.**
BALBASHOV, A. M. CHERVONENKIS, A. YA.
ANTONOV, A. V.
FIZ. TVERD. TELA
15 (10), 3095–7, 1973.
(FOR ENGLISH TRANSLATION SEE E55069)

55069 **MAGNETOOPTIC PROPERTIES OF MATERIALS WITH A CYLINDRICAL DOMAIN STRUCTURE.**
BALBASHOV, A. M. CHERVONENKIS, A. YA.
ANTONOV, A. V.
SOV. PHYS. SOLID STATE
15 (10), 2066–7, 1974.
(ENGLISH TRANSLATION OF FIZ. TVERD. TELA, 15 (10), 3095–7, 1973; FOR ORIGINAL SEE E55068)

55072 **MAGNETIC PROPERTIES OF CHALCOGENIDE SPINELS.**
BELOV, K. P. TRET'YAKOV, YU. D.
GORDEEV, I. V. KOROLEVA, L. I. PED'KO, A. V.
BATOROVA, S. D. ALFEROV, V. A.
SAKSONOV, YU. G. SHALIMOVA, M. A.
FIZ. TVERD. TELA
15 (10), 3106–8, 1973.
(FOR ENGLISH TRANSLATION SEE E55073)

55073 **MAGNETIC PROPERTIES OF CHALCOGENIDE SPINELS.**
BELOV, K. P. TRET'YAKOV, YU. D.
GORDEEV, I. V. KOROLEVA, L. I. PED'KO, A. V.
BATOROVA, S. D. ALFEROV, V. A.
SAKSONOV, YU. G. SHALIMOVA, M. A.
SOV. PHYS. SOLID STATE
15 (10), 2076–7, 1974.
(ENGLISH TRANSLATION OF FIZ. TVERD. TELA, 15 (10), 3106–8, 1973; FOR ORIGINAL SEE E55072)

55074 **PHASE TRANSITIONS IN ZINC TIN ARSENIDE.**
RUD', YU. V. TASHTANOVA, M.
FIZ. TVERD. TELA
15 (10), 3108–11, 1973.
(FOR ENGLISH TRANSLATION SEE E55075)

55075 **PHASE TRANSITIONS IN ZINC TIN ARSENIDE.**
RUD', YU. V. TASHTANOVA, M.
SOV. PHYS. SOLID STATE
15 (10), 2078–9, 1974.
(ENGLISH TRANSLATION OF FIZ. TVERD. TELA, 15 (10), 3108–11, 1973; FOR ORIGINAL SEE E55074)

55078 **ANISOTROPY OF THE TRANSPORT COEFFICIENTS OF MANGANESE SILICON.**
MEIZER, K. I. KRENTSIS, R. P.
FROLOV, A. A. GEL'D, P. V.
FIZ. TVERD. TELA
15 (10), 3123–5, 1973.
(FOR ENGLISH TRANSLATION SEE E55079)

EPIC Number | Bibliographic Citation

55079 **ANISOTROPY OF THE TRANSPORT COEFFICIENTS OF MANGANESE SILICON.**
MEIZER, K. I. KRENTSIS, R. P.
FROLOV, A. A. GEL'D, P. V.
SOV. PHYS. SOLID STATE
15 (10), 2090–1, 1974.
(ENGLISH TRANSLATION OF FIZ. TVERD. TELA, 15 (10), 3123–5, 1973; FOR ORIGINAL SEE E55078)

55085 **DEVELOPMENT OF GALLIUM ARSENIDE SOLAR CELLS.**
ION PHYSICS CORP
ION PHYSICS CORP., BURLINGTON, MASS.
43PP., 1973.
(N73-30977, NASA-CR-135510, AVAIL. NTIS)

55086 **PROPERTIES OF MULTILAYER FILTERS.**
BAUMEISTER, P. W.
ROCHESTER UNIV., N. Y., INST. OF OPTICS
23PP., 1973.
(NASA-CR-135671, N73-32537, AVAIL. NTIS)

55087 **SOLID STATE PHYSICS PROGRAM. THE DIELECTRIC PROPERTIES OF SEVERAL INSULATORS.**
ANDEEN, C. FONTANELLA, J. SCHUELE, D.
CASE WESTERN RESERVE UNIV., CLEVELAND, OHIO
22PP., 1972.
(COO-623-182, N73-21662, AVAIL. NTIS)

55088 **ELECTRICAL CONDUCTIVITY OF CALCIUM OXIDE DOPED NONSTOICHIOMETRIC CERIUM DIOXIDE FROM 700 TO 1500 C.**
BLUMENTHAL, R. N. BRUGNER, F. S.
GARNIER, J. E.
MARQUETTE UNIV., MILWAUKEE, WIS.
38PP., 1972.
(COO-1441-16, N73-21473, AVAIL. NTIS)

55089 **TEMPERATURE DEPENDENCE OF THE ELECTRICAL CONDUCTIVITY OF NONSTOICHIOMETRIC CERIUM OXIDE.**
BLUMENTHAL, R. N. HOFMAIER, R. L.
MARQUETTE UNIV., MILWAUKEE, WIS.
32PP., 1972.
(COO-1441-17, N73-21474, AVAIL. NTIS)

55092 **SUPERCONDUCTIVITY AND MAGNETISM OF INTERCALATED AND INTERMETALLIC COMPOUNDS.**
GEBALLE, T. H.
STANFORD UNIV., DEPT. OF APPL. PHYS., CALIF.
13PP., 1972.
(AD-751 497, N73-16751, AFOSR-TR-72-1972, AVAIL. NTIS)

55095 **GROWTH AND CHARACTERIZATION OF GALLIUM ARSENIDE AND CHARACTERIZATION OF GALLIUM ARSENIDE AND MIXED III-V SEMICONDUCTOR COMPOUNDS.**
VINCENT, F. S. Y.
UNIVERSITY OF SOUTHERN CALIF., LOS ANGELES,
PH.D. THESIS
234PP., 1973.
(AD-763 761, N73-30722, USCEE-455, AVAIL. NTIS)

55096 **EFFECT OF OXYGEN AND OTHER IMPURITIES ON INFRARED ABSORPTION IN II-VI AND II-V COMPOUNDS.**
WHELAN, J. M. GERSHENZON, M.
UNIVERSITY OF SOUTHERN CALIF., LOS ANGELES
4-6, 1972.
(AD-764 904, N73-33730, USCEE-443, AFCRL-TR-73-0054, AVAIL. NTIS)

55097 **OPTIMIZATION OF ALKALI HALIDE WINDOW MATERIALS.**
SHLICHTA, P. J. CHANEY, R. E.
UNIVERSITY OF SOUTHERN CALIF., LOS ANGELES
7-11, 1972.
(AD-764 904, N73-33730, USCEE-443,AFCRL-TR-73-0054)

55098 **FABRICATION OF POLYCRYSTALLINE INFRARED WINDOW MATERIALS.**
COPLEY, S. M. WHELAN, J. M. RANA, V.
BERKSTRESSER, G.
UNIVERSITY OF SOUTHERN CALIF., LOS ANGELES
17-20, 1972.
(AD-764 904, N73-33730, USCEE-443, AFCRL-TR-73-0054, AVAIL. NTIS)

55099 **STUDY OF DEFECTS IN II-VI COMPOUNDS.**
KROGER, F. A. GERZHENZON, M. CHERN, S. S.
VYDYANATH, H. R.
UNIVERSITY OF SOUTHERN CALIF., LOS ANGELES
32-6, 1972.
(AD-764 904, N73-33730, USCEE-443, AFCRL-TR-73-0054, AVAIL. NTIS)

55100 **THEORETICAL STUDIES OF ABSORPTION MECHANISMS IN INFRARED WINDOW MATERIALS.**
HELLWARTH, R. W.
UNIVERSITY OF SOUTHERN CALIF., LOS ANGELES
37-49, 1972.
(AD-764 904, N73-33730, USCEE-443, AFCRL-TR-73-0054, AVAIL. NTIS)

55101 **TECHNIQUES FOR INDIRECT MEASUREMENT OF SMALL ABSORPTIVE LOSSES.**
STEIER, W. H. NIEH, S. T. K.
UNIVERSITY OF SOUTHERN CALIF., LOS ANGELES
50-4, 1972.
(AD-764 904, N73-33730, USCEE-443, AFCRL-TR-73-0054, AVAIL. NTIS)

EPIC Number | Bibliographic Citation

55102 **POSSIBILITY OF USING TRIPLE SEMICONDUCTOR COMPOUNDS IN THERMOELECTRIC AND PHOTOELECTRIC CONVERTERS.**
BERGER, L. I.
KHIM. REAKTIVY PREPARATY TRUDY IRYEA
32, 315-20, 1970.
(FOR ENGLISH TRANSLATION SEE E55103)

55103 **POSSIBILITY OF USING TRIPLE SEMICONDUCTOR COMPOUNDS IN THERMOELECTRIC AND PHOTOELECTRIC CONVERTERS.**
BERGER, L. I.
ARMY FOREIGN SCIENCE AND TECHNOLOGY CENTER, CHARLOTTESVILLE, VA.
6PP., 1972.
(ENGLISH TRANSLATION OF KHIM. REAKTIVY PREPARATY TRUDY IRYEA (32), 315-20, 1970; FOR ORIGINAL SEE E55102)
(AD-765 730, N73-33734, FSTC-HT-23-346-73, AVAIL. NTIS)

55104 **ELECTRICAL PROPERTIES OF SILVER DOPED ANTIMONY TELLURIDE.**
KARIMOV, J. MAVLONOV, SH. SHEROV, P.
IZV. AKAD. NAUK TADZH. SSR, OTD. FIZ.-MATEMATICHESKIKH GEOL. KHIM. NAUK
(3), 20-5, 1970.
(FOR ENGLISH TRANSLATION SEE E55105)

55105 **ELECTRICAL PROPERTIES OF SILVER DOPED ANTIMONY TELLURIDE.**
KARIMOV, J. MAVLONON, SH. SHEROV, P.
ARMY FOREIGN SCIENCE AND TECHNOLOGY CENTER, CHARLOTTESVILLE, VA.
9PP., 1972.
(ENGLISH TRANSLATION OF IZV. AKAD. NAUK TADZN. SSR, OTD. FIZ.-MATEMATICHESKIKH GEOL. KHIM. NAUK (3), 20-5, 1970; FOR ORIGINAL SEE E55104)
(AD-765 780, N74-10702, FSTC-HT-23-1005-72, AVAIL. NTIS)

55106 **RESEARCH ON THE PROPERTIES OF AMORPHOUS SEMICONDUCTORS AT HIGH TEMPERATURES.**
DE NEUFVILLE, J. P.
ENERGY CONVERSION DEVICES, INC., TROY, MICH.
263PP., 1973.
(AD-766 141, N74-10696, ECD-516-6, AVAIL. NTIS)

55107 **RESEARCH ON THE PROPERTIES OF AMORPHOUS SEMICONDUCTORS AT HIGH TEMPERATURES.**
DE NEUFVILLE, J. P.
ENERGY CONVERSION DEVICES, INC., TROY, MICH.
85PP., 1973.
(AD-766 143, N74-10694, ECD-516-5, AVAIL. NTIS)

55109 **INFRARED DOUBLE RESONANCE IN BORON TRICHLORIDE.**
HOUSTON, P. L. NOWAK, A. V. STEINFELD, J. I.
J. CHEM. PHYS.
58 (8), 3373-80, 1973.
(AD-772 498, AFOSR-TR-73-2257)

55111 **PREPARATION AND PROPERTIES OF ONE-DIMENSIONAL METALS IN DIELECTRIC MATRICES.**
LABES, M. M. WALATKA, V. V., JR.
DEPT. OF CHEMISTRY, TEMPLE UNIV., PHILADELPHIA, PA.
15PP., 1973.
(AS-772 741, AFOSR-TR-73-2318)

55112 **HIGH TEMPERATURE ELECTRICAL CONDUCTIVITY MEASUREMENT TECHNIQUES.**
FREDERIKSE, H. P. R. HOSLER, W. R.
NATIONAL BUREAU OF STANDARDS, WASHINGTON, D. C.
32PP., 1973.
(AD-772 776, ARL-73-0156)

55113 **BAND STRUCTURE AND ELECTRICAL PROPERTIES OF AMORPHOUS SEMICONDUCTORS.**
ADLER, D.
MASSACHUSETTS INST. OF TECHNOLOGY, CAMBRIDGE
34PP., 1973.
(AD-772 779, AROD-9181:24-P, ARPA-1562)

55115 **EXCESS CARRIERS INDUCED IN INDIUM ANTIMONIDE WITH A CARBON-DIOXIDE LASER.**
FOSSUM, H. J. CHEN, W. S. ANCKER-JOHNSON, B.
PHYS. REV.
8 B (6), 2857-68, 1973.
(AD-773 085, AFOSR-TR-73-2255)

55117 **GRAVIMETRIC AND ELECTRICAL CONDUCTIVITY STUDIES OF PURE AND DOPED NIOBIUM PENTOXIDE.**
TRIPP, W. C. WIMMER, J. M.
SYSTEMS RESEARCH LABS INC., DAYTON, OHIO
35PP., 1973.
(AD-773 175, ARL-73-0157)

55119 **DEVELOPMENT OF A STABLE PIEZOELECTRIC CERAMIC FOR SONAR.**
JAFFE, B.
VERNITRON PIEZOELECTRIC DIV., BEDORD, OHIO
63PP., 1974.
(AD-773 948)

EPIC Number	Bibliographic Citation

55120 **PHOTON ECHOES IN LANTHANUM TRIFLUORIDE AND YTTRIUM ALUMINUM GARNET.**
TAKEUCHI, N. CHANDRA, S. CHEN, Y. C.
HARTMANN, S. R.
PHYS. LETT.
46 A (2), 97–8, 1973.
(AD–773 974)

55121 **CORRELATION BETWEEN ELECTRON SPIN RESONANCE AND SUPERCONDUCTIVITY IN GADOLINIUM RUTHENIUM RARE EARTH ALLOYS.**
DAVIDOV, D. RETTORI, C. BABERSCHKE, K.
CHOCK, E. P. ORBACH, R.
DEPT. OF PHYSICS, CALIFORNIA UNIV., LOS ANGELES
9PP., 1973.
(AD–774 073)

55125 **CRITERIA FOR SUPERCONDUCTING TRANSITION TEMPERATURES.**
MATTHIAS, B. T.
PHYSICA
69, 54–6, 1973.
(AD–775 191, AFOSR–TR–74–0238)

55126 **NOTES ON THE NEGATIVE TEMPERATURE COEFFICIENT OF RESISTANCE AND SUPERCONDUCTIVITY OF NIOBIUM NITRIDE THIN FILMS.**
AYER, J. W., JR. ROSE, K.
PHYS. LETTERS
45 A (2), 333–4, 1973.
(AD–773 212, AFOSR–TR–74–0002)

55127 **ELASTIC-WAVE FORMULATION OF ELECTROELASTIC WAVES IN UNBOUNDED PIEZOELECTRIC CRYSTALS.**
EPSTEIN, S.
PHYS. REV.
7 B (4), 1636–44, 1973.
(AD–775 500)

55129 **PRESSURE DEPENDENCE OF TRANSITION TEMPERATURE FOR GOLD PALLADIUM GALLIUM ALLOYS.**
SMITH, T. F. SHELTON, R. N. SCHIRBER, J. E.
PHYS. REV.
8 B (7), 3479–81, 1973.
(AD–775 190, AFOSR–TR–74–0239)

55132 **THE SUPERCONDUCTING ISOTOPE EFFECT OF IRON IN URANIUM INTERMETALLIC IRON.**
ENGELHARDT, J. J.
SOLID STATE COMMUN.
13, 1355–6, 1973.
(AD–775 192, AFOSR–TR–74–0237)

55135 **THE OPTICAL PROPERTIES OF THIN FILMS OF ANTIMONY SESQUIOXIDE.**
BUTTERFIELD, A. W. MC DERMOTT, I. T.
THIN SOLID FILMS
18, 111–6, 1973.
(AD–776 050)

55137 **MODULATION SPECTROSCOPY OF DISORDERED SOLIDS.**
SERAPHIN, B. O. KOTTKE, M.
OPTICAL SCIENCES CENTER, ARIZONA UNIV., TUCSON
75PP., 1974.
(AD–775 830)

55139 **CRYSTAL CHEMISTRY AND MAGNETIC PROPERTIES OF CHROMIUM (II) B (III) FLUORIDE COMPOUNDS.**
TRESSAUD, A. DANCE, J. M. RAVEZ, J.
PORTIER, J. GOODENOUGH, J. B.
MATER. RES. BULL.
8, 1467–78, 1973.
(AD–775 933)

55144 **USE OF AIRBORNE RESISTIVITY SURVEYS FOR GRAVEL LOCATION.**
CULLEY, R. W.
CAN. INST. MIN. METALL. BULL.
66 (733), 70–4, 1973.

55149 **STUDY OF THE EFFECTS OF RADIATION ON THE ELECTRICAL AND OPTICAL PROPERTIES OF MERCURY CADMIUM TELLURIDE.**
COLWELL, J. F. GREEN, B. A. LEADON, R.
MALLON, C. E. NABER, J. A.
INTELCOM RAD TECH., SAN DIEGO, CALIF.
62PP., 1973.
(AD–775 389, AFCRL–TR–73–0761)

55150 **AN INVESTIGATION OF THE DYNAMIC SUSCEPTIBILITY OF NEODYMIUM (1–X) SAMARIUM (X) COBALT SINGLE CRYSTALS AND THE EFFECT OF HYDROGEN ABSORPTION.**
MAARTENSE, I.
DEPT. OF PHYSICS, MANITOBA UNIV., WINNIPEG
50PP., 1973.
(AD–775 717, AFML–TR–73–250)

55151 **STUDY OF PHASE EQUILIBRIA IN THE SYSTEMS THALLIUM ARSENIC SULFIDE AND THALLIUM ARSENIC SELENIDE.**
ROLAND, G. W. FEICHTNER, J. D.
MC HUGH, J. P.
WESTINGHOUSE RESEARCH LABS, PITTSBURGH, PA.
112PP., 1973.
(AD–775 401, AFML–TR–74–6)

55152 **HIGH ENERGY LASER WINDOWS.**
RICE, R. W.
NAVAL RESEARCH LAB., WASHINGTON, D. C.
84PP., 1973.
(AD–774 701, ARPA–2031)

55153 **THEORETICAL STUDIES OF HIGH-POWER INFRARED WINDOW MATERIALS.**
SPARKS, M. S. DUTHLER, C. J.
XONICS INC., VAN NUYS, CALIF.
263—., 1973.
(AD–775 649, ARPA–1969)

55156 **STUDIES RELATIVE TO POSSIBLE LASER PUMPED BY NUCLEAR BETA RAYS. I. OPTICAL SPECTRA OF LITHIUM THULIUM FLUORIDE DOPES WITH A RARE EARTH ION.**
MORRISON, C. A. WORTMAN, D. C.
HARRY DIAMOND LABS, WASHINGTON, D. C.
27PP., 1973.
(AD–775 424, HDL–TR–1621)

55157 **SUPERCONDUCTIVITY AT THE SURFACE OF LEAD TELLURIDE.**
MILLER, D. L.
COORDINATED SCIENCE LAB., ILLINOIS UNIV., URBANA
107PP., 1973.
(AS–776 144, CSL–R–620)

55160 **INVESTIGATION OF DIELECTRIC OPTICAL COATINGS FOR LASERS.**
WOOD, R. M. TAYLOR, R. T. READ, M.
GENERAL ELECTRIC CO. LTD, WEMBLEY (ENGLAND), CENTRAL LABS.,
25PP., 1973.
(AD–917 645, DRIC–BR–38606)

55161 **INTERBAND CARRIER TRANSFER IN SEMICONDUCTORS AT VERY HIGH PRESSURES.**
PITT, G. D.
STANDARD TELECOMMUNICATION LABS, LTD, HARLOW (ENGLAND)
26PP., 1973.
(AD–917 776, DRIC–BR–38581)

55163 **LUMINESCENT MATERIAL PREPARATION AND SPECTROSCOPY.**
ANDERSON, W. W. CHANG, H. J.
OHIO STATE UNIV., RESEARCH FOUNDATION, COLUMBUS
31PP., 1973.
(AD 775 473, OSURF–3032A1–TR–73F, AROD–6835.6–E)

55164 **HIGH ELECTRIC FIELD ELECTRON VELOCITY IN INDIUM ARSENIDE.**
OWEN, E. F. GANDHI, O. P.
MICROWAVE DEVICE AND PHYSICS LAB., UTAH UNIV., SALT LAKE CITY
44–61, 1972.
(AD–758 914, MDL–Q40)

55165 **SOLID-STATE OPTICAL DETECTOR.**
PETERSEN, C. K. KRIGBAUM, W. G.
URE, R. W., JR.
MICROWAVE DEVICE AND PHYSICS LAB., UTAH UNIV., SALT LAKE CITY
62–83, 1972.
(AD–758 914, MDL–Q40)

55167 **SUBMILLIMETER SPECTROSCOPY OF SEMICONDUCTORS.**
GERSHENZON, E. M. GOLTSMAN, G. N.
PTITSINA, N. G.
ZH. EKSP. TEOR. FIZ.
64 (2), 587–98, 1973.
(FOR ENGLISH TRANSLATION SEE E55168 AND E62582)

55168 **SUBMILLIMETER SPECTROSCOPY OF SEMICONDUCTORS.**
GERSHENZON, E. M. GOLTSMAN, G. N.
PTITSINA, N. G.
FOREIGN TECHNOLOGY DIV., WRIGHT–PATTERSON AIR FORCE BASE, OHIO
26PP., 1974.
(ENGLISH TRANSLATION OF ZH. EKSP. TEOR. FIZ. 64 (2), 587–98, 1973; FOR ORIGINAL SEE E55167)

55170 **MAGNETIC BALANCE FOR MEASURING THE SUSCEPTIBILITY OF WEAKLY MAGNETIC SUBSTANCES.**
OZERETSKOVSKII, I. N. PCHELKIN, V. A.
LUK'YANOV, V. F.
RUSS. J. PHYS. CHEM.
47 (5), 752–4, 1973.
(ENGLISH TRANSLATION OF ZH. FIZ. KHIM., 47 (5), 1324–6, 1973; FOR ORIGINAL SEE E51349)

55171 **X-RAY ELECTRON STUDY OF COBALT COMPOUNDS.**
NEFEDOV, V. I. BARANOVSKII, I. B.
MOLODKIN, A. K. OMURALIEVA, U. O.
RUSS. J. INORG. CHEM.
18 (5), 684–5, 1973.
(ENGLISH TRANSLATION OF ZH. NEORG. KHIM., 18 (5), 1295–7, 1973; FOR ORIGINAL SEE E51316)

55174 **ANALYTIC NATURE OF THE DEPENDENCE OF THE ELECTRIC STRENGTH ON THE PARAMETERS OF A DISORDERED CONDENSED SYSTEM.**
KORZO, V. F.
FIZ. TVERD. TELA
15 (11), 3214–21, 1973.
(FOR ENGLISH TRANSLATION SEE E55175)

EPIC Number	Bibliographic Citation

55175 **ANALYTIC NATURE OF THE DEPENDENCE OF THE ELECTRIC STRENGTH ON THE PARAMETERS OF A DISORDERED CONDENSED SYSTEM.**
KORZO, V. F.
SOV. PHYS. SOLID STATE
15 (11), 2145–9, 1974.
(ENGLISH TRANSLATION OF FIZ. TVERD. TELA, 15 (11), 3214–21, 1973; FOR ORIGINAL SEE E55174)

55176 **ESR AND OPTICAL SPECTRA OF EUROPIUM DIPOSITIVE IONS IN A SINGLE CRYSTAL OF LITHIUM BARIUM FLUORIDE.**
AL'TSHULER, N. S. KORABLEVA, S. L.
LIVANOVA, L. D. STOLOV, A. L.
FIZ. TVERD. TELA
15 (11), 3231–4, 1973.
(FOR ENGLISH TRANSLATION SEE E55177)

55177 **ESR AND OPTICAL SPECTRA OF EUOPIUM DIPOSITIVE IONS IN A SINGLE CRYSTAL OF LITHIUM BARIUM FLUORIDE.**
AL'TSHULER, N. S. KORABLEVA, S. L.
LIVANOVA, L. D. STOLOV, A. L.
SOV. PHYS. SOLID STATE
15 (11), 2155–7, 1974.
(ENGLISH TRANSLATION OF FIZ. TVERD. TELA, 15 (11), 3231–4, 1973; FOR ORIGINAL SEE E55176)

55180 **ENHANCEMENT OF THE SPIN–ORBIT INTERACTION BY THE INFLUENCE OF A HEAVY CATION IN AN SODIUM NITRITE: THALLIUM CRYSTAL.**
REZNIK, L. E. GARBER, P. R. FESUN, A. V.
FIZ. TVERD. TELA
15 (11), 3280–5, 1973.
(FOR ENGLISH TRANSLATION SEE E55181)

55181 **ENHANCEMENT OF THE SPIN–ORBIT INTERACTION BY THE INFLUENCE OF A HEAVY CATION IN AN SODIUM NITRITE: THALLIUM CRYSTAL.**
REZNICK, L. E. GARBER, P. R. FESUN, A. V.
SOV. PHYS. SOLID STATE
15 (11), 2185–8, 1974.
(ENGLISH TRANSLATION OF FIZ. TVERD. TELA, 15 (11), 3280–5, 1973; FOR ORIGINAL SEE E55180)

55184 **MAGNETOELASTIC COUPLING OF COBALT DIPOSITIVE IONS IN THE YTTRIUM IRON GARNET STRUCTURE.**
PROTOPOPOVA, L. M. PETRAKOVSKII, G. A.
SMOKOTIN, E. M. PETROV, R. A.
FIZ. TVERD. TELA
15 (11), 3290–2, 1973.
(FOR ENGLISH TRANSLATION SEE E55185)

55185 **MAGNETOELASTIC COUPLING OF COBALT DIPOSITIVE IONS IN THE YTTRIUM IRON GARNET STRUCTURE.**
PROTOPOPOVA, L. M. PETRAKOVSKII, G. A.
SMOKOTIN, E. M. PETROV, R. A.
SOV. PHYS. SOLID STATE
15 (11), 2192–3, 1974.
(ENGLISH TRANSLATION OF FIZ. TVERD. TELA, 15 (11), 3290–2, 1973; FOR ORIGINAL SEE E55184)

55190 **SURFACE EFFECTS IN THE SPECTRA OF CADMIUM SELENIDE SINGLE CRYSTALS.**
DAVYDOVA, N. A. MYASNIKOV, E. N.
STRASHNIKOVA, M. I.
SOV. PHYS. SOLID STATE
15 (11), 2217–20, 1974.
(ENGLISH TRANSLATION OF FIZ. TVERD. TELA, 15 (11), 3332–7, 1973; FOR ORIGINAL SEE E54646)

55191 **QUANTUM THEORY OF GALVANOMAGNETIC EFFECTS IN SEMICONDUCTORS.**
BRYKSIN, V. V. FIRSOV, YU. A.
FIZ. TVERD. TELA
15 (11), 3344–53, 1973.
(FOR ENGLISH TRANSLATION SEE E55192)

55192 **QUANTUM THEORY OF GALVANOMAGNETIC EFFECTS IN SEMICONDUCTORS.**
BRYKSIN, V. V. FIRSOV, YU. A.
SOV. PHYS. SOLID STATE
15 (11), 2224–9, 1974.
(ENGLISH TRANSLATION OF FIZ. TVERD. TELA, 15 (11), 3344–53, 1973; FOR ORIGINAL SEE E55191)

55193 **ELEVATION OF THE SUPERCONDUCTING TRANSITION TEMPERATURE IN THIN SEMICONDUCTING FILMS ON METAL SUBSTRATES.**
AGRANOVICH, V. M. ANTONYUK, B. P.
FIZ. TVERD. TELA
15 (11), 3392–4, 1973.
(FOR ENGLISH TRANSLATION SEE E55194)

55194 **ELEVATION OF THE SUPERCONDUCTING TRANSITION TEMPERATURE IN THIN SEMICONDUCTING FILMS ON METAL SUBSTRATES.**
AGRANOVICH, V. M. ANTONYUK, B. P.
SOV. PHYS. SOLID STATE
15 (11), 2254–5, 1974.
(ENGLISH TRANSLATION OF FIZ. TVERD. TELA, 15 (11), 3392–4, 1973; FOR ORIGINAL SEE E55193)

55195 **CERIUM IN YTTRIUM AND LUTETIUM ORTHOPNOSPHATE CRYSTALS.**
STAROSTIN, N. V. TITOV, S. A.
FIZ. TVERD. TELA
15 (11), 3398–3400, 1973.
(FOR ENGLISH TRANSLATION SEE E55196)

55196 **CERIUM IN YTTRIUM AND LUTETIUM ORTHOPHOSPHATE CRYSTALS.**
STAROSTIN, N. V. TITOV, S. A.
SOV. PHYS. SOLID STATE
15 (11), 2259–60, 1974.
(ENGLISH TRANSLATION OF FIZ. TVERD. TELA, 15 (11), 3398–3400, 1973; FOR ORIGINAL SEE E55195)

55197 **HOLE BANDS OF A CALCIUM FLUORIDE CRYSTAL.**
STAROSTIN, N. V. GANIN, V. A.
FIZ. TVERD. TELA
15 (11), 3404–7, 1973.
(FOR ENGLISH TRANSLATION SEE E55198)

55198 **HOLE BANDS OF A CALCIUM FLUORIDE CRYSTAL.**
STAROSTIN, N. V. GANIN, V. A.
SOV. PHYS. SOLID STATE
15 (11), 2265–6, 1974.
(ENGLISH TRANSLATION OF FIZ. TVERD. TELA, 15 (11), 3404–7, 1973; FOR ORIGINAL SEE E55197)

55199 **ANISOTROPY OF THE ELECTRICAL RESISTIVITY OF GERMANIUM TELLURIDE.**
NOVIKOVA, S. I. SHELIMOVA, L. E.
ABRIKOSOV, N. KH. AVILOV, A. S.
KORZHUEV, M. A.
FIZ. TVERD. TELA
15 (11), 3407–9, 1973.
(FOR ENGLISH TRANSLATION SEE E55200)

55200 **ANISOTROPY OF THE ELECTRICAL RESISTIVITY OF GERMANIUM TELLURIDE.**
NOVIKOVA, S. I. SHELIMOVA, L. E.
ABRIKOSOV, N. KH. AVILOV, A. S.
KORZHUEV, M. A.
SOV. PHYS. SOLID STATE
15 (11), 2267–8, 1974.
(ENGLISH TRANSLATION OF FIZ. TVERD. TELA, 15 (11), 3407–9, 1973; FOR ORIGINAL SEE E55199)

55203 **TRAPPING LEVELS IN STRONTIUM TITANIUM OXIDE SINGLE CRYSTALS.**
KUNIN, V. YA. TSIKIN, A. N. SHTURBINA, N. A.
FIZ. TVERD. TELA
15 (11), 3417–9, 1973.
(FOR ENGLISH TRANSLATION SEE E55204)

55204 **TRAPPING LEVELS IN STRONTIUM TITANIUM OXIDE SINGLE CRYSTALS.**
KUNIN, V. YA. TSIKIN, A. N. SHTURBINA, N. A.
SOV. PHYS. SOLID STATE
15 (11), 2276–7, 1974.
(ENGLISH TRANSLATION OF FIZ. TVERD. TELA, 15 (11), 3417–9, 1973; FOR ORIGINAL SEE E55203)

55207 **OPTICAL TRANSITIONS FROM THE VALENCE BAND TO A LOCAL LEVEL IN THE FORBIDDEN BAND OF ZINC SULFIDE AND IN ALKALI HALIDE CRYSTAL PHOSPHORS.**
KUZNETSOV, A. S.
FIZ. TVERD. TELA
15 (11), 3428–30, 1973.
(FOR ENGLISH TRANSLATION SEE E55208)

55208 **OPTICAL TRANSITIONS FROM THE VALENCE BAND TO A LOCAL LEVEL IN THE FORBIDDEN BAND OF ZINC SULFIDE AND IN ALKALI HALIDE CRYSTAL PHOSPHORS.**
KUZNETSOV, A. S.
SOV. PHYS. SOLID STATE
15 (11), 2285–6, 1974.
(ENGLISH TRANSLATION OF FIZ. TVERD. TELA, 15 (11), 3428–30, 1973; FOR ORIGINAL SEE E55207)

55213 **PROPERTIES OF A SUPERCONDUCTING ALLOY NIOBIUM ALUMINUM PREPARED BY VACUUM EVAPORATION.**
GOLOVASHKIN, A. I. LEVCHENKO, I. S.
MOTULEVICH, G. P.
FIZ. TVERD. TELA
15 (11), 3448–9, 1973.
(FOR ENGLISH TRANSLATION SEE E55214)

55214 **PROPERTIES OF A SUPERCONDUCTING ALLOY NIOBIUM ALUMINUM PREPARED BY VACUUM EVAPORATION.**
GOLOVASHKIN, A. I. LEVCHENKO, I. S.
MOTULEVICH, G. P.
SOV. PHYS. SOLID STATE
15 (11), 2302–3, 1974.
(ENGLISH TRANSLATION OF FIZ. TVERD. TELA, 15 (11), 3448–9, 1973; FOR ORIGINAL SEE E55213)

55217 **TEMPERATURE DEPENDENCE OF THE ELECTRICAL CONDUCTIVITY OF LIQUID SEMICONDUCTORS OF THE ARSENIC SELENIDE–ARSENIC TELLURIDE SYSTEM.**
ANDREEV, A. A. LEBEDEV, E. A.
SHMURATOV, E. A. SHPUNT, V. KH.
FIZ. TVERD. TELA
15 (11), 3456–7, 1973.
(FOR ENGLISH TRANSLATION SEE E55218)

EPIC Number | Bibliographic Citation

55218 TEMPERATURE DEPENDENCE OF THE ELECTRICAL CONDUCTIVITY OF LIQUID SEMICONDUCTORS OF THE ARSENIC SELENIDE–ARSENIC TELLURIDE SYSTEM.
ANDREEV, A. A. LEBEDEV, E. A.
SHMURATOV, E. A. SHPUNT, V. KH.
SOV. PHYS. SOLID STATE
15 (11), 2310–11, 1974.
(ENGLISH TRANSLATION OF FIZ. TVERD. TELA, 15 (11), 3456–7, 1973; FOR ORIGINAL SEE E55217)

55219 INFLUENCE OF COBALT DIPOSITIVE IONS ON THE MAGNETOSTRICTION OF A W–TYPE HEXAFERRITE.
KUNTSEVICH, S. P. PALEKHIN, V. P.
FIZ. TVERD. TELA
15 (11), 3460–2, 1973.
(FOR ENGLISH TRANSLATION SEE E55220)

55220 INFLUENCE OF COBALT DIPOSITIVE IONS ON THE MAGNETOSTRICTION OF A W–TYPE HEXAFERRITE.
KUNTSEVICH, S. P. PALEKHIN, V. P.
SOV. PHYS. SOLID STATE
15 (11), 2314–5, 1974.
(ENGLISH TRANSLATION OF FIZ. TVERD. TELA, 15 (11), 3460–2, 1973; FOR ORIGINAL SEE E55219)

55221 FORMATION OF IMPURITY COMPLEXES ASSOCIATED WITH THE APPEARANCE OF THE U BAND IN POTASSIUM CHLORIDE.
PERSHITS, YA. N. SHONIN, V. N.
FIZ. TVERD. TELA
15 (11), 3462–5, 1973.
(FOR ENGLISH TRANSLATION SEE E55222)

55222 FORMATION OF IMPURITY COMPLEXES ASSOCIATED WITH THE APPEARANCE OF THE U BAND IN POTASSIUM CHLORIDE.
PERSHITS, YA. N. SHONIN, V. N.
SOV. PHYS. SOLID STATE
15 (11), 2316–7, 1974.
(ENGLISH TRANSLATION OF FIZ. TVERD. TELA, 15 (11), 3462–5, 1973; FOR ORIGINAL SEE E55221)

55223 MANIFESTATIONS OF THE BAND STRUCTURE OF SPHALERITE–TYPE CRYSTALS IN X–RAY AND PHOTOELECTRIC EMISSION SPECTRA.
NEMOSHKALENKO, V. V. ALESHIN, V. G.
PANCHENKO, M. T. SENKEVICH, A. I.
FIZ. TVERD. TELA
15 (11), 3465–7, 1973.
(FOR ENGLISH TRANSLATION SEE E55224)

55224 MANIFESTATIONS OF THE BAND STRUCTURE OF SPHALERITE–TYPE CRYSTALS IN X–RAY AND PHOTOELECTRIC EMISSION SPECTRA.
NEMOSHKALENKO, V. V. ALESHIN, V. G.
PANCHENKO, M. T. SENKEVICH, A. I.
SOV. PHYS. SOLID STATE
15 (11), 2318–9, 1974.
(ENGLISH TRANSLATION OF FIZ. TVERD. TELA, 15 (11), 3465–7, 1973; FOR ORIGINAL SEE E55223)

55225 DISORDER IN A CONDENSED MEDIUM AND DEVIATIONS FROM STEADY–STATE CONDITIONS DURING BREAKDOWN.
KORZO, V. F.
FIZ. TVERD. TELA
15 (11), 3476–8, 1973.
(FOR ENGLISH TRANSLATION SEE E55226)

55226 DISORDER IN A CONDENSED MEDIUM AND DEVIATIONS FROM STEADY–STATE CONDITIONS DURING BREAKDOWN.
KORZO, V. F.
SOV. PHYS. SOLID STATE
15 (11), 2328–9, 1974.
(ENGLISH TRANSLATION OF FIZ. TVERD. TELA, 15 (11), 3476–8, 1973; FOR ORIGINAL SEE E55225)

55229 CONDUCTION–BAND FORMATION IN METAL LAYERS INTERCALATED IN TANTALUM SULFIDE: NUCLEAR RESONANCE OF TIN, MERCURY, AND LEAD IN TANTALUM SULFIDE.
GOSSARD, A. C. DI SALVO, F. J. YASUOKA, H.
PHYS. REV.
9 B (10), 3965–8, 1974.

55237 OPTICAL ABSORPTION ON LOCALIZED LEVELS IN GALLIUM ARSENIDE.
BOIS, D. PINARD, P.
PHYS. REV.
9 B (10), 4171–7, 1974.

55241 USE OF ORTHOGONALIZED–PLANE–WAVE BANDS AND WAVE FUNCTIONS IN THE CALCULATION OF ACOUSTIC DEFORMATION POTENTIALS.
IVEY, J. L.
PHYS. REV.
9 B (10), 4281–5, 1974.

55242 LATTICE VIBRATIONS OF SILVER GALLIUM SULFIDE, SILVER GALLIUM SELENIUM, AND COPPER GALLIUM SULFIDE.
VAN DER ZIEL, J. P. MEIXNER, A. E.
KASPER, H. M. DITZENBERGER, J. A.
PHYS. REV.
9 B (10), 4286–94, 1974.

55243 FAR–INFRARED RECOMBINATION RADIATION FROM N–TYPE GERMANIUM AND GALLIUM ARSENIDE.
THOMAS, S. R. FAN, H. Y.
PHYS. REV.
9 B (10), 4295–4305, 1974.

55244 SURFACE AND BULK PHOTORESPONSE OF CRYSTALLINE ARSENIC SULFIDE.
BLOSSEY, D. F. ZALLEN, R.
PHYS. REV.
9 B (10), 4306–13, 1974.

55245 MODEL CALCULATIONS FOR RADIATIVE RECOMBINATION IN ZINC–NITROGEN–DOPED GALLIUM ARSENIC PHOSPHIDE IN THE DIRECT AND INDIRECT COMPOSITION REGION.
CAMPBELL, J. C. HOLONYAK, N., JR.
KUNZ, A. B. CRAFORD, M. G.
PHYS. REV.
9 B (10), 4314–22, 1974.

55246 THEORY OF MAGNETOPHONON STRUCTURE IN THE LONGITUDINAL MAGNETOTHERMAL ELECTRO–MOTIVE–FORCE.
ARORA, V. K. PETERSON, R. L.
PHYS. REV.
9 B (10), 4323–8, 1974.

55247 SMALL–POLARON EFFECTS ON THE DC CONDUCTIVITY AND THERMOELECTRIC POWER OF THE ONE–DIMENSIONAL MOTT SEMICONDUCTOR.
BARI, R. A.
PHYS. REV.
9 B (10), 4329–39, 1974.

55248 CALCULATED FAR–INFRARED LATTICE ABSORPTION SPECTRA OF OF CADMIUM TELLURIDE DOPED WITH BERYLLIUM.
TALWAR, D. N. AGRAWAL, B. K.
PHYS. REV.
9 B (10), 4362–72, 1974.

55249 PHOTOEMISSION STUDIES OF CRYSTALLINE AND AMORPHOUS ANTIMONY SELENIDE.
HURYCH, Z. DAVIS, D. BUCZEK, D.
WOOD, C. LAPEYRE, G. J. BAER, A. D.
PHYS. REV.
9 B (10), 4392–4404, 1974.

55250 QUADRATIC JAHN–TELLER EFFECT IN THE EMISSION OF POTASSIUM IODIDE: THALLIUM–TYPE PHOSPHORS.
RANFAGNI, A. VILIANI, G.
PHYS. REV.
9 (10), 4448–54, 1974.

55251 INFRARED–ACTIVE LOCALIZED PAIR MODES IN THE GAP REGION OF POTASSIUM IODIDE.
WARD, R. W. CLAYMAN, B. P.
PHYS. REV.
9 B (10), 4455–60, 1974.

55252 OPTICAL PROPERTIES OF LITHIUM FLUORIDE.
MICKISH, D. J. KUNZ, A. B. COLLINS, T. C.
PHYS. REV.
9 B (10), 4461–7, 1974.
(AD–A7756)

55254 TUNNELING RECOMBINATION OF TRAPPED ELECTRONS AND HOLES IN POTASSIUM CHLORIDE: SILVER CHLORIDE AND POTASSIUM CHLORIDE: THALLIUM CHLORIDE.
DELBECQ, C. J. TOYOZAWA, Y. YUSTER, P. H.
PHYS. REV.
9 B (10), 4497–4505, 1974.

55255 THERMAL EXPANSIONS OF HIGH–PURITY AND HYDROXIDE DOPED SODIUM CHLORIDE AT TEMPERATURES BELOW 30 K.
CASE, C. R., II. SWENSON, C. A.
PHYS. REV.
9 B (10), 4506–11, 1974.

55257 DONOR–ACCEPTOR PAIR LINES IN ZINC SELENIDE: AN ADDENDIUM.
MERZ, J. L.
PHYS. REV.
9 B (10), 4593–6, 1974.

55261 DEFECT STRUCTURE OF TANTALUM OXIDE.
STROUD, J. E. TRIPP, W. C. WIMMER, J. M.
J. AMER. CERAM. SOC.
57 (4), 172–5, 1974.
(AD–A007 639, ARL–75–0067)

55263 PROCESSING PARAMETERS AND PROPERTIES OF LITHIUM FERRITE SPINEL.
BANDYOPADHYAY, G. FULRATH, R. M.
J. AMER. CERAM. SOC.
57 (4), 182–6, 1974.

55264 PHASE RELATIONS AT LOW TEMPERATURES IN THE IRON–MAGNESIUM–OXIDE SYSTEM.
KRAWITZ, A. COHEN, J. B.
J. AMER. CERAM. SOC.
57 (4), 186–90, 1974.

55267 ELECTROCHEMISTRY OF CERAMIC ELECTROLYTES.
WORRELL, W. L.
AMER. CERAM. SOC. BULL.
53 (5), 425–33, 1974.

55275 HIGH–FIELD ELECTRICAL CONDUCTIVITY OF AMORPHOUS SEMICONDUCTORS.
SMID, V.
CESKOSLOVENSKY CASOPIS PRO FYSIKU
23 A (6), 584–596, 1973.

EPIC Number	Bibliographic Citation

55278 **DEFECT FERROELECTRIC MATERIAL OF THE LEAD SODIUM TITANIUM OXIDE TYPE.**
KAKEGAWA, K. MORI, J.
YAMAMURA, H. SHIRASAKI, S.
JAP. J. APPL. PHYS.
12 (11), 1821-2, 1973.

55279 **TEMPERATURE DEPENDENCE OF THE MAGNETIC EASY DIRECTION OF PRASEODYMIUM-(COBALT, COPPER) INTERMETALLIC COMPOUNDS.**
MAEDA, H.
JAP. J. APPL. PHYS.
12 (11), 1825-6, 1973.

55281 **NUMERICAL SOLUTION OF THE MODE-EQUATION OF PLANAR DIELECTRIC WAVEGUIDES TO DETERMINE THEIR REFRACTIVE INDEX AND THICKNESS BY MEANS OF A PRISM-FILM COUPLER.**
KERSTEN, R. T.
OPTICS COMMUNICATIONS
9, 427-431, 1973.

55285 **TRANSPORT PHENOMENA IN P-TYPE ANTIMONY THALLIUM DITELLURIDE.**
GITSU, D. V. KANTSER, CH. T. STRATAN, G. I.
CHEBAN, A. G.
FIZ. TEKH. POLUPROV.
7 (10), 1874-7, 1973.
(FOR ENGLISH TRANSLATION SEE E59242)

55287 **DETERMINATION OF THE PARAMETERS OF IMPURITY CENTERS IN SEMICONDUCTOR MATERIALS BY CHARGING THEM BY ELECTROMAGNETIC RADIATION.**
KARPENKO, V. P. KASHERININOV, P. G.
MATVEEV, O. A. TOMASOV, A. A.
FIZ. TEKH. POLUPROV.
7 (10), 1901-7, 1973.
(FOR ENGLISH TRANSLATION SEE E59245)

55288 **ANISOTROPY OF THERMOEMF. OF CADMIUM ZINC ANTIMONIDE SOLID-SOLUTION SINGLE CRYSTALS.**
BUDA, I. S. PILAT, I. M. SOLICHUK, K. D.
FIZ. TEKH. POLUPROV.
7 (10), 1925-8, 1973.
(FOR ENGLISH TRANSLATION SEE E59247)

55289 **PHOTOCURRENT OSCILLATIONS IN CADMIUM SULFIDE DETECTORS.**
ZAVERTANNAYA, L. S. RVACHEV, A. L.
FIZ. TEKH. POLUPROV.
7 (10), 1929-35, 1973.
(FOR ENGLISH TRANSLATION SEE E59248)

55290 **INDUCED MOTT TRANSITION IN COMPENSATED GALLIUM ARSENIDE.**
VUL, B. M. ZAVARITSKAYA, E. I. GALKIN, G. N.
VORONOVA, I. D. ROZHDESTVENSKAYA, N. V.
FIZ. TEKH. POLUPROV.
7 (10), 1942-5, 1973.
(FOR ENGLISH TRANSLATION SEE E59249)

55292 **PHOTOELECTRIC PHENOMENA IN CADMIUM SILICON PHOSPHIDE SINGLE CRYSTALS DOPED BY GROUP IIB ELEMENTS.**
BYCHKOV, A. G. POTYKEVICH, I. V.
RADZIVIL, V. P. TKACHUK, I. YU.
TYCHINA, I. I.
FIZ. TEKH. POLUPROV.
7 (10), 1961-4, 1973.
(FOR ENGLISH TRANSLATION SEE E59251)

55294 **SATURATION OF INTERBAND LIGHT ABSORPTION IN A SEMICONDUCTOR TAKING INTO ACCOUNT FIELD SPATIAL HETEROGENEITY.**
POLUEKTOV, I. A. POPOV, YU. M.
ROITBERG, V. S.
FIZ. TEKH. POLUPROV.
7 (11), 2114-18, 1973.
(FOR ENGLISH TRANSLATION SEE E59268)

55295 **PHOTOCONDUCTIVITY OF GOLD-DOPED CADMIUM GALLIUM INDIUM SULFIDE SINGLE CRYSTALS. RECOMBINATION SCHEME.**
ABDULLAEV, G. B. DZHURAEV, V. B.
ANTONOV, V. B. NANI, R. KH. SALAEV, E. YU.
FIZ. TEKH. POLUPROV.
7 (11), 2144-8, 1973.
(FOR ENGLISH TRANSLATION SEE E59271)

55296 **NATURES OF CENTERS OF FAST RECOMBINATION IN CADMIUM SELENIDE CRYSTALS.**
MARTINAITIS, A. SAKALAS, A.
JANUSKEVICIUS, Z.
FIZ. TEKH. POLUPROV.
7 (11), 2232-4, 1973.
(FOR ENGLISH TRANSLATION SEE E59280)

55298 **INDUCED IMPURITY PHOTOCONDUCTIVITY IN ZINKENITE.**
DMYTRIV, A. YU. KOVAL'SKII, P. N.
MAKARENKO, V. V.
FIZ. TEKH. POLUPROV.
7 (11), 2241-3, 1973.
(FOR ENGLISH TRANSLATION SEE E59283)

55300 **ANISOTROPY OF PIEZOELECTRIC SCATTERING IN SEMICONDUCTORS WITH WURTZITE STRUCTURE.**
BULAT, L. P.
FIZ. TEKH. POLUPROV.
7 (9), 1732-40, 1973.
(FOR ENGLISH TRANSLATION SEE E59225)

55303 **HOT ELECTRONS AT LOW TEMPERATURES IN COMPENSATED GALLIUM ARSENIDE.**
VUL, B. M. ZAVARITSKAYA, E. I.
VORONOVA, I. D. ROZHDESTVENSKAYA, N. V.
FIZ. TEKH. POLUPROV.
7 (9), 1766-70, 1973.
(FOR ENGLISH TRANSLATION SEE E59228)

55305 **EFFECT OF A MAGNETIC FIELD ON THE IONIZATION ENERGY OF FINELY DIVIDED DONOR IMPURITIES IN GALLIUM ARSENIDE AND INDIUM PHOSPHIDE.**
GUSLIKOV, V. M. EMEL'YANENKO, O. V.
NASLEDOV, D. N. NEDEOGLO, D. D.
TIMCHENKO, I. N.
FIZ. TEKH. POLUPROV.
7 (9), 1785-9, 1973.
(FOR ENGLISH TRANSLATION SEE E59230)

55306 **NATURE OF A 1.0 EV RADIATION IMPURITY BAND IN THE PHOTOLUMINESCENCE SPECTRUM OF EPITAXIAL GALLIUM ARSENIDE.**
BATAVIN, V. V. POPOVA, G. V.
FIZ. TEKH. POLUPROV.
7 (9), 1790-5, 1973.
(FOR ENGLISH TRANSLATION SEE E59231)

55307 **ELECTROREFLECTION SPECTRA AND BAND STRUCTURE OF GERMANIUM ZINC ARSENIDE.**
KRIVAITE, G. SHILEIKA, A.
FIZ. TEKH. POLUPROV.
7 (9), 1796-800, 1973.
(FOR ENGLISH TRANSLATION SEE E59232)

55308 **PHOTOCONDUCTIVITY OF GALLIUM ARSENIDE-ALUMINUM ARSENIDE SOLID SOLUTIONS.**
BERDZENISHVILI, A. I. DZHAKHUTASHVILI, T. V.
LOBZHANIDZE, Z. V. MIRTSKHULAVA, A. A.
PEKAR, I. E. CHIKOVANI, R. I.
SHKOL'NIK, A. L.
FIZ. TEKH. POLUPROV.
7 (9), 1806-8, 1973.
(FOR ENGLISH TRANSLATION SEE E59233)

55309 **DOMAIN ELECTRIC INSTABILITY IN N-CADMIUM TELLURIDE.**
CHAPNIN, V. A. MARINENKO, S. M.
GOLUBTSOV, V. V.
FIZ. TEKH. POLUPROV.
7 (9), 1814-17, 1973.
(FOR ENGLISH TRANSLATION SEE E59234)

55310 **EFFECT OF IMPURITIES ON THE NATURAL ABSORPTION EDGE IN HEXAGONAL ALPHA-SILICON CARBIDE.**
VIOLINA, G. N. SELEZNEV, B. I.
TAIROV, YU. M.
FIZ. TEKH. POLUPROV.
7 (9), 1821-2, 1973.
(FOR ENGLISH TRANSLATION SEE E59235)

55312 **DIFFUSION LENGTH OF MINORITY CARRIERS IN GERMANIUM-DOPED P-ALUMINUM GALLIUM ARSENIDE SOLID SOLUTIONS.**
ROGULIN, V. YU. FILLER, A. S.
SHLENSKII, A. A.
FIZ. TEKH. POLUPROV.
7 (9), 1828-30, 1973.
(FOR ENGLISH TRANSLATION SEE E59237)

55315 **EXCESS CIRCULAR POLARIZATION OF LUMINESCENCE DURING OPTICAL ORIENTATION IN A SEMICONDUCTOR WITH A CUBIC LATTICE.**
DZHIOEV, R. I. ZAKHARCHENYA, B. P.
FLEISHER, V. G. VEKUA, V. L.
FIZ. TEKH. POLUPROV.
7 (9), 1849-51, 1973.
(FOR ENGLISH TRANSLATION SEE E59240)

55316 **EXCITED STATES OF DONORS IN GALLIUM ARSENIDE.**
GERSHENZON, E. M. GOL'TSMAN, G. N.
PTITSYNA, N. G.
FIZ. TEKH. POLUPROV.
7 (10), 1870-3, 1973.
(FOR ENGLISH TRANSLATION SEE E59241)

55319 **DRIFT VELOCITY AND AVERAGE ENERGY OF HOT ELECTRONS IN N-INDIUM ANTIMONIDE.**
VOROB'EV, L. E. GNESIN, M. M.
STAFEEV, V. I.
FIZ. TEKH. POLUPROV.
7 (10), 1982-6, 1973.
(FOR ENGLISH TRANSLATION SEE E59254)

55320 **EFFECT OF THE CONCENTRATION OF AN IMPURITY IN P-INDIUM ANTIMONIDE AT 4.2 K ON PIEZORESISTANCE.**
ALADASHVILI, D. I. GALAVANOV, V. V.
OBUKHOV, S. A.
FIZ. TEKH. POLUPROV.
7 (10), 2019-20, 1973.
(FOR ENGLISH TRANSLATION SEE E59256)

EPIC Number	Bibliographic Citation

55321 ELECTRIC AND PHOTOELECTRIC CHARACTERISTICS OF GALLIUM PHOSPHIDE-BASED N-NU- AND P-NU-N-STRUCTURES.
NASLEDOV, D. N. POPOV, YU. G.
PUTILOVSKAYA, M. YU. SLOBODCHIKOV, S. V.
FIZ. TEKH. POLUPROV.
7 (10), 2021-4, 1973.
(FOR ENGLISH TRANSLATION SEE E59257)

55322 CHANGE IN THE ELECTRIC CONDUCTIVITY OF GALLIUM SELENIDE IN HIGH SUPERHIGH-FREQUENCY ELECTRIC FIELDS.
AKHUNDOV, G. A. ABDINOV, A. SH.
KYAZYM-ZADE, A. G. MEKHTIEV, N. M.
FIZ. TEKH. POLUPROV.
7 (10), 2030-1, 1973.
(FOR ENGLISH TRANSLATION SEE E59258)

55323 FIELD EFFECT IN LEAD SULFIDE EPITAXIAL FILMS.
MURTAZIN, A. M. ZARIF'YANTS, YU. A.
FIZ. TEKH. POLUPROV.
7 (10), 2041-3, 1973.
(FOR ENGLISH TRANSLATION SEE E59259)

55325 CONDITIONS OF BREAKDOWN REVERSIBILITY IN CHALCOGENIDE GLASSES.
KOLOMIETS, B. T. LEBEDEV, E. A.
TAKSAMI, I. A. SHPUNT, V. KH.
FIZ. TEKH. POLUPROV.
7 (10), 2045-7, 1973.
(FOR ENGLISH TRANSLATION SEE E59261)

55326 EFFECTIVE MASS OF CHARGE CARRIERS IN COPPER SULFOTELLURIDE.
CORBACHEV, V. V. PUTILIN, I. M.
FIZ. TEKH. POLUPROV.
7 (10), 2049-50, 1973.
(FOR ENGLISH TRANSLATION SEE E59262)

55327 OBSERVATION OF OSCILLATING MAGNETOABSORPTION IN INDIUM PHOSPHIDE CRYSTALS.
ABDULLAEV, M. A. ZAKHARCHENYA, B. P.
SEISYAN, R. P.
FIZ. TEKH. POLUPROV.
7 (10), 2055-7, 1973.
(FOR ENGLISH TRANSLATION SEE E59263)

55328 BAND STRUCTURE OF III - V - II - VI -TYPE SOLID SOLUTIONS. EXTREME CONDITIONS OF INTERBAND INTERACTION.
BUZEVICH, G. I. SKOROBOGATOVA, L. A.
KHABAROV, E. N.
FIZ. TEKH. POLUPROV.
7 (11), 2079-85, 1973.
(FOR ENGLISH TRANSLATION SEE E59264)

55330 STARK BROADENING OF PHOTOTHERMAL IONIZATION SPECTRA OF DONORS IN GALLIUM ARSENIDE.
BERMAN, L. V. KOGAN, SH. M. SAGINOV, L. D.
SIDOROV, V. I. TELEGIN, A. A.
FIZ. TEKH. POLUPROV.
7 (11), 2094-8, 1973.
(FOR ENGLISH TRANSLATION SEE E59266)

55331 THEORY OF ELECTROLUMINESCENCE OR HEAVILY DOPED SEMICONDUCTORS.
OSIPOV, V. V.
FIZ. TEKH. POLUPROV.
7 (11), 2106-13, 1973.
(FOR ENGLISH TRANSLATION SEE E59267)

55332 EFFECT OF THE INTENSITY OF IRRADIATION ON ACCUMULATION OF RADIATION DEFECTS IN SEMICONDUCTORS.
BOLOTOV, V. V. VASIL'EV, A. V.
SMIRNOV, L. S.
FIZ. TEKH. POLUPROV.
7 (11), 2132-6, 1973.
(FOR ENGLISH TRANSLATION SEE E59269)

55333 ELECTRIC CONDUCTIVITY OF DEFORMED P-GERMANIUM IN A HIGH MAGNETIC FIELD.
NORMANTAS, E. FILIPAVICHUS, V.
FIZ. TEKH. POLUPROV.
7 (11), 2137-43, 1973.
(FOR ENGLISH TRANSLATION SEE E59270)

55334 IONIZATION ENERGIES OF DONOR SUBSTITUTION IMPURITIES IN GALLIUM ARSENIDE.
BAZHENOV, V. K. SOLOSHENKO, V. I.
FOIGEL, M. G.
FIZ. TEKH. POLUPROV.
7 (11), 2149-52, 1973.
(FOR ENGLISH TRANSLATION SEE E59272)

55336 ENERGY SPECTRUM OF IMPURITY LEVELS AND FEATURES OF RECOMBINATION IN OXYGEN-DOPED GALLIUM ARSENIDE.
PEKA, G. P. SHEPEL, L. G. MIRETS, L. Z.
FIZ. TEKH. POLUPROV.
7 (11), 2159-64, 1973.
(FOR ENGLISH TRANSLATION SEE E59274)

55337 PROPERTIES OF IONIZATION DOMAINS IN MANGANESE-ACTIVATED SODIUM ZINC GERMANATE CRYSTALS.
DEVYATYKH, E. V. L'VOVA, E. YU.
STOPACHINSKII, V. B. FANG, P.-N. FOK, M. V.
FIZ. TEKH. POLUPROV.
7 (11), 2165-71, 1973.
(FOR ENGLISH TRANSLATION SEE E59275)

55338 THERMOELECTRICITY AND EFFECTIVE MASS OF HOLES IN P-SILICON ZINC ARSENIDE CRYSTALS.
AVERKIEVA, G. K. PROCHUKHAN, V. D.
RUD, YU. V. SKRIPKIN, V. A.
TASHTANOVA, M.
FIZ. TEKH. POLUPROV.
7 (11), 2172-4, 1973.
(FOR ENGLISH TRANSLATION SEE E59276)

55339 LUMINESCENCE PROPERTIES OF EPITAXIAL FILMS OF ALUMINUM GALLIUM PHOSPHIDE SOLID SOLUTIONS WHEN $0 \leq X \leq 0.85$.
ALFEROV, ZH. I. GARBUZOV, D. Z.
KONNIKOV, S. G. KOP'EV, P. S.
MISHURNYI, V. N.
FIZ. TEKH. POLUPROV.
7 (11), 2175-8, 1973.
(FOR ENGLLSH TRANSLATION SEE E59277)

55340 SPECTRAL OSCILLATIONS OF BARRIER PHOTOEMF. IN INDIUM ANTIMONIDE IN QUANTIZING MAGNETIC FIELDS.
BELOV, N. A. KIM, G. D. KOSOGOV, O. V.
MARAMZINA, M. A.
FIZ. TEKH. POLUPROV.
7 (11), 2179-83, 1973.
(FOR ENGLISH TRANSLATION SEE E59278)

55341 ELECTROLUMINESCENCE OF GALLIUM ARSENIDE PHOSPHIDE CRYSTALS IN THE REGION OF COMPOSITIONS WITH INDIRECT BAND STRUCTURE.
PIKHTIN, A. N. RAZBEGAEV, V. N.
YAS'KOV, D. A.
FIZ. TEKH. POLUPROV.
7 (11), 2184-8, 1973.
(FOR ENGLISH TRANSLATION SEE E59279)

55342 QUENCHING OF AN INJECTION CURRENT IN COPPER-DOPED GALLIUM ARSENIDE.
BRODOVOI, V. A. DRIKOT, N. Z.
SHCHERBATYI, N. I.
FIZ. TEKH. POLUPROV.
7 (11), 2245-7, 1973.
(FOR ENGLISH TRANSLATION SEE E59284)

55343 THERMOELECTRICITY OF HEAVILY COMPENSATED P-INDIUM ANTIMONIDE.
ABRIKOSOV, N. KH. LAPTEV, A. V.
MIRGALOVSKAYA, M. S. RAUKHMAN, M. R.
SKRIPKIN, V. A.
FIZ. TEKH. POLUPROV.
7 (11), 2253-4, 1973.
(FOR ENGLISH TRANSLATION SEE E59285)

55345 SPECIFIC CONDUCTANCES OF SODIUM HEXAFLUORO-ALUMINATE-SODIUM CHLORIDE AND SODIUM HEXAFLUORO-ALUMINATE-BARIUM CHLORIDE MELTS.
KUVAKIN, M. A. EVSTIFEEV, E. N.
ISPOLIN, V. A. TAIANOVA, L. I.
RUSS. J. PHYS. CHEM.
47 (4), 589, 1973.
(ENGLISH TRANSLATION OF ZH. FIZ. KHIM., 47 (4), 1036, 1973; FOR ORIGINAL SEE E51347)

55346 PROPERTIES AND FORMATION CONDITIONS OF CONDUCTIVE COATINGS WITH TWO-DIMENSIONALLY ORIENTED FILLER STRUCTURE.
SHCHIBRYA, N. G. GUL', V. E.
COLLOID J., USSR
35 (3), 471-5, 1973.
(ENGLISH TRANSLATION OF KOLL. ZH., 35 (3), 511-6, 1973; FOR ORIGINAL SEE E51962)

55347 ELECTRICAL CONDUCTIVITY OF URANIUM BETA-DIOXIDE MODIFIED BY ADDITIONS OF MAGNESIUM OXIDE, STRONTIUM OXIDE, AND NIOBIUM PENTOXIDE.
VLASOV, V. G. PIS'MENKO, V. T.
ULYASHEV, S. P. SHALAGINOV, V. N.
BEKETOV, A. R.
J. APPL. CHEM., USSR
46 (1), 34-7, 1973.
(ENGLISH TRANSLATION OF ZH. PRIKL. KHIM., 46 (1), 36-40, 1973; FOR ORIGINAL SEE E51317)

55350 MEASUREMENT OF THE OPTICAL PROPERTIES OF POLYCRYSTALLINE ALUMINUM NITRIDE AT 0.10-25 MU.
KUTOLIN, S. A. LUKINA, L. L.
SAMOILOVA, R. N.
INORG. MAT., USSR
9 (6), 862-4, 1973.
(ENGLISH TRANSLATION OF IZV. AKAD. NAUK SSSR, NEORG. MATER., 9 (6), 964-6, 1973; FOR ORIGINAL SEE E53779)

55351 FAR-INFRARED MEASUREMENTS OF THE OPTICAL PROPERTIES OF CESIUM IODIDE BETWEEN 12 AND 300 K, COMPARED WITH CALCULATIONS BASED ON CUBIC ANHARMONICITY ONLY.
BEAIRSTO, J. A. B. ELDRIDGE, J. E.
CAN. J. PHYS.
51 (24), 2550-63, 1973.

55353 SPIN-DEPENDENT CONDUCTION IN SEMICONDUCTORS.
MORIGAKI, K.
KOTAI BUTSURI
8 (11), 577-84, 1973.

EPIC Number	Bibliographic Citation
55357	**PROPERTIES OF ELECTRON CENTERS.** KLINCK, C. C. POINT DEFECTS SOLIDS 1, 291–325PP., 1972. (EDITED BY J. H. CRAWFORD, JR., PLENUM: NEW YORK)
55362	**MEASUREMENT OF SURFACE CONDUCTIVITY OF SEMICONDUCTOR CRYSTALS.** NEKRASOV, M. M. RYABCHENKO, G. V. VOP. MIKROELEKTRON., MATER. SEMIN. ELEM. USTROISTVA MIKROELEKTRON 69–71, 1971.
55364	**RAMAN SPECTRA AND OPTICAL CONSTANTS OF CADMIUM FLUORIDE.** GOBEAU, J. HEURET, M. MON, J. P. RECKER, K. PHYS. STATUS SOLIDI 20 A (2), 687–93, 1973.
55366	**TEMPERATURE AND CURRENT STUDIES OF THE RELAXATION EFFECT OF ION–ELECTRON EMISSION ON SILICON.** OMEL'YANOVSKAYA, N. M. LEBEDEV, S. YA. PANIN, S. D. FIZ. TVERD. TELA (LENINGRAD) 14 (7), 2185–7, 1972. (FOR ENGLISH TRANSLATION SEE E60745)
55375	**ON THE THEORY OF ELECTRICAL CONDUCTIVITY IN SEMICONDUCTING THIN FILMS UNDER A HIGH ELECTRIC FIELD.** ILKOVIC, V. FYZ. CAS. 22 (4), 207–18, 1972.
55377	**HIGH PURITY GALLIUM ARSENIDE.** WOLFE, C. M. STILLMAN, G. E. GALLIUM ARSENIDE RELAT. COMPOUNDS, PROC. INT. SYMP., 3RD 3–17, 1971.
55380	**EPITAXIAL INDIUM PHOSPHIDE AND INDIUM PHOSPHIDE ARSENIDE.** HALES, M. C. KNIGHT, J. R. WILKINS, C. W. GALLIUM ARSENIDE RELAT. COMPOUNDS, PROC. INT. SYMP., 3RD 50–6, 1971.
55384	**ELECTROLUMINESCENCE IN INDIUM GALLIUM PHOSPHIDE.** ONTON, A. LORENZ, M. R. GALLIUM ARSENIDE RELAT. COMPOUNDS, PROC. INT. SYMP., 3RD 222–30, 1971.
55386	**TEMPERATURE DEPENDENCE OF ELECTROCONDUCTIVITY AND PHOTOSENSITIVITY IN CADMIUM SULFIDE FILMS.** AKRAMOV, KH. T. TESHABAEV, A. LULDASHEV, B. D. KHUSANOV, M. M. GELIOTEKHNIKA (2), 9–12, 1972. (FOR ENGLISH TRANSLATION SEE E75456)
55387	**THERMOELECTRIC PROPERTIES OF GALLIUM SYSTEM ALLOYS UNDER STANDARD CONDITIONS.** IORDANISHVILI, E. K. KARTENKO, N. H. ORLOV, A. G. FINOGENOV, A. D. GELIOTEKHNIKA (4), 36–42, 1972. (FOR ENGLISH TRANSLATION, SEE E 88429)
55403	**POLYTYPISM AND LUMINESCENCE OF LEAD(II) IODIDE CRYSTALS.** BLONSKII, I. V. GORBAN, I. S. GUBANOV, V. A. LYUTER, YA. A. POPERENKO, L. V. STRAHNIKOVA, M. I. FIZ. TVERD. TELA (LENINGRAD) 15 (12), 3664–8, 1973. (FOR ENGLISH TRANSLATION SEE E57814)
55404	**MAGNETIC PROPERTIES OF SYSTEMS WITH A COOPERATIVE JAHN–TELLER EFFECT.** KAPLAN, M. D. VEKHTER, B. G. FIZ. TVERD. TELA (LENINGRAD) 15 (12), 3675–6, 1973. (FOR ENGLISH TRANSLATION SEE E57815)
55405	**MAGNETIC STATE OF CHROMIUM(3+) ION IN CHROMIUM COPPER OXIDE.** BELOV, K. P. GORYAGA, A. N. ANTOSHINA, L. G. KORAIEM, T. FIZ. TVERD. TELA (LENINGRAD) 15 (12), 3687–8, 1973. (FOR ENGLISH TRANSLATION SEE E57820)
55406	**MAGNETIC IMPURITY STATES IN EUROPIUM GADOLINIUM OXIDE.** SAMOKHVALOV, A. A. ARBUZOVA, T. I. SIMONOVA, M. I. FAL'KOVSKAYA, L. D. FIZ. TVERD. TELA (LENINGRAD) 15 (12), 3690–2, 1973. (FOR ENGLISH TRANSLATION SEE E57821)
55407	**PHOTOINDUCED CHANGE IN THE MAGNETIC PROPERTIES OF HYDROGEN SILICON YTTRIUM OXIDE.** KUTS, P. S. KOVALENKO, V. F. RUBAN, V. A. FIZ. TVERD. TELA (LENINGRAD) 15 (12), 3707–8, 1973. (FOR ENGLISH TRANSLATION SEE E57824)
55409	**NEGATIVE LONGITUDINAL MAGNETORESISTANCE IN CADMIUM MERCURY TELLURIDE.** BERCHENKO, N. N. PASHKOVSKII, M. V. FIZ. TVERD. TELA (LENINGRAD) 15 (12), 3716–18, 1973. (FOR ENGLISH TRANSLATION SEE E57830)
55422	**BISMUTH IRON OXIDE STUDY BY MOESSBAUER EFFECT.** HANZEL, D. MOLJK, A. FIZIKA (ZAGRED) 5 (3), 145–53, 1973.
55444	**EFFECT OF ATOMIC ORDERING ON THE MAGNETIC PROPERTIES OF THE ALLOY GOLD–COPPER CONTAINING AN IRON IMPURITY.** KUZ'MENKO, P. P. KAL'NAYA, G. I. SUPRUNENKO, P. A. FIZ. METAL. METALLOVED. 35 (6), 1179–83, 1973.
55457	**CALCULATION OF HALL COEFFICIENTS OF FERROMAGNETS.** IGOSHEVA, T. N. FIZ. METAL. METALLOVED. 36 (2), 404–7, 1973.
55465	**MAGNETIC REVERSAL OF ORIENTED MANGANESE–BISMUTH FILMS.** ABAKUMOV, B. M. BAIKOVA, N. D. SHISHKOV, A. G. FIZ. METAL. METALLOVED. 36 (4), 717–20, 1973.
55470	**MAGNETIC PROPERTIES OF THE CHROMIUM MANGANESE ANTIMONIDE ALLOY IN HIGH PULSED MAGNETIC FIELDS.** ZAINULLINA, R. I. SHASHURINA, L. F. FIZ. METAL. METALLOVED. 36 (4), 890–2, 1973.
55473	**MAGNETIC CRYSTALLINE ANISOTROPY OF THE INTERMETALLIC COMPOUND SAMARIUM–COBALT.** KOROLEF, A. V. ERMOLENKO, A. S. FIZ. METAL. METALLOVED. 36 (5), 957–64, 1973.
55474	**MAGNETIC AND HYSTERETIC PROPERTIES OF COMPOUNDS OF RARE EARTH METALS WITH IRON.** BISLIEV, A. M. NIKITIN, S. A. SAVITSKII, E. M. TEREKHOVA, V. F. KOLESNICHENKO, V. E. FIZ. METAL. METALLOVED. 36 (5), 965–70, 1973.
55477	**MAGNETIC PROPERTIES AND CRYSTAL POWDERS OF PRASEODYMIUM–SAMARIUM–COBALT ALLOYS.** MAGAT, L. M. KOROTKOVA, M. N. SHCHERBAKOVA, E. V. ERMOLENKO, A. S. FIZ. METAL. METALLOVED. 36 (6), 1308–10, 1973.
55479	**ELECTRICAL PROPERTIES OF RARE EARTH CHALCOGENIDES.** ZHUZE, V. P. GONCHAROVA, E. V. KHAL'KOGENIDOV REDKOZEMEL. ELEM. 58–122, 1973.
55480	**MAGNETIC PROPERTIES OF RARE EARTH CHALCOGENIDES.** LOGINOV, G. M. FIZ. SVOISTVA KHAL'KOGENIDOV REDKOZEMEL. ELEM. 179–222, 1973.
55490	**ELECTRIC PROPERTIES OF ZINC DIPHOSPHIDE.** POLYKEVICH, I. V. TYCHINA, I. I. FEDOTOVSKII, A. V. FIZ. TVERD. TELA 23–5PP., 1972.
55491	**LONG-WAVE FUNDAMENTAL ABSORPTION EDGE OF BISMUTH OXIDE.** FIDRYA, A. K. FIZ. TVERD. TELA 34–40, 1972.
55492	**ELECTRICAL PROPERTIES OF CADMIUM SILICON PHOSPHIDE SINGLE CRYSTALS DOPED WITH GROUP II AND III ELEMENTS.** BYCHKOV, A. G. RADZIVIL, V. P. TKACHUK, I. YU. TYCHINA, I. I. FIZ. TVERD. TELA 41–7PP., 1972.
55493	**PIEZORESISTANCE IN SEMICONDUCTORS CONTAINING DEEP ENERGY LEVELS.** SEMENYUK, A. K. PANKEVICH, E. V. FEDOSOV, A. V. DOSKOCH, V. P. FIZ. TVERD. TELA 48–52, 1972.
55494	**MAGNETOSTRICTIVE NICKEL–COBALT FERRITES.** KIRICHOK, P. P. KUSTOVSKII, L. G. PODVAL'NYKH, G. S. SHAMANOV, M. A. FIZ. TVERD. TELA 55–61, 1972.

EPIC Number | Bibliographic Citation

55500 THERMOLUMINESCENT PROPERTIES OF LITHIUM BORATE ACTIVATED BY SILVER.
THOMPSON, J. J. ZIEMER, P. L.
HEALTH PHYS.
25 (4), 435–41, 1973.

55511 LINEAR AND NONLINEAR OPTICAL PROPERTIES OF SOME TERNARY SELENIDES.
BOYD, G. D. MCFEE, J. H. STORZ, F. G.
KASPER, H. M.
IEEE JOURNAL OF QUANTUM ELECTRONICS
QE-8, 900–908, 1972.

55512 MECHANISMS FOR SELF-FOCUSING IN OPTICAL GLASSES.
FELDMAN, A. HOROWITZ, D. WAXLER, R. M.
IEEE J. QUANTUM ELECTRON.
9 (11), 1054–61, 1973.

55521 RESISTIVITY OF MAGNESIUM OXIDE POWDER AT ELEVATED TEMPERATURES.
RITGER, R. J. SANDOR, B. I.
IEEE TRANS. ELEC. INSUL.
8 (4), 133–6, 1973.

55522 INFLUENCE OF FIELD NONUNIFORMITY ON THE BREAKDOWN CHARACTERISTICS OF SULFUR HEXAFLUORIDE.
AZER, A. A. COMSA, R. P.
IEEE TRANS. ELEC. INSUL.
8 (4), 136–42, 1973.

55524 INFLUENCE OF SURFACE CONDITIONS ON THE COERCIVE FORCE OF SAMARIUM-COBALT PARTICLES.
SEARLE, C. W. FREDERICK, W. G. D.
GARRETT, H. J.
IEEE TRANS. MAGN.
9 (3), 164–7, 1973.

55525 MAGNETIC PROPERTIES OF FLUID-QUENCHED COBALT-SAMARIUM MAGNETS.
DOSER, M. SMEGGIL, J. G.
IEEE TRANS. MAGN.
9 (3), 168–71, 1973.

55527 NEW HIGH COERCIVE FORCE GAMMA-FERRIC OXIDE EXHIBITING COERCIVE FORCE AS HIGH AS 450–470 OERSTED.
YADA, Y. MIYAMOTO, S. KAWAGOE, H.
IEEE TRANS. MAGN.
9 (3), 185–8, 1973.

55529 MAGNETIC PROPERTIES OF COBALT-SAMARIUM LODEX AND COBALT-SAMARIUM-LEAD COMPOSITES.
DOSER, M. SUMMITT, R.
IEEE TRANS. MAGN.
9 (3), 194–7, 1973.

55530 OBSERVATION OF MAGNETIC DOMAINS IN NEODYMIUM-COBALT USING AN ELECTROETCHING TECHNIQUE.
EVANS, D. J. GARRETT, H. J.
IEEE TRANS. MAGN.
9 (3), 197–201, 1973.

55531 OBSERVATION OF DOMAIN STRUCTURES IN SAMARIUM-COBALT BY ELECTRON MICROSCOPY.
RILEY, A. JONES, G. A.
IEEE TRANS. MAGN.
9 (3), 201–3, 1973.

55542 LIQUID PHASE EPITAXY FILMS OF BISMUTH-SUBSTITUTED BUBBLE GARNET.
ITO, S. MIKAMI, I. SUGITA, Y.
TANIGUCHI, S.
IEEE TRANS. MAGN.
9 (3), 460–3, 1973.

55558 LIGAND FIELD THEORY OF THE MAGNETIC AND OPTICAL PROPERTIES OF COBALT(II) AMMONIUM AND POTASSIUM SULFATE HEXAHYDRATES.
GHOSH, D. PAL, D.
INDIAN J. PHYS.
47 (9), 513–27, 1973.

55579 ADVANCED HARDENED ANTENNA WINDOW MATERIALS STUDY III.
BRAZEL, J. P.
ARMY MATERIALS AND MECHANICS RESEARCH CENTER, WATERTOWN, MASSACHUSETTS
254PP., 1973.
(AD–768 225, AMMRC-CTR–73–26)

55588 TECHNIQUES FOR THE MEASUREMENT OF THE SEMICONDUCTOR PROPERTIES OF THERMOELECTRIC MATERIALS.
RYDEN, D. J.
AT. ENERGY RES. ESTABL., HARWELL, ENGLAND
28PP., 1973.
(AERE–R–6996)

55592 MAGNETIC PROPERTIES OF URANIUM TRICHLORIDE, URANIUM TRIBROMIDE, NEPTUNIUM TRICHLORIDE, NEPTUNIUM TRIBROMIDE, AND PLUTONIUM TRICHLORIDE.
JONES, E. R., JR. HENDRICKS, M. E.
STONE, J. A. KARRAKER, D. G.
SAVANNAH RIVER LAB., E. I. DU PONT DE NEMOURS AND CO., AIKEN, S. C.
17PP., 1972.
(DP–MS–71–84)

55593 MOESSBAUER SPECTRA AND MAGNETIC PROPERTIES OF DICESIUM HEXACHLORONEPTUNATE, BIS(TETRAMETHYLAMMONIUM) HEXACHLORONEPTUNATE, AND BIS(TETRAETHYLAMMONIUM) HEXACHLORONEPTUNATE.
STONE, J. A. KARRAKER, D. G.
SAVANNAH RIVER LAB., E. I. DU PONT DE NEMOURS AND CO., AIKEN, S. C.
15PP., 1972.
(DP–MS–71–86)

55608 OPTICAL ABSORPTION SPECTRA OF YTTERBIUM(3+) IN ALKALI HALIDE SINGLE CRYSTALS.
RAO, V. J.
INDIAN J. PURE APPL. PHYS.
11 (6), 441–2, 1973.

55614 PHOTOLUMINESCENCE IN COPPER AND MANGANESE-ACTIVATED STRONTIUM SULFIDE PHOSPHORS.
KANARI, P. S.
INDIAN J. PURE APPL. PHYS.
11 (7), 499–503, 1973.

55618 DECAY AND THERMOLUMINESCENCE STUDIES ON CALCIUM SULFIDE PHOSPHORS ACTIVATED WITH ARSENIC.
JAIN, K. L. RANADE, J. D.
INDIAN J. PURE APPL. PHYS.
11 (8), 602–4, 1973.

55620 PERMITTIVITY AND DIELECTRIC LOSS IN COLORED AND UNCOLORED SODIUM IODIDE CRYSTALS.
SARMA, G. C. MAHANTA, P. C.
INDIAN J. PURE APPL. PHYS.
11 (9), 666–8, 1973.

55627 CHARACTERIZATION OF GALLIUM ARSENIDE BY FAR-INFRARED REFLECTIVITY.
PERKOWITZ, S. BREECHER, J.
INFRARED PHYS.
13 (4), 321–6, 1973.

55637 MAGNETIC INVESTIGATIONS OF SEVERAL RARE EARTH OXIDES.
SCHREINER, P. CZOPNIK, A.
INST. TECH. JAD., AGH REP.
(39/PS), 15PP., 1973.

55648 DIELECTRIC MEASUREMENTS AT THE EARLY STAGES OF HARDENING OF MONOMINERAL CEMENTS.
SVATOVSKAYA, L. B. SHIBALLO, V. G.
J. APPL. CHEM., USSR
46 (6), 1302–5, 1973.
(ENGLISH TRANSLATION OF ZH. PRIKL. KHIM., 46 (6), 1219–23, 1973; FOR ORIGINAL SEE E52387)

55654 COERCIVE FIELD OF HARD MAGNETIC MATERIALS.
KRONMUELLER, H. HILZINGER, H.
INT. J. MAGN.
5 (1–3), 27–32, 1973.

55659 NEGATIVE MAGNETORESISTANCE EFFECT IN SOME MANGANESE COMPOUNDS WITH PEROVSKITE STRUCTURE.
BAYER, E. SCHMELZ, H.
INT. J. MAGN.
5 (1–3), 71–3, 1973.

55660 THEORETICAL TEMPERATURE DEPENDENCE OF THE PARAMAGNETIC SUSCEPTIBILITY OF A FERRIMAGNET WITH FIVE SUBLATTICES.
FLORESCU, V.
INT. J. MAGN.
5 (1–3), 81–4, 1973.

55663 MAGNETIC PROPERTIES OF THE FERRIMAGNET SODIUM NICKEL IRON FLUORIDE AND THE LINEAR ANTIFERROMAGNET SODIUM NICKEL ALUMINUM FLUORIDE.
HEGER, G.
INT. J. MAGN.
5 (1–3), 119–24, 1973.

55670 FIELD DEPENDENCE OF RESISTIVITY IN MAGNETIC SEMICONDUCTORS.
FELDTKELLER, E. TREITINGER, L.
INT. J. MAGN.
5 (1–3), 237–41, 1973.

55687 PHYSICAL PROPERTIES OF SAMARIUM TELLURIDES.
KARABEKOV, A. K. YAREMBASH, E. I.
TYURIN, E. G.
IZV. AKAD. NAUK KIRG. SSR
(6), 68–72, 1973.

55692 ELECTRICAL STABILITY OF A SERIES OF ELECTRONEGATIVE GASES IN A UNIFORM FIELD AT HIGH PRESSURES.
LYAPIN, A. G. SEMENOV, YU. N.
IZV. AKAD. NAUK SSSR, ENERG. TRANSP.
(1), 107–15, 1973.

55694 CALCULATION OF THE WATER VAPOR ABSORPTION COEFFICIENT IN THE 8–13 MU RANGE.
NESMELOVA, L. I. TVOROGOV, S. D.
FOMIN, V. V.
IZV. AKAD. NAUK SSSR, FIZ. ATMOS. OKEANA
9 (11), 1205–8, 1973.

EPIC Number	Bibliographic Citation

55706 ELASTIC AND ELECTRICAL PROPERTIES OF ZINCITE IN THE 4.2-700 K RANGE.
TOKAREV, E. F. KARYAKINA, N. F.
KOBYAKOV, I. V. KUZ'MINA, I. P.
LOBACHEV, A. N.
IZV. AKAD. NAUK SSSR, SER. FIZ.
37 (11), 2401-3, 1973.

55710 EFFECT OF FAST-ELECTRON IRRADIATION ON THE ELECTROPHYSICAL PROPERTIES OF N-GALLIUM ANTIMONIDE.
ANNAEV, R. G. MEL'NIKOVA, L. L.
IZV. AKAD. NAUK TURKM. SSR, SER. FIZ.-TEKH., KHIM.
(5), 25-30, 1973.

55711 KINETIC PROPERTIES OF COPPER SELENIDE.
ASTAKHOV, O. P. BERGER, L. I.
DOVLETOV, K. TASHLIEV, K.
IZV. AKAD. NAUK TURKM. SSR, SER. FIZ.-TEKH., KHIM. GEOL. NAUK
(5), 101-3, 1973.

55713 PIEZORESISTANCE OF P-GALLIUM ANTIMONIDE.
SAIDOV, M. S. SAIDOV, A. S. NIKITIN, V. V.
IZV. AKAD. NAUK UZB. SSR, SER. FIZ.-MAT. NAUK
17 (4), 65-8, 1973.

55721 TWO-PHOTON INDIRECT TRANSITIONS IN GALLIUM PHOSPHIDE CRYSTAL.
YEE, J. H. CHAU, H. H. M.
OPT. COMMUN.
10 (1), 56-8, 1974.

55726 SINGLE-PARTICLE MODEL FOR THE FREQUENCY DEPENDENCE WEAK INFRARED ABSORPTION IN CRYSTALS AND MOLECULES AT T = 0 K.
YUKON, S. P. BENDOW, B.
OPT. COMMUN.
10 (1), 53-5, 1974.
(AD-778 830)

55728 PIEZOOPTICAL EFFECTS.
BALSLEV, I.
SEMICOND. SEMIMETALS
9, 403-56, 1972.
(EDITED BY ROBERT K. WILLARDSON, ACADEMIC: NEW YORK, N. Y.)

55729 OPTICAL MAGNETO-ABSORPTION IN HEAVILY DOPED SEMI-CONDUCTORS.
VAN CONG, H.
PHIL. MAG.
28 (5), 983-91, 1973.

55733 TEFLON CELL TECHNIQUE TO MEASURE THERMOPOWER OF LIQUIDS AND SOLIDS AT HIGH PRESSURES.
RESHAMWALA, A. S. RAMESH, T. G.
J. PHYS.
7 E (2), 133-6, 1974.

55739 ANOMALOUS RESISTIVITY NEAR CURIE TEMPERATURE DUE TO THE CRITICAL SCATTERING.
KASUYA, T. KONDO, A.
SOLID STATE COMMUN.
14 (3), 253-9, 1974.

55740 ELECTRONIC STRUCTURE OF AMORPHOUS MATERIALS.
EDWARDS, S. F.
NEW DEVELOP. SEMICOND., MC GILL SUMMER SCH. LECT.
249-87, 1971.
(EDITED BY P. R. WALLACE, NOORDHOFF INT. PUBL.: LEIDEN, NETH)

55758 THERMOELECTRIC PROPERTIES OF COPPER IODIDE AND CHLORIDE.
ASTAKHOV, O. P. FEDOROV, V. I.
TEPLOFIZ. VYS. TEMP.
11 (6), 1305-7, 1973.
(FOR ENGLISH TRANSLATION SEE E57781)

55759 ROLE OF MICROFIELDS OF PLASMA TYPE IN IONIC MELTS.
KURILENKOV, YU. K.
TEPLOFIZ. VYS. TEMP.
11 (6), 1291-3, 1973.
(FOR ENGLISH TRANSLATION SEE E57778)

55771 PREPARATION AND SOME PHYSICAL PROPERTIES OF CRYSTALS AND GLASSES FROM I-V-VI(2)-TYPE COMPOUNDS.
BOGDANOVA, A. V. GOLOVEI, M. I.
MIKHAL'KO, I. P. KIKINESHI, A. A.
SEMAK, D. G. TURYANITSA, I. D.
IZV. VYSSH. UCHEB. ZAVED., KHIM. KHIM. TEKHNOL.
16 (8), 1288-91, 1973.

55772 PHYSICAL CHEMICAL PROPERTIES OF COBALT OXIDE - ALUMINUM OXIDE SYSTEMS.
TRUNOV, A. M. UMINSKIY, M. V.
KRAEVSKAYA, E. A. PRESNOV, V. A.
IZV. VYSSH. UCHEB. ZAVED., KHIM. KHIM. TEKHNOL.
16 (9), 1356-8, 1973.
(FOR ENGLISH TRANSLATION SEE E68956)

55777 FORMATION OF F CENTERS AND COLORATION DEPTH IN SODIUM CHLORIDE AND POTASSIUM CHLORIDE SINGLE CRYSTALS DURING ORIENTED (ALONG CRYSTALLOGRAPHIC AXES [100]) IRRADIATION BY 10-50 KEV ELECTRONS.
KULESHOV, E. A. SHIPATOV, E. T.
UKR. FIZ. ZH. (RUSS. ED.)
18 (12), 2029-33, 1973.

55786 CRYSTAL DATA ON GAMMA-INDIUM SULFIDE STABILIZED BY ARSENIC AND ANTIMONY.
DIEHL, R. NITSCHE, R. CARPENTIER, C. D.
J. APPL. CRYSTALLOGR.
6 (PT. 6), 497-8, 1973.

55794 IONIC CONDUCTIVITY OF OXIDES BASED ON LITHIUM ORTHOSILICATE.
WEST, A. R.
J. APPL. ELECTROCHEM.
3 (4), 327-35, 1973.

55795 PRELIMINARY DATA ON THE OPTICAL PROPERTIES OF SOLID AMMONIA AND SCATTERING PARAMETERS FOR AMMONIA CLOUD PARTICLES.
TAYLOR, F. W.
J. ATMOS. SCI.
30, 677-683, 1973.

55796 SEARCH FOR THE E-EFFECT IN THE ATMOSPHERIC WATER VAPOR CONTINUUM.
TOMASI, C. GUZZI, R. VITTORI, O.
J. ATMOS. SCI.
31 (1), 255-60, 1974.

55802 CHEMICAL SYNTHESIS AND PROPERTIES OF COPPER (I) IODIDE SINGLE CRYSTALS.
POPOLITOV, V. I. LOBACHEV, A. N.
IZV. AKAD. NAUK SSSR, NEORG. MATER.
9 (6), 1062-3, 1973.

55807 ELECTRICAL PROPERTIES OF IRON SELENIDES.
AKHMEDOV, N. R. DZHALILOV, N. Z.
ABDINOV, D. SH.
IZV. AKAD. NAUK SSSR, NEORG. MATER.
9 (8), 1429-30, 1973.

55817 ELECTRIC PROPERTIES OF ANTIMONY BISMUTH IODIDE SELENIDE CRYSTALS AND FILMS.
BELOTSKII, D. P. GAVRILENKO, N. V.
KATERINYUK, D. M. KUSHNIR, YA. I.
LAPSHIN, V. F. MOIK, I. B.
IZV. AKAD. NAUK SSSR, NEORG. MATER.
9 (9), 1537-41, 1973.

55820 DEFECT FORMATION PROCESSES IN VANADIUM PENTOXIDE.
VOLZHENSKII, D. S. PASHKOVSKII, M. V.
FEDORKO, V. F.
IZV. AKAD. NAUK SSSR, NEORG. MATER.
9 (9), 1581-4, 1973.

55822 BEHAVIOR OF TIN IMPURITIES IN ANTIMONY TELLURIDE SINGLE CRYSTALS.
SHEROV, P. MAVLONOV, SH. KARIMOV, S.
IZV. AKAD. NAUK SSSR, NEORG. MATER.
9 (9), 1637-9, 1973.

55823 LEAD-TIN-TELLURIUM POLYTHERMAL CROSS SECTION AND PREPARATION OF SINGLE CRYSTALS OF THE ALLOY LEAD TIN TELLURIDE.
SHELIMOVA, L. E. ABRIKOSOV, N. KH.
IZV. AKAD. NAUK SSSR, NEORG. MATER.
9 (9), 1642-3, 1973.

55824 EFFECT OF IONIC ORDERING ON THE PULSED PROPERTIES OF A LITHIUM FERRITE.
DUGAR-ZHABON, K. D.
IZV. AKAD. NAUK SSSR, NEORG. MATER.
9 (9), 1646-7, 1973.

55826 VOLUME-TYPE RESISTORS WITH A CURRENT-CONDUCTING PHASE FROM TITANIUM CARBIDE.
GREBENKINA, V. G. YUSOV, YU. P.
SOROKIN, V. N. PEREVEZENTSEV, A. V.
IZV. AKAD. NAUK SSSR, NEORG. MATER.
9 (10), 1827-8, 1973.

55828 SPECTROSCOPIC PROPERTIES OF NEODYMIUM TRIPOSITIVE-ACTIVATED STRONTIUM ALUMINATE CRYSTALS.
KEVORKOV, A. M. KAMINSKII, A. A.
BAGDASAROV, KH. S. TEVOSYAN, T. T.
SARKISOV, S. E.
IZV. AKAD. NAUK SSSR, NEORG. MATER.
9 (10), 1839-40, 1973.

55830 ELECTRIC CONDUCTIVITY AND THERMOELECTRIC POTENTIAL OF ALPHA-FERRIC OXIDE IN OXYGEN - CARBON DIOXIDE - SULFUR DIOXIDE GAS MIXTURES.
KONEV, V. N. CHEBOTIN, V. V. SUNTSOV, N. V.
DVOENKO, E. P.
IZV. AKAD. NAUK SSSR, NEORG. MATER.
9 (10), 1847-51, 1973.

55832 REFRACTIVE INDICES AND ELECTRO-OPTIC COEFFICIENTS OF THE EULITITES BISMUTH GERMANATE AND BISMUTH SILICATE.
BORTFELD, D. P. MEIER, H.
J. APPLIED PHYSICS
43, 5110, 5111, 1972.

EPIC Number | Bibliographic Citation

55835 OPTICAL AND ELECTRICAL PROPERTIES OF PROTONBOMBARDED P-TYPE GALLIUM ARSENIDE.
DYMENT, J. C. NORTH, J. C. D ASARO, L. A.
J. OF APPLIED PHYSICS
44, 207–213, 1973.

55840 ION–IMPLANTED NITROGEN IN GALLIUM ARSENIDE.
KACHARE, A. H. SPITZER, W. G.
KAHAN, A. EULER, F. K. WHATLEY, T. A.
J. APPL. PHYS.
44 (10), 4393–9, 1973.

55841 MULTIPHONON ABSORPTION BY IONIC CRYSTALS. TEMPERATURE DEPENDENCE.
ROSENSTOCK, H. B.
J. APPL. PHYS.
44 (10), 4473–7, 1973.

55851 SECONDARY ELECTRON EMISSION FROM GOLD, MOLYBDENUM, AND COPPER – BERYLLIUM BY HIGH–CHARGE–NUMBER LASER–PRODUCED METAL IONS.
CANO, G. L.
J. APPL. PHYS.
44 (12), 5293–300, 1973.

55859 ANALYSES OF SOME POTENTIAL PROBELMS IN CYLINDRICAL COORDINATES IN CONNECTION WITH FOUR–POINT PROBE TECHNIQUE.
MURASHIMA, S.
JAP. J. OF APPLIED PHYSICS
12, 1244–1250, 1973.

55860 ELECTRICAL CONDUCTIVITY AND OPTICAL PROPERTIES OF SOLUTION–GROWN GALLIUM INDIUM PHOSPHIDE ALLOYS.
SONOMURA, H. OHTA, Y. MIYAUCHI, T.
JAP. J. APPL. PHYS.
12 (9), 1338–42, 1973.

55864 TEMPERATURE DEPENDENCE OF THE COERCIVE FORCE AND THE ANISOTROPY CONSTANT IN MANGANESE – BISMUTH THIN FILM.
KOBAYASHI, K. TANAKA, M. NISHIMURA, Y.
JAP. J. APPL. PHYS.
12 (9), 1471–3, 1973.

55866 HETEROEPITAXIAL GROWTH OF LOWER BORON PHOSPHIDE ON SILICON SUBSTRATE USING PHOSPHINE–DIBORANE–HYDROGEN SYSTEM.
TAKIGAWA, M. HIROYAMA, M. SHOHNO, K.
JAP. J. APPL. PHYS.
12 (10), 1504–9, 1973.

55871 EXCITATION MECHANISM OF ELECTROLUMINESCENT ERBIUM TRIPOSITIVE ION–DOPED ZINC SULFIDE THIN FILMS.
KOBAYASHI, H. TANAKA, S. SASAKURA, H.
JAP. J. APPL. PHYS.
12 (10), 1637–8, 1973.

55872 OPTICAL ENERGY GAP OF THE MIXED CRYSTAL CADMIUM SULFIDE TELLURIDE.
OHATA, K. SARAIE, J. TANAKA, T.
JAP. J. APPL. PHYS.
12 (10), 1641–2, 1973.

55873 IMPROVED POWDER–PATTERN TECHNIQUE FOR DELINEATING FERROELECTRIC DOMAINS.
HATANO, J. SUDA, F. FUTAMA, H.
JAP. J. APPL. PHYS.
12 (10), 1644–5, 1973.

55874 OPTICAL ABSORPTION IN CADMIUM INDIUM SULFIDE.
NAKANISHI, H. ENDO, S. IRIE, T.
JAP. J. APPL. PHYS.
12 (10), 1646–7, 1973.

55876 SEMICONDUCTING AND DIELECTRIC PROPERTIES OF C–AXIS ORIENTED ANTIMONY SULFIDE IODIDE THIN FILM.
YOSHIDA, M. YAMANAKA, K. HAMAKAWA, Y.
JAP. J. APPL. PHYS.
12 (11), 1699–705, 1973.

55877 EFFECTS OF DENSIFICATION ON ELECTRICAL AND OPTICAL PROPERTIES OF CHALCOGENIDE GLASSES.
ARAI, K. HATTORI, Y. NAMIKAWA, H.
SAITO, S.
JAP. J. APPL. PHYS.
12 (11), 1717–22, 1973.

55879 SULFUR–MODIFIED CHROMIUM DIOXIDE.
KAWAMATA, T. HIROTA, E. MIHARA, T.
TERADA, Y.
JAP. J. APPL. PHYS.
12 (11), 1737–41, 1973.

55881 ELECTRON INJECTION MECHANISM IN ELECTROLUMINESCENT TERBIUM TRIPOSITIVE ION–DOPED ZINC SULFIDE FILMS.
KOBAYASHI, H. TANAKA, S. SASAKURA, H.
HAMAKAWA, Y.
JAP. J. APPL. PHYS.
12 (12), 1854–61, 1973.

55887 OBSERVATION OF B–H HYSTERESIS LOOP OF YTTERBIUMORTHOFERRITE BY FARADAY ROTATION.
HASEGAWA, M. DAIDO, K. SAITO, M.
JAP. J. APPL. PHYS.
12 (12), 1904–6, 1973.

55888 PROPERTIES AND MEMORY APPLICATIONS OF CYLINDRICAL DOMAINS IN MANGANESE – BISMUTH FILMS.
ONO, Y. NAGAO, M.
JAP. J. APPL. PHYS.
12 (12), 1907–13, 1973.

55889 DIELECTRIC CONSTANT OF ALPHA–MERCURIC SULFIDE IN MICROWAVE REGION.
OHMIYA, T.
JAP. J. APPL. PHYS.
12 (12), 1958.

55890 EFFECT OF HYDROSTATIC PRESSURE ON THE CURIE TEMPERATURE OF FERROELECTRIC RUBIDIUM TRIHYDROGEN SELENITE.
GESI, K. OZAWA, K. MAKITA, Y.
JAP. J. APPL. PHYS.
12 (12), 1963–4, 1973.

55891 THEORY OF DIELECTRIC LOSSES IN IONIC CRYSTALS.
TANKONOGOV, M. P. MIRONOV, V. A.
IZV. VYSSH. UCHEB. ZAVED., FIZ.
15 (8), 7–14, 1972.

55893 BAND STRUCTURE OF III – V – II – VI SOLID SOLUTIONS. II. SELF–ABSORPTION EDGE IN STRONGLY DOPED N–INDIUM ARSENIDE AND IN INDIUM ARSENIDE–CADMIUM TELLURIDE SOLID SOLUTIONS.
SEMIKOLENOVA, N. A. KHABAROV, E. N.
IZV. VYSSH. UCHEB. ZAVED., FIZ.
16 (6), 82–8, 1973.

55897 TEMPERATURE DEPENDENCE OF THE ANISOTROPY OF SINGLE–CRYSTAL FILMS OF LITHIUM FERRITE.
GAVRILIN, V. P. MUTLIN, V. M.
KOSHKIN, L. I. BRATASHEVSKII, YU. A.
PAFOMOV, N. N.
IZV. VYSSH. UCHEB. ZAVED., FIZ.
16 (8), 113–16, 1973.

55899 ELECTRIC CONDUCTIVITY OF ZINC OXIDE IN ATOMIC NITROGEN.
SOKOLOV, V. A. URUSOV, B. G. MARKIN, YU. A.
RABADANOV, R. A.
IZV. VYSSH. UCHEB. ZAVED., FIZ.
16 (8), 134–6, 1973.

55905 ENERGY BAND STRUCTURE OF SILICA.
BREEZE, A. PERKINS, P. G.
J. CHEM. SOC., FARADAY TRANS. 2
69 (PT. 8), 1237–42, 1973.

55913 VARIATION OF THERMOELECTRONIC EXTRACTION FUNCTION OF POWDERED SEMICONDUCTORS UNDER ELECTROMAGNETIC IRRADIATION. I. CONSTRUCTION OF AN EXPERIMENTAL DEVICE.
BOURASSEAU, S. MARTIN, J. R. JUILLET, F.
TEICHNER, S. J.
J. CHIM. PHYS. PHYSICOCHIM. BIOL.
70 (10), 1467–71, 1973.

55914 VARIATION OF THE THERMOELECTRONIC EXTRACTION FUNCTION OF POWDERED SEMICONDUCTORS UNDER ELECTROMAGNETIC RADIATION. II. PHOTODESORPTION OF OXYGEN FROM TITANIUM DIOXIDE (ANATASE).
BOURASSEAU, S. MARTIN, J. R. JUILLET, F.
TEICHNER, S. J.
J. CHIM. PHYS. PHYSIOCHIM. BIOL.
70 (10), 1472–7, 1973.

55915 ELECTRONIC PROPERTIES OF BISMUTH SELENIDE PELLETS. EXISTENCE REGION.
DUMON, A. LICHANOT, A. GROMB, S.
J. CHIM. PHYS. PHYSICOCHIM. BIOL.
70 (10), 1546–54, 1973.

55917 GROWTH AND SOME PHYSICAL PROPERTIES OF SEMICONDUCTING COPPER LEAD ANTIMONIDE SULFIDE CRYSTALS.
FRUMAR, M. KALA, T. HORAK, J.
J. CRYST. GROWTH
20 (3), 239–44, 1973.

55921 EFFECT OF LEAD AND TELLURIUM SATURATION ON CARRIER CONCENTRATIONS IN IMPURITY–DOPED LEAD(II) TELLURIDE.
STRAUSS, A. J.
J. ELECTRON. MATER.
2 (4), 553–69, 1973.

55935 ARMCO IRON. NEW CONCEPT AND BROAD–DATA BASE JUSTIFY ITS USE AS A THERMAL CONDUCTIVITY REFERENCE MATERIAL.
LUCKS, C. F.
J. TEST. EVAL.
1 (5), 422–31, 1973.

55943 LOW TEMPERATURE PROPERTIES OF THE METALLIC ANTIFERROMAGNET ERBIUM–ZINC.
STEWART, A. M. DUNLOP, J. B. ANDREONE, D.
COSTA, G.
J. PHYS. CHEM. SOLIDS
34 (11), 1939–48, 1973.

EPIC Number	Bibliographic Citation
55944	**OBSERVATION OF A DONOR-ACCEPTOR PAIR RECOMBINATION IN THE EDGE EMISSION OF A ZINC SELENIDE CRYSTAL BY ELECTROLUMINESCENCE.** IKEDA, K. UCHIDA, K. HAMAKAWA, Y. J. PHYS. CHEM. SOLIDS 34 (11), 1985-91, 1973.
55945	**STRUCTURAL AND MAGNETIC PROPERTIES OF THE YTTRIUM - THORIUM - IRON AND LUTETIUM - THORIUM - IRON SYSTEMS.** KUNESH, C. J. NARASIMHAN, K. S. V. L. BUTERA, R. A. J. PHYS. CHEM. SOLIDS 34 (11), 2003-9, 1973.
55956	**A.C. ELECTROLUMINESCENCE OF SILVER ACTIVATED CALCIUM SULFIDE PHOSPHORS.** LAWANGAR, R. D. NARLIKAR, A. V. J. SHIVAJI UNIV. 5 (10), 1-4, 1972.
55961	**ELECTRICAL TRANSPORT PROPERTIES AND PREPARATION OF THE METAL-AMMONIA COMPOUND LITHIUM TETRAAMMINE.** ROSENTHAL, M. D. MAXFIELD, B. W. J. SOLID STATE CHEM. 7 (2), 109-23, 1973.
55962	**LUMINESCENCE OF CHROMIUM TRIPOSITIVE IONS IN ORDERED AND DISORDERED LITHIUM ALUMINUM OXIDE.** POTT, G. T. MCNICOL, B. D. J. SOLID STATE CHEM. 7 (2), 132-7, 1973.
55963	**TRANSITION METAL IODATES. II. CRYSTALLOGRAPHIC, MAGNETIC, AND NONLINEAR OPTIC SURVEY OF THE 3D IODATES.** ABRAHAMS, S. C. SHERWOOD, R. C. BERSTEIN, J. L. NASSAU, K. J. SOLID STATE CHEM. 7 (2), 205-12, 1973.
55964	**ELECTRICAL PROPERTIES OF INDIUM OXIDE.** DE WIT, J. H. W. J. SOLID STATE CHEM. 8 (2), 142-9, 1973.
55965	**ELECTRICAL CONDUCTIVITY AT LOW TEMPERATURES OF THE BINARY COMPOUNDS CHROMIUM(II) AND CHROMIUM(II, III) SULFIDES, SELENIDES, OR TELLURIDES.** BABOT, D. CHEVRETON, M. J. SOLID STATE CHEM. 8 (2), 166-74, 1973.
55966	**MAGNETIC PROPERTIES AND ELECTRIC CONDUCTIVITY OF THE CHROMIUM SELENIDE TELLURIDE TERNARY COMPOUNDS.** BABOT, D. WINTENBERGER, M. LAMBERT-ANDRON, B. CHEVRETON, M. J. SOLID STATE CHEM. 8 (2), 175-81, 1973.
55967	**FACTORS RESPONSIBLE FOR HIGH IONIC CONDUCTIVITY IN SIMPLE SOLID COMPOUNDS.** ARMSTRONG, R. D. BULMER, R. S. DICKEINSON, T. J. SOLID STATE CHEM. 8 (3), 219-28, 1973.
55968	**OPTICAL PROPERTIES OF SOME ALKALI METAL TUNGSTEN BRONZES FROM 0.1 TO 38 ELECTRON VOLTS.** LYNCH, D. W. ROSEI, R. WEAVER, J. H. OLSON, C. G. J. SOLID STATE CHEM. 8 (3), 252-52, 1973.
55972	**TRANSFERENCE NUMBERS AND CATIONIC CONDUCTIVITY IN CALCIUM AND STRONTIUM OXIDES.** GAUTHIER, M. DUCLOT, M. HAMMOU, A. DEPORTES, C. J. SOLID STATE CHEM. 9 (1), 15-23, 1974.
55973	**ELECTRICAL AND MAGNETIC PROPERTIES OF LANTHANUM EUROPIUM BORIDE SOLID SOLUTIONS.** MERCURIO, J. P. ETOURNEAU, J. NASLAIN, R. HAGENMULLER, P. GOODENOUGH, J. B. J. SOLID STATE CHEM. 9 (1), 37-47, 1974.
55974	**BEHAVIOR OF VANADIUM DIOXIDE SINGLE CRYSTALS SYNTHESIZED UNDER VARIOUS OXYGEN PARTIAL PRESSURES AT 1500 K.** KIMIZUKA, N. ISHII, M. KAWADA, I. SAEKI, M. NAKAHIRA, M. J. SOLID STATE CHEM. 9 (1), 69-77, 1974.
55987	**MOBILITY OF ELECTRONS AS A PERFECTION CRITERION FOR II - VI-TYPE CRYSTALS.** GROIS, A. SH. KHAL'KOGENIDY TSINKA, KADMIYA RTUTI 147-50, 1973.
55993	**EFFECT OF ADSORPTION ON THE LUMINESCENCE OF SEMICONDUCTORS. I. RECOMBINATION LUMINESCENCE.** VOL'KENSHTEIN, F. F. PEKA, G. P. MALAKHOV, V. V. KINET. KATAL. 14 (4), 1052-7, 1973.
56005	**CURIE POINT OF A WIDE-GAP FERROELECTRIC IN RELATION TO THE NONEQUILIBRIUM CONCENTRATION OF CARRIERS.** KONSIN, P. I. KRISTOFEL, N. N. KRISTALLOGRAFIYA 17 (4), 712-15, 1972.
56006	**CRYSTALLIZATION IN THE GERMANIUM DIOXIDE - ANTIMONY TRIOXIDE - POTASSIUM FLUORIDE-WATER HYDROTHERMAL SYSTEM.** TSEITLIN, M. N. PLAKHOV, G. F. LOBACHEV, A. N. POPOLITOV, V. I. SIMONOV, M. A. BELOV, N. V. KRISTALLOGRAFIYA 18 (4), 836-9, 1973.
56008	**DISLOCATION CHARGE IN SODIUM CHLORIDE CRYSTALS WITH AN ANION IMPURITY.** TYAPUNINA, N. A. KOLOMIITSEV, A. I. KRISTALLOGRAFIYA 18 (4), 868-70, 1973. (FOR ENGLISH TRANSLATION SEE E63234)
56011	**CRYSTAL OPTICAL PROPERTIES OF ALKALINE EARTH METAVANADATES.** GLAZYRIN, M. P. IVAKIN, A. A. GUREVICH, V. A. KRISTALLOGRAFIYA 18 (5), 1088-9, 1973. (FOR ENGLISH TRANSLATION SEE E76600)
56014	**DOMAIN WALLS, ANTIPHASE BOUNDARIES, AND DISLOCATIONS IN GADOLINIUM MOLYBDATE SINGLE CRYSTALS.** MELESHINA, V. A. INDENBOM, V. L. BAGDASAROV, KH. S. POLKHOVSKAYA, T. M. KRISTALLOGRAFIYA 18 (6), 1218-26, 1973.
56015	**ELECTRON-CRYSTAL STRUCTURE AND PROPERTIES OF BARIUM FERRITE DOPED WITH RARE EARTH OXIDES.** SAMSONOV, G. V. GORBATYUK, V. A. SHCHEGOLEV, N. F. KRISTALLOKHIM. TUGOPLAVKIKH SOEDIN. 104-14, 1972.
56028	**EFFECT OF THE GROWTH RATE OF SILICON DIOXIDE FILMS ON SOME OF THEIR PROPERTIES.** VIRTMANIS, A. ZHAATA, L. KALNINA, R. FELTINS, I. FREIBERGA, L. LATV. PSR ZINAT. AKAD. VESTIS, FIZ. TEH. ZINAT. SER. (4), 8-13, 1973.
56038	**ELECTRICAL CONDUCTIVITY OF PHOSPHORUS NITRIDE AND OXYNITRIDE.** UBELE, I. MILLERS, T. LATV. PSR ZINAT. AKAD. VESTIS, KIM. SER. (5), 540-2, 1973.
56044	**SEMIEMPIRICAL CALCULATION OF ELECTRON BAND STRUCTURE IN CUBIC BORON NITRIDE.** SHIFROVICH, E. I. BALEVICIUS, L. BATARUNAS, J. LIET. FIZ. RINKINYS 13 (2), 221-5, 1973.
56055	**FORMATION CONDITIONS AND PROPERTIES OF THIN CADMIUM INDIUM TELLURIDE FILMS.** PAULAVICIUS, A. JASUTIS, V. VESIENE, T. TOLUTIS, V. LIET. FIZ. RINKINYS 13 (4), 561-7, 1973.
56062	**MAGNETIC PROPERTIES OF GADOLINIUM-ACTIVATED CALCIUM SULFIDE PHOSPHORS.** THAKAR, J. RANADE, J. D. MADHYA BHARATI, PART 2 18 A (18), 127-30, 1970.
56067	**DOMAIN STRUCTURE AND REMAGNETIZATION PROCESSES IN SINGLE-CRYSTAL PARTICLES OF SAMARIUM - COBALT ALLOY.** LAGUTIN, A. E. UL'YANOV, A. I. GRECHISHKIN, R. M. MAGN., MAGNITOMEKH. ELEK. SVOISTVA FERROMAGN. 110-19, 1972.
56073	**LUMINESCENCE OF LITHIUM ZINC VANADATE.** BUYSERD, J. BLASSE, G. J. INORG. NUCL. CHEM. 35 (10), 3631-2, 1973.
56074	**ENERGY BANDS IN RUTILE STRUCTURE WITH AN APPLICATION TO VANADIUM DIOXIDE.** ZHANG, H. L. ZHANG, H. J. M. J. KOREAN PHYS. SOC. 5 (2), 57-62, 1972.

EPIC Number	Bibliographic Citation
56077	**SUPERCONDUCTIVITY OF LANTHANUM-OSMIUM.** LAWSON, A. C. CANNON, J. F. ROBERTSON, D. L. HALL, H. T. J. LESS-COMMON METALS 32 (1), 173-4, 1973. (AD-779 189)
56084	**ELECTRIC PROPERTIES OF METAL HALIDES CONTAINING METAL-METAL BONDS.** KEPERT, D. L. MARSHALL, R. E. J. LESS-COMMON METALS 34 (1), 153-63, 1974.
56099	**ELECTRIC CONDUCTIVITY OF URANIUM DIOXIDE - THORIUM DIOXIDE SOLID SOLUTIONS.** LEE, H. M. J. NUCL. MATER. 48 (2), 107-17, 1973.
56101	**PHOTOELASTIC CONSTANTS OF AMMONIUM DIHYDROGEN PHOSPHATE.** NARASIMHAMURTY, T. S. RAO, K. V. PETTERSEN, H. E. J. MATER. SCI. 8 (4), 577-80, 1973.
56106	**FLUX GROWTH OF TITANOMAGNETITE FROM BARIUM OXIDE-BORON OXIDE FLUX IN AN IRON CRUCIBLE.** HAUPTMAN, Z. WANKLYN, B. M. SMITH, S. H. J. MATER. SCI. 8 (12), 1695-8, 1973.
56110	**LASER-EXCITED FLUORESCENCE SPECTRUM OF NITROGEN DIOXIDE.** ABE, K. J. MOL. SPECTROSC. 48 (2), 395-408, 1973.
56120	**PRESSURE EFFECTS ON ELECTRIC CONDUCTION IN GLASSES.** ARAI, K. KUMATA, K. KADOTA, K. YAMAMOTO, K. NAMIKAWA, H. SAITO, S. J. NON-CRYST. SOLIDS 13 (1), 131-9, 1973.
56122	**OPTICAL ABSORPTION IN VITREOUS ANTIMONY GERMANIUM SELENIDE.** FRUMAR, M. TICHA, H. KLIKORKA, J. TOMISKA, P. J. NON-CRYST. SOLIDS 13 (1), 173-8, 1973.
56124	**AMPLIFIED LASER ABSORPTION - DETECTION OF NITRIC OXIDE.** CHACKERIAN, C., JR. OPTICAL SOCIETY OF AMERICA, JOURNAL 63, 342-345, 1973.
56136	**REFRACTIVE INDEX MEASUREMENT BY THE MOIRE TECHNIQUE.** RANGANAYAKAMMA, B. PRASAD, C. R. J. PHYS. 6 E (12), 1186-8, 1973.
56142	**ABSORPTION SPECTRUM OF CERIUM AND THE GAMMA-ALPHA PHASE TRANSITION.** OTTEWELL, D. STEWARDSON, E. A. WILSON, J. E. J. PHYS. 6 B (10), 2184-96, 1973.
56148	**BASIC PHYSICOCHEMICAL PROPERTIES OF FLUXES FOR ELECTRO SLAG HEATING.** LOPAEV, B. E. MASH. TEKHNOL. OBRAB. METAL. DAVLENIEM LITEINOE PROIZVOD. 223-7, 1971.
56149	**A THERMAL ANNEALING PROCEDURE FOR THE REDUCTION OF 10.6 MU-M OPTICAL LOSSES IN CADMIUM TELLURIDE.** GENTILE, A. L. KIEFER, J. E. KYLE, N. R. WINSTON, H. V. MATER. RES. BULL. (USA) 8 (5), 523-32, 1973.
56152	**SINGLE CRYSTAL GROWTH AND ELECTRICAL PROPERTIES OF THALLIUM TELLURIDE.** CRUCEANU, E. SLADARU, ST. IVANCIU, O. MATER. RES. BULL. 8 (9), 1021-6, 1973.
56154	**NONLINEAR OPTICAL PROPERTIES OF INDIUM THIOPHOSPHATE.** BRIDENBAUGH, P. M. MATER. RES. BULL. 8 (9), 1055-60, 1973.
56156	**PHASE EQUILIBRIUM AND DIELCTRIC CHARACTERIZATION OF STRONTIUM NIOBATE AND SODIUM NIOBATE MIXTURES.** MORIN, D. COLIN, J. P. LE ROUX, G. PATEAU, L. TOLEDANO, J. C. MATER. RES. BULL. 8 (9), 1089-102, 1973.
56160	**PHASE DIAGRAM AND PROPERTIES OF COPPER ANTIMONY SELENIDE AND OTHER I(3)-V-VI(4) COMPOUNDS.** SCOTT, W. KENCH, J. R. MATER. RES. BULL. 8 (10), 1257-67, 1973.
56161	**ELECTRIC RESISTIVITY OF IRON TYPE RARE EARTH SILICIDES.** FELNER, I. MAYER, I. MATER. RES. BULL. 8 (11), 1317-19, 1973.
56162	**MAGNETIC PROPERTIES OF SOME RARE EARTH FERRITES.** DROFENIK, M. HANZEL, D. ZUPAN, J. MATER. RES. BULL. 8 (12), 1337-42, 1973.
56163	**THERMAL VARIATION OF THE MAGNETIC SUSCEPTIBILITY AND MAGNETIZATION OF THE DICALCIUM FERRITE.** GRENIER, J. C. POUCHARD, M. GEORGES, R. MATER. RES. BULL. 8 (12), 1413-20, 1973.
56164	**ELECTRIC AND MAGNETIC PROPERTIES OF THE TRANSITION IN NICKEL SULFIDE.** BARTHELEMY, E. GOROCHOV, O. MC KINZIE, H. MATER. RES. BULL. 8 (12), 1401-12, 1973.
56165	**SINGLE CRYSTALS IN THE BISMUTH(III) OXIDE-MOLYBDENUM(VI) OXIDE BSYSTEM. GROWTH AND OPTICAL PROPERTIES.** MIYAZAWA, S. KAWANA, A. KOIZUMI, H. IWASAKI, H. MATER. RES. BULL. 9 (1), 41-57, 1974.
56168	**IONIC CONDUCTIVITY OF RUBIDIUM CHLORIDE.** JURCZAK, P. WHITMORE, D. H. MATER. SCI. RES. 6, 49-54, 1973.
56172	**STUDY OF METALLURGICAL PROCESSES BY THERMOPOWER MEASUREMENTS. GOLD-COPPER ALLOYS.** BARNARD, R. D. CHIVERS, A. J. M. METAL SCI. J. 7, 147-52, 1973.
56205	**CONDITIONS FOR MAINTAINING LIGHT TOTALS IN THE PHOSPHOR BISMUTH-ACTIVATED CALCIUM SULFIDE.** BATURICHEVA, Z. B. SMIRNOVA, O. M. MAIDANOVA, E. A. TITAR, V. P. MONOKRIST. TEKH. (5), 44-7, 1971.
56208	**DETERMINATION OF THE NORMAL AND ANOMALOUS PHOTOELECTRIC ABSORPTION COEFFICIENTS OF POTASSIUM CHLORIDE SINGLE CRYSTALS.** CHAIKOVSKII, E. F. ZAGARII, L. B. MONOKRIST. TEKH. (7), 21-6, 1972.
56210	**ELECTROCHEMISTRY OF POLYCRYSTALLINE POTASSIUM DIHYDROGEN PHOSPHATE.** ITOU, K. ISHIHARA, K. MATSUI, N. YAMADA, T. NAGOYA KOGYO DAIGAKU GAKUHO 23, 113-7, 1971.
56213	**SPECTRAL CHARACTERISTICS OF THE PHOTOLUMINESCENCE OF GALLIUM ARSENIDE DOPED WITH GROUP IV ELEMENTS.** MIL'VIDSKII, M. G. PROSHKO, G. P. SHERSHAKOVA, I. N. NAUCH. TR., NAUCH.-ISSLED. PROEKT. INST. REDKOMETAL. PROM. (46), 56-62, 1973.
56217	**ELECTRICAL AND OPTICAL PROPERTIES AND EPR OF MANGANESE DIPOSITIVE IONS IN ZINC CADMIUM SULFIDE.** BULANYI, M. F. KODZHESPIROV, F. F. MOZHAROVSKII, L. A. SHMIGEL'SKII, S. S. NEKOT. AKTUAL. VOP. SOVREM. ESTESTVOZN. 53-7, 1971.
56218	**ELECTROLUMINESCENCE OF A SUBLIMATE PHOSPHOR.** POLEZHAEV, B. A. NEKOT. AKTUAL. VOP. SOVREM. ESTESTVOZN. 57-9, 1971.
56220	**ELECTRICAL AND OPTICAL PROPERTIES OF MANGANESE-ACTIVATED ZINC SULFIDE SINGLE CRYSTALS.** BORISENKO, N. D. KODZHESPIROV, F. F. NEKOT. AKTUAL. VOP. SOVREM. ESTESTVOZN. 63-5, 1971.
56225	**ANOMALOUS PHOTOVOLTAGE IN CADMIUM TELLURIDE FILMS IN A WIDE RANGE OF LIGHT INTENSITIES.** KORSUNSKII, M. I. SOMINSKII, M. M. NEKOT. VOP. OBSHCH. PRIKL. FIZ. 59-70, 1972.
56236	**ELECTRICAL CONDUCTIVITY AND CISCOISTY OF THE MOLTEN LEAD(II) CHLORIDE-ZINC CHLORIDE BINARY SYSTEM.** UMETSU, Y. ISHII, Y. NIPPON KINZOKU GAKKAISHI 37 (9), 997-1004, 1973.
56247	**BAND-GAP EXCITONS IN GALLIUM SELENIDE.** MOOSER, E. SCHLUETER, M. NUOVO CIMENTO SOC. ITAL. FIS. 18 B (1), 164-208, 1973.

EPIC Number	Bibliographic Citation
56259	**INTERFEROMETRIC DETERMINATION OF THE REFRACTIVE INDEX OF CARBON DIOXIDE IN THE ULTRAVIOLET REGION.** BIDEAU-MEHU, A. GUERN, Y. ABJEAN, R. JOHANNIN-GILLES, A. OPT. COMMUN. 9 (4), 432-4, 1973.
56262	**MANUFACTURING METHODS, STRUCTURE AND PHYSICO-CHEMICAL PROPERTIES OF OPTICAL CERAMICS.** VOLYNETS, F. K. OPT.-MEKH. PROM. 40 (9), 48-61, 1973. (FOR ENGLISH TRANSLATION SEE E76721)
56265	**TITANIUM NITRIDE THIN FILMS PRODUCED BY D.C. SPUTTERING.** NAKAMURA, T. GOTO, T. YAMANAKA, S. OYO BUTSURI 42 (5), 491-7, 1973.
56266	**OPTICAL PROPERTIES OF EVAPORATED ALPHA-TELLURIUM DIOXIDE FILMS.** KOBAYASHI, S. SAITO, N. OYO BUTSURI 42 (10), 968-74, 1973.
56280	**MAGNETIC CHARACTERISTICS OF LANTHANIDE - COPPER COMPOUNDS WITH THE CERIUM - COPPER STRUCTURE.** COLDEA, M. POP, I. PHIL. MAG. 28 (4), 881-90, 1973.
56284	**SOLID STATE PHYSICS. ACCOMPLISHMENTS AND FUTURE PROSPECTS.** BARDEEN, J. PHYS. 50 (FIFTY) YEARS LATER, GEN. ASSEM. INT. UNION PURE APPL. PHYS., 14TH 165-90, 1973. (EDITED BY SANBORN CONNER BROWN, NASA: WASHINGTON, D.C.)
56286	**ITINERANT THEORY OF MAGNETISM.** BRINKMAN, W. F. PHYS. FEEN. 8 (2-3), 253-75, 1973.
56287	**OPTICS AND MAGNETOOPTICS OF THIN METALLIC FILMS.** CAREY, R. THOMAS, B. W. J. WARD, L. PHYS. BULL. 24 (7), 423-5, 1973.
56300	**STRUCTURE AND SOME ELECTROPHYSICAL PROPERTIES OF ANTIMONY THALLIUM SULFIDE FILMS.** ZOZULYA, L. P. VOINOVA, L. G. BAZAKUTSA, V. A. IZV. VYSSH. UCHEB. ZAVED., FIZ. 16 (9), 37-40, 1973.
56302	**FERROMAGNETIC RESONANCE AND MAGNETIC CRYSTALLOGRAPHIC ANISOTROPY OF LITHIUM FERRITE SINGLE CRYSTAL FILMS.** GAVRILIN, V. P. BEREZIN, D. G. MIROSHNIKOV, YU. F. IZV. VYSSH. UCHEB. ZAVED., FIZ. 16 (9), 86-9, 1973.
56306	**IONIC CONDUCTIVITY OF ALKALI HALIDE CRYSTAL WHISKERS.** DERYABIN, P. E. MELIK-GAIKAZYAN, I. YA. ZAKHAROV, V. F. IZV. VYSSH. UCHEB. ZAVED., FIZ. 16 (9), 126-8, 1973.
56315	**LOCAL LEVELS IN ZINC SULFIDE FILM.** ATAKOVA, M. M. RAMAZANOV, P. E. SAL'MAN, E. G. IZV. VYSSH. UCHEB. ZAVED., FIZ. 16 (10), 95-8, 1973.
56317	**ELECTROPHYSICAL PARAMETERS OF TERNARY COMPOUNDS OF GERMANIUM, SULFUR, AND RARE EARTH ELEMENTS.** STEPANETS, M. P. SEREBRENNIKOV, V. V. AGAFONNIKOV, V. F. GORDIEVSKIKH, A. I. IZV. VYSSH. UCHEB. ZAVED., FIZ. 16 (10), 137-9, 1973.
56318	**X-RAY LUMINESCENCE AND THERMOLUMINESCENCE OF FLUORITE CRYSTALS ACTIVATED BY IRON GROUP IONS.** KAZAKOV, B. N. STOLOV, A. L. YAKOVLEVA, ZH. S. IZV. VYSSH. UCHEB. ZAVED., FIZ. 16 (10), 139-41, 1973.
56321	**LUMINESCENCE PROPERTIES OF ADDITIVELY COLORED SILVER-ACTIVATED POTASSIUM BROMIDE CRYSTALS.** GOLUB, S. I. SIVAK, V. D. IZV. VYSSH. UCHEB. ZAVED., FIZ. 16 (11), 81-5, 1973.
56322	**ELECTRICAL CONDUCTIVITY OF PRELIMINARILY IRRADIATED AND THERMALLY DECOLORIZED CALCIUM FLUORIDE CRYSTALS.** LISITSYN, V. M. MORGUNOV, V. L. FEDOROV, V. A. IZV. VYSSH. UCHEB. ZAVED., FIZ. 16 (11), 115-18, 1973.
56325	**MAGNETIC ANISOTROPY OF MAGNESIUM MANGANESE FERRITE FILMS.** DUNAEVA-MITLINA, T. A. GAVRILIN, V. P. GERASIMENKO, N. V. IZV. VYSSH. UCHEB. ZAVED., FIZ. 16 (11), 151-3, 1973.
56328	**HALL MOBILITY IN COMPENSATED GALLIUM ARSENIDE.** KRIVOV, M. A. MALYANOV, S. V. MELEV, V. G. IZV. VYSSH. UCHEB. ZAVED., FIZ. 16 (12), 135-7, 1973.
56329	**HALL EFFECT AND ELECTRIC PROPERTIES OF FILMS PREPARED FROM DYSPROSIUM-COBALT.** BOCHKAREV, V. F. BURAVIKHIN, V. A. SUKHOMLIN, V. T. EGOROV, V. A. IZV. VYSSH. UCHEB. ZAVED., FIZ. 16 (12), 145-8, 1973.
56330	**INVESTIGATION OF THE PHONON DRAG EFFECT IN GALLIUM ARSENIDE.** KRIGER, E. D. KRAVCHENKO, A. F. MOROZOV, B. V. POLOVINKIN, V. G. SKOK, E. M. PHYS. STATUS SOLIDI, (APPL. RES.) 13 A 389-398, 1972.
56333	**PHOTOELECTRIC PROPERTIES OF GALLIUM SELENIUM.** ADDUCI, F. FERRARA, M. TANTALO, P. CINGOLANI, A. MINAFRA, A. PHYSICA STATUS SOLIDI - APPLIED RESEARCH 15 A 303-310, 1973.
56334	**DIELECTRIC LOSS MEASUREMENTS ON HYDROXYL ION DIPOLES IN POTASSIUM BROMIDE WITH CALORIC TECHNIQUES.** REYMANN, G. A. LUTY, F. PHYS. STATUS SOLIDI 16 A (2), 561-8, 1973. (AD 781 560)
56335	**ELECTRICAL PROPERTIES OF GERMANIUM ZINC PHOSPHIDE AT RELATIVELY LOW TEMPERATURES.** SOMOGYI, K. PHYS. STATUS SOLIDI 18 A (2), K95-K97, 1973.
56341	**FAST THERMAL DETECTORS MADE FROM CADMIUM ARSENIDE FILMS.** GOLDSMID, H. J. ERTL, M. E. PHYS. STATUS SOLIDI 19 A (1), K19-K21, 1973.
56342	**SWITCHING IN FERROMAGNETIC SEMICONDUCTORS CAUSED BY MAGNETIC MECHANISM.** HAUSMANN, K. MUELLER, K. H. WOLF, M. PHYS. STATUS SOLIDI 19 A (1), K27-K29, 1973.
56343	**EFFECT OF PRESSURE ON THE FERRIMAGNETIC CURIE TEMPERATURE OF IRON SELENIDE CONTAINING VACANCIES.** OZAWA, K. YOSHIMI, T. ANZAI, S. YANAGISAWA, S. PHYS. STATUS SOLIDI 19 A (1), K39-K41, 1973.
56344	**DIELECTRIC AND PIEZOELECTRIC PROPERTIES OF AMMONIUM FLUOROBERYLLATE.** SORGE, G. SCHMIDT, G. FREIDANK, W. KLAPPERSTUECK, U. PHYS. STATUS SOLIDI 19 A (1), K43-K46, 1973.
56345	**DENSITY-OF-STATES EFFECTIVE ELECTRON MASS IN CADMIUM PHOSPHIDE.** RADAUSTAN, S. I. ARUSHANOV, E. K. NATEPROV, A. N. MARUSHYAK, L. S. PHYS. STATUS SOLIDI 19 A (1), K71-K73, 1973.
56346	**HIGH FIELD RESISTIVITY OF LEAD SULFIDE AT 77 K.** FINLAYSON, D. M. YAU, K. L. PHYS. STATUS SOLIDI 19 A (1), K79-K83, 1973.
56347	**MAGNETIC STRUCTURE OF URANIUM PHOSPHIDE.** MURASIK, A. LIGENZA, S. LECIEJEWICZ, J. TROC, R. PHYS. STATUS SOLIDI 19 A (1), K89-K91, 1973.
56351	**FRANZ-KELDYSH EFFECT IN EMISSION OF ELECTROLUMINESCENT COPPER- AND CHLORINE-DOPED ZINC SULFIDE FILMS.** VLASENKO, N. A. KHOMCHENKO, V. S. PHYS. STATUS SOLIDI 19 A (2), K137-K141, 1973.
56352	**MAGNETIC PROPERTIES OF PRASEODYMIUM-INDIUM.** STALINSKI, B. CZOPNIK, A. ILIEW, N. MYDLARZ, T. PHYS. STATUS SOLIDI 19 A (2), K161-K164, 1973.

EPIC Number	Bibliographic Citation

56353 ELECTRICAL RESISTIVITY OF RARE EARTH–TIN SINGLE CRYSTALS (RE = LANTHANUM, CERIUM, PRASEODYMIUM, AND NEODYMIUM).
STALINSKI, B. KLETOWSKI, Z. HENKIE, Z.
PHYS. STATUS SOLIDI
19 A (2), K165–K168, 1973.

56354 INFLUENCE OF CHEMISORPTION OF OXYGEN ON THE LUMINESCENCE OF CADMIUM SULFIDE SINGLE CRYSTALS.
HEINE, G. WANDEL, K.
PHYS. STATUS SOLIDI
19 A (2), 415–21, 1973.

56356 ELECTRICAL RESISTANCE OF THE PALLADIUM–SILVER–HYDROGEN ALLOYS FROM 4 TO 300 K.
SZAFRANSKI, A. W.
PHYS. STATUS SOLIDI
19 A (2), 459–66, 1973.

56362 CORRELATION BETWEEN ABSORPTION BANDS AND IMPLANTED ALKALI IONS IN LITHIUM FLUORIDE.
DAVENAS, J. PEREZ, A.
THEVENARD, P. DUPUY, C. H. S.
PHYS. STATUS SOLIDI
19 A (2), 679–86, 1973.

56364 INFLUENCE OF PRESSURE ON THE ELECTRICAL PROPERTIES OF CADMIUM ZINC ARSENIDE SOLID SOLUTIONS.
CISOWSKI, J. ZDANOWICZ, W.
PHYS. STATUS SOLIDI
19 A (2), 741–5, 1973.

56369 SUPPRESSION AND FIELD ENHANCEMENT OF THE MANGANESE (2+) ION LUMINESCENCE IN ZINC SULFIDE–TYPE COMPOUNDS.
ROEPPISCHER, H. KLOPFLEISCH, M.
PHYS. STATUS SOLIDI
20 A (1), K21–4, 1973.

56370 ELECTRICAL PROPERTIES OF IRON SELENIDES, AND NICKEL IRON SELENIDE SINGLE CRYSTALS.
ABDULLAEV, G. B. AKHMEDOV, N. R.
DZHALILOV, N. Z. ABDINOV, D. SH.
PHYS. STATUS SOLIDI
20 A (1), K29–31, 1973.

56372 SURFACE RECOMBINATION ON EPITAXIAL GALLIUM ARSENIDE FILMS.
DMITRUK, N. L. LYASHENKO, V. I.
TERESHCHENKO, A. K. SPEKTOR, S. A.
PHYS. STATUS SOLIDI
20 A (1), 53–62, 1973.

56374 ELECTRIC RESISTIVITY OF SINGLE CRYSTAL IN THE VICINITY OF THE CURIE TEMPERATURE IN AN EXTERNAL MAGNETIC FIELD.
HENKIE, Z. KLAMUT, J.
PHYS. STATUS SOLIDI
20 A (1), K69–72, 1973.

56375 HIGH–RESOLUTION STUDIES OF THE ENERGY DISTRIBUTION OF THERMALLY STIMULATED EXOELECTRONS FROM LITHIUM FLUORIDE.
SAMUELSSON, L. I. HAGSTROM, S. B. M.
CARLSSON, C. A.
PHYS. STATUS SOLIDI
20 A (1), K79–81, 1973.

56390 MAGNETIC ORDERING IN URANIUM COMPOUNDS WITH GOLD – COPPER–TYPE LATTICE.
MURASIK, A. LECIEJEWICZ, J.
LIGENZA, S. MISIUK, A.
PHYS. STATUS SOLIDI
20 A (1), 395–401, 1973.

56391 LUMINESCENCE OF LITHIUM NIOBATE.
BLASSE, G.
PHYS. STATUS SOLIDI
20 A (2), K99–102, 1973.

56392 DETERMINATION OF THE IMPURITY PARAMETERS IN GALLIUM PHOSPHIDE FROM HALL DATA.
SOMOGYI, K.
PHYS. STATUS SOLIDI
20 A (2), K127–30, 1973.

56393 LOW TEMPERATURE TRANSITION OF MAGNETITE IN A MAGNETIC FIELD AND ITS INFLUENCE ON THE MAGNETORESISTANCE.
KOSTOPOULOS, D.
PHYS. STATUS SOLDI
20 A (2), K139–42, 1973.

56394 ELECTRON SCATTERING IN CADMIUM SULFIDE CRYSTALS.
PODOR, B.
PHYS. STATUS SOLIDI
20 A (2), K143–46, 1973.

56395 DECAY KINETICS OF PHOTOLUMINESCENCE IN VITREOUS AND CRYSTALLINE ARSENIC SELENIDE AND ARSENIC SULFIDE.
IVASHCHENKO, YU. N. KOLOMIETS, B. T.
MAMONTOVA, T. N. SMORGONSKAYA, E. A.
STATUS SOLIDI
20 A (2), 429–34, 1973.

56398 PHOTOELECTRONIC PROPERTIES OF PHOTOCONDUCTING CADMIUM SELENIDE.
MANFREDOTTI, C. MURRI, R. PEPE, E.
SEMISA, D.
PHYS. STATUS SOLIDI
20 A (2), 477–86, 1973.

56399 VARIATION OF LUMINESCENCE INTENSITIES OF RARE EARTH–DOPED LANTHANUM OXIDE POWDERS PREPARED AT VARIOUS TEMPERATURES.
RATINEN, H.
PHYS. STATUS SOLIDI
20 A (2), 521–6, 1973.

56407 CALCULATED BAND STRUCTURE AND REFLECTIVITY SPECTRA OF GERMANIUM ZINC PHOSPHIDE.
VAREA DE ALVAREZ, C. COHEN, M. L.
PHYS. REV. LETT.
30 (20), 979–82, 1973.

56408 BAND STRUCTURE OF GERMANIUM ZINC PHOSPHIDE AND SILICON ZINC PHOSPHIDE TERNARY COMPOUNDS WITH PSEUDODIRECT ENERGY GAPS.
SHAY, J. L. TELL, B. BUEHLER, E.
WERNICK, J. H.
PHYS. REV. LETT.
30 (20), 983–6, 1973.

56417 ANGULAR DEPENDENCE OF PHOTOEMISSION FROM THE (110) FACE OF GALLIUM ARSENIDE.
SMITH, N. V. TRAUM, M. M.
PHYS. REV. LETT.
31 (20), 1247–50, 1973.

56428 MAGNETIC SUSCEPTIBILITIES OF NICKEL CHLORIDE HEXAHYDRATE.
HAMBURGER, A. I. FRIEDBERG, S. A.
PHYSICA (UTRECHT)
69 (1), 67–75, 1973.

56440 HIGH–FIELD MAGNETORESISTANCE OF THE EXCHANGE ENHANCED PARAMAGNETIC AND WEAKLY FERROMAGNETIC COMPOUNDS OF THE NICKEL – ALUMINUM AND NICKEL – GALLIUM SERIES.
CHANG, K. H. VAN DER LINDE, R. H.
SIEVERTS, E. G.
PHYSICA (UTRECHT)
69 (2), 467–84, 1973.

56441 PHASE TRANSITIONS IN AN ANTIFERROMAGNET WITH A HIDDEN CANTING.
METSELAAR, J. W. DE KLERK, D.
PHYSICA (UTRECHT)
69 (2), 499–534, 1973.

56460 EQUIPMENT FOR NONDESTRUCTIVE MEASUREMENTS OF THE RESISTIVITY OF SEMICONDUCTOR EPITAXIAL LAYERS BY THE THREE–POINT PROBE TECHNIQUE.
ROSINSKI, A. SIENNICKI, A. WISNIEWSKI, R.
POMIARY, AUTOMAT. KONT.
18, 246,247, 1972.

56462 EFFECTS OF PORE STURCTURE ON THE ELECTRICAL AND MECHANICAL PROPERTIES OF PIEZOELECTRIC CERAMICS.
OKAZAKI, K. NAGATA, K. HASEGAWA, A.
PORE STRUCT. PROP. MATER., PROC. INT. SYMP.
RILEM/IUPAC
PART 2, E165–82, 1973.

56463 PORE STURCTURE AND MAGNETIC PROPERTIES OF FERRITES.
IGARASHI, H. OKAZAKI, K.
PORE STRUCT. PROP. MATER., PROC. INT. SYMP.
RILEM/IUPAC
PART 2, E183–98, 1973.

56469 MECHANISM OF ELECTRIC CONDUCTIVITY OF MOLYBDENUM DISELENIDE – TANTALUM DISELENIDE QUASIBINARY ALLOYS.
KALIKHMAN, V. L. KASIYAN, I. M.
MIKAILYUK, I. P.
POROSH. MET.
(11), 75–9, 1973.
(FOR ENGLISH TRANSLATION SEE E76678)

56473 ELECTRIC PROPERTIES OF NONSTOICHIOMETRIC TITANIUM CARBIDE.
NESHPOR, V. S. NIKITIN, V. P.
SKALETSKAYA, N. A.
POROSH. MET.
13 (8), 54–7, 1973.

56475 SINGLE CRYSTALS OF REFRACTORY COMPOUNDS. II /SURVEY/
ANDRIEVSKII, R. A. RYMASHEVSKII, G. A.
SINEL'NIKOVA, V. S.
POROSH. MET.
12, 30–45, 1972.

56477 PHYSICOMECHANICAL PROPERTIES OF FIBER CARBIDES.
KATS, S. M. GORIN, A. I. SEMENOV, M. V.
POROSH. METAL.
12, 87–92, 1972.

EPIC Number	Bibliographic Citation
56479	**EFFECT OF MILLED POWDER QUANTITY ON ELECTROMAGNETIC PROPERTIES OF MAGNESIUM MANGANESE ALUMINUM IRON OXIDE.** CHO, S. A. POWDER MET. INT. 5 (3), 142–6, 1973.
56496	**THIN-FILM EVAPORATION BY AN ELECTRON GUN.** HEJDUK, A. MARCHWICKI, Z. OHLY, T. SZRETER, M. PR. NAUK. INST. TECHNOL. ELEKTRON. POLITECH. WROCLAW. (10), 133–41, 1970.
56509	**KINETICS OF SCINTILLATOR LUMINESCENCE.** MEDVEDEV, M. N. KONDRATENKOV, YU. B. PRIB. TEKH. EKSP. (4), 79–81, 1973.
56514	**ELECTRIC BREAKDOWN OF NITROUS OXIDE.** DUTTON, J. HARRIS, F. M. HUGHES, D. B. PROC. INST. ELEC. ENG. 120 (8), 941–4, 1973.
56520	**LASER INDUCED FLUORESCENCE IN HOLMIUM TRIPOSITIVE ION DOPED LANTHANUM FLUORIDE SINGLE CRYSTAL.** BANSILAL RAO, D. R. PROC. NUCL. PHYS. SOLID STATE PHYS. SYMP., 17TH C, 151–4, 1973.
56523	**SHALLOW ELECTRON TRAPS IN REDUCED STRONTIUM TITANATE SINGLE CRYSTALS.** LAL, H. B. PROC. NUCL. PHYS. SOLID STATE PHYS. SYMP., 17TH C, 91–6, 1973.
56525	**ELECTRICAL CONDUCTION IN AMORPHOUS GALLIUM ARSENIDE FILMS.** NARASIMHAN, K. L. GUHA, S. PROC. NUCL. PHYS. SOLID STATE PHYS. SYMP., 17TH C, 105–9, 1973.
56526	**EUROPIUM TUNGSTATE SINGLE CRYSTALS.** LAL, H. B. KUMAR, A. PROC. NUCL. PHYS. SOLID STATE PHYS. SYMP., 17TH C, 85–9, 1972.
56527	**SYNTHETIC CRYSTALS OF ARSENIC TRISULFIDE. ELECTRICAL CONDUCTIVITY AND ITS TEMPERATURE DEPENDENCE.** GHOSH, B. KOTHIYAL, G. P. PROC. NUCL. PHYS. SOLID STATE PHYS. SYMP., 17TH C, 79–84, 1973.
56528	**DISPERSION OF RESISTIVTY AND DIELECTRIC CONSTANTS IN SEMICONDUCTING BARIUM TITANATE.** BRAHMECHA, B. G. SINHA, K. P. PROC. NUCL. PHYS. SOLID STATE PHYS. SYMP., 17TH C, 61–6, 1973.
56533	**OBSERVATION OF FERRIMAGNETIC DOMAIN WALLS IN COBALT FERRITES WITH A HIGH VOLTAGE TRANSMISSION ELECTRON MICROSCOPY.** DE JONGHE, L. C. PROC., ELECTRON MISCROSC. SOC. AMER. 31, 26–7, 1973.
56537	**ION IMPLANTATION OF TELLURIUM AND ANTIMONY IN GALLIUM ARSENIDE.** GAMO, K. TAKAI, M. MASUDA, K. NAMBA, S. PROC. CONF. SOLID STATE DEVICES, 4TH 130–5, 1973.
56541	**GREEN-LIGHT-EMITTING DIODES OF GALLIUM PHSPHIDE DOPED WITH OXYGEN AND INDIUM.** TANAKA, A. KOBAYASHI, H. ITOH, H. HARA, K. SUKEGAWA, T. PROC. CONF. SOLID STATE DEVICES, 4TH 264–8, 1973.
56542	**CADMIUM SULFIDE ELECTROLUMINESCENT DIODES PRODUCED BY NITROGEN ION-IMPLANTATION.** SHIRAKI, Y. SHIMADA, T. IKEZU, T. KOMATSUBARA, K. F. PROC. CONF. SOLID STATE DEVICES, 4TH 269–75, 1973.
56544	**PHOTOELECTRON SPECTRUM OF SULFUR TRIOXIDE. JAHN-TELLER DISTROTION IN (SULFUR TRIOXIDE)(+) ION.** MINES, G. W. THOMAS, R. K. PROC. ROY. SOC. LONDON 336 A (1606), 355–64, 1974.
56545	**ATOMIC DISPLACEMENT EFFECTS ON THE CATHODOLUMINESCENCE OF ZINC SELENIDE IMPLANTED WITH YTTERBIUM IONS.** BRYANT, F. J. GOODWIN, G. K. HAGSTON, W. E. PROC. ROY. SOC. LONDON 337 A (1608), 21–47, 1974.
56566	**NEGATIVE RESISTANCE IN CADMIUM SELENIDE POWDER. RELATIVE ABSORPTION COEFFICIENT.** NICASTRO, L. J. OFFENBACHER, E. L. RCA REV. 34 (3), 442–56, 1973.
56572	**ELECTRON IRRADIATION OF COPPER-GOLD.** GILBERT, J. HERMAN, H. DAMASK, A. C. RADIAT. EFF. 20 (1–2), 37–42, 1973.
56574	**LOW-TIME-LAG ENERGY TRANSFER IN ALKALI METAL HALIDE CRYSTALS AND EFFECT OF AN EXTERNAL ELECTRIC FIELD.** NAGLI, L. E. PLYAVINYA, I. K. SHEKHTMAN, V. A. RADIATS. FIZ. 7, 61–114, 1973.
56575	**INFLUENCE OF IMPURITIES ON THE INITIAL RATE OF RADIATION FORMATION OF F-CENTERS IN POTASSIUM IODIDE CRYSTALS.** PARFIANVICH, I. A. SHURALEVA, E. I. LOBANOV, B. D. SMOL'SKAYA, L. P. PENZINA, E. E. MAKAROVA, L. A. RADIATS. FIZ. NEMETAL. KRIST. 3 (PT. 3), 32–8, 1971.
56576	**LOW-TIME-LAG MIGRATION OF STABLE ELECTRON EXCITATIONS IN THALLIUM-ACTIVATED POTASSIUM IODIDE.** POLOGRUDOV, V. V. MARTYNOVICH, E. F. PARFIANOVICH, I. A. RADIATS. FIZ. NEMETAL. KRIST. 3 (PT. 3), 59–65, 1971.
56580	**HALL MOBILITY OF ELECTRONS IN THE SPACE-CHARGE REGION OF CADMIUM SELENIDE FILMS.** KALININ, A. N. KARPOVICH, I. A. BEDNYI, B. I. RADIOTEKH. ELEKTRON. 18 (10), 2208–9, 1973.
56581	**PHOTOELECTRON EMISSION FROM GALLIUM INDIUM ARSENIDE ACTIVATED BY CESIUM AND OXYGEN.** MUSATOV, A. L. BYKOV, V. A. KOROTKIKH, V. L. RADIOTEKH. ELEKTRON. 18 (10), 2210–12, 1973.
56584	**TRANSITION PROCESSES IN GALLIUM PHOSPHIDE LIGHT DIODES.** TARASOV, V. M. AFINOGENOV, YU. A. RADIOTEKH. ELEKTRON. 18 (11), 2448–51, 1973.
56585	**FORMATION, STOICHIOMETRY, AND PROPERTIES OF I-III-VI(2) SEMICONDUCTING CRYSTALS.** KASPER, H. M. REACTIV. SOLIDS, PROC. INT. SYMP., 7TH 46–55PP., 1972.
56587	**RECENT WORK ON IONIC TRANSPORT IN SOLIDS WITH TUNNEL AND LAYER STRUCTURES.** WHITTINGHAM, M. S. HUGGINS, R. A. REACTIV. SOLIDS, PROC. INT. SYMP., 7TH 125–39, 1972.
56588	**CHARACTERIZATION AND PHASE TRANSFORMATION OF AMORPHOUS FERRIC HYDROXIDE.** OKAMOTO, S. SEKIZAMA, H. OKAMOTO, S. I. REACTIV. SOLIDS, PROC. INT. SYMP., 7TH 341–53, 1972.
56591	**ELECTRICAL PROPERTIES OF VACUUM-DEPOSITED ZINC TELLURIDE FILMS.** WATANABE, H. REP. RES. INST. ELEC. COMMUN., TOHOKU UNIV. 24 (3–4), 89–95, 1973.
56592	**GAS PHASE TRANSPORT OF THE YTTRIUM IRON GARNET BY HYDROGEN CHLORIDE.** LAUNAY, J. C. ONILLON, M. POUCHARD, M. REV. CHIM. MINER. 9 (1), 41–9, 1972.
56593	**ON THE STRUCTURAL AND PHYSICAL PROPERTIES OF THE RARE EARTH MOLYBDATES.** BRIXNER, L. H. REV. CHIM. MINER. 10 (1–2), 47–61, 1973.
56604	**ELECTROPHYSICAL PROPERTIES OF INDIUM OXIDE PHROLYTIC FILM WITH DISORDERED STRUCTURE.** KORZO, V. F. CHERNYAEV, V. N. PHYS. STATUS SOLIDI 20 A (2), 695–705, 1973.
56607	**MAGNETOELASTIC COUPLING INVESTIGATION OF BISMUTH-CALCIUM-IRON-VANADIUM GARNETS.** SMOKOTIN, E. M. PETROV, R. A. VELICHKO, V. V. YAKOVLEV, YU. M. PHYS. STATUS SOLIDI 21 A (1), K9–K12, 1974.

EPIC Number	Bibliographic Citation
56610	EFFECT OF PRESSURE ON THE CURIE TEMPERATURE OF HOLMIUM–NICKEL AND ERBIUM–NICKEL. JAAKOLA, S. PARVIAINEN, S. PHYS. STATUS SOLIDI 21 A (1), K53–K56, 1974.
56613	CONDUCTION ELECTRONS IN POTASSIUM BROMIDE AT FIELDS CLOSE TO BREAKDOWN. MOESTL, K. PHYS. STATUS SOLIDI 21 A (1), 123–33, 1974.
56617	REACTION KINETIC CALCULATIONS SIMULATING OSCILLATIONS IN ZINC SELENIDE CRYSTALS. GSCHWIND, G. HABERLAND, D. H. NELKOWSKI, H. STAIS, A. PHYS. STATUS SOLIDI 21 A (1), 167–75, 1974.
56620	LUMINESCENT TRANSITIONS AND CONDUCTIVITY IN ZINC OXIDE. BAUR, G. FREYDORF, E. V. KOSCHEL, W. H. PHYS. STATUS SOLIDI 21 A (1), 247–51, 1974.
56621	MOLYBDENUM TRIOXIDE LAYERS. OPTICAL PROPERTIES, COLOR CENTERS, AND HOLOGRAPHIC RECORDING. TUBBS, M. R. PHYS. STATUS SOLIDI 21 A (1), 253–60, 1974.
56623	LUMINESCENT PROPERTIES OF LANTHANIDE IONS IN MAGNESIUM OXIDE AND CALCIUM OXIDE FILMS PREPARED BY RADIO FREQUENCY SPUTTERING. RATINEN, H. PHYS. STATUS SOLIDI 21 A (1), 275–80, 1974.
56627	GALVANOMAGNETIC PHENOMENA IN PLATINUM ANTIMONIDE IN HIGH MAGNETIC FIELDS. ABDULLAEV, A. A. ANGELOVA, L. A. KUZNETSOV, V. K. ORMONT, A. B. PASHINTSEV, YU. I. PHYS. STATUS SOLIDI 21 (1), 339–43, 1974.
56629	MECHANISM OF THE RECOMBINATION OF CHARGE CARRIERS IN SEMIINSULATING CHROMIUM–DOPED GALLIUM ARSENIDE. VOROB'EVA, N. V. VOROB'EV, YU. V. KARKHANIN, YU. I. KOLOMIETS, I. A. TRETYAK, O. V. PHYS. STATUS SOLIDI 21 A (1), 369–76, 1974.
56630	MEASUREMENT OF THE TEMPERATURE COEFFICIENT OF THE REFRACTIVE INDEX OF INFRARED MATERIALS WITH THE AID OF A CARBON DIOXIDE LASER. KOLOSOVSKII, O. A. USTIMENKO, L. N. OPT. SPEKTROSK. 33, (10), 781–82, 1972. (FOR ENGLISH TRANSLATION SEE E57756)
56636	OPTICAL CONSTANTS OF FERRIC OXIDE IN THE INFRARED SPECTRAL REGION. POPOVA, S. I. TOLSTYKH, T. S. IVLEV, L. S. OPT. SPEKTROSK. 35 (5), 954–5, 1973.
56638	EFFECT OF TEMPERATURE AND EXCITATION INTENSITY ON THE EDGE EMISSION OF ALUMINUM– AND NITROGEN–DOPED BETA–SILICON CARBIDE. NGUYEN, N. L. NEDZVETSKII, D. S. OPT. SPEKTROSK. 35 (6), 1111–15, 1973. (FOR ENGLISH TRANSLATION SEE E76649)
56639	PHOTOSTIMULATED THERMOLUMINESCENCE OF FLUORITE CRYSTALS CONTAINING A RARE EARTH ION IMPURITY. KORNIENKO, L. S. LOZHNIKOV, A. A. NAZAROV, V. I. CHERNOV, P. OPT. SPEKTROSK. 35 (6), 1120–5, 1973. (FOR ENGLISH TRANSLATION SEE E76650)
56640	FLUORITE RADIATION DEFECTS UNSTABLE AT 77 K. KASK, N. E. KORNIENKO, L. S. CHERNOV, P. V. OPT. SPEKTROSK. 35 (6), 1180–1, 1973. (FOR ENGLISH TRANSLATION SEE E76652)
56642	FERROELECTRIC DOMAINS INSIDE THICK CRYSTALS OF POTASSIUM NIOBATE. KULKARNI, R. H. CHAUDHARI, R. M. INGLE, S. G. J. PHYS. 6 D (15), 1816–21, 1973.
56645	ELECTRON DRIFT VELOCITY AND BREAKDOWN IN SILVER CHLORIDE. MOESTL, K. J. PHYS. 6 D (17), 2131–6, 1973.
56646	SECONDARY ELECTRON EMISSION OF CESIUM IODIDE. VERMA, R. L. J. PHYS. 6 D (17), 2137–41, 1973.
56652	MAGNETOOPTIC DETERMINATION OF THE REFRACTIVE INDEXES OF FERRIC BORATE. HAISMA, J. PRINS, H. J. VAN MIERLOO, K. L. L. J. PHYS. 7 D (1), 162–8, 1974.
56653	TEMPERATURE DEPENDENCE OF CATHODOLUMINESCENCE IN N–TYPE GALLIUM ARSENIDE. JONES, G. A. C. NAG, B. R. GOPINATH, A. J. PHYS. 7 D (1), 183–93, 1974.
56672	SUPERCONDUCTIVITY AND STRUCTURAL INSTABILITY OF (HAFNIUM, ZIRCONIUM) VANADIUM AND (HAFNIUM, TANTALUM) VANADIUM ALLOYS AT HIGH PRESSURE. SMITH, T. F. SHELTON, R. N. LAWSON, A. C. J. PHYS. 3 F (12), 2157–68, 1973. (AD 778 290)
56673	PRESSURE DEPENDENCE OF THE CURIE TEMPERATURE OF RARE EARTH–COBALT COMPOUNDS. BROUHA, M. BUSCHOW, K. H. J. J. PHYS. 3 F (12), 2218–26, 1973.
56678	ANOMALOUS DISPLACEMENT OF THE LUMINESCENCE BAND IN SOME SEMICONDUCTORS. DAMASKIN, I. A. PYSHKIN, S. L. RADAUTSAN, S. I. TEZLEVAN, V. E. PIS'MA ZH. EKSP. TEOR. FIZ. 18 (4), 239–42, 1973. (FOR ENGLISH TRANSLATION SEE E76683)
56687	PHONON CYCLOTRON RESONANCE IN INDIUM ANTIMONIDE. IVANOV–OMSKII, V. I. KOLOMIETS, B. T. SHEREGII, E. M. PIS'MA ZH. EKSP. TEOR. FIZ. 18 (6), 337–9, 1973.
56692	INTERFERENCE STATES OF LIGHT EXCITONS. OBSERVATION OF ACCESSORY. KISELEV, V. A. RAZBIRIN, B. S. URAL'TSEV, I. N. PIS'MA ZH. EKSP. TEOR. FIZ. 18 (8), 504–7, 1973.
56696	GIANT FARADAY EFFECT AND OPTICAL ABSORPTION IN YTTRIUM BISMUTH ALUMINUM FERRATE EPITAXIAL FILMS. BALBASHOV, A. M. CERVONENKIS, A. YA. CHERKASOV, A. P. BAKHTEUZOV, V. E. TSVETKOVA, A. A. CHEPARIN, V. P. PIS'MA ZH. EKSP. TEOR. FIZ. 18 (9), 572–5, 1973.
56697	BIEXCITON IN THE CADMIUM SULFIDE SPECTRUM AND INDUCED RADIATIVE DECAY OF EXCITON–IMPURITY RADIATIVE DECAY OF EXCITON–IMPURITY COMPLEXES. DITE, A. F. REVENKO, V. I. TIMOFEEV, V. B. ALTUKHOV, P. D. PIS'MA ZH. EKSP. TEOR. FIZ. 18 (9), 579–83, 1973.
56699	LASER GENERATION OF NEODYMIUM IONS IN QUARTZ GLASS. GALANT, E. I. KONDRAT'EV, YU. N. PRZHEVUSKII, A. K. PROKHOROVA, T. I. TOLSTOI, M. N. SHAPOVALOV, V. N. PIS'MA ZH. EKSP. TEOR. FIZ. 18 (10), 635–7, 1973.
56703	EXPERIMENTAL DEVICE FOR SPECTRAL ANALYSIS IN THE CATHODOLUMINESCENCE STUDIES: APPLICATION TO ZINC SELENIDE SAMPLES. GUILLARD, J. M. HITIER, G. REV. PHYS. APPL. 8 (4), 337–40, 1973.
56706	ELECTRICAL CONDUCTIVITY OFF INTERMETALLIC COMPOUNDS OF THE CERIUM–THALLIUM SYSTEM. CISMARU, G. D. SPACU, P. REV. ROUM. CHIM. 18 (8), 1345–51, 1973.
56714	DIRECT READING MOBILITY INDICATOR. HOWES, M. J. REV. SCI. INSTRUM. 44 (9), 1223–5, 1973.
56718	FOUR PROBE CELL FOR RAPID RESISTIVITY MEASUREMENTS. CAHEN, D. HAHN, J. R. ANDERSON, J. R. REV. SCI. INSTRUM. 44 (11), 1567–8, 1973.
56720	EMISSION PROPERTIES OF OXIDE CATHODES USING PHOTORESIST BINDER. GRAY, H. F. HAAS, G. A. REV. SCI. INSTRUM. 44 (11), 1616–17, 1973.

EPIC Number	Bibliographic Citation

56730 **FORMATION OF EPITAXIAL LAYERS OF GALLIUM ARSENIDE FROM THE GAS PHASE.**
FEDORENKO, V. N. RAINOV, YU. A.
GRIBOV, V. T. AKHIN'KO, A. T.
KOZYRKIN, B. I. SOKOLOV, E. B.
SB. NAUCH. TR. PROBL. MIKROELEKTRON., MOSK. INST. ELEKTRON. TEKH.
(13), 141–3, 1972.

56731 **ELECTRIC PROPERTIES OF TRANSITION METAL SILICIDES.**
VIGDOROVICH, V. N. KONDRATOV, N. M.
SB. NAUCH. TR. PROBL. MIKROELEKTRON., MOSK. INST. ELEKTRON. TEKH.
(13), 169–75, 1972.

56733 **DOPING OF CADMIUM SELENIDE SINGLE CRYSTALS DURING GROWTH FROM A MELT BY THE BRIDGMAN METHOD.**
DRACHEV, V. V. DAVYDOV, A. A.
KARTUSHINA, A. A. KRUPYSHEV, R. S.
SOKOLOV, E. B.
SB. NAUCH. TR. PROBL. MIKROELEKTRON., MOSK. INST. ELEKTRON. TEKH.
(13), 193–6, 1972.

56734 **ELECTRICAL PROPERTIES OF CADMIUM ANTIMONIDE DOPED WITH RARE EARTH ELEMENTS.**
KORSAKOVA, M. D. YAREMBASH, E. I.
SB. NAUCH. TR. PROBL. MIKROELEKTRON., MOSK. INT. ELEKTRON. TEKH.
(13), 197–200, 1972.

56738 **EFFECT OF THE CHARGE CALCINATION TEMPERATURE ON THE LUMINESCENCE OF CALCIUM TUNGSTATE.**
GURVICH, A. M. MIKHALEV, A. A.
TOMBAK, M. I.
SB. NAUCH. TR., VSES. NAUCH.-ISSLED. INST. LYUMINOFOROV OSOBO CHIST. VESHCHESTV
(7), 18–26, 1972.

56739 **EFFECTS OF THE DEGREE OF PURIFICATION AND HEAT TREATMENT ON THE THERMOLUMINESCENCE OF CALCIUM TUNGSTATE.**
KRONGAUZ, V. G. MIKHALEV, A. A.
KAPLENOV, I. G.
SB. NAUCH. TR., VSES. NAUCH.-ISSLED. INST. LYUMINOFOROV OSOBO CHIST. VESHCHESTV
(7), 27–32, 1972.

56742 **EFFECT OF FREQUENCY ON THE DIELECTRIC LOSS TANGENT IN ALUMINUM OXIDE FILMS.**
ERASHOV, A. N. MARKIN, V. V.
SHCHEVELEV, M. I.
SB. TR. POLUPROV. MATER., PRIB. IKH PRIMEN.
43–5, 1971.

56749 **INTRODUCTION TO PRINCIPLES OF THE SOLID STATE.**
WELLER, P. F.
SOLID STATE CHEM. PHYS.
1, 1–65, 1973.
(EDITED BY PAUL F. WELLER, DEKKER: NEW YORK)

56765 **ELECTRICAL PROPERTIES OF SOLIDS.**
PERLSTEIN, J. H.
SOLID STATE CHEM. PHYS.
1, 189–293, 1973.
(EDITED BY PAUL F. WELLER, DEKKER: NEW YORK)

56767 **OPTICAL PROPERTIES OF SOLIDS.**
AXE, J. D.
SOLID STATE CHEM. PHYS.
1, 411–500, 1973.
(EDITED BY PAUL F. WELLER, DEKKER: NEW YORK)

56768 **TIN DIOXIDE FILMS ON GLASS.**
HASKOVA, E.
SKLAR KERAM.
23 (5), 144–7, 1973.

56769 **COMPOUND TELLURIDES AND THEIR ALLOYS FOR PELTIER COOLING - A REVIEW.**
YIM, W. M. ROSI, F. D.
SOLID-STATE ELECTRONICS
15, 1121–1140, 1972.

56771 **SEMICONDUCTOR AND SEMI-INSULATOR RESISTIVITY MEASUREMENTS USING A DIRECT CURRENT FOUR POINT PROBE APPARATUS WITH NON-PENETRATING TIPS.**
HEILIG, K.
SOLID-STATE ELECTRONICS
16, 503–506, 1973.

56775 **FIELD-INDUCED ABSORPTION IN GOLD AURUM-CADMIUM SULFUR AND COPPER CUPRUM SULFUR-CADMIUM SULFUR DIODES**
CHANG, C. C. SHIMODA, R. Y.
SOLID-STATE ELECTRON.
16 (9), 1079–81, 1973.

56785 **TWO-PHONON LATTICE ABSORPTION IN INDIUM PHOSPHIDE, INDIUM ARSENIDE, INDIUM ARSENIDE PHOSPHIDE, AND INDIUM ARSENIDE PHOSPHIDE COMPOUNDS.**
KEKELIDZE, N. P. KEKELIDZE, G. P.
SHATBEROVA, E. B. GURVICH, L. V.
SOOBSHCH. AKAD. NAUK GRUZ. SSR
72 (1), 69–72, 1973.

EPIC Number	Bibliographic Citation

56801 **EFFECT OF OXIDES OF RARE EARTH ELEMENTS ON THE DIELECTRIC PROPERTIES OF BARIUM - TITANIUM CERAMICS.**
IORDANOVA, M. TOMOVA, E.
STROIT. MATER. SILIKAT. PROM.
14 (3), 21–3, 1973.

56806 **STRUCTURE AND PROPERTIES OF BETA-SILVER SULFIDE SEMICONDUCTOR THIN FILMS.**
ICHIMESCU, A.
STUD. CERCET. FIZ.
25 (4), 403–24, 1973.

56807 **MAGNETIC AND STRUCTURAL PROPERTIES OF IRON, COBALT, AND NICKEL RARE EARTH ALLOYS.**
BURZO, E.
STUD. CERCET. FIZ.
25 (4), 425–45, 1973.

56816 **EFFECT OF BISMUTH STANNATE ON THE ELECTRIC PROPERTIES OF BARIUM TITANATE CERAMIC MATERIALS.**
PROHASKA, K.
SZKLO CERAM.
24 (9), 266–70, 1973.

56818 **SURFACE PHOTOVOLTAGE SPECTROSCOPY AND SURFACE PIEZOELECTRIC EFFECT IN GALLIUM ARSENIDE.**
LAGOWSKI, J. BALTOV, I. GATOS, H. C.
SURFACE SCI.
40 (2), 216–26, 1973.

56837 **EFFICIENCY AND PERSISTENCE OF ELECTROLUMINESCENCE OF POWDERED ZINC SULFIDE PHOSPHORS.**
REBANE, K.
TARTU RIIKLIKU ULIKOOLI TOIM.
(292), 3–12, 1972.

56838 **STABILITY OF POWDERED ELECTROLUMINOPHORS WITH PROTECTIVE ELECTROCHEMICAL COATINGS.**
SOSHCHIN, N. P. TALVISTE, E. TAMMIK, A.
TARTU RIIKLIKU ULIKOOLI TOIM.
(292), 13–25, 1972.

56851 **PHOTOLUMINESCENCE STUDY ON LATTICE DEFECTS IN CADMIUM TELLURIDE.**
TAGUCHI, T. SHIRAFUJI, J. INUISHI, Y.
TECHNOL. REP. OSAKA UNIV.
23 (1090–1120), 195–203, 1973.

56854 **PROPERTIES OF INDIUM NITRIDE FILMS.**
ANDREEVA, A. F.
TEKHNOL. POLUCH. NOVYKH MATER.
116–20, 1972.

56855 **ELECTRICAL RESISTIVITY OF TRANSITION METAL DISILICIDES AT LOW TEMPERATURES.**
KONONENKO, T. K.
TEKHNOL. POLUCH. NOVYKH MATER.
190–6, 1972.

56856 **EXPERIMENTAL STUDY OF BASIC CHARACTERISTICS OF TEMPERATURE-SENSITIVE MAGNETIC MATERIALS.**
YAMASAWA, K. MURAKAMI, K.
TECHNOL. REP. TOHOKU UNIV.
38 (1), 225–36, 1973.

56859 **RADIATION CHARACTERISTICS OF WATER VAPOR AND CARBON DIOXIDE.**
POPOV, YU. A. SHVARTSBLAT, R. L.
TEPLOFIZ. VYS. TEMP.
11 (4), 741–9, 1973.

56861 **KINETIC PROPERTIES OF THE SOLID SOLUTION COPPER SULFIDE TELLURIDE.**
ASTAKHOV, O. P.
TEPLOFIZ. VYS. TEMP.
11 (5), 1121–3, 1973.
(FOR ENGLISH TRANSLATION SEE E57295)

56862 **EFFECT OF LEAD AND BISMUTH IMPURITIES ON THE ELECTRIC CONDUCTIVITY AND THERMOELECTRICITY OF ANTIMONY TRISELENIDE IN THE LIQUID STATE.**
KAZANDZHAN, B. I. MISHUTKINA, T. I.
TSEDERBERG, N. V.
TEPLOFIZ. VYS. TEMP.
11 (5), 1124–5, 1973.
(FOR ENGLISH TRANSLATION SEE E57296)

56872 **TEMPERATURE DEPENDENCE OF THE ELECTRIC CONDUCTIVITY OF ZINC OXIDE FILMS.**
KOTERA, Y. MIYAYAMA, A.
TOKYO KOGYO SHIKENSHO HOKOKU
68 (4), 168–72, 1973.

56873 **BORON NITRIDE AND ITS PHOTOLUMINESCENCE.**
LUBYANSKII, G. A.
TR. ALTAI. POLITEKH. INST.
(4), 248–54, 1972.

56875 **HISTORY OF THE DISCOVERY OF THE FERROELECTRIC PROPERTIES OF BARIUM TITANATE.**
VUL, B. M.
TITANAT BARIYA, MATER, SEMIN., POSVYASHCH. 25-LETIYU OTKRYTIYA SEGNETOELEKTRICHESKIKH SVOISTV TITANATA BARIYA
5–7, 1973.

EPIC Number	Bibliographic Citation
56876	**SIGNIFICANCE OF THE DISCOVERY OF THE FERROELECTRIC NATURE OF BARIUM TITANATE FOR SCIENCE AND INDUSTRY.** BOGDANOV, S. V. TITANAT BARIYA, MATER, SEMIN., POSVYASHCH. 25-LETIYU OTKRYTIYA SEGNETOELEKTRICHESKIKH SVOISTV TITANATA YU BARIYA 7–10, 1973.
56878	**BARIUM TITANATE-ANCESTOR OF THE PEROVSKITE FAMILY OF FERROELECTRIC SUBSTANCES.** VENEVTSEV, YU. N. ZHDANOV, G. S. TITANAT BARIYA, MATER, SEMIN., POSVYASHCH. 25-LETIYU OTKRYTIYA SEGNETOELEKTRICHESKIKH SVOISTV TITANATA YU BARIYA 19–28, 1973.
56879	**BARIUM TITANATE FAMILY.** FESENKO, E. G. TITANAT BARIYA, MATER, SEMIN., POSVYASHCH. 25-LETIYU OTKRYTIYA SEGNETOELEKTRICHESKIKH SVOISTV TITANATA YU BARIYA 28–40, 1973.
56880	**EFFECT OF EXTERNAL INFLUENCES ON THE DOMAIN STRUCTURE AND POLARIZATION OF BARIUM TITANATE SINGLE CRYSTALS.** SINYAKOV, E. V. TITANAT BARIYA, MATER, SEMIN., POSVYASHCH. 25-LETIYU OTKRYTIYA SEGNETOELEKTRICHESKIKH SVOISTV TITANATA YU BARIYA 50–9, 1973.
56881	**DIELECTRIC SPECTRUM OF BARIUM TITANATE.** DEM'YANOV, V. V. SOLOV'EV, S. P. TITANAT BARIYA, MATER, SEMIN., POSVYASHCH. 25-LETIYU OTKRYTIYA SEGNETOELEKTRICHESKIKH SVOISTV TITANATA YU BARIYA 60–6, 1973.
56882	**DISPERSION OF DIELECTRIC CONSTANT IN BARIUM TITANATE IN THE FERROELECTRIC REGION.** POPLAVKO, YU. M. PEREVERZEVA, L. P. TITANAT BARIYA, MATER, SEMIN., POSVYASHCH. 25-LETIYU OTKRYTIYA SEGNETOELEKTRICHESKIKH SVOISTV TITANATA YU BARIYA 67–70, 1973.
56883	**SEMICONDUCTOR PROPERTIES OF BARIUM TITANATE.** GURO, G. M. IVANCHIK, I. I. KOVTONYUK, N. F. TITANAT BARIYA, MATER, SEMIN., POSVYASHCH. 25-LETIYU OTKRYTIYA SEGNETOELEKTRICHESKIKH SVOISTV TITANATA YU BARIYA 71–7, 1973.
56885	**BASIC PROPERTIES OF FERROELECTRIC SOLID SOLUTIONS OF BARIUM TITANATE TYPE.** FRITSBERG, V. YA. TITANAT BARIYA, MATER, SEMIN., POSVYASHCH. 25-LETIYU OTKRYTIYA SEGNETOELEKTRICHESKIKH SVOISTV TITANATA YU BARIYA 86–93, 1973.
56887	**STRUCTURE, SYNTHESIS, PROPERTIES, AND USES OF THE FERROELECTRICS LITHIUM NIOBATE AND LITHIUM TANTALATE.** VENEVTSEV, YU. N. FEDULOV, S. A. SHAPIRO, Z. I. KLYUEV, V. P. TITANAT BARIYA, MATER, SEMIN., POSVYASHCH. 25-LETIYU OTKRYTIYA SEGNETOELEKTRICHESKIKH SVOISTV TITANATA YU BARIYA 118–33, 1973.
56888	**PYROELECTRIC EFFECT IN OCTAHEDRAL OXY-FERROELECTRIC COMPOUNDS.** ROITBERG, M. B. RABINOVICH, A. Z. PYATIGORSKAYA, L. I. SHAPIRO, Z. I. TITANAT BARIYA, MATER, SEMIN., POSVYASHCH. 25-LETIYU OTKRYTIYA SEGNETOELEKTRICHESKIKH SVOISTV TITANATA YU BARIYA 133–40, 1973.
56894	**MAGNETOSTRICTION AND PARALLEL SUSCEPTIBILITY IN IN ANTIFERROMAGNETIC COBALT FLUORIDE.** PROKHOROV, A. S. RUDASHEVSKII, E. G. TR. FIZ. INST., AKAD. NAUK SSSR 67, 74–7, 1973.
56897	**ULTRAVIOLET LUMINESCENCE OF ZINC SULFIDE DURING ELECTRONIC AND OPTICAL EXCITATIONS.** VORONOV, YU. V. TR. FIZ. INST., AKAD. NAUK SSSR 68, 3–94, 1973.
56898	**IONIZATION DOMAINS IN STRONG FIELDS AND MOTION OF LUMINESCENT AREAS IN CRYSTALS.** FOK, M. V. L'VOVA, E. YU. TR. FIZ. INST., AKAD. NAUK SSSR 68, 95–110, 1973.
56899	**RADIATIVE RECOMBINATION IN CADMIUM TELLURIDE CRYSTALS.** PANOSYAN, ZH. R. TR. FIZ. INST., AKAD. NAUK SSSR 68, 147–202, 1973.
56900	**BAND STRUCTURE OF SEMICONDUCTORS STUDIED BY DIFFERENTIAL OPTICAL METHODS.** DZHIOEVA, S. G. TR. FIZ. INST., AKAD. NAUK SSSR 68, 203–31, 1973.
56901	**DELAY OF LUMINESCENCE AND DETERMINATION OF THE TIMES OF RADIATIONLESS RELAXATION.** NOLLE, E. L. TR. FIZ. INST., AKAD. NAUK SSSR 68, 232–8, 1973.
56904	**EFFECTS OF LOW-SYMMETRY CRYSTAL FIELDS ON THE MAGNETIC PROPERTIES OF COBALT TUNGSTATE.** KHATS'KO, E. N. ZVYAGIN, A. I. TR. FIZ.-TEKH. INST. NIZK. TEMP., AKAD. NAUK UKR. SSR (18), 3–14, 1972.
56905	**MAGNETIC PROPERTIES AND RESONANCE OF LITHIUM NEODYMIUM MOLYBDATE.** KALININ, P. S. ZVYAGIN, A. I. EL'CHANINOVA, S. D. PELIKH, L. N. CHERNYI, A. S. YURKO, V. G. TR. FIZ.-TEKH. INST. NIZK. TEMP., AKAD. NAUK UKR. SSR (20), 85–90, 1972.
56906	**MAGNETIC PROPERTIES OF POTASSIUM YTTRIUM MOLYBDATE WITH DYSPROSIUM IMPURITIES.** STEPENKO, T. S. YURKO, V. G. EL'CHANINOVA, S. D. ZVYAGIN, A. I. TR. FIZ.-TEKH. INST. NIZK. TEMP., AKAD. NAUK UKR. SSR (20), 91–3, 1972.
56907	**ROLE OF PHONONS IN THE ELECTRIC RESISTIVITY OF THE ANTIFERROMAGNETIC SEMICONDUCTOR MANGANESE TELLURIDE.** PEREVERZEV, YU. V. POVSTYANYI, L. V. TR. FIZ.-TEKH. INST. NIZK. TEMP., AKAD UKR. SSR (20), 94–101, 1972.
56913	**ELECTRIC CONDUCTIVITY OF FLUOROBERYLLATE GLASSES AND CRYSTALLINE CALCIUM FLUORIDE.** DANILKIN, V. I. LEONOV, I. L. PETROVSKII, G. T. TSURIKOVA, G. A. TR., GOS. INST. PRIKL. KHIM. (65), 78–81, 1970.
56921	**GROWTH MECHANISM OF URANIUM DIOXIDE SEMISPHERICAL DEPOSITS ON AN ELECTRODE TIP.** PUZAKOV, V. V. BARABOSHKIN, A. N. KALIEV, K. A. TARASOVA, K. P. TR. INST. ELEKTROKHIM., URAL. NAUCH. TSENTR, AKAD. NAUK SSSR (18), 99–105, 1972.
56936	**EFFECTS OF AN ELECTRIC FIELD ON THE OPTICAL PROPERTIES OF POLYCRYSTALLINE CADMIUM SULFIDE FILMS.** KHIRIN, V. N. TR. MOSK. ENERG. INST. (142), 14–22, 1972.
56938	**LUMINESCENCE PROPERTIES OF ZINC SULFIDE FILMS HEAT-TREATED IN ZINC VAPOR.** MOROZOVA, N. K. KARETNIKOV, I. A. LONGINOV, V. V. TR. MOSK. ENERG. INST. (142), 29–36, 1972.
56939	**ELECTRICAL INSTABILITY IN CADMIUM TELLURIDE THIN FILMS.** BOROVOV, G. I. VORONKOV, E. N. MURAV'EV, L. N. TR. MOSK. ENERG. INST. (142), 37–42, 1972.
56940	**PRODUCTION AND STUDY OF GALLIUM INDIUM ANTIMONIDE SOLID-SOLUTION THIN FILMS.** VARGANOV, S. V. TR. MOSK. ENERG. INST. (142), 43–6, 1972.
56941	**ANNEALING OF MERCURIC TELLURIDE THIN FILMS.** SHNITNIKOV, A. S. MUKHINA, O. B. GEORGOV, R. P. TR. MOSK. ENERG. INST. (142), 47–51, 1972.
56942	**DEPTH OF INTRINSIC DEFECT LEVELS AND THE EDGE LUMINESCENCE OF ZINC SULFIDE POWDERS.** KOROLEV, O. I. MOROZOVA, N. K. TR. MOSK. ENERG. INST. (142), 52–7, 1972.
56943	**INFRARED ABSORPTION AND RATE OF ETCHING OF SILICON NITRIDE LAYERS OBTAINED BY AN ION-PLASMA METHOD.** SOLDATOV, V. S. SAV'YALOV, YU. P. MEDVEDEV, K. S. NIKOLAENKO, O. G. USKOVA, Z. A. TR. MOSK. ENERG. INST. (142), 71–5, 1972.

EPIC Number	Bibliographic Citation
56944	EFFECTS OF CATHODIC-REACTIVE-SPUTTERING DIELECTRIC DEPOSITION CONDITIONS ON THE ELECTRICAL CONDUCTIVITY OF CADMIUM SULFIDE FILMS. KORNETOV, V. N. SMOTRAKOV, A. A. KHANIN, V. A. SHAPOSHNIKOV, N. P. TR. MOSK. ENERG. INST. (142), 81–8, 1972.
56945	CRYSTALLIZATION OF INDIUM ANTIMONIDE THIN FILMS. TARASOV, V. L. GULYAEV, A. M. SKVORTSOVA, V. V. TR. MOSK. ENERG. INST. (142), 89–95, 1972.
56946	PRODUCTION OF VANADIUM DIOXIDE THIN FILMS BY CATHODE REACTIVE SPUTTERING AND STUDY OF THEIR ELECTRIC PROPERTIES. MAKROUSOV, V. V. CHIRKOV, V. G. TR. MOSK. ENERG. INST. (142), 96–101, 1972.
56947	OPTICAL PROPERTIES OF ZINC OXIDE POWDERS. SATYBAEV, N. M. MALOV, M. M. TR. MOSK. ENERG. INST. (142), 102–8, 1972.
56948	OPTICAL CHARACTERISTICS AND THE EPR SIGNAL OF ZINC SULFIDE SINGLE CRYSTALS HEAT-TREATED IN ZINC VAPORS. ARKHANGEL'SKII, G. E. MALOV, M. M. MOROZOVA, N. K. TR. MOSK. ENERG. INST. (142), 132–4, 1972.
56950	HEXAFERRITES DOPED WITH SCANDIUM TRIPOSITIVE, ALUMINUM TRIPOSITIVE, AND GALLIUM TRIPOSITIVE IONS. CHEPARIN, V. P. CHERKASOV, A. P. SVESHNIKOV, YU. A. TR. MOSK. ENERG. INST. (143), 65–9, 1972.
56957	PROPERTIES OF EPITAXIAL FILMS GROWN BY ZONE MELTING WITH A TEMPERATURE GRADIENT FROM GALLIUM ARSENIDE SYSTEMS. KEDA, A. I. LUNIN, L. S. TR. NOVOCHERKASSK. POLITEKH. INST. (259), 50–9, 1972.
56958	DISPERSION OF THE REAL AND IMAGINARY PARTS OF THE DIELECTRIC CONSTANTS OF TITANIUM DIOXIDE FILMS IN AND NEAR THE FUNDAMENTAL ABSORPTION REGION. TEKUCHEVA, I. A. TR. RYAZAN. RADIOTEKH. INST. (37), 83–91, 1972.
56959	ELECTRON HEATING IN DEGENERATE INDIUM ANTIMONIDE IN PARALLEL ELECTRIC AND QUANTIZING MAGNETIC FIELDS. BYKOVSKII, YU. A. GARIFULLIN, I. A. ELESIN, V. F. KADUSHKIN, V. I. PROTASOV, E. A. RODIONOV, A. G. TR. RYAZAN. RADIOTEKH. INST. (37), 96–101, 1972.
56960	DEPENDENCE OF THE DIELECTRIC PROPERTIES OF OXIDE SEMICONDUCTORS ON THE SINTERING TEMPERATURE. PERELYGIN, A. I. TLEUBAEVA, A. K. KOROLEVA, G. I. TR. RYAZAN. RADIOTEKH. INST. (37), 119–24, 1972.
56966	PROPERTIES OF GALLIUM ARSENIDE-ZINC SELENIDE SYSTEM. KIROVSKAYA, I. A. MULIKOVA, G. M. TR. TOMSK. GOS. UNIV. 240, 160–6, 1973.
56971	TEMPERATURE-DEPENDENT HALL EFFECT MEASUREMENTS IN ALUMINA. GREEN, B. A. DAVIS, M. V. TRANS. AM. NUCL. SOC. 16, 75–6, 1973.
56972	MICROWAVE DIELECTRIC PROPERTIES OF MULLITE. PERRY, G. S. TRANS. J. BRIT. CERAM. SOC. 72 (6), 279–83, 1973.
56978	INTERMETALLIC FLUORITE-TYPE COMPOUND PLATINUM-MANGANESE-TIN IN THE PLATINUM-MANGANESE-TIN SYSTEM AND ITS MAGNETIC PROPERTIES. MASUMOTO, H. WATANABE, K. TRANS. JAP. INST. METALS 14 (5), 408–14, 1973.
56980	PRODUCTION AND STUDY OF TIN ZINC ARSENIDE SINGLE CRYSTALS WITH SPHALERITE AND CHALCOPYRITE STRUCTURES. KORNEEV, E. F. TROIN. POLUPROV. 80–3PP., 1972.
56981	ELECTRICAL CONDUCTIVITY OF SOME II - IV - V-TYPE COMPOUNDS IN SOLID AND LIQUID STATES. GUBSKAYA, G. F. EVFIMOVSKII, I. V. GORYUNOVA, N. A. SEREDNII, A. P. TYCHINA, I. I. KOVALEVA, I. S. KRANCHEVICH, K. S. TROINYE POLUPROV. 133–9PP., 1972.
56982	PREPARATION, STRUCTURE, AND SOME PROPERTIES OF GERMANIUM ZINC ARSENIDE DENDRITES. DASHEVSKII, M. YA. KHASIKOV, V. V. TROIN. POLUPROV. 83–8PP., 1972.
56983	REGION OF GLASS FORMATION IN THE CADMIUM - GERMANIUM - ARSENIC SYSTEM. VAIPOLIN, A. A. KUZ'MENKO, G. S. OSMANOV, E. O. TROIN. POLUPROV. 90–2PP., 1972.
56986	EFFECT OF TEMPERATURE ON THE EFFECTIVE ELECTRON MASS IN CADMIUM GERMANIUM ARSENIDE. MAL'TSEV, YU. V. PICHAKHCHI, G. I. POLUSHINA, I. K. UPATOVA, T. V. UKHANOV, YU. I. TROIN. POLUPROV. 119–21PP., 1972.
56988	PHOTOLUMINESCENCE OF CADMIUM SILICON PHOSPHIDE SINGLE CRYSTALS. BYCHKOV, A. G. KROLEVETS, N. M. LYUBCHENKO, A. V. POLYKEVICH, I. V. SHEINMAN, M. K. TROIN. POLUPROV. 125–7PP., 1972.
56989	OPTICAL ANISOTROPY OF II - IV - V COMPOUNDS. BORSHCHEVSKII, A. S. GRIGOR'EVA, V. S. IVANOV, E. K. PROCHUKHAN, V. D. SMIRNOVA, A. D. UNDALOV, YU. K. UPATOVA, T. V. TROIN. POLUPROV. 149–51PP., 1972.
56990	ELECTRICAL AND PHOTOELECTRIC PROPERTIES OF CADMIUM SILICON PHOSPHIDE. LYUBCHENKO, A. V. BYCHKOV, A. G. POTYKEVICH, I. V. RADZIVIL, V. P. TYCHINA, I. I. TROIN. POLUPROV. 159–68PP., 1972.
56991	BAND STRUCTURE OF CADMIUM TIN ARSENIDE. VUL, S. P. KARYMSHAKOV, R. K. POLYANSKAYA, T. A. SHMARTSEV, YU. V. TROIN. POLUPROV. 170–3PP., 1972.
56992	PROPERTIES OF CADMIUM TIN ARSENIDE AND CADMIUM GERMANIUM ARSENIDE SINGLE CRYSTALS. RUSSU, G. T. KRETSU, I. V. CHEBAN, A. G. CHINIK, B. S. TROIN. POLUPROV. 173–6PP., 1972.
56993	ELECTRICAL PROPERTIES OF CADMIUM INDIUM SULIFIDE. MOLODYAN, I. P. RUSSU, E. V. TEZLEVAN, V. E. REVENKO, F. N. TROIN. POLUPROV. 214–17PP., 1972.
56995	CADMIUM GALLIUM SELENIDE SINGLE CRYSTALS AND THIN FILMS. TYRZIU, V. G. TYRZIU, M. P. TROIN. POLUPROV. 220–2PP., 1972.
56996	PHOTOCONDUCTIVITY OF CADMIUM INDIUM SULFIDE UNDER LASER EXCITATION. DAMASKIN, I. A. PYSHKIN, S. L. RADAUTSAN, S. I. TEZLEVAN, V. E. TROIN. POLUPROV. 222–5PP., 1973.
56997	BASIC PHYSICAL PROPERTIES OF THE THREE-LAYER INDIUM ZINC SULFIDE POLYTYPE. ANDRIESH, A. M. DONIKA, F. G. MUSTYA, I. G. SHMIGLYUK, M. I. TROIN. POLUPROV. 225–8PP., 1972.
56998	PHYSICAL-CHEMICAL STUDIES ON SOME RARE EARTH COMPOUNDS. RUSTAMOV, P. G. KARAEV, Z. SH. NASIBOV, I. O. SULTANOV, T. I. MURTUZOV, M. I. GAMIDOV, R. S. TROIN. POLUPROV. II - IV - V(2), II - III(2) - VI(4) 239–41, 1972.
56999	ELECTROOPTICAL REFLECTION SPECTRUM OF CADMIUM TIN PHOSPHIDE. KAVALIAUSKAS, J. GORYUNOVA, N. A. LEONOV, E. I. ORLOV, V. M. SILCIKA, A. TROINYE POLUPROV. 155–9PP., 1972.
57000	PREPARATION AND ELECTRICAL PROPERTIES OF GROUP II–V SEMICONDUCTORS CONTAINING ARSENIC. 1. PREPARATION AND ELECTRICAL PROPERTIES OF ZINC ARSENIDE THIN FILM. WEI, C.-C. SUN, Y.-Y. HSU, T.-Y. LIN, T.-B. TS'AI LIAO K'O HSUEH 4 (1), 1–7, 1972.

EPIC Number	Bibliographic Citation
57001	**PHOTOCONDUCTIVE PROPERTIES OF CADMIUM SULFIDE THIN FILMS PREPARED BY A SOLUTION SPRAY TECHNIQUE.** WU, T.-S. HUNG, K.-E. LO, T.-T. TS'AI LIAO K'O HSUEH 4 (2), 77-83, 1972.
57002	**ASRDI OXYGEN TECHNOLOGY SURVEY: VOLUMN IV: LOW TEMPERATURE MEASUREMENT.** SPARKS, L. L. NATL. AERONAUTICS AND SPACE ADMINISTRATION, WASHINGTON, D. C. 155PP., 1974. (NASA-SP-3073)
57004	**MAGNETIC PROPERTIES OF URANIUM BORIDE-DYSPROSIUM BORIDE AND URANIUM BORIDE-ERBIUM BORIDE SYSTEMS.** ALI-ZADE, N. KH. RAMAZANZADE, M. G. CHECHERNIKOV, V. I. GUSEINOV, N. G. SLOVYANSKII, V. K. UCH. ZAP., AZERB. INST. NEFTI KHIM. 9 (8), 54-6, 1972.
57006	**ELECTRIC CONDUCTIVITY OF ALKALI METAL SULFATES IN CRYSTALLINE AND FUSED STATES.** POLISHCHUK, A. F. SHURKHAL, T. M. ROMASHCHENKO, N. A. UKR. KHIM. ZH. 39 (8), 760-7, 1973.
57008	**POTASSIUM OXIDE - CALCIUM OXIDE - SILICON DIOXIDE - WATER SYSTEM AT 280.** BUKHOVETS, V. G. SHOR, O. I. SAZHIN, V. S. UKR. KHIM. ZH. 39 (8), 774-8, 1973.
57010	**THERMOELECTRIC PROPERTIES OF LEAD CHLORIDE-LEAD BROMIDE AND LEAD CHLORIDE-LEAD IODIDE MELTS.** MARKOV, B. F. KUZYAKIN, E. B. LOICHENKO, V. YA. UKR. KHIM. ZH. 39 (10), 984-8, 1973.
57016	**CRYSTALLOOPTICAL PROPERTIES OF SOME CALCIUM PYROPHOSPHATES.** KAMALOV, Z. ZDUKOS, A. T. SVISTUNOV, V. A. UZB. KHIM. ZH. 17 (4), 6-9, 1973.
57017	**NATURE OF LUMINESCENCE CENTERS OF ALKALI HALIDE PHOSPHORS.** IVANOVA, N. I. TARASOVA, L. I. USP. FOTONIKI (3), 128-58, 1973.
57025	**MAGNETIC PROPERTIES OF LANTHANUM NICKEL OXIDE - ALUMINUM LANTHANUM OXIDE SOLID SOLUTIONS.** BRACH, B. YA. MEL'NIK, G. I. CHEZHINA, N. V. VESTN. LENINGRAD. UNIV., FIZ., KHIM. (3), 143-5, 1973.
57026	**EFFECT OF CHEMICAL PREHISTORY AND CONDITIONS OF SINTERING ON THE MAGNETIC PROPERTIES OF NICKEL ZINC FERRITES.** ANASTASYUK, N. V. LEBEDEVA, E. V. OLEINIKOV, N. N. PIL'SHCHIKOV, A. I. TRET'YAKOV, YU. D. VESTN. MOSK. UNIV., KHIM. 14 (4), 451-4, 1973.
57030	**ELECTRICAL CONDUCTIVITY AND STRUCTURE OF VACUUM CONDENSATES OF TITANIUM, ZIRCONIUM, AND NIOBIUM CARBIDES.** FAT'YANOV, V. M. USHAKOVA, S. E. ASTAPCHIKA, S. A. SYCHEV, G. T. VESTSI AKAD. NAVUK BELARUS. SSR, SER. FIZ.-TEKH. NAVUK (3), 44-7, 1973.
57038	**ENERGY SPECTRUM OF ELECTRONS EMITTED BY ALKALI HALIDE CRYSTALS UNDER BOMBARDMENT BY INERT-GAS IONS AND ATOMS.** ARIFOV, U. A. RAKHIMOV, R. R. GAIPOV, S. PARILIS, E. S. VSES. SIMP. VZAIMODEISTVIYU AT. CHASTITS TVERD. TELOM, 2ND 20-3PP., 1972.
57039	**ELECTRON EMISSION OF POTASSIUM BROMIDE, SODIUM CHLORIDE, AND LITHIUM FLUORIDE FILMS DURING BOMBARDMENT BY SLOW KRYPTON POSITIVE, ARGON POSITIVE, AND NEON POSITIVE IONS.** RADKHIMOV, R. R. GAIPOV, S. VSES. SIMP. VZAIMODEISTVIYU AT. CHASTITS TVERD. TELOM, 2ND 50-3PP., 1972.
57053	**A STUDY ON THE NONSTOICHIOMETRIC VANADIUM OXIDE COMPOUNDS.** OSHIMA, H. YOGYO-KYOKAI-SHI 81 (932), 162-5, 1973.
57056	**OXONICKELATES(II) OF ALKALI METALS. POTASSIUM NICKELATE(II), RUBIDIUM NICKELATE(II), AND CESIUM NICKELATE(II).** RIECK, H. HOPPE, R. Z. ANORG. ALLG. CHEM. 400 (3), 311-20, 1973.
57057	**OXIDE SYSTEM WITH TRANSITION METAL IONS IN DIFFERENT OXIDATION STATES. XIII. SINGLE CRYSTALS IN THE MAGNESIUM VANADIUM OXIDE SYSTEM.** PICKARDT, J. REUTER, B. RIEDEL, E. SOECHTIG, J. Z. ANORG. ALLG. CHEM. 401 (1), 29-36, 1973.
57058	**OXIDE SYSTEMS OF TRANSITION METAL IONS IN DIFFERENT OXIDATION STATES. XV. ZINC IRON VANADIUM OXIDE SPINEL.** COLSMANN, G. REUTER, B. RIEDEL, E. Z. ANORG. ALLG. CHEM. 401 (1), 41-52, 1973.
57059	**OXIDE SYSTEMS WITH TRANSITION METAL IONS IN DIFFERENT OXIDATION STATES. XIV. PREPARATION AND STUDY OF SINGLE CRYSTALS IN THE ZINC VANADIUM OXIDE SYSTEM.** PICKARDT, J. REUTER, B. Z. ANORG. ALLG. CHEM. 401 (1), 37-40, 1973.
57065	**MAGNETIC STUDIES OF CERIUM AMMONIUM SULFATE IN RELATION TO CRYSTAL STRUCTURE.** SINGHAL, O. P. Z. NATURFORSCH., TEIL 28 B (3-4), 158-60, 1973.
57070	**TEMPERATURE DEPENDENCE OF PHOSPHORESCENCE AND FLUORESCENCE IN POTASSIUM HEXAFLUOROCHROMATE(III).** KOGLIN, E. KRASSER, W. Z. NATURFORSCH., TEIL 28 A (7), 1131-5, 1973.
57072	**THERMOELECTRIC POWER OF THE MOLTEN SYSTEMS (SILVER + M) IODIDE AND (COPPER + M) IODIDE (M = SODIUM, POTASSIUM, RUBIDIUM, CESIUM).** PEZZATI, E. SCHIRALDI, A. MAGISTRIS, A. Z. NATURFORSCH., TEIL 28 A (8), 1334-7, 1973.
57073	**THERMOLUMINESCENCE OF COPPER-DOPED CUBIC AND HEXAGONAL ZINC SULFIDE.** GRASSER, R. SCHARMANN, A. WETZEL, G. Z. NATURFORSCH., TEIL 28 A (8), 1378-9, 1973.
57075	**PERMITTIVITY OF TITANIUM DIOXIDE-ENRICHED BARIUM TITANATE CERAMICS.** HOFFMANN, B. LAUER, R. Z. NATURFORSCH., TEIL 28 A (9), 1489-91, 1973.
57080	**SUPERCONDUCTIVITY IN THE PALLADIUM-HYDROGEN AND THE PALLADIUM-DEUTERIUM SYSTEMS.** STRITZKER, B. BUCKEL, W. Z. PHYS. 257 (1), 1-8, 1972.
57082	**THEORY FOR SUPERCONDUCTIVITY IN PALLADIUM-HYDROGEN AND PALLADIUM-DEUTERIUM SYSTEMS.** BENNEMANN, K. H. GARLAND, J. W. Z. PHYS. 260 (5), 367-74, 1973.
57091	**INFLUENCE OF THE CHANNELING EFFECT ON THE LUMINESCENCE OF SODIUM CHLORIDE SINGLE CRYSTALS UNDER ION BOMBARDMENT.** SCHALCH, D. SCHARMANN, A. Z. PHYS. 264 (1), 73-84, 1973.
57103	**DOUBLE HYSTERESIS LOOPS IN GADOLINIUM MOLYBDATE(VI).** KUMADA, A. J. PHYS. SOC. JAP. 35 (3), 941, 1973.
57104	**PHONON STRUCTURES IN THE EXCITATION SPECTRA OF THE INTRINSIC LUMINESCENCE OF POTASSIUM IODIDE UNDER TWO PHOTON EXCITATION.** YOSHINARI, T. HIRAI, M. J. PHYS. SOC. JAP. 35 (3), 942, 1973.
57106	**FERROELECTRIC TYPE OF HYSTERESIS LOOP OBSERVED IN BERYLLIUM OXIDE.** SAWADA, S. HIROTSU, S. IWAMURA, H. SHIROISHI, Y. J. PHYS. SOC. JAP. 35 (3), 946, 1973.
57107	**MAGNETIC PROPERTIES OF (IRON-METAL) CARBIDES WHERE M = CHROMIUM OR NICKEL.** SHIGEMATSU, T. NAKANISHI, N. KACHI, S. J. PHYS. SOC. JAP. 35 (4), 1250, 1973.

EPIC Number	Bibliographic Citation
57108	**MAGNETIC PROPERTIES OF COMPOUNDS IN THE CHROMIUM–SELENIUM SYSTEM.** YUZURI, M. J. PHYS. SOC. JAP. 35 (4), 1252, 1973.
57110	**ELECTRICAL PROPERTIES OF CHROMIUM(III) SULFIDE SINGLE CRYSTALS.** SUGIURA, T. MASUDA, Y. J. PHYS. SOC. JAP. 35 (4), 1254, 1973.
57111	**HIGH–FIELD MAGNETIC SUSCEPTIBILITY OF IRON–PLATINUM ALLOYS.** SUMIYAMA, K. GRAHAM, G. M. NAKAMURA, Y. J. PHYS. SOC. JAP. 35 (4), 1255, 1973.
57112	**HALL MOBILITY IN TIN(IV) SULFIDE SINGLE CRYSTALS.** ISHIZAWA, Y. FUJIKI, Y. J. PHYS. SOC. JAP. 35 (4), 1259, 1973.
57113	**RELAXED EXCITED STATES OF THE PAIRED SILVER NEGATIVE ION CENTER IN POTASSIUM CHLORIDE.** TAKEZOE, H. ONAKA, R. J. PHYS. SOC. JAP. 35 (4), 1260, 1973.
57114	**NEGATIVE MAGNETORESISTANCE IN P–ZINC ARSENIDE.** IWAMI, M. FUJISHIMA, K. KAWABE, K. J. PHYS. SOC, JAP. 35 (4), 1261, 1973.
57115	**HYDROSTATIC PRESSURE EFFECT ON THE ELECTRICAL PROPERTIES OF NICKEL COPPER SULFIDE AND NICKEL COBALT SULFIDE.** YOMO, S. MORI, N. MITSUI, T. OGAWA, S. J. PHYS. SOC. JAP. 35 (4), 1263, 1973.
57117	**DISPERSION OF REFRACTIVE INDEXES ON A NEW FERROELECTRIC SINGLE CRYSTAL LEAD NIOBIUM OXIDE.** KONDO, Y. J. PHYS. SOC. JAP. 35 (4), 1266, 1973.
57118	**MICROWAVE PERMITTIVITY OF POTASSIUM TRIDEUTERIUM SELENITE.** DAS, S. N. J. PHYS. SOC. JAP. 35 (4), 1267, 1973.
57119	**EFFECT OF HYDROSTATIC PRESSURE ON THE FERROELECTRIC CURIE TEMPERATURE OF RUBIDIUM BISULFATE.** GESI, K. OZAWA, K. J. PHYS. SOC. JAP. 35 (4), 1268, 1973.
57120	**NEUTRON DIFFRACTION STUDIES OF FERROELECTRIC LEAD GERMANATE ABOVE THE CURIE POINT.** IWATA, Y. KOYANO, N. SHIBUYA, I. J. PHYS. SOC. JAP. 35 (4), 1269, 1973.
57124	**MAGNETIC AND MOESSBAUER STUDIES OF THE ORDERED PEROVSKITES IRON RHENIUM STRONTIUM OXIDE.** ABE, M. NAKAGAWA, T. NOMURA, S. J. PHYS. SOC. JAP. 35 (5), 1360–5, 1973.
57127	**LATTICE VIBRATIONS OF CADMIUM MAGNESIUM TELLURIDE MIXED CRYSTALS.** NAKASHIMA, S. FUKUMOTO, T. MITSUISHI, A. ITOH, K. J. PHYS. SOC. JAP. 35 (5), 1437–41, 1973.
57129	**MAGNETIC PROPERTIES OF IRON TITANIUM SULFIDE.** MURANAKA, S. J. PHYS. SOC. JAP. 35 (5), 1553, 1973.
57135	**BAND STRUCTURE OF CADMIUM ANTIMONIDE.** YAMADA, Y. J. PHYS. SOC. JAP. 35 (6), 1600–7, 1973.
57138	**SILVER(1–) ION CENTERS IN ALKALI HALIDES. IV. CHARACTERISTIC FEATURES OF SILVER(1–) ION CENTERS.** SHIMANUKI, S. J. PHYS. SOC. JAP. 35 (6), 1680–7, 1973.
57141	**IONIC TRANSPORT PROPERTIES OF LEAD–DOPED RUBIDIUM CHLORIDE.** MISRA, K. D. SHARMA, M. N. J. PHYS. SOC. JAP. 36 (1), 154–7, 1974.
57142	**EXCITON LUMINESCENCE IN THALLIUM BROMIDE AND THALLIUM CHLORIDE.** SHIMIZU, R. KODA, T. MURAHASHI, T. J. PHYS. SOC. JAP. 36 (1), 161–8, 1974.
57143	**EFFECT OF HIGH–DENSITY EXCITONS ON THE EXCITON BANDS IN COPPER(I) CHLORIDE.** KATO, Y. GOTO, T. FUJII, T. UETA, M. J. PHYS. SOC. JAP. 36 (1), 169–76, 1974.
57144	**LITHIUM GADOLINIUM MOLYBDATE. NEW PARAMAGNETIC, FERROELECTRIC CRYSTAL.** PANDEY, R. K. J. PHYS. SOC. JAP. 36 (1), 177–8, 1974.
57146	**PARAMAGNETIC RESONANCE AND STATIC SUSCEPTIBILITY MEASUREMENTS IN GADOLINIUM–ZINC.** DEBRAY, D. RYBA, E. J. PHYS. 32 (2–3), (SUPPL.), 11–30–2, 1971.
57148	**SUPERCONDUCTIVITY AND FERROMAGNETISM OF URANIUM COMPOUNDS.** MATTHIAS, B. T. J. PHYS. (PARIS) 32 (2–3) 607–8, 1971.
57149	**CRYSTALLOGRAPHIC, MAGNETIC, AND ELASTIC PROPERTIES OF RUBIDIUM COBALT FLUORIDE.** ALLAIN, Y. DENIS, J. HERPIN, A. LECOMTE, J. MERIEL, P. NOUET, J. PLICQUE, F. ZAREMBOVITCH, A. J. PHYS. 32 (2–3) (SUPPL.), 611–13, 1971.
57152	**MAGNETIC ANISOTROPIC BEHAVIOR OF RUBIDIUM COBALT NICKEL FLUORIDE.** ELBINGER, G. JAEGER, E. KEILIG, W. PERTHEL, R. J. PHYS. 32 (2–3) (SUPPL.), 625–6, 1971.
57153	**MAGNETIC ANISOTROPY IN RUBIDIUM NICKEL FLUORIDE WITH COBALT AND CALCIUM SUBSTITUTIONS.** MC GUIRE, T. R. SHAFER, M. W. J. PHYS. 32 (2–3) (SUPPL.), 627–8, 1971.
57154	**THERMAL EXPANSION AND MAGNETOSTRICTION OF WEAK ITINERANT FERROMAGNETS SCANDIUM–INDIUM AND ZIRCONIUM–ZINC.** FAWCETT, E. MEINCKE, P. P. M. J. PHYS. 32 (2–3) (SUPPL.), 629–31, 1971.
57157	**MAGNETIC ORDER OF THE COMPOUND SERIES RARE EARTH–MANGANESE–IRON.** KIRCHMAYR, H. R. STEINER, W. J. PHYS. 32 (2–3) (SUPPL.), 665–7, 1971.
57168	**MAGNETIC BEHAVIOR OF THE TWO–DIMENSIONAL ANTIFERROMAGNET BARIUM IRON FLUORIDE.** EIBSCHUETZ, M. HOLMES, L. GUGGENHEIM, H. J. COX, D. E. J. PHYS. 32 (2–3) (SUPPL.), 759–60, 1971.
57169	**IRREVERSIBLE PHOTOINDUCED CHANGE IN THE OPTICAL ABSORPTION OF SILICON–DOPED YTTRIUM IRON GARNET ON IRRADIATION.** DILLON, J. F., JR. GYORGY, E. M. REMEIKA, J. P. J. PHYS. 32 (2–3) (SUPPL.), 794–5, 1971.
57171	**ANISOTROPY OF NICKEL(II) AND –(III) IONS IN CUBIC SITES.** POINTON, A. J. ROBERTSON, J. M. WETTON, G. A. J. PHYS. 32 (2–3) (SUPPL.), 850–2, 1971.
57173	**MAGNETIC PROPERTIES OF TETRAGOLD TYPE ORDERED ALLOYS.** SATO, H. YESSIK, M. NOAKES, J. E. J. PHYS. (PARIS) (SUPPL.) 32 (2–3), 865–7, 1971.
57177	**LINEAR CHAIN ANTIFERROMAGNET POTASSIUM COPPER FLUORIDE AND FERROMAGNET POTASSIUM COPPER FLUORIDE.** HIRAKAWA, K. YAMADA, I. KUROGI, Y. J. PHYS. 32 (2–3) (SUPPL.), 890–1, 1971.
57179	**NUCLEAR MAGNETIC RESONANCE AND RELAXATION IN PLUTONIUM–URANIUM–ALUMINUM.** FRADIN, F. Y. BRODSKY, M. B. ARKO, A. J. J. PHYS. 32 (2–3) (SUPPL.), 905–6, 1971.

EPIC Number	Bibliographic Citation
57180	EFFECT OF CARBON CONCENTRATION ON THE MAGNETIC PROPERTIES AND HYPERFINE INTERACTIONS OF NEPTUNIUM MONOCARBIDE. LAM, D. J. MUELLER, M. H. PAULIKAS, A. P. LANDER, G. H. J. PHYS. 32 (2-3) (SUPPL.), 917-19, 1971.
57181	NEAR-INFRARED PHOTOLUMINESCENCE OF THE EUROPIUM CHALCOGENIDES AND A PROPOSED MAGNETIC POLARON MODEL. BUSCH, G. STREIT, P. WACHTER, P. J. PHYS. 32 (2-3) (SUPPL.), 926-7, 1971.
57182	OPTICAL TRANSITIONS AND THE ENERGY LEVEL SCHEME OF THE EUROPIUM CHALCOGENIDES. BUSCH, G. GUENTHERODT, G. WACHTER, P. J. PHYS. 32 (2-3) (SUPPL.), 928-9, 1971.
57183	TEMPERATURE DEPENDENCE OF PHOTOCONDUCTIVITY IN CADMIUM CHROMIUM SELENIDE. BERGER, S. B. AMITH, A. J. PHYS. 32 (2-3) (SUPPL.), 934-6, 1971.
57187	MAGNETIZATION PROCESSES IN HELICAL MANGANESE PHOSPHIDE. NAGAMIYA, T. HIYAMIZU, S. J. PHYS. 32 (2-3) (SUPPL.), 972-3, 1971.
57190	HEAT CAPACITY OF FOUR MANGANESE DOUBLE CHLORIDES. BLOTE, H. W. J. HUISKAMP, W. J. J. PHYS. 32 (2-3) (SUPPL.), 1005-7, 1971.
57194	HYSTERESIS MEASUREMENTS ON RARE EARTH-COBALT MICROPARTICLES. ZIJLSTRA, H. J. PHYS. 32 (2-3) (SUPPL.), 1039-40, 1971.
57195	METAL-INSULATOR TRANSITIONS IN TRANSITION METAL OXIDES. MC WHAN, D. B. MENTH, A. REMEIKA, J. P. J. PHYS. (SUPPL.) (PARIS) 32 (2-3), 1079-85, 1971.
57198	MAGNETIC SUSCEPTIBILITY AND NUCLEAR RESONANCE STUDIES OF METAL-INSULATOR TRANSITION OF CHROMIUM VANADIUM OXIDE AND ALUMINUM VANADIUM OXIDE. MENTH, A. GOSSARD, A. C. REMEIKA, J. P. J. PHYS. 32 (2-3) (SUPPL.), 1107-9, 1971.
57208	RESEARCH OF THE DEPARTMENT OF SOLID STATE PHYSICS. KOZLOWSKI, L. PIECH, T. ZESZ. NAUK. AKAD. GORN.-HUTN., CRACOW, MET. ODLEW. (51), 55-66, 1973.
57210	STRAIN SENSITIVITY OF P-TYPE GALLIUM PHOSPHIDE. LEVCHENKO, P. V. MAR'YAMOVA, I. I. ZB. NAUK. ROB. ASPIR. L'VIV. POLITEKH. INST. (7), 122-8, 1973.
57216	SPECIFIC HEAT OF THE ANTIFERROMAGNETIC GARNET CALCIUM GERMANIUM MANGANESE OXIDE. BELOV, K. P. VALYANSKAYA, T. V. MAMSUROVA, L. G. SOKOLOV, V. I. ZH. EKSP. TEOR. FIZ. 65 (3), 1133-40, 1973.
57217	NATURE OF THE MAGNETIZATION DISCONTINUITY IN THE MANGANESE-BISMUTH PARTICLES. SHTOL'TS, E. V. KAUNOV, N. G. ZH. EKSP. TEOR. FIZ. 65 (4), 1454-9, 1973.
57222	MAGNETIC PROPERTIES OF ULTRAFINE IRON OXIDE PARTICLES. KRUPYANSKII, YU. F. SUZDALEV, I. P. ZH. EKSP. TEOR. FIZ. 65 (4), 1715-25, 1973.
57229	ENERGY STATES OF LOCALIZED ELECTRONS IN STRONGLY COMPENSATED N-INDIUM ANTIMONIDE. ARENDARCHUK, V. V. GERSHENZON, E. M. LITVAK-GORSKAYA, L. B. RABINOVICH, R. I. ZH. EKSP. TEOR. FIZ. 65 (6), 2387-98, 1973.
57231	MAGNETIC SUSCEPTIBILITY AND WEAK FERROMAGNETISM IN NICKEL(II) FLUORIDE AT 4.2 K. BAZHAN, A. N. ZH. EKSP. TEOR. FIZ. 65 (6), 2479-86, 1973.
57235	OPTICAL PROPERTIES OF SOME COMPOUNDS OF POTASSIUM AND SODIUM WITH SULFUR. VLADIMIROV, P. S. DMITRIEVA, A. M. ZH. FIZ. KHIM. 47 (8), 2169, 1973.
57238	ELECTRIC CONDUCTIVITY OF RUBIDIUM NITRATE AT HIGH HYDROSTATIC PRESSURES. MURIN, I. V. KORNEEV, B. F. ZH. FIZ. KHIM. 47 (9), 2405-6, 1973.
57239	MEASUREMENT OF THE TRANSFERENCE NUMBERS OF SOME ALKALI METAL CHROMATES. BURMISTROVA, N. P. KULESHOV, V. P. ZH. FIZ. KHIM. 47 (10), 2491-4, 1973.
57245	DISPERSION OF THE REFRACTIVE INDEX, REFRACTION, AND POLARIZABILITY OF CARBON DIOXIDE. TIMOSHENKO, N. I. KHOLODOV, E. P. YAMNOV, A. L. ZH. FIZ. KHIM. 47 (11), 2952, 1973.
57249	EFFECT OF A SENSITIZING DYE ON THE EFFECTIVE MOBILITY OF CURRENT CARRIERS IN LAYERS OF POLYCRYSTALLINE ZINC OXIDE. POVKHAN, T. I. AKIMOV, I. A. ZH. NAUCH. PRIKL. FOTOGR. KINEMATOGR. 18 (5), 378-80, 1973.
57259	ENERGY GAP VARIATIONS AND STRUCTURAL PHASE CHANGES IN CADMIUM SULFIDE-TELLURIUM ALLOY THIN FILMS. HILL, R. RICHARDSON, D. THIN SOLID FILMS 18 (1), 25-8, 1973.
57266	OPTICAL PROPERTIES OF THIN FILMS OF ANTIMONY TRIOXIDE. BUTTERFIELD, A. W. MC DERMOTT, I. T. THIN SOLID FILMS 18 (1), 111-16, 1973.
57272	BARRIER-LIMITED MOBILITY IN THIN SEMICONDUCTOR FILMS. ANDERSON, J. C. THIN SOLID FILMS 18 (2), 239-45, 1973.
57273	PREPARATION AND PROPERTIES OF THIN FILMS OF ZINC OXIDE FOR HYPERSONIC TRANSDUCERS. CHERNETS, A. N. KENIGSBERG, N. L. THIN SOLID FILMS 18 (2), 247-55, 1973.
57279	OPTICAL PROPERTIES OF ZIRCONIUM DIBORIDE THIN FILMS. LINTON, R. C. THIN SOLID FILMS 20 (1), 17-21, 1973.
57281	PROPERTIES OF GALLIUM SELENIDE THIN FILMS FORMED BY THE THREE-TEMPERATURE METHOD. PERSIN, M. PERSIN, A. POPOVIC, S. CELUSTKA, B. THIN SOLID FILMS 20 (1), 75-80, 1973.
57286	INFRARED ABSORPTION BY SMALL AMORPHOUS QUARTZ SPHERES. STEYER, T. R. DAY, K. L. HUFFMAN, D. R. APPL. OPT. 13 (7), 1586-90, 1974.
57287	REFRACTIVE INDEX DETERMINATION OF LAYERED COMPOUND ZINC INDIUM SULFIDE. ANEDDA, A. APPL. OPT. 13 (7), 1595-8, 1974.
57288	PULSED DYE LASER SYSTEM FOR RAMAN AND LUMINESCENCE SPECTROSCOPY. BELL, M. I. TYTE, R. N. APPL. OPT. 13 (7), 1610-14, 1974.
57289	INTERFEROMETRIC NULL METHOD FOR MEASURING STRESS-INDUCED BIREFRINGENCE. BIRNBAUM, G. CORY, E. GOW, K. APPL. OPT. 13 (7), 1660-9, 1974.
57295	KINETIC PROPERTIES OF THE ALLOY COPPER SULFUR TELLURIDE. ASTAKHOV, O. P. HIGH TEMP. 11 (5), 1000-2, 1973. (ENGLLISH TRANSLATION OF TEPLOFIZ. VYS. TEMP., 11 (5), 1121-3, 1973; FOR ORIGINAL SEE E56861)
57296	EFFECT OF ADDITIONS OF LEAD AND BISMUTH ON THE ELECTRICAL CONDUCTIVITY AND THERMO-ELECTRO-MOTIVE-FORCE OF ANTIMONY SELENIDE IN THE LIQUID STATE. KAZANDZHAN, B. I. MISHUTKINA, T. I. TSEDERBERG, N. V. HIGH TEMP. 11 (5), 1003-4, 1973. (ENGLISH TRANSLATION OF TEPLOFIZ. VYS. TEMP., 11 (5), 1124-5, 1973; FOR ORIGINAL SEE E56862)

EPIC Number *Bibliographic Citation*

57297 PROPERTIES AND STRUCTURE OF GLASSES IN THE SYSTEM LEAD MONOXIDE–GERMANIUM DIOXIDE–SILICON DIOXIDE.
TOPPING, J. A. FUCHS, P. MURTHY, M. K.
J. AMER. CERAM. SOC.
57 (5), 205–8, 1974.

57298 PROPERTIES AND STRUCTURE OF GLASSES IN THE SYSTEM LEAD MONOXIDE–GERMANIUM DIOXIDE.
TOPPING, J. A. HARROWER, I. T. MURTHY, M. K.
J. AMER. CERAM. SOC.
57 (5), 209–12, 1974.

57299 MAGNETIC PROPERTIES OF AN AMORPHOUS ANTIFERROMAGNET.
FRIEBELE, E. J. KOON, N. C. WILSON, L. K.
KINSER, D. L.
J. AMER. CERAM. SOC.
57 (6), 237–41, 1974.

57300 ELECTRICAL CONDUCTION IN SINGLE-CRYSTAL AND POLYCRYSTALLINE ALUMINUM OXIDE AT HIGH TEMPERATURES.
KITAZAWA, K. COBLE, R. L.
J. AMER. CERAM. SOC.
57 (6), 245–50, 1974.

57302 ELECTRICAL AND OPTICAL PROPERTIES OF TIN OXIDE FILMS.
ROHATGI, A. VIVERITO, T. R. SLACK, L. H.
J. AMER. CERAM. SOC.
57 (6), 278–9, 1974.

57303 DAMAGE OF SINGLE-CRYSTAL ALUMINUM OXIDE BY 14–ME V NEUTRONS.
BUNCH, J. M. CLINARD, F. W., JR.
J. AMER. CERAM. SOC.
57 (6), 279–80, 1974.

57305 ANALYSIS OF THE BEHAVIOR OF ERBIUM TRIPOSITIVE IN ZIRCON-STRUCTURE SYSTEMS.
VISHWAMITTAR PURI, S. P.
PHYS. REV.
9 B (11), 4673–89, 1974.

57306 COMPARISON OF THE JAHN-TELLER EFFECT IN FOUR TRIPLY DEGENERATE STATES OF MANGANESE IN RUBIDIUM MANGANESE FLUORIDE.
SOLOMON, E. I. MC CLURE, D. S.
PHYS. REV.
9 B (11), 4690–4718, 1974.

57310 EVALUATION OF THE COUPLED PROTON-OPTIC-MODE MODEL FOR POTASSIUM DIHYDROGEN PHOSPHATE AND ISOMORPHOUS RUBIDIUM DIHYDROGEN PHOSPHATE.
PEERCY, P. S.
PHYS. REV.
9 B (11), 4868–71, 1974.

57319 ENERGY BANDS AND FERMI SURFACE OF GOLD TIN.
ARLINGHAUS, F. J.
PHYS. REV.
9 B (12), 5071–6, 1974.

57322 TEMPERATURE DEPENDENCE OF THE BAND STRUCTURE OF GERMANIUM- AND ZINC-BLENDE-TYPE SEMICONDUCTORS.
AUVERGNE, D. CAMASSEL, J. MATHIEU, H.
CARDONA, M.
PHYS. REV.
9 B (12), 5168–77, 1974.

57323 POLARIZED-LIGHT PHOTEMISSION STUDIES OF WURTZITE CADMIUM SULFIDE.
DERBENWICK, G. F. POWELL, R. A.
SPICER, W. E.
PHYS. REV.
9 B (12), 5178–82, 1974.

57324 ANOMALOUS MOBILITY BEHAVIOR IN CADMIUM SULFIDE AND CADMIUM TELLURIDE: ELECTRICAL EVIDENCE FOR IMPURITY PAIRS.
WOODBURY, H. H.
PHYS. REV.
9 B (12), 5188–94, 1974.

57325 SHALLOW-DONOR IONIZATION ENERGIES IN THE II–VI COMPOUNDS.
WOODBURY, H. H. AVEN, M.
PHYS. REV.
9 B (12), 5195–5202, 1974.

57326 SOME PROPERTIES OF SILVER ALUMINUM TELLURIDE, SILVER GALLIUM TELLURIDE, AND SILVER INDIUM TELLURIDE.
TELL, B. SHAY, J. L. KASPER, H. M.
PHYS. REV.
9 B (12), 5203–8, 1974.

57334 INVESTIGATION OF THERMAL CONDUCTIVITY, THERMAL DIFFUSIVITY, AND EMITTANCE OF SEMITRANSPARENT MATERIALS AT HIGH TEMPERATURES.
MEN, A. A. SERGEEV, O. A.
HIGH TEMP. HIGH PRESSURES
5 (1), 19–28, 1973.

57337 LUMINESCENCE SPECTRUM FINE STRUCTURE OF CADMIUM SULFIDE SINGLE CRYSTALS IN THE REGION OF LOCALIZED STATES.
BRODIN, M. S. VITRIKHOVSKII, N. I.
KRITSKII, A. V.
UKR. FIZ. ZH.
17 (5), 825–9, 1972.

57344 STUDY OF INFRARED AND THERMAL EXTINCTION OF LUMINESCENCE AND PHOTOCONDUCTIVITY IN COPPER AND CHLORINE DOPED ZINC CADMIUM SULFIDE.
VLASENKO, N. A. KONOVETS, K.
UKR. FIZ. ZH.
17 1582–1591, 1972.

57346 HIGH TEMPERATURE INVESTIGATIONS OF THE STEADY AND NONEQUILIBRIUM ELECTRICAL CONDUCTIVITY OF CADMIUM SULFIDE CRYSTALS.
RUD, IU. V. SANIN, K. V.
UKR. FIZ. ZH.
18, 610–615, 1973.

57348 INFLUENCE OF INTERVALLEY SCATTERING ON THE SIZE EFFECT IN THE ELECTRICAL CONDUCTIVITY OF SEMICONDUCTORS.
GORKUN, YU. I.
UKR. FIZ. ZH.
18, 739–748, 1973.

57349 TEMPERATURE DEPENDENCE OF PARAMAGNETIC SUSCEPTIBILITY IN INDIUM- AND ALUMINUM-SUBSTITUTED FERRITES OF M TYPE.
EFIMOVA, N. N. MAMALUI, YU. A.
UKR. FIZ. ZH.
18 (7), 1114–16, 1973.

57353 LUMINESCENCE OF NICKEL-ACTIVATED LITHIUM CHLORIDE CRYSTALS.
ANTONYAK, O. T. VISHNEVSKII, V. N.
PIDZYRAILO, N. S. TOKARIVSKII, M. V.
UKR. FIZ. ZH. (RUSS. ED.)
18 (8), 1338–43, 1973.

57354 EFFECT OF HEAT TREATMENT OF ELECTRICAL AND MECHANICAL PROPERTIES OF CRYSTALS WITH CENTERS OF THE COLLOID TYPE.
RAKITYANSKAYA, O. F. MOZGOVAYA, L. A.
UKR. FIZ. ZH. (RUSS. ED.)
18 (8), 1354–7, 1973.

57355 INVESTIGATION OF THE ELECTRICAL CONDUCTIVITY OF SINGLE CADMIUM SELENIUM CRYSTALS AT HIGH TEMPERATURES.
RUD', IU. V. SANIN, K. V.
UKR. FIZ. ZH.
18, 1373–9, 1973.

57356 ELECTRICAL CONDUCTIVITY OF CADMIUM SELENIDE SINGLE CRYSTALS IN A HIGH-TEMPERATURE RANGE.
RUD, YU. V. SANIN, K. V.
UKR. FIZ. ZH. (RUSS. ED.)
18 (8), 1377–83, 1973.

57361 MECHANISM OF INDUCED MAGNETIC ANISOTROPY IN SOME FERRITES WITH SPINEL STRUCTURES.
LETYUK, L. M.
UKR. FIZ. ZH. (RUSS. ED.)
18 (9), 1481–5, 1973.

57365 IMPURITY INFRARED ABSORPTION IN HEXAGONAL ALPHA-SILICON CARBIDE.
ODARICH, V. A.
UKR. FIZ. ZH.
18 (9), 1562–4, 1973.

57367 RECOMBINATION FEATURES AND ELECTRICAL INSTABILITY IN GALLIUM ARSENIDE COMPENSATED WITH CHROMIUM.
VOROB'EVA, N. V. VOROB'EV, YU. V.
ZAKHARCHENKO, V. N. KARKHANIN, YU. I.
TRETYAK, O. V.
UKR. FIZ. ZH. (RUSS. ED.)
18 (10), 1664–8, 1973.

57371 PHOTOCONDUCTIVITY OF ACTIVATED CADMIUM BROMIDE SINGLE CRYSTALS.
KUSHNIR, O. B.
UKR. FIZ. ZH. (RUSS. ED.)
18 (10), 1732–4, 1973.

57375 EFFECT OF INFRARED RADIATION ON THE CHARGE EXCHANGE OF IMPURITY CENTERS IN HEXAGONAL ALPHA-SILICON CARBIDE CRYSTALS.
GORBAN, I. S. LUGOVOI, V. I.
SLOBODYANYUK, A. V.
UKR. FIZ. ZH. (RUSS. ED.)
18 (11), 1769–72, 19739

57378 POLARIZATION PROPERTIES OF DOPED ANTIMONY IODIDE SULFIDE.
TURYANITSA, I. D. KOPERLES, B. M.
SEMAK, D. G. MIKHAL'KO, I. M.
KININESHI, A. A.
UKR. FIZ. ZH. (RUSS. ED.)
18 (11), 1918–20, 1973.

EPIC Number	Bibliographic Citation

57387 LIGHT EMISSION FROM HOT ELECTRONS IN ZINC SELENIDE.
TURBEY, K. ALLEN, J. W.
J. PHYS.
6 C (19), 2887-97, 1973.

57390 HALL AND DRIFT MOBILITY OF POLAR P-TYPE SEMICONDUCTORS. I. THEORY.
KRANZER, D.
J. PHYS.
6 C (20), 2967-76, 1973.

57391 HALL AND DRIFT MOBILITY OF POLAR P-TYPE SEMICONDUCTORS. II. APPLICATION TO ZINC TELLURIDE, CADMIUM TELLURIDE, AND ZINC SELENIDE.
KRANZER, D.
J. PHYS.
6 C (20), 2977-87, 1973.

57392 AVERAGE NUCLEAR EFFECTIVE CHARGE IN TETRAHEDRAL SEMICONDUCTORS.
GARBATO, L. MANCA, P. MULA, G.
J. PHYS.
6 C (20), 2988-92, 1973.

57395 OSCIALLATORY MAGNETORESISTANCE OF HEAVILY DOPED SEMICONDUCTORS AT LOW TEMPERATURES.
VAN CONG, H.
J. PHYS.
6 C (22), 3275-81, 1973.

57396 MAGNETOPHONON EFFECT IN GALLIUM ARSENIDE AND INDIUM PHOSPHIDE TO HIGH PRESSURES.
PITT, G. D. LEES, J. HOULT, R. A.
STRADLING, R. A.
J. PHYS.
6 C (22), 3282-94, 1973.

57398 ELECTRONIC PROPERTIES OF II-VI SEMICONDUCTORS.
GARBATO, L. MANCA, P. MULA, G.
J. PHYS.
6 C (23), L441-4, 1973.

57400 RELIABILITY OF THE SEMIEMPIRICAL TIGHT-BINDING METHOD FOR BAND STRUCTURE CALCULATIONS.
CASULA, F. EDMONDSON, D. R.
J. PHYS.
6 C (23), 3403-12, 1973.

57403 CALCULATIONS OF IMPURITY STATES IN SEMICONDUCTORS. II. OXYGEN-DOPED GALLIUM PHOSPHIDE.
JAROS, M. ROSS, S. F.
J. PHYS.
6 C (23), 3451-6, 1973.

57404 THEORY FOR THE MULTIPLET STRUCTURE OF THE FAR-INFRARED ABSORPTION BY OFF-CENTERED IMPURITIES. II. (111) OFF-CENTERED IMPURITIES.
PANDEY, G. K. SHUKALA, D. K. PANDEY, A.
J. PHYS.
6 C (23), 3514-24, 1973.

57405 BAND STRUCTURE AND PHOTOEMISSION STUDIES OF TIN(IV) SULFIDE AND TIN(IV) SELENIDE. I. EXPERIMENTAL.
WILLIAMS, R. H. MURRAY, R. B.
GOVAN, D. W. THOMAS, J. M. EVANS, E. L.
J. PHYS.
6 C (24), 3631-42, 1973.

57406 BAND STRUCTRE AND PHOTOEMISSION STUDIES OF TIN(IV) SULFIDE AND TIN(IV) SELENIDE. II. THEORETICAL.
MURRAY, R. B. WILLIAMS, R. H.
J. PHYS.
6 C (24), 3643-51, 1973.

57407 THEORY OF PHOTOCONDUCTIVITY IN AMORPHOUS SEMICONDUCTORS CONTAINING SLOWLY-VARYING TRAP DISTRIBUTIONS.
SIMMONS, J. G. TAYLOR, G. W.
J. PHYS.
6 C (24), 3706-18, 1973.

57423 ANISOTROPIC AND ANOMALOUS SUSCEPTIBLITIES OF THE ONE-DIMENSIONAL ANTIFERROMAGNET POTASSIUM TRIFLUOROCUPRATE(II).
HIRAKAWA, K. MIKE, H.
PHYS. LETT.
45 A (2), 79-80, 1973.

57426 FORMATION AND GROWTH OF F-CENTERS IN CADMIUM-DOPED SODIUM CHLORIDE CRYSTALS. THERMOLUMINESCENCE STUDIES.
SANSORES, L. E. MUNOX, E.
VALLADARES, A. A.
PHYS. LETT.
45 A (2), 125-6, 1973.

57428 PERTURBATION OF INTRINSIC LUMINESCENCE BY LATTICE DEFECTS IN SODIUM CHLORIDE.
IKEYA, M. CRAWFORD, J. H., JR.
PHYS. LETT.
45 A (3), 213-14, 1973.

57431 CRITICAL PHENOMENA OF FERROMAGNETIC COBALT DISULFIDE.
JIBU, M. ISHIKAWA, Y. TAJIMA, K.
PHYS. LETT.
45 A (3), 235-6, 1973.

EPIC Number	Bibliographic Citation

57438 NEGATIVE TEMPERATURE COEFFICIENT OF RESISTANCE AND SUPERCONDUCTIVITY OF NIOBIUM NITRIDE THIN FILMS.
AYER, W. J., JR. ROSE, K.
PHYS. LETT.
45 A (4), 333-4, 1973.

57440 IMPURITY STATES IN OXYGEN-DOPED GALLIUM ARSENIDE.
ROSS, S. F. JAROS, M.
PHYS. LETT.
45 A (5), 355-6, 1973.

57444 IONICITY, VALENCY, AND BAND INVERSION IN LEAD TIN TELLURIDE.
WEMPLE, S. H.
PHYS. LETT.
45 A (5), 401-3, 1973.

57446 LOW TEMPERATURE MAGNETIZATION OF TERBIUM - ALUMINUM SINGLE CRYSTALS.
PURWINS, H. G. WALKER, E. BARBARA, B.
ROSSIGNOL, M. F.
PHYS. LETT.
45 A (5), 427-8, 1973.

57448 POTASSIUM IODATE. FIRST FERROELECTRIC WITH NONREORIENTABLE AND NON- 180 DEGREES SWITCHABLE COMPONENTS OF SPONTANEOUS POLARIZATION.
IVANOV, N. R. SHUVALOV, L. A.
CHIKHLADZE, O. A.
PHYS. LETT.
45 A (6), 437-8, 1973.

57453 OPTICAL PROPERTIES OF THE LAYER COMPOUND GALLIUM TELLURIDE.
GRASSO, V. MONDIO, G. SAITTA, G.
PHYS. LETT.
46 A (2), 95-6, 1973.

57454 MAGNETOOPTICAL STUDIES OF ACCEPTOR STATES IN MERCURY TELLURIDE.
BASTARD, G. GULDNER, Y. RIGAUX, C.
NGUYEN, H. H. VIEREN, J. P. MENANT, M.
MYCIELSKI, A.
PHYS. LETT.
46 A (2), 99-100, 1973.

57461 THE ENERGY BANDS AND THE FERMI SURFACE OF BETA PRIME SILVER ZINC.
SKRIVER, H. L.
PHYS. STATUS SOLIDI
58 (2), 721-35, 1973.

57468 OPTICAL PROPERTIES AND ENERGY GAP OF GERMANIUM TELLURIDE FROM REFLECTANCE STUDIES.
LEWIS, J. W.
PHYS. STATUS SOLIDI
59 B (1), 367-77, 1973.

57469 SHALLOW DONOR LEVELS IN GALLIUM ARSENIDE.
BASHENOV, V. K.
PHYS. STATUS SOLIDI
59 B (2), K93-6, 1973.

57471 FERROELECTRIC PHASE TRANSITION IN SMALL CRYSTALS OF BARIUM TITANATE.
BAEUERLE, D. GENZEL, L. MARTIN, T. P.
PHYS. STATUS SOLIDI
59 B (2), 459-64, 1973.

57472 PROPERTIES OF INDIUM ANTIMONIDE BISMUTHIDE OR ALLOYS. III. THEORETICAL ESTIMATION OF BANDGAPS.
JEAN-LOUIS, A. M. DURAFFOURG, G.
PHYS. STATUS SOLIDI
59 B (2), 495-503, 1973.

57475 PHONON-ASSISTED D.C. HOPPING CONDUCTIVITY OF AMORPHOUS SEMICONDUCTORS AND SEMICONDUCTING GLASSES.
CAPEK, V.
PHYS. STATUS SOLIDI
60 B (1), K5-K9, 1973.

57479 OPTICAL PHONONS OF BISMUTH(III) TELLURIDE.
UNKELBACH, K. H. BECKER, CH. KOEHLER, H.
MIDDENDORFF, A. V.
PHYS. STATUS SOLIDI
60 B (1), K41-4, 1973.

57480 SURFACE PHOTOVOLTAGE OF MOLYBDENUM(IV) SULFIDE.
MC GOVERN, I. T. WILLIAMS, R. H.
MEE, C. H. B.
PHYS. STATUS SOLIDI
60 B (1), K53-K55, 1973.

57481 ANTIFERROMAGNETISM OF NEPTUNIUM-PLATINUM.
SMITH, J. L. HILL, H. H.
PHYS. STATUS SOLIDI
60 B (1), K61-3, 1973.

57483 VARIATIONAL METHOD IN THE THEORY OF RECIPROCAL ELECTRON AND PHONON DRAG IN SEMICONDUCTORS.
PINCHUK, I. I. LUSTE, O. YA.
PHYS. STATUS SOLIDI
60 B (1), 107-16, 1973.

EPIC Number	Bibliographic Citation

57485 **MOBILITY OF HOLES IN DEFORMED SEMICONDUCTORS.**
DUESTER, F. LABUSCH, R.
PHYS. STATUS SOLIDI
60 B (1), 161–8, 1973.

57486 **ABSORPTION EDGE AND URBACH'S RULE IN ZINC OXIDE.**
JENSEN, G. H. SKETTRUP, T.
PHYS. STATUS SOLIDI
60 B (1), 169–73, 1973.

57487 **CONDUCTANCE OF AMMONIA NEAR THE TRIPLE POINT.**
LEONIDOVA, G. G. POLANDOV, I. N.
RUSS. J. PHYS. CHEM.
47 (5), 709, 1973.
(ENGLISH TRANSLATION OF ZH. FIZ. KHIM., 47 (5), 1261, 1973; FOR ORIGINAL SEE E51348)

57490 **ELECTRICAL CONDUCTIVITY OF ZIRCONIUM AND HAFNIUM TETRACHLORIDES.**
ALEKSEEVA, L. V. BYSTROVA, O. N.
DENISOVA, N. D. KUTSEVA, V. S.
RUSS. J. PHYS. CHEM.
47 (5), 760–1, 1973.
(ENGLISH TRANSLATION OF ZH. FIZ. KHIM., 47 (5), 1338, 1973; FOR ORIGINAL SEE E52377)

57493 **NATURE OF EXO-ELECTRON EMISSION FROM CRYSTAL I. SULPHIDES.**
KRYLOVA, I. V. KONYUSHKINA, N. I.
RUSS. J. PHYS. CHEM.
47 (6), 829–31, 1973.
(ENGLISH TRANSLATION OF ZH. FIZ. KHIM., 47 (6), 1475–8, 1973; FOR ORIGINAL SEE E52380)

57496 **MAGNETIC PROPERTIES OF COBALT OXIDE–ZINC OXIDE SOLID SOLUTIONS.**
KEROVA, L. S. LOGINOV, G. M.
MOROZOVA, M. P.
RUSS. J. PHYS. CHEM.
47 (6), 921–2, 1973.
(ENGLISH TRANSLATION OF ZH. FIZ. KHIM., 47 (6), 1620, 1973; FOR ORIGINAL SEE E52384)

57497 **ELECTRON SPIN RESONANCE AND SUPERCONDUCTIVITY IN GADOLINIUM–LANTHANUM–ALUMINUM INTERMETALLIC COMPOUNDS.**
DAVIDOV, D. CHELKOWSKI, A. RETTORI, C.
ORBACH, R. MAPLE, M. B.
PHYS. REV.
7 B (3), 1029–38, 1973.
(AD 771 556)

57500 **MAMAGNETIC PROPERTIES OF DYSPROSIUM–GOLD AND DYSPROSIUM – SILVER.**
MIURA, S. KANEKO, T. OHASHI, M.
KAMIGAKI, K.
J. PHYS. (PARIS)
32 (2–3), 1124–5, 1971.

57502 **MAGNETIC SUSCEPTIBILITY, ELECTRONIC SPECIFIC HEAT, AND TRANSPORT PROPERTIES OF SOME INTERMETALLIC COMPOUNDS OF CERIUM.**
COOPER, J. R. RIZZUTO, C. OLEESE, G.
J. PHYS. (PARIS)
32 (2–3), 1136–8, 1971.

57503 **MAGNETIC PROPERTIES PF PALLADIUM–RARE EARTH PHASES.**
GARDNER, W. E. PENFOLD, J. HARRIS, I. R.
J. PHYS. (PARIS)
32 (2–3), 1139–40, 1971.

57509 **PROPERTIES OF NARROW WALLS IN FERROMAGNETIC SUBSTANCES WITH STRONG ANISOTROPY.**
BARBARA, B.
J. PHYS. (PARIS)
34 (11–12), 1039–46, 1973.

57513 **ANALYSIS OF COMPLEX THERMOLUMINESCENCE GLOW CURVES.**
ONNIS, S. RUCCI, A.
J. LUMIN.
6 (5), 404–13, 1973.

57516 **CERIUM AND TERBIUM LUMINESCENCE IN LANTHANUM MAGNESIUM ALUMINATE.**
VERSTEGEN, J. M. P. J. SOMMERDIJK, J. L.
VERRIET, J. G.
J. LUMIN.
6 (5), 425–31, 1973.

57518 **SPECTRUM OF TERBIUM TRIPOSITIVE ION IN TERBIUM ALUMINUM GARNET.**
JOSHI, B. D. PAGE, A. G.
J. LUMIN.
6 (5), 441–8, 1973.

57519 **ELECTROLUMINESCENCE COMETS IN ZINC SULFIDE:COPPER SINGLE CRYSTALS SCANNED WITH A NEEDLE ELECTRODE.**
HAUPT, H. NELKOWSKI, H.
J. LUMIN.
6 (5), 449–54, 1973.

57520 **CALCIUM OXIDE PHOSPHORS.**
LEHMANN, W.
J. LUMIN.
6 (5), 455–70, 1973.

57521 **EXCITATION MIGRATION AMONG INHOMOGENEOUSLY BROADENED LEVELS OF EUROPIUM TRIPOSITIVE IONS.**
MOTEGI, N. SHIONOYA, S.
J. LUMIN.
8 (1), 1–17, 1973.

57522 **DONOR–ACCEPTOR PAIR SPECTRA IN 6H AND 4H SILICON CARBIDE DOPED WITH NITROGEN AND ALUMINUM.**
HAGEN, S. H. VAN KEMENADE, A. W. C.
VAN DER DOES DE BYE, J. A. W.
J. LUMIN.
8 (1), 18–31, 1973.

57524 **RADIATIVE AND RADIATIONLESS PROCESSES ON ERBIUM TRIPOSITIVE IONS IN MANGANESE(II) FLUORIDE.**
FLAHERTY, J. M. DI BARTOLO, B.
J. LUMIN.
8 (1), 51–70, 1973.

57527 **LUMINESCENCE OF INSULATING BERYLLIUM–DOPED AND LITHIUM–DOPED GALLIUM NITRIDE.**
PANKOVE, J. I. DUFFY, M. T. MILLER, E. A.
BEKEYHEISER, J. E.
J. LUMIN.
8 (1), 89–93, 1973.

57528 **LUMINESCENCE OF HEXAVALENT URANIUM IN ORDERED PEROVSKITES.**
DE HAIR, J. TH. W. BLASSE, G.
J. LUMIN.
8 (1), 97–100, 1973.

57529 **DIELECTRIC CONSTANT OF GALLIUM PHOSPHIDE FROM A REFINED ANALYSIS OF DONOR–ACCEPTOR PAIR LUMINESCENCE, AND THE DEVIATION OF THE PAIR ENERGY FROM THE COULOMB LAW.**
VINK, A. T. VAN DER HEYDEN, R. L. A.
VAN DER DOES DE BYE, J. A. W.
J. LUMIN.
8 (2), 105–25, 1973.

57530 **INFLUENCE OF THE HOST LATTICE ON THE INFRARED–EXCITED BLUE LUMINESCENCE OF YTTERBIUM TRIPOSITIVE, THULIUM TRIPOSITIVE–DOPED COMPOUNDS.**
SOMMERDIJK, J. L.
J. LUMIN.
8 (2), 126–30, 1973.

57533 **GUDDEN–POHL EFFECT AND SURFACE STATES IN ZINC SULFIDE PHOSPHORS.**
PEKA, G. P. PROSKURA, A. I.
J. LUMIN.
8 (2), 164–75, 1973.

57534 **LUMINESCENCE IN ZINC SELENIDE WITH SODIUM AND ALUMINUM DOPING.**
CHATTERJEE, P. K. ROSA, A. J.
STREETMAN, B. G.
J. LUMIN.
8 (2), 176–82, 1973.

57537 **LASER INDUCED FLUORESCENCE OF CN RADICALS.**
JACKSON, W. M.
J. CHEM. PHYS.
59 (2), 960–1, 1973.

57538 **CRYSTAL SPECTRUM OF PROMETHIUM TRIPOSITIVE IN LANTHANUM CHLORIDE.**
BAER, W. CONWAY, J. G. DAVIS, S. P.
J. CHEM. PHYS.
59 (5), 2294–302, 1973.

57543 **POSSIBLE APPLICATIONS OF SURFACE ELECTROMAGNETIC WAVES TO MEASURE ABSORPTION COEFFICIENTS.**
ALEXANDER, R. W., JR. BELL, R. J.
WARD, C. A. WEAVER, J. H. TYLER, I. L.
FISCHER, B.
J. CHEM. PHYS.
59 (7), 3492–4, 1973.
(AD 779 161)

57547 **MOLECULAR ROTATIONAL ZEEMAN EFFECT IN HYPOFLUOROUS ACID, A COMPARISON WITH WATER, OXYGEN DIFLUORIDE, AND OTHER FLUORINE CONTAINING MOLECULES. DIPOLE MOMENTS OF HYPOFLUOROUS ACID AND DEUTERATED HYPOFLUOROUS ACID.**
ROCK, S. L. PEARSON, E. F. APPLEMAN, E. H.
NORRIS, C. L. FLYGARE, W. H.
J. CHEM. PHYS.
59 (8), 3940–5, 1973.

57557 **ESCA STUDIES OF SOME III–V COMPOUNDS WITH GALLIUM AND ARSENIC.**
LEONHARDT, G. BERNDTSSON, A.
HEDMAN, J. KLASSON M. NILSSON, R.
NORDLING, C.
PHYS. STATUS SOLIDI
60 B (1), 241–8, 1973.

57559 **OPTICAL ABSORPTION BY FREE POLARONS IN CADMIUM OXIDE.**
FINKENRATH, H. FRICKE, W. UHLE, N.
PHYS. STATUS SOLIDI
60 B (1), 341–4, 1973.

EPIC Number	Bibliographic Citation
57560	PHOTOEMISSION AND DENSITY OF VALENCE STATES OF THE II–VI COMPOUNDS. II. ZINC SELENIDE, CADMIUM SULFIDE, AND MERCURY(II) SULFIDE. SHEVCHIK, N. J. TEJEDA, J. LANGER, D. W. CARDONA, M. PHYS. STATUS SOLIDI 60 B (1), 345–55, 1973. (AD 782 812)
57562	DENSITY OF STATES AND CONDUCTIVITY IN HIGHLY IMPURE SEMICONDUCTORS. LUKES, T. ROGERS, B. A. PHYS. STATUS SOLIDI 60 B (1), 385–97, 1973.
57563	PHONON DRAG IN WURTZITE–TYPE SEMICONDUCTORS. BULAT, L. P. PHYS. STATUS SOLIDI 60 B (1), 451–9, 1973.
57565	SPECIFIC HEAT AND RESISTIVITY OF P–TYPE GALLIUM ANTIMONIDE BETWEEN 0.3 AND 4 K. SAINT PAUL, M. JAY–GERIN, J. P. BRIGGS, A. PHYS. STATUS SOLIDI 60 B (2), K83–6, 1973.
57568	CYCLOTRON RESONANCE IN N–TYPE INDIUM PHOSPHIDE AND GALLIUM ARSENIDE. SIMMONDS, P. E. MEHTEIEV, A. SH. PHYS. STATUS SOLIDI 60 B (2), K127–9, 1973.
57571	SUSCEPTIBILITY OF HOLMIUM ARSENATE NEAR THE MAGNETIC PHASE TRANSITION. BECHER, W. KALBFLEISCH, H. PHYS. STATUS SOLIDI 60 B (2), 557–62, 1973.
57573	BAND STRUCTURE OF VANADIUM(II) OXIDE BY THE AUGMENTED PLANE WAVE – LINEAR COMBINATION OF ATOMIC ORBITALS METHOD. KRAAN, D. J. PHYS. STATUS SOLIDI 60 B (2), 587–94, 1973.
57579	GALLIUM ARSENIDE LUMINESCENCE TRANSITIONS TO ACCEPTORS IN MAGNETIC FIELDS. WILLMANN, F. DREYBRODT, W. BETTINI, M. BAUSER, E. BIMBERG, D. PHYS. STATUS SOLIDI 60 B (2), 751–9, 1973.
57584	ANOMALOUS TEMPERATURE DEPENDENCE OF CHARGE CARRIER DENSITY AND MOTT TRANSITION IN FERROMAGNETIC SEMICONDUCTORS. GRIGIN, A. P. NAGAEV, E. L. PHYS. STATUS SOLIDI 61 B (1), 65–75, 1974.
57587	SHUBNIKOV–DE HAAS OSCILLATIONS IN CADMIUM MERCURY SELENIDE. STANKIEWICZ, J. GIRIAT, W. DOBROWOLSKI, W. PHYS. STATUS SOLIDI 61 B (1), 267–76, 1974.
57588	TWO–PHOTON PHOTOCONDUCTIVITY MEASUREMENTS IN A HEXAGONAL ZINC OXIDE CRYSTAL. KOREN, G. PHYS. STATUS SOLIDI 61 B (1), 277–84, 1974.
57589	LUMINESCENCE SPECTRA DUE TO HIGH–DENSITY EXCITONS IN COPPER BROMIDE CHLORIDE MIXED CRYSTALS. SUGA, S. KODA, T. PHYS. STATUS SOLDI 61 B (1), 291–302, 1974.
57590	GALVANO– AND THERMOMAGNETIC PHENOMENA IN N–TYPE INDIUM ANTIMONIDE SEMICONDUCTORS AT INELASTIC OPTICAL SCATTERING. TOLPYGO, KH. I. PHYS. STATUS SOLIDI 61 B (1), 311–23, 1974.
57594	ELECTRICAL CONDUCTIVITY AND STRUCTURE OF MOLTEN BINARY LITHIUM FLUORIDE–ALUMINUM FLUORIDE AND SODIUM FLUORIDE–ALUMINUM FLUORIDE MIXTURES. MATIASOVSKY, K. DANEK, V. J. ELECTROCHEM. SOC. 120 (7), 919–22, 1973.
57595	ELECTRIC PROPERTIES OF VAPOR–DEPOSITED SILICON NITRIDE FILMS MEASURED IN STRONG ELECTRIC FIELDS. CHAUDHARI, P. K. FRANZ, J. M. ACKER, C. P. J. ELECTROCHEM. SOC. 120 (7), 991–3, 1973.
57596	EMISSION OF EUROPIUM(3+) IN SOME CALCIUM GERMANATES. ISAACS, T. J. PRICE, A. A. J. ELECTROCHEM. SOC. 120 (7), 997–9, 1973.
57597	REDUCTION OF CARRIER CONCENTRATION IN LEAD TIN TELLURIDE BY CADMIUM DIFFUSION AND DOPING WITH ZINC. LINDEN, K. J. J. ELECTROCHEM. SOC. 120 (8), 1131–4, 1973.
57598	ELLIPSOMETRY OF MULTILAYERED DIELECTRICS ON SILICON, APPLIED TO MNOS (METAL–NITRIDE–OXIDE–SILICON) LUNDKVIST, L. J. ELECTROCHEM. SOC. 120 (8), 1140–2, 1973.
57599	MAGNETIC PLATING ON NONCONDUCTORS. DE PEW, J. R. J. ELECTROCHEM. SOC. 120 (9), 1187–92, 1973.
57600	EFFECT OF 3D IMPURITIES ON THE SUPERCONDUCTING TRANSITION TEMPERATURE OF THE LAYERED COMPOUND NIOBIUM(IV) SELENIDE. HAUSER, J. J. ROBBINS, M. DI SALVO, F. J. PHYS. REV. 8 B (3), 1038–42, 1973.
57610	FLATBAND ELECTROREFLECTANCE OF GALLIUM ARSENIDE. II. COMPARISON OF THEORY AND EXPERIMENT. POND, S. F. HANDLER, P. PHYS. REV. 8 B (6), 2869–79, 1973.
57613	NONCOLLINEAR–BEAM SECOND–HARMONIC GENERATION IN COPPER(I) CHLORIDE. HAUEISEN, D. C. MAHR, H. PHYS. REV. 8 B (6), 2969–74, 1973.
57614	MECHANISM OF ION MOVEMENT IN ALKALI HALIDES. RAMDAS, S. SHUKLA, A. K. RAO, C. N. R. PHYS. REV. 8 B (6), 2975–81, 1973.
57618	MOESSBAUER STUDY OF FERRIMAGNETIC IRON SELENIDE. OK, H. N. LEE, S. W. PHYS. REV. 8 B (9), 4267–9, 1973.
57622	STUDY OF V CENTERS IN CESIUM IODIDE CRYSTAL. SIDLER, T. PELLAUX, J.–P. NOUAIHAT, A. SOLID STATE COMMUN. 13 (4), 479–82, 1973.
57624	PARAMAGNETIC SUSCEPTIBILITY AND TRANSITION AT LOW TEMPERATURE. II. SUPERCONDUCTIVITY OF A–15 COMPOUNDS AND THEIR MAGNETIC PROPERTIES. KODESS, B. N. SOLID STATE COMMUN. 13 (5), 527–30, 1973.
57629	DEEP TRAPS IN ZINC TELLURIDE CRYSTALS. RIBEIRO, C. A. PAUTRAT, J. L. SOLID STATE COMMUN. 13 (5), 589–93, 1973.
57633	MIXED ANIONIC CONDUCTION IN LEAD(II) FLUORIDE CHLORIDE. SCHOONMAN, J. HALFF, A. F. BLASSE, G. SOLID STATE COMMUN. 13 (6), 677–9, 1973.
57637	PHONON REPLICA OF EXCITED LEVEL OF FREE EXCITON IN CADMIUM SULFIDE. BONNOT, A. PLANEL, R. BENOIT A LA GUILLAUME, C. SOLID STATE COMMUN. 13 (7), 733–6, 1973.
57638	STRESS–INDUCED FERROELECTRICITY IN POTASSIUM TANTALATE(V). UWE, H. UNOKI, H. FUJII, Y. SAKUDO, T. SOLID STATE COMMUN. 13 (7), 737–9, 1973.
57641	NEAR INFRARED PROPERTIES OF SCANDIUM FLUORIDE–DOPED CADMIUM FLUORIDE. LANGER, J. M. PEARSON, G. L. LANGER, T. KRUKOWSKA–FULDE, B. SOLID STATE COMMUN. 13 (7), 767–70, 1973.
57643	MAGNETORESISTANCE AND PHOTOMAGNETORESISTANCE OF EUROPIUM(II) OXIDE THIN FILMS NEAR THE CURIE TEMPERATURE. LLINARES, C. DUCHEMIN, C. BORDURE, G. SOLID STATE COMMUN. 13 (7), 785–8, 1973.
57645	SLOW PHOTOCONDUCTIVE KINETICS IN CHLORINE– AND GALLIUM–DOPED CADMIUM TELLURIDE. LOSEE, D. L. KHOSLA, R. P. RANADIVE, D. K. SMITH, F. T. J. SOLID STATE COMMUN. 13 (7), 819–22, 1973.

EPIC Number	Bibliographic Citation
57646	**STRONG POLARIZATION DEPENDENCE AND SELENIUM LONEPAIRS IN THE PHOTOEMISSION SPECTRA OF ANTIMONY SELENIDE.** HURYCH, Z. BUCZEK, D. WOOD, C. LAPEYRE, G. J. BAER, A. D. SOLID STATE COMMUN. 13 (7), 823–7, 1973. (AD 778 405)
57651	**SURFACE SPIN-EXCHANGE SCATTERING OF POLARIZED ELECTRONS EMITTED FROM MAGNETIC MATERIALS.** HELMAN, J. S. SIEGMANN, H. C. SOLID STATE COMMUN. 13 (7), 891–3, 1973.
57654	**MAGNETIC TRANSITION IN CHROMIUM VANADIUM NITRIDE.** NASR-EDDINE, M. BERTAUT, E. F. MOLLARD, P. CHAUSSY, J. SOLID STATE COMMUN. 13 (7), 905–8, 1973.
57655	**THIRD NEIGHBOR LINEAR-COMBINATION-OF-ATOMIC-ORBITALS ENERGY BANDS OF ZINC BLENDE.** KRAUT, E. A. SOLID STATE COMMUN. 13 (7), 923–6, 1973.
57657	**VIBRATIONAL SPECTRA OF CHALCOGEN HYDRIDE MOLECULES IN ALKALI HALIDES.** KOEPP, S. HAUSMANN, A. SOLID STATE COMMUN. 13 (7), 931–4, 1973.
57658	**MAGNETOELECTRICITY IN THE RARE EARTH HYDROXIDE OXIDES ROOH (R = ERBIUM, TERBIUM, DYSPROSIUM).** CHRISTENSEN, A. N. HORNREICH, R. M. SHARON, B. SOLID STATE COMMUN. 13 (7), 963–6, 1973.
57660	**RADIO AND THERMOLUMINESCENCE STUDIES IN CESIUM IODIDE DOPED WITH F-CENTERS.** PELLAUX, J. P. SIDLER, T. NOUAILHAT, A. AEGERTER, M. A. SOLID STATE COMMUN. 13 (7), 979–81, 1973.
57662	**EFFECT OF CRITICAL FLUCTUATIONS OF THE ELECTRICAL RESISTIVITY OF GADOLINIUM ANTIMONIDE AND HOLMIUM ANTIMONIDE ABOVE THE NEEL TEMPERATURE.** TAUB, H. WILLIAMSON, S. J. SOLID STATE COMMUN. 13 (7), 1021–5, 1973.
57666	**ELECTRIC RESISTIVITY OF INTERCALATED MOLYBDENUM DISULFIDE.** HERMANN, A. M. SOMOANO, R. HADEK, V. REMBAUM, A. SOLID STATE COMMUN. 13 (8), 1065–8, 1973.
57667	**DENSITY-OF-STATES IN THE VALENCE BAND OF SOME ALLOYS ON A GOLD BASE.** NEMOSHKALENKO, V. V. ALESHIN, V. G. SENKEVICH, A. I. SOLID STATE COMMUN. 13 (8), 1069–72, 1973.
57670	**CHARACTERIZATION AND STUDY BY THE MOESSBAUER EFFECT OF A NEW HIGH-PRESSURE VARIETY OF IRON HYDROXI:E OXIDE.** PERNET, M. CHENAVAS, J. JOUBERT, J. C. SOLID STATE COMMUN. 13 (8), 1147–54, 1973.
57678	**POSITION OF THE COPPER ACCEPTOR LEVEL IN ZINC OXIDE SINGLE CRYSTALS.** MOLLWO, E. MUELLER, G. WAGNER, P. SOLID STATE COMMUN. 13 (8), 1283–7, 1973.
57680	**MAGNETIC PROPERTIES OF STOICHIOMETRIC IRON SULFIDE SINGLE CRYSTALS NEAR THE ALPHA-TRANSITION TEMPERATURE.** TAKAHASHI, T. SOLID STATE COMMUN. 13 (9), 1335–7, 1973.
57683	**VARIATION OF ENERGY GAPS IN SEMICONDUCTING ALLOY SYSTEMS.** SONG, K. S. SOLID STATE COMMUN. 13 (9), 1397–400, 1973.
57687	**ENERGY GAP INDUCED BY MAGNETIC FIELD IN ZERO-GAP SEMICONDUCTORS.** KOWALSKI, J. ZAWADZKI, W. SOLID STATE COMMUN. 13 (9), 1433–6, 1973.
57692	**IMPURITY CONDUCTION ASSOCIATED WITH THE L-MINIMA IN TELLURIUM-DOPED N-GALLIUM ANTIMONIDE.** SUN, R.-Y. BECKER, W. M. SOLID STATE COMMUN. 13 (9), 1481–3, 1973.
57694	**OPTICAL PROPERTIES OF POSITIVE HOLE CENTERS OBTAINED IN X-IRRADIATED STRONTIUM CHLORIDE DOPED WITH AN ALKALINE CATION.** RZEPKA, E. MITROAICA, G. LEFRANT, S. TAUREL, L. SOLID STATE COMMUN. 13 (9), 1499–501, 1973.
57695	**ANISOTROPIC RESISTIVITY AND ANISOTROPIC MAGNETORESISTANCE OF THE MAGNETIC SEMICONDUCTOR IRON CHROMIUM SULFIDE.** GOLDSTEIN, L. LYONS, D. H. GIBART, P. SOLID STATE COMMUN. 13 (9), 1503–6, 1973.
57701	**DOPED SEMICONDUCTORS IN AN INHOMOGENEOUS MAGNETIC FIELD.** CUNNINGHAM, S. L. WALLIS, R. F. SOLID STATE COMMUN. 13 (10), 1713–16, 1973.
57702	**ANOMALOUS MAGNETORESISTANCE IN A ZERO-GAP SEMICONDUCTOR.** LIU, L. TAN, M. SOLID STATE COMMUN. 13 (10), 1747–9, 1973.
57706	**MODEL CALCULATIONS FOR THE PHASE TRANSITION IN SAMARIUM SULFIDE.** HERBST, J. F. WATSON, R. E. WILKINS, J. W. SOLID STATE COMMUN. 13 (11), 1771–4, 1973. (AD 777 514)
57708	**OPTICAL PROPERTIES OF A QUASI-DISORDERED SEMICONDUCTOR, ZINC INDIUM SULFIDE.** BOSACCHI, A. BOSACCHI, B. FRANCHI, S. HERNANDEZ, L. SOLID STATE COMMUN. 13 (11), 1805–9, 1973.
57710	**ABSORPTION SPECTRA OF EXCITONS IN ALKALI HALIDES IN THE VACUUM-ULTRAVIOLET REGION.** SATOKO, C. SOLID STATE COMMUN. 13 (11), 1851–4, 1973.
57712	**ANOMALOUS TEMPERATURE DEPENDENCE OF THE ENERGY GAP OF SILVER GALLIUM SULFIDE.** YU, P. W. ANDERSON, W. J. PARK, Y. S. SOLID STATE COMMUN. 13 (11), 1883–7, 1973. (AD-786 298, ARL-74-0043)
57714	**INTRINSIC LOW-TEMPERATURE MAGNETIC AND TRANSPORT PROPERTIES OF NICKEL - ALUMINUM.** WHILLHITE, J. R. WELSH, L. B. YOSHITOMI, T. BRITTAIN, J. O. SOLID STATE COMMUN. 13 (11), 1907–10, 1973.
57719	**PRESSURE-INDUCED REVERSAL OF THE SIGN OF THE HYDROSTATIC PIEZOELECTRIC CONSTANT OF LITHIUM TANTALATE.** GRAHAM, R. A. SOLID STATE COMMUN. 13 (12), 1965–7, 1973.
57720	**RAMAN STUDY OF SOFT ZONE-BOUNDARY PHONONS AND ANTIFERRODISTORTIVE PHASE TRANSITION IN BARIUM TETRAFLUOROMANGANATE(II).** RAYAN, J. F. SCOTT, J. F. SOLID STATE COMMUN. 14 (1), 5–9, 1974.
57725	**EFFECT OF MOBILE SODIUM IONS ON FIELD ENHANCEMENT DIELECTRIC BREAKDOWN IN SILICON DIOXIDE FILMS ON** OSBURN, C. M. RAIDER, S. I. J. ELECTROCHEM. SOC. 120 (10), 1369–76, 1973.
57726	**REPRODUCIBLE HIGH-EFFICIENCY GALLIUM PHOSPHIDE GREEN-EMITTING DIODES GROWN BY OVERCOMPENSATION.** LORIMOR, O. G. HACKETT, W. H., JR. BACHRACH, R. Z. J. ELECTROCHEM. SOC. 120 (10), 1424–8, 1973.
57727	**SOLID-STATE IONICS. HIGH-CONDUCTIVITY SOLID COPPER ION CONDUCTORS. N-ALKYL(OR HYDRO) HEXAMETHYLENETETRAMINE HALIDE-COPPER(I)HALIDE DOUBLE SALTS.** TAKAHASHI, T. YAMAMOTO, O. IKEDA, S. J. ELECTROCHEM. SOC. 120 (10), 1431–4, 1973.
57728	**SOLID ELECTROLYTE PROPERTIES AND CRYSTAL FORMS OF LEAD FLUORIDE.** KENNEDY, J. H. MILES, R. HUNTER, J. J. ELECTROCHEM. SOC. 120 (1), 1441–6, 1973.

EPIC Number	Bibliographic Citation
57729	**ANODIZATION OF SILICON IN AN R.F. (RADIO FREQUENCY) PLASMA.** PULFREY, D. L. HATHORN, F. G. M. YOUNG, L. J. ELECTROCHEM. SOC. 120 (11), 1529–35, 1973.
57730	**INTERSTITIAL MODEL FOR THE DIELECTRIC RELAXATION OF ZINC FLUORIDE DOPED WITH LITHIUM.** ROTH, T. A. J. ELECTROCHEM. SOC. 120 (11), 1547–50, 1973.
57731	**SURFACE OXIDE ON ETCHED ALUMINUM.** SMITH, A. W. J. ELECTROCHEM. SOC. 120 (11), 1551–7, 1973.
57732	**GROWTH AND CHARACTERIZATION OF INDIUM GALLIUM ARSENIDE PHOSPHIDE LATTICE–MATCHED HETEROJUNCTIONS.** ANTIYPAS, G. A. MOON, R. L. J. ELECTROCHEM. SOC. 120 (11), 1574–7, 1973.
57733	**ELECTRIC CONDUCTION AT ELEVATED TEMPERATURES IN THERMALLY GROWN SILICON DIOXIDE FILMS.** MILLS, T. G. KROGER, F. A. J. ELECTROCHEM. SOC. 120 (11), 1582–6, 1973.
57735	**SOLID–STATE IONICS. SOLID ELECTROLYTES IN THE SILVER SULFIDE, SELENIDE, OR TELLURIDE–SILVER IODIDE–MERCURY(II) IODIDE.** TAKAHASHI, T. KUWABARA, K. YAMAMOTO, O. J. ELECTROCHEM. SOC. 120 (12), 1607–12, 1973.
57736	**TRANSPORT PROPERTIES OF LANTHANUM FLUORIDE THIN FILMS.** LILLY, A. C., JR. LA ROY, B. C. TILLER, C. O. WHITING, B. J. ELECTROCHEM. SOC. 120 (12), 1673–6, 1973.
57737	**EFFECTS OF COMMINUTION ON THE LUMINESCENCE OF** KUBONIWA, S. HOSHINA, T. NARAHARA, T. KANAMARU, M. J. ELECTROCHEM. SOC. 120 (12), 1734–41, 1973.
57738	**INDIUM PHOSPHIDE. I. PHOTOLUMINESCENCE MATERIALS STUDY.** WILLIAMS, E. W. ELDER, W. ASTELS, M. G. WEBB, M. MULLIN, J. B. STRAUGHAN, B. TUFTON, P. J. J. ELECTROCHEM. SOC. 120 (12), 1741–9, 1973.
57739	**INDIUM PHOSPHIDE. II. LIQUID EPITAXIAL GROWTH.** ASTLES, M. G. SMITH, F. G. H. WILLIAMS, E. W. J. ELECTROCHEM. SOC. 120 (12), 1750–7, 1973.
57740	**INDIUM PHOSPHIDE. III. DOUBLE EPITAXY LIGHT EMITTING DIODES WITH 1.5 EFFICIENCY AT 300 K.** WILLIAMS, E. W. PORTEOUS, P. ASTLES, M. G. DEAN, P. J. J. ELECTROCHEM. SOC. 120 (12), 1757–60, 1973.
57742	**SILICIDE FORMATION IN TUNGSTEN AND OTHER REFRACTORY METALLIZATIONS ON PLATINUM SILICIDE ON SILICON.** SINHA, A. K. READ, M. H. SMITH, T. E. J. ELECTROCHEM. SOC. 120 (12), 1775–8, 1973.
57743	**SYMMETRY OF LUMINESCING TUNGSTATE(VI) GROUPS IN CALCIUM TUNGSTATE(VI).** BHALLA, R. J. R. S. B. J. ELECTROCHEM. SOC. 120 (12), 1778–80, 1973.
57744	**VAPOR–PHASE EPITAXIAL GROWTH OF GALLIUM NITRIDE ON GALLIUM ARSENIDE, GALLIUM PHOSPHIDE, SILICON, AND AMMONIA.** MORIMOTO, Y. UCHIHO, K. USHIO, S. J. ELECTROCHEM. SOC. 120 (12), 1783–5, 1973.
57745	**GREEN DIRECT CURRENT ELECTROLUMINESCENCE FROM LEAD–DOPED ZINC SULFIDE POWDER PHOSPHORS.** WAITE, M. S. VECHT, A. J. ELECTROCHEM. SOC. 121 (1), 109–13, 1974.
57748	**HIGH–TEMPERATURE DIELECTRIC BEHAVIOR OF CALCIUM–DOPED CERIUM(IV) OXIDE.** SEITZ, M. A. HOLLIDAY, T. B. J. ELECTROCHEM. SOC. 121 (1), 122–6, 1974.
57749	**TEMPERATURE AND COMPOSITIONAL DEPENDENCE OF THE ELECTRIC CONDUCTIVITY OF NONSTOICHIOMETRIC CERIUM OXIDE.** BLUMENTHAL, R. N. HOFMAIER, R. L. J. ELECTROCHEM. SOC. 121 (1), 126–31, 1974.
57750	**SYNTHESIS AND PHOTOLUMINESCENCE OF M(II) M(III)(2) (SULFIDE, SELENIUM)(4).** DONOHUE, P. C. HANLON, J. E. J. ELECTROCHEM. SOC. 121 (1), 137–42, 1974.
57751	**CANDOLUMINESCENCE IN TRANSITION–ION–ACTIVATED OXIDE PHOSPHORS.** HESS, J. W., JR. SWEET, J. R. WHITE, W. B. J. ELECTROCHEM. SOC. 121 (1), 142–5, 1974.
57752	**CRYSTAL GROWTH AND CHARACTERIZATION OF GALLIUM NITRIDE.** CHU, T. L. ITO, K. SMELTZER, R. K. CHU, S. S. C. J. ELECTROCHEM. SOC. 121 (1), 159–62, 1974.
57753	**HIGH–TEMPERATURE DIELECTRIC BEHAVIOR OF POLYCRYSTALLINE ZINC OXIDE.** SEITZ, M. A. SOKOLY, T. O. J. ELECTROCHEM. SOC. 121 (1), 163–9, 1974.
57756	**MEASUREMENT OF THE TEMPERATURE COEFFICIENT OF THE REFRACTIVE INDEX OF INFRARED MATERIALS USING A CARBON DIOXIDE LASER.** KOLOSOVSKII, O. A. USTIMENKO, L. N. OPT. SPECTROS., USSR 33 (3), 430–1, 1972. (ENGLISH TRANSLATION OF OPT. SPEKTROSK., 33, 781–2, 1972; FOR ORIGINAL SEE E56630)
57761	**INFLUENCE OF A STRONG MAGNETIC FIELD ON THE PHOTOLUMINESCENCE SPECTRUM OF N–TYPE GALLIUM ARSENIDE.** ZVEREV, L. P. MIN'KOV, G. M. NEGASHEV, S. A. SOV. PHYS. SEMICOND. 7 (8), 1056–7, 1974. (ENGLISH TRANSLATION OF FIZ. TEKH. POLUPROV., 7 (8), 1585–8, 1973; FOR ORIGINAL SEE E52520)
57762	**OPTICAL ABSORPTION IN NICKEL–DOPED GALLIUM ARSENIDE.** BAZHENOV, V. K. RASHEVSKAYA, E. P. SOLOV'EV, N. N. FOIGEL, M. G. SOV. PHYS. SEMICOND. 7 (8), 1067–8, 1974. (ENGLISH TRANSLATION OF FIZ. TEKH. POLUPROV., 7 (8), 1601–4, 1973; FOR ORIGINAL SEE E52521)
57763	**EXCITON INTERACTION IN LASER EMISSION FROM CADMIUM TELLURIDE.** GOLUBEV, G. P. SYSUN, V. V. YAKOVLEV, V. A. SOV. PHYS. SEMICOND. 7 (8), 1071, 1974. (ENGLISH TRANSLATION OF FIZ. TEKH. POLUPROV., 7 (8), 1606–7, 1973; FOR ORIGINAL SEE E52522)
57764	**DIFFUSION THERMOELECTRIC POWER IN N–TYPE INDIUM ANTIMONIDE.** KOSAREV, V. V. TAMARIN, P. V. SOV. PHYS. SEMICOND. 7 (8), 1079–,0, 1974. (ENGLISH TRANSLATION OF FIZ. TKH. POLUPROV., 7 (8), 1617–20, 1973; FOR ORIGINAL SEE E52523)
57766	**INFLUENCE OF THE MAGNETIC FIELD ON THE HEATING OF ELECTRONS IN N–TYPE INDIUM ANTIMONIDE.** IL'IN, V. A. LITVAK–GORSKAYA, L. B. RABINOVICH, R. I. SHAPIRO, E. Z. SOV. PHYS. SEMICOND. 7 (8), 1089–90, 1974. (ENGLISH TRANSLATION OF FIZ. TEKH. POLUPROV., 7 (8), 1631–3, 1973; FOR ORIGINAL SEE E52525)
57769	**PHOTOELECTRIC PROPERTIES OF ZINKENITE.** DMYTRIV, A. YU. KOVAL'SKII, P. N. MAKARENKO, V. V. SOV. PHYS. SEMICOND. 7 (8), 1097–8, 1974. (ENGLISH TRANSLATION OF FIZ. TEKH. POLUPROV., 7 (8), 1641–3, 1973; FOR ORIGINAL SEE E52528)
57770	**MECHANISM OF THE COMPENSATION OF IRON–DOPED SEMIINSULATING GALLIUM ARSENIDE.** GANAPOL'SKII, E. M. OMEL'YANOVSKII, E. M. PERVOVA, L. YA. FISTUL, V. I. SOV. PHYS. SEMICOND. 7 (8), 1099, 1974. (ENGLISH TRANSLATION OF FIZ. TEKH. POLUPROV., 7 (8), 1643–5, 1973; FOR ORIGNAL SEE E52529)

EPIC Number	Bibliographic Citation

57771 **DETERMINATION OF THE PARAMETERS OF TRAPS IN CADMIUM SELENIDE FROM THE TEMPERATURE DEPENDENCE OF THE ACOUSTIC GAIN.**
KOCHNEVA, N. S. VASIL'EV, B. P.
SOV. PHYS. SEMICOND.
7 (8), 1104–5, 1974.
(ENGLISH TRANSLATION OF FIZ. POLUPROV., 7 (8), 1650–2, 1973; FOR ORIGINAL SEE E52530)

57772 **PHOTOCONDUCTIVITY OF LEAD SULFIDE.**
ZUBKOVA, T. I. IL'IN, V. I.
SOV. PHYS. SEMICOND.
7 (8), 1106–7, 1974.
(ENGLISH TRANSLATION OF FIZ. TEKH. POLUPROV., 7 (8), 1653–4, 1973; FOR ORIGINAL SEE E52531)

57773 **INFLUENCE OF IMPURITY IONS ON THE BAND STRUCTURE UNDER MODERATE DOPING CONDITONS.**
KLOTYN'SH, E. E. PETROC, V. K.
SOV. PHYS. SEMICOND.
7 (8), 1108–9, 1974.
(ENGLISH TRANSLATION OF FIZ. TEKH. POLUPROV., 7 (8), 1655–7, 1973; FOR ORIGINAL SEE E52532)

57778 **THE ROLE OF MICROFIELDS OF PLASMA TYPE IN IONIC MELTS.**
KURILENKOV, YU. K.
HIGH TEMP.
11 (6), 1154–6, 1973.
(ENGLISH TRANSLATION OF TEPLOFIZ. VYS. TEMP., 11 (6), 1291–3, 1973; FOR ORIGINAL SEE E55759)

57781 **THERMOELECTRIC PROPERTIES OF COPPER IODIDE AND CHLORIDE.**
ASTAKHOV, O. P. FEDOROV, V. I.
HIGH TEMP.
11 (6), 1170–2, 1973.
(ENGLISH TRANSLATION OF TEPLOFIZ. VYS. TEMP., 11 (6), 1305–7, 1973; FOR ORIGINAL SEE E55758)

57785 **LUMINESCENCE AND ABSORPTION SPECTRA OF RARE EARTH ORTHOPHOSPHATES ACTIVATED BY NEODYMIUM, EUROPIUM, AND TERBIUM IONS.**
IONKINA, E. A. MOROZOV, N. N.
MURAV'EV, E. N. ORLOVSKII, V. P.
REPKO, V. P.
INORG. MAT., USSR
9 (7), 1130–2, 1973.
(ENGLISH TRANSLATION OF IZV. AKAD. NAUK SSSR, NEORG. MATER., 9 (7), 1270–1, 1973; FOR ORIGINAL SEE E52560)

57786 **PROPERTIES OF GALLIUM ARSENIDE DOPED BY INFORPORATION OF TELLURIUM IONS.**
ZELEVINSKAYA, V. M. KACHURIN, G. A.
SMIRNOV, L. S.
INORG. MAT., USSR
9 (8), 1171–3, 1973.
(ENGLISH TRANSLATION OF IZV. AKAD. NAUK SSSR, NEORG. MATER., 9 (8), 1316–9, 1973; FOR ORIGINAL SEE E52561)

57787 **AMORPHOUS–POLYCRYSTALLINE PHASE TRANSITION IN THIN FILMS OF CARBON, SILICON, GERMANIUM, GERMANIUM SELENIDE, AND GERMANIUM TELLURIDE, AND ITS INFLUENCE ON ELECTRICAL CONDUCTIVITY AND OPTICAL DENSITY.**
ZAKHAROV, V. P. ZALIVA, V. I.
INORG. MAT., USSR
9 (8), 1178–81, 1973.
(ENGLISH TRANSLATION OF IZV. AKAD. NAUK SSSR, NEORG. MATER., 9 (8), 1325–9, 1973; FOR ORIGINAL SEE E52562)

57788 **ELECTRICAL CONDUCTIVITY MECHANISM AND BAND MODEL OF QUASIBINARY ALLOYS TUNGSTEN DISELENIDE – NIOBIUM SELENIDE.**
KALIKHMAN, V. L. KASIYAN, I. M.
INORG. MAT., USSR
9 (8), 1185–9, 1973.
(ENGLISH TRANSLATION OF IZV. AKAD. NAUK SSSR, NEORG. MATER., 9 (8), 1333–8, 1973; FOR ORIGINAL SEE E52563)

57789 **MAGNETIC AND ELECTRICAL PROPERTIES OF EUROPIUM TELLURIDES AND SELENIDES.**
BUTUSOV, O. B. CHECHERNIKOV, V. I.
PECHENNIKOV, A. V. YAREMBASH, E. I.
SADOVSKAYA, O. A. TYURIN, E. G.
INORG. MAT., USSR
9 (8), 1190–1, 1973.
(ENGLISH TRANSLATION OF IZV. AKAD. NAUK SSSR, NEORG. MATER., 9 (8), 1339–41, 1973; FOR ORIGINAL SEE E52564)

57791 **MAGNETIC SUSCEPTIBILITY AND ELECTRICAL RESISTANCE OF IRON, COBALT, AND NICKEL MONOBORIDES.**
BUDOZHAPOV, V. D. ZELENIN, L. I.
CHEMERINSKAYA, L. S. SIDORENKO, F. A.
GEL'D, P. V.
INORG. MAT., USSR
9 (8), 1290–1, 1973.
(ENGLISH TRANSLATION OF IZV. AKAD. NAUK SSSR, NEORG. MATER., 9 (8), 1447–8, 1973; FOR ORIGINAL SEE E52566)

57792 **USE OF MOSSBAUER SPECTROSCOPY TO INVESTIGATE FORMATION OF HEMATITE FROM AMORPHOUS IRON HYDROXIDE.**
LOSEVA, G. V. MURASHKO, N. V.
INORG. MAT., USSR
9 (8), 1301–2, 1973.
(ENGLISH TRANSLATION OF IZV. AKAD. NAUK SSSR, NEORG. MATER., 9 (8), 1456–7, 1973; FOR ORIGINAL SEE E52567)

57794 **THE EFFECTS OF NEUTRON IRRADIATION DAMAGE ON THE SUPERCONDUCTING PROPERTIES OF NIOBIUM TIN.**
BETT, R.
CRYOGENICS
14 (7), 361–6, 1974.

57797 **ION DEPLETION OF GLASS AT A BLOCKING ANODE: II, PROPERTIES OF ION–DEPLETED GLASSES.**
CARLSON, D. E. HANG, K. W. STOCKDALE, G. F.
J. AMER. CERAM. SOC.
57 (7), 295–300, 1974.

57798 **OPTICAL ABSORPTION OF THE TRANSITION ELEMENTS IN VITREOUS SILICA.**
SCHULTZ, P. C.
J. AMER. CERAM. SOC.
57 (7), 309–13, 1974.

57799 **FAR–INFRARED ABSORPTION OF COPPER(I) CHLORIDE.**
IKEZAWA, M.
J. PHYS. SOC. JAP.
35 (1), 309, 1973.

57800 **ACOUSTOELECTRONIC EFFECTS AND PHOTOCONDUCTIVITY IN SEMICONDUCTORS IN A MAGNETIC FIELD.**
BACHININ, YU. G.
FIZ. TVERD. TELA
15 (12), 3504–7, 1973.
(FOR ENGLISH TRANSLATION SEE E57801)

57801 **ACOUSTOELECTRONIC EFFECTS AND PHOTOCONDUCTIVITY IN SEMICONDUCTORS IN A MAGNETIC FIELD.**
BACHININ, YU. G.
SOV. PHYS. SOLID STATE
15 (12), 2344–5, 1974.
(ENGLISH TRANSLATION OF FIZ. TVERD. TELA, 15 (12), 3504–7, 1973; FOR ORIGINAL SEE E57800)

57802 **POLYMORPHISM OF BISMUTH SELENIDE AT HIGH PRESSURES AND TEMPERATURES.**
ATABAEVA, E. YA. BENDELIANI, N. A.
FIZ. TVERD. TELA
15 (12), 3508–12, 1973.
(FOR ENGLISH TRANSLATION SEE E57803)

57803 **POLYMORPHISM OF BISMUTH SELENIDE AT HIGH PRESSURES AND TEMPERATURES.**
ATABAEVA, E. YA. BENDELIANI, N. A.
POPOVA, S. V.
SOV. PHYS. SOLID STATE
15 (12), 2346–8, 1974.
(ENGLISH TRANSLATION OF FIZ. TVERD. TELA, 15 (12), 3508–12, 1973; FOR ORIGINAL SEE E57802)

57805 **EXCITON–MAGNON TRANSITIONS IN THE ABSORPTION SPECTRA OF POTASSIUM MANGANESE–COBALT FLUORIDE SOLID SOLUTIONS.**
BELYAEVA, A. I. EREMENKO, V. V.
GAPON, N. V. KOTLYARSKII, M. M.
FIZ. TVERD. TELA
15 (12), 3532–4, 1973.
(FOR ENGLISH TRANSLATION SEE E57806)

57806 **EXCITON–MAGNON TRANSITIONS IN THE ABSORPTION SPECTRA OF POTASSIUM MANGANESE–COBALT FLUORIDE SOLID SOLUTIONS.**
BELYAEVA, A. I. EREMENKO, V. V.
GAPON, N. V. KOTLYARSKII, M. M.
SOV. PHYS. SOLID STATE
15 (12), 2360–1, 1974.
(ENGLISH TRANSLATION OF FIZ. TVERD. TELA, 15 (12), 3532–4, 1973; FOR ORIGINAL SEE E57805)

57807 **MAGNETIC ANISOTROPY OF CUBIC CRYSTALS.**
ZAPASSKII, V. S.
FIZ. TVERD. TELA
15 (12), 3544–9, 1973.
(FOR ENGLISH TRANSLATION SEE E57808)

57808 **MAGNETIC ANISOTROPY OF CUBIC CRYSTALS.**
ZAPASSKII, V. S.
SOV. PHYS. SOLID STATE
15 (12), 2367–9, 1974.
(ENGLISH TRANSLATION OF FIZ. TVERD. TELA, 15 (12), 3544–9, 1973; FOR ORIGINAL SEE E57807)

57814 **POLYTYPISM AND LUMINESCENCE OF LEAD DIOXIDE CRYSTALS.**
BLONSKII, I. V. GORBAN', I. S.
GUBANOV, V. A. LYUTER, YA. A.
POPERENKO, L. V. STRASHNIKOVA, M. I.
SOV. PHYS. SOLID STATE
15 (12), 2439–41, 1974.
(ENGLISH TRANSLATION OF FIZ. TVERD. TELA, 15 (12), 3664–8, 1973; FOR ORIGINAL SEE E55403)

EPIC Number	Bibliographic Citation
57815	MAGNETIC PROPERTIES OF SYSTEMS EXHIBITING A COOPERATIVE JAHN-TELLER EFFECT. KAPLAN, M. D. VEKHTER, B. G. SOV. PHYS. SOLID STATE 15 (12), 2446-7, 1974. (ENGLISH TRANSLATION OF FIZ. TVERD. TELA, 15 (12), 3675-6, 1973; FOR ORIGINAL SEE E55404)
57816	SUBSTRUCTURE OF DOMAINS IN MAGNESIUM-MANGANESE FERRITE FILMS. DUNAEVA-MITLINA, T. A. FIZ. TVERD. TELA 15 (12), 3678-81, 1973. (FOR ENGLISH TRANSLATION SEE E57817)
57817	SUBSTRUCTURE OF DOMAINS IN MAGNESIUM-MANGANESE FERRITE FILMS. DUNAEVA-MITLINA, T. A. SOV. PHYS. SOLID STATE 15 (12), 2449-50, 1974. (ENGLISH TRANSLATION OF FIZ. TVERD. TELA, 15 (12), 3678-81, 1973; FOR ORIGINAL SEE E57816)
57818	FINE STRUCTURE IN THE ABSORPTION SPECTRUM OF SILVER-DOPED POTASSIUM IODIDE CRYSTALS. NEDZVETSKAYA, I. V. IVANOVA, N. I. FIZ. TVERD. TELA 15 (12), 3685-7, 1973. (FOR ENGLISH TRANSLATION SEE E57819)
57819	FINE STRUCTURE IN THE ABSORPTION SPECTRUM OF SILVER-DOPED POTASSIUM IODIDE CRYSTALS. NEDZVETSKAYA, I. V. IVANOVA, N. I. SOV. PHYS. SOLID STATE 15 (12), 2455, 1974. (ENGLISH TRANSLATION OF FIZ. TVERD. TELA, 15 (12), 3685-7, 1973; FOR ORIGINAL SEE E57818)
57820	MAGNETIC STATE OF THE CHROMIUM TRIPOSITIVE ION IN THE COMPOUND COPPER CHROMIUM OXIDE. BELOV, K. P. GORYAGA, A. N. ANTOSHINA, L. G. KORAIEM, T. SOV. PHYS. SOLID STATE 15 (12), 2456, 1974. (ENGLISH TRANSLATION OF FIZ. TVERD. TELA, 15 (12), 3687-8, 1973; FOR ORIGINAL SEE E55405)
57821	MAGNETIC IMPURITY STATES IN EUROPIUM (1-X) GADOLINIUM (X) OXIDE. SAMOKHVALOV, A. A. ARBUZOVA, T. I. SIMONOVA, M. I. FAL'KOVSKAYA, L. D. SOV. PHYS. SOLID STATE 15 (12), 2459-60, 1974. (ENGLISH TRANSLATION OF FIZ. TVERD. TELA, 15 (12), 3690-2, 1973; FOR ORIGINAL SEE E55406)
57822	TEMPERATURE DEPENDENCE OF THE FORBIDDEN-BAND WIDTH OF BARIUM (0.50) STRONTIUM (0.50) NIOBIUM OXIDE SINGLE CRYSTALS IN THE PHASE TRANSITION REGION. SAVITSKII, V. G. KOVTUN, R. N. ALEKSYUK, V. E. PROTSAKH, P. F. FIZ. TVERD. TELA 15 (12), 3696-8, 1973. (FOR ENGLISH TRANSLATION SEE E57823)
57823	TEMPERATURE DEPENDENCE OF THE FORBIDDEN-BAND WIDTH OF BARIUM (0.50) STRONTIUM (0.50) NIOBIUM OXIDE SINGLE CRYSTALS IN THE PHASE TRANSITION REGION. SAVITSKII, V. G. KOVTUN, R. N. ALEKSYUK, V. E. PROTSAKH, P. F. SOV. PHYS. SOLID STATE 15 (12), 2464, 1974. (ENGLISH TRANSLATION OF FIZ. TVERD. TELA, 15 (12), 3696-8, 1973; FOR ORIGINAL SEE E57822)
57824	PHOTOINDUCED CHANGES IN THE MAGNETIC PROPERTIES OF YTTRIUM IRON (5-X) SILICON (X) OXIDE. KUTS, P. S. KOVALENKO, V. F. RUBAN, V. A. SOV. PHYS. SOLID STATE 15 (12), 2471-2, 1974. (ENGLISH TRANSLATION OF FIZ. TVERD. TELA, 15 (12), 3707-8, 1973; FOR ORIGINAL SEE E55407)
57825	NEGATIVE PHOTOPLASTIC EFFECT IN CADMIUM SULFIDE. OSIP'YAN, YU. A. SHIKHSAIDOV, M. SH. FIZ. TVERD. TELA 15 (12), 3711-2, 1973. (FOR ENGLISH TRANSLATION SEE E57826)
57826	NEGATIVE PHOTOPLASTIC EFFECT IN CADMIUM SULFIDE. OSIP'YAN, YU. A. SHIKHSAIDOV, M. SH. SOV. PHYS. SOLID STATE 15 (12), 2475-6, 1974. (ENGLISH TRANSLATION OF FIZ. TVERD. TELA, 15 (12), 3711-2, 1973; FOR ORIGINAL SEE E57825)
57828	THEORY OF THE MAGNETIC ANISOTROPY OF RARE EARTH COBALT COMPOUNDS. KARPENKO, V. P. FIZ. TVERD. TELA 15 (12), 3714-6, 1973. (FOR ENGLISH TRANSLATION SEE E57829)
57829	THEORY OF THE MAGNETIC ANISOTROPY OF RARE EARTH COBALT COMPOUNDS. KARPENKO, V. P. SOV. PHYS. SOLID STATE 15 (12), 2478, 1974. (ENGLISH TRANSLATION OF FIZ. TVERD. TELA, 15 (12), 3714-6, 1973; FOR ORIGINAL SEE E57828)
57830	NEGATIVE LONGITUDINAL MAGNETORESISTANCE OF CADMIUM(X) MERCURY (1-X) TELLURIDE. BERCHENKO, N. N. PASHKOVSKII, M. V. SOV. PHYS. SOLID STATE 15 (12), 2479-80, 1974. (ENGLISH TRANSLATION OF FIZ. TVERD. TELA, 15 (12), 3716-8, 1973; FOR ORIGINAL SEE E55409)
57831	FINE GRAINED ALUMINA SUBSTRATES: II, PROPERTIES. MISTLER, R. E. MORZENTI, P. T. SHANEFIELD, D. J. BULL. AMER. CERAM. SOC. 53 (8), 564-8, 1974.
57834	AVERAGED INFRARED ABSORPTION COEFFICIENTS OF WATER VAPOR. CALFEE, R. F. SCHWIESOW, R. L. NATL. OCEANIC ATMOS. ADM., WAVE PROPAGATION LAB., BOULDER, COLORADO 25PP., 1973. (NOAA-TR-ERL-274)
57837	THERMOLUMINESCENCE AND COLOR CENTERS IN RARE EARTH DOPED CERIA CRYSTALS. LAND, P. L. AEROSP. RES. LAB., WRIGHT-PATTERSON AIR FORCE BASE, OHIO 64PP., 1973. (ARL-73-0171)
57841	ELECTROLUMINESCENCE IN II-VI COMPOUNDS. II. ELECTROLUMINESCENCE FROM ACOUSTOELECTRIC DOMAINS IN CADMIUM SELENIDE. MACOMBER, W. G. U. S., AEROSP. RES. LAB. 45-58, 1973. (ARL-73-0130)
57843	GROWTH OF LARGE BAND GAP (GROUP) I-III-VI(2) CRYSTALS. COOK, W. R., JR. U. S. AEROSP. RES. LAB. 16PP., 1973. ARL-73-0154 AD 773180
57844	GRAVIMETRIC AND ELECTRICAL CONDUCTIVITY STUDIES OF PURE AND DOPED NIOBIUM PENTOXIDE. WIMMER, J. M. TRIPP, W. C. U. S. AEROSPACE RES. LAB. 29PP., 1973. (ARL-73-0157)
57852	SATURATED PHOTOVOLTAGE OF A P-N JUNCTION. PARROTT, J. E. IEEE TRANS. ELECTRON DEVICES 21 (1), 89-93, 1974.
57859	ELLIPSOMETRIC METHOD FOR MEASURING OPTICAL CONSTANTS AND THE THICKNESS OF THIN ABSORBING FILMS ON A METALLIC SUBSTRATE. SHKLYAREVSKII, I. N. EL-SHAZLY, A. F. A. YAROVAYA, R. G. KOSTYUK, V. P. OPT. SPEKTROSK. 36 (1), 199-204, 1974. (FOR ENGLISH TRANSLATION SEE E59207)
57860	REEXAMINATION OF THE HIGH-TEMPERATURE RESISTIVITY ANOMALY IN (CHROMIUM-VANADIUM OXIDE). HONIG, J. M. CHANDRASHEKHAR, G. V. SINHA, A. P. B. PHYS. REV. LETT. 32 (1), 13-15, 1974.
57861	MULTIPHONON ABSORPTION IN SODIUM FLUORIDE. POHL, D. W. MEIER, P. F. PHYS. REV. LETT. 32 (2), 58-61, 1974.
57862	DISPERSION AND DIFFRACTION BY ANISOTROPIC CENTERS IN ALKALI HALIDES. SCHNEIDER, I. PHYS. REV. LETT. 32 (8), 412-15, 1974.
57864	DENSITY LINES OF STATES IN COMPENSATED CADMIUM TELLURIDE CRYSTALS. AGRINSKAYA, N. V. ARKAD'EVA, E. N. KRYMOVA, E. D. PROBL. FIZ. SOEDIN. A-II B-VI, MATER, VSES. SOVESHCH., 3RD 1, 294-9, 1972.
57869	LEAD TELLURIDE-GALLIUM TELLURIDE SYSTEM. ABILOV, CH. I. RUSTAMOV, P. G. ALIDZHANOV, M. A. IZV. AKAD. NAUK SSSR, NEORG. MATER. 10 (1), 142-3, 1974. (FOR ENGLISH TRANSLATION SEE E64881)

EPIC Number	Bibliographic Citation
57870	THERMAL DIFFUSION IN IONIC CRYSTALS. DUPUY, J. PHYS. ELECTROLYTES 2, 699–745, 1972.
57871	DYNAMICAL JAHN-TELLER SPLITTING OF THE B ABSORPTION BAND IN ALKALI HALIDE PHOSPHORS ACTIVATED WITH THALLIUM(1+)-TYPE IONS. ASANO, S. TOMISHIMA, Y. REP. RES. LAB. SURFACE SCI., OKAYAMA UNIV. 4 (1), 1–22, 1973.
57879	ELECTRICAL PROPERTIES OF SILVER(I) NITRATE, THALLIUM(I) NITRATE, AND AMMONIUM NITRATE. FERMOR, J. H. KJEKSHUS, A. ACTA CHEM. SCAND. 27 (10), 3712–20, 1973.
57880	CRYSTAL STRUCTURE OF ZINC ARSENIDE. FLEET, M. E. ACTA CRYSTALLOGR. 30 B (1), 122–6, 1974.
57885	PHOTOCONDUCTION OF VANADIUM PENTOXIDE. HEVESI, I. LANG, J. CHEMIERESYUK, G. G. ACTA PHYS. CHEM. 19 (1–2), 25–8, 1973.
57887	DIAMAGNETIC ANISOTROPY OF MIXED CRYSTAL PENTACHLOROPHENOL-HEXACHLOROBENZENE. FULINSKA-WOJCIK, G. ROHLEDER, J. W. ACTA PHYS. POL. 45 A (1), 3–7, 1974.
57888	DOMAIN STRUCTURE OF LITHIUM FERRITE. DEMBINSKA, M. ACTA PHYS. POL. 45 A (1), 33–41, 1974.
57892	TEMPERATURE DEPENDENCE OF THE CHANGES OF THE TRANSVERSE ACOUSTIC WAVE ATTENUATION IN N-INDIUM ANTIMONIDE DUE TO THE MAGNETIC FIELD. HRIVNAK, L. KOVAR, J. STELINA, J. ACTA PHYS. SLOVACA 23 (4), 212–16, 1973.
57897	HIGH MOBILITY INDIUM ANTIMONIDE FILMS. TRANIELLO, G. R. ALTA FREQ. 42 (10), 560–2, 1973.
57898	CURIE TEMPERATURES OF SUBSTITUTED YTTRIUM - GADOLINIUM GARNETS. LLABRES, J. CARMONA, F. AN. FIS. 69 (10–12), 375–8, 1973.
57902	REFRACTIVE INDEX MEASUREMENTS ON MAGNETIC GARNET FILMS. MCCOLLUM, B. C. BEKEBREDE, W. R. KESTIGIAN, M. SMITH, A. B. APPL. PHYS. LETT. 23 (12), 702–3, 1973.
57903	THE RADIO-FREQUENCY SPUTTERED ALUMINUM NITRIDE FILMS ON SAPPHIRE. SHUSKUS, A. J. REEDER, T. M. PARADIS, E. L. APPL. PHYS. LETT. 24 (4), 155–6, 1974.
57905	EFFICIENT ELECTROLUMINESCENCE FROM INDIUM PHOSPHIDE DIODES GROWN BY LIQUID-PHASE EPITAXY FROM TIN SOLUTIONS. SHAY, J. L. BACHMANN, K. J. BUEHLER, E. APPL. PHYS. LETT. 24 (4), 192–4, 1974.
57908	ELECTRICAL PROPERTIES OF TIN(IV) OXIDE FILMS PREPARED BY CHEMICAL VAPOR DEPOSITION. MUTO, R. FURUUCHI, S. ASAHI GARASU KENKYU HOKOKU 23 (1), 27–44, 1973.
57912	SMALL ABSORPTION COEFFICIENT MEASUREMENT BY CALORIMETRIC AND SPECTRAL EMITTANCE TECHNIQUES. LIPSON, H. G. SKOLNIK, L. H. STIERWALT, D. L. APPL. OPT. 13 (8), 1741–4, 1974. (AD 787 243)
57914	MEASUREMENTS OF SMALL SIGNAL ABSORPTION AT HIGH TEMPERATURE FOR THE 001–100 BAND OF CARBON DIOXIDE. LEONARD, R. L. APPL. OPT. 13 (8), 1920–2, 1974.
57915	MEASUREMENT OF THE ABSORPTION COEFFICIENT OF ATMOSPHERIC DUST. LINDBERG, J. D. LAUDE, L. S. APPL. OPT. 13 (8), 1923–7, 1974.
57916	MAGNETIC NEUTRON SCATTERING ON MANGANESE(II) OXIDE NEAR NEEL TEMPERATURE. LEDER, H. RAUCH, H. ATOMKERNENERGIE 22 (3), 196–8, 1973.
57922	PRODUCTION OF CADMIUM TELLURIDE AND ZINC TELLURIDE SINGLE CRYSTALS FROM SOLUTION IN TELLURIUM. DZISIOW, A. WOJCIECHOWSKI, S. NOWAK, Z. PIOTROWSKI, J. BIUL. WOJSK. AKAD. TECH. 22 (9), 61–4, 1973.
57928	PHENOMENOLOGICAL INTERPRETATION OF CERTAIN DIELECTRIC PROPERTIES OF POLYCRYSTALLINE BARIUM TITANATE. MICHERON, F. BULL. SOC. FR. CERAM. (100), 15–29, 1973.
57933	CONSEQUENCES OF THE FORMATION OF IRON DIPOSITIVE ION IN A SINGLE CRYSTAL OF IRON LITHIUM OXIDE PREPARED UNDER IODINE VAPOR PRESSURE. MARAIS, A. MAKRAM, H. C. R. ACAD. SCI. 277 B (19), 545–8, 1973.
57938	MAGNETIC PROPERTIES OF IRON LANTHANUM SULFIDE. COLLIN, G. BARTHELEMY, E. GOROCHOV, O. C. R. ACAD. SCI. 277 C (17), 775–8, 1973.
57939	MECHANISM OF ELECTRIC CONDUCTION IN THE HEXABORIDES OF EUROPIUM AND YTTERBIUM. GOODENOUGH, J. B. MERCURIO, J. P. ETOURNEAU, J. NASLAIN, R. HAGENMULLER, P. C. R. ACAD. SCI. 277 C (22), 1239–42, 1973.
57940	ANTIFERROMAGNETISM IN TWO ANTIMONATES WITH A TRIRUTILE STRUCTURE. TURBIL, J. P. BERNIER, J. C. C. R. ACAD. SCI. 277 C (24), 1347–9, 1973.
57941	LIQUID PHASE EPITAXY OF ALUMINUM GALLIUM ANTIMONIDE. NGUYEN, V. M. GOUSKOV, A. A. AVEROUS, M. BOUGNOT, G. C. R. ACAD. SCI. 278 B (1), 15–17, 1974.
57944	DIELECTRIC LOSS MEASUREMENTS ON NONPOLAR LIQUIDS IN THE MICROWAVE REGION 8 TO 12 GHZ. DAGG, I. R. REESOR, G. E. CAN. J. PHYS. 52 (1), 29–32, 1974.
57955	DIELECTRIC MEASUREMENTS USING ALTERNATING CURRENTS AND IONIC THERMOCURRENTS. PERLMAN, M. M. UNGER, S. J. APPL. PHYS. 45 (6), 2389–93, 1974.
57957	ELECTRIC FIELD DEPENDENCE OF THE DIELECTRIC CONSTANT OF PZT FERROELECTRIC CERAMICS. BAR-CHAIM, N. BRUNSTEIN, M. GRUNBERG, J. SEIDMAN, A. J. APPL. PHYS. 45 (6), 2398–2405, 1974.
57958	THERMAL CONDUCTIVITY OF MAGNESIUM PLUMBIDE. MARTIN, J. J. SHANKS, H. R. J. APPL. PHYS. 45 (6), 2428–31, 1974.
57959	DIELECTRIC PROPERTIES OF AMORPHOUS SELENIUM BISMUTH AND SELENIUM BISMUTH ARSENIC FILMS. GOLDSTEIN, I. S. J. APPL. PHYS. 45 (6), 2447–51, 1974.
57960	MICROWAVE PROPERTIES OF LIQUIDS AND SOLIDS USING A RESONANT MICROWAVE CAVITY AS A PROBE. HONG, K. H. ROBERTS, J. A. J. APPL. PHYS. 45 (6), 2452–6, 1974.
57962	OBLIQUE INCIDENCE OF A ELECTROMAGNETIC WAVE AT A MOVING FERRITE MEDIUM. MUKHERJEE, P. K. TALWAR, S. P. J. APPL. PHYS. 45 (6), 2521–9, 1974.
57966	CONCENTRATION DEPENDENCE OF THE REFRACTIVE INDEX FOR N - AND P - TYPE GALLIUM ARSENIDE BETWEEN 1.2 AND 1.8 EV. SELL, D. D. CASEY, H. C., JR. WECHT, K. W. J. APPL. PHYS. 45 (6), 2650–7, 1974.
57968	EXTRINSIC ABSORPTION IN 10.6- MU M-LASER-WINDOW MATERIALS DUE TO MOLECULAR-ION IMPURITIES. DUTHLER, C. J. J. APPL. PHYS. 45 (6), 2668–71, 1974.

EPIC Number	Bibliographic Citation
57969	DYNAMIC PROPERTIES OF HIGH-MOBILITY GARNET FILMS IN THE PRESENCE OF IN-PLANE MAGNETIC FIELDS. SHAW, R. W. MOODY, J. W. SANDFORT, R. M. J. APPL. PHYS. 45 (6), 2672-7, 1974.
57970	OPTICAL ABSORPTION IN ION-BOMBARDED MAGNETIC GARNET FILMS. SEMAN, J. A. WEMPLE, S. H. NORTH, J. C. J. APPL. PHYS. 45 (6), 2700-4, 1974.
57971	THEORY OF BLOCH-LINE AND BLOCH-WALL MOTION. SLONCZEWSKI, J. C. J. APPL. PHYS. 45 (6), 2705-15, 1974.
57974	SATURATION MAGNETIZATION OF GALLIUM-SUBSTITUTED YTTRIUM IRON GARNET. HANSEN, P. ROSCHMANN, P. TOLKSDORF, W. J. APPL. PHYS. 45 (6), 2728-32, 1974.
57975	INFLUENCE OF THE CRYSTALLINE ELECTRIC FIELD ON THE HEAT CAPACITY AND RESISTIVITY OF PRASEODYMIUM ALUMINUM. MAHONEY, J. V. WALLACE, W. E. CRAIG, R. S. J. APPL. PHYS. 45 (6), 2733-8, 1974.
57976	UNDOPED HIGH-RESISTIVITY CADMIUM TELLURIDE FOR NUCLEAR RADIATION DETECTORS. TRIBOULET, R. MARFAING, Y. CORNET, A. SIFFERT, P. J. APPL. PHYS. 45 (6), 2759-65, 1974.
57977	REFRACTIVE INDEX OF GALLIUM ARSENIDE (0.62) PHOSPHORUS (0.38) BETWEEN 1.2 AND 2.0 EV. CASEY, H. C., JR. J. APPL. PHYS. 45 (6), 2766-7, 1974.
57978	SUPERCONDUCTIVE TUNNELING IN JUNCTIONS CONTAINING LEAD-GOLD LAYERED FILMS. BASAVAIAH, S. LAHIRI, S. K. J. APPL. PHYS. 45 (6), 2773-4, 1974.
57980	DIFFUSION EFFECTS IN ONE-CARRIER SPACE-CHARGE-LIMITED CURRENTS WITH TRAPPING. ROSENTAL, A. SAPAR, A. J. APPL. PHYS. 45 (6), 2787-8, 1974.
57984	LOW-FREQUENCY DIELECTRIC CONSTANTS OF ALPHA-QUARTZ, SAPPHIRE, MAGNESIUM FLUORIDE AND MAGNESIUM OXIDE. FONTANELLA, J. ANDEEN, C. SCHUELE, D. J. APPL. PHYS. 45 (7), 2852-4, 1974.
57985	ELECTRICAL AND OPTICAL PROPERTIES OF THIN FILMS OF LEAD DIPOSITIVE AND SILICON DOPED YTTRIUM IRON GARNET PRODUCED BY LIQUID PHASE EPITAXY. LARSEN, P. K. ROBERTSON, J. M. J. APPL. PHYS. 45 (7), 2867-73, 1974.
57986	GALVANOMAGNETIC MEASUREMENTS ON THIN LEAD SELENIDE EPITAXIAL FILMS AS A FUNCTION OF OXYGEN AND HYDROGEN EXPOSURE. MC LANE, G. F. J. APPL. PHYS. 45 (7), 2926-30, 1974.
57987	FLUORESCENCE QUENCHING OF THE F(3/2) STATE IN NEODYMIUM-DOPED YTTRIUM ALUMINUM GARNET BY MULTIPHONON RELAXATION. LIAO, P. F. WEBER, H. P. J. APPL. PHYS. 45 (7), 2931-4, 1974.
57988	INFRARED REFLECTION OF ION-IMPLANTED GALLIUM ARSENIDE. KACHARE, A. H. SPITZER, W. G. EULER, F. K. KAHAN, A. J. APPL. PHYS. 45 (7), 2938-46, 1974. (AD 786 150)
57989	CHARACTERISTICS OF A LASER-PUMPED 1.5 MU-M INFRARED QUANTUM COUNTER. STOKOWSKI, S. E. J. APPL. PHYS. 45 (7), 2957-60, 1974.
57991	PHOTOCONDUCTIVITY IN THE AMORPHOUS GERMANIUM-RICH GERMANIUM TELLURIUM SYSTEM. SCHARNHORST, K. P. RIEDL, H. R. J. APPL. PHYS. 45 (7), 2971-9, 1974.

EPIC Number	Bibliographic Citation
57993	PREPARATION AND PROPERTIES OF HIGH - TRANSITION TEMPERATURE NIOBIUM GERMANIUM FILMS. GAVALER, J. R. JANOCKO, M. A. JONES, C. K. J. APPL. PHYS. 45 (7), 3009-13, 1974.
57994	ELECTRON LIFETIME AND DIFFUSION CONSTANT IN GERMANIUM-DOPED GALLIUM ARSENIDE. ACKET, G. A. NIJMAN, W. LAM, H. 'T J. APPL. PHYS. 45 (7), 3033-40, 1974.
57997	RADIO FREQUENCY REACTIVELY SPUTTERED SUPERCONDUCTING NIOBIUM NITRIDE FILMS. KESKAR, K. S. YAMASHITA, T. ONODERA, Y. GOTO, Y. ASO, T. J. APPL. PHYS. 45 (7), 3102-5, 1974.
57998	STATIC BUBBLE DOMAIN PROPERTIES OF AMORPHOUS GADOLINIUM COBALT FILMS. HASEGAWA, R. J. APPL. PHYS. 45 (7), 3109-12, 1974.
57999	ANNEALING BEHAVIOR AND TEMPERATURE DEPENDENCE OF THE BROWTH-INDUCED MAGNETIC ANISOTROPY IN EPITAXIAL SAMARIUM-YTTRIUM IRON GARNET. HAGEDORN, F. B. J. APPL. PHYS. 45 (7), 3123-8, 1974.
58000	DOMAIN PATTERNS OF A MAGNETIC GARNET BUBBLE FILM IN AN ARBITRARILY ORIENTED FIELD. SHIMADA, Y. J. APPL. PHYS. 45 (7), 3154-8, 1974.
58001	SECONDARY EMISSION AND PHOTOEMISSION FROM NEGATIVE ELECTRON AFFINITY GALLIUM PHOSPHIDE: CESIUM. MARTINELLI, R. U. J. APPL. PHYS. 45 (7), 3203-4, 1974.
58002	PHOTOVOLTAIC POLARITY OF CADMIUM TELLURIDE FILMS OBLIQUELY DEPOSITED IN VACUUM. ONISHI, H. KUROKAWA, S. LEYASU, K. J. APPL. PHYS. 45 (7), 3205-6, 1974.
58003	TEMPERATURE AND FIELD DEPENDENCE OF MAGNETIZATION OF SILICON-DOPED YTTRIUM IRON GARNET CRYSTALS. PANDEY, R. K. J. APPL. PHYS. 45 (7), 3216-7, 1974.
58006	CRYSTALLOGRAPHY, MAGNETISM, AND BAND STRUCTURE OF MANGANESE NICKEL BISMUTH - TYPE COMPOUNDS. SUITS, J. C. STREET, G. B. LEE, K. GOODENOUGH, J. B. PHYS. REV. 10 B (1), 120-7, 1974.
58007	HIGH-PRESSURE STUDIES ON FERRITES. HALASA, N. A. DE PASQUALI, G. DRICKAMER, H. G. PHYS. REV. 10 B (1), 154-64, 1964.
58008	DETERMINATION OF EXCHANGE INTEGRALS J (1) AND J (2) AND MAGNETIC SURFACE-ANISOTROPY ENERGY IN EUROPIUM SULFIDE FROM STANDING-SPIN-WAVE RESONANCE. SCHWOB, P. K. TACHIKI, M. EVERETT, G. E. PHYS. REV. 10 B (1), 165-78, 1974.
58010	MAGNETIC-ION-LATTICE INTERACTION: RARE-EARTH ANTIMONIDES. MULLEN, M. E. LUTHI, B. WANG, P. S. BUCHER, E. LONGINOTTI, L. D. MAITA, J. P. OTT, H. R. PHYS. REV. 10 B (1), 186-99, 1974.
58014	SULFUR K BETA X-RAY EMISSION SPECTRA AND ELECTRONIC STRUCTURES OF SOME METAL SULFIDES. SUGIURA, C. GOHSHI, Y. SUZUKI, I. PHYS. REV. 10 B (2), 338-43, 1974.
58015	EFFECTS OF THERMAL-NEUTRON IRRADIATION ON THE ELASTIC CONSTANTS OF COPPER. REHN, L. E. HOLDER, J. GRANATO, A. V. COLTMAN, R. R. YOUNG, F. W., JR. PHYS. REV. 10 B (2), 349-62, 1974.
58018	CORE EXCITONS IN AMORPHOUS MAGNESIUM ALLOYS. SLOWIK, J. H. PHYS. REV. 10 B (2), 416-31, 1974.

EPIC Number	Bibliographic Citation

58023 **ELECTRONIC BAND STRUCTURES AND CHARGE DENSITIES OF NIOBIUM CARBIDE AND NIOBIUM NITRIDE.**
CHADI, D. J. COHEN, M. L.
PHYS. REV.
10 B (2), 496–500, 1974.

58028 **SPACE–CHARGE–LIMITED CURRENT FLOW IN GALLIUM NITRIDE THIN FILMS.**
VESELY, J. C. SHATZKES, M. BURKHARDT, P. J.
PHYS. REV.
10 B (2), 582–90, 1974.

58029 **FREE–EXCITON–IMPURITY INTERACTION IN ALUMINUM ARSENIC.**
ONTON, A. CHICOTKA, R. J.
PHYS. REV.
10 B (2), 591–5, 1974.

58030 **ELECTRONIC DENSITY OF STATES AND BONDING IN CHALCOPYRITE–TYPE SEMICONDUCTORS.**
DE ALVAREZ, C. V. COHEN, M. L. LEY, L.
KOWALCZYK, S. P. MC FEELY, F. R.
SHIRLEY, D. A. GRANT, R. W.
PHYS. REV.
10 B (2), 596–8, 1974.

58031 **MAGNETICALLY RESOLVED FINE STRUCTURE AT THE E(1) EDGE OF INDIUM ANTIMONY.**
SARI, S. O.
PHYS. REV.
10 B (2), 599–602, 1974.

58032 **THEORY FOR TWO–BEAM TWO–PHOTON PHOTOCONDUCTIVITY IN SOLIDS AND ITS APPLICATION TO ZINC SULFIDE CRYSTALS.**
YEE, J. H.
PHYS. REV.
10 B (2), 603–6, 1974.

58033 **THEORY OF LOCALIZED STATES IN SEMICONDUCTORS. I. NEW RESULTS USING AN OLD METHOD.**
PANTELIDES, S. T. SAH, C. T.
PHYS. REV.
10 B (2), 621–37, 1974.
(AD 785 451)

58034 **THEORY OF LOCALIZED STATES IN SEMICONDUCTORS. II. THE PSEUDO IMPURITY THEORY APPLICATION TO SHALLOW AND DEEP DONORS IN SILICON.**
PANTELIDES, S. T. SAH, C. T.
PHYS. REV.
10 B (2), 638–58, 1974.
(AD 785 452)

58035 **LUMINESCENCE LINE SHAPE AS A TEMPERATURE PROBE: THE THERMAL RELAXATION OF HIGHLY EXCITED CADMIUM SULFIDE.**
SHAH, J. LEHENY, R. F. BRINKMAN, W. F.
PHYS. REV.
10 B (2), 659–64, 1974.

58036 **FRANZ–KELDYSH EFFECT AND INTERNAL FIELDS IN ZINC SULFIDE CRYSTALS.**
YACOBI, B. G. BRADA, Y.
PHYS. REV.
10 B (2), 665–70, 1974.

58037 **FUNDAMENTAL ENERGY GAP OF GALLIUM NITRIDE FROM PHOTOLUMINESCENCE EXCITATION SPECTRA.**
MONEMAR, B.
PHYS. REV.
10 B (2), 676–81, 1974.

58038 **CYCLOTRON RESONANCE IN INDIUM ANTIMONY AND GALLIUM ARSENIDE WITH MAGNETIC FIELDS UP TO 140 T.**
HERLACH, F. DAVIS, J. SCHMIDT, R.
SPECTOR, H.
PHYS. REV.
10 B (2), 682–7, 1974.

58040 **SECOND–HARMONIC GENERATION IN INDIUM ANTIMONY, INDIUM PHOSPHIDE, AND ALUMINUM ANTIMONY.**
LEE, C. C. FAN, H. Y.
PHYS. REV.
10 B (2), 703–9, 1974.

58041 **ELECTRON ORBITAL ENERGIES OF OXYGEN ADSORBED ON SILICON SURFACES AND OF SILICON DIOXIDE.**
IBACH, H. ROWE, J. E.
PHYS. REV.
10 B (2), 710–8, 1974.

58042 **SIMPLE TREATMENT OF THE ANOMALOUS INTERBAND DIELECTRIC CONSTANT OF ZERO–GAP SEMICONDUCTORS.**
BAILYN, M. LIU, L.
PHYS. REV.
10 B (2), 759–66, 1974.

58043 **EFFECTIVE CHARGES AND PIEZOELECTRICITY.**
HARRISON, W. A.
PHYS. REV.
10 B (2), 767–70, 1974.

58045 **PROPOSED SEARCH FOR SUPERCONDUCTIVITY IN THE SEMICONDUCTOR SILICON TELLURIDE.**
DALVEN, R.
PHYS. REV.
10 B (3), 870–1, 1974.
(ERRATUM: TITLE IBID, AUTHOR IBID, J. IBID, 10 (11), 4812, 1974.)

58047 **THERMODYNAMIC PROPERTIES OF RUBIDIUM DIHYDROGEN ARSENATE.**
FAIRALL, C. W. REESE, W.
PHYS. REV.
10 B (3), 882–5, 1974.

58048 **EFFECT OF ANTIFERROMAGNETIC TRANSITION ON THE OPTICAL–ABSORPTION EDGE IN MANGANESE OXIDE, ALPHA–MANGANESE SULFIDE, AND COBALT OXIDE.**
CHOU, H.–H. FAN, H. Y.
PHYS. REV.
10 B (3), 901–10, 1974.

58050 **ABSORPTION SPECTRA OF YTTRIUM IRON OXIDE (YTTRIUM IRON GARNET) AND YTTRIUM GALLIUM OXIDE: IRON.**
SCOTT, G. B. LACKLISON, D. E. PAGE, J. L.
PHYS. REV.
10 (3), 971–86, 1974.

58051 **INFRARED BAND GAP AT THE METAL–NONMETAL TRANSITION IN NICKEL SULFIDE.**
BARKER, A. S., JR. REMEIKA, J. P.
PHYS. REV.
10 B (3), 987–94, 1974.

58052 **BAND MODEL FOR THE METAL–SEMICONDUCTOR TRANSITION IN NICKEL SULFIDE.**
MATTHEISS, L. F.
PHYS. REV.
10 B (3), 995–1005, 1974.

58053 **MAGNETIC PROPERTIES OF NEPTUNIUM LAVES PHASES: NEPTUNIUM ALUMINATE, NEPTUNIUM OSMIUM, NEPTUNIUM IRIDIUM, AND NEPTUNIUM RUTHENIUM.**
ALDRED, A. T. DUNLAP, B. D. LAM, D. J.
NOWIK, I.
PHYS. REV.
10 B (3), 1011–19, 1974.

58055 **HYDROSTATIC–PRESSURE STUDIES OF MAGNETIC MODES IN THE FAR INFRARED.**
JOHNSON, K. C. SIEVERS, A. J.
PHYS. REV.
10 B (3), 1027–37, 1974.

58057 **OPTICAL EXCITATION OF PLASMONS IN A QUASI–ONE–DIMENSIONAL CONDUCTOR.**
WILLIAMS, P. F. BUTLER, M. A.
ROUSSEAU, D. L.
PHYS. REV.
10 B (3), 1109–11, 1974.

58058 **MAGNETIC SUSCEPTIBILITY OF ANTIFERROMAGNETIC IRIDIUM COMPLEXES.**
DE, I. DESAI, V. P. CHAKRAVARTY, A. S.
PHYS. REV.
10 B (3), 1113–7, 1974.

58059 **PREPARATION OF HIGH–COERCIVITY BARIUM IRON OXIDE.**
HANEDA, K. MIYAKAWA, C. KOJIMA, H.
J. AMER. CERAM. SOC.
57 (8), 354–7, 1974.

58062 **STUDY OF EDGE LUMINESCENCE IN GALLIUM SELENIDE SINGLE CRYSTALS.**
ABDULLAEV, G. V. BELEN'KII, G. L.
SALAEV, E. YU. SULEIMANOV, R. A.
KHALILOV, V. KH.
FIZ. TVERD. TELA
16 (1), 19–24, 1974.
(FOR ENGLISH TRANSLATION SEE E58063)

58063 **STUDY OF EDGE LUMINESCENCE IN GALLIUM SELENIDE SINGLE CRYSTALS.**
ABDULLAEV, G. V. BELEN'KII, G. L.
SALAEV, E. YU. SULEIMANOV, R. A.
KHALILOV, V. KH.
SOV. PHYS. SOLID STATE
16 (1), 11–4, 1974.
(ENGLISH TRANSLATION OF FIZ. TVERD. TELA, 16 (1), 19–24, 1974; FOR ORIGINAL SEE E58062)

58064 **ELECTROOPTICAL CONSTANTS OF IONIC CRYSTALS.**
LARIONOV, A. L. MALKIN, B. Z.
FIZ. TVERD. TELA
16 (1), 36–41, 1974.
(FOR ENGLISH TRANSLATION SEE E58065)

58065 **ELECTROOPTICAL CONSTANTS OF IONIC CRYSTALS.**
LARIONOV, A. L. MALKIN, B. Z.
SOV. PHYS. SOLID STATE
16 (1), 21–4, 1974.
(ENGLISH TRANSLATION OF FIZ. TVERD. TELA, 16 (1), 36–41, 1974; FOR ORIGINAL SEE E58064)

EPIC Number	Bibliographic Citation
58066	**SPECTRAL CHARACTERISTICS OF THE RADIATION PRODUCED WHEN TRANSPARENT DIELECTRICS ARE FRACTURED BY LASER LIGHT.** ARKHIPOV, YU. V. MORACHEVSKII, N. V. MOROZOV, V. V. FAIZULLOV, F. S. FIZ. TVERD. TELA 16 (1), 71–6, 1974. (FOR ENGLISH TRANSLATION SEE E58067)
58067	**SPECTRAL CHARACTERISTICS OF THE RADIATION PRODUCED WHEN TRANSPARENT DIELECTRICS ARE FRACTURED BY LASER LIGHT.** ARKHIPOV, YU. V. MORACHEVSKII, N. V. MOROZOV, V. V. FAIZULLOV, F. S. SOV. PHYS. SOLID STATE 16 (1), 43–5, 1974. (ENGLISH TRANSLATION OF FIZ. TVERD. TELA, 16 (1), 71–6, 1974; FOR ORIGINAL SEE E58066)
58068	**ELECTRON EFFECTIVE MASSES IN INDIUM ANTIMONY CRYSTALS DOPED WITH VARIOUS IMPURITIES.** LANG, I. G. NASLEDOV, D. N. PAVLOV, S. T. RADAIKINA, L. N. FILIPCHENKO, A. S. FIZ. TVERD. TELA 16 (1), 92–7, 1974. (FOR ENGLISH TRANSLATION SEE E58069)
58069	**ELECTRON EFFECTIVE MASSES IN INDIUM ANTIMONY CRYSTALS DOPED WITH VARIOUS IMPURITIES.** LANG, I. G. NASLEDOV, D. N. PAVLOV, S. T. RADAIKINA, L. N. FILIPCHENKO, A. S. SOV. PHYS. SOLID STATE 16 (1), 54–6, 1974. (ENGLISH TRANSLATION OF FIZ. TVERD. TELA, 16 (1), 92–7, 1974; FOR ORIGINAL SEE E58068)
58070	**MAGNETIC STRUCTURE OF BARIUM (0.4) STRONTIUM (1.6) ZINC (2) FERRITE IN A MAGNETIC FIELD.** SIZOV, R. A. FIZ. TVERD. TELA 16 (1), 98–101, 1974. (FOR ENGLISH TRANSLATION SEE E58071)
58071	**MAGNETIC STRUCTURE OF BARIUM (0.4) STRONTIUM (1.6) ZINC (2) FERRITE IN A MAGNETIC FIELD.** SIZOV, R. A. SOV. PHYS. SOLID STATE 16 (1), 57–8, 1974. (ENGLISH TRANSLATION OF FIZ. TVERD. TELA, 16 (1), 98–101, 1974; FOR ORIGINAL SEE E58070)
58072	**LIFSHITS ELECTRONIC PHASE TRANSITIONS IN BISMUTH.** BRANDT, N. B. YASTREBOVA, V. A. PONOMAREV, YA. G. FIZ. TVERD. TELA 16 (1), 102–9, 1974. (FOR ENGLISH TRANSLATION SEE E58073)
58073	**LIFSHITS ELECTRONIC PHASE TRANSITIONS IN BISMUTH.** BRANDT, N. B. YASTREBOVA, V. A. PONOMAREV, YA. G. SOV. PHYS. SOLID STATE 16 (1), 59–63, 1974. (ENGLISH TRANSLATION OF FIZ. TVERD. TELA, 16 (1), 102–9, 1974; FOR ORIGINAL SEE E58072)
58074	**SPONTANEOUS ELECTROOPTICAL ABSORPTION EFFECT IN BARIUM TITANATE SINGLE CRYSTALS.** SONIN, A. S. GUSEVA, L. M. PLESHAKOV, I. A. FIZ. TVERD. TELA 16 (1), 110–4, 1974. (FOR ENGLISH TRANSLATION SEE E58075)
58075	**SPONTANEOUS ELECTROOPTICAL ABSORPTION EFFECT IN BARIUM TITANATE SINGLE CRYSTALS.** SONIN, A. S. GUSEVA, L. M. PLESHAKOV, I. A. SOV. PHYS. SOLID STATE 16 (1), 64–6, 1974. (ENGLISH TRANSLATION OF FIZ. TVERD. TELA, 16 (1), 110–4, 1974; FOR ORIGINAL SEE E58074)
58082	**EFFECT OF DEGREE OF UNIPOLARITY ON SECOND-HARMONIC GENERATION AND ELECTROOPTIC PROPERTIES OF BARIUM SODIUM NIOBATE CRYSTALS.** VORONOV, V. V. ZHARIKOV, E. V. KUZ'MINOV, YU. S. OSIKO, V. V. TOBIS, V. I. SHUMSKAYA, L. S. FIZ. TVERD. TELA 16 (1), 162–6, 1974. (FOR ENGLISH TRANSLATION SEE E58083)
58083	**EFFECT OF DEGREE OF UNIPOLARITY ON SECOND-HARMONIC GENERATION AND ELECTROOPTIC PROPERTIES OF BARIUM SODIUM NIOBATE CRYSTALS.** VORONOV, V. V. ZHARIKOV, E. V. KUZ'MINOV, YU. S. OSIKO, V. V. TOBIS, V. I. SHUMSKAYA, L. S. SOV. PHYS. SOLID STATE 16 (1), 96–8, 1974. (ENGLISH TRANSLATION OF FIZ. TVERD. TELA, 16 (1), 162–6, 1974; FOR ORIGINAL SEE E58082)
58084	**TEMPERATURE DEPENDENCE OF VIBRATIONAL ABSORPTION BY MOLECULAR CENTERS IN ALKALI-HALIDE CRYSTALS.** TSYASHCHENKO, YU. P. PASECHNYI, V. A. TARASENKO, A. V. ZAPOROZHETS, V. M. FIZ. TVERD. TELA 16 (1), 167–72, 1974. (FOR ENGLISH TRANSLATION SEE E58085)
58085	**TEMPERATURE DEPENDENCE OF VIBRATIONAL ABSORPTION BY MOLECULAR CENTERS IN ALAKLI-HALIDE CRYSTALS.** TSYASHCHENKO, YU. P. PASECHNYI, V. A. TARASENKO, A. V. ZAPOROZHETS, V. M. SOV. PHYS. SOLID STATE 16 (1), 99–102, 1974. (ENGLISH TRANSLATION OF FIZ. TVERD. TELA, 16 (1), 167–72, 1974; FOR ORIGINAL SEE E58084)
58086	**SOME PYROELECTRIC PROPERTIES OF A PLASTICALLY DEFORMED LITHIUM FLUORIDE CRYSTAL.** KORNFEL'D, M. I. FIZ. TVERD. TELA 16 (1), 180–3, 1974. (FOR ENGLISH TRANSLATION SEE E58087)
58087	**SOME PYROELECTRIC PROPERTIES OF A PLASTICALLY DEFORMED LITHIUM FLUORIDE CRYSTAL.** KORNFEL'D, M. I. SOV. PHYS. SOLID STATE 16 (1), 107–8, 1974. (ENGLISH TRANSLATION OF FIZ. TVERD. TELA, 16 (1), 180–3, 1974; FOR ORIGINAL SEE E58086)
58088	**EMISSION, ABSORPTION, AND REFLECTION SPECTRA OF HIGH-DENSITY EXCITONS IN A CADMIUM SELENIDE CRYSTAL.** AKOPYAN, I. KH. RAZBIRIN, B. S. FIZ. TVERD. TELA 16 (1), 189–91, 1974. (FOR ENGLISH TRANSLATION SEE E58089)
58089	**EMISSION, ABSORPTION, AND REFLECTION SPECTRA OF HIGH-DENSITY EXCITONS IN A CADMIUM SELENIDE CRYSTAL.** AKOPYAN, I. KH. RAZBIRIN, B. S. SOV. PHYS. SOLID STATE 16 (1), 113–4, 1974. (ENGLISH TRANSLATION OF FIZ. TVERD. TELA, 16 (1), 189–91, 1974; FOR ORIGINAL SEE E58088)
58090	**NONMONOTONIC DEPENDENCE OF THE ACOUSTOELECTRIC ELECTRO-MOTIVE-FORCE ON THE CONDUCTIVITY OF A PIEZOELECTRIC SEMICONDUCTOR.** TIMAN, B. L. RYZHIKOV, V. D. FIZ. TVERD. TELA 16 (1), 191–4, 1974. (FOR ENGLISH TRANSLATION SEE E58091)
58091	**NONMONOTONIC DEPENDENCE OF THE ACOUSTOELECTRIC ELECTRO-MOTIVE-FORCE ON THE CONDUCTIVITY OF A PIEZOELECTRIC SEMICONDUCTOR.** TIMAN, B. L. RYZHIKOV, V. D. SOV. PHYS. SOLID STATE 16 (1), 115–6, 1974. (ENGLISH TRANSLATION OF FIZ. TVERD. TELA, 16 (1), 191–4, 1974; FOR ORIGINAL SEE E58090)
58092	**POSITIVE ISOTROPIC MAGNETORESISTANCE OF YTTRIUM IRON GARNET.** KSENDZOV, YA. M. MAKAROV, V. V. FIZ. TVERD. TELA 16 (1), 194–5, 1974. (FOR ENGLISH TRANSLATION SEE E58093)
58093	**POSITIVE ISOTROPIC MAGNETORESISTANCE OF YTTRIUM IRON GARNET.** KSENDZOV, YA. M. MAKAROV, V. V. SOV. PHYS. SOLID STATE 16 (1), 117–8, 1974. (ENGLISH TRANSLATION OF FIZ. TVERD. TELA, 16 (1), 194–5, 1974; FOR ORIGINAL SEE E58092)
58094	**PROPERTIES OF SINGLE CRYSTALS OF THE FERROELECTRIC LEAD GERMANIUM OXIDE.** SAL'NIKOV, V. D. STEFANOVICH, S. YU. CHECHKIN, V. V. TOMASHPOL'SKII, YU. YA. VENEVTSEV, YU. I. FIZ. TVERD. TELA 1P (1), 196–9, 1974. (FOR ENGLISH TRANSLATION SEE E58095)
58095	**PROPERTIES OF SINGLE CRYSTALS OF THE FERROELECTRIC LEAD GERMANIUM OXIDE.** SAL'NIKOV, V. D. STEFANOVICH, S. YU. CHECHKIN, V. V. TOMASHPOL'SKII, YU. YA. VENEVTSEV, YU. I. SOV. PHYS. SOLID STATE 16 (1), 119–20, 1974. (ENGLISH TRANSLATION OF FIZ. TVERD. TELA, 16 (1), 196–9, 1974; FOR ORIGINAL SEE E58094)
58096	**INFLUENCE OF A STRONG ELECTRIC FIELD ON THE MAGNETIC ANISOTROPY OF YTTRIUM IRON GARNET.** PEREKALINA, T. M. ZHELUDEV, I. S. SMIRNOVSKAYA, E. M. FONTON, S. S. KONOPLEV, N. A. FIZ. TVERD. TELA 16 (1), 199–201, 1974. (FOR ENGLISH TRANSLATION SEE E58097)

EPIC Number	Bibliographic Citation

58097 **INFLUENCE OF A STRONG ELECTRIC FIELD ON THE MAGNETIC ANISOTROPY OF YTTRIUM IRON GARNET.**
PEREKALINA, T. M. ZHELUDEV, I. S.
SMIRNOVSKAYA, E. M. FONTON, S. S.
KONOPLEV, N. A.
SOV. PHYS. SOLID STATE
16 (1), 121–2, 1974.
(ENGLISH TRANSLATION OF FIZ. TVERD. TELA, 16 (1), 199–201, 1974; FOR ORIGINAL SEE E58096)

58098 **ANOMALOUS ULTRASONIC DAMPING IN ANTIMONY SULFIDE.**
SAMULIONIS, V. I. ORLYUKAS, A. S.
GRIGAS, I. P.
FIZ. TVERD. TELA
16 (1), 206–8, 1974.
(FOR ENGLISH TRANSLATION SEE E58099)

58099 **ANOMALOUS ULTRASONIC DAMPING IN ANTIMONY SULFIDE.**
SAMULIONIS, V. I. ORLYUKAS, A. S.
GRIGAS, I. P.
SOV. PHYS. SOLID STATE
16 (1), 127–8, 1974.
(ENGLISH TRANSLATION OF FIZ. TVERD, TELA, 16 (1), 206–8, 1974; FOR ORIGINAL SEE E58098)

58100 **ABSORPTION AND REFLECTION SPECTRA OF MANGANESE FLUORIDE IN THE VACUUM ULTRAVIOLET REGION.**
GALUZA, A. I. EREMENKO, V. V.
KIRICHENKO, A. P.
FIZ. TVERD. TELA
16 (1), 208–10, 1974.
(FOR ENGLISH TRANSLATION SEE E58101)

58101 **ABSORPTION AND REFLECTION SPECTRA OF MANGANESE FLUORIDE IN THE VACUUM ULTRAVIOLET REGION.**
GALUZA, A. I. EREMENKO, V. V.
KIRICHENKO, A. P.
SOV. PHYS. SOLID STATE
16 (1), 129–30, 1974.
(ENGLISH TRANSLATION OF FIZ. TVERD. TELA, 16 (1), 208–10, 1974; FOR ORIGINAL SEE E58100)

58102 **EFFECT OF BAND INVERSION ON THE MAGNETIC SUSCEPTIBILITY OF LEAD (1–X) TIN (X) TELLURIDE AND LEAD (1–X) TIN (X) SELENIDE.**
TOVSTYUK, K. D. LASHKAREV, G. V.
ORLETSKII, V. B. SHEVCHENKO, A. D.
FIZ. TVERD. TELA
16 (1), 221–3, 1974.
(FOR ENGLISH TRANSLATION SEE E58103)

58103 **EFFECT OF BAND INVERSION ON THE MAGNETIC SUSCEPTIBILITY OF LEAD (1–X) TIN (X) TELLURIDE AND LEAD (1–X) TIN (X) SELENIDE.**
TOVSTYUK, K. D. LASHKAREV, G. V.
ORLETSKII, V. B. SHEVCHENKO, A. D.
SOV. PHYS. SOLID STATE
16 (1), 140–1, 1974.
(ENGLISH TRANSLATION OF FIZ. TVERD. TELA, 16 (1), 221–3, 1974; FOR ORIGINAL SEE E58102)

58108 **MAGNETIC PROPERTIES OF RARE–EARTH ORTHOVANADITES.**
BAZUEV, G. V. MATVEENKO, I. I.
SHVEIKIN, G. P.
FIZ. TVERD. TELA
16 (1), 240–3, 1974.
(FOR ENGLISH TRANSLATION SEE E58109)

58109 **MAGNETIC PROPERTIES OF RARE–EARTH ORTHOVANADITES.**
BAZUEV, G. V. MATVEENKO, I. I.
SHVEIKIN, G. P.
SOV. PHYS. SOLID STATE
16 (1), 155–6, 1974.
(ENGLISH TRANSLATION OF FIZ. TVERD. TELA, 16 (1), 240–3, 1974; FOR ORIGINAL SEE E58108)

58110 **CONCENTRATION DEPENDENCE OF DRIFT MOBILITY IN CONDUCTING BARIUM TITANIUM OXIDE CRYSTALS.**
GRUSHEVSKII, YU. A. GIRSHBERG, YA. G.
BURSIAN, E. V.
FIZ. TVERD. TELA
16 (1), 248–50, 1974.
(FOR ENGLISH TRANSLATION SEE E58111)

58111 **CONCENTRATION DEPENDENCE OF DRIFT MOBILITY IN CONDUCTING BARIUM TITANIUM OXIDE CRYSTALS.**
GRUSHEVSKII, YU. A. GIRSHBERG, YA. G.
BURSIAN, E. V.
SOV. PHYS. SOLID STATE
16 (1), 161–2, 1974.
(ENGLISH TRANSLATION OF FIZ. TVERD. TELA, 16 (1), 248–50, 1974; FOR ORIGINAL SEE E58110)

58112 **PHOTOELECTRIC EMISSION FROM CRYSTALS AND GLASSES OF VARIOUS CHALCOGENIDES.**
BENTSA, V. M. TURYANITSA, I. D.
FIZ. TVERD. TELA
16 (1), 259–60, 1974.
(FOR ENGLISH TRANSLATION SEE E58113)

58113 **PHOTOELECTRIC EMISSION FROM CRYSTALS AND GLASSES OF VARIOUS CHALCOGENIDES.**
BENTSA, V. M. TURYANITSA, I. D.
SOV. PHYS. SOLID STATE
16 (1), 170, 1974.
(ENGLISH TRANSLATION OF FIZ. TVERD. TELA, 16 (1), 259–60, 1974; FOR ORIGINAL SEE E58112)

58114 **INFRARED LUMINESCENCE OF DEEP DONORS IN SILICON CARBIDE.**
GORBAN', I. S. SLOBODYANYUK, A. V.
FIZ. TVERD. TELA
16 (1), 263–6, 1974.
(FOR ENGLISH TRANSLATION SEE E58115)

58115 **INFRARED LUMINESCENCE OF DEEP DONORS IN SILICON CARBIDE.**
GORBAN', I. S. SLOBODYANYUK, A. V.
SOV. PHYS. SOLID STATE
16 (1), 173–4, 1974.
(ENGLISH TRANSLATION OF FIZ. TVERD. TELA, 16 (1), 263–6, 1974; FOR ORIGINAL SEE E58114)

58116 **MAGNETIC SPECIFIC HEAT OF LANTHANUM ORTHOVANADITE.**
BORUKHOVICH, A. S. BAZUEV, G. V.
FIZ. TVERD. TELA
16 (1), 273–6, 1974.
(FOR ENGLISH TRANSLATION SEE E58117)

58117 **MAGNETIC SPECIFIC HEAT OF LANTHANUM ORTHOVANADITE.**
BORUKHOVICH, A. S. BAZUEV, G. V.
SOV. PHYS. SOLID STATE
16 (1), 181–2, 1974.
(ENGLISH TRANSLATION OF FIZ. TVERD. TELA, 16 (1), 273–6, 1974; FOR ORIGINAL SEE E58116)

58120 **INFLUENCE OF IMPURITIES ON THE CURIE TEMPERATURE OF CHAIN CRYSTALS.**
BALETSKII, D. YU. BERCHA, D. M.
KOPERLES, B. M. TURYANITSA, I. D.
FIZ. TVERD. TELA
16 (1), 278–81, 1974.
(FOR ENGLISH TRANSLATION SEE E58121)

58121 **INFLUENCE OF IMPURITIES ON THE CURIE TEMPERATURE OF CHAIN CRYSTALS.**
BALETSKII, D. YU. BERCHA, D. M.
KOPERLES, B. M. TURYANITSA, I. D.
SOV. PHYS. SOLID STATE
16 (1), 185–6, 1974.
(ENGLISH TRANSLATION OF FIZ. TVERD. TELA, 16 (1), 278–81, 1974; FOR ORIGINAL SEE E58120)

58122 **ANOMALIES OF THE SPECIFIC HEAT AND MAGNETIC THERMODYNAMIC PARAMETERS OF YTTRIUM ORTHOVANADITE.**
BORUKHOVICH, A. S. BAZUEV, G. V.
SHVEIKIN, G. P.
FIZ. TVERD. TELA
16 (1), 286–9, 1974.
(FOR ENGLISH TRANSLATION SEE E58123)

58123 **ANOMALIES OF THE SPECIFIC HEAT AND MAGNETIC THERMODYNAMIC PARAMETERS OF YTTRIUM ORTHOVANADITE.**
BORUKHOVICH, A. S. BAZUEV, G. V.
SHVEIKIN, G. P.
SOV. PHYS. SOLID STATE
16 (1), 191–2, 1974.
(ENGLISH TRANSLATION OF FIZ. TVERD. TELA, 16 (1), 286–9, 1974; FOR ORIGINAL SEE E58122)

58124 **ALLOWANCE FOR THE SATURATION IN MANY–PHOTON IONIZATION PROCESSES IN ACTIVATED ALKALI HALIDE CRYSTALS.**
ASEEV, G. I. KATS, M. L. NIKOL'SKII, V. K.
FIZ. TVERD. TELA
16 (1), 293–5, 1974.
(FOR ENGLISH TRANSLATION SEE E58125)

58125 **ALLOWANCE FOR THE SATURATION IN MANY–PHOTON IONIZATION PROCESSES IN ACTIVATED ALKALI HALIDE CRYSTALS.**
ASEEV, G. I. KATS, M. L. NIKOL'SKII, V. K.
MEDVEDEV, B. A. SILKINA, T. G.
SOV. PHYS. SOLID STATE
16 (1), 197–8, 1974.
(ENGLISH TRANSLATION OF FIZ. TVERD. TELA, 16 (1), 293–5, 1974; FOR ORIGINAL SEE E58124)

58126 **PARAPROCESS IN LITHIUM FERRITE–TITANATES.**
BELOV, K. P. GORYAGA, A. N. PED'KO, A. V.
KOKOREV, A. I.
FIZ. TVERD. TELA
16 (1), 295–8, 1974.
(FOR ENGLISH TRANSLATION SEE E58127)

58127 **PARAPROCESS IN LITHIUM FERRITE–TITANATES.**
BELOV, K. P. GORYAGA, A. N. PED'KO, A. V.
KOKOREV, A. I.
SOV. PHYS. SOLID STATE
16 (1), 199–200, 1974.
(ENGLISH TRANSLATION OF FIZ. TVERD. TELA, 16 (1), 295–8, 1974; FOR ORIGINAL SEE E58126)

EPIC Number	Bibliographic Citation
58128	**SPECTRA OF THE PHOTOELECTRIC YIELD OF LITHIUM HYDRIDE AND LITHIUM DEUTERIDE IN THE ULTRASOFT X-RAY REGION.** MAISTE, A. A. CHOLAKH, S. O. GAVRILOV, F. F. ELANGO, M. A. FIZ. TVERD. TELA 16 (1), 301–3, 1974. (FOR ENGLISH TRANSLATION SEE E58129)
58129	**SPECTRA OF THE PHOTOELECTRIC YIELD OF LITHIUM HYDRIDE AND LITHIUM DEUTERIDE IN THE ULTRASOFT X-RAY REGION.** MAISTE, A. A. CHOLAKH, S. O. GAVRILOV, F. F. ELANGO, M. A. SOV. PHYS. SOLID STATE 16 (1), 200–4, 1974. (ENGLISH TRANSLATION OF FIZ. TVERD. TELA, 16 (1), 301–3, 1974; FOR ORIGINAL SEE E58128)
58130	**AVERAGE INTERNAL POTENTIAL AND MAGNETIC SUSCEPTIBILITY OF SEMICONDUCTOR CRYSTALS.** ANDRIANOV, D. G. ZHUKOVA, L. A. SAVEL'EV, A. S. FISTUL', V. I. FIZ. TVERD. TELA 16 (1), 309–11, 1974. (FOR ENGLISH TRANSLATION SEE E58131)
58131	**AVERAGE INTERNAL POTENTIAL AND MAGNETIC SUSCEPTIBILITY OF SEMICONDUCTOR CRYSTALS.** ANDRIANOV, D. G. ZHUKOVA, L. A. SAVEL'EV, A. S. FISTUL', V. I. SOV. PHYS. SOLID STATE 16 (1), 209–10, 1974. (ENGLISH TRANSLATION OF FIZ. TVERD. TELA, 16 (1), 309–11, 1974; FOR ORIGINAL SEE E58130)
58132	**CONTACT PHENOMENA IN A PYROELECTRIC.** KORNFEL'D, M. I. FIZ. TVERD. TELA 16 (1), 311–2, 1974. (FOR ENGLISH TRANSLATION SEE E58133)
58133	**CONTACT PHENOMENA IN A PYROELECTRIC.** KORNFEL'D, M. I. SOV. PHYS. SOLID STATE 16 (1), 211, 1974. (ENGLISH TRANSLATION OF FIZ. TVERD. TELA, 16 (1), 311–2, 1974; FOR ORIGINAL SEE E58132)
58134	**EFFECTS OF PLASTIC DEFORMATION ON THE DIELECTRIC PROPERTIES OF ICE.** MAE, S. HIGASHI, A. CRYST. LATTICE DEFECTS 4 (4), 295–308, 1973.
58136	**CYLINDRICAL MAGNETIC DOMAINS IN EPITAXIAL FERRITE THIN FILMS.** SUK, K. KRATOCHVILOVA, E. KRUPICKA, S. CZECH. J. PHYS. 23 (12), 1413–14, 1973.
58137	**BAND STRUCTURE OF ALUMINUM ANTIMONIDE.** TOPOL, I. NEUMANN, H. HESS, E. CZECH. J. PHYS. 24 (1), 107–12, 1974.
58140	**LUMINESCENCE OF EUROPIUM-ACTIVATED SODIUM BROMIDE AND SODIUM IODIDE PHOSPHORS.** IVAKHNENKO, P. S. VILITKEVICH, A. I. DAL'NEVOST. FIZ. SB. 1, 147–59, 1971.
58144	**THERMOELECTROMOTIVE FORCE OF COUPLES OF MOLYBDENUM WITH FIBROUS INTERSTITIAL COMPOUNDS PREPARED IN AN ELECTRIC DISCHARGE.** TAKAHASHI, T. ITOH, H. TOMITA, H. DENKI KAGAKU 41 (11), 853–8, 1973.
58155	**DEEP ACCEPTOR LEVELS IN LEAD CHALCOGENIDES AND THEIR SOLID SOLUTIONS.** KASIMOV, S. ULUGKHODZHAEVA, M. MAKHMUDOV, M. DOKL. AKAD. NAUK TADZH. SSR 16 (11), 16–19, 1973.
58156	**ELECTRICAL PROPERTIES OF THALLIUM-DOPED N-INDIUM ARSENIDE.** MAKHMATKULOV, M. MAVLONOV, SH. DOKL. AKAD. NAUK TADZH. SSR 16 (11), 20–4, 1973.
58158	**RADIO- AND THERMOLUMINESCENCE OF RARE EARTH ELEMENTS IN YTTRIUM ALUMINATE-RARE EARTH TRIPOSITIVE ION CRYSTALS.** ARSEN'EV, P. A. VAKHIDOV, SH. A. IBRAGIMOVA, E. M. DOKL. AKAD. NAUK UZB. SSR 30 (5), 32–4, 1973.
58160	**PHYSICAL PROPERTIES OF 3-D METAL SILICIDES.** SAMSONOV, G. V. FOMENKO, V. S. PODGRUSHKO, N. F. OKHREMCHUK, L. N. PODCHERNYAEVA, I. A. DOPROV. AKAD. NAUK UKR. RSR, SER. 35 B (12), 1102–5, 1973.
58164	**EFFECT OF ELECTRIC FIELD STRENGTH ON THE ELECTRIC CONDUCTIVITY OF MOLTEN LITHIUM, SODIUM, AND POTASSIUM CHLORIDES.** SHABANOV, O. M. GADZHIEV, S. M. TAGIROV, S. M. ELEKTROKHIMIYA 9 (12), 1828–32, 1973.
58175	**USE OF THE PHOTOEFFECT AT THE SEMICONDUCTOR-ELECTROLYTE BOUNDARY FOR DETERMINING THE ENERGY GAP OF SEMICONDUCTORS.** KLUG, H. P. LERCHE, K. H. ERNST, H. G. THIELEMANN, W. EXP. TECH. PHYS. 21 (5), 425–30, 1973.
58178	**CHARACTERISTICS OF RADIO-FREQUENCY-SPUTTERED LEAD BISMUTH LANTHANUM IRON ZIRCONIUM NIOBATE FERROELECTRIC THIN FILMS.** SPENCE, W. MILLER, P. M. WU, N. FERROELECTRICS 5 (3–4), 201–5, 1973.
58179	**FERROELECTRIC AND ANTIFERROELECTRIC MATERIALS.** SUBBARAO, E. C. FERROELECTRICS 5 (3–4), 267–80, 1973.
58180	**COMPOUND SEMICONDUCTOR ALLOYS.** ONTON, A. FESTKOERPERPROBLEME 13, 59–84, 1973.
58183	**PROPERTIES OF VACUUM CONDENSATES OF TITANIUM, ZIRCONIUM, AND NIOBIUM CARBIDES.** USHAKOVA, S. E. FAT'YANOV, V. M. FIZ. KHIM. OBRAB. MATER. (6), 131–4, 1973.
58193	**NARROW-BAND DOMAIN STRUCTURE OF SINGLE-CRYSTAL NICKEL-ZINC-COBALT FERRITE FILMS.** GUSEVA, E. G. KOSHKIN, I. I. STRYGIN, YU. F. FIZ. PLAST., UPRUGOSTI MET. ELEKTRODIN. YAVLENIYA FERRITAKH (1), 85–8, 1972.
58194	**THE DELTA R/R EFFECT IN FILMS OF MAGNESIUM MANGANESE FERRITES.** MITLINA, L. A. FIZ. PLAST., UPRUGOSTI MET. ELEKTRODIN. YAVLENIYA FERRITAKH (1), 107–15, 1972.
58195	**ANOMALIES IN THE ELECTRIC CONDUCTIVITY OF FILMS OF MAGNESIUM MANGANESE FERRITES AT 77–903 K.** MITLINA, L. A. FIZ. PLAST., UPRUGOSTI MET. ELEKTRODIN. YAVLENIYA FERRITAKH (1), 115–21, 1972.
58197	**KINETIC PHENOMENA IN N-SILVER TELLURIDE.** ALIEV, S. A. SUYUNOV, U. KH. ALIEV, M. I. FIZ. TEKH. POLUPROV. 7 (10), 2024–7, 1973.
58199	**LUMINESCENCE PROPERTIES OF GALLIUM INDIUM PHOSPHIDE SOLID SOLUTIONS AT $0.45 < X < 0.50$.** ALFEROV, ZH. I. GARBUZOV, D. Z. MISHURNYI, V. A. RUMYANTSEV, V. D. TRET'YAKOV, D. N. FIZ. TEKH. POLUPROV. 7 (12), 2305–11, 1973.
58200	**IMPURITY RECOMBINATION EMISSION IN ALUMINUM ANTIMONIDE.** LUKOMSKII, A. I. FIZ. TEKH. POLUPROV. 7 (12), 2349–51, 1973. (FOR ENGLISH TRANSLATION SEE E59205)
58201	**MAGNESIUM FERRITE OF THE SYSTEM.** BIBIK, V. P. KIRICHOK, P. P. PODVAL'NYKH, G. S. FIZ. TVERD. TELA 66–70, 1972. (EDITED BY V. P. DUSHCHENKO, KIEV. GOS. PEDAGOG. INST.: KIEV. USSR)
58202	**CURRENT-VOLTAGE CHARACTERISTICS OF GLASSY CADMIUM GERMANIUM PHOSPHIDE.** KIRILENKO, M. M. SERYI, V. I. TYCHINA, I. I. POTYKEVICH, I. V. FIZ. TVERD. TELA 19–23, 1972. (EDITED BY F. P. DUSHCHENKO, KIEV. GOS. PEDAGOG. INST.: KIEV, USSR)
58203	**THERMOEMF. IN GALLIUM ARSENIDE-ZINC TELLURIDE SEMICONDUCTOR ALLOYS.** ANISHCHENKO, V. A. VOITSEKHOVSKII, A. V. FIZ. TVERD. TELA 26–9, 1972.

EPIC Number	Bibliographic Citation
58209	**KINETIC EFFECTS IN A GERMANIUM LEAD TELLURIDE SOLID SOLUTION.** PROKOF'EVA, L. V. NIKULIN, YU. A. BUZYLEVA, L. V. FIZ. TEKH. POLUPROV. 7 (10), 1865–9, 1973. (FOR ENGLISH TRANSLATION SEE E59204)
58210	**SPECTRAL DEPENDENCE OF ONE- AND TWO-PHOTON ABSORPTION IN CADMIUM SULFIDE-TYPE CRYSTALS AND NONPARABOLIC CHARACTER OF THEIR CONDUCTION BANDS.** BRODIN, M. S. DEMIDENKO, Z. A. DIMITRENKO, K. A. REZNICHENKO, V. YA. STRASHNIKOVA, M. I. FIZ. TEKH. POLUPROV. 8 (1), 74–9, 1974. (FOR ENGLISH TRANSLATION SEE E59206)
58212	**ABSORPTION COEFFICIENT ON INFRARED LASER WINDOW MATERIALS.** DEUTSCH, T. F. J. PHYS. CHEM. SOLIDS 34 (12), 2091–104, 1973.
58213	**FREE CARRIER ABSORPTION IN N-TYPE CADMIUM TELLURIDE.** JENSEN, B. J. PHYS. CHEM. SOLIDS 34 (12), 2235–45, 1973.
58223	**URBACH RULE IN CADMIUM SELENIDE.** NITECKI, R. GAJ, J. A. PHYS. STATUS SOLIDI 62 B (1), K17–19, 1974.
58225	**USE OF SOME II - VI COMPOUNDS FOR REGULATION OF LASER PULSES.** IGNATAVICIUS, M. PISKARSKAS, A. STABINIS, A. PROBL. FIZ. SOEDIN. II - VI, MATER. VSES. SOVESHCH., 3RD 1, 121–5, 1972.
58226	**EQUIVALENT REFRACTIVE INDEX OF MULTILAYER FILMS OF DIFFERENT MATERIALS.** CHOPRA, K. L. SHARMA, S. K. YADAVA, V. N. THIN SOLID FILMS 20 (2), 209–15, 1974.
58227	**REFLECTION SPECTRA OF DEFORMED POTASSIUM IODIDE SINGLE CRYSTALS WITH OBLIQUE INCIDENCE OF BEAMS IN THE 240–150 NM RANGE.** VISHNEVSKII, V. N. MARCHUK, E. P. KULIK, Z. S. KULIK, L. N. UKR. FIZ. ZH. (RUSS. ED.) 19 (1), 58–60, 1974.
58234	**CRYSTAL GROWTH AND ELECTRICAL PROPERTIES OF MANGANESE-DOPED TIN TELLURIDE. II.** INOUE, M. YAGI, H. MORISHITA, S. FUKUI DAIGAKU KOGAKUBU KENKYU HOKOKU 21 (2), 93–100, 1973.
58240	**MAGNETOSTRICTION OF RARE EARTH GARNETS CONTAINING GALLIUM AND EUROPIUM. OLD THEORY FOR NEW PROBLEMS.** WHITE, R. L. IEEE TRANS. MAGN. 9 (4), 606–9, 1973.
58242	**HYSTERESIS PROPERTIES OF SINTERED SAMARIUM-COBALT PERMANENT MAGNETS.** ALFF, E. GIVORD, D. HABERER, J. P. IEEE TRANS. MAGN. 9 (4), 631–5, 1973.
58248	**EFFECTS OF ELECTRON RADIATION ON THE ELECTRICAL AND OPTICAL PROPERTIES OF MERCURY CADMIUM TELLURIDE.** MALLON, C. E. NABER, J. A. COLWELL, J. F. GREEN, B. A. IEEE TRANS. NUCL. SCI. 20 (6), 214–19, 1973.
58255	**PHOTOELECTRON SPECTRUM OF SILICON DIFLUORIDE.** FEHLNER, T. P. TURNER, D. W. INORG. CHEM. 13 (3), 754–5, 1974.
58280	**SOLID SOLUTIONS OF SULFUR AND SELENIUM IN COPPER TELLURIDE.** KONEV, V. N. KRUSHATINA, N. A. KOCHETKOVA, A. A. IZV. AKAD. NAUK SSSR, NEORG. MATER. 10 (1), 140–1, 1974. (FOR ENGLISH TRANSLATION SEE E77075)
58287	**SECONDARY ELECTRON EMISSION OF CALCIUM OXIDE EPITAXIAL FILMS ON MOLYBDENUM.** MALYSHEV, S. V. ANDRONOV, A. N. KHOMENKO, V. V. IZV. AKAD. NAUK SSSR, SER. FIZ. 37 (12), 2553–6, 1973.
58291	**ION-DOPED BASE OF A MOLECULARLY SPRAY-COATED OXIDE CATHODE.** VOLODIN, YU. A. DRUZHININ, A. V. KNYAZEV, A. YA. KULICHIKHINA, S. I. IZV. AKAD. NAUK SSSR, SER. FIZ. 37 (12), 2528–31, 1973.
58292	**ION DOPING OF AN OXIDE CATHODE BASE.** ATABEK, B. A. DRUZHININ, A. V. KONDRASHENKOV, YU. A. NEKRASOV, V. I. IZV. AKAD. NAUK SSSR, SER. FIZ. 37 (12), 2523–7, 1973.
58294	**DEFECTS INDUCED IN EMITTERS BY ELECTRONS AND THEIR ROLE IN THE DECREASE OF THE SECONDARY ELECTRON EMISSION COEFFICIENT.** TYUTIKOV, A. M. TOISEVA, M. N. IZV. AKAD. NAUK SSSR, SER. FIZ. 37 (12), 2557–61, 1973.
58299	**MICROPHOTODEFORMATION EFFECT IN CADMIUM SULFIDE SINGLE CRYSTALS.** KAIPNAZAROV, D. K. KOSAEV, E. K. IZV. AKAD. NAUK UZB. SSR, SER. FIZ.-MAT. NAUK 17 (6), 59–60, 1973.
58300	**LUMINESCENCE PHENOMENA IN TERBIUM TRIPOSITIVE DOPED LANTHANUM NIOBATE CRYSTALS.** VAKHIDOV, SH. A. MOROZOV, A. M. NURULLAEV, E. IZV. AKAD. NAUK UZB. SSSR, SER. FIZ.-MAT. NAUK 17 (6), 62–4, 1973.
58305	**THERMIONIC PROPERTIES OF LANTHANUM HEXABORIDE-BASED CATHODES UNDER GAS-DISCHARGE CONDITIONS.** VIKHREV, YU. I. POTSAR, A. A. IZV. LENINGRAD. ELEKTROTEKH. INST. (117), 58–66, 1972.
58309	**SUPEREXCHANGE INTERACTION IN RARE EARTH DIELECTRICS.** SIDOROV, A. A. FAL'KOVSKAYA, L. D. IZV. VYSSH. UCHEB. ZAVED., FIZ. 16 (12), 78–82, 1973.
58310	**DEFORMATION CHANGES IN THE OPTICAL PROPERTIES OF SOME ALKALI HALIDE CRYSTALS.** VISHNEVSKII, V. N. STEFANSKII, I. V. KUZYK, M. P. KULIK, Z. S. KULIK, L. N. IZV. VYSSH. UCHEB. ZAVED., FIZ. 16 (12), 86–91, 1973.
58312	**STATIONARY TRANSTHRESHOLD SUSCEPTIBILITY OF AN YTTRIUM FERRITE GARNET UNDER PARALLEL PUMPING CONDITIONS.** SIGAL, M. A. IZV. VYSSH. UCHEB. ZAVED., FIZ. 16 (12), 128–30, 1973.
58314	**ELECTROMOTIVE FORCE IN LITHIUM HYDRIDE CRYSTALS.** ASTAF'EVA, L. V. GAVRILOV, F. F. DVINYANINOV, B. L. IZV. VYSSH. UCHEB. ZAVED., FIZ. 17 (1), 139–41, 1974.
58320	**STRONG TEMPERATURE DEPENDENCE OF THE COERCIVITY OF PRASEODYMIUM COPPER COMPOUNDS.** MAEDA, H. JAP. J. APPL. PHYS. 12 (12), 1959–60, 1973.
58321	**CRYSTALLOGRAPHIC, ELECTRIC, AND THERMOCHEMICAL PROPERTIES OF THE PEROVSKITE-TYPE LANTHANIDE ELEMENT STRONTIUM COBALT OXIDE.** OHBAYASHI, H. KUDO, T. GEJO, T. JAP. J. APPL. PHYS. 13 (1), 1–7, 1974.
58322	**PIEZOELECTRIC AND ELASTIC PROPERTIES OF LITHIUM GERMANATE(IV) SINGLE CRYSTAL.** HIRANO, H. MATSUMURA, S. JAP. J. APPL. PHYS. 13 (1), 17–23, 1974.
58326	**NONSTOICHIOMETRY OF TELLURIUM-DOPED GALLIUM ARSENIDE.** NISHIZAWA, J. OTSUKA, H. YAMAKOSHI, S. ISHIDA, K. JAP. J. APPL. PHYS. 13 (1), 46–56, 1974.
58327	**ELECTRIC AND OPTICAL PROPERTIES OF GERMANIUM-DOPED GALLIUM PHOSPHIDE.** AOKI, M. TAJIMA, M. JAP. J. APPL. PHYS. 13 (1), 118–25, 1974.
58330	**UNDOPED N-TYPE GALLIUM ANTIMONIDE GROWN BY LIQUID PHASE EPITAXY.** MIKI, H. SEGAWA, K. FUJIBAYASHI, K. JAP. J. APPL. PHYS. 13 (1), 203–4, 1974.
58335	**QUANTUM EFFICIENCY OF DIFFUSION LIMITED ENERGY TRANSFER IN LANTHANUM CERIUM TERBIUM PHOSPHATE.** BOURCET, J. C. FONG, F. K. J. CHEM. PHYS. 60 (1), 34–9, 1974.
58336	**ELECTRONIC PROPERTIES OF TIN SULFIDE DOPED WITH ANTIMONY.** LICHANOT, A. GROMB, S. J. CHIM. PHYS. PHSIOCHIM. BIOL. 70 (11–12), 1592–9, 1973.

EPIC Number	Bibliographic Citation
58340	IONIC AND ELECTRONIC CONDUCTIVITY IN YTTRIUM(III) OXIDE-DOPED MONOCLINIC ZIRCONIUM(IV) OXIDE. NASRALLAH, M. M. DOUGLASS, D. L. J. ELECTROCHEM. SOC. 121 (2), 255–62, 1974.
58341	ELLIPSOMETRIC STUDY OF THE PLASMA OXIDATION OF TANTALUM. LESLIE, J. D. KNORR, K. J. ELECTROCHEM. SOC. 121 (2), 263–7, 1974.
58343	PREPARATION AND PROPERTIES OF BORON ARSENIDE FILMS. CHU, T. L. HYSLOP, A. E. J. ELECTROCHEM. SOC. 121 (3), 412–15, 1974.
58345	VAPOR-GROWN INDIUM GALLIUM PHOSPHIDE ELECTROLUMINESCENT JUNCTIONS ON GALLIUM ARSENIDE. NUESE, C. J. SIGAI, A. G. GANNON, J. J. ZAMEROWSKI, T. J. ELECTRON. MATER. 3 (1), 51–7,, 1974.
58346	PROPERTIES OF COPPER TIN SELENIDE, COPPER GERMANIUM SELENIDE, AND OTHER A(2)(I) B(IV) C(3)(VI) COMPOUNDS. SCOTT, W. J. ELECTRON. MATER. 3 (1), 209–23, 1974.
58360	RESISTANCE AND MAGNETORESISTANCE OF LITHIUM TETRAAMMINE. ROSENTHAL, M. D. MAXFIELD, B. W. J. LOW TEMP. PHYS. 14 (1–2), 15–27, 1974.
58426	RESONANCE FLUORESCENCE SPECTRUM OF NITROGEN DIOXIDE. ABE, K. MYERS, F. MCCUBBIN, T. K., JR. POLO, S. R. J. MOL. SPECTROSC. 50, 413–23, 1974.
58431	MOLECULAR CALCULATION OF ELECTRONIC PROPERTIES OF LAYERED CRYSTAL. II. PERIODIC SMALL CLUSTER CALCULATION FOR GRAPHITE AND BORON NITRIDE. ZUNGER, A. J. PHYS. 7 C (1), 96–106, 1974.
58432	HIGH-PRESSURE ELECTRICAL AND PHASE PROPERTIES OF MERCURY TELLURIDE - GALLIUM TELLURIDE ALLOYS. MORRISSY, J. H. PITT, G. D. VYAS, M. K. R. J. PHYS. 7 C (1), 113–26, 1974.
58435	CONTRIBUTION OF IRON DIPOSITIVE IONS TO THE MAGNETOCRYSTALLINE ANISOTROPY CONSTANT K(1) OF IRON TITANIUM OXIDE. FLETCHER, E. J. O'REILLY, W. J. PHYS. 7 C (1), 171–8, 1974.
58436	PHOTOEMISSION FROM GALLIUM SELENIDE USING SYNCHROTRON RADIATION. WILLIAMS, R. H. WILLIAMS, G. P. NORRIS, C. HOWELLS, M. R. MUNCRO, I. H. J. PHYS. 7 C (2), L29–32, 1974.
58437	ZEEMAN EFFECT IN THE SPECTRUM OF EXCITONS BOUND TO ISOELECTRONIC BISMUTH IN INDIUM PHOSPHIDE. WHITE, A. M. DEAN, P. J. FAIRHURST, K. M. BARDSLEY, W. DAY, B. J. PHYS. 7 C (2), L35–9, 1974.
58441	COMPARISON OF THE OPTICAL AND DIELECTRIC PROPERTIES OF CRYSTALLINE AND MOLTEN LITHIUM FLUORIDE. MEAD, D. G. J. PHYS. 7 C (2), 445–53, 1974.
58487	DETERMINATION OF THE REFRACTION INDEX OF TRANSPARENT BODIES WITH THE AID OF SCRATCHES AND IMMERSION LIQUIDS. FEDYUKINA, G. N. ZLENKO, V. YA. ZAP. VSES. MINERAL. OBSCHCHEST. 101 (3), 374–5, 1972.
58505	MAGNETIC PROPERTIES OF IRON(III) CHLORIDE-GRAPHITE COMPOUNDS. I. MOESSBAUER STUDIES. OHHASHI, K. TSUJIKAWA, I. J. PHYS. SOC. JAP. 36 (2), 422–30, 1974.
58509	THEORY OF THE GIANT MAGNETOSTRICTION IN IRON TITANATE. KATAOKA, M. J. PHYS. SOC. JAP. 36 (2), 456–63, 1974.
58511	ELECTRONIC AND VIBRONIC SPECTRA OF CERIUM TRIPOSITIVE ION IN YTTRIUM PHOSPHATE AND LUTETIUM PHOSPHATE. NAKAZAWA, E. SHIONOYA, S. J. PHYS. SOC. JAP. 36 (2), 504–10, 1974.
58519	TERNARY METAL CHROMIUM SELENIDES WHERE METAL IS IRON, COPPER, ZINC, OR CADMIUM. MURASHKO, N. I. GORYACHEV, YU. M. OBOLONCHIK, V. A. KHIM. SVYAZ KRIST. POLUPROV. POLUMETALLOV 171–6, 1973.
58523	POTASSIUM IODATE, THE FIRST FERROELECTRIC ALLOWING ONLY 120 DEGREES SWITCHING OF FERROELECTRIC POLARIZATION. SHUVALOV, L. A. IVANOV, N. R. CHIKHLADZE, O. A. IZRAILENKO, A. N. KRISTALLOGRAFIYA 18 (6), 1207–13, 1973.
58526	GROWTH AND SOME PHYSICAL PROPERTIES OF LEAD GERMANATE SINGLE CRYSTALS. GABRIELYAN, V. T. IONOV, P. V. MIKHAILINA, K. A. ARAKELOV, O. A. KRISTALLOGRAFIYA 19 (1), 176–8, 1974. (FOR ENGLISH TRANSLATION SEE E66302)
58530	BAND STRUCTURE OF GROUP II–V COMPOUND SEMICONDUCTOR, CADMIUM ANTIMONIDE. III. OPTICAL AND ELECTRICAL PROPERTIES. YAMADA, Y. KYUSHU DAIGAKU KOGAKU SHUHO 46 (6), 719–23, 1973.
58531	ELECTRIC CONDUCTIVITY OF BETA-SILICON CARBIDE POLYCRYSTALLINE FILMS. KRIVICH, A. P. MACHEVSKII, E. N. NEIMANE, I. PROKOPOVICH, I. M. FELTINS, I. LATV. PSR ZINAT. AKAD. VESTIS, FIZ. TEH. ZINAT. SER. (5), 45–9, 1973.
58532	NEW DATA ON THALLIUM-ACTIVATED POTASSIUM IODIDE LUMINESCENCE EXCITED IN THE A-ABSORPTION BAND. TRINKLERS, M. ZOLOVKINA, I. S. LATV. PSR ZINAT. AKAD. VESTIS, FIZ. TEH. ZINAT. SER. (6), 28–35, 1973.
58540	NONSTOICHIOMETRY OF LITHIUM - SODIUM FERRITE UNDER EQUILIBRIUM CONDITIONS. GRANIK, V. A. METLIN, YU. G. OLEINIKOV, N. N. TRET'YAKOV, YU. D. MATER. MEZHOTRASL. SOVESHCH. METOD. POLUCH. ANAL. FERRITOVYKH, SEGNETO-P'EZOELEKTRICHESKIKH MATER. SYR'YA NIKH, 3RD 3, 3–9, 1971.
58541	EFFECT OF FERRITIZATION AND THE GRINDING OF POWDERS ON THE PROPERTIES OF FERRITES WITH SQUARE HYSTERESIS LOOPS OBTAINED BY THE COPRECIPITATION OF CARBONATES. GULIDA, B. G. KRIGER, E. M. NAZAROVA, E. A. KOROL, V. P. KUCHINSKAYA, E. A. MATER. MEZHOTRASL. SOVESHCH. METOD. POLUCH. ANAL. FERRITOVYKH, SEGNETO-P'EZOELEKTRICHESKIKH MATER. SYR'YA NIKH, 3RD 3, 13–20, 1971.
58542	EFFECT OF THE ROASTING OF FERRITE MASSES ON THE PROPERTIES OF MANGANESE - ZINC FERRITES. GULIDA, B. G. RADINA, L. V. GUTOROVA, E. V. MATER. MEZHOTRASL. SOVESHCH. METOD. POLUCH. ANAL. FERRITOVYKH, SEGNETO-P'EZOELEKTRICHESKIKH MATER. SYR'YA NIKH, 3RD 3, 20–6, 1971.
58543	EFFECT OF FERRITE POWDER PRODUCTION PROCESSES ON THE DYNAMIC PARAMETERS OF MAGNETOSTRICTION MATERIALS. OBUKHOV, A. A. ERASTOVA, V. I. MOCHALOV, G. P. ARON, P. M. MATER. MEZHOTRASL. SOVESHCH. METOD. POLUCH. ANAL. FERRITOVYKH, SEGNETO, P'EZOELEKTRICHESKIKH MATER. SYR'YA NIKH, 3RD 3, 40–7, 1971.
58545	REPRODUCIBILITY OF HYSTERESIS LOOP PARAMETS FOR MANGANESE ZINC FERRITES. AMINOV, T. G. SHISHKIN, V. N. MATER. MEZHOTRASL. SOVESHCH. METOD. POLUCH. ANAL. FERRITOVYKH, SEGNETO-P'EZOELEKTRICHESKIKH MATER. SYR'YA NIKH, 3RD 3, 193–8, 1971.
58546	SINTERING OF FERRITE PRODUCTS. GRANIK, V. A. OLEINIKOV, N. N. TRET'YAKOV, YU. D. MATER. MEZHOTRASL. SOVESHCH. METOD. POLUCH. ANAL. FERRITOVYKH, SEGNETO-P'EZOELEKTRICHESKIKH MATER. SYR'YA NIKH, 3RD 3, 220–8, 1971.

EPIC Number	Bibliographic Citation
58547	EFFECT OF SUBSTRATES USED DURING HEAT TREATMENT ON THE PROPERTIES OF LITHIUM SODIUM FERRITE. GRANIK, V. A. METLIN, YU. G. OLEINIKOV, N. N. TRET'YAKOV, YU. D. MATER. MEZHOTRASL. SOVESHCH. METOD. POLUCH. ANAL. FERRITOVYKH, SEGNETO-P'EZOELEKTRICHESKIKH MATER. SYR'YA NIKH, 3RD 3, 228–32, 1971.
58548	POSSIBLE REDUCTION IN DIELECTRIC LOSSES IN FERRITE GARNETS. KRASNOVA, V. A. RYBACHUK, I. S. SIL'VESTROVICH, I. I. MATER. MEZHOTRASL. SOVESHCH. METOD. POLUCH. ANAL. FERRITOVYKH, SEGNETO-P'EZOELEKTRICHESKIKH MATER. SYR'YA NIKH, 3RD 3, 233–7, 1971.
58550	FLUORESCENCE AND X-RAY DATA OF EUROPIUM FLUORIDE CHLORIDE. BRIXNER, L. H. BIERLEIN, J. D. MATER. RES. BULL. 9 (2), 99–104, 1974.
58551	SINGLE CRYSTALS OF SAMARIUM HEXABORIDE FOR CONDUCTIVITY AND OTHER MEASUREMENTS. STURGEON, G. D. MERCURID, J. P. ETOURNEAU, J. HAGENMULLER, P. MATER. RES. BULL. 9 (2), 117–19, 1974.
58553	ELECTRIC PROPERTIES OF CHROMIUM SILICIDE THIN FILMS CONDENSED ON HEATED CERAMIC SUBSTRATES. STARYI, I. B. CHEPOK, O. L. METALLOFIZIKA (45), 97–100, 1973.
58559	MAGNETIC MEASUREMENTS IN THE SYSTEMS, (ZIRCONIUM, HAFNIUM)–(IRON, COBALT, NICKEL)–OXYGEN. SOBEZAK, R. MONATSH. CHEM. 104 (6), 1526–9, 1973.
58561	PRODUCTION OF MACROCRYSTALLINE GALLIUM SELENIDE SEMICONDUCTOR SAMPLES. GAL'CHINETSKII, L. P. GUR'EV, V. R. KHODEEVA, N. V. MONOKRIST. TEKH. (7), 58–9, 1972.
58565	BAND STRUCTURE AND TRANSPORT PROPERTIES OF MAGNETIC SEMICONDUCTORS. HAAS, C. NEW DEVELOP. SEMICOND., MC GILL SUMMER SCH. LECT. 1–34, 1973.
58566	FERROMAGNETIC AND SEMICONDUCTING CHALCOGENIDES. METHFESSEL, S. NEW DEVELOP. SEMICOND., MC GILL SUMMER SCH. LECT. 35–61, 1973.
58572	ZERO-BANDGAP TRANSITION IN SEMICONDUCTING ALLOYS. VERIE, C. NEW DEVELOP. SEMICOND., MC GILL SUMMER SCH. LECT. 511–74, 1971.
58579	EFFECT OF THERMAL DECOMPOSITION ON THE ELECTRICAL CONDUCTIVITY OF AMMONIUM SULPHATE. KHAIRETDINOV, E. F. MEERSON, E. E. BOLDYREV, V. V. RUSS. J. PHYS. CHEM. 47 (7), 995–6, 1973. (ENGLISH TRANSLATION OF ZH. FIZ. KHIM., 47 (7), 1763–5, 1973; FOR ORIGINAL SEE E52386)
58586	NEW APPARATUS FOR HALL STUDIES ON VACUUM-DEPOSITED THIN FILMS. PRAKASH, O. INDIAN J. PURE APPL. PHYS. 11 (11), 846–50, 1973.
58589	OPTICAL PROPERTIES OF SINGLE CRYSTALS OF HEXAGONAL SILVER IODIDE. COCHRANE, G. J. PHYS. 7 D (5), 748–58, 1974.
58590	PHOTOVOLTAGE IN PHOTOGRAPHIC SILVER HALIDE CRYSTALS. BARSHCHEVSKII, B. U. TREKHOV, E. S. KOLLOID. ZH. 36 (1), 9–10, 1974.
58591	ELECTRICAL PROPERTIES OF NON-CRYSTALLINE SEMICONDUCTORS. YAMADA, S. NIPPON BUTSURI GAKKAISHI 27 (5), 390–4, 1972.
58597	EFFECT OF DIRECTIONAL DEFORMATIONS ON BIREFRINGENCE OF CADMIUM SULFIDE. BABONAS, G. REZA, A. A. SHILEIKA, A. YU. PROBL. FIZ. SOEDIN. II - VI, MATER, VSES. SOVESHCH., 3RD 1, 97–101, 1972.
58604	FREE CARRIER INFRARED ABSORPTION IN N-INDIUM ARSENIDE. KEKELIDZE, N. P. KEKELIDZE, G. P. SHATBERASHVILI, E. B. VOSKOBOINIK, N. B. SOOBSHCH. AKAD. NAUK GRUZ. SSR 73 (1), 45–8, 1974.
58606	ELECTRICAL PROPERTIES AND SPECTRAL RESPONSE OF LEAD TELLURIDE-GERMANIUM HETEROJUNCTIONS. CORSI, C. MILLER, M. THIN SOLID FILMS 20 (2), S41–S43, 1974.
58630	THEORY OF HALL COEFFICIENT MAGNETROPHONON OSCILLATIONS IN GALLIUM ARSENIDE. BARKER, J. R. MCSHEEHY, C. J. PHYS. LETT. 46 A (4), 237–8, 1973.
58633	MAGNETIC SUSCEPTIBILITY OF ALPHA-SODIUM FERRATE(III). HABBAL, F. WATSON, G. E. ELLISTON, P. R. PHYS. LETT. 46 A (4), 283–4, 1973.
58635	PRESSURE DEPENDENCE OF THE SUPERCONDUCTING TRANSITION TEMPERATURES OF PALLADIUM HYDRIDE AND PALLADIUM DEUTERIDE. SCHIRBERT, J. W. PHYS. LETT. 46 A (4), 285–6, 1973.
58641	PHOTOLUMINESCENCE OF TIN(IV) SULFIDE SINGLE CRYSTALS. KUZUBA, T. ERA, K. ISHIZAWA, Y. PHYS. LETT. 46 A (6), 413–14, 1974.
58651	LUMINESCENCE AND PHOTOCURRENT OF GALLIUM SULFIDE. CATALANO, I. M. FERRARA, M. TANTALO, P. PHYS. STATUS SOLIDI 20 A (2), K135–8, 1973.
58652	STRUCTURAL DEFECTS IN NEODYMIUN-DOPED YTTRIUM ALUMINATE. ARSEN'EV, P. A. VAKHIDOV, S. A. IBRAGIMOVA, E. M. PHYS. STATUS SOLIDI 21 A (1), K35–8, 1974.
58659	ZEEMAN EFFECT ON ACCEPTOR CENTERS AND NEGATIVE MAGNETORESISTANCE IN TELLURIUM. BIR, G. L. KRIGEL, V. G. PIKUS, G. E. FARBSHTEIN, I. I. PIS'MA ZH. EKSP. TEOR. FIZ. 19 (1), 48–51, 1974.
58660	INCREASE IN THE ELECTRIC STRENGTH OF WATER IN A SYSTEM WITH DIFFUSION ELECTRODES. VOROB'EV, V. V. KAPITONOV, V. A. KRUGLYAKOV, E. P. PIS'MA ZH. EKSP. TEOR. FIZ. 19 (2), 95–8, 1974.
58662	VERIFICATION OF THREE SCALING FUNCTIONS FOR IRON YTTRIUM OXIDE. KAMILOV, I. K. ALIEV, KH. K. MAGOMEDOV, M. M. PIS'MA ZH. EKSP. TEOR. FIZ. 19 (2), 128–31, 1974.
58674	ELECTROABSORPTION IN DEEP LOCAL CENTERS IN BROADBAND SEMICONDUCTORS. BUDYANSKII, V. I. SAL'KOV, E. A. SHEINKMAN, M. K. SHEPEL'SKII, G. A. PROBL. FIZ. SOEDIN. A-II B-VI, MATER. VSES. SOVESHCH., 3RD 1, 87–91, 1972.
58678	ELECTRIC AND PHOTOELECTRIC PROPERTIES OF CADMIUM SELENIDE SINGLE CRYSTALS CONTAINING DOUBLY CHARGED ACCEPTOR CENTERS. ABRAMOV, A. A. DOVTONYUK, N. F. GERSHMAN, L. S. PROBL. FIZ. SOEDIN. A-II B-VI, MATER. VSES. SOVESHCH., 3RD 1, 270–5, 1972.
58679	TRANSFER PHENOMENA IN CADMIUM ZINC TELLURIDE SINGLE CRYSTALS ALLOYED WITH TELLURIUM AND STUDY OF CADMIUM TELLURIDE SINGLE CRYSTALS. ANDRONIN, I. K. LISTUNOV, G. P. SUSHKEVICH, K. D. PROBL. FIZ. SOEDIN. A-II B-VI, MATER. VSES. SOVESHCH., 3RD 1, 300–4, 1972.
58680	MAGNETISM OF CADMIUM TELLURIDE LATTICE DEFECTS. IVANOV-OMSKII, V. I. KOLOMIETS, B. T. OGORODNIKOV, U. K. RUD, YU. V. TSMOTS, V. M. PROBL. FIZ. SOEDIN. A-II B-VI, MATER. VSES. SOVESHCH., 3RD 1, 311–15, 1972.

EPIC Number | Bibliographic Citation

58681 SYNTHESIS OF ZINC SLENIDE SINGLE CRYSTALS FROM THE VAPOR PHASE AND FROM SOLUTION.
GAUGASH, P. V. KAS'YAN, V. A.
PROBL. FIZ. SOEDIN. A-II B-VI, MATER. VSES. SOVESHCH., 3RD
1, 316-20, 1972.

58683 MAXIMUM PHOTOLUMINESCENCE AND PHOTOCURRENT QUENCHING RATES IN WIDE-BAND SEMICONDUCTORS.
LYUBCHENKI, A. V. SHEINKMAN, M. K.
PROBL. FIZ. SOEDIN. A-II B-VI, MATER. VSES. SOVESHCH., 3RD
2, 34-9, 1972.

58685 THERMOSTIMULATED CONDUCTIVITY AND THERMOLUMINESCENCE OF CADMIUM SULFIDE CRYSTALS.
AIDLA, A. KIRS, J.
PROBL. FIZ. SOEDIN. A-II B-VI, MATER. VSES. SOVESHCH., 3RD
2, 56-60, 1972.

58686 ORIGIN OF ORANGE AND RED LUMINESCENCE IN CADMIUM SULFIDE.
KELLE, H. KIRS, J. TULVA, L.
PROBL. FIZ. SOEDIN. A-II B-VI, MATER. VSES. SOVESHCH., 3RD
2, 85-9, 1972.

58690 ELASTIC, PIEZOELECTRIC, AND DIELECTRIC CONSTANTS OF CADMIUM SELENIDE AND ZINC OXIDE OVER A WIDE TEMPERATURE RANGE.
TOKAREV, E. F. PADO, G. S.
CHERNOZATONSKII, L. A. DAN'KOV, A. A.
KOBYAKOV, I. B.
PROBL. FIZ. SOEDIN. A-II B-VI, MATER. VSES. SOVESHCH., 3RD
2, 354-7, 1972.

58691 PHOTOCONDUCTIVITY AND LUMINESCENCE OF CADMIUM INDIUM SULFIDE SINGLE CRYSTALS.
ABDULLAEV, G. B. ANTONOV, V. B.
BELEN'KII, G. L. GUSEINOV, D. T.
LARIONKINA, L. S. NANI, R. KH.
SALAEV, E. YU.
PROBL. FIZ. SOEDIN. A-II B-VI, MATER. VSES. SOVESHCH., 3RD
2, 358-62, 1972.

58694 DENSITY DEPENDENCE OF THE REFRACTIVITY OF GASES.
BUCKINGHAM, A. D. GRAHAM, C.
PROC. ROY. SOC. LONDON, SER.
337 A (1609), 275-91, 1974.

58696 THEORY OF THE URBACH-MARTIENSSEN RULE FOR MIXED CRYSTALS. APPLICATION OF CPA (COHERENT POTENTIAL APPROXIMATION).
SAWAI, T. UENO, S. MATSUBARA, T.
PROGR. THEOR. PHYS., SUPPL.
53, 222-39, 1973.

58697 RADIATION-STIMULATED PHENOMENA IN CALCIUM FLUORIDE CRYSTALS ACTIVATED BY RARE EARTH IONS.
VAKHIDOV, SH. A. KAIPOV, B.
TAVSHUNSKII, G. A.
RADIATS. EFF. MONOKRIST.
152-68, 1973.

58698 COLOR CENTERS AND PHOTOLUMINESCENCE IN CORUNDUM.
VAKHIDOV, SH. A. KHATAMOV, D. K.
YANGIBAEV, M.
RADIATS. EFF. MONOKRIST.
169-74, 1973.

58699 RADIATION-STIMULATED PHENOMENA IN RARE EARTH TRIPOSITIVE ION-ACTIVATED YTTRIUM ALUMINUM GARNET AND RARE EARTH ALUMINUM GARNET CRYSTALS.
VAKHIDOV, SH. A. IBRAGIMOVA, E.
YUSUPOV, A. A.
RADIATS. EFF. MONOKRIST.
175-89, 1973.

58700 INFLUENCE OF IRRADIATION WITH NEUTRONS AND GAMMA-QUANTA ON THE CATHODOLUMINESCENCE SPECTRA OF GALLIUM ARSENIDE.
VIL'KOTSKII, V. A. DOMANEVSKII, D. S.
LOMAKOV, V. M.
RADIATS. FIZ. NEMETAL. KRIST.
3 (PT. 2), 10-16, 1971.

58702 NATURE OF THE RED BAND OF CATHODE LUMINESCENCE OF IRRADIATED BETA-SILICON CARBIDE.
GEITSI, I. I. GORIN, S. I. NESTEROV, A. A.
PLETYUSHKIN, A. A.
RADIATS. FIZ. NEMETAL. KRIST.
3 (PT. 2), 97-105, 1971.

58704 CALCULATION OF THE CAPACITANCE MODULATION COEFFICIENTS OF SUPERHIGH-FREQUENCY NONLINEAR FERROELECTRIC-BASED CAPACITORS.
VENDIK, O. G. KOZYREV, A. B.
RADIOTEKH. ELEKTRON.
18 (12), 2649-52, 1973.

58713 INFLUENCE OF THE TEMPERATURE OF HOT PRESSING ON THE PROPERTIES OF MATERIALS BASED ON LEAD TITANATE ZIRCONATE.
PETROVA, V. Z. ZHABOTINSKII, V. A.
KUSHNARENKO, V. V. KOCHETGOV, V. V.
SB. NAUCH. TR. PROBL. MIKROELEKTRON., MOSK. INST. ELEKTRON. TEKH.
(13), 28-32, 1972.

58714 PHOTOSTIMULATED LUMINESCENCE OF CALCIUM TUNGSTATE.
KRONGAUZ, V. G. MERZLYAKOV, A. T.
KAPLENOV, I. G. GURVICH, A. M.
MIKHALEV, A. A.
SB. NAUCH. TR., VSES. NAUCH.-ISSLED. INST. LYUMINOFOROV OSOBO CHIST. VESHCHESTV
(7), 72-4, 1972.

58722 TRANSMITTED SECONDARY ELECTRONS FROM GALLIUM ARSENIDE THIN FILMS.
MINAGAWA, C. YOSHIDA, S.
SHINKU
16 (10), 366-71, 1973.

58726 VALUE OF THE DEFORMATION POTENTIAL IN INDIUM ARSENIDE AND PHOSPHIDE COMPOUNDS.
KEKELIDZE, N. P. GOGIASHVILI, V. A.
KEKELIDZE, G. P.
SOOBSHCH. AKAD. NAUK GRUZ. SSR
72 (2), 313-16, 1973.

58734 WORK FUNCTION OF A SINGLE CRYSTAL OF THE METAL COMPOUND(EPSILON PHASE) IN THE MOLYBDENUM-RHODIUM SYSTEM.
SAVITSKII, E. M. BUROV, I. V.
STRUKT. SVOISTVA MONOKRIST TUGOPLAVKIKH METAL.
211-16, 1973.
(FOR ENGLISH TRANSLATION SEE E68941)

58738 ELECTRIC TRANSPORT IN MOLTEN MONOVALENT NITRATES. III. METHODS. IV. EXPERIMENTAL RESULTS. V. CONCLUSIONS.
TOPOR, D.
STUD. CERCET. CHIM.
21 (11), 1235-54, 1973.

58740 FERROMAGNETISM OBSERVED IN CHROMIUM SEQUIOXIDE.
GHOSH, P. K. MAITY, G. C.
BHATTACHARYA, R. C.
TECHNOLOGY
10 (1-2), 137-8, 1973.

58747 BARIUM TITANATE AS THE BASIS OF A NEW TYPE OF NONLINEAR ELEMENT-VARIKOND.
VERBITSKAYA, T. N.
TITANAT BARIYA, MATER, SEMIN., POSVYASHCH. 25-LETIYU OTKRYTIYA SEGNETOELEKTRICHESKIKN SVOISTV TITANATA BARIYA
171-9, 1973

58749 UTILIZATION OF AUTOSTABILIZATION PHENOMENA IN BARIUM TITANATE SINGLE CRYSTALS AND CERAMICS.
MIRONOVA, E. I. TOKAREV, A. I.
PLUZHNIKOV, V. M.
TITANAT BARIYA, MATER, SEMIN., POSVYASHCH. 25-LETIYU OTKRYTIYA SEGNETOELEKTRICHESKIKN SVOISTV TITANATA BARIYA
185-8, 1973.

58756 MAGNETIC PROPERTIES OF SINGLE CRYSTALS OF THE COBALT(II) TUNGSTATE-ZINC TUNGSTATE SYSTEM.
KATS'KO, E. N. ZVYAGIN, A. I. PELIKH, L. N.
TR. FIZ.-TEKH. INST. NIZK. TEMP., AKAD. NAUK USSR
(21), 28-33, 1972.

58760 VARIATION OF THE RESISTIVITY OF DEIONIZED WATER WITHIN A TEMPERATURE CYCLE.
KEVANISHVILI, G. S. KAKHADZE, A. E.
GABUNIYA, K. E.
TR. GRUZ. POLITEKH. INST.
(5), 83-5, 1972.

58761 CALCIUM SULFIDE AND OXIDE PHOSPHORS DOPED WITH THALLIUM, INDIUM, AND GALLIUM IMPURITIES IN DIFFERENT VALENCE STATES.
PARTS, T. HUTT, G. JACK, I.
TR. INST. FIZ. ASTRON., AKAD. NAUK EST. SSR
(41), 12-28, 1972.

58762 STRUCTURE AND OPTICAL CHARACTERISTICS OF BISMUTH CENTERS IN CALCIUM SULFIDE.
JACK, I. ELLERVEE, A.
TR. INST. FIZ. ASTRON., AKAD. NAUK EST. SSR
(41), 29-40, 1972.

58763 SILVER CENTERS IN CALCIUM OXIDE AND CALCIUM SULFIDE PHOSPHORS.
PARTS, T. PUNG, L. HALDRE, U. HUTT, G.
JACK, I.
TR. INST. FIZ. ASTRON., AKAD. NAUK EST. SSR
(41), 41-56, 1972.

EPIC Number	Bibliographic Citation
58764	ELECTRON SPIN RESONANCE AND SOME OPTICAL CHARACTERISTICS OF CHROMIUM CENTERS IN CALCIUM SULFIDE. PUNG, L. REALO, K. HALDRE, U. JAEK, I. TR. INST. FIZ. ASTRON., AKAD. NAUK EST. SSR (41), 57–65, 1972.
58765	ROLE OF OXYGEN TREATMENT ON PROPERTIES OF CALCIUM SULFIDE PHOSPHORS. ALLSALU, M. PEDAK, E. REALO, K. JACK, I. TR. INST. FIZ. ASTRON., AKAD. NAUK EST. SSR (41), 66–78, 1972.
58767	DEFECT PRODUCTION IN CALCIUM SULFIDE DURING MECHANICAL COMPRESSION. JACK, I. KUZNETSOV, A. S. OTS, A. TR. INST. FIZ. ASTRON., AKAD. NAUK EST. SSR (41), 105–17, 1972.
58768	LUMINESCENCE PROPERTIES OF COPPER–ACTIVATED STRONTINIUM SULFIDE PHOSPHORS. PEDAK, E. ALLSALU, M. MUST, M. TR. INST. FIZ. ASTON., AKAD. NAUK EST. SSR (41), 118–28, 1972.
58769	ORIGIN OF RED AND ORANGE EMISSION BANDS IN CADMIUM SULFIDE. KELLE, H. KIRS, J. TULVA, L. TR. INST. FIZ. ASTRON., AKAD. NAUK EST. SSR (41), 129–45, 1972.
58770	SPECTRAL CHARACTERISTICS OF SILVER– OR ZINC–ACTIVATED CALCIUM SULFIDE CRYSTAL PHOSPHORS. JACK, I. HUTT, G. TR. INST. FIZ. ASTRON., AKAD. NAUK EST. SSR (41), 233–5, 1972.
58771	STRUCTURE OF THE STIMULATION SPECTRA OF PHOSPHORS BASED ON ALKALINE EARTH AND ZINC SULFIDES. NISOVTSEV, V. V. MIKHAILIN, V. V. TR. INST. FIZ. ASTRON., AKAD. NAUK EST. SSR (41), 146–65, 1972.
58772	DETERMINING THE PARAMETERS OF TRAPPING LEVELS IN SEMICONDUCTORS. LOUK, P. PIILMA, M. TR. INST. FIZ. ASTRON., AKAD. NAUK EST. SSR (41), 171–95, 1972.
58773	ABSOLUTE THERMOLUMINESCENCE OUTPUTS OF CRYSTAL PHOSPHORS UNDER ALPHA OR GAMMA–RADIATIONS. SAVIKHIN, F. A. TR. INST. FIZ. ASTRON., AKAD. NAUK EST. SSR (41), 240–2, 1972.
58792	MAGNETOSTRICTION IN ALPHA–FERRIC OXIDE– AND NICKEL(II) OXIDE–TYPE ANTIFERROMAGNETS. FARZTDINOV, M. M. UCH. ZAP., BASHKIR. UNIV. (57), 104–13, 1972.
58797	PHOTOPRODUCTION OF DISORDER IN LEAD AZIDE AND THALLIUM AZIDE. WIEGAND, D. A. PHYS. REV. 10 B (4), 1241–7, 1974.
58802	ELECTRONIC STRUCTURE OF SILICON OXIDE. I. THEORY AND SAMPLE CALCULATIONS. YIP, K. L. FOWLER, W. B. PHYS. REV. 10 B (4), 1391–9, 1974.
58803	ELECTRONIC STRUCTURE OF SILICON OXIDE. II. CALCULATIONS AND RESULTS. YIP, K. L. FOWLER, W. B. PHYS. REV. 10 B (4), 1400–8, 1974.
58804	OPTICAL, ELECTRICAL–TRANSPORT, AND HEAT–CAPACITY STUDIES OF THE SOLID SOLUTIONS TITANIUM TANTALUM SULFIDE, ZIRCONIUM TANTALUM SULFIDE, AND TITANIUM NIOBIUM SELENIDE. BENDA, J. A. PHYS. REV. 10 B (4), 1409–20, 1974.
58805	PERCOLATION AND CONDUCTIVITY: A COMPUTER STUDY. I. PIKE, G. E. SEAGER, C. H. PHYS. REV. 10 B (4), 1421–34, 1974.
58806	PERCOLATION AND CONDUCTIVITY: A COMPUTER STUDY. II. SEAGER, C. H. PIKE, G. E. PHYS. REV. 10 (4), 1435–46, 1974.
58808	PRESSURE DEPENDENCE OF ENERGY GAPS AND REFRACTIVE INDICES OF TETRAHEDRALLY BONDED SEMICONDUCTORS. TSAY, T. F. MITRA, S. S. BENDOW, B. PHYS. REV. 10 B (4), 1476–81, 1974. (AD–787 240, AFCRL–TR–74–0465) (AD–A012 553, N76–12355)
58810	BOND–ORBITAL MODEL. II. HARRISON, W. A. CIRACI, S. PHYS. REV. 10 B (4), 1516–27, 1974.
58811	STRUCTURAL STUDIES OF GLASSY COPPER ARSENIC SELENIDE ALLOYS. LIANG, K. S. BIENENSTOCK, A. BATES, C. W. PHYS. REV. 10 B (4), 152,–38, 1974.
58812	THERMOELECTRIC POWER OF THE EXTRINSIC MOTT SEMICONDUCTOR. BARI, R. A. PHYS. REV. 10 B (4), 1560–3, 1974.
58814	DECAY KINETICS OF THE RED LUMINESCENCE OF GALLIUM EQUILIBRIUM CONDITIONS. NEUMARK, G. F. PHYS. REV. 10 B (4), 1574–84, 1974.
58816	PHASE TRANSITIONS IN RUBIDIUM CALCIUM FLUORIDE. MODINE, F. A. SONDER, E. UNRUH, W. P. FINCH, C. B. WESTBROOK, R. D. PHYS. REV. 10 B (4), 1623–34, 1974.
58817	METHOD FOR MEASURING THE CONTRIBUTION OF THE NONLINEAR DIPOLE MEMENT TO MULTIPHONON ABSORPTION. HELLWARTH, R. MANGIR, M. PHYS. REV. 10 B (4), 1635–41, 1974.
58818	TEMPERATURE DEPENDENCE OF TRANSVERSE– AND LONGITUDINAL–OPTIC MODES IN TITANIUM OXIDE (RUTILE). GERVAIS, F. PIRIOU, B. PHYS. REV. 10 B (4), 1642–54, 1974.
58819	USE OF 3D–IMPURITY–ION ABSORPTION TO STUDY THE DISTRIBUTION OF RADIATION DAMAGE IN CRYSTALS. YUN, S. I. LEE, K. H. SIBLEY, W. A. VEHSE, W. E. PHYS. REV. 10 B (4), 1665–72, 1974.
58821	PIEZO–OPTIC STUDY OF THE F CENTER IN ALAKALI HALIDES–EVIDENCE FOR STRUCTURE IN THE F BAND OF POTASSIUM CHLORIDE, POTASSIUM BROMIDE, AND SODIUM CHLORIDE. PERREGAUX, A. ASCARELLI, G. PHYS. REV. 10 B (4), 1683–98, 1974.
58822	ABSORPTION COEFFICIENT OF ALKALI HALIDES IN THE MULTIPHONON REGIME: EFFECTS OF NONLINEAR DIPOLE MOMENTS. MILLS, D. L. MARADUDIN, A. A. PHYS. REV. 10 B (4), 1713–24, 1974.
58823	VALENCE–BAND STRUCTURE OF COPPER GALLIUM INDIUM SULFIDE ALLOYS. TELL, B. SHAY, J. L. KASPER, H. M. BARNS, R. L. PHYS. REV. 10 B (4), 1748–50, 1974.
58825	RECOMBINATION PROCESSES INVOLVING ZINC AND NITROGEN IN GALLIUM ARSENIC–PHOSPHIDE. CAMPBELL, J. C. HOLONYAK, N., JR. LEE, M. H. KUNZ, A. B. PHYS. REV. 10 B (4), 1755–7, 1974.
58826	IMPURITY CONDUCTION IN MANGANESE–DOPED GALLIUM ARSENIDE. SEAGER, C. H. PIKE, G. E. PHYS. REV. 10 (4), 1760–1, 1974.
58827	LINEWIDTHS IN X–RAY PHOTOEMISSION AND X–RAY EMISSION SPECTROSCOPIES: WHAT DO THEY MEASURE. CITRIN, P. H. EISENBERGER, P. M. MARRA, W. C. ABERG, T. UTRIAINEN, J. KALLNE, E. PHYS. REV. 10 B (4), 1762–5, 1974.
58835	MAGNETIC PROPERTIES OF INTERMETALLIC COMPOUNDS RUTHENIUM–VANADIUM, ZIRCONIUM–VANADIUM, HAFNIUM–VANADIUM, ZIRCONIUM–RUTHENIUM–VANADIUM, AND HAFNIUM–RUTHENIUM–VANADIUM IN RELATION TO TEMPERATURE. AKHVERDYAN, M. M. CHECHERNIKOVA, O. I. RAEVSKAYA, M. V. SOKOLOVSKAYA, E. M. VESTN. MOSK. UNIV., KHIM. 14 (6), 736–7, 1973.
58840	BREAKDOWN VOLTAGES OF DIELECTRIC FILMS DURING AGING. MIKHAILOVSKII, I. P. VYCHISL. SIST. (52), 59–63, 1972.

EPIC Number	Bibliographic Citation

58851 **ANISOTROPY OF THERMOELECTRIC PROPERTIES OF CRYSTALS.**
OSIPOV, E. V. PILAT, I. M.
VOP. MIKROELEKTRON., MATER. SEMIN. ELEM. USTROISTVA MIKROELEKTRON.
76–83, 1971.

58853 **PREPARATION AND STUDY OF ALUMINUM NITRIDE FILMS.**
SLAVNIKOV, V. S.
VOP. MIKROELEKTRON., MATER. SEMIN. ELEM. USTROISTVA MIKROELEKTRON.
160–3, 1971.

58865 **MECHANISM OF PHOTOCHROMIC PROCESSES IN SILVER HALIDE-BASED GLASSES STUDIED BY A LUMINESCENCE METHOD.**
BELOUS, V. M. DOLBINOVA, E. A.
TSEKHOMSKII, V. A.
ZH. NAUCH. PRIKL. FOTOGR. KINEMATOGR.
18 (6), 465–7, 1973.

58866 **EFFECT OF DEVIATIONS FROM STOICHIOMETRY ON PROPERTIES OF THE SEMICONDUCTOR ZINC SILICON ARSENIDE.**
AVERKIEVA, G. K. PROCHUKHAN, V. D.
TASHTANOVA, M.
BULL. ACAD. SCI. USSR, PHYS. CHEM. SECT.
206 (3), 800–2, 1972.
(ENGLISH TRANSLATION OF DOKL. AKAD. NAUK SSSR, 206 (3), 638–40, 1972; FOR ORIGINAL SEE E49811)

58870 **LITHIUM, SODIUM, POTASSIUM, RUBIDIUM, OR CESIUM ANTIMONY SULFIDE OR SELENIDE TERNARY CHALCOGENIDE COMPOUNDS.**
BAZAKUTSA, V. A. GNIDASH, N. I.
LAZAREV, V. B. ROGACHEVA, E. I.
SALOV, A. V. SUKHORIKOVA, L. N.
VASIL'EVA, M. P. BERUL, S. I.
ZH. NEORG. KHIM.
18 (12), 3234–9, 1973.

58893 **STRUCTURAL AND OPTICAL PROPERTIES OF INDIUM ARSENIDE FILMS.**
GOSWAMI, A. RAO, B. V. SINGH, P.
INDIAN J. PURE APPL. PHYS.
12 (1), 17–20, 1974.

58894 **PREPARATION OF LEAD TELLURIDE FILMS IN A QUASICLOSED VOLUME.**
SMIRNOV, N. K. CHERKASHIN, G. A.
IZV. AKAD. NAUK SSSR, NEORG. MATER.
10 (2), 221–3, 1974.
(FOR ENGLISH TRANSLATION SEE E64883)

58895 **LEAD SELENIDE-TIN SELENIDE SYSTEM.**
SHTANOV, V. I. ZLOMANOV, V. P.
NOVOSELOVA, A. V.
IZV. AKAD. NAUK SSSR, NEORG. MATER.
10 (2), 224–7, 1974.
(FOR ENGLISH TRANSLATION SEE E64884)

58898 **DETERMINATION OF THE SIGNS OF THE RATIOS OF STRAIN-OPTICAL CONSTANTS MEASURED ULTRASONICALLY.**
PETERSEN, H. E. NARASIMHAMURTY, T. S.
J. ACOUST. SOC. AMER.
54 (6), 1635–8, 1973.

58902 **ELECTRIC CONDUCTIVITY OF URANIUM OXIDE.**
LEE, H. M.
J. NUCL. MATER.
50 (1), 25–30, 1974.

58909 **MAGNETISM AND RESISTIVITY OF SOME DILUTE RARE EARTH-ZINC COMPOUNDS.**
STEWART, A. M. COLES, B. R.
J. PHYS.
4 F (3), 458–65, 1974.

58912 **STRESS AND MAGNETOOPTICAL STUDIES ON TETRAHEDRAL AND TETRAGONAL F CENTERS IN STRONTIUM CHLORIDE AND BARIUM CHLORIDE FLUORIDE.**
DURAN, J. LEMOYNE, D. LEFRANT, S.
YUSTE, M.
J. PHYS. (PARIS), COLLOQ.
(9), 131–2, 1973.

58913 **APPLICATION OF CHI SQUARE TESTS TO FITTING OF IONIC CONDUCTIVITY.**
FRIAUF, R. J.
J. PHYS. (PARIS), COLLOQ.
(9), 403–14, 1973.

58922 **EXCITONIC PHASE IN SEMIMETALS.**
MASE, S.
KOTAI BUTSURI
9 (2), 59–72, 1974.

58928 **KONDO RESISTIVITY OF PRASEODYMIUM-CERIUM ALLOYS.**
ALTUNBAS, M. TAYLOR, K. N. R.
WILKINSON, G. A.
PHIL. MAG.
29 (2), 349–71, 1974.

58934 **LATTICE INSTABILITIES AND SUPERCONDUCTIVITY OF (HAFNIUM, ZIRCONIUM)-VANADIUM COMPOUNDS.**
TAKASHIMA, T. HAYASHI, H.
PHYS. LETT.
47 A (3), 209–10, 1974.

58935 **PHONONS IN SURFACE PHOTOVOLTAGE OF GALLIUM ARSENIDE.**
MORAWSKI, A. LAGOWSKI, J.
PHYS. LETT.
47 A (3), 219–20, 1974.

58941 **CORRELATED CHANGES OF FLOW STRESS AND OPTICAL ABSORPTION IN POTASSIUM BROMIDE GAMMA-RAYED AT LNT (LIQUID NITROGEN TEMPERATURE).**
NARAMOTO, H. OZAWA, K. OKADA, T.
SUITA, T.
PHYS. STATUS SOLIDI
22 A (2), 445–53, 1974.

58944 **KONDO EFFECT IN THE TRANSPORT PROPERTIES OF THE CESIUM CHLORIDE-TYPE COMPOUNDS IRON-TITANIUM. I. THEIR ANOMALOUS BEHAVIORS IN TITANIUM-RICH COMPOSITIONS.**
IKEDA, K.
PHYS. STATUS SOLIDI
62 B (2), 655–64, 1974.

58947 **EXCITON-PHONON INTERACTIONS IN RECRYSTALLIZED ZINC TELLURIDE FILMS.**
BERLULIS, K. KURIK, M. V. MANZHARA, V. S.
TOLUTIS, V. JASUTIS, V.
PROBL. FIZ. SOEDIN. A-II B-VI, MATER. VSES. SOVESHCH., 3RD
1, 170–4, 1972.

58949 **USE OF HOLOGRAPHY FOR STUDYING THE EXTERNAL AND INTERNAL MORPHOLOGY OF CRYSTALS.**
GUSEVA, I. N. GINZBURG, V. M.
LEKHTSIER, E. N. SEMENOV, E. G.
PRIB. TEKH. EKSP.
(1), 180–2, 1974.
(FOR ENGLISH TRANSLATION SEE E65919)

58955 **EVAPORATION-DEPOSITED CHROMIUM-CARBON FILMS.**
LASSAK, L. LORENZ, H. P.
SIEMENS FORSCH.-ENTWICKLUNGSBER.
3 (1), 1–4, 1974.

58958 **ELLIPSOMETRIC STUDIES OF CHEMISORPTION OF GALLIUM PHOSPHIDE (110) SINGLE CRYSTALS.**
MORGAN, A. E.
SURFACE SCI.
43 (1), 150–72, 1974.

58961 **OPTICAL DISPERSION OF HOMOGENEOUSLY MIXED ZINC SULFIDE-MAGNESIUM FLUORIDE.**
YADAVA, V. N. SHARMA, S. K. CHOPRA, K. L.
THIN SOLID FILMS
22 (1), 57–66, 1974.

58962 **URBACH RULE FOR THE SODIUM AND POTASSIUM HALIDES.**
TOMIKI, T. MIYATA, T. TSUKAMOTO, H.
Z. NATURFORSCH., TEIL
29 A (1), 145–57, 1974.

58968 **SYNTHESIS AND CERTAIN OPTICAL PROPERTIES OF GLASSY AND CRYSTALLINE ANTIMONY SULFUR BROMIDE.**
CHEPUR, D. V. TURYANITSA, I. D.
GERZANICH, E. I. KOPERLES, B. M.
SLIVKA, V. YU. PUGA, P. P.
IZV. VYSSH. UCHEB. ZAVED. FIZ.
14 (2), 114–6, 1971.
(FOR ENGLISH TRANSLATION SEE E58969)

58969 **SYNTHESIS AND CERTAIN OPTICAL PROPERTIES OF GLASSY AND CRYSTALLINE ANTIMONY SULFUR BROMIDE.**
CHEPUR, D. V. TURYANITSA, I. D.
GERZANICH, E. I. KOPERLES, B. M.
SLIVKA, V. YU. PUGA, P. P.
SOV. PHYS. J.
(2), 234–6, 1971.
(ENGLISH TRANSLATION OF IZV. VYSSH. UCHEB. ZAVED. FIZ., (2), 114–6, 1971; FOR ORIGINAL SEE E58968)

58977 **SUSPENSION BALANCE EMPLOYING A LARGE PERMANENT MAGNET.**
PANKEY, T.
REV. SCI. INSTRUM.
33 (4), 431–3, 1962.

58978 **SERVO-CONTROLLED MEASURING BRIDGE FOR SEMICONDUCTORS OF HIGH RESISTIVITY.**
FERMOR, J. H. KJEKSHUS, A.
REV. SCI. INSTRUM.
36 (6), 763–6, 1965.

58979 **SPECIMEN HOLDER FOR HIGH TEMPERATURE ELECTRON TRANSPORT PROPERTY MEASUREMENTS.**
HYDE, G. R. RAO, N. G.
REV. SCI. INSTRUM.
41, 593–4, 1970.

58980 **DOUBLE MODULATION METHOD FOR HALL EFFECT MEASURMENTS ON PHOTOCONDUCTING MATERIALS.**
EISELE, I. KEVAN, L.
REV. SCI. INSTRUM.
43 (2), 189–94, 1972.

EPIC Number	Bibliographic Citation
58992	**EFFECT OF DEFORMATION ON THE THERMOELECTRIC PROPERTIES OF BISMUTH TELLURIDE - BISMUTH SELENIDE.** KULIEV, A. Z. OKHOTIN, A. S. ASADOV, D. A. KAKHRAMANOV, K. SH. TEPLOFIZ. SVOISTVA TVERD. TEL VYS. TEMP., TR. VSES. KONF. 30–3, 1971. (FOR ENGLISH TRANSLATION SEE E90003)
58994	**HALL COEFFICIENT AND SPECIFIC ELECTRICAL RESISTIVITY OF LIQUID METAL ALLOYS.** BUSCH, G. GUNTHERODT, H. J. PHYS. KONDENS. MATER. 6, 325–62, 1967.
58997	**UNIVERSAL INSTRUMENT TO MEASURE THE GALVANOMETRIC EFFECTS IN SEMICONDUCTORS.** FIVAZ, R. HELV. PHYS. ACTA 36, 1052–8, 1963.
58999	**INFRARED SPECTRA FROM REFLECTION STUDIES OF CARBON MONOXIDE ON EVAPORATED NICKEL FILMS.** MCCOY, E. F. SMART, R. ST. C. SURFACE SCI. 39, 109–20, 1973.
59001	**ELECTRIC PROPERTIES OF LIQUID METALS AND SEMICONDUCTORS.** ALEKSSEV, V. A. ANDREEV, A. A. PROKHORENKO, V. YA. USP. FIZ. NAUK 106 (3–4), 393–29, 1972. (FOR ENGLISH TRANSLATION SEE E59002)
59002	**ELECTRIC PROPERTIES OF LIQUID METALS AND SEMICONDUCTORS.** ALEKSSEV, V. A. ANDREEV, A. A. PROLHORENKO, V. YA. SOV. PHYS. - USP. 15 (2), 139–250, 1972. (ENGLISH TRANSLATION OF USP. FIZ. NAUK, 106 (304), 393–298 1972; FOR ORIGINAL SEE E59001)
59014	**THEORY OF IMPURITY SCATTERING IN SEMICONDUCTORS.** CONWELL, E. WEISSKOPF, V. F. PHYS. REV. 77 (3), 388–90, 1950.
59015	**NEUTRAL IMPURITY SCATTERING IN SEMICONDUCTORS.** ERGINSOY, C. PHYS. REV. 79, 1013–4, 1950.
59036	**THE ELECTRICAL RESISTANCE OF METALLIC MELTS. II. THE ELECTRICAL RESISTANCE OF MOLTEN COPPER–TIN, SILVER–TIN AND MAGNESIUM LEAD ALLOYS.** ROLL, A. MOTZ, H. Z. METALLK. 48 (8), 435–44, 1957.
59037	**THE ELECTRICAL RESISTANCE OF METALLIC MELTS. IV. THE ELECTRICAL RESISTANCE OF MOLTEN GOLD–TIN, GOLD–LEAD—, AND SILVER–LEAD–ALLOYS.** ROLL, A. UHL, E. Z. METALLK. 50 (3), 159–65, 1959.
59041	**MAGNETIC PROPERTIES OF SINGLE CRYSTALS OF YTTERBIUM OXYSULFIDE.** ROSSAT–MIGNOD, J. BALLESTRACCI, R. VETTIER, C. LE GAL, H. QUEZEL, G. J. PHYS. COLLOQ. 32 (2–3), C1–1031–C1–1033, 1971.
59050	**INVESTIGATION OF THE ELECTRICAL RESISTIVITY OF ZIRCONIUM AND HAFNIUM NITRIDES.** PETROVA, I. I. PETROV, V. A. ERMAKOV, B. G. SOKOLOV, V. V. TEPLOFIZ. VYS. TEMP. 10 (5), 1007–12, 1972. (FOR ENGLISH TRANSLATION SEE E59051)
59051	**INVESTIGATION OF THE ELECTRICAL RESISTIVITY OF ZIRCONIUM AND HAFNIUM NITRIDES.** PETROVA, I. I. PETROV, V. A. ERMAKOV, B. G. SOKOLOV, V. V. HIGH TEMP. 10 (5), 905–9, 1972. (ENGLISH TRANSLATION OF TEPLOFIZ. VYS. TEMP., 10 (5), 1007–12, 1972; FOR ORIGINAL SEE E59050)
59068	**ELECTROPHYSICAL PROPERTIES OF ALLOYED COPPER SULFIDE AND COPPER TELLURIDE.** ASTAKHOV, O. P. LOBANKOV, V. V. SGIBNEV, I. V. SURKOV, B. M. TEPLOFIZ. VYS. TEMP. 10 (3), 654–5, 1972. (FOR ENGLISH TRANSLATION SEE E59069)
59069	**ELECTROPHYSICAL PROPERTIES OF ALLOYED COPPER SULFIDE AND COPPER TELLURIDE.** ASTAKHOV, O. P. LOBANKOV, V. V. SGIBNEV, I. V. SURKOV, B. M. HIGH TEMP. 10 (3), 586–7, 1972. (ENGLISH TRANSLATION OF TEPLOFIZ. VYS. TEMP., 10 (3), 654–5, 1972; FOR ORIGINAL SEE E59068)
59070	**ROOM TEMPERATURE TRANSPORT PROPERTIES OF P–TYPE LEAD TELLURIDE.** HARRIS, J. J. RIDLEY, B. K. J. PHYS. CHEM. SOLIDS 33 (7), 1455–64, 1972.
59071	**TEMPERATURE DEPENDENCE OF CARRIER MOBILITY IN BARIUM TITANATE.** BURSIAN, E. V. GIRSHBERG, YA. G. STAROV, E. N. FIZ. TVERD. TELA 14 (4), 1019–22, 1972. (FOR ENGLISH TRANSLATION SEE E59072)
59072	**TEMPERATURE DEPENDENCE OF CARRIER MOBILITY IN BARIUM TITANATE.** BURSIAN, E. V. GIRSHBERG, YA. G. STAROV, E. N. SOV. PHYS. SOLID STATE 14 (4), 872–5, 1972. (ENGLISH TRANSLATION OF FIZ. TVERD. TELA, 14 (4), 1019–22, 1972; FOR ORIGINAL SEE E59071)
59075	**MEASUREMENT OF THE RESISTIVITY INHOMOGENEITY OF PHOTOSENSITIVE SEMICONDUCTING MATERIALS BY THE DARK PROBE METHOD.** BUGRIENKO, V. I. RYBIN, V. N. FIZ. TEKH. POLUPROV. 3 (10), 1593–7, 1969. (FOR ENGLISH TRANSLATION SEE E59076)
59076	**MEASUREMENT OF THE RESISTIVITY INHOMOGENEITY OF PHOTOSENSTIVE SEMICONDUCTING MATERIALS BY THE DARK PROBE METHOD.** BUGRIENKO, V. I. RYBIN, V. N. SOV. PHYS. SEMICOND. 3 (10), 1340–2, 1970. (ENGLISH TRANSLATION OF FIZ. TEKH. POLUPROV., 3 (10), 1593–7, 1969; FOR ORIGINAL SEE E59075)
59077	**INFRARED ABSORPTION IN N– AND P–TYPE SILICON CARBIDE SINGLE CRYSTALS.** IL'IN, M. A. MIKHAILOVA, N. G. RASHEVSKAYA, E. P. FIZ. TEKH. POLUPROV. 7 (3), 586–90, 1973. (FOR ENGLISH TRANSLATION SEE E59078)
59078	**INFRARED ABSORPTION IN N– AND P–TYPE SILICON CARBIDE SINGLE CRYSTALS.** IL'IN, M. A. MIKHAILOVA, N. G. RASHEVSKAYA, E. P. SOV. PHYS. SEMICOND. 7 (3), 406–8, 1973. (ENGLISH TRANSLATION OF FIZ. TEKH. POLUPROV., 7, 586–90, 1973; FOR ORIGINAL SEE E59077)
59093	**FERROELECTRIC TRANSITIONS IN POTASSIUM DIHYDROGEN PHOSPHATE AND POTASSIUM DIDEUTERIUM PHOSPHATE STUDIED BY INFRARED POLARIZED REFLECTION.** LEVIN, S. PELAH, I. WIENER–AVNEAR, E. PHYS. STATUS SOLIDI 58 B (1), 61–9, 1973.
59111	**ELECTRIC RESISTIVITY AND THERMAL EXPANSION OF DYSPROSIUM GOLD.** OHASHI, M. KANEKO, T. MIURA, S. KAMIGAKI, K. J. PHYS. SOC. JAPAN 34, 553, 1973.
59128	**ELECTRICAL RESISTIVITY OF ALUMINUM APPLIED TO A BACKING BY PLASMA GAS–FLAME DEPOSITION.** SMIRNOV, E. V. SHKLYAREVSKII, E. E. INZH. FIZ. ZH. 16 (4), 713–6, 1969. (FOR ENGLISH TRANSLATION SEE E59129)
59129	**ELECTRICAL RESISTIVITY OF ALUMINUM APPLIED TO A BACKING BY PLASMA GAS–FLAME DEPOSITION.** SMIRNOV, E. V. SHKLYAREVSKII, E. E. J. ENG. PHYS. 16 (4), 493–5, 1969. (ENGLISH TRANSLATION OF INZH. FIZ. ZH., 16 (4), 713–6, 1969; FOR ORIGINAL SEE E59128)
59134	**THERMAL RADIATIVE PROPERTIES OF A SMOOTH AIR–WATER INTERFACE.** ARMALY, B. F. CROSBIE, A. L. LOOK, D. C. NELSON, H. F. INT. J. HEAT MASS TRANSFER 16, 1477–87, 1973.

EPIC Number	Bibliographic Citation
59135	**PERFORMANCE OF LEAD TELLURIDE AND BISMUTH SESQUITELLURIDE AS SOLAR THERMOELECTRIC GENERATOR MATERIALS.** PRASAD, S. RAO, A. B. INDIAN J. PURE APPL. PHYS. 10 (1), 36–8, 1972.
59151	**MICROWAVE PERMITTIVITY OF THE GALLIUM ARSENIDE LATTICE AT TEMPERATURES BETWEEN 100 K AND 600 K.** LU, T. GLOVER, G. H. CHAMPLIN, K. S. APPL. PHYS. LETT. 13 (12), 404, 1968.
59156	**THERMAL CONDUCTIVITY OF SOME DOUBLE AND TRIPLE SELENIDES OF TRANSITION ELEMENTS.** ABDULLAEV, G. B. ALIEV, G. M. IVANOVA, V. A. ABDINOV, D. SH. HEAT TRANSFER–SOV. RES. 5 (2), 30–3, 1973.
59164	**SINGLE ELECTROMETER METHOD OF MEASURING TRANSPORT PROPERTIES OF HIGH–RESISTIVITY SEMICONDUCTORS.** BALESHTA, T. M. KEYS, J. D. AMER. J. PHYS. 36, 23–6, 1968.
59166	**EFFECT OF EXCHANGE COUPLING ON THE SPECTRA OF TRANSITION METAL IONS. CRYSTAL STRUCTURE AND OPTICAL SPECTRUM OF CESIUM CHROMIUM TRIBROMIDE.** LI, T.–I. STUCKY, G. D. ACTA CRYSTALLOGR., SECT. 29 B (7), 1529–32, 1973.
59167	**A SIMPLE APPARATUS FOR RECORDING THE VARIATION OF HALL COEFFICIENT WITH TEMPERATURE.** PUTLEY, E. H. J. SCI. INSTRUM. 33, 164, 1956.
59174	**APPARATUS FOR AUTOMATIC ELECTRICAL MEASUREMENTS ON SEMICONDUCTORS FROM LIQUID HELIUM TEMPERATURE TO 400 K.** ELLIOTT, C. T. WILSON, D. J. J. PHYS. 2 E (SERIES 2), 956–8, 1969.
59175	**A DIGITAL RECORDING SYSTEM FOR MEASURING THE ELECTRICAL PROPERTIES OF SEMI–CONDUCTORS.** CARTER, R. H. A. HOWARTH, D. J. PUTLEY, D. H. J. SCI. INSTRUM. 35, 115–6, 1958.
59176	**CRYOSTAT FOR MEASURING THE ELECTRICAL PROPERTIES OF RESISTANCE SEMICONDUCTORS AT LOW TEMPERATURES.** MITCHELL, W. H. PUTLEY, E. H. J. SCI. INSTRUM. 36, 134–6, 1959.
59177	**RESISTIVITY MEASURING CIRCUIT USING CHOPPED DIRECT CURRENT.** EDWARDS, W. D. J. SCI. INSTRUM. 42, 432–4, 1965.
59185	**A METHOD OF MEASURING THE RESISTIVITY AND HALL COEFFICIENT OF LAMELLAE OF ARBITRARY SHAPE.** VAN DER PAUW, L. J. PHILIPS TECH. REV. 20 (8), 220–4, 1958–9.
59188	**ELECTRICAL AND OPTICAL PROPERTIES OF GALLIUM PHOSPHIDE FILMS.** ZYKOV, A. M. SAMORUKOV, B. E. IZV. VYSSH. UCHEB. ZAVED., FIZ. 14 (6), 54–8, 1971. (FOR ENGLISH TRANSLATION SEE E59189)
59189	**ELECTRICAL AND OPTICAL PROPERTIES OF GALLIUM PHOSPHIDE FILMS.** ZYKOV, A. M. SAMORUKOV, B. E. SOV. PHYS. J. 14 (6), 761–4, 1971. (ENGLISH TRANSLATION OF IZV. VYSSH. UCHEB., ZAVED. FIZ., 14, (6), 54–8, 1971; FOR ENGLISH TRANSLATION SEE E59188)
59204	**INVESTIGATION OF THE TRANSPORT PHENOMENA IN THE SOLID SOLUTION LEAD GERMANIUM TELLURIDE.** PROKOF'EVA, L. V. NIKULIN, YU. A. BUZYLEVA, L. V. SOV. PHYS. SEMICOND. 7 (10), 1245–7, 1974. (ENGLISH TRANSLATION OF FIZ. TEKH. POLUPROV., 7 (10), 1865–9, 1973; FOR ORIGINAL SEE E58209)
59205	**IMPURITY RADIATIVE RECOMBINATION IN ALUMINUM ANTIMONIDE.** LUKOMSKII, A. I. SOV. PHYS. SEMICOND. 7 (12), 1562–3, 1974. (ENGLISH TRANSLATION OF FIZ. TEKH. POLUPROV., 7 (12), 2349–51, 1973; FOR ORIGINAL SEE E58200)
59206	**FREQUENCY DEPENDENCES OF THE ONE– AND TWO–PHOTON ABSORPTION OF CRYSTALS WITH NONPAROBOLIC CONDUCTION BANDS SIMILAR TO CADMIUM SULFIDE.** BRODIN, M. S. DEMIDENKO, Z. A. DMITRENKO, K. A. REZNICHENKO, V. YA. STRASHNIKOVA, M. I. SOV. PHYS. SEMICOND. 8 (1), 43–6, 1974. (ENGLISH TRANSLATION OF FIZ. TEKH. POLUPROV., 8 (1), 74–9, 1974; FOR ORIGINAL SEE E58210)
59207	**ELLIPSOMETRIC METHOD FOR MEASURING OPTICAL CONSTANTS AND THICKNESS OF THIN ABSORBING FILMS ON METAL SUBSTRATES.** SHKLYAREVSKII, I. N. EL–SHAZLY, A. F. A. YAROVAYA, R. G. KOSTYUK, V. P. OPT. SPECTROS., USSR 36 (1), 116–8, 1974. (ENGLISH TRANSLATION OF OPT. SPEKTROSK., 36 (1), 199–204, 1974; FOR ORIGINAL SEE E57859)
59208	**EFFECT OF CONTAMINATION WITH CADMIUM ON THE ELECTRICAL CONDUCTIVITY AND THE THERMOELECTROMOTIVE FORCE OF MOLTEN THALLIUM (I) TELLURIDE.** KAZANDZHAN, B. I. TSURIKOV, A. A. RUSS. J. PHYS. CHEM. 47 (4), 566–6, 1973. (ENGLISH TRANSLATION OF ZH. FIZ. KHIM., 47 (4), 1002–4, 1973; FOR ORIGINAL SEE E51346)
59223	**EXPERIMENTAL DETERMINATION OF THE THERMAL AND ELECTRICAL CONDUCTIVITY OF HYDROGEN AND SULFUR HEXAFLUORIDE IN THE ELECTRIC ARC.** MOTSCHMANN, H. Z. PHYS. 191, 10–23, 1966.
59225	**ANISOTROPY OF THE PIEZOELECTRIC SCATTERING IN WURTZITE–TYPE SEMICONDUCTORS.** BULAT, L. P. SOV. PHYS. SEMICOND. 7 (9), 1157–62, 1974. (ENGLISH TRANSLATION OF FIZ. TEKH. POLUPROV., 7 (9), 1732–40, 1973; FOR ORIGINAL SEE E55300)
59228	**HOT ELECTRONS AT LOW TEMPERATURES IN COMPENSATED GALLIUM ARSENIDE.** VUL, B. M. ZAVARITSKAYA, E. I. VORONOVA, I. D. ROZHDESTVENSKAYA, N. V. SOV. PHYS. SEMICOND. 7 (9), 1179–81, 1974. (ENGLISH TRANSLATION OF FIZ. TEKH. POLUPROV., 7 (9), 1766–70, 1973; FOR ORIGINAL SEE E55303)
59230	**INFLUENCE OF A MAGNETIC FIELD ON THE IONIZATION ENERGY OF SHALLOW DONOR IMPURITIES IN GALLIUM ARSENIDE AND INDIUM PHOSPHIDE.** GULLIKOV, V. M. EMEL'YANENKO, O. V. NASLEDOV, D. N. NEDEOGLO, D. D. TIMCHENKO, I. N. SOV. PHYS. SEMICOND. 7 (9), 1191–3, 1974. (ENGLISH TRANSLATION OF FIZ. TEKH. POLUPROV., 7 (9), 1785–9, 1973; FOR ORIGINAL SEE E55305)
59231	**1.0 E V IMPURITY BAND IN THE PHOTOLUMINESCENCE SPECTRUM OF EPITAXIAL GALLIUM ARSENIDE.** BATAVIN, V. V. POPOVA, G. V. SOV. PHYS. SEMICOND. 7 (9), 1194–7, 1974. (ENGLISH TRANSLATION OF FIZ. TEKH. POLUPROV., 7 (9), 1790–5, 1973; FOR ORIGINAL SEE E55306)
59232	**ELECTROREFLECTION SPECTRA AND BAND STRUCTURE OF ZINC GERMANIUM ARSENIDE.** KRIVAITE, G. Z. SHILEIKA, A. YU. SOV. PHYS. SEMICOND. 7 (9), 1198–1200, 1974. (ENGLISH TRANSLATION OF FIZ. TEKH. POLUPROV., 7 (9), 1796–1800, 1973; FOR ORIGINAL SEE E55307)
59233	**PHOTOCONDUCTIVITY OF GALLIUM ARSENIDE–ALUMINUM ARSENIDE SOLID SOLUTIONS.** BERDZENISHVILI, A. I. DZHAKHUTASHVILI, T. V. LOBZHANIDZE, Z. V. MIRTSKHULAVA, A. A. PEKAR, I. E. CHIKOVANI, R. I. SHKOL'NIK, A. L. SOV. PHYS. SEMICOND. 7 (9), 1204–5, 1974. (ENGLISH TRANSLATION OF FIZ. TEKH. POLUPROV., 7 (9), 1806–8, 1973; FOR ORIGINAL SEE E55308)
59234	**DOMAIN ELECTRICAL INSTABILITY IN N–TYPE CADMIUM TELLURIDE.** CHAPNIN, V. A. MARINENKO, S. M. GOLUBTSOV, V. V. SOV. PHYS. SEMICOND. 7 (9), 1210–2, 1974. (ENGLISH TRANSLATION OF FIZ. TEKH. POLUPROV., 7 (9), 1814–7, 1973; FOR ORIGINAL SEE E55309)

EPIC Number	Bibliographic Citation
59235	INFLUENCE OF IMPURITIES ON THE FUNDAMENTAL ABSORPTION EDGE OF HEXAGONAL ALPHA-SILICON CARBIDE. VIOLINA, G. N. SELEZNEV, V. I. TAIROV, YU. M. SOV. PHYS. SEMICOND. 7 (9), 1215-6, 1974. (ENGLISH TRANSLATION OF FIZ. TEKH. POLUPROV., 7 (9), 1821-2, 1973; FOR ORIGINAL SEE E55310)
59237	DIFFUSION LENGTH OF THE MINORITY CARRIERS IN GERMANIUM-DOPED P-TYPE ALUMINUM GALLIUM ARSENIDE. ROGULIN, V. YU. FILLER, A. S. SHLENSKII, A. A. SOV. PHYS. SEMICOND. 7 (9), 1221-2, 1974. (ENGLISH TRANSLATION OF FIZ. TEKH. POLUPROV., 7 (9), 1828-30, 1973; FOR ORIGINAL SEE E55312)
59240	EXCESS CIRCULAR POLARIZATION OF THE LUMINESCENCE AS A RESULT OF OPTICAL ORIENTATION OF SPINS IN A CUBIC SEMICONDUCTOR. DZHIOEV, R. I. ZAKHARCHENYA, B. P. FLEISHER, V. G. VEKUA, V. L. SOV. PHYS. SEMICOND. 7 (9), 1237-8, 1974. (ENGLISH TRANSLATION OF FIZ. TEKH. POLUPROV., 7 (9), 1849-51, 1973; FOR ORIGINAL SEE E55315)
59241	INVESTIGATION OF EXCITED DONOR STATES IN GALLIUM ARSENIDE. GERSHENZON, E. M. GOL'TSMAN, G. N. PTITSYNA, N. G. SOV. PHYS. SEMICOND. 7 (10), 1248-50, 1974. (ENGLISH TRANSLATION OF FIZ. TEKH. POLUPROV., 7 (10), 1870-3, 1973; FOR ORIGINAL SEE E55316)
59242	TRANSPORT PHENOMENA IN P-TYPE THALLIUM ANTIMONY DITELLURIDE. GITSU, D. V. KANTSER, CH. T. STRATAN, G. I. CHEBAN, A. G. SOV. PHYS. SEMICOND. 7 (10), 1251-3, 1974. (ENGLISH TRANSLATION OF FIZ. TEKH. POLUPROV., 7 (10), 1874-7, 1973; FOR ORIGINAL SEE E55285)
59245	DETERMINATION OF THE PARAMETERS OF IMPURITY CENTERS IN SEMICONDUCTING MATERIALS BY THE METHOD OF CHARGE REVERSAL WITH THE AID OF ELECTROMAGNETIC RADIATION. KARPENKO, V. P. KASHERININOV, P. G. MATVEEV, O. A. TOMASOV, A. A. SOV. PHYS. SEMICOND. 7 (10), 1268-72, 1974. (ENGLISH TRANSLATION OF FIZ. TEKH. POLUPROV., 7 (10), 1901-7, 1973; FOR ORIGINAL SEE E55287)
59247	ANISOTROPY OF THE THERMOELECTRIC POWER OF CADMIUM ZINC ANTIMONIDE SINGLE CRYSTALS. BUDA, I. S. PILAT, I. M. SOLICHUK, K. D. SOV. PHYS. SEMICOND. 7 (10), 1284-6, 1974. (ENGLISH TRANSLATION OF FIZ. TEKH. POLUPROV., 7 (10), 1925-8, 1973; FOR ORIGINAL SEE E55288)
59248	OSCILLATIONS OF THE PHOTOCURRENT IN CADMIUM SULFIDE RADIATION DETECTORS. ZAVERTANNAYA, L. S. RVACHEV, A. L. SOV. PHYS. SEMICOND. 7 (10), 1287-91, 1974. (ENGLISH TRANSLATION OF FIZ. TEKH. POLUPROV., 7 (10), 1929-35, 1973; FOR ORIGINAL SEE E55289)
59249	INDUCED MOTT TRANSITION IN COMPENSATED GALLIUM ARSENIDE. VUL, B. M. ZAVARITSKAYA, E. I. VORONOVA, I. D. GALKIN, G. N. ROZHDESTVENSKAYA, N. V. SOV. PHYS. SEMICOND. 7 (10), 1295-7, 1974. (ENGLISH TRANSLATION OF FIZ. TEKH. POLUPROV., 7 (10), 1942-5, 1973; FOR ORIGINAL SEE E55290)
59251	PHOTOELECTRIC EFFECTS IN CADMIUM SILICON PHOSPHIDE SINGLE CRYSTALS DOPED WITH IIB ELEMENTS. BYCHKOV, A. G. POTYKEVICH, I. V. RADZIVIL, V. P. TKACHUK, I. YU. TYCHINA, I. I. SOV. PHYS. SEMICOND. 7 (10), 1308-10, 1974. (ENGLISH TRANSLATION OF FIZ. TEKH. POLUPROV., 7 (10), 1961-4, 1973; FOR ORIGINAL SEE E55292)
59254	DRIFT VELOCITY AND AVERAGE ENERGY OF HOT ELECTRONS IN N-TYPE INDIUM ANTIMONIDE. VOROB'EV, L. E. GNESIN, M. M. STAFEEV, V. I. SOV. PHYS. SEMICOND. 7 (10), 1322-4, 1974. (ENGLISH TRANSLATION OF FIZ. TEKH. POLUPROV., 7 (10), 1982-6, 1973; FOR ORIGINAL SEE E55319)
59256	DEPENDENCE OF THE 4.2 K PIEZORESISTANCE OF P-TYPE INDIUM ANTIMONIDE ON THE IMPURITY CONCENTRATION. ALADASHVILI, D. I. GALAVANOV, V. V. OBUKHOV, S. A. SOV. PHYS. SEMICOND. 7 (10), 1349-50, 1974. (ENGLISH TRANSLATION OF FIZ. TEKH. POLUPROV., 7 (10), 2019-20, 1973; FOR ORIGINAL SEE E55320)
59257	SOME ELECTRICAL AND PHOTOELECTRIC CHARACTERISTICS OF N-V AND P-V-N STRUCTURES MADE OF GALLIUM PHOSPHIDE. NASLEDOV, D. N. POPOV, YU. G. PUTILOVSKAYA, M. YU. SLOBODCHIKOV, S. V. SOV. PHYS. SEMICOND. 7 (10), 1351-2, 1974. (ENGLISH TRANSLATION OF FIZ. TEKH. POLUPROV., 7 (10), 2021-4, 1973; FOR ORIGINAL SEE E55321)
59258	CHANGE IN THE ELECTRICAL CONDUCTIVITY OF GALLIUM SELENIDE IN STRONG MICROWAVE ELECTRIC FIELDS. AKHUNDOV, G. A. ABDINOV, A. SH. KYAZYM-ZADE, A. G. MEKHTIEV, N. M. SOV. PHYS. SEMICOND. 7 (10), 1357, 1974. (ENGLISH TRANSLATION OF FIZ. TEKH. POLUPROV., 7 (10), 2030-1, 1973; FOR ORIGINAL SEE E55322)
59259	FIELD EFFECT IN EPITAXIAL FILMS OF LEAD SULFIDE. MURTAZIN, A. M. ZARIF'YANTS, YU. A. SOV. PHYS. SEMICOND. 7 (10), 1364-5, 1974. (ENGLISH TRANSLATION OF FIZ. TEKH. POLUPROV., 7 (10), 2041-3, 1973; FOR ORIGINAL SEE E55323)
59261	INVESTIGATION OF THE CONDITIONS FOR THE REVERSIBILITY OF BREAKDOWN IN CHALCOGENIDE GLASSES. KOLOMIETS, B. T. LEBEDEV, E. A. TAKSAMI, I. A. SHPUNT, V. KH. SOV. PHYS. SEMICOND. 7 (10), 1368-9, 1974. (ENGLISH TRANSLATION OF FIZ. TEKH. POLUPROV., 7 (10), 2045-7, 1973; FOR ORIGINAL SEE E55325)
59262	EFFECTIVE MASS OF CARRIERS IN COPPER SULFOTELLURIDE. GORBACHEV, V. V. PUTILIN, I. M. SOV. PHYS. SEMICOND. 7 (10), 1372, 1974. (ENGLISH TRANSLATION OF FIZ. TEKH. POLUPROV., 7 (10), 2049-50, 1973; FOR ORIGINAL SEE E55326)
59263	OBSERVATIONS OF OSCILLATORY MAGNETOABSORPTION IN INDIUM PHOSPHIDE CRYSTALS. ABDULLAEV, M. A. ZAKHARCHENYA, B. P. SEISYAN, R. P. SOV. PHYS. SEMICOND. 7 (10), 1377-8, 1974. (ENGLISH TRANSLATION OF FIZ. TEKH. POLUPROV., 7 (10), 2055-7, 1973; FOR ORIGINAL SEE E55327)
59264	BAND STRUCTURE A (III) B (V)-A (II) B (VI) SOLID SOLUTIONS. EXTREMAL CONDITIONS FOR THE INTERBAND INTERACTION. BUZEVICH, G. I. SKOROBOGATOVA, L. A. KHABAROV, E. N. SOV. PHYS. SEMICOND. 7 (11), 1389-92, 1974. (ENGLISH TRANSLATION OF FIZ. TEKH. POLUPROV., 7 (11), 2079-85, 1973; FOR ORIGINAL SEE E55328)
59266	STARK BROADENING OF PHOTOTHERMAL IONIZATION SPECTRA OF DONORS IN GALLIUM ARSENIDE. BERMAN, L. V. KOGAN, SH. M. SAGINOV, L. D. SIDOROV, V. I. TELEGIN, A. A. SOV. PHYS. SEMICOND. 7 (11), 1398-1400, 1974. (ENGLISH TRANSLATION OF FIZ. TEKH. POLUPROV., 7 (11), 2094-8, 1973; FOR ORIGINAL SEE E55330)
59267	THEORY OF THE ELECTROLUMINESCENCE OF HEAVILY DOPED SEMICONDUCTORS. OSIPOV, V. V. SOV. PHYS. SEMICOND. 7 (11), 1405-9, 1974. (ENGLISH TRANSLATION OF FIZ. TEKH. POLUPROV., 7 (11), 2106-13, 1973; FOR ORIGINAL SEE E55331)
59268	SATURATION OF THE INTERBAND ABSORPTION OF LIGHT IN SEMICONDUCTORS WITH AN ALLOWANCE FOR SPATIAL FIELD INHOMOGENEITIES. POLUEKTOV, I. A. POPOV, YU. M. ROITBERG, V. S. SOV. PHYS. SEMICOND. 7 (11), 1410-2, 1974. (ENGLISH TRANSLATION OF FIZ. TEKH. POLUPROV., 7 (11), 2114-8, 1973; FOR ORIGINAL SEE E55294)
59269	DEPENDENCE OF THE RATE OF ACCUMULATION OF RADIATION DEFECTS IN SEMICONDUCTORS ON THE RADIATION INTENSITY. BOLOTOV, V. V. VASIL'EV, A. V. SMIRNOV, L. S. SOV. PHYS. SEMICOND. 7 (11), 1421-3, 1974. (ENGLISH TRANSLATION OF FIZ. TEKH. POLUPROV., 7 (11), 2132-6, 1973; FOR ORIGINAL SEE E55332)

EPIC Number | Bibliographic Citation

59270 **ELECTRICAL CONDUCTIVITY OF STRAINED P-TYPE GERMANIUM IN STRONG MAGNETIC FIELDS.**
NORMANTAS, E. FILIPAVICHUS, V.
SOV. PHYS. SEMICOND.
7 (11), 1424–7, 1974.
(ENGLISH TRANSLATION OF FIZ. TEKH. POLUPROV., 7 (11), 2137–43, 1973; FOR ORIGINAL SEE E55333)

59271 **PHOTOCONDUCTIVITY OF CADMIUM GALLIUM INDIUM SULFIDE SINGLE CRYSTALS DOPED WITH GOLD. RECOMBINATION SCHEME.**
ABDULLAEV, G. B. DZHURAEV, N. D.
ANTONOV, V. B. NANI, R. KH. SALAEV, E. YU.
SOV. PHYS. SEMICOND.
7 (11), 1428–31, 1974.
(ENGLISH TRANSLATION OF FIZ. TEKH. POLUPROV., 7 (11), 2144–8, 1973; FOR ORIGINAL SEE E55295)

59272 **IONIZATION ENERGIES OF SUBSTITUTIONAL DONOR IMPURITIES IN GALLIUM ARSENIDE.**
BAZHENOV, V. K. SOLOSHENKO, V. I.
FOIGEL, M. G.
SOV. PHYS. SEMICOND.
7 (11), 1432–4, 1974.
(ENGLISH TRANSLATION OF FIZ. TEKH. POLUPROV., 7 (11), 2149–52, 1973; FOR ORIGINAL SEE E55334)

59274 **ENERGY SPECTRUM OF IMPURITY LEVELS AND SOME FEATURES OF RECOMBINATION IN OXYGEN-DOPED GALLIUM ARSENIDE.**
PEKA, G. P. SHEPEL', L. G. MIRETS, L. Z.
SOV. PHYS. SEMICOND.
7 (11), 1439–42, 1974.
(ENGLISH TRANSLATION OF FIZ. TEKH. POLUPROV., 7 (11), 2159–64, 1973; FOR ORIGINAL SEE E55336)

59275 **PROPERTIES OF IONIZATION DOMAINS IN MANGANESE ACTIVATED SODIUM ZINC GERMANATE CRYSTALS.**
DEVYATYKH, E. V. L'VOVA, E. YU.
STOPACHINSKII, V. B. FAN, PA-N. FOK, M. V.
SOV. PHYS. SEMICOND.
7 (11), 1443–6, 1974.
(ENGLISH TRANSLATION OF FIZ. TEKH. POLUPROV., 7 (11), 2165–71, 1973; FOR ORIGINAL SEE E55337)

59276 **THERMOELECTRIC POWER AND EFFECTIVE MASS OF HOLES IN P-TYPE SILICON ZINC ARSENIDE CRYSTALS.**
AVERKIEVA, G. K. PROCHUKHAN, V. D.
SOV. PHYS. SEMICOND.
7 (11), 1447–8, 1974.
(ENGLISH TRANSLATION OF FIZ. TEKH. POLUPROV., 7 (11), 2172–4, 1973; FOR ORIGINAL SEE E55338)

59277 **LUMINESCENCE OF EPITAXIAL FILMS OF ALUMINUM GALLIUM PHOSPHIDE SOLID SOLUTIONS WITH $0 \leq X \leq 0.85$.**
ALFEROV, ZH. I. GARBUZOV, D. Z.
KONNIKOV, S. G. KOP'EV, P. S.
SOV. PHYS. SEMICOND.
7 (11), 1449–50, 1974.
(ENGLISH TRANSLATION OF FIZ. TEKH. POLUPROV., 7 (11), 2175–8, 1973; FOR ORIGINAL SEE E55339)

59278 **SPECTRAL OSCILLATIONS OF THE BARRIER PHOTO-ELECTRO-MOTIVE-FORCE OF INDIUM ANTIMONIDE IN QUANTIZING MAGNETIC FIELDS.**
BELOV, N. A. KIM, G. D. KOSOGOV, O. V.
MARAMZINA, M. A.
SOV. PHYS. SEMICOND.
7 (11), 1451–3, 1974.
(ENGLISH TRANSLATION OF FIZ. TEKH. POLUPROV., 7 (11), 2179–83, 1973; FOR ORIGINAL SEE E55340)

59279 **ELECTROLUMINESCENCE OF GALLIUM ARSENIDE PHOSPHIDE CRYSTALS IN THE RANGE OF COMPOSITIONS CORRESPONDING TO THE INDIRECT BAND STRUCTURE.**
PIKHTIN, A. N. RAZBEGAEV, V. N.
YAS'KOV, D. A.
SOV. PHYS. SEMICOND.
7 (11), 1454–6, 1974.
(ENGLISH TRANSLATION OF FIZ. TEKH. POLUPROV., 7 (11), 2184–8, 1973; FOR ORIGINAL SEE E55341)

59280 **NATURE OF FAST-RECOMBINATION CENTERS IN CADMIUM SELENIDE CRYSTALS.**
MARTINAITIS, A. V. SAKALAS, A. P.
YANUSHKEVICHYUS, Z. V.
SOV. PHYS. SEMICOND.
7 (11), 1486–7, 1974.
(ENGLISH TRANSLATION OF FIZ. TEKH. POLUPROV., 7 (11), 2232–4, 1973; FOR ORIGINAL SEE E55296)

59281 **INFLUENCE OF A SURFACE ELECTRIC FIELD ON THE ABSORPTION OF LIGHT IN GALLIUM ARSENIDE.**
KRAVCHENKO, A. F. TEREKHOV, A. S.
SOV. PHYS. SEMICOND.
7 (11), 1488, 1974.
(ENGLISH TRANSLATION OF FIZ. TEKH. POLUPROV., 7 (11), 2234–5, 1973; FOR ORIGINAL SEE E54645)

59283 **INDUCED IMPURITY PHOTOCONDUCTIVITY OF LEAD ANTIMONY SULFIDE.**
DMYTRIV, A. YU. KOVAL'SKII, P. N.
MAKARENKO, V. V.
SOV. PHYS. SEMICOND.
7 (11), 1493–4, 1974.
(ENGLISH TRANSLATION OF FIZ. EKH. POLUPROV., 7 (11), 2241–3, 1973; FOR ORIGINAL SEE E55298)

59284 **QUENCHING OF THE INJECTION CURRENT IN COPPER-DOPED GALLIUM ARSENIDE.**
BRODOVOI, V. A. DERIKOT, N. Z.
SHCHERBATYI, N. I.
SOV. PHYS. SEMICOND.
7 (11), 1496–7, 1974.
(ENGLISH TRANSLATION OF FIZ. TEKH. POLUPROV., 7 (11), 2245–7, 1973; FOR ORIGINAL SEE E55342)

59285 **THERMOELECTRIC POWER OF STRONGLY COMPENSATED P-TYPE INDIUM ANTIMONIDE.**
ABRIKOSOV, N. KH. LAPTEV, A. V.
MIRGALOVSKAYA, M. S. RAUKHMAN, M. R.
SKRIPKIN, V. A.
SOV. PHYS. SEMICOND.
7 (11), 1502–3, 1974.
(ENGLISH TRANSLATION OF FIZ. TEKH. POLUPROV., 7 (11), 2253–4, 1973; FOR ORIGINAL SEE E55343)

59290 **MAGNETIC MEASUREMENTS ON SINGLE CRYSTALS IN THE YTTRIUM COBALT-IRON AND PRASEODYMIUM COBALT-IRON SYSTEMS.**
SHANLEY, C. W.
SCHOOL ENG., UNIV. DAYTON, DAYTON, OHIO
36PP., 1973.
(AFML-TR-276-I)

59291 **LOW-FREQUENCY DIELECTRIC CONSTANTS OF ALPHA-QUARTZ, SAPPHIRE, MAGNESIUM FLUORIDE, AND MAGNESIUM OXIDE.**
FONTANELLA, J. ANDEEN, C. SCHUELE, D.
U. S. NAVAL ACAD., ANNAPOLIS, MD.
18PP., 1973.
(COO-623-198)

59293 **LOW-FREQUENCY DIELECTRIC CONSTANT OF VITREOUS ARSENIC TRISULFIDE.**
FONTANELLA, J. ANDEEN, C. SCHUELE, D.
U. S. NAVAL ACAD., ANNAPOLIS, MD.
6PP., 1973.
(COO-623-196)

59303 **SYNTHESIS OF RARE EARTH COMPOUNDS CONTAINING TRIVALENT EUROPIUM AND PROMETHIUM-147 IONS AND THE STUDY OF LUMINESCENCE UNDER BETA- EXCITATION.**
BABUSIAUX, A.
COMM. ENERG. AT., GIF-SUR-YVETTE, FR.
67PP., 1973.
(CEA-R-4503)

59309 **HIGH FIELD SUPERCONDUCTIVITY IN ALKALI METAL INTERCALATES OF MOLYBDENUM SULFIDE.**
WOOLLAM, J. A. FLOOD, D. J. WAGONER, D. E.
SOMOANO, R. B. REMBAUM, A.
NASA, LEWIS RESEARCH CENTER, CLEVELAND, OHIO
14PP., 1973.
(NASA-TM-X-68206, N73-20794)

59311 **ANALYSIS OF OPTICAL SURFACE SCATTERING FROM EPITAXIAL FILMS.**
BROWN, R. N.
AIR FORCE CAMBRIDGE RES. LAB., L. G. HANSCOM FIELD, BEDFORD, MASS.
9PP., 1973.
(AFCRL-PSRP-577, AD-775753)

59319 **BEHAVIOR OF SEMICONDUCTOR STRUCTURAL ELEMENTS AT LOW TEMPERATURES.**
LENGELER, B. MATULA, S. SPORMANN, J.
DURCANSKY, G.
BER. KERNFORSCHUNGSANLAGE JUELICH
JUL-1021-FF, 47PP., 1973.

59322 **FAR-INFRARED OPTICAL ABSORPTION OF MANGANESE FLUORIDE.**
NEIMANIS, J. TIMUSK, T.
CAN. J. PHYS.
52 (3), 223–6, 1974.

59347 **THERMAL CONDUCTIVITY AND COEFFICIENT OF ABSORPTION OF ZINC SELENIDE IN THE 300–580 K RANGE.**
MEN, A. A. CHECHEL'NITSKII, A. Z.
SOKOLOV, V. A. SHOLODOVA, L. A.
IZV. AKAD. NAUK SSSR, NEORG. MATER.
10 (3), 548–9, 1974.
(FOR ENGLISH TRANSLATION SEE E64885)

59352 **PHOTOEFFECTS IN ZINC SILICON DIPHOSPHIDE.**
KRUSE, P. W. SCHULZE, R. G.
J. ELECTRON. MATER.
3 (2), 431–49, 1974.

59353 **OPTICAL PROPERTIES OF INFRARED TRANSMITTING MATERIALS.**
BENDOW, B.
J. ELECTRON. MATER. (USA)
3 (1), 101–35, 1974.

59354 **HIGH-TEMPERATURE SOLID SOLUBILITY LIMIT OF CARBON IN NIOBIUM AND TANTALUM.**
HORZ, G. LINDENMAIER, K. KLAISS, R.
J. LESS-COMMON MET.
35 (1), 97–105, 1974.

EPIC Number	Bibliographic Citation

59358 JAHN-TELLER EFFECT IN THE 3T1(P) ABSORPTION BAND OF NICKEL(2+) ION IN ZINC SULFIDE AND ZINC OXIDE.
KAUFMANN, U. G. KOIDL, P.
J. PHYS.
7 C (4), 791-806, 1974.

59370 PREPARATION OF LEAD TELLURIDE WITH A VARIABLE DISTRIBUTION OF THE CONCENTRATION OF CARRIERS.
RAEVSKII, S. D. CHEBAN, A. G.
KANTSER, CH. T. BARDETSKAYA, A. F.
MAKLOVICH, A. S. BYGU, P. V.
MATER. DOKL. NAUCH.-TEKH. KONF., KISHINEV. POLITEKH. INST., 9TH
109-10, 1973.

59372 EFFECT OF OXYGEN AND CADMIUM ON THE ELECTRIC CONDUCTIVITY OF COPPER.
MIRCHEV, M. PASKALEV, P. SPASOV, S.
METALURGIYA (SOFIA)
(2), 25-6, 1973.

59375 SPECTRAL EMITTANCE MEASUREMENTS ON SEVERAL CRYSTALLINE SAMPLES.
STIERWALT, D. L.
NAT. BUR. STAND. (U. S.), SPEC. PUBL.
387, 250-3, 1973.

59376 NONLINEAR REFRACTIVE INDEX MEASUREMENTS IN LASER MEDIA.
OWYOUNG, A.
NAT. BUR. STAND. (U. S.), SPEC. PUBL.
387, 11-25, 1973.

59378 PROPERTIES OF SELECTED SUPERCONDUCTIVE MATERIALS. 1974 SUPPLEMENT.
ROBERTS, B. W.
NAT. BUR. STAND. (U.S.), TECH. NOTE
825, 3PP., 1974.
(NBS-TN-825-SUPPL., COM-74-50460)

59379 PREPARATION OF OXIDE AND NITRIDE DIELECTRICS BY HIGH-FREQUENCY SPUTTERING.
GASHTOL'D, V. N. KUTOLIN, S. A.
SHAKORYAN, L. M. REZNIKOV, A. A.
NIZKOTEMP. PLAZMA TEKHNOL. NEORG. VESHCHESTV, TR. VSES. SEMIN., 2ND
40-5, 1971.

59381 MEASUREMENT OF BIREFRINGENCE BY THE METHOD OF THE INTERFERENCE OF POLARIZED RAYS IN CRYSTALS WITH THE POINT DELTA-N = 0 SITUATED IN THE REGION OF TRANSPARENCY.
SHALDIN, A. V. BELOGUROV, D. A.
OPT. SPEKTROSK.
36 (3), 599-600, 1974.
(FOR ENGLISH TRANSLATION SEE E62041)

59384 ELECTRON-PHONON INTERACTION AND SUPERCONDUCTIVITY IN TRANSITION METAL AND TRANSITION METAL CARBIDES.
KLEIN, B. M. PAPACONSTANTOPOULOS, D. A.
PHYS. REV. LETT.
32 (21), 1193-5, 1974.

59386 QUENCHING EFFECT IN GADOLINIUM - INFLUENCE OF HYDROGEN.
ASTY, M. LEMARIE, P. H.
PHYS. STATUS SOLIDI (GERMANY)
21 (2), 457-61, 1974.

59393 ANTIMONY CENTRES IN POTASSIUM HALIDES.
RADHAKRISHNA, S. KARGUPPIKAR, A. M.
PHYS. STATUS SOLIDI (GERMANY)
61 B (2), 687-94, 1974.

59397 INTERFERENCE APPARATUS FOR STUDYING THE THERMO- AND ELECTROOPTICAL PROPERTIES OF CRYSTALS.
KOPYLOV, YU. L.
PRIB. TEKH. EKSP.
(1), 202-4, 1974.
(FOR ENGLISH TRANSLATION SEE E65920)

59398 THERMALLY INDUCED ABSORPTION BANDS WITH VIBRONIC STRUCTURE IN LITHIUM FLUORIDE CRYSTALS.
CRITTENDEN, G. C. TOWNSEND, P. D.
RADIAT. EFF.
20 (3), 145-8, 1973.

59403 MICROSTRUCTURES AND BEHAVIOR NEAR THE CURIE TEMPERATURE OF GADOLINIUM AND GADOLINIUM-CARBON ALLOYS.
WONG, R. C. MILSTEIN, F. BALDWIN, J. A., JR.
SPINGARN, J.
SOLID STATE COMMUN. (USA)
14 (3), 235-8, 1974.

59409 ABSORPTION EDGE OF UNIAXIALLY DEFORMED CADMIUM SULFUR SINGLE CRYSTALS.
IVITRIKHOVSKII, N. L. KURIK, M. V.
MANZHARA, V. S.
SOV. PHYS.-SEMICOND. (USA)
7 (5), 632-4, 1973.
(ENGLISH TRANSLATION OF FIZ. TEKH. POLUPROVODN., 7 (5), 931-4, 1973; FOR ORIGINAL SEE E62163)

59411 ANISOTROPIC DEMBER PHOTO-E.M.F. OF A SEMICONDUCTOR WITH A PERIODIC DOPING PROFILE.
GIRBNIKOV, Z. S.
SOV. PHYS.-SEMICOND. (USA)
7 (6), 823-5, 1973.
(ENGLISH TRANSLATION OF FIZ. TEKH. POLUPROVODN. 7 (6), 1225-9, 1973; FOR ORIGINAL SEE E62165)

59413 ENERGY-TRANSFER CHARACTERISTICS IN TRANSLUCENT MATERIALS.
BEZRUKOVA, N. MEN, A. A. SERGEEV, O. A.
SETTAROVA, Z. S.
TEPLOFIZ. SVOISTVA TVERD. VESHCHESTV, MATER. VSES. TEPLOFIZ. KONF. SVOISTVAM VESHCHESTV VYS. TEMP., 4TH
97-101PP., 1973.

59418 EFFECT OF THE PHASE REDISTRIBUTION OF IMPURITIES ON THE ABSORPTION OF LIGHT BY FREE CARRIERS IN P-CADMIUM TELLURIDE.
ZAKHARCHUK, A. P. MALINKO, V. N.
NOVOSELETSKII, N. E. TOVSTYUK, K. D.
TSEBULYA, G. G.
UKR. FIZ. ZH. (RUSS. ED.)
19 (3), 513-15, 1974.

59423 CRYSTAL STRUCTURE AND BIREFRINGENCE OF DISORDERED ZINC SULFIDE SINGLE CRYSTALS.
NELKOWSKI, H. PFUETZENREUTER, O., II
ACTA CRYSTALLOGR., SECT.
27 A (PT. 3), 296-8, 1971.

59433 ABSORPTION BY FREE CHARGE CARRIERS IN POLAR SEMICONDUCTORS.
KOENIG, W. M.
ACTA PHYS. AUSTR.
33 (3-4), 275-84, 1971.

59436 METHOD OF MEASUREMENT OF A SMALL BIREFRINGENCE.
WARDZYNSKI, W.
ACTA PHYS. POL.
39 A (1), 21-7, 1971.

59438 METHOD FOR DETERMINING OPTICAL CONSTANTS OF THIN FILMS.
DOBIERZEWSKA-MOZRZYMAS, E. LEWANOWICZ, S.
MOZRZYMAS, J.
ACTA PHYS. POL.
41 A (3), 251-7, 1972.

59443 DETERMINATION OF OPTICAL CONSTANTS OF METALS.
HOFFMANN, GY. BAUER, F. FARKAS, L.
ACTA TECH. (BUDAPEST)
71 (3-4), 1971.

59462 THEORY OF ELECTRICAL CONDUCTIVITY MEASUREMENTS IN SEMICONDUCTOR FILMS BY MEANS OF PROBES.
KON'KOV, V. L. RUBTSOVA, R. A.
IZV. VYSSH. UCHEB. ZAVED., FIZ.
(1), 135-41, 1965.
(FOR ENGLISH TRANSLATION SEE E59463)

59463 THEORY OF ELECTRICAL CONDUCTIVITY MEASUREMENTS IN SEMICONDUCTOR FILMS BY MEANS OF PROBES.
KON'KOV, V. L. RUBTSOVA, R. A.
SOV. PHYS. J.
(1), 97-101, 1965.
(ENGLISH TRANSLATION OF IZV. VYSSH. UCHEB. ZAVED. FIZ., (1), 135-41, 1965; FOR ORIGINAL SEE E59462)

59464 ON THE THEORY OF THE PROBE METHOD OF ELECTRICAL CONDUCTIVITY MEASUREMENT IN SEMICONDUCTORS.
KON'KOV, V. L.
FIZ. TVERD. TELA
6 (1), 304-6, 1964.
(FOR ENGLISH TRANSLATION SEE E59465)

59465 ON THE THEORY OF THE PROBE METHOD OF ELECTRICAL CONDUCTIVITY MEASUREMENT IN SEMICONDUCTORS.
KON'KOV, V. L.
SOV. PHYS. SOLID STATE
6 (1), 244-6, 1964.
(ENGLISH TRANSLATION OF FIZ. TVERD. TELA, 6 (1), 304-6, 1964; FOR ORIGINAL SEE E59464)

59478 THEORY OF THE FOUR-POINT PROBE TECHNIQUE AS APPLIED TO THE MEASUREMENT OF THE CONDUCTIVITY OF THIN LAYERS ON CONDUCTING SUBSTRATES.
BROWN, M. A. C. S. JAKEMAN, E.
BRIT. J. APPL. PHYS.
17, 1143-8, 1966.

59479 CORRECTION DEVISORS FOR THE FOUR-POINT PROBE RESISTIVITY MEASUREMENT ON CYLINDRICAL SEMICONDUCTORS.
MURASHIMA, S. KANAMORI, H. ISHIBASHI, F.
JAP. J. APPL. PHYS.
9 (1), 58-67, 1970.

59484 THE GEOMETRIC FACTOR IN SEMICONDUCTOR FOUR-PROBE RESISTIVITY MEASUREMENTS.
MIRCEA, A.
SOLID STATE ELECTON.
6, 459-62, 1963.

EPIC Number	Bibliographic Citation
59485	POTENTIAL DISTRIBUTION IN A RECTANGULAR SEMICONDUCTOR BAR FOR USE WITH FOUR-POINT PROBE MEASUREMENTS. REBER, J. M. SOLID STATE ELECTRON. 7, 525-9, 1964.
59513	TELLURIDE SEMICONDUCTORS. XVII. THERMOEMF., ELECTRICAL CONDUCTIVITY, AND THERMAL CONDUCTIVITY OF GERMANIUM TELLURIDE NEAR STOICHIOMETRIC COMPOSITION. MALY, D. NIEKE, H. ANN. PHYS. (LEIPSIG) 27 (1), 94-100, 1971.
59520	ELECTROPHYSICAL PROPERTIES OF ZINC TELLURIDE, CADMIUM TELLURIDE, AND LEAD TELLURIDE THIN FILMS. SPINULESCU-CARNARU, I. DRAGHICI, I. BALTATEANU, N. AN. UNIV. BUCURESTI, SER. STIINT. NATUR., FIZ. 17, 83-102, 1968.
59532	EFFECT OF UNIAXIAL DEFORMATION ON FUNDAMENTAL ABSORPTION IN GALLIUM ARSENIDE. KRAVCHENKO, A. F. MAKAROV, E. A. MARDEZHOV, A. S. ARSENID GALLIYA (3), 103-12, 1970.
59542	A STUDY OF THE PHYSICAL PROPERTIES OF BORON. COSTATO, M. FONTANESI, S. ATTI SEMIN. MAT. FIS. UNIV. MODENA (ITALY) 18 (2), 231-81, 1969.
59552	STUDY OF THE ELECTRIC CONDUCTIVITY AND THE THERMOELECTRIC POWER OF URANIUM OXIDE AT HIGH TEMPERATURE. SORRIAUX, A. DJERASSI, H. C. R. HEBD. SEAN. ACAD. SCI., FRANCE 272 B (24), 1373-6, 1971.
59553	COMPARATIVE STUDY OF THE ELECTRIC CONDUCTIVITY AS A FUNCTION OF GRAIN SIZE OF CALCINATED URANIUM OXIDE. RUBIO, A. C.R. HEBD. SEAN. ACAD. SCI. 272 B (25), 1435-8, 1971.
59557	REVIEW OF OPTICAL AND ELECTRICAL PROPERTIES OF AMORPHOUS SEMICONDUCTORS. STUKE, J. J. NON-CRYST. SOLIDS 4, 1-26, 1970.
59561	SPIN-DISORDER EFFECTS IN THE ELECTRICAL RESISTIVITIES OF METALS AND ALLOYS. COLES, B. R. ADVAN. PHYS. (SUPPL. PHIL. MAG.) 7 (8), 40-71, 1958.
59563	LATTICE DEFECTS AND THE ELECTRICAL RESISTIVITY OF METALS. BROOM, T. ADVAN. PHYS. (SUPPL. PHIL. MAG.) 3, 26-83, 1954.
59568	ON THE GALVANOMAGNETIC, THERMOMAGNETIC, AND THERMO-ELECTRIC EFFECTS IN ISOTROPIC METALS AND SEMICONDUCTORS. MOORE, E. J. AUST. J. PHYS. 11, 235-54, 1958.
59572	THE CLASSIFICATION AND QUALITY CONTROL OF THIN FILMS BY THE RECOGNITION OF X-RAY DIFFRACTION LINES. KAWARAI, S. KOIKE, R. SHINTANI, M. FURUYA, N. ELECTRON. COMMUN. JAP. 56 (1), 79-84, 1973.
59573	MEASURING SEMI-CONDUCTOR PROPERTIES OF THERMOELECTRIC MATERIALS. RYDEN, D. J. ELECTRON. ENGINEERING 46 (551), 59,61,63, 1974.
59575	PHOTOMODULATED CONTACTLESS TECHNIQUE FOR MEASUREMENT OF SPECIFIC RESISTANCE OF HIGH RESISTANCE FILMS. VOROBECHIKOV, E. S. NALIVAYKO, B. A. ELEKTRON. TEKH. (USSR) 1, 12 (7), 39-42, 1971.
59578	CAMEL'S BACK STRUCTURE OF THE CONDUCTION BAND IN GALLIUM PHOSPHIDE. LAWAETZ, P. SOLID STATE COMMUN. 16 (1), 65-7, 1975.
59579	THEORY OF THE PHOTOELECTRIC EMISSION FROM SMALL QUASIMETALLIC CENTRES. ADAMYAN, V. M. GLAUBERMAN, A. E. KHLOPKOV, V. N. FIZ. TVER. TELA 13 (6), 1663-67, 1971. (FOR ENGLISH TRANSLATION SEE E61328)
59580	NONLINEAR ELECTRICAL CONDUCTIVITY OF ZERO-GAP SEMICONDUCTORS. BENESLAVSKII, S. D. FIZ. TVER. TELA (USSR) 13 (6), 1727-33, 1971. (FOR ENGLISH TRANSLATION SEE E61329)
59583	NEGATIVE MAGNETORESISTANCE IN INDIUM SELENIDE SINGLE CRYSTALS. ROMEO, N. PHYS. STATUS SOLIDI 26 A (2), K187-90, 1974.
59584	ELECTRON AND HOLE MOBILITIES IN GALLIUM INDIUM ARSENIDE. NEUMANN, H. STAUDTE, M. BUTTER, E. STARY, J. PHYS. STATUS SOLIDI 27 A (1), K9-11, 1975.
59585	MAGNETIZATION OF TRANSITION METAL BERYLLIDE ALLOYS. JESSER, R. HERR, A. PHYS. STATUS SOLIDI 27 A (1), K13-15, 1975.
59587	METHOD FOR MEASURING THERMOELECTRIC PARAMETERS. AGAEV, YA. MIKHAILOV, A. R. GELIOTEKHNIKA (USSR) 31-5PP., 1966. (FOR ENGLISH TRANSLATION SEE E63247)
59588	ELECTRICAL CONDUCTIVITY OF MATERIALS UNDER SHOCK COMPRESSION. STYRIS, D. L. DUVALL, G. E. HIGH TEMP.-HIGH PRESSURES 2 (5), 477-99, 1970.
59589	ELECTRICAL PROPERTIES OF TIN-CHALCOGENIDE FILMS. GOSWAMI, A. JOG, R. H. INDIAN J. PHYS. 43 (10), 563-74, 1969.
59594	TRANSPORT PROPERTIES OF FERROMAGNETIC SYSTEMS NEAR THE CRITICAL POINT: ELECTRICAL RESISTIVITY. KAWATRA, M. P. BUDNICK, J. I. INT. J. MAGN. 1 (1), 61-74, 1970.
59598	MEASUREMENT OF THE FUNDAMENTAL ELECTRO-PHYSICAL PARAMETERS OF THIN SEMICONDUCTOR LAYERS BY THE INSULATED CRYSTAL METHOD. KOVTONYUK, N. M. AMRINOV, N. M. MAGOMEDOV, A. A. IZV. VUZ FIZ. (USSR) (5), 105-9, 1971. (FOR ENGLISH TRANSLATION SEE E62174)
59601	ULTRAVIOLET-FLASH EFFECT IN CHEMICALLY DEPOSITED LEAD SULFIDE LAYERS. RYERSON, R. J. BUBE, R. H. J. APPL. PHYS. 41 (13), 5355, 1970.
59602	CONCENTRATION STUDY DETERMINATION OF THE 6P, 6I, AND 6D ENERGY LEVELS OF GADOLINIUM(3+) ION IN STRONTIUM FLUORIDE AT A C(4) NU SITE. DETRIO, J. A. FERRALLI, M. W. YANEY, P. P. J. CHEM. PHYS. 53 (11), 4372-7, 1970.
59607	SUPERCONDUCTIVITY OF COLD-DEPOSITED BERYLLIUM FILMS. ALEKSEEVSKII, N. E. TSEBRO, V. I. T. J. LOW TEMP. PHYS. 4 (6), 679-96, 1971.
59609	STUDY OF ISOTHERMAL PRECEIPITATION IN A URANIUM-TITANIUM ALLOY WITH 2.5 TITANIUM. STELLY, M. J. NUCL. MATER. (NETHERLANDS) 49 (3), 245-56, 1974.
59611	INFRARED ABSORPTION IN IONIC INSULATORS DUE TO MULTIPHONON PROCESSES. MCGILL, T. C. J. PHYS. AND CHEM. SOLIDS 34 (12), 2105-15, 1973. (AD-A025 873)
59614	DISPERSION OF OPTICAL COEFFICIENTS IN SEMICONDUCTORS. PURSEY, H. J. PHYS. 4 C (10), 1223-5, 1971.
59615	CELLS FOR FAR INFRARED ABSORPTION MEASUREMENTS ON POLAR LIQUIDS. FLEMING, J. W. DAVIES, G. J. J. PHYS. 4 E (8), 620-2, 1971.
59622	THE ELECTRICAL RESISTIVITY DURING PRE-PRECEIPITATION PROCESSES. ROSSITER, P. L. WELLS, P. PHIL. MAG. 24 (188), 425-36, 1971.

EPIC Number	Bibliographic Citation
59623	**SPACE CHARGE CONDUCTION IN PRESENCE OF A GAUSSIAN DISTRIBUTION OF LOCALIZED STATES.** GRENET, J. VAUTIER, C. CARLES, D. CHABRIER, J. J. PHILOS. MAG. 28 (6), 1265–77, 1973.
59626	**EVIDENCE OF STRUCTURE IN THE F BAND IN POTASSIUM CHLORIDE, POTASSIUM BROMIDE AND SODIUM CHLORIDE.** PERREGAUX, A. ASCARELLI, G. PHYS. LETT. (NETHERLANDS) 35 A (6), 455–6, 1971.
59640	**THERMOFORCE, ELECTRICAL AND THERMAL CONDUCTIVITY OF CRYSTALS OF THE SYSTEM INDIUM TELLURIDE–THALLIUM TELLURIDE.** NIEKE, H. SANDT, P. R. ANN. PHYSIK (LEIPZIG) 26 (3), 235–45, 1971.
59642	**ON THE GENERATION OF VACANCIES BY MOVING DISLOCATIONS.** SEITZ, F. ADVAN. PHYS. 1, 43–90, 1952.
59646	**ELECTRICAL CONDUCTIVITY AND THERMO–ELECTRO–MOTIVE–FORCE OF DITHALLIUM CHALCOGENIDES IN THE LIQUID STATE.** KAZANDZHAN, B. I. LOBANOV, A. A. SELIN, YU. I. TSURIKOV, A. A. IZV. AKAD. NAUK SSSR, NEORG. MATER. 7 (6), 1061–2, 1971. (FOR ENGLISH TRANSLATION SEE E59647)
59647	**ELECTRICAL CONDUCTIVITY AND THERMO–ELECTRO–MOTIVE–FORCE OF DITHALLIUM CHALCOGENIDES IN THE LIQUID STATE.** KAZANDZHAN, B. I. LOBANOV, A. A. SELIN, YU. I. TSURIKOV, A. A. INORG. MAT., USSR 7 (6), 941–2, 1971. (ENGLISH TRANSLATION OF IZV. AKAD. NAUK SSSR, NEORG. MATER., 7 (6), 1061–2, 1971; FOR ORIGINAL SEE E59646)
59648	**THE SYSTEM BISMUTH SELENIDE–BISMUTH IODIDE.** BELOTSKII, D. P. LAPSHIN, V. F. BOICHUK, R. F. IZV. AKAD. NAUK SSSR, NEORG. MATER. 7 (11), 1936–8, 1971. (FOR ENGLISH TRANSLATION SEE E59649)
59649	**THE SYSTEM BISMUTH SELENIDE–BISMUTH IODIDE.** BELOTSKII, D. P. LAPSHIN, V. F. BOICHUK, R. F. INORG. MAT., USSR 7 (11), 1724–6, 1971. (ENGLISH TRANSLATION OF IZV. AKAD. NAUK SSSR, NEORG. MATER., 7 (11), 1936–8, 1971; FOR ORIGINAL SEE E59648)
59668	**TRANSITION TEMPERATURE OF SUPERCONDUCTING INDIUM, THALLIUM, AND LEAD GRAINS.** WATSON, J. H. P. PHYS. REV. 2 B (5), 1282–6, 1970.
59674	**TEMPERATURE COEFFICIENT OF THE REFRACTIE INDEX OF DIAMOND– AND ZINC–BLEND–TYPE SEMICONDUCTORS.** YU, P. Y. CARDONA, M. PHYS. REV. 2 B (8) 3193–7, 1970.
59675	**UNRELAXED 2S STATE OF THE F CENTER IN ALKALI HALIDES STUDIED BY THE STARK EFFECT.** GRASSANO, U. M. MARGARITONDO, G. ROSEI, R. PHYS. REV. 2 B (8), 3319–22, 1970.
59678	**5F MAGNETISM IN PALLADIUM–ACTINIDE SOLID SOLUTIONS.** NELLIS, W. J. BRODSKY, M. B. PHYS. REV. 4 B (5), 1594–601, 1971.
59681	**EFFICIENCY CALCULATIONS FOR SOME P–N AND N–P HETEROJUNCTIONS.** SREEDHAR, A. K. SHARMA, B. I. PUROHIT, R. K. PHYS. STATUS SOLIDI (GERMANY) 3 A (3), K217–21, 1970.
59683	**FINITE SIZE EFFECTS AND I.R. OPTICAL ABSORPTION OF CYLINDRICAL PARTICLES OF IONIC CRYSTALS.** PASTRNAK, J. PHYS. STATUS SOLIDI (GERMANY) 3 A (3), 657–63, 1970.
59684	**ON THE EFFECT OF STRUCTURE ON THE ELECTRICAL RESISTIVITY OF SOME ORDERING SOLID SOLUTIONS.** VAROTTO, C. F. VIDOZ, A. E. PHYS. STATUS SOLIDI (GERMANY) 3 A (3), 697–706, 1970.

EPIC Number	Bibliographic Citation
59690	**SIMPLE METHOD FOR DETERMINING PHOTO–IONIZATION CROSS SECTIONS.** BJORKLUND, G. GRIMMEISS, H. G. PHYS. STATUS SOLIDI (GERMANY) 42 (1), K1–4, 1970.
59691	**INTERBAND OPTICAL TRANSITIONS IN DISORDERED SEMICONDUCTORS.** BONCH–BRUEVICH, V. L. PHYS. STATUS SOLIDI (GERMANY) 42 (1), 35–42, 1970.
59694	**TWO–PHOTON ABSORPTION SPECTRUM BY EXITONS IN CADMIUM SULPHIDE.** PRADERE, F. MYSYROWICZ, A. PROCEEDINGS OF THE 10TH INTERNATIONAL CONFERENCE ON THE PHYSICS OF SEMICONDUCTORS, CAMBRIDGE, MASS., USA 101–6PP., 1970.
59695	**ENERGY DEPENDENCE OF CONDUCTION IN BAND TAILS.** REDFIELD, D. CRANDALL, R. S. PROCEEDINGS OF THE 10TH INTERNATIONAL CONFERENCE ON THE PHYSICS OF SEMICONDUCTORS, CAMBRIDGE, MASS. 574–77PP., 1970.
59698	**THE THEORY OF TRANSPORT PHENOMENA FOR A LOW–MOBILITY SEMICONDUCTOR IN A HIGH ELECTRIC FIELD.** BRYXIN, V. V. FIRSOV, YU. A. PROCEEDINGS OF THE 10TH INTERNATIONAL CONFERENCE ON THE PHYSICS OF SEMICONDUCTORS, CAMBRIDGE, MASS. 767–73PP., 1970.
59699	**ELECTRICAL PROPERTIES OF SEMICONDUCTOR MELTS.** REGEL, A. R. ANDREEV, A. A. KAZANDZHAN, B. I. LOBANOV, A. A. MAMADALIEV, M. SMIRNOV, I. A. SHADRICHEV, E. V. PROCEEDINGS OF THE 10TH INTERNATIONAL CONFERENCE ON THE PHYSICS OF SEMICONDUCTORS, CAMBRIDGE, MASS. 773–84PP., 1970.
59704	**EXAMINATION OF MATERIALS WITH A VIEW TO HEAT RECOVERY BY THERMOELECTRIC MEANS.** MAHENC, J. ROUTIE, R. REV. PHYS. APPL. 5 (4), 653–8, 1970.
59711	**ELECTRONIC PROPERTIES OF CLEAN CLEAVED GALLIUM ARSENIDE SURFACES.** DINAN, J. H. GALBRAITH, L. K. FISCHER, T. E. SURFACE SCI. 26 (2), 587–604, 1971.
59716	**A PROPOSED ANALYSIS OF THE SPACE–CHARGE WAVE AND NEGATIVE RESISTANCE OF IV–ELEMENT SEMICONDUCTOR BULK.** KAWARMURA, M. MORISHITA, S. TRANS. INST. ELECTRONICS COMM1N. ENGRS. JAPAN, ABC 52 (10), 44–53, 1969.
59717	**CHANGES OF SURFACE CONDUCTIVITY IN GERMANIUM DURING X–IRRADIATION.** KREUTZ, E. W. PAGNIA, H. WAIDELICH, W. Z. ANGEW. PHYS. (GERMANY) 30 (2–3), 145–50, 1970.
59718	**INVESTIGATIONS OF SOME A–B(3) SUPERLATTICE–PHASES.** PREDEL, B. SCHWERMANN, W. Z. METALLK. (GERMANY) 62 (7), 517–24, 1971.
59721	**THEORY OF THERMALLY ASSISTED ELECTRON HOPPING IN AMORPHOUS SOLIDS.** BRENIG, W. DOHLER, G. WOLFLE, P. Z. PHYS. (GERMANY) 246 (1), 1–12, 1971.
59722	**FINE STRUCTURE OF THE EXCITON ABSORPTION SPECTRUM OF GALLIUM ARSENIDE CRYSTALS.** SEISYAN, R. P. ABDULLAEV, M. A. FIZ. TEKH. POLUPROVODN. (USSR) 7 (4), 811–15, 1973. (FOR ENGLISH TRANSLATION SEE E59723)
59723	**FINE STRUCTURE OF THE EXCITON ABSORPTION SPECTRUM OF GALLIUM ARSENIDE CRYSTALS.** SEISYAN, R. P. ABDULLAEV, M. A. SOV. PHYS. SEMICOND. 7 (4), 554–6, 1973. (ENGLISH TRANSLATION OF FIZ. TEKH. POLUPROV., 7 (4), 811–15, 1973; FOR ORIGINAL SEE E59722)
59724	**OPTICAL ABSORPTION IN N–TYPE SILICON CARBIDE (4H).** SELEZNEV, B. I. TAITOV, YU. M. FIZ. TEKH. POLUPROVODN. (USSR) 7 (5), 996–6, 1973. (FOR ENGLISH TRANSLATION SEE E59725)
59725	**OPTICAL ABSORPTION IN N–TYPE SILICON CARBIDE (4H).** SELEZNEV, B. I. TAIROV, YU. M. SOV. PHYS. SEMICOND. 7 (5), 680, 1973. (ENGLISH TRANSLATION OF FIZ. TEKH. POLUPROV., 7 (5), 996, 1973; FOR ORIGINAL SEE E59724)

EPIC Number	Bibliographic Citation
59726	VACANCY CONCENTRATION IN RELATION TO PLASTIC DEFORMATION IN SODIUM CHLORIDE CRYSTALS. TYAPUNINA, N. A. TSELEBROVSKII, A. N. KRISTALLOGRAFIYA (USSR) 18 (3), 649–50, 1973. (FOR ENGLISHS TRANSLATION SEE E59727)
59727	VACANCY CONCENTRATION IN RELATION TO PLASTIC DEFORMATION IN SODIUM CHLORIDE CRYSTALS. TYAPUNINA, N. A. TSELEBROVSKII, A. N. SOV. PHYS. CRYSTALLOGR. 18 (3), 410, 1973. (ENGLISH TRANSLATION OF KRISTALLOGRAFIYA, 18 (3), 649–50, 1973; FOR ORIGINAL SEE E59726)
59755	DESIGN OF GERMANIUM FOR THERMOMETRIC APPLICATIONS. BLAKEMORE, J. S. REV. SCI. INSTRUM. 33 (1), 106–12, 1962.
59758	WIDE RANGE MAGNETIC FIELD MEASUREMENTS AT 4.2 K. LUBELL, M. S. CHANDRASEKHAR, B. S. REV. SCI. INSTRUM. 35, 906–8, 1964.
59770	ANALYTICAL DETERMINATION OF OPTICAL CONSTANTS BASED ON THE POLARIZED REFLECTANCE AT A DIELECTRIC–CONDUCTOR INTERFACE. POTTER, R. F. J. OPT. SOC. AMER. 54 (7), 904–6, 1964.
59773	ELLIPSOMETRIC METHOD FOR THE DETERMINATION OF ALL THE OPTICAL PARAMETERS OF THE SYSTEM OF AN ISOTROPIC NONABSORBING FILM ON AN ISOTROPIC ABSORBING SUBSTRATE. OPTICAL CONSTANTS OF SILICON. VEDAM, K. KNAUSENBERGER, W. LUKES, F. J. OPT. SOC. AMER. 59 (1), 64–71, 1969.
59799	THE DIELECTRIC CONSTANT OF IONIC SOLIDS AND ITS CHANGE WITH HYDROSTATIC PRESSURE. JONES, B. W. PHIL. MAG. 16, 1085–96, 1967.
59800	CONDUCTION IN NON–CRYSTALLINE MATERIALS. III. LOCALIZED STATES IN A PSEUDOGAP AND NEAR EXTREMITIES OF CONDUCTION AND VALENCE BANDS. MOTT, N. F. PHIL. MAG. 19, 835–52, 1969.
59805	THERMOELECTRIC FIGURE OF MERIT OF PURE AND DOPED BISMUTH–ANTIMONY ALLOYS IN MAGNETIC FIELDS. IVANOV, G. A. KULIKOV, V. A. NALETOV, V. L. PANARIN, A. F. REGEL, A. R. FIZ. TEKH. POLUPROV. 6 (7), 1296–9, 1972. (FOR ENGLISH TRANSLATION SEE E59806)
59806	THERMOELECTRIC FIGURE OF MERIT OF PURE AND DOPED BISMUTH–ANTIMONY ALLOYS IN MAGNETIC FIELDS. IVANOV, G. A. KULIKOV, V. A. NALETOV, V. L. PANARIN, A. F. REGEL, A. R. SOV. PHYS. SEMICOND. 6 (7), 1134–7, 1973. (ENGLISH TRANSLATION OF FIZ. TEKH. POLUPROV., 6 (7), 1296–9, 1972; FOR ORIGINAL SEE E59805)
59810	SEMICONDUCTING GLASSES. PART I: GLASS AS AN ELECTRONIC CONDUCTOR. OWEN, A. E. CONTEMP. PHYS. 11 (3), 227–55, 1970.
59831	BAND STRUCTURE OF SEMICONDUCTOR ALLOYS BEYOND THE VIRTUAL CRYSTAL APPROXIMATION EFFECT OF COMPOSITIONAL DISORDER ON THE ENERGY GAPS IN GALLIUM PHOSPHIDE ARSENIDE. BALDERESCHI, A. MASCHKE, K. SOLID STATE COMMUN. 16 (1), 99–102, 1975.
59839	PHEONOMENA OBSERVED DURING IMPLANTATION OF NITROGEN ION INTO CADMIUM SULFIDE. KOMATSUBARA, K. SHIRAKI, Y. SHIMADA, T. BUSSEI 13 (8), 457–70, 1972.
59847	EFFECT OF HYDROSTATIC PRESSURE ON THE PHASE TRANSITION OF FEROELECTRIC LEAD TITANATE OXIDE. IKEDA, T. SOLID STATE COMMUN. 16 (1), 103–4, 1975.
59866	BEHAVIOR UNDER PRESSURE OF ALLOYS WITH RARE EARTH IMPURITIES. COQBLIN, B. COLLOQ. INT. CENT. NAT. RECH. SCI. (188), 179–90, 1970.
59867	VARIATION OF THE RADIATIVE EMISSION AND PHOTOVOLTAIC EFFECT OF LEAD SELENIDE UNDER PRESSURE. MARTINEZ, G. CHAMBOULEYRON, I. BESSON, J. M. BALKANSKI, M. COLLOQ. INT. CENT. NAT. RECH. SCI. (188), 241–6, 1970.
59881	SYNTHETIC METALS BASED ON GRAPHITE. UBBELOHDE, A. R. CONF. IND. CARBONS GRAPHITE, PAP. 3RD, 43–8, 1971. (EDITED BY G. J. GREGORY, SOC. CHEM. IND.: LONDON, ENGLAND)
59900	THERMOELECTRIC POWER OF N–TYPE BISMUTH SELENIDE IN STRONG TRANSVERSE MAGNETIC FIELDS. MIDDENDORFF, A. KOHLER, H. LANDWEHR, G. PHYS. STATUS SOLIDI 57 B (1), 203–10, 1973.
59903	OPTICAL PROPERTIES OF CRYSTALS OF CUPROUS SULPHIDES. (CHALCOSITE, DJURLEITE, COPPER SULFIDE, AND DIGENITE). MULDER, B. J. PHYS. STATUS SOLIDI 13 A, 79–88, 1972.
59904	THE FEATURES OF THE THERMO–ELECTRIC SKIN EFFECT IN THE PRESENCE OF SHALLOW LEVELS. MAEV, R. G. TOKAREV, E. F. PHYS. STATUS SOLIDI 13 A (1), 285–91, 1972.
59928	SPLIT–BEAM ELLIPSOMETRY OF THIN FILMS DEPOSITED ON SEMICONDUCTORS. KOMIYA, Y. SAKAMOTO, T. TARUI, Y. DENSHI GIJUTSU SOGO KENKYUJO IHO 36 (1/2), 96–103, 1972.
59932	ATOMIC, MOLECULAR, AND IONIC INTERACTIONS (IN DIELECTRICS). KRANBUEHL, D. E. DIG. LIT. DIELEC. 34, 65–86PP., 1972.
59933	CONDUCTION PHENOMENA IN DIELECTRIC SOLIDS. TANAKA, T. KOSAKI, M. DIG. LIT. DIELEC. 34, 87–125, 1972.
59951	PROPERTIES OF THE GERMANIUM TELLURIDE–SILVER ANTIMONY DITELLURIDE SYSTEM. BORISOVA, L. D. DECHEVA, S. K. DIMITROVA, S. K. MORALIISKI, P. D. DOKL. BOLG. AKAD. NAUK 24 (11), 1461–3, 1971.
59952	PHOTOVOLTAIC EFFECT ON CADMIUM SULFIDE–TIN SULFIDE. STOYANOV, V. E. VASILEV, I. S. STEFANOV, R. R. DOKL. BOLG. AKAD. NAUK 24 (11), 1469–71, 1971.
59955	ANNEALING AND THICKNESS EFFECTS ON THE ELECTRICAL RESISTANCE OF VACUUM–DEPOSITED TIN ANTIMONIDE ALLOY FILMS. DAMODARA DAS, V. JAGADEESH, M. S. THIN SOLID FILMS 24 (2), 203–10, 1974.
59967	ON THE ROLE OF POLARIZATION CHARGE IN ELECTROLUNINESCENCE OF ZINC SELENIDE THIN FILMS. BUZNITSKII, E. A. POSATSKAYA, A. S. YUGAS, B. S. UKR. FIZ. ZH. 19 (12), 1937–42, 1974.
59977	PHOTOVOLTAIC JUNCTIONS FORMED ON SILK–SCREENED CADMIUM SULFIDE LAYERS. VOJDANI, S. SHARIFNAI, A. DOROUDIAN, M. ELECTRON. LETT. 9 (6), 128–9, 1973.
59984	EFFECT OF THE SAMPLE SURFACE STATE ON THE ABSORPTION EDGE IN GALLIUM ARSENIDE. TURSKA, I. ELECTRON TECHNOL. 4 (1–2), 13–20, 1971.
59994	NONCONTACT METHODS FOR MEASURING THE CONDUCTIVITY OF SINGLE CRYSTALS AND MULTILAYER STRUCTURES OF A SEMICONDUCTOR. DEMIDOV, E. S. USKOV, V. A. SHUTOV, YU. N. ELEKTRON. TEKH., SER. UPR. KACH. STAND. 12, (5), 18–26, 1970.
59995	THERMAL STABILITY AND ELECTRICAL PROPERTIES OF CERIUM GROUP RARE–EARTH ELEMENT THIOGERMANATES. BESKROVNAYA, R. A. SEREBRENNIKOV, V. V. ELEKTRON. TEKH. SER.: UPR. KACH. STAND. 12, 12 (1), 113–15, 1971.

EPIC Number	Bibliographic Citation
59997	**TECHNOLOGY EFFECT ON THE ELECTRICAL CONDUCTIVITY OF THERMOELECTRIC MATERIALS.** REHAK, J. ELEKTROTECH. CAS. 22 (4), 255–67, 1971.
59998	**MEASUREMENT OF CONDUCTIVITY AND PERMITTIVITY OF SEMICONDUCTORS FOR MICROWAVES.** HABOVCIK, P. DROBNY, V. ELEKTROTECH. CAS. 23 (1), 28–39, 1972.
59999	**ANOMALOUS BEHAVIOR OF THE TRANSPORT PROPERTIES OF BISMUTH TELLURIDE SELENIDE.** RYDEN, D. J. ENERGY CONVERS. 11 (4), 161–9, 1971.
60019	**PHYSICAL PROPERTIES OF THIN FILMS OF ANTIMONY THALLIUM TELLURIDE TERNARY SEMICONDUCTOR COMPOUNDS.** BAZAKUTSA, V. A. VOINOVA, L. G. DEMBOVSKII, S. A. LISOVSKII, L. G. KUL'CHITSKAYA, A. K. FIZ. ELEKTRON. (LVOV) (2), 104–6, 1970.
60020	**ELECTRON–HOLE SCATTERING IN SEMICONDUCTORS WITH NARROW BAND GAPS.** BORONYUK, P. I. TOVSTYUK, K. D. FIZ. ELEKTRON. (LVOV) (2), 13–18, 1970.
60021	**FIELD DEPENDENCES OF MAGNETOTHERMOELECTRIC EFFECTS IN SEMIMETALS AND MERCURY(II) TELLURIDE NARROW–BAND SEMICONDUCTORS.** TSYUTSYURA, D. I. SHNEIDER, A. D. FIZ. ELEKTRON. (LVOV) (5), 15–17, 1972.
60023	**OPTICAL ABSORPTION AND REFLECTION IN MERCURY TELLURIDE.** IVANOV–OMSKII, V. I. KOLOMIETS, B. T. MAL'KOVA, A. A. MEKHTIEV, A. SH. FIZ. ELEKTRON. RESPUB. MIZHVIDOM. NAUK.–TEKH. ZB. (4), 16–20, 1971.
60042	**PHOTOCONDUCTIVITY AND PHOTOVOLTAIC EFFECT IN THERMALLY TREATED CADMIUM TELLURIDE.** DESNICA, U. V. URLI, N. B. FIZIKA 2 (3), 145–53, 1970.
60077	**APPLICATION OF EFFECTS OF ANOMALOUS DISPERSION IN REFRACTOMETRIC MEASUREMENTS. IV. SYSTEMS OF TWO SOLIDS.** MIOC, D. A. MIOC, U. B. GLAS. HEM. DRUS., BEOGRAD 37 (3–4), 119–28, 1972.
60090	**INFLUENCE OF THERMIONIC EMISSION ON MEASUREMENTS OF ELECTRICAL PROPERTIES OF REFRACTORY MATERIALS AT HIGH TEMPERATURES.** LOUP, J. P. JONKIERE, N. ANTHONY, A. M. HIGH TEMP.–HIGH PRESSURES 2 (1), 75–88, 1970.
60095	**MEASUREMENT OF HIGH ELECTRIC RESISTANCE IN THE CLOSED PRESSURE APPARATUS.** DIREL, A. NEUHAUS, A. HIGH TEMP.–HIGH PRESSURES 3 (1), 81–7, 1971.
60098	**PHOTOCONDUCTIVITY OF CRYSTALS I.** NOZAKI, H. IIDA, T. HYOMEN 8 (12), 807–17, 1970.
60099	**PHOTOCONDUCTIVITY OF CRYSTALS. III.** NOZAKI, H. IIDA, T. HYOMEN 9 (2), 78–92, 1971.
60102	**PHOTOVOLTAIC EFFECTS IN GRADED–BANDGAP STRUCTURES.** MARFAING, Y. CHEVALLIER, J. IEEE TRANS. ELECTRON DEVICES 18 (8), 465–71, 1971.
60103	**PHOTOVOLTAIC EFFECT IN THE COPPER–CADMIUM–SULFUR SYSTEM.** VAN AERSCHODT, A. E. CAPART, J. J. DAVID, K. H. FABBRICOTTI, M. HEFFELS, K. H. LOFERSKI, J. J. REINHARTZ, K. K. IEEE TRANS. ELECTRON DEVICES 18 (8), 471–82, 1971.
60135	**THERMAL ELECTRO–MOTIVE–FORCE OF COPPER OXIDE AND ITS DEPENDENCE ON THE OXYGEN PARTIAL PRESSURE.** ZUEV, K. P. DOLGINTSEV, V. D. IZV. VYSSH. UCHEB. ZAVED. FIZ. 14 (2), 110–2, 1971. (FOR ENGLISH TRANSLATION SEE E60136)

EPIC Number	Bibliographic Citation
60136	**THERMAL ELECTRO–MOTIVE–FORCE OF COPPER OXIDE AND ITS DEPENDENCE ON THE OXYGEN PARTIAL PRESSURE.** ZUEV, K. P. DOLGINTSEV, V. D. SOV. PHYS. J. 14 (2), 228–30, 1971. (ENGLISH TRANSLATION OF IZV. VYSSH. UCHEB. ZAVED. FIZ., 14 (2), 110–2, 1971; FOR ORIGINAL SEE E60135)
60139	**THERMOELECTRIC PARAMETERS OF THIN FILMS ON THALLIUM BISMUTH SELENIDE, AND THALLIUM BISMUTH TELLURIDE.** VOINOVA, L. G. BAZAKUTSA, V. A. DEMBOVSKII, S. A. LISOVSKII, L. G. SOKOL, E. P. KANTSER, CH. T. IZV. VYSSH. UCHEB. ZAVED. FIZ. 14 (5), 154–5, 1971. (FOR ENGLISH TRANSLATION SEE E60140)
60140	**THERMOELECTRIC PARAMETERS OF THIN FILMS ON THALLIUM BISMUTH SELENIDE, AND THALLIUM BISMUTH TELLURIDE.** VOINOVA, L. G. BAZAKUTSA, V. A. DEMBOVSKII, S. A. LISOVSKII, L. G. SOKOL, E. P. KANTSER, CH. T. SOV. PHYS. J. 14 (5), 713–4, 1971. (ENGLISH TRANSLATION OF IZV. VYSSH. UCHEB. ZAVED. FIZ., 14 (5), 154–5, 1971; FOR ORIGINAL SEE E60139)
60141	**THERMAL PROBE MEASUREMENT OF THE THERMOEMF OF EPITAXIAL FILMS.** ANATYCHUK, L. I. DIMITRASHCHUK, V. T. LUSTE, O. YA. MEL'NIK, A. P. IZV. VYSSH. UCHEB. ZAVED., FIZ. 14 (9), 71–5, 1971. (FOR ENGLISH TRANSLATION SEE E60142)
60142	**THERMAL PROBLE MEASUREMENT OF THE THERMOEMF OF EPITAXIAL FILMS.** ANATYCHUK, L. I. DIMITRASHCHUK, V. T. LUSTE, O. YA. MEL'NIK, A. P. SOV. PHYS. J. 14 (9), 1218–21, 1971. (ENGLISH TRANSLATION OF IZV. VYSSH. UCHEB. ZAVED., FIZ., 14 (9), 71–5, 1971; FOR ORIGINAL SEE E60141)
60155	**X–RAY INTERFERENCES AT LIQUID (MERCURY, GALLIUM, CARBON TETRACHLORIDE).** MENKE, H. PHYSIK. Z. 33 (16), 593–604, 1932.
60161	**OPTICAL AND THERMAL ENERGY GAP OF SOLID SOLUTION LEAD TIN TELLURIDE.** SIZOV, F. F. ORLETSKI, V. B. GRINEVA, S. G. TOVSTYUK, K. D. UKR. FIZ. ZH. 19 (12), 1979–84, 1974.
60165	**PHYSICAL AND ELECTRICAL PROPERTIES OF THIN–FILM BARIUM TITANATE PREPARED BY RADIO FREQUENCY SPUTTERING ON SILICON SUBSTRATES.** MAHER, G. H. DIEFENDORF, R. J. IEEE TRANS. PARTS, HYBRIDS, PACKAG. 8 (3), 11–15, 1972.
60173	**OXYGEN–ENHANCED SULBLIMATION OF P–TYPE LEAD TELLURIDE THERMOELECTRIC MATERIALS.** EGGERS, P. MUELLER, J. J. INTERSOC. ENERGY CONVERS. ENG. CONF., PROC. 963–9, 1971.
60177	**PHOTOVOLTAIC EFFECTS IN LATERALLY ILLUMINATED P–N JUNCTIONS.** CONSTANTINESCU, C. GOLDENBLUM, A. SOSTARICH, M. INT. J. ELECTRON. 35 (1), 65–72, 1973.
60185	**PHYSICAL PROPERTIES OF INDIUM PHOSPHIDE–INDIUM ARSENIDE ALLOYS.** KEKELIDZE, N. P. ISSLED. MATER. NOV. TEKH., DOKL. NAUCH.–TEKH. KONF. 127–32, 1971. (EDITED BY F. N. TAVADZE, METSNIEREBA: TIFLIS, USSR)
60192	**EFFECT OF INTRINSIC CONDUCTIVITY ON THE PROPERTIES OF BISMUTH ANTIMONY TELLURIDE SELENIDE SOLID SOLUTIONS.** SARKISYAN, V. SH. GOL'TSMAN, B. M. GORBACHEVA, A. N. IZV. AKAD. NAUK ARM. SSR, FIZ. 6 (4), 255–61, 1971.
60193	**METHOD OF MEASURING THE CONDUCTIVITY OF LIQUIDS.** ZOLYAN, T. S. IZV. AKAD. NAUK ARM. SSR, FIZ. 6 (4), 315–18, 1971.

EPIC Number	Bibliographic Citation
60216	**MEASUREMENT OF THE SPECIFIC RESISTANCE OF SEMICONDUCTOR SINGLE CRYSTALS IN THE SHAPES OF CYLINDERS AND TUBES.** POLYAKOV, N. N. KUKUI, A. S. PAVLOV, N. I. GOLUBEV, V. I. IZV. AKAD. NAUK SSSR, SER. FIZ. 35 (3), 53,-43, 1971. (FOR ENGLISH TRANSLATION SEE E63197)
60217	**MEASUREMENT OF THE SPECIFIC RESISTANCE OF PLANAR SINGLE CRYSTALS BY A CONTACTLESS METHOD.** KUKUI, A. S. KUSHCH, V. V. CHUMACHENKO, T. L. IZV. AKAD. NAUK SSSR, SER. FIZ. 35 (3), 544-5, 1971. (FOR ENGLISH TRANSLATION SEE E63198)
60221	**IMPURITY PHOTOEMF. OF P-N JUNCTIONS IN INDIUM PHOSPHIDE.** BERKELIEV, A. DURDYEV, K. IZV. AKAD. NAUK TURKM. SSR, SER. FIZ.-TEKH., KHIM. GEOL. NAUK (4), 79-32, 1971.
60225	**EFFECT OF EXTENSION ON THE CHARACTER OF THE ANOMALOUSLY LARGE PHOTOVOLTAGE EFFECT.** ADIROVICH, E. I. MIRZAMAKHMUDOV, T. YUABOV, YU. M. IZV. AKAD. NAUK UZB. SSR, SER. FIZ.-MAT. NAUK 15 (1), 36-9, 1971.
60230	**PHOTOCONDUCTIVITY AND PHOTOELECTROMOTIVE FORCE SENSITIZATION IN HEAVY METAL AZIDES COLORED BY ORGANIC DYES.** GAVRISHCHENKO, YU. V. SAVEL'EV, G. G. ZAKHAROV, YU. A. IZV. TOMSK. POLITEKH. INST. (185), 69-71, 1970.
60252	**TEMPERATURE DEPENDENCE OF THE BIREFRINGENCE FOR LANTHANUM-DOPED LEAD ZIRCONATE-TITANATE 7/65/35 AND AN NIOBIUM-MODIFIED LEAD ZIRCONATE-TITANATE.** KAPLIT, M. EDDY, D. S. J. AMER. CERAM. SOC. 57 (9), 409, 1974.
60253	**TEMPERATURE CHANGE OF THE REFRACTIVE INDEX OF CHEMICAL VAPOR DEPOSITED ZINC SELENIDE AT 10.6 MU M.** SKOLNIK, L. H. CLARK, O. M. APPL. OPT. 13 (9), 1999-2001, 1974.
60255	**OPTICAL COATINGS FOR HIGH ENERGY ZINC SELENIDE LASER WINDOWS.** RUDISILL, J. E. BRAUNSTEIN, M. BRAUNSTEIN, A. I. APPL. OPT. 13 (9), 2075-80, 1974.
60256	**REFRACTIVE INDEX PROFILE MEASUREMENTS OF DIFFUSED OPTICAL WAVEGUIDES.** MARTIN, W. E. APPL. OPT. 13 (9), 2112-6, 1974.
60259	**FARADAY ROTATION OPTICAL ISOLATOR FOR 10.6-MU M RADIATION.** JACOBS, S. D. TEEGARDEN, K. J. AHRENKIEL, R. K. APPL. OPT. 13 (10), 2313-6, 1974.
60260	**NONOXIDE CHALCOGENIDE GLASS FILMS FOR INTEGRATED OPTICS.** WATTS, R. K. DE WIT, M. HOLTON, W. C. APPL. OPT. 13 (10), 2329-32, 1974.
60261	**DIFFUSION KINETICS AND OPTICAL WAVEGUIDING PROPERTIES OF OUTDIFFUSED LAYERS IN LITHIUM NIOBATE AND LITHIUM TANTALATE.** CARRUTHERS, J. R. KAMINOW, I. P. STULZ, L. W. APPL. OPT. 13 (10), 2333-42, 1974.
60265	**PRESSURE AND STRESS DEPENDENCE OF THE REFRACTIVE INDEX OF TRANSPARENT CRYSTALS.** BENDOW, B. GIANINO, P. D. TSAY, Y.-F. MITRA, S. S. APPL. OPT. 13 (10), 2382-96, 1974. (AD-A012 553, N76-12355, AD-B013 807L)
60270	**HALOGEN VAPOR DEPOSITION OF CHALCOGENIDE CRYSTALS LEAD SULFIDE.** KWAN, S. H. FONSTAD, C. G. COLOZZI, A. LINZ, A. J. APPL. PHYS. 45 (8), 3273-6, 1974.
60275	**ELECTRONIC DENSITY OF STATES IN TITANIUM NICKEL INTERMETALLICS.** MITCHELL, M. A. WANG, F. E. CULLEN, J. R. J. APPL. PHYS. 45 (8), 3337-9, 1974.
60279	**HELICAL INSTABILITY IN INJECTED SEMICONDUCTOR PLASMAS.** TACANO, M. CHEN, W. S. J. APPL. PHYS. 45 (8), 3407-20, 1974.
60281	**A FLASHLAMP-PUMPED NEODYMIUM DOPED YTTRIUM ALUMINUM GARNET WAVEGUIDE LASER.** MOCKEL, P. OBERBACHER, R. RAUSCHER, W. J. APPL. PHYS. 45 (8), 3460-2, 1974.
60283	**LEAD TIN TELLURIUM INTERMETALLIC LAYERS BY RADIO FREQUENCY MULTICATHODE SPUTTERING.** CORSI, C. J. APPL. PHYS. 45 (8), 3467-71, 1974.
60284	**EFFECTS OF PRESSURE ON OPTICALLY PUMPED GALLIUM ANTIMONIDE, INDIUM ARSENIDE, AND INDIUM ANTIMONIDE LASERS.** MENYUK, N. PINE, A. S. KAFALAS, J. A. STRAUSS, A. J. J. APPL. PHYS. 45 (8), 3477-84, 1974.
60286	**GROWTH AND PROPERTIES OF CADMIUM SULFIDE EPITAXIAL LAYERS BY THE CLOSE-SPACED TECHNIQUE.** YOSHIKAWA, A. SAKAI, Y. J. APPL. PHYS. 45 (8), 3521-9, 1974.
60287	**EFFECTS OF DIFFUSION CURRENT ON GALVANOMAGNETIC PROPERTIES IN THIN INTRINSIC INDIUM ANTIMONY AT ROOM TEMPERATURE.** FUJISADA, H. J. APPL. PHYS. 45 (8), 3530-40, 1974.
60290	**OPTICAL STUDIES OF DEEP-CENTER LUMINESCENCE IN CADMIUM SULFIDE.** SHIRAKI, Y. SHIMADA, T. KOMATSUBARA, K. F. J. APPL. PHYS. 45 (8), 3554-61, 1974.
60291	**EFFECT OF CUBIC, TILTED UNIAXIAL, AND ORTHORHOMBIC ANISOTROPIES ON HOMOGENEOUS NUCLEATION IN A GARNET BUBBLE FILM.** HUBERT, A. MALOZEMOFF, A. P. DELUCA, J. C. J. APPL. PHYS. 45 (8), 3562-71, 1974.
60293	**MOSSBAUER AND CRYSTALLOGRAPHIC STUDY OF DYSPROSIUM IRON NICKEL COMPOUNDS.** TASI, S. C. NARASIMHAN, K. S. V. L. KUNESH, C. J. BUTERA, R. A. J. APPL. PHYS. 45 (8), 3582-6, 1974.
60295	**EFFECTS OF HIGH NONSTOICHIOMETRY ON EUROPIUM OXIDE PROPERTIES.** MASSENET, O. CAPIOMONT, Y. DANG, N. V. J. APPL. PHYS. 45 (8), 3593-9, 1974.
60297	**MAGNETIC ORDER IN NICKEL MANGANESE ALLOYS.** PATTON, C. E. BAKER, G. L. J. APPL. PHYS. 45 (8), 3611-3, 1974.
60298	**EFFECT OF THERMAL CYCLING ON THE MAGNETIC DOMAIN STRUCTURE OF DIRECTIONALLY SOLIDIFIED COBALT - COBALT NIOBIUM EUTECTIC.** ARNSON, H. L. ALBRIGHT, D. L. J. APPL. PHYS. 45 (8), 3614-6, 1974.
60299	**BUBBLE DYNAMICS AND GROWTH-INDUCED ANISOTROPY IN (YTTRIUM, EUROPIUM, THULIUM) (GALLIUM, IRON) OXIDE.** TABOR, W. J. VELLA-COLEIRO, G. P. HAGEDORN, F. B. VAN UITERT, L. G. J. APPL. PHYS. 45 (8), 3617-20, 1974.
60302	**ANISOTROPY AND MAGNETOSTRICTION OF GALLIUM-SUBSTITUTED YTTRIUM IRON GARNET.** HANSEN, P. J. APPL. PHYS. 45 (8), 3638-42, 1974.
60303	**KERR-EFFECT ENHANCEMENT AND IMPROVEMENT OF READOUT CHARACTERISTICS IN MANGANESE BUSMUTH FILM MEMORY.** EGASHIRA, K. YAMADA, T. J. APPL. PHYS. 45 (8), 3643-8, 1974.
60304	**SUBTHRESHOLD VELOCITY-FIELD CHARACTERISTICS FOR BULK AND EPITAXIAL INDIUM PHOSPHIDE.** MAGERFELD, A. POTTER, K. E. ROBSON, P. N. J. APPL. PHYS. 45 (8), 3681-2, 1974.

EPIC Number	Bibliographic Citation
60305	**SUPERCONDUCTIVITY IN METASTABLE SIMPLE CUBIC ALLOYS.** JOHNSON, W. L. POON, S. J. J. APPL. PHYS. 45 (8), 3683–4, 1974.
60307	**REFRACTIVE INDICES OF CONGRUENTLY MELTING LITHIUM NIOBATE.** NELSON, D. F. MIKULYAK, R. M. J. APPL. PHYS. 45 (8), 3688–9, 1974.
60308	**PREPARATION OF NONEQUILIBRIUM SOLID SOLUTIONS OF (GALLIUM ARSENIC) SILICON.** NOREIKA, A. J. FRANCOMBE, M. H. J. APPL. PHYS. 45 (8), 3690–1, 1974.
60309	**SOME ELECTRICAL PROPERTIES OF SILVER GALLIUM SULFIDE.** YU, P. W. MANTHURUTHIL, J. PARK, Y. S. J. APPL. PHYS. 45 (8), 3694–6, 1974. (AD–A8124)
60322	**POWDER METALLURGY REVIEW 7 SILICON NITRIDE (PART 2).** CUTLER, I. B. CROFT, W. J. POWDER MET. INTERN. 6 (3), 144–8, 1974.
60325	**DIMERIZATION OF A LINEAR HEISENBERG CHAIN IN THE INSULATING PHASES OF VANADIUM CHROMIUM OXIDE.** POUGET, J. P. LAUNOIS, H. RICE, T. M. DERNIER, P. GOSSARD, A. VILLENEUVE, G. HAGENMULLER, P. PHYS. REV. 10 B (5), 1801–15, 1974.
60334	**NEUTRON AND MAGNETIZATION STUDIES OF THE URANIUM PHOSPHIDE–URANIUM SULFIDE SYSTEM.** MAGLIC, R. C. LANDER, G. H. MUELLER, M. H. CRANGLE, J. WILLIAMS, G. S. PHYS. REV. 10 B (5), 1943–50, 1974.
60335	**LATTICE MODES IN FERROELECTRIC PEROVSKITES. II. LEAD BARIUM TITANIUM OXIDE INCLUDING BARIUM TITANIUM OXIDE.** BURNS, G. PHYS. REV. 10 B (5), 1951–9, 1974.
60336	**OPTICAL INVESTIGATION OF THE METAMAGNETIC PROPERTIES OF IRON CHLORIDE.** GRIFFIN, J. A. SCHNATTERLY, S. E. FARGE, Y. REGIS, M. FONTANA, M. P. PHYS. REV. 10 B (5), 1960–6, 1974.
60337	**NUCLEAR MAGNETIC COOLING TO 1.6 MILLIKELVIN AND NUCLEAR FERROMAGNETISM IN PRASEODYMIUM THALLIUM.** ANDRES, K. DARACK, S. PHYS. REV. 10 B (5), 1967–74, 1974.
60338	**THEORY FOR THE EFFECTS OF THE LOCAL ATOMIC ENVIRONMENT ON THE FORMATION OF MAGNETIC MOMENTS.** AOI, K. DEULING, H. BENNEMANN, K. H. PHYS. REV. 10 B (5), 1975–8, 1974.
60340	**MAGNETICALLY INDUCED LATTICE DISTORTIONS IN ACTINIDE COMPOUNDS.** LANDER, G. H. MUELLER, M. H. PHYS. REV. 10 B (5), 1994–2003, 1974.
60341	**NEUTRON–SCATTERING STUDIES OF SPIN WAVES IN RARE–EARTH ORTHOFERRITES.** SHAPIRO, S. M. AXE, J. D. REMEIKA, J. P. PHYS. REV. 10 B (5), 2014–21, 1974.
60348	**MAGNETIC ANISOTROPY AND HYPERFINE INTERACTIONS IN CERIUM IRON, GADOLINIUM IRON, AND LUTETIUM IRON.** ATZMONY, U. DARIEL, M. P. PHYS. REV. 10 B (5), 2060–7, 1974.
60350	**MANGANESE NUCLEAR ACOUSTIC RESONANCE IN ANTIFERROMAGNETIC RUBIDIUM MANGANESE FLUORIDE NEAR THE NEEL TEMPERATURE.** JIMBO, T. ELBAUM, C. PHYS. REV. 10 B (5), 2131–3, 1974.
60353	**ELECTRONIC STATES OF BOUBLY IONIZED AMMONIA.** APPELL, J. HORSLEY, J. A. J. CHEM. PHYS. 60 (9), 3445–8, 1974.
60354	**COLLECTIVE OSCILLATION IN LIQUID WATER.** HELLER, J. M., JR. HAMM, R. N. BIRKHOFF, R. D. PAINTER, L. R. J. CHEM. PHYS. 60 (9), 3483–6, 1974.
60355	**DISSOCIATION ENERGIES OF LITHIUM DEUTERIUM.** STWALLEY, W. C. WAY, K. R. VELASCO, R. J. CHEM. PHYS. 60 (9), 3611–2, 1974.
60356	**PRESSURE DEPENDENCE OF THE DIELECTRIC CONSTANT OF HYDROGEN OXIDE AND DEUTERIUM OXIDE.** SRINIVASAN, K. R. KAY, R. L. J. CHEM. PHYS. 60 (9), 3645–9, 1974.
60358	**OXIDATION OF NIOBIUM AS STUDIED BY THE ULTRA VIOLET PHOTOEMISSION TECHNIQUE.** LINDAU, I. SPICER, W. E. J. APPL. PHYS. 45 (9), 3720–5, 1974.
60359	**SPACE CHARGE EFFECTS IN PROUSTITE (SILVER ARSENIC SULFIDE).** BYER, H. H. BOBB, L. C. J. APPL. PHYS. 45 (9), 3738–41, 1974.
60363	**ELECTRONIC STATES OF MANGANESE IONS IN BARIUM STRONTIUM TITANATE SINGLE CRYSTALS.** NAKAHARA, M. MURAKAMI, T. J. APPL. PHYS. 45 (9), 3795–3800, 1674.
60367	**THERMIONIC EMISSION OF BORON– AND LANTHANUM–COATED BORON FILAMENTS.** WOLFF, E. G. J. APPL. PHYS. 45 (9), 3840–3, 1974.
60369	**WEAK–FIELD MAGNETORESISTANCE IN CZOCHRALSKI–GROWN LEAD TIN TELLURIDE.** HOFF, G. F. JENSEN, J. D. J. APPL. PHYS. 45 (9), 3883–6, 1974.
60371	**PROPERTIES OF ZINC–DOPED GALLIUM NITRIDE. II. PHOTOCONDUCTIVITY.** PANKOVE, J. I. BERKEYHEISER, J. E. J. APPL. PHYS. 45 (9), 3892–5, 1974.
60372	**ELECTRON TRANSPORT AND EMISSION CHARACTERISTICS OF NEGATIVE ELECTRON AFFINITY ALUMINUM GALLIUM ARSENIC ALLOYS.** MARTINELLI, R. U. ETTENBERG, M. J. APPL. PHYS. 45 (9), 3896–8, 1974.
60373	**PHOTON RECYCLING IN SEMICONDUCTOR LASERS.** STERN, F. WOODALL, J. M. J. APPL. PHYS. 45 (9), 3904–6, 1974.
60374	**AN 8 PERCENT EFFICIENT LAYERED SCHOTTKY–BARRIER SOLAR CELL.** ANDERSON, W. A. DELAHOY, A. E. MILANO, R. A. J. APPL. PHYS. 45 (9), 3913–5, 1974.
60377	**RECOMBINATION PROCESSES IN HIGHLY EXCITED CADMIUM SULFIDE.** FISCHER, T. BILLE, J. J. APPL. PHYS. 45 (9), 3937–42, 1974.
60379	**NITRIC OXIDE SPECTROSCOPY BY PULSED LEAD SULFIDE SELENIDE DIODE LASERS.** PREIER, H. RIEDEL, W. J. APPL. PHYS. 45 (9), 3955–8, 1974.
60380	**INFRARED ABSORPTION IN LOW LOSS POTASSIUM CHLORIDE SINGLE CRYSTALS NEAR 10.6 MU M.** HASS, M. DAVISSON, J. W. KLEIN, P. H. BOYER, L. L. J. APPL. PHYS. 45 (9), 3959–64, 1974.
60382	**PROTON BOMBARDMENT AND ISOCHRONAL ANNEALING OF RHO–TYPE LEAD TIN TELLURIDE.** WANG, C. C. TAO, T. F. SUNIER, J. W. J. APPL. PHYS. 45 (9), 3981–7, 1974.
60385	**A SINGLE MECHANISM FOR SLOW DOMAIN WALL MOTION IN BOTH FERROELECTRICS AND FERROMAGNETS.** BALDWIN, J. A., JR. MILSTEIN, F. J. APPL. PHYS. 45 (9), 4013–5, 1974.
60387	**MAGNETIZATION AND MAGNETIC ENTROPY OF DYSPROSIUM TITANIUM OXIDE.** FLOOD, D. J. J. APPL. PHYS. 45 (9), 4041–4, 1974.

EPIC Number	Bibliographic Citation

60388 **EFFECTS OF HEAT TREATMENT AND DOPING WITH ZIRCONIUM ON THE SUPERCONDUCTING CRITICAL CURRENT DENSITIES OF MULTIFILAMENTARY NIOBIUM TIN WIRES.**
SUENAGA, M. LUHMAN, T. S. SAMPSON, W. B.
J. APPL. PHYS.
45 (9), 4049–53, 1974.

60390 **PREPARATION AND PROPERTIES OF SUBMICRON HEXAGONAL IRON NITROGEN, $2 < X < 3$.**
BOUCHARD, R. J. FREDERICK, C. G. JOHNSON, V.
J. APPL. PHYS.
45 (9), 4067–70, 1974.

60392 **INTERACTION OF DOMAIN WALLS WITH LOCALIZED STRESS FIELDS IN MAGNETOSTRICTIVE FILMS.**
DISHMAN, J. M. PIERCE, R. D. ROMAN, B. J.
J. APPL. PHYS.
45 (9), 4076–83, 1974.

60393 **MOBILITY IN EPITAXIAL GALLIUM ARSENIDE UNDER 1–MEV ELECTRON IRRADIATION.**
DRESNER, J.
J. APPL. PHYS.
45 (9), 4118–9, 1974.

60397 **LONGITUDIANL AND TRANSVERSE THERMOELECTRIC ELECTRO–MOTIVE–FORCE OF SPECIMENS OF FINITE DIMENSIONS IN A MAGNETIC FIELD.**
KOZLOV, V. A. LIDORENKO, N. S.
NAGAEV, E. L.
FIZ. TVERD. TELA
16 (2), 328–34, 1974.
(FOR ENGLISH TRANSLATION SEE E60398)

60398 **LONGITUDINAL AND TRANSVERSE THERMOELECTRIC ELECTRO–MOTIVE–FORCE OF SPECIMENS OF FINITE DIMENSIONS IN A MAGNETIC FIELD.**
KOZLOV, V. A. LIDORENKO, N. S.
NAGAEV, E. L.
SOV. PHYS. SOLID STATE
16 (2), 217–20, 1974.
(ENGLISH TRANSLATION OF FIZ. TVERD. TELA, 16 (2), 328–34, 1974; FOR ORIGINAL SEE E60397)

60399 **QUADRATIC ELECTROOPTICAL EFFECT IN CRYSTALS HAVING THE FLUORITE STRUCTURE.**
KAPLYANSKII, A. A. MALKIN, B. Z.
MEDVEDEV, V. N. SKVORTSOV, A. P.
FIZ. TVERD. TELA
16 (2), 335–40, 1974.
(FOR ENGLISH TRANSLATION SEE E60400)

60400 **QUADRATIC ELECTROOPTICAL EFFECT IN CRYSTALS HAVING THE FLUORITE STRUCTURE.**
KAPLYANSKII, A. A. MALKIN, B. Z.
MEDVEDEV, V. N. SKVORTSOV, A. P.
SOV. PHYS. SOLID STATE
16 (2), 221–4, 1974.
(ENGLISH TRANSLATION OF FIZ. TVERD. TELA, 16 (2), 335–40, 1974; FOR ORIGINAL SEE E60399)

60407 **FORMATION OF ANION AND CATION DEFECTS IN POTASSIUM BROMIDE WHISKER CRYSTALS.**
YAANSON, N. A. GINDINA, R. I.
FIZ. TVERD. TELA
16 (2), 379–83, 1974.
(FOR ENGLISH TRANSLATION SEE E60408)

60408 **FORMATION OF ANION AND CATION DEFECTS IN POTASSIUM BROMIDE WHISKER CRYSTALS.**
YAANSON, N. A. GINDINA, R. I.
LUSHCHIK, CH. B.
SOV. PHYS. SOLID STATE
16 (2), 248–50, 1974.
(ENGLISH TRANSLATION OF FIZ. TVERD. TELA, 16 (2), 379–83, 1974; FOR ORIGINAL SEE E60407)

60409 **ULTRASOLFT X–RAY SPECTRA OF SILICIDES OF TRANSITION METALS OF THE SECOND PERIOD.**
SHULAKOV, A. S. ZIMKINA, T. M.
FOMICHEV, V. A. NESHPOR, V. S.
FIZ. TVERD. TELA
16 (2), 401–5, 1974.
(FOR ENGLISH TRANSLATION SEE E60410)

60410 **ULTRASOFT X–RAY SPECTRA OF SILICIDES OF TRANSITION METALS OF THE SECOND PERIOD.**
SHULAKOV, A. S. ZIMKINA, T. M.
FOMICHEV, V. A. NESHPOR, V. S.
SOV. PHYS. SOLID STATE
16 (2), 261–3, 1974.
(ENGLISH TRANSLATION OF FIZ. TVERD. TELA, 16 (2), 401–5, 1974; FOR ORIGINAL SEE E60409)

60411 **OPTICAL AND MAGNETOOPTIC SPECTRA OF LITHIUM FERRITE IN THE RANGE 1.8–4.1 EV.**
MALAKHOVSKII, A. V. EDEL'MAN, I. S.
GAVRILIN, V. P. BARINOV, G. I.
FIZ. TVERD. TELA
16 (2), 410–3, 1974.
(FOR ENGLISH TRANSLATION SEE E60412)

60412 **OPTICAL AND MAGNETOOPTIC SPECTRA OF LITHIUM FERRITE IN THE RANGE 1.8–4.1 EV.**
MALAKHOVSKII, A. V. EDEL'MAN, I. S.
GAVRILIN, V. P. BARINOV, G. I.
SOV. PHYS. SOLID STATE
16 (2), 266–8, 1974.
(ENGLISH TRANSLATION OF FIZ. TVERD. TELA, 16 (2), 410–3, 1974; FOR ORIGINAL SEE E60411)

60413 **SUPERCONDUCTIVITY OF POLAR SEMICONDUCTORS AND SEMIMETALS.**
PASHITSKII, E. A. MAKAROV, V. L.
TERESHCHENKO, S. D.
FIZ. TVERD. TELA
16 (2), 427–37, 1974.
(FOR ENGLISH TRANSLATION SEE E60414)

60414 **SUPERCONDUCTIVITY OF POLAR SEMICONDUCTORS AND SEMIMETALS.**
PASHITSKII, E. A. MAKAROV, V. L.
TERESHCHENKO, S. D.
SOV. PHYS. SOLID STATE
16 (2), 276–81, 1974.
(ENGLISH TRANSLATION OF FIZ. TVERD. TELA, 16 (2), 427–37, 1974; FOR ORIGINAL SEE E60413)

60415 **ACOUSTOELECTRIC CURRENT INSTABILITY IN CADMIUM SELENIUM TELLURIDE CRYSTALS.**
BELYAEV, A. D. MISELYUK, E. G.
OLIKH, YA. M. TSEKVAVA, B. E.
FIZ. TVERD. TELA
16 (2), 438–43, 1974.
(FOR ENGLISH TRANSLATION SEE E60416)

60416 **ACOUSTOELECTRIC CURRENT INSTABILITY IN CADMIUM SELENIUM TELLURIDE CRYSTALS.**
BELYAEV, A. D. MISELYUK, E. G.
OLIKH, YA. M. TSEKVAVA, B. E.
SOV. PHYS. SOLID STATE
16 (2), 282–5, 1974.
(ENGLISH TRANSLATION OF FIZ. TVERD. TELA, 16 (2), 438–43, 1974; FOR ORIGINAL SEE E60415)

60421 **CHANGE OF CHARGE ON IMPURITY TIN ATOMS IN ARSENIC SELENIDE IN THE TRANSITION CRYSTAL–GLASS.**
SAGATOV, M. A. BOLTAKS, B. I.
VASIL'EV, L. N. SEREGIN, P. P.
FIZ. TVERD. TELA
16 (2), 462–5, 1974.
(FOR ENGLISH TRANSLATION SEE E60422)

60422 **CHANGE OF CHARGE ON IMPURITY TIN ATOMS IN ARSENIC SELENIDE IN THE TRANSITION CRYSTAL–GLASS.**
SAGATOV, M. A. BOLTAKS, B. I.
VASIL'EV, L. N. SEREGIN, P. P.
SOV. PHYS. SOLID STATE
16 (2), 297–8, 1974.
(ENGLISH TRANSLATION OF FIZ. TVERD. TELA, 16 (2), 462–5, 1974; FOR ORIGINAL SEE E60421)

60423 **PHENOMENOLOGICAL THEORY OF THE MAGNETIC ANISOTROPY OF RARE EARTH COBALT COMPOUNDS.**
IRKHIN, YU. P. ROZENFEL'D, E. V.
FIZ. TVERD. TELA
16 (2), 485–9, 1974.
(FOR ENGLISH TRANSLATION SEE E60424)

60424 **PHENOMENOLOGICAL THEORY OF THE MAGNETIC ANISOTROPY OF RARE EARTH COBALT COMPOUNDS.**
IRKHIN, YU. P. ROZENFEL'D, E. V.
SOV. PHYS. SOLID STATE
16 (2), 310–2, 1974.
(ENGLISH TRANSLATION OF FIZ. TVERD. TELA, 16 (2), 485–9, 1974; FOR ORIGINAL SEE E60423)

60425 **FIELD EMISSION FROM GERMANIUM DURING OXYGEN ADSORPTION.**
IVANOV, V. G. ROZOVA, T. T.
FURSEI, G. N. SMIRNOVA, T. P.
FIZ. TVERD. TELA
16 (2), 495–501, 1974.
(FOR ENGLISH TRANSLATION SEE E60426)

60426 **FIELD EMISSION FROM GERMANIUM DURING OXYGEN ADSORPTION.**
IVANOV, V. G. ROZOVA, T. T.
FURSEI, G. N. SMIRNOVA, T. P.
SOV. PHYS. SOLID STATE
16 (2), 316–9, 1974.
(ENGLISH TRANSLATION OF FIZ. TVERD. TELA, 16 (2), 495–501, 1974; FOR ORIGINAL SEE E60425)

60427 **PIEZOELECTRIC AND ELASTIC PROPERTIES OF HEXAGONAL ALPHA ZINC SULFIDE.**
FIRSOVA, M. M.
FIZ. TVERD. TELA
16 (2), 549–52, 1974.
(FOR ENGLISH TRANSLATION SEE E60428)

60428 **PIEZOELECTRIC AND ELASTIC PROPERTIES OF HEXAGONAL ALPHA ZINC SULFIDE.**
FIRSOVA, M. M.
SOV. PHYS. SOLID STATE
16 (2), 350–1, 1974.
(ENGLISH TRANSLATION OF FIZ. TVERD. TELA, 16 (2), 549–52, 1974; FOR ORIGINAL SEE E60427)

EPIC Number	Bibliographic Citation

60429 **ANOMALOUS CHANGES IN THE PARAMETERS OF FERRITES WITH OVER-BALANCED HYSTERESIS LOOPS DURING MAGNETIZATION.**
ROZENBAUM, L. B.
FIZ. TVERD. TELA
16 (2), 552-5, 1974.
(FOR ENGLISH TRANSLATION SEE E60430)

60430 **ANOMALOUS CHANGES IN THE PARAMETERS OF FERRITES WITH OVER-BALANCED HYSTERESIS LOOPS DURING MAGNETIZATION.**
ROZENBAUM, L. B.
SOV. PHYS. SOLID STATE
16 (2), 352-3, 1974.
(ENGLISH TRANSLATION OF FIZ. TVERD. TELA, 16 (2), 552-5, 1974; FOR ORIGINAL SEE E60429)

60431 **EFFECT OF ANNEALING ON THE DOMAIN STRUCTURE OF LITHIUM METANIOBATE SINGLE CRYSTALS.**
EVLANOVA, N. F. RASHKOVICH, L. N.
FIZ. TVERD. TELA
16 (2), 555-7, 1974.
(FOR ENGLISH TRANSLATION SEE E60432)

60432 **EFFECT OF ANNEALING ON THE DOMAIN STRUCTURE OF LITHIUM METANIOBATE SINGLE CRYSTALS.**
EVLANOVA, N. F. RASHKOVICH, L. N.
SOV. PHYS. SOLID STATE
16 (2), 354-5, 1974.
(ENGLISH TRANSLATION OF FIZ. TVERD. TELA, 16 (2), 555-7, 1974; FOR ORIGINAL SEE E60431)

60433 **ELECTRON SCATTERING BY LOCAL MAGNETIC MOMENTS IN SEMICONDUCTORS.**
POLNIKOV, V. G.
FIZ. TVERD. TELA
16 (2), 562-4, 1974.
(FOR ENGLISH TRANSLATION SEE E60434)

60434 **ELECTRON SCATTERING BY LOCAL MAGNETIC MOMENTS IN SEMICONDUCTORS.**
POLNIKOV, V. G.
SOV. PHYS. SOLID STATE
16 (2), 360-1, 1974.
(ENGLISH TRANSLATION OF FIZ. TVERD. TELA, 16 (2), 562-4, 1974; FOR ORIGINAL SEE E60433)

60437 **COUNTERPOLARIZATION IN ANTIMONY SULFIDE IODIDE.**
ADONIN, A. A. GREKOV, A. A.
FIZ. TVERD. TELA
16 (2), 566-7, 1974.
(FOR ENGLISH TRANSLATION SEE E60438)

60438 **COUNTERPOLARIZATION IN ANTIMONY SULFIDE IODIDE.**
ADONIN, A. A. GREKOV, A. A.
SOV. PHYS. SOLID STATE
16 (2), 364, 1974.
(ENGLISH TRANSLATION OF FIZ. TVERD. TELA, 16 (2), 566-7, 1974; FOR ORIGINAL SEE E60437)

60439 **ELECTRICAL PROPERTIES AND NONMETAL-METAL TRANSITIONS IN EUROPIUM GADOLINIUM OXIDE.**
SAMOKHVALOV, A. A. AFANAS'EV, A. YA.
GIZHEVSKII, B. A. LOSHKAREVA, N. N.
SIMONOVA, M. I.
FIZ. TVERD. TELA
16 (2), 568-70, 1974.
(FOR ENGLISH TRANSLATION SEE E60440)

60440 **ELECTRICAL PROPERTIES AND NONMETAL-METAL TRANSITIONS IN EUROPIUM GADOLINIUM OXIDE.**
SAMOKHVALOV, A. A. AFANAS'EV, A.YA.
GIZHEVSKII, B. A. LOSHKAREVA, N. N.
SIMONOVA, M. I.
SOV. PHYS. SOLID STATE
16 (2), 365-6, 1974.
(ENGLISH TRANSLATION OF FIZ. TVERD. TELA, 16 (2), 568-70, 1974; FOR ORIGINAL SEE E60439)

60441 **HOLE ZONES IN STRONTIUM FLUORIDE AND BARIUM FLUORIDE CRYSTALS.**
STAROSTIN, N. V. GANIN, V. A.
FIZ. TVERD. TELA
16 (2), 572-4, 1974.
(FOR ENGLISH TRANSLATION SEE E60442)

60442 **HOLE ZONES IN STRONTIUM FLUORIDE AND BARIUM FLUORIDE CRYSTALS.**
STAROSTIN, N. V. GANIN, V. A.
SOV. PHYS. SOLID STATE
16 (2), 369-70, 1974.
(ENGLISH TRANSLATION OF FIZ. TVERD. TELA, 16 (2), 572-4, 1974; FOR ORIGINAL SEE E60441)

60445 **PIEZOSPECTROSCOPIC INVESTIGATION OF HEXAGONAL ZINC SULFIDE SINGLE CRYSTALS.**
KOBYAKOV, I. B. SUSLINA, L. G.
FEDOROV, D. L.
FIZ. TVERD. TELA
16 (2), 578-81, 1974.
(FOR ENGLISH TRANSLATION SEE E60446)

60446 **PIEZOSPECTROSCOPIC INVESTIGATION OF HEXAGONAL ZINC SULFIDE SINGLE CRYSTALS.**
KOBYAKOV, I. B. SUSLINA, L. G.
FEDOOROV, D. L.
SOV. PHYS. SOLID STATE
16 (2), 374-5, 1974.
(ENGLISH TRANSLATION OF FIZ. TVERD. TELA, 16 (2), 578-81, 1974; FOR ORIGINAL SEE E60445)

60447 **ELECTROLUMINESCENCE AND IMPACT IONIZATION IN ALKALI HALIDE CRYSTALS.**
LEBEDEVA, N. I.
FIZ. TVERD. TELA
16 (2), 585-6, 1974.
(FOR ENGLISH TRANSLATION SEE E60448)

60448 **ELECTROLUMINESCENCE AND IMPACT IONIZATION IN ALKALI HALIDE CRYSTALS.**
LEBEDEVA, N. I.
SOV. PHYS. SOLID STATE
16 (2), 378-9, 1974.
(ENGLISH TRANSLATION OF FIZ. TVERD. TELA, 16 (2), 585-6, 1974; FOR ORIGINAL SEE E60447)

60449 **EFFECT OF TEMPERATURE ON THE SPECTRUM OF THE TRANSVERSE PHOTOCURRENT IN P-TYPE INDIUM ANTIMONIDE.**
PROTASOV, E. A. RODINOV, A. G.
FIZ. TVERD. TELA
16 (2), 595-7, 1974.
(FSOR ENGLISH TRANSLATION SEE E60450)

60450 **EFFECT OF TEMPERATURE ON THE SPECTRUM OF THE TRANSVERSE PHOTOCURRENT IN P-TYPE INDIUM ANTIMONIDE.**
PROTASOV, E. A. RODINOV, A. G.
SOV. PHYS. SOLID STATE
16 (2), 387-8, 1974.
(ENGLISH TRANSLATION OF FIZ. TVERD. TELA, 16 (2), 595-7, 1974; FOR ORIGINAL SEE E60449)

60451 **SIZE EFFECT OF ENHANCED SUPERCONDUCTING TRANSITION TEMPERATURE IN THIN FILMS.**
ANTONYUK, B. P.
FIZ. TVERD. TELA
16 (2), 604- , 1974.
(FOR ENGLISH TRANSLATION SEE E60452)

60452 **SIZE EFFECT OF ENHANCED SUPERCONDUCTING TRANSITION TEMPERATURE IN THIN FILMS.**
ANTONYUK, B. P.
SOV. PHYS. SOLID STATE
16 (2), 395, 1974.
(ENGLISH TRANSLATION OF FIZ. TVERD. TELA, 16 (2), 604- , 1974; FOR ORIGINAL SEE E60451)

60459 **STIMULATED PHOTO-ELECTRO-MOTIVE-FORCE OF INHOMOGENEOUSLY EXCITED ZINC SULFIDE: COPPER SINGLE CRYSTALS.**
GORDIENKO, YU. N. KODZHESPIROV, F. F.
FIZ. TVERD. TELA
16 (2), 623-5, 1974.
(FOR ENGLISH TRANSLATION SEE E60460)

60460 **STIMULATED PHOTO-ELECTRO-MOTIVE-FORCE OF INHOMOGENEOUSLY EXCITED ZINC SULFIDE: COPPER SINGLE CRYSTALS.**
GORDIENKO, YU. N. KODZHESPIROV, F. F.
SOV. PHYS. SOLID STATE
16 (2), 411-2, 1974.
(ENGLISH TRANSLATION OF FIZ. TVERD. TELA, 16 (2), 623-5, 1974; FOR ORIGINAL SEE E60459)

60461 **CRYSTAL FIELD AND SUPEREXCHANGE.**
SIDOROV, A. A.
FIZ. TVERD. TELA
16 (2), 625-7, 1974.
(FOR ENGLISH TRANSLATION SEE E60462)

60462 **CRYSTAL FIELD AND SUPEREXCHANGE.**
SIDOROV, A. A.
SOV. PHYS. SOLID STATE
16 (2), 413-4, 1974.
(ENGLISH TRANSLATION OF FIZ. TVERD. TELA, 16 (2), 625-7, 1974; FOR ORIGINAL SEE E60461)

60463 **SPECTROSCOPIC PROPERTIES OF OPTICAL TRANSITIONS IN THE LATTICE VIBRATION REGION FOR IONIC CRYSTALS.**
TOLSTYKH, T. S. SHAGANOV, I. I.
LIBOV, V. S.
FIZ. TVERD. TELA
16 (3), 657-62, 1974.
(FOR ENGLISH TRANSLATION SEE E60464)

60464 **SPECTROSCOPIC PROPERTIES OF OPTICAL TRANSITIONS IN THE LATTICE VIBRATION REGION FOR IONIC CRYSTALS.**
TOLSTYKH, T. S. SHAGANOV, I. I.
LIBOV, V. S.
SOV. PHYS. SOLID STATE
16 (3), 431-4, 1974.
(ENGLISH TRANSLATION OF FIZ. TVERD. TELA, 16 (3), 657-62, 1974; FOR ORIGINAL SEE E60463)

EPIC Number	Bibliographic Citation

60465 **CURRENT OSCILLATIONS IN NIOBIUM TIN TUNNEL JUNCTIONS AT VOLTAGES ABOVE THE SUPERCONDUCTING GAP.**
VEDENEEV, S. I. GOLOVASHKIN, A. I.
MOTULEVICH, G. P.
FIZ. TVERD. TELA
16 (3), 668–71, 1974.
(FOR ENGLISH TRANSLATION SEE E60466)

60466 **CURRENT OSCILLATIONS IN NIOBIUM TIN TUNNEL JUNCTIONS AT VOLTAGES ABOVE THE SUPERCONDUCTING GAP.**
VEDENEEV, S. I. GOLOVASHKIN, A. I.
MOTULEVICH, G. P.
SOV. PHYS. SOLID STATE
16 (3), 439–41, 1974.
(ENGLISH TRANSLATION OF FIZ. TVERD. TELA, 16 (3), 668–71, 1974; FOR ORIGINAL SEE E60465)

60467 **SELF-OSCILLATION OF THE MAGNETIZATION DURING PARALLEL PUMPING OF SPIN WAVES.**
ZAUTKIN, V. V. STAROBINETS, S. S.
FIZ. TVERD. TELA
16 (3), 678–86, 1974.
(FOR ENGLISH TRANSLATION SEE E60468)

60468 **SELF-OSCILLATION OF THE MAGNETIZATION DURING PARALLEL PUMPING OF SPIN WAVES.**
ZAUTKIN, V. V. STAROBINETS, S. S.
SOV. PHYS. SOLID STATE
16 (3), 446–51, 1974.
(ENGLISH TRANSLATION OF FIZ. TVERD. TELA, 16 (3), 678–86, 1974; FOR ORIGINAL SEE E60467)

60469 **HOLE SCATTERING IN COPPER OXIDE.**
TAZENKOV, B. A. GRUZDEV, F. A.
FIZ. TVERD. TELA
16 (3), 702–8, 1974.
(FOR ENGLISH TRANSLATION SEE E60470)

60470 **HOLE SCATTERING IN COPPER OXIDE.**
TAZENKOV, B. A. GRUZDEV, F. A.
SOV. PHYS. SOLID STATE
16 (3), 460–3, 1974.
(ENGLISH TRANSLATION OF FIZ. TVERD. TELA, 16 (3), 702–8, 1974; FOR ORIGINAL SEE E60469)

60471 **VIBRATIONAL AND DIELECTRIC SPECTRA OF CADMIUM PYRONIOBATE.**
POPLAVKO, YU. M. KNYAZEV, A. S.
ZAKHAROV, V. P. TSYKALOV, V. G.
ALEKSEEV, V. V.
FIZ. TVERD. TELA
16 (3), 713–8, 1974.
(FOR ENGLISH TRANSLATION SEE E60472)

60472 **VIBRATIONAL AND DIELECTRIC SPECTRA OF CADMIUM PYRONIOBATE.**
POPLAVKO, YU. M. KNYAZEV, A. S.
ZAKHAROV, V. P. TSYKALOV, V. G.
ALEKSEEV, V. V.
SOV. PHYS. SOLID STATE
16 (3), 466–9, 1974.
(ENGLISH TRANSLATION OF FIZ. TVERD. TELA, 16 (3), 713–8, 1974; FOR ORIGINAL SEE E60471)

60479 **POSSIBLE INCREASE IN SUPERCONDUCTING TRANSITION TEMPERATURE IN DOPED SEMICONDUCTORS.**
ELESIN, V. F. KOPAEV, YU. V.
FIZ. TVERD. TELA
16 (3), 840–2, 1974.
(FOR ENGLISH TRANSLATION SEE E60480)

60480 **POSSIBLE INCREASE IN SUPERCONDUCTING TRANSITION TEMPERATURE IN DOPED SEMICONDUCTORS.**
ELESIN, V. F. KOPAEV, YU. V.
SOV. PHYS. SOLID STATE
16 (3), 540–1, 1974.
(ENGLISH TRANSLATION OF FIZ. TVERD. TELA, 16 (3), 840–2, 1974; FOR ORIGINAL SEE E60479)

60481 **EFFECT OF IMPURITIES ON THE VIBRATIONAL SPECTRA OF II–VI SEMICONDUCTOR COMPOUNDS.**
VODOP'YANOV, L. K. VINOGRADOV, E. A.
VINOGRADOV, V. S.
FIZ. TVERD. TELA
16 (3), 849–55, 1974.
(FOR ENGLISH TRANSLATION SEE E60482)

60482 **EFFECT OF IMPURITIES ON THE VIBRATIONAL SPECTRA OF II–VI SEMICONDUCTOR COMPOUNDS.**
VODOP'YANOV, L. K. VINOGRADOV, E. A.
VINOGRADOV, V. S.
SOV. PHYS. SOLID STATE
16 (3), 545–9, 1974.
(ENGLISH TRANSLATION OF FIZ. TVERD. TELA, 16 (3), 849–55, 1974; FOR ORIGINAL SEE E60481)

60487 **THERMAL STABILITY OF IMPURITY COMPLEXES AND THEIR TRANSFORMATION IN POTASSIUM CHLORIDE.**
PERSHITS, YA. N. SHONIN, V. N.
FIZ. TVERD. TELA
16 (3), 914–6, 1974.
(FOR ENGLISH TRANSLATION SEE E60488)

EPIC Number	Bibliographic Citation

60488 **THERMAL STABILITY OF IMPURITY COMPLEXES AND THEIR TRANSFORMATION IN POTASSIUM CHLORIDE.**
PERSHITS, YA. N. SHONIN, V. N.
SOV. PHYS. SOLID STATE
16 (3), 586–7, 1974.
(ENGLISH TRANSLATION OF FIZ. TVERD. TELA, 16 (3), 914–6, 1974; FOR ORIGINAL SEE E60487)

60489 **UNIAXIAL ANISOTROPY IN BISMUTH–CALCIUM–VANADIUM FERROGARNET SINGLE CRYSTALS.**
FILONICH, V. S. YAKOVLEV, YU. M.
DEVYATOVA, T. A.
FIZ. TVERD. TELA
16 (3), 921–2, 1974.
(FOR ENGLISH TRANSLATION SEE E60490)

60490 **UNIAXIAL ANISOTROPY IN BISMUTH–CALCIUM–VANADIUM FERROGARNET SINGLE CRYSTALS.**
FILONICH, V. S. YAKOVLEV, YU. M.
DEVYATOVA, T. A.
SOV. PHYS. SOLID STATE
16 (3), 592, 1974.
(ENGLISH TRANSLATION OF FIZ. TVERD. TELA, 16 (3), 921–2, 1974; FOR ORIGINAL SEE E60489)

60493 **MAGNETORESISTANCE OF A (0001) FILM OF MANGANESE FERRITE.**
DYMPILOV, R. M. KICHMARENKO, F. S.
FIZ. TVERD. TELA
16 (3), 932–3, 1974.
(FOR ENGLISH TRANSLATION SEE E60494)

60494 **MAGNETORESISTANCE OF A (0001) FILM OF MANGANESE FERRITE.**
DYMPILOV, R. M. KICHMARENKO, F. S.
SOV. PHYS. SOLID STATE
16 (3), 600, 1974.
(ENGLISH TRANSLATION OF FIZ. TVERD. TELA, 16 (3), 932–3, 1974; FOR ORIGINAL SEE E60493)

60501 **OPTICAL CENTERS AND EXCITATION ENERGY TRANSFER IN POLYCRYSTALLINE LANTHANUM TANTALUM OXIDE: NEODYMIUM.**
ZUEV, M. G. ROZHDESTVENSKII, F. A.
KRYLOV, E. I.
FIZ. TVERD. TELA
16 (3), 950–2, 1974.
(FOR ENGLISH TRANSLATION SEE E60502)

60502 **OPTICAL CENTERS AND EXCITATION ENERGY TRANSFER IN POLYCRYSTALLINE LANTHANUM TANTALUM OXIDE: NEODYMIUM.**
ZUEV, M. G. ROZHDESTVENSKII, F. A.
KRYLOV, E. I.
SOV. PHYS. SOLID STATE
16 (3), 613–4, 1974.
(ENGLISH TRANSLATION OF FIZ. TVERD. TELA, 16 (3), 950–2, 1974; FOR ORIGINAL SEE E60501)

60503 **DETERMINATION OF COUPLING COEFFICIENT IN SECOND HARMONIC GENERATION OF ACOUSTIC SURFACE WAVES.**
ALIPPI, A. PALMA, A. PALMIERI, L.
SOCINO, G.
J. APPL. PHYS.
45 (10), 4347–9, 1974.

60508 **SILICON-DEFECT CONCENTRATIONS IN HEAVILY SILICON-DOPED GALLIUM ARSENIDE: CHANGES INDUCED BY ANNEALING.**
KUNG, J. K. SPITZER, W. G.
J. APPL. PHYS.
45 (10), 4477–86, 1974.

60509 **LUMINESCENT PROPERTIES OF COPPER GALLIUM SULFIDE DOPED WITH CADMIUM OR ZINC.**
SHAY, J. L. BRIDENBAUGH, P. M. KASPER, H. M.
J. APPL. PHYS.
45 (10), 4491–4, 1974.

60516 **BAND STRUCTURE ENHANCEMENT AND OPTIMIZATION OF RADIATIVE RECOMBINATION IN GALLIUM ARSENIDE PHOSPHORUS: NITROGEN (AND INDIUM GALLIUM PHOSPHORUS: NITROGEN).**
CAMPBELL, J. C. HOLONYAK, N., JR.
CRAFORD, M. G. KEUNE, D. L.
J. APPL. PHYS.
45 (10), 4543–53, 1974.

60517 **3PTICAL ABSORPTION EDGE OF LITHIUM NIOBIUM OXIDE.**
REDFIELD, D. BURKE, W. J.
J. APPL. PHYS.
45 (10), 4566–71, 1974.

60521 **DETERMINATION OF THE ANISOTROPY FIELD OF GARNET BUBBLE MATERIALS FROM DOMAIN OBSERVATION.**
SHIMADA, Y. KOJIMA, H. SAKAI, K.
J. APPL. PHYS.
45 (10), 4598–4600, 1974.

60523 **MAGNETIC-FIELD-INDUCED RECRYSTALLIZATION IN MANGANESE BISMUTH.**
CHEN, T. STUTIUS, W. E.
J. APPL. PHYS.
45 (10), 4622–5, 1974.

EPIC Number	Bibliographic Citation
60528	**ANALYSIS OF CONVERSION EFFICIENCY OF ORGANIC-SEMICONDUCTOR SOLAR CELLS.** FANG, P. H. J. APPL. PHYS. 45 (10), 4672-3, 1974.
60530	**CRYSTALLINE THORIUM BORATE.** BASKIN, Y. HARADA, Y. HANDWERK, J. H. J. AMER. CERAM. SOC. 44 (9), 456-9, 1961.
60532	**THERMAL AND ELECTRICAL CONDUCTIVITY OF THE LANTHANUM CHROMIUM OXIDE-CHROMIUM CERMETS.** BARYKIN, B. M. GORDON, V. G. LEVINOV, B. M. REKOV, A. I. SPIRIDONOV, E. G. HIGH TEMP. HIGH PRESSURES 6 (1), 47-52, 1974.
60533	**STUDIES OF THE PROPERTIES OF AMORPHOUS TETRAHEDRALLY-COORDINATED SEMICONDUCTORS.** CONNELL, G. A. N. PAUL, W. HIGH TEMP. HIGH PRESSURES 6 (1), 85-94, 1974.
60534	**INFLUENCE OF PRESSURE ON THE ELECTRON CONCENTRATION AND MOBILITY IN MERCURY SELENIDE AT 77 K.** BAJ, M. POROWSKI, S. HIGH TEMP. HIGH PRESSURES 6 (1), 95-100, 1974.
60536	**SEMICONDUCTING PROPERTIES OF VITREOUS ARSENIC SELENIDE UNDER PRESSURE.** KOLOMIETS, B. T. RASPOPOVA, E. M. HIGH TEMP. HIGH PRESSURES 6 (1), 107-10, 1974.
60537	**OBSERVATION OF METASTABLE DONOR STATES IN N-TYPE INDIUM ANTIMONY.** KONCZYKOWSKI, M. POROWSKI, S. CHROBOCZEK, J. HIGH TEMP. HIGH PRESSURES 6 (1), 111-4, 1974.
60544	**ELECTRICAL PROPERTIES OF COPPER TELLURIDE.** MUSAEV, A. M. AGAEV, K. A. KERIMOV, I. G. CHIRAGOV, M. I. IZV. AKAD. NAUK SSSR, NEORG. MATER. 8 (9), 1577-81, 1972. (FOR ENGLISH TRANSLATION SEE E60545)
60545	**ELECTRICAL PROPERTIES OF COPPER TELLURIDE.** MUSAEV, A. M. AGAEV, K. A. KERIMOV, I. G. CHIRAGOV, M. I. INORG. MAT., USSR 8 (9), 1385-8, 1972. (ENGLISH TRANSLATION OF IZV. AKAD. NAUK SSSR, NEORG. MATER., 8 (9), 1577-81, 1972; FOR ORIGINAL SEE E60544)
60546	**INFRARED ABSORPTION STUDIES IN NEUTRON- AND ELECTRON-IRRADIATED GALLIUM ARSENIDE.** VAIDYANATHAN, K. V. WATT, L. A. K. PROC. INTERN. CONF. RADIATION EFFECTS SEMICONDUCTORS 293-300, 1971.
60551	**THE ELECTRICAL CONDUCTIVITY, THE THERMAL EXPANSION AND THE HARDNESS OF MAGNESIUM-ZINC ALLOYS.** GRUBE, G. BURKHARDT, A. Z. ELEKTROCHEM. 35 (6), 315-32, 1929.
60555	**THE ELECTRICAL RESISTIVITY AND PHASE DIAGRAM OF BINARY ALLOYS. THE LITHIUM-CADMIUM SYSTEM.** GRUBE, G. VOSSKUHLER, H. VOGT, H. Z. ELEKTROCHEM. 38 (11), 869-80, 1932.
60558	**PHYSICAL PRINCIPLES, MATERIALS GUIDELINED, AND MATERIALS LIST FOR HIGH POWER 10.6 MICROMETER WINDOWS.** SPARKS, M. RAND CORP., SANTA MONICA, CALIF. 27PP., 1973. (AD-776 818, R-863-PR)
60560	**INFRARED OPTICAL MATERIALS WITH TRANSMISSION IN THE 8-14 MICRON AND 1-10 MILLIMETER REGIONS.** SMAKULA, A. DEPT. OF THE NAVY, OFFICE OF NAVAL RESEARCH, WASHINGTON, D. C. 20PP., 1963. (AD-431 928)
60561	**DEVELOPMENT OF A SEMICONDUCTOR FILM-TYPE THERMOCOUPLE ENERGY CONVERTER.** MINNEAPOLIS-HONEYWELL REGULATOR COMP., RES. CTR., HOPKINS, MINNESOTA PICATINNY ARSENAL, DOVER, NEW JERSEY 24PP., 1960. (AD-242 514)
60562	**INVESTIGATION OF THE SURFACE OPTICAL PROPERTIES OF OXIDES AS A FUNCTION OF COMPOSITION.** FRERICHS, R. WHITMORE, D. H. AIR FORCE MATERIALS LAB., WRIGHT PATTERSON AIR FORCE BASE, OHIO 188PP., 1964. (AD-434 372, RTD-TDR-63-4196)
60566	**DETECTOR INVESTIGATION FOR 8-15 AND 100-4000 MICRON REGIONS.** WALLIS, R. F. SHENKER, H. U. S. NAVAL RESEARCH LABORATORY, WASHINGTON, D. C. 48PP., 1963. (NRL-5996)
60573	**NUCLEAR MAGNETIC RESONANCE, MAGNETIC SUSCEPTIBILITY, AND LATTICE CONSTANTS OF SOLID AND LIQUID GOLD GALLIUM, GOLD PALLADIUM GALLIUM, AND GOLD INDIUM.** WARREN, W. W., JR. SHAW, R. W., JR. MENTH, A. DISALVO, F. J. STORM, A. R. WERNICK, J. H. PHYS. REV. 7 B (4), 1247-63, 1973.
60575	**ABSORPTION FROM NEUTRAL ACCEPTORS IN GALLIUM ARSENIDE AND GALLIUM PHOSPHIDE.** CHRISTENSEN, O. PHYS. REV. 7 B (4), 1426-32, 1973.
60578	**RESISTIVITY AND ONE DIMENSIONALITY IN TITANIUM OXIDE.** VAN ZANDT, L. L. EKLUND, P. C. PHYS. REV. 7 B (4), 1454-79, 1973.
60579	**GROUND STATE ENERGY OF A WANNIER EXCITON IN A APOLAR CRYSTAL.** DE VOOGHT, J. G. KAJAJ, K. K. PHYS. REV. 7 B (4), 1472-9, 1973.
60580	**QUANTUM DIELECTRIC THEORY OF ELECTRONEGATIVITY IN COVALENT SYSTEMS. III. PRESSURE-TEMPERATURE PHASE DIAGRAMS, HEATS OF MIXING, AND DISTRIBUTION COEFFICIENTS.** VAN VECHTEN, J. A. PHYS. REV. 7 B (4), 1479-1507, 1973.
60581	**ELECTRON HOLE LIQUIDS IN SEMICONDUCTORS.** BRINKMAN, W. F. RICE, T. M. PHYS. REV. 7 B (4), 1508-23, 1973.
60582	**HIGH RESOLUTION REFLECTION SPECTRA OF ALKALI HALIDES IN THE FAR ULTRAVIOLET.** ANTINORI, M. BALZAROTTI, A. PIACENTINI, M. PHYS. REV. 7 B (4), 1541-9, 1973.
60583	**LUMINESCENCE LIFETIME IN POTASSIUM CHLORIDE CRYSTALS CONTAINING ALPHA FLUORIDE CENTERS.** BENCI, S. MANFREDI, M. PHYS. REV. 7 B (4), 1549-53, 1973.
60584	**PHOTOEMISSION FROM CESIUM IODIDE: EXPERIMENT.** DISTEFANO, T. H. SPICER, W. E. PHYS. REV. 7 B (4), 1554-64, 1973.
60585	**PHOTOEMISSION FROM CESIUM IODIDE: CALCULATION.** DISTEFANO, T. H. PHYS. REV. 7 B (4), 1564-71, 1973.
60586	**QUANTUM-MECHANICAL CALCULATIONS OF THE INFRARED PROPERTIES OF HYDROGEN IONS IN POTASSIUM HALIDES.** WOOD, R. F. GANGULY, B. N. PHYS. REV. 7 B (4), 1591-1602, 1973.
60587	**SPACE-CHARGE EFFECTS IN CESIUM IODIDE ELECTROLUMINESCENCE.** PARACCHINI, C. PHYS. REV. 7 B (4), 1603-8, 1973.
60588	**STRESS-INDUCED DICHROISM AND ENERGY SHIFTS IN THE A, B, AND C ABSORPTION BANDS IN POTASSIUM CHLORIDE: THALLIUM.** LEMOS, A. M. KROLIK, C. PHYS. REV. 7 B (4), 1608-16, 1973.
60590	**OPTICAL-ABSORPTION SPECTRUM OF TETRAHEDRAL IRON IN CADMIUM INDIUM SULFIDE: INFLUENCE OF A WEAK JAHN-TELLER COUPLING.** WITTEKOEK, S. VAN STAPELE, R. P. WIJMA, A. W. J. PHYS. REV. 7 B (4), 1667-77, 1973.

EPIC Number	Bibliographic Citation

60591 D-BAND SURFACE STATES ON TRANSITION-METAL PEROVSKITE CRYSTALS: I. QUALITATIVE FEATURES AND APPLICATION TO STRONTIUM TITANIUM OXIDE.
WOLFRAM, T. KRAUT, W. A. MORIN, F. J.
PHYS. REV.
7 B (4), 1677–94, 1973.

60592 RELAXED EXCITED STATES OF THE F CENTER: A STUDY OF THE NEARLY DEGENERATE STATES OF A BOUND LATTICE POLARON.
WANG, S. MATSUURA, M. WONG, C. C.
INOUE, M.
PHYS. REV.
7 B (4), 1695–1712, 1973.

60593 INTERPRETATION OF DEAN AND HARTMAN'S 6H-SILICON CARBIDE MAGNETO-OPTICAL DATA.
PATRICK, L.
PHYS. REV.
7 B (4), 1719–21, 1973.

60594 SELF-CONSISTENT ENERGY BANDS OF LITHIUM FLUORIDE
BRENER, N. E.
PHYS. REV.
7 B (4), 1721–3, 1973.

60596 STRONG-FIELD ASSIGNMENT KN 4F 5D LEVELS OF YTTERBIUM IN STRONTIUM CHLORIDE.
LOH, E.
PHYS. REV.
7 B (5), 1846–50, 1973.

60600 METAL-INSULATOR TRANSITIONS IN PURE AND DOPED VANADIUM OXIDE.
MC WHAN, D. B. MENTH, A. REMEIKA, J. P.
BRINKMAN, W. F. RICE, T. M.
PHYS. REV.
7 B (5), 1920–31, 1973.

60603 POLARIZED-NEUTRON STUDY OF THE INDUCED MAGNETIC MOMENT IN THULIUM ANTIMONY.
LANDER, G. H. BRUN, T. O. VOGT, O.
PHYS. REV.
7 B (5), 1988–2004, 1973.

60604 MAGNETIC-MOMENT DISTRIBUTION IN NICKEL IRON AND GOLD IRON ALLOYS.
CABLE, J. W. WOLLAN, E. O.
PHYS. REV.
7 B (5), 2005–16, 1973.

60605 SPECIFIC HEAT OF TWO-DIMENSIONAL HEISENBERG ANTIFERROMAGNETS: POTASSIUM MANGANESE FLUORIDE AND POTASSIUM NICKEL FLUORIDE.
SALAMON, M. B. IKEDA, H.
PHYS. REV.
7 B (5), 2017–24, 1973.

60606 MAGNETIC TRANSITIONS IN CESIUM NICKEL CHLORIDE.
YELON, W. B. COX, D. E.
PHYS. REV.
7 B (5), 2024–7, 1973.

60609 MAGNETIC AND THERMAL PROPERTIES OF GADOLINIUM (HYDROXIDE).
SKJELTORP, A. T. CATANESE, C. A.
MEISSNER, H. E. WOLF, W. P.
PHYS. REV.
7 B (5), 2062–91, 1973.

60610 HALL EFFECT IN VANADIUM OXIDE NEAR THE SEMICONDUCTOR-TO-METAL TRANSITION.
ROSEVEAR, W. H. PAUL, W.
PHYS. REV.
7 B (5), 2109–11, 1973.

60611 SUPERCONDUCTIVITY, FERROELECTRICITY, AND THE MOTT INSULATOR.
BARI, R. A.
PHYS. REV.
7 B (5), 2128–32, 1973.

60623 LOW-ENERGY-ELECTRON-DIFFRACTION INTENSITY PROFILES AND ELECTRONIC ENERGY BANDS FOR LITHIUM FLUORIDE.
LARAMORE, G. E. SWITENDICK, A. C.
PHYS. REV.
7 B (8), 3615–28, 1973.

60626 QUENCHING AND ENHANCEMENT OF FLUORESCENCE FROM BOUND EXCITONS BY FAR-INFRARED RADIATION.
GUNDERSEN, M. FAUST, W. L.
PHYS. REV.
7 B (8), 3681–5, 1973.

60627 PHONON TUNNELING SPECTROSCOPY IN N-GERMANIUM SCHOTTKY BARRIERS UNDER PRESSURE.
GUETIN, P. SCHREDER, G.
PHYS. REV.
7 B (8), 3697–3702, 1973.

60628 THEORY OF INTERNAL PHOTOEMISSION.
HELMAN, J. S. SANCHEZ-SINENCIO, F.
PHYS. REV.
7 B (8), 3702–6, 1973.

60629 THEORY OF ISOTHERMAL CURRENTS AND THE DIRECT DETERMINATION OF TRAP PARAMETERS IN SEMICONDUCTORS AND INSULATORS CONTAINING ARBITRARY TRAP DISTRIBUTIONS.
SIMMONS, J. G. TAM, M. C.
PHYS. REV.
7 B (8), 3706–13, 1973.

60630 THERMALLY STIMULATED CURRENTS IN SEMICONDUCTORS AND INSULATORS HAVING ARBITRARY TRAP DISTRIBUTIONS.
SIMMONS, J. G. TAYLOR, G. W. TAM, M. C.
PHYS. REV.
7 B (8), 3714–9, 1973.

60632 RESONANCE RAMAN SPECTRA OF SEMICONDUCTING CADMIUM FLUORIDE: INDIUM CRYSTALS.
O'HORO, M. P. WHITE, W. B.
PHYS. REV.
7 B (8), 3748–53, 1973.

60633 ENERGY BANDS OF METALLIC VANADIUM OXIDE.
CARUTHERS, E. KLEINMAN, L. ZHANG, H. I.
PHYS. REV.
7 B (8), 3753–60, 1973.

60634 REFRACTIVE-INDEX BEHAVIOR OF AMORPHOUS SEMICONDUCTORS AND GLASSES.
WEMPLE, S. H.
PHYS. REV.
7 B (8), 3737–77, 1973.

60636 DISPERSION OF RAMAN CORSS SECTION IN CADMIUM SULFIDE AND ZINC OXIDE OVER A WIDE ENERGY RANGE.
CALLENDER, R. H. SUSSMAN, S. S.
SELDERS, M. CHANG, R. K.
PHYS. REV.
7 B (8), 3788–98, 1973.

60638 EFFECT OF STRAIN ON THE SECONDARY BAND EXTREMA OF LEAD SULFIDE, LEAD SELENIDE, LEAD TELLURIDE, AND TIN TELLURIDE.
RABII, S.
PHYS. REV.
7 B (8), 3830–6, 1973.
(AD-A004 661)

60640 INFRARED-REFLECTANCE SPECTRA OF LAYERED GROUP -IV AND GROUP -VI TRANSITION-METAL DICHALCOGENIDES.
LUCOVSKY, G. WHITE, R. M. BENDA, J. A.
REVELLI, J. F.
PHYS. REV.
7 B (8), 3859–70, 1973.

60642 WAVE FUNCTIONS FOR THE F CENTER IN SODIUM AZIDE.
BARTRAM, R. H. JAIN, P. K. KEMMEY, P. J.
PHYS. REV.
7 B (8), 3878–84, 1973.

60643 PRESSURE AND TEMPERATURE DEPENDENCE OF THE STATIC DIELECTRIC CONSTANTS OF POTASSIUM CHLORIDE SODIUM CHLORIDE, LITHIUM FLUORIDE, AND MAGNESIUM OXIDE.
BARTELS, R. A. SMITH, P. A.
PHYS. REV.
7 B (8), 3885–92, 1973.

60644 PHONON SIDEBANDS IN THE EMISSION SPECTRUM OF OXYGEN IN ALKALI-HALIDE CRYSTALS.
ROLFE, J. IKEZAWA, M. TIMUSK, T.
PHYS. REV.
7 B (8), 3913–25, 1973.

60645 DIFFERENTIAL OPTICAL SPECTRA AND BAND STRUCTURE OF STRONTIUM TITANIUM OXIDE.
YACOBY, Y. NAVEH, O.
PHYS. REV.
7 B (8), 3991–4000, 1973.

60646 POTENTIAL OF FLUORIDE IN SODIUM BROMIDE.
QUIGLEY, R. J. DAS, T. P.
PHYS. REV.
7 B (8), 4004–5, 1973.

60647 POTENTIAL OF FLUORIDE IN SODIUM BROMIDE.
ROLLEFSON, R. J.
PHYS. REV.
7 B (8), 4006, 1973.

60648 NEW MULTIPLET STRUCTURE IN PHOTOEMISSION FROM MANGANESE FLUORIDE.
KOWALCZYK, S. P. LEY, L. POLLAK, R. A.
MCFEELY, F. R. SHIRLEY, D. A.
PHYS. REV.
7 B (8), 4009–11, 1973.

60649 SURFACE PROPERTIES OF RUBIDIUM IODIDE.
SYDOR, M.
PHYS. REV.
7 B (8), 4012–6, 1973.

60652 ELECTRONIC TRANSPORT IN RHENIUM OXIDE: DIRECT CURRENT CONDUCTIVITY AND HALL EFFECT.
PEARSALL, T. P. LEE, C. A.
PHYS. REV.
10 B (6), 2190–4, 1974.

EPIC Number	Bibliographic Citation

60654 **OPTICAL PROPERTIES OF CHROMIUM OXIDE AND MOLYBDENUM OXIDE FROM 0.1 TO 6 EV.**
CHASE, L. L.
PHYS. REV.
10 B (6), 2226–31, 1974.

60657 **THEORY OF MULTIPHONON ABSORPTION DUE TO NONLINEAR ELECTRIC MOMENTS IN CRYSTALS.**
BENDOW, B. YUKON, S. P. YING, S.–C.
PHYS. REV.
10 B (6), 2286–99, 1974.

60658 **SOFT X–RAY RESPONSE OF TRANSITION–METAL LAYER COMPOUNDS.**
SONNTAG, B. BROWN, F. C.
PHYS. REV.
10 B (6), 2300–6, 1974.

60664 **OPTICAL PROPERTIES OF THE CADMIUM ARSENIDE–CADMIUM PHOSPHIDE SEMICONDUCTOR ALLOY SYSTEM.**
ZIVITZ, M. STEVENSON, J. R.
PHYS. REV.
10 B (6), 2457–68, 1974.

60665 **INPROVED CALCULATIONS OF THE COMPLEX DIELECTRIC CONSTANT OF SEMICONDUCTORS.**
BRECKENRIDGE, R. A. SHAW, R. W., JR.
SHER, A.
PHYS. REV.
10 B (6), 2483–9, 1974.

60668 **COOPERATIVE JAHN–TELLER PHASE TRANSITION IN PRASEODYMIUM ALUMINUM OXIDE.**
BIRGENEAU, R. J. KJEMS, J. K. SHIRANE, G.
VAN UITERT, L. G.
PHYS. REV.
10 B (6), 2512–34, 1974.

60670 **MAGNETO–OPTICAL MEASUREMENTS ON HYDROGEN–IMPLANTED 6H SILICON CARBON.**
CHOYKE, W. J. PARTICK, L. DEAN, P. J.
PHYS. REV.
10 B (6), 2554–65, 1974.

60671 **STIMULATED–EMISSION CROSS SECTION AND FLUORESCENT QUANTUM EFFICIENCY OF NEWODYMIUM IN YTTRIUM ALUMINUM GARNET AT ROOM TEMPERATURE.**
SINGH, S. SMITH, R. G. VAN UITERT, L. G.
PHYS. REV.
10 B (6), 2566–72, 1974.

60672 **INFRARED ABSORPTION BY THE HIGHER–ORDER–DIPOLE–MOMENT MECHANISM.**
SPARKS, M.
PHYS. REV.
10 B (6), 2581–9, 1974.

60673 **CORRELATION EFFECTS IN ENERGY–BAND THEORY.**
PANTELIDES, S. T. MICKISH, D. J. KUNZ, A. B.
PHYS. REV.
10 B (6), 2602–13, 1974.

60677 **EVIDENCE FOR A GRADUAL MOBILITY TRANSITION IN BAND TAISL OF HEAVILY DOPED GALLIUM ARSENIDE.**
REDFIELD, D.
J. NON–CRYST. SOLIDS
8 (9), 602–5, 1972.
(AD–744 708, PRRL–72–CR–26)

60678 **STATISTICAL PROPERTIES OF DISORDERED SEMICONDUCTORS.**
REDFIELD, D.
PHYS. REV. LETT.
27 (11), 730–5, 1971.
(AD–744 708, PRRL–72–CR–26)

60679 **TRANSPORT PROPERTIES AND BAND STRUCTURES OF GRAY TIN.**
GROVES, S. H.
GORDON MC KAY LAB., HARVARD UNIV., CAMBRIDGE, MASS.
128PP., 1963.
(AD–432 897, HP–10, NR–017–308)

60682 **SIMILARITIES IN THE VALENCE BANDS OF AMORPHOUS AND CRYSTALLINE GERMANIU M TELLURIDE DETERMINED BY X–RAY PHOTOEMISSION.**
SHEVCHIK, N. J. TEJEDA, J. LANGER, D. W.
CARDONA, M.
PHYS. REV. LETT.
30 (14), 659–62, 1973.

60685 **TUNABLE FAR–INFRARED RADIATIONS FROM HOT–ELECTRONS IN N–TYPE INDIUM ANTIMONY.**
KOBAYASHI, K. L. I. KOMATSUBARA, K. F.
OTSUKA, E.
PLHYS. REV. LETT.
30 (15), 702–5, 1973.

60690 **ELECTRICAL AND OPTICAL PROPERTIES OF III–V SEMICONDUCTORS.**
KALMA, A. H. BERGER, R. A. LEADON, R. E.
NABER, J. A.
AIR FORCE CAMBRIDGE RESEARCH LABS., BEDFORD, MASS.
84PP., 1971.
(AD–736 418, AFCRL–71–0494, GULF–RT–A10824)

EPIC Number	Bibliographic Citation

60691 **DETERMINATION OF REFRACTIVE INDEX OF THIN FILMS FROM INTERFERENCE–FRINGE REFLECTION SPECTRA.**
JAEGER, J. B.
AIR FORCE INST. OF TECHNOLOGY, WRIGHT–PATTERSON AIR FORCE BASE, OHIO, M. S. THESIS
92PP., 1974.
(AD–777 843, GEP–PH–74–9)

60692 **A STUDY OF SEMICONDUCTOR LASER MODAL FIELDS AND THEIR RADIATION PATTERNS.**
BUTLER, J. K. VOGES, R. C. SANZGIRI, S. M.
ZOROOFCHI, J. WANG, C. S.
DEPT. OF ELECTRICAL ENGR., SOUTHERN METHODIST UNIVERSITY, DALLAS, TEX.
115PP., 1974.
(AD–777 521)

60693 **LASER WINDOW SURFACE FINISHING AND COATING TECHNOLOGY.**
BRAUNSTEIN, M.
HUGHES RESEARCH LABS., MALIBU, CALIF.
44PP., 1973.
(AD–777 888, AFCRL–TR–74–0032)

60694 **PHYSICAL CHARACTERIZATION OF ELECTRONIC MATERIALS.**
KULIN, S. A. KREDER, K. NESHE, P.
MANLABS, INC., CAMBRIDGE, MASS.
73PP., 1973.
(AD–778 091, AFCRL–TR–73–0652)

60699 **EXCITON SPECTRUM OF PHOTOCONDUCTIVITY IN ZINC SULFIDE CRYSTALS.**
IL'INSKII, A. V. NOVIKOV, V. B.
SUSLINA, L. G. SHADRIN, E. B.
FIZ. TVERD. TELA
14 (7), 1933–7, 1972.
(FOR ENGLISH TRANSLATION SEE E60700)

60700 **EXCITON SPECTRUM OF PHOTOCONDUCTIVITY IN ZINC SULFIDE CRYSTALS.**
IL'INSKII, A. V. NOVIKOV, B. V.
SUSLINA, L. G. SHADRIN, E. B.
SOV. PHYS. SOLID STATE
14 (7), 1673–7, 1973.
(ENGLISH TRANSLATION OF FIZ. TVERD. TELA, 14 (7), 1933–7, 1972; FOR ORIGINAL SEE E60699)

60701 **FINE STRUCTURE OF THE BIELECTRON OR BIHOLE ENERGY LEVELS IN BISMUTH IODIDE CRYSTALS.**
GROSS, E. F. STAROSTIN, N. V.
SHEPILOV, M. P. SHEKHMAMET'EV, R. I.
FIZ. TVERD. TELA
14 (7), 1942–7, 1972.
(FOR ENGLISH TRANSLATION SEE E60702)

60702 **FINE STRUCTURE OF THE BIELECTRON OR BIHOLE ENERGY LEVELS IN BISMUTH IODIDE CRYSTALS.**
GROSS, E. F. STAROSTIN, N. V.
SHEPILOV, M. P. SHEKHMAMET'EV, R. I.
SOV. PHYS. SOLID STATE
14 (7), 1681–5, 1973.
(ENGLISH TRANSLATION OF FIZ. TVERD. TELA, 14 (7), 1942–7, 1972; FOR ORIGINAL SEE E60701)

60703 **KINETICS OF THE PHOTOPLASTIC EFFECT AND ITS DEPENDENCE ON ORIENTATION.**
OSIP'YAN, YU. A. SAVCHENKO, I. B.
FIZ. TVERD. TELA
14 (7), 1993–6, 1972.
(FOR ENGLISH TRANSLATION SEE E60704)

60704 **KINETICS OF THE PHOTOPLASTIC EFFECT AND ITS DEPENDENCE ON ORIENTATION.**
OSIP'YAN, YU. A. SAVCHENKO, I. B.
SOV. PHYS. SOLID STATE
14 (7), 1723–5, 1973.
(ENGLISH TRANSLATION OF FIZ. TVERD. TELA, 14 (7), 1993–6, 1972; FOR ORIGINAL SEE E60703)

60705 **EFFECT OF A UNIAXIAL MECHANICAL STRESS ON THE DIELECTRIC CONSTANT OF POTASSIUM DIHYDRATE PHOSPHIDE IN THE REGION OF POSITIVE TEMPERATURES.**
SAVINKO, A. I. SHASKOL'SKAYA, M. P.
PETROV, V. M. TITOV, V. A.
FIZ. TVERD. TELA
14 (7), 2008–11, 1972.
(FOR ENGLISH TRANSLATION SEE E60706)

60706 **EFFECT OF A UNIAXIAL MECHANICAL STRESS ON THE DIELECTRIC CONSTANT OF POTASSIUM DIHYDRATE PHOSPHIDE IN THE REGION OF POSITIVE TEMPERATURES.**
SAVINKO, A. I. SHASKOL'SKAYA, M. P.
PETROV, V. M. TITOV, V. A.
SOV. PHYS. SOLID STATE
14 (7), 1735–7, 1973.
(ENGLISH TRANSLATION OF FIZ. TVERD. TELA, 14 (7), 2008–11, 1972; FOR ORIGINAL SEE E60705)

60707 **METHOD OF CHANGING AND CONTROLLING OPTICAL PROPERTIES OF PHOTOSEMICONDUCTORS.**
MAEV, R. G. POLUEKTOV, I. A.
PUSTOVOIT, V. I.
FIZ. TVERD. TELA
14 (7), 2012–20, 1972.
(FOR ENGLISH TRANSLATION SEE E60708)

EPIC Number	Bibliographic Citation

60708 **METHOD OF CHANGING AND CONTROLLING OPTICAL PROPERTIES OF PHOTOSEMICONDUCTORS.**
MAEV, R. G. POLUEKTOV, I. A.
PUSTOVOIT, V. I.
SOV. PHYS. SOLID STATE
14 (7), 1738–44, 1973.
(ENGLISH TRANSLATION OF FIZ. TVERD. TELA, 14 (7), 2012–20, 1972; FOR ORIGINAL SEE E60707)

60709 **TEMPERATURE DEPENDENCE OF EXTRAORDINARY HALL CONSTANT OF COPPER–NICKEL FERRITES.**
ABDEL'GANI, A. MIRYASOV, N. Z.
FIZ. TVERD. TELA
14 (7), 2021–4, 1972.
(FOR ENGLISH TRANSLATION SEE E60710)

60710 **TEMPERATURE DEPENDENCE OF EXTRAORDINARY HALL CONSTANT OF COPPER–NICKEL FERRITES.**
ABDEL'GANI, A. MIRYASOV, N. Z.
SOV. PHYS. SOLID STATE
14 (7), 1745–7, 1973.
(ENGLISH TRANSLATION OF FIZ. TVERD. TELA, 14 (7), 2021–4, 1972; FOR ORIGINAL SEE E60709)

60713 **POSSIBLE MECHANISM FOR THE TWO STAGES OF EXOELECTRON EMISSION DURING OXIDATION OF A METAL.**
GEL'MAN, A. G. FAINSHTEIN, A. I.
FIZ. TVERD. TELA
14 (7), 2030–4, 1972.
(FOR ENGLISH TRANSLATION SEE E60714)

60714 **POSSIBLE MECHANISM FOR THE TWO STAGES OF EXOELECTRON EMISSION DURING OXIDATION OF A METAL.**
GEL'MAN, A. G. FAINSHTEIN, A. I.
SOV. PHYS. SOLID STATE
14 (7), 1752–5, 1973.
(ENGLISH TRANSLATION OF FIZ. TVERD. TELA, 14 (7), 2030–4, 1972; FOR ORIGINAL SEE E60713)

60715 **ELECTROOPTICAL EFFECT IN FERROELECTRIC CRYSTALS HAVING A SMEARED PHASE TRANSITION.**
BEREZHNOI, A. A.
FIZ. TVERD. TELA
14 (7), 2035–40, 1972.
(FOR ENGLISH TRANSLATION SEE E60716)

60716 **ELECTROOPTICAL EFFECT IN FERROELECTRIC CRYSTALS HAVING A SMEARED PHASE TRANSITION.**
BEREZHNOI, A. A.
SOV. PHYS. SOLID STATE
14 (7), 1756–60, 1973.
(ENGLISH TRANSLATION OF FIZ. TVERD. TELA, 14 (7), 2035–40, 1972, FOR ORIGINAL SEE E60715)

60717 **PHOTOCONDUCTIVITY OF SEMICONDUCTORS IN STRONG MAGNETIC FIELDS.**
MALOV, A. D. RYZHII, V. I.
FIZ. TVERD. TELA
14 (7), 2048–52, 1972.
(FOR ENGLISH TRANSLATION SEE E60718)

60718 **PHOTOCONDUCTIVITY OF SEMICONDUCTORS IN STRONG MAGNETIC FIELDS.**
MALOV, A. D. RYZHII, V. I.
SOV. PHYS. SOLID STATE
14 (7), 1766–9, 1973.
(ENGLISH TRANSLATION OF FIZ. TVERD. TELA, 14 (7), 2048–52, 1972; FOR ORIGINAL SEE E60717)

60719 **ANOMALOUS BEHAVIOR OF THE DIELECTRIC NONLINEARITY COEFFICIENT IN STRONTIUM TITANATE NEAR THE PHASE TRANSITION AT 110 K.**
BUZIN, I. M. IVANOV, I. V. RUKIN, E. I.
CHUPRAKOV, V. F.
FIZ. TVERD. TELA
14 (7), 2053–7, 1972.
(FOR ENGLISH TRANSLATION SEE E60720)

60720 **ANOMALOUS BEHAVIOR OF THE DIELECTRIC NONLINEARITY COEFFICIENT IN STRONTIUM TITANATE NEAR THE PHASE TRANSITION AT 110 K.**
BUZIN, I. M. IVANOV, I. V. RUKIN, E. I.
CHUPRAKOV, V. F.
SOV. PHYS. SOLID STATE
14 (7), 1770–3, 1973.
(ENGLISH TRANSLATION OF FIZ. TVERD. TELA, 14 (3), 2053–7, 1972; FOR ORIGINAL SEE E60719)

60721 **EFFECT OF INELEASTIC INTERACTION OF CARRIERS ON THE ABSORPTION OF LIGHT IN SEMICONDUCTORS.**
VLASOV, G. K.
FIZ. TVERD. TELA
14 (7), 2083–91, 1972.
(FOR ENGLISH TRANSLATION SEE E60722)

60722 **EFFECT OF INELASTIC INTERACTION OF CARRIERS ON THE ABSORPTION OF LIGHT IN SEMICONDUCTORS.**
VLASOV, G. K.
SOV. PHYS. SOLID STATE
14 (7), 1794–1800, 1973.
(ENGLISH TRANSLATION OF FIZ. TVERD. TELA, 14 (7), 2083–91, 1972; FOR ORIGINAL SEE E60721)

EPIC Number	Bibliographic Citation

60723 **EFFECT OF FLUCTUONS ON THE EQUILIBRIUM PROPERTIES OF SEMICONDUCTORS.**
KRIVOGLAZ, M. A.
FIZ. TVERD. TELA
14 (7), 2092–2101, 1972.
(FOR ENGLISH TRANSLATION SEE E60724)

60724 **EFFECT OF FLUCTUONS ON THE EQUILIBRIUM PROPERTIES OF SEMICONDUCTORS.**
KRIVOGLAZ, M. A.
SOV. PHYS. SOLID STATE
14 (7), 1801–9, 1973.
(ENGLISH TRANSLATION OF FIZ. TVERD. TELA, 14 (7), 2092–2101, 1972; FOR ORIGINAL SEE E60723)

60725 **IMPURITY CENTERS IN AMMONIUM CHLORIDE CRYSTALS ACTIVATED WITH IRON GROUP IONS.**
STOLOV, A. L. YAKOVLEVA, ZH. S.
FIZ. TVERD. TELA
14 (7), 2102–4, 1972.
(FOR ENGLISH TRANSLATION SEE E60726)

60726 **IMPURITY CENTERS IN AMMONIUM CHLORIDE CRYSTALS ACTIVATED WITH IRON GROUP IONS.**
STOLOV, A. L. YAKOVLEVA, ZH. S.
SOV. PHYS. SOLID STATE
14 (7), 1810–2, 1973.
(ENGLISH TRANSLATION OF FIZ. TVERD. TELA, 14 (7), 2102–4, 1972; FOR ORIGINAL SEE E60725)

60727 **RECOMBINATION LUMINESCENCE IN THE CRYSTALS YTTRIUM ALUMINUM OXIDE–TWO RARE–EARTH ACTIVATORS.**
BATYGOV, S. KH. VORON'KO, YU. K.
DENKER, B. I. OSIKO, V. V.
FIZ. TVERD. TELA
14 (7), 2114–7, 1972.
(FOR ENGLISH TRANSLATION SEE E60728)

60728 **RECOMBINATION LUMINESCENCE IN THE CRYSTALS YTTRIUM ALUMINUM OXIDE–TWO RARE–EARTH ACTIVATORS.**
BATYGOV, S. KH. VORON'KO, YU. K.
DENKER, B. I. OSIKO, V. V.
SOV. PHYS. SOLID STATE
14 (7), 1820–2, 1973.
(ENGLISH TRANSLATION OF FIZ. TVERD. TELA, 14 (7), 2114–7, 1972; FOR ORIGINAL SEE E60727)

60729 **INDIRECT EXCHANGE INTERACTION INVOLVING PHOTOELECTRONS.**
BERDYSHEV, A. A. LETFULOV, B. M.
FIZ. TVERD. TELA
14 (7), 2119–21, 1972.
(FOR ENGLISH TRANSLATION SEE E60730)

60730 **INDIRECT EXCHANGE INTERACTION INVOLVING PHOTOELECTRONS.**
BERDYSHEV, A. A. LETFULOV, B. M.
SOV. PHYS. SOLID STATE
14 (7), 1824–5, 1973.
(ENGLISH TRANSLATION OF FIZ. TVERD. TELA, 14 (7), 2119–21, 1972; FOR ORIGINAL SEE E60729)

60731 **ANTIPARALLEL SWITCHING IN ALPHA–DOMAIN BARIUM TITANATE CRYSTALS.**
DUDA, V. M. DUDNIK, E. F. SINYAKOV, E. V.
FIZ. TVERD. TELA
14 (7), 2138–40, 1972.
(FOR ENGLISH TRANSLATION SEE E60732)

60732 **ANTIPARALLEL SWITCHING IN ALPHA–DOMAIN BARIUM TITANATE CRYSTALS.**
DUDA, V. M. DUDNIK, E. F. SINYAKOV, E. V.
SOV. PHYS. SOLID STATE
14 (7), 1844–5, 1973.
(ENGLISH TRANSLATION OF FIZ. TVERD. TELA, 14 (7), 2138–40, 1972; FOR ORIGINAL SEE E60731)

60735 **ANOMALOUS BEHAVIOR OF THE OPTICAL ABSORPTION COEFFICIENT OF LEAD MAGNONIOBATE SINGLE CRYSTALS IN THE REGION OF A BROAD FERROELECTRIC TRANSITION.**
KAMZINA, L. S. KRAINIK, N. N.
NESTEROVA, N. N.
FIZ. TVERD. TELA
14 (7), 2147–50, 1972.
(FOR ENGLISH TRANSLATION SEE E60736)

60736 **ANOMALOUS BEHAVIOR OF THE OPTICAL ABSORPTION COEFFICIENT OF LEAD MAGNONIOBATE SINGLE CRYSTALS IN THE REGION OF A BROAD FERROELECTRIC TRANSITION.**
KAMZINA, L. S. KRAINIK, N. N.
NESTEROVA, N. N.
SOV. PHYS. SOLID STATE
14 (7), 1853–5, 1973.
(ENGLISH TRANSLATION OF FIZ. TVERD. TELA, 14 (7), 2147–50, 1972; FOR ORIGINAL SEE E60735)

60737 **MAGNETIC PROPERTIES OF COPPER–CHROMIUM CHALCOGENIDES.**
BELOV, K. P. TRET'YAKOV, YU. D.
GORDEEV, I. V. KOROLEVA, L. I.
PED'KO, A. V. SMIRNOVSKAYA, E. I.
ALFEROV, V. A. SAKSONOV, YU. G.
FIZ. TVERD. TELA
14 (7), 2155–7, 1972.
(FOR ENGLISH TRANSLATION SEE E60738)

EPIC Number	Bibliographic Citation

60738 **MAGNETIC PROPERTIES OF COPPER-CHROMIUM CHALCOGENIDES.**
BELOV, K. P. TRET'YAKOV, YU. D.
GORDEEV, I. V. KOROLEVA, L. I.
PED'KO, A. V. SMIRNOVSKAYA, E. I.
ALFEROV, V. A. SAKSONOV, YU. G.
SOV. PHYS. SOLID STATE
14 (7), 1862-3, 1973.
(ENGLISH TRANSLATION OF FIZ. TVERD. TELA, 14 (7), 2155-7, 1972; FOR ORIGINAL SEE E60737)

60739 **SWITCHING EFFECT IN PYROLYTIC VANADIUM OXIDE FILMS.**
ZHDAN, A. G. DAREVSKII, A. S.
CHUGUNOVA, M. E. SERBINOV, I. A.
FIZ. TVERD. TELA
14 (7), 2170-2, 1972.
(FOR ENGLISH TRANSLATION SEE E60740)

60740 **SWITCHING EFFECT IN PYROLYTIC VANADIUM OXIDE FILMS.**
ZHDAN, A. G. DAREVSKII, A. S.
CHUGUNOVA, M. E. SERBINOV, I. A.
SOV. PHYS. SOLID STATE
14 (7), 1879-80, 1973.
(ENGLISH TRANSLATION OF FIZ. TVERD. TELA, 14 (7), 2170-2, 1972; FOR ORIGINAL SEE E60739)

60741 **TEMPERATURE BROADENING AND SHIFT OF PHONONLESS LINED IN LUMINESCENCE SPECTRA OF CRYSTALS OF URANYL COMPOUNDS.**
SHCHEKOKOV, R. N. KRASILOV, YU. I.
KARASEV, V. E.
FIZ. TVERD. TELA
14 (7), 2175-7, 1972.
(FOR ENGLISH TRANSLATION SEE E60742)

60742 **TEMPERATURE BROADENING AND SHIFT OF PHONONLESS LINED IN LUMINESCENCE SPECTRA OF CRYSTALS OF URANYL COMPOUNDS.**
SHCHEKOKOV, R. N. KRASILOV, YU. I.
KARASEV, V. E.
SOV. PHYS. SOLID STATE
14 (7), 1885-6, 1973.
(ENGLISH TRANSLATION OF FIZ. TVERD. TELA, 14 (7), 2175-7, 1972; FOR ORIGINAL SEE E60741)

60745 **TEMPERATURE AND CURRENT STUDIES OF THE RELAXATION EFFECT IN ION-ELECTRON EMISSION IN SILICON.**
OMEL'YANOVSKAYA, N. M. LEBEDEV, S. YA.
PANIN, S. D.
SOV. PHYS. SOLID STATE
14 (7), 1895-6, 1973.
(ENGLISH TRANSLATION OF FIZ. TVERD. TELA, 14 (7), 2185-7, 1972; FOR ORIGINAL SEE E55366)

60748 **TRANSIENT RADI1TION EFFECTS.**
BERGER, R. A. COLWELL, J. F. FISHER, C. J.
FLANAGAN, T. M. GREEN, B. A.
INTELCOM RAD TECH, SAN DIEGO, CALIF.
77PP., 1973.
(AD-778 811, HDL-TR-197-1)

60749 **INVESTIGATION OF THE VALENCE BAND OF LEAD TELLURIDE BY USING THE TRANSFER EFFECT.**
CHERNIK, I. A. KAIDANOV, V. N.
VINOGRADOVA, M. I. KOLOMOETS, N. V.
FIZ. TEKH. POLUPROV.
2 (6), 773-80, 1968.
(FOR ENGLISH TRANSLATION SEE E60750)

60750 **INVESTIGATION OF THE VALENCE BAND OF LEAD TELLURIDE BY USING THE TRANSFER EFFECT.**
CHERNIK, I. A. KAIDANOV, V. N.
VINOGRADOVA, M. I. KOLOMOETS, N. V.
ARMY FOREIGN SCIENCE AND TECHNOLOGY CENTER, CHARLOTTESVILLE, VA.
16PP., 1974.
(ENGLISH TRANSLATION OF FIZ. TEKH. POLUPROV., 2 (6), 773-80, 1968 FOR ORIGINAL SEE E60749)
(AD-781 249, FSTC-HT-23-2035-72)

60751 **ION IMPLANTATION IN SEMI-CONDUCTORS AND SEMI-INSULATORS.**
RODINE, E. T. SHIN, B. K. BARTELHEIMER, D. L
SYSTEMS RESEARCH LABS., INC., DAYTON, OHIO
162PP., 1974.
(AD-781 193, ARL-74-0025, SRL-6739-12)

60752 **A DEVICE FOR MEASURING THERMOELECTRIC AND THERMOMAGNETIC EFFICIENCY OF SEMICONDUCTORS.**
SUPOSTAT, S. A. TIKHOMIROV, B. G.
NIZKOTEMP. TERMOELEK. MATER.
35-9, 1970.
(FOR ENGLISH TRANSLATION SEE E60753)

60753 **A DEVICE FOR MEASURING THERMOELECTRIC AND THERMOMAGNETIC EFFICIENCY OF SEMICONDUCTORS.**
SUPOSTAT, S. A. TIKHOMIROV, B. G.
ARMY FOREIGN SCIENCE AND TECHNOLOGY CENTER, CHARLOTTESVILLE, VA.
5PP., 1974.
(ENGLISH TRANSLATION OF NIZKOTEMP. TERMOELEK. MATER. 35-9, 1970; FOR ORIGINAL SEE E60752)
(AD-781 247, FSTC-HT-23-2245-72)

60754 **IR WINDOW STUDIES.**
KROGER, F. A. MARBURGER, J. H.
UNIV. OF SOUTHERN CALIF., LOS ANGELES
ELECTRONIC SCIENCES LAB.
77PP., 1973.
(AD-780 504, AFCRL-TR-73-0680, USCEE-457)

60755 **CHARACTERIZATION OF SEMICONDUCTING GLASSES FOR USE AS BOLOCON LAYERS.**
MACKENZIE, J. D.
CALIFORNIA UNIV., SCHOOL OF ENGINEERING AND APPLIED SCIENCE, LOS ANGELES
73PP., 1973.
(AD-780 118, UCLA-ENG-7358)

60774 **TRANSFERRED ELECTRON PHOTOEMISSION FROM INDIUM PHOSPHIDE.**
BELL, R. L. JAMES, L. W. MOON, R. I.
APPL. PHYS. LETT.
25 (11), 645-6, 1974.

60789 **AMORPHOUS CARBON RESISTANCE THERMOMETER-HEATERS FOR MAGNETIC AND CALORIMETRIC INVESTIGATIONS AT TEMPERATURES BELOW 1 K.**
GIAUQUE, W. F. STOUT, J. W. CLARK, C. W.
J. AMER. CHEM. SOC.
60, 1053-60, 1938.

60793 **CHEMISORPTION OF METHANOL AND ELECTRICAL CONDUCTIVITY CHANGES ON VANADIUM PENTOXIDE CATALYSTS.**
BHATTACHARYYA, S. K. MAHANTI, P.
J. CATAL.
25 (3), 438-41, 1972.

60796 **AUTOMATIC SYSTEM FOR MEASURING HALL EFFECT IN SEMICONDUCTORS.**
LOEBNER, E. DIESEL, T. J. SCHADE, C. M.
HEWLETT - PACKARD J.
18, 9-15, 1966.

60802 **EDGE ABSORPTION OF CADMIUM INDIUM SULFIDE SINGLE CRYSTALS IN THE REGION OF INDIRECT TRANSITIONS.**
RADAUTSAN, S. I. SYRBU, N. N.
TEZLEVAN, V. E. SHERBAN, K. F. BARAN, N. P.
PHYS. STATUS SOLIDI
57 B, K93-K97, 1973.

60833 **SELF-FOCUSING IN YTTRIUM ALUMINUM GARNET AND OPTICAL GLASSES.**
FELDMAN, A. HOROWITZ, D. WAXLER, R. M.
NATIONAL BUREAU OF STANDARDS
26-35, 1973.
(NBS-SP-387, N74-20087)

60835 **LASER SURFACE DAMAGE STUDIES AT BENDIX.**
BRAUNLICH, P. CARRICO, J. ROSENBLUM, B.
SCHMID, A.
NATIONAL BUREAU OF STANDARDS
9U-102, 1973.
(NBS-SP-387, N74-20096)

60837 **PULSED CARBON DIOXIDE LASER DAMAGE STUDIES OF WINDOWS AND WINDOW COATINGS.**
BRAUNSTEIN, A. I. WANG, V. BRAUNSTEIN, M.
RUDISILL, J. E. WADA, J.
NATIONAL BUREAU OF STANDARDS
151-6, 1973.
(NBS-SP-387, N74-20103)

60838 **PULSED CARBON DIOXIDE LASER DAMAGE STUDIES OF METAL AND DIELECTRIC COATED MIRRORS.**
WANG, V. BRAUNSTEIN, A. I. BRAUNSTEIN, M.
RUDISILL, J. E. WADA, Y.
NATIONAL BUREAU OF STANDARDS
157-69, 1973.
(NBS-SP-387, N74-20104)

60840 **STUDIES OF INTRINSIC OPTICAL BREAKDOWN.**
FRADIN, D. W. BASS, M.
NATIONAL BUREAU OF STANDARDS
225-38, 1973.
(NBS-SP-387, N74-20113)

60841 **A SENSITIVE INTERFEROMETRIC NULL METHOD FOR MEASURING STRESS-INDUCED BIREFRINGENCE.**
BIRNBAUM, G. CORY, E.
NATIONAL BUREAU OF STANDARDS
254-8, 1973.
(NBS-SP-387, N74-20116)

60866 **COATING SCIENCE AND TECHNOLOGY.**
KNOX, B. E. VEDAM, K.
PENNSYLVANIA STATE UNIV., UNIVERSITY PARK
18PP., 1973.
(AD-777 886, AFCRL-TR-74-0038)

60867 **A DOPPLER SHIFT INTERFEROMETRIC TECHNIQUE FOR MEASURING SMALL ABSORPTION COEFFICIENTS.**
SKOLNIK, L. H. KAHAN, A. HORDVIK, A.
CLARK, M.
AIR FORCE CAMBRIDGE RES. LABS., L. G. HANSCOM FIELD, MASS.
32PP., 1973.
(AD-778 077, AFCRL-TR-74-0001)

EPIC Number	Bibliographic Citation
60868	**RESEARCH ON HALIDE SUPERALLOY WINDOWS.** MILES, P. A. READEY, D. W. NEWBERG, R. T. RAYTHEON COMP., WALTHAM, MASS. 176PP., 1973. (AD-778 108, AFCRL-TR-73-0758)
60879	**ANOMALOUS DISPERSION OF BIREFRINGENCE OF SAPPHIRE AND MAGNESIUM FLUORIDE IN THE VACUUM ULTRAVIOLET.** CHADRASEKHARAN, V. DAMANY, H. APPL. OPT. 8 (3), 671-6, 1969.
60888	**COMPENDIUM ON HIGH POWER INFRARED LASER WINDOW MATERIALS (LQ-10 PROGRAM).** SAHAGIAN, C. S. PITHA, C. A. AIR FORCE CAMBRIDGE RESEARCH LABS., L. G. HANSCOM FIELD, MASS. 196PP., 1972. (AD-901 886L, AFCRL-72-0170)
60891	**MICROSTRUCTURAL ANALYSIS OF EVAPORATED AND PYROLYTIC SILICON THIN FILMS.** ANDERSON, R. M. J. ELECTROCHEM. SOC. 120 (11), 1540-6, 1973.
60892	**THERMAL OXIDATION OF SILICON AFTER ION IMPLANTATION.** FRITZSCHE, C. R. ROTHEMUND, W. J. ELECTROCHEM. SOC. 120 (11), 1603-5, 1973.
60899	**SWITCHING EFFECT IN LIQUID SEMICONDUCTORS.** REGEL, A. R. ANDREEV, A. A. MAMADALIEV, M. J. NON-CRYST. SOLIDS 8-10, 455-60, 1972.
60905	**IS THERE AN INTIMATE RELATION BETWEEN AMORPHOUS AND CRYSTALLINE SEMICONDUCTORS.** CONNELL, G. A. N. PAUL, W. J. NON-CRYST. SOLIDS 8-10, 215-22, 1972.
60911	**EFFECT OF ION BOMBARDMENT ON CRYSTALLINE AND AMORPHOUS FILMS OF ARSENIC TRISELENIDE AND SELENIUM.** OLLEY, J. A. YOFFE, A. D. J. NON-CRYST. SOLIDS 8-10, 850-6, 1972.
60915	**PREPARATION OF THERMOLUMINESCENT LITHIUM FLUORIDE.** ROSSITER, M. J. REES-EVANS, D. B. ELLIS, S. C. J. PHYS. 3 D (12), 1816-23, 1970.
60920	**DETERMINATION OF THE OPTICAL CONSTANTS OF THIN FILMS FROM MEASUREMENTS OF REFLECTANCE AND TRANSMITTANCE AT NORMAL INCIDENCE.** DENTON, R. E. CAMPBELL, R. D. TOMLIN, S. G. J. PHYS. 5 D (4), 852-63, 1972.
60922	**PHOTOVOLTAIC PROPERTIES OF SINGLE-CRYSTAL CADMIUM SULFIDE-COPPER SULFIDE CELLS.** WILSON, J. I. B. WOODS, J. J. PHYS. 5 (9), 1700-11, 1972.
60928	**APPARATUS FOR MEASURING RESISTIVITY AND HALL COEFFICIENT OF HEAVILY DOPED SEMICONDUCTORS AT HIGH TEMPERATURES.** ROWE, D. M. BUNCE, R. W. J. PHYS. 4 E (11), 902-4, 1971.
60929	**NEW METHOD FOR THE MEASUREMENT OF THE THERMOELECTRIC POWER OF SINTERED SEMICONDUCTORS.** CRUCQ, A. DEGOLS, L. J. PHYS. 5 E (1), 81-3, 1972.
60930	**MEASUREMENT OF HEAT FLOW BY MEANS OF NERNST EFFECT.** GOLDSMID, H. J. KNITTEL, T. SA VIDES, N. UHER, C. J. PHYS. 5 E (4), 313-14, 1972.
60932	**MEASUREMENT OF PHOTOLUMINESCENCE AND OPTICAL ABSORPTION.** MORRISON, G. I. WRIGHT, H. C. J. PHYS. 5 E (7), 632-3, 1972.
60933	**RAPID NONDESTRUCTIVE METHOD FOR MEASURING THE REFRACTIVE INDEX AND THICKNESS OF THIN DIELECTRIC FILMS.** RAIF, J. BEN-YOSEF, N. ORON, M. J. PHYS. 6 E (1), 48-50, 1973.
60950	**ELECTRICAL RESISTANCE NEAR FERROMAGNETIC CURIE POINTS.** ZUMSTEG, F. C. PARKS, R. D. J. PHYS. (PARIS), COLLOQ. (1), (PT. 1), C1-534-C1-535, 1971.
60954	**ONSET OF SUPERCONDUCTIVITY IN SODIUM AND POTASSIUM INTERCALATED MOLYBDENUM DISULFIDE.** SOMOANO, R. B. REMBAUM, A. JPL QUART. TECH. REV. 1 (3), 33-7, 1971.
60959	**EVOLUTION OF RESISTIVITY BETWEEN 90 AND 278 K AND** COLIN, G. BOISSONNEAU, J. F. J. SOLID STATE CHEM. 5 (3), 342-5, 1972.
60960	**RELATIONS BETWEEN STRUCTURE AND THE OPTICAL AND ELECTRICAL PROPERTIES OF AMORPHOUS SILICON AND GERMANIUM FILMS.** BRODSKY, M. H. J. VAC. SCI. TECHNOL. 8 (1), 125-34, 1971.
60961	**ELECTRONIC CONDUCTION IN AMORPHOUS SEMICONDUCTORS.** JONSCHER, A. K. J. VAC. SCI. TECHNOL. 8 (1), 135-44, 1971.
60962	**EXPERIMENTAL DATA ON THE EFFECT OF COBALT IONS ON THE ANISOTROPY OF CADMIUM CHROMIUM SELENIDE.** JAGIELINSKI, T. BERKOWSKI, M. PHYS. STATUS SOLIDI 27 A (1), K17-20, 1975.
60963	**LOCALLIZED LEVELS IN THE LEAD(II) IODIDE BAND GAP INDUCED BY THERMAL TREATMENT AND IRRADIATION.** BALTOG, I. CONSTANTINESCU, M. GHITA, C. GHITA, L. PHYS. STATUS SOLIDI 27 A (1), K39-41, 1975.
60964	**SURVEY OF OPTICAL AND ELECTRICAL PROPERTIES OF THIN FILMS OF II-VI SEMICONDUCTING COMPOUNDS.** LUDEKE, R. J. VAC. SCI. TECHNOL. 8 (1), 199-209, 1971.
60965	**REVIEW OF THE ELECTRICAL AND OPTICAL PROPERTIES OF III-V COMPOUND SEMICONDUCTOR FILMS.** WIEDER, H. H. J. VAC. SCI. TECHNOL. 8 (1), 210-23, 1971.
60976	**SURFACE PHOTOVOLTAGE SPECTROSCOPY. NEW APPROACH TO THE STUDY OF HIGH-GAP SEMICONDUCTOR SURFACES.** GATOS, H. C. LAGOWSKI, J. J. VAC. SCI. TECHNOL. 10 (1), 130-5, 1973.
61000	**APPARATUS FOR PREPARING FILMS OF THERMOELECTRIC MATERIALS.** NAER, V. A. KRAVCHUK, V. V. KHOLOD. TEKH. TEKHNOL. (10), 44-8, 1970. (FOR ENGLISH TRANSLATION SEE E62297)
61007	**BAND TAILS IN IMPURE SEMICONDUCTORS.** MORIGAKI, K. YONEZAWA, F. KOTAI BUTSURI 7 (3), 133-44, 1972.
61009	**SELF-REVERSAL OF EXCITON LUMINESCENCE LINES AND FINE STRUCTURE OF EXCITON ABSORPTION IN CADMIUM TELLURIDE.** GIPPIUS, A. A. VAVILOV, V. S. PANOSYAN, YA. R. USHAKOV, V. V. KRATK. SOOBSHCH. FIZ. (7), 8-14, 1970.
61011	**PHYSICAL PROPERTIES OF SODIUM CHLORIDE AND POTASSIUM CHLORIDE CRYSTALS GROWN BY A MODIFIED KYROPOULOS METHOD.** SUSZYNSKA, M. LEBL, M. ZEMLICKA, J. KRIST. TECH. 7 (8), 943-55, 1972.
61015	**MEASUREMENT OF THE ELECTRIC CONDUCTIVITY OF LIQUID METALS AND SEMICONDUCTORS.** LEE, T. N. KUMSOK HAKHOE CHI 10 (4), 292-9, 1972.
61023	**THERMALLY STIMULATED VOLTAIC EFFECT IN ZINC SULFIDE SINGLE CRYSTALS.** ALZETTA, G. CHELLA, G. SCARMOZZINO, R. LETT. NUOVO CIMENTO SOC. ITAL. FIS. SR.2 3 (1), 1-4, 1972.
61025	**EFFECT OF UNIAXIAL STRESS ON THE DISPERSION OF HELICONS IN A MANY-VALLEY SEMICONDUCTOR.** POZELA, J. RIAUKA, V. TOLUTIS, R. LIET. FIZ. RINKINYS 10 (2), 243-50, 1970.
61027	**SURFACE PHOTOEMF IN HIGH-RESISTANCE CADMIUM SELENIDE CRYSTALS.** VENGRIS, S. VISCAKAS, J. KABYALKA, V. I. LIET. FIZ. RINKINYS 10 (5), 751-5, 1970.

EPIC Number	Bibliographic Citation
61029	EFFECT OF THE TRANSITION SURFACE LAYER ON THE OPTICAL PROPERTIES OF CADMIUM SELENIDE SINGLE CRYSTALS. VISCAKAS, J. MEDEISIS, A. LIET. FIZ. RINKINYS 11 (1), 81–6, 1971.
61035	EFFECT OF MECHANICAL STRESSES ON THE PHOTOVOLTAIC EFFECT IN POLYCRYSTALLINE CADMIUM TELLURIDE FILMS. BAKUTIS, J. VALACKA, K. VENISLOVEINE, R. LIET. FIZ. RINKINYS 12 (5), 851–6, 1972.
61039	STUDY OF INTERNAL MACRO-VOLTAGES IN THIN CADMIUM TELLURIDE FILMS. BAKUTIS, I. P. VALATSKA, K. K. VENISLOVENE, R. I. LITOV. FIZ. SB. (USSR) 13 (3), 415–20, 1973.
61059	CYLINDRICAL ERBIUM OXIDE RADIATOR STRUCTURES FOR THERMO-PHOTOVOLTAIC GENERATORS. GUAZZONI, G. KITTL, E. U. S. ARMY ELECTRONICS COMMAND, FORT MONMOUTH, N. J. 27PP., 1974. (ECOM-4249)
61061	STUDY OF THE DEFECT STRUCTURE OF THE SEMI-CONDUCTING III - V COMPOUNDS AND OTHER RELATED MATERIALS. SPITZER, W. G. AIR FORCE CAMBRIDGE RESEARCH LAB. 50PP., 1972. (AFCRL-72-0296, AD-751 052, USCEE-421)
61068	OPTICAL PROPERTIES OF THIN BORON NITRIDE FILMS. BARONIAN, W. MATER. RES. BULL. 7 (2), 119–24, 1972.
61070	ELECTRON TRANSPORT PROPERTIES OF TRANSITION METAL OXIDE SYSTEMS WITH THE POTASSIUM TETRAFLUORONICKELATE(II) STRUCTURE. GANGULY, P. RAO, C. N. R. MATER. RES. BULL. 8 (4), 405–12, 1973.
61074	PSEUDO POTENTIALS AND THEIR FOURIER COEFFICIENTS FOR ATOMS AND IONS WITH S- AND P-CLOSED SHELLS. MIYAKAWA, T. MEM. DEF. ACAD. (JAPAN) 13 (2), 173–208, 1973.
61077	OPTICAL AND ELECTRICAL PROPERTIES OF (ZINC, CADMIUM, MERCURY) SULFIDE AND CADMIUM (SULFIDE, SELENIDE) SOLID SOLUTIONS. KAWAI, S. KIRIYAMA, R. NAKAHARA, F. MEM. INST. SCI. IND. RES., OSAKA UNIV. 2,, 101–12, 1971.
61079	THERMOELECTRIC POWER MEASUREMENTS ON SEMICONDUCTORS. SOMOGYI, K. PODOR, B. BODO, B. MERES AUTOM. (HUNGARY) 21 (4), 130–5, 1973.
61104	POSSIBILITY OF INVESTIGATING THE INHOMOGENEITY OF SEMICONDUCTOR MATERIALS BY USING PROBE METHODS. ORZHEVSKII, O. B. FISTUL, V. I. ZAVOD. LAB. 27 (10), 1236–9, 1961. (FOR ENGLISH TRANSLATION, SEE E61105)
61105	POSSIBILITY OF INVESTIGATING THE INHOMOGENEITY OF SEMICONDUCTOR MATERIALS BY USING PROBE METHODS. ORZHEVSKII, O. B. FISTUL, V. I. IND. LAB., USSR 27 (10), 1239–42, 1961. (ENGLISH TRANSLATION OF ZAVOD. LAB., 27 (10), 1236–9, 1961; FOR ORIGINAL SEE E61104)
61106	INVESTIGATION OF THE HOMOGENEITY OF HIGH-ALLOY SEMICONDUCTORS BY MEANS OF A HEATED THERMOCOUPLE PROBE. KOKOSHKIN, V. A. ZAVOD. LAB. 31 (4), 461–3, 1965. (FOR ENGLISH TRANSLATION SEE E61107)
61107	INVESTIGATION OF THE HOMOGENEITY OF HIGH-ALLOY SEMICONDUCTORS BY MEANS OF A HEATED THERMOCOUPLE PROBE. KOKOSHKIN, V. A. IND. LAB., USSR 31 (4), 562–4, 1965. (ENGLISH TRANSLATION OF ZAVOD. LAB., 31 (4), 461–3, 1965; FOR ORIGINAL SEE E67106)
61133	PREPARATION OF MATERIALS FOR THERMOELECTRIC FREEZING DEVICES BASED ON BISMUTH TELLURIDE. JAKLOVSZKY, J. IONESCU, R. NISTOR, N. NICULESCU, D. METALURGIA (BUCHAREST) 24 (7), 482–5, 1972.
61141	OPTICAL ABSORPTION IN SILVER HALIDES. HIROSHI, K. NIPPON SHASHIN GAKKAI KAISHI 28 (4), 165–72, 1965.
61151	SOME FINITE-TEMPERATURE PROPERTIES OF SUPERCONDUCTING BISMUTH THALLIUM. VASHISHTA, P. CARBOTTE, J. P. PHYS. REV. 10 B (7), 2789–91, 1974.
61152	RELATIONSHIP BETWEEN SUPERCONDUCTING TRANSITION TEMPERATURE AND FERMI LEVEL: AN NMR STUDY OF VANADIUM GALLIUM SILICON. FRADIN, F. Y. WILLIAMSON, J. D. PHYS. REV. 10 B (7), 2803–11, 1974.
61156	FAR-INFRARED SPECTROSCOPY OF TERBIUM PHOSPHATES. LEWIS, J. F. L. PRINZ, G. A. PHYS. REV. 10 B (7), 2892–9, 1974.
61157	GROUND-STATE MAGNETIC RESONANCE OF DYSPROSIUM PHOSPHATES IN THE FAR INFRARED. PRINZ, G. A. LEWIS, J. F. L. WAGNER, R. J. PHYS. REV. 10 B (7), 2907–14, 1974.
61159	MAGNETIC PROPERTIES OF SOME CUBIC RARE-EARTH ELPASOLITE HEXAFLUORIDES. BUCHER, E. GRUGGENHEIM, H. J. ANDRES, K. HULL, G. W., JR. COOPER, A. S. PHYS. REV. 10 B (7), 2945–51, 1974.
61161	ELASTIC AND MAGNETOELASTIC PROPERTIES OF POLYCRYSTALLINE RARE-EARTH-IRON LAVES COMPOUNDS. KLIMKER, H. ROSEN, M. DARIEL, M. P. ATZMONY, U. PHYS. REV. 10 B (7), 2968–72, 1974.
61166	CHEMISORPTION OF OXYGEN ON PARTIALLY REDUCED VANADIUM OXIDE STUDIED BY ELECTRON PARAMAGNETIC RESONANCE. DYREK, K. BULL. ACAD. POL. SCI., SER. SCI. CHIM. 22 (7), 605–12, 1974.
61167	MAGNETIC PHASE DIAGRAM OF THE URANIUM ARSENIDE-URANIUM PHOSPHIDE SYSTEM. TROC, R. BULL. ACAD. POL. SCI., SER. SCI. CHIM. 22 (7), 613–9, 1974.
61168	ELECTRICAL RESISTIVITY OF URANIUM PHOSPHIDE AND URANIUM ARSENIDE. TROC, R. KLETOWSKI, Z. BULL. ACAD. POL. SCI., SER. SCI. CHIM. 22 (7), 621–4, 1974.
61171	DIELECTRIC PROPERTIES OF FRESH AND SEA ICE AT 10 AND 35 GHZ. VANT, M. R. GRAY, R. B. RAMSEIER, R. O. MAKIOS, V. J. APPL. PHYS. 45 (11), 4712–7, 1974.
61179	OPTICAL ABSORPTION IN EPITAXIAL LEAD TELLURIDE FILMS ON BARIUM FLUORIDE. MC CARTHY, S. L. WEBER, W. H. MIKKOR, M. J. APPL. PHYS. 45 (11), 4907–11, 1974.
61180	ANNEALING BEHAVIOR OF UNIMPLANTED AND ZINC-IMPLANTED GALLIUM ARSENIDE. ITOH, T. KASAHARA, J. J. APPL. PHYS. 45 (11), 4915–9, 1974.
61181	KINETICS OF RECOMBINATION IN NITROGEN-DOPED GALLIUM PHOSPHIDE. DAPKUS, P. D. HACKETT, W. H., JR. LORIMOR, O. G. BACHRACH, R. Z. J. APPL. PHYS. 45 (11), 4920–30, 1974.
61182	HOT ELECTRON GALVANOMAGNETIC CONDUCTION IN CADMIUM SULFIDE-A MONTE CARLO INVESTIGATION. CHATTOPADHYAY, D. J. APPL. PHYS. 45 (11), 4931–3, 1974.
61183	TRANSIENT PHOTOCONDUCTIVITY CURRENT-TIME PROFILES IN LOW CARRIER MOBILITY SOLIDS. FLEMING, R. J. J. APPL. PHYS. 45 (11), 4944–9, 1974.
61185	INVESTIGATION OF INFRARED LOSS MECHANISMS IN HIGH-RESISTIVITY GALLIUM ARSENIDE. CHRISTENSEN, C. P. JOINER, R. NIEH, S. T. K. STEIER, W. H. J. APPL. PHYS. 45 (11), 4957–60, 1974.

EPIC Number | Bibliographic Citation

61186 ROOM-TEMPERATURE DEEP-STATE EMISSION SPECTRA, RADIATIVE EFFICIENCY, AND LIFETIME OF SOME GALLIUM PHOSPHIDE: TELLURIUM, NITROGEN CRYSTALS.
BACHRACH, R. Z. DAPKUS, P. D. LORIMOR, O. G.
J. APPL. PHYS.
45 (11), 4971-3, 1974.

61187 OPTICAL SPECTRA AND LASER ACTION IN NOEDYMIUM TRIPOSITIVE ION DOPED CALCIUM YTTRIUM MAGNESIUM GERMANIUM OXIDE.
SHARP, E. J. MILLER, J. E. HOROWITZ, D. J.
LINZ, A. BELRUSS, V.
J. APPL. PHYS.
45 (11), 4974-9, 1974.

61188 INFRARED-STIMULATED LUMINESCENCE IN ZINC SULFIDE GROWN BY CHEMICAL VAPOR DEPOSITION.
ZUCCA, R. CORY, E. S. ESPINOSA, G. P.
HENGSTENBERG, D. H. LIM, T. C.
J. APPL. PHYS.
45 (11), 4986-92, 1974.

61190 PHOTOELECTROMAGNETIC EFFECT IN N-GALLIUM SELENIDE.
ADDUCI, F. CINGOLANI, A. FERRARA, M.
MINAFRA, A. TANTALO, P.
J. APPL. PHYS.
45 (11), 5000-1, 1974.

61193 STATIC AND DYNAMIC COERCIVITIES OF HARD MAGNETIC BUBBLES.
PATTERSON, R. W.
J. APPL. PHYS.
45 (11), 5018-22, 1974.

61194 PREPARATION AND PROPERTIES OF A MULTIFILAMENTARY VANADIUM GALLIUM COMPOSITE.
CRITCHLOW, P. R. GREGORY, E. MARANCIK, W.
J. APPL. PHYS.
45 (11), 5027-32, 1974.

61195 NONLINEAR REVERSIBLE PROCESSES IN YTTRIUM IRON GARNET: AN EXPLANATION FOR THE RAYLEIGH LOOP ANOMALIES.
FEU, A. TRUEBA, A.
J. APPL. PHYS.
45 (11), 5033-6, 1974.

61196 MAGNETIZATION REVERSAL PROCESS IN RARE-EARTH ELEMENT COBALT PARTICLES AND SINTERED PERMANENT MAGNETS.
SEARLE, C. W. GARRETT, H. J.
J. APPL. PHYS.
45 (11), 5037-42, 1974.

61198 X-RAY CONTINUUM FROM THICK ELEMENTAL TARGETS FOR 10-50-KE V.
RAO-SAHIB, T. S. WITTRY, D. B.
J. APPL. PHYS.
45 (11), 5060-8, 1974.

61199 SINGLE-HETEROSTRUCTURE LEAD SULFIDE SELENIDE DIODE LASERS.
SLEGER, K. J. MC LANE, G. F. STROM, U.
BISHOP, S. G. MITCHELL, D. L.
J. APPL. PHYS.
45 (11), 5069-71, 1974.

61200 MEASUREMENT OF THE DRIFT VELOCITY OF CHARGE CARRIERS IN MERCURIC IODIDE.
MINDER, R. MAJNI, G. CANALI, C.
OTTAVIANI, G. STUCK, R. PONPON, J. P.
SCHWAB, C. SIFFERT, P.
J. APPL. PHYS.
45 (11), 5074-6, 1974.

61202 FLUORESCENCE IN LITHIUM NEODYMIUM ULTRA-PHOSPHATE SINGLE CRYSTALS.
YAMADA, T. OTSUKA, K. NAKANO, J.
J. APPL. PHYS.
45 (11), 5096-7, 1974.

61209 ELECTRON TRANSPORT IN GRAPHITES AND CARBONS.
SAUNDERS, G. A.
MOD. ASPECTS GRAPHITE TECHNOL.
79-127, 1970.
(EDITED BY L. C. F. BLACKMAN, ACADEMIC: LONDON, ENGLAND)

61219 ANISOTROPY OF SYNTHETIC METALS.
UBBELOHDE, A. R.
NATURE (LONDON)
232 (5305), 43-4, 1971.

61220 INTERFEROMETRIC METHOD FOR DETERMINING REFRACTIVE INDEX AND THICKNESS OF THIN FILMS.
ISRAELACHVILI, J.
NATURE (LONDON), PHYS. SCI.
229 (3), 85-6, 1971.

61228 KONDO EFFECT IN SEMICONDUCTORS.
KHABIBULLIN, B. M. NIKITIN, B. S.
NEKOT. VOP. MAGN. RADIOSPEKTROSK. KVANTOVOI AKUST., SEKTS. FIZ., MATER. NAUCH. KONG.
151-3, 1967.
(EDITED BY B. M. KOZYREV, KAZAN. FIZ.-TEKH. INST. AKAD. NAUK SSSR: KAZAN, USSR.)

61240 ELECTRICAL AND THERMOELECTRIC PROPERTIES OF THALLIUM-BASED TERNARY COMPOUNDS.
GITSU, D. V. KANTSER, CH. T. KRETSU, I. V.
CHUMAK, G. D.
MIZKOTEMP. TERMOELEK. MATER.
17-21, 1970.

61243 THEORY OF THERMOEMF. ANISOTROPY OF SEMICONDUCTORS WITH AN ANISOTROPIC MASS OF CURRENT CARRIERS.
NITSOVICH, M. V. LUTSYAK, V. S.
NITSOVICH, V. M.
NIZKOTEMP. TERMOELEK. MATER.
69-72, 1970.
(EDITED BY D. V. GITSU, RED.-IZD. OTD. AKAD. NAUK MOLD. SSR: KISHINEV, USSR)

61245 ELECTRON-PHONON DRAG IN THIN SEMICONDUCTOR FILMS.
SARDARYAN, V. S. ERMAGANBETOV, K. T.
NIZKOTEMP. TERMOELEK. MATER.
138-43, 1970.

61248 ENERGY POSSIBILITIES OF LOW-TEMPERATURE THERMOELECTRIC MATERIALS.
BANAGA, M. P. GOL'TSMAN, B. M.
GROMOV, B. D. IORDANISHVILI, E. K.
SHAPIRO, E. KH.
NIZKOTEMP. TERMOELEK. MATER.
176-81, 1970.
(EDITED BY D. V. GITSU, REDL-IZD. OTD. AKAD. NAUK MOLD, SSR: KISHINEV, USSR)

61262 ELECTRICAL AND OPTICAL PROPERTIES OF ZINC-DOPED ALKALI HALIDES.
RADHAKRISHNA, S.
NUOVO CIMENTO SOC. ITAL. FIS.
[11] 4 B (2), 169-76, 1971.

61268 SYSTEM FOR MEASURING THE CONDUCTIVITY OF SEMICONDUCTORS IN A HIGH ELECTRIC D.C. FIELD.
NEUBERT, R. HOERSTEL, W. KUSNICK, D.
SPITZER, M.
EXP. TECH. PHYS. (GERMANY)
22 (1), 7-15, 1974.

61285 THE HALL EFFECT AND SOME OTHER PHYSICAL CONSTANTS OF ALLOYS. PT. VII. THE ALUMINIUM-SILVER SERIES OF ALLOYS.
POWELL, H. EVANS, E. J.
PHIL. MAG.
34 (230), 145-61, 1943.

61287 SURFACE STATES AND RECTIFICATION AT A METAL SEMI-CONDUCTOR CONTACT.
BARDEEN, J.
PHYS. REV.
71, 717-27, 1947.

61305 THE ELECTRICAL RESISTANCE OF DILUTE COPPER ALLOYS AT VERY LOW TEMPERATURES.
WHITE, G. K.
CAN. J. PHYS.
33 (3-4), 119-24, 1955.

61307 THE PREPARATION AND SEMICONDUCTING PROPERTIES OF ZINC ANTIMONY SINGLE CRYSTALS.
MASUMOTO, K. KOMIYA, H.
JAPAN. INST. METALS, J.
28, 273-81, 1964.

61308 INVESTIGATIONS OF ZINC CADMIUM ANTIMONY SOLID-SOLUTION SINGLE CRYSTALS.
PILAT, I. M. OSIPOV, E. V.
FIZ. TEKH. POLUPROV.
2 (1), 64-8, 1968.
(FOR ENGLISH TRANSLATION SEE E61309)

61309 INVESTIGATIONS OF ZINC CADMIUM ANTIMONY SOLID-SOLUTION SINGLE CRYSTALS.
PILAT, I. M. OSIPOV, E. V.
SOV. PHYS. SEMICOND.
2 (1), 53-6, 1968.
(ENGLISH TRANSLATION OF FIZ. TEKH. POLUPROV., 2 (1), 64-8, 1968; FOR ORIGINAL SEE E61308)

61324 MEASUREMENT OF THE DIELECTRIC CONSTANTS OF MOLTEN ZINC CHLORIDE AND ZINC BROMIDE.
DOUCET, Y. CHAREYRE, J.-P. SANTINI, R.
TETE, A.
COMPT. REND.
273, (9), 339-41, 1971.

61325 THE ELECTRICAL RESISTIVITY OF METALLIC MELTS. III. THE ELECTRICAL RESISTIVITY OF ALLOY MELTS OF THE MIXED CRYSTAL SYSTEMS SILVER-GOLD AND COPPER-GOLD AS WELL AS THE EUTECTIC SYSTEMS SILVER-COPPER, TIN-ZINC AND ALUMINUM-ZINC.
ROLL, A. MOTZ, H.
Z. METALLK.
48 (9), 495-502, 1957.

EPIC Number	Bibliographic Citation

61328 THEORY OF ELECTRON PHOTOEMISSION FROM SMALL QUASIMETALLIC CENTERS.
ADAMYAN, V. M. GLAUBERMAN, A. E.
KHLOPKOV, B. N.
SOV. PHYS. SOLID STATE
13 (6), 1392–5, 1971.
(ENGLISH TRANSLATION OF FIZ. TVERD. TELA, 13 (6), 1663–7, 1971; FOR ORIGINAL SEE E59579)

61329 NONLINEAR ELECTRICAL CONDUCTIVITY OF GAPLESS SEMICONDUCTORS.
BENESLAVSKII, S. D.
SOV. PHYS. SOLID STATE
13 (6), 1444–8, 1971.
(ENGLISH TRANSLATION OF FIZ. TVERD. TELA, 13 (6), 1727–33, 1971; FOR ORIGINAL SEE E59580)

61333 HIGH TEMPERATURE ABSORPTION IN CARBON DIOXIDE AT 10.6 MU M.
STRILCHUK, A. R. OFFENBERGER, A. A.
APPL. OPT.
13 (11), 2643–6, 1974.

61337 ANODIC PROTON INJECTION IN GLASSES.
CARLSON, D. E.
J. AMER. CERAM. SOC.
57 (11), 461–6, 1974.

61339 PROPERTIES OF SURFACE BARRIER LAYER FORMED ON A SEMICONDUCTING BARIUM TITANIUM OXIDE CERAMIC.
WAKINO, K.
J. AMER. CERAM. SOC.
57 (11), 472–3, 1974.

61340 DC CONDUCTIVITY OF GERMANIUM SULFIDE SILVER AND ARSENIC SULFIDE SILVER GLASSES.
KAWAMOTO, Y. NAGURA, N. TSUCHIHASHI, S.
J. AMER. CERAM. SOC.
57 (11), 489–91, 1974.

61342 HOT–PRESSING OF LITHIUM OXIDE–STABILIZED BETA–ALUMINA.
VIRKAR, A. V. TENNENHOUSE, G. J.
GORDON, R. S.
J. AMER. CERAM. SOC.
57 (11), 508, 1974.

61351 TRANSIENT CARRIER DECAY AND TRANSPORT PROPERTIES IN MERCURY CADMIUM TELLURIDE.
NIMTZ, G. BAUER, G. DORNHOUS, R.
MULLER, K. H.
PHYS. REV.
10 B (8), 3302–10, 1974.

61352 DIRECT EXCITONS IN CUBIC SEMICONDUCTORS IN A MAGNETIC FIELD.
SWIERKOWSKI, L.
PHYS. REV.
10 B (8), 3311–5, 1974.

61354 DEEP HOLE TRAPS IN P–TYPE GALLIUM SELENIDE SINGLE CRYSTALS.
MANFREDOTTI, C. MURRI, R. RIZZO, A.
GALASSINI, S. RUGGIERO, L.
PHYS. REV.
10 B (8), 3387–93, 1974.

61356 CORRECTIONS TO THE FERMI LEVEL IN HEAVILY DOPED GALLIUM ARSENIDE.
RIMBEY, P. R. MAHAN, G. D.
PHYS. REV.
10 B (8), 3419–25, 1974.

61357 DIAMAGNETISM OF DIELECTRICS.
WHITE, R. M.
PHYS. REV.
10 B (8), 3426–32, 1974.

61358 BAND INVERSION AND TRANSPORT PROPERTIES OF L MINIMA IN N–GALLIUM ANTIMONY (TELLURIDE).
SUN, R.–Y. BECKER, W. M.
PHYS. REV.
10 B (8), 3436–50, 1974.

61360 RESONANT RAMAN SCATTERING IN GALLIUM SELENIDE.
HOFF, R. M. IRWIN, J. C.
PHYS. REV.
10 B (8), 3464–70, 1974.

61361 TOW–PHOTON ABSORPTION SPECTRUM OF CADMIUM SULFIDE IN THE A– AND B– EXCITONIC REGION AT 20 K BY THE NEW TWIN–LASER TECHNIQUE.
STAFFORD, R. G. SONDERGELD, M.
PHYS. REV.
10 B (8), 3471–9, 1974.

61362 LATTICE VIBRATIONAL MODES OF LITHIUM GERMANIUM OXIDE MEASUIRED BY INFRARED AND RAMAN TECHNIQUES.
LURIO, A. BURNS, G.
PHYS. REV.
10 B (8), 3512–7, 1974.

61363 COUPLED MODES WITH A(1) SYMMETRY IN TETRAGONAL BARIUM TITANIUM OXIDE.
CHAVES, A. KATIYAR, R. S. PORTO, S. P. S.
PHYS. REV.
10 B (8), 3522–33, 1974.

61365 ELASTIC AND PIEZOELECTRIC CONSTANTS OF SILVER–IODIDE: STUDY OF A MATERIAL AT THE COVALENT–IONIC PHASE TRANSITION.
FJELDLY, T. A. HANSON, R. C.
PHYS. REV.
10 B (8), 3569–77, 1974.

61369 CHARGE–DENSITY–WAVE STATE IN VANADIUM SULFIDE.
LIU, S. H.
PHYS. REV.
10 B (8), 3619–25, 1974.

61371 VIBRATIONAL ABSORPTION OF TUNNELING MOLECULAR DEFECTS IN CRYSTALS. I. TUNNELING MOLECULES IN ELECTRIC FIELDS (HYDROXIDE ION DOPED POTASSIUM CHLORIDE).
LUTY, F.
PHYS. REV.
10 B (8), 3667–76, 1974.

61372 VIBRATIONAL ABSORPTION OF TUNNELING MOLECULAR DEFECTS IN CRYSTALS. II. TUNNELING MOLECULES UNDER APPLIED STRESS (CYANIDE ION DOPED POTASSIUM CHLORIDE).
LUTY, F.
PHYS. REV.
10 B (8), 3677–91, 1974.

61373 DISTRIBUTION FUNCTION OF PHOTOEXCITED CARRIERS IN HIGHLY EXCITED GALLIUM ARSENIDE.
SHAH, J.
PHYS. REV.
10 B (8), 3697–9, 1974.

61375 SHARP COUPLING TRANSITION OF GADOLINIUM IN ALUMINUM GALLIUM SOLVENTS.
KOCH, E. N. FLYNN, C. P.
PHYS. REV.
10 B (10), 4071–8, 1974.

61379 MICROSCOPIC MAGNETIC PROPERTIES OF VANADIUM OXIDES.
GOSSARD, A. C. DI SALVO, F. J.
ERICH, L. C. REMEIKA, J. P. YASUOKA, H.
KOSUGE, K. KACHI, S.
PHYS. REV.
10 B (10), 4178–83, 1974.

61382 BAND NONPARABOLICITIES, BROADENING, AND INTERNAL FIELD DISTRIBUTIONS: THE SPECTROSCOPY OF FRANZ–KELDYSH OSCILLATIONS.
ASPNES, D. E.
PHYS. REV.
10 B (10), 4228–38, 1974.

61383 HALL COEFFICIENT AND MOBILITY IN LEAD TIN TELLURIDE WITH HIGH CARRIER DENSITIES.
OCIO, M.
PHYS. REV.
10 B (10), 4274–83, 1974.

61386 ANALYSIS OF THE THERMALLY STIMULATED CAPACITOR–DISCHARGE METHOD FOR CHARACTERIZING LOCALIZED STATES IN AMORPHOUS SEMICONDUCTORS.
AGARWAL, S. C.
PHYS. REV.
10 B (10), 4340–50, 1974.

61387 ATTEMPTS TO MEASURE THERMALLY STIMULATED CURRENTS IN CHALCOGENIDE GLASSES.
AGARWAL, S. C. FRITZSCHE, H.
PHYS. REV.
10 B (10), 4351–7, 1974.

61388 DENSITY OF VALENCE STATES OF COPPER CHLORIDE, COPPER BROMIDE, COPPER IODIDE, AND SILVER IODIDE.
GOLDMANN, A. TEJEDA, J. SHEVCHIK, N. J.
CARDONA, M.
PHYS. REV.
10 B (10), 4388–4402, 1974.

61390 ELECTRIC FIELD EFFECTS ON THE UV ABSORPTION OF SODIUM IODIDE, POTASSIUM IODIDE, AND RUBIDIUM IODIDE.
MENES, M.
PHYS. REV.
10 B (10), 4469–79, 1974.

61391 ISOTOPE SPLITTING OF THE CHLORIDE GAP MODE IN POTASSIUM IODIDE.
SHOTTS, W. J. SIEVERS, A. J.
PHYS. REV.
10 B (10), 4495–7, 1974.

61394 MAGNETIC EXCITATIONS IN TERBIUM ANTIMONIDE.
HOLDEN, T. M. SVENSSON, E. C.
BUYERS, W. J. L. VOGT, O.
PHYS. REV.
10 B (9), 3864–76, 1974.

EPIC Number | Bibliographic Citation

61395 MAGNETIC PROPERTIES OF EUROPIUM TITANATES.
CHIEN, C.-L. DE BENEDETTI, S.
BARROS, F. S.
PHYS. REV.
10 B (9), 3913-22, 1974.

61398 MAGNETIC EXCITATION SPECTRUM OF COBALT CHLORIDE WATER.
FOGEDBY, H. C.
PHYS. REV.
10 B (9), 4000-13, 1974.

61400 EFFECT OF LATTICE TRANSFORMATION ON THE PRESSURE DEPENDENCE OF T C OF VANADIUM SILICON SINGLE CRYSTALS.
HUANG, S. CHU, C. W.
PHYS. REV.
10 B (9), 4030-2, 1974.

61409 THE THEORY OF OPTICAL ABSORPTION IN DISORDERED SYSTEMS.
FEDIRKO, V. A.
IZV. VUZ FIZ. (USSR)
(2), 21-5, 1974.
(FOR ENGLISH TRANSLATION SEE E95265)

61410 SUPERCONDUCTIVITY AND CORRELATION OF MAGNETIC MOMENTS IN CERIUM-TERBIUM-RUTHENIUM INTERMETALLIC.
ROTH, S. IBEL, K. JUST, W.
J. APPL. CRYSTALLOGR.
7 (PT. 2), 230-2, 1974

61413 EFFECT OF THIN-FILM THICKNESS ON ABELES-TYPE INDEX MEASUREMENTS.
BURNS, W. K. LEE, A. B.
J. OPT. SOC. AM. (USA)
64 (1), 108-9, 1974.

61421 TEMPERATURE DEPENDENCE OF ELECTRICAL CONDUCTION MECHANISM IN AMORPHOUS SEMICONDUCTOR.
TAKEDA, T.
JAP. J. APPL. PHYS.
13 (3), 541-2, 1974.

61430 PREPARATION AND PROPERTIES OF POLYMERIC INTERCALATED DICHALCOGENIDES.
HSU, C.-H. LABES, M. M.
NATURE (PHYS. SCI.)
246, (155), 122-3, 1973.

61432 EFFECTS OF DOPING AND FREE CARRIERS ON THE REFRACTIVE INDEX OF DIRECT-GAP SEMICONDUCTORS.
CROSS, M. ADAMS, M. J.
OPTOELECTRONICS
6 (3), 199-216, 1974.

61433 THERMAL CONDUCTIVITY AND NATURAL REFRACTIVE INDEX OF POLYCRYSTALLINE MAGNESIUM FLUORIDE.
MEN, A. A. CHECHEL'NITSKII, A. Z.
VOLYNETS, F. K. SMIRNAYA, E. P.
OPT.-MEKH. PROM.
41 (1), 41-3, 1974.
(FOR ENGLISH TRANSLATION SEE E65922)

61435 THE ELECTRICAL CONDUCTIVITY FOR IMPERFECT CRYSTALS AT FINITE TEMPERATURE.
VAN ZUYLEN, H. J. LODDER, A.
PHYSICA (NETHERLANDS)
71 (2), 341-70, 1974.

61441 OPTICAL PROPERTIES OF STRONGLY EXCITED DIRECT BAND GAP MATERIALS.
LEVY, R. GRUN, J. B.
PHYS. STATUS SOLIDI (GERMANY)
22 A (1), 11-38, 1974.

61443 SCATTERING OF ELECTRONS IN SEMICONDUCTORS BY A CHARGED DISLOCATION.
GERLACH, E.
PHYS. STATUS SOLIDI (GERMANY)
62 B (1), K43-5, 1974.

61445 INVESTIGATION OF THE INFRARED-ACTIVE LATTICE VIBRATION IN STRONTIUM CHLORIDE.
DROSTE, R. GEICK, R.
PHYS. STATUS SOLIDI (GERMANY)
62 B (2), 511-17, 1974.

61449 INFLUENCE OF SUPERFIEICIAL SPACE CHARGE REGIONS ON THE OPTICAL ABSORPTION OF ZINC SULFIDE POLYCRYSTALLINE THIN FILMS.
BUGNET, P.
REV. PHYS. APPL. (FRANCE)
9 (2), 447-50, 1974.

61450 STATIC ULTRAHIGH PRESSURES ABOVE 500 KILOBARS.
LORENT, R. E.
REV. SCI. INSTRUM. (USA)
44 (12), 1691-3, 1973.

61451 LOW TEMPERATURE MAGNETO-RESISTANCE, LOGARITHMIC RESISTIVITY RISE AND ANISOTROPIC SUPERCONDUCTIVITY IN TA S(2)(PYRIDINE)(1/2).
THOMPSON, A. H.
SOLID STATE COMMUN. (USA)
13 (11), 1911-13, 1973.

EPIC Number | Bibliographic Citation

61452 COMMENTS ON DIRECT CURRENT CONDUCTIVITY IN AMORPHOUS SEMICONDUCTORS.
POLLAK, M.
SOLID STATE COMMUN.
13 (7), 869-72, 1973.

61454 ON JUMP CONDUCTION IN DISORDERED SEMICONDUCTORS.
BONCH-BRUEVICH, V. L. KAIPER, R.
VESTIN. MOSK. UNIV. FIZ. ASTRON. (USSR)
14 (6), 667-73, 1973.

61459 EFFECTS OF HOLE AND PLASMA CURRENTS ON THE INFRARED ABSORPTION OF INDIUM ANTIMONIDE.
BAUMGARDNER, C. A.
UNIVERSITY OF IDAHO, PH.D. THESIS
96PP., 1971.

61472 INDEXES OF REFRACTION OF ZINC SULFIDE, ZINC SELENIDE, ZINC TELLURIDE, CADMIUM SULFIDE, AND CADMIUM TELLURIDE IN THE FAR INFRARED.
HATTORI, T. HOMMA, Y. MITSUISHI, A.
TACKE, M.
OPT. COMMUN.
7 (3), 229-32, 1973.

61477 ANISOTROPIC RADIATION THERMOELEMENT.
ANATYCHUK, L. I. BOGOMOLOV, P. A.
KUPCHINSKII, O. I. LUSTE, O. YA.
YURTSENYUK, S. P.
OPT.-MEKH. PROM.
38 (1), 27-9, 1971.
(FOR ENGLISH TRANSLATION SEE E65921)

61478 PHOTOVOLTAIC EFFECTS IN COPPER SELENIDE - N-TYPE SILICON (GALLIUM ARSENIDE) JUNCTIONS.
MAKABE, R.
OSAKA KOGYO GIJUTSU SHIKENSHO KIHO
22 (4), 253-9, 1971.

61479 DOUBLE-CATHODE SPUTTERING SYSTEM AND ITS APPLICATION TO THE PREPARATION OF TANTALUM AND NIOBIUM FILMS.
GOTO, T. YAMANAKA, S.
OYO BUTSURI
40 (3), 269-75, 1971.

61481 COPPER SELENIDE - CADMIUM SELENIDE PHOTOVOLTAIC CELLS.
OTAKE, T. ONNAGAWA, H. MIYASHITA, K.
WADA, M.
OYO BUTSURI
40 (11), 1224-6, 1971.

61482 INTERFEROMETRIC DETERMINATION OF THE REFRACTIVE INDEX IN THE INFRARED REGION. I. CALCULATION METHOD FOR THE TRANSMITTANCE OF THE FABRY-PEROT INTERFEROMETER.
SZTRAKA, L. GROFESIK, A. JOBBAGY, A.
PERIOD. POLYTECH., CHEM. ENG.
14 (3-4), 309-19, 1970.

61493 SEMICONDUCTORS. FUNDAMENTAL PRINCIPLES.
MADELUNG, O.
PHYS. CHEM.
10, 331-70, 1970.
(EDITED BY HENRY EYRING, ACADEMIC: NEW YORK)

61494 PHOTOCONDUCTIVITY OF SEMICONDUCTORS.
BUBE, R. H.
PHYS. CHEM.
10, 515-77, 1970.
(EDITED BY HENRY EYRING, ACADEMIC: NEW YORK)

61498 EVALUATION OF RAMAN SPECTRA, PHONON RELAXATION TIME, AND INFRARED AND ULTRAVIOLET ABSORPTIONS INDUCED BY THALLIUM ION SUBSTITUTIONAL IN POTASSIUM IODIDE.
BENEDEK, G. TERZI, N.
PHYS. IMPURITY CENT. CRYST., PROC. INT. SEMIN. SELEC. PROBL. THEORY IMPURITY CENT. CRYST.
321-42, 1972.
(EDITED BY G. S. ZAVT, AKAD. NAUK EST. SSR, INST. FIZ. ASTRONL: TALLIN, USSR)

61505 DIFFUSION AND OPTICAL PROPERTIES OF GROUP III IMPURITIES IN ZINC SELENIDE.
BJERKELAND, H. HOLWECH, I.
PHYS. NOV.
6 (3-4), 139-45, 1972.

61508 OPTICAL DISPERSION AND IONICITY OF ALUMINUM PHOSPHIDE AND ALUMINUM ARSENIDE.
MONEMAR, B.
PHYS. SCR.
3 (3-4), 193-5, 1971.

61512 HIGH-PRESSURE PHENOMENA IN SOLIDS.
JAYARAMAN, A.
PHYS. SOLID STATE
255-75, 1969.
(EDITED BY S. BALAKRISHNA, ACADEMIC: LONDON, ENGLAND)

61514 SEARCH FOR HIGH-TEMPERATURE SUPERCONDUCTORS.
MATTHAIS, B. T.
PHYS. TODAY
24 (8), 23-8, 1971.

EPIC Number	Bibliographic Citation

61519 ACTIVATION ENERGY OF HOPPING CONDUCTION.
SHKLOVSKII, B. I. EFROS, A. L.
YANCHEV, I. YA.
PIS'MA ZH. EKSP. TEOR. FIZ.
14 (5), 348–51, 1971.
(FOR ENGLISH TRANSLATION SEE E63219)

61532 OPTICAL PROPERTIES OF THIN LAYERS OF ZINC, SELENIDE–CADMIUM SELENIDE AND ZINC TELLURIDE–CADMIUM TELLURIDE SYSTEMS PRODUCED BY THE WEDGE ON WEDGE METHOD.
KOT, M. V. TYRZIU, V. G.
POLUPROV. SOEDIN. IKH TVERD. RASTVORY
31–8, 1970.
(EDITED BY S. I. RADAUTSAN, RED.–IZD. OTD. AKAD. NAUK MOLD. SSR: KISHINEV, USSR)

61533 OPTICAL PROPERTIES OF GALLIUM SESQUISELENIDE IN THIN LAYERS.
TYRZIU, M. P. TYRZIU, V. G.
POLUPROV. SOEDIN. IKH TVERD. RASTVORY
118–24, 1970.

61540 NEW OBSERVATIONS ON NEON BAND–DEGE LUMINESCENCE IN GALLIUM ARSENIDE PHOSPHIDE.
ROESSLER, D. M. WU, T.–Y.
APPL. PHYS. LETT.
25 (12), 718–20, 1974.

61548 SOLID MATERIALS STUDIED IN THE SUBMILLIMETER WAVE REGION.
ALESHECHKIN, V. N. KRAFTMAKHER, G. A.
MERIAKRI, V. V. USHATKIN, E. F.
PRIB. TEKH. EKSP.
(4), 150–1, 1971.
(FOR ENGLISH TRANSLATION SEE E65901)

61549 MEASUREMENT OF THE REFRACTIVE INDEXES OF DIELECTRICS IN THE MILLIMETER WAVE REGION.
KOZLOV, G. V.
PRIB. TEKH. EKSP.
(4), 152–4, 1971.
(FOR ENGLISH TRANSLATION SEE E65902)

61550 MEASUREMENT OF PHOTOLUMINESCENCE, PHOTOEMF., AND ELECTRICAL LUMINESCENCE OF SEMICONDUCTOR MATERIALS AND STRUCTURES.
KNAB, O. D. MAGALYAS, V. I. FROLOV, V. D.
SHVEIKIN, V. I. SHMERKIN, I. A.
PRIB. TEKH. EKSP.
(4), 225–6, 1971.
(FOR ENGLISH TRANSLATION SEE E65905)

61554 METHOD FOR DETERMINING ELECTRICAL RESISTANCE AT HIGH PRESSURES AND TEMPERATURES.
CHERNOV, D. B. SHINYAEV, A. YA.
PRIB. TEKH. EKSP.
(4), 223–4, 1971.
(FOR ENGLISH TRANSLATION SEE E65904)

61555 LIQUID DIELECTRICS AT SUBMILLIMETER WAVELENGTHS.
APLETALIN, V. N. MERIAKRI, V. V.
CHIGRYAI, E. E.
PRIB. TEKH. EKSP.
(5), 149–50, 1971.
(FOR ENGLISH TRANSLATION SEE E65906)

61558 CRYOSTAT WITH A PNEUMATIC DEVICE FOR OPTICAL MEASUREMENTS IN THE FAR INFRARED REGION.
VODOP'YANOV, L. K. KOPANEV, V. D.
PRIB. TEKH. EKSP.
(6), 182–4, 1971.
(FOR ENGLISH TRANSLATION SEE E65909)

61559 REFLECTING ATTACHMENT FOR AN INFRARED SPECTROMETER.
KARPINOS, D. M. LISTOVNICHAYA, S. P.
AIVAZOV, V. YA.
PRIB. TEKH. EKSP.
(6), 190–1, 1971.
(FOR ENGLISH TRANSLATION SEE E65910)

61562 AUTOMATIC MEASUREMENT OF THE HALL EFFECT AND ELECTRICAL CONDUCTIVITY IN HEAVILY DOPED SEMICONDUCTORS.
GRUZINOV, B. F. KONSTANTINOV, P. P.
PRIB. TEKH. EKSP.
(5), 225–7, 1972.
(FOR ENGLISH TRANSLATION SEE E65913)

61563 PREPARATION OF SAMPLES OF SILICON EPITAXIAL FILMS FOR VAN DER PAUW MEASUREMENTS.
SOMODI, K.
PRIB. TEKH. EKSP.
(6), 206–8, 1972.
(FOR ENGLISH TRANSLATION SEE E65914)

61564 MEASUREMENT OF THE OPTICAL DENSITY OF LIQUIDS USING SCANNING DEVICES.
GOS'KOV, P. I. ZHELTOVSKII, G. A.
PRIB. TEKH. EKSP.
(1), 201–3, 1973.
(FOR ENGLISH TRANSLATION SEE E65915)

61578 COMPRESSIBILITIES AND ELECTRICAL RESISTANCE UNDER PRESSURE, WITH SPECIAL REFERENCE TO INTERMETALLIC COMPOUNDS.
BRIDGMAN, P. W.
PROC. AMERICAN ACAD. ARTS SCI.
70 (7), 285–317, 1936.

61595 THERMOELECTRIC POWER OF CELLS WITH IONIC COMPOUNDS INVOLVING IONIC AND ELECTRONIC CONDUCTION.
WAGNER, C.
PROGR. SOLID STATE CHEM.
7, 1–37, 1972.

61662 ANALYSIS OF THE THERMOELECTRIC POWER IN LEAD TIN TELLURIDE.
OCIO, M.
REV. PHYS. APPL.
7 (3), 151–4, 1972.

61670 INFLUENCE OF THERMAL TREATMENT ON THE PHOTOVOLTAIC EFFECT ARISING FROM THE CONTACT OF THIN TELLURIUM LAYERS WITH ZINC.
GHEORGHITA–OANCEA, C. BARBICI, L. ZAMFIR, E.
REV. ROUM. PHYS.
15 (8), 865–8, 1970.

61672 THERMOELECTRIC PROPERTIES OF QUATERNARY SOLID SOLUTIONS COMPOSED OF BISMUTH AND ANTIMONY TELLURIDES AND SELENIDES.
NICULESCU, D. IONESCU, R. JAKLOVSZKY, J.
NISTOR, N.
REV. ROUM. PHYS.
16 (8), 819–26, 1971.

61678 THERMOELECTRIC N–P TESTER USING A.C. BIAS FOR GALLIUM ARSENIDE AND GALLIUM PHOSPHIDE.
WOLFSTIRN, K. B. FOCHT, M. W.
REV. SCI. INSTRUM.
42 (1), 152–4, 1971.

61683 NEW DOUBLE BEAM OPTICAL LEVER REFRACTOMETER AND THE VARIATION OF THE REFRACTIVE INDEX OF SODIUM CHLORIDE WITH TEMPERATURE.
PEREIRA, F. N. D. D. HALLETT, A. C. H.
REV. SCI. INSTRUM.
42 (4), 490–3, 1971.

61706 MULTIPLET EXCITON BANDS OF ALKALI HALIDES IN THE EXTREME ULTRAVIOLET REGION.
SAITO, H.
SCI. LIGHT (TOKYO)
20 (1), 1–44, 1971.

61726 SIMULTANEOUS MEASUREMENTS OF RESISTIVITY AND THERMOELECTRIC POWER DURING ORDERING OF GOLD COPPER INTERMETALLIC COMPOUND.
VAN DER LEE, K. VAN DEN BEUKEL, A.
SCR. MET.
5 (10), 901–4, 1971.

61736 SOLAR CELLS. NEW SOURCES OF ELECTRICAL ENERGY.
POTMESILOVA, A.
SLABOPROUDLY OBZ.
33 (6), 284–6, 1972.

61741 STRUCTURE OF CADMIUM SULFIDE–COPPER(I) SULFIDE HETEROJUNCTION LAYERS.
DAVID, J. P. MARTINUZZI, S.
CABANE–BROUTY, F. SORBIER, J. P.
MATHIEU, J. M. ROMAN, J. M. BRETZNER, J. F.
SOL. CELLS, PROC. INT. COLLOQ.
81–94, 1971.

61742 INFRARED RESPONSE OF CADMIUM SULFIDE IN CONTACT WITH METALS.
BUTENDEICH, R. RUPPEL, W.
SOL. CELLS, PROC. INT. COLLOQ.
111–19, 1971.

61743 PARTIAL RESULTS ON CADMIUM SULFIDE AND CADMIUM TELLURIDE THIN–FILM SOLAR CELL SPATIAL RELIABILITY.
BERNARD, J. BERRY, J. BUISSON, J. P.
PAILLOUS, A.
SOL. CELLS, PROC. INT. COLLOQ.
229–40, 1971.

61754 CALCULATION OF THE REFRACTIVE INDEX OF CALCIUM FLUORIDE USING EXPERIMENTALLY DETERMINED OSCILLATOR PARAMETERS.
FIELD, G. R. WILKINSON, G. R.
SPECTROCHIM. ACTA
29 A (4), 659–64, 1973.

61758 DETERMINATION OF SURFACE STATE ENERGY POSITIONS BY SURFACE PHOTOVOLTAGE SPECTROMETRY: CADMIUM SULFIDE.
BALESTRA, C. L. LAGOWSKI, J. GATOS, H. C.
SURFACE SCI.
26 (1), 317–20, 1971.

61760 PHOTOVOLTAGE INVERSION EFFECT AND ITS APPLICATION TO SEMICONDUCTOR SURFACE STUDIES. CADMIUM SULFIDE.
LAGOWSKI, J. BALESTRA, C. L. GATOS, H. C.
SURFACE SCI.
27 (3), 547–58, 1971.

EPIC Number	Bibliographic Citation
61763	**WAVELENGTH DEPENDENCE OF THE SURFACE PHOTOVOLTAGE IN VACUUM CLEAVED CADMIUM SULFIDE.** STEINRISSER, F. HETRICK, R. E. SURFACE SCI. 28 (2), 607–20, 1971.
61764	**EFFECT OF ADSORBED WATER ON THE SURFACE PHOTOVOLTAGE OF GALLIUM ARSENIDE.** KATZ, M. J. FOX, D. C. HAAS, K. J. SURFACE SCI. 28 (2), 627–31, 1971.
61767	**PHOTOVOLTAGE INVERSION EFFECT RESULTING FROM A CONTINUOUS SPECTRUM OF SURFACE STATES. ZINC OXIDE.** LAGOWSKI, J. SPROLES, E. S., JR. GATOS, H. C. SURFACE SCI. 30 (3), 653–8, 1972.
61768	**EFFECT OF SURFACE STATES ON THE TRANSPORT COEFFICIENTS OF THIN SEMICONDUCTOR FILMS.** HARRIS, J. J. CROCKER, A. J. SURFACE SCI. 30 (3), 692–6, 1972.
61770	**SURFACE PHOTOVOLTAGE AND INTERNAL PHOTOEMISSION AT THE ANODIZED INDIUM ANTIMONIDE SURFACE.** LILE, D. L. SURFACE SCI. 34 (2), 337–67, 1973.
61774	**ELECTRICAL CONDUCTIVITY AND STRUCTURAL FEATURES OF ALUMINOSILICATE MELTS.** ZHMOIDIN, G. I. SVOISTVA STRUKT. SHLAKOVYKH RASPLAVOV 101–7, 1970. (EDITED BY I. S. KULIKOV, NAUKA: MOSCOW, USSR)
61807	**INVESTIGATIONS OF THE HALL EFFECT AND CONDUCTIVITY OF INDIUM GALLIUM ANTIMONIDE.** SZLENK, K. BYSZEWSKI, P. OLEMPSKA, Z. PHYS. STATUS SOLIDI 27 A (1), 49–58, 1975.
61824	**REGION OF SOLID SOLUTIONS OF GERMANIUM TELLURIDE IN ANTIMONY SESQUITELLURIDE.** ABRIKOSOV, N. KH. DANILOVA-DOBRYAKOVA, G. T. DOBRYNINA, N. A. IZV. AKAD. NAUK SSSR NEORG. MATER. 9 (4), 568–71, 1973. (FOR ENGLISH TRANSLATION SEE E61825)
61825	**REGION OF SOLID SOLUTIONS OF GERMANIUM TELLURIDE IN ANTIMONY TELLURIDE.** ABRIKOSOV, N. KH. DANILOVA-DOBRYAKOVA, G. T. DOBRYNINA, N. A. INORG. MATER., USSR 9 (4), 512–4, 1973. (ENGLISH TRANSLATION OF IZV. AKAD. NAUK SSSR, NEORG. MATER., 9 (4), 568–71; FOR ORIGINAL SEE E61824)
61826	**MEASUREMENT OF THERMAL AND ELECTRICAL CONDUCTIVITIES OF SMALL CROSS SECTION SAMPLES IN THE 80–400 K RANGE.** GOL'TSMAN, B. M. KOMISSARCHIK, M. G. INZH.-FIZ. ZH. (USSR) 20 (3), 527–33, 1971. (FOR ENGLISH TRANSLATION SEE E61827)
61827	**MEASUREMENT OF THERMAL AND ELECTRICAL CONDUCTIVITIES OF SMALL CROSS SECTION SAMPLES IN THE 80–400 K RANGE.** GOL'TSMAN, B. M. KOMISSARCHIK, M. G. J. ENG. PHYS. 20 (3), 385–9, 1971. (ENGLISH TRANSLATION OF INZH. FIZ. ZH., 20 (3), 527–33, 1971; FOR ORIGINAL SEE E61826)
61830	**OPTICAL CHARACTERISTICS OF LARGE SINGLE CRYSTALS OF FLUORIDES.** CHERNEUSKAYA, E. G. ALEKSEEVA, T. A. BAKHSHIEVA, G. F. LOUKOV, A. U. TIKHOMIROV, A. I. SHELUD'KO, R. N. KALININA, M. U. SOV. J. OPT. TECHNOL. 40 (6), 379–80, 1973. (ENGLISH TRANSLATION OF OPT. MEKH. PROM., 40 (6), 47–8, 1973; FOR ORIGINAL SEE E52216)
61845	**LONGITUDIANL PHOTOCONDUCTIVITY AND PHOTOEMF. IN CRYSTALS AND THIN FILMS OF II - VI COMPOUNDS.** KOT, M. V. PANASYUK, L. M. SIMASHKEVICH, A. V. SHERBAN, D. A. TR. FIZ. POLUPROV. KISHINEV. UNIV. (2), 64–71, 1969.
61851	**REFRACTION OF MELTS. SODIUM CHLORIDE-POTASSIUM CHLORIDE SYSTEM.** SMIRNOV, M. V. MUKATOV, T. KHAIMENOV, A. P. TR. INST. ELEKTROKHIM., AKAD. NAUK SSSR, URAL. FILIAL (14), 73–81, 1970.
61852	**REFRACTIVE INDEXES OF FUSED LITHIUM, SODIUM, AND POTASSIUM FLUORIDES.** SMIRNOV, M. V. MUKATOV, T. TR. INST. ELEKTROKHIM. URAL. FIL. AKAD. NAUK SSSR (16), 40–1, 1970.
61853	**MOLAR REFRACTION OF SODIUM CHLORIDE-RUBIDIUM CHLORIDE AND SODIUM CHLORIDE-CESIUM CHLORIDE MELTS.** SMIRNOV, M. V. MUKATOV, T. TR. INST. ELEKTROKHIM., URAL. NAUCH. TSENTR., AKAD. NAUK SSSR (17), 15–17, 1971.
61867	**THERMOELECTRIC AND THERMOPHYSICAL PROPERTIES OF GROUP V LIQUID CHALCOGENIDES.** VUKALOVICH, M. P. ALEKSANDROV, A. A. KAZANDZHAN, B. I. MACHUEV, V. I. OKHOTIN, V. S. FEDOROV, V. I. MISHUTKIN, T. I. TR. VSES. NAUCH.-TEKH. KONF. TERMODIN. SEKTS. TEPLOFIZ. SVOISTVA VESHCH. 95–101, 1969.
61876	**CONTROL OF SEMICONDUCTOR CRYSTALLIZATION BY PASSING AN ELECTRIC CURRENT THROUGH A CRYSTAL-MELT SYSTEM.** LEVINZON, D. I. TSVET. METAL. (2), 60–2, 1973.
61886	**EFFECT OF ENVIRONMENT ON THE PHOTOVOLTAIC PROPERTIES OF EPITAXIAL CADMIUM TELLURIDE FILMS.** NOVIK, F. T. REISSE, G. UCH. ZAP. LENINGRAD. GOS. UNIV., SER. FIZ. GEOL. NAUK (354), 41–6, 1970.
61890	**SYNTHETIC GRAPHITE METALS.** UBBELOHDE, A. R. UMSCHAU 71 (21), 786–7, 1971.
61906	**PHOTOELECTROMOTIVE FORCE AND STRUCTURE OF LEAD SULFIDE THIN FILMS AS A FUNCTION OF SUBSTRATE TEMPERATURE AND SPRAYING SPEED.** RUDENOK, M. I. CHASOVNIKOVA, L. I. VESTN. LENINGRAD. UNIV., FIZ., KHIM. (4), 52–62, 1972.
61908	**COEFFICIENT OF ABSORPTION IN THE ENERGY RANGE LESS THAN THE ENERGY GAP REGION IN THE PRESENCE OF RESONANCE SCATTERING.** KAIPER, R. VESTN. MOSK. UNIV., FIZ., ASTRON. 13 (3), 287–92, 1972.
61918	**MAGNETIC PROPERTIES OF URANIUM CHALCOGENIDES. I. URANIUM YTTRIUM-TYPE COMPOUNDS.** SUSKI, W. REIZER-NETTER, H. BULL. ACAD. POLON. SCI., SER. SCI. CHIM. 22 (8), 701–7, 1974.
61928	**REFRACTIVE INDEX AND DIAMETER DETERMINATIONS OF STEP INDEX OPTICAL FIBERS AND PREFORMS.** PRESBY, H. M. MARCUSE, D. APPL. OPT. 13 (12), 2882–5, 1974.
61934	**THERMAL TRANSFORMATIONS OF X CENTERS IN SODIUM CHLORIDE CRYSTALS.** BODRYAGIN, V. I. ANDYSHULA, N. A. FIZ. TVERD. TELA 16 (4), 1010–4, 1974. (FOR ENGLISH TRANSLATION SEE E61935)
61935	**THERMAL TRANSFORMATIONS OF X CENTERS IN SODIUM CHLORIDE CRYSTALS.** BODRYAGIN, V. I. ANDYSHULA, N. A. SOV. PHYS. SOLID STATE 16 (4), 653–5, 1974. (ENGLISH TRANSLATION OF FIZ. TVERD. TELA, 16 (4), 1010–4, 1974; FOR ORIGINAL SEE E61934)
61936	**MAGNETIC INTERACTIONS OF IRON ATOMS IN THE GALLIUM ARSENIDE LATTICE.** ISAEVIVANOV, V. V. KOLCHANOVA, N. M. MASTEROV, V. F. NASLEDOV, D. N. TALALAKIN, G. N. FIZ. TVERD. TELA 16 (4), 1044–50, 1974. (FOR ENGLISH TRANSLATION SEE E61937)
61937	**MAGNETIC INTERACTIONS OF IRON ATOMS IN THE GALLIUM ARSENIDE LATTICE.** ISAEVIVANOV, V. V. KOLCHANOVA, N. M. MASTEROV, V. F. NASLEDOV, D. N. TALALAKIN, G. N. SOV. PHYS. SOLID STATE 16 (4), 674–7, 1974. (ENGLISH TRANSLATION OF FIZ. TVERD. TELA 16 (4), 1044–50, 1974; FOR ORIGINAL SEE E61936)
61944	**AGGREGATION OF EUROPIUM DIPOSITIVE ION-VACANCY CENTERS IN EUROPIUM-ACTIVATED ALKALI HALIDE CRYSTALS.** SAVEL'EV, V. P. AVDONIN, V. P. DUGAROVA, L. D. NEDASHKOVSKII, A. P. PLACHENOV, B. T. FIZ. TVERD. TELA, 16 (4), 1090–3, 1974. (FOR ENGLISH TRANSLATION SEE E61945)

EPIC Number	Bibliographic Citation

61945 **AGGREGATION OF EUROPIUM DIPOSITIVE ION-VACANCY CENTERS IN EUROPIUM-ACTIVATED ALKALI HALIDE CRYSTALS.**
SAVEL'EV, V. P. AVDONIN, V. P.
DUGAROVA, L. D. NEDASHKOVSKII, A. P.
PLACHENOV, B. T.
SOV. PHYS. SOLID STATE
16 (4), 700–2, 1974.
(ENGLISH TRANSLATION OF FIZ. TVERD. TELA, 16 (4), 1090–3, 1974; FOR ORIGINAL SEE E61944)

61952 **SOME FEATURES OF THE SPECTRAL PROPERTIES OF CADMIUM SELENIDE SINGLE CRYSTALS ARISING FROM THEIR SURFACES.**
DAVYDOVA, N. A. MYASNIKOV, E. N.
STRASHNIKOVA, M. I.
FIZ. TVERD. TELA
16 (4), 1173–6, 1974.
(FOR ENGLISH TRANSLATION SEE E61953)

61953 **SOME FEATURES OF THE SPECTRAL PROPERTIES OF CADMIUM SELENIDE SINGLE CRYSTALS ARISING FROM THEIR SURFACES.**
DAVYDOVA, N. A. MYASNIKOV, E. N.
STRASHNIKOVA, M. I.
SOV. PHYS. SOLID STATE
16 (4), 752–4, 1974.
(ENGLISH TRANSLATION OF FIZ. TVERD. TELA, 16 (4), 1173–6, 1974; FOR ORIGINAL SEE E61952)

61958 **PERMITTIVITY OF STRONTIUM TITANATE FILMS IN THE TEMPERATURE RANGE 4.2–100 DEGREES K.**
VENDIK, O. G. KOZYREV, A. B. LOOS, G. D.
PAVLYUK, E. G. RUBAN, A. S.
TER-MARTIROSYAN, L. T.
FIZ. TVERD. TELA
16 (4), 1222–4, 1974.
(FOR ENGLISH TRANSLATION SEE E61959)

61959 **PERMITTIVITY OF STRONTIUM TITANATE FILMS IN THE TEMPERATURE RANGE 4.2–100 DEGREES K.**
VENDIK, O. G. KOZYREV, A. B. LOOS, G. D.
PAVLYUK, E. G. RUBAN, A. S.
TER-MARTIROSYAN, L. T.
SOV. PHYS. SOLID STATE
16 (4), 788–9, 1974.
(ENGLISH TRANSLATION OF FIZ. TVERD. TELA, 19 (4), 1222–4, 1974; FOR ORIGINAL SEE E61958)

61960 **DOMAIN CONTRIBUTION TO THE DIELECTRIC CONSTANT OF FERROELECTRICS.**
TURIK, A. V. BONDARENKO, E. I.
FIZ. TVERD. TELA
16 (4), 1240–2, 1974.
(FOR ENGLISH TRANSLATION SEE E61961)

61961 **DOMAIN CONTRIBUTION TO THE DIELECTRIC CONSTANT OF FERROELECTRICS.**
TURIK, A. V. BONDARENKO, E. I.
SOV. PHYS. SOLID STATE
16 (4), 804, 1974.
(ENGLISH TRANSLATION OF FIZ. TVERD. TELA, 16 (4), 1240–2, 1974; FOR ORIGINAL SEE E61960)

61962 **STUDY OF THE PHASE TRANSITIONS IN BARIUM TITANATE BY THE OPTICAL SECOND HARMONIC METHOD.**
MITIN, G. G. GORELIK, V. S.
MATSONASHVILI, B. N. SUSHCHINSKII, M. M.
FIZ. TVERD. TELA
16 (5), 1261–4, 1974.
(FOR ENGLISH TRANSLATION SEE E61963)

61963 **STUDY OF THE PHASE TRANSITIONS IN BARIUM TITANATE BY THE OPTICAL SECOND HARMONIC METHOD.**
MITIN, G. G. GORELIK, V. S.
MATSONASHVILI, B. N. SUSHCHINSKII, M. M.
SOV. PHYS. SOLID STATE
16 (5), 817–8, 1974.
(ENGLISH TRANSLATION OF FIZ. TVERD. TELA, 19 (5), 1261–4, 1974; FOR ORIGINAL SEE E61962)

61970 **TWO-PHOTON ABSORPTION SPECTRUM OF CADMIUM SULFIDE.**
BREDIKHIN, V. I. GENKIN, V. N.
FIZ. TVERD. TELA
16 (5), 1332–5, 1974.
(FOR ENGLISH TRANSLATION SEE E61971)

61971 **TWO-PHOTON ABSORPTION SEPCTRUM OF CADMIUM SULFIDE.**
BREDIKHIN, V. I. GENKIN, V. N.
SOV. PHYS. SOLID STATE
16 (5), 860–2, 1974.
(ENGLISH TRANSLATION OF FIZ. TVERD. TELA, 16 (5), 1332–5, 1974; FOR ORIGINAL SEE E61970)

61980 **ELECTROREFLECTION SPECTRA OF ZINC CADMIUM TELLURIDE SINGLE CRYSTALS.**
TYAGAI, V. A. SNITKO, O. V.
BONDARENKO, V. N. VITRIKHOVSKII, N. I.
POPOV, V. B. KRASIKO, A. N.
FIZ. TVERD. TELA
16 (5), 1373–82, 1974.
(FOR ENGLISH TRANSLATION SEE E61981)

61981 **ELECTROREFLECTION SPECTRA OF ZINC CADMIUM TELLURIDE SINGLE CRYSTALS.**
TYAGAI, V. A. SNITKO, O. V.
BONDARENKO, V. N. VITRIKHOVSKII, N. I.
POPOV, V. B. KRASIKO, A. N.
SOV. PHYS. SOLID STATE
16 (5), 885–90, 1974.
(ENGLISH TRANSLATION OF FIZ. TVERD. TELA, 16 (5), 1373–82, 1974; FOR ORIGINAL SEE E61980)

61984 **EFFECT PF COBALT DIPOSITIVE ON SPIN-WAVE DAMPING IN SUBSTITUTED LITHIUM FERRITES.**
BUNINA, M. P. LEBEDEVA, E. V.
PIL'SHCHIKOV, A. I. SEMIKHIN, V. I.
SIL'VESTROVICH, I. I.
FIZ. TVERD. TELA
16 (5), 1406–9, 1974.
(FOR ENGLISH TRANSLATION SEE E61985)

61985 **EFFECT OF COBALT DIPOSITIVE ON SPIN-WAVE DAMPING IN SUBSTITUTED LITHIUM FERRITES.**
BUNINA, M. P. LEBEDEVA, E. V.
PIL'SHCHIKOV, A. I. SEMIKHIN, V. I.
SIL'VESTROVICH, I. I.
SOV. PHYS. SOLID STATE
16 (5), 905–6, 1974.
(ENGLISH TRANSLATION OF FIZ. TVERD. TELA, 16 (5), 1406–9, 1974; FOR ORIGINAL SEE E61984)

61986 **EFFECT OF DIRECTIONAL STRESS ON THE BIREFRINGENCE OF CADMIUM SELENIDE.**
REZA, A. A. BABONAS, G. A.
FIZ. TVERD. TELA
16 (5), 1414–8, 1974.
(FOR ENGLISH TRANSLATION SEE E61987)

61987 **EFFECT OF DIRECTIONAL STRESS ON THE BIREFRINGENCE OF CADMIUM SELENIDE.**
REZA, A. A. BABONAS, G. A.
SOV. PHYS. SOLID STATE
16 (5), 909–11, 1974.
(ENGLISH TRANSLATION OF FIZ. TVERD. TELA, 16 (5), 1414–8, 1974; FOR ORIGINAL SEE E61986)

61988 **OPTICAL PROPERTIES OF CADMIUM TELLURIDE IN THE FAR INFRARED.**
VODOP'YANOV, L. K. VINOGRADOV, E. A.
KOLOTKOV, V. V. MITYAGIN, YU. A.
FIZ. TVERD. TELA
16 (5), 1419–25, 1974.
(FOR ENGLISH TRANSLATION SEE E61989)

61989 **OPTICAL PROPERTIES OF CADMIUM TELLURIDE IN THE FAR INFRARED.**
VODOP'YANOV, L. K. VINOGRADOV, E. A.
KOLOTKOV, V. V. MITYAGIN, YU. A.
SOV. PHYS. SOLID STATE
16 (5), 912–5, 1974.
(ENGLISH TRANSLATION OF FIZ. TVERD. TELA, 16 (5), 1419–25, 1974; FOR ORIGINAL SEE E61988)

61992 **INTERACTION OF LIGHT WITH LATTICE VIBRATIONS IN THIN FILMS OF A(2) B(6) SEMICONDUCTING COMPOUNDS.**
VODOP'YANOV, L. K. VINOGRADOV, E. A.
FIZ. TVERD. TELA
16 (5), 1432–8, 1974.
(FOR ENGLISH TRANSLATION SEE E61993)

61993 **INTERACTION OF LIGHT WITH LATTICE VIBRATIONS IN THIN FILMS OF A(2) B(6) SEMICONDUCTING COMPOUNDS.**
VODOP'YANOV, L. K. VINOGRADOV, E. A.
SOV. PHYS. SOLID STATE
16 (5), 919–22, 1974.
(ENGLISH TRANSLATION OF FIZ. TVERD. TELA, 16 (5), 1432–8, 1974; FOR ORIGINAL SEE E61992)

61996 **PHOTODIELECTRIC RESEARCH ON PHOTODIELECTRIC PROCESSES IN IONIC CRYSTALS.**
OSIPOV, P. K.
FIZ. TVERD. TELA
16 (5), 1476–8, 1974.
(FOR ENGLISH TRANSLATION SEE E61997)

61997 **PHOTODIELECTRIC RESEARCH ON PHOTODIELECTRIC PROCESSES IN IONIC CRYSTALS.**
OSIPOV, P. K.
SOV. PHYS. SOLID STATE
16 (5), 945–6, 1974.
(ENGLISH TRANSLATION OF FIZ. TVERD. TELA, 16 (5), 1476–8, 1974; FOR ORIGINAL SEE E61996)

62000 **RELAXATION OF DIELECTRIC PERMITTIVITY IN SINGLE-CRYSTAL BISMUTH TITANATE.**
SINYAKOV, E. V. DUDNIK, E. F. DUDA, V. M.
PODOL'SKII, V. A. GORFUNKEL, M. A.
FIZ. TVERD. TELA
16 (5), 1515–7, 1974.
(FOR ENGLISH TRANSLATION SEE E62001)

EPIC Number | Bibliographic Citation

62001 RELAXATION OF DIELECTRIC PERMITTIVITY IN SINGLE-CRYSTAL BISMUTH TITANATE.
SINYAKOV, E. V. DUDNIK, E. F. DUDA, V. M.
PODOL'SKII, V. A. GORFUNKEL, M. A.
SOV. PHYS. SOLID STATE
16 (5), 979–80, 1974.
(ENGLISH TRANSLATION OF FIZ. TVERD. TELA, 16 (5), 1515–7, 1974; FOR ORIGINAL SEE E62000)

62004 GENERATION OF CATION VACANCIES DURING THE FORMATION AND DESTRUCTION OF COLLOIDS IN POTASSIUM CHLORIDE CRYSTALS.
D'YACHENKO, N. G. TYURIN, A. V.
SHEVELEVA, A. S.
FIZ. TVERD. TELA
16 (5), 1527–30, 1974.
(FOR ENGLISH TRANSLATION SEE E62005)

62005 GENERATION OF CATION VACANCIES DURING THE FORMATION AND DESTRUCTION OF COLLOIDS IN POTASSIUM CHLORIDE CRYSTALS.
D'YACHENKO, N. G. TYURIN, A. V.
SHEVELEVA, A. S.
SOV. PHYS. SOLID STATE
16 (5), 990–1, 1974.
(ENGLISH TRANSLATION OF FIZ. TVERD. TELA, 16 (5), 1527–30, 1974; FOR ORIGINAL SEE E62004)

62006 STABILITY OF CENTERS IN POTASSIUM CHLORIDE AND POTASSIUM BROMIDE CRYSTALS WITH CATION AND ANION SUBSTITUTIONAL IMPURITIES.
KATS, M. L. GYUNSBURG, K. E.
GOLUBENTSEVA, L. I. ZVERZDOVA, N. P.
FIZ. TVERD. TELA
16 (5), 1534–6, 1974.
(FOR ENGLISH TRANSLATION SEE E62007)

62007 STABILITY OF CENTERS IN POTASSIUM CHLORIDE AND POTASSIUM BROMIDE CRYSTALS WITH CATION AND ANION SUBSTITUTIONAL IMPURITIES.
KATS, M. L. GYUNSBURG, K. E.
GOLUBENTSEVA, L. I. ZVERZDOVA, N. P.
SOV. PHYS. SOLID STATE
16 (5), 996–7, 1974.
(ENGLISH TRANSLATION OF FIZ. TVERD. TELA, 16 (5), 1534–6, 1974; FOR ORIGINAL SEE E62006)

62010 SPECTRAL, TEMPERATURE, AND CONCENTRATION DEPENDENCE OF THE INTERBAND ABSORPTION IN BARIUM TITANATE.
SHAPKIN, V. V. GRUSHEVSKII, YU. A.
GRISHBERG, YA. G. BURSIAN, E. V.
FIZ. TVERD. TELA
16 (5), 1546–9, 1974.
(FOR ENGLISH TRANSLATION SEE E62011)

62011 SPECTRAL, TEMPERATURE, AND CONCENTRATION DEPENDENCE OF THE INTERBAND ABSORPTION IN BARIUM TITANATE.
SHAPKIN, V. V. GRUSHEVSKII, YU. A.
GRISHBERG, YA. G. BURSIAN, E. V.
SOV. PHYS. SOLID STATE
16 (5), 1006–7, 1974.
(ENGLISH TRANSLATION OF FIZ. TVERD. TELA, 16 (5), 1546–9, 1974; FOR ORIGINAL SEE E62010)

62012 EFFECT OF PLASTIC DEFORMATION ON OPTICAL ABSORPTION OF CESIUM IODIDE CRYSTALS.
METOLIDI, E. N. NEKLYUDOV, I. M.
PANOVA, A. N.
FIZ. TVERD. TELA
16 (5), 1549–51, 1974.
(FOR ENGLISH TRANSLATION SEE E62013)

62013 EFFECT OF PLASTIC DEFORMATION ON OPTICAL ABSORPTION OF CESIUM IODIDE CRYSTALS.
METOLIDI, E. N. NEKLYUDOV, I. M.
PANOVA, A. N.
SOV. PHYS. SOLID STATE
16 (5), 1008–9, 1974.
(ENGLISH TRANSLATION OF FIZ. TVERD. TELA, 16 (5), 1549–51, 1974; FOR ORIGINAL SEE E62012)

62018 LIFETIME OF SPIN CORRELATION FORMATIONS AT THE CURIE POINT OF YTTRIUM IRON GARNET.
BELOV, K. P. SHEBALDIN, N. V.
FIZ. TVERD. TELA
16 (5), 1571–4, 1974.
(FOR ENGLISH TRANSLATION SEE E62019)

62019 LIFETIME OF SPIN CORRELATION FORMATIONS AT THE CURIE POINT OF YTTRIUM IRON GARNET.
BELOV, K. P. SHEBALDIN, N. V.
SOV. PHYS. SOLID STATE
16 (5), 1027–8, 1974.
(ENGLISH TRANSLATION OF FIZ. TVERD. TELA, 16 (5), 1571–4; FOR ORIGINAL SEE E62018)

62020 SINGULARITIES IN THE INTRINSIC ABSORPTION EDGES OF ZINC SILICON PHOSPHIDE AND ZINC GERMANIUM PHOSPHIDE SINGLE CRYSTALS.
GORBAN', I. S. GORYNYA, V. A.
LUGOVSKII, V. V. TYCHINA, I. I.
FIZ. TVERD. TELA
16 (5), 1574–6, 1974.
(FOR ENGLISH TRANSLATION SEE E62021)

62021 SINGULARITIES IN THE INTRINSIC ABSORPTION EDGES OF ZINC SILICON PHOSPHIDE AND ZINC GERMANIUM PHOSPHIDE SINGLE CRYSTALS.
GORBAN', I. S. GORYNYA, V. A.
LUGOVSKII, V. V. TYCHINA, I. I.
SOV. PHYS. SOLID STATE
16 (5), 1029–30, 1974.
(ENGLISH TRANSLATION OF FIZ. TVERD. TELA, 16 (5), 1574–6, 1974; FOR ORIGINAL SEE E62020)

62023 ACOUSTO-OPTIC PROPERTIES OF SOME CHALCOGENIDE CRYSTALS.
GOTTLIEB, M. ISAACS, T. J. FEICHTNER, J. D.
ROLAND, G. W.
J. APPL. PHYS.
45 (12), 5145–51, 1974.

62027 PROPERTIES AND STRUCTURE OF BORIC OXIDE-GERMANIUM OXIDE GLASSES.
SHELBY, J. E.
J. APPL. PHYS.
45 (12), 5272–7, 1974.

62028 ELECTRICAL PROPERTIES OF COPPER GALLIUM SULFIDE SINGLE CRYSTALS.
YU, P. W. DOWNING, D. L. PARK, Y. S.
J. APPL. PHYS.
45 (12), 5283–8, 1974.

62029 OPTICAL GUIDED WAVES IN CADMIUM SULFUR SELENIDE DIFFUSED LAYERS.
BRILLSON, L. J. CONWELL, E. M.
J. APPL. PHYS.
45 (12), 5289–93, 1974.

62030 PHOTOCONDUCTIVITY IN SOLUTION-GROWN COPPER-DOPED GALLIUM PHOSPHIDE.
SCHULZE, R. G. PETERSEN, P. E.
J. APPL. PHYS.
45 (12), 5307–11, 1974.

62032 PHOTOCONDUCTIVITY IN ANODIC TANTALUM OXIDE FORMED ON NITROGEN-DOPED TANTALUM FILMS.
THOMAS, J. H., III
J. APPL. PHYS.
45 (12), 5349–55, 1974.

62033 ELECTRICAL PROPERTIES OF SILVER INDIUM SELENIDE.
TELL, B. KASPER, H. M.
J. APPL. PHYS.
45 (12), 5367–70, 1974.

62036 MAGNETOSTRICTIVE PROPERTIES OF HOLMIUM TERBIUM IRON INTERMETALLIC COMPOUNDS.
KOON, N. C. SCHINDLER, A. I. WILLIAMS, C. M.
CARTER, F. L.
J. APPL. PHYS.
45 (12), 5389–91, 1974.

62037 EFFECT OF STRONG MAGNETIC FIELDS ON SUPERCONDUCTING TRANSITION OF SINGLE-CRYSTAL NIOBIUM SELENIDE.
LEUPOLD, H. A. ROTHWARF, F. WINTER, J. J.
BRESLIN, J. T. ROSS, R. L. AU COIN, T. R.
DUBECK, L. W.
J. APPL. PHYS.
45 (12), 5399–5405, 1974.

62039 ON THE GAMMA-GAMMA AND GAMMA-CHI TRANSITIONS OF THE GALLIUM INDIUM PHOSPHIDE ALLOYS
JOULLIE, A. M. ALIBERT, C.
J. APPL. PHYS.
45 (12), 5472–4, 1974.

62041 MEASUREMENT OF BIREFRINGENCE USING THE INTERFERENCE OF POLARIZED BEAMS IN CRYSTALS AT A POINT DELTA-N = 0 IN THE TRANSPARENT REGION.
SHALDIN, A. V. BELOGUROV, D. A.
OPT. SPECTROS., USSR
36 (3), 346, 1974.
(ENGLISH TRANSLATION OF OPT. SPEKTROSK., 36 (3), 599–600, 1974; FOR ORIGINAL SEE E59381)

62044 BAND NARROWING AND CHARGE TRANSFER IN SIX INTERMETALLIC COMPOUNDS.
MORUZZI, V. L. WILLIAMS, A. R. JANAK, J. F.
PHYS. REV.
10 B (12), 4856–62, 1974.

62048 X-RAY PHOTOELECTRON STUDIES OF THORIUM, URANIUM, AND THEIR DIOXIDES.
VEAL, B. W. LAM, D. J.
PHYS. REV.
10 B (12), 4902–8, 1974.

62055 ADSORPTION OF OXYGEN ON CLEAN CLEAVED (110) GALLIUM-ARSENIDE SURFACES.
DORN, R. LUTH, H. RUSSELL, G. J.
PHYS. REV.
10 B (12), 5049–56, 1974.

62056 ELECTRICAL PROPERTIES AND THE METAL-INSULATOR TRANSITION IN (SCANDIUM TITANIUM) OXIDE
CHANDRASHEKHAR, G. V. VAN ZANDT, L. L.
HONIG, J. M. JAYARAMAN, A.
PHYS. REV.
10 B (12), 5063–8, 1974.

EPIC Number	Bibliographic Citation

62059 **BAND STRUCTURE OF CADMIUM GERMANIUM ARSENIDE NEAR K=O.**
KILDAL, H.
PHYS. REV.
10 B (12), 5082–7, 1974.
(AD–A7761)

62060 **+HOTOLUMINESCENCE OF TITANIUM IN FOUR SILICON CARBIDE POLYTYPES.**
PATRICK, L. CHOYKE, W. J.
PHYS. REV.
10 B (12), 5091–4, 1974.

62062 **STRUCTURAL INTERPRETATION OF THE INFRARED AND RAMAN SPECTRA OF GLASSES IN THE ALLOY SYSTEM GERMANIUM SULFIDE.**
LUCOVSKY, G. GALEENER, F. L. KEEZER, R. C.
GEILS, R. H. SIX, H. A.
PHYS. REV.
10 B (12), 5134–46, 1974.

62063 **K.P PERTURBATION THEORY IN SEMICONDUCTOR ALLOYS.**
SIGGIA, E. D.
PHYS. REV.
10 B (12), 5147–58, 1974.

62064 **CALCULATED AND MEASURED REFLECTIVITY OF ZINC GERMANIUM PHOSPHIDE.**
VAREA DE ALVAREZ, C. COHEN, M. L.
KOHN, S. E. PETROFF, Y. SHEN, Y. R.
PHYS. REV.
10 B (12), 5175–83, 1974.

62065 **ELECTRONIC STRUCTURE AND PROPERTIES OF MAGNESIUM OXIDE.**
PANTELIDES, S. T. MICHISH, D. J. KUNZ, A. B.
PHYS. REV.
10 B (12), 5203–12, 1974.

62066 **DIFFERENCE IN CONDUCTIVITY BETWEEN LITHIUM DEUTERIUM AND LITHIUM HYDROGEN CRYSTALS.**
VAROTSOS, P. A. MOURIKIS, S.
PHYS. REV.
10 B (12), 5220–4, 1974.

62068 **THERMOLUMINESCENCE AND CONTINUOUS DISTRIBUTIONS OF TRAPS.**
BOSACCHI, A. FRANCHI, S. BOSACCHI, B.
PHYS. REV.
10 B (12), 5235–8, 1974.

62074 **OCCURRENCE OF POLARITY REVERSAL OF PHOTOINDUCED VOLTAGE IN MERCURIC IODIDE.**
ENDO, T. NAKAMURA, K.
WASEDA DAIGAKU RIKOGAKU KENKYUSHO HOKOKU
(52), 139–48, 1971.

62077 **DETERMINATION OF OPTICAL CONSTANTS OF N-TYPE GALLIUM ARSENIDE FROM REFLECTIVITY AND TRANSMISSION MEASUREMENTS IN THE FAR INFRARED.**
SOBOTTA, H. RIED, V.
WISS. Z. KARL–MARX–UNIV. LEIPSIG. MATH.–NATURWISS. REIHE
20 (1), 147–54, 1971.

62078 **APPARATUS FOR ELECTRODELESS MEASUREMENT OF ELECTRICAL RESISTIVITY.**
TSCHIRNER, H. U.
WISS. Z., TECH. HOCHSCH. KARL–MARX–STADT
12 (4), 427–41, 1970.

62084 **PERMITTIVITY OF MOLTEN SODIUM NITRATE.**
DOUCET, Y. SANTINI, R. TETE, A.
C. R. HEBD. SEANCES ACAD. SCI.
279 B (26), 637–9, 1974.

62085 **CRYSTALLOGRAPHIC AND MAGNETIC PROPERTIES OF THREE MIXED OXIDES WITH PEROVSKITE STRUCTURE.**
PADEL, L. GRENET, J.–C. POIX, P.
C. R. HEBD. SEANCES ACAD. SCI.
279 C (12), 505–7, 1974.

62097 **ANISOTROPY AND TEMPERATURE BEHAVIOR OF A 1.3 ELECTRON VOLTS OPTICAL ABSORPTION BAND IN ALPHA–SILICON CARBIDE (6 H).**
ODARICH, V. A.
ZH. PRIKL. SPEKTROSK.
14 (4), 732–4, 1971.
(FOR ENGLISH TRANSLATION SEE E64880)

62098 **OPTICAL CONSTANTS OF ALPHA–SILICON CARBIDE (6H) IN THE SELF–ABSORPTION REGION.**
ODARICH, V. A.
ZH. PRIKL. SPEKTROSK.
15 (1), 160–2, 1971.
(FOR ENGLISH TRANSLATION SEE E67085)

62099 **DETERMINATION OF THE CONCENTRATION LIMIT OF THE ISOMORPHIC SUBSTITUTION OF LEAD IN SODIUM CHLORIDE–LEAD AND POTASSIUM CHLORIDE–LEAD SYSTEMS.**
ARTEMOVA, V. B. DOBRZHANSKII, G. F.
KORTUKOVA, E. I. KREININ, O. L.
LEBEDEVA, V. N. ROZIN, K. M.
ZH. PRIKL. SPEKTROSK.
16 (2), 285–9, 1972.
(FOR ENGLISH TRANSLATION SEE E67086)

62100 **OPTICAL ABSORPTION IN NEUTRON–IRRADIATED GALLIUM PHOSPHIDE.**
PIVOVAROV V. YA. TKACHEV, V. D.
ZH. PRIKL. SPEKTROSK.
18 (2), 283–8, 1973.
(FOR ENGLISH TRANSLATION SEE E89715)

62127 **THE PREPARATION OF SEMI–INSULATING GALLIUM ARSENIDE BY CHROMIUM DOPING.**
CRONIN, G. R. HAISTY, R. W.
J. ELECTROCHEM. SOC.
111 (7), 874–7, 1964.

62161 **SUPERCONDUCTIVITY.**
MATTHAIS, B. T. GEBALLE, T. H.
COMPTON, V. B.
REV. MODERN PHYS.
35 (1), 1–22, 1963.

62163 **ABSORPTION EDGE OF UNIAXIALLY DEFORMED CADMIUM SULFIDE SINGLE CRYSTALS.**
VITRIKHOVSKII, N. I. KURIK, M. V.
MANZHARA, V. S.
FIZ. TEKH. POLUPROV.
7 (5), 931–4, 1973.
(FOR ENGLISH TRANSLATION SEE E59409)

62165 **ANISOTROPIC DEMBER PHOTO–EMF OF A SEMICONDUCTOR WITH A PERIODIC DOPING PROFILE.**
GRIBNIKOV, Z. S.
FIZ. TEKH. POLUPROV.
7 (6), 1225–9, 1973.
(FOR ENGLISH TRANSLATION SEE E59411)

62170 **MAGNETIC PROPERTIES OF COMPOUNDS OF RARE–EARTH METALS WITH IRON.**
BELOV, K. P. NIKITIN, S. A. BISLIEV, A. M.
SAVITSKII, E. M. TEREKHOVA, V. F.
KOLESNICHENKO, V. E.
SOV. PHYS. JETP
37 (6), 1086–8, 1973.
(ENGLISH TRANSLATION OF ZH. EKSP. TEOR. FIZ., 64 (6), 2154–9, 1973; FOR ORIGINAL SEE E51313)

62171 **OPTICAL ORIENTATION OF EXCITONS IN UNIAXIAL CRYSTALS. LARGE EXCHANGE SPLITTING.**
BIR, G. L. PIKUS, G. E.
SOV. PHYS. JETP
37 (6), 1116–21, 1973.
(ENGLISH TRANSLATION OF ZH. EKSP. TEOR. FIZ., 64 (6), 2210–21, 1973; FOR ORIGINAL SEE E51314)

62174 **INSULATED–CRYSTAL METHOD FOR MEASURING ELECTRICAL PROPERTIES OF THIN SEMICONDUCTING FILMS.**
KOVTONYUK, N. F. AMRINOV, N. M.
MAGOMEDOV, A. A.
SOV. PHYS. J.
(5), 653–6, 1971.
(ENGLISH TRANSLATION OF IZV. VYSSH. UCHEB. ZAVED. FIZ., (5), 105–9, 1971; FOR ORIGINAL SEE E59598)

62185 **CHARACTERISTIC SPECTRA OF ENERGY ABSORPTION FOR DIELECTRIC SOLIDS.**
PLENDL, J. N.
APPL. OPT.
9 (12), 2768–86, 1970.

62186 **RADIATION–INDUCED CHANGES IN REFRACTIVE INDEX AND ABSORPTION COEFFICIENT FOR SEVERAL OPTICAL MATERIALS.**
OLSON, D. R. DIESELMAN, H. D.
SCHROEDER, J. B.
APPL. OPT.
10 (1), 81–6, 1971.

62190 **FORMULAS FOR THE DERIVATIVES OF THE COMPLEX INDEX OF REFRACTION WITH RESPECT TO DELTA, PSI, PHI, AND D.**
LOESCHER, D. H.
APPL. OPT.
10 (5), 1031–3, 1971.

62194 **ION–IMPLANTATION INDUCED OPTICAL ABSORPTION EDGE SHIFTS IN GALLIUM PHOSPHIDE.**
DAVEY, J. E. PANKEY, T. MALMBERG, P. R.
LUCKE, W. H.
APPL. PHYS. LETT.
1M (8), 323–5, 1970.

62195 **N–P JUNCTION PHOTOVOLTAIC DETECTORS IN LEAD TELLURIDE PRODUCED BY PROTON BOMBARDMENT.**
DONNELLY, J. P. HARMAN, T. C.
FOYT, A. G., JR.
APPL. PHYS. LETT.
18 (6), 259–61, 1971.

62200 **ABSORPTION AT 10.6 MU VIA IONIC DIPOLE–DIPOLE INTERACTIONS.**
NICOLAI, V. O.
APPL. PHYS. LETT.
20 (12), 486–7, 1972.

62201 **FABRICATION OF SINGLE–CRYSTAL SEMICONDUCTOR OPTICAL WAVEGUIDES BY SOLID–STATE DIFFUSION.**
TAYLOR, H. F. MARTIN, W. E. HALL, D. B.
SMILEY, V. N.
APPL. PHYS. LETT.
21 (3), 95–8, 1972.

EPIC Number	Bibliographic Citation

62222 **PHOTOELECTROCHEMICAL PROCESSES AND PHOTOCATALYSIS ON ZINC OXIDE SUSPENSIONS AND ZINC OXIDE LAYERS.**
GERISCHER, H. CAMMANN, K.
BER. BUNSENGES. PHYS. CHEM.
76 (5), 392–5, 1972.

62230 **EFFECT OF OXYGEN ON THE TEMPERATURE DEPENDENCE OF ELECTRICAL PROPERTIES OF REACTIVELY SPUTTERED TANTALUM FILMS.**
WATERHOUSE, N. WESTWOOD, W. D.
CAN. J. PHYS.
49 (17), 2250–63, 1971.

62235 **PHOTOVOLTAIC FILMS OF CADMIUM TELLURIDE DEPOSITED ON MOVING SUBSTRATE.**
BENDA, M.
CESK. CAS. FYS. (CZECHOSLOVAKIA)
20 A (4), 366–9, 1970.

62243 **A. C. POTENTIOMETRIC METHOD FOR HIGH TEMPERATURE RESISTIVITY AND PHASE BOUNDARY DETERMINATION.**
CHIOTTI, P.
AMES LAB., IOWA STATE UNIVERSITY
19PP., 1971.
(IS–2683, N72–30406, CONF–710926–2)

62246 **GALLIUM NITRIDE FOR LED APPLICATIONS.**
PANKOVE, J. I.
RADIO CORP. OF AMERICA, PRINCETON, N. J.
64PP., 1973.
(N73–27676, NASA–CR–132263, PRRL–73–CR–32)

62248 **MATERIALS FOR HIGH-POWER CARBON DIOXIDE LASERS.**
RUDKO, T. I. HORRIGAN, F. A.
RESEARCH DIVISION, RAYTHEON CO., WALTHAM, MASS.
100PP., 1969.
(AD–693 311)

62250 **METHODS OF MEASUREMENT FOR SEMICONDUCTOR MATERIALS, PROCESS CONTROL, AND DEVICES.**
BULLIS, W. M.
NATIONAL BUREAU OF STANDARDS, WASHINGTON, D. C.
62PP., 1970.
(AD–710 906, NBS–TN–527)

62251 **THRESHOLD REQUIREMENTS AND CARRIER INTERACTION EFFECTS IN GALLIUM ARSENIDE PLATELET LASERS.**
ROSSI, J. A. KEUNE, D. L. HOLONYAK, N., JR.
DAPKUS, P. D. BURNHAM, R. D.
J. APPL. PHYS.
41 (1), 31l–20, 1970.
(AD–714 533, AFML–TR–70–149)

62252 **LASER RECOMBINATION TRANSITION IN P-TYPE GALLIUM ARSENIDE.**
ROSSI, J. A. HOLONYAK, N., JR. DAPKUS, P. D.
APPL. PHYS. LETT.
15 (4), 109–10, 1969.
(AD–714 533, AFML–TR–70–149)

62253 **GALLIUM ARSENIDE JUNCTION LASERS CONTAINING THE AMPHOTERIC DOPANTS GERMANIUM AND SILICON.**
BURNHAM, R. D. DAPKUS, P. D.
HOLONYAK, N., JR. KEUNE, D. L.
ZWICKER, H. R.
SOLID STATE ELECTRON.
13, 199–205, 1970.
(AD–714 533, AFML–TR–70–149)

62254 **LASER OPERATION AND SPECTROSCOPY OF EPITAXIAL GALLIUM ARSENIDE GUNN OSCILLATOR WAFERS.**
HOLONYAK, N., JR. KEUNE, D. L. ROSSI, J. A.
LAWLEY, K. L. WALLINE, R. E. WILLIAMS, F. V.
J. APPL. PHYS.
40 (12), 4998–9, 1969.
(AD–714 533, AFML–TR–70–149)

62255 **DIRECT OBSERVATION OF A DYNAMIC BURNSTEIN SHIFT IN GALLIUM ARSENIDE: GERMANIUM PLATELET LASER.**
DAPKUS, P. D. HOLONYAK, N., JR.
BURNHAM, R. D. KEUNE, D. L.
APPL. PHYS. LETT.
16 (3), 93–5, 1970.
(AD–714 533, AFML–TR–70–149)

62256 **STIMULATED EMISSION IN LOSSY SEMICONDUCTOR LASER MODES.**
KEUNE, D. L. HOLONYAK, N., JR. DAPKUS, P. D.
BURNHAM, R. D.
J. APPL. PHYS.
41 (6), 2725–7, 1970.
(AD–714 533, AFML–TR–70–149)

62260 **MICROWAVE METHODS OF STUDYING SEMICONDUCTING MATERIALS.**
GRIFFIN, D. W.
SCHOOL OF ELECTRICAL ENGINEERING, CORNELL UNIV., ITHACA, N. Y.
182PP., 1971.
(AD–719 869, RADC–TR–71–28)

62262 **DEVELOPMENT OF GALLIUM ARSENIDE INFRARED WINDOW MATERIAL.**
THOMPSON, A. G.
ELECTRONIC MATERIALS LAB., BELL AND HOWELL COMP., PASADENA, CALIF.
48PP., 1970.
(AD–720 390)

62263 **METHODS OF MEASUREMENT FOR SEMICONDUCTOR MATERIALS, PROCESS CONTROL, AND DEVICES.**
BULLIS, W. M.
NATIONAL BUREAU OF STANDARDS, WASHINGTON, D. C.
58PP., 1971.
(AD–723 671, NBS–TN–571)

62264 **HETEROJUNCTION PHOTOVOLTAIC SOLAR CELLS.**
NOWAK, W. B. SMITH, K. P. FENER, A. R.
NORTHEASTERN UNIV., BOSTON, MASS.
64–159, 1971.
(AD–726 114, AFCRL–71–0163)

62266 **METHODS OF MEASUREMENT FOR SEMICONDUCTOR MATERIALS, PROCESS CONTROL, AND DEVICES.**
BULLIS, W. M.
NATIONAL BUREAU OF STANDARDS, WASHINGTON, D. C.
72PP., 1971.
(AD–728 611, NBS–TN–592)

62269 **RESEARCH ON THE PROPERTIES OF AMORPHOUS SEMICONDUCTORS AT HIGH TEMPERATURES.**
DENEUFVILLE, J. P.
ENERGY CONVERSION DEVICES, INC., TROY, MICH.
178PP., 1971.
(AD–730 449, ECD–516–2,)

62272 **SEMICONDUCTOR CONDUCTIVITY USING A HIGH-SENSITIVITY TECHNIQUE.**
DIXON, S., JR. DIORDANO, R. F. JACOBS, H.
ARMY ELECTRONICS COMMAND, FORT MONMOUTH, N. J.
61PP., 1971.
(AD–736 366, ECOM–3507)

62273 **ELECTRO-OPTIC CHARACTERISTICS OF CADMIUM TELLURIDE AT 3.39 AND 10.6 MU.**
KIEFER, J. F.
APPL. PHYS. LETT.
15 (1), 26–7, 1969.
(AD–744 500, AROD–7893:11–P)

62274 **THEORETICAL STUDIES OF HIGH-POWER INFRARED WINDOW MATERIALS.**
SPARKS, M.
XONICS INC., VAN NUYS, CALIFORNIA
179PP., 1973.
(AD–765 354)

62275 **HIGH ENERGY LASER WINDOWS.**
RICE, R. W.
NAVAL RESEARCH LAB., WASHINGTON, D. C.
57PP., 1972.
(AD–765 514)

62276 **STUDY OF LASER-IRRADIATED THIN FILMS.**
DESHAZER, L. G. LEUNG, K. M. NEWMAN, B. E.
UNIVERSITY OF SOUTHERN CALIF., LOS ANGELES, CALIF.
130PP., 1973.
(AD–774 022, AFCRL–TR–73–0585, USCEE–461)

62277 **THERMOELECTRIC MATERIALS AT 300 K.**
DEVORE, R. ANDERSON, W. W. HARPSTER, J. W.
SEPSY, C. F. SHAPIRO, D. E.
DEPT. OF MECHANICAL ENGR., OHIO STATE UNIV., COLUMBUS. OHIO
218PP., 1974.
(AD–781 545, OSURF–3714–1)
(N75–23356)

62285 **PARAELASTIC ALIGNMENT OF OH(–) IONS IN RUBIDIUM BROMIDE AND RUBIDIUM IODIDE.**
JIMINIZ, R. V. LUTY, F.
PHYS. STATUS SOLIDI
52 B, K27–K31, 1972.
(AD–781 561, AF–AFOSR–1645–69)

62286 **STUDY OF THE PARAELECTRIC BEHAVIOR OF OH(–) IONS IN ALKALI HALIDES WITH OPTICAL AND CALORIC METHODS. I. STATICS OF DIPOLE ALIGNMENT.**
KAPPHAN, S. LUTY, F.
J. PHYS. CHEM. SOLIDS
34, 969–87, 1973.
(AD–781 562, AF–AFOSR–1645–69)

62287 **INDICES OF REFRACTION OF MOLTEN FLUORIDES OF LITHIUM, SODIUM, AND POTASSIUM.**
SMIRNOV, M. V. MUKATOV, T.
ELEKTROKHIM. RASPLAV. SOLEV. I TVERD. ELEKTRO.
(16), 40–1, 1970.
(FOR ENGLISH TRANSLATION SEE E62288)

EPIC Number	Bibliographic Citation
62288	**INDICES OF REFRACTION OF MOLTEN FLUORIDES OF LITHIUM, SODIUM, AND POTASSIUM.** SMIRNOV, M. V. MUKATOV, T. ARMY FOREIGN SCIENCE AND TECHNOLOGY CENTER, CHARLOTTESVILLE, VIRGINIA 4PP., 1973. (ENGLISH TRANSLATION OF ELEKTROKHIM. RASPLAV. SOLEV. I TVERD. ELEKTRO., (16), 40–1, 1970; FOR ORIGINAL SEE E62287) (AD–781 736, FSTC–HT–23–1341–73)
62289	**LOW ABSORPTANCE METALLIC COATINGS FOR METALLIC SUBSTRATES.** KURDOCK, J. R. PERKIN–ELMER CORP., NORWALK, CONN. 81PP., 1974. (AD–781 790, AFWL–TR–74–28)
62293	**THERMOPHOTOVOLTAIC CELLS.** SCHWARTZ, R. J. GARDNER, N. F. MUNRO, P. LAMMERT, M. SCHOOL OF ELECTRICAL ENGR., PURDUE UNIVERSITY, LAFAYETTE, IND. 80PP., 1974. (AD–782 833, N74–34662, ECOM–0281–72–F)
62294	**ION BOMBARDMENT AND OPTICAL STUDIES OF LEAD AZIDE.** COOPER, C. B. MILLER, J. H. DEPT. OF PHYSICS, DELAWARE UNIV., NEWARK 19PP., 1974. (AD–782 884, AROD–11666.1–A)
62295	**GROWTH AND HARDENING OF ALKALI HALIDES FOR USE IN INFRARED LASER WINDOWS.** SIBLEY, W. A. BUTLER, C. T. HOPKINS, J. R. MARTIN, J. J. DEPT. OF PHYSICS, OKLAHOMA STATE UNIV., STILLWATER 31PP., 1974. (AD–783 328, N74–34918, AFCRL–TR–74–0220)
62296	**IR WINDOW STUDIES.** KROGER, F. MARBURGER, J. H. ELECTRONIC SCIENCES LAB., UNIV. OF SOUTHERN CALIF., LOS ANGELES 89PP., 1973. (AD–783 331, AFCRL–TR–74–0060)
62297	**APPARATUS FOR PRODUCING FILMS OF THERMOELECTRIC MATERIALS.** NAER, V. A. KRAVCHUK, V. V. ARMY FOREIGN SCIENCE AND TECHNOLOGY CENTER, CHARLOTTESVILLE, VIRGINIA 7PP., 1974. (ENGLISH TRANSLATION OF KHOLOD. TEKH. TEKHNOL., (10), 44–8, 1970; FOR ORIGINAL SEE E61000) (AD–783 731, FSTC–HT–23–2034–72)
62298	**THERMOELECTRIC SEMICONDUCTOR MATERIALS BASED ON BISMUTH TELLURIDE.** GOLTSMAN, B. M. KUDINOV, B. A. SMIRNOV, I. A. MONO. POLUPROVODNIKOVYE TERMOELEKTRICHESKIE MATERIALY NA OSNOVE, MOSCOW 320PP., 1972. (FOR ENGLISH TRANSLATION SEE E62299)
62299	**THERMOELECTRIC SEMICONDUCTOR MATERIALS BASED ON BISMUTH TELLURIDE.** GOLTSMAN, B. M. KUDINOV, B. A. SMIRNOV, I. A. ARMY FOREIGN SCIENCE AND TECHNOLOGY CENTER, CHARLOTTESVILLE, VIRGINA 346PP., 1973. (ENGLISH TRANSLATION OF MONO. POLUPROVODNIKOVYE TERMOELEKTRICHESKIE MATERIALY NA OSNOVE, MOSCOW, 320PP., 1972; FOR ORIGINAL SEE E62298) (AD–783 734, FSTC–HT–23–1782–73)
62300	**DEVICES BASED ON THERMOELECTRICAL PHENOMENA.** GORODETSKII, A. F. KRAVCHENKO, A. F. SAMOILOV, E. M. MONO. OSNOVY FIZ. POLUPROVOD. I POLUPROVOD. PRIB. 315–26, 1966. (FOR ENGLISH TRANSLATION SEE E62301)
62301	**DEVICES BASED ON THERMOELECTRICAL PHENOMENA.** GORODETSKII, A. F. KRAVCHENKO, A. F. SAMOILOV, E. M. ARMY FOREIGN SCIENCE AND TECHNOLOGY CENTER, CHARLOTTESVILLE, VIRGINIA 24PP., 1974. (ENGLISH TRANSLATION OF MONO. OSNOVY FIZ. POLUPROVOD. I POLUPROVOD. PRIB., N. P., 315–26, 1966; FOR ORIGINAL SEE E62300) (AD–783 821, FSTC–HT–23–45–74)
62302	**THE AIR FORCE WEAPONS LABORATORY LASER WINDOW TEST APPARATUS.** DUEWEKE, P. W. PREONAS, D. D. PETERSON, D. G., JR. OHIO RESEARCH INST., DAYTON UNIV. 144PP., 1974. (AD–783 852, N75–11329, AFWL–TR–73–181)

EPIC Number	Bibliographic Citation
62303	**INDIRECTLY FUNDED RESEARCH AND EXPLORATORY DEVELOPMENT AT THE APPLIED PHYSICS LABORATORY.** HART, R. W. APPLIED PHYSICS LAB., JOHNS HOPKINS UNIV., SILVER SPRING, MD. 161PP., 1973. (AD–783 996, APL–TG–1241)
62305	**LOW LOSS WINDOW MATERIALS FOR CHEMICAL LASERS.** HARRINGTON, J. A. DEPT. OF PHYSICS, ALABAMA UNIV., HUNTSVILLE 28PP., 1974. (AD–784 326, UAH–RR–154)
62306	**THEORETICAL STUDIES OF HIGH–POWER ULTRAVIOLET AND INFRARED MATERIALS.** SPARKS, M. S. DUTHLER, C. J. XONICS INC., VAN NUYS, CALIF. 245PP., 1974. (AD–784 327)
62307	**IR WINDOW STUDIES.** KROGER, F. A. MARBURGER, J. H. BASS, M. COPLEY, S. M. CROWELL, C. R. DE SHAZER, L. HELLWARTH, R. W. PARKS, J. SHLICKTA, P. J. STEIER, W. H. WHELAN, J. M. WILCOX, W. J. ELECTRONIC SCIENCES LAB., UNIV. OF SOUTHERN CALIF., LOS ANGELES 17–9, 1974. (AD–784 655)
62308	**APPARATUS FOR THE HIGH–SPEED MEASUREMENT OF THE THERMOELECTRICAL PARAMETERS OF SEMICONDUCTOR MATERIALS IN THE 150–500 K RANGE.** ERASOVA, N. A. KAIDANOV, V. I. NOVICHKOV, A. I. NUROMSKII, A. B. ARMY FOREIGN SCIENCE AND TECHNOLOGY CENTER, CHARLOTTESVILLE, VIRGINIA 15PP., 1974. (ENGLISH TRANSLATION OF TR. LENINGRAD. POLITEKH. INST., (325), 10–5, 1971; FOR ORIGINAL SEE E49756) (AD–784 739, FSTC–HT–23–1881–73, N75–11789)
62309	**GROWTH AND HARDENING OF ALKALI HALIDES FOR USE IN INFRARED LASER WINDOWS.** BUTLER, C. T. MARTIN, J. J. MERKLE, L. D. SIBLEY, W. A. SILL, E. L. DEPT. PF PHYSICS, OKLAHOMA STATE UNIV., STILLWATER 13PP., 1974.
62310	**SYNTHESIS AND CHARACTERIZATION OF EUROPIUM SULFIDE.** ANANTH, K. P. GIELISSE, P. J. ROCKETT, T. J. DIV. OF ENGINEERING RESEARCH, RHODE ISLAND UNIV., KINGSTON 17–29, 1973. (AD–784 806, AFCRL–TR–74–0295, URI–9804–4258)
62312	**HIGH PRESSURE POLYMORPHISM IN CADMIUM SULFIDE, CADMIUM SELENIDE, AND CADMIUM TELLURIDE.** YU, W. C. GIELISSE, P. J. MATER. RES. BULL. 6 (7), 621–38, 1971. (AD–784 806, AFCRL–TR–74–0295, URI–9804–4258)
62313	**HIGH ENERGY LASER WINDOWS.** RICE, R. W. NAVAL RESEARCH LAB., WASHINGTON, D. C. 1–3, 1974. (AD–784 991)
62314	**THEORY OF INTRINSIC MULTIPHONON ABSORPTION AND COMPARISON WITH EXPERIMENT.** BOYER, L. L. ROSENSTOCK, H. B. NAVAL RESEARCH LAB., WASHINGTON, D. C. 47–58, 1974. (AD–784 991)
62315	**IMPURITY EFFECTS ON VACUUM ULTRAVIOLET AND INFRARED MULTIPHONON SPECTRA OF LASER–WINDOW MATERIALS.** KLEIN, P. H. KRULFELD, M. CLOFFY, E. W. NAVAL RESEARCH LAB., WASHINGTON, D. C. 59–71, 1974. (AD–784 991)
62316	**SPECTRAL EMITTANCE STUDIES OF SURFACE AND BULK ABSORPTION.** HASS, M. STIERWALT, D. L. NAVAL RESEARCH LAB., WASHINGTON, D. C. 81–8, 1974. (AD–784 991)
62317	**SEPARATION OF SURFACE AND BULK ABSORPTION IN LASER CALORIMETRY.** BABISKIN, J. HASS, M. NAVAL RESEARCH LAB., WASHINGTON, D. C. 91–8, 1974. (AD–784 991)
62318	**LARGE POLARIZATION DEPENDENT VOLTAGES IN FERROELECTRIC CERAMICS.** BRODY, P. S. CROWNE, F. HARRY DIAMOND LABS., WASHINGTON, D. C. 12PP., 1973. (AD–785 608)

EPIC Number	Bibliographic Citation
62320	**LEAD TELLURIDE ALLOYED WITH INDIUM AND LANTHANUM.** GORBACHEV, V. V. LINSKY, V. A. MAKAROV, E. F. ZHEMCHUZHINA, E. A. IVANOV, A. I. MONO. KHIMICH. SVYAZ V POLUPROVOD. I POLUMETALLAKH, MINSK 374–82, 1972. (FOR ENGLISH TRANSLATION SEE E62321)
62321	**LEAD TELLURIDE ALLOYED WITH INDIUM AND LANTHANUM.** GORBACHEV, V. V. LINSKY, V. A. MAKAROV, E. F. ZHEMCHUZHINA, E. A. IVANOV, A. I. ARMY FOREIGN SCIENCE AND TECHNOLOGY CENTER, CHARLOTTESVILLE, VIRGINIA 16PP., 1974. (ENGLISH TRANSLATION OF MONO. KHIMICH. SVYAZ V POLUPROVOD. I POLUMETALLAKH, MINSK 374–82, 1972; FOR ORIGINAL SEE E62320) (AD–786 794, FSTC–HT–23–728–74)
62322	**THE APPLICATION OF PHYSICAL VAPOR DEPOSITION TO SEMICONDUCTOR MATERIALS FOR USE AS HIGH POWER INFRARED WINDOWS.** SHIOZAWA, L. R. JOST, J. M. ROBERTS, D. A. GOULD INV., CLEVELAND, OHIO 130PP., 1973. (AD–918 931L, AFML–TR–73–163)
62323	**IR WINDOW STUDIES.** KROGER, F. A. MARBURGER, J. H. ELECTRONIC SCIENCES LAB., UNIV. OF SOUTHERN CALIF., LOS ANGELES 67PP., 1974. (AD–787 852, AFCRL–TR–74–0268)
62324	**CARBON DIOXIDE LASER WINDOWS.** GOTTLIEB, G. W. NICOLAI, V. O. AIR FORCE WEAPONS LAB., KIRTLAND AFB, N. MEX. 22PP., 1969. (AD–859 306, AFWL–TR–69–108)
62325	**HIGH POWER C. W. AND PULSE OPERATED CARBON DIOXIDE LASER WINDOWS.** ELYARD, C. A. LAMBERT, R. CENTRAL LABS., GENERAL ELECTRIC COMP., LTD, WEMBLEY, ENGLAND 15PP., 1973. (AD–915 053, DRIC–BR–37701)
62327	**INVESTIGATIONS OF THE NEW TRIGONAL GADOLINIUM TRIPOSITIVE ESR CENTER PRODUCED IN IRRADIATED ALKALINE–EARTH FLUORIDE CRYSTALS.** LEE, S. YANG, C.–C. BEVOLO, A. J. PHYS. REV. 10 B (11), 4515–22, 1974.
62328	**EFFICIENT PHONON–ASSISTED LONG–LIFETIME NEODYMIUM TRIPOSITIVE IONS FLUOROSCENCE IN CESIUM SODIUM NEODYMIUM CHLORIDE.** TOFIELD, B. C. WEBER, H. P. PHYS. REV. 10 B (11), 1230–7, 1974.
62337	**ANOMALOUS MAGNETIZATION OF AMORPHOUS TERBIUM IRON, GADOLINIUM IRON, AND YTTRIUM IRON.** RHYNE, J. J. SCHELLENG, J. H. KOON, N. C. PHYS. REV. 10 B (11), 4672–9, 1974.
62340	**MAGNETIC INTERACTIONS IN COBALT DIBROMIDE HEXAHYDRATE.** KOPINGA, K. BROM, P. W. M. DE JONG, W. J. M. PHYS. REV., B 10 (11), 4690–6, 1974.
62346	**RESISTIVITY AND HALL EFFECT OF EUROPIUM SELENIDE IN FIELDS UP TO 150 KOE.** SHAPIRA, Y. FONER, S. OLIVEIRA, N. F., JR. REED, T. B. PHYS. REV. 10 B (11), 4765–80, 1974.
62347	**EFFECT OF SPIN SPLITTING OF THE CONDUCTION BAND ON THE RESISTIVITY AND HALL COEFFICIENT: MODEL FOR THE POSITIVE MAGNETORESISTANCE IN EUROPIUM SELENIDE.** SHAPIRA, Y. KAUTZ, R. L. PHYS. REV. 10 B (11), 4781–94, 1974.
62354	**REFRACTIVE INDEX OF NEODYMIUM DOPED CALCIUM FLUORIDE AND SOME NEODYMIUM DOPED GLASSES AS A FUNCTION OF WAVELENGTH, NEODYMIUM, AND TEMPERATURE.** GUNTER, R. C., JR. CLOSS, J. V. APPL. OPT. 14 (1), 174–6, 1975.
62356	**THERMOELECTRIC CURRENT GENERATING.** HESSE, J. BRENNST.–WARME–KRAFT 22 (12), 590–6, 1970.
62370	**INVESTIGATION OF THE ELECTRICAL CONDUCTIVITY OF SEMICONDUCTORS AND INTERMETALLIC COMPOUNDS IN THE SOLID AND LIQUID STATES. I.** BLUM, A. I. MOKROVSKII, N. P. REGEL', A. R. IZV. AKAD. NAUK SSSR, SER. FIZ. 16, (2), 139–53, 1952.
62372	**SPECIFIC RESISTANCE MEASUREMENT OF SEMICONDUCTORS BY THE ALTERNATING CURRANT–FOUR POINT METHOD.** HARTMANN, U. EXP. TECH. PHYS. 18, (6), 429–38, 1970.
62375	**INVESTIGATION OF SUPERCONDUCTING INTERACTIONS AND AMORPHOUS SEMICONDUCTORS.** JANOCKO, M. A. JONES, C. K. GAVALER, J. R. DEIS, D. W. ASHKIN, M. MATHUR, M. P. BAUERLE, J. E. WESTINGHOUSE ELECTRIC CORP., PITTSBURGH, PA. 245PP., 1972. (N73–13731, NASA–CR–129524, AVAIL. NTIS)
62376	**SURVEY OF THE PROPTERTIES OF THE HYDROGEN ISOTOPES BELOW THEIR CRITICAL TEMPERATURES.** RODER, H. M. CHILDS, G. E. MC CARTY, R. D. ANGERHOFER, P. E. CRYOGENICS DIV., NATIONAL BUREAU OF STANDARDS, BOULDER, COLORADO 121PP., 1973. (N74–10664, NBS–TN–641)
62384	**THE ROLE OF THE ELECTRONIC POLARON IN THE SOFT X–RAY ABSORPTION OF THE LITHIUM HALIDES.** KUNZ, A. B. DEVREESE, J. T. COLLINS, T. C. J. PHYS., SOLID STATE PHYS. 5 C, 3259–63, 1972. (AD–757 004, ARL–73–0036)
62386	**ACOUSTO–OPTIC INTERACTIONS.** LEAN, E. G. IBM WATSON RESEARCH CENTER, YORKTOWN HEIGHTS, N. Y. 60PP., 1973. (AD–758 719)
62387	**THE STRUCTURE OF TETRAHEDRALLY COORDINATED AMORPHOUS SEMICONDUCTORS.** SHEVCHIK, N. J. DIV. OF ENGINEERING AND APPLIED PHYSICS, HARVARD UNIV., CAMBRIDGE, MASS. 352PP., 1972. (AD–746 638, N73–12821, HP–29, ARPA–TR–44, AVAIL. NTIS)
62407	**CRYSTAL STRUCTURE OF REACTIVELY SPUTTERED SILVER FILMS AND THERMAL DESORPTION OF OXYGEN FROM THESE FILMS.** TANAKA, S. TETSUYA, A. YAMASHINA, T. CHEM. LETT. (6), 599–602, 1974.
62410	**IRRADIATION EFFECTS IN SUPERCONDUCTING MAGNETS.** ONISHI, T. DENSHI GIJUTSU SOGO KENKYUJO CHOSA HOKOKU (175), 1–56, 1973.
62427	**CYCLOTRON RESONANCE IN N–INDIUM ANTIMONIDE IN STRONG MAGNETIC FIELDS.** GERSHENZON, E. M. SEREBRYAKOVA, N. A. SMIRNOVA, V. B. FIZ. TEKH. POLUPROV. 8 (3), 476–80, 1974. (FOR ENGLISH TRANSLATION SEE E65330)
62428	**STRUCTURE OF ALLOWED BAND EDGES IN N–INDIUM ARSENIDE STUDIED BY THE OPTICAL ABSORPTION METHOD.** ZOTOVA, N. V. GARYAGDYEV, G. NASLEDOV, D. N. FIZ. TEKH. POLUPROV. 8 (5), 921–7, 1974. (FOR ENGLISH TRANSLATION SEE E65331)
62432	**ANOMALOUS LARGE PHOTOVOLTAIC EFFECT IN CADMIUM TELLURIDE THIN FILMS.** KRETSU, I. P. MALKOCH, N. K. RAZLOGA, M. P. CHEBAN, A. G. FIZ. TEKH. POLUPROV. 8 (6), 1198–201, 1974. (FOR ENGLISH TRANSLATION SEE E65334)
62435	**INVESTIGATION OF SOME FACTORS INFLUENCING THE CRITICAL CURRENT OF NIOBIUM SPECIMENS OBTAINED BY A DIFFUSION METHOD.** ERMOLOV, V. A. EFREMOV, YU. N. ALEKSEEVSKII, N. E. ZAITSEV, G. S. IZV. AKAD. NAUK SSSR MET. (6), 169–72, 1973. (FOR ENGLISH TRANSLATION SEE E66134)
62436	**PREPARATION AND STUDY OF THE PROPERTIES OF AMORPHOUS SILICON PHOSPHIDE AND SILICON ARSENIDE FILMS.** DOMASHEVSKAYA, E. P. UGAI, YA. A. MIROSHNICHENKO, S. N. ALFEEVA, M. S. NIKONOV, I. F. IZV. AKAD. NAUK SSSR, NEORG. MATER. 10 (4), 731–2, 1974. (FOR ENGLISH TRANSLATION SEE E67079)

EPIC Number	Bibliographic Citation

62447 **BISMUTH TELLURIDE–INDIUM TELLURIDE SYSTEM.**
DOVLETOV, K. SAMOKHOTINA, N. K.
ANIKIN, A. V. ASHIROV, A.
IZV. AKAD. NAUK TURKM. SSR, SER. FIZ.–TEKH., KHIM.
GEOL. NAUK
(6), 85–8, 1973.

62457 **DISTINCTION BETWEEN OPTICAL ABSORPTION EDGES AND PHOTOEMISSION EDGES IN SOLIDS.**
KUNZ, A. B.
J. PHYS.
7 C (12), L231–L234, 1974.

62465 **OPTICAL AND RESISTIVITY STUDIES OF INTERCALATED LAYER COMPOUNDS.**
BENDA, J. A. HOWARD, R. E. PHILLIPS, W. A.
J. PHYS. CHEM. SOLIDS
35 (8), 937–45, 1974.

62479 **ABSORPTION OF X–COLOURED STRONTIUM DOPED RUBIDIUM CHLORIDE IN THE FLUORIDE REGION.**
KATZ, I. KRISTIANPOLLER, N. ENGLMAN, R.
PHILOS. MAG.
29 (2), 373–82, 1974.

62480 **PHOTOVOLTAIC EFFICIENCIES OF COPPER SULFIDE PHASES IN THE TOPOTAXIAL HETEROJUNCTION COPPER SULFIDE–CADMIUM SULFIDE.**
TE VELDE, T. S. DIELEMAN, J.
PHILIPS RES. REP.
28 (6), 573–95, 1973.

62485 **SUPERCONDUCTIVITY AT THE SURFACE OF LEAD TELLURIDE (AND LEED OF EPITAXIAL LAYERS).**
MILLER, D. L. STRONGIN, M. KAMMERER, O. F.
STREETMAN, B. G.
PHYS. REV.
8 B (9), 4416–19, 1973.

62493 **TEMPERATURE DEPENDENCE OF THE BAND GAP IN ZINC OXIDE FROM REFLECTION DATA.**
HVEDSTRUP, J. G.
PHYS. STATUS SOLIDI
64 B (1), K51–K54, 1974.

62496 **EFFECTS OF UNIAXIAL STRESS ON THE OPTICAL PROPERTIES OF SEMICONDUCTORS.**
WARDZYNSKI, W.
POSTEPY FIZ.
25 (1), 101–19, 1974.

62504 **SUBHALIDES OF TELLURIUM. ELECTRIC CONDUCTIVITY IN RELATION TO DRYSTAL STRUCTURE.**
VON ALPEN, U. KNIEP, R.
SOLID STATE COMMUN.
14 (10), 1033–6, 1974.

62513 **CHANGES IN ELECTROCONDUCTIVITY OF CRYSTALS AT DISLOCATION AGING.**
VENGLINSKAYA, S. V. KORNYUSHIN, YU. V.
UKR. FIZ. ZH. (USSR)
19 (4), 590–5, 1974.

62520 **TEMPERATURE DEPENDENCE OF THE ELASTO–OPTICAL CONSTANTS P(11) AND P(12) OF SODIUM CHLORIDE, POTASSIUM CHLORIDE, POTASSIUM BROMIDE AND POTASSIUM IODIDE CRYSTALS.**
PAKHNEV, A. V. GORBACH, S. S.
SHASKOL'SKAYA, M. P.
KRISTALLOGRAFIYA (USSR)
18 (5), 1090–1, 1973.
(FOR ENGLISH TRANSLATION SEE E62521)

62521 **TEMPERATURE DEPENDENCE OF THE ELASTO–OPTICAL CONSTANTS P(11) AND P(12) OF SODIUM CHLORIDE, POTASSIUM CHLORIDE, POTASSIUM BROMIDE AND POTASSIUM IODIDE CRYSTALS.**
PAKHNEV, A. V. GORBACH, S. S.
SHASKOL'SKAYA, M. P.
SOV. PHYS. CRYSTALLOGR.
18 (5), 687, 1974.
(ENGLISH TRANSLATION OF KRISTALLOGRAFIYA, 18 (5), 1090–1, 1973; FOR ORIGINAL SEE E62520)

62523 **ELECTRICAL CONDUCTIVITY OF LIQUID SULFUR AND PHOSPHORUS MIXTURES.**
STEUNENBERG, R. K. TRAPP, C. YONCO, R. M.
CAIRNS, E. J.
ADVAN. CHEM. SER.
110, 190–200, 1972.

62525 **THE 10.6–MU–M ABSORPTION OF POTASSIUM CHLORIDE.**
DEUTSCH, T. F.
APPL. PHYS. LETT.
25 (2), 109–12, 1974.

62528 **FUNDAMENTAL ABSORPTION SPECTRUM OF INDIUM PHOSPHIDE IN THE 1.40–1.70 E V RANGE.**
EMLIN, R. V. ZVEREV, L.
FIZ. TEKH. POLUPROV.
8 (6), 1225–6, 1974.
(FOR ENGLISH TRANSLATION SEE E64431)

62529 **OPTICAL ABSORPTION OF GALLIUM ARSENIDE NEAR THE FUNDAMENTAL BAND AT HIGH TEMPERATURES.**
BILENKO, D. I. TSIPORUKHA, V. D.
FIZ. TEKH. POLUPROV.
8 (6), 1235–7, 1974.
(FOR ENGLISH TRANSLATION SEE E64432)

62535 **OPTICAL ABSORPTION LINE SHAPE FOR THE B BAND OF THALLIUM(+) LIKE IONS IN ALKALI HALIDES.**
HONMA, A. OOAKU, S. MABUCHI, T.
J. PHYS. SOC. JAP.
36 (6), 1708, 1974.

62547 **INFRARED ABSORPTION BY ALKALI HALIDES IN THE TRANSPARENT REGIME AND ITS TEMPERATURE DEPENDENCE.**
NAMJOSHI, K. V. MITRA, S. S.
SOLID STATE COMMUN.
15 (2), 317–20, 1974.
(AD–A012 553, N76–12355)

62548 **INFRARED ABSORPTION IN GALLIUM NITRIDE GROWN BY VAPOUR PHASE EPITAXY USING GALLIUM BROMIDE AND AMMONIA.**
MORIMOTO, Y. USHIO, S.
JAP. J. APPL. PHYS. (JAPAN)
13 (5), 905–6, 1974.

62549 **SIMPLIFIED REFRACTIVE INDEX DISPERSION RELATIONSHIPS FOR DIELECTRIC FILMS USED IN SEMICONDUCTOR TECHNOLOGY.**
PLISKIN, W. A.
J. ELECTROCHEM. SOC.
121 C (3), 88PP., 1974.

62550 **EPITAXIAL GROWTH AND PROPERTIES OF GALLIUM ARSENIDE ON MAGNESIUM ALUMINATE SPINEL.**
WANG, C. C. DOUGHERTY, F. C.
J. ELECTROCHEM. SOC. (USA)
121 (4), 571–82, 1974.

62555 **THALLIUM(2+) ION CENTER IN THALLIUM CHLORIDE DOPED POTASSIUM CHLORIDE.**
DELBECQ, C. J. HUTCHINSON, E. YUSTER, P. H.
J. PHYS. SOC. JAP. (JAPAN)
36 (3), 913, 1974.

62566 **PHOTOVOLTAIC EFFECT IN ANODIC OXIDE FILMS ON BISMUTH.**
IKONOPISOV, S. KLEIN, E. ANDREEVA, L.
NIKOLOV, TS.
THIN SOLID FILMS
22 (1), S11–S13, 1974.

62567 **STUDY OF BARIUM, CESIUM AND CESIUM CHLORIDE ADSORPTION ON YTTRIUM AND SCANDIUM SURFACE.**
PANCHISHIN, R. S. STASYUK, Z. V.
UKR. FIZ. ZH.
19 (5), 769–72, 1974.

62582 **SUBMILLIMETRE SPECTROSCOPY OF SEMICONDUCTORS.**
GERSHENZON, E. M. GOL'TSMAN, G. N.
PTITSINA, N. G.
SOV. PHYS. JETP
37 (2), 299–304, 1973.
(ENGLISH TRNSLATION OF ZH. EKSP. TEOR. FIZ., 64 (2), 587–98, 1973; FOR ORIGINAL SEE E55167)

62585 **INFLUENCE OF THE IMPURITY CONCENTRATION ON THE HOPPING CONDUCTION IN SEMICONDUCTORS.**
SKAL, A. S. SHKLOVSKII, B. I.
FIZ. TEKH. POLUPROV. (USSR)
7 (8), 1589–92, 1973.
(FOR ENGLISH TRANSLATION SEE E62586)

62586 **INFLUENCE OF THE IMPURITY CONCENTRATION ON THE HOPPING CONDUCTION IN SEMICONDUCTORS.**
SKAL, A. S. SHKLOVSKII, B. I.
SOV. PHYS. SEMICOND.
7 (8), 1058–9, 1974.
(ENGLISH TRANSLATION OF FIZ. TEKH. POLUPROV3D., 7 (8), 1589–92, 1973; FOR ORIGINAL SEE E62585)

62589 **THERMOELECTRIC POWER OF A THIN SEMICONDUCTOR FILM IN THE CASE OF STRONG SURFACE BAND BENDING.**
POLNIKOV, V. G.
FIZ. TEKH. POLUPROVODN. (USSR)
7 (8), 1657–9, 1973.
(FOR ENGLISH TRANSLATION SEE E62590)

62590 **THERMOELECTRIC POWER OF A THIN SEMICONDUCTOR FILM IN THE CASE OF STRONG SURFACE BAND BENDING.**
POLNIKOV, V. G.
SOV. PHYS. SEMICOND.
7 (8), 1110–11, 1974.
(ENGLISH TRANSLATION OF FIZ. TEKH. POLUPROVOD., 7 (8), 1657–9, 1973; FOR ORIGINAL SEE E62589)

62591 **DETERMINATION OF THE CROSS SECTION FOR THE ABSORPTION OF LIGHT BY NONEQUILIBRIUM CARRIERS GENERATED BY RUBY LASER RADIATION IN INDIUM SELENIDE CRYSTALS.**
ABDULLAEV, G. B. AKHUNDOV, G. A.
AGAEVA, A. A. SALMANOV, V. M.
SHARONOV, YU. P. YAROSHETSKII, I. D.
FIZ. TEKH. POLUPROVODN. (USSR)
7 (11), 2225–7, 1973.
(FOR ENGLISH TRANSLATION SEE E62592)

EPIC Number | Bibliographic Citation

62592 **DETERMINATION OF THE CROSS SECTION FOR THE ABSORPTION OF LIGHT BY NONEQUILIBRIUM CARRIERS GENERATED BY RUBY LASER RADIATION IN INDIUM SELENIDE CRYSTALS.**
ABDULLAEV, G. B. AKHUNDOV, G. A.
AGAEVA, A. A. SALMANOV, V. M.
SHARONOV, YU. P. YAROSHETSKII, I. D.
SOV. PHYS. SEMICOND.
7 (11), 1480–1, 1974.
(ENGLISH TRANSLATION OF FIZ. TEKH. POLUPROVOD., 7 (11), 2225–7, 1973; FOR ORIGINAL SEE E62591)

62595 **ALUMINUM NITRIDE AS A DIELECTRIC FOR SILICON DEVICES.**
KELM, R. W.
SOUTHERN METHODIST UNIV., DALLAS, TEXAS, PH. D. THESIS
142PP., 1973.
(UNIV. MICROFILMS NO. 74-5171, N74-21352)

62600 **KODAK IRTRAN INFRARED OPTICAL MATERIALS. CONDENSED DATA FOR KODAK IRTRAN INFRARED OPTICAL MATERIALS.**
EASTMAN KODAK COMPANY
EASTMAN KODAK COMPANY
57PP., 1971.
(KODAK PUBL. NO. U-72, KODAK PUBL. NO. U-71)

62602 **TEMPERATURE DEPENDENCE OF THE ABSORPTION COEFFICIENT OF GALLIUM ARSENIDE AND ZINC SELENIDE AT 10.6 MICROMETERS.**
SKOLNIK, L. H. LIPSON, H. G. BENDOW, B.
SCHOTT, J. T.
APPL. PHYS. LETT.
25 (8), 442–5, 1974.
(AD-A000 980, AFCRL-TR-74-0529)
(AD-B013 807L)

62603 **TRANSPORT AND LOCALIZED LEVELS IN AMORPHOUS BINARY CHALCOGENIDES.**
BUBE, R. H. MAHAN, J. E. SHIAH, R. T. S.
VANDER PLAS, H. A.
APPL. PHYS. LETT.
25 (7), 419–41, 1974.
(AD-A001 163)

62605 **MICROWAVE HIGH DIELECTRIC CONSTANT MATERIAL.**
SMOKE, E. J. KASTENBEIN, E. L.
FREEMAN, J. R. JOHNSON, H. C.
U. S. ARMY ELECTRONICS COMMAND, FORT MONMOUTH, N. J.
95 PP., 1974.
(ECOM-69-0109-F)

62620 **PHOTOMAGNETOELECTRIC EFFECT IN CADMIUM TELLURIDE FILMS WITH ANOMALOUSLY LARGE PHOTOVOLTAGE.**
KORSUNSKII, M. I. SOMINSKII, M. M.
SMURYGIN, V. M.
KODL. AKAD. NAUK SSSR
203 (2), 332–5, 1972.
(FOR ENGLISH TRANSLATION SEE E64435)

62623 **OPTOELECTRONIC VOLTAGE TRANSFORMER.**
ADIROVICH, E. I. NAIMANBAEV, R. N.
YUABOV, YU. M.
DOKL. AKAD. NAUK SSSR
208 (1), 73–61, 1973.
(FOR ENGLISH TRANSLATION SEE E65120)

62640 **THE INFLUENCE OF ZINC AND SCANDIUM HEAT TREATMENT ON THE EXCITON SPECTRA OF ZINC SCANDIUM SINGLE CRYSTALS.**
ROPPISCHER, H. JACOBS, J. NOVIKOV, B. V.
PHYS. STATUS SOLIDI
27 A (1), 123–7, 1975.

62658 **CONDUCTIVITY INVESTIGATION OF CALCIUM VANADATE (V).**
BELYANINOV, YU. N. GRUNIN, V. S.
ZONN, Z. N. IOFFE, V. A. PATRINA, I. B.
YANCHEVSKAYA, I. S.
PHYS. STATUS SOLIDI
27 A (1), 165–73, 1975.

62674 **HALL MOBILITY IN SINGLE CRYSTALS OF NICKEL OXIDE AS A FUNCTION OF TEMPERATURE AND DEVIATION FROM STOICHIOMETRY.**
FRIEDMAN, F. WEICHMAN, F. L.
TANNHAUSER, D. S.
PHYS. STATUS SOLIDI
27 A (1), 273–9, 1975.

62678 **ELASTIC, OPTICAL, AND DIELECTRIC PROPERTIES AND THEIR PRESSURE DERIVATIVES OF RUTILE-STRUCTURE OXIDES IN A MODIFIED RIGID ION APPROXIMATION.**
STRIEFLER, M. E. BARSCH, G. R.
PHYS. STATUS SOLIDI
67 B (1), 143–56, 1975.

62679 **FERROELECTRIC DOMAINS AND POLARIZATION REVERSAL IN LEAD ZIRCONIUM NIOBATE.**
NOMURA, S. KOJIMA, F.
JAP. J. APPL. PHYS.
13 (12), 2004–8, 1974.

62680 **DOMAIN-WALL ENERGY IN MANGANESE ANTIMONIDE AND CHROMIUM-MODIFIED MANGANESE ANTIMONIDE.**
SUZUKI, M. WAKIYAMA, T. ANAYAMA, T.
JAP. J. APPL. PHYS.
13 (12), 2019–24, 1974.

62687 **THEORY OF LIGHT ABSORPTION BY FREE CARRIERS IN SEMICONDUCTORS POSSESSING NONPARABOLIC BANDS.**
ALIEV, T. A. GASHIMZADE, F. M.
FIZ. TEKH. POLUPROV.
6 (3), 458–61, 1972.
(FOR ENGLISH TRANSLATION SEE E64415)

62689 **OPTICAL ABSORPTION OF GALLIUM MONOTELLURIDE.**
GRAMATSKII, V. I. KARAMAN, M. I.
MUSHINSKII, V. P.
FIZ. TEKH. POLUPROV.
6 (3), 550–2, 1972.
(FOR ENGLISH TRANSLATION SEE E64417)

62691 **PHOTOELECTRIC PHENOMENA NEAR THE GALLIUM ARSENIDE SURFACE AT LOW TEMPERATURES.**
TERESHCHENKO, A. K. DMITRUK, N. L.
BORKOVSKAYA, O. YU.
FIZ. TEKH. POLUPROV.
6 (3), 585, 1972.

62693 **KINETICS OF PHOTOEMF. IN INDIUM ARSENIDE P-N JUNCTIONS.**
ANDRUSHKO, A. I. NASLEDOV, D. N.
SLOBODCHIKOV, S. V.
FIZ. TEKH. POLUPROV.
6 (5), 822–5, 1972.
(FOR ENGLISH TRANSLATION SEE E64420)

62695 **MEASUREMENTS OF BIREFRINGENCE DISPERSION OF CADMIUM SULFIDE SINGLE CRYSTALS.**
LISITSA, M. P. MALINKO, V. N.
TEREKHOVA, S. F.
FIZ. TEKH. POLUPROV.
6 (5), 926–7, 1972.
(FOR ENGLISH TRANSLATION SEE E64422)

62698 **IMAGINARY PART OF COMPLEX LOW-FREQUENCY CONDUCTIVITY IN A HIGH ELECTRICAL FIELD.**
ZUEV, V. V.
FIZ. TEKH. POLUPROV.
6 (5), 965–8, 1972.
(FOR ENGLISH TRANSLATION SEE E64429)

62703 **ELECTRONIC PROPERTIES OF COMPENSATED SEMICONDUCTORS HAVING CORRELATED IMPURITY DISTRIBUTION.**
GAL'PERN, YU. S. EFROS, A. L.
FIZ. TEKH. POLUPROV.
6 (6), 1081–8, 1972.
(FOR ENGLISH TRANSLATION SEE E65300)

62704 **HOPPING CONDUCTION OF WEAKLY DOPED SEMIDONDUCTORS.**
SHKLOVSKII, B. I.
FIZ. TEKH. POLUPROV.
6 (7), 1197–226, 1972.
(FOR ENGLISH TRANSLATION SEE E65123)

62705 **PROPERTIES OF IRON-DOPED CADMIUM TELLURIDE.**
VUL, B. M. IVANOV, V. S.
RUKAVISHNIKOV, V. A. SAL'MAN, V. M.
CHAPNIN, V. A.
FIZ. TEKH. POLUPROV.
6 (7), 1264–7, 1972.
(FOR ENGLISH TRANSLATION SEE E65301)

62706 **OPTICAL PROPERTIES OF SUPERLATTICES MADE FROM SEMICONDUCTORS WITH COMPLEX BAND STRUCTURES.**
SHIK, A. YA.
FIZ. TEKH. POLUPROV.
6 (7), 1268–77, 1972.
(FOR ENGLISH TRANSLATION SEE E65302)

62707 **INTRINSIC LIGHT ABSORPTION IN THE NONPARABOLIC REGION IN LEAD TELLURIDE AND LEAD TELLURIDE-TIN TELLURIDE SOLID SOLUTIONS.**
DRABKIN, I. A. MORGOVSKII, L. YA.
NEL'SON, I. V. RAVICH, YU. I.
FIZ. TEKH. POLUPROV.
6 (7), 1323–6, 1972.
(FOR ENGLISH TRANSLATION SEE E65303)

62710 **USE OF A SCHOTTKY BARRIER FOR DETERMINING THE COEFFICIENT OF LIGHT ABSORPTION IN A SEMICONDUCTOR.**
GUTKIN, A. A. DMITRIEV, M. V.
NASLEDOV, D. N.
FIZ. TEKH. POLUPROV.
6 (7), 1394–5, 1972.
(FOR ENGLISH TRANSLATION SEE E65306)

62713 **EXCITON ABSORPTION ON DEFORMED CRYSTAL SURFACES AND POLYCRYSTALS.**
SKAISTIS, E. SUGAKOV, V. I.
FIZ. TEKH. POLUPROV.
6 (9), 1637–42, 1972.
(FOR ENGLISH TRANSLATION SEE E65309)

62715 **ELECTROMOTIVE FORCE GENERATED BY ILLUMINATION OF A SEMICONDUCTOR BY A MOVING LIGHT BEAM.**
KHOMUTOVA, M. D.
FIZ. TEKH. POLUPROV.
6 (9), 1836–7, 1972.
(FOR ENGLISH TRANSLATION SEE E65311)

EPIC Number	Bibliographic Citation
62716	**ANISOTROPY OF THE ELECTRICAL PROPERTIES OF TELLURIUM-, INDIUM-, AND LEAD-DOPED BISMUTH SELENIDE SINGLE CRYSTALS.** BOECHKO, V. F. PSAREV, V. I. FIZ. TEKH. POLUPROV. 6 (10), 2042–4, 1972. (FOR ENGLISH TRANSLATION SEE E65312)
62717	**INTRABAND TRANSITION IN N-ALUMINUM ANTIMONIDE.** AGAEV, YA. BEKMEDOVA, N. G. MIKHAILOV, A. R. FIZ. TEKH. POLUPROV. 6 (10), 2059–61, 1972. (FOR ENGLISH TRANSLATION SEE E65313)
62718	**SHAPE OF THE INTRINSIC ABSORPTION EDGE IN CADMIUM SELENIDE.** VOLKOVA, L. V. VOLKOV, V. V. MENTSER, A. N. KIREEV, P. S. FIZ. TEKH. POLUPROV. 6 (10), 2085, 1972. (FOR ENGLISH TRANSLATION SEE E65314)
62719	**EFFECT OF A BISMUTH IMPURITY ON THE ENERGY SPECTRUM AND ELECTRON SCATTERING IN LEAD TELLURIDE.** KAIDANOV, V. I. MEL'NIK, R. B. SHAPIRO, L. A. FIZ. TEKH. POLUPROV. 6 (11), 2140–3, 1972. (FOR ENGLISH TRANSLATION SEE E65315)
62720	**CHANGE IN SEMICONDUCTOR CONDUCTIVITY UNDER THE EFFECT OF SOUND.** GULYAEV, YU. V. LISTVINA, N. N. FIZ. TEKH. POLUPROV. 6 (11), 2169–74, 1972. (FOR ENGLISH TRANSLATION SEE E65316)
62723	**HOPPING CONDUCTION OF SEMICONDUCTORS IN A STRONG ELECTRIC FIELD.** SHKLOVSKII, B. I. FIZ. TEKH. POLUPROV. 6 (12), 2335–40, 1972. (FOR ENGLISH TRANSLATION SEE E65319)
62726	**PROPERTIES OF TITANIUM- AND COBALT-COMPENSATED GALLIUM ARSENIDE AND DIODE STRUCTURES MADE FROM IT.** BEKMURATOV, M. F. MURYGIN, V. I. FIZ. TEKH. POLUPROV. 7 (1), 83–7, 1973. (FOR ENGLISH TRANSLATION SEE E65322)
62727	**HOPPING CONDUCTIVITY OF HEAVILY DOPED SEMICONDUCTORS.** SHKLOVSKII, B. I. FIZ. TEKH. POLUPROV. 7 (1), 112–18, 1973. (FOR ENGLISH TRANSLATION SEE E65323)
62728	**CAPABILITIES OF INJECTION THERMOELECTRIC ELEMENTS.** LUKISHKER, E. M. KOLOMOETS, N. V. FIZ. TEKH. POLUPROV. 7 (1), 172–6, 1973. (FOR ENGLISH TRANSLATION SEE E65324)
62729	**LEAD TELLURIDE FILMS PREPARED BY THE CLOSED-VOLUME METHOD.** KONDRATOV, A. V. TIMOFEEV, YU. V. SMIRNOV, N. K. CHERKASHIN, G. A. CHUDNOVSKII, A. F. FIZ. TEKH. POLUPROV. 7 (1), 178–80, 1973. (FOR ENGLISH TRANSLATION SEE E65325)
62730	**THEORY OF THE IMPURITY ABSORPTION OF SEMICONDUCTORS WITH COMPLEX BAND STRUCTURE.** SHIK, A. YA. FIZ. TEKH. POLUPROV. 7 (1), 193–6, 1973. (FOR ENGLISH TRANSLATION SEE E65326)
62731	**DIMENSIONAL DEPENDENCE OF THE THERMOELECTROMOTIVE FORCE OF SEMICONDUCTORS.** PRIMA, N. A. FIZ. TEKH. POLUPROV. 7 (2), 338–45, 1973. (FOR ENGLISH TRANSLATION SEE E65327)
62733	**SELECTIVE PHOTOCELLS FROM SILICON-DOPED ALUMINUM GALLIUM ARSENIDE P-N VARIABLE-GAP STRUCTURES.** TSARENKOV, B. V. DANILOVA, T. N. IMENKOV, A. N. YAKOVLEV, YU. P. FIZ. TEKH. POLUPROV. 7 (7), 1426–9, 1973. (FOR ENGLISH TRANSLATION SEE E65329)
62735	**LASER MEASUREMENT OF OPTICAL ABSORPTION IN LIQUIDS.** WHINNERY, J. R. ACCOUNTS CHEM. RES. 7 (7), 225–31, 1974.
62737	**A SIMPLE SAMPLE HOLDER AND CRYOSTAT FOR MEASURING THERMOELECTRIC POWER OF SEMICONDUCTORS IN THE TEMPERATURE RANGE OF 80–400 K.** SOMOGYI, K. PODOR, B. ACTA TECH. ACAD. SCI. HUNG. (HUNGARY) 76 (1–2), 177–81, 1974.

EPIC Number	Bibliographic Citation
62740	**HIGH-VOLTAGE BULK PHOTOVOLTAIC EFFECT AND THE PHOTOREFRACTIVE PROCESS IN LITHIUM NIOBATE.** GLASS, A. M. VON DER LINDE, D. NEGRAN, T. J. APPL. PHYS. LETT. 25 (4), 233–5, 1974.
62748	**MAGNETIC PROPERTIES OF AMORPHOUS GADOLINIUM COBALT FILMS.** TOO, L. J. GAMBINO, R. J. KIRKPATRICK, S. CUOMO, J. J. LILIENTHAL, H. AIP CONF. PROC. 18 (1), 641–5, 1973.
62753	**MAGNETIC AND STRUCTURAL TRANSITIONS IN NEODYMIUM SULFIDE, DYSPROSIUM SULFIDE AND ERBIUM SULFIDE.** TAO, L. J. TORRANCE, J. B. HOLTZBERG, F. AIP CONF. PROC. 18 (1), 340, 1973.
62758	**THE OPTICAL ABSORPTION PRODUCED BY SMALL SODIUM METAL PARTICLES IN SODIUM CHLORIDE.** SMITHARD, M. A. TRAN, M. Q. HELV. PHYS. ACTA (SWITZERLAND) 46 (6), 869–88, 1974.
62782	**INHOMOGENEOUS TRANSPORT REGIME AND METAL-NONMETAL TRANSITIONS IN DISORDERED MATERIALS.** COHEN, M. H. JORTNER, J. J. PHYS. (PARIS), COLLOQ. (4), 345–66, 1974.
62785	**ENERGY DISTRIBUTION OF EXOELECTRONS EMITTED INTO VACUUM FROM PLASTICALLY DEFORMED, OXIDE COVERED ALUMINIUM AT LOW TEMPERATURES.** SUJAK, B. GIEROSZYNSKI, A. GIEROSZYNSKA, K. ACTA PHYS. POL. 46 A (1), 3–17, 1974.
62804	**MEASUREMENT OF THE REFRACTIVE INDEX OF THIN WEAKLY ABSORBING FILMS BY THE ABELES METHOD.** BUGNIN, G. A. OPT. SPEKTROSK. 37 (1), 197–8, 1974. (FOR ENGLISH TRANSLATION SEE E65343)
62805	**BRILLOUIN ZONE EFFECTS ON THE CRITICAL TEMPERATURE OF SUPERCONDUCTORS AND SOME RELATED NORMAL METAL PROPERTIES.** HAVINGA, E. E. VAN MAAREN, M. H. PHYS. REP. 10 C (3), 107–50, 1974.
62806	**SUPERCONDUCTIVITY OF MAGNESIUM-BASED ALLOYS.** CLAESON, T. PHYS. SCR. (SWEDEN) 9 (6), 353–6, 1974.
62811	**THEORY OF THE URBACH-MARTIENSSEN RULE FOR MIXED CRYSTALS. APPLICATION OF CPA.** SAWAI, T. UENO, S. MATSUBARA, T. PROG. THEOR. PHYS. SUPPL. (JAPAN) (53), 222–39, 1973.
62815	**OPTICAL PROPERTIES OF INFRARED TRANSMITTING MATERIALS (LQ-10 POWER LASER WINDOW PROGRAM).** BENDOW, B. CONF. PREPARATION AND PROPERTIES OF ELECTRONIC MATERIALS 35PP., 1973.
62816	**CALCULATIONS OF THE FREQUENCY DEPENDENCE OF ELASTO-OPTIC CONSTANTS OF INFRARED LASER WINDOW MATERIALS.** BENDOW, B. GIANINO, P. D. AIR FORCE CAMBRIDGE RES. LAB., HANSCOM AFB, MASS. 111PP., 1974. (AFCRL-TR-74-0533)
62826	**SEMICONDUCTOR RESISTIVITY AND CONDUCTIVITY TYPE DETERMINATION.** YEAGER, J. R. SOLID STATE TECHNOL. 17 (3), 14–16, 1974.
62829	**STUDY OF THERMOELECTRIC AND THERMIONIC POWER CONVERSION.** JASINSKI, R. J. WALD, F. TYCO LABS., INC., WALTHAM, MASS. 233PP., 1967. (AD-661 455)
62833	**BREAKDOWN CHARACTERISTICS IN THIN SILICATE OXIDE** HAMANO, K. JAP. J. APPL. PHYS. 13 (7), 1085–92, 1974.
62845	**PHOTOEMF. IN AN ANTIMONY SULFIDE IODIDE FERROELECTRIC SEMICONDUCTOR.** BEZDETNYI, N. M. GORBATOV, G. Z. ZEINALLY, A. KH. LEBEDEVA, N. N. SHEINKMAN, M. K. FIZ. TVERD. TELA (LENINGRAD) 14 (2), 574–5, 1972. (FOR ENGLISH TRANSLATION SEE E65172)

EPIC Number | Bibliographic Citation

62850 MULTIPHOTON EXCITATION AND IONIZATION OF THALLIUM ION IMPURITY CENTERS IN ALKALI HALIDE CRYSTALS.
ASEEV, G. I. KATS, M. L.
FIZ. TVERD. TELA (LENINGRAD)
14 (5), 1365–8, 1972.
(FOR ENGLISH TRANSLATION SEE E65169)

62853 COMPOSITE MATRIX ELEMENT OF A TWO-PHOTON INTERBAND TRANSITION IN SEMICONDUCTORS.
MEDNIS, P. M.
FIZ. TVERD. TELA (LENINGRAD)
14 (9), 2531–4, 1972.
(FOR ENGLISH TRANSLATION SEE E65179)

62856 PHOTOEMF. SPECTRUM OF A SILVER BROMIDE EMULSION LAYER.
KOROTAEV, N. N. MEIKLYAR, P. V.
FIZ. TVERD. TELA (LENINGRAD)
14 (10), 3099–100, 1972.
(FOR ENGLISH TRANSLATION SEE E65177)

62858 TWO-PHOTON ABSORPTION AND OPTICAL ORIENTATION OF FREE CARRIERS IN CUBIC CRYSTALS.
IVCHENKO, E. L.
FIZ. TVERD. TELA (LENINGRAD)
14 (12), 3489–97, 1972.
(FOR ENGLISH TRANSLATION SEE E65181)

62861 MECHANICAL STRESSES IN BISMUTH, ANTIMONY TELLURIDE SOLID-SOLUTION FILMS.
GOL'TSMAN, B. M. KOMISSARCHIK, M. G.
FIZ. TVERD. TELA (LENINGRAD)
15 (1), 301–3, 1973.
(FOR ENGLISH TRANSLATION SEE E65168)

62862 EFFECT OF UNIAXIAL MECHANICAL DEFORMATIONS ON THE OPTICAL PROPERTIES OF ALKALI HALIDE CRYSTALS.
VISHNEVSKII, V. N. STEFANSKII, I. V.
KUZYK, M. P. KULIK, Z. S. KULIK, L. N.
FIZ. TVERD. TELA (LENINGRAD)
15 (1), 325–7, 1973.
(FOR ENGLISH TRANSLATION SEE E65167)

62863 ABNORMALLY LARGE SPONTANEOUS ROTATIONAL ELECTROOPTICAL EFFECT IN THE FERROELECTRIC AMMONIUM SODIUM SELANATE DIHYDRATE.
ALEKSANDROV, K. S. ANISTRATOV, A. T.
IVANOV, N. R. MEL'NIKOVA, S. V.
SHUVALOV, L. A.
FIZ. TVER. TELA (LENINGRAD)
15 (2), 456–8, 1973.
(FOR ENGLISH TRANSLATION SEE E65166)

62865 DIELECTRIC AND ELECTRO-OPTIC PROPERTIES OF PEROVSKITE-TYPE POTASSIUM LEAD ZINC NIOBATE CRYSTAL.
KOHIMA, F. KAWAKATSU, A. NOMURA, S.
JAP. J. APPL. PHYS.
14 (1), 59–63, 1975.

62876 THE SCINTILLATION PROCESS OF SODIUM IODIDE (THALLIUM).
ISHIKANE, M. KAWANISHI, M.
JAP. J. APPL. PHYS.
14 (1), 64–9, 1975.

62877 SILICATE CARBON WHISKER AS A FIELD EMITTER.
KUDO, J. NAKAMURA, S.
JAP. J. APPL. PHYS.
14 (1), 151–2, 1975.

62889 OPTICAL PROPERTIES OF HETERO-EPITAXIAL CADMIUM SULFIDE FILMS.
YOSHIKAWA, A. SAKAI, Y.
JAP. J. APPL. PHYS.
13 (9), 1353–61, 1974.

62894 PHOTOLUMINESCENCE OF NITROGEN-IMPLANTED GALLIUM ARSENIDE PHOSPHIDE NEAR THE DIRECT-INDIRECT-TRANSITION POINT.
MAKITA, Y. GONDA, S.
JAP. J. APPL. PHYS.
14 (1), 155–6, 1975.

62913 RADIATIVE RECOMBINATION FROM NON-EQUILIBRIUM STATES IN CATHODOEXCITED SEMICONDUCTORS.
ZEHE, A. ROPKE, G.
PHYS. STATUS SOLIDI
67 B (1), 169–79, 1975.

62914 STRUCTURE AND ELECTRICAL PROPERTIES OF EVAPORATED AND SPUTTERED TITANIUM FILMS.
GERSTENBERG, D.
ANN. PHYSIK
11 (7), 354–64, 1963.

62927 MAGNETIC PROPERTIES OF CHROMIUM BETWEEN 0 AND 350 C.
COLLINGS, E. W. HEDGCOCK, F. T.
SIDDIQUI, A.
PHIL MAG.
6, 155–8, 1961.

62952 AN ELECTRON BEAM METHOD FOR MEASURING HIGH SHEET RESISTANCES OF THIN FILMS.
CHESTER, A. N. KOSICKI, B. B.
REV. SCI. INSTRUM.
41 (12), 1817–24, 1970.

62960 EFFECTS OF PRESSURE ON THE ELECTRICAL PROPERTIES OF SEMICONDUCTORS.
LONG, D.
PHYS. REV.
101 (4), 1256–63, 1956.

62975 EXCEITED-STATE ABSORPTION IN RUBY, EMERALD, AND MAGNESIUM OXIDE:CHROMIUM.
FAIRBANK, W. M., JR. KLAUMINZER, G. K.
SCHAWLOW, A. L.
PHYS. REV.
11 B (1), 30–76, 1975.

62976 FLUORESCENCE LINE NARROWING OF TRIVALENT PRASEODYMIUM IN LANTHANUM TRIFLUORIDE SINGLE CRYSTAL-PHONON-INDUCED RELAXATION.
ERICKSON, L. E.
PHYS. REV.
11 B (1), 77–81, 1975.

62977 ANALYSIS OF THE OPTICAL SPECTRUM OF THULIUM IN LITHIUM YTTRIUM FLUORIDE.
JENSSEN, H. P. LINZ, A. LEAVITT, R. P.
MORRISON, C. A. WORTMAN, D. E.
PHYS. REV.
11 B (1), 92–101, 1975.

62979 EFFECT OF CRYSTAL DAMAGE ON SUPERCONDUCTIVITY IN THE TRANSITION-METAL LAYER COMPOUNDS.
TSANG, J. C. SHAFER, M. W. CROWDER, B. L.
PHYS. REV.
11 B (1), 155–62, 1975.

63000 NONOHMIC EFFECTS IN MERCURY TELLURIDE AT LOW TEMPERATURES.
BENESLAVSKII, S. D. IVANOV-OMSKII, V. I.
KOLOMIETS, B. T. SMIRNOV, V. A.
FIZ. TVERD. TELA
16 (6), 1620–9, 1974.
(FOR ENGLISH TRANSLATION SEE E63001)

63001 NONOHMIC EFFECTS IN MERCURY TELLURIDE AT LOW TEMPERATURES.
BENESLAVSKII, S. D. IVANOV-OMSKII, V. I.
KOLOMIETS, B. T. SMIRNOV, V. A.
SOV. PHYS. SOLID STATE
16 (6), 1058–63, 1974.
(ENGLISH TRANSLATION OF FIZ. TVERD. TELA 16 (6), 1620–9, 1974; FOR ORIGINAL SEE E63000)

63002 MAGNETOELASTIC INTERACTIONS IN CRYSTALS WITH A COOPERATIVE JOHN-TELLER EFFECT.
VEKHTER, B. G. KAPLAN, M. D.
FIZ. TVERD. TELA
16 (6), 1630–4, 1974.
(FOR ENGLISH TRANSLATION SEE E63003)

63003 MAGNETOELASTIC INTERACTIONS IN CRYSTALS WITH A COOPERATIVE JAHN-TELLER EFFECT.
VEKHTER, B. G. KAPLAN, M. D.
SOV. PHYS. SOLID STATE
16 (6), 1064–6, 1974.
(ENGLISH TRANSLATION OF FIZ. TVERD. TELA 16 (6), 1630–4, 1974; FOR ORIGINAL SEE E63002)

63010 PHOTOCONDUCTIVITY IN THE MAGNETIC SEMICONDUCTOR CADMIUM CHROMIUM SELENIDE.
AMINOV, T. G. VESELAGO, V. G.
KALINNIKOV, V. T. UTROBIN, V. P.
SHAPSHEVA, N. P.
FIZ. TVERD. TELA
16 (6), 1673–7, 1974.
(FOR ENGLISH TRANSLATION SEE E63011)

63011 PHOTOCONDUCTIVITY IN THE MAGNETIC SEMICONDUCTOR CADMIUM CHROMIUM SELENIDE.
AMINOV, T. G. VESELAGO, V. G.
VINOGRADOVA, G. I. KALINNIKOV, V. T.
UTROBIN, V. P. SHAPSHEVA, N. P.
SOV. PHYS. SOLID STATE
16 (6), 1090–2, 1974.
(FOR ENGLISH TRANSLATION OF FIZ. TVERD. TELA, 16 (6), 1673–7, 1974; FOR ORIGINAL SEE E63010)

63012 THERMAL BROADENING OF THE PHONONLESS LINES IN THE LUMINESCENCE SPECTRUM OF THE NITRITE ION IN A POTASSIUM CHLORIDE CRYSTAL.
REBANE, L. A. FREIBERG, A. M.
FIZ. TVERD. TELA
16 (6), 1686–9, 1974.
(FOR ENGLISH TRANSLATION SEE E63013)

63013 THERMAL BROADENING OF THE PHONONLESS LINES IN THE LUMINESCENCE SPECTRUM OF THE NITRITE ION IN A POTASSIUM CHLORIDE CRYSTAL.
REBANE, L. A. FREIBERG, A. M.
SOV. PHYS. SOLID STATE
16 (6), 1097–8, 1974.
(ENGLISH TRANSLATION OF FIZ. TVERD. TELA, 16 (6), 1686–9, 1974; FOR ORIGINAL SEE E63012)

EPIC Number	Bibliographic Citation

63014 **MAGNETIZATION-REVERSAL NUCLEI IN MAGNETICALLY UNIAXIAL HIGH-ANISOTROPY FERROMAGNETS.**
GASS, V. G. SHUR, YA. S. GLAZER, A. A.
FIZ. TVERD. TELA
16 (6), 1704-9, 1974.
(FOR ENGLISH TRANSLATION SEE E63015)

63015 **MAGNETIZATION-REVERSAL NUCLEI IN MAGNETICALLY UNIAXIAL HIGH-ANISOTROPY FERROMAGNETS.**
GASS, V. G. SHUR, YA. S. GLAZER, A. A.
SOV. PHYS. SOLID STATE
16 (6), 1108-11, 1974.
(ENGLISH TRANSLATION OF FIZ. TVERD. TELA 16 (6), 1704-9, 1974; FOR ORIGINAL SEE E63014)

63016 **EXCITON AND BAND EFFECTS IN POTASSIUM SPECTRA OF LITHIUM IN IONIC COMPOUNDS.**
MAISTE, A. A. SAAR, A. M. E. ELANGO, M. A.
FIZ. TVERD. TELA
16 (6), 1720-4, 1674.
(FOR ENGLISH TRANSLATION SEE E63017)

63017 **EXCITON AND BAND EFFECTS IN POTASSIUM SPECTRA OF LITHIUM IN IONIC COMPOUNDS.**
MAISTE, A. A. SAAR, A. M. E. ELANGO, M. A.
SOV. PHYS. SOLID STATE
16 (6), 1118-20, 1974.
(ENGLISH TRANSLATION OF FIZ. TVERD. TELA 16 (6), 1720-4, 1974; FOR ORIGINAL SEE E63016)

63022 **INVESTIGATION OF THE PHOTOPLASTIC EFFECT IN GAMMA-IRRADIATED SODIUM CHLORIDE CRYSTALS.**
ERMAKOV, G. A. KOROVKIN, E. V.
SOIFER, YA. M.
FIZ. TVERD. TELA
16 (6), 1756-60, 1974.
(FOR ENGLISH TRANSLATION SEE E63023)

63023 **INVESTIGATION OF THE PHOTOPLASTIC EFFECT IN GAMMA-IRRADIATED SODIUM CHLORIDE CRYSTALS.**
ERMAKOV, G. A. KOROVKIN, E. V.
SOIFER, YA. M.
SOV. PHYS. SOLID STATE
16 (6), 1139-41, 1974.
(ENGLISH TRANSLATION OF FIZ. TVERD. TELA 16 (6) 1756-60, 1974; FOR ORIGINAL SEE E63022)

63024 **LOW-TEMPERATURE PHASE TRANSFORMATION IN MANGANESE SILICON.**
KALISHEVICH, G. I. VERESHCHAGIN, YU. A.
GEL'D, P. V.
FIZ. TVERD. TELA
16 (6), 1774-5, 1974.
(FOR ENGLISH TRANSLATION SEE E63025)

63025 **LOW-TEMPERATURE PHASE TRANSFORMATION IN MANGANESE SILICON.**
KALISHEVICH, G. I. VERESHCHAGIN, YU. A.
GEL'D, P. V.
SOV. PHYS. SOLID STATE
16 (6), 1151, 1974.
(ENGLISH TRANSLATION OF FIZ. TVERD. TELA 16 (6), 1774-5, 1974; FOR ORIGINAL SEE E63024)

63028 **DEEP IMPURITY STATES AND INEQUIVALENT ATOMIC POSITIONS IN THE 33R POLYTYPE OF SILICON CARBIDE.**
GORBAN', I. S. SLOBODYANYUK, A. V.
FIZ. TVERD. TELA
16 (6), 1789-91, 1974.
(FOR ENGLISH TRANSLATION SEE E63029)

63029 **DEEP IMPURITY STATES AND INEQUIVALENT ATOMIC POSITIONS IN THE 33R POLYTYPE OF SILICON CARBIDE.**
GORBAN', I. S. SLOBODYANYUK, A. V.
SOV. PHYS. SOLID STATE
16 (6), 1163-4, 1974.
(ENGLISH TRANSLATION OF FIZ. TVERD. TELA 16 (6) 1789-91, 1974; FOR ORIGINAL SEE E63028)

63032 **STUDY OF THE PHASE CHANGE IN ANTIMONY SULFIDE AT MICROWAVE FREQUENCIES.**
MESHKAUSKAS, I. GRIGAS, I.
FIZ. TVERD. TELA
16 (6), 1804-6, 1974.
(FOR ENGLISH TRANSLATION SEE E63033)

63033 **STUDY OF THE PHASE CHANGE IN ANTIMONY SULFIDE AT MICROWAVE FREQUENCIES.**
MESHKAUSKAS, I. GRIGAS, I.
SOV. PHYS. SOLID STATE
16 (6), 1175-6, 1974.
(ENGLISH TRANSLATION OF FIZ. TVERD. TELA 16 (6) 1804-6, 1974; FOR ORIGINAL SEE E63032)

63036 **QUANTIU OSCILLATIONS OF THE KNIGHT SHIFT IN SINGLE-CRYSTAL INDIUM ANTIMONY.**
KONDRAT'EV, M. B. STARTSEV, V. V.
KHABIBULLIN, B. M.
FIZ. TVERD. TELA
16 (6), 1812-4, 1974.
(FOR ENGLISH TRANSLATION SEE E63037)

63037 **QUANTUM OSCILLATIONS OF THE KNIGHT SHIFT IN SINGLE-CRYSTAL INDIUM ANTIMONY.**
KONDRAT'EV, M. B. STARTSEV, V. V.
KHABIBULLIN, B. M.
SOV. PHYS. SOLID STATE
16 (6), 1182-3, 1974.
(ENGLISH TRANSLATION OF FIZ. TVERD TELA 16 (6) 1812-4, 1974; FOR ORIGINAL SEE E 63036)

63040 **EFFECT OF TEMPERATURE ON THE OPTICAL-ABSORPTION SPECTRA OF DEEP CENTERS IN SEMICONDUCTORS.**
KOPYLOV, A. A. PIKHTIN, A. N.
FIZ. TVERD. TELA
16 (7), 1837-43, 1974.
(FOR ENGLISH TRANSLATION SEE E63041)

63041 **EFFECT OF TEMPERATURE ON THE OPTICAL-ABSORPTION SPECTRA OF DEEP CENTERS IN SEMICONDUCTORS.**
KOPYLOV, A. A. PIKHTIN, A. N.
SOV. PHYS. SOLID STATE
16 (7), 1200-3, 1975.
(ENGLISH TRANSLATION OF FIZ. TVERD. TELA, 16 (7), 1837-43, 1974; FOR ORIGIANL SEE E63040)

63044 **MODEL FOR THE COMPLEX DOMAIN STRUCTURE OF A MAGNETICALLY UNIAXIAL CRYSTAL.**
KANDAUROVA, G. S. BEKETOV, V. N.
FIZ. TVERD. TELA
16 (7), 1857-62, 1974.
(FOR ENGLISH TRANSLATION SEE E63045)

63045 **MODEL FOR THE COMPLEX DOMAIN STRUCTURE OF A MAGNETICALLY UNIAXIAL CRYSTAL.**
KANDAUROVA, G. S. DEKETOV, V. N.
SOV. PHYS. SOLID STATE
16 (7), 1213-6, 1975.
(ENGLISH TRANSLATION OF FIZ. TVERD. TELA 16 (7), 1857-62, 1974; FOR ORIGINAL SEE E63044)

63046 **ELECTRON TRANSPORT IN SINGLE CRYSTALS OF VANADIUM OXIDE BRONZES.**
VINOGRADOV, A. A.
FIZ. TVERD. TELA
16 (7), 1874-8, 1974.
(ENGLISH TRANSLATION SEE E63047)

63047 **ELECTRON TRANSPORT IN SINGLE CRYSTALS OF VANADIUM OXIDE BRONZES.**
INOGRADOV, A. A.
SOV, PHYS. SOLID STATE
16 (7), 1224-6, 1975.
(ENGLISH TRANSLATION OF FIZ. TVERD. TELA, 16 (7) 1874-8, 1974; FOR ORIGINAL SEE E63046)

63050 **THERMOELECTRIC PROPERTIES OF SOLID ELECTROLYTE RUBIDIUM SILVER.**
DANILOV, A. V. IVANOV, V. E. KARPOV, S. V.
FIZ. TVERD. TELA
16 (7), 1929-32, 1974.
(FOR ENGLISH TRANSLATION SEE E63051)

63051 **THERMOELECTRIC PROPERTIES OF SOLID ELECTROLYTE RUBIDIUM SILVER.**
DANILOV, A. V. IVANOV, V. E. KARPOV, S. V.
SOV. PHYS. SOLID STATE
16 (7), 1259-60, 1975.
(ENGLISH TRANSLATION OF FIZ. TVERD. TELA 16 (7), 1929-32, 1974; FOR ORIGINAL SEE E63050)

63054 **LOW-TEMPERATURE ABSORPTION AND REFLECTION SPECTRA OF BISMUTH IODIDE SINGLE CRYSTALS.**
LISITSA, M. P. GUDYMENKO, L. F.
MOTSNYI, F. V. BELETSKAN, D. I.
FIZ. TVERD. TELA
16 (7), 1965-73, 1974.
(FOR ENGLISH TRANSLATION SEE E63055)

63055 **LOW-TEMPERATURE ABSORPTION AND REFLECTION SPECTRA OF BISMUTH IODIDE SINGLE CRYSTALS.**
LISITSA, M. P. GUDYMENKO, L. F.
MOTSNYI, F. V. BELETSKAN, D. I.
SOV. PHYS. SOLID STATE
16 (7), 1280-5, 1975.
(ENGLISH TRANSLATION OF FIZ. TVERD. TELA 16 (7), 1965-73, 1974; FOR ORIGINAL SEE E63054)

63056 **ANISOTROPIC IONIC CONDUCTIVITY IN MAGNESIUM FLUORIDE.**
GORLACH, V. V. LISITSYN, V. M.
FIZ. TVERD. TELA
16 (7), 1988-90, 1974.
(FOR ENGLISH TRANSLATION SEE E63057)

63057 **ANISOTROPIC IONIC CONDUCTIVITY IN MAGNESIUM FLUORIDE.**
GORLACH, V. V. LISITSYN, V. M.
SOV. PHYS. SOLID STATE
16 (7), 1293-4, 1975.
(ENGLISH TRANSLATION OF FIZ. TVERD. TELA 16 (7), 1988-90, 1974; FOR ORIGINAL SEE E63056)

63060 **CONCENTRATION DEPENDENCES OF THE PROPERTIES OF COMPOUNDS OF VARIABLE COMPOSITION ACCORDING TO THE CLUSTER-COMPONENT MODEL.**
KAMYSHOV, V. M. MEN, A. N. GORBATOV, A. G.
FIZ. TVERD. TELA
16 (7), 2051-4, 1974.
(FOR ENGLISH TRANSLATION, SEE E63061)

EPIC Number	Bibliographic Citation
63061	CONCENTRATION DEPENDENCES OF THE PROPERTIES OF COMPOUNDS OF VARIABLE COMPOSITION ACCORDING TO THE CLUSTER-COMPONENT MODEL. KAMYSHOV, V. M. MEN, A. N. GORBATOV, A. G. SOV. PHYS. SOLID STATE 16 (7), 1332-3, 1975. (ENGLISH TRANSLATION OF FIZ. TVERD. TELA, 16 (7), 2051-4, 1974; FOR ORIGINAL, SEE E63060)
63074	STRUCTURE OF THE STRIP DOMAINS OF FILMS MAGNETIZED BY CONSTANT AND ALTERNATING FIELDS . GOROKHOV, E. A. BURAVIKHIN, V. A. SELIN, G. N. FIZ. TVERD. TELA 16 (7), 2099-2100, 1974. (FOR ENGLISH TRANSLATION, SEE E63075)
63075	STRUCTURE OF THE STRIP DOMAINS OF FILMS MAGNETIZED BY CONSTANT AND ALTERNATING FIELDS. GOROKHOV, E. A. BURAVIKHIN, V. A. SELIN, G. N. SOV. PHYS. SOLID STATE 16 (7), 1367, 1975. (ENGLISH TRANSLATION OF FIZ. TVERD. TELA, 16 (7), 2099-2100, 1974; FOR ORIGINAL, SEE E63074)
63076	PROPERTIES OF FILMS OF SUPERCONDUCTING NIOBIUM GALLIUM ALLOYS PRODUCED BY EVAPORATION IN VACUO. GOLOVASHKIN, A. I. LEVCHENKO, I. S. MOTULEVICH, G. P. FIZ. TVERD. TELA 16 (7), 2100-2, 1974. (FOR ENGLISH TRANSLATION, SEE E63077)
63077	PROPERTIES OF FILMS IF SUPERCONDUCTING NIOBIUM GALLIUM ALLOYS PRODUCED BY EVAPORATION IN VACUO. GOLOVASHKIN, A. I. LEVCHENKO, I. S. MOTULEVICH, G. P. SOV. PHYS. SOLID STATE 16 (7), 1368-9, 1975. (ENGLISH TRANSLATION OF FIZ, TVERD. TELA, 16 (7), 2100-2, 1974; FOR ORIGINAL, SEE E63076)
63078	TWO-STATE DRAG OF ELECTRONS BY PHONONS IN QUANTIZING MAGNETIC FIELDS. KOZLOV, V. A. FIZ. TVERD. TELA 16 (8), 2161-7, 1974. (FOR ENGLISH TRANSLATION SEE E63079)
63079	TWO-STATE DRAG OF ELECTRONS BY PHONONS IN QUANTIZING MAGNETIC FIELDS. KOZLOV, V. A. SOV. PHYS. SOLID STATE 16 (8), 1413-6, 1975. (ENGLISH TRANSLATION OF FIZ. TVERD. TELA, 16 (8), 2161-7, 1974; FOR ORIGINAL SEE E63078)
63080	FIELD DEPENDENCE OF MAGNETIC ANISOTROPY CONSTANTS OF RARE EARTH IRON GARNETS IN STRONG FIELDS. DEMIDOV, V. G. ZVEZDIN, A. K. LEVITIN, R. Z. MARKOSYAN, A. S. POPOV, A. I. FIZ. TVERD. TELA 16 (7), 2114-7, 1974. (FOR ENGLISH TRANSLATION, SEE E63081)
63081	FIELD DEPENDENCE OF MAGNETIC ANISOTROPY CONSTANTS OF RARE EARTH IRON GARNETS IN STRONG FIELDS. DEMIDOV, V. G. ZVEZDIN, A. K. LEVITIN, R. Z. MARKOSYAN, A. S. POPOV, A. I. AOV. PHYA. SOLID STATE 16 (7), 1379-80, 1975. (ENGLISH TRANSLATION OF FIZ. TVERD. TELA, 16 (7), 2114-7, 1974; FOR ORIGINAL, SEE E63080)
63082	ENERGY-GAP WIDTH OF THE SOLID SOLUTION BISMUTH TELLURIDE SELENIUM SULFIDE. BEKDURDYEV, CH. D. GOL'TSMAN, B. M. KUTASOV, V. A. PETROV, A. V. FIZ. TVERD. TELA 16 (7), 2121-2, 1974. (FOR ENGLISH TRANSLATION, SEE E63083)
63083	ENERGY-GAP WIDTH OF THE SOLID SOLUTION BISMUTH TELLURIDE SELENIUM SULFIDE. BEKDURDYEV, CH. D. GOL TSMAN, B. M. KUTASOV, V. A. PETROV, A. V. SOV. PHYS. SOLID STATE 16 (7), 1385, 1975. (ENGLISH TRANSLATION OF FIZ. TVERD. TELA, 16 (7), 2121-2, 1974; FOR ORIGINAL, SEE E63082)
63084	ANOMALOUSLY LARGE REMAGNETIZATION JUMPS IN ORTHOFERRITES. NENAST EV, V. P. RUDYAK, V. M . FIZ. TVERD. TELA 16 (7), 2125-7, 1974. (FOR ENGLISH TRANSLATION, SEE E63085)
63085	ANOMALOUSLY LARGE REMAGNETIZATION JUMPS IN ORTHOFERRITES. NENAST EV, V. P. RUDYAK, V. M. SOV. PHYS, SOLID STATE 16 (7), 1388, 1975. (ENGLISH TRANSLATION OF FIZ. TVERD. TELA, 16 (7), 2125-7, 1974; FOR ORIGINAL, SEE E63084)
63088	ELECTRIC PERMITTIVITY OF VANADIUM PERTOXIDE. CHERNENKO, I. M. IVON, A. I. FIZ. TVERD. TELA 16 (7), 2130-2, 1974. (FOR ENGLISH TRANSLATION, SEE E63089)
63089	ELECTRIC PERMITTIVITY OF VANADIUM PENTOXIDE. CHERNENKO, I. M. IVON, A. I. SOV. PHYS. SOLID STATE 16 (7), 1391-2, 1975. (ENGLISH TRANSLATION OF FIZ. TVERD. TELA, 16 (7), 2130-2, 1974; FOR ORIGINAL, SEE E63088)
63090	THERMAL DIFFUSIVITY OF MANGANESE ANTIMONIDE. ALTSEV, M. I. ARASLY, D. G. GUSEINOV, R. E. DZHABBAROV, R. M. FIZ. TVERD. TELA 16 (7), 2139-41, 1974. (FOR ENGLISH TRANSLATION, SEE E63091)
63091	THERMAL DIFFUSIVITY OF MANGANESE ANTIMONIDE. ALTSEV, M. I. ARASLY, D. G. GUSEINOV, R. E. DZHABBAROV, R. M. SOV. PHYS. SOLID STATE 16 (7), 1399-1400, 1975. (ENGLISH TRANSLATION OF FIZ. TVERD. TELA, 16 (7), 2139-41, 1974; FOR ORIGINAL, SEE E63090)
63102	VIBRATIONAL AND DIELECTRIC SPECTRA OF CADMIUM TITANATE. KNYAZEV, A. S. POPLAVKO, YU. M. ZAKHAROV, V. P. FIZ. TVERD. TELA 16 (8), 2215-8, 1974. (FOR ENGLISH TRANSLATION, SEE E63103)
63103	VIBRATIONAL AND DIELECTRIC SPECTRA OF CADMIUM TITANATE. KNYAZEV, A. S. POPLAVKO, YU. M. ZAKHAROV, V. P. SOV. PHYS. SOLID STATE 16 (8), 1446-8, 1975. (ENGLISH TRANSLATION OF FIZ. TVERD. TELA, 16 (8), 2215-8, 1974; FOR ORIGINAL, SEE E63102)
63106	RAMAN SCATTERING AND REORIENTATION OF SULFUR IONS IN POTASSIUM IODIDE. REBANE, L. A. TRESHCHALOV, A. B. KHAL DRE, T. YU. FIZ. TVERD. TELA 16 (8), 2236-40, 1974. (FOR ENGLISH TRANSLATION, SEE E 63107)
63107	RAMAN SCATTERING AND REORIENTATION OF SULFUR IONS IN POTASSIUM IODIDE. REBANE, L. A. TRESHCHALOV, A. B. KHAL DRE, T. YU. SOV. PHYS. SOLID STATE 16 (8), 14460-2, 1975. (ENGLISH TRANSLATION OF FIZ. TVERD. TELA, 16 (8), 2236-40, 1974; FOR ORIGINAL, SEE E63106)
63112	DYNAMIC THEORY OF POTASSIUM DEUTERIUM PHOSPHATE TYPE FERROELECTRICS. KONSIN, P. I. FIZ. TVERD. TELA 16 (8), 2337-41, 1974. (FOR ENGLISH TRANSLATION SEE E63113)
63113	DYNAMIC THEORY OF POTASSIUM DEUTERIUM PHOSPHATE TYPE FERROELECTRICS. KONSIN, P. I. SOV. PHYS. SOLID STATE 16 (8), 1521-3, 1975. (ENGLISH TRANSLATION OF FIZ. TVERD. TELA, 16 (8), 2337-41, 1974; FOR ORIGINAL, SEE E63112)
63116	GALLIUM ARSENIDE PRESSURE SENSOR. VYAS, M. K. R. HIGH TEMP. HIGH PRESSURES 6 (2), 237-40, 1974.
63117	PHASE DIAGRAM OF CADMIUM ANTIMONIDE SEMICONDUCTIVE COMPOUND TO 80 KBAR. BELASH, I. T. PONYATOVSKII, E. G. HIGH TEMP. HIGH PRESSURES 6 (2), 241-4, 1974.
63126	ANOMALOUS TEMPERATURE DEPENDENCE OF THE OPTICAL PROPERTIES OF VANADIUM DIOXIDE NEAR THE SEMICONDUCTOR-METAL PHASE TRANSITION. VALIEV, K. A. MOKEROV, V. G. GALIEV, G. B. FIZ. TVERD. TELA 16 (8), 2361-4, 1974. (FOR ENGLISH TRANSLATION, SEE E63127)
63127	ANOMALOUS TEMPERATURE DEPENDENCE OF THE OPTICAL PROPERTIES OF VANADIUM DIOXIDE NEAR THE SEMICONDUCTOR-METAL PHASE TRANSITION, VALIEV, K. A. MOKEROV, V. G. GALIEV, G. B. SOV. PHYS. SOLID STATE 16 (8), 1535-6, 1975. (ENGLISH TRANSLATION OF FIZ. TVERD. TELA, 16 (8), 2361-4, 1974; FOR ORIGINAL, SEE E63126)

EPIC Number	Bibliographic Citation
63128	DIELECTRIC PROPERTIES OF ANTIMONY SULFUR IODIDE UNDER THE ACTION OF UNIAXIAL MECHANICAL STRESSES. NAKONECHNYI, YU. S. TURYANITSA, I. D. FIZ. TVERD. TELA 16 (8), 2365–8, 1974. (FOR ENGLISH TRANSLATION, SEE E63129)
63129	DIELECTRIC PROPERTIES OF ANTIMONY SULFUR IODIDE UNDER THE ACTION OF UNIAXIAL MECHANICAL STRESSES. NAKONECHNYI, YU. S. TURYANITSA, I. D. SOV. PHYS. SOLID STATE 16 (8), 1537–9, 1975. (ENGLISH TRANSLATION OF FIZ. TVERD. TELA, 16 (8), 2365–8, 1974; FOR ORITINAL, SEE E63128)
63131	MAGNETIC SUSCEPTIBILITY AND ELECTRICAL PROPERTIES OF P-TYPE LEAD TIN TELLURIDE. LASHKAREV, G. V. MIGLEI, D. F. TOVSTYUK, K. D. SHEVCHENKO, A. D. FIZ. TEKH. POLUPROV. 8 (8), 1425–30, 1974. (FOR ENGLISH TRANSLATION SEE E63132)
63132	MAGNETIC SUSCEPTIBILITY AND ELECTRICAL PROPERTIES OF P-TYPE LEAD TIN TELLURIDE. LASHKAREV, G. V. MIGLEI, D. F. TOVSTYUK, K. D. SHEVCHENKO, A. D. SOV. PHYS. SEMICOND. 8 (8), 929–32, 1975. (ENGLISH TRANSLATION OF FIZ. TEKH. POLUPROV., 8 (8), 1425–30, 1974; FOR ORIGINAL SEE E63131)
63138	ELECTROTRANSPORT IN SOME LIQUID METAL ALLOYS. VERHOEVEN, J. D. UNIVERSITY OF MICHIGAN, PH. D. THESIS 292PP., 1963. (UNIV. MICROFILM NO. 63–6964)
63141	THE LOW-TEMPERATURE PHOTOLUMINESCENCE OF BISMUTH IODIDE. LISITSA, M. I. GUDYMENKO, L. F. MOTSNYI, F. V. BLETSKAN, D. I. FIZ. TVERD. TELA 16 (8), 2400, 1974. (FOR ENGLISH TRANSLATION, SEE E63142)
63142	THE LOW-TEMPERATURE PHOTOLUMINESCENCE OF BISMUTH IODIDE. LISITSA, M. I. GUDYMENKO, L. F. MOTSNYI, F. V. BLETSKAN, D. I. SOV. PHYS. SOLID STATE 16 (8), 1559, 1975. (ENGLISH TRANSLATION OF FIZ. TVERD. TELA, 16 (8), 2400, 1974; FOR ORIGINAL, SEE 63141)
63143	EFFECT OF DEFECTS ON THE RESONANCE-RAMAN AND HOT-LUMINESCENCE SPECTRA OF CRYSTALS. PERMOGOROV, S. A. REZNITSKII, A. N. MOROZENKO, YA. V. KAZENNOV, B. A. FIZ. TVERD. TELA 16 (8), 2403–4, 1974. (FOR ENGLISH TRANSLATION, SEE E63144)
63144	EFFECT OF DEFECTS ON THE RESONANCE-RAMAN AND HOT-LUMINESCENCE SPECTRA OF CRYSTALS. PERMOGOROV, S. A. REZNITSKII, A. N. MOROZENKO, YA. V. KAZENNOV, B. A. SOV. PHYS. SOLID STATE 16 (8), 1562–3, 1975. (ENGLISH TRANSLATION OF FIZ. TVERD. TELA, 16 (8), 2403–4, 1974; FOR ORIGINAL SEE E63143)
63147	FEATURES OF THE PHOTOVOLTAIC EFFECT IN CRYSTALS OF BARIUM TITANATE. VOLK, T. R. KOCHEV, K. D. FIZ. TVERD. TELA 16 (8), 2419–21, 1974. (FOR ENGLISH TRANSLATION SEE E63148)
63148	FEATURES OF THE PHOTOVOLTAIC EFFECT IN CRYSTALS OF BARIUM TITANATE. VOLK, T. R. KOCHEV, K. D. SOV. PHYS. SOLID STATE 16 (8), 1575–6, 1975. (ENGLISH TRANSLATION OF FIZ. TVERD. TELA, 16 (8), 2419–21, 1974; FOR ORIGINAL SEE E63147)
63149	PHASE TRANSITIONS DURING SPIN REORIENTATION IN DYSPROSIUM IRON COBALT OXIDE. BELOV, K. P. GAPEEV, A. K. KADOMTSEVA, A. M. KRYNETSKII, I. B. LUKINA, M. M. OVCHINNIKOVA, T. L. FIZ. TVERD. TELA 16 (8), 2422–4, 1974. (FOR ENGLISH TRANSLATION SEE E63150)
63150	PHASE TRANSITIONS DURING SPIN REORIENTATION IN DYSPROSIUM IRON COBALT OXIDE. BELOV, K. P. GAPEEV, A. K. KADOMTSEVA, A. M. KRYNETSKII, I. B. LUKINA, M. M. OVCHINNIKOVA, T. L. SOV. PHYS. SOLID STATE 16 (8), 1577–8, 1975. (ENGLISH TRANSLATION OF FIZ. TVERD. TELA, 16 (8), 2422–4, 1974; FOR ORIGINAL SEE E63149)
63153	TEMPERATURE CHARACTERISTICS OF DEFORMATION SENSITIZATION. BREDIKHIN, S. I. SHMURAK, S. Z. FIZ. TVERD. TELA 16 (8), 2430–2, 1974. (FOR ENGLISH TRANSLATION SEE E 63154)
63154	TEMPERATURE CHARACTERISTICS OF DEFORMATION SENSITIZATION. BREDIKHIN, S. I. SHMURAK, S. Z. SOV. PHYS. SOLID STATE 16 (8), 1583–4, 1975. (ENGLISH TRANSLATION OF FIZ. TVERD. TELA, 16 (8), 2430–2, 1974; FOR ORIGINAL SEE E 63153)
63155	RESONANT SCATTERING OF POLARONS. SHMELEV, G. M. FIZ. TVERD. TELA 16 (8), 2432–4, 1974. (FOR ENGLISH TRANSLATION SEE E63156)
63156	RESONANT SCATTERING OF POLARONS. SHMELEV, G. M. SOV. PHYS. SOLID STATE 16 (8), 1585–6, 1975. (ENGLISH TRANSLATION OF FIZ. TVERD. TELA, 16 (8), 2432–4, 1974; FOR ORIGINAL SEE E 63155)
63157	NATURE OF THE RUSSELL EFFECT. MITROFANOV, V. V. SOKOLOV, V. I. FIZ. TVERD. TELA 16 (8), 2435–7, 1974. (FOR ENGLISH TRANSLATION SEE E 63158)
63158	NATURE OF THE RUSSELL EFFECT. MITROFANOV, V. V. SOKOLOV, V. I. SOV. PHYS. SOLID STATE 16 (8), 1587–8, 1975. (ENGLISH TRANSLATION OF FIZ. TVERD. TELA, 16 (8), 2435–7, 1974; FOR ORIGINAL SEE E63157)
63159	BEHAVIOR OF 180 DEGREE DOMAIN WALLS OF BARIUM TITANATE SINGLE CRYSTALS DURING THE FATIGUE AND RECOVERY OF SWITCHING PROPERTIES. KUDZIN, A. YU. PANCHENKO, T. V. YUDIN, S. P. FIZ. TVERD. TELA 16 (8), 2437–40, 1974. (FOR ENGLISH TRANSLATION SEE E63160)
63160	BEHAVIOR OF 180 DEGREE DOMAIN WALLS OF BARIUM TITANATE SINGLE CRYSTALS DURING THE FATIGUE AND RECOVERY OF SWITCHING PROPERTIES. KUDZIN, A. YU. PANCHENKO, T. V. YUDIN, S. P. SOV. PHYS. SOLID STATE 16 (8), 1589–90, 1975. (ENGLISH TRANSLATION OF FIZ. TVERD. TELA, 16 (8), 2437–40, 1974; FOR ORIGINAL SEE E63159)
63161	ANOMALOUS BEHAVIOR OF THE ELECTRICAL PROPERTIES OF TETRAGONAL-DISTORTED COPPER FERRITE. BELOV, K. P. GORYAGA, A. N. ANTOSHINA, L. L. FIZ. TVERD. TELA 16 (8), 2446–7, 1974. (FOR ENGLISH TRANSLATION SEE E63162)
63162	ANOMALOUS BEHAVIOR OF THE ELECTRICAL PROPERTIES OF TETRAGONAL-DISTORTED COPPER FERRITE. BELOV, K. P. GORYAGA, A. N. ANTOSHINA, L. L. SOV. PHYS. SOLID STATE 16 (8), 1596–7, 1975. (ENGLISH TRANSLATION OF FIZ. TVERD. TELA, 16 (8), 2446–7, 1974; FOR ORIGINAL SEE E63161)
63165	MAGNETIC ANOMALY OF THE THERMAL EXPANSION OF ANTIFERROMAGNETIC IRON FLUORIDE. GORDIENKO, V. A. ZUBENKO, V. V. NIKOLAEV, V. I. FIZ. TVERD. TELA 16 (8), 2459–62, 1974. (FOR ENGLISH TRANSLATION SEE E63166)
63166	MAGNETIC ANOMALY IN THE THERMAL EXPANSION OF ANTIFERROMAGNETIC IRON FLUORIDE. GORDIENKO, V. A. ZUBENKO, V. V. NIKOLAEV, V. I. SOV. PHYS. SOLID STATE 16 (8), 1608–9, 1975. (ENGLISH TRANSLATION OF FIZ. TVERD. TELA, 16 (8), 2459–62, 1974; FOR ORIGINAL SEE E63165)
63173	CHANGES IN THE RESISTIVITY OF THE ORDERED ALLOY NICKEL MANGANESE DURING BOMBARDMENT WITH FISSION FRAGMENTS. RAYETSKIY, V. M. NAUMINIKOV, V. I. KISELEV, L. M. SVIRIDOV, A. F. PHYS. METALS METALLOGR., USSR. 35 (5), 33–7, 1973. (ENGLISH TRANSLATION OF FIZ. METAL METALLOVED., 35 (5), 932–6, 1973; FOR ORIGINAL, SEE E51686)

EPIC Number	Bibliographic Citation

63179 **NEUTRON DIFFRACTION ANALYSIS OF MAGNETIC AND ATOMIC STRUCTURES OF THE ORDERED ALLOY IRON-PLATINUM OF EQUIATOMIC COMPOSITION.**
KELAREV, V. V. VOKHMYANIN, A. P.
DOROFEYEV, YU. A. SIDOROV, S. K.
PHYS. METALS METALLOGR., USSR
35 (6), 169–70, 1973.
(ENGLISH TRANSLATION OF FIZ. METAL. METALOVVED., 35 (6), 1302–3, 1973; FOR ORIGINAL SEE E51540)

63180 **X-RAY PHOTOEMISSION SPECTROSCOPY AND THE BAND STRUCTURE OF SOLIDS.**
SOKOLOV, O. B. FINASHKIN, V. K.
PHYS. METALS METALLOGR,. USSR
36 (1), 1–11, 1973.
(ENGLISH TRANSLATION OF FIZ. METAL. METALLOVED., 36 (1), 7–17, 1973; FOR ORIGINAL, SEE E51688)

63182 **PECULIARITIES OF MAGNETIC HYSTERESIS IN SINGLE CRYSTALS OF RARE EARTH METAL - COBALT OR YTTRIUM - COBALT COMPOUNDS.**
YERMOLENKO, A. S. KOROLEV, A. B.
PHYS. METALS METALLOGR., USSR
36 (1), 44–51, 1973.
(ENGLISH TRANSLATION OF FIZ. METAL. METALLOVED., 36 (1), 52–9, 1973; FOR ORIGINAL, SEE E51689)

63197 **ON MEASURING THE RESISTIVITY OF CYLINDRICAL AND TUBULAR SEMICONDUCTOR SINGLE CRYSTALS.**
POLYAKOV, N. N. KUKUI, A. S. PAVLOV, N. I.
GOLUBEV, V. I.
BULL. ACAD. SCI., USSR, PHYS. SER.
35 (3), 492–6, 1971.
(ENGLISH TRANSLATION OF IZV. AKAD. NAUK SSSR, SER. FIZ., 35 (3), 538–43, 1971; FOR ORIGINAL SEE E60216)

63198 **CONTACTLESS RESISTIVITY MEASUREMENTS ON FLAT SINGLE CRYSTALS.**
KUKUI, A. S. KUSHCH, V. V.
CHUMACHENKO, T. L.
BULL. ACAD. SCI., USSR, PHYS. SER.
35 (3), 497–8, 1971.
(ENGLISH TRANSLATION OF IZV. AKAD. NAUK SSSR, SER. FIZ., 35 (3), 544–5, 1971; FOR ORIGINAL SEE E60217)

63207 **POLARIZATION-OPTICAL INVESTIGATION OF MAGNETIZATION PROCESSES NEAR DISLOCATIONS IN YTTRIUM IRON GARNET SINGLE CRYSTALS.**
VLASKO-VLASOV, V. K. DEDUKH, L. M.
NIKITENKO, V. I.
SOV. PHYS. JETP
38 (1), 184–94, 1974.
(ENGLISH TRANSLATION OF ZH. EKSP. TEOR. FIZ., 65 (1), 376–95, 1973; FOR ORIGINAL SEE E52369)

63208 **MAGNETIC ANISOTROPY AND MAGNETOSTRICTION OF NEODYMIUM-SUBSTITUTED YTTRIUM IRON GARNETS.**
VOLKOVA, N. V. RAITSIS, V. I.
SOV. PHYS. JETP
38 (2), 339–41, 1974.
(ENGLISH TRANSLATION OF ZH. EKSP. TEOR. FIZ., 65 (2), 688–92, 1973; FOR ORIGINAL SEE E52370)

63209 **EFFECT OF DISLOCATIONS ON THE ELECTRIC PROPERTIES OF P-GERMANIUM.**
OSIP'YAN, YU. A. SHEVCHENKO, S. A.
SOV. PHYS. JETP
38 (2), 345–8, 1974.
(ENGLISH TRANSLATION OF ZH. EKSP. TEOR. FIZ., 65 (2), 698–704, 1973; FOR ORIGINAL SEE E52373)

63212 **ON THE THEORY OF IMPURITY FERROMAGNETISM IN SEMICONDUCTORS.**
ABRIKOSOV, A. A.
SOV. PHYS. JETP
38 (2), 403–7, 1974.
(ENGLISH TRANSLATION OF ZH. EKSP. TEOR. FIZ. 65 (2), 814–22, 1973; FOR ORIGINAL SEE E52372)

63219 **ACTIVATION ENERGY OF JUMP CONDUCTIVITY.**
SHKLOVSKII, B. I. EFROS, A. L.
YANCHEV, I. YA.
JETP LETTERS
14 (5), 233–5, 1971.
(ENGLISH TRANSLATION OF PIS'MA ZH. EKSP. TEOR. FIZ., 14 (5), 348–51, 1971; FOR ORIGINAL SEE E61519)

63230 **MORPHOLOGY OF THE DOMAIN STRUCTURE OS ANTIMONY IODIDE SULFIDE CRYSTALS.**
ZADOROZHNAYA, L. A. LYAKHOVITSKAYA, V. A.
BELYAEV, L. M.
SOV. PHYS. CRYSTALLOGR.
18 (3), 363–5, 1973.
(ENGLISH TRANSLATION OF KRISTALLOGRAFIYA, 18 (3), 579–83, 1973; FOR ORIGINAL, SEE E 51932)

63232 **ELECTRONIC MECHANISM OF THE INFLUENCE OF RADIATION ON THE PROCESS OF REPOLARIZATION OF FERROELECTRICS.**
GREKOV, A. A. MALITSKAYA, M. A.
FRIDKIN, V. M.
SOV. PHYS. CRYSTALLOGR.
18 (4), 494–8, 1974.
(ENGLISH TRANSLATION OF KRISTALLOGRAFIYA, 18 (4), 788–95, 1973; FOR ORIGINAL, SEE E 51934)

63233 **GROWTH AND STUDY OF CRYSTALS OF DOUBLE OXIDES OF CADMIUM WITH STRUCTURES OF THE PEROVSKITE TYPE. I. CADMIUM HAFNATE.**
SPINKO, R. I. LEBEDEV, V. N. KOLESOVA, R. V.
FESENKO, E. G.
SOV. PHYS. CRYSTALLOGR.
18 (4), 536–7, 1974.
(ENGLISH TRANSLATION OF KRISTALLOGRAFIYA 18 (4), 849–51, 1973; FOR ORIGINAL SEE E52665)

63234 **CHARGE ON DISLOCATIONS IN SODIUM CHLORIDE CRYSTALS CONTAINING AN ANIONIC IMPURITY.**
TYAPUNINA, N. A. KOLOMIITSEV, A. I.
SOV. PHYS. CRYSTALLOGR.
18 (4), 549–50, 1974.
(ENGLISH TRANSLATION OF KRISTALLOGRAFIYA 18 (4), 868–70, 1973; FOR ORIGINAL SEE E56008)

63242 **THE OPTICAL AND OTHER PHYSICAL PROPERTIES OF INFRA-RED OPTICAL MATERIALS.**
BALLARD, S. S. COMBES, L. S. HYDE, W. L.
GRIFFITH, G. E. MC CARTHY, K. A.
BAIRD ASSOCIATES, INC., CAMBRIDGE, MASS.
282PP., 1949.

63246 **INFLUENCE OF EXTERNAL FACTORS ON THE ELECTROPHYSICAL PROPERTIES OF PIEZOELECTRIC CERAMICS MADE FROM SOLID SOLUTIONS LEAD BARIUM NIOBATE.**
ANAN'EVA, A. A. UGRYUMOVA, M. A.
SHAEVICH, T. A.
SOV. PHYS. ACOUST.
19 (4), 318–9, 1974.
(ENGLISH TRANSLATION OF AKUST. ZH. 19 (4), 494–7, 1973; FOR ORIGINAL SEE E52500)

63247 **METHOD FOR MEASURING THERMOELECTRIC PARAMETERS.**
AGAEV, YA. MIKHAILOV, A. R.
APPL. SOLAR ENERGY, USSR
2 (6), 31–5, 1966.
(ENGLISH TRANSLATION OF GELIOTEKHNIKA, 2 (6), 41–6, 1966; FOR ORIGINAL SEE E59587)

63252 **PROPERTIES AND STRUCTURE OF GLASSES IN THE SYSTEM BISMUTH OXIDE - SILICON OXIDE - GERMANIUM OXIDE.**
TOPPING, J. A. CAMERON, N. MURTHY, M. K.
J. AMER. CERAM. SOC.
57 (12), 519–21, 1974.

63253 **EVALUATION OF LATTICE SITE AND VALENCE OF MANGANESE AND IRON IN POLYCRYSTALLINE LEAD TITANIUM OXIDE BY ELECTRON SPIN RESONANCE AND THERMOGRAVIMETRY.**
HENNINGS, D. POMPLUN, H.
J. AMER. CERAM. SOC.
57 (12), 527–30, 1974.

63254 **INTERNAL FRICTION OF GLASSES WITH LOW WATER CONTENTS.**
DAY, D. E.
J. AMER. CERAM. SOC.
57 (12), 530–3, 1974.

63255 **10.6-MICROMETER ABSORPTION DEPENDENCE ON ROUGHNESS OF UHV-COATED SUPERSMOOTH MIRRORS.**
SAITO, T. T. KURDOCK, J. R. AUSTIN, R. R.
SOILEAU, M. J.
APPL. OPT.
14 (2), 266–7, 1975.

63256 **HEAT FLOW ANALYSIS OF LASER ABSORPTION CALORIMETRY.**
ENRIQUE BERNAL, G.
APPL. OPT.
14 (2), 314–21, 1975.

63258 **NONLINEAR LONGITUDINAL POTASSIUM TANTALATE - NIOBATE MODULATOR.**
FOX, A. J.
APPL. OPT.
14 (2), 343–52, 1975.

63265 **CRYSTAL-FIELD CALCULATIONS FOR ENERGY LEVELS OF URANIUM IN ZIRCONIUM SILICON OXIDE.**
MACKEY, D. J. RUNCIMAN, W. A. VANCE, E. R.
PHYS. REV.
11 B (1), 211–8, 1975.

63269 **LOW-TEMPERATURE RESISTIVITY OF YTTERBIUM IN GOLD, SILVER, AND GOLD - SILVER ALLOYS.**
TALMOR, Y. SIERRO, J.
PHYS. REV.
11 B (1), 300–8, 1975.

63274 **MAGNETOCRYSTALLINE ANISOTROPY OF SAMARIUM COBALT AND ITS INTERPRETATION ON A CRYSTAL-FIELD MODEL.**
SANKAR, S. G. RAO, V. U. S. SEGAL, E.
WALLACE, W. E. FREDERICK, W. G. D.
GARRETT, H. J.
PHYS. REV.
11 B (1), 435–9, 1975.

63275 **ELECTRONIC PROPERTIES OF BERYLLIDES OF THE RARE EARTH AND SOME ACTINIDES.**
BUCHER, E. MAITA, J. P. HULL, G. W.
FULTON, R. C. COOPER, A. S.
PHYS. REV.
11 B (1), 440–9, 1975.

EPIC Number	Bibliographic Citation
63276	**MAGNETIC AND SOME THERMAL PROPERTIES OF CHALCOGENIDES OF PRASEODYMIUM AND THULIUM AND A FEW OTHER RARE EARTHS.** BUCHER, E. ANDRES, K. DI SALVO, F. J. MAITA, J. P. GOSSARD, A. C. COOPER, A. S. HULL, G. W., JR. PHYS. REV. 11 B (1), 500–13, 1975.
63278	**MAGNETIC PROPERTIES OF NEPTUNIUM LAVES PHASES: NEPTUNIUM MANGANESE, NEPTUNIUM IRON, NEPTUNIUM COBALT, AND NEPTUNIUM NICKEL.** ALDRED, A. T. DUNLAP, B. D. LAM, D. J. LANDER, G. H. MUELLER, M. H. NOWIK, I. PHYS. REV. 11 B (1), 530–44, 1975.
63284	**ELECTRONIC STRUCTURE OF LEAD SELENIDE AND LEAD TELLURIDE. I. BAND STRUCTURES, DENSITIES OF STATES, AND EFFECTIVE MASSES.** MARTINEZ, G. SCHLUTER, M. COHEN, M. L. PHYS. REV. 11 B (2), 651–9, 1975.
63285	**ELECTRONIC STRUCTURE OF LEAD SELENIDE AND LEAD TELLURIDE. II. OPTICAL PROPERTIES.** MARTINEZ, G. SCHLUTER, M. COHEN, M. L. PHYS. REV. 11 B (2), 660–70, 1975.
63292	**TEMPERATURE DEPENDENCE OF FAR–INFRARED ABSORPTION IN GALLIUM ARSENIDE.** STOLEN, R. H. PHYS. REV. 11 B (2), 767–70, 1975.
63293	**TWO–PHOTON PHOTOCONDUCTIVITY PHEONOMENA IN SEMICONDUCTORS AND INSULATORS.** KOREN, G. PHYS. REV. 11 B (2), 802–21, 1975.
63295	**ENERGY TRANSFER IN SAMARIUM–DOPED CALCIUM TUNGSTATE CRYSTALS.** TREADAWAY, M. J. POWELL, R. C. PHYS. REV. 11 B (2), 862–74, 1975.
63296	**RESONANT RAMAN SCATTERING BY A LOCALIZED MODE IN CESIUM IODIDE.** MARTIN, T. P. PHYS. REV. 11 B (2), 875–80, 1975.
63297	**ROLE OF HYDROGEN AND DEUTERIUM ON THE V – CENTER FORMATION IN MAGNESIUM OXIDE.** CHEN, Y. ABRAHAM, M. M. TEMPLETON, L. C. UNRUH, W. P. PHYS. REV. 11 B (2), 881–90, 1975.
63298	**ELECTRONIC EXCITATIONS IN PRASEODYMIUM ALUMINUM OXIDE.** LYONS, K. B. BIRGENEAU, R. J. BLOUNT, E. I. VAN UITERT, L. G. PHYS. REV. 11 B (2), 891–900, 1975.
63299	**LOCALIZED–MODE SURFACE POLARITONS.** BISHOP, M. F. PHYS. REV. 11 B (2), 901–4, 1975.
63300	**EXCITONS IN MOLYBDENUM DISULPHIDE.** FORTIN, E. RAGA, F. PHYS. REV. 11 B (2), 905–12, 1975.
63301	**FLUORESCENCE TRANSITION FROM STATE 4T2 TO STATE 4A2 AND PHOSPHORESCENCE TRANSITION FROM STATE 2E TO 4A2 IN MAGNESIUM OXIDE: CHROMIUM.** CASTELLI, F. FORSTER, L. S. PHYS. REV. 11 B (2), 920–8, 1975.
63303	**INTERNAL PHOTOEMISSION OF HOLES FROM A SEMICONDUCTOR INTO A SEMICONDUCTOR.** CAROLI, C. HELMAN, J. S. SANCHEZ–SINENCIO, F. PHYS. REV. 11 B (2), 980–2, 1975.
63304	**ELECTRON PARAMAGNETIC RESONANCE OF GADOLINIUM TRIPOSITIVE IN C(S) SYMMETRY AND CRYSTALLOGRAPHIC STUDY OF RARE–EARTH ULTRAPHOSPHATES. CASE OF GADOLINIUM TRIPOSITIVE, EUROPIUM TRIPOSITIVE, AND GADOLINIUM EUROPIUM ULTRAPHOSPHATES.** PARROT, R. BARTHOU, C. CANNY, B. BLANZAT, B. COLLIN, G. PHYS. REV. 11 B (3), 1001–12, 1975.
63305	**MAGNETIC PROPERTIES OF NEPTUNIUM LAVES PHASES: NEPTUNIUM OSMIUM – RUTHENIUM PSEUDOBINARY SYSTEM.** ALDRED, A. T. LAM, D. J. HARVEY, A. R. DUNLAP, B. D. PHYS. REV. 11 B (3), 1169–75, 1975.
63306	**EFFECT OF PRESSURE ON THE ZONE–CENTER PHONONS OF LEAD TITANIUM OXIDE AND ON THE FERROELECTRIC–PARAELECTRIC PHASE TRANSITION.** CERDEIRA, F. HOLZAPFEL, W. B. BAUERLE, D. PHYS. REV. 11 B (3), 1188–92, 1975.
63320	**ELECTRONIC STRUCTURE AND OPTICAL PROPERTIES OF 3C – SILICON CARBIDE.** LUBINSKY, A. R. ELLIS, D. E. PAINTER, G. S. PHYS. REV. 11 B (4), 1537–46, 1975.
63321	**TEMPERATURE–GRADIENT INSTABILITIES IN SEMICONDUCTOR JUNCTIONS.** HANDEL, P. H. PHYS. REV. 11 B (4), 1595–9, 1975.
63322	**SCREENED–EXCHANGE PLUS COULOMB–HOLE CORRELATED HARTREE–FOCK ENERGY BANDS FOR LITHIUM FLUORIDE.** BRENER, N. E. PHYS. REV. 11 B (4), 1600–8, 1975. (AD–A008 076, ARL–75–0096)
63323	**MAGNETIC PROPERTIES OF GADOLINIUM OXIDE.** MOON, R. M. KOEHLER, W. C. PHYS. REV. 11 B (4), 1609–22, 1975.
63324	**LOCAL–FIELD EFFECTS ON INELASTIC ELECTRON SCATTERING.** NAGEL, S. R. WITTEN, T. A., JR. PHYS. REV. 11 B (4), 1623–35, 1975.
63326	**ANOMALOUS HIGH–TEMPERATURE IONIC CONDUCTIVITY IN THE SILVER HALIDES.** ABOAGYE, J. K. FRIAUF, R. J. PHYS. REV. 11 B (4), 1654–64, 1975.
63327	**MULTIPHONON ABSORPTION IN IONIC CRYSTALS.** BOYER, L. L. HARRINGTON, J. A. HASS, M. ROSENSTOCK, H. B. PHYS. REV. 11 B (4), 1665–80, 1975. (AD–B008 044L)
63328	**LINEAR DICHROISM IN THE ABSORPTION AND TRIPLET–STATE EXCITATION SPECTRA OF FLUORIDE CENTERS IN POTASSIUM CHLORIDE.** ENGSTROM, H. PHYS. REV. 11 B (4), 1689–99, 1975.
63329	**ELECTRONIC STRUCTURE OF LITHIUM HYDRIDE AND SODIUM HYDRIDE.** KUNZ, A. B. MICKISH, D. J. PHYS. REV. 11 B (4), 1700–4, 1975.
63331	**MULTIPLET SPLITTING OF THE MANGANESE 2(P) AND 3(P) LEVELS IN MANGANESE FLUORIDE SINGLE CRYSTALS.** KOWALCZYK, S. P. LEY, L. MCFEELY, F. R. SHIRLEY, D. A. PHYS. REV. 11 B (4), 1721–7, 1975.
63332	**THEORY OF THE OPTICAL PROPERTIES OF IONIC CRYSTAL CUBES.** FUCHS, R. PHYS. REV. 11 B (4), 1732–40, 1975.
63334	**COUPLED–MODE THEORY, MORI DAMPING, AND THE SHAPE OF LATTICE–ABSORPTION BANDS.** SILVERMAN, B. D. PHYS. REV. 11 B (4), 1768–9, 1975.
63336	**ACOUSTO–OPTIC PROPERTIES OF DENSE FLINT GLASSES.** ESCHLER, H. WIEDINGER, F. J. APPL. PHYS. 46 (1), 65–70, 1975.
63337	**HYDROXYL IONS AND THE 200–NM ABSORPTION BAND IN MAGNESIUM AND TITANIUM DOPED THERMOLUMINESCENT LITHIUM FLUORIDE SINGLE CRYSTALS.** VORA, H. JONES, J. H. STOEBE, T. G. J. APPL. PHYS. 46 (1), 71–7, 1975.
63342	**PHOTOELECTRIC PROPERTIES OF CUPROUS OXIDE.** POLLACK, G. P. TRIVICH, D. J. APPL. PHYS. 46 (1), 163–72, 1975.

EPIC Number	Bibliographic Citation
63344	EVALUATION OF THE AGGLOMERATION OF ACICULAR MAGNETIC OXIDE PARTICLES IN POLYMER SUBSTRATE USING THE MAXWELL-WAGNER EFFECT. DASGUPTA, S. CONNER, W. P. J. APPL. PHYS. 46 (1), 204–7, 1975.
63345	ELECTROMECHANICAL RESPONSE OF PZT 65/35 SUBJECTED TO AXIAL SHOCK LOADING. LYSNE, P. C. BARTEL, L. C. J. APPL. PHYS. 46 (1), 222–9, 1975.
63346	PREDICTION OF DIELECTRIC BREAKDOWN IN SHCOK-LOADED FERROELECTRIC CERAMICS. LYSNE, P. C. J. APPL. PHYS. 46 (1), 230–2, 1975.
63348	CONCENTRATION DEPENDENCE OF THE ABSORPTION COEFFICIENT FOR N- AND P-TYPE GALLIUM ARSENIDE BETWEEN 1.3 AND 1.6 EV. CASEY, H. C., JR. SELL, D. D. WECHT, K. W. J. APPL. PHYS. 46 (1), 2507, 1975.
63349	INFRARED STRESS BIREFRINGENCE IN POTASSIUM BROMIDE, POTASSIUM CHLORIDE, LITHIUM FLUORIDE, AND ZINC SELENIDE. CHEN, C. S. SZCZESNIAK, J. P. CORELLI, J. C. J. APPL. PHYS. 46 (1), 303–9, 1975. (AD-A018 871)
63350	ELECTRICAL CONDUCTION AND DIELECTRIC BREAKDOWN IN CRYSTALLINE NICKEL OXIDE AND NICKEL OXIDE (LITHIUM) FILMS. JUSCHILLO, N. LALEVIC, B. LEUNG, B. J. APPL. PHYS. 46 (1), 310–6, 1975.
63351	BEHAVIOR OF CARRIER LIFETIME SPECTRA OF (77 K) IN GALLIUM ARSENIDE PHOSPHIDE. LEE, M. H. HOLONYAK, N., JR. NELSON, R. J. KEUNE, D. L. GROVES, W. O. J. APPL. PHYS. 46 (1), 323–31, 1975.
63356	CATHODOLUMINESCENCE OF COMPOSITIONALLY GRADED LAYERS OF GALLIUM ARSENIDE PHOSPHIDE. KASANO, H. HOSOKI, S. J. APPL. PHYS. 46 (1), 394–401, 1975.
63357	A DYNAMIC MODEL FOR FLUX JUMPS IN TYPE-II SUPERCONDUCTORS. BUSSIERE, J. F. LE BLANC, M. A. R. J. APPL. PHYS. 46 (1), 406–12, 1975.
63358	UNIAXIAL ANISOTROPY IN MAGNESIUM IRON ALUMINUM OXIDE. BORRELLI, N. F. J. APPL. PHYS. 46 (1), 430–5, 1975.
63361	INDEX OF REFRACTION OF BARIUM OXIDE. ANDERSON, C. J. HENSLEY, E. B. J. APPL. PHYS. 46 (1), 443, 1975.
63362	LOCALIZED VIBRATIONAL MODE ABSORPTION OF ION-IMPLANTED BERYLLIUM IN ZINC TELLURIDE. VODOPYANOV, L. K. KACHARE, A. H. SPITZER, W. G. WILSON, R. G. J. APPL. PHYS. 46 (1), 446–8, 1975.
63363	CARRIER CONCENTRATION RATIO AND HALL MOBILITY OF SEMI-INSULATING GALLIUM ARSENIDE UPON PHOTOEXCITATION AND ELECTRON BOMBARDMENT. EUTHYMIOU, P. C. NOMICOS, C. D. THEODOROU, D. E. J. APPL. PHYS. 46 (1), 449–51, 1975.
63367	FAR-FIELD EMISSION PATTERNS OF SINGLE HETERSTRUCTURE GALLIUM ARSENIDE LASERS. HENSHALL, G. D. WHITEAWAY, J. E. A. ELECTRON. LETT. 10 (15), 326–7, 1974.
63373	THE ELECTRONIC CHARGE DENSITIES IN SEMICONDUCTING LAYER AND CHAIN STRUCTURES. MOOSER, E. SCHLUTER, I. CH. SCHLUTER, M. J. PHYS. CHEM. SOLIDS 35 (9), 1269–84, 1974.
63375	ON THE HOT ELECTRON CONDUCTIVITY IN A POLAR SEMICONDUCTOR. LICEA, I. J. PHYS. CHEM. SOLIDS 35 (9), 1344–6, 1974.
63380	COEXISTENCE OF FERROMAGNETISM AND SUPERCONDUCTIVITY IN A SUPERCONDUCTING ALLOY. SMIT, W. A. VERTOGEN, G. KRAAK, J. PHYSICA 74 (1), 97–109, 1974.
63390	INFRARED ABSORPTION IN MICROCRYSTALS OF MAGNESIUM OXIDE. LAGARDE, P. NERENBERG, M. A. PHYS. STATUS SOLIDI (GERMANY) 64 B (2), 567–74, 1974.
63393	FREE-CARRIER PIEZOBIREFRINGENCE IN GALLIUM PHOSPHORUS. GLURDGYDZE, L. N. REMENYUK, A. D. SHMARTSEV, YU. V. SOLID STATE COMMUN. 15 (2), 143–4, 1974.
63399	HOPPING CONDUCTION IN AMORPHOUS SEMICONDUCTORS. GRANT, A. J. DAVIS, E. A. SOLID STATE COMMUN. 15 (3), 563–6, 1974.
63405	EVALUATION OF DEEP LEVELS IN SEMICONDUCTORS USING FIELD EFFECT TRANSCONDUCTANCE. WADA, O. YANAGISAWA, S. TAKANASHI, H. JAP. J. APPL. PHYS. 14 (1), 157–8, 1975.
63406	ABSORPTION IN MATERIALS USED FOR OPTICAL FIBERS. ZAGANIARIS, A. BOUVY, G. ANN. TELECOMMUN. 29 (5–6), 189–94, 1974. (FOR ENGLISH TRANSLATION SEE E93191)
63413	SUPERCONDUCTIVITY AND CRYSTAL LATTICE STABILITY. KODESS, B. N. SOLID STATE COMMUN. 16 (3), 269–73, 1975.
63423	STATE OF THIN FILMS OF SILICON, CHROMIUM, AND CHROMIUM SILICIDES. SHABALINA, O. K. BAUM, B. A. GEL'D, P. V. IZV. AKAD. NAUK SSSR, NEORG. MATER. 7 (10), 1864–5, 1971. (FOR ENGLISH TRANSLATION SEE E67074)
63424	CALCULATION OF OPTICAL CONSTANTS OF SEMICONDUCTORS FROM DIFFUSE REFLECTION SPECTRA OF THEIR POWDERS. VERGER, L. I. PETROV, V. M. IZV. AKAD. NAUK SSSR, NEORG. MATER. 7 (11), 1905–8, 1971. (FOR ENGLISH TRANSLATION SEE E67075)
63428	TIN TELLURIDE-LEAD SELENIDE SYSTEM. BOROVIKOVA, R. P. DUDKIN, L. D. KAZANSKAYA, O. A. KOSOLAPOVA, E. F. IZV. AKAD. NAUK SSSR, NEORG. MATER. 8 (10), 1762–4, 1972. (FOR ENGLISH TRANSLATION SEE E67082)
63429	ELECTRICAL CONDUCTIVITY AND THERMOEMF. OF BISMUTH SESQUITELLURIDE-ANTIMONY SESQUISULFIDE MOLTEN ALLOYS. CHIZHEVSKAYA, S. N. ABRIKOSOV, N. KH. IZV. AKAD. NAUK SSSR, NEORG. MATER. 8 (11), 2031–2, 1972. (FOR ENGLISH TRANSLATION SEE E67081)
63434	LASER PHOTOLUMINESCENCE SPECTROSCOPY OF PHOTODISSOCIATION FRAGMENTS. JACKSON, W. M. CODY, R. J. J. CHEM. PHYS. 61 (10), 4183–5, 1974.
63435	THE SUPERCONDUCTING TRANSITION TEMPERATURE AND ITS HIGH-PRESSURE BEHAVIOR OF TETRAGONAL NIOBIUM TIN. CHU, C. W. VIELAND, L. J. J. LOW TEMP. PHYS. 17 (1–2), 25–9, 1974.
63444	RESTORATION OF SOME PROPERTIES OF NICKEL DURING ANNEALING AFTER COLD DEFORMATION. SIKOROV, V. N. UMANSKII, Y. S. EPSHTEIN, G. N. IZV. VYSSH. UCHEB. ZAVED., CHERN. MET. 14 (11), 143–7, 1971.
63449	INVESTIGATION OF THE INFLUENCE OF PORES AND GRAIN BOUNDARIES ON THE ELECTRICAL AND THERMAL CONDUCTIVITIES OF THERMOELECTRIC MATERIALS. GOL'TSMAN, B. M. SARKISYAN, V. SH. STIL'BANS, L. S. SHLYKOV, V. V. IZV. AKAD. NAUK SSSR, NEORG. MATER. 5 (2), 283–6, 1969. (FOR ENGLISH TRANSLATION SEE E63450)

EPIC Number	Bibliographic Citation

63450 INVESTIGATION OF THE INFLUENCE OF PORES AND GRAIN BOUNDARIES ON THE ELECTRICAL AND THERMAL CONDUCTIVITIES OF THERMOELECTRIC MATERIALS.
GOL'TSMAN, B. M. SARKISYAN, V. SH.
STIL'BANS, L. S. SHLYKOV, V. V.
INORG. MATER.
5 (2), 235-7, 1969.
(ENGLISH TRANSLATION OF IZV. AKAD. NAUK, SSSR, NEORG. MATER., 5 (2), 283-6, 1969; FOR ORIGINAL SEE E63449)

63457 REFRACTOMETRY WITH SOLID SUBSTANCES HAVING LOW REFRACTIVE INDEXES.
BOURDINAUD, M. POIVILLIERS, J.
TAULEMESSE, C. THEVENIN, J. C.
COMMIS. ENERG. AT., CEN, GIF-SUR-YVETTE, FR.
12PP., 1973.
(CEA-N-1671)

63458 PHOTOELECTRIC AND ELECTROPHYSICAL PROPERTIES OF COPPER-DOPED GALLIUM ARSENIDE.
VOITSEKHOVSKII, A. V. ZAKHAROVA, G. A.
KRIVOV, M. A. MALISOVA, E. V.
IZV. VYSSH. UCHEB. ZAVED., FIZ.
13 (9), 40-4, 1970.
(FOR ENGLISH TRANSLATION SEE E65158)

63462 PHOTOELECTRIC PROPERTIES OF P-N JUNCTIONS IN SINGLE-CRYSTAL LEAD SULFIDE FILMS.
BATUKOVA, L. M.
IZV. VYSSH. UCHEB. ZAVED., FIZ.
14 (5), 146-8, 1971.
(FOR ENGLISH TRANSLATION SEE E65164)

63465 MEASUREMENT OF THE ANISOTROPY OF SEMICONDUCTOR LAYER ELECTRICAL CONDUCTIVITY BY A FOUR-PROBE METHOD.
ISLYAMOV, Z. I. KON'KOV, V. L.
IZV. VYSSH. UCHEB. ZAVED., FIZ.
14 (8), 143-6, 1971.
(FOR ENGLISH TRANSLATION SEE E65154)

63468 MEASUREMENT OF THE CONDUCTIVITY OF HETEROGENEOUS SEMICONDUCTOR LAYERS BY A PROBE METHOD.
KON'KOV, V. L. PAVLOV, N. I. POLYAKOV, N. N.
IZV. VYSSH. UCHEB. ZAVED., FIZ.
14 (10), 33-8, 1971.
(FOR ENGLISH TRANSLATION SEE E65157)

63469 EFFECT OF ELECTRON IRRADIATION ON PHOTODIODES BASED ON GALLIUM ARSENIDE.
BRUDNYI, V. N. VORONKOV, V. P.
KRIVOV, M. A. MALYANOV, S. V.
IZV. VYSSH. UCHEB. ZAVED., FIZ.
15 (1), 106-7, 1972.
(FOR ENGLISH TRANSLATION SEE E65147)

63472 OPTICAL PROPERTIES OF INDIUM SELENIUM TELLURIUM SINGLE CRYSTALS.
MUSHINSKII, V. P. KOBOLEV, V. I.
IZV. VYSSH. UCHEB. ZAVED., FIZ.
15 (5), 65-8, 1972.
(FOR ENGLISH TRANSLATION SEE E65150)

63474 USE OF THE METHOD OF ATTENUATED TOTAL INTERNAL REFLECTION FOR SEMICONDUCTOR METRICS.
BILENKO, D. I. DVORKIN, V. A.
SHEKHTER, Z. V.
IZV. VYSSH. UCHEB. ZAVED., FIZ.
15 (6), 19-23, 1972.
(FOR ENGLISH TRANSLATION SEE E65152)

63478 UNIFORMITY OF BETA-SILICON CARBIDE SINGLE CRYSTALS STUDIED BY USING VOLUME-GRADIENT PHOTOEMF.
AIVAZOVA, L. S. ALTAISKII, YU. M.
SIDYAKIN, V. G.
IZV. VYSSH. UCHEB. ZAVED., FIZ.
15 (10), 113-14, 1972.
(FOR ENGLISH TRANSLATION SEE E65927)

63482 PHOTOEMF. OCCURRING IN GALLIUM ARSENIDE-BASED P-N JUNCTIONS UNDER THE ACTION OF NATURAL RECOMBINATION RADIATION.
OKUNEV, V. D. GAMAN, V. I.
IZV. VYSSH. UCHEB. ZAVED., FIZ.
16 (1), 138-9, 1973.
(FOR ENGLISH TRANSLATION SEE E65161)

63486 DIELECTRIC CONSTANT AND CONDUCTIVITY MEASUREMENT OF POWDER SAMPLES BY THE CAVITY PERTURBATION METHOD.
KOBAYASHI, H. OGAWA, S.
JAP. J. APPL. PHYS.
10 (3), 345-50, 1971.

63491 PHOTOVOLTAIC POLARITIES OF OBLIQUELY DEPOSITED ZINC SULFIDE FILMS DOPED WITH CHLORINE AND ZINC.
TAKEDA, S. SAITO, Y.
JAP. J. APPL. PHYS.
11 (6), 915-16, 1972.

63492 OPTICAL ABSORPTION DUE TO ACCEPTOR LEVELS IN UNDOPED ZINC TELLURIDE.
HORIKOSHI, Y. EBINA, A. TAKAHASHI, T.
JAP. J. APPL. PHYS.
11 (7), 992-1001, 1972.

63503 PHOTOVOLTAIC PROPERTIES OF ZINC SULFIDE CRYSTALS AND A COMPARATIVE STUDY WITH LUMINESCENCE.
SCARMOZZINO, R.
J. APPL. PHYS.
43 (11), 4652-7, 1972.

63504 EFFECT OF NITROGEN ON THE ELECTRICAL AND STRUCTURAL PROPERTIES OF TRIODE-SPUTTERED TANTALUM FILMS.
WILLMOTT, D. J.
J. APPL. PHYS.
43 (12), 4865-71, 1972.

63506 PHOTOELECTRIC SPECTRAL RESPONSE OF CERTAIN SOLIDS.
JONES, J. E.
J. APPL. PHYS.
44 (1), 96-9, 1973.

63510 PHOTOVOLTAIC EFFECTS IN THE IONIZATION RESPONSE OF TANTALUM CAPACITORS.
BAKER, R. T. FLANAGAN, T. M. LEADON, R. E.
J. APPL. PHYS.
44 (3), 995-1002, 1973.

63515 PHOTOVOLTAIC EFFECT DUE TO TWO-PHOTON PROCESS IN P-N JUNCTION DEVICES IN THE PRESENCE OF A BUILT-IN FIELD.
DEB, S. MUKHERJEE, M. K. BASU, A. K.
J. APPL. PHYS.
44 (8), 3689-93, 1973.

63527 EFFECT OF PRESSURE ON THE OPTICAL ABSORPTION OF REF CENTRES IN CERIUM AND TERBIUM DOPED CALACIUM FLUORIDE.
DROTNING, W. D. DRICKAMER, H. G.
J. CHEM. PHYS.
59 (7), 3482-4, 1973.

63536 MEASUREMENT OF RESISTIVITY OF EPITAXIAL WAFERS USING A VOLTAGE RELAXATION TECHNIQUE.
AGATSUMU, T.
J. ELECTROCHEM. SOC.
119 (2), 237-44, 1972.

63537 EFFECT OF HYDROGEN CHLORIDE AND MOLECULAR CHLORINE ON THE THERMAL OXIDATION OF SILICON.
KRIEGLER, R. J. CHENG, Y. C. COLTON, D. R.
J. ELECTROCHEM. SOC.
119 (3), 388-92, 1972.

63538 SELECTIVE PHOTOETCHING OF GALLIUM ARSENIDE.
KUHN-KUHNENFELD, F.
J. ELECTROCHEM. SOC.
119 (8), 1063-8, 1972.

63542 RESISTIVITY CHARACTERIZATION OF SEMICONDUCTOR CRYSTAL INGOTS.
PADOVANI, F. VALANT, G.
J. ELECTROCHEM. SOC.
120 (4), 585-7, 1973.

63549 MEASUREMENTS ON THE EFFECT OF GRAIN BOUNDARIES ON THE ELECTRICAL RESISTIVITY OF URANIUM DIOXIDE.
SCHIKARSKI, W. ONDRACEK, G.
J. NUCL. MATER.
45 (2), 171-3, 1972.

63562 PIEZOELECTRIC CONSTANT AND CONDUCTIVITY RELAXATION IN N-TYPE INDIUM PHOSPHIDE FROM ULTRASONIC ATTENUATION MEASUREMENTS.
BOYLE, W. F. SLADEK, W. F.
SOLID STATE COMMUN.
16 (3), 323-6, 1975.

63564 METHODS FOR DETERMINING FILM THICKNESS AND OPTICAL CONSTANTS OF FILMS AND SUBSTRATES.
RUIZ-URBIETA, M. SPARROW, E. M.
ECKERT, E. R. G.
J. OPT. SOC. AMER.
61 (3), 351-9, 1971.

63568 INTENSITY METHOD FOR STRESS-OPTICAL MEASUREMENTS. STRESS-OPTICAL DISPERSION OF SINGLE-CRYSTAL SODIUM FLUORIDE.
VASUDEVAN, T. N. MICHAEL, A. J.
J. OPT. SOC. AMER.
62 (3), 344-7, 1972.

63580 SHARPNESS OF TRANSITION AND EFFECT OF TUNNELLING IN FERROELECTRIC BEAN-RODBELL MODEL OF KDP.
NETTLETON, R. E.
J. PHYS.
7 C (20), 3785-96, 1974.

63585 DISPERSION OF OPTICAL AND ELECTROOPTICAL COEFFICIENTS IN SEMICONDUCTORS.
PURSEY, H. PAGE, P. A.
J. PHYS.
3 C (2), 431-7, 1970.

63586 OPTICAL ABSORPTION IN SEMICONDUCTORS WITH HIGH IMPURITY CONCENTRATIONS IN THE PRESENCE OF AN ELECTRIC FIELD.
LUKES, T. SOMARATNA, K. T. S.
J. PHYS.
3 C (10), 2044-56, 1970.

EPIC Number	Bibliographic Citation
63587	**IMPROVEMENT OF THE PERFORMANCE OF PELTIER JUNCTIONS FOR THERMOELECTRIC COOLING.** LANDECKER, K. J. PHYS. 3 C (10), 2146–50, 1970.
63588	**THEORY OF L BANDS IN FACE-CENTRED CUBIC ALKALI HALIDES.** DAWBER, P. G. PARKER, I. M. J. PHYS. 3 C (10), 2186–99, 1970.
63591	**DEPENDENCE OF THE ELECTRICAL RESISTIVITY ON SHORT-RANGE ORDER.** ROSSITER, P. L. WELLS, P. J. PHYS. 4 C (3), 354–63, 1971.
63593	**DISPERSION OF OPTICAL COEFFICIENTS IN SEMICONDUCTORS.** PURSEY, H. J. PHYS. 4 C (10), L223–L225, 1971.
63594	**COMPARISON BETWEEN THE TRANSPORT PROPERTIES OF SINGLE-CRYSTAL, POLYCRYSTAL, AND POWDER ANISOTROPIC SEMICONDUCTORS.** RYDEN, D. J. J. PHYS. 4 C (10), 1193–206, 1971.
63597	**CALCULATED INFRARED ABSORPTION INDUCED BY IMPURITIES IN CESIUM CHLORIDE AND CESIUM IODIDE.** MARTIN, T. P. J. PHYS. 4 C (15), 2269–77, 1971.
63600	**POLARIZATION DEPENDENCE OF THE TWO-PHOTON ABSORPTION COEFFICIENT IN CRYSTALS.** DENISOV, M. M. MAKAROV, V. P. J. PHYS. 5 C (18), 2651–64, 1972.
63601	**OPTICAL PROPERTIES OF GRAPHITE AND BORON NITRIDE.** ZUPAN, J. KOLAR, D. J. PHYS. 5 C (21), 3097–100, 1972.
63603	**DAMPING THEORY OF THE MAGNETOPHONON STRUCTURE IN THE LONGITUDINAL SEEBECK EFFECT IN SEMICONDUCTORS.** BARKER, J. R. J. PHYS. 6 C (3), L52–L54, 1973.
63624	**POSSIBLE EXPLANATIONS FOR THE LOW TEMPERATURE RESISTIVITIES OF NICKEL-ALUMINUM AND NICKEL-GALLIUM ALLOYS IN TERMS OF SPIN DENSITY FLUCTUATION THEORIES.** FLUITMAN, J. H. J. BOOM, R. DE CHATEL, P. F. SCHINKEL, C. J. TILANUS, J. L. L. DE VRIES, B. R. J. PHYS. 3 F (1), 109–17, 1973.
63632	**INTERPRETATION OF THE OPTICAL AND PHOTOEMISSIVE PROPERTIES OF CADMIUM TELLURIDE.** SARAVIA, L. R. CASAMAYOU, L. J. PHYS. CHEM. SOLIDS 33 (1), 145–55, 1972.
63636	**OPTICAL AND PHOTOELECTRIC PROPERTIES OF GALLIUM ANTIMONIDE.** DIVRECHY, A. ROBIN-KANDARE, S. ROBIN, J. J. PHYS. CHEM. SOLIDS 34 (3), 413–20, 1973.
63637	**TEMPERATURE DEPENDENCE OF THE CONTRIBUTION TO THE TRANSPORT COEFFICIENTS OF NEARLY FERROMAGNETIC METALS FROM ELECTRON-PARAMAGNON SCATTERING.** MILLS, D. L. J. PHYS. CHEM. SOLIDS 34 (4), 679–86, 1973.
63643	**FILLING-IN OF THE PSEUDOGAP IN AMORPHOUS MAGNESIUM - BISMUTH ALLOYS.** SUTTON, C. M. SOLID STATE COMMUN. 16 (3), 327–30, 1975.
63651	**OPTICAL ABSORPTION OF TETRAHEDRAL CHROMIUM(2+) ION IN ZINC BLENDE ZINC TELLURIDE.** KOMURA, H. SEKINOBU, M. J. PHYS. SOC. JAP. 29 (4), 1100, 1970.
63653	**PARAMAGNETIC SPIN WAVE EXCITATIONS BY LIGHT. I. TWO-MAGNON PROCESSES.** KAWASAKI, T. J. PHYS. SOC. JAPAN 29 (5), 1144–52, 1970.
63666	**EXCITATION OF TRAPPED ELECTRONS IN ANTIMONY IODOSULFIDE.** IRIE, K. J. PHYS. SOC. JAP. 34 (6), 1530–5, 1973.

EPIC Number	Bibliographic Citation
63677	**IONIZATION QUANTUM YIELDS AND ABSORPTION COEFFICIENTS OF SELECTED COMPOUNDS AT 58.4 AND 73.6–74.4 NM.** REBBERT, R. E. AUSLOOS, P. J. RES. NAT. BUR. STAND., SECT. 75 A (5), 481–5, 1971.
63685	**EMISSION OF X ELECTRONS FROM (110) GALLIUM ARSENIDE ACTIVATED TO NEGATIVE ELECTRON AFFINITY.** BURT, M. G. INKSON, J. C. J. PHYS. 8 D (1), L3–5, 1975.
63697	**INTRABAND EDGE ABSORPTION OR LIGHT IN SEMICONDUCTORS.** ZORINA, E. L. OPT. SPEKTROSK. 32 (5), 966–73, 1972. (FOR ENGLISH TRANSLATION SEE E65339)
63698	**ABSORPTION AND AMPLIFICATION COEFFICIENTS OF A GALLIUM ARSENIDE INJECTION LASER.** GLADKII, B. I. POTYKEVICH, I. V. OPT. SPEKTROSK. 32 (6), 1163–6, 1972. (FOR ENGLISH TRANSLATION SEE E65340)
63699	**DISPERSION OF INFRARED LIGHT BY CYLINDRICAL PARTICLES OF DIELECTRICS, SEMICONDUCTORS, AND METALS.** LEBEDEVA, V. N. OPT. SPEKTROSK. 32 (6), 1185–9, 1972. (FOR ENGLISH TRANSLATION SEE E65341)
63700	**MEASUREMENT OF THE REFRACTIVE INDEX TEMPERATURE COEFFICIENT OF INFRARED MATERIALS USING A CARBON DIOXIDE LASER.** KOLOSOVSKII, O. A. USTIMENKO, L. N. OPT. SPEKTROSK. 33 (4), 781–2, 1972. (FOR ENGLISH TRANSLATION SEE E65342)
63709	**THE LUMINESCENCE OF EUROPIUM DOPED TIN IV OXIDE.** CRABTREE, D. F. J. PHYS. 8 D (1), 107–116, 1975.
63722	**ELECTRICAL PROPERTIES OF THE MOLTEN INDIUM-TELLURIUM SYSTEM.** NINOMIYA, Y. NAKAMURA, Y. SHIMOJI, M. PHIL. MAG. 26 (4), 953–60, 1972.
63748	**MATERIALS RESEARCH FOR PERMANENT MAGNETS.** ZIJLSTRA, H. PHILIPS TECH. REV. 34 (8), 193–207, 1974.
63751	**RESISTIVE TRANSITION OF SUPERCONDUCTING LAYER COMPOUNDS.** LITTLE, W. A. PHYS. LETT. 36 (1), 17–18, 1971.
63759	**MAPPING OF ELECTRIC FIELDS IN ZINC SULFIDE.** BRADA, Y. STEINBERGER, I. T. STONE, B. PHYS. LETT. 38 A (4), 263–4, 1972.
63761	**OPTICAL PROPERTIES OF LASER-TYPE GALLIUM ARSENIDE.** THOMAS, B. THOMAS, R. ADAMS, M. J. CROSS, M. PHYS. LETT. 38 A (7), 537–8, 1972.
63763	**ANISOTROPY OF THE OPTICAL CONSTANTS OF GALLIUM SELENIDE NEAR THE BAND EDGE.** WASSCHER, J. D. DIELEMAN, J. PHYS. LETT. 39 A (4), 279–80, 1972.
63772	**OPTICAL ABSORPTION NEAR THE THRESHOLD IN N-TYPE CRYSTALS INDIUM PHOSPHIDE, INDIUM ARSENIDE, AND THEIR SOLID SOLUTIONS INDIUM PHOSPHORUS ARSENIDE.** KEKELIDZE, N. P. KEKELIDZE, G. P. PHYS. LETT. 42 A (2), 129–30, 1972.
63774	**NONLOCAL OPTICAL PROPERTIES OF AN IONIC CRYSTAL FILM.** FUCHS, R. PHYS. LETT. 43 A (1), 42–4, 1973.
63775	**TEMPERATURE DEPENDENCE OF BRILLOUIN SCATTERING IN POTASSIUM CHLORIDE AND SODIUM CHLORIDE.** KATO, E. PHYS. LETT. 43 A (1), 51–2, 1973.
63782	**STRESS-OPTICAL DISPERSION IN RUBIDIUM CHLORIDE AND RUBIDIUM BROMIDE CRYSTALS.** VASUDEVAN, T. N. KRISHNAN, R. S. PHYS. LETT. 43 A (5), 461–2, 1973.

EPIC Number	Bibliographic Citation
63783	**CHEMISTRY OF THE OPTICAL CONSTANTS OF SOLIDS.** HOPFIELD, J. J. PHYS. OPTO-ELECTRON. MATER., PROC. SYMP. 1-16, 1971.
63787	**ELECTRONIC BAND STRUCTURE AND OPTICAL PROPERTIES OF 3C-SILICON CARBIDE, BORON PHOSPHIDE, AND BORON NITRIDE.** HEMSTREET, L. A., JR. FONG, C. Y. PHYS. REV. 6 B (4), 1464-80, 1972.
63788	**ASSIGNMENTS OF THE TWO-PHONON INFRARED ABSORPTION SPECTRUM OF LITHIUM FLUORIDE.** ELDRIDGE, J. E. PHYS. REV. 6 B (4), 1510-19, 1972.
63793	**PRESSURE DEPENDENCE OF THE REFRACTIVE INDEX OF AMORPHOUS LONE-PAIR SEMICONDUCTORS.** KASTNER, M. PHYS. REV. 6 B (6), 2273-9, 1972.
63804	**INFRARED LATTICE VIBRATIONS AND FREE-ELECTRON DISPERSION IN GALLIUM NITRIDE.** BARKER, A. S., JR. ILEGEMS, M. PHYS. REV. 7 B (2), 743-50, 1973.
63807	**THERMO- AND ELASTO-OPTIC PARAMETERS OF SODIUM FLUORIDE AND THEIR IMPLICATIONS FOR LIGHT SCATTERING FROM SECOND SOUND.** POHL, D. W. SCHWARZ, S. E. PHYS. REV. 7 B (6), 2735-9, 1973.
63810	**A MODEL FOR INDUCED MOMENT FERROMAGNETISM IN SOME PRASEODYMIUM-TRANSITION METAL COMPOUNDS.** ZUCKERMANN, M. J. J. PHYS. 4 F (10), 1800-18, 1974.
63811	**DOMINANT SECOND-ORDER DIPOLE-MOMENT CONTRIBUTION IN THE INFRARED ABSORPTION OF GROUP IIIA-VA COMPOUNDS.** FLYTZANIS, C. PHYS. REV. LETT. 29 (12), 772-5, 1972.
63819	**SUPERCONDUCTIVITY IN THE PALLADIUM-HYDROGEN AND PALLADIUM-NICKEL-HYDROGEN SYSTEMS.** SKOSKIEWICZ, T. PHYS. STATUS SOLIDI 11 A (2), K123-6, 1972.
63823	**PHYSICAL PROPERTIES OF VITREOUS ARSENIC SELENIDE DOPED WITH IIIA GROUP ELEMENTS.** LEZAL, D. TRKAL, V. SRB, I. DOKOUPIL, S. SMID, V. ROSICKA, V. PHYS. STATUS SOLIDI 12 A (1), K39-K42, 1972.
63824	**THERMAL ANNEALING OF X-RAY-INDUCED DEFECTS IN STRONTIUM-DOPED POTASSIUM CHLORIDE CRYSTALS.** KATZ, I. CHENFOUX, B. KRISTIANPOLLER, N. PHYS. STATUS SOLIDI 12 A (1), 307-15, 1972.
63827	**EFFECT OF PARTIAL SUBSTITUTION OF LEAD BY GALLIUM, INDIUM, AND THALLIUM ON THERMOELECTRIC PROPERTIES OF LEAD TELLURIDE.** RUSTAMOV, P. G. ALIDZHANOV, M. A. ABILOV, KH. I. PHYS. STATUS SOLIDI 12 A (2), K103-7, 1972.
63838	**PHOTOELECTRIC PROPERTIES OF GALLIUM SELENIDE.** ADDUCI, F. FERRARA, M. TANTALO, P. CINGOLANI, A. MINAFRA, A. PHYS. STATUS SOLIDI 15 (1), 303-10, 1973.
63847	**ENERGY SPECTRUM OF A BOUND POLARON.** BAJAJ, K. K. CLARK, T. D. PHYS. STATUS SOLIDI 52 (1), 195-206, 1972.
63848	**OPTICAL ABSORPTION EDGE OF HEAVILY DOPED SEMICONDUCTORS AT LOW TEMPERATURES.** VAN CONG, H. MESNARD, G. PHYS. STATUS SOLIDI 52 B (2), 553-69, 1972.
63849	**FREE CARRIER ABSORPTION IN CADMIUM SULFUR SELENIDE SINGLE CRYSTALS.** LISITSA, M. P. DEMIDENKO, Z. A. MALINKO, V. N. PIDLISNYI, E. V. VALAKH, M. YA. VITRIKHOVSKII, N. I. PHYS. STATUS SOLIDI 53 B (1), 55-64, 1972.
63879	**MECHANISM FOR THE PHOTOVOLTAIC EFFECT IN HEAT-TREATED CUPROUS SULFIDE-CADMIUM SULFIDE HETEROJUNCTIONS.** GILL, W. D. BUBE, R. H. PROC. INT. CONF. PHOTOCOND., 3RD 395-401, 1971. (EDITED BY E. M. PELL, PERGAMON: OXFORD, ENGLAND)
63880	**OPTICAL PROPERTIES OF THE LAYER STRUCTURES GALLIUM TELLURIDE, GALLIUM SELENIDE AND GALLIUM SULFIDE.** BREBNER, J. L. FISCHER, G. PROC. INTERN. CONF., PHYS. SEMICOND., EXETER, ENGL. 760-5, 1962.
63881	**OPTICAL PROPERTIES OF GALLIUM NITRIDE.** PANKOVE, J. I. MARUSKA, H. P. PROC. INT. CONF. PHYS. SEMICOND., 10TH 593-7, 1970. (EDITED BY SEYMOUR P. KELLER, NATL. TECH. INF. SERV.: SPRINGFIELD, VA.)
63884	**ELECTRONIC PROPERTIES OF SOME SEMICONDUCTING GLASSES BASED ON CADMIUM DIARSENIDE.** ABRAHAM, A. GREGORA, I. HRUBY, A. MATYAS, M. STOURAC, L. TAUC, J. VORLICEK, V. ZAVETOVA, M. PROC. INT. CONF. PHYS. SEMICOND., 10TH 784-9, 1970.
63887	**PHOTOELECTRIC PROPERTIES OF CADMIUM TIN PHOSPHIDE - COPPER(I) SULFIDE HETEROJUNCTIONS.** GORYUNOVA, N. A. ANSHON, A. V. KARPOVICH, I. A. LEONOV, E. I. ORLOV, V. M. PROC. INT. CONF. PHYS. CHEM. SEMICOND. HETEROJUNCTIONS LAYER STRUCT. 2, 275-82, 1971.
63890	**THEORY OF HIGH PHOTOVOLTAGES IN SEMICONDUCTING FILMS.** SOSNOWSKI, L. PROC. INT. CONF. PHYS. CHEM. SEMICOND. HETEROJUNCTIONS LAYER STRUCT. 4, 29-40, 1971. (EDITED BY G. SZIGETI, AKAD. KIADO: BUDAPEST, HUNGARY)
63892	**EFFECT OF THE STRUCTURE ON ELECTRICAL AND OPTICAL PROPERTIES OF INDIUM ANTIMONIDE, GALLIUM ANTIMONIDE, AND INDIUM GALLIUM SULFIDE ALLOYS SINGLE CRYSTALLINE FILMS.** KAS'YAN, V. A. NIKOL'SKII, YU. A. PASECHNIK, F. I. PROC. INT. CONF. PHYS. CHEM. SEMICOND. HETEROJUNCTIONS LAYER STRUCT. 4, 133-42, 1971. (EDITED BY G. SZIGETI, AKAD. KIADO: BUDAPEST, HUNGARY)
63893	**GENERATION OF ANOMALOUS PHOTOVOLTAGES.** ORLOWSKI, B. PROC. INT. CONF. PHYS. CHEM. SEMICOND. HETEROJUNCTIONS LAYER STRUCT. 4, 195-203, 1971. (EDITED BY G. SZIGETI, AKAD. KIADO: BUDAPEST, HUNGARY)
63899	**PIEZO-OPTIC CONSTANTS OF CADMIUM TELLURIDE.** WEIL, R. SUN, M. J. PROC. INT. SYMP. CADMIUM TELLURIDE, MATER. GAMMA-RAY DETECTORS XIX-1-XIX-6, 1972. (EDITED BY P. SIFFERT, CENT. RECH. NUCL.: STRASBOURG, FRANCE)
63912	**DETERMINATION OF SEMICONDUCTOR RESISTIVITY BY MICROWAVE MEASUREMENTS.** HEATON, A. G. PAL, D. K. PROC. INST. ELEC. ENG. 115 (5), 742-6, 1968.
63913	**THE ELECTRONIC CHARACTERIZATION OF MAGNESIUM OXIDE.** MILEK, J. T. HUGHES AIRCRAFT COMP., CULVER CITY, CALIF. 37PP., 1966. (EPIC-IR-22)
63932	**PRODUCTION OF THIN FILMS BY EVAPORATION OF RARE EARTH METALS AND STUDY OF THEIR PHYSICOCHEMICAL PROPERTIES.** SAMSONOV, G. V. SERVETSKAYA, M. G. ISAEVA, L. P. SEREBRYAKOVA, T. I. REDKOZEMEL. METAL. IKH. SOEDIN. 76-81PP., 1970.
63955	**EFFECTS OF PLASMA AND HOLE CURRENT ON THE OPTICAL ABSORPTION OF INDIUM ANTIMONIDE.** BALLEGEER, D. J. BAUMGARDNER, C. A. SOLID STATE COMMUN. 10 (1), 111-14, 1972.

EPIC Number	Bibliographic Citation
63961	**ELLIPSOMETRICAL METHOD FOR THE DETERMINATION OF THE THICKNESS AND THE DISPERSION OF THE OPTICAL CONSTANTS OF THIN ABSORBING FILMS EVAPORATED ON METAL SUBSTRATES.** SHKLYAREVSKII, I. N. EL-SHAZLY, A. F. A. KOSTYUK, V. P. SOLID STATE COMMUN. 10 (11), 1045-8, 1972.
63962	**PHOTOELASTIC PROPERTIES OF AMORPHOUS ARSENIC SESQUISULFIDE.** GALKIEWICZ, R. K. TAUC, J. SOLID STATE COMMUN. 10 (1I), 1261-4, 1972.
63966	**EVIDENCE FOR A SECOND VALENCE BAND IN P-TYPE BISMUTH SESQUITELLURIDE FROM MAGNETO-SEEBECK AND SHUBNIKOV-DE HAAS DATA.** VON MIDDENDORFF, A. LANDWEHR, G. SOLID STATE COMMUN. 11 (1), 203-7, 1972.
63967	**NATURE OF SUPERCONDUCTING NIOBIUM AND TANTALUM MONOCARBIDES.** DUBROVSKAYA, L. B. RABIN'KIN, A. G. GEL'D, P. V. ZH. EKSP. TEOR. FIZ. 62 (1), 300-6, 1972. (FOR ENGLISH TRANSLATION SEE E68424)
63978	**RESONANCE OF THE ELECTRONIC POLARON APPEARING IN THE OPTICAL ABSORPTION OF ALKALI HALIDES.** DEVREESE, J. T. KUNZ, A. B. COLLINS, T. C. SOLID STATE COMMUN. 11 (5), 673-8, 1972.
63980	**HIGH-TEMPERATURE PARAMAGNON MODIFICATIONS IN NEARLY MAGNETIC METALS.** BEAL-MONOD, M. T. SOLID STATE COMMUN. 11 (5), 683-7, 1972.
63995	**PHOTOVOLTAIC AND ELECTRON-VOLTAIC PROPERTIES OF DIFFUSED AND SCHOTTKY BARRIER GALLIUM ARSENIDE DIODES.** KALIBJIAN, R. MAYEDA, K. SOLID-STATE ELECTRON. 14 (7), 529-40, 1971.
63998	**AUTOPHOTOVOLTAIC MEASUREMENT OF ABSORPTION COEFFICIENT AND DIFFUSION LENGTHS OF LIGHT EMITTING DIODES.** FULOP, W. KONIDARIS, S. SOLID-STATE ELECTRON. 15 (8), 923-31, 1972.
64069	**ELECTRIC CONDUCTIVITY AND STRUCTURE OF DISCONTINUOUS METAL FILMS ON DIELECTRIC.** BIOKO, B. T. PALATNIK, L. S. SINEL'NIKOV, A. N. THIN SOLID FILMS 7 (5), 305-11, 1971.
64072	**VERY PURE THIN-FILM TANTALUM PHASE.** SCHAUER, A. PETERS, W. JUERGENS, W. THIN SOLID FILMS 8 (3), R9-R12, 1971.
64074	**AMORPHOUS SEMICONDUCTING THIN FILMS.** GRIGOROVICI, R. THIN SOLID FILMS 9 (1), 1-23, 1972.
64075	**ULTRATHIN RHENIUM FILM RESISTORS.** DANIELSSON, H. KASEMO, B. MARKLUND, I. THIN SOLID FILMS 9 (1), 121-32, 1972.
64079	**STRUCTURE AND ELECTRICAL PROPERTIES OF TANTALUM FILMS SPUTTERED IN ARGON-OXYGEN.** FEINSTEIN, L. G. GERSTENBERG, D. THIN SOLID FILMS 10 (1), 79-89, 1972.
64085	**THEORY OF HIGH-FIELD CONDUCTIVITY.** MURGATROYD, P. N. THIN SOLID FILMS 11 (1), 125-33, 1972.
64092	**MOSAIC HETEROJUNCTION PHOTOEMF. IN EVAPORATED ZINC SULFIDE-CADMIUM SULFIDE.** ANDREICHIN, R. IVANOVA, A. GESHEVA, K. STANISLAVOVA, YU. THIN SOLID FILMS 12 (1), 149-52, 1972.
64094	**COMPARISON BETWEEN THIN-FILM LIGHT POSITION SENSORS OPERATING IN PHOTOVOLTAIC AND PHOTOCONDUCTIVE MODES IN CADMIUM SULFIDE STRUCTURES.** BILLINGS, A. R. JOHANSEN, E. THIN SOLID FILMS 13 (1), 41-5, 1972.

EPIC Number	Bibliographic Citation
64098	**CHOICE OF CRITERIA FOR ELLIPSOMETRIC DETERMINATIONS ON THIN FILMS.** CAMAGNI, P. MANARA, A. THIN SOLID FILMS 13 (2), 341-50, 1972.
64100	**PHOTOELECTRONIC PROPERTIES OF INDIUM ARSENIDE ANTIMONIDE FILMS.** WIEDER, H. H. CLAWSON, A. R. THIN SOLID FILMS 15 (2), 217-21, 1973.
64150	**ELECTRICAL RESISTIVITY OF SOME VANADIUM-OXYGEN ALLOYS.** STAROSTINA, L. S. MAKSIMOV, YU. A. ZH. FIZ. KHIM. 45 (11), 2789-91, 1971. (FOR ENGLISH TRANSLATION SEE E68412)
64184	**TRANSITION TEMPERATURE OF STRONG COUPLING SUPERCONDUCTORS.** HERTEL, P. Z. PHYS. 248 (3), 272-84, 1971.
64232	**CADMIUM SULPHIDE SUMMARY REVIEW AND DATA SHEETS.** NEUBERGER, M. HUGHES AIRCRAFT CO., CULVER CITY, CALIF. 155PP., 1963. (AD-413 667 EPIC-DS-124)
64236	**PREPARATION AND PROPERTIES OF THIN FILMS OF EUROPIUM SULFIDE.** PALATNIK, L. S. LASHKAREV, G. V. SOROKIN, V. K. MARINCHEVA, V. E. ZOZULYA, L. P. IZV. AKAD. NAUK SSSR, NEORG. MAT. 9 (1), 42-5, 1973. (FOR ENGLISH TRANSLATION SEE E64237)
64237	**PREPARATION AND PROPERTIES OF THIN FILMS OF EUROPIUM SULFIDE.** PALATNIK, L. S. LASHKAREV, G. V. SOROKIN, V. K. MARINCHEVA, V. E. ZOZULYA, L. P. INORG. MAT., USSR 9 (1), 37-40, 1973. (ENGLISH TRANSLATION OF IZV. AKAD. NAUK SSSR, NEORG. MAT., 9 (1), 42-5, 1973; FOR ORIGINAL SEE E64236)
64246	**PHASE DIAGRAM OF THE SYSTEM TITANIUM - OXIDE AND SOME PROPERTIES OF THE ALLOYS OF THIS SYSTEM.** KORNILOV, I. I. GLAZOVA, V. V. NATIONAL AERONAUTICS SPACE ADMINISTRATION 12-28, 1965. (NASA-TT-F-338, N66-10278)
64247	**MODIFICATION OF THE FAR INFRARED ABSORPTION SPECTRUM OF AMMONIUM DIHYDROGEN PHOSPHATE AT THE ANTIFERROELECTRIC TRANSITION.** BREHAT, F. HADNI, A. REV. PHYS. APPL. 9 (2), 443-5, 1974.
64248	**FITTING THE SELLMEIER DISPERSION EQUATION TO THE REFRACTIVE INDICES OF IRTRAN-1.** OLSEN, A. L. BROWNE, H. N. APPL. OPT. 3 (8), 982-3, 1964.
64251	**PHASE EQUILIBRIUM OF ALLOYS OF THE SECTION TRITITANIUM ALUMINIDE - ZIRCONIUM OF THE TERNARY SYSTEM TITANIUM - ALUMINUM - ZIRCONIUM.** KORNILOV, I. I. NARTOVA, T. T. SAVEL'YEVA, M. M. NATIONAL AERONAUTICS SPACE ADMINISTRATION 53-7, 1965. (NASA-TT-F-338, N66-10282)
64254	**LATTICE INFRARED SPECTRA OF BORON NITRIDE AND BORON MONO-PHOSPHIDE.** GIELISSE, P. J. MITRA, S. S. PLENDL, J. N. GRIFFIS, R. C. MANSUR, L. C. MARSHALL, R. PASCOE, E. A. ILLINOIS INSTITUTE OF TECHNOLOGY 35PP., 1966. (AD-644019, AFCRL-66-615, IITRI-A-6138)
64255	**THE INFRARED AND RAMAN-ACTIVE LATTICE VIBRATIONS IN ZINC SELENIDE.** MITRA, S. S. CARVALL, E. MARSHALL, R. MC DEVITT, N. T. BULL. AMER. PHYS. SOC. 10, 1086-, 1965. (AD-644019, AFCRL-66-615, IITRI-A-6138)
64256	**TEMPERATURE DEPENDENCE OF INFRARED DISPERSION IN IONIC CRYSTALS LITHIUM FLUORIDE AND MAGNESIUM OXIDE.** JASPERSE, J. R. KAHAN, A. PLENDL, J. N. PHYS. REV. 146 (2), 526-42, 1966. (AD-644019, AFCRL-66-615, IITRI-A-6138)

EPIC Number	Bibliographic Citation

64257 **U CENTERS IN CESIUM BROMIDE.**
MITRA, S. S. BRADA, Y.
PHYS. REV.
145 (2), 626–7, 1966.
(AD–644019, AFCRL–66–615, IITRI–A–6138)

64258 **ELECTRONIC STRUCTURE OF THE U CENTER.**
SPECTOR, H. N. MITRA, S. S.
SCHNEISING, H. N.
ILLINOIS INSTITUTE OF TECHNOLOGY
100–39, 1966.
(AD–644019, AFCRL–66–615, IITRI–A–6138)

64266 **DIAMAGNETIC SUSCEPTIBILITY OF HIGH–PURITY THORIUM DIOXIDE CRYSTALS.**
SMITH, H. M. CLARK, G. W.
ATOMIC ENERGY COMMISSION
P. 4, 1968.
(ORNL–4370)

64268 **TRANSPORT PROPERTIES OF URANIUM NITRIDE.**
MOORE, J. P. FULKERSON, W. MCELROY, D. L.
ATOMIC ENERGY COMMISSION
26–8, 1968.
(ORNL–4370)

64269 **ELECTRICAL RESISTIVITY OF URANIUM (CARBON, NITROGEN).**
DODD, C. V. LEITNAKER, J. M. POTTER, R. A.
MOORE, J. P. FULKERSON, W.
ATOMIC ENERGY COMMISSION
28, 1968.
(ORNL–4370)

64270 **OXIDATION OF NICKEL.**
CATHEART, J. V. PETERSON, F. G.
ATOMIC ENERGY COMMISSION
47–9, 1968.
(ORNL–4370)

64273 **IMPPRUTY PHOTOVOLLAIC EFFECT IN CADMIUM SULFIDE.**
BLAIR, J.
PROC. PHOTOVOLTAIC SPECIALISTS CONF., 5TH
1, 39PP., 1965.
(NASA–CR–70168, N66–17316)

64286 **TEMPERATURE DEPENDENCES OF THE FORMATION OF F–CENTERS IN POTASSIUM CHLORIDE–POTASSIUM BROMIDE SOLID SOLUTIONS.**
ZAVADOVSKAYA, E. K. ANNENKOV, YU. M.
FRANGUL'YAN, T. S.
OPT. SPEKTROSK.
29 (4), 721–6, 1970.
(FOR ENGLISH TRANSLATION SEE E68416)

64287 **ELECTRON HALL MOBILITY AND PHOTOCONDUCTIVITY OF COLOURED POTASSIUM BROMIDE CRYSTALS AT MODERATE TEMPERATURES.**
AL–SAFFAR, I. S. CALDERWOOD, J. H.
J. PHYS. AND CHEM. SOLIDS
36 (3), 213–14, 1975.

64288 **METHODS FOR USING THE KRAMERS–KRONIG RELATION FOR CALCULATING THE OPTICAL CONSTANT OF CONDENSED MEDIA FROM THE REFLECTION SPECTRUM.**
SOLOV'EVA, G. S. LIBOV, V. S.
OPT. SPEKTROSK.
33 (3), 513–19, 1972.
(FOR ENGLISH TRANSLATION SEE E68417)

64324 **PHOTOELECTRONIC PROPERTIES OF DEFECTS IN CADMIUM SELENIDE SINGLE CRYSTALS.**
ROBINSON, A. L.
AIR FORCE MATER. LAB., WPAFB, OHIO
245PP., 1971.
(AFML–TR–71–96)

64326 **MAGNETIC PROPERTIES OF INTERMETALLIC COMPOUNDS RARE EARTH SILVER.**
MIURA, S. KANEKO, T. OHASHI, M.
YAMAUCHI, H.
J. PHYS. SOC. JAP.
37 (5), 1464, 1974.

64327 **THE PRESSURE EFFECT ON THE NEEL POINT OF AN ANTIFERROMAGNETIC COMPOUND CHROMIUM ANTIMONY.**
KANEKO, T. YOSHIDA, H. OHASHI, M.
ABE, S. KAMIGAKI, K.
J. PHYS. SOC. JAP.
37 (5), 1465, 1974.

64328 **THE DECAY MECHANISM OF HOT INDIRECT EXCITONS IN THALLIUM BROMIDE.**
SHIMIZU, R. KODA, T.
J. PHYS. SOC. JAP.
37 (5), 1468, 1974.

64329 **MAGNETOCRYSTALINE ANISOTROPY OF IRON PHOSPHIDE AND IRON NICKEL PHOSPHIDE COMPOUNDS.**
TUJII, H. KAMIGAICHI, T. HOKABE, T.
OKAMOTO, T.
J. PHYS. SOC. JAP.
37 (6), 1712, 1974.

64338 **SOFT X–RAY STUDIES OF THE SATELLITES OF SODIUM, MAGNESIUM, ALUMINUM, AND SILICON AND THE OPTICAL PROPERTIES OF MAGNESIUM OXIDE AND MAGNESIUM FLUORIDE.**
HANSON, W. F. ARAKAWA, E. T.
OAK RIDGE NATIONAL LAB., OAK RIDGE, TENN.
122PP., 1971.
(ORNL–TM–3564)

64344 **STUDIES, RESEARCH AND INVESTIGATIONS OF THE OPTICAL PROPERTIES OF THIN FILMS OF METALS SEMI–CONDUCTORS AND DIELECTRIC.**
HADLEY, L. N., JR.
DEPT. OF PHYSICS, COLORADO STATE UNIVERSITY, FORT COLLINS, COLORADO
15PP., 1961.
(AD–284 583)

64411 **STUDY OF THERMAL RADIATION WITH SOLIDS AND INTERNALLY ABLATING COMPOUNDS.**
KIRCHNER, H. P. COMNITZ, H. G.
VASSALLO, F. A.
WRIGHT PATTERSON AIR FORCE BASE, OHIO
48PP., 1960.
(AD–237 839)

64415 **THEORY OF LIGHT ABSORPTION BY FREE CARRIERS IN SEMICONDUCTORS WITH A NONPARABOLIC BAND.**
ALIEV, T. A. GASHIMZADE, F. M.
SOV. PHYS. SEMICOND.
6 (3), 395–7, 1972.
(ENGLISH TRANSLATION OF FIZ. TEKH. POLUPROV., 6 (3), 458–61, 1972; FOR ORIGINAL SEE E62687)

64417 **ABSORPTION OF LIGHT IN GALLIUM MONOTELLURIDE.**
GRAMATSKII, V. I. KARAMAN, M. I.
MUSHINSKII, V. P.
SOV. PHYS. SEMICOND.
6 (3), 475–7, 1972.
(ENGLISH TRANSLATION OF FIZ. TEKH. POLUPROV., 6 (3), 550–2, 1972; FOR ORIGINAL SEE E62689)

64420 **INVESTIGATIONS OF THE KINETICS OF THE PHOTO–EMF OF INDIUM ARSENIDE P–N JUNCTIONS.**
ANDRUSHKO, A. I. NASLEDOV, D. N.
SLOBODCHIKOV, S. V.
SOV. PHYS. SEMICOND.
6 (5), 712–4, 1972.
(ENGLISH TRANSLATION OF FIZ. TEKH. POLUPROV., 6 (5), 822–5, 1972; FOR ORIGINAL SEE E62693)

64422 **COMMENTS ON MEASUREMENTS OF THE DISPERSION OF THE BIREFRINGENCE OF CADMIUM SULFIDE SINGLE CRYSTALS.**
LISITSA, M. P. MALINKO, V. N.
TEREKHOVA, S. F.
SOV. PHYS. SEMICOND.
6 (5), 798–9, 1972.
(ENGLISH TRANSLATION OF FIZ. TEKH. POLUPROV., 6 (5), 926–7, 1972; FOR ORIGINAL SEE E62695)

64426 **INFRARED LATTICE ABSORPTION IN IONIC AND HOMOPOLAR CRYSTALS.**
LAX, M. BURSTEIN, E.
SYRACUSE UNIVERSITY
60PP., 1954.
(AD–24 363)

64429 **IMAGINARY PART OF THE COMPLEX LOW–FREQUENCY CONDUCTIVITY IN STRONG ELECTRIC FIELDS.**
ZUEV, V. V.
SOV. PHYS. SEMICOND.
6 (5), 839–41, 1972.
(ENGLISH TRANSLATION OF FIZ. TEKH. POLUPROV., 6 (5), 965–8, 1972; FOR ORIGINAL SEE E62698)

64431 **FUNDAMENTAL ABSORPTION SPECTRUM OF INDIUM PHOSPHIDE IN THE PHOTON ENERGY RANGE 1.40– 1.70 EV.**
EMLIN, R. V. ZVEREV, L. P. RUT, O. E.
SOV. PHYS. SEMICOND.
8 (6), 796, 1974.
(ENGLISH TRANSLATION OF FIZ. TEKH. POLUPROV., 8 (6), 1225–6, 1974; FOR ORIGINAL SEE E62528)

64432 **HIGH–TEMPERATURE OPTICAL ABSORPTION IN GALLIUM ARSENIDE NEAR THE FUNDAMENTAL BAND.**
BILENKO, D. I. TSIPORUKHA, V. D.
SOV. PHYS. SEMICOND.
8 (6), 804–5, 1974.
(ENGLISH TRANSLATION OF FIZ. TEKH. POLUPROV., 8 (6), 1235–7, 1974; FOR ORIGINAL SEE E62529)

64435 **PHOTOMAGNETIC EFFECT IN CADMIUM TELLURIDE FILMS HAVING AN ANOMALOUSLY HIGH PHOTOVOLTAGE.**
KORSUNSKII, M. I. SOMINSKII, M. M.
SMURYGIN, V. M.
SOV. PHYS. DOKL.
17 (3), 268–71, 1972.
(ENGLISH TRANSLATION OF DOKL. AKAD. NAUK SSSR, 203 (2), 332–5, 1972; FOR ORIGINAL SEE E62620)

64456 **BEHAVIOR OF MATERIALS AT LOW TEMPERATURES.**
ROSENBERG, H. M.
ADV. CRYOG.
77–101, 1971.
(EDITED BY C. A. BAILEY; PLENUM: LONDON, ENGLAND)

EPIC Number | Bibliographic Citation

64457 **ELECTRON TRANSPORT PHENOMENA IN SMALL-GAP SEMICONDUCTORS.**
ZAWADZKI, W.
ADV. PHYS.
23 (3), 435–522, 1974.

64464 **SEMICONDUCTOR DEVICES SUITABLE FOR USE IN CRYOGENIC ENVIRONMENTS.**
LENGELER, B.
CRYOGENICS
14 (8), 439–47, 1974.

64477 **INFRARED OPTICAL MATERIALS FOR 8–13 MU–M. CURRENT DEVELOPMENTS AND FUTURE PROSPECTS.**
MARSH, K. J. SAVAGE, J. A.
INFRARED PHYS.
14 (2), 85–97, 1974.

64485 **DEVELOPMENT OF THE VAN DER PAUW METHOD FOR ALTERNATING CURRENT MEASUREMENTS IN AN ALTERNATING MAGNETIC FIELD.**
MACHEVSKII, E. N. FELTINS, I.
LATV. PSR ZINAT. AKAD. VESTIS, FIZ. TEH. ZINAT. SER.
(4), 50–4, 1974.

64488 **ABSORPTION STUDIES OF CADMIUM TELLURIDE AND ZINC SELENIDE.**
DUTT, B. V. SPITZER, W. G.
UNIVERSITY OF SOUTHERN CALIFORNIA, LOS ANGELES
68–73, 1974.
(AD–A003 393, AFCRL–TR–74–0441)

64489 **OPTIMIZATION OF ALKALI HALIDE WINDOW MATERIALS.**
SHLICHTA, P. J. YEE, J.
UNIVERSITY OF SOUTHERN CALFORNIA, LOS ANGELES
3–15, 1974.
(AD–A003 393, AFCRL–TR–74–0441)

64490 **STUDY OF DEFECTS IN II–VI COMPOUNDS.**
KROGER, F. A. SELIM, F.
UNIVERSITY OF SOUTHERN CALFORNIA, LOS ANGELES
28–38, 1974.
(AD–A003 393, AFCRL–TR–74–0441)

64493 **INVESTIGATION OF INFRARED LOSS MECHANISMS IN HIGH RESISTIVITY GALLIUM ARSENIDE.**
CHRISTENSEN, C. P. JOINER, R.
NIEH, S. T. K. STEIER, W. H.
UNIVERSITY OF SOUTHERN CALIFORNIA, LOS ANGELES
43–58, 1974.
(AD–A003 393, AFCRL–TR–74–0441)

64494 **ALKALI HALIDE SURFACE STUDIES WITH ACOUSTIC PROBE TECHNIQUES.**
PARKS, J. H. ROCKWELL, D. A. COLBERT, T. S.
UNIVERSITY OF SOUTHERN CALIFORNIA, LOS ANGELES
59–67, 1974.
(AD–A003 393, AFCRL–TR–74–0441)

64495 **OPTICAL PROPERTIES OF INFRARED TRANSMITTING MATERIALS (LQ–10 HIGH POWER LASER WINDOW PROGRAM).**
BENDOW, B.
AIR FORCE CAMBRIDGE RESEARCH LABS., HANSCOM AFB, OHIO
35PP., 1973.
(AD–A003 397, AFCRL–TR–74–0576)

64496 **GALVANOMAGNETIC EFFECTS IN GALLIUM ANTIMONIDE.**
BECKER, W. M. FAN, H. Y.
DEPARTMENT OF PHYSICS, PURDUE UNIVERSITY
1–2, 25–7, 1961.
(AD–263 209)

64497 **INFRARED ABSORPTION IN N–TYPE GALLIUM ANTIMONIDE.**
RAMDAS, A. K. FAN, H. Y.
DEPARTMENT OF PHYSICS, PURDUE UNIVERSITY
3–4, 28–9, 1961.
(AD–263 209)

64508 **DOMAIN OBSERVATION IN AMMONIUM HYDROGEN SULFATE CRYSTALS.**
KONDO, T. ISHIBASHI, Y. TAKAGI, Y.
J. PHYS. SOC. JAP.
37 (6), 1708, 1974.

64516 **SURFACE PHOTOEMF OF CADMIUM SELENIDE FILMS.**
OMAROV, A. M.
PRIKL. FIZ. TVERD. TELA
22–6, 1973.

64519 **THERMOELECTRIC PROPERTIES OF SOME II – IV – V(2) TYPE COMPOUNDS IN THE LIQUID AND SOLID STATES.**
AIDAMIROV, M. A. ALIEV, S. N. ALIEVA, KH. O.
MAGOMEDOV, YA. B.
PRIKL. FIZ. TVERD. TELA
178–81, 1973.

64535 **OPTICAL PROPERTIES OF GRAPHITE AND BORON NITRIDE.**
ZUPAN, J. KOLAR, D.
J. PHYS. C, SOLID STATE PHYS.
5 (21), 3097–3100, 1972.

64536 **INHOMOGENEITY IN REFRACTIVE INDEX OF EVAPORATED MAGNESIUM FLUORIDE FILM.**
NAGATA, K.–I.
JAP. J. APPL. PHYS.
7 (10), 1181–5, 1968.

EPIC Number | Bibliographic Citation

64537 **FAR–INFRARED ABSORPTION DUE TO ELECTRONIC TRANSITIONS OF IRON (2+) – DOPED MAGNESIUM FLUORIDE AND IRON (2+) – DOPED ZINC FLUORIDE.**
DURR, U. WEBER, R.
PHYS. STATUS SOLIDI
60 B (2), 733–8, 1973.

64538 **ON THE INTERPRETATION OF THE VIBRATIONAL SPECTRA OF FUSED SILICA.**
WADIA, W. BALLOMAL, L. S.
PHYS. CHEM. GLASSES
9 (4), 115–24, 1968.

64539 **VARIATION OF REFRACTIVE INDEX WITH WAVELENGTH IN FUSED SILICA OPTICAL FIBERS AND PREFORMS.**
PRESBY, H. M.
APPL. PHYS. LETT.
24 (9), 422–4, 1974.

64540 **BOROSILICATE CLAD FUSED SILICA CORE FIBER OPTICAL WAVEGUIDE WITH LOW TRANSMISSION LOSS PREPARED BY A HIGH–EFFICIENCY PROCESS.**
DABBY, F. W. PINNOW, D. A.
OSTERMAYER, F. W., JR. VAN UITERT, L. G.
SAIFI, M. A. CAMLIBEL, I.
APPL. PHYS. LETT.
25 (12), 714–5, 1974.

64541 **INFLUENCE OF INTERFERENCE IN A SILICON DIOXIDE FILM ON THE REFLECTION SPECTRUM OF THE SILICA – SILICON SYSTEM IN THE 9 MU REGION.**
RAKOV, A. V. POTAPOV, E. V.
MIZGIREVA, L. P.
OPT. SPEKTROSK.
25 (1), 168–9, 1968.
(FOR ENGLISH TRANSLATION SEE E64542)

64542 **INFLUENCE OF INTERFERENCE IN A SILICON DIOXIDE FILM ON THE REFLECTION SPECTRUM OF THE SILICA – SILICON SYSTEM IN THE 9 MR REGION.**
RAKOV, A. V. POTAPOV, E. V.
MIZGIREVA, L. P.
OPT. SPECTROS., USSR
25 (1), 89–90, 1968.
(ENGLISH TRANSLATION OF OPT. SPEKTROSK., 25 (1), 168–9, 1968; FOR ORIGINAL SEE E64541)

64543 **FUSED SILICA CORE GLASS FIBER AS A LOW–LOSS OPTICAL WAVEGUIDE.**
KATO, D.
APPL. PHYS. LETT.
22 (1), 3–4, 1973.

64544 **FUNDAMENTAL OPTICAL ATTENUATION LIMITS IN THE LIQUID AND GLASSY STATE WITH APPLICATION TO FIBER OPTICAL WAVEGUIDE MATERIALS.**
PINNOW, D. A. RICH, T. C.
OSTERMAYER, F. W., JR. DI DOMENICO, M., JR.
APPL. PHYS. LETT.
22 (10), 527–9, 1973.

64545 **RAMAN SCATTERING AND INFRARED ABSORPTION FROM LOW LYING MODES IN VITREOUS SILICON DIOXIDE, GERMANIUM DIOXIDE, AND BORON DIOXIDE.**
STOLEN, R. H.
PHYS. CHEM. GLASSES
11 (3), 83–7, 1970.

64547 **OPTICAL ABSORPTION IN FUSED SILICA DURING IRRADIATION: RADIATION ANNEALING OF THE C–BAND.**
PALMA, G. E. GAGOSZ, R. M.
J. PHYS. CHEM. SOLIDS
33 (1), 177–89, 1972.

64548 **REFRACTIVE INDICES OF FUSED SILICA AT LOW TEMPERATURES.**
WAXLER, R. M. CLEEK, G. W.
J. RES. NAT. BUR. STAND.
75 A (4), 279–81, 1971.

64549 **OPTICAL ABSORPTION AND LUMINESCENCE OF IRRADIATED MAGNESIUM FLUORIDE.**
FACEY, O. E. SIBLEY, W. A.
PHYS. REV.
186 (3), 926–32, 1969.

64551 **REFRACTIVE INDICES OF INFRARED OPTICAL MATERIALS AND COLOR CORRECTION OF INFRARED LENSES.**
HERZBERGER, M. SALZBERG, C. D.
J. OPT. SOC. AMER.
52 (4), 420–7, 1962.

64570 **TWO–PHOTON ABSORPTION IN CADMIUM SELENIDE.**
BRUECKNER, F. DNEPROVSKII, V. S.
KHATTATOV, V. U.
KVANTOVAYA ELEKTRON. (MOSCOW)
1 (6), 1360–4, 1974.
(FOR ENGLISH TRANSLATION SEE E88316)

64576 **ABSORPTION OF LIGHT IN INTRINSIC SEMICONDUCTORS IN THE PRESENCE OF HIGH–POWER LASER RADIATION.**
SINYAVSKII, E. P.
OPT. SPEKTROSK.
37 (3), 495–503, 1974.
(FOR ENGLISH TRANSLATION SEE E86907)

EPIC Number	Bibliographic Citation

64577 **SYSTEMATIC STUDY OF PYROELECTRICITY. FERROELECTRICITY AND PYROELECTRICITY IN THE PEROVSKITES.**
BELL, M. I. RACCAH, P. M.
U. S. ARMY ELECTRONICS COMMAND, FORT MONMOUTH, N. J.
40PP., 1975.

64583 **PHOTOVOLTAIC EFFECT ON THIN LAYERS OF LEAD TELLURIDE.**
ZAMFIR, E. OANCEA, C.
AN. UNIV. BUCURESTI, FIZ.
22, 5–9, 1973.

64585 **TYPE OF CONDUCTIVITY OF 3-D TRANSITION METAL SILICIDES.**
NIKITIN, E. N. TARASOV, V. I.
KRISTALLOGRAFIYA
16 (2), 372–6, 1971.
(FOR ENGLISH TRANSLATION SEE E68414)

64713 **ANTIFERROMAGNETIC SUSCEPTIBILITY OF RUBIDIUM MANGANESE FLUORIDE. EVIDENCE FOR A TEMPERATURE DEPENDENCE OF THE EXCHANGE CONSTANT.**
DE JONG, L. J. BREED, D. J.
SOLID STATE COMMUN.
15, 1061–5, 1974.

64714 **SPIN WAVE THEORY AND THE FIELD DEPENDENT CRITICAL BEHAVIOUR OF THE ANTIFERROMAGNETIC PERPENDICULAR SUSCEPTIBILITY IN (BISDIETHYL-AMMONIUM TETRACHLOROCUPRATE) AND COBALT BROMIDE HEXAHYDRATE.**
METSELAAR, J. W. DE JONH, L. J.
SOLID STATE COMMUN.
14, 1303–8, 1974.
(COMMUNICATIONS FROM THE KAMERLINGH ONNES LABORATORY OF THE UNIVERSITY OF LEIDEN, NO. 405)

64715 **CHANGES IN FERROELECTRIC PROPERTIES OF POTASSIUM DEUTERIUM PHOSPHIDE CRYSTALS DOPED WITH MANGANESE DIPOSITIVE IONS.**
BUTKIEWICZ, J. HILCZER, B. YURIN, V. A.
DOBRZHANSKII, G. F.
BULL. ACAD. POL. SCI., SER. SCI. MATH. ASTRON. PHYS.
22 (11), 1173–7, 1974.

64748 **EVALUATION OF OPTICAL PROPERTIES OF IRDOMES FOR SIDEWINDER 1C MISSILES.**
OLSEN, A. L.
U. S. NAVAL ORDNANCE TEST STATION, CHINA LAKE, CALIF.
22PP., 1963.
(AD–345 739, NAVWEPS–8366, NOTS–TP–3265)

64749 **DUAL MODE DOME DESIGN PROBLEMS.**
GRAY, B. C. TURNER, W. L.
WRIGHT AIR DEVELOPMENT DIVISION, WRIGHT–PATTERSON AIR FORCE BASE, OHIO
43–56, 1960.
(AD–321 784, WADD–TR–60–274, VOL. II)

64750 **RESEARCH ON PHOTOSTIMULATION IN ALKALI HALIDES.**
HERSH, H.
RESEARCH DEPARTMENT, ZENITH RADIO CORPORATION, CHICAGO, ILLINOIS
38PP., 1963.
(AD–334 334L, ZRC–63–42)

64751 **CERAMIC FIBER OPTICA.**
VUKASOVICH, M. S.
HORIZONS INCORPORATED, CLEVELAND, OHIO
26PP., 1963.
(AD–338 093)

64763 **HALL COEFFICIENT, ELECTRICAL RESISTIVITY AND THE NATURE OF ELECTRON STATES IN LIQUID ALLOYS OF MONOVALENT NOBLE METALS.**
BUSCH, G. GUNTHERODT, H. J.
ADVAN. PHYS.
16 (64), 651–6, 1967.

64818 **LOW TEMPERATURE ELECTRICAL PROPERTIES OF ZINC–DOPED ZINC–OXIDE.**
LI, P. W. HAGEMARK, K. I.
J. SOLID STATE CHEM.
12 (3–4), 371–5, 1975.

64819 **SUBMILLIMETER WAVE DIELECTRIC DISPERSION IN WATER.**
ZAFAR, M. S. HASTED, J. B. CHAMBERLAIN, J.
NATURE (LONDON) PHYS. SCI.
243 (129), 106–9, 1973.
(AD–783 223, EOARD–TR–75–2)

64844 **OPTICAL ABSORPTION INVOLVING HYDROGEN–LIKE CENTERS IN SEMICONDUCTORS.**
ROZNERITSA, YA. A. MATRONITSKII, YA. S.
IZV. VYSSH. UCHEB. ZAVED. FIZ.
(11), 119–21, 1970.
(FOR ENGLISH TRANSLATION SEE E64845)

64845 **OPTICAL ABSORPTION INVOLVING HYDROGEN–LIKE CENTERS IN SEMICONDUCTORS.**
ROZNERITSA, YA. A. MATRONITSKII, YA. S.
SOV. PHYS. J.
(11), 1505–6, 1970.
(ENGLISH TRANSLATION OF IZV. VYSSH. UCHEB. ZAVED. FIZ., (11), 119–21, 1970; FOR ORIGINAL SEE E64844)

64846 **OPTICAL CONSTANTS AND SPECTRAL MICROCHARACTERISTICS OF SODIUM OXIDE – SILICON OXIDE GLASSES IN THE IR REGION OF THE SPECTRUM.**
GIRIN, O. P. KONDRATEV, YU. N.
RAABEN, E. L.
OPT. SPEKTROSK.
29, 745–50, 1970.
(FOR ENGLISH TRANSLATION SEE E64847)

64847 **OPTICAL CONSTANTS AND SPECTRAL MICROCHARACTERISTICS OF SODIUM OXIDE – SILICON OXIDE GLASSES IN THE IR REGION OF THE SPECTRUM.**
GIRIN, O. P. KONDRATEV, YU. N.
RAABEN, E. L.
OPT. SPECTROS., USSR
29, 397–400, 1970.
(ENGLISH TRANSLATION OF OPT. SPEKTROSK., 29, 745–50, 1970; FOR ORIGINAL SEE E64846)

64850 **STUDY OF SODIUM SILICATE GLASSES IN THE INFRARED BY MEANS OF THIN FILMS.**
CROZIER, D. DOUGLAS, R. W.
PHYS. CHEM. GLASSES
6 (6), 240–5, 1965.

64851 **QUANTUM TRANSPORT AND OPTICAL STUDY OF SILICON, GERMANIUM, AND INDIUM ANTIMONIDE BY CYCLOTRON RESONANCE.**
OTSUKA, E. MURASE, K. OHYAMA, T.
KOBAYASHI, K.
PROC. INT. CONF. PHYS. SEMICOND., 10TH
561–5, 1970.

64854 **INFLUENCE OF SECOND–PHASE INCLUSIONS ON ELECTRICAL CONDUCTIVITY AND HALL EFFECT.**
VORONKOV, V. V. VORONKOVA, G. I.
IGLITSYN, M. I.
FIZ. TEKH. POLUPROV.
4 (12), 2263–6, 1970.
(FOR ENGLISH TRANSLATION SEE E64855)

64855 **INFLUENCE OF SECOND–PHASE INCLUSIONS ON ELECTRICAL CONDUCTIVITY AND HALL EFFECT.**
VORONKOV, V. V. VORONKOVA, G. I.
IGLITSYN, M. I.
SOV. PHYS. SEMICOND.
4 (12), 1949–52, 1971.
(ENGLISH TRANSLATION OF FIZ. TEKH. POLUPROV., 4 (12), 2263–6, 1970; FOR ORIGINAL SEE E64854)

64857 **INFRARED ABSORPTION SPECTRA DUE TO LOCALIZED VIBRATION IN THE II–VI COMPOUNDS.**
MITSUISHI, A. MANABE, A. YOSHINAGA, H.
IBUKI, S. KOMIYA, H.
PROGR. THEOR. PHYS., SUPPL.
(45), 21–35, 1970.

64877 **CHEMICAL SHIFT OF THE K LEVEL IN PHOTOELECTRON SPECTRA.**
MAZALOV, L. N. SADOVSKII, A. P.
MURAKHTANOV, V. V. GUZHAVINA, T. I.
J. STRUCT. CHEM., USSR
14 (3), 436–40, 1973.
(ENGLISH TRANSLATION OF ZH. STRUKT. KHIM., 14 (3), 477–82, 1973; FOR ORIGINAL SEE E51330)

64880 **THE ANISOTROPY AND TEMPERATURE BEHAVIOR OF THE 1.3 ELECTRON VOLTS OPTICAL ABSORPTION BAND IN ALPHA – SILICON CARBIDE.**
ODARICH, V. A.
J. APPL. SPECTROS., USSR
14 (4), 540–1, 1971.
(ENGLISH TRANSLATION OF ZH. PRIKL. SPEKTROSK., 14 (4), 732–4, 1971; FOR ORIGINAL SEE E62097)

64881 **THE SYSTEM LEAD TELLURIDE – GALLIUM TELLURIDE.**
ABILOV, CH. I. RUSTAMOV, P. G.
ALIDZHANOV, M. A.
INORG. MAT., USSR
10 (1), 115–6, 1974.
(ENGLISH TRANSLATION OF IZV. AKAD. NAUK SSSR, NEORG. MATER., 10 (1), 142–3, 1974; FOR ORIGINAL SEE E57869)

64883 **PREPARATION OF LEAD TELLURIDE FILMS IN A QUASICLOSED VOLUME.**
SMIRNOV, N. K. CHERKASHIN, G. A.
INORG. MAT., USSR
10 (2), 188–90, 1974.
(ENGLISH TRANSLATION OF IZV. AKAD. NAUK SSSR, NEORG. MATER., 10 (2), 221–3, 1974; FOR ORIGINAL SEE E58894)

64884 **THE SYSTEM LEAD SELENIDE – TIN SELENIDE.**
SHTANOV, V. I. ZLOMANOV, V. P.
NOVOSELOVA, A. V.
INORG. MAT., USSR
10 (2), 191–3, 1974.
(ENGLISH TRANSLATION OF IZV. AKAD. NAUK SSSR, NEORG. MATER., 10 (2), 224–7, 1974; FOR ORIGINAL SEE E58895)

EPIC Number	Bibliographic Citation

64885 **THERMAL CONDUCTIVITY AND ABSORPTION COEFFICIENT OF ZINC SELENIDE AT 300–580 K.**
MEN', A. A. CHECHEL'NITSKII, A. Z.
SOKOLOV, V. A. KHOLODOVA, L. A.
INORG. MAT., USSR
10 (3), 468–9, 1974.
(ENGLISH TRANSLATION OF IZV. AKAD. NAUK SSSR, NEORG. MATER., 10 (3), 548–9, 1974; FOR ORIGINAL SEE E59347)

64890 **ON THE APPROXIMATE CORRELATION BETWEEN THE BONDING ENERGY OF OXYGEN IN METAL OXIDES AND THE WIDTH OF THEIR FORBIDDEN ZONES.**
KLISSURSKI, D. G.
SOLID STATE COMMUN.
15 (11–12), 1789–92, 1974.

64940 **THE INCLUSION OF WATER IN GLASSES. IV. INFLUENCE OF THE TEMPERATURE.**
SCHOLZE, H.
GLASTECHN. BER.
32 (8), 314–20, 1959.

64941 **THE DETERMINATION OF THE OPTICAL CONSTANTS, N. K FROM REFLECTIVITY MEASUREMENTS.**
NEUROTH, N.
Z. PHYSIK.
144, 85–90, 1956.

64959 **PIEZOOPTICAL PHENOMENA DUE TO FREE CHARGE CARRIERS IN GALLIUM ANTIMONIDE.**
GLURDZHIDZE, L. N. REMENYUK, A. D.
VUL, A. YA. GOLUBEV, L. V.
FIZ. TEKH. POLUPROVODN.
8 (9), 1720–4, 1974.
(FOR ENGLISH TRANSLATION SEE E68432)

64980 **PHONON RESISTIVITIES OF DILUTE TRANSITION METAL COMPOUNDS.**
DUNLOP, J. B. GRUENER, G. NAPOLI, F.
SOLID STATE COMMUN.
15 (1), 13–17, 1974.

64981 **NEW CORRELATION. SUPERCONDUCTING CRITICAL TEMPERATURE VERSUS NUMBER OF NATURALLY OCCURRING ISOTOPES AMONG SUPERCONDUCTING ELEMENTS.**
WANG, F. E. MITCHELL, M. A.
SOLID STATE COMMUN.
15 (5), 867–9, 1974.

64986 **STRESS-INDUCED AMPLIFICATION OF THE PHOTOVOLTAIC EFFECT IN NONCENTROSYMMETRIC SEMICONDUCTORS. CADMIUM SULFIDE.**
LAGOWSKI, J. MORAWSKI, A. GATOS, H. C.
SURF. SCI.
45 (1), 325–8, 1974.

64995 **APPLICATIONS OF SEMICONDUCTORS TO PHOTOEMISSION AND SECONDARY EMISSION.**
PIAGET, C. JARRY, PH.
AVISEM 71, COLLOQ. INT. APPL. TECH. VIDE IND.
SEMICOND. COMPOSANTS ELECTRON. MICROELECTRON.,
[C.R.], 3RD
427–42PP., 1971.

64997 **SEMICONDUCTING PROPERTIES OF TITANIUM DIOXIDE.**
ALBELLA, J. M. MORAN, A. PAJARES, J. A.
SORIA, J. A.
ACTA CIENT. VENEZ., SUPL.
24 (2), 195–200, 1973.

65000 **VARIATION OF THE OPTICAL PROPERTIES OF LEVO- AND DEXTROROTATORY SODIUM BROMATE WITH CRYSTAL-GROWTH TEMPERATURE.**
DAS, J. N. VERMA, N.
ACTA CRYSTALLOGR., SECT.
29 B (1), 4–7, 1973.

65002 **PHOTOEMISSION OF GALLIUM ARSENIDE IN THE REFLECTION AND TRANSMISSION MODE.**
FRANK, G. GARBE, S.
ACTA ELECTRON.
16 (3), 237–44, 1973.

65011 **TIME DELAYED LUMINESCENCE SPECTRA OF LEAD ACTIVATED ZINC SULFIDE PHOSPHORS EXCITED BY A RUBY LASER.**
FRACSKOWIAK, M. GERHOLD, W. SUSLA, W.
ACTA PHYS. CHEM.
19 (4), 393–402, 1973.

65013 **SOME OPTICAL PROPERTIES OF SILICON OXIDE FILMS ON SILICON SUBSTRATE.**
VAN PHUC, D.
ACTA TECH. ACAD. SCI. HUNG.
74 (3–4), 263–74, 1973.

65015 **OPTICAL INTERFEROMETRY AT HIGH PRESSURES.**
VEDAM, K.
BATTELLE MEMORIAL INST., COLUMBUS, OHIO
39–44, 1971.
(NBS-SP-326, N71-26481)

65020 **STUDY OF PHASE TRANSITIONS IN INSULATORS BY THE DIELECTRIC CONSTANT TECHNIQUE.**
SAMARA, G. A. CHRISMAN, W. L.
BATTELLE MEMORIAL INST., COLUMBUS, OHIO
243–50, 1971.
(NBS-SP-326, N71-26503)

65038 **ELECTRONIC TRANSITIONS IN THE FAR-INFRARED ABSORPTION SPECTRUM OF ERBIUM(3+): CALCIUM FLUORIDE.**
WARD, R. W. CLAYMAN, B. P.
J. PHYS.
7 C (16), L322–L324, 1974.

65041 **OPTICAL PROPERTIES AND ELECTRONIC DENSITY OF STATES.**
CARDONA, M.
NATIONAL BUREAU OF STANDARDS, WASHINGTON, D. C.
77–91, 1971.
(NBS-SP-323, N72-21713)

65042 **THEORETICAL ELECTRON DENSITY OF STATES STUDY OF TETRAHEDRALLY BONDED SEMICONDUCTORS.**
STUKEL, D. J. COLLINS, T. C. EUWEMA, R. N.
NATIONAL BUREAU OF STANDARDS, WASHINGTON, D. C.
93–103, 1971.
(NBS-SP-323, N72-21714)

65043 **ELECTRONIC DENSITY OF STATES IN EUROPIUM CHALCOGENIDES.**
CHE, S. J.
NATIONAL BUREAU OF STANDARDS, WASHINGTON, D. C.
105–9, 1971.
(NBS-SP-323, N72-21715)

65044 **ENERGY BAND STRUCTURE AND DENSITY OF STATES IN TETRAGONAL GERMANIUM OXIDE.**
ARLINGHAUS, F. J. ALBERS, W. A., JR.
NATIONAL BUREAU OF STANDARDS, WASHINGTON, D. C.
111–3, 1971.
(NBS-SP-323, N72-21716)

65045 **CALCULATION OF THE DENSITY OF STATES AND OPTICAL PROPERTIES OF LEAD TELLURIDE FROM APW-LCAO ENERGY BANDS.**
BUSS, D. D. SCHIRF, V. E.
NATIONAL BUREAU OF STANDARDS, WASHINGTON, D. C.
115–23, 1971.
(NBS-SP-323, N72-21717)

65048 **OPTICAL DENSITY OF STATES ULTRAVIOLET PHOTOELECTRIC SPECTROSCOPY.**
SPICER, W. E.
NATIONAL BUREAU OF STANDARDS, WASHINGTON, D. C.
139–58, 1971.
(NBS-SP-323, N72-21720)

65050 **ELECTRONIC DENSITIES OF STATES FROM X-RAY PHOTOELECTRON SPECTROSCOPY.**
FADLEY, C. S. SHIRLEY, D. A.
NATIONAL BUREAU OF STANDARDS, WASHINGTON, D. C.
163–79, 1971.
(NBS-SP-323, N72-21722)

65061 **ORBITAL SYMMETRY CONTRIBUTIONS TO ELECTRONIC DENSITY OF STATES OF GOLD ALUMINUM.**
SWITENDICK, A. C.
NATIONAL BUREAU OF STANDARDS, WASHINGTON, D. C.
297–302, 1971.
(NBS-SP-323, N72-21738)

65062 **SOFT X-RAY EMISSION SPECTRUM OF ALUMINUM IN GOLD ALUMINUM.**
WILLIAMS, M. L. DOBBYN, R. C. CUTHILL, J. R.
MC ALISTER, A. J.
NATIONAL BUREAU OF STANDARDS, WASHINGTON, D. C.
303–5, 1971.
(NBS-SP-323, N72-21739)

65065 **THE INFLUENCE OF GENERALIZED ORDER-DISORDER ON THE ELECTRON STATES IN FIVE CLASSES OF COMPOUND FORMING BINARY ALLOY SYSTEMS.**
COLLINGS, E. W. ENDERBY, J. E. HO, J. C.
NATIONAL BUREAU OF STANDARDS, WASHINGTON, D. C.
483–92, 1971.
(NBS-SP-323, N72-21762)

65066 **LOCALIZED STATES IN NARROW BAND AND AMORPHOUS SEMICONDUCTORS.**
ADLER, D. FEINLEIB, J.
NATIONAL BUREAU OF STANDARDS, WASHINGTON, D. C.
493–504, 1971.
(NBS-SP-323, N72-21763)

65067 **A CLUSTER THEORY OF THE ELECTRONIC STRUCTURE OF DISORDERED SYSTEMS.**
FROED, K. F. COHEN, M. H.
NATIONAL BUREAU OF STANDARDS, WASHINGTON, D. C.
505–8, 1971.
(NBS-SP-323, N72-21764)

65069 **DENSITY OF STATES OF SILVER GOLD, SILVER PALLADIUM, AND SILVER INDIUM ALLOYS STUDIED BY MEANS OF THE PHOTOEMISSION TECHNIQUE.**
NILSSON, P. O.
NATIONAL BUREAU OF STANDARDS, WASHINGTON, D. C.
551–5, 1971.
(NBS-SP-323, N72-21770)

EPIC Number	Bibliographic Citation

65073 **RELEVANCE OF KNIGHT SHIFT MEASUREMENTS TO THE ELECTRONIC DENSITY OF STATES.**
BENNETT, L. H. WATSON, R. E. CARTER, G. C.
NATIONAL BUREAU OF STANDARDS, WASHINGTON, D. C.
601–43, 1971.
(NBS–SP–323, N72–21776)

65080 **NONLINEAR OPTICAL SUSCEPTIBILITY OF SEMICONDUCTORS WITH ZINCBLENDE STRUCTURE.**
BELL, M. I.
NATIONAL BUREAU OF STANDARDS, WASHINGTON, D. C.
757–66, 1971.
(NBS–SP–323, N72–21792)

65081 **MODEL DENSITY OF STATES FOR HIGH TRANSITION TEMPERATURES BETA–TUNGSTEN SUPERCONDUCTORS.**
COHEN, R. W. CODY, G. D. VIELAND, L. J.
NATIONAL BUREAU OF STANDARDS, WASHINGTON, D. C.
767–73, 1971.
(NBS–SP–323, N72–21793)

65083 **A NOTE ON THE POSITION OF THE GOLD 5D BANDS IN GOLD ALUMINUM AND GOLD GALLIUM.**
CHAN, P. D. SHIRLEY, D. A.
NATIONAL BUREAU OF STANDARDS, WASHINGTON, D. C.
791–3, 1971.
(NBS–SP–323, N72–21796)

65104 **CALCULATIONS OF THE FREQUENCY DEPENDENCE OF ELASTO–OPTIC CONSTANTS OF INFRARED LASER WINDOW MATERIALS.**
BENDOW, B. GIANINO, P. D.
AIR FORCE CAMBRIDGE RESEARCH LABS., HANSCOM AFB, MASS.
100PP., 1974.
(AD–A003 621, AFCRL–TR–74–0533, AFCRL–PSRP–608)
(N75–26848)

65105 **LASER WINDOW SURFACE FINISHING AND COATING TECHNOLOGY.**
BRAUNSTEIN, M.
HUGHES RESEARCH LABS., MALIBU, CALIF.
55PP., 1974.
(AD–A003 666, AFCRL–TR–74–0425)

65107 **INVESTIGATION OF BASIC ELECTRONIC TRANSPORT, RECOMBINATION AND OPTICAL PROPERTIES IN INDIUM ARSENIDE (1–X) PHOSPHIDE (X) ALLOY SYSTEMS AND THE GALLIUM ANTIMONIDE EPITAXIAL FILMS FOR 1–2 MICROMETER IR APPLICATIONS.**
LI, S. S.
DEPT. OF ELECTRICAL ENGINEERING, FLORIDA UNIV., GAINESVILLE
84PP., 1974.
(AD–A003 981)

65109 **ELECTRONIC AND MAGNETIC PROPERTIES OF HIGH TEMPERATURE ELECTROLYTES.**
NACHTRIEB, N. H.
DEPT. OF CHEMISTRY, CHICAGO UNIV., ILLINOIS
43PP., 1974.
(AD–A004 136, AFOSR–TR–75–0060)

65110 **INFRARED REFLECTIVITY AND FREE CARRIER ABSORPTION OF SILICON DOPED, N–TYPE GALLIUM ARSENIDE.**
KUNG, J. SPITZER, W. G.
J. ELECTROCHEM. SOC.
121 (11), 1482–7, 1974.
(AD–A004 065, AFOSR–TR–75–0006)

65111 **OPTIVAL ABSORPTION OF COPPER IRON SULFIDE AND IRON–DOPED COPPER ALUMINUM SULFIDE AND COPPER GALLIUM SULFIDE.**
KONDO, K. TERANISHI, T. SATO, K.
J. PHYS. SOC. JAP.
36 (1), 311, 1974.

65112 **SPECTRAL VARIATION OF INDEX OF REFRACTION.**
DAVIDSON, R. M.
J. OPT. SOC. AMER.
53, 1006, 1963.

65120 **OPTOELECTRONIC VOLTAGE TRANSFORMER.**
ADIROVICH, E. I. NAIMANBAEV, R. N.
YUABOV, YU. M.
SOV. PHYS. DOKL.
18 (1), 67–9, 1973.
(ENGLISH TRANSLATION OF DOKL. AKAD. NAUK SSSR, 208 (1), 73–6, 1973; FOR ORIGINAL SEE E62623)

65123 **HOPPING CONDUCTION IN LIGHTLY DOPED SEMICONDUCTORS (REVIEW).**
SHKLOVSKII, B. I.
SOV. PHYS. SEMICOND.
6 (7), 1053–75, 1973.
(ENGLISH TRANSLATION OF FIZ. TEKH. POLUPROVOD., 6 (7), 1197–1226, 1972; FOR ORIGINAL SEE E62704)

65147 **EFFECTS OF ELECTRON IRRADIATION ON GALLIUM ARSENIDE PHOTODIODES.**
BRUDNYI, V. N. VORONKOV, V. P.
KRIVOV, M. A. MALYANOV, S. V.
SOV. PHYS. J.
15 (1), 83–4, 1972.
(ENGLISH TRANSLATION OF IZV. VYSSH. UCHEB. ZAVED., FIZ., 106–7, 1972; FOR ORIGINAL SEE E63469)

65150 **INVESTIGATION OF THE OPTICAL PROPERTIES OF INDIUM SELENIDE TELLURIDE SINGLE CRYSTALS.**
MUSHINSKII, V. P. KOBOLEV, V. I.
SOV. PHYS. J.
15 (5), 682–5, 1972.
(ENGLISH TRANSLATION OF IZV. VYSSH. UCHEB. ZAVED., FIZ., 15 (5), 65–8, 1972; FOR ORIGINAL SEE E63472)

65152 **USE OF THE METHOD OF BROKEN TOTAL INTERNAL REFLECTION TO DETERMINE SEMICONDUCTOR PROPERTIES.**
BILENKO, D. I. DVORKIN, B. A.
SHEKHTER, Z. V.
SOV. PHYS. J.
15 (6), 793–7, 1972.
(ENGLISH TRANSLATION OF IZV. VYSSH. UCHEB. ZAVED., FIZ., 15 (6), 19–23, 1972; FOR ORIGINAL SEE E63474)

65154 **MEASUREMENT OF ELECTRICAL–CONDUCTIVITY ANISOTROPY IN SEMICONDUCTOR LAYERS BY FOUR–PROBE METHOD.**
ISLYAMOV, Z. I. KON'KOV, V. L.
SOV. PHYS. J.
14 (8), 1143–5, 1971.
(ENGLISH TRANSLATION OF IZV. VYSSH. UCHEB. ZAVED., FIZ. 14 (8), 143–6, 1971; FOR ORIGINAL SEE E63465)

65157 **MEASUREMENT OF THE CONDUCTIVITY OF NONUNIFORM SEMICONDUCTOR LAYERS BY A PROBE METHOD.**
KON'KOV, V. L. PAVLOV, N. I.
POLYAKOV, N. N.
SOV. PHYS. J.
14 (10), 1336–40, 1971.
(ENGLISH TRANSLATION OF IZV. VYSSH. UCHEB. ZAVED., FIZ., 14 (10), 33–8, 1971; FOR ORIGINAL SEE E63468)

65158 **SOME PHOTOELECTRIC AND ELECTRICAL PROPERTIES OF COPPER–DOPED GALLIUM ARSENIDE.**
VOITSEKHOVSKII, A. V. ZAKHAROVA, G. A.
KRIVOV, M. A. MALISOVA, E. V.
SOV. PHYS. J.
13 (9), 1154–7, 1970.
(ENGLISH TRANSLATION OF IZV. VYSSH. UCHEB. ZAVED., FIZ., 13 (9), 40–4, 1970; FOR ORIGINAL SEE E63458)

65161 **THE PHOTO–EMF IN GALLIUM ARSENIDE JUNCTIONS PRODUCED BY NATURAL RECOMBINATION RADIATION.**
OKUNEV, V. D. GAMAN, V. I.
SOV. PHYS. J.
16 (1), 111–3, 1973.
(ENGLISH TRANSLATION OF IZV. VYSSH. UCHEB. ZAVED., FIZ., 16 (1), 138–9, 1973; FOR ORIGINAL SEE E63482)

65164 **PHOTOELECTRIC PROPERTIES OF P–N JUNCTIONS IN SINGLE–CRYSTAL LEAD SULFIDE FILMS.**
BATUKOVA, L. M.
SOV. PHYS. J.
14 (5), 701–3, 1971.
(ENGLISH TRANSLATION OF IZV. VYSSH. UCHED. ZAVED., FIZ., 14 (5), 146–8, 1971; FOR ORIGINAL SEE E63462)

65166 **ANOMALOUSLY LARGE SPONTANEOUS ROTARY ELECTROOPTIC EFFECT IN FERROELECTRIC AMMONIUM SODIUM SELENATE DIHYDRATE.**
ALEKSANDROV, K. S. ANISTRATOV, A. T.
IVANOV, N. R. MEL'NIKOVA, S. V.
SHUVALOV, L. A.
SOV. PHYS. SOLID STATE
15 (2), 324–5, 1973.
(ENGLISH TRANSLATION OF FIZ. TVERD. TELA, 15 (2), 456–8, 1973; FOR ORIGINAL SEE E62863)

65167 **INFLUENCE OF UNIAXIAL MECHANICAL DEFORMATION ON THE OPTICAL PROPERTIES OF ALKALI HALIDE CRYSTALS.**
VISHNEVSKII, V. N. STEFANSKII, I. V.
KUZYK, M. P. KULIK, Z. S. KULIK, L. N.
SOV. PHYS. SOLID STATE
15 (1), 242–3, 1973.
(ENGLISH TRANSLATION OF FIZ. TVERD. TELA, 15 (1), 325–7, 1973; FOR ORIGINAL SEE E62862)

65168 **MECHANICAL STRESSES IN FILMS OF (BISMUTH ANTIMONY) TELLURIDE.**
GOL'TSMAN, B. M. KOMISSARCHIK, M. G.
SOV. PHYS. SOLID STATE
15 (1), 219–20, 1973.
(ENGLISH TRANSLATION OF FIZ. TVERD. TELA, 15 (1), 301–3, 1973; FOR ORIGINAL SEE E62861)

65169 **MANY–PHOTON EXCITATION AND IONIZATION OF THALLIUM IMPURITY CENTERS IN ALKALI HALIDE CRYSTALS.**
ASEEV, G. I. KATS, M. L.
SOV. PHYS. SOLID STATE
14 (5), 1173–6, 1972.
(ENGLISH TRANSLATION OF FIZ. TVERD. TELA, 14 (5), 1365–8, 1972; FOR ORIGINAL SEE E62850)

EPIC Number	Bibliographic Citation
65172	CHARACTERISTICS OF THE PHOTOELECTRIC EMF OF ANTIMONY SULFIDE IODIDE. BEZDETNYI, N. M. GORBATOV, G. Z. ZEINALLY, A. KH. LEBEDEVA, N. N. SHEINKMAN, M. K. SOV. PHYS. SOLID STATE 14 (2), 477–8, 1972. (ENGLISH TRANSLATION OF FIZ. TVERD. TELA, 14 (2), 574–5, 1972; FOR ORIGINAL SEE E62845)
65177	PHOTO-EMF SPECTRUM OF A SILVER BROMIDE EMULSION FILM. KOROTAEV, N. N. MEIKLYAR, P. V. SOV. PHYS. SOLID STATE 14 (10), 2656–7, 1973. (ENGLISH TRANSLATION OF FIZ. TVERD. TELA, 14 (10), 3099–3100, 1972; FOR ORIGINAL SEE E62856)
65179	JOINT MATRIX ELEMENT FOR TWO-PHOTON INTERBAND TRANSITIONS IN SEMICONDUCTORS. MEDIS, P. M. SOV. PHYS. SOLID STATE 14 (9), 2195–7, 1973. (ENGLISH TRANSLATION OF FIZ. TVERD. TELA, 14 (9), 2531–4, 1972; FOR ORIGINAL SEE E62853)
65181	TWO-PHOTON ABSORPTION AND OPTICAL ORIENTATION OF FREE CARRIERS IN CUBIC CRYSTALS. IVCHENKO, E. L. SOV. PHYS. SOLID STATE 14 (12), 2942–6, 1973. (ENGLISH TRANSLATION OF FIZ. TVERD. TELA, 14 (12), 3489–97, 1972; FOR ORIGINAL SEE E62858)
65191	OSCILLATIONS OF THE CURRENT IN THE CASE OF CARRIER EXCLUSION IN SEMICONDUCTORS CONTAINING DEEP LEVELS. KNIGIN, P. I. KOROLEV, YU. S. FIZ. TEKH. POLUPROVODN. 7 (9), 1811–14, 1973. (FOR ENGLISH TRANSLATION SEE E65192)
65192	OSCILLATIONS OF THE CURRENT IN THE CASE OF CARRIER EXCLUSION IN SEMICONDUCTORS CONTAINING DEEP LEVELS. KNIGIN, P. I. KOROLEV, YU. S. SOV. PHYS. SEMICOND. 7 (9), 1208–9, 1974. (ENGLISH TRANSLATION OF FIZ. TEKH. POLUPROV., 7 (9), 1811–4, 1973; FOR ORIGINAL SEE E65191)
65199	ELECTRICAL AND OPTICAL PROPERTIES OF IRON OXIDE. BOWEN, H. K. ADLER, D. AUKER, B. H. J. SOLID STATE CHEM. 12 (3–4), 355–9, 1975.
65201	THE CRYSTALLIZATION OF VITREOUS SEMICONDUCTOR ARSENIC SELENIDE TELLURIDE. ITO, S. IGAKI, K. TECHNOL. REP. TOHOKU UNIV. 38 (2), 733–42, 1973.
65212	THE PREPARATION AND PROPERTIES OF BARIUM TANTALUM SULFIDE, BARIUM NIOBIUM SULFIDE, AND BARIUM TANTALUM SELENIDE. DONOHUE, P. C. WEIHER, J. F. J. SOLID STATE CHEM. 10 (2), 142–4, 1974.
65213	THE PREPARATION AND CHARACTERIZATION OF CADMIUM IRIDIUM HYDROXIDE AND ZINC IRIDIUM HYDROXIDE. SARKOZY, R. CHAMBERLAND, B. L. J. SOLID STATE CHEM. 10 (2), 145–50, 1974.
65217	INVESTIGATION OF THE OPTICAL AND MAGNETIC PROPERTIES OF THE VARIOUS PHASES OF THE ZINC BORATE SYSTEM. SPEED, A. R. HAGSTON, W. E. GARLICK, G. F. J. PHYS. STATUS SOLIDI 23 A (2), 689–701, 1974.
65239	AN ITERATIVE CALCULATION OF GALVANOMAGNETIC COEFFICIENTS AND ALTERNATING CURRENT CONDUCTIVITY OF POLAR SEMICONDUCTORS. NAG, B. R. J. PHYS. 7 C (19), 3541–6, 1974.
65241	ELECTRON PROBE MICROANALYSIS USING OXYGEN X-RAYS: I. MASS ABSORPTION COEFFICIENTS. LOVE, G. COX, M. G. C. SCOTT, V. D. J. PHYS. 7 D (15), 2131–41, 1974.
65242	FAR INFRARED OPTICAL PROPERTIES OF FREE CARRIERS IN GALLIUM ARSENIDE. ZITTER, R. N. AS'SAADI, K. J. PHYS CHEM. SOLIDS 35 (12), 1593–4, 1974.
65250	INTERSERIAL PHOTOTRANSITIONS OF EXCITIONS IN SEMICONDUCTORS. KHADSHI, P. I. MOSKALENKO, S. A. PHYS. STATUS SOLIDI (GERMANY) 65 B (2), 833–45, 1974.
65257	THEORY OF MULTIPHONON ABSORPTION IN THE WINGS OF INTERNAL VIBRATIONAL MODES OF IMPURITIES IN IONIC CRYSTALS. BENDOW, B. SOLID STATE COMMUN. 15 (8), 1395–9, 1974. (AD-A010 455, AFCRL-TR-74-0442)
65265	LUMINESCENCE CENTERS OF COPPER-ACTIVATED ZINC SULFIDE. DVORAK, L. KUPKA, Z. ACTA UNIV. PALACKI. OLOMUC., FAC. RERUM NATUR. 41, PHYSICAL 13, 15–32, 1973.
65266	PHOTOELECTROLUMINESCENT EFFECTS IN COPPER-ACTIVATED ZINC SULFIDE ELECTROLUMINESCENT POWDERS. KUPKA, Z. DVORAK, L. ACTA UNIV. PALACKI. OLOMUC., FAC. RERUM NATUR. 13, 159–64, 1973.
65271	ELECTRONIC CONFIGURATION AND ELECTRICAL CONDUCTIVITY IN CERAMICS. ADLER, D. AMER. CERAM. SOC., BULL. 52 (2), 154–9, 1973.
65282	LARGE PHOTOVOLTAGES IN FERROELECTRIC CERAMICS. BRODY, P. S. AM. CERAM. SOC. BULL. 52 (8), 631, 1973.
65286	PLASMA TORCH TECHNIQUE FOR THE PREPARATION OF LOW OPTICAL LOSS VITREOUS SILICA. NASSAU, K. SHIEVER, J. W. AM. CERAM. SOC. BULL. 52 (9), 703, 1973.
65288	PHOTOCONDUCTIVITY AND RECOMBINATION KINETICS IN AMORPHOUS BULK AND FILM ARSENIDE SILICATE TELLURIDE. AMOLDUSSEN, T. C. BUBE, R. H. AM. CERAM. SOC. BULL. 52 (9), 714, 1973.
65300	ELECTRONIC PROPERTIES OF COMPENSATED SEMICONDUCTORS WITH CORRELATED IMPURITY DISTRIBUTIONS. GAL'PERN, YU. S. EFROS, A. L. SOV. PHYS. SEMICOND. 6 (6), 941–6, 1972. (ENGLISH TRANSLATION OF FIZ. TEKH. POLUPROV., 6 (6), 1081–8, 1972; FOR ORIGINAL SEE E62703)
65301	PROPERTIES OF IRON-DOPED CADMIUM TELLURIDE. VUL, B. M. IVANOV, V. S. RUKAVISHNIKOV, V. A. SAL'MAN, V. M. CHAPNIN, V. A. SOV. PHYS. SEMICOND. 6 (7), 1106–9, 1973. (ENGLISH TRANSLATION OF FIZ. TEKH. POLUPROV., 6 (7), 1264–7, 1972; FOR ORIGINAL SEE E62705)
65302	OPTICAL PROPERTIES OF SEMICONDUCTOR SUPERLATTICES WITH COMPLEX BAND STRUCTURES. SHIK, A. YA. SOV. PHYS. SEMICOND. 6 (7), 1110–7, 1973. (ENGLISH TRANSLATION OF FIZ. TEKH. POLUPROV., 6 (7), 1268–77, 1972; FOR ORIGINAL SEE E62706)
65303	FUNDAMENTAL ABSORPTION OF LIGHT IN THE NONPARABOLIC REGION OF LEAD TELLURIDE AND IN LEAD TELLURIDE - TIN TELLURIDE SOLID SOLUTIONS. DRABKIN, I. A. MORGOVSKII, L. YA. NEL'SON, I. V. RAVICH, YU. I. SOV. PHYS. SEMICOND. 6 (7), 1156–8, 1973. (ENGLISH TRANSLATION OF FIZ. TEKH. POLUPROV., 6 (7), 1323–6, 1972; FOR ORIGINAL SEE E62707)
65306	USE OF A SCHOTTKY BARRIER IN DETERMINATION OF THE OPTICAL ABSORPTION COEFFICIENT OF A SEMICONDUCTOR. GUTKIN, A. A. DMITRIEV, M. V. NASLEDOV, D. N. SOV. PHYS. SEMICOND. 6 (7), 1218–9, 1973. (ENGLISH TRANSLATION OF FIZ. TEKH. POLUPROV., 6 (7), 1394–5, 1972; FOR ORIGINAL SEE E62710)
65309	EXCITON ABSORPTION DUE TO SURFACE IRREGULARITIES IN CRYSTALS AND POLYCRYSTALS. SKAISTIS, E. SUGAKOV, V. I. SOV. PHYS. SEMICOND. 6 (9), 1417–21, 1973. (ENGLISH TRANSLATION OF FIZ. TEKH. POLUPROV., 6 (9), 1637–42, 1975; FOR ORIGINAL SEE E62713)
65311	ELECTROMOTIVE FORCE GENERATED IN A SEMICONDUCTOR BY A MOVING LIGHT BEAM. KHOMUTOVA, M. D. SOV. PHYS. SEMICOND. 6 (9), 1590–1, 1973. (ENGLISH TRANSLATION OF FIZ. TEKH. POLUPROV., 6 (9), 1836–7, 1972; FOR ORIGINAL SEE E62715)

EPIC Number	Bibliographic Citation
65312	**ANISOTROPY OF ELECTRICAL PROPERTIES OF DOPED (TELLURIDE, INDIUM, LEAD) BISMUTH SELENIDE SINGLE CRYSTALS.** BOECHKO, V. F. PSAREV, V. I. SOV. PHYS. SEMICOND. 6 (10), 1737–9, 1973. (ENGLISH TRANSLATION OF FIZ. TEKH. POLUPROV., 6 (10), 2042–4, 1972; FOR ORIGINAL SEE E62716)
65313	**INTERBAND TRANSITIONS IN N-TYPE ALUMINUM ANTIMONIDE.** AGAEV, YA. BEKMEDOVA, N. G. MIKHAILOV, A. R. SOV. PHYS. SEMICOND. 6 (10), 1752–3, 1973. (ENGLISH TRANSLATION OF FIZ. TEKH. POLUPROV., 6 (10), 2059–61, 1972; FOR ORIGINAL SEE E62717)
65314	**PROFILE OF THE FUNDAMENTAL ABSORPTION EDGE OF CADMIUM SELENIDE.** VOLKOVA, L. V. VOLKOV, V. V. MENTSER, A. N. KIREEV, P. S. SOV. PHYS. SEMICOND. 6 (10), 1776, 1973. (ENGLISH TRANSLATION OF FIZ. TEKH. POLUPROV., 6 (10), 2085, 1972; FOR ORIGINAL SEE E62718) (ORIGINAL ARTICLE SUBMITTED TO THE ALL UNION SCIENTIFIC AND TECH. INFORMATION INST., MOSCOW, A-219, BALTIISKAYA UL. 14)
65315	**INFLUENCE OF BISMUTH IMPURITIES ON THE ENERGY SPECTRUM AND ELECTRON SCATTERING IN LEAD TELLURIDE.** KAIDANOV, V. I. MEL'NIK, R. B. SHAPIRO, L. A. SOV. PHYS. SEMICOND. 6 (11), 1815–7, 1973. (ENGLISH TRANSLATION OF FIZ. TEKH. POLUPROV., 6 (11), 2140–3, 1972; FOR ORIGINAL SEE E62719)
65316	**EFFECT OF ACOUSTIC WAVES ON THE CONDUCTIVITY OF SEMICONDUCTORS.** GULYAEV, YU. V. LISTVINA, N. N. SOV. PHYS. SEMICOND. 6 (11), 1835–8, 1973. (ENGLISH TRANSLATION OF FIZ. TEKH. POLUPROV., 6 (11), 2169–74, 1972; FOR ORIGINAL SEE E62720)
65319	**HOPPING CONDUCTION IN SEMICONDUCTORS SUBJECTED TO A STRONG ELECTRIC FIELD.** SHKLOVSKII, B. I. SOV. PHYS. SEMICOND. 6 (12), 1964–7, 1973. (ENGLISH TRANSLATION OF FIZ. TEKH. POLUPROV., 6 (12), 2335–40, 1972; FOR ORIGINAL SEE E62723)
65322	**INVESTIGATION OF SOME PROPERTIES OF TITANIUM AND COBALT COMPENSATED GALLIUM ARSENIDE CRYSTALS AND DIODE STRUCTURES.** BEKMURATOV, M. F. MURYGIN, V. I. SOV. PHYS. SEMICOND. 7 (1), 55–8, 1973. (ENGLISH TRANSLATION OF FIZ. TEKH. POLUPROV., 7 (1), 83–7, 1973; FOR ORIGINAL SEE E62726)
65323	**HOPPING CONDUCTION IN HEAVILY DOPED SEMICONDUCTORS.** SHKLOVSKII, B. I. SOV. PHYS. SEMICOND. 7 (1), 77–80, 1973. (ENGLISH TRANSLATION OF FIZ. TEKH. POLUPROV., 7 (1), 112–8, 1973; FOR ORIGINAL SEE E62727)
65324	**CAPABILITIES OF INJECTION THERMOELECTRIC DEVICES.** LUKISHKER, E. M. KOLOMOETS, N. V. SOV. PHYS. SEMICOND. 7 (1), 119–21, 1973. (ENGLISH TRANSLATION OF FIZ. TEKH. POLUPROV., 7 (1), 172–6, 1973; FOR ORIGINAL SEE E62728)
65325	**INVESTIGATION OF LEAD TELLURIDE FILMS PREPARED BY THE CLOSED VOLUME METHOD.** KONDRATOV, A. V. TIMOFEEV, YU. V. SMIRNOV, N. K. CHERKASHIN, G. A. CHUDNOVSKII, A. F. SOV. PHYS. SEMICOND. 7 (1), 124–5, 1973. (ENGLISH TRANSLATION OF FIZ. TEKH. POLUPROV., 7 (1), 178–80, 1973; FOR ORIGINAL SEE E62729)
65326	**THEORY OF IMPURITY ABSORPTION IN SEMICONDUCTORS WITH COMPLICATED BAND STRUCTURE.** SHIK, A. YA. SOV. PHYS. SEMICOND. 7 (1), 138–9, 1973. (ENGLISH TRANSLATION OF FIZ. TEKH. POLUPROV., 7 (1), 193–6, 1973; FOR ORIGINAL SEE E62730)
65327	**SIZE DEPENDENCE OF THE THERMO ELECTROMOTIVE FORCE IN SEMICONDUCTORS.** PRIMA, N. A. SOV. PHYS. SEMICOND. 7 (2), 241–5, 1973. (ENGLISH TRANSLATION OF FIZ. TEKH. POLUPROV., 7 (2), 338–45, 1973; FOR ORIGINAL SEE E62731) (ERRATA: TITLE IBID, AUTHOR IBID, J. IBID, 7 (5), 703, 1973)

EPIC Number	Bibliographic Citation
65329	**SELECTIVE PHOTOCELLS BASED ON VARIABLE-GAP GALLIUM ALUMINUM ARSENIDE: SILICON P-N STRUCTURES.** TSARENKOV, B. V. DANILOVA, T. N. IMENKOV, A. N. YAKOVLEV, YU. P. SOV. PHYS. SEMICOND. 7 (7), 954–5, 1974. (ENGLISH TRANSLATION OF FIZ. TEKH. POLUPROV., 7 (7), 1426–9, 1973; FOR ORIGIANL SEE E62733)
65330	**HIGH FIELD CYCLOTRON RESONANCE IN N-TYPE INDIUM ANTIMONIDE.** GERSHENZON, E. M. SEREBRYAKOVA, N. A. SMIRNOVA, V. B. SOV. PHYS. SEMICOND. 8 (3), 306–8, 1974. (ENGLISH TRANSLATION OF FIZ. TEKH. POLUPROV., 8 (3), 476–80, 1974; FOR ORIGINAL SEE E62427)
65331	**INVESTIGATION OF THE STRUCTURE OF THE ALLOWED-BAND EDGES OF N-TYPE INDIUM ARSENIDE BY THE OPTICAL ABSORPTION METHOD.** ZOTOVA, N. V. GARYAGDYEV, G. NASLEDOV, D. N. SOV. PHYS. SEMICOND. 8 (5), 593–6, 1974. (ENGLISH TRANSLATION OF FIZ. TEKH. POLUPROV., 8 (5), 921–7, 1974; FOR ORIGINAL SEE E62428)
65334	**SOME ASPECTS OF THE ANOMALOUS PHOTO-EMF IN THIN CADMIUM TELLURIDE FILMS.** KRETSU, I. P. MALKOCH, N. K. RAZLOGA, M. P. CHEBAN, A. G. SOV. PHYS. SEMICOND. 8 (6), 777–8, 1974. (ENGLISH TRANSLATION OF FIZ. TEKH. POLUPROV., 8 (6), 1198–1201, 1974; FOR ORIGINAL SEE E62432)
65339	**INTRABAND EDGE ABSORPTION OF LIGHT IN SEMICONDUCTORS.** ZORINA, E. L. OPT. SPECTROS., USSR 32 (5), 518–21, 1972. (ENGLISH TRANSLATION OF OPT. SPEKTROSK., 32 (5), 966–73, 1972; FOR ORIGINAL SEE E63697)
65340	**ABSORPTION COEFFICIENT AND GAIN OF A GALLIUM ARSENIDE INJECTION LASER.** GLADKII, B. I. POTYKEVICH, I. V. OPT. SPECTROS., USSR 32 (6), 630–2, 1972. (ENGLISH TRANSLATION OF OPT. SPEKTROSK., 32 (6), 1163–6, 1972; FOR ORIGINAL SEE E63698)
65341	**SCATTERING OF INFRARED RADIATION BY CYLINDRICAL DIELECTRIC, SEMICONDUCTOR, AND METAL PARTICLES.** LEBEDEVA, V. N. OPT. SPECTROS., USSR 32 (6), 644–6, 1972. (ENGLISH TRANSLATION OF OPT. SPEKTROSK., 32 (6), 1185–9, 1972; FOR ORIGINAL SEE E63699)
65342	**MEASUREMENT OF THE TEMPERATURE COEFFICIENT OF THE REFRACTIVE INDEX OF INFRARED MATERIALS USING A CARBON DIOXIDE LASER.** KOLOSOVSKII, O. A. USTIMENKO, L. N. OPT. SPECTROS., USSR 33 (4), 430–1, 1972. (ENGLISH TRANSLATION OF OPT. SPEKTROSK., 33 (4), 781–2, 1972; FOR ORIGINAL SEE E63700)
65343	**MEASUREMENT OF THE INDEX OF REFRACTION OF LOW-ABSORBING THIN FILMS BY THE ABELES METHOD.** BUGNIN, G. A. OPT. SPECTROS., USSR 37 (1), 111, 1974. (ENGLISH TRANSLATION OF OPT. SPEKTROSK., 37 (1), 197–8, 1974; FOR ORIGINAL SEE E62804)
65344	**THE RESISTANCE OF 72 ELEMENTS, ALLOYS AND COMPOUNDS TO 100,000 KG/CM.** BRIDGMAN, P. W. PROC. AMER. ACAD. ARTS SCI. 81 (4), 165–251, 1952.
65348	**FREE AND BOUND EXCITONS IN BETA-SILICON CARBIDE CRYSTALS.** NEDZVETSKII, D. S. NOVIKOV, B. V. PROKOF'EVA, N. K. REIFMAN, M. B. FIZ. TEKH. POLUPROV. 2 (8), 1089–96, 1968. (FOR ENGLISH TRANSLATION SEE E65349)
65349	**FREE AND BOUND EXCITONS IN BETA-SILICON CARBIDE CRYSTALS.** NEDZVETSKII, D. S. NOVIKOV, B. V. PROKOF'EVA, N. K. REIFMAN, M. B. SOV. PHYS. SEMICOND. 2 (8), 914–9, 1969. (ENGLISH TRANSLATION OF FIZ. TEKH. POLUPROV., 2 (8), 1089–96, 1968; FOR ORIGINAL SEE E65348)
65350	**OPTICAL ABSORPTION DUE TO EXCITATION OF ELECTRONS BOUND TO SILICON AND SULFUR IN GALLIUM PHOSPHIDE.** ONTON, A. PHYS. REV. 186 (3), 786–90, 1969.

EPIC Number	Bibliographic Citation

65351 **MAGNETIC PROPERTIES OF VANADIUM SULFIDE.**
OKA, Y. KOSUGE, K. KACHI, S.
PHYS. LETT.
50 A (4), 311–12, 1974.

65353 **OPTICAL ABSORPTION IN N-TYPE ALPHA SILICON CARBIDE (6 H) NEAR 0.6 MU M.**
DUBROVSKY, G. B. RADOVANOVA, E. I.
PHYS. LETT.
28 A (4), 283–4, 1968.

65354 **OPTICAL ABSORPTION ASSOCIATED WITH SUPERLATTICE IN SILICON CARBIDE CRYSTALS.**
DUBROVSKII, G. B. LEPNEVA, A. A.
RADOVANOVA, E. I.
PHYS. STATUS SOLIDI
57 B (1), 423–31, 1973.

65357 **LUMINESCENT CHARACTERISTICS OF CERTAIN ALKALI-BORATE GLASSES ACTIVATED WITH LEAD (II) CHLORIDE.**
BELYI, M. U. OKHRIMENKO, B. A. ROS', N. V.
YABLOCHKOV, S. M.
UKR. FIZ. ZH.
20 (1), 1–4, 1975.

65371 **QUANTUM OSCILLATIONS OF THE LONGITUDINAL MAGNETORESISTANCE OF P-TYPE INDIUM ANTIMONIDE.**
BIR, G. L. PARFEN'EV, R. V.
FIZ. TVERD. TELA
16 (9), 2595–2606, 1974.
(FOR ENGLISH TRANSLATION SEE E65372)

65372 **QUANTUM OSCILLATIONS OF THE LOGITUDINAL MAGNETORESISTANCE OF P-TYPE INDIUM ANTIMONIDE.**
BIR, G. L. PARFEN'EV, R. V.
SOV. PHYS. SOLID STATE
16 (9), 1686–92, 1975.
(ENGLISH TRANSLATION OF FIZ. TVERD. TELA, 16 (9), 2595–2606, 1974; FOR ORIGINAL SEE E65371)

65375 **NATURE OF A TRANSITION FROM WEAKLY FERROMAGNETIC TO ANTIFERROMAGNETIC STATE IN ORTHOFERRITES.**
BELOV, K. P. ZVEZDIN, A. K.
KADOMTSEVA, A. M. KRYNETSKII, I. B.
OVCHINNIKOVA, T. L.
FIZ. TVERD. TELA
16 (9), 2615–20, 1974.
(FOR ENGLISH TRANSLATION SEE E65376)

65376 **NATURE OF A TRANSITION FROM WEAKLY FERROMAGNETIC TO ANTIFERROMAGNETIC STATE IN ORTHOFERRITES.**
BELOV, K. P. ZVEZDIN, A. K.
KADOMTSEVA, A. M. KRYNETSKII, I. B.
OVCHINNIKOVA, T. L.
SOV. PHYS. SOLID STATE
16 (9), 1698–1700, 1975.
(ENGLISH TRANSLATION OF FIZ. TVERD. TELA, 16 (9), 2615–20, 1974; FOR ORIGINAL SEE E65375)

65377 **CONDUCTION MECHANISM AND SUPERCONDUCTING TRANSITION TEMPERATURE FOR GRANULAR TIN SAMPLES.**
MOROZOV, YU. G. NAUMENKO, I. G.
PETINOV, V. I.
FIZ. TVERD. TELA
16 (9), 2621–5, 1974.
(FOR ENGLISH TRANSLATION SEE E65378)

65378 **CONDUCTION MECHANISM AND SUPERCONDUCTING TRANSITION TEMPERATURE FOR GRANULAR TIN SAMPLES.**
MOROZOV, YU. G. NAUMENKO, I. G.
PETINOV, V. I.
SOV. PHYS. SOLID STATE
16 (9), 1701–3, 1975.
(ENGLISH TRANSLATION OF FIZ. TVERD. TELA, 16 (9), 2621–5, 1974; FOR ORIGINAL SEE E65377)

65379 **INHOMOGENEOUS BROADENING AND SHIFT OF THE PHONONLESS LINES IN THE LUMINESCENCE SPECTRUM OF SUPEROXIDE ION IN POTASSIUM CHLORIDE.**
FREIBERG, A. M. REBANE, L. A.
FIZ. TVERD. TELA
16 (9), 2626–32, 1974.
(FOR ENGLISH TRANSLATION SEE E65380)

65380 **INHOMOGENEOUS BROADENING AND SHIFT OF THE PHONONLESS LINES IN THE LUMINESCENCE SPECTRUM OF SUPEROXIDE ION IN POTASSIUM CHLORIDE.**
FREIBERG, A. M. REBANE, L. A.
SOV. PHYS. SOLID STATE
16 (9), 1704–7, 1975.
(ENGLISH TRANSLATION OF FIZ. TVERD. TELA, 16 (9), 2626–32, 1974; FOR ORIGINAL SEE E65379)

65383 **MAGNETIC MOMENTS OF MANGANESE IONS IN SOLID SOLUTIONS OF SYSTEM MANGANESE ARSENIDE - MANGANESE ANTIMONIDE.**
SIROTA, N. N. RYZHKOVSKII, V. M.
FIZ. TVERD. TELA
16 (9), 2643–7, 1974.
(FOR ENGLISH TRANSLATION SEE E65384)

65384 **MAGNETIC MOMENTS OF MANGANESE IONS IN SOLID SOLUTIONS OF SYSTEM MANGANESE ARSENIDE - MANGANESE ANTIMONIDE.**
SIROTA, N. N. RYZHKOVSKII, V. M.
SOV. PHYS. SOLID STATE
16 (9), 1714–6, 1975.
(ENGLISH TRANSLATION OF FIZ. TVERD. TELA, 16 (9), 2643–7, 1974; FOR ORIGINAL SEE E65383)

65389 **FERROELECTRIC NUCLEI IN BARIUM TITANATE.**
TOMASHPOL'SKII, YU. YA. SEVOST'YANOV, M. A.
FIZ. TVERD. TELA
16 (9), 2689–92, 1974.
(FOR ENGLISH TRANSLATION SEE E65390)

65390 **FERROELECTRIC NUCLEI IN BARIUM TITANATE.**
TOMASHPOL'SKII, YU. YA. SEVOST'YANOV, M. A.
SOV. PHYS. SOLID STATE
16 (9), 1739–40, 1975.
(ENGLISH TRANSLATION OF FIZ. TVERD. TELA, 16 (9), 2689–92, 1974; FOR ORIGINAL SEE E65389)

65391 **CONCENTRATION DEPENDENCE OF THE CURIE-WEISS CONSTANT AND OF THE CURIE-WEISS POINT OF (BARIUM, STRONTIUM) TITANIUM OXIDE TYPE FERROELECTRICS.**
KONSIN, P. I.
FIZ. TVERD. TELA
16 (9), 2709–12, 1974.
(FOR ENGLISH TRANSLATION SEE E65392)

65392 **CONCENTRATION DEPENDENCE OF THE CURIE-WEISS CONSTANT AND OF THE CURIE-WEISS POINT OF (BARIUM, STRONTIUM) TITANIUM OXIDE TYPE FERROELECTRICS.**
KONSIN, P. I.
SOV. PHYS. SOLID STATE
16 (9), 1751–2, 1975.
(ENGLISH TRANSLATION OF FIZ. TVERD. TELA, 16 (9), 2709–12, 1974; FOR ORIGINAL SEE E65391)

65397 **DIELECTRIC PROPERTIES AND TWIN STRUCTURE OF BISMUTH VANADIUM OXIDE SINGLE CRYSTALS.**
DUDNIK, E. F. GENE, V. V. AKIMOV, S. V.
KREICHEREK, A. YA.
FIZ. TVERD. TELA
16 (9), 2733–4, 1974.
(FOR ENGLISH TRANSLATION SEE E65398)

65398 **DIELECTRIC PROPERTIES AND TWIN STRUCTURE OF BISMUTH VANADIUM OXIDE SINGLE CRYSTALS.**
DUDNIK, E. F. GENE, V. V. AKIMOV, S. V.
KREICHEREK, A. YA.
SOV. PHYS. SOLID STATE
16 (9), 1767, 1975.
(ENGLISH TRANSLATION OF FIZ. TVERD. TELA, 16 (9), 2733–4, 1974; FOR ORIGINAL SEE E65397)

65403 **INFLUENCE OF IMPURITIES ON THE LATTICE ABSORPTION SPECTRUM OF ALPHA - SILICON CARBIDE (6H) CRYSTALS.**
KOLESNIKOV, A. A. MAKAROV, E. A.
ROMANOV, A. A.
FIZ. TVERD. TELA
16 (9), 2769–71, 1974.
(FOR ENGLISH TRANSLATION SEE E65404)

65404 **INFLUENCE OF IMPURITIES ON THE LATTICE ABSORPTION SPECTRUM OF ALPHA - SILICON CARBIDE (6H) CRYSTALS.**
KOLESNIKOV, A. A. MAKAROV, E. A.
ROMANOV, A. A.
SOV. PHYS. SOLID STATE
16 (9), 1795–6, 1975.
(ENGLISH TRANSLATION OF FIZ. TVERD. TELA, 16 (9), 2769–71, 1974; FOR ORIGINAL SEE E65403)

65411 **HALL EFFECT, ELECTRICAL RESISTIVITY, AND THERMOELECTRIC POWER OF COBALT TUNGSTEN HEXAFERRITE SINGLE CRYSTALS.**
BELOV, K. P. SVIRINA, E. P. KARNEEVA, S. S.
FIZ. TVERD. TELA
16 (9), 2783–4, 1974.
(FOR ENGLISH TRANSLATION SEE E65412)

65412 **HALL EFFECT, ELECTRICAL RESISTIVITY, AND THERMO-ELECTRIC POWER OF COBALT TUNGSTEN HEXAFERRITE SINGLE CRYSTALS.**
BELOV, K. P. SVIRINA, E. P. KARNEEVA, S. S.
SOV. PHYS. SOLID STATE
16 (9), 1806–7, 1975.
(ENGLISH TRANSLATION OF FIZ. TVERD. TELA, 16 (9), 2783–4, 1974; FOR ORIGINAL SEE E65411)

65413 **VIBRATIONAL SPECTRA OF ANTIFERROELECTRICS.**
KNYAZEV, A. S. POPLAVKO, YU. M.
ZAKHAROV, V. P. KOSAKOVSKII, L. G.
FIZ. TVERD. TELA
16 (9), 2785–6, 1974.
(FOR ENGLISH TRANSLATION SEE E65414)

65414 **VIBRATIONAL SPECTRA OF ANTIFERROELECTRICS.**
KNYAZEV, A. S. POPLAVKO, YU. M.
ZAKHAROV, V. P. KOSAKOVSKII, L. G.
SOV. PHYS. SOLID STATE
16 (9), 1808–9, 1975.
(ENGLISH TRANSLATION OF FIZ. TVERD. TELA, 16 (9), 2785–6, 1974; FOR ORIGINAL SEE E65413)

EPIC Number	Bibliographic Citation
65419	**EFFECT OF THE ELECTRON - MAGNON INTERACTION ON THE ELECTRON MOBILITY IN FERROMAGNETIC SEMICONDUCTORS.** GRIGIN, A. P. KOZLOV, V. A. NAGAEV, E. A. FIZ. TVERD. TELA 16 (9), 2808–10, 1974. (FOR ENGLISH TRANSLATION SEE E65420)
65420	**EFFECT OF THE ELECTRON - MAGNON INTERACTION ON THE ELECTRON MOBILITY IN FERROMAGNETIC SEMICONDUCTORS.** GRIGIN, A. P. KOZLOV, V. A. NAGAEV, E. A. SOV. PHYS. SOLID STATE 16 (9), 1827–8, 1975. (ENGLISH TRANSLATION OF FIZ. TVERD. TELA, 16 (9), 2808–10, 1974; FOR ORIGINAL SEE E65419)
65427	**RECRYSTALLIZATION OF THERMALLY EVAPORATED CADMIUM SULFIDE FILMS VIA AN HYDROGEN SULFIDE HEAT TREATMENT PROCESS.** FRAAS, L. M. BLEHA, W. P. BRAATZ, P. J. APPL. PHYS. 46 (2), 491–5, 1975.
65428	**ELECTRICAL PROPERTIES OF SALINE ICE AT 1 KILOCYCLE HERTZ DOWN TO - 150 C.** ADDISON, J. R. J. APPL. PHYS. 46 (2), 513–22, 1975.
65429	**STRUCTURAL AND ELECTRICAL PROPERTIES OF FILMS SPUTTERED FROM A PLATINUM CATHODE IN ARGON - OXYGEN MIXTURES.** BENNEWITZ, C. D. WESTWOOD, W. D. BROWN, J. D. J. APPL. PHYS. 46 (2), 558–67, 1975.
65434	**GROWTH AND CHARACTERIZATION OF LIQUID–PHASE EPITAXIAL INDIUM GALLIUM ARSENIDE.** NAHORY, R. E. POLLACK, M. A. DE WINTER, J. J. APPL. PHYS. 46 (2), 775–82, 1975.
65438	**OPTICAL PROPERTIES OF SEMICONDUCTOR SUPERLATTICE.** TSU, R. KOMA, A. ESAKI, L. J. APPL. PHYS. 46 (2), 845–5, 1975.
65439	**SATURATION AND RECOVERY OF THE DIRECT INTERBAND ABSORPTION IN SEMICONDUCTORS.** REINTJES, J. F. MC GROODY, J. C. BLAKESLEE, A. E. J. APPL. PHYS. 46 (2), 879–82, 1975.
65440	**REFLECTANCE–CIRCULAR DICHROISM OF THE MAGNETIC INSULATOR COBALT CADMIUM CHROMIUM SULFIDE.** AHRENKIEL, R. K. LYU, S. L. COBURN, T. J. J. APPL. PHYS. 46 (2), 894–9, 1975.
65441	**MONOLITHIC MEASUREMENT OF OPTICAL GAIN AND ABSORPTION IN LEAD TELLURIDE.** CROSS, P. S. OLDHAM, W. G. J. APPL. PHYS. 46 (2), 952–4, 1975.
65442	**BURIED OPTICAL WAVEGUIDES IN FUSED SILICA BY HIGH–ENERGY OXYGEN ION IMPLANTATION.** RAO, E. V. K. MOUTONNET, D. J. APPL. PHYS. 46 (2), 955–7, 1975.
65446	**A STUDY OF MICROPOROUS SILICON DIOXIDE FILMS BY PERTURBED TOTAL INTERNAL REFLECTION.** ZOLOTAREV, V. M. PERVEEV, A. F. ARKATOVA, T. G. MURANOVA, G. A. ZH. PRIKL. SPEKTROSK. 16 (2), 331–8, 1972. (FOR ENGLISH TRANSLATION SEE E65447)
65447	**A STUDY OF MICROPOROUS SILICON DIOXIDE FILMS BY PERTURBED TOTAL INTERNAL REFLECTION.** ZOLOTAREV, V. M. PERVEEV, A. F. ARKATOVA, T. G. MURANOVA, G. A. J. APPL. SPECTROS., USSR 16 (2), 248–53, 1972. (ENGLISH TRANSLATION OF ZH. PRIKL. SPEKTROSK., 16 (2), 331–8, 1972; FOR ORIGINAL SEE E65446)
65448	**REFLECTION SPECTRA OF CRYSTALLINE AND VITREOUS MODIFICATIONS OF GERMANIUM DIOXIDE AND SILICON DIOXIDE IN THE 5–50 MU REGION.** VENEDIKTOV, A. A. MOROZOV, V. N. POLUKHIN, V. N. ZH. PRIKL. SPEKTROSK. 10 (6), 969–71, 1969. (FOR ENGLISH TRANSLATION SEE E65449)
65449	**REFLECTION SPECTRA OF CRYSTALLINE AND VITREOUS MODIFICATIONS OF GERMANIUM DIOXIDE AND SILICON DIOXIDE IN THE 5–50 MU REGION.** VENEDIKTOV, A. A. MOROZOV, V. N. POLUKHIN, V. N. J. APPL. SPECTROS., USSR 10 (6), 656–7, 1969. (ENGLISH TRANSLATION OF ZH. PRIKL. SPEKTROSK., 10 (6), 969–71, 1969; FOR ORIGINAL SEE E65448)
65450	**ELECTROPHYSICAL PROPERTIES OF TITANIUM DIBORIDE AND ALLOYS IN THE SYSTEM TITANIUM - BORON - NITROGEN.** AIVAZOV, M. I. DOMASHNEV, I. A. IZV. AKAD. NAUK SSSR, NEORG. MATER. 7 (10), 1735–8, 1971. (FOR ENGLISH TRANSLATION SEE E65451)
65451	**ELECTROPHYSICAL PROPERTIES OF TITANIUM DIBORIDE AND ALLOYS IN THE SYSTEM TITANIUM - BORON - NITROGEN.** AIVAZOV, M. I. DOMASHNEV, I. A. INORG. MAT., USSR 7 (10), 1551–3, 1971. (ENGLISH TRANSLATION OF IZV. AKAD. NAUK SSSR, NEORG. MATER., 7 (10), 1735–8, 1971; FOR ORIGINAL SEE E65450)
65456	**MIXED–FIELD MEASUREMENTS ON THE MAGNETIC SEMICONDUCTORS CADMIUM CHROMIUM SELENIDE AND MERCURY CHROMIUM SELENIDE.** MANASSE, F. K. KYLLONEN, E. W. J. APPL. PHYS. 46 (2), 977–9, 1975.
65457	**MECHANISM OF ELECTRICAL BREAKDOWN IN SILICON OXIDE FILMS.** RIDLEY, B. K. J. APPL. PHYS. 46 (3), 998–1007, 1975.
65459	**FUSION AND HEAT COMPRESSION OF NONOXIDE REFRACTORY COMPOUNDS, BORIDES, CARBIDES, NITRIDES AND SILICIDES.** PASTOR, H. IND. CERAM. (615), 89–104, 1969.
65462	**OHMIC CONTACT AND IMPURITY CONDUCTION IN P–DOPED CADMIUM TELLURIDE.** GU, J. KITAHARA, T. KAWAKAMI, K. SAKAGUCHI, T. J. APPL. PHYS. 46 (3), 1184–5, 1975.
65463	**EMISSION CROSS SECTION AND FLUORESCENCE QUENCHING OF NEODYMIUM LANTHANUM PENTAPHOSPHATE.** SINGH, S. MILLER, D. C. POTOPOWICZ, J. R. SHICK, L. K. J. APPL. PHYS. 46 (3), 1191–6, 1975.
65464	**ELECTRICAL PROPERTIES OF EPITAXIALLY GROWN INDIUM ARSENIDE PHOSPHIDE FILMS.** LI, S. S. ANDERSON, J. R. KENNEDY, J. K. J. APPL. PHYS. 46 (3), 1223–8, 1975.
65468	**LIFETIME SPECTRA (77 K) OF NITROGEN–DOPED GALLIUM ARSENIDE PHOSPHIDE.** LEE, M. H. HOLONYAK, N., JR. NELSON, R. J. KEUNE, D. L. GROVES, W. O. J. APPL. PHYS. 46 (3), 1290–8, 1975.
65471	**MAGNETIC PROPERTIES OF SOME LIGHT RARE–EARTH COMPOUNDS WITH CESIUM CHLORIDE STRUCTURE.** BUSCHOW, K. H. J. DE JONG, J. P. ZANDBERGEN, H. W. VAN LAAR, B. J. APPL. PHYS. 46 (3), 1352–4, 1975.
65472	**MAGNETIC PROPERTIES AND PRESSURE DEPENDENCE OF THE CURIE TEMPERATURE OF LANTHANUM COBALT COPPER.** BROUHA, M. BUSCHOW, K. H. J. J. APPL. PHYS. 46 (3), 1355–8, 1975.
65473	**MODEL FOR NONCOHERENT MAGNETIZATION REVERSAL.** BRADY, L. J. J. APPL. PHYS. 46 (3), 1365–71, 1975.
65475	**PHOTOVOLTAIC EFFECTS IN SEMI–INSULATING GALLIUM ARSENIDE.** ZUCCA, R. WOOD, E. J. J. APPL. PHYS. 46 (3), 1396–8, 1975.
65476	**POOLE–FRENKEL CONDUCTION AND THE NEUTRAL TRAP.** ARNETT, P. C. KLEIN, N. J. APPL. PHYS. 46 (3), 1399–1400, 1975.
65477	**PHOTOEFFECTS IN CADMIUM TELLURIDE WITH ACID–GROWN TELLURIDE LAYERS.** ZITTER, R. N. CHAVDA, D. L. J. APPL. PHYS. 46 (3), 1405–6, 1975.

EPIC Number	Bibliographic Citation
65484	**ANGULAR-RESOLVED ULTRAVIOLET PHOTOEMISSION SPECTROSCOPY AND ITS APPLICATION TO THE LAYER COMPOUNDS TANTALUM SELENIDE AND TANTALUM SULFIDE.** SMITH, N. V. TRAUM, M. M. PHYS. REV. 11 B (6), 2087–2108, 1975.
65487	**X-RAY PHOTOELECTRON SPECTROSCOPIC STUDIES OF THE ELECTRONIC STRUCTURE OF COBALT OXIDE.** KIM, K. S. PHYS. REV. 11 B (6), 2177–85, 1975.
65490	**MANY BODY AND HOT PHONON EFFECTS IN THE RADIATIVE EMISSION SPECTRUM OF CADMIUM SULFIDE UNDER HIGH EXCITATION INTENSITIES.** MENESES, E. A. JANNUZZI, N. RAMOS, J. G. P. LUZZI, R. LEITE, R. C. C. PHYS. REV. 11 B (6), 2213–21, 1975.
65491	**NEW METHOD FOR THE CALCULATION OF THE BINDING ENERGY OF EXCITON COMPLEXES: THE EXCITON-IONIZED-DONOR COMPLEX.** ELKOMOSS, S. G. AMER. A. S. PHYS. REV. 11 B (6), 2222–8, 1975.
65492	**TEMPERATURE DEPENDENCE OF THE 2.2-ELECTRON VOLTS PAIR-RECOMBINATION BAND IN GALLIUM PHOSPHIDE (SULFUR, CALCIUM) CRYSTALS.** HALPERIN, A. ZACKS, E. PHYS. REV. 11 B (6), 2237–42, 1975.
65493	**EXCITON-EXCITON AND EXCITON-CARRIER SCATTERING IN GALLIUM SELENIDE.** MERCIER, A. VOITCHOVSKY, J. P. PHYS. REV. 11 B (6), 2243–50, 1975.
65494	**BAND-GAP SHRINKAGE OF SEMICONDUCTORS.** AUVERGNE, D. CAMASSEL, J. MATHIEU, H. PHYS. REV. 11 B (6), 2251–9, 1975.
65495	**CLUSTER CALCULATIONS OF THE EFFECTS OF SINGLE VACANCIES OF THE ELECTRONIC PROPERTIES OF LEAD SULFIDE.** HEMSTREET, L. A., JR. PHYS. REV. 11 B (6), 2260–70, 1975.
65496	**OSCILLATORY COMPONENT OF THE MAGNETOCONDUCTIVITY TENSOR FOR NONDEGENERATE SEMICONDUCTOR THIN FILMS.** MACKEY, H. J. DERRING, W. D. RATER, L. M. PHYS. REV. 11 B (6), 2297–8, 1975.
65497	**OPTICAL ABSORPTION AND TRANSPORT IN SEMICONDUCTING STRONTIUM TITANIUM OXIDE.** LEE, C. DESTRY, J. BREBNER, J. L. PHYS. REV. 11 B (6), 2299–2310, 1975.
65498	**BRILLOUIN SCATTERING, PIEZOBIREFRINGENCE, AND DISPERSION OF PHOTOELASTIC COEFFICIENTS OF CADMIUM SULFIDE AND ZINC OXIDE.** BERKOWICZ, R. SKETTRUP, T. PHYS. REV. 11 B (6), 2316–26, 1975.
65499	**POINT DEFECTS IN HEXAGONAL BORON NITRIDE. I. ELECTRON-PARAMAGNETIC, THERMOLUMINESCENCE, AND THERMALLY-STIMULATED-CURRENT MEASUREMENTS.** KATZIR, A. SUSS, J. T. ZUNGER, A. HALPERIN, A. PHYS. REV. 1 B (6), 2370–7, 1975.
65500	**POINT DEFECTS IN HEXAGONAL BORON NITRIDE. II. THEORETICAL STUDIES.** ZUNGER, A. KATZIR, A. PHYS. REV. 11 B (6), 2378–90, 1975.
65501	**ELECTRONIC EXCITATION ENERGIES AND THE SOFT-X-RAY ABSORPTION SPECTRA OF ALKALI HALIDES.** PANTELIDES, S. T. PHYS. REV. 11 B (6), 2391–2411, 1975.
65504	**INTEGRATED OPTICS: A REPORT ON THE 2ND OSA TOPICAL MEETING.** POLE, R. V. CONWELL, E. M. KOGELNIK, H. TIEN, P. K. WHINNERY, J. R. YARIV, A. DE MARIA, A. J. APPL. OPT. 14 (3), 569–79, 1975.
65506	**EFFECT OF DISPERSION ON THE REFLECTION AND TRANSMISSION EXTREMA FROM A MONOLAYER.** SEESER, J. W. APPL. OPT. 14 (3), 640–2, 1975.
65507	**PRECISION BEAM SPLITTERS FOR CARBON DIOXIDE LASERS.** FRANZEN, D. L. APPL. OPT. 14 (3), 647–52, 1975.
65508	**LASER INDUCED DAMAGE IN OPTICAL MATERIALS: 6TH AMER. SOC. FOR TEST. AND MATER. SYMPOSIUM.** GLASS, A. J. GUENTHER, A. H. APPL. OPT. 14 (3), 698–715, 1975.
65511	**HIGH FREQUENCY POLARIZATION MODULATION METHOD FOR MEASURING BIREFRINGENCE.** MODINE, F. A. MAJOR, R. W. SONDER, E. APPL. OPT. 14 (3), 757–60, 1975.
65518	**ELECTRICAL CONDUCTIVITY OF PURE, NONSTOICHIOMETRIC MANGANESE OXIDE.** ALBELLA, J. M. PAJARES, J. A. SORIA, J. A. AN. QUIM. 69 (2), 189–97, 1973.
65519	**NICLE-ZINC FERRITES WITH CURIE TEMPERATURE IN THE DOMAIN OF 0 C.** LUCA, E. PASNICU, C. REZLESCU, AN. STIINT. 'AL. I. CUZA' IASI (SER. NOWA) I 19 (1), 53–9, 1973.
65522	**EFFECT OF THE RATE OF COOLING ON THE MAGNETIC THERMOREMANENCE COERCIVITY.** PAPUSOI, C. AN. STIINT. UNIV. AL. I. CUZA IASI 19 (SECT. 1B) (2), 143–54, 1973.
65524	**INFLUENCE OF SINTERING TEMPERATURE ON ELECTRICAL AND MAGNETIC PROPERTIES OF NICKEL - ZINC FERRITES WITH CURIE POINT.** PASNICU, C. AN. STIINT. UNIV. AL. I. CUZA IASI 19 (SECT. 1B), (2), 161–7, 1973.
65532	**REACTIVELY EVAPORATED FILMS OF SCANDIA AND YTTRIA.** HEITMANN, W. APPL. OPT. 12 (2), 394–7, 1973.
65533	**REFRACTIVE INDEX MEASUREMENTS OF SILVER BROMIDE IN THE INFRARED.** MCCARTHY, D. E. APPL. OPT. 12 (2), 409, 1973.
65537	**MEASUREMENT OF OPTICAL ABSORPTION IN DIELECTRIC REFLECTORS.** AHRENS, H. WELLING, H. SCHEEL, H. E. APPL. PHYS. 1 (1), 69–71, 1973.
65539	**DETERMINATION OF THE INTRINSIC CARRIER CONCENTRATION IN INDIUM ANTIMONIDE BY HELICON WAVES.** BERNOT, H. HINSCH, H. APPL. PHYS. 1 (3), 147–51, 1973.
65543	**PHOTOLUMINESCENCE OF N-GALLIUM ARSENIDE AT TRANSPARENT SCHOTTKY CONTACTS.** LANGMANN, U. APPL. PHYS. 1 (4), 219–21, 1973.
65547	**FIELD ELECTRON EMISSION FROM AN ALUMINUM OXIDE COVERED TUNGSTEN PLANE AT TEMPERATURES UP TO 1700 K.** VANSELOW, R. APPL. PHYS. 2 (5), 229–35, 1973.
65549	**A CAVITY RESONATOR METHOD FOR MEASURING THE COMPLEX PERMITTIVITY ON SMALL AMOUNTS OF LIQUIDS IN THE FREQUENCY RANGE 0.7–25 GHZ.** KAATZE, U. APPL. PHYS. 2 (5), 241–6, 1973.
65550	**IONIZED IMPURITY SCATTERING IN DEGENERATE INDIUM OXIDE.** CLANGET, R. APPL. PHYS. 2 (5), 247–56, 1973.
65571	**ELECTRICAL PROPERTIES AND PHOTOCONDUCTIVITY OF THIN CADMIUM SULFIDE LAYERS PRODUCED IN A HYDROGEN ATMOSPHERE.** AKRAMOV, KH. T. YULDASHEV, B. D. SAIDKHANOV, A. GELIOTEKHNIKA (USSR) 9 (2), 3–5, 1973. (FOR ENGLISH TRANSLATION SEE E65572)

EPIC Number	Bibliographic Citation
65572	ELECTRICAL PROPERTIES AND PHOTOCONDUCTIVITY OF THIN CADMIUM SULFIDE LAYERS PRODUCED IN A HYDROGEN ATMOSPHERE. AKRAMOV, KH. T. YULDASHEV, B. D. SAIDKHANOV, A. APPL. SOL. ENERGY 9 (1-2), 47-9, 1973. (ENGLISH TRANSLATION OF GELIOTEKHNIKA, 9 (2), 3-5, 1973; FOR ORIGINAL SEE E65571)
65583	THE ORIGIN OF THE LOW-ENERGY OPTICAL ABSORPTION TAIL IN CHALCOGENIDE GLASSES. VANCU, A. SLADARU, ST. GRIGOROVICI, R. 5TH INTERNATIONAL CONFERENCE ON AMORPHOUS AND LIQUID SEMICONDUCTORS, VOL. I, GARMISCH-PARTENKIRCHEN, GERMANY 631-7PP., 1974.
65584	OPTICAL PROCESSES AND ELECTRON STATES IN AMORPHOUS CHALCOGENIDES. DAVIS, E. A. 5TH INTERNATIONAL CONFERENCE ON AMORPHOUS AND LIQUID SEMICONDUCTORS, VOL. I, GARMISCH-PARTENKIRCHEN, GERMANY 519-32PP., 1974.
65585	OPTICAL ABSORPTION, PHOTOCONDUCTIVITY AND THE MOBILITY EDGE OF AMORPHOUS GALLIUM PHOSPHIDE. YATES, D. A. PENCHINA, C. M. DAVEY, J. E. 5TH INTERNATIONAL CONFERENCE ON AMORPHOUS AND LIQUID SEMICONDUCTORS, VOL. I, GARMISCH-PARTENK2RCHEN, 617-20, 1974.
65596	TRANSPORT PROPERTIES OF VITREOUS CHALCOGENIDES. MARSHALL, J. M. FISHER, F. D. OWEN, A. E. INTERN. CONF. AMORPHOUS AND LIQUID SEMICONDUCTORS. 1305-10, 1973.
65598	THE COMPOSITION AND TEMPERATURE DEPENDENCES OF THE BREAKDOWN VOLTAGE IN AMORPHOUS ARSENIC SELENIDE - ARSENIC TELLURIDE. KOLOMIETS, B. T. LEBEDEV, E. A. TSENDIN, K. D. INTERN. CONF. AMORPHOUS LIQUID SEMICONDUCTORS 1317-20PP., 1973.
65606	ELECTRICAL RESISTIVITY MINIMUM IN AMORPHOUS IRON FILMS. YOSHIE, T. YAMAKAWA, K. FUJITA, F. E. J. PHYS. SOC. JAP. (JAPAN) 37 (2), 572, 1974.
65612	DEPENDENCE OF IMPURITY ABSORPTION BANDS ON LATTICE PARAMETERS IN ALKALI HALIDE CRYSTALS. TYAGI, R. C. SETHI, V. C. PHYS. STATUS SOLIDI (GERMANY) 65 B (2), K123-7, 1974.
65614	AMORPHOUS SEMICONDUCTORS. LASOCKA, M. MATYJA, H. POSTEPY FIZ. 25 (4), 373-404, 1974.
65616	FAR ULTRAVIOLET ABSORPTION SPECTRUM OF THE K(+) ION IN KCL. BALZAROTTI, A. BIANCONI, A. BURATTINI, E. STRINATI, G. SOLID STATE COMMUN. (USA) 15 (8), 1431-4, 1974.
65617	OPTICAL AND PARAMAGNETIC PROPERTIES OF ZINC OXIDE-CRYSTALS SIMULTANEOUSLY DOPED WITH COPPER AND HYDROGEN. MOLLWO, E. MULLER, G. ZWINGEL, D. SOLID STATE COMMUN. (USA) 15 (8), 1475-9, 1974.
65619	RADIATIVE RECOMBINATION WITH COULOMB INTERACTION SHIELDING IN CADMIUM SULFIDE CRYSTALS. TIMOFEEV, V. B. LYSENKO, V. G. REVENKO, V. I. TRAMAS, T. G. ZH. ESKP. TEOR. FIZ. PIS'MA 20 (3), 180-5, 1974. (FOR ENGLISH TRANSLATION SEE E68418)
65623	PHOTOCONDUCTIVITY ANOMALIES NEAR THE CURIE POINT OF CADMIUM CHROMIUM SELENIDE LIGHTLY DOPED WITH GALLIUM. KALINNIKOV, V. T. AMINOV, T. G. SHABUNINA, G. G. SHAPSHEVA, N. R. BELOV, K. P. KOROLEVA, L. I. BATOROVA, S. D. SHALIMOVA, M. A. ZH. ESKP. TEOR. FIZ. PIS'MA 20 (3), 191-5, 1974. (FOR ENGLISH TRANSLATION SEE E68419)
65625	DETERMINATION OF THE OPTICAL CONSTANTS OF THE SILICON-SILICA SYSTEM BY THE METHOD OF THE ANGULAR MODULATION OF REFLECTANCE. PICOZZI, P. SANTUCCI, S. BALZAROTTI, A. SURF. SCI. 45 (1), 227-37, 1974.
65637	IONIC CONDUCTIVITY OF LIQUID AMMONIUM CHLORIDE FROM TRIPLE POINT TO CRITICAL POINT. BUBACK, M. FRANCK, E. U. BER. BUNSENGES. PHYS. CHEM. 77 (12), 1074-9, 1973.
65641	CHANGES OF THE WORK FUNCTION OF BISMUTH MOLYBDATE CATALYSTS ON ADSORPTION OF OXYGEN. GRZYBOWSKA, B. HABER, J. NOWOTNY, J. NOWOTNY, J. T. BULL. ACAD. POL. SCI., SER. SCI. CHIM. 21 (1), 51-6, 1973.
65651	SEMICONDUCTING PROPERTIES OF RARE EARTH CUPRIC KENJO, T. YAJIMA, S. BULL. CHEM. SOC. JAP. 46 (5), 1329-33, 1973.
65652	DIELECTRIC RELAXATION OF GAMMA-ALUMINA. KONDO, S. MUROYA, M. FUJIWARA, H. YAMAGUCHI, N. BULL. CHEM. SOC. JAP. 46 (5), 1362-5, 1973.
65654	CRYSTAL GROWTH AND DIELECTRIC PROPERTIES OF FERROELECTRIC SBN. SAKAMOTO, K. UNOKI, H. SAKUDO, T. BULL. ELECTROTECH. LAB. 37 (4), 429-36, 1973.
65656	MAGNETIC PROPERTIES OF YTTRIUM - COBALT POWDER MAGNETS AND HEAT TREATMENT EFFECT. SHIBATA, T. KATAYAMA, T. MIZOE, M. TSUCHIYA, S. BULL. ELECTROTECH. LAB. 37 (11), 1013-23, 1973.
65663	PREPARATION OF BARIUM-FERRITES BY WET METHOD (MAGNETIC CHARACTERISATION). HANEDA, K. MIYAKAWA, C. KOJIMA, H. BULL. RES. INST. SCI. MEAS. TOHOKU UNIV. 22 (1), 67-78, 1973.
65676	HOW TO DETERMINE NEEL'S TEMPERATURE OF ALPHA-CHROMIUM OXIDE FROM THE TEMPERATURE RELATIONSHIP OF THE EPR-SPECTRA. ANGELOV, S. A. MEHANDJIEV, D. R. C. R. ACAD. BULG. SCI. 26 (9) 1213-6, 1973.
65678	MAGNETIC SUSCEPTIBILITIES OF SOME COMPOUNDS OF SULFUR. KENNEDY, M. B. LISTER, M. W. MARSON, R. POYNTZ, R. B. CAN. J. CHEM. 51 (5), 674-9, 1973.
65685	EFFECT OF THE EXCITATION PROCESS ON THE THERMOLUMINESCENCE OF TRICALCIUM SILICATE. FIERENS, P. TIRLOCQ, J. VERHAEGEN, J. P. CEM. CONCR. RES. 3 (3), 227-32, 1973.
65693	SURFACE PROPERTIES OF VACUUM EVAPORATED CADMIUM SULFIDE FILMS. TANAKA, K. CHIBA DAIGAKU KOGAKUBU KENKYU HOKOKU 25 (47), 53-9, 1973.
65696	FIELD EMISSION OF ELECTRONS FROM SEMICONDUCTOR CRYSTALS. MITSKIS, A. YU. YU. RADIOTEKHNIKA (USSR) 27 (12), 83PP., 1973. (FOR ENGLISH TRANSLATION SEE E65697)
65697	FIELD EMISSION OF ELECTRONS FROM SEMICONDUCTOR CRYSTALS. MITSKIS, A. YU. YU. TELECOMMUN. RADIO ENG. 27 (12), (PT. 2), 102, 1972. (ENGLISH TRANSLATION OF RADIOTEKHNIKA, 27 (12), 83, 1972; FOR ORIGINAL SEE E65696)
65723	SPONTANEOUS AND STIMULATED EMISSION FROM ELECTRON-BEAM-EXCITED GALLIUM SELENIDE. ABDULLAEV, G. B. ANTONOV, V. B. MEKHTIEV, T. E. SALEEV, E. YU. KVANTOVAYA ELEKTRON., MOSKVA (USSR) 1 (1), 143-6, 1974. (FOR ENGLISH TRANSLATION SEE E65724)
65724	SPONTANEOUS AND STIMULATED EMISSION FROM ELECTRON-BEAM-EXCITED GALLIUM SELENIDE. ABDULLAEV, G. B. ANTONOV, V. B. MEKHTIEV, T. E. SALEEV, E. YU. SOV. J. QUANTUM ELECTRON. 4 (1), 80-1, 1974. (ENGLISH TRANSLATION OF KVANTOVAYA ELEKTRON., 1 (1), 143-6, 1974; FOR ORIGINAL SEE E65723)

EPIC Number	Bibliographic Citation

65725 **ABSORPTION OF CARBON DIOXIDE LASER LINES IN OSMIUM OXIDE VAPOUR.**
BAZAROV, E. N. GERASIMOV, G. A.
POSUDIN, YU. I.
KVANTOVAYA ELEKTRON., MOSKVA (USSR)
1 (1), 180–3, 1974.
(FOR ENGLISH TRANSLATION SEE E65726)

65726 **ABSORPTION OF CARBON DIOXIDE LASER LINES IN OSMIUM OXIDE VAPOUR.**
BAZAROV, E. N. GERASIMOV, G. A.
POSUDIN, YU. I.
SOV. J. QUANTUM ELECTRON.
4 (1), 106–7, 1974.
(ENGLISH TRANSLATION OF KVANTOVAYA ELEKTRON., 1 (1), 180–3, 1974; FOR ORIGINAL SEE E65725)

65732 **LUMINESCENT PROPERTIES OF MANGANESE ACTIVATED BARIUM ZINC SULFIDE.**
VECHT, A. HIGTON, M. WILLIAMSON, J. H.
MEGSON, B. NICHOLAS, D.
J. ELECTROCHEM. SOC.
121 C (3), 94, 1974.

65737 **CONDUCTIVITY OF SINGLE CRYSTAL SODIUM BETA-ALUMINA.**
FIELDER, W. L. KAUTZ, H. E. FORDYCE, J. S.
SINGER, J.
J. ELECTROCHEM. SOC.
121 C (3), 101, 1974.

65738 **HIGH TEMPERATURE ELECTRICAL CONDUCTIVITY OF ALUMINUM NITRIDE.**
FRANCIS, R. W. WORRELL, W. L.
J. ELECTROCHEM. SOC.
121 C (3), 103, 1974.

65747 **MOESSBAUER EFFECT AND RESISTIVITY IN STUDIES IN NONSTOICHIOMETRIC IRON TELLURIDE.**
HERMON, E. NOLAN, R. D. SHTRIKMAN, S.
ISR. J. CHEM.
9 (1), 1–5, 1971.

65758 **INFRARED AND VISIBLE PHOTON UPCONVERSION IN LANTHANUM CHLORIDE : PRASEODYMIUM TRIPOSITIVE (NEODYMIUM TRIPOSITIVE).**
ZALUCHA, D. J. SELL, J. A. FONG, F. K.
J. CHEM. PHYS.
60 (4), 1660–7, 1974.

65759 **STANDARD MATERIALS FOR MEASUREMENTS ON CERAMICS.**
WACHTMAN, J. B., JR.
BULL. AMER. CERAM. SOC.
50 (3), 242–7, 1971.

65760 **CALCIUM OXIDE – ALUMINUM OXIDE – SILICON OXIDE COMPOSITION FOR USE AS A SUBSTRATE FOR THIN FILMS.**
WILLIAMS, J. C.
BULL. AMER. CERAM. SOC.
50 (9), 726–9, 1971.

65761 **PREPARATION OF HIGH DENSITY CERAMIC TITANIUM OXIDE HAVING LOW DIELECTRIC LOSS AT MICROWAVE FREQUENCIES.**
EGERTON, L. THOMSON, J., JR.
BULL AMER. CERAM. SOC.
50 (11), 924–8, 1971.

65762 **DETERMINATION OF THE DIELECTRIC CONSTANTS OF ORGANIC AND INORGANIC MIXTURES.**
DIXON, G. D. WESTERVELT, D. C.
BULL. AMER. CERAM. SOC.
52 (6), 501–4, 1973.

65763 **LASERS AND GLASS TECHNOLOGY.**
SNITZER, E.
BULL. AMER. CERAM. SOC.
52 (6), 516–25, 1973.

65771 **MACROSCOPIC INHOMOGENEITIES IN AMORPHOUS SEMICONDUCTORS; CONTACTLESS CONDUCTIVITY.**
STROM, U. TAYLOR, P. C.
PHYS. REV. LETT.
30 (1), 13–6, 1973.

65772 **OPTICAL PROPERTIES OF FERROMAGNETIC POTASSIUM CHROMIUM CHLORIDE.**
DAY, P. GREGSON, A. K. LEECH, D. H.
PHYS. REV. LETT.
30 (1), 19–22, 1973.

65773 **THERMOPOWER ANOMALY IN GADOLINUM NICKEL: SPIN SCATTERING MODEL VERSUS STATIC ENTROPY MODEL.**
ZORIC, I. THOMAS, G. A. PARKS, R. D.
PHYS. REV. LETT.
30 (1), 22–5, 1973.

65810 **CHEMICALLY, THERMALLY, AND RADIATION-INDUCED CHANGES IN THE THERMALLY STIMULATED EXOELECTRON EMISSION CHARACTERISTICS OF CERAMIC BERYLLIUM OXIDE.**
GAMMAGE, R. B. BECKER, K. CRASE, K. W.
DAN. A. E. C., RISOE REP.
249 (PT. 2), 573–88, 1971.

65811 **CHARACTERISTICS OF SELECTED PHOSPHORS FOR STIMULATED EXOELECTRON EMISSION DOSIMETRY.**
ZIEMER, P. L. MACARTHUR, W. C.
MCMANAMAN, V. L. SMITH, G. D.
DAN. A. E. C., RISOE REP.
249 (PT. 2), 632–53, 1971.

65812 **THERMALLY STIMULATED EXOELECTRON EMISSION RESPONSE OF CERAMIC BERYLLIUM OXIDE COVERED WITH DIFFERENT ABSORBERS DURING GAMMA- AND X-RAY IRRADIATION.**
ROTONDI, E. SUPPA, T.
DAN. A. E. C., RISOE REP.
249 (PT. 2), 480–9, 1971.

65825 **LATTICE THERMAL CONDUCTIVITY OF COPPER GERMANIUM CHALCOGENIDES.**
IRIE, T. ENDO, S. SUDO, I.
CONF. THERM. CONDUCTIVITY, PAP., 9TH
34–42, 1970.

65841 **PREPARATION OF THIN ZINC ARSENIDE FILMS DEPOSITED BY THERMAL EVAPORATION IN VACUUM.**
PAWLIKOWSKI, J. M.
ANAL. INSTRUM.
(1), 33–46, 1969.

65845 **THEORY OF DIELECTRIC BREAKDOWN IN CRYSTALS.**
KIM, Y. I.
CHOSON MINJUJUUI INMIN KONGHWAGUK KWAHAGWON TONGBO
(1), 15–19, 1971.

65858 **ELECTRICAL CONDUCTIVITY AND THERMOELECTRIC POWER OF ALLOYS IN THE ARSENIDE – TELLURIDE AND ARSENIDE TELLURIDE INDIUM MOLTEN SYSTEMS.**
OBERAFO, A. A.
J. PHYS.
8 C (4), 469–78, 1975.

65859 **RELAXED EXCITON FORMATION THROUGH THE H CENTER RECOMBINATION WITH THE F CENTER IN KILOBAR.**
TANIMURA, K. FUJIWARA, M. OKADA, T.
SUITA, T.
PHYS. LETT.
50 A (4), 301–2, 1974.

65864 **IMPURITY ABSORPTION OF INFRARED RADIATION IN N-TYPE SILICON CARBIDE (6 H).**
VAKULENKO, O. V. GOVOROVA, O. A.
SHUTOV, B. M.
FIZ. TVERD. TELA
14 (1), 291–2, 1972.
(FOR ENGLISH TRANSLATION SEE E65865)

65865 **IMPURITY ABSORPTION OF INFRARED RADIATION IN N-TYPE SILICON CARBIDE (6 H).**
VAKULENKO, O. V. GOVOROVA, O. A.
SHUTOV, B. M.
SOV. PHYS. SOLID STATE
14 (1), 242, 1972.
(ENGLISH TRANSLATION OF FIZ. TVERD. TELA, 14 (1), 291–2, 1972; FOR ORIGINAL SEE E65864)

65866 **IMPURITY ABSORPTION SPECTRA OF SILICON CARBIDE IN THE NEAR INFRARED REGION.**
GORBAN', I. S. MARAZUEV, YU. A.
SKIRDA, A. S.
FIZ. TVERD. TELA
14 (3), 780–3, 1972.
(FOR ENGLISH TRANSLATION SEE E65867)

65867 **IMPURITY ABSORPTION SPECTRA OF SILICON CARBIDE IN THE NEAR INFRARED REGION.**
GORBAN', I. S. MARAZUEV, YU. A.
SKIRDA, A. S.
SOV. PHYS. SOLID STATE
14 (3), 664–7, 1972.
(ENGLISH TRANSLATION OF FIZ. TVERD. TELA, 14 (3), 780–3, 1972; FOR ORIGINAL SEE E65866)

65869 **REFRACTIVE INDEX, DISPERSION, AND BIREFRINGENCE OF SILICON CARBIDE POLYTYPES.**
SHAFFER, P. T.
APPL. OPT.
10 (5), 1034–6, 1971.

65877 **REFRACTIVE INDEX OF OPTICAL MATERIALS IN THE INFRARED REGION. DATA SHEETS.**
MOSES, A. J.
HUGHES AIRCRAFT CO., CULVER CITY, CALIFORNIA
255PP., 1970.
(AD-704 555, EPIC-DS-166, N70-36221)

65878 **OPTICAL PROPERTIES OF II-IV-V2 AND I-III-V12 CRYSTALS WITH PARTICULAR REFERENCE TO TRANSMISSION LIMITS.**
BHAR, G. C. SMITH, R. C.
PHYS. STATUS SOLIDI
13 A (1), 157–68, 1972.

65879 **REFLECTIVITY SPECTRA AND ENERGY BAND STRUCTURE OF MAGNESIUM X CRYSTALS.**
SOBOLEV, V. V.
PHYS. STATUS SOLIDI
49 B (2), K209–K214, 1972.

EPIC Number	Bibliographic Citation

65883 **PHOTOIONIZATION ABSORPTION OF ATOMS IN POLYATOMIC MOLECULES IN THE ULTRASOFT X-RAY RADIATION REGION.**
ZIMKINA, T. M. VINOGRADOV, A. S.
IZV. AKAD. NAUK SSSR, SER. FIZ.
36 (2), 248–54, 1972.
(FOR ENGLISH TRANSLATION SEE E65884)

65884 **PHOTOIONIZATION ABSORPTION OF ATOMS IN POLYATOMIC MOLECULES IN THE ULTRASOFT X-RAY RADIATION REGION.**
ZIMKINA, T. M. VINOGRADOV, A. S.
BULL. ACAD. SCI., USSR, PHYS. SER.
36 (2), 229–35, 1972.
(ENGLISH TRANSLATION OF IZV. AKAD. NAUK SSSR, SER. FIZ., 36 (2), 248–54, 1972; FOR ORIGINAL SEE E65883)

65887 **ABSORPTION SPECTRUM OF THE SILICON CARBIDE RADICAL IN THE GASEOUS PHASE.**
VERMA, R. D. NAGARAJ, S.
CAN. J. PHYS.
52 (19), 1938–48, 1974.

65891 **RARE EARTH METALS ALREADY LESS RARE.**
GUNTHER, G.
TEK. TIDSKR.
104 (13), 21–3, 1974.

65897 **SPECTRAL LOSSES OF UNCLAD FIBERS MADE FROM HIGH-GRADE VITREOUS SILICA.**
KAISER, P.
APPL. PHYS. LETT.
23 (1), 45–6, 1973.

65901 **INVESTIGATION OF SOLID MATERIALS AT SUBMILLIMETER WAVELENGTHS.**
ALESHECHKIN, V. N. KRAFTMAKHER, G. A.
MERIAKRI, V. V. USHATKIN, E. F.
INSTRUM. EXP. TECH., USSR
(4), 1123–5, 1971.
(ENGLISH TRANSLATION OF PRIB. TEKH. EKSP., (4), 150–1, 1971; FOR ORIGINAL SEE E61548)

65902 **MEASUREMENT OF THE REFRACTIVE INDICES OF DIELECTRICS AT MILLIMETER WAVELENGTHS.**
KOZLOV, G. V.
INSTRUM. EXP. TECH., USSR
(4), 1126–8, 1971.
(ENGLISH TRANSLATION OF PRIB. TEKH. EKSP., (4), 152–4, 1971; FOR ORIGINAL SEE E61549)

65904 **METHOD OF DETERMINING THE ELECTRICAL RESISTIVITY AT PRESSURES AND TEMPERATURES.**
CHERNOV, D. B. SHINYAEV, I. YA.
INSTRUM. EXP. TECH., USSR
(4), 1216–8, 1971.
(ENGLISH TRANSLATION OF PRIB. TEKH. EKSP., (4), 223–4, 1971; FOR ORIGINAL SEE E61554)

65905 **MEASUREMENT OF THE PHOTOLUMINESCENCE, PHOTO-EMF, AND ELECTROLUMINESCENCE OF SEMICONDUCTOR MATERIALS AND STRUCTURES.**
KNAB, O. D. MAGALYAS, V. I. FROLOV, V. D.
SHVEIKIN, V. I. SHMERKIN, I. A.
INSTRUM. EXP. TECH., USSR
(4), 1219–21, 1971.
(ENGLISH TRANSLATION OF PRIB. TEKH. EKSP., (4), 225–6, 1971; FOR ORIGINAL SEE E61550)

65906 **INVESTIGATION OF LIQUID DIELECTRICS AT SUB-MILLIMETER WAVELENGTHS.**
APLETALIN, V. N. MERIAKRI, V. V.
CHIGRYAI, E. E.
INSTRUM. EXP. TECH., USSR
(5), 1437–9, 1971.
(ENGLISH TRANSLATION OF PRIB. TEKH. EKSP., (5), 149–50, 1971; FOR ORIGINAL SEE E61555)

65909 **CRYOSTAT WITH A PNEUMATIC DEVICE FOR OPTICAL MEASUREMENTS IN THE FAR INFRARED REGION.**
VODOP'YANOV, L. K. KOPANEV, V. D.
INSTRUM. EXP. TECH., USSR
(6), 1798–9, 1971.
(ENGLISH TRANSLATION OF PRIB. TEKH. EKSP., (6), 182–4, 1971; FOR ORIGINAL SEE E61558)

65910 **REFLECTING ATTACHMENT FOR AN INFRARED SPECTROMETER.**
KARPINOS, D. M. LISTOVNICHAYA, S. P.
AIVAZOV, V. YA.
INSTRUM. EXP. TECH., USSR
(6), 1809–10, 1971.
(ENGLISH TRANSLATION OF PRIB. TEKH. EKSP., (6), 190–1, 1971; FOR ORIGINAL SEE E61559)

65913 **AUTOMATIC MEASUREMENT OF THE HALL EFFECT AND THE ELECTRICAL CONDUCTIVITY IN HEAVILY DOPED SEMICONDUCTORS.**
GRUZINOV, B. F. KONSTANTINOV, P. P.
INSTRUM. EXP. TECH., USSR
(5), 1557–8, 1972.
(ENGLISH TRANSLATION OF PRIB. TEKH. EKSP., (5), 225–7, 1972; FOR ORIGINAL SEE E61562)

65914 **PREPARATION OF SAMPLES OF EPITAXIAL SILICON FILMS FOR MEASUREMENTS BY THE VAN DER PAUW METHOD.**
SZOMODY, K.
INSTRUM. EXP. TECH., USSR
(6), 1859–60, 1972.
(ENGLISH TRANSLATION OF PRIB. TEKH. EKSP., (6), 206–8, 1972; FOR ORIGINAL SEE E61563)

65915 **MEASUREMENT OF THE OPTICAL DENSITY OF LIQUIDS BY MEANS OF SCANISTORS.**
GOS'KOV, P. I. ZHELTOVSKII, G. A.
INSTRUM. EXP. TECH., USSR
(1), 246–8, 1973.
(ENGLISH TRANSLATION OF PRIB. TEKH. EKSP., (1), 201–3, 1973; FOR ORIGINAL SEE E61564)

65916 **USE OF A PHOTOELECTRON MULTIPLIER OPERATING IN THE LOGARITHMIC MODE FOR THE INVESTIGATION OF THE DECAY KINETICS OF LUMINESCENCE.**
BACHERIKOV, V. V. KAGAIN, V. E.
MAKAROV, YU. A. NIKOLAEV, YU. N.
TARASOV, V. M.
INSTRUM. ECP. TECH., USSR
(3), 900–1, 1973.
(ENGLISH TRANSLATION OF PRIB. TEKH. EKSP., (3), 206–7, 1973; FOR ORIGINAL, SEE E 51084)

65917 **MEASUREMENT OF THE PERMITTIVITY OF LIQUIDS IN STRONG ELECTRIC FIELDS.**
GARBER, R. I. SLIPCHENKO, V. I.
INSTRUM. EXP. TECH., USSR
(3), 928–30, 1973.
(ENGLISH TRANSLATION OF PROB. TEKH, EKSP., (3), 227–9, 1973; FOR ORIGINAL, SEE E 51085)

65919 **THE USE OF HOLOGRAPHY FOR THE INVESTIGATION OF THE EXTERNAL AND INTERNAL MORPHOLOGY OF CRYSTALS.**
GUSEVA, I. N. GINZBURG, V. M.
LEKHTSIER, E. N. SEMENOV, E. G.
INSTRUM. EXP. TECH., USSR
(1), 206–8, 1974.
(ENGLISH TRANSLATION OF PRIB. TEKH. EKSP., (1), 180–2, 1974; FOR ORIGINAL SEE E58949)

65920 **INTERFERENCE INSTALLATION FOR INVESTIGATIONS OF THE THERM- AND ELECTRO-OPTICAL PROPERTIES OF CRYSTALS.**
KOPYLOV, YU. L.
INSTRUM. EXP. TECH., USSR
(1), 231–3, 1974.
(ENGLISH TRANSLATION OF PRIB. TEKH. EKSP., (1), 202–4, 1974; FOR ORIGINAL SEE E59397)

65921 **ANISOTROPIC RADIATION DETECTOR.**
ANATYCHUK, L. I. BOGOMOLOV, P. A.
KUPCHINSKII, O. I. LUSTE, O. YA.
YURTSENYUK, S. P.
SOV. J. OPT. TECHNOL.
3, (1), 22–3, 1971.
(ENGLISH TRANSLATION OF OPT. MEKH. PROM., 38 (1), 27–9, 1971; FOR ORIGINAL SEE E61477)

65922 **THERMAL CONDUCTIVITY AND NATURAL ABSORPTION COEFFICIENT OF POLYCRYSTALLINE MAGNESIUM FLUORIDE.**
MEN', A. A. CHECHEL'NITSKII, A. Z.
VOLYNETS, F. K. SMIRNAYA, E. P.
SOV. J. OPT. TECHNOL.
41 (1), 37–8, 1974.
(ENGLISH TRANSLATION OF OPT. MEKH. PROM., 41 (1), 41–3, 1974; FOR ORIGINAL SEE E61433)

65927 **THE BULK-GRADIENT PHOTO-EMF AND THE HOMOGENEITY OF BETA - SILICON CARBIDE SINGLE CRYSTALS.**
AIVAZOVA, L. S. ALTAISKII, YU. M.
SIDYAKIN, V. G.
SOV. PHYS. J.
15 (10), 1479–81, 1972.
(ENGLISH TRANSLATION OF IZV. VYSSH. UCHEB. ZAVED. FIZ., 15 (10), 113–4, 1972; FOR ORIGINAL SEE E63478)

65932 **PREPARATION AND CHARACTERIZATION OF A NEW HIGH-ENERGY OXIDIZER.**
SILVERMAN, J.
RESEARCH AND TECHNOLOGY DIVISION, AIR FORCE SYSTEMS COMMAND, EDWARDS, CALIFORNIA
29PP., 1964.
(AD-350 869)

65933 **DEVELOPMENT OF DIELECTRIC MATERIALS.**
PETZE, C. L., JR.
DELAWARE RESEARCH AND DEVELOPMENT CORP., WILMINGTON, DELAWARE
81PP., 1955.
(AD-82 684)

65935 **REDUCTION OF REFLECTIVITY FROM TRANSPARENT MATERIALS: A MEMORANDUM IN EVALUATION OF TECHNIQUES APPLICABLE TO PLASTIC HELICOPTER CANOPIES.**
BEACH, N. E.
PLASTICS TECHNICAL EVALUATION CENTER, PICATINNY ARSENAL, DOVER, NEW JERSEY
31 PP., 1962.
(AD-294 117, PLASTEC REPORT-9)

EPIC Number	Bibliographic Citation

65939 **ELECTRON–ELECTRON SCATTERING IN SEMICONDUCTORS, THEORY AND EXPERIMENT.**
APPEL, J. BRAY, R. WIKNER, E. G.
PROC. INT. CONF. PHYS. SEMICOND.
64–74, 1962.

65940 **DIPOLE SCATTERING IN SEMICONDUCTORS.**
STRATTON, R.
PROC. INT. CONF. PHYS. SEMICOND.
81–5, 108, 1962.

65942 **A THEORY OF THERMOELECTRIC AND THERMOMAGNETIC EFFECTS.**
KOLODZIEJCZAK, J. SOSNOWSKI, L.
ZAWADZKI, W.
PROC. INT. CONF. PHYS. SEMICOND.
94–8, 1962.

65944 **LOW MOBILITY TRANSPORT PHENOMENA IN SEMICONDUCTORS.**
KLINGER, M. J.
PROC. INT. CONF. PHYS. SEMICOND.
205–15, 1962.

65945 **ON THE THEORY OF DEGENERATE SEMICONDUCTORS.**
BONCH–BRUEVICH, V. L.
PROC. INT. CONF. PHYS. SEMICOND.
216–9, 1962.

65946 **THEORY OF THE BAND STRUCTURE OF VERY DEGENERATE SEMICONDUCTORS.**
WOLFF, P. A.
PROC. INT. CONF. PHYS. SEMICOND.
220–6, 1962.

65947 **BAND STRUCTURE OF HEAVILY DOPED SEMICONDUCTORS.**
CONWELL, E. M. LEVINGER, B. W.
PROC. INT. CONF. PHYS. SEMICOND.
227–33, 1962.

65948 **ENERGY BANDS IN IMPURE SEMICONDUCTORS.**
KANE, E. O.
PROC. INT. CONF. PHYS. SEMICOND.
252–8, 263, 1962.

65951 **ABSORPTION AND EMISSION OF EXCITONS AND IMPURITIES IN GALLIUM ANTIMONIDE.**
JOHNSON, E. J. FILINSKI, I. FAN, H. Y.
PROC. INT. CONF. PHYS. SEMICOND.
375–83, 1962.

65952 **ADDITIONAL LIGHT WAVES IN CRYSTALS IN THE REGION OF EXCITON ABSORPTION.**
PEKAR, S. I.
PROC. INT. CONF. PHYS. SEMICOND.
419–30, 1962.

65955 **RECENT PROGRESS IN BAND THEORY OF SEMICONDUCTORS.**
PINCHERLE, L.
PROC. INT. CONF. PHYS. SEMICOND.
541–51, 602, 1962.

65956 **GALVANO AND THERMOMAGNETIC EFFECTS IN SEMICONDUCTORS WITH DEGENERATE BANDS.**
BIR, G. L. NORMANTAS, E. PIKUS, G. E.
PROC. INT. CONF. PHYS. SEMICOND.
559–63, 1962.

65958 **CALCULATION OF THE BAND STRUCTURE OF CRYSTAL COMPLEXES BY THE FREE–ELECTRON NETWORK MODEL.**
DELLA RICCIA, G.
PROC. INT. CONF. PHYS. SEMICOND.
570–6, 1962.

65960 **LANDAU LEVELS IN THE VALENCE BANDS OF DIAMOND–TYPE SEMICONDUCTORS.**
EVTUHOV, V.
PROC. INT. CONF. PHYS. SEMICOND.
590–8, 1962.

65961 **ENERGY BANDS AND IMPURITY LEVELS IN AMORPHOUS SEMICONDUCTORS.**
GUBANOV, A. I.
PROC. INT. CONF. PHYS. SEMICOND.
599–601, 1962.

65962 **OPTICAL AND ELECTRICAL PROPERTIES OF CADMIUM MERCURY TELLURIDE ALLOYS.**
STRAUSS, A. J. HARMAN, T. C.
MAVROIDES, J. G. DICKEY, D. H.
DRESSELHAUS, M. S.
PROC. INT. CONF. PHYS. SEMICOND.
703–10, 792, 1962.

65963 **ELECTRICAL AND OPTICAL PROPERTIES OF HIGH–PURITY MERCURY TELLURIDE.**
QUILLIET, A. RODOT, H. RODOT, M.
PROC. INT. CONF. PHYS. SEMICOND.
711, 792, 1962.

65967 **REFRACTIVE INDEX MEASUREMENTS.**
MALITSON, I. H. DODGE, M. J.
NATIONAL BUREAU OF STANDARDS, WASHINGTON, D. C.
17–24, 1964.
(AD–457 871, NBS–REPT.–8626)

65968 **THERMOPHYSICAL PROPERTIES OF SOME CANDIDATE SUPERORBITAL HEAT SHIELD AND INSULATION MATERIALS.**
CHARLESWORTH, J. H.
AERONAUTICAL SYSTEMS DIVISION, AIR FORCE SYSTEMS COMMAND, U. S. AIR FORCE, WRIGHT PATTERSON, AFB, OHIO
4PP., 1963.
(AD–414 173, ASRC–TM–63–16)

65970 **STUDY OF NON–OXIDE MATERIALS WITH DEFECT STRUCTURES.**
BUCKNER, D. A. KREIDL, N. J.
BAUSCH AND LOMB, INC., ROCHESTER, N. Y.
22PP., 1961.
(AD–431 115)

65971 **THE EFFECT OF ARC PLASMA DEPOSITION ON THE STABILITY OF NON–METALLIC MATERIALS.**
KRAMER, B. E. LEVINSTEIN, M. A.
GRENIER, J. W.
FLIGHT PROPULSION LAB. DEPT., GENERAL ELECTRIC, CINCINNATI, OHIO
57PP., 1961.
(AD–264 602)

65974 **INVESTIGATION OF MAGNETHOHYDRODYNAMIC POWER GENERATION. VOLUME IV. MATERIALS.**
MARKOWSKI, S. J. SEAWARD, E. T.
EMANUELSON, R. C. HARRISON, W. J. BACON, J.
PRATT AND WHITNEY AIRCRAFT, DIV. OF UNITED AIRCRAFT CORP., EAST HARTFORD, CONNECTICUT
115 PP., 1962.
(AD–411 915, RADC–TR–62–464–VOL IV, PWA–2125)

65975 **PYROLYZED RAYON FIBER REINFORCED PLASTICS.**
SCHMIDT, D. L. HAWKINS, H. T.
AIR FORCE MATERIALS LAB., WRIGHT PATTERSON AIR FORCE BASE, OHIO
71PP., 1964.
(AD–438 892, ML–TDR–64–47)

65977 **OPTIMIZATION OF THERMOELECTRIC ENERGY CONVERTERS.**
KLEIN, P. H.
AIRCRAFT ACCESSORY TURBINE DEPT., GENERAL ELECTRIC
48PP., 1960.
(AD–265 461)

65978 **INFRARED COATING STUDIES.**
RESEARCH AND DEVELOPMENT, BAUSCH AND LOMB.
DEPT. OF THE ARMY ENGINEER RESEARCH AND DEVELOPMENT LAB., FORT BELVOIR, VIRGINIA
23PP., 1965.
(AD–460 357)

65981 **STUDY OF A THERMOPHOTOVOLTAIC CONVERTER.**
ENGINEERING PHYSICS LAB., GM DEFENSE RESEARCH LAB.
GENERAL MOTORS CORPORATION
36PP., 1963.
(AD–424 672)

65983 **LITHIUM–ALUMINUM SILICATES AS CERAMIC MATERIALS.**
MEHMEL, M.
GLASS–EMAIL–KERAMO–TECH.
10 (9), 337–40, 1959.
(FOR ENGLISH TRANSLATION SEE E65984)

65984 **LITHIUM–ALUMINUM SILICATES AS CERAMIC MATERIALS.**
MEHMEL, M.
DEPT. OF RESEARCH AND DEVELOPMENT SERVICES, ADMIRALTY
11PP., 1963.
(ENGLISH TRANSLATION OF GLASS–EMAIL–KERAMO–TECH., 10 (9), 337–40, 1959; FOR ORIGINAL SEE E65983)
(AD–406341, A.C.S.I.L.–TRANS.–1396)

65985 **OPTICAL AND ELECTRICAL PROPERTIES OF SOME LEAD TIN TELLURIDE ALLOYS.**
DIONNE, G. WOOLLEY, J. C.
J. NONMETALS
1 (3), 239–49, 1973.

66020 **OPTICAL STUDIES ON ANODIC OXIDE FILMS ON ALUMINIUM.**
SAKAE, T.
INSTITUTE OF MODERN LANGUAGES, INC., WASHINGTON, D.C.
31PP., 1966.
(AD–631 171, AERDL–T–1824–66)

66022 **A REVIEW OF THE PHYSICAL PROPERTIES OF SOME NEW SEMICONDUCTORS OF THE GROUPS III–V.**
SEROCZYNSKA–WOJAS, B.
POSTEPY FIZ.
17 (1), 29–41, 1966.
(FOR ENGLISH TRANSLATION SEE E66023)

66023 **A REVIEW OF THE PHYSICAL PROPERTIES OF SOME NEW SEMICONDUCTORS OF THE GROUPS III–V.**
SEROCZYNSKA–WOJAS, B.
FOREIGN TECHNOLOGY DIVISION, WRIGHT PATTERSON AIR FORCE BASE, OHIO
14PP., 1967.
(ENGLISH TRANSLATION OF POSTEPY FIZ., 17 (1), 1966; FOR ORIGINAL SEE E66022)
(AD 838 861)

EPIC Number	Bibliographic Citation
66024	**ULTRASONIC METHODS FOR THE INVESTIGATION OF SEMICONDUCTING PIEZOELECTRIC MATERIALS.** VASIL'EV, V. S. KANEVSKII, I. N. AKUST. ZH. 169-91PP., 1970. (FOR ENGLISH TRANSLATION SEE E66025)
66025	**ULTRASONIC METHODS FOR THE INVESTIGATION OF SEMICONDUCTING PIEZOELECTRIC MATERIALS.** VASIL'EV, V. S. KANEVSKII, I. N. SOV. PHYS. ACOUST. 16 (2), 145-62, 1970. (ENGLISH TRANSLATION OF AKUST. ZH., 16 (2), 169-91, 1970; FOR ORIGINAL SEE E66024)
66036	**A STUDY OF THE BREAKDOWN MECHANISM OF A SILICON MONOXIDE FILM.** BOROB'YEV, G. A. MUKHACHEV, V. A. RADIO ELECTRON. (USSR) 18 (4), 882-3, 1973. (FOR ENGLISH TRANSLATION SEE E66037)
66037	**A STUDY OF THE BREAKDOWN MECHANISM OF A SILICON MONOSIDE FILM.** VOROB'YEV, G. A. MUKHACHEV, V. A. RADIO ENG. ELECTRON. PHYS. 18 (4), 645-7, 1973. (ENGLISH TRANSLATION OF RADIOTEKH. ELEKTRON., 18 (4), 882-3, 1973; FOR ORIGINAL SEE E66036)
66038	**CALCULATION OF THE SECONDARY ELECTRON EMISSION OF SEMICONDUCTOR SYSTEMS WITH A NEGATIVE AFFINITY WITH CURRENT REMOVAL TAKEN INTO CONSIDERATION.** AUTHOR ANON. RADIO ENG. ELECTRON. PHYS. 18 (6), 904-9, 1973. (ENGLISH TRANSLATION OF RADIOTEKH. ELEKTRON., 18 (6), 1237-43, 1973; FOR ORIGINAL SEE E52160)
66053	**HIGH-TEMPERATURE MAGNETOSTRICTION OF MAGNETITE.** KLAPEL, G. D. SHIVE, P. N. J. GEOPHYS. RES. 79 (17), 2629-33, 1974.
66068	**THE BISMUTH TELLURIDE-BISMUTH SELENIDE SYSTEM.** NEUBERGER, M. ELECTRONIC PROPERTIES INFORMATION CENTER, CULVER CITY, CALIFORNIA 144PP., 1966. (AD 477 558, EPIC-DS-147)
66096	**LANTHANUM-MODIFIED BARIUM STRONTIUM NIOBATE FERROELECTRIC CRYSTALS AND THEIR APPLICATIONS AS INFRARED RADIATION DETECTORS.** LIU, S. T. MACIOLEK, R. B. 1973 INTERNATIONAL ELECTRON DEVICES MEETING TECHNICAL DIGEST 259-62PP., 1973.
66101	**FERROELECTRIC, CONDUCTIVITY AND SECONDARY EMISSION CHARACTERTISTICS OF A POTASSIUM DIDENTERIUM PHOSPHATE LIGHT VALVE.** CASASENT, D. KEICHER, W. INTERNATIONAL ELECTRON DEVICES MEETING TECHNICAL DIGEST 426-9PP., 1973.
66102	**EXOELECTRON EMISSION FROM ZINC OXIDE. [OXYGEN ADSORPTION EFFECT].** KRIEGSEIS, W. SCHARMANN, A. INTERNATIONAL SYMPOSIUM ON EXOELECTRON EMISSION AND DOSIMETRY, 4TH 96-9PP., 1974.
66103	**THERMALLY STIMULATED FIELD EMISSION OF EXOELECTRONS FROM LITHIUM NIOBATE.** ROSENBLUM, B. BRAUNLICH, P. CARRICO, J. P. INTERNATIONAL SYMPOSIUM ON EXOELECTRON EMISSION AND DOSIMETRY, 4TH 100-1PP., 1974.
66104	**ON THE PROBLEM OF EXOELECTRON ENERGY SPECTRUM.** KORTOV, V. S. ZOLNIKOV, P. P. INTERNATIONAL SYMPOSIUM ON EXOELECTRON EMISSION AND DOSIMETRY, 4TH 102-6PP., 1974.
66105	**A NEW APPROACH IN THE DESCRIPTION OF THERMAL STIMULATED ELECTRON EMISSION GLOW CURVES.** DOERFEL, H. PIESCH, E. INTERNATIONAL SYMPOSIUM ON EXOELECTRON EMISSION AND DOSIMETRY, 4TH 107-10PP., 1974.
66109	**THERMOSTIMULATED EMISSION FROM SODIUM CHLORIDE.** KONYUSHKINA, N. I. KRYLOVA, I. V. INTERNATIONAL SYMPOSIUM ON EXOELECTRON EMISSION AND DOSIMETRY, 4TH 154-8PP., 1974.
66110	**EMISSION PHENOMENA IN METALS AND SEMICONDUCTORS.** RAMSEY, J. A. INTERNATIONAL SYMPOSIUM ON EXOELECTRON EMISSION AND DOSIMETRY, 4TH 193-208PP., 1974.

EPIC Number	Bibliographic Citation
66112	**INTRINSIC MAGNETIC AFTER EFFECT.** HUNTER, J. UNIVERSITY OF DURHAM, ENGLAND 1-, 1973.
66116	**NATURE OF CONDUCTIVITY IN SOME IRON SELENIDES.** AKHMEDOV, N. R. DZHALILOV, N. Z. ABDINOV, D. SH. GASANOVA, N. A. IZV. AKAD. NAUK AZERB. SSR, SER. FIZ.-TEKH. MAT. NAUK (3), 35-7, 1973.
66119	**SPACE-CHARGE-LIMITED CURRENTS IN P-GALLIUM SELENIDE SINGLE CRYSTALS.** TAGIEV, B. G. GADZHIEV, V. A. ABDULLAEVA, S. G. MAMEDOV, G. M. IZV. AKAD. NAUK AZERB. SSR, SER. FIZ.-TEKH. MAT. NAUK (3), 58-60, 1973.
66120	**RECOMBINATION LUMINESCENCE IN SILVER-ACTIVATED SODIUM CHLORIDE PHOSPHORS.** ALIEV, F. G. IZV. AKAD. NAUK AZERB. SSR, SER. FIZ.-TEKH. MAT. NAUK (3), 70-6, 1973.
66121	**ELECTRIC PROPERTIES OF GALLIUM ARSENIDE-INDIUM ARSENIDE SINGLE CRYSTALS AT LOW GALLIUM ARSENIDE CONCENTRATIONS.** ALIEV, M. I. KHALILOV, KH. A. IZV. AKAD. NAUK AZERB. SSR, SER. FIZ.-TEKH. MAT. NAUK (3), 91-5, 1973.
66125	**MAGNETIC PROPERTIES OF URANIUM SULFIDE SELENIDE AND URANIUM SULFIDE TELLURIDE COMPOUNDS.** PLETYUSHKIN, V. A. CHECHERNIKOV, V. I. SLOVYANSKIKH, V. K. VESTN. MOSK. UNIV., FIZ., ASTRON. 12 (5), 605-6, 1971.
66128	**LUMINESCENT PROPERTIES OF ERBIUM TRIPOSITIVE IONS IN ZINC SULFIDE-CADMIUM SULFIDE MIXED LUMINOPHORS.** SENASHENKO, M. V. VESTN. MOSK. UNIV., FIZ., ASTRON. 13 (4), 467-9, 1972.
66129	**FERROELECTRIC PROPERTIES OF SOLID SOLUTIONS IN THE AMMONIUM SULFATE-AMMONIUM FLUOROBERYLLATE SYSTEM. AMMONIUM SULFATE-RICH.** LEVINA, M. E. KOLBENEVA, G. I. VESTN. MOSK. UNIV., KHIM. 12 (6), 683-5, 1971.
66134	**EXAMINATION OF SOME FACTORS WHICH INFLUENCE THE CRITICAL CURRENT OF NIOBIUM STANNIDE OBTAINED BY DIFFUSION.** ERMOLOV, V. A. EFREMOV, YU. N. ALEKSEEVSKII, N. E. ZAYTSEV, G. S. RUSS. MET. (6), 99-102, 1973. (ENGLISH TRANSLATION OF IZV. AKAD. NAUK SSSR, METAL., (6), 169-72, 1973; FOR ORIGINAL SEE E62435)
66138	**ELECTRICAL CONDUCTIVITY OF IONIC CRYSTALS.** BALBAKOV, D. ZH. KHALMURZAEV, S. SHALPYKOV, A. V. VLIYANIE PRIMESEI DEFEKTOV SVOISTVA KRIST. 106-12, 1970.
66150	**EFFECT OF ANTIMONY(III) OXIDE ADDITION ON THE ELECTRIC RESISTANCE OF THERMISTORS FROM A SEMICONDUCTING BARIUM TITANATE CERAMIC.** SIMEONOV, K. SIVOVA, R. STUKLO FINA KERAM., NAUCHNO-TEKH. KONF., 3RD 137-43, 1972.
66152	**INTERFEROMETRIC MEASUREMENTS OF THE FAR-INFRARED REFRACTIVE INDEX OF SODIUM FLUORIDE AT LOW TEMPERATURES.** RANDALL, C. M. LAB. OPER., AEROSPACE CORP., EL SEGUNDO, CALIF. 26PP., 1970. (AD-711 064)
66156	**CADMIUM SULFIDE. DATA SHEETS.** NEUBERGER, M. HUGHES AIRCRAFT CO., CULVER CITY, CALIFORNIA, ELECTRONIC PROPERTIES INFORMATION CENTER 256PP., 1967. (AD 810 354, EPIC-DS-124/2E)
66157	**VANADIUM SILICIDE. DATA SHEET.** GRIGSBY, D. L. HUGHES AIRCRAFT CO., CULVER CITY, CALIF. 49PP., 1967. (AD-810 374, EPIC-DS-154)
66180	**PROPERTIES AND STRUCTURE OF VITREOUS SILICA. I.** BRUCKNER, R. J. NON-CRYST. SOLIDS 5, 123-75, 1970.

EPIC Number	Bibliographic Citation

66184 **OPTICAL ABSORPTION OF SILICON CARBIDE INVESTIGATED AS A SURFACE-BARRIER DIODE.**
MAKAROV, V. V.
FIZ. TEKH. POLUPROV.
6 (9), 1805–7, 1972.
(FOR ENGLISH TRANSLATION SEE E66185)

66185 **OPTICAL ABSORPTION OF SILICON CARBIDE INVESTIGATED AS A SURFACE-BARRIER DIODE.**
MAKAROV, V. V.
SOV. PHYS. SEMICOND.
6 (9), 1556–7, 1973.
(ENGLISH TRANSLATION OF FIZ. TEKH. POLUPROV., 6 (9), 1805–7, 1972; FOR ORIGINAL SEE E66184)

66186 **FAR-INFRARED ABSORPTION BANDS OF SILICON CARBIDE.**
IL'IN, M. A. KARSHTEDT, E. M.
RASHEVSKAYA, E. P.
FIZ. TEKH. POLUPROV.
6 (11), 2230–2, 1972.
(FOR ENGLISH TRANSLATION SEE E66187)

66187 **FAR-INFRARED ABSORPTION BANDS OF SILICON CARBIDE.**
IL'IN, M. A. KARSHTEDT, E. M.
RASHEVSKAYA, E. P.
SOV. PHYS. SEMICOND.
6 (11), 1877–8, 1973.
(ENGLISH TRANSLATION OF FIZ. TEKH. POLUPROV., 6 (11), 2230–2, 1972; FOR ORIGINAL SEE E66186)

66193 **PROPERTIES AND STRUCTURE OF VITREOUS SILICA. II.**
BRUCKNER, R.
J. NON-CRYST. SOLIDS
5, 177–216, 1971.

66197 **SPECTROPHOTOMETRIC COMPOSITIONAL ANALYSIS OF TANTALUM-ALUMINUM ALLOY FILMS.**
HUBER, F. JAFFE, D.
J. VAC. SCI. TECHNOL.
8 (3), 480–7, 1971.

66199 **THE DETERMINATION OF THE OPTICAL CONSTANTS OF SEMICONDUCTORS OF THE TYPE A(III) B(V) IN THE INFRARED.**
OSWALD, F. SCHADE, R.
Z. NATURFORSCH.
9 A, 611–7, 1954.

66202 **REFRACTIVE INDEX BEHAVIOR OF GARNETS.**
WEMPLE, S. H. TABOR, W. J.
J. APPL. PHYS.
44 (3), 1395–6, 1973.

66204 **PREPARATION AND PROPERTIES OF INFRARED-TO-VISIBLE CONVERSION PHOSPHORS.**
OSTERMAYER, F. W., JR.
MET. TRANS.
2 (3), 747–55, 1971.

66213 **TRANSMISSION SPUTTERING AND RECOIL IMPLANTATION FROM THIN METAL FILMS UNDER ION BOMBARDMENT.**
PERKINS, J. G. STROUD, P. T.
NUCL. INSTRUM. METHODS
102 (1), 109–15, 1972.

66214 **PHOTOEMISSION DENSITIES OF INTRINSIC SURFACE STATES FOR SILICON, GERMANIUM, AND GALLIUM ARSENIDE.**
EASTMAN, D. E. GROBMAN, W. D.
PHYS. REV. LETT.
28 (21), 1378–81, 1972.

66215 **OPTICAL PROPERTIES OF LASER-TYPE GALLIUM ARSENIDE.**
THOMAS, B. THOMAS, R. ADAMS, M. J.
CROSS, M.
PHYS. LETT.
38 A (7), 537–8, 1972.

66222 **ABSORPTION SATURATION IN GERMANIUM, SILICON, AND GALLIUM ARSENIDE AT 10.6 MU M.**
GIBSON, A. F. ROSITO, C. A. RAFFO, C. A.
KIMMITT, M. F.
APPL. PHYS. LETT.
21 (8), 356–7, 1972.

66227 **THE TEMPERATURE DEPENDENCE OF THE ABSORPTION EDGE IN SOME AMORPHOUS SEMICONDUCTORS.**
CONNELL, N.
PHYS. STATUS SOLIDI
53 B (1), 213–8, 1972.

66229 **RADIATIVE TRANSFER THROUGH A CLOUD OF ABSORBING-SCATTERING PARTICLES.**
SANDERS, C. F., JR. LENOIR, J. M.
AICHE J.
18 (1), 155–60, 1972.

66230 **CHALCOGENIDE GLASSES FOR HIGH ENERGY LASER APPLICATIONS.**
HILTON, A. R. HAYES, D. J. RECHTIN, M. D.
TEXAS INSTRUMENTS INC., CENTRAL RESEARCH LAB., DALLAS, TEXAS
76PP., 1974.
(AD-782 036, TI-08-74-44)

EPIC Number	Bibliographic Citation

66262 **HIGHLY SENSITIVE HALL-EFFECT MEASURING DEVICE.**
KANEDA, T.
KEISO
15 (7), 78–81, 1972.

66263 **HALL EFFECT IN P-TYPE SEMICONDUCTORS.**
MISHRA, U. K.
LIBYAN J. SCI.
2, 89–103, 1972.

66264 **ANOMALOUS MAGNETIC RESONANCE BEHAVIOR OF COBALT DOPED BISMUTH-CALCIUM-IRON-VANADIUM GARNET CRYSTALS.**
KRISHNAN, R. HODGES, J. A.
DE LACHEISSERIE, E.
MAGN. RESONANCE RELAT. PHENOMENA, PROC. CONGR. AMPERE, 16TH
473–6, 1971.

66266 **TRANSPARENT HEXAGONAL FERROMAGNETIC RUBIDIUM TRIFLUORONICKELATE (SYNTHESIS OF SINGLE CRYSTALS AND MAGNETIC PROPERTIES).**
SMOLENSKII, G. A. SYRNIKOV, P. P.
YUDIN, V. M.
MATER. MEZHOTRASL. SOVESHCH. METOD. POLUCH. ANAL. FERRITOVYKH MATER. SYR'YA NIKH, 2ND
1, 61–70PP., 1968.

66268 **EFFECT OF COMPENSATING IMPURITIES AND HEAT TREATMENT ON RADIATIVE RECOMBINATION IN GALLIUM ARSENIDE.**
VIL'KOTSKII, V. A. DOMANEVSKII, D. S.
LOMAKO, V. M. TKACHEV, V. D.
MATER. VSES. SOVESHCH. DEFEKTAM STRUKT. POLUPROV.
2, 128–35, 1970.

66269 **ANISOTROPY OF HOLE MOBILITY IN INDIUM ANTIMONIDE.**
KRAVCHENKO, A. F. PALKIN, A. M.
MATER. VSES. SOVESHCH. DEFEKTAM STRUKT. POLUPROV.
2, 173–7, 1970.

66270 **ENERGY LEVELS OF DEFECTS IN GALLIUM ARSENIDE DOPED WITH GROUP II AND VI IMPURITIES.**
MARONCHUK, YU. E. SHERSTYAKOVA, V. N.
SHERSTYAKOV, A. P.
MATER. VSES. SOVESHCH. DEFEKTAM STRUKT. POLUPROV.
2, 186–91, 1970.

66271 **MANIFESTATION OF GALLIUM ARSENIDE STRUCTURE IN PHOTOELECTRIC EMISSION IN THE X-RAY SPECTRAL REGION.**
NIKOLAENYA, A. Z. NEKRASHEVICH, I. G.
MATER. VSES. SOVESHCH. DEFEKTAM STRUKT. POLUPROV.
2, 204–8, 1970.

66283 **PHYSICAL PROPERTIES OF GROUP IV-VI TRANSITION METAL GERMANIDES.**
GRECHKO, O. G. L'VOV, S. N. BONDAREV, V. N.
METALLIDY-STR., SVOISTVA, PRIMEN.
142–9, 1971.

66284 **ELECTRICAL RESISTIVITY AND SUSCEPTIBILITY OF TRANSITION METAL HYDRIDES.**
NEMCHENKO, V. F.
METALLIDY-STR., SVOISTVA, PRIMEN.
149–57, 1971.

66285 **RESISTIVITY OF TRANSITION METAL GERMANIDES.**
BONDAREV, V. N. PODERGIN, V. A.
GRECHKO, O. G. PERMINOV, V. P.
METALLOTERM. METODY POLUCH. SOEDIN. SPLAVOV
65–7, 1972.

66296 **OPTICAL ABSORPTION IN CRYSTALS AND SOLUTIONS OF POTASSIUM HALIDES WITH LEAD HALIDE IMPURITY.**
PERSHITS, YA. N. VASIL'EV, N. N.
IZV. VYSSH. UCHEB. ZAVED., FIZ.
14 (12), 71–6, 1971.
(FOR ENGLISH TRANSLATION SEE E66297)

66297 **OPTICAL ABSORPTION IN CRYSTALS AND SOLUTIONS OF POTASSIUM HALIDES WITH LEAD HALIDE IMPURITY.**
PERSHITS, YA. N. VASIL'EV, N. N.
SOV. PHYS. J.
14 (12), 1664–8, 1971.
(ENGLISH TRANSLATION OF IZV. VYSSH. UCHEB. ZAVED., FIZ., 14 (12), 71–6, 1971; FOR ORIGINAL SEE E66296)

66298 **ABSORPTION SPECTRA OF GALLIUM ARSENIDE EXPOSED TO 5 - ME V PROTONS.**
KRIVOV, M. A. RED'KO, V. P. RAMAZANOV, P. E.
BUDNITSKII, D. L.
IZV. VYSSH. UCHEB. ZAVED., FIZ.
15 (4), 158–60, 1972.
(FOR ENGLISH TRANSLATION SEE E66299)

66299 **ABSORPTION SPECTRA OF GALLIUM ARSENIDE EXPOSED TO 5 - ME V PROTONS.**
KRIVOV, M. A. RED'KO, V. P.
RAMAZANOV, P. E. BUDNITSKII, D. L.
SOV. PHYS. J.
15 (4), 612–4, 1972.
(ENGLISH TRANSLATION OF IZV. VYSSH. UCHEB. ZAVED., FIZ., 15 (4), 158–60, 1972; FOR ORIGINAL SEE E66298)

EPIC Number | Bibliographic Citation

66302 **GROWING SINGLE CRYSTALS OF 5 LEAD OXIDE - 3 GERMANIUM OXIDE AND SOME OF THEIR OPTICAL ELECTRICAL PROPERTIES.**
GABRIELYAN, V. T. IONOV, P. V.
MIKHAILINA, K. A. ARAKELOV, O. A.
SOV. PHYS. CRYSTALLOGR.
19 (1), 106-7, 1974.
(ENGLISH TRANSLATION OF KRISTALLOGRAFIYA, 19 (1), 176-8, 1974; FOR ORIGINAL SEE E58526)

66308 **OPTICAL RADIATION EMITTED AT HEAVY-ION BOMBARDMENT OF SOLIDS.**
BRAUN, M. EMMOTH, B. MARTINSON, I.
PHYS. SCRIPTA
10 (3), 133-8, 1974.

66310 **INTERBAND TRANSITIONS AND EXCITON EFFECTS IN SEMICONDUCTORS.**
WELKOWSKY, M. BRAUNSTEIN, R.
PHYS. REV.
5 B (2), 497-509, 1972.
(AD-743 581)

66313 **FIBER REINFORCED GLASS.**
LARE, P. J. DIVECHA, A. P. HAHN, H.
MELPAR INC., FALLS CHURCH, VIRGINIA
21PP., 1968.
(AD-845 650)

66316 **OPTOELECTRONIC FUNCTIONAL ELECTRONIC BLOCKS.**
BIARD, J. R.
TEXAS INSTRUMENTS INC., DALLAS, TEXAS
71PP., 1964.
(AD-609 509, TI-03-64-88)

66317 **BEHAVIOR OF ULTRA-SMALL COLLOID PARTICLES.**
CARUSO, R.
THIOKOL CHEMICAL CORP., DENVILLE, N. J.
45PP., 1967.
(AD-655 906, AFOSR-67-0933)

66334 **CALCULATION OF THE BAND STRUCTURE OF NIOBIUM NITRIDE.**
SCHWARZ, K.
MONATSH. CHEM.
102 (5), 1400-18, 1971.

66343 **MAGNETOCRYSTALLINE ANISOTROPY OF FERRO- AND FERRIMAGNETICS.**
DARBY, M. I. ISAAC, E. D.
IEEE TRANS. MAGN.
MAG-10 (2), 259-304, 1974.

66363 **ELECTRICAL PROPERTY OF AN INTERCALATED COMPOUND.**
KANAMARU, F. KOIZUMI, M.
JAP. J. APPL. PHYS. (JAPAN)
13 (8), 1319-20, 1974.

66368 **STRONG AND WEAK FERROMAGNETISM IN NICKEL-IRON ALLOYS.**
CAMPBELL, I. A.
J. PHYS.
4 F (8), L181-3, 1974.

66369 **CHARACTERISATION AND SYNTHESIS IN HYDROTHERMAL CONDITIONS OF VANADIUM OXYHYDROXIDE AND A NEW ALLOTROPIC VARIETY OF VANADIUM DIOXIDE.**
MULLER, J. JOUBERT, J. C.
J. SOLID STATE CHEM. (USA)
11 (2), 79-87, 1974.

66375 **THE DYNAMICAL CONDUCTIVITY FOR IONIZED IMPURITY SCATTERING.**
GERLACH, E. RAUTENBERG, M.
PHYS. STATUS SOLIDI (GERMANY)
65 B (1), K13-17, 1974.

66380 **ELECTRON SPIN RESONANCE AND OPTICAL ABSORPTION OF DEFECTS IN THE INORGANIC AZIDES.**
OWENS, F. J.
RADIAT. EFF.
21 (1), 1-17, 1974.

66386 **DEVELOPMENT TRENDS OF INORGANIC DIELECTRIC MATERIALS.**
ANTONIEWICZ, J.
WIAD. ELEKTROTECH.
42 (7), 149-52, 1974.

66395 **THE USE OF ION BOMBARDMENT TO STUDY AMORPHOUS SOLIDS.**
OLLEY, J. A. YOFFE, A. D.
INTERN. CONF. AMORPHOUS AND LIQUID SEMICONDUCTORS
73-8PP., 1974.

66431 **INSTABILITY IN THE ABSORPTION OF LIGHT BY FREE CARRIERS IN SEMICONDUCTORS.**
PUCHKOV, V. I. EPSHTEIN, E. M.
FIZ. TEKH. POLUPROV.
7 (10), 1878-81, 1973.
(FOR ENGLISH TRANSLATION SEE E66432)

66432 **INSTABILITY IN THE ABSORPTION OF LIGHT BY FREE CARRIERS IN SEMICONDUCTORS.**
PUCHKOV, V. I. EPSHTEIN, E. M.
SOV. PHYS. SEMICOND.
7 (10), 1254-5, 1974.
(ENGLISH TRANSLATION OF FIZ. TEKH. POLUPROV., 7 (10), 1878-81, 1973; FOR ORIGINAL SEE E66431)

EPIC Number | Bibliographic Citation

66433 **ELECTRICAL CONDUCTIVITY OF A SEMICONDUCTOR WITH A CLASSICAL SUPERLATTICE IN THE DIFFUSION APPROXIMATION.**
GRIBNIKOV, Z. S.
FIZ. TEKH. POLUPROV.
7 (10), 1948-55, 1973.
(FOR ENGLISH TRANSLATION SEE E66434)

66434 **ELECTRICAL CONDUCTIVITY OF A SEMICONDUCTOR WITH A CLASSICAL SUPERLATTICE IN THE DIFFUSION APPROXIMATION.**
GRIBNIKOV, Z. S.
SOV. PHYS. SEMICOND.
7 (10), 1300-4, 1974.
(ENGLISH TRANSLATION OF FIZ. TEKH. POLUPROV., 7 (10), 1948-55, 1973; FOR ORIGINAL SEE E66433)

66435 **TRANSPORT EFFECTS IN THE VICINITY OF A SEMICONDUCTOR SURFACE UNDER STRONG BAND-BENDING CONDITIONS.**
BASKIN, E. M. ENTIN, M. V.
FIZ. TEKH. POLUPROV.
8 (1), 64-73, 1974.
(FOR ENGLISH TRANSLATION SEE E66436)

66436 **TRANSPORT EFFECTS IN THE VICINITY OF A SEMICONDUCTOR SURFACE UNDER STRONG BAND-BENDING CONDITIONS.**
BASKIN, E. M. ENTIN, M. V.
SOV. PHYS. SEMICOND.
8 (1), 37-42, 1974.
(ENGLISH TRANSLATION OF FIZ. TEKH. POLUPROV., 8 (1), 64-73, 1974; FOR ORIGINAL SEE E66435)

66438 **PHASE STATE OF OXYGEN IN SILICON.**
MALYSHEV, V. A.
FIZ. TEKH. POLUPROV.
8 (1), 148-53, 1974.
(FOR ENGLISH TRANSLATION SEE E66439)

66439 **PHASE STATE OF OXYGEN IN SILICON.**
MALYSHEV, V. A.
SOV. PHYS. SEMICOND.
8 (1), 92-5, 1974.
(ENGLISH TRANSLATION OF FIZ. TEKH. POLUPROV., 8 (1), 148-53, 1974; FOR ORIGINAL SEE E66438)

66446 **GALLIUM NITRIDE: BAND STRUCTURE, PROPERTIES, AND POTENTIAL APPLICATIONS.**
KESAMANLY, F. P.
FIZ. TEKH. POLUPROV.
8 (2), 225-41, 1974.
(FOR ENGLISH TRANSLATION SEE E66447)

66447 **GALLIUM NITRIDE: BAND STRUCTURE, PROPERTIES, AND POTENTIAL APPLICATIONS.**
KESAMANLY, F. P.
SOV. PHYS. SEMICOND.
8 (2), 147-56, 1974.
(ENGLISH TRANSLATION OF FIZ. TEKH. POLUPROV., 8 (2), 225-41, 1974; FOR ORIGINAL SEE E66446)

66448 **ANISOTROPY OF TWO-PHOTON ABSORPTION IN CADMIUM DIPHOSPHIDE.**
LISITSA, M. P. MOZOL', P. E.
POTYKEVICH, I. V. KOVAL', V. S.
FEKESHGAZI, I. V.
FIZ. TEKH. POLUPROV.
8 (2), 242-6, 1974.
(FOR ENGLISH TRANSLATION SEE E66449)

66449 **ANISOTROPY OF TWO-PHOTON ABSORPTION IN CADMIUM DIPHOSPHIDE.**
LISITSA, M. P. MOZOL', P. E.
POTYKEVICH, I. V. KOVAL', V. S.
FEKESHGAZI, I. V.
SOV. PHYS. SEMICOND.
8 (2), 157-9, 1974.
(ENGLISH TRANSLATION OF FIZ. TEKH. POLUPROV., 8 (2), 242-6, 1974; FOR ORIGINAL SEE E66448)

66450 **CAPTURE OF IMPURITY ATOMS BY VACANCIES IN IMPLANTED LAYERS.**
ZELEVINSKAYA, V. M. KACHURIN, G. A.
BOGOMYAKOV, N. P. AZIKOV, B. S.
SHIROKOV, L. L.
FIZ. TEKH. POLUPROV.
8 (2), 254-7, 1974.
(FOR ENGLISH TRANSLATION SEE E66451)

66451 **CAPTURE OF IMPURITY ATOMS BY VACANCIES IN IMPLANTED LAYERS.**
ZELEVINSKAYA, V. M. KACHURIN, G. A.
BOGOMYAKOV, N. P. AZIKOV, B. S.
SHIROKOV, L. L.
SOV. PHYS. SEMICOND.
8 (2), 164-6, 1974.
(ENGLISH TRANSLATION OF FIZ. TEKH. POLUPROV., 8 (2), 254-7, 1974; FOR ORIGINAL SEE E66450)

66452 **CHARACTERISTICS OF THE TRANSPORT PHENOMENA IN THE SPACE CHARGE REGION NEAR THE SURFACE OF A SEMICONDUCTOR.**
KOLOMETS, N. V. POLNIKOV, V. G.
FIZ. TEKH. POLUPROV.
8 (2), 391-3, 1974.
(FOR ENGLISH TRANSLATION SEE E66453)

EPIC Number	Bibliographic Citation
66453	**CHARACTERISTICS OF THE TRANSPORT PHENOMENA IN THE SPACE CHARGE REGION NEAR THE SURFACE OF A SEMICONDUCTOR.** KOLOMETS, N. V. POLNIKOV, V. G. SOV. PHYS. SEMICOND. 8 (2), 250–1, 1974. (ENGLISH TRANSLATION OF FIZ. TEKH. POLUPROV., 8 (2), 391–3, 1974; FOR ORIGINAL SEE E66452)
66454	**SIZE DEPENDENT THERMOELECTRIC POWER IN MANY-VALLEY SEMICONDUCTORS.** PRIMA, N. A. FIZ. TEKH. POLUPROV. 8 (2), 397–400, 1974. (FOR ENGLISH TRANSLATION SEE E66455)
66455	**SIZE DEPENDENT THERMOELECTRIC POWER IN MANY-VALLEY SEMICONDUCTORS.** PRIMA, N. A. SOV. PHYS. SEMICOND. 8 (2), 254–6, 1974. (ENGLISH TRANSLATION OF FIZ. TEKH. POLUPROV., 8 (2), 397–400, 1974; FOR ORIGINAL SEE E66454)
66481	**ELECTRICAL PROPERTIES OF IMPLANTED LAYERS IN GALLIUM ARSENIDE.** TANSEY, J. E. UNIVERSITY OF SURREY, ENGLAND 1–, 1973.
66483	**APPLICATION OF MOS TRANSISTOR FOR THE COMPENSATION OF A BRIDGE IN MEASUREMENT OF THE MAGNETORESISTANCE OF AMORPHOUS SEMICONDUCTORS.** KUBELIK, I. TRISKA, A. CESK. CAS. FIS. 24 A (1), 58–60, 1974.
66484	**MOBILITY IN GALLIUM ANTIMONIDE.** DNEPROVSKAYA, T. S. VESTN. MOSK. UNIV., FIZ., ASTRON. 11 (6), 622–6, 1970.
66486	**ELECTRICAL PROPERTIES OF MERCURY TELLURIDE SINGLE CRYSTALS.** ANTONIV, I. P. VOLZHENSKAYA, L. G. VISN. L'VIV. UNIV. SER. FIZ. (5), 73–4, 1969.
66490	**TEMPERATURE DEPENDENCE OF CATHODOLUMINESCENCE OF GALLIUM ARSENIDE, GALLIUM PHOSPHIDE, AND GALLIUM ARSENIDE PHOSPHIDE.** MARCINIAK, H. C. WITTRY, D. B. NAT. CONF. ELECTRON PROBE ANAL., PROC., 7TH 27A–27C, 1972.
66491	**ELECTRONIC CONDUCTION IN GLASS.** TRAP, H. I. L. NACHRICHTENTECH. Z. 24 (7), 353–60, 1971.
66509	**THE CLASSIFICATION AND QUALITY CONTROL OF THIN FILMS BY THE RECOGNITION OF X-RAY DIFFRACTION LINES.** KAWARAI, S. KOIKE, R. SHINTANI, M. FURUYA, N. ELECTRON. COMMUN. JAPAN 56 C (1), 79–84, 1973.
66510	**CONTACT POTENTIAL DIFFERENCE IN SILICON CRYSTAL RECTIFIERS.** MEYERHOF, W. E. PHYS. REV. 71 (10), 727–35, 1947.
66514	**APPLICATION OF ELLIPSOMETRY TO OXIDATION STUDIES OF BINARY TITANIUM – ALUMINUM ALLOYS.** JOHNSON, D. L. TAO, L. C. SURFACE SCI. 16, 390–7, 1969.
66515	**THE FUNDAMENTAL ABSORPTION EDGE OF ALUMINUM ARSENDIE AND ALUMINUM PHOSPHIDE.** LORENZ, M. R. CHICOTKA, R. PETTIT, G. D. DEAN, P. J. SOLID STATE COMMUN. 8 (9), 693–7, 1970.
66518	**FLUORESCENCE AND ABSORPTION STUDIES OF STRONTIUM GADOLINIUM CERIUM FLUORIDE.** YANEY, P. P. SCHAEFFER, D. M. WOLF, J. L. PHYS. REV. 11 B (7), 2460–77, 1975.
66530	**HEAT CAPACITY OF EUROPIUM OXIDE NEAR THE CURIE TEMPERATURE.** KORNBLIT, A. AHLERS, G. PHYS. REV. 11 B (7), 2678–88, 1975.
66532	**REFRACTIVE INDEX OF ALKALI HALIDES AND ITS WAVELENGTH AND TEMPERATURE DERIVATIVES.** LI, H. H. J. PHYS. CHEM. REF. DATA 5 (2), 329–528, 1976. (CINDAS–EPIC–1)
66541	**THERMAL BROADENING, SHIFT, AND PROFILE OF PHONONLESS LINES IN THE SPECTRA OF OXIDE AND SULFIDE MOLECULAR CENTERS.** REBANE, L. A. FREIBERG, A. M. KONI, YU. YA. FIZ. TVERD. TELA 15 (11), 3318–24, 1973. (FOR ENGLISH TRANSLATION SEE E66542)
66542	**THERMAL BROADENING, SHIFT, AND PROFILE OF PHONONLESS LINES IN THE SPECTRA OF OXIDE AND SULFIDE MOLECULAR CENTERS.** REBANE, L. A. FREIBERG, A. M. KONI, YU. YA. SOV. PHYS. SOLID STATE 15 (11), 2209–12, 1974. (ENGLISH TRANSLATION OF FIZ. TVERD. TELA, 15 (11), 3318–24, 1973; FOR ORIGINAL SEE E66541)
66549	**PHOTOMAGNETIC EFFECT AND PHOTOCONDUCTIVITY OF P-TYPE SEMICONDUCTORS IN THE CASE OF A NONEQUILINRIUM PHOTOELECTRON DISTRIBUTION.** LYAGUSHCHENKO, R. I. YASSIEVICH, I. N. FIZ. TEKH. POLUPROV. 7 (10), 1887–91, 1973. (FOR ENGLISH TRANSLATION SEE E66550)
66550	**PHOTOMAGNETIC EFFECT AND PHOTOCONDUCTIVITY OF P-TYPE SEMICONDUCTORS IN THE CASE OF A NONEQUILINRIUM PHOTOELECTRON DISTRIBUTION.** LYAGUSHCHENKO, R. I. YASSIEVICH, I. N. SOV. PHYS. SEMICOND. 7 (10), 1259–61, 1974. (ENGLISH TRANSLATION OF FIZ. TEKH. POLUPROV., 7 (10), 1887–91, 1973; FOR ORIGINAL SEE E66549)
66551	**IMPURITY CONDUCTION IN N-TYPE GALLIUM ARSENIDE.** EMELYANENKO, O. V. LAGUNOVA, T. S. NASLEDOV, D. N. NEDEOGLO, D. D. TIMCHENKO, I. N. FIZ. TEKH. POLUPROV. 7 (10), 1919–24, 1973. (FOR ENGLISH TRANSLATION SEE E66552)
66552	**IMPURITY CONDUCTION IN N-TYPE GALLIUM ARSENIDE.** EMELYANENKO, O. V. LAGUNOVA, T. S. NASLEDOV, D. N. NEDEOGLO, D. D. TIMCHENKO, I. N. SOV. PHYS. SEMICOND. 7 (10), 1280–3, 1974. (ENGLISH TRANSLATION OF FIZ. TEKH. POLUPROV., 7 (10), 1919–24, 1973; FOR ORIGINAL SEE E66551)
66553	**CRITERION FOR INCREASING THE PHOTORESPONSE OF SEMICONDUCTORS BY INHOMOGENEOUS DOPING.** EVDOKIMOV, V. M. FIZ. TEKH. POLUPROV. 7 (10), 1956–60, 1973. (FOR ENGLISH TRANSLATION SEE E66554)
66554	**CRITERION FOR INCREASING THE PHOTORESPONSE OF SEMICONDUCTORS BY INHOMOGENEOUS DOPING.** EVDOKIMOV, V. M. SOV. PHYS. SEMICOND. 7 (10), 1305–7, 1974. (ENGLISH TRANSLATION OF FIZ. TEKH. POLUPROV., 7 (10), 1956–60, 1973; FOR ORIGINAL SEE E66553)
66555	**METHOD FOR THE DETERMINATION OF THE COMPONENTS OF THE MOBILITY TENSOR OF THE MINORITY CARRIERS IN ANISOTROPIC SEMICONDUCTORS.** ZHADKO, I. P. ROMANOV, V. A. FIZ. TEKH. POLUPROV. 7 (10), 2027–9, 1973. (FOR ENGLISH TRANSLATION SEE E66556)
66556	**METHOD FOR THE DETERMINATION OF THE COMPONENTS OF THE MOBILITY TENSOR OF THE MINORITY CARRIERS IN ANISOTROPIC SEMICONDUCTORS.** ZHADKO, I. P. ROMANOV, V. A. SOV. PHYS. SEMICOND. 7 (10), 1355–6, 1974. (ENGLISH TRANSLATION OF FIZ. TEKH. POLUPROV., 7 (10), 2027–9, 1973; FOR ORIGINAL SEE E66555)
66558	**THEORY OF DEEP CENTERS IN SEMICONDUCTORS.** ROITSIN, A. B. FIZ. TEKH. POLUPROV. 8 (1), 3–29, 1974. (FOR ENGLISH TRANSLATION SEE E66559)
66559	**THEORY OF DEEP CENTERS IN SEMICONDUCTORS.** ROITSIN, A. B. SOV. PHYS. SEMICOND. 8 (1), 1–17, 1974. (ENGLISH TRANSLATION OF FIZ. TEKH. POLUPROV., 8 (1), 3–29, 1974; FOR ORIGINAL SEE E66558)
66560	**INVESTIGATION OF THE ELECTRICAL PROPERTIES OF N-CADMIUM TIN ARSENIDE UNDER HYDROSTATIC PRESSURE.** DAUNOV, M. I. MAGOMEDOV, A. B. FIZ. TEKH. POLUPROV. 8 (1), 45–9, 1974. (FOR ENGLISH TRANSLATION SEE E66561)

EPIC Number	Bibliographic Citation
66561	**INVESTIGATION OF THE ELECTRICAL PROPERTIES OF N-CADMIUM TIN ARSENIDE UNDER HYDROSTATIC PRESSURE.** DAUNOV, M. I. MAGOMEDOV, A. B. SOV. PHYS. SEMICOND. 8 (1), 26-8, 1974. (ENGLISH TRANSLATION OF FIZ. TEKH. POLUPROV., 8 (1), 45-9, 1974; FOR ORIGINAL SEE E66560)
66562	**BEHAVIOR OF GROUP IV ELEMENTS INTRODUCED INTO INDIUM ARSENIDE BY ION IMPLANTATION.** GUSEVA, M. I. ZOTOVA, N. V. KOVAL', A. V. NASLEDOV, D. N. FIZ. TEKH. POLUPROV. 8 (1), 59-63, 1974. (FOR ENGLISH TRANSLATION SEE E66563)
66563	**BEHAVIOR OF GROUP IV ELEMENTS INTRODUCED INTO INDIUM ARSENIDE BY ION IMPLANTATION.** GUSEVA, M. I. ZOTOVA, N. V. KOVAL', A. V. NASLEDOV, D. N. SOV. PHYS. SEMICOND. 8 (1), 34-6, 1974. (ENGLISH TRANSLATION OF FIZ. TEKH. POLUPROV., 8 (1), 59-63, 1974; FOR ORIGINAL SEE E66562)
66570	**CONDUCTIVITY OF ZINC SILICON ARSENIDE AT THE MELT PHASE TRANSITION.** AVERKIEVA, G. K. PROCHUKHAN, V. D. RUD', YU. V. TASHTANOVA, M. FIZ. TEKH. POLUPROV. 8 (1), 157-8, 1974. (FOR ENGLISH TRANSLATION SEE E66571)
66571	**CONDUCTIVITY OF ZINC SILICON ARSENIDE AT THE MELT PHASE TRANSITION.** AVERKIEVA, G. K. PROCHUKHAN, V. D. RUD', YU. V. TASHTANOVA, M. SOV. PHYS. SEMICOND. 8 (1), 98-9, 1974. (ENGLISH TRANSLATION OF FIZ. TEKH. POLUPROV., 8 (1), 157-8, 1974; FOR ORIGINAL SEE E66570)
66572	**TEMPERATURE DEPENDENCE OF THE PIEZORESISTANCE CONSTANT OF N-TYPE SILICON CARBIDE (6H).** GUK, G. N. LYUBIMSKII, V. M. GOFMAN, E. P. ZINOV'EV, V. B. CHALYI, E. A. FIZ. TEKH. POLUPROV. 8 (1), 164-5, 1974. (FOR ENGLISH TRANSLATION SEE E66573)
66573	**TEMPERATURE DEPENDENCE OF THE PIEZORESISTANCE CONSTANT OF N-TYPE SILICON CARBIDE (6H).** GUK, G. N. LYUBIMSKII, V. M. GOFMAN, E. P. ZINOV'EV, V. B. CHALYI, E. A. SOV. PHYS. SEMICOND. 8 (1), 104, 1974. (ENGLISH TRANSLATION OF FIZ. TEKH. POLUPROV., 8 (1), 164-5, 1974; FOR ORIGINAL SEE E66572)
66574	**CRYSTAL-MELT PHASE TRANSITION AND CONDUCTIVITY OF CADMIUM GERMANIUM PHOSPHIDE.** BORSHCHEVSKII, A. S. RUD', YU. V. TASHTANOVA, M. UNDALOV, YU. K. FIZ. TEKH. POLUPROV. 8 (1), 165-8, 1974. (FOR ENGLISH TRANSLATION SEE E66575)
66575	**CRYSTAL-MELT PHASE TRANSITION AND CONDUCTIVITY OF CADMIUM GERMANIUM PHOSPHIDE.** BORSHCHEVSKII, A. S. RUD', YU. V. TASHTANOVA, M. UNDALOV, YU. K. SOV. PHYS. SEMICOND. 8 (1), 105-6, 1974. (ENGLISH TRANSLATION OF FIZ. TEKH. POLUPROV., 8 (1), 165-8, 1974; FOR ORIGINAL SEE E66574)
66578	**RESIDUAL CONDUCTANCE OF EPITAXIAL FILMS OF GALLIUM ARSENIDE.** SYTENKO, T. N. TYAGUL'SKII, I. P. FIZ. TEKH. POLUPROV. 8 (1), 171-4, 1974. (FOR ENGLISH TRANSLATION SEE E66579)
66579	**RESIDUAL CONDUCTANCE OF EPITAXIAL FILMS OF GALLIUM ARSENIDE.** SYTENKO, T. N. TYAGUL'SKII, I. P. SOV. PHYS. SEMICOND. 8 (1), 109-10, 1974. (ENGLISH TRANSLATION OF FIZ. TEKH. POLUPROV., 8 (1), 171-4, 1974; FOR ORIGINAL SEE E66578)
66580	**NONLINEAR INDUCTION EFFECT IN SEMICONDUCTORS IN AN ALTERNATING INHOMOGENEOUS MAGNETIC FIELD.** MEILIKOV, E. Z. ARONZON, B. A. FIZ. TEKH. POLUPROV. 8 (1), 183-5, 1974. (FOR ENGLISH TRANSLATION SEE E66581)
66581	**NONLINEAR INDUCTION EFFECT IN SEMICONDUCTORS IN AN ALTERNATING INHOMOGENEOUS MAGNETIC FIELD.** MEILIKOV, E. Z. ARONZON, B. A. SOV. PHYS. SEMICOND. 8 (1), 118-9, 1974. (ENGLISH TRANSLATION OF FIZ. TEKH. POLUPROV., 8 (1), 183-5, 1974; FOR ORIGINAL SEE E66580)
66586	**DIRECT ALLOWED TRANSITIONS IN ANTIMONY SILICIDE.** ZEINALLY, A. KH. AGASIEV, A. A. EFENDIEV, SH. M. FIZ. TEKH. POLUPROV. 8 (1), 197-200, 1974. (FOR ENGLISH TRANSLATION SEE E66587)
66587	**DIRECT ALLOWED TRANSITIONS IN ANTIMONY SILICIDE.** ZEINALLY, A. K. AGASIEV, A. A. EFENDIEV, SH. M. SOV. PHYS. SEMICOND. 8 (1), 128-9, 1974. (ENGLISH TRANSLATION OF FIZ. TEKH. POLUPROV., 8 (1), 197-200, 1974; FOR ORIGINAL SEE E66586)
66588	**CATHODOLUMINESCENCE OF GALLIUM NITRIDE SINGLE CRYSTALS.** PIKHTIN, A. N. PICHUGIN, I. G. GIZITI, S. E. FIZ. TEKH. POLUPROV. 8 (1), 204-8, 1974. (FOR ENGLISH TRANSLATION SEE E66589)
66589	**CATHODOLUMINESCENCE OF GALLIUM NITRIDE SINGLE CRYSTALS.** PIKHTIN, A. N. PICHUGIN, I. G. GIZITI, S. E. SOV. PHYS. SEMICOND. 8 (1), 134-6, 1974. (ENGLISH TRANSLATION OF FIZ. TEKH. POLUPROV., 8 (1), 204-8, 1974; FOR ORIGINAL SEE E66588)
66590	**ELECTROLUMINESCENCE OF P-N JUNCTIONS IN GALLIUM INDIUM PHOSPHIDE SOLID SOLUTIONS.** ALFEROV, ZH. I. ARSENT'EV, I. N. GARBUZOV, D. Z. MISHURNYI, V. A. RUMYANTSEV, V. D. TRET'YAKOV, D. N. FIZ. TEKH. POLUPROV. 8 (1), 208-10, 1974. (FOR ENGLISH TRANSLATION SEE E66591)
66591	**ELECTROLUMINESCENCE OF P-N JUNCTIONS IN GALLIUM INDIUM PHOSPHIDE SOLID SOLUTIONS.** ALFEROV, ZH. I. ARSENT'EV, I. N. GARBUZOV, D. Z. MISHURNYI, V. A. RUMYANTSEV, V. D. TRET'YAKOV, D. N. SOV. PHYS. SEMICOND. 8 (1), 137-8, 1974. (ENGLISH TRANSLATION OF FIZ. TEKH. POLUPROV., 8 (1), 208-10, 1974; FOR ORIGINAL SEE E66590)
66592	**SOME CHARACTERISTICS OF EPITAXIAL P-N JUNCTIONS IN LEAD TIN SELENIDE.** ANTONOV, V. B. KURBANOVA, E. I. SALDEV, E. YU. FIZ. TEKH. POLUPROV. 8 (1), 219-21, 1974. (FOR ENGLISH TRANSLATION SEE E66593)
66593	**SOME CHARACTERISTICS OF EPITAXIAL P-N JUNCTIONS IN LEAD TIN SELENIDE.** ANTONOV, V. B. KURBANOVA, E. I. SALDEV, E. YU. SOV. PHYS. SEMICOND. 8 (1), 146, 1974. (ENGLISH TRANSLATION OF FIZ. TEKH. POLUPROV., 8 (1), 219-21, 1974; FOR ORIGINAL SEE E66592)
66594	**FREQUENCY DISPERSION OF AMBIPOLAR MOBILITY IN SEMICONDUCTORS WITH DEEP TRAPS.** SABLIKOV, V. A. FIZ. TEKH. POLUPROV. 8 (2), 247-53, 1974. (FOR ENGLISH TRANSLATION SEE E66595)
66595	**FREQUENCY DISPERSION OF AMBIOPOLAR MOBILITY IN SEMICONDUCTORS WITH DEEP TRAPS.** SABLIKOV, V. A. SOV. PHYS. SEMICOND. 8 (2), 160-3, 1974. (ENGLISH TRANSLATION OF FIZ. TEKH. POLUPROV., 8 (2), 247-53, 1974; FOR ORIGINAL SEE E66594)
66598	**QUENCHING OF THE PHOTOCONDUCTIVITY OF GERMANIUM DOPED GALLIUM PHOSPHIDE.** IVASHCHENKO, A. I. RADAUTSAN, S. I. SAMORUKOV, B. E. SLOBODCHIKOV, S. V. SOLOMONOV, A. I. FIZ. TEKH. POLUPROV. 8 (2), 278-84, 1974. (FOR ENGLISH TRANSLATION SEE E66599)
66599	**QUENCHING OF THE PHOTOCONDUCTIVITY OF GERMANIUM DOPED GALLIUM PHOSPHIDE.** IVASHCHENKO, A. I. RADAUTSAN, S. I. SAMORUKOV, B. E. SLOBODCHIKOV, S. V. SOLOMONOV, A. I. SOV. PHYS. SEMICOND. 8 (2), 179-82, 1974. (ENGLISH TRANSLATION OF FIZ. TEKH. POLUPROV., 8 (2), 278-84, 1974; FOR ORIGINAL SEE E66598)

EPIC Number	Bibliographic Citation

66600 **INFLUENCE OF A MAGNETIC FIELD ON THE HOPPING CONDUCTION IN N-TYPE INDIUM ANTIMONIDE.**
GERSHENZON, E. M. IL'IN, V. A. LITVAK-GORSKAYA, L. B.
FIZ. TEKH. POLUPROV.
8 (2), 295–300, 1974.
(FOR ENGLISH TRANSLATION SEE E66601)

66601 **INFLUENCE OF A MAGNETIC FIELD ON THE HOPPING CONDUCTION IN N-TYPE INDIUM ANTIMONIDE.**
GERSHENZON, E. M. IL'IN, V. A. LITVAK-GORSKAYA, L. B.
SOV. PHYS. SEMICOND.
8 (2), 189–91, 1974.
(ENGLISH TRANSLATION OF FIZ. TEKH. POLUPROV., 8 (2), 295–300, 1974; FOR ORIGINAL SEE E66600)

66614 **INVESTIGATION OF THE PHYSICAL PROPERTIES OF SOME BINARY BORIDE SYSTEMS.**
KUNITSKII, YU. A. FOMENKO, V. S.
TEPLOFIZ. VYS. TEMP.
12 (4), 910–2, 1974.
(FOR ENGLISH TRANSLATION SEE E66615)

66615 **INVESTIGATION OF THE PHYSICAL PROPERTIES OF SOME BINARY BORIDE SYSTEMS.**
KUNITSKII, YU. A. FOMENKO, V. S.
HIGH TEMP.
12 (4), 801–2, 1974.
(ENGLISH TRANSLATION OF TEPLOFIZ. VYS. TEMP., 12 (4), 910–2, 1974; FOR ORIGINAL SEE E66614)

66617 **ELECTRIC ENERGY GENERATION BY SHOCK COMPRESSION OF FERROELECTRIC CERAMICS: NORMAL-MODE RESPONSE OF LEAD ZIRCONIUM TITANATE 95/5.**
LYSNE, P. C. PERCIVAL, C. M.
J. APPL. PHYS.
46 (4), 1519–25, 1975.

66619 **PHOTOELECTRON EMISSION FROM ALUMINUM AND NICKEL MEASURED IN AIR.**
SMITH, T.
J. APPL. PHYS.
46 (4), 1553–8, 1975.

66621 **EFFECT OF BULK CARRIERS ON PROM SENSITIVITY.**
SPRAGUE, R. A.
J. APPL. PHYS.
46 (4), 1673–8, 1975.

66624 **TEMPERATURE DEPENDENCE OF SPONTANEOUS PEAK WAVELENGTH IN GALLIUM ARSENIDE AND GALLIUM ALUMINUM ARSENIDE ELECTROLUMINESCENT LAYERS.**
DYMENT, J. C. CHENG, Y. C. SPRING THORPE, A. J.
J. APPL. PHYS.
46 (4), 1739–43, 1975.

66627 **ANALYSIS OF THE ELECTRICAL AND LUMINESCENT PROPERTIES OF COPPER INDIUM SELENIDE.**
MIGLIORATO, P. SHAY, J. L. KASPER, H. M. WAGNER, S.
J. APPL. PHYS.
46 (4), 1777–82, 1975.

66637 **INVESTIGATION OF THE POSSIBILITY OF COMPENSATION OF CARRIERS IN MOLTEN THALLIUM SELENIDE.**
KAZANDZHAN, B. I. RAZUMEICHENKO, L. A. TSURIKOV, A. A.
FIZ. TEKH. POLUPROV.
8 (2), 343–8, 1974.
(FOR ENGLISH TRANSLATION SEE E66638)

66638 **INVESTIGATION OF THE POSSIBILITY OF COMPENSATION OF CARRIERS IN MOLTEN THALLIUM SELENIDE.**
KAZANDZHAN, B. I. RAZUMEICHENKO, L. A. TSURIKOV, A. A.
SOV. PHYS. SEMICOND.
8 (2), 219–22, 1974.
(ENGLISH TRANSLATION OF FIZ. TEKH. POLUPROV., 8 (2), 343–8, 1974; FOR ORIGINAL SEE E66637)

66639 **PHOTOMAGNETIC EFFECT SPECTRUM OF MULTILAYER STRUCTURES WITH P–N JUNCTIONS.**
ADIROVICH, E. I. ARNOV, D. A. MASTOV, E. M. YUABOV, YU. M.
FIZ. TEKH. POLUPROV.
8 (2), 354–61, 1974.
(FOR ENGLISH TRANSLATION SEE E66640)

66640 **PHOTOMAGNETIC EFFECT SPECTRUM OF MULTILAYER STRUCTURES WITH P–N JUNCTIONS.**
ADIROVICH, E. I. ARNOV, D. A. MASTOV, E. M. YUABOV, YU. M.
SOV. PHYS. SEMICOND.
8 (2), 226–30, 1974.
(ENGLISH TRANSLATION OF FIZ. TEKH. POLUPROV., 8 (2), 354–61, 1974; FOR ORIGINAL SEE E66639)

66643 **SENSITIZATION OF PHOTOLYSIS OF LEAD AZIDE BY INORGANIC SEMICONDUCTORS.**
ZAKHAROV, YU. A. SUROVIO, E. P.
FIZ. TEKH. POLUPROV.
8 (2), 385–7, 1974.
(FOR ENGLISH TRANSLATION SEE E66644)

66644 **SENSITIZATION OF PHOTOLYSIS OF LEAD AZIDE BY INORGANIC SEMICONDUCTORS.**
ZAKHAROV, YU. A. SUROVIO, E. P.
SOV. PHYS. SEMICOND.
8 (2), 245–6, 1974.
(ENGLISH TRANSLATION OF FIZ. TEKH. POLUPROV., 8 (2), 385–7, 1974; FOR ORIGINAL SEE E66643)

66647 **BAND PARAMETERS OF THE INDIUM ANTIMONIDE CADMIUM TELLURIDE SOLID SOLUTION SYSTEM.**
SKOROBGATOVA, L. A. KHABAROV, E. N.
FIZ. TEKH. POLUPROV.
8 (2), 401–3, 1974.
(FOR ENGLISH TRANSLATION SEE E66648)

66648 **BAND PARAMETERS OF THE INDIUM ANTIMONIDE CADMIUM TELLURIDE SOLID SOLUTION SYSTEM.**
SKOROBGATOVA, L. A. KHABAROV, E. N.
SOV. PHYS. SEMICOND.
8 (2), 257–8, 1974.
(ENGLISH TRANSLATION OF FIZ. TEKH. POLUPROV., 8 (2), 401–3, 1974; FOR ORIGINAL SEE E66647)

66655 **FREE EXCITONS IN THE LUMINESCENCE SPECTRA OF UNDOPED GALLIUM PHOSPHIDE AND OF INDIUM GALLIUM PHOSPHIDE AND ALUMINUM GALLIUM PHOSPHIDE.**
GARBUZOV, D. Z. KOP'EV, P. S. MISHURNYI, V. A.
FIZ. TEKH. POLUPROV.
8 (2), 418–21, 1974.
(FOR ENGLISH TRANSLATION SEE E66656)

66656 **FREE EXCITONS IN THE LUMINESCENCE SPECTRA OF UNDOPED GALLIUM PHOSPHIDE AND OF INDIUM GALLIUM PHOSPHIDE AND ALUMINUM GALLIUM PHOSPHIDE.**
GARBUZOV, D. Z. KOP'EV, P. S. MISHURNYI, V. A.
SOV. PHYS. SEMICOND.
8 (2), 270–1, 1974.
(ENGLISH TRANSLATION OF FIZ. TEKH. POLUPROV., 8 (2), 418–21, 1974; FOR ORIGINAL SEE E66655)

66659 **ANOMALOUS HALL MOBILITY IN GALLIUM ARSENIDE.**
KRIVOV, M. A. MALYANOV, S. V. MELEV, V. G.
FIZ. TEKH. POLUPROV.
8 (2), 430–3, 1974.
(FOR ENGLISH TRANSLATION SEE E66660)

66660 **ANOMALOUS HALL MOBILITY IN GALLIUM ARSENIDE.**
KRIVOV, M. A. MALYANOV, S. V. MELEV, V. G.
SOV. PHYS. SEMICOND.
8 (2), 279–80, 1974.
(ENGLISH TRANSLATION OF FIZ. TEKH. POLUPROV., 8 (2), 430–3, 1974; FOR ORIGINAL SEE E66659)

66668 **ELECTRONIC STRUCTURE AND FERMI-SURFACE-RELATED INSTABILITIES IN 1T - TANTALUM SELENIDE.**
MYRON, H. W. FREEMAN, A. J.
PHYS. REV.
11 B (8), 2735–9, 1975.

66679 **ELASTIC CONSTANTS AND LATTICE ANHARMONICITY OF GALLIUM ANTIMONIDE AND GALLIUM PHOSPHIDE FROM ULTRASONIC VELOCITY MEASUREMENTS BETWEEN 4.2 AND 300 K.**
BOYLE, W. F. SLADEK, R. J.
PHYS. REV.
11 B (8), 2933–40, 1975.

66680 **INFRARED VIBRATIONAL SPECTRUM OF CRYSTALLINE ARSENIC SULFIDE.**
TREACY, D. TAYLOR, P. C.
PHYS. REV.
11 B (8), 2941–7, 1975.

66682 **THEORY OF BAND-POPULATION EFFECTS IN ELECTRO-REFLECTANCE.**
BOTTKA, N. JOHNSON, D. L.
PHYS. REV.
11 B (8), 2969–78, 1975.

66683 **PHONON-GENERATED MICROFIELDS AND TEMPERATURE DEPENDENCE OF THE ABSORPTION EDGE IN II–VI COMPOUNDS.**
YACOBI, B. G. BRADA, Y. LACHISH, U. HIRSCH, C.
PHYS. REV.
11 B (8), 2990–8, 1975.

66684 **STRUCTURE OF THE VALENCE BANDS OF ZINC-BLENDE-TYPE SEMICONDUCTORS.**
PANTELIDES, S. T. HARRISON, W. A.
PHYS. REV.
11 B (8), 3006–21, 1975.

66685 **LANDAU LEVELS AT THE E(1) EDGE IN SEMICONDUCTORS.**
INKSON, J. C.
PHYS. REV.
11 B (8), 3022–30, 1975.

66686 **NONLINEAR CONDUCTIVITY TENSOR IN GRADED MIXED SEMICONDUCTORS.**
LEIBLER, L. MYCIELSKI, J. FURDYNA, J. K.
PHYS. REV.
11 (8), 3037–44, 1975.

EPIC Number	Bibliographic Citation

66687 COEXISTENCE OF TETRAGONAL WITH ORTHORHOMBIC OR TRIGONAL JAHN-TELLER DISTORTIONS IN AN OXYGEN COMPLEX: A PLAUSIBLE INTERPRETATION OF ALKALI-HALIDE PHOSPHORS LUMINESCENCE.
BACCI, M. RANFAGNI, A. FONTANA, M. P.
VILIANI, G.
PHYS. REV.
11 B (8), 3052-9, 1975.

66688 DYNAMICS OF EXCITON-POLARITON RECOMBINATION IN CADMIUM SULFIDE.
WIESNER, P. HEIM, U.
PHYS. REV.
11 B (8), 3071-7, 1975.

66689 TUNNELING STATES OF CYANIDE IN VARIOUS ALKALI HALIDES: STUDY OF RESOLVED TUNNELING STRUCTURES AND PARAELASTIC SIDEBANDS IN THE VIBRATIONAL ABSORPTION OF CYANIDE.
BEYELER, H. U.
PHYS. REV.
11 B (8), 3078-97, 1975.

66690 OPTICAL ABSORPTION AND ELECTRIC CONDUCTIVITY OF SILICON CARBIDE FILMS PRODUCED BY ION IMPLANATATION.
ROTHEMUND, W. FRITZSCHE, C. R.
J. ELECTROCHEM. SOC.
121 (4), 586-8, 1974.

66691 OPTICAL ABSORPTION EDGE IN GALLIUM SELENIDE UNDER HYDROSTATIC PRESSURE.
BESSON, J. M. JAIN, K. P. KUHN, A.
PHYS. REV. LETT.
32 (17), 936-9, 1974.

66692 SPECTRA OF LIGHT REFLECTED OFF CADMIUM MERCURY TELLURIDE THIN FILMS.
IGNATOWICZ, S. A. KISIEL, A. ZIMNAL, M.
THIN SOLID FILMS
21 (2), 231-6, 1974.

66696 NONLOCAL DIELECTRIC SUSCEPTIBILITY OF A SEMIINFINITE INSULATOR.
HYZHNYAKOV, V. V. MARADUDIN, A. A.
MILLS, D. L.
PHYS. REV.
11 B (8), 3149-62, 1975.

66698 STRUCTURE AND PROPERTIES OF NIOBIUM TIN HYDROXIDE.
VIELAND, L. J. WICKLUND, A. W. WHITE, J. G.
PHYS. REV.
11 B (9), 3311-6, 1975.

66700 ELECTRICAL CONDUCTIVITY IN NARROW-BAND MATERIALS.
ESWARAN, M. KIMBALL, J. C.
PHYS. REV.
11 B (9), 3420-30, 1975.

66701 ENERGY BANDS, ELECTRONIC PROPERTIES, AND MAGNETIC ORDERING OF CHROMIUM BROMIDE.
LIU, S. H. KOPP, L. ENGLAND, W. B.
MYRON, H. W.
PHYS. REV.
11 B (9), 3463-8, 1975.

66703 TEMPERATURE DEPENDENCE OF MAGNETORESISTANCE IN THE NICKEL ALUMINUM SYSTEM.
HAMBOURGER, P. D. OLWERT, R. J. CHU, C. W.
PHYS. REV.
11 B (9), 3501-3, 1975.

66708 THE EFFECT OF LATTICE PARAMETER MISMATCH IN NEGATIVE ELECTRON AFFINITY GALLIUM ARSENIDE PHOTOCATHODES GROWN ON GALLIUM PHOSPHIDE/INDIUM GALLIUM PHOSPHIDE SUBSTRATES.
ENSTROM, R. E. FISHER, D. G.
J. APPL. PHYS.
46 (5), 1976-82, 1975.

66711 HIGH-CONTRAST OPTICAL STORAGE IN VANADIUM DIOXIDE FILMS.
BALBERG, I. TROKMAN, S.
J. APPL. PHYS.
46 (5), 2111-9, 1975.

66713 REDUCED DEGRADATION IN INDIUM GALLIUM ARSENIDE ELECTROLUMINESCENT DIODES.
ETTENBERG, M. NUESE, C. J.
J. APPL. PHYS.
46 (5), 2137-42, 1975.

66714 TEMPERATURE DEPENDENCE OF MINORITY-CARRIER LIFETIME IN VAPOR-GROWN GALLIUM PHOSPHIDE.
WESSELS, B. W.
J. APPL. PHYS.
46 (5), 2143-6, 1975.

66715 SPECTRAL DISTRIBUTION OF PHOTOIONIZATION CROSS SECTIONS BY PHOTOCONDUCTIVITY MEASUREMENTS.
GRIMMEISS, H. G. LEDEBO, L. A.
J. APPL. PHYS.
46 (5), 2155-62, 1975.

66716 SELF-FOCUSING OF NEAR-INFRARED LASER BEAMS IN GALLIUM ARSENIDE.
MILLER, R. C. NORDLAND, W. A., JR.
J. APPL. PHYS.
46 (5), 2177-80, 1975.

66717 OPTICAL WAVEGUIDING IN LITHIUM NIOBIUM OXIDE SINGLE CRYSTAL FILM GROWN BY THE EPITAXIAL-GROWTH-BY-MELTING TECHNIQUE.
MIYAZAWA, S. SUGII, K. UCHIDA, N.
J. APPL. PHYS.
46 (5), 2223-8, 1975.

66719 FABRICATION OF FLEXIBLE SUPERCONDUCTING NIOBIUM ALUMINUM TAPE.
HARASYN, D. E. TOTH, L. E.
J. APPL. PHYS.
46 (5), 2232-6, 1975.

66720 SUPERCONDUCTING PROPERTIES OF GETTER-SPUTTERED VANADIUM ALUMINUM THIN FILMS AS A FUNCTION OF SPUTTERING GAS, PRESSURE, AND SUBSTRATE TEMPERATURE.
SCHMIDT, P. H. BACON, D. D. BARZ, H.
COOPER, A. S.
J. APPL. PHYS.
46 (5), 2237-43, 1975.

66723 ELECTROLUMINESCENCE IN ALUMINUM - ALUMINUM OXIDE - GOLD DIODES.
PONG, W. INOUYE, C. MATSUNAGA, F.
MORIWAKI, M.
J. APPL. PHYS.
46 (5), 2310-2, 1975.

66726 PERMITTIVITY AND INSTABILITY OF THE UNIFORM STATE OF NARROW-BAND FERROMAGNETIC SEMICONDUCTORS.
ZIL'BERVARG, V. E. NAGAEV, E. L.
FIZ. TVERD. TELA
16 (10), 2834-41, 1974.
(FOR ENGLISH TRANSLATION SEE E66727)

66727 PERMITTIVITY AND INSTABILITY OF THE UNIFORM STATE OF NARROW-BAND FERROMAGNETIC SEMICONDUCTORS.
ZIL'BERVARG, V. E. NAGAEV, E. L.
SOV. PHYS. SOLID STATE
16 (10), 1838-41, 1975.
(ENGLISH TRANSLATION OF FIZ. TVERD. TELA, 16 (10), 2834-41, 1974; FOR ORIGINAL SEE E66726)

66728 MEASUREMENT OF THE ELECTRON HALL MOBILITY IN ALKALINE-EARTH OXIDE CRYSTALS.
KOVALEV, N. N. KRASIN'KOVA, M. V.
FIZ. TVERD. TELA
16 (10), 2842-8, 1974.
(FOR ENGLISH TRANSLATION SEE E66729)

66729 MEASUREMENT OF THE ELECTRON HALL MOBILITY IN ALKALINE-EARTH OXIDE CRYSTALS.
KOVALEV, N. N. KRASIN'KOVA, M. V.
SOV. PHYS. SOLID STATE
16 (10), 1842-5, 1975.
(ENGLISH TRANSLATION OF FIZ. TVERD. TELA, 16 (10), 2842-8, 1974; FOR ORIGINAL SEE E66728)

66730 MAGNETIC SPECTRA OF CADMIUM AND COPPER CHALCOGENIDE CHROMITES.
PODSEKIN, A. K. DEM'YANOV, V. V.
ALFEROV, V. A. GORDEEV, I. V.
TRET'YAKOV, YU. D.
FIZ. TVERD. TELA
16 (10), 2868-72, 1974.
(FOR ENGLISH TRANSLATION SEE E66731)

66731 MAGNETIC SPECTRA OF CADMIUM AND COPPER CHALCOGENIDE CHROMITES.
PODSEKIN, A. K. DEM'YANOV, V. V.
ALFEROV, V. A. GORDEEV, I. V.
TRET'YAKOV, YU. D.
SOV. PHYS. SOLID STATE
16 (10), 1857-9, 1975.
(ENGLISH TRANSLATION OF FIZ. TVERD. TELA, 16 (10), 2868-72, 1974; FOR ORIGINAL SEE E66730)

66732 OSCILLATION OF THE MAGNETORESISTANCE OF N-INDIUM ANTIMONIDE IN A HIGH ELECTRIC FIELD.
KADUSHKIN, V. I.
FIZ. TVERD. TELA
16 (10), 2903-6, 1974.
(FOR ENGLISH TRANSLATION SEE E66733)

66733 OSCILLATION OF THE MAGNETORESISTANCE OF N-INDIUM ANTIMONIDE IN A HIGH ELECTRIC FIELD.
KADUSHKIN, V. I.
SOV. PHYS. SOLID STATE
16 (10), 1879-81, 1975.
(ENGLISH TRANSLATION OF FIZ. TVERD. TELA, 16 (10), 2903-6, 1974; FOR ORIGINAL SEE E66732)

66734 EFFECT OF PRESSURE ON IMPURITY CONDUCTION ON N-TYPE INDIUM ANTIMONIDE.
ITSKEVICH, E. S. KASHIRSKAYA, L. M.
FIZ. TVERD. TELA
16 (10), 2917-24, 1974.
(FOR ENGLISH TRANSLATION SEE E66735)

EPIC Number	Bibliographic Citation
66735	**EFFECT OF PRESSURE ON IMPURITY CONDUCTION ON N-TYPE INDIUM ANTIMONIDE.** ITSKEVICH, E. S. KASHIRSKAYA, L. M. SOV. PHYS. SOLID STATE 16 (10), 1888-92, 1975. (ENGLISH TRANSLATION OF FIZ. TVERD. TELA, 16 (10), 2917-24, 1974; FOR ORIGINAL SEE E66734)
66736	**MAGNETIC FREEZE-OUT IN N-TYPE INDIUM ANTIMONIDE UNDER PRESSURE.** ITSKEVICH, E. S. KASHIRSKAYA, L. M. SUKHOPAROV, V. A. FIZ. TVERD. TELA 16 (10), 2925-33, 1974. (FOR ENGLISH TRANSLATION SEE E66737)
66737	**MAGNETIC FREEZE-OUT IN N-TYPE INDIUM ANTIMONIDE UNDER PRESSURE.** ITSKEVICH, E. S. KASHIRSKAYA, L. M. SUKHOPAROV, V. A. SOV. PHYS. SOLID STATE 16 (10), 1893-8, 1975. (ENGLISH TRANSLATION OF FIZ. TVERD. TELA, 16 (10), 2925-33, 1974; FOR ORIGINAL SEE E66736)
66740	**DOMAIN STRUCTURE OF RARE EARTH ORTHOFERRITES IN THE SPIN-SWITCHING REGION.** IVANOV, B. A. KRASNOV, V. P. FIZ. TVERD. TELA 16 (10), 2971-7, 1974. (FOR ENGLISH TRANSLATION SEE E66741)
66741	**DOMAIN STRUCTURE OF RARE EARTH ORTHOFERRITES IN THE SPIN-SWITCHING REGION.** IVANOV, B. A. KRASNOV, V. P. SOV. PHYS. SOLID STATE 16 (10), 1922-5, 1975. (ENGLISH TRANSLATION OF FIZ. TVERD. TELA, 16 (10), 2971-7, 1974; FOR ORIGINAL SEE E66740)
66742	**ROLE OF R CENTERS IN FORMATION OF AN EXCITON STRUCTURE IN THE PHOTOCONDUCTIVITY SPECTRA OF CADMIUM SULFIDE CRYSTALS.** IL'INSKII, A. V. NOVIKOV, B. V. SUTULOVA, S. I. FIZ. TVERD. TELA 16 (10), 3029-33, 1974. (FOR ENGLISH TRANSLATION SEE E66743)
66743	**ROLE OF R CENTERS IN FORMATION OF AN EXCITON STRUCTURE IN THE PHOTOCONDUCTIVITY SPECTRA OF CADMIUM SULFIDE CRYSTALS.** IL'INSKII, A. V. NOVIKOV, B. V. SUTULOVA, S. I. SOV. PHYS. SOLID STATE 16 (10), 1957-9, 1975. (ENGLISH TRANSLATION OF FIZ. TVERD. TELA, 16 (10), 3029-33, 1974; FOR ORIGINAL SEE E66742)
66744	**ELECTRICAL CONDUCTIVITY AND THERMAL ELECTROMOTIVE FORCE OF ALKALI EARTH METAL OXIDES AT 700-2000 K.** KOVALEV, N. N. KRASIN'KOVA, M. V. FIZ. TVERD. TELA 16 (10), 3034-8, 1974. (FOR ENGLISH TRANSLATION SEE E66745)
66745	**ELECTRICAL CONDUCTIVITY AND THERMAL ELECTROMOTIVE FORCE OF ALKALI EARTH METAL OXIDES AT 700-2000 K.** KOVALEV, N. N. KRASIN'KOVA, M. V. SOV. PHYS. SOLID STATE 16 (10), 1960-2, 1975. (ENGLISH TRANSLATION OF FIZ. TVERD. TELA, 16 (10), 3034-8, 1974; FOR ORIGINAL SEE E66744)
66752	**NEW TYPE OF DOMAIN STRUCTURE IN EPITAXIAL YTTRIUM - BISMUTH - GALLIUM GARNET FILMS.** BALBASHOV, A. M. CHERVONENKIS, A. YA. CHERKASOV, A. P. BAKHTEUZOV, V. E. FIZ. TVERD. TELA 16 (10), 3102-3, 1974. (FOR ENGLISH TRANSLATION SEE E66753)
66753	**NEW TYPE OF DOMAIN STRUCTURE IN EPITAXIAL YTTRIUM - BISMUTH - GALLIUM GARNET FILMS.** BALBASHOV, A. M. CHERVONENKIS, A. YA. CHERKASOV, A. P. BAKHTEUZOV, V. E. SOV. PHYS. SOLID STATE 16 (10), 2002, 1975. (ENGLISH TRANSLATION OF FIZ. TVERD. TELA, 16 (10), 3102-3, 1974; FOR ORIGINAL SEE E66752)
66754	**ELECTRICAL CONDUCTIVITY AND OPTICAL TRANSMISSION OF HIGHLY DISPERSE CADMIUM SULFIDE FILMS.** PETROV, YU. I. MANAEVSKII, M. A. FIZ. TVERD. TELA 16 (10), 3104-5, 1974. (FOR ENGLISH TRANSLATION SEE E66755)
66755	**ELECTRICAL CONDUCTIVITY AND OPTICAL TRANSMISSION OF HIGHLY DISPERSE CADMIUM SULFIDE FILMS.** PETROV, YU. I. MANAEVSKII, M. A. SOV. PHYS. SOLID STATE 16 (10), 2003-4, 1975. (ENGLISH TRANSLATION OF FIZ. TVERD. TELA, 16 (10), 3104-5, 1974; FOR ORIGINAL SEE E66754)
66756	**FIELD EFFECTS IN VANADIUM DIOXIDE FILMS.** MOKROUSOV, V. V. KORNETOV, V. N. FIZ. TVERD. TELA 16 (10), 3106-7, 1974. (FOR ENGLISH TRANSLATION SEE E66757)
66757	**FIELD EFFECTS IN VANADIUM DIOXIDE FILMS.** MOKROUSOV, V. V. KORNETOV, V. N. SOV. PHYS. SOLID STATE 16 (10), 2005, 1975. (ENGLISH TRANSLATION OF FIZ. TVERD. TELA, 16 (10), 3106-7, 1974; FOR ORIGINAL SEE E66756)
66760	**ENERGY STRUCTURE OF BERYLLIUM DIBORIDE.** TUPITSYN, I. I. LYAKHOVSKAYA, I. I. NAKHMANSON, M. S. SUKHIKH, A. S. FIZ. TVERD. TELA 16 (10), 3117-9, 1974. (FOR ENGLISH TRANSLATION SEE E66761)
66761	**ENERGY STRUCTURE OF BERYLLIUM DIBORIDE.** TUPITSYN, I. I. LYAKHOVSKAYA, I. I. NAKHMANSON, M. S. SUKHIKH, A. S. SOV. PHYS. SOLID STATE 16 (10), 2015-6, 1975. (ENGLISH TRANSLATION OF FIZ. TVERD. TELA, 16 (10), 3117-9, 1974; FOR ORIGINAL SEE E66760)
66762	**POSITION OF THE FUNDAMENTAL ABSORPTION EDGE OF CRYSTALLINE TITANIUM DIOXIDE.** PAK, V. N. FIZ. TVERD. TELA 16 (10), 3127-8, 1974. (FOR ENGLISH TRANSLATION, SEE E66763)
66763	**POSITION OF THE FUNDAMENTAL ABSORPTION EDGE OF CRYSTALLINE TITANIUM DIOXIDE.** PAK, V. N. SOV. PHYS. SOLID STATE 16 (10), 2023, 1975. (ENGLISH TRANSLATION OF FIZ. TVERD. TELA, 16 (10), 3127-8, 1974; FOR ORIGINAL SEE E66762)
66770	**HYPERFINE FIELDS IN GADOLINIUM IRON AND YTTRIUM IRON INTERMETALLIC COMPOUNDS.** NIKITIN, S. A. VASIL'KOVSKII, V. A. KOVTUN, N. M. KUPRIYANOV, A. K. OSTROVSKII, V. F. FIZ. TVERD. TELA 16 (10), 3137-9, 1974. (FOR ENGLISH TRANSLATION SEE E66771)
66771	**HYPERFINE FIELDS IN GADOLINIUM IRON AND YTTRIUM IRON INTERMETALLIC COMPOUNDS.** NIKITIN, S. A. VASIL'KOVSKII, V. A. KOVTUN, N. M. KUPRIYANOV, A. K. OSTROVSKII, V. F. SOV. PHYS. SOLID STATE 16 (10), 2031-2, 1975. (ENGLISH TRANSLATION OF FIZ. TVERD. TELA, 16 (10), 3137-9, 1974; FOR ORIGINAL SEE E66770)
66774	**PHOTOFERROMAGNETIC EFFECT AND PHOTOCONDUCTIVITY OF THE CADMIUM ZINC CHROMIUM SELENIDE SYSTEM.** MAKHOTKIN, V. E. SHABUNINA, G. G. AMINOV, T. G. VINOGRADOVA, G. I. VESELAGO, V. G. FIZ. TVERD. TELA 16 (10), 3141-2, 1974. (FOR ENGLISH TRANSLATION SEE E66775)
66775	**PHOTOFERROMAGNETIC EFFECT AND PHOTOCONDUCTIVITY OF THE CADMIUM ZINC CHROMIUM SELENIDE SYSTEM.** MAKHOTKIN, V. E. SHABUNINA, G. G. AMINOV, T. G. VINOGRADOVA, G. I. VESELAGO, V. G. SOV. PHYS. SOLID STATE 16 (10), 2034-5, 1975. (ENGLISH TRANSLATION OF FIZ. TVERD. TELA, 16 (10), 3141-2, 1974; FOR ORIGINAL SEE E66774)
66778	**ELECTRON-CAPTURE CROSS SECTION OF HOLE ACTIVATOR CENTERS IN POTASSIUM CHLORIDE : EUROPIUM.** NEDASHKOVSKII, A. P. AVDONIN, V. P. DOUGAROVA, L. D. PLACHENOV, B. T. SAVEL'EV, V. P. FIZ. TVERD. TELA 16 (10), 3151-2, 1974. (FOR ENGLISH TRANSLATION SEE E66779)

EPIC Number	Bibliographic Citation
66779	**ELECTRON-CAPTURE CROSS SECTION OF HOLE ACTIVATOR CENTERS IN POTASSIUM CHLORIDE : EUROPIUM.** NEDASHKOVSKII, A. P. AVDONIN, V. P. DOUGAROVA, L. D. PLACHENOV, B. T. SAVEL'EV, V. P. SOV. PHYS. SOLID STATE 16 (10), 2044–5, 1975. (ENGLISH TRANSLATION OF FIZ. TVERD. TELA, 16 (10), 3151–2, 1974; FOR ORIGINAL SEE E66778)
66782	**OPTICAL AND THERMAL DEPTH OF ENERGY LEVELS OF PHOTOSENSITIVE PARAMAGNETIC CENTERS IN II–VI SINGLE CRYSTALS.** KODZHESPIROV, F. F. BULANYI, M. F. TEREB, I. A. FIZ. TVERD. TELA 16 (10), 3159–62, 1974. (FOR ENGLISH TRANSLATION SEE E66783)
66783	**OPTICAL AND THERMAL DEPTH OF ENERGY LEVELS OF PHOTOSENSITIVE PARAMAGNENTIC CENTERS IN II–VI SINGLE CRYSTALS.** KODZHESPIROV, F. F. BULANYI, M. F. TEREB, I. A. SOV. PHYS. SOLID STATE 16 (10), 2052–3, 1975. (ENGLISH TRANSLATION OF FIZ. TVERD. TELA, 16 (10), 3159–62, 1974; FOR ORIGINAL SEE E66782)
66784	**DISLOCATION EXCITONS IN POTASSIUM IODIDE CRYSTALS.** MARKOVA–OSORGINA, I. A. SHMURAK, S. Z. FIZ. TVERD. TELA 16 (10), 3164–6, 1974. (FOR ENGLISH TRANSLATION SEE E66785)
66785	**DISLOCATION EXCITONS IN POTASSIUM IODIDE CRYSTALS.** MARKOVA–OSORGINA, I. A. SHMURAK, S. Z. SOV. PHYS. SOLID STATE 16 (10), 2056–7, 1975. (ENGLISH TRANSLATION OF FIZ. TVERD. TELA, 16 (10), 3164–6, 1974; FOR ORIGINAL SEE E66784)
66786	**POSSIBLE MECHANISM OF THE FORMATION OF A THROUGH NUCLEUS OF MAGNETIZATION SWITCHING IN ORTHOFERRITES.** NENAST'EV, V. P. RUDYAK, V. M. FIZ. TVERD. TELA 16 (10), 3167–9, 1974. (FOR ENGLISH TRANSLATION SEE E66787)
66787	**POSSIBLE MECHANISM OF THE FORMATION OF A THROUGH NUCLEUS OF MAGNETIZATION SWITCHING IN ORTHOFERRITES.** NENAST'EV, V. P. RUDYAK, V. M. SOV. PHYS. SOLID STATE 16 (10), 2059–60, 1975. (ENGLISH TRANSLATION OF FIZ. TVERD. TELA, 19 (10), 3167–9, 1974; FOR ORIGINAL SEE E66786)
66788	**INDUCED ELECTROOPTIC ABSORPTION EFFECT IN A BARIUM TITANATE SINGLE CRYSTAL.** SONIN, A. S. GUSEVA, L. M. PLESHAKOV, I. A. KASHLAKOVA, I. V. FIZ. TVERD. TELA 16 (10), 3172–3, 1974. (FOR ENGLISH TRANSLATION SEE E66789)
66789	**INDUCED ELECTROOPTIC ABSORPTION EFFECT IN A BARIUM TITANATE SINGLE CRYSTAL.** SONIN, A. S. GUSEVA, L. M. PLESHAKOV, I. A. KASHLAKOVA, I. V. SOV. PHYS. SOLID STATE 16 (10), 2063–4, 1975. (ENGLISH TRANSLATION OF FIZ. TVERD. TELA, 16 (10), 3172–3, 1974; FOR ORIGINAL SEE E66788)
66790	**INFLUENCE OF THE MAGNETIC ORDERING ON THE PHOTOCONDUCTIVITY OF CADMIUM CHROMIUM SELENIDE.** SALYGANOV, V. I. SHIL'NIKOV, YU. R. YAKOVLEV, YU. M. FEDOROV, V. L. VINNIK, M. A. RUBAL'SKAYA, E. V. FIZ. TVERD. TELA 16 (10), 3174–6, 1974. (FOR ENGLISH TRANSLATION SEE E66791)
66791	**INFLUENCE OF THE MAGNETIC ORDERING ON THE PHOTOCONDUCTIVITY OF CADMIUM CHROMIUM SELENIDE.** SALYGANOV, V. I. SHIL'NIKOV, YU. R. YAKOVLEV, YU. M. FEDOVOV, V. L. VINNIK, M. A. RUBAL'SKAYA, E. V. SOV. PHYS. SOLID STATE 16 (10), 2065–6, 1975. (ENGLISH TRANSLATION OF FIZ. TVERD. TELA, 16 (10), 3174–6, 1974; FOR ORIGINAL SEE E66790)
66796	**FERROELECTRIC AND FERROMAGNETIC PROPERTIES OF THIN CONDENSED FILMS.** TOMASHPOL'SKII, YU. YA. FIZ. TVERD. TELA 16 (10), 3191–2, 1974. (FOR ENGLISH TRANSLATION SEE E66797)
66797	**FERROELECTRIC AND FERROMAGNETIC PROPERTIES OF THIN CONDENSED FILMS.** TOMASHPOL'SKII, YU. YA. SOV. PHYS. SOLID STATE 16 (10), 2081, 1975. (ENGLISH TRANSLATION OF FIZ. TVERD. TELA, 16 (10), 3191–2, 1974; FOR ORIGINAL SEE E66796)
66798	**HYSTERESIS OF TEMPERATURE DEPENDENCE OF PHOTOCURRENT ON CADMIUM SULFIDE SINGLE CRYSTALS.** ZOTOV, V. V. MATER. NAUK. KONF. MOLODIKH UCH. UNIV., ODES. DERZH. UNIV. 236–8, 1968.
66801	**PREPARATION AND PROPERTIES OF CHROMIUM–DOPED SEMICONDUCTING AND SEMIINSULATING GALLIUM ARSENIDE SINGLE CRYSTALS.** PODOR, B. ZSINDELY, S. PAPP, E. KOZL. MAGY. TUD. AKAD. MUSZ. FIZ. KUT. INTEZ. (.0–3), 43–51, 1971.
66806	**EXOEMISSION OF IONIC COMPOUNDS. RECENT DEVELOPMENTS AND BASIC PROBLEMS.** KAAMBRE, H. INTERN. SYMP. EXOELECTRON EMISSION AND DOSIMETRY, 4TH 57–71PP., 1974.
66807	**EXOELECTRON EMISSION OF EVAPORATED LITHIUM FLUORIDE FILMS.** HUZIMURA, R. MAEDA, M. TAKAHASHI, A. INTERN. SYMP. EXOELECTRON EMISSION AND DOSIMETRY, 4TH 72–4PP., 1974.
66808	**EMISSION OF HIGH ENERGY ELECTRONS BY MECHANICAL TREATMENT OF ALKALI HALIDES.** LINKE, E. WOLLBRANDT, J. INTERN. SYMP. EXOELECTRON EMISSION AND DOSIMETRY, 4TH 75–8PP., 1974.
66809	**EXOELECTRON EMISSION FROM CESIUM IODIDE.** ONSGAARD, J. ENNOW, K. R. INTERN. SYMP. EXOELECTRON EMISSION AND DOSIMETRY, 4TH 79–81PP., 1974.
66810	**SHIFT OF THERMALLY STIMULATED EXOELECTRON EMISSION MAXIMUM AND EXOELECTRON YIELD DURING THE THERMAL TREATMENT OF BERYLLIUM OXIDE POWDER. [DOSIMETER PREPARATION].** MLITZKE, E. INTERN. SYMP. EXOELECTRON EMISSION AND DOSIMETRY, 4TH 82–4PP., 1974.
66811	**EXOELECTRON EMISSION OF BERYLLIUM OXIDE.** EULER, M. SCHARMANN, A. INTERN. SYMP. EXOELECTRON EMISSION AND DOSIMETRY, 4TH 85–9PP., 1974.
66812	**ENERGY ANALYSIS OF THERMALLY STIMULATED EXOELECTRONS FROM BERYLLIUM OXIDE.** PETERSON, D. D. REGULLA, D. F. WACHSMANN, F. INTERN. SYMP. EXOELECTRON EMISSION AND DOSIMETRY, 4TH 90–2PP., 1974.
66813	**TRAPPING CENTERS AND ACTIVATORS IN THERMALOX BERYLLIUM OXIDE [EPR CHARACTERIZATION AND ROLE IN EXOELECTRON EMISSION].** GAMMAGE, R. B. GARRISON, A. K. INTERN. SYMP. EXOELECTRON EMISSION AND DOSIMETRY, 4TH 93–5PP., 1974.
66814	**CALIBRATION AND RESOLUTION IN THERMALLY STIMULATED EXOELECTRON EMISSION TRAP SPECTROSCOPY.** HOLZAPFEL, G. WOLBER, L. INTERN. SYMP. EXOELECTRON EMISSION AND DOSIMETRY, 4TH 111–13PP., 1974.
66817	**OPTICALLY STIMULATED EXOELECTRON EMISSION FROM SIMPLE AND COMPLEX COMPOUNDS.** HOLZAPFEL, G. NINK, R. INTERN. SYMP. EXOELECTRON EMISSION AND DOSIMETRY, 4TH 133–6PP., 1974.
66818	**RETARDING FIELD MEASUREMENTS ON OPTICALLY STIMULATED EXOELECTRON EMISSION FROM POTASSIUM SULFATE SURFACES.** BRUNSMANN, U. SCHARMANN, A. INTERN. SYMP. EXOELECTRON EMISSION AND DOSIMETRY, 4TH 137–41PP., 1974.
66819	**THE PHYSICO–CHEMICAL NATURE OF EXOELECTRON EMISSION.** KRYLOVA, I. V. INTERN. SYMP. EXOELECTRON EMISSION AND DOSIMETRY, 4TH 145–53PP., 1974.
66821	**EXOELECTRON–EMISSION, RESEARCH AND APPLICATION IN CHEMISTRY AND BIOLOGY.** ROBOCK, K. INTERN. SYMP. EXOELECTRON EMISSION AND DOSIMETRY, 4TH 162–77PP., 1974.

EPIC Number	Bibliographic Citation

66825 APPLICATION OF LITHIUM OXIDE TREATED BERYLLIUM OXIDE CERAMICS FOR THE DETECTION OF FAST NEUTRONS IN MIXED RADIATION FIELDS.
KRIEGSEIS, W. SCHARMANN, A.
INTERN. SYMP. EXOELECTRON EMISSION AND DOSIMETRY, 4TH
236–40PP., 1974.

66826 ABOUT THE ENERGY DEPENDENCE OF THE EXOELECTRON EMISSION OF BERYLLIUM OXIDE IRRADIATED BY PHOTONS. [DOSIMETER].
KIRKS, H. J. SIEGEL, V.
INTERN. SYMP. EXOELECTRON EMISSION AND DOSIMETRY, 4TH
241–3PP., 1974.

66828 SIMULTANEOUS THERMOLUMINESCENCE AND THERMALLY STIMULATED EXOELECTRON EMISSION MEASUREMENTS ON SOME THERMAL LUMINESCENCE DEVICE MATERIALS.
PETEL, M. HOLZAPFEL, G.
INTERN. SYMP. EXOELECTRON EMISSION AND DOSIMETRY, 4TH
252–4PP., 1974.

66845 ELECTRICAL CONDUCTIVITY OF SINGLE-CRYSTAL AND POLYCRYSTALLINE NICKEL OXIDE AT HIGH TEMPERATURES.
DEREN, J. JARZEBSKI, Z. M. MROWEC, S.
WALEC, T.
BULL. ACAD. POL. SCI., SER. SCI. CHIM.
19 (2), 147–52, 1971.

66847 STIMULATION OF PHOTOELECTRIC EMISSION FROM SEMICONDUCTORS.
BORZYAK, P. G.
TRANS. IMEKO (INT. MEAS. CONFED.) SYMP. PHOTON DETECTORS, 4TH
13–28PP., 1970.

66848 OPTICAL AND PHOTOELECTRIC PROPERTIES OF THIN CESIUM OXIDE LAYERS.
HOENE, E. L.
TRANS. IMEKO (INT. MEAS. CONFED.) SYMP. PHOTON DETECTORS, 4TH
29–41PP., 1970.

66855 PLASTIC DEFORMATION OF IONIC CRYSTALS IN THE PRESENCE OF VARIOUS EXTERNAL EFFECTS.
ZAGORUIKO, N. V.
TR. UNIV. DRUZHBY NAR.
(62), 99–112, 1972.

66864 ELECTROOPTIC CERAMICS.
LAND, C. E. THACHER, P. D. HAERTLING, G. H.
APPL. SOLID STATE SCI.
4, 137–233, 1974.

66865 NARROW-GAP SEMICONDUCTORS.
HARMAN, T. C. MELNGAILIS, I.
APPL. SOLID STATE SCI.
4, 1–94, 1974.

66869 THE CHARACTERISTIC PROPERTIES OF MATERIALS FOR OPTICAL FIBRES.
PASSARET, M.
ANN. TELECOMMUN.
29 (5–6), 179–88, 1974.

66874 ELECTROLUMINESCENT DIODES OF EPITAXIAL GALLIUM ARSENIDE.
PIQUERAS, J. MENDEZ, E. FERNANDEZ, A.
MUNOZ, E.
AN. FIS.
70 (1), 106–9, 1974.

66876 CRYSTAL GROWTH AND OPTICAL PROPERTIES OF GALLIUM NITRIDE.
AOKI, M. MATSUMOTO, T. SANO, M.
ANNU. REP. ENG. RES. INST. FAC. ENG. UNIV. TOKYO
32, 115–20, 1973

66878 EMISSION PHENOMENA IN HOLMIUM TRIPOSITIVE-ACTIVATED LANTHANUM NIOBATE CRYSTALS.
VAKHIDOV, SH. A. MOROZOV, A. M.
NURULLAEV, E.
IZV. AKAD. NAUK UZB. SSR, SER. FIZ.-MAT. NAUK
18 (3), 96–8, 1974.

66879 ALTERNATIVE INTERPRETATIONS OF DIELECTRIC MEASUREMENTS WITH PARTICULAR REFERENCE TO POLAR LIQUIDS.
SHEPPARD, R. J. GRANT, E. H.
ADV. MOL. RELAXATION PROCESSES
6 (1), 61–7, 1974.

66880 RESULTS OF INVESTIGATION OF DIRECT CURRENT ARC BURNING IN AN ATMOSPHERE OF WATER VAPOR.
PAVLOVIC, B. IKONOMOV, N. TODOROVIC, M.
ACTA CHIM. ACAD. SCI. HUNG.
82 (2), 193–9, 1974.

66882 EFFECTS OF HEAT TREATMENT ON THE MAGNETIC PROPERTIES OF AN EPITAXIAL GALLIUM DOPED YTTRIUM IRON GARNET.
SAKURAI, Y. MINAGAWA, S.
IEEE TRANS. MAGN.
MAG-9 (4), 624–6, 1973.

EPIC Number	Bibliographic Citation

66884 THE DIRECT CURRENT AND MICROWAVE-BIASED PHOTOCONDUCTIVE RESPONSE IN CADMIUM SULFIDE CRYSTALS.
HERCZFELD, P. R. HANLON, L. R.
IEEE TRANS. MICROWAVE THEORY TECH.
21 (2), 109–11, 1973.

66893 EFFECTS OF ELECTRON RADIATION ON THE ELECTRICAL AND OPTICAL PROPERTIES OF MERCURY CADMIUM TELLURIDE.
MALLON, C. E. NABER, J. A. COLWELL, J. F.
GREEN, B. A.
IEEE TRANS. NUCL. SCI.
20 (6), 214–19, 1973.

66899 PARTICLE-INITIATED BREAKDOWN BETWEEN COAXIAL ELECTRODES IN COMPRESSED SULFUR HEXAFLUORIDE.
COOKSON, A. H. FARISH, O.
IEEE TRANS. POWER APP. SYST.
92 (3), 871–6, 1973.

66903 MAGNETIC PHASE TRANSITIONS IN FOUR MANGANESE DOUBLE CHLORIDES.
BLOTE, H. W. J. HUISKAMP, W. J.
PHYSICA
53 (3), 445–70, 1971.

66910 SCANNING CATHODOLUMINESCENCE ANALYSES OF COMPOUND SEMICONDUCTORS.
HOSOKI, S. OKANO, H.
PROC. INT. CONF. X-RAY OPT. MICROANAL., 6TH
589–95, 1972.

66918 EVIDENCE FOR PARAELECTRIC BEHAVIOR IN LEAD TELLURIDE AND PSEUDOBINARIES BASED ON LEAD TELLURIDE.
BATE, R. T. CARTER, D. L. WROBEL, J. S.
PROC. INT. CONF. PHYS. SEMICOND., 10TH
125–9PP., 1970.

66920 LUMINESCENCE SPECTRA OF EUROPIUM COMPOUNDS AND NICKEL OXIDE.
TSU, R. ESAKI, L.
PROC. INT. CONF. PHYS. SEMICOND., 10TH
282–5PP., 1970.

66927 OPTICAL PROPERTIES OF SUBSTITUTIONAL DONORS IN CADMIUM SULFIDE.
NASSAU, K. HENRY, C. H. SHIEVER, J. W.
PROC. INT. CONF. PHYS. SEMICOND., 10TH
629–32, 1970.

66928 EFFECT OF DISORDER ON THE BAND STRUCTURE OF SILICON GERMANIDE.
STROUD, D. EHRENREICH, H.
PROC. INT. CONF. PHYS. SEMICOND., 10TH
652–7, 1970.

66929 THE D.C. CONDUCTIVITY, OPTICAL ABSORPTION, AND PHOTOCONDUCTIVITY OF AMORPHOUS ARSENIC TELLURIDE - ARSENIC SELENIDE FILMS.
WEISER, K. FISCHER, R. BRODSKY, M. H.
PROC. INT. CONF. PHYS. SEMICOND., 10TH
667–72, 1970.

66930 LUMINESCENCE OF NUCLEAR EMULSIONS EXCITED BY ALPHA- AND BETA-RADIATION.
BELOUS, V. M. KARTUZHANSKII, A. L.
KEKHVA, T. E. PLACHENOV, B. T. SHUR, L. I.
PROC. INT. CONF. NUCL. PHOTOGR. SOLID STATE TRACK DETECTORS, 8TH
1, 88–94, 1972.

66933 EFFECT OF LITHIUM OXIDE ADDITION ON THE DENSITY AND ELECTRIC CONDUCTIVITY OF NICKEL(II) OXIDE SINTERED SAMPLES.
STIGLIC, R. TRBOJEVIC, LJ. STEVANOVIC, M.
POWDER TECHNOL. PUBL. SER.
4, 75–9, 1972.

66935 PHYSICAL PROPERTIES OF LOWER NICKEL PHOSPHIDES.
SAMSONOV, G. V. PADERNO, YU. B.
LAZORENKO, V. I. VITYAZ, P. A.
POROSH. MET.
11 (7), 68–72, 1971.

66936 PERSPECTIVES ON THE PRACTICAL USE OF POWDERED GALLIUM AND INDIUM PHOSPHIDES.
YARMOLA, T. M.
POROSH. MET.
11 (3), 97–100, 1971.

66959 NEW LABORATORY MEASUREMENTS OF THE TRANSITIONS OF CALCIUM HYDRIDE.
BERG, L. E. KLYNNING, L.
ASTRON. ASTROPHYS., SUPPL. SER.
13 (3), 325–44, 1974.

66970 SOME ASPECTS OF DIELECTRIC AND HALL EFFECT MEASUREMENTS AT MICROWAVE FREQUENCIES.
PETHIG, R. SOUTH, R. B.
CPEM 74 DIGEST: CONFERENCE ON PRECISION ELECTROMAGNETIC MEASUREMENTS
231–2PP., 1974.

66974 BASIC SOLID-STATE PHYSICS.
OLMSTEAD, J. A.
AUTOMOTIVE ELECTRONICS
3–15PP., 1974.

EPIC Number	Bibliographic Citation
66976	**EFFECT OF SCREENING ON THE MOBILITY OF CHARGE CARRIERS IN COMPENSATED MATERIALS.** AVAK'YANTS, G. M. DZHEREDZHYAN, A. A. KARAYAN, G. S. IZV. AKAD. NAUK ARM. SSR, FIZ. 7 (4), 267–77, 1972.
66977	**HIGH-TEMPERATURE STUDY OF THE SPECIFIC ELECTRICAL RESISTANCE OF IRON-ALUMINUM-SILICON ORDERED ALLOYS.** ARUTYUNYAN, S. V. IZV. AKAD. NAUK ARM. SSR, SER. TEKH. NAUK 24 (5), 54–7, 1971.
66984	**MAGNETORESISTANCE OF N-GALLIUM ARSENIDE EPITAXIAL LAYERS.** EMEL'YANENKO, O. V. NASLEDOV, D. N. NEDEOGLO, D. D. TIMCHENKO, I. N. IZV. AKAD. NAUK MOLD. SSR, SER. FIZ.-TEKH. MAT. NAUK (1), 64–7, 1972.
66986	**SPECTRAL DISTRIBUTION OF PHOTOCONDUCTIVITY IN ORIGINAL AND NONSTOICHIOMETRIC GALLIUM ANTIMONIDE.** BURDIYAN, I. I. KOLCHANOVA, N. M. MIRONOV, I. F. IZV. AKAD. NAUK MOLD. SSR, SER. FIZ.-TEKH. MAT. NAUK (3), 73–5, 1971.
66990	**REFRACTION IN RUBIDIUM CARBONATE TRI-HYDRATE.** SOKOL, V. I. DZYATKEVICH, B. S. DOBRYNINA, T. A. IZV. AKAD. NAUK SSSR, SER. KHIM. (12), 2654–7, 1971.
66991	**DETERMINATION OF THE FORBIDDEN BAND OF SINGLE CRYSTALS OF THALLIUM TELLURIDE.** KARIMOV, S. K. TURSUNOV, N. IZV. AKAD. NAUK TADZH. SSR, OTD. FIZ.-MAT. GEOL.-KHIM. NAUK (2), 19–27, 1972.
66992	**THALLIUM CHALCOGENIDES IN THE LIQUID AND SOLID STATES.** ABDUSALYAMOVA, M. N. IZV. AKAD. NAUK TADZH. SSR, OTD. FIZ.-MAT. GEOL.-KHIM. NAUK (2), 40–4, 1972.
66993	**DENSITY DEPENDENCE ON OPTICAL EFFECTIVE MASS OF CONDUCTION ELECTRONS IN III - V SEMICONDUCTOR COMPOUNDS.** DZHOTYAN, A. P. KAZARYAN, E. M. IZV. AKAD. NAUK ARM. SSR, FIZ. 6 (3), 197–202, 1971.
66997	**TEMPERATURE DEPENDENCE OF OPTICAL EFFECTIVE MASS OF ELECTRON IN III - V -TYPE SEMICONDUCTOR COMPOUNDS.** KAZARYAN, E. M. MAILYAN, G. L. IZV. AKAD. NAUK ARM. SSR, FIZ. 6 (5), 380–5, 1971.
66998	**EFFECT OF HIGH PRESSURE ON ELECTRICAL PROPERTIES OF P-GALLIUM ARSENIDE.** SVIRIDOV, I. F. PRESNOV, V. A. IZV. AKAD. NAUK ARM. SSR, FIZ. 6 (6), 487–91, 1971.
67004	**ANGULAR DEPENDENCE OF PHOTOEMISSION FROM GALLIUM ARSENIDE.** WOOTEN, F. HUEN, T. WINSOR, H. V. ELECTRON SPECTROSC., PROC. INT. CONF. 283–7PP., 1972.
67020	**MAGNETIC ORDERING IN PEROVSKITES.** BANKS, E. TASHIMA, N. FERRITES, PROC. INT. CONF. 581–4PP., 1971.
67028	**PHOTOEMISSION PROPERTIES OF BISMUTH-CESIUM LAYERS.** NANEV, K. NIKOLOV, B. IZV. INST. ELEKTRON., BULG. AKAD. NAUK. 5, 29–38, 1971.
67029	**INTEGRAL SENSITIVITY OF CESIUM ANTIMONIDE.** NANEV, K. IZV. INST. ELEKTRON., BULG. AKAD. NAUK. 5, 39–45, 1971.
67030	**DEVICE FOR PULSE MEASUREMENTS OF THE HALL AND MAGNETORESISTANCE EFFECTS IN SEMICONDUCTORS AND METALS.** VICHEV, B. IZV. INST. ELEKTRON., BULG. AKAD. NAUK. 5, 97–108, 1971.
67035	**MEASUREMENT OF THE PARAMETERS OF GALLIUM ARSENIDE FOR GUNN DIODES.** KOSTYREVA, I. V. ARISTARKHOV, A. I. MATKHANOVA, I. P. IZV. LENINGRAD. ELEKTROTEKH. INST. (96), 54–6, 1970.
67036	**PHYSICAL ADSORPTION ON SEMICONDUCTING SURFACES.** PESHEV, O. IZV. OTD. KHIM. NAUKI, BULG. AKAD. NAUK. 5 (2), 199–205, 1972.

EPIC Number	Bibliographic Citation
67037	**SENSITIZATION OF THE PHOTOCONDUCTIVITY AND PHOTO-EMF. OF AZIDES OF HEAVY METALS, COLORED BY ORGANIC DYES.** GAVRISHCHENKO, YU. V. SAVEL'EV, G. G. ZAKHAROV, YU. A. IZV. TOMSK. POLITEKH. INST. 185, 69–71, 1970.
67038	**ELECTRICAL STRENGTH OF SOME LIQUID DIELECTRICS IN THE NANOSECOND RANGE OF VOLTAGE ACTION.** KOROLEV, V. S. TORBIN, N. M. IZV. TOMSK. POLITEKH. INST. 180, 154–7, 1971.
67039	**ELECTRICAL PROPERTIES OF CRYSTALS OF SOLID SOLUTIONS OF POTASSIUM CHLORIDE-POTASSIUM BROMIDE SYSTEM COMPOUNDS.** ANNENKOV, YU. M. GRISHUKOV, V. A. IZV. TOMSK. POLITEKH. INST. 180, 164–6, 1971.
67046	**DETERMINATION OF THE CONCENTRATIONS AND MOBILITIES OF ELECTRONS AND HOLES ACCORDING TO THE RELATION OF THE HALL COEFFICIENT TO MAGNETIC INDUCTION.** KHARAKHORIN, F. F. BOYARINTSEV, P. K. ISSLED. MATER. NOV. TEKH., DOKL. NAUCH.-TEKH. KONF. 164–9, 1971.
67048	**EMISSION SPECTRA OF CADMIUM GALLIUM SULFIDE CRYSTALS.** ZHITAR, V. F. TARAN, N. I. DONIKA, T. V. ISSLED. STOZHN. POLUPROV. 89–97PP., 1970.
67049	**EFFECT OF FERRIC OXIDE CONCENTRATION ON MAGNETIZATION AND SQUARENESS OF THE HYSTERESIS LOOP IN MANGANESE FERRITE EPITAXIAL FILMS.** KOSHKIN, L. I. ISSLED. FIZ. METOD. FIZ. ASTRON. 31–5, 1970.
67050	**GALVANOMAGNETIC PHENOMENA IN MAGNESIUM-MANGANESE FERRITES.** KOSHKIN, L. I. MITLINA, L. A. VEDENEV, A. P. ISSLED. FIZ. METOD. FIZ. ASTRON. 36–9, 1970.
67054	**REACTION OF III(2) - VI(3) -TYPE INDIUM CHALCOGENIDES WITH CHALCOGENS.** RUSTAMOV, P. G. MELIKOVA, Z. D. MAMODALIEV, F. D. ISSLED. MATER. NOVOI TEKH. 158–63, 1971.
67057	**USE OF INDIUM ANTIMONIDE AS A MATERIAL FOR PRESSURE TRANDUCERS.** IVANOVA, E. M. CHAPUTOVICH, E. E. IZMER. TEKH. (9), 22–3, 1972.
67060	**ELECTROMAGNETIC PROPERTIES OF HOT-PRESSED FERRITES.** PROKOSHKIN, D. A. BYKOV, YU. A. SOKOLENKO, L. M. NAZARCHIK, N. A. KAMNEVA, R. V. SHIMENSAS, KH. YA. IZV. VYSSH. UCHEB. ZAVED., MASHINOSTR. (9), 114–17, 1972.
67062	**TEMPERATURE DEPENDENCE OF THE PIEZO-OPTIC COEFFICIENT OF LIQUIDS.** GOTTLIEB, M. J. ACOUST. SOC. AMER. 49 (5), (PT. 2), 1442–7, 1971.
67067	**EDGE EMISSION AND DEEP CENTRE LUMINESCENCE IN ZINC SELENIDE.** GEZCI, S. UNIVERSITY OF DURHAM, ENGLAND 1– , 1973.
67074	**THE STATE OF THIN FILMS OF SILICON, CHROMIUM, AND CHROMIUM SILICIDES.** SHABALINA, O. K. BAUM, B. A. GEL'D, P. V. INORG. MAT., USSR 7 (10), 1664–5, 1971. (ENGLISH TRANSLATION OF IZV. AKAD. NAUK SSSR, NEORG. MATER., 7 (10), 1864–5, 1971; FOR ORIGINAL SEE E63423)
67075	**CALCULATING THE OPTICAL CONSTANTS OF SEMICONDUCTORS FROM DIFFUSE REFLECTION SPECTRA OF POWDERS.** BERGER, L. I. PETROV, V. M. INORG. MAT., USSR 7 (11), 1699–1702, 1971. (ENGLISH TRANSLATION OF IZV. AKAD. NAUK SSSR, NEORG. MATER., 7 (11), 1905–8, 1971, FOR ORIGINAL SEE E63424)

EPIC Number	Bibliographic Citation
67079	**PREPARATION OF AMORPHOUS SILICON PHOSPHIDE AND SILICON ARSENIDE FILMS AND INVESTIGATION OF THEIR PROPERTIES.** DOMASHEVSKAYA, E. P. UGAI, YA. A. MIROSHNICHENKO, S. N. ALFEEVA, M. S. NIKONOV, I. F. INORG. MAT., USSR 10 (4), 625-6, 1974. (ENGLISH TRANSLATION OF IZV. AKAD. NAUK SSSR, NEORG. MATER., 10 (4), 731-2, 1974; FOR ORIGINAL SEE E62436)
67081	**ELECTRICAL CONDUCTIVITY AND THERMO-EMF OF LIQUID ALLOYS IN THE SYSTEM BISMUTH SESQUITELLURIDE - ANTIMONY SESQUISULFIDE.** CHIZHEVSKAYA, S. N. ABRIKOSOV, N. KH. INORG. MAT., USSR 8 (11), 1786-7, 1972. (ENGLISH TRANSLATION OF IZV. AKAD. NAUK SSSR, NEORG. MATER., 8 (11), 2031-2, 1972; FOR ORIGINAL SEE E63429)
67082	**THE SYSTEM TIN TELLURIDE - LEAD SELENIDE.** BOROVIKOVA, R. P. DUDKIN, L. D. KAZANSKAYA, O. A. KOSOLAPOVA, E. F. INORG. MAT., USSR 8 (10), 1550-2, 1972. (ENGLISH TRANSLATION OF IZV. AKAD. NAUK SSSR, NEORG. MATER., 8 (10), 1762-4, 1972; FOR ORIGINAL SEE E63428)
67085	**OPTICAL CONSTANTS OF ALPHA-SILICON CARBIDE IN THE INTRINSIC ABSORPTION REGION.** OBARICH, V. A. J. APPL. SPECTROSC., USSR 15 (1), 959-61, 1971. (ENGLISH TRANSLATION OF ZH. PRIKL. SPEKTROSK., 15 (1), 160-2, 1971; FOR ORIGINAL SEE E62098)
67086	**THE CONCENTRATION LIMIT OF ISOMORPHIC SUBSTITUTION OF LEAD IN SODIUM CHLORIDE-LEAD AND POTASSIUM CHLORIDE LEAD SYSTEMS.** ARTEMOVA, V. B. DOBRZHANSKII, G. F. KORTUKOVA, E. I. KREININ, O. L. LEBEDEVA, V. N. ROZIN, K. M. J. APPL. SPECTROSC., USSR 16 (2), 212-5, 1972. (ENGLISH TRANSLATION OF ZH. PRIKL. SPEKTROSK., 16 (2), 285-9, 1972; FOR ORIGINAL SEE E62099)
67104	**PHASE MEMORY EFFECTS IN LOW FREQUENCY PHOTOCURRENT OSCILLATIONS IN EVAPORATED CADMIUM SULFIDE AND AND (CADMIUM - ZINC) SULFIDE THIN FILMS.** YOSHIE, O. JAP. J. APPL. PHYS. 13 (7), 1177-8, 1974.
67106	**DESIGN AND OPERATION OF AN AUTOMATED, HIGH-TEMPERATURE ELLIPSOMETER.** VAN DER MEULEN, Y. J. HIEN, N. C. J. OPT. SOC. AM. (USA) 64 (6), 804-11, 1974.
67107	**RADIATION-INDUCED COLORATION IN KBR CRYSTALS SUBJECTED TO AC ELECTRIC FIELDS.** GOVINDA, S. J. PHYS. 7 C (20), L374-8, 1974.
67124	**CHEMISORPTION ON (001), (110) AND (111) NICKEL SURFACES. A CORRELATED STUDY USING LEED SPECTRA, AUGER SPECTRA AND WORK FUNCTION CHANGE MEASUREMENTS.** DEMUTH, J. E. RHODIN, T. N. SURF. SCI. 45 (1), 249-307, 1974.
67143	**THERMODYNAMIC PROPERTIES AND DEFECT STRUCTURE OF INTERMETALLIC COMPOUNDS.** STEVENSON, D. A. DEPT. MATER. SCI., STANFORD UNIV., STANFORD, CALIF. 80PP., 1970. (SU-326-P-25-10)
67166	**THE INFLUENCE OF PARTIAL SUBSTITUTIONS OF GERMANIUM BY NEODYMIUM AND GADOLINIUM ON THE THERMOELECTRIC PROPERTIES OF GERMANIUM TELLURIDE.** ZEINALOV, A. A. VERDIEVA, N. A. NASIROV, YA. N. PHYS. STATUS SOLIDI (GERMANY) 5 A (3), K203-4, 1971.
67175	**TRANSPORT PROPERTIES OF SEMICONDUCTOR SURFACE LAYERS.** DORDA, G. ELECTRON. FIS. APL. (SPAIN) 17 (1-2), 203-8, 1974.
67182	**OPTICAL PROPERTIES OF ALPHA GERMANIUM, ALPHA SILICON, AND ALPHA III - V COMPOUNDS.** THEYE, M. L. INTERN. CONF. AMORPHOUS AND LIQUID SEMICONDUCTORS I, 479-98PP., 1974.
67192	**EFFECT OF HEAT TREATMENTS ON THE SEMICONDUCTOR PROPERTIES OF A COMMERCIALLY ELECTRODEPOSITED MANGANESE DIOXIDE.** FOSTER, I. B. LEE, J. A. TYE, F. L. J. APPL. CHEM. BIOTECHNOL. 22 (10), 1085-93, 1972.
67201	**ARSENIC TRISELENIDE. PREPARATION AND ELECTRICAL CONDUCTIVITY AT HIGH TEMPERATURES.** WEBB, L. M. BAKER, E. H. J. CHEM. SOC., DALTON TRANS. (6), 769-72, 1972.
67203	**TRANSVERSE PHOTOCONDUCTIVITY IN TELLURIDE-BASED AND APPLICATION TO ARRAYS OF LIGHT SENSORS. I. RECOMBINATION AND TRAPPING PROCESSES.** CASSANHIOL, B. CORNET, J. ROSSIER, D. INTERNATIONAL CONFERENCE ON AMORPHOUS AND LIQUID SEMICONDUCTORS, 5TH 571-9PP., 1974.
67205	**OPTICAL AND ELECTRICAL PROPERTIES OF AMORPHOUS SILICON CARBIDE FILMS.** FAGEN, E. A. INTERNATIONAL CONFERENCE ON AMORPHOUS AND LIQUID SEMICONDUCTORS, 5TH 601-7PP., 1974.
67211	**EFFECT OF PRECIPITATING TEMPERATURE ON PERMEABILITY OF FERRITE BY COPRECIPITATION METHOD.** TASAKI, J. ITO, T. PROCEEDINGS OF THE 5TH COLLOQUIUM ON MICROWAVE COMMUNICATION SM-27/335-41PP., 1974.
67232	**BREAKDOWN TIME LAG OF SHORT GAPS IN VARIOUS GASES.** SHIBUYA, Y. INTERNATIONAL CONFERENCE ON GAS DISCHARGES, 3RD 132-5PP., 1974.
67234	**TIME LAGS IN SULFUR HEXAFLUORIDE IN A UNIFORM-FIELD GAP.** PEDERSEN, A. NIELSEN, T. M. INTERNATIONAL CONFERENCE ON GAS DISCHARGES, 3RD 105-8PP., 1974.
67235	**THE TEMPORAL GROWTH OF IONISATION IN LONG UNIFORM FIELD GAPS IN AIR AND SULPHUR HEXAFLUORIDE.** CRICHTON, B. H. TEDFORD, D. J. CHALMERS, P. INTERNATIONAL CONFERENCE ON GAS DISCHARGES, 3RD 100-4PP., 1974.
67238	**HIGH VOLTAGE BREAKDOWN MECHANISMS IN SULFUR HEXAFLUORIDE GAS.** REIN, A. ARNESEN, A. INTERNATIONAL CONFERENCE ON GAS DISCHARGES, 3RD 399-402PP., 1974.
67240	**ELECTRICAL STRENGTH OF SULPHUR HEXAFLUORIDE AT HIGH PRESSURE AND AT THE LIQUID STATE.** TORSHIN, Y. V. INTERNATIONAL CONFERENCE ON GAS DISCHARGES, 3RD 389-93PP., 1974.
67241	**PARTICLE MOVEMENT AND GAS BREAKDOWN IN HIGH PRESSURE NITROGEN AND SULPHUR HEXAFLUORIDE.** COOKSON, A. H. WOOTTON, R. E. INTERNATIONAL CONFERENCE ON GAS DISCHARGES, 3RD 385-8, 1974.
67244	**DIELECTRIC CHARACTERISTICS OF MIXTURES OF SULFUR HEXAFLUORIDE AND NITROGEN.** BAUMGARTNER, R. G. INTERNATIONAL CONFERENCE ON GAS DISCHARGES, 3RD 366-9PP., 1974.
67247	**DIELECTRIC BREAKDOWN ON LITHIUM FLORIDE CLEAVAGE SURFACES IN COMPRESSED NITROGEN GAS.** DAVISSON, J. W. ANN. CONF. ELECT. INSULATION DIELECTRIC PHENOMENA 215-21PP., 1974.
67248	**CRYSTAL GROWTH AND PROPERTIES OF SILVER INDIUM SULFIDE.** OKAMOTO, K. REP. UNIV. ELECTRO-COMMUN. 24 (1), 113-7, 1973.
67252	**ABSORPTION OF AMMONIA IN THE WAVELENGTH REGION AROUND 40 MICROMETER.** LEUPOLT, A. INFRARED PHYS. 14 (2), 99-126, 1974.
67255	**FINE-GRAINED SULPHIDE PHOSPHORS.** JESIONEK, J. GIERDALSKA, B. PR. OSRODKA BADAW.-ROZWOJOWEGO ELEKTRON. PROZNIOWEJ 2 (2), 57-70, 1974.
67259	**EFFECT OF TEMPERATURE ON RECOMBINATION LUMINESCENCE AND ELECTRON TUNNELLING.** ERSHOV, B. G. KIEFFER, F. NATURE 252 (5479), 118-19, 1974.

EPIC Number	Bibliographic Citation

67264 **RADIATION-INDUCED DEFECTS IN ALKALI HALIDES, AND THEIR ROLE IN RECOMBINATION PROCESSES.**
MURRAY, R. B.
DEPT. PHYS., UNIV. DELAWARE, NEWARK, DEL.
13PP., 1971.
(NYO-3842-12)

67267 **MAGNETIC PROPERTIES OF HOLMIUM - SILVER.**
NERESON, M.
LOS ALAMOS SCIENTIFIC LAB., LOS ALAMOS, N. MEX.
5PP., 1972.
(LA-DC-72-1247)

67269 **EVALUATION OF DYSPROSIUM-DOPED CALCIUM SULFATE AND THULIUM-DOPED CALCIUM SULFATE THERMOLUMINESCENCE DOSIMETRY FOR MEASUREMENT OF SMALL GAMMA-RAY EXPOSURES.**
SHAMBON, A.
HEALTH SAF. LAB., AEC, NEW, N. Y.
13PP., 1972.
(HASL-270)

67271 **ELECTROLUMINESCENT-DIODE FORMATION IN ION-IMPLANTED ZINC TELLURIDE.**
MARINE, J.
C.E.N., COMMIS. ENERG. AT., GRENOBLE, FR.
101PP., 1972.
(CEA-R-4313)

67273 **TEMPERATURE DEPENDENCE OF THE ELECTRICAL CONDUCTIVITY OF NONSTOICHIOMETRIC CERIUM OXIDE.**
BLUMENTHAL, R. N. HOFMAIER, R. L.
COLLEGE OF ENGINEERING, MARQUETTE UNIV., MILWAUKEE, WIS.
35PP., 1971.
(COO-1441-13)

67274 **DEFECT STRUCTURE OF NONSTOICHIOMETRIC CERIUM DIOXIDE.**
BLUMENTHAL, R. N.
COLL. ENG., MARQUETTE UNIV., MILWAUKEE, WIS.
23PP., 1970.
(COO-1441-12)

67275 **ELECTRICAL CONDUCTIVITY OF CALCIUM OXIDE-DOPED NONSTOICHIOMETRIC CERIUM OXIDE FROM 700 TO 1500.**
BRUGNER, F. S BLUMENTHAL, R. N.
COLLEGE OF ENGINEERING, MARQUETTE UNIV., MILWAUKEE, WIS.
30PP., 1971.
(COO-1441-14)

67276 **ELECTRICAL CONDUCTIVITY OF CALCIUM OXIDE-DOPED NONSTOICHIOMETRIC CERIUM DIOXIDE FROM 700 TO 1500.**
BLUMENTHAL, R. N. BRUGNER, F. S.
GARNIER, J. E.
COLLEGE OF ENGINEERING, MARQUETTE UNIV., MILWAUKEE, WIS.
38PP., 1972.
(COO-1441-16)

67281 **PRESENT STATE OF TRANSPORT THEORY FOR DISORDERED SYSTEMS.**
BRENIG, W.
INTERN. CONF. AMORPHOUS AND LIQUID SEMICONDUCTORS I, 31-47, 1974.

67288 **HALL MOBILITY IN ARSENIC SELENIDE, ARSENIC TELLURIDE, AND ARSENIC TELLURIDE SELENIDE GLASSES.**
ROILOS, M. MYTILINEOU, E.
INTERNATIONAL CONFERENCE ON AMORPHOUS AND LIQUID SEMICONDUCTORS, 5TH
319-24PP., 1973.

67289 **CONDUCTION IN LOCALIZED BAND-TAIL AND IN EXTENDED STATES. I. EXPERIMENTAL STUDIES OF TRANSPORT IN AMORPHOUS ARSENIC TELLURIDE.**
GRANT, A. J. MOUSTAKAS, T. D. PENNEY, T.
WEISER, K.
INTERN. CONF. AMORPHOUS AND LIQUID SEMICONDUCTORS I, 325-33, 1973.

67290 **TRANSPORT PROPERTIES OF POLAR SEMICONDUCTORS IN A MAGNETIC FIELD.**
SONDHEIMER, E. H.
INTERN. CONF. ON THE APPL. HIGH MAGNETIC FIELDS SEMICONDUCTOR PHYS.
240-8, 1974.

67300 **PERMANENT MAGNETS WITH HIGH COERCIVE FIELD.**
SMIT, P. C.
POLYTECH. TIJDSCHR. ELEKTROTECH. ELECKTRON.
29 (15), 485-7, 1974.

67314 **HALL EFFECT AND ELECTRICAL CONDUCTIVITY IN LEAD SULFIDE POLYCRYSTALLINE LAYERS.**
BELOV, A. F. IL'IN, V. I.
TR. LENINGR. POLITEKH. INST.
(325), 19-23, 1972.

67315 **THERMAL STABILITY OF BARIUM - GOLD FILMS.**
KIRSANOVA, T. S. ZHUKOVSKII, A. N.
TR. LENINGRAD. POLITEKH. INST.
(311), 59-62, 1970.

67317 **EMISSION OF CHARGED PARTICLES FROM SOME DIELECTRICS CAUSED BY 0.2-30 KILOELECTRON VOLT HYDROGEN IONS.**
PETROV, N. N. SERGEEV, E. A.
TR. LENINGRAD. POLITEKH. INST.
(311), 89-93, 1970.

67319 **EXCITATION OF ELECTRONS AND THE FORMATION OF RADIATION DEFECTS DURING BOMBARDMENT OF SILICON CARBIDE SINGLE CRYSTALS BY HYDROGEN IONS.**
MAKAROV, V. V.
TR. LENINGRAD. POLITEKH. INST.
(311), 1308, 1970.

67320 **BASIC OPTICAL ABSORPTION EDGE IN N-TYPE LEAD SULFIDE, LEAD SELENIDE, AND LEAD TELLURIDE EPITAXIAL FILMS.**
ZHURAVLEVA, V. M.
TR. LENINGRAD. POLITEKH. INST.
(325), 23-8, 1971.

67321 **SPECTRAL DISTRIBUTION OF QUANTUM SENSITIVITY OF PHOTOCONDUCTORS OF LEAD SULFIDE TYPE.**
VINCHAKOV, V. N. PODVYAZNIKOVA, N. K.
TR. LENINGRAD. POLITEKH. INST.
(325), 28-32, 1971.

67323 **COMPRESSED GASES IN A STUDY OF POLYCRYSTALLINE LEAD SULFIDE FILMS.**
IL'IN, V. I.
TR. LENINGRAD. POLITEKH. INST.
(325), 56-62, 1971.

67324 **LUMINESCENCE OF DIVALENT SAMARIUM IN SULFATES OF ALKALINE EARTH METALS.**
BYKOVSKII, P. I. PISARENKO, V. F.
TR. KRASNODAR. GOS. PEDAGOG. INST.
(123), 47-64, 1969.

67325 **TWO TYPES OF LUMINESCENCE CENTERS IN CRYOLITE ACTIVATED WITH LANTHANIDE IONS.**
BREGEDA, I. D. PISARENKO, V. F.
TR. KRASNODAR. GOS. PEDAGOG. INST.
(123), 27-31, 1969.

67326 **IONIC CONDUCTIVITY AND OPTICAL CENTERS OF CALCIUM FLUORIDE ACTIVATED WITH LANTHANIDE IONS.**
POPOV, V. V. PISARENKO, V. F.
TR. KRASNODAR. GOS. PEDAGOG, INST.
(123), 6-19, 1969.

67327 **POSTRADIATIONAL CHANGES IN THE ELECTRICAL CONDUCTIVITY, THERMOELECTROMOTIVE FORCE AND DIELECTRIC LOSS TANGENT OF AMMONIUM PERCHLORATE.**
ZAKHAROV, YU. A. SHECHKOV, G. T.
TR. KONF. MOLODYKH UCH.-KHIM. GORODA TOMSKA, 1ST
81-5, 1971.

67332 **NATURE OF THE ELECTRICAL CONDUCTIVITY OF TITANIUM, VANADIUM, CHROMIUM, AND IRON ORTHOTANTALATES AT HIGH TEMPERATURES.**
KRYLOV, E. I. ROZHDESTVENSKII, F. A.
KASIMOV, G. G. POTEKHIN, O. G.
NEUIMIN, A. D.
TR. INST. KHIM., AKAD. NAUK SSSR, URAL. FILIAL
(23), 13-17, 1971.

67337 **HIGHLY SENSITIVE HALL ELECTROMOTIVE FORCE GENERATORS FROM INDIUM ANTIMONIDE SINGLE-CRYSTAL FILMS.**
KAS'YAN, V. A. PASECHNIK, F. I.
TR. FIZ. POLUPROV.
(3), 95-102, 1971.

67340 **THERMOLUMINESCENT PHOSPHORS BASED ON BERYLLIUM OXIDE.**
YASUNO, Y. YAMASHITA, T.
THIRD INT. CONF. LUMIN. DOSIM., PROC.
290-304, 1971.

67341 **THERMOLUMINESCENCE OF LITHIUM FLUORIDE DOPED WITH VARIOUS ACTIVATORS.**
ROBERTSON, M. E. A. GILBOY, W. B.
THIRD INT. CONF. LUMIN. DOSIM., PROC.
350-6, 1971.

67349 **ELECTRICAL AND THERMAL CONDUCTIVITY CHANGE OF LITHIUM FLUORIDE SINGLE CRYSTALS DURING X-IRRADIATION AND HEAT TREATMENT.**
GOLUBEVA, L. A. LISKER, I. S.
PCHELINSKAYA, S. N. SHISHELOV, A. A.
TEPLO-MASSOPERENOS TVERD. TELAKH, ZHIDK. GAZAKH
38-44, 1970.

67350 **SECONDARY ELECTRON EMISSION OF TUNGSTEN WITH BARIUM OXIDE FILMS OF VARIOUS THICKNESSES AT PRIMARY-ELECTRON ENERGIES OF 1-50 ELECTRON VOLTS.**
SHUL'MAN, A. R. BAZHANOVA, N. P.
TR. LENINGRAD. POLITEKH. INST.
328, 18-22, 1973.

67353 **TYPES OF EFFECTIVE [SECONDARY ELECTRON] EMITTERS AND THEIR PRACTICAL USE.**
LEPESHINSKAYA, V. N.
TR. LENINGRAD. POLITEKH. INST.
328, 3-11, 1973.

EPIC Number	Bibliographic Citation
67355	**FURTHER IMPROVEMENT IN A NEW METHOD OF PURIFYING SUBSTANCES.** STROITELEV, S. A. TR. KHIM. KHIM., TEKHNOL. (4), 26–7, 1973.
67357	**SPECTROSCOPIC STUDIES OF STRONTIUM ORTHOVANADATE.** KORDYUKOV, N. I. GAVRILOV, F. F. TR. INST. KHIM., URAL. NAUCH. TSENTR, AKAD. NAUK SSSR 25, 63–5, 1973.
67359	**MUTUAL SOLUBILITY OF CALCIUM TUNGSTATE AND MOLYBDATE.** ZHUKOVSKII, V. M. DOBROVINSKII, R. YU. PETROV, A. N. FETISOV, V. B. TKACHENKO, E. V. BOGDANOVICH, M. I. TR. INST. KHIM., URAL. NAUCH. TSENTR, AKAD. NAUK SSSR 25, 105–7, 1973.
67360	**ELECTRIC CONDUCTIVITY OF OXYGEN VANADIUM BRONZES.** KAPUSTKIN, V. K. PLETNEV, R. N. TR. INST. KHIM., URAL. NAUCH. TSENTR. AKAD. NAUK SSSR 25, 82–4, 1973.
67361	**LUMINESCENCE OF BARIUM AND CADMIUM ORTHOVANADATES ACTIVATED BY EUROPIUM.** KORDYUKOV, N. I. KARA-USHANOV, V. YU. TR. INST. KHIM., URAL. NAUCH. TSENTR, AKAD. NAUK SSSR 25, 66–70, 1973.
67362	**NATURAL LUMINESCENCE OF DOUBLE ORTHOVANADATES.** FOTIEV, A. A. KARA-USHANOV, V. YU. GAVRILOV, F. F. TR. INST. KHIM., URAL. NAUCH. TSENTR, AKAD. NAUK SSSR 25, 71–4, 1973.
67363	**ELECTRONIC SPECTRA OF YTTRIUM ORTHONIOBATE.** SLEPUKHIN, V. K. KRYLOV, E. I. LIOZNYANSKII, V. M. SHUL'GIN, B. V. SOMOV, S. I. TR. INST. KHIM., URAL. NAUCH. TSENTR, AKAD. NAUK SSSR 25, 77–81, 1973.
67365	**SPECTROSCOPIC STUDIES OF CALCIUM ORTHOVANADATE.** KORDYUKOV, N. I. TR. INST. KHIM., URAL. NAUCH. TSENTR, AKAD. NAUK SSSR 25, 57–62, 1973.
67368	**MAGNETIC SUSCEPTIBILITY OF VANADIUM TRIOXIDE, TITANIUM SESQUIOXIDE, AND THEIR SOLID SOLUTIONS IN THE 20–600 RANGE.** PERELYAEV, V. A. SHVEIKIN, G. P. TR. INST. KHIM., URAL. NAUCH. TSENTR. AKAD. NAUK SSSR 25, 13–14, 1973.
67369	**EFFECT OF TRANSITION METAL CATIONS ON THE MAGNETIC TRANSITION IN VANADIUM TRIOXIDE.** PERELYAEV, V. A. SHVEIKIN, G. P. BAZUEV, G. V. TR. INST. KHIM., URAL. NAUCH. TSENTR, AKAD. NAUK SSSR 25, 8–12, 1973.
67370	**MAGNETIC SUSCEPTIBILITY AND MAGNETIC STRUCTURE OF CHROMIUM TITANIUM OXIDE AND CHROMIUM VANADIUM OXIDE SOLID SOLUTIONS.** ZUBOV, V. G. MATVEENKO, I. I. GEL'D, P. V. TR. INST. KHIM., URAL. NAUCH. TSENTR, AKAD. NAUK SSSR 25, 35–8, 1973.
67371	**LUMINESCENCE OF RARE EARTH ORTHOVANADATES.** MOSKVIN, A. S. KHODOS, M. YA. SHUL'GIN, B. V. TR. INST. KHIM., URAL. NAUCH. TSENTR. AKAD. NAUK SSSR 25, 39–43, 1973.
67379	**ELECTRIC CONDUCTIVITY IN THE REGION OF EXISTENCE OF THE COMPOUNDS SAMARIUM ZIRCONIUM OXIDE AND GADOLINIUM ZIRCONIUM OXIDE WITH PYROCHLORE STRUCTURE.** FOMINA, L. V. PAL'GUEV, S. F. FIZ. KHIM. ELEKTROKHIM. RASPLAV. SOLEI TVERD. ELEKTROLIT. (1), 142–3, 1973.
67387	**ELECTROSPARK MACHINING OF HIGH-RESISTANCE CADMIUM SULFIDE.** IVANOVSKII, V. N. NEFED'EV, V. A. ELEKTRON. OBRAB. MATER. (6), 10–12, 1973.
67400	**MEASUREMENT OF THE P20 (00 1–10 0) TRANSITION PROBABILITY OF CARBON DIOXIDE AND IMPACT BROADENING DURING COLLISIONS WITH CARBON DIOXIDE, NITROGEN, AND HELIUM.** DANILOV, V. V. KRUGLYAKOV, E. P. SHUN'KO, E. V. ZH. PRIKL. MEKH. TEKH. FIZ. (6), 24–8, 1972.
67403	**LOW TEMPERATURE FLASH OF THALLIUM DOPED POTASSIUM CHLORIDE ACTIVATOR RECOMBINATION LUMINESCENCE UNDER EXCITATION IN FUNDAMENTAL ABSORPTION REGION.** ALUKER, E. D. LUSIS, D. YU. LATV. PSR ZINAT. AKAD. VESTIS FIZ. TEH. SER. (1), 17–19, 1974.
67411	**STRUCTURE OF THE CONDUCTIVITY BAND IN MERCURY TELLURIDE.** ALIEV, S. A. GADZHIEV, T. G. ALIEV, E. M. ALIEV, M. I. IZV. AKAD. NAUK AZERB. SSR, SER. FIZ.-TEKH. MAT. NAUK (6), 83–7, 1969.
67413	**STRUCTURE OF THE CONDUCTION BAND AND MECHANISM OF ELECTRON SCATTERING IN INDIUM GALLIUM ANTIMONIDE.** ZEINALOV, S. A. ALIEV, S. A. ALIEV, M. I. IZV. AKAD. NAUK AZERB. SSR, SER. FIZ.-TEKH. MAT. NAUK (5), 12–17, 1969.
67414	**SYNTHESIS AND STUDY OF THE ELECTRICAL PROPERTIES OF GADOLINIUM GALLIUM TRISELENIDE.** BABAEV, S. KH. KARAEV, Z. SH. RUSTAMOV, A. G. IZV. AKAD. NAUK AZERB. USSR, SER. FIZ.-TEKH. MAT. NAUK (3), 56–60, 1970.
67415	**MEASUREMENT OF THE HALL MOBILITY OF CURRENT CARRIERS IN SEMICONDUCTORS AT SUPERHIGH FREQUENCIES.** PASHAEV, A. M. IZV. AKAD. NAUK AZERB. SSR, SER. FIZ.-TEKH. MAT. NAUK (5), 67–9, 1970.
67419	**THEORY OF THE TRANSVERSE PHOTOMAGNETOELECTRIC EFFECT IN SEMICONDUCTORS.** ARONOV, D. A. SHAMASOV, R. G. IZV. AKAD. NAUK UZB. SSR, SER. FIZ.-MAT. NAUK 14 (5), 45–50, 1970.
67420	**SECONDARY EMISSION OF RUBIDIUM BROMIDE, SELENIUM, AND CADMIUM TELLURIDE DURING BOMBARDMENT WITH SODIUM IONS AND ATOMS.** ARIFOV, U. A. FLYANTS, N. N. RAKHIMOV, R. R. IZV. AKAD. NAUK UZB. SSR, SER. FIZ.-MAT NAUK 14 (4), 45–8, 1970.
67421	**PHOTOCONDUCTIVITY OF GALLIUM SELENIDE AND GALLIUM TELLURIDE SINGLE CRYSTALS DOPED WITH TIN.** ALIEVA, M. KH. BELEN'KII, G. L. MAMEDOVA, A. Z. ALLEV, T. I. ISAEV, F. K. IZV. AKAD. NAUK AZERB. SSR, SER. FIZ.-TEKH. MAT. NAUK (3), 117–20, 1970.
67423	**MEASUREMENT OF SOME PHYSICAL PARAMETERS OF GADOLINIUM SESQUISELENIDE SINGLE CRYSTALS GROWN BY A GAS TRANSPORT METHOD.** AGAEV, A. B. DZHALILOV, N. Z. IZV. AKAD. NAUK AZERB. SSR, SER. FIZ.-TEKH. MAT. NAUK (3), 92–5, 1970.
67430	**ELECTROLUMINESCENCE COMETS IN COPPER DOPED ZINC SULFIDE SINGLE CRYSTALS SCANNED WITH A NEEDLE ELECTRODE. COMMENTS.** MAXIA, V. MUNTONI, C. MURGIA, M. LETT. NUOVO COMENTO SOC. ITAL. FIS. 10 (13), 568–70, 1974.
67431	**THERMOLUMINESCENCE OF CERIUM ACTIVATED LEAD CHLORIDE SINGLE CRYSTALS.** CZEGLEDY, S. FELSZERFALVI, J. SAMSONI, Z. Z. PHYS. CHEM., FRANKFURT 73 (4–6), 184–7, 1970.
67432	**ELECTRICAL CONDUCTIVITIES AND DEFECT STRUCTURES OF PURE NICKEL OXIDE AND CHROMIUM-DOPED NICKEL OXIDE.** MEIER, G. H. RAPP, R. A. Z. PHYS. CHEM., FRANKFURT 74 (3–4), 1971.
67461	**TEMPERATURE DEPENDENCE OF THE DIELECTRIC CONSTANT OF STRONTIUM TITANATE.** GINTEL, J. POZNAN. TOW. PRZYJ. NAUK, PR. KOM. MAT.-PRZYR., FIZ. DIELEK. RADIOSPEKTROSK. 5 (2), 293–4, 1972.
67464	**RECOMBINATION CENTERS DETERMINING THE HIGH SENSITIVITY OF N-CADMIUM ANTIMONIDE PHOTORESISTORS.** MALYUTENKO, V. K. POLUPROV. TEKH. MIKROELEKTRON. RESPUB. MEZHVEDOM. SB. (9), 84–9, 1972.
67465	**PARAMETERS OF CADMIUM TELLURIDE LAYERS OBTAINED BY VACUUM DEPOSITION.** POLUDIN, V. P. SAFRONOVA, L. I. FILIPOVA, A. I. CHALAYA, V. G. POLUPROV. TEKH. MIKROELEKTRON. RESPUB. MEZHVEDOM. SB. (9), 81–4, 1972.
67466	**PHOTOSENSITIVE HIGH-RESISTANCE CADMIUM SULFIDE LAYERS.** MALOVICHKO, A. V. CHALAYA, V. G. SHUL'GA, E. P. POLUPROV. TEKH. MIKROELEKTRON. RESPUB. MEZHVEDOM. SB. (9), 20–5, 1972.
67469	**TANTALUM NITRIDE THIN FILM RESISTORS WITH LOW TEMPERATURE COEFFICIENT OF RESISTANCE.** SATO, A. ODA, Y. HISHINUMA, Y. PROC. ELECTRONIC COMPONENTS CONF. 58–62, 1970.

EPIC Number	Bibliographic Citation
67476	**THE ELECTRIC STRENGTH OF ALUMINA: THE EFFECT OF POROSITY.** MORSE, C. T. HILL, G. J. PROC. BRIT. CERAM. SOC. 23-35PP., 1970.
67485	**MAGNETIC STUDIES OF DIPOTASSIUM CHROMIUM TETRACHLORIDE.** GARDNER, W. E. GREGSON, A. K. PROGR. VAC. MICROBALANCE TECH. 2, 183-7, 1973.
67506	**PRESSURE DEPENDENCE OF THE METAL-SEMICONDUCTOR TRANSITION OF POTASSIUM BROMOCYANOPLATINATE HYDRATE.** MUELLER, W. H. G. JEROME, D. J. PHYS. (PARIS), LETT. 35 (7-8), L103-L105, 1974.
67515	**HIGH ENERGY DENSITY, LOW IMPEDANCE CAPACITORS USING PRESSURIZED WATER AS A DIELECTRIC.** MILLER, A. R. PROCEEDINGS OF THE SYMPOSIUM ON ENGINEERING PROBLEMS OF FUSION RESEARCH, 5TH 471-4PP., 1974.
67519	**SYNTHESIS AND GROWTH OF GALLIUM ARSENIDE SINGLE CRYSTALS.** THYAGARAJAN, R. NARULA, R. C. MOHAN, M. INDIAN J. TECHNOL. 10 (1), 25-8, 1972.
67524	**POLARIZATION OF POTASSIUM DIHYDROGEN PHOSPHATE IN THE PHASE TRANSITION REGION.** SIDNENKO, E. V. GLADKII, V. V. KRISTALLOGRAFIYA 18 (1), 138-42, 1973.
67526	**ELECTROOPTICAL PROPERTIES OF POTASSIUM DIHYDROGEN PHOSPHATE CRYSTALS WITH VARYING DEGREES OF DEUTERATION.** VOLKOVA, E. N. VELICHKO, I. A. KRISTALLOGRAFIYA 18 (2), 409-10, 1973.
67531	**ON THE CALCULATION OF ACTIVATION ENERGIES FROM THE THERMOLUMINESCENT GLOW CURVES.** LIEM, P. SVISZT, P. TOTH, B. KOZL. MAGY. TUD. AKAD. MUSZ. FIZ. KUT. INTEZ. (0-9), 17-30, 1973.
67543	**EFFECT OF ELECTRON BOMBARDMENT AND OF THE EXPOSURE OF POROUS ALKALI HALIDE FILMS TO AIR ON THEIR SECONDARY-EMISSION PROPERTIES.** IVANOV, A. V. NAUGOL'NYKH, O. V. FRIDRIKHOV, S. A. TR. LENINGRAD. POLITEKH. INST. 328, 44-6, 1973.
67544	**EFFECT OF THE SUBSTRATE MATERIAL ON FIELD ENHANCED SECONDARY ELECTRON EMISSION OF ALKALI HALIDE FILMS.** IVANOV, A. V. PALTS, T. FRIDRIKHOV, S. A. TR. LENINGRAD. POLITEKH. INST. 328, 47-50, 1973.
67548	**PHOTOEMISSION OF SINGLE-CRYSTAL GALLIUM ARSENIDE(III) WITH A REDUCED WORK FUNCTION.** KAPITSA, M. L. NEMCHENOK, R. L. PALTS, T. TR. LENINGRAD. POLITEKH. INST. 328, 68-72, 1973.
67552	**ANGULAR RELATIONS OF SECONDARY EMISSION FROM CRYSTALS IRRADIATED WITH SLOW IONS.** GOL'DADE, V. A. PETROV, N. N. RUMYANTSEV, I. S. TR. LENINGRAD. POLITEKH. INST. 328, 84-9, 1973.
67554	**USE OF SURFACE-BARRIER DIODES TO STUDY THE INTERACTION OF IONIZING RADIATION WITH SEMICONDUCTORS.** MAKAROV, V. V. TR. LENINGRAD. POLITEKH. INST. 328, 140-3, 1973.
67558	**ELECTRIC CONDUCTIVITY OF FUSED HALIDES NEAR THE MELTING POINT.** BYSTRAI, G. P. DESYATNIK, V. N. TR. URAL. POLITEKH. INST. 220, 31-5, 1973.
67577	**MAGNETIC PROPERTIES OF YTTRIUM-COBALT POWDER MAGNETS AND HEAT TREATMENT EFFECT.** SHIBATA, T. KATAYAMA, T. MIZOE, M. TSUCHIYA, S. DENSHI GIJUTSU SOGO KENKYUJO IHO 37 (11), 1013-23, 1973.
67578	**OBSERVATION OF MAGNETIC DOMAIN IN RARE EARTH GARNETS BOMBARDED WITH ENERGETIC IONS.** TSURUSHIMA, T. SUGIYAMA, Y. TANOUE, H. YAMADA, H. KATAOKA, S. DENSHI GIJUTSU SOGO KENKYUJO IHO 37 (3), 296-303, 1973.
67579	**EFFECT OF WATER AND POROSITY ON IONIC CONDUCTION OF SINTERED BARIUM FLUORIDE.** MIZUTA, S. SHIRASAWA, K. YANAGIDA, H. DENKI KAGAKU 41 (12), 913-18, 1973.
67586	**EQUIVALENT CONDUCTIVITY OF MOLTEN RARE-EARTH CHLORIDES. PRASEODYMIUM TRICHLORIDE, NEODYMIUM TRICHLORIDE, GADOLINIUM TRICHLORIDE, AND DYSPROSIUM TRICHLORIDE.** CHO, K. KURODA, T. DENKI KAGAKU 40 (11), 837-9, 1972.
67588	**HALL EFFECT IN SEMICONDUCTORS.** ALOMAN, A. VISA, I. ELENA, E. VISA, C. CERCET. MET., INST. CERCET. MET., BUCHAREST 13, 611-28, 1972.
67598	**ION TRANSPORT NUMBER OF MULLITE WITH EXCESS SILICON DIOXIDE.** KOMATSU, S. ISHITANI, S. IGI, S. KOZUKA, Z. NIPPON KINZOKU GAKKAISHI 37 (4), 455-62, 1973.
67610	**SPECTRAL SENSITIZATION OF PHOTOCONDUCTION IN CADMIUM SULFIDE POWDER BY CYANINE DYES. III.** NAKATSUI, H. HISHIKI, Y. NIPPON SHASHIN GAKKAISHI 35 (2), 83-9, 1972.
67618	**LOCAL DETERMINATION OF GALVANOMAGNETIC PROPERTIES IN SEMICONDUCTORS - AN APPLICATION OF THE SOLUTION OF A BOUNDARY VALUE PROBLEM IN POTENTIAL THEORY.** LASZLO, G. KOZL. MAGY. TUD. AKAD. MUSZ. FIZ. KUT. INTEZ. (1-12), V-XIIIPP., 1-154, 1974.
67619	**A NOTE ON THE TEMPERATURE DEPENDENCE OF ELECTRON MOBILITY IN GALLIUM ARSENIDE.** PODOR, B. NADOR, N. KOZL. MAGY. TUD. AKAD. MUSZ. FIZ. KUT. INTEZ. (0-13), 55-60, 1974.
67623	**EVORPORATED THIN FILMS OF IRON OXIDES.** NOSE, H. TASHIRO, I. HASHIMOTO, M. KIMURA, R. TRANS. NAT. RES. INST. METALS 12 (4), 123-9, 1970.
67624	**KINETIC AND BAND PARAMETERS OF COBALT DISILICIDE.** OSTROVSKII, F. I. KRENTSIS, R. P. GEL'D, P. V. TR. URAL. POLITEKH. INST. (186), 164-6, 1970.
67629	**ENERGY SPECTRA OF DEFECTS IN EPITAXIAL N-GALLIUM PHOSPHIDE, IRRADIATED BY FAST NEUTRONS.** PIVOVAROV, V. YA. TKACHEV, V. D. VESTN. BELORUSS. UNIV. 1 (1), 45-8, 1970.
67630	**DETERMINATION OF THE ELECTROPHYSICAL PARAMETERS OF HEAVILY DOPED ION-IMPLANTED LAYERS OF SILICON, GERMANIUM, AND GALLIUM ARSENIDE FROM THEIR REFLECTION SPECTRA.** STREL'TSOV, L. N. KHAILBULIN, I. B. FIZ. OSN. IONNO-LUCHEVOGO LEGIROVANIYA (2), 186-90, 1972.
67636	**STUDY OF LOCALIZED LEVELS BY MEANS OF ELECTRICAL AND OPTICAL MEASUREMENTS.** MARFAING, Y. TRIBOULET, R. PROC. INT. SYMP. CADMIUM TELLURIDE, MATER. GAMMA-RAY DETECTORS X-1-X-6, 1972.
67637	**PHOTOCONDUCTIVITY STUDIES OF NATIVE DEFECTS AND DEFECTS CREATED BY ELECTRON IRRADIATION IN N-TYPE CADMIUM TELLURIDE.** CAILLOT, M. PROC. INT. SYMP. CADMIUM TELLURIDE, MATER. GAMMA-RAY DETECTORS XIII-1-XIII-5, 1972.
67638	**PROPERTIES OF CADMIUM TELLURIDE DOPED WITH IRON.** VUL, B. M. IVANOV, V. S. RUKAVISHNIKOV, V. A. SAL'MAN, V. M. CHAPNIN, V. A. PROC. INT. SYMP. CADMIUM TELLURIDE, MATER. GAMMA-RAY DETECTORS XIV-1-XIV-8, 1972.
67639	**DOUBLE ACCEPTORS IN CADMIUM TELLURIDE.** VUL, B. M. VAVILOV, V. S. IVANOV, V. S. STOPACHINSKII, V. B. CHAPNIN, V. A. PROC. INT. SYMP. CADMIUM TELLURIDE, MATER. GAMMA-RAY DETECTORS XI-I-XI-9, 1972.

EPIC Number	Bibliographic Citation
67646	EXPERIMENTAL ASSEMBLY FOR OBTAINING THE SECONDARY ELECTRON EMISSION SPECTRA OF METALS AND SEMICONDUCTORS. SALMERON, M. BARO, A. M. PRADAL, F. AN. FIS. 67 (9–10), 405–7, 1971.
67652	TECHNOLOGY OF THIN ZINC MERCURY TELLURIDE LAYERS. NOWAK, Z. BIUL. WOJSK. AKAD. TECH. 21 (5), 99–104, 1972.
67654	IONIC CONDUCTIVITY OF SOLID CALCIUM SULFIDE AT 65 TO 1000. NAGATA, K. GOTO, K. S. MET. TRANS. 5 (4), 899–903, 1974.
67668	LUMINESCENCE SPECTRA OF CRYSTALLOPHOSPHORS OF YTTRIUM AND LANTHANUM OXIDES ACTIVATED BY RARE EARTH METALS. ANTONOV, A. V. KULEVSKII, L. V. MELAMED, SH. G. NAUCHN. TR., NAUCHNO-ISSLED. PROEKTN. INST. REDKOMET. PROM-STI (47), 209–18, 1973.
67690	RELATIONS OF EQUATIONS OF STATISTICAL AND QUANTUM CONDUCTIVITY MODELS IN SOLIDS. NEMILOV, S. V. STEKLOOBRAZNOE SOSTOYANIE 5 (1), 61–8, 1970.
67712	PARTICIPATION OF DOPING IMPURITIES IN FORMING RADIATION DEFECTS IN GALLIUM ARSENIDE. BRAILOVSKII, E. YU. KONOZENKO, I. D. RADIATS. FIZ. NEMETAL. KRIST. 91–6, 1970.
67719	ENERGY SPECTRUM OF RADIATION DAMAGE IN EPITAXIAL N-TYPE GALLIUM PHOSPHIDE. PIVOVAROV, V. YA. TKACHEV, V. D. RADIATS. FIZ.-NEMETAL. KRIST. 3 (2), 3–10, 1971.
67721	LOW-FREQUENCY PHOTOCURRENT NOISES IN NEUTRON-IRRADIATED GALLIUM ARSENIDE. GIORGADZE, M. P. KURDIANI, N. I. RADIATS. FIZ. NEMETAL. KRIST. 3 (2), 26–32, 1971.
67723	ELECTRIC PROPERTIES OF GAMMA-IRRADIATED P-TYPE CADMIUM TELLURIDE. ARONS, A. A. MATLAK, V. V. NIKONYUK, E. S. UST'YANOV, V. I. RADIATS. FIZ. NEMETAL. KRIST. 3 (2), 54–68, 1971.
67724	CHANGES IN PHOTOELECTRIC PROPERTIES OF CADMIUM SELENIDE DURING IRRADIATION. UST'YANOV, V. I. TARABROVA, L. I. RADIATS. FIZ. NEMETAL. KRIST. 3 (2), 78–91, 1971.
67725	EFFECT OF PENETRATING NUCLEAR RADIATION ON THE II - IV - V(2) SEMICONDUCTOR COMPOUNDS IN CRYSTALLINE AND VITREOUS STATES. AKSENOV, V. V. ZAITOV, F. A. NIYAZOVA, O. R. KHARAKHORIN, F. F. RADIATS. FIZ. NEMETAL KRIST. 3 (2), 91–7, 1971.
67726	CHARACTERISTICS OF RADIATION-ALTERED ELECTROPHYSICAL PROPERTIES IN SOLID SOLUTIONS OF ALKALI HALIDE CRYSTALS. ZAVADOVSKAYA, E. K. GRISHUKOV, V. A. CHOLOKOV, K. S. RADIATS. FIZ. NEMETAL. KRIST. 3 (3), 55–9, 1971.
67731	RELATIONS BETWEEN THE SEMICONDUCTIVE AND CATALYTIC PROPERTIES OF CERTAIN OXIDES. CLAUDEL, B. IND. CHIM. BELGE 39 (2), 149–59, 1974.
67738	SOFT MODES OF POTASSIUM DIHYDROGEN PHOSPHATE. RANDOM PHASE APPROXIMATION THEORY BASED ON THE KOBAYASHI MODEL. OHNARI, I. KUROSAWA, H. OHMURA, N. TAKADA, S. KANAGAWA DAIGAKU KOGAKUBU KENKYU HOKOKU 12, 14–19, 1974.
67740	ELECTRIC RESISTIVITY OF NICKEL-COPPER-ZINC FERRITES. BEKBULATOV, M. S. DZHUMABAEV, B. A. IZV. AKAD. NAUK KAZ. SSR, SER. FIZ.-MAT. 12 (2), 70–2, 1974.
67743	EFFECT OF A CHROMIUM IMPURITY ON THE PHOTOCONDUCTIVITY OF CADMIUM SULFIDE. ABDULLAEV, G. A. IZV. AKAD. NAUK UZB. SSR, SER. FIZ.-MAT. NAUK 18 (2), 84–5, 1974.
67746	HIGH-TEMPERATURE THERMOLUMINESCENCE OF CALCIUM FLUORIDE-RARE EARTH FLUORIDE GAMMA-IRRADIATED CRYSTALS. KAIPOV, B. TAVSHUNSKII, G. A. KALEKOV, A. IZV. AKAD. NAUK UZB. SSR, SER. FIZ.-MAT. NAUK 18 (1), 68–9, 1974.
67747	ELECTRICAL CONDUCTIVITY AND HALL EFFECT TAKING INTO ACCOUNT THE FIELD OF IMPURITY IONS IN SEMICONDUCTORS WITH SILICON-TYPE BAND STRUCTURE. EREZHEPOV, M. IZV. AKAD. NAUK UZB. SSR, SER. FIZ.-MAT. NAUK 18 (2), 51–5, 1974.
67748	EFFECT OF OXYGEN ADSORPTION DURING GAMMA-IRRADIATION ON THE ELECTRICAL CONDUCTIVITY OF LEAD SULFIDE AND ZINC SULFIDE. KALAMAZOV, R. U. KOKKOZOV, R. IZV. AKAD. NAUK UZB. SSR, SER. FIZ.-MAT. NAUK 18 (3), 98–9, 1974.
67749	PHOTOCONDUCTIVITY AND ENERGY SPECTRUM OF LOCAL CENTERS IN P-SILICON ZINC ARSENIDE CRYSTALS. AVERKIEVA, G. K. IMENKOV, A. N. PROCHUKHAN, V. D. RUD, YU. V. TAIROV, M. A. TASHTANOVA, M. IZV. AKAD. NAUK UZB. SSR, SER. FIZ.-MAT. NAUK 18 (4), 42–4, 1974.
67753	CURIE TEMPERATURE OF FERRITES WITH WEAKLY DISTURBED STOICHIOMETRY. DZHUMABAEV, B. A. BEKBULATOV, M. S. DZHUNUSOV, A. S. IZV. AKAD. NAUK KAZ. SSR, SER. FIZ.-MAT. 12 (2), 86–8, 1974.
67756	THERMOLUMINESCENCE OF MAGNESIUM OXIDE ACTIVATED BY THE CHEMISORPTION OF OXYGEN. MAKSIMOVA, N. D. RUFOV, YU. N. IZV. AKAD. NAUK SSSR, SER. KHIM. (3), 696–8, 1974.
67757	EFFECT OF THE SORPTION OF TIN TETRACHLORIDE ON THE ELECTRICAL RESISTANCE AND THERMOEMF. OF TIN(II) OXIDE. ALEN'KINA, K. V. PETROV, E. S. KUZNETSOV, YU. P. IZV. SIB. OTD. AKAD. NAUK SSSR, SER. KHIM. NAUK (2), 104–9, 1974.
67759	ELECTRIC PROPERTIES OF PURE AND DOPED P-SILICON ZINC ARSENIDE SINGLE CRYSTALS. AVERKIEVA, G. K. PROCHUKHAN, V. D. RUD, YU. V. TASHTANOVA, M. IZV. AKAD. NAUK UZB. SSR, SER. FIZ.-MAT. NAUK 18 (2), 46–50, 1974.
67765	CALCULATION OF THE DENSITY-OF-STATES EFFECTIVE MASS, TAKING INTO CONSIDERATION ANISOTROPIC SCATTERING. SARDARYAN, V. S. KRAVCHENKO, A. F. ARSENID GALLIYA, DOKL., VSES. SOVESHCH. 53–4, 1969.
67766	ELECTRICAL PROPERTIES OF EPITAXIAL LAYERS OF P-GALLIUM ARSENIDE. KATAEV, YU. G. LAVRENT'EVA, L. G. ARSENID GALLIYA, DOKL., VSES. SOVESHCH. 377–85, 1969.
67767	ADSORPTION, CATALYTIC, AND ELECTROPHYSICAL PROPERTIES OF GALLIUM ARSENIDE. MAIDANOVSKAYA, L. G. KIROVSKAYA, I. A. ARSENID GALLIYA, DOKL., VSES. SOVESHCH. 401–10, 1969.
67768	CHARACTERISTICS OF ELECTROLUMINESCENT CAPACITOR CHANGING THE COLOR OF THE LUMINESCENCE FROM THE FREQUENCY OF FEED VOLTAGE. VEDEKHIN, A. F. KOVALEV, B. A. DANILOV, V. P. SB. NAUCH. TR., VSES. NAUCH.-ISSLED. INST. LYUMINOFOROV OSOBO CHIST. VESHCHESTV 3, 52–8, 1973.
67769	SURFACE PROPERTIES OF CADMIUM SULFIDE INSULATING LAYERS. GIRAEV, M. A. SB. STATEI MOLODYKH UCH. DAGESTAN. FIL. AKAD. NAUK 31–4, 1969.
67772	PHOTOCONDUCTIVITY OF LEAD SULFIDE PHOTOCONDUCTIVE CELLS IN STRONG ELECTRIC FIELDS. CHECHURIN, S. N. UCH. ZAP. LENINGRAD. GOS. UNIV., SER. FIZ. GEOL. NAUK (354), 33–7, 1970.
67773	ACTIVATION ENERGY OF THE ELECTRICAL CONDUCTIVITY OF GLASSES BASED ON TETRAHEDRAL PHASES. BOLTOVETS, N. S. BORISOVA, Z. U. GORYUNOVA, N. A. KOUZOVA, N. I. OSMANOV, E. O. VESTN. LENINGRAD. UNIV., FIZ., KHIM. (1), 60–4, 1971.

EPIC Number	Bibliographic Citation
67785	**ELECTRON EMITTERS OF NIGATIVE ELECTRON AFFINITY AS PHOTOCATHODES.** BORDAN, P. WISS. BER. ALLG. ELEK.-GES. -TELEFUNKEN 45 (3), 127-9, 1972.
67787	**FIELD EMISSION OF TANTALUM COATED BY A THIN SILICON MONOXIDE AND ALUMINUM SESQUIOXIDE LAYER.** BOBEV, K. MIREVA, Z. IZV. INST. ELEKTRON. 7 11-17, 1974.
67788	**SPECTRAL DEPENDENCE OF THE PHOTOELECTRON ESCAPE DEPTH FROM CESIUM RUBIDIUM ANTIMONIDE.** NANEV, K. NIKOLOV, B. TILEVA, D. IZV. INST. ELEKTRON. 7 19-22, 1974.
67789	**PHOTOEMISSIVE PROPERTIES OF THE ANTIMONY - CESIUM - BISMUTH INTERMETALLIC COMPOUNDS WITH VARIABLE COMPOSITION.** NANEV, K. NIKOLOV, B. IZV. INST. ELEKTRON. 7 23-7, 1974.
67800	**ELECTRON SPIN RESONANCE AND MICROWAVE DIELECTRIC MEASUREMENTS OF GAMMA-IRRADIATED FERROELECTRIC AMMONIUM HYDROGEN SULFATE.** BARBUR, I. BODI, A. POPESCU, G. D. MILITARU, V. MAGN. RESONANCE RELAT. PHENOMENA, PROC. CONGR. AMPERE, 17TH 199-201, 1973.
67801	**MUCLEAR MAGNETIC RESONANCE STUDY OF THE TEMPERATURE DEPENDENCE OF THE LITHIUM-7 QUADRUPOLE COUPLING CONSTANT ABOVE AND BELOW THE CURIE TEMPERATURE IN FERROELECTRIC LITHIUM TANTALATE.** SLOTFELDT-ELLINGSEN, D. MAGN. RESONANCE RELAT. PHENOMENA, PROC. CONGR. AMPERE, 17TH 350-2, 1973.
67802	**POLYMORPHISM OF BISMUTH SELENIDE AT HIGH PRESSURES AND TEMPERATURES.** ATABAEVA, E. YA. BENDELIANI, N. A. POPOVA, S. V. FIZ. TVERD. TELA AMPERE, 17TH 15 (12), 3508-12, 1973. (FOR ENGLISH TRANSLATION SEE E57803)
67803	**ORBACH PROCESS IN PARAELECTRIC RELAXATION AT LOW TEMPERATURES.** KNOP, K. KAENZIG, W. MAGN. RESONANCE RELAT. PHENOMENA, PROC. CONGR. AMPERE, 17TH 434-6, 1973.
67807	**VARIATION OF CRYSTAL FERMI ENERGY AS A METHOD OF OBTAINING DIFFERENT CHARGE STATES OF IONS FOR ELECTRON SPIN RESONANCE STUDY.** OHLSEN, W. D. MAGN. RESONANCE RELAT. PHENOMENA. PROC. CONGR. AMPERE, 17TH 513-16, 1973.
67808	**OPTICAL DETECTION OF THE EPR OF LOOSE F AGGREGATE CENTERS IN POTASSIUM CHLORIDE.** SCHNEGG, P. A. RUEDIN, Y. AEGERTER, M. A. JACCARD, C. MAGN. RESONANCE RELAT. PHENOMENA, PROC. CONGR. AMPERE, 17TH 521-3, 1973.
67813	**GALLIUM PHOSPHIDE LIQUID PHASE EPITAXIAL GROWTH AND LIGHT EMITTING DIODES. II. GALLIUM PHOSPHIDE LIQUID PHASE EPITAXIAL GROWTH FOR GREEN LIGHT EMITTING DIODES.** DAZAI, K. AKITA, K. NAKAI, S. FUJITSU SCI. TECH. J. 9 (3), 149-72, 1973.
67817	**OBTAINING CERAMIC DIELECTRICS WITH REOXIDATED FILM.** BARBULESCU, A. MATER. CONSTR. (BUCHAREST) 3 (4), 203-5, 1973.
67820	**PHOTOELECTRON SPECTRA OF CESIUM HALIDES.** TIMOSHENKO, M. M. AKOPYAN, M. E. KHIM. VYS. ENERG. 8 (3), 211-14, 1974.
67821	**LOW-TEMPERATURE EXOELECTRON EMISSION FROM THE SURFACE OF IRRADIATED OXIDES. I. ALUMINUM OXIDE EMISSION IN THE ABSENCE OF ADSORBED GASES.** DOLIDZE, G. M. KOLBANOVSKII, YU. A. POLAK, L. S. SAKVARELIDZE, V. S. KHIM. VYS. ENERG. 8 (4), 291-5, 1974.
67824	**MAGNETIC PROPERTIES OF SCANDIUM- AND CHROMIUM-CONTAINING AND SCANDIUM- AND INDIUM-CONTAINING FERRITES.** BONDAREV, D. E. REDK. ELEM. 6, 150-1, 1971.
67825	**COPPER - MANGANESE-SYSTEM FERRITES WITH ADDITIONS OF SCANDIUM OXIDE.** KHOMYAKOV, YU. M. REDK. ELEM. 6, 154-8, 1971.
67826	**THE X-RAY DIFFRACTION STUDY OF LOCAL DISTORTIONS AND THEIR EFFECT ON THE MAGNETIC PROPERTIES OF SCANDIUM-CONTAINING FERRITES.** BONDAREV, D. E. KIRICHOK, P. P. PODVAL'NYKH, G. S. SHARANEVICH, L. N. REDK. ELEM. 6, 168-72, 1971.
67837	**STATISTICS OF ELECTRON EMISSION.** SAVINOV, E. P. SHCHEMELEV, V. N. UCH. ZAP. LENINGRAD. GOS. UNIV. SER. FIZ. GEOL. NAUK (354), 111-18, 1970.
67840	**CHANGES IN THE ENERGY SPECTRUM OF CAPTURE CENTERS OF CADMIUM SULFIDE CRYSTALS SUBJECTED TO ELECTRON BOMBARDMENT.** GRIGOR'EV, R. V. NOVIKOV, B. V. SHESTAKOVA, T. V. UCH. ZAP. LENINGRAD. GOS. UNIV., SER. FIZ. GEOL. NAUK (354), 91-6, 1970.
67845	**EFFECT OF THE MAGNITUDE OF THE MAGNETIZING FIELD AND TEMPERATURE ON THE MAGNETIC CHARACTERISTICS OF PERMANENT MAGNETS FROM SAMARIUM - COBALT POWDERS.** SPIDCHENKO, V. K. BULYGINA, T. I. SERGEEV, V. V. REDKOZEMEL. METAL., SPLAVY SOEDIN., MATER. SOVESHCH., 7TH 71-4, 1973.
67847	**MAGNETIZATION PROCESS IN FERROMAGNETIC RARE EARTH INTERMETALLIC COMPOUNDS WITH STRONG ANISOTROPY.** BARBARA, B. LEMAIRE, R. REDKOZEMEL. METAL., SPLAVY SOEDIN., MATER. SOVESHCH., 7TH 92-7, 1973.
67849	**MAGNETOCRYSTALLINE ANISOTROPY OF CERIUM - COBALT SINGLE CRYSTALS.** SKOKOV, A. D. EIDINOV, A. YA. POTAPOV, N. N. VETOSHKIN, I. D. SADCHIKOV, V. V. KRASAVIN, YU. I. REDKOZEMEL. METAL., SPLAVY SOEDIN., MATER. SOVESHCH., 7TH 104-6, 1973.
67851	**THEORY OF THE COERCIVE FORCE OF RARE EARTH METAL-COBALT ALLOYS.** MISHIN, D. D. GRECHISHKIN, R. M. REDKOZEMEL. METAL., SPLAVY SOEDIN., MATER. SOVESHCH., 7TH 109-11, 1973.
67852	**DOMAIN STRUCTURE AND MAGNETIC REVERSAL PROCESSES IN THE SAMARIUM - COBALT ALLOY.** GRECHISHKIN, R. M. MISHIN, D. D. LEONOVICH, I. G. KUDREVATYKH, N. V. REDKOZEMEL. METAL., SPLAVY SOEDIN., MATER. SOVESHCH., 7TH 112-15, 1973.
67853	**PERMANENT MAGNETS FROM COBALT-RARE EARTH METAL ALLOYS.** GRECHISHKIN, R. M. LEONOVICH, I. G. MISHIN, D. D. TSIRKOV, A. I. REDKOZEMEL. METAL., SPLAVY SOEDIN., MATER. SOVESHCH., 116-20, 1973.
67854	**MAGNETIC PROPERTIES OF INTERMETALLIC RARE EARTH METAL COMPOUNDS OF TIN OR LEAD.** STALINSKI, B. CZOPNIK, A. ILIEV, N. MYDLARZ, T. REDKOZEMEL. METAL., SPLAVY SOEDIN., MATER. SOVESHCH., 7TH 121-2, 1973.
67856	**ELECTROPHYSICAL PROPERTIES OF SEMIMETALLIC SILICIDES OF RARE EARTH METALS.** LAZORENKO, V. I. RUD, B. M. DVORINA, L. A. PADERNO, YU. B. REDKOZEMEL. METAL., SPLAVY SOEDIN., MATER. SOVESHCH., 7TH 251-3, 1973.
67865	**EUROPIUM DIPHOSPHIDE WITH SEMICONDUCTOR PROPERTIES.** MIRONOV, E. BRYGALINA, G. P. REDKOZEMEL. METAL., SPLAVY SOEDIN., MATER. SOVESHCH., 7TH 305, 1973.

EPIC Number	Bibliographic Citation
67868	**PHOTOMAGNETIC PHENOMENA.** ENZ, U. UMSCHAU 72 (12), 393, 1972.
67877	**ENERGY-BAND STRUCTURE THEORY.** OKAZAKI, M. INOUE, M. J. FAC. ENG., UNIV. TOKYO SER. A (9), 44–5, 1971.
67881	**EFFECT OF NEUTRONS ON CADMIUM SULFIDE CRYSTAL DETECTORS FOR LIGHT AND HIGH-ENERGY QUANTA.** MIKOSZA, H. TRANS. IMEKO SYMP. PHOTON DETECTORS, 4TH 135–52, 1970.
67891	**PRACTICAL LIMITS TO THE THERMOELECTRIC FIGURE OF MERIT–II.** URE, R. W., JR. ENERGY CONVERS. 12 (2), 45–52, 1972.
67892	**ON THE ELECTRICAL CONDUCTIVITY OF CERTAIN METALS AT LOW TEMPERATURES.** MC LENNAN, J. C. HOWLETT, L. E. WILHELM, J. O. TRANS. ROY. SOC. CAN. 23 (SERIES 3), 287–306, 1930.
67894	**A BIBLIOGRAPHY ON METHODS FOR THE MEASUREMENT OF INHOMOGENEITIES IN SEMICONDUCTORS.** SCHAFFT, H. A. NEEDHAM, S. G. NATIONAL BUREAU OF STANDARDS 45PP., 1968. (NBS–TN–445)
67895	**OBSERVATIONS USING THE VAN DER PAUW METHOD OF RESISTIVITY MEASUREMENT.** GORETZKI, H. PRAKT. METALLOGR. (2), 85–95, 1968.
67914	**LUMINESCENCE KINETICS OF SCINTILLATORS.** MEDVEDEV, M. N. KONDRATENKOV, YU. B. PRIB. TEKH. EKSP., 19 (4), (PT. 1), 79–81, 1973. (FOR ENGLISH TRANSLATION SEE E 67915)
67915	**LUMINESCENCE KINETICS OF SCINTILLATORS.** MEDVEDEV, M. N. KONDRATENKOV, YU. B. INSTRUM. EXP. TECH., USSR 16 (4), (PT. 1), 1077–9, 1973. (ENGLISH TRANSLATION OF PRIB. TEKH. EKSP., 19 (4), (PT. 1), 79–81, 1973; FOR ORIGINAL SEE E67914)
67920	**CRYOSTAT FOR MEASURING THE MAGNETOSTRICTION CONSTANTS OF FERRITES BY THE FERROMAGNETIC RESONANCE METHOD.** VOLKOVA, N. V. RAITSIS, V. I. PRIB. TEKH. EKSP. 16 (2), (PT. 2), 236–8, 1973. (FOR ENGLISH TRANSLATION SEE E 67921)
67921	**CRYOSTAT FOR MEASURING THE MAGNETOSTRICTION CONSTANTS OF FERRITES BY THE FERROMAGNETIC RESONANCE METHOD.** VOLKOVA, N. V. RAITSIS, V. I. INSTRUM. EXP. TECH., USSR 16 (2), (PT. 2), 614–6, 1973. (ENGLISH TRANSLATION OF PRIB. TEKH. EKSP., 16 (2), (PT. 2), 236–8, 1973; FOR ORIGINAL SEE E 67920)
67946	**A COMPARISON OF THE PROPERTIES OF CAST AND SINTERED LANTHANUM HEXABORIDES (CASTING USING CONSUMABLE ELECTRODES).** KOSYACHKOV, A. A. STEPANCHUK, A. N. SHLYUKO, V. YA. POROSH. MET. 13 (3), 74–6, 1974. (FOR ENGLISH TRANSLATION SEE E67947)
67947	**A COMPARISON OF THE PROPERTIES OF CAST AND SINTERED LANTHANUM HEXABORIDES (CASTING USING CONSUMABLE ELECTRODES).** KOSYACHKOV, A. A. STEPANCHUK, A. N. SHLYUKO, V. YA. SOV. POWDER METAL. MET. CERAM., 13 (3), 230–1, U.MJ. (ENGLISH TRANSLATION OF POROSH. MET., 13 (3), 74–6, 1974; FOR ORIGINAL SEE E 67946)
67958	**EFFECT OF DOPING WITH IODINE AND ANTIMONY ON THE THERMOELECTRIC PROPERTIES OF THALLIUM TELLURIDE.** TSEDERBERG, N. V. KAZANDZHAN, B. I. TSURIKOV, A. A. TEPLOFIZ. VYS. TEMP. 10 (5), 1120–1, 1972. (FOR ENGLISH TRANSLATION SEE E 67959)
67959	**EFFECT OF DOPING WITH IODINE AND ANTIMONY ON THE THERMOELECTRIC PROPERTIES OF THALLIUM TELLURIDE** TSEDERBERG, N. V. KAZANDZHAN, B. I. TSURIKOV, A. A. HIGH TEMP. 10 (5), 1005–7, 1972. (ENGLISH TRANSLATION OF TEPLOFIZ. VYS. TEMP., 10 (5), 1120–1, 1972; FOR ORIGINAL SEE E 67958)
67982	**ELECTRICAL PROPERTIES AND LUMINESCENCE OF OXYGEN-DOPED CADMIUM TELLURIDE CRYSTALS.** AGRINSKAYA, N. V. ALEKSANDROVA, G. I. ARKAD'EVA, E. N. ATABEKOV, B. A. MATVEEV, O. A. PEREPELOVA, G. B. SHMANENKOVA, G. I. FIZ. TEKH. POLUPROV. 8 (2), 317–20, 1974. (FOR ENGLISH TRANSLATION SEE E67983)
67983	**ELECTRICAL PROPERTIES AND LUMINESCENCE OF OXYGEN-DOPED CADMIUM TELLURIDE CRYSTALS.** AGRINSKAYA, N. V. ALEKSANDROVA, G. I. ARDAD'EVA, E. N. ATABEKOV, B. A. MATVEEV, O. A. PEREPELOVA, G. B. PROKOF'EV, S. V. SHMANENKOVA, G. I. SOV. PHYS. SEMICOND. 8 (2), 202–3, 1974. (ENGLISH TRANSLATION OF FIZ. TEKH. POLUPROV., 8 (2), 317–20, 1974; FOR ORIGINAL SEE E67982)
67984	**HIGH TEMPERATURE GREEN LUMINESCENCE OF CADMIUM SULFIDE SINGLE CRYSTALS DOPED HEAVILY WITH CHLORINE.** MOIN, M. D. PEKAR', G. S. SAL'KOV, E. A. FIZ. TEKH. POLUPROV. 8 (1), 202–4, 1974. (FOR ENGLISH TRANSLATION SEE E 67985)
67985	**HIGH TEMPERATURE GREEN LUMINESCENCE OF CADMIUM SULFIDE SINGLE CRYSTALS DOPED HEAVILY WITH CHLORINE.** MOIN, M. D. PEKAR', G. S. SAL'KOV, E. A. SOV. PHYS. SEMICOND. 8 (1), 132–3, 1974. (ENGLISH TIANSLATION OF FIZ. TEKH. POLUPROV., 8 (1), 202–4, 1974; FOR ORIGINAL SEE E 67984)
67986	**EQASIENXCITON NATURE OF THE ENERGY SPECTRUM AND POSSIBILITY OF A PHASE TRANSITION OF THE FIRST KIND IN A DEGENERATE ELECTRON-HOLE PLASMA IN SEMICONDUCTORS.** FISHMAN, I. M. SHRETER, YU. G. FIZ. TEKH. POLUPROV. 8 (2), 362–7, 1974. (FOR ENGLISH TRANSLATION SEE E 67987)
67987	**EQASIEXCITON NATURE OF THE ENERGY SPECTRUM AND POSSIBILITY OF A PHASE TRANSITION OF THE FIRST KIND IN A DEGENERATE ELECTRON-HOLE PLASMA IN SEMICONDUCTORS.** FISHMAN, I. M. SHRETER, YU. G. SOV. PHYS. SEMICOND. 8 (2), 231–3, 1974. (ENGLISH TRANSLATION OF FIZ. TEKH. POLUPROV., 8 (2), 362–7, 1974; FOR ORIGINAL SEE E 67986)
67988	**SPECTRA OF THE ABSORPTION AND EXCITATION OF LUMINESCENCE IN SILVER-ACTIVATED POTASSIUM IODIDE, POTASSIUM SILVER IODIDE, AND SILVER IODIDE.** NEDZVETSKAYA, I. V. OPT. SPEKTROSK. 36 (1), 145–9, 1974. (FOR ENGLISH TRANSLATION SEE E67989)
67989	**SPECTRA OF THE ABSORPTION AND EXCITATION OF LUMINESCENCE IN SILVER-ACTIVATED POTASSIUM IODIDE, POTASSIUM SILVER IODIDE, AND SILVER IODIDE.** NEDZVETSKAYA, I. V. OPT. SPECTROS., USSR 36 (1), 83–5, 1974. (ENGLISH TRANSLATION OF OPT. SPEKTROSK., 36 (1), 145–9, 1974; FOR ORIGINAL SEE E67988)
68005	**EQUIPMENT FOR MEASURING THE HALL CONSTANT OF SEMICONDUCTORS AT TEMPERATURES UP TO 1000 DEGREES C.** ASTAKHOV, O. P. SGIBNEV, I. V. IZMER. TEKH. 16 (4), 61, 1973. (FOR ENGLISH TRANSLATION SEE E 68006)
68006	**EQUIPMENT FOR MEASURING THE HALL CONSTANT OF SEMICONDUCTORS AT TEMPERATURES UP TO 1000 DEGREES C.** ASTAKHOV, O. P. SGIBNEV, I. V. MEAS. TECH., USSR 16 (4), 575–6, 1973. (ENGLISH TRANSLATION OF IZMER. TEKH., 16 (4), 61, 1973; FOR ORIGINAL SEE E 68005)
68007	**MEASURING THE CONDUCTANCE AND ITS RELATION TO THE TEMPERATURE OF POLYCRYSTALLINE SEMICONDUCTORS UNDER PRESSURE.** ALIKIN, V. I. IZMER. TEKH. 16 (2), 52–4, 1973. (FOR ENGLISH TRANSLATION SEE E 68008)

EPIC Number	Bibliographic Citation
68008	**MEASURING THE CONDUCTANCE AND ITS RELATION TO THE TEMPERATURE OF POLYCRYSTALLINE SEMICONDUCTORS UNDER PRESSURE.** ALIKIN, V. I. MEAS. TECH., USSR 16 (2), 240–3, 1973. (ENGLISH TRANSLATION OF IZMER. TEKH., 16 (2), 52–4, 1973; FOR ORIGINAL SEE E 68007)
68020	**ELECTRICAL CONDUCTIVITY OF COPPER OXIDE WHEN EQUILIBRIUM WITH THE GAS PHASE IS DISTURBED.** ZUEV, K. P. BURTSEV, A. F. IZV. AKAD. NAUK SSSR, NEORG. MATER. 9 (3), 395–8, 1973. (FOR ENGLISH TRANSLATION SEE E 68021)
68021	**ELECTRICAL CONDUCTIVITY OF COPPER OXIDE WHEN EQUILIBRIUM WITH THE GAS PHASE IS DISTURBED.** ZUEV, K. P. BURTSEV, A. F. INORG. MAT., USSR 9 (3), 352–4, 1973. (ENGLISH TRANSLATION OF IZV. AKAD. NAUK SSSR, NEORG. MATER., 9 (3), 395–8, 1973; FOR ORIGINAL SEE E68020)
68031	**ELECTRICAL PROPERTIES OF CERIUM SULFIDE.** GOLIKOVA, O. A. RUDNIK, N. M. SERGEEVA, V. M. IZV. AKAD. NAUK SSSR, NEORG. MATER. 9 (5), 755–9, 1973. (FOR ENGLISH TRANSLATION SEE E 68032)
68032	**ELECTRICAL PROPERTIES OF CERIUM SULFIDE.** GOLIKOVA, O. A. RUDNIK, N. M. SERGEEVA, V. M. INORG. MAT., USSR 9 (5), 677–80, 1973. (ENGLISH TRANSLATION OF IZV. AKAD. NAUK SSSR, NEORG. MATER., 9 (5), 755–9, 1973; FOR ORIGINAL SEE E 68031)
68034	**DOPING OF ZINC SILICON ARSENIDE.** AVERKIEVA, G. K. PROCHUKHAN, V. D. TASHTANOVA, M. IZV. AKAD. NAUK SSSR, NEORG. MATER. 9 (3), 487–8, 1973. (FOR ENGLISH TRANSLATION SEE E68035)
68035	**DOPING OF ZINC SILICON ARSENIDE.** AVERKIEVA, G. K. PROCHUKHAN, V. D. TASHTANOVA, M. INORG. MAT., USSR 9 (3), 435–6, 1973. (ENGLISH TRANSLATION OF IZV. AKAD. NAUK SSSR, NEORG. MATER., 9 (3), 487–8, 1973; FOR ORIGINAL SEE E 68034)
68038	**PHASE TRANSITION IN BARIUM TITANIUM OXIDE.** DEM'YANOV, V. V. IZV. AKAD. NAUK SSSR, NEORG. MATER. 9 (3), 404–8, 1973. (FOR ENGLISH TRANSLATION SEE E 68039)
68039	**PHASE TRANSITION IN BARIUM TITANIUM OXIDE.** DEM'YANOV, V. V. INORG. MAT., USSR 9 (3), 359–62, 1973. (ENGLISH TRANSLATION OF IZV. AKAD. NAUK SSSR, NEORG. MATER., 9 (3), 404–8, 1973; FOR ORIGINAL SEE E 68038)
68040	**PREPARATION OF NIOBIUM TIN COATINGS FROM THE GAS PHASE.** PETRUSEVICH, I. V. KOZLOV, F. N. BOGDANOV, V. P. NISEL'SON, L. A. IZV. AKAD. NAUK SSSR, NEORG. MATER., 9 (6), 952–5, 1973. (FOR ENGLISH TRANSLATION SEE E 68041)
68041	**PREPARATION OF NIOBIUM TIN COATINGS FROM THE GAS PHASE.** PETRUSEVICH, I. V. KOZLOV, F. N. BOGDANOV, V. P. NESEL'SON, L. A. INORG. MAT., USSR, 9 (6), 852–4, 1973. (ENGLISH TRANSLATION OF IZV. AKAD. NAUK SSSR, NEORG. MATER., 9 (6), 952–5, 1973; FOR ORIGINAL SEE E 68040)
68076	**RADIO FREQUENCY AND DIRECT CURRENT REACTIVE SPUTTERING FOR CRYSTALLINE AND AMORPHOUS VANADIUM DIOXIDE THIN FILM DEPOSITION.** DUCHENE, J. TERRAILLON, M. PAILLY, M. C.E.N., COMMIS. ENERGY. AT., GRENBOLE, FR., 11 PP., 1972. (CEA–CONF–2133)
68077	**ENERGY LEVELS OF TERBIUM TRIPOSITIVE IN LANTHANUM BROMIDE.** JOSHI, B. D. PATEL, B. M. PAGE, A. G. BANGIA, T. R. SAXENA, R. N. RADIOCHEM DIV., BHABHA AT. RES. CENT., BOMBAY 21 PP., 1972. (B.A.R.C.–588)

EPIC Number	Bibliographic Citation
68078	**ELECTRICAL RESISTIVITY OF MAGNETICALLY ORDERED ALLOYS. CHROMIUM TELLURIDE.** RAO, U. R. K. YAKHMI, J. V. KARKHANAVALA, M. D. RADIOCHEM DIV., BHABHA AT. RES. CENT., BOMBAY 7 PP., 1971. (B.A.R.C.–545)
68079	**ELECTRICAL CONDUCTIVITY OF REFIRED SINTERED URANIUM DIOXIDE PETTETS.** RAO, S. V. K. AGNIHOTRI, P. K. ANANDAN, N. S. PRASAD, G. E. MOORTHY, V. K. METALL. DIV., BHABHA, AT. RES. CENT., BOMBAY 6 PP., 1972. (B.A.R.C.–596)
68080	**ELECTRICAL RESISTIVITY OF IRON SELENIDE.** RAO, U. R. K. YAKHMI, J. V. CHEM. DIV., BHABHA AT. RES. CENT., BOMBAY 5 PP., 1971. (B.A.R.C.–546)
68082	**EXPOSURE RATE DEPENDENCE OF THE THERMOLUMINESCENT RESPONSE.** ZANETIC, J. INST. FIS., UNIV. SAO PAULO, SAO PAULO 79 PP., 1972. (INIS–MF–1110)
68114	**LEAD TELLURIDE–TIN TELLURIDE.** NEUBERGER, M. HUGHES AIRCRAFT CO., CULVER CITY, CALIF. 211PP., 1970. (AD–701 075, EPIC–DS–164)
68115	**IV–VI SEMICONDUCTING COMPOUNDS DATA TABLES.** NEUBERGER, M. HUGHES AIRCRAFT CO., CULVER CITY, CALIF. 102PP., 1969. (AD–699 260, EPIC–S–12)
68126	**VAPOR PHASE GROWTH SYSTEM AND ITS USE IN THE PREPARATION OF SEVERAL III–V COMPOUND SEMICONDUCTORS.** ENSTROM, R. E. MILLER, E. A. SIGAI, A. G. RCA LAB., PRINCETON, N. J. 104 PP., 1971. (NASA–CR–1886)
68127	**SPECTROSCOPIC MEASUREMENTS OF WATER VAPOR PLASMAS AT HIGH RESOLUTION. THE OPTICAL TRANSITION PROBABILITIES FOR OK (A (2) – X (2) II).** KLEIN, L. GREYRAD CORP., PRINCETON, N. J. 146 PP., 1972. (NASA–CR–2069)
68133	**ULTRAVACUUM IN THE STUDY OF ELECTRON EMISSION FROM ION BOMBARDMENT.** CATONI, F. CIPOLLONI, G. LAB. ELETTRON. COM. NAZ. ENERG. NUCL, ROME, ITALY 17 PP., 1971. (RT–EL–71–4)
68149	**FLUORESCENCE AND PHOSPHORESCENCE OF PHOTO–MULTIPLIER WINDOW MATERIALS UNDER ELECTRON IRRADIATION.** VIEHMANN, W. EUBANKS, A. G. BREDEKAMP, J. H. NASA, GODDARD SPACE FLIGHT CENTER, GREENBELT, MD. 38 PP., 1974. (N74–28136, NASA–TM–X–70695, X755–74–210)
68153	**LASER WINDOW SURFACE FINISHING AND COATING TECHNOLOGY.** BRAUNSTEIN, M. HUGHES RESEARCH LABS., MALIBU, CALIF. 45PP., 1973. (N74–27936, AD–777 888, AFCRL–TR–74–0032)
68159	**COMPOSITION AND OPTICAL PROPERTIES OF MANGANESE - BISMUTH THIN FILMS PREPARED BY VACUUM EVAPORATION.** LUTTER, A. OPT. DEP., CENT. RES. INST. PHYS., BUDAPEST, HUNG. 12 PP., 1974. (KFKI–74–2)
68189	**GROWTH AND DOPING CHARACTERISTICS OF FLASH EVAPORATED THIN FILM GALLIUM ARSENIDE.** HU, D. H. UNIV. MISSOURI, COLUMBIA, PH. D. THESES, 106 PP., 1970. (UNIV. MICROFILMS NO. 71–3339)
68192	**IMPURITY ANALYSIS OF EPITAXIAL GALLIUM ARSENIDE WITH AN ACCURATE HALL EFFECT APPARATUS.** DAVIS, M. E. OHIO STATE UNIV., COLUMBUS, PH. D. THESES 147 PP., 1973. (N74–26204 UNIV. MICROFILMS NO. 74–10942)
68205	**COLOR CENTRES AND THERMOLUMINESCENCE IN LITHIUM FLOURIDE.** MAYHUGH, M. R. DARTMOUTH COLL., HANOVER, N. H., PH. D. THESIS 74 PP., 1970. (UNIV. MICROFORMS NO. 70–20684)

EPIC Number | Bibliographic Citation

68207 **OPTICAL PROPERTIES AND ELECTRICAL CONDUCTIVITY OF SEVERAL INTERMETALLIC COMPOUNDS.**
KIEWIT, D. A.
NORTHWESTERN UNIV., EVANSTON, ILL., PH. D. THESIS
191 PP., 1968.
(N70-11317 UNIV. MICROFILMS NO. 69-1865)

68209 **ELECTRICAL PROPERTIES OF III-V SEMICONDUCTORS.**
SHERWOOD, N. T.
PURDUE UNIV., LAFAYETTE, IND., PH. D. THESIS
131 PP., 1970.
(UNIV. MICROFILMS NO. 71-2687)

68210 **THE ELECTRICAL PROPERTIES OF GRAIN BOUNDARIES IN NICKEL OXIDE AND MAGNESIUM OXIDE.**
OSBURN, C. M.
PURDUE UNIV., LAFAYETTE, IND., PH. D. THESIS
295PP., 1970.
(UNIV. MICROFILMS NO. 71-2662)

68214 **MAGNETIC SUSCEPTIBILITIES OF TITANIUM AND VANADIUM IN CORUNDUM STRUCTURES.**
ARNOLD, D. J.
TEXAS TECH. UNIV., LUBBOCK, PH. D. THESIS
110PP., 1970.
(UNIV. MICROFILMS NO. 71-523)

68216 **THERMOLUMINESCENCE OF THORIUM OXIDE SINGLE CRYSTALS.**
RODINE, E. T.
UNIV NEBRASKA, LINCOLN, PH. D. THESIS
140 PP., 1970.
(UNIV. MICROFILMS NO9 71-3654)

68217 **RARE EARTH ION PAIR ABSORPTION AT LOW CONCENTRATIONS IN LANTHANUM TRICHLORIDE.**
BLATT, J. H.
UNIV. ALABAMA, PH. S. THESIS
119PP., 1970.
(UNIV. MICROFILMS NO. 71-1225)

68244 **THE OPTICAL CONSTANTS (N, K) OF AMMONIUM SULFATE IN THE INFRARED.**
CHERMACK, E. E. A.
NEW YORK UNIV., N. Y., PH. D. THESIS
122PP., 1970.
(UNIV. MICROFILMS NO. 70-18992)

68246 **A STUDY OF THERMALLY STIMULATED LUMINESCENCE IN STANNIC OXIDE.**
EAGLETON, R. D.
OKLAHOMA STATE UNIV., STILLWATER, PH. D. THESIS
91PP., 1969.
(UNIV. MICROFILMS. NO. 70-21376)

68253 **DETERMINATION OF REFRACTIVE INDEX OF THIN FILMS FROM INTERFERENCE-FRINGE REFLECTION SPECTRA.**
JAEGER, J. B.
AIR FORCE INST. OF TECH., WPAFB, OHIO, M. S. THESIS
94PP., 1974.
(N74-28217, AD-777 843, GEP/PH/74-9)

68271 **II-VI SEMICONDUCTING COMPOUNDS DATA TABLES.**
NEUBERGER, M.
HUGHES AIRCRAFT CO., CULVER CITY, CALIF.
156PP., 1969.
(AD-698 341, EPIC-S-11)

68313 **ZINC SELENIDE. DATA SHEETS.**
NEUBERGER, M.
HUGHES AIRCRAFT CO., CULVER CITY, CALIF.
31PP., 1963.
(AD-421 964, EPIC-DS-132, N64-27558)

68323 **OPTICAL PROPERTIES AND THERMAL CONDUCTIVITY OF ALUMINUM OXIDE.**
NEUBERGER, M.
HUGHES AIRCRAFT CO., CULVER CITY, CALIF.
62PP., 1965.
(AD-464 823, EPIC-S-6)

68325 **CADMIUM OXIDE. DATA SHEETS.**
NEUBERGER, M.
HUGHES AIRCRAFT CO., CULVER CITY, CALIF.
63PP., 1966.
(AD-486 595, EPIC-DS-149)

68345 **THE ELECTRICAL ANDNOPTICAL PROPERTIES OF ZINC SELENIDE.**
JONES, G.
UNIV. DURHAM, ENGLAND, M. S. THESIS
1973.

68348 **PERMANENT MAGNET PROPERTIES OF YTTRIUM-(COBALT, COPPER) AND YTTRIUM-(IRON COBALT, COPPER) INTERMETALLIC COMPOUNDS.**
TOSHIKAZU, K. TSUGIO, S.
DENSHI GIJUTSU SOGO KENKYUJO IHO
36 (11), 768-76, 1972.

68350 **EXCITON-PHONON INTERACTIONS IN URANYL COMPOUND CRYSTALS.**
VOLOD'KO, L. V. SEVCHENKO, A. N.
KOMYAK, A. I. UMREIKO, D. S.
DOKL. AKAD. NAUK B. SSSR
18 (7), 601-3, 1974.

68351 **EXCITON STATES IN CADMIUM TELLURIDE AT 80-293 K.**
IVANOV, V. S. NOLLE, E. L.
STOPACHINSKII, V. B.
EKSITONY POLUPORV.
88-92, 1971.

68353 **EXCITON PHOTOLUMINESCENCE AND ABSORPTION IN CADMIUM TELLURIDE CRYSTALS.**
GIPPIUS, A. A. VAVILOV, V. S.
PANOSYAN, ZH. R. USHAKOV, V. V
EKSITONY POLYPROV.
68-87, 1971.

68361 **LEAD SULFIDE. DATA SHEETS.**
NEUBERGER, M.
HUGHES AIRCRAFT CO., CULVER CITY, CALIF.
114PP., 1966.
(AD-803 886, EPIC-DS-150)

68368 **LEAD OXIDE.**
NEUBERGER, M.
HUGHES AIRCRAFT CO., CULVER CITY, CALIF.
84PP., 1967.
(AD-814 147, EPIC-DS-155)

68371 **CADMIUM TELLURIDE AND THE CADMIUM TELLURIDE-MERCURY SYSTEM.**
NEUBERGER, M.
HUGHES AIRCRAFT CO., CULVER CITY, CALIF.
200PP., 1967.
(AD-819 287, EPIC-DS-157)

68372 **NIOBIUM TIN. PART 1. STRUCTURE SENSITIVE PROPERTIES. DATA SHEETS.**
GRIGSBY, D. L.
HUGHES AIRCRAFT CO., CULVER CITY, CALIF.
158PP., 1968.
(AD-830 330, EPIC-DS-159)

68373 **NIOBIUM TIN. PART II. DATA SHEETS.**
GRIGSBY, D. L.
HUGHES AIRCRAFT CO., CULVER CITY, CALIF.
180PP., 1968.
(AD-838 460, EPIC-DS-160)

68374 **BORON NITRIDE. DATA SHEETS.**
NEUBERGER, M.
HUGHES AIRCRAFT CO., CULVER CITY, CALIF.
95PP., 1967.
(AD-824 733, EPIC-DS-158)

68396 **ION DOPING OF CADMIUM TELLURIDE.**
AGRINSKAYA, N. V. ARKAD'EVA, E. N.
GUSEVA, M. U. MASLOVA, L. V.
MATVEEV, O. A. RYVKIN, S. M.
STARININ, K. V. SLADKOVA, V. A.
FIZ. OSN. IONNO-LUCHEVOGO LEGIR., MATER. NAUCH. KONF.
2, 227-30, 1972.

68402 **ANGULAR DISTRIBUTION OF ELECTRONS EMITTED DURING THE PHOTOIONIZATION OF FREE ATOMS AND MOLECULES.**
MILYAEV, V. M. VILESOV, F. I.
KHIM. VYS. ENERG.
6 (4), 354-6, 1972.

68409 **INFLUENCE OF HYDROSTATIC PRESSURE ON THE FERROELECTRIC PHASE TRANSITION IN AMMONIUM TETRAFLUOROBERYLLATE.**
SORGE, G. FRENZEL, CH.
PHYS. STATUS SOLIDI
22 A (1), K31-K36, 1974.

68412 **RESISTIVITY OF VANADIUM - OXYGEN ALLOYS.**
STAROSTINA, L. S. MAKSIMOV, YU. A.
RUSS. J. PHYS. CHEM.
45 (11), 1581-3, 1971.
(ENGLISH TRANSLATION OF ZH. FIZ. KHIM., 45 (11), 2789-91, 1971; FOR ORIGINAL SEE E64150)

68414 **CONDUCTIVITY TYPE OF 3-D TRANSITION METAL SILICIDES.**
NIKITIN, E. N. TARASOV, V. I.
SOV. PHYS. CRYSTALLOGR.
16 (2), 305-8, 1971.
(ENGLISH TRANSLATION OF KRISTALLOGRAFIYA, 16 (2), 372-6, 1971; FOR ORIGINAL SEE E64585)

68416 **TEMPERATURE DEPENDENCES OF F-CENTER FORMATION IN POTASSIUM CHLORIDE - POTASSIUM BROMIDE SOLID SOLUTIONS.**
ZAVADOVSKAYA, E. K. ANNENKOV, YU. M.
FRANGULYAN, T. S.
OPT. SPECTROS., USSR
29 (4), 385-8, 1970.
(ENGLISH TRANSLATION OF OPT. SPEKTROSK., 29 (4), 721-6, 1970; FOR ORIGINAL SEE E64286)

68417 **METHOD OF APPLYING THE KRAMERS-KRONIG RELATION TO THE CALCULATION OF OPTICAL CONSTANTS OF CONDENSED MEDIA FROM THE REFLECTION SPECTRUM.**
SOLOVEVA, G. S. LIBOV, V. S.
OPT. SPECTROS., USSR
33 (3), 276-9, 1972.
(ENGLISH TRANSLATION OF OPT. SPEKTROSK., 33 (3), 513-9, 1972; FOR ORIGINAL SEE E64288)

EPIC Number	Bibliographic Citation

68418 **RADIATIVE RECOMBINATION UNDER CONDITIONS OF SCREENING OF THE COULOMB INTERACTION IN CADMIUM SULFIDE CRYSTALS.**
LYSENKO, V. G. REVENKO, V. I. TRATAS, T. G.
TIMOFEEV, V. B.
JETP LETT.
20 (3), 77–9, 1974.
(ENGLISH TRANSLATION OF ZH. EKSP. TEOR. FIZ., PIS'MA RED., 20 (3), 180–5, 1974; FOR ORIGINAL SEE E65619)

68419 **ANOMALIES OF THE PHOTOCONDUCTIVITY IN THE REGION OF THE CURIE POINT OF THE COMPOUND CADMIUM CHROMIUM SELENIDE WEAKLY DOPED WITH GALLIUM.**
BELOV, K. P. KOROLEVA, L. I. BATOROVA, S. D.
SHALIMOVA, M. A. KALINNIKOV, V. T.
AMINOV, T. G. SHABUNINA, G. G.
SHAPSHEVA, N. P.
JETP LETT.
20 (3), 82–3, 1974.
(ENGLISH TRANSLATION OF ZH. EKSP. TEOR. FIZ., PIS'MA RED., 20 (3), 191–5, 1974; FOR ORIGINAL SEE E65623)

68424 **ON THE NATURE OF SUPERCONDUCTING NIOBIUM AND TANTALUM MONOCARBIDES.**
DUBROVSKAYA, L. B. RABIN'KIN, A. G.
GEL'D, P. V.
SOV. PHYS. JETP
35 (1), 161–4, 1972.
(ENGLISH TRANSLATION OF ZH. EKSP. TEOR. FIZ., 62 (1), 300–6, 1972; FOR ORIGINAL SEE E63967)

68432 **PIEZOOPTICAL PHENOMENA DUE TO FREE CHARGE CARRIERS IN GALLIUM ANTIMONIDE.**
GLURDZHIDZE, L. N. REMENYUK, A. D.
VUL', A. YA. GOLUBEV, L. V.
SOV. PHYS. SEMICOND.
8 (9), 1114–6, 1975.
(ENGLISH TRANSLATION OF FIZ. TEKH. POLUPROV., 8 (9), 1720–4, 1974; FOR ORIGINAL SEE E64959)

68518 **TRANSVERSE NERNST-ETTINGSHAUSEN EFFECT IN PURE AND DOPED INDIUM ANTIMONIDE CRYSTALS.**
ERMOLOVICH, YU. B.
DIELEKTR. POLUPROVODN. NEZHVED. NAUCHN. SB.
(3), 13–16, 1973.

68520 **TEMPERATURE DEPENDENCE OF THE LUMINESCENCE SPECTRUM OF ALUMINUM-DOPED BETA-SILICON CARBIDE.**
ALTAISKII, YU. M. KALABUKHOV, N. P.
PUGACH, O. V.
DIELEKTR. POLUPROVODN. MEZHVED. NAUCHN. SB.
(3), 17–20, 1973.

68540 **CHARACTERISTICS OF THERMIOELECTRIC PROPERTIES OF ANTIMONY SELENIDE MELTS WITH ADDITIVES.**
KAZANDZHAN, B. I. LOBANOV, A. A.
MISHUTKINA, T. I.
TR. MOSK. ENERG. INST.
75, 185–91, 1970.

68546 **THE OPTICAL TRANSPARENCY OF YTTRIUM IRON GARNET IN THE NEAR INFRARED.**
LECRAW, R. C. WOOD, D. L. DILLON, J. F., JR.
REMEIKA, J. P.
APPL. PHYS. LETT.
7 (1), 27–8, 1965.

68551 **PHYSICAL PROPERTIES AND ELECTRONIC STRUCTURE OF THE TERNARY ALLOY (VANADIUM CHROMIUM) SILICON.**
SURIKOV, V. I. PRYADEIN, V. I.
SHTOL'TS, A. K. STEPANOV, A. P. GEL'D, P. V.
PREKUL, A. F. ZAGRYAZHSKII, V. L.
FIZ. METAL. METALLOVED.
33 (6), 1222–7, 1972.
(FOR ENGLISH TRANSLATION SEE E68552)

68552 **PHYSICAL PROPERTIES AND ELECTRONIC STRUCTURE OF THE TERNARY ALLOY (VANADIUM CHROMIUM) SILICON.**
SURIKOV, V. I. PRYADEIN, V. I.
SHTOL'TS, A. K. STEPANOV, A. P.
GEL'D, P. V. PREKUL, A. F.
ZAGRYAZHSKII, V. L.
PHYS. METALS METALLOGR.
33 (6), 93–8, 1972.
(ENGLISH TRANSLATION OF FIZ. METAL. METALLOVED., 33 (6), 1222–7, 1972; FOR ORIGINAL SEE E68551)

68553 **THERMOLUMINESCENCE OF IRRADIATED ORTHOVANADATES OF GROUP III ELEMENTS.**
KHODOS, M. YA. SHUL'GIN, B. V.
FOTIEV, A. A. GAVRILOV, F. F.
IZV. AKAD. NAUK SSSR, NEORG. MATER.
8 (9), 1678–9, 1972.
(FOR ENGLISH TRANSLATION SEE E68554)

68554 **THERMOLUMINESCENCE OF IRRADIATED ORTHOVANADATES OF GROUP III ELEMENTS.**
KHODOS, M. YA. SHUL'GIN, B. V.
FOTIEV, A. A. GAVRILOV, F. F.
INORG. MAT., USSR
8 (9), 1475–6, 1972.
(ENGLISH TRANSLATION OF IZV. AKAD. NAUK SSSR, NEORG. MATER., 8 (9), 1678–9, 1972; FOR ORIGINAL SEE E68553)

68558 **THERMO ELECTRO-MOTIVE-FORCE AND SEEBECK COEFFICIENT OF LITHIUM DOPED NICKEL OXIDE AT HIGH TEMPERATURE.**
STEVANOVIC, M. STIGLIC, R.
THERMOPHYSICAL PROPERTIES OF SOLIDS AT HIGH TEMP., EUROPEAN CONF., 4TH
93–6, 1974.

68590 **FERROELECTRIC AND OPTICAL PROPERTIES OF LEAD POTASSIUM NIOBATE.**
NAKANO, J. YAMADA, T.
J. APPL. PHYS.
46 (6), 2361–5, 1975.

68596 **NEW INTERPRETATION OF THE FAR-INFRARED SULFUR DIOXIDE LASER SPECTRUM.**
STEENBECKELIERS, G. BELLET, J.
J. APPL. PHYS.
46 (6), 2620–6, 1975.

68597 **EFFECT OF DISLOCATIONS ON GREEN ELECTROLUMINESCENCE EFFICIENCY IN GALLIUM PHOSPHIDE GROWN BY LIQUID PHASE EPITAXY.**
BRANTLEY, W. A. LORIMOR, O. G. DAPKUS, P. D.
HASZKO, S. E. SAUL, R. H.
J. APPL. PHYS.
46 (6), 2629–37, 1975.

68601 **HIGH TEMPERATURE ELECTRON AND HOLE MOBILITIES IN PURE AND DOPED CADMIUM SULFIDE.**
VYDYANATH, H. R. KROGER, F. A.
J. APPL. PHYS.
46 (6), 2670–4, 1975.

68602 **TEMPERATURE DEPENDENCE OF THE BAND GAP AND COMPARISON WITH THE THRESHOLD FREQUENCY OF PURE GALLIUM ARSENIDE LASERS.**
CAMASSEL, J. AUVERGNE, D. MATHIEU, H.
J. APPL. PHYS.
46 (6), 2683–9, 1975.

68606 **OPTICAL WAVEGUIDES IN ION-IMPLANTED ZINC TELLURIDE.**
VALETTE, S. LABRUNIE, G. LIZET, J.
J. APPL. PHYS.
46 (6), 2731–2, 1975.

68607 **A HIGHLY SENSITIVE REVERSIBLE AND NONVOLATILE HYBRID PHOTOCONDUCTIVE/MAGNETO-OPTIC STORAGE MATERIAL.**
KRUMME, J. P. HILL, B. KRUGER, J.
WITTER, K.
J. APPL. PHYS.
46 (6), 2733–6, 1975.

68609 **SYNTHESIS AND MAGNETIC BEHAVIOR OF GADOLINIUM NITRIDE.**
CUTLER, R. A. LAWSON, A. W.
J. APPL. PHYS.
46 (6), 2739–44, 1975.

68612 **CALIBRATION OF THE PRESSURE DEPENDENCE OF THE R(1) RUBY FLUORESCENCE LINE TO 195 KILOBAR.**
PIERMARINI, G. J. BLOCK, S. BARNETT, J. D.
FORMAN, R. A.
J. APPL. PHYS.
46 (5), 2774–80, 1975.

68613 **OPTICAL AND DIELECTRIC CONSTANTS OF HAFNIUM AND ITS ANODIC OXIDE FILMS.**
SAXENA, A. N. MITTAL, K. L.
J. APPL. PHYS.
46 (6), 2788–9, 1975.

68614 **EVIDENCE OF ABSENCE OF ELECTRODE-LIMITED CONDUCTION IN THIN (140) TANTALUM OXIDE FILMS.**
YOUNG, P. L.
J. APPL. PHYS.
46 (6), 2794–5, 1975.

68615 **CONTROL OF THE UNIAXIAL MAGNETIC ANISOTROPY IN LIQUID PHASE EPITAXY GROWN IRON GARNET FILMS BY SMALL RUTHENIUM SUBSTITUTIONS.**
KRUMME, J. P. HANSEN, P. BARTELS, G.
MATEIKA, D.
J. APPL. PHYS.
46 (6), 2801–3, 1975.

68616 **EFFECT OF ELASTIC UNIAXIAL STRAIN ON THE ELECTRICAL RESISTANCE OF INDIUM BISMUTH SINGLE-CRYSTAL WHISKERS.**
KEY, W. S. DAVIS, J. H.
J. APPL. PHYS.
46 (6), 2806–7, 1975.

68617 **PIEZOELECTRIC EFFECT IN TETRAGONAL CRYSTALS.**
ADHAV, R. S.
J. APPL. PHYS.
46 (6), 2808, 1975.

68626 **PYROELECTRIC PROPERTIES OF TOURMALINE AND CANCRINITE CRYSTALS IN A WIDE RANGE OF TEMPERATURES.**
DROZHDIN, S. N. NOVIK, V. K. KOPTSIK, V. A.
KOBYAKOV, I. B.
FIZ. TVERD. TELA
16 (11), 3266–9, 1974.
(FOR ENGLISH TRANSLATION SEE E68627)

EPIC Number	Bibliographic Citation

68627 **PYROELECTRIC PROPERTIES OF TOURMALINE AND CANCRINITE CRYSTALS IN A WIDE RANGE OF TEMPERATURES.**
DROZHDIN, S. N. NOVIK, V. K. KOPTSIK, V. A.
KOBYAKOV, I. B.
SOV. PHYS. SOLID STATE
16 (11), 2122–3, 1975.
(ENGLISH TRANSLATION OF FIZ. TVERD. TELA, 16 (11), 3266–9, 1974; FOR ORIGINAL SEE E68626)

68630 **ABSORPTION OF LIGHT IN ANTIFERROMAGNETIC NICKEL AND COBALT TUNGSTATES.**
EREMENKO, V. V. LITVINENKO, YU. G.
KAZAKOVA, T. I.
FIZ. TVERD. TELA
16 (11), 3282–7, 1974.
(FOR ENGLISH TRANSLATION SEE E68631)

68631 **ABSORPTION OF LIGHT IN ANTIFERROMAGNETIC NICKEL AND COBALT TUNGSTATES.**
EREMENKO, V. V. LITVINENKO, YU. G.
KAZAKOVA, T. I.
SOV. PHYS. SOLID STATE
16 (11), 2132–5, 1975.
(ENGLISH TRANSLATION OF FIZ. TVERD. TELA, 16 (11), 3282–7, 1974; FOR ORIGINAL SEE E68630)

68636 **EFFECT OF CONDITIONS AT THE SURFACE ON THE SIZE OF THE SURFACE SPACE CHARGE LAYER IN GALLIUM ARSENIDE.**
CHERNIKOV, N. G. ARSEN'EVA–GEIL', A. N.
FIZ. TVERD. TELA
16 (11), 3388–90, 1974.
(FOR ENGLISH TRANSLATION SEE E68637)

68637 **EFFECT OF CONDITIONS AT THE SURFACE ON THE SIZE OF THE SURFACE SPACE CHARGE LAYER IN GALLIUM ARSENIDE.**
CHERNIKOV, N. G. ARSEN'EVA–GEIL', A. N.
SOV. PHYS. SOLID STATE
16 (11), 2195–6, 1975.
(ENGLISH TRANSLATION OF FIZ. TVERD. TELA, 16 (11), 3388–90, 1974; FOR ORIGINAL SEE E68636)

68644 **SUPERPARAMAGNETISM OF IRON–DOPED GALLIUM ARSNEIDE.**
ISAEV'IVANOV, V. V. MASTEROV, V. F.
NASLEDOV, D. N.
FIZ. TVERD. TELA
16 (11), 3485–7, 1974.
(FOR ENGLISH TRANSLATION SEE E68645)

68645 **SUPERPARAMAGNETISM OF IRON–DOPED GALLIUM ARSENIDE.**
ISAEV'IVANOV, V. V. MASTEROV, V. F.
NASLEDOV, D. N.
SOV. PHYS. SOLID STATE
16 (11), 2260–1, 1975.
(ENGLISH TRANSLATION OF FIZ. TVERD. TELA, 16 (11), 3485–7, 1974; FOR ORIGINAL SEE E68644)

68646 **PREBREAKDOWN PHENOMENA IN POLYCRYSTALLINE BARIUM TITANATE.**
KHOTCHENKOV, A. G.
FIZ. TVERD. TELA
16 (11), 3493–5, 1974.
(FOR ENGLISH TRANSLATION SEE E68647)

68647 **PREBREAKDOWN PHENOMENA IN POLYCRYSTALLINE BARIUM TITANATE.**
KHOTCHENKOV, A. G.
SOV. PHYS. SOLID STATE
16 (11), 2267–8, 1975.
(ENGLISH TRANSLATION OF FIZ. TVERD. TELA, 16 (11), 3493–5, 1974; FOR ORIGINAL SEE E68646)

68650 **INFLUENCE OF PORES AND DISLOCATIONS ON MAGNETIZATION SWITCHING IN POLYCRYSTALLINE FERRITES WITH RECTANGULAR HYSTERESIS LOOPS.**
AGAPOVA, N. N. AGARKOV, B. N. BOKOV, V. A.
IGNAT'EVA, Z. SH.
FIZ. TVERD. TELA
16 (11), 3500–2, 1974.
(FOR ENGLISH TRANSLATION SEE E68651)

68651 **INFLUENCE OF PORES AND DISLOCATIONS ON MAGNETIZATION SWITCHING IN POLYCRYSTALLINE FERRITES WITH RECTANGULAR HYSTERESIS LOOPS.**
AGAPOVA, N. N. AGARKOV, B. N. BOKOV, V. A.
IGNAT'EVA, Z. SH.
SOV. PHYS. SOLID STATE
16 (11), 2273–4, 1975.
(ENGLISH TRANSLATION OF FIZ. TVERD. TELA, 16 (11), 3500–2, 1974; FOR ORIGINAL SEE E68650)

68652 **DEPENDENCE OF THE PARAMETERS OF THE MECHANICALLY INDUCED EXOEMISSION FROM ALKALI HALIDE CRYSTALS ON THE ANNEALING TEMPERATURE.**
KUZNETSOV, V. A. YANOVA, L. P.
KALLAEV, S. N. TOLSTAYA, S. N.
FIZ. TVERD. TELA
16 (11), 3507–9, 1974.
(FOR ENGLISH TRANSLATION SEE E68653)

68653 **DEPENDENCE OF THE PARAMETERS OF THE MECHANICALLY INDUCED EXOEMISSION FROM ALKALI HALIDE CRYSTALS ON THE ANNEALING TEMPERATURE.**
KUZNETSOV, V. A. YANOVA, L. P.
KALLAEV, S. N. TOLSTAYA, S. N.
SOV. PHYS. SOLID STATE
16 (11), 2278–9, 1975.
(ENGLISH TRANSLATION OF FIZ. TVERD. TELA, 16 (11), 3507–9, 1974; FOR ORIGINAL SEE E68652)

68654 **DOMAIN STRUCTURE OF FERRITES IN THE VICINITY OF THE COMPENSATION POINT.**
BAR'YAKHTAR, V. G. YABLONSKII, D. A.
FIZ. TVERD. TELA
16 (11), 3511–3, 1974.
(FOR ENGLISH TRANSLATION SEE E68655)

68655 **DOMAIN STRUCTURE OF FERRITES IN THE VICINITY OF THE COMPENSATION POINT.**
BAR'YAKHTAR, V. G. YABLONSKII, D. A.
SOV. PHYS. SOLID STATE
16 (11), 2282–3, 1975.
(ENGLISH TRANSLATION OF FIZ. TVERD. TELA, 16 (11), 3511–3, 1974; FOR ORIGINAL SEE E68654)

68656 **WEAK FERROMAGNETISM OF MANGANESE SILICON.**
SUDAKOVA, N. P. NIKHEL'SON, A. V.
KRENTSIS, R. P. KALISHEVICH, G. I.
GEL'D, P. V.
FIZ. TVERD. TELA
16 (11), 3515–8, 1974.
(FOR ENGLISH TRANSLATION SEE E68657)

68657 **WEAK FERROMAGNETISM OF MANGANESE SILICON.**
SUDAKOVA, N. P. MIKHEL'SON, A. V.
KRENTSIS, R. P. KALISHEVICH, G. I.
GEL'D, P. V.
SOV. PHYS. SOLID STATE
16 (11), 2286–7, 1975.
(ENGLISH TRANSLATION OF FIZ. TVERD. TELA, 16 (11), 3515–8, 1974; FOR ORIGINAL SEE E68656)

68660 **STOICHIOMETRY OF LITHIUM METANIOBATE AND SPONTANEOUS PARAMETRIC SCATTERING OF LIGHT.**
GEORGIEV, G. M. KITAEVA, G. KH.
MIKHAILOVSKII, A. G. PENIN, A. N.
RUBININA, N. M.
FIZ. TVERD. TELA
16 (11), 3524–6, 1974.
(FOR ENGLISH TRANSLATION SEE E68661)

68661 **STOICHIOMETRY OF LITHIUM METANIOBATE AND SPONTANEOUS PARAMETRIC SCATTERING OF LIGHT.**
GEORGIEV, G. M. KITAEVA, G. KH.
MIKHAILOVSKII, A. G. PENIN, A. N.
RUBININA, N. M.
SOV. PHYS. SOLID STATE
16 (11), 2293–4, 1975.
(ENGLISH TRANSLATION OF FIZ. TVERD. TELA, 16 (11), 3524–6, 1974; FOR ORIGINAL SEE E68660)

68662 **ANTIFERROELECTRIC AND FERROELASTIC PROPERTIES OF LEAD ORTHOVANADATE.**
GENE, V. V. DUDNIK, E. F. SINYAKOV, E. V.
FIZ. TVERD. TELA
16 (11), 3530–2, 1974.
(FOR ENGLISH TRANSLATION SEE E68663)

68663 **ANTIFERROELECTRIC AND FERROELASTIC PROPERTIES OF LEAD ORTHOVANADATE.**
GENE, V. V. DUDNIK, E. F. SINYAKOV, E. V.
SOV. PHYS. SOLID STATE
16 (11), 2299, 1975.
(ENGLISH TRANSLATION OF FIZ. TVERD. TELA, 16 (11), 3530–2, 1974; FOR ORIGINAL SEE E68662)

68673 **LATTICE DYNAMICS OF TETRAHEDRALLY BONDED SEMICONDUCTORS CONTAINING ORDERED VACANT SITES.**
FINKMAN, E. TAUC, J. KERSHAW, R.
WOLD, A.
PHYS. REV.
11 B (10), 3785–94, 1975.

68674 **THEORY OF THE ISOTOPE SHIFT FOR ZERO–PHONON OPTICAL TRANSITIONS AT TRAPS IN SEMICONDUCTORS.**
HEINE, V. HENRY, C. H.
PHYS. REV.
11 B (10), 3795–3803, 1975.

68675 **HIGH ENERGY OPTICAL ABSORPTION BANDS OF TRANSITION METAL IONS IN FLUORIDE HOST CRYSTALS.**
SABATINI, J. F. SALWIN, A. E.
MC CLURE, D. S.
PHYS. REV.
11 B (10), 3832–41, 1975.
(AD–A12 037)

68676 **VALENCE TRANSITIONS OF SAMARIUM IN MONOSULFIDE SOLID SOLUTIONS.**
TAO, L. J. HOLTZBERG, F.
PHYS. REV.
11 B (10), 3842–9, 1975.

EPIC Number	Bibliographic Citation

68677 **CONDUCTION IN AMORPHOUS MAGNESIUM GERMANIUM AND TIN COMPOUNDS.**
HAUSER, J. J.
PHYS. REV.
11 B (10), 3860–6, 1975.

68678 **ULTRAVIOLET PHOTOELECTRON SPECTROSCOPY OF LEAD TELLURIDE: DIRECT VERSUS NONDIRECT TRANSITIONS AND ENERGY-LOSS MECHANISMS.**
BRAICOVICH, L. CIUCCI, G.
PHYS. REV.
11 B (10), 3896–9, 1975.

68679 **SPIN DEPENDENT HALL EFFECT IN SEMICONDUCTORS.**
CHAZALVIEL, J. N.
PHYS. REV.
11 B (10), 3918–34, 1975.

68681 **ELECTRONIC STRUCTURES OF ARSENIC SELENIDE AND SELENIUM.**
CHEN, I.
PHYS. REV.
11 B (10), 3976–83, 1975.

68687 **ALTERNATIVE FORM OF THE NONLOCAL P POTENTIAL IN THE EMPIRICAL PSEUDOPOTENTIAL METHOD.**
FONG, C. Y. CHADI, D. J. COHEN, M. L.
PHYS. REV.
11 B (10), 4063–4, 1975.

68690 **ABSORPTION OF INFRARED RADIATION BY NEUTRAL DONOR-PAIR MOLECULES IN III–V AND II–VI COMPOUNDS.**
GOLKA, J.
J. PHYS.
7 C (22), L407–10, 1974.

68692 **EFFECT OF VACANCIES ON ELECTRICAL AND OPTICAL PROPERTIES OF AMOPRHOUS GALLIUM ARSENIDE FILMS.**
NARASIMHAN, K. L. GUHA, S.
J. NON-CRYST. SOLIDS (NETHERLANDS)
16 (1), 143–7, 1974.

68702 **GADOLINIUM AND CERIUM IMPURITIES IN THE LANTHANUM INDIUM, TIN, LEAD COMPOUNDS: A NUCLEAR-MAGNETIC-RESONANCE STUDY.**
WELSH, L. B. WILEY, C. L. FRADIN, F. Y.
PHYS. REV.
11 B (11), 4156–67, 1975.

68703 **CONFIGURATION MIXING IN THE 3 S-HOLE STATE OF TRANSITION METAL IONS.**
VIINIKKA, E.-K. OHRN, Y.
PHYS. REV.
11 B (11), 4168–78, 1975.

68704 **MOSSBAUER STUDY OF ANTIFERROMAGNETIC IRON CHROMIUM SELENIDE.**
HONG, S. R. OK, H. N.
PHYS. REV.
11 B (11), 4176–8, 1975.

68705 **ELECTRON SPIN RESONANCE AND OPTICAL ABSORPTION OF BOUND SMALL POLARONS IN YTTRIUM ALUMINUM OXIDE.**
SCHIRMER, O. F. BLAZEY, K. W. BERLINGER, W.
DIEHL, R.
PHYS. REV.
11 B (11), 4201–11, 1975.

68709 **PREPARATION AND ANALYSIS OF SUPERCONDUCTING NIOBIUM - GERMANIUM FILMS.**
TESTARDI, L. R. MEEK, R. L. POATE, J. M.
ROYER, W. A. STORM, A. R. WERNICK, J. H.
PHYS. REV.
11 B (11), 4304–17, 1975.

68710 **HEAT CAPACITY OF V(3) X COMPOUNDS AND THE RELATIONSHIP BETWEEN THE SUPERCONDUCTING TRANSITION TEMPERATURE AND ANHARMONICITY.**
KNAPP, G. S. BADER, S. D. CULBERT, H. V.
FRADIN, F. Y. KLIPPERT, T. E.
PHYS. REV.
11 B (11), 4331–8, 1975.

68711 **ANISOTROPY ENERGY MEASUREMENTS ON SINGLE-CRYSTAL TERBIUM HOLMIUM IRON.**
WILLIAMS, C. M. KOON, N. C.
PHYS. REV.
11 B (11), 4360–3, 1975.

68712 **OPTICAL ABSORPTION OF CUBIC SILICON CARBIDE AT 3.1 ELECTRON VOLTS.**
ALTAISKII, YU. M. RODINOV, V. N.
IZV. AKAD. NAUK SSSR, NEORG. MATER.
10 (6), 1147–9, 1974.
(FOR ENGLISH TRANSLATION SEE E68713)

68713 **OPTICAL ABSORPTION OF CUBIC SILICON CARBIDE AT 3.1 EV.**
ALTAISKII, YU. M. RODIONOV, V. N.
INORG. MAT., USSR
10 (6), 985–6, 1974.
(ENGLISH TRANSLATION OF IZV. AKAD. NAUK SSSR, NEORG. MATER., 10 (6), 1147–9, 1974; FOR ORIGINAL SEE E68712)

68777 **SUM RULE CONSTRAINTS IN REFLECTANCE EXTRAPOLATION FOR KRAMERS-KRONIG ANALYSIS.**
ELLIS, H. W. STEVENSON, J. R.
J. APPL. PHYS.
46 (7), 3066–9, 1975.

68792 **ONE MICRON PHOTODETECTORS.**
ATALLA, M. M. BUBE, R. H. DIESEL, J.
GOWEN, E. KOYAMA, R. Y. LOEBNER, E. E.
U. S. ARMY ENGINEER RESEARCH AND DEVELOPMENT LABS, FT. BELVOIR, VA.
92PP., 1964.
(AD-446 671L)

68817 **HIGH POWER INFRARED LASER WINDOW MATERIALS (LQ-10 PROGRAM).**
SOLID STATE SCIENCE LABORATORY
AIR FORCE CAMBRIDGE RESEARCH LABS., L. G. HAMSCOM FIELD, MASS.
120PP., 1973.
(AD-919 928L, AFCRL-SR-165)

68823 **OPTICAL PROCESSING OF ALKALI HALIDES AND POLYCRYSTALLINE ZINC SELENIDE FOR HIGH POWER LASER APPLICATIONS.**
KURDOCK, J. R.
AIR FORCE MATERIALS LAB., WRIGHT PATTERSON AFB, OHIO
130PP., 1974.
(AD-B001 507L, AFML-TR-74-166-PT. 1)

68831 **LOW ABSORPTION COATING TECHNOLOGY.**
BRAUNSTEIN, M.
AIR FORCE WEAPONS LAB., KIRTLAND, AFB, N. M.
134PP., 1974.
(AD-917 927L, AFWL-TR-74-10)

68832 **RESEARCH IN OPTICAL MATERIALS AND STRUCTURES FOR HIGH POWER LASERS.**
HORRIGAN, F. A. DEUTSCH, T. F.
RAYTHEON RESEARCH DIVISION, WALTHAM, MASS.
54PP., 1972.
(AD-893 673L)

68839 **0.85 MICRON SOLID STATE LASER MATERIAL EVALUATION. PART II.**
CHICKLIS, E. P. FOLWELLER, R. C.
NAIMAN, C. S.
AIR FORCE AVIONICS LAB., WPAFB, OHIO
53PP., 1973.
(AD-917 091L, AFAL-TR-73-94-PT. 2)

68841 **ABSORPTION MEASUREMENTS ON HIGH POWER LASER WINDOW MATERIALS.**
DEUTSCH, T. F.
CONF. HIGH POWER INFRARED LASER WINDOW MATERIALS, 3RD
1, 13–29, 1973.
(AD-918 230L, AFCRL-SR-174-VOL. 1)

68842 **GROWTH, FINISHING, AND OPTICAL ABSORPTION OF PURE POTASSIUM CHLORIDE SINGLE CRYSTALS.**
DAVISSON, J. W. HASS, M. KLEIN, P. H.
KRULFELD, M.
CONF. HIGH POWER INFRARED LASER WINDOW MATERIALS, 3RD
1, 31–42, 1973.
(AD-918 230L, AFCRL-SR-174-VOL. 1)

68843 **TEMPERATURE DEPENDENCE OF THE ABSORPTION COEFFICIENT OF SOME WINDOW MATERIAL SAMPLES.**
STIERWALT, D. L.
CONF. HIGH POWER INFRARED LASER WINDOW MATERIALS, 3RD
1, 43–8, 1973.
(AD-918 230L, AFCRL-SR-174-VOL. 1)

68844 **EVALUATION OF THE OPTICAL PROPERTIES OF WINDOW MATERIALS FOR HIGH POWER IR LASERS.**
JOHNSTON, G. T. LEWIS, J. F.
CONF. HIGH POWER INFRARED LASER WINDOW MATERIALS, 3RD
1, 49–68, 1973.
(AD-918 230L, AFCRL-SR-174-VOL. 1)

68845 **INFRARED TRANSMISSION IN CHALCOGENIDE GLASSES.**
MAKLAD, M. MOHR, R. HOWARD, R.
MACEDO, F. B. MOYNIHAN, C. T.
CONF. HIGH POWER INFRARED LASER WINDOW MATERIALS, 3RD
1, 69–95, 1973.
(AD-918 230L, AFCRL-SR-174-VOL. 1)

68846 **INVESTIGATION OF BASIC INFRARED LOSS MECHANISM IN HIGH RESISTIVITY GALLIUM ARSENIDE.**
CHRISTENSEN, C. P. JOINER, R. NIEH, S. T. K.
STEIER, W. H.
CONF. HIGH POWER INFRARED LASER WINDOW MATERIALS, 3RD
1, 97–103, 1973.
(AD-918 230L, AFCRL-SR-174-VOL. 1)

68847 **THEORY OF FREQUENCY AND TEMPERATURE DEPENDENCE OF INTRINSIC MULTIPHONON ABSORPTION IN LASER WINDOW MATERIALS.**
BENDOW, B. YING, S.-C. YUKON, S. P.
CONF. HIGH POWER INFRARED LASER WINDOW MATERIALS, 3RD
1, 105–60, 1973.
(AD-918 230L, AFCRL-SR-174-VOL. 1)

EPIC Number	Bibliographic Citation
68849	INFRARED ABSORPTION DUE TO MULTIPHONON-PROCESSES IN THE TRANSPARENT REGIME OF SOLIDS AND ITS TEMPERATURE DEPENDENCE. NAMJOSHI, K. V. MITRA, S. S. CONF. HIGH POWER INFRARED LASER WINDOW MATERIALS, 3RD 1, 171–90, 1973. (AD-918 230L, AFCRL-SR-174-VOL. 1)
68850	TEMPERATURE DEPENDENCE OF MULTIPHONON ABSORPTION. HARRINGTON, J. A. HASS, M. CONF. HIGH POWER INFRARED LASER WINDOW MATERIALS, 3RD 1, 191–203, 1973. (AD-918 230L, AFCRL-SR-174-VOL. 1)
68851	MULTIPHONON ABSORPTION IN ALKALI HALIDES QUANTUM TREATMENT OF MORSE POTENTIAL. ROSENSTOCK, H. B. CONF. HIGH POWER INFRARED LASER WINDOW MATERIALS, 3RD 1, 205–19, 1973. (AD-918 230L, AFCRL-SR-174-VOL. 1)
68852	THEORETICAL STUDIES OF HIGH POWER INFRARED WINDOW MATERIALS. SPARKS, M. DUTHLER, C. J. CHOW, H. C. SHAM. L. J. MARADUDIN, A. A. MILLS, D. L. CONF. HIGH POWER INFRARED LASER WINDOW MATERIALS, 3RD 1, 221–36, 1973. (AD-918 230L, AFCRL-SR-174-VOL. 1)
68853	IMPURITY ABSORPTION IN POTASSIUM CHLORIDE WINDOWS. LIPSON, H. G. LARKIN, J. J. BENDOW, B. MITRA, S. S. CONF. HIGH POWER INFRARED LASER WINDOW MATERIALS, 3RD 1, 237–65, 1973. (AD-918 230L, AFCRL-SR-174-VOL. 1)
68854	PHOTOLUMINESCENT ANALYSES OF ZINC SELENIDE LASER WINDOW MATERIALS. REYNOLDS, D. C. LITTON, C. W. NAAS, D. W. JOHNSON, D. E. CONF. HIGH POWER INFRARED LASER WINDOW MATERIALS, 3RD 1, 267–79, 1973. (AD-918 230L, AFCRL-SR-174-VOL. 1)
68855	THEORY OF MULTIPHONON ABSORPTION INCLUDING THE IMPURITY VIBRATIONAL MODE FOR AN IONIC CRYSTAL. TING, C. S. BIRMAN, J. L. BENDOW, B. CONF. HIGH POWER INFRARED LASER WINDOW MATERIALS, 3RD 1, 281–8, 1973. (AD-918 230L, AFCRL-SR-174-VOL. 1)
68857	THE COMPUTATION OF THE ABSORPTION COEFFICIENT FROM CALORIMETRIC DATA. KAHAN, A. LIPSON, H. G. SKOLNIK, L. H. CONF. HIGH POWER INFRARED LASER WINDOW MATERIALS, 3RD 1, 307–23, 1973. (AD-918 230L, AFCRL-SR-174-VOL. 1)
68859	SMALL ABSORPTION COEFFICIENT MEASUREMENT BY CALORIMETRIC AND SPECTRAL EMITTANCE TECHNIQUES. LIPSON, H. G. SKOLNIK, L. H. STIERWALT, D. L. CONF. HIGH POWER INFRARED LASER WINDOW MATERIALS, 3RD 1, 337–52, 1973. (AD-918 230L, AFCRL-SR-174-VOL. 1)
68860	MEASUREMENT OF STRESS-INDUCED BIREFRINGENCE IN ALKALI HALIDES. WILKENING, W. W. FRIEDMAN, J. PITHA, C. A. CONF. HIGH POWER INFRARED LASER WINDOW MATERIALS, 3RD 1, 353–66, 1973. (AD-918 230L, AFCRL-SR-174-VOL. 1)
68861	STRESS AND PRESSURE DEPENDENCE OF THE REFRACTIVE INDEX OF LASER WINDOW MATERIALS. BENDOW, B. GIANINO, P. D. MITRA, S. S. TSAY, Y.-F. CONF. HIGH POWER INFRARED LASER WINDOW MATERIALS, 3RD 1, 367–402, 1973. (AD-918 230L, AFCRL-SR-174-VOL. 1)
68863	THE DEFECT STRUCTURE OF CADMIUM TELLURIDE AND ITS USE AS AN IR WINDOW MATERIAL. KROGER, F. A. CHERN, S. S. VYDYANATH, H. R. CONF. HIGH POWER INFRARED LASER WINDOW MATERIALS, 3RD 2, 437–61, 1973. (AD-918 231L, AFCRL-SR-174-VOL. 2)
68864	THE TEMPERATURE AND ORIENTATION DEPENDENCE OF PLASTIC DEFORMATION IN GALLIUM ARSENIDE SINGLE CRYSTALS. SWAMINATHAN, V. COPLEY, S. M. CONF. HIGH POWER INFRARED LASER WINDOW MATERIALS, 3RD 2, 477–90, 1973. (AD-918 231L, AFCRL-SR-174-VOL. 2)
68865	FLUORIDE WINDOW MATERIALS FOR USE AS LASER WINDOWS IN THE 2 TO 6 MICRON SPECTRAL REGION. PASTOR, R. C. ROBINSON, M. TURK, R. R. BRAUNSTEIN, A. ALLEN, S. STAFSUDD, O. WINSTON, H. CONF. HIGH POWER INFRARED LASER WINDOW MATERIALS, 3RD 2, 509–35, 1973. (AD-918 231L, AFCRL-SR-174-VOL. 2)
68866	PREPARATION AND PROPERTIES OF RUBIDIUM CHLORIDE DOPED SOLID SOLUTIONS. O'CONNOR, J. J. LARKIN, J. J. PICKERING, N. E. ARAINGTON, A. F. CONF. HIGH POWER INFRARED LASER WINDOW MATERIALS, 3RD 2, 537–45, 1973. (AD-918 231L, AFCRL-SR-174-VOL. 2)
68867	THE PROPERTIES OF POTASSIUM CHLORIDE - STRONTIUM CHLORIDE ALLOYS AND THEIR FABRICATION BY CASTING. READEY, D. W. NEWBERG, R. T. MILES, P. A. CONF. HIGH POWER INFRARED LASER WINDOW MATERIALS, 3RD 2, 555–78, 1973. (AD-918 231L, AFCRL-SR-174-VOL. 2)
68868	STRENGTHENING BEHAVIOR IN POLYCRYSTALLINE POTADDIUM CHLORIDE. BECHER, P. F. FREIMAN, S. W. KLEIN, P. H. RICE, R. W. CONF. HIGH POWER INFRARED LASER WINDOW MATERIALS, 3RD 2, 579–600, 1973. (AD-918 231L, AFCRL-SR-174-2)
68869	THE STRUCTURE AND PROPERTIES OF HOT ROLLED POTASSIUM CHLORIDE CRYSTALS. KOEPKE, B. G. ANDERSON, R. H. BERNAL, E. CONF. HIGH POWER INFRARED LASER WINDOW MATERIALS, 3RD 2, 601–13, 1973. (AD-918 231L, AFCRL-SR-174-VOL. 2)
68870	MECHANICAL AND OPTICAL PROPERTIES OF RECRYSTALLIZED ALKALI HALIDE ALLOYS. HARRISON, W. B. HENDRICKSON, G. O. STARLING, J. E. CONF. HIGH POWER INFRARED LASER WINDOW MATERIALS, 3RD 2, 615–35, 1973. (AD-918 231L, AFCRL-SR-174-VOL. 2)
68871	CHARACTERISTICS OF LARGE POTASSIUM CHLORIDE INGOTS FOR THE PRODUCTION OF 10.6 MU M LASER OPTICAL ELEMENTS. SWINEHART, C. F. MOSS, R. H. JABLON, E. A. SFILIGOJ, M. STOTLAP, S. C. HAMMOND, D. A. CONF. HIGH POWER INFRARED LASER WINDOW MATERIALS, 3RD 2, 675–81, 1973. (AD-918 231L, AFCRL-SR-174-VOL. 2)
68874	PROTECTIVE COATINGS FOR ALKALI HALIDE OPTICAL COMPONENTS. CHAFFIN, J. H. CONF. HIGH POWER INFRARED LASER WINDOW MATERIALS, 3RD 3, 891–8, 1973. (AD-918 232L, AFCRL-SR-174-VOL. 3)
68875	OPTICAL COATINGS FOR HIGH ENERGY ZINC SELENIDE LASER WINDOWS. BRAUNSTEIN, M. RUDISILL, J. E. BRAUNSTEIN, A. I. CONF. HIGH POWER INFRARED LASER WINDOW MATERIALS, 3RD 3, 917–23, 1973.
68878	RESEARCH, STUDIES, AND INVESTIGATIONS OF MATERIALS SENSITIVE TO RADIATION IN THE 8 TO 14-MICRON REGION OF THE INFRARED SPECTRUM. SEILER, M. R. CHAPMAN, C. M. MOODY, J. W. HIMES, R. C. SHILLIDAY, T. S. BATTELLE MEMORIAL INSTITUTE, COLUMBUS, OHIO 14PP., 1963. (AD-406 176L)
68901	DEVELOPMENT OF LEAD TELLURIDE AND (LEAD, TIN) TELLURIDE PHOTOVOLTAIC DETECTORS BY A VACUUM SUBLIMATION. HOHNKE, D. K. HOLLOWAY, H. KAISER, S. FORD MOTOR CO., DEARBORN, MICHIGAN 88PP., 1973. (AD-917 388L)
68907	THEORETICAL STUDIES OF HIGH POWER INFRARED WINDOW MATERIALS. SPARKS, M. AZZARELLI, T. XONICS INC., VAN NUYS, CALIF. 50PP., 1972. (AD-894 577L)
68939	C. THERMOELECTRIC TRANSDUCERS. YAMAGUCHI, K. SASAKI, K. DENSHI KAGAKU 21 (5), 39–45, 1971. (FOR ENGLISH TRANSLATION SEE E68940)
68940	C. THERMOELECTRIC TRANSDUCERS. YAMAGUCHI, K. SASAKI, K. FOREIGN SCIENCE AND TECHNOLOGY CENTER 19PP., 1972. (ENGLISH TRANSLATION OF DENSHI KAGAKU, 21 (5), 39–45, 1971; FOR ORIGINAL SEE E68939) (AD-894 828L, FSTC-HT-23-248-72)

EPIC Number	Bibliographic Citation
68941	**WORK FUNCTION OF A SINGLE CRYSTAL OF THE METAL COMPOUND (EPSILON PHASE) IN THE MOLYBDENUM - RHODIUM SYSTEM.** SAVITSKII, E. M. BUROV, I. V. FOREIGN TECHNOLOGY DIVISION, WPAFB, OHIO 6PP., 1974. (ENGLISH TRANSLATION OF STRUKT. SVOISTVA MONOKRIST TUGOPLAVKIKH METAL., 211-16, 1973; FOR ORIGINAL SEE E58734) (AD-923 744L, FTD-HC-23-2468-74)
68956	**PHYSICAL CHEMICAL PROPERTIES OF COBALT OXIDE - ALUMINUM OXIDE SYSTEMS.** TRUNOV, A. M. UMINSKIY, M. V. KRAEVSKAYA, E. A. PRESNOV, V. A. FOREIGN SCIENCE AND TECHNOLOGY CENTER, CHARLOTTESVILLE, VA. 3PP., 1974. (ENGLISH TRANSLATION OF IZV. VYSSH. UCHEB. ZAVED., KHIM. KHIM., TEKHNOL., 16 (9), 1356-8, 1973; FOR ORIGINAL SEE E55772) (AD-B001 672L, FSTC-HT-23-337-75)
68992	**NEW HIGH POWER BROADBAND COATED ALUMINUM OXIDE WINDOWS.** LESENSKY, L. TISDALE, L. U. S. ARMY ELECTRONICS COMMAND, FORT MONMOUTH, N.J. 43PP., 1972. (AD-903 707L, ECOM-316-F)
68995	**CASCADED THERMOELECTRIC COOLING DEVICES UTILIZING THE DISTRIBUTED PELTIER EFFECT.** BUIST, R. FENTON, J. TUOMI, D. BORG-WARNER CORP., DES PLAINES, ILL. 77PP., 1972. (AD-900 626L)
69937	**GROWTH AND SOME PROPERTIES OF DONOR-IMPURITY-DOPED ZINC SULFIDE SINGLE CRYSTALS.** ADAMOV, L. S. SARKISOV, L. A. SYSOEV, L. A. MONOKRIST. TEKH. (6), 91-6, 1972.
70072	**MAGNETO-VOLUME EFFECTS IN RARE-EARTH TRANSITION METAL INTERMETALLICS.** BROUHA, M. BUSCHOW, K. H. J. MIEDEMA, A. R. IEEE TRANS. MAGN. 10 (2), 182-5, 1974.
70149	**INFRARED OPTICAL PROPERTIES OF LITHIUM-7 FLUORIDE AND NATURAL LITHIUM FLUORIDE AT VARIOUS TEMPERATURES, CALCULATED WITH SHELL-MODEL LATTICE-DYNAMICAL DATA.** ELDRIDGE, J. E. HOWARD, R. PHYS. REV. 7 B (10), 4652-65, 1973.
70259	**LOW-RESISTANCE CARBIDE RESISTORS.** GREBENKINA, V. G. YUSOV, YU. P. SOROKIN, V. N. PEREVEZENTSEV, A. V. POROSH. MET. 13 (4), 97-100, 1973. (FOR ENGLISH TRANSLATION SEE E93221)
70334	**NEW METHOD FOR THE DETERMINATION OF THE THICKNESS AND THE REFRACTIVE INDEX OF THIN DIELECTRIC FILMS EVAPORATED ON METAL SUBSTRATES.** SHKLYAREVSKII, I. N. EL-SHAZLY, A. F. A. IDEZAK, E. SOLID STATE COMMUN. 9 (20), 1737-40, 1971.
70339	**INTERBAND LIGHT ABSORPTION IN STRONGLY DOPED SEMICONDUCTORS.** SHKLOVSKII, B. I. EFROS, A. L. ZH. EKSP. TEOR. FIZ. (USSR) 59 (4), 1343-52, 1970. (FOR ENGLISH TRANSLATION SEE E79434)
70363	**CADMIUM TELLURIDE LAYERS AND SOLAR CELLS.** KAASE, H. SCHNEIDER, G. Z. NATURFORSCH. 26 A (10), 1691-8, 1971.
70390	**MAGNETIC PROPERTIES OF AMARIUM .** HAMANO, M. YAJIMA, S. TRANS. JAP. INST. MET. (JAPAN) 15 (4), 273-5, 1974.
70392	**X-RAY DIFFRACTION AND ELECTRICAL RESISTIVITY STUDY OF DISILVER-INDIUM AND HIGH TEMPERATURE TRISILVER-INDIUM PHASES.** SATOW, T. UEMURA, O. YAMAKAWA, S. TRANS. JAP. INST. MET. 15 (4), 253-5, 1974.
70398	**OPTICAL DISTORITON BY HEATED WINDOWS IN HIGH-POWER LASER SYSTEMS.** SPARKS, M. J. APPL. PHYS. 42 (12), 5029-46, 1971.
70404	**ION IMPLANTATION OF NITROGEN INTO CADMIUM SULFIDE.** SHIRAKI, Y. SHIMADA, T. KOMATSUBARA, K. F. J. APPL. PHYS. 43 (2), 710-18, 1972.
70440	**A CORRELATION BETWEEN THE MAGNITUDES OF DIELECTRIC BREAKDOWN FIELDS IN ALKALI HALIDES AND THEIR LATTICE CONSTANTS.** VIJH, A. K. J. MATER. SCI. (GB) 9 (12), 2052-3, 1974.
70490	**ELECTROMODULATION OF THE OPTICAL PROPERTIES OF THALLIUM-ACTIVATED POTASSIUM BROMIDE.** GIORGIANNI, U. GRASSO, V. SAITTA, G. PHYS. REV. [3] 2 B (12), 5007-9, 1970.
70494	**LAYERED COMPOUNDS, INTERCALATION, AND MAGNETIC SUSCEPTIBILITY MEASUREMENTS.** DI SALVO, F. J. LOW TEMP. PHYS.-LT 13, PROC. INT. CONF. LOW TEMP. PHYS., 13TH 3, 417-27, 1974.
70499	**POLARON EFFECTS ON THE OPTICAL PROPERTIES OF SEMICONDUCTORS.** HECK, R. J. WOODRUFF, T. O. PHYS. REV. [3] 3 B (6), 2056-9, 1971.
70519	**OPTICAL ABSORPTION BY IMPURITIES IN P-TYPE GALLIUM PHOSPHIDE.** DISHMAN, J. M. DI DOMENICO, M., JR. PHYS. REV. [3] 4 B (8), 2621-34, 1971.
70528	**SPECTROSCOPIC INVESTIGATIONS OF A NEW TYPE OF COLOUR CENTRES IN ADDITIVELY COLOURED PURE ALKALINE EARTH FLUORIDE CRYSTALS.** RAUCH, R. SENFF, I. PHYS. STATUS SOLIDI (GERMANY) 26 A (2), 537-45, 1974.
70530	**CONDUCTIVITY IN ANISOTROPIC SEMICONDUCTORS. APPLICATION TO LONGITUDINAL RESISTIVITY AND HALL EFFECT IN SATURATION-STRESSED DEGENERATELY DOPED N-TYPE GERMANIUM.** KRIEGER, J. B. MEEKS, T. ESPOSITO, E. PHYS. REV. [3] 5 B (4), 1499-504, 1972.
70535	**EFFECTS OF INTERCALATION ON ELECTRON TRANSPORT IN TANTALUM DISULFIDE.** THOMPSON, A. H. GAMBLE, F. R. KOCHLER, R. F., JR. PHYS. REV. [3] 5 B (8), 2811-16, 1972.
70542	**EXCESS-CARRIER TRANSPORT IN ANISOTROPIC SEMICONDUCTORS. PHOTOVOLTAIC EFFECT.** SHAH, R. M. SCHETZINA, J. F. PHYS. REV. [3] 5 B (10), 4014-21, 1972.
70543	**TEMPERATURE DEPENDENCE OF LONG-WAVELENGTH OPTIC PHONONS OF SODIUM FLUORIDE SINGLE CRYSTALS.** CHANG, I. F. MITRA, S. S. PHYS. REV. [3] 5 B (10), 4094-101, 1972.
70545	**SPIN FLUCTUATIONS IN PLUTONIUM AND OTHER ACTINIDE METALS AND COMPOUNDS.** ARKO, A. J. BRODSKY, M. B. NELLIS, W. J. PHYS. REV. [3] 5 B (11), 4564-9, 1972.
70568	**REMARKS TO THE OVSHINSKY EFFECT.** BOER, K. W. PHYS. STATUS SOLIDI (GERMANY) 1 A (1), K21-4, 1970.
70570	**THE KINETICS OF ANOMALOUS PHOTOVOLTAGE IN CADMIUM TELLURIDE VACUUM EVAPORATED FILMS.** BENDA, M. SVOBODA, J. PHYS. STATUS SOLIDI (GERMANY) 1 A (2), K57-9, 1970.
70573	**ROLE OF CHEMISORBED OXYGEN ON DARK CURRENT AND AND ANOMALOUS PHOTOVOLTAIC EFFECT IN CADMIUM SULFIDE EVAPORATED LAYERS.** LEGRE, J. P. MARTINUZZI, S. PHYS. STATES SOLIDI (GERMANY) 1 A (4), 689-93, 1970.
70576	**METHOD FOR DETERMINING OPTICAL EXCITATION DENSITIES DUE TO PHOTOIONIZATION OF IMPURITIES AND TO INTERBAND TRANSITIONS IN THIN CADMIUM SULFIDE-TYPE CRYSTALS FROM PHOTOCONDUCTIVITY MEASUREMENTS.** WRUCK, D. PHYS. STATUS SOLIDI (GERMANY) 2 A (4), 679-91, 1970.
70577	**THE ANOMALOUS PHOTOVOLTAGE IN VACUUM DEPOSITED FILMS OF GALLIUM TELLURIDE.** BENDA, M. PHYS. STATUS SOLIDI (GERMANY) 2 A (4), K225-6, 1970.

EPIC Number | Bibliographic Citation

70578 ANOMALOUS PHOTOVOLTAIC EFFECT IN ZINC SULFIDE THIN FILMS.
MARCHAL, G. PALZ, W.
PHYS. STATUS SOLIDI (GERMANY)
2 A (4), K257-9, 1970.

70582 THEORY OF HIGH PHOTOVOLTAGES IN SEMICONDUCTING FILMS.
SOSNOWSKI, L. ORLOWSKI, B.
PHYS. STATUS SOLIDI (GERMANY)
3 A (1), 117-30, 1970.

70587 EFFECT OF STATIC ATOMIC DISPLACEMENTS AND SHORT-RANGE ORDER ON THE ELECTRICAL RESISTIVITY.
WELLS, P. ROSSITER, P. D.
PHYS. STATUS SOLIDI
4 A (1), 151-7, 1971.

70591 CONTACT AND PHOTOVOLTAIC PROPERTIES OF GEL-GROWN BETA-SILVER IODIDE SINGLE CRYSTALS.
HENISCH, H. K. SURI, S. K.
PHYS. STATUS SOLIDI
5 A (1), K65-K68, 1971.

70599 CHEMICAL METHOD OF PREPARING PHOTOCONDUCTING LEAD SULFIDE FILMS.
ACHARYA, H. N. BOSE, H. N.
PHYS. STATUS SOLIDI
6 A (1), K43-K45, 1971.

70600 SURFACE PHOTOVOLTAIC EFFECTS IN PHOTOCONDUCTING CADMIUM SULFIDE CRYSTALS.
HALES, M. C. REED, C. E. SCOTT, C. G.
PHYS. STATUS SOLIDI
6 A (1), 45-53, 1971.

70607 PROPERTIES OF CARBIDE ALLOYS OF ZIRCONIUM AND NIOBIUM IN REGIONS OF THEIR HOMOGENEITY.
SAMSONOV, G. V. NAUMENKO, V. YA.
RYABOKON, L. P. VERKHOTUROV, A. D.
POROSHK. METALL.
(1), 54-8, 1975.
(FOR ENGLISH TRANSLATION SEE E93225)

70608 RECOMBINATION OF HOT ELECTRONS ON DISLOCATIONS AND THE POSSIBILITY OF NEGATIVE DIFFERENTIAL CONDUCTIVITY.
PATAKI, G.
PHYS. STATUS SOLIDI
8 A (2), 411-22, 1971.

70645 KRAMERS-KRONIG ANALYSIS OF EXCITON SPECTRA IN CASE OF SPATIAL RESONANCE DISPERSION.
SKETTRUP, T.
PHYS. STATUS SOLIDI
42 (2), 813-19, 1970.

70646 OPTICAL ABSORPTION IN CRYSTALS CONTAINING IMPURITIES.
HACKER, K.
PHYS. STATUS SOLIDI
42 B (2), 687-92, 1970.

70647 INFRARED MODULATION AND ENERGY BAND PARAMETERS IN MULTIVALLEY SEMICONDUCTORS THROUGH UNIAXIAL STRESS DEPENDENCE OF FREE CARRIER CONTRIBUTION TO OPTICAL CONSTANTS.
WALTON, A. K.
PHYS. STATUS SOLIDI
43 B (1), 379-86, 1971.

70649 TEMPERATURE DEPENDENCE OF THE RESISTIVITY IN THE KONDO SIDE-BAND MODEL.
MARANZANA, F. E. BIANCHESSI, P.
PHYS. STATUS SOLIDI
43 B (2), 601-10, 1971.

70652 THEORY OF OPTICAL INTERBAND TRANSITIONS IN THE PRESENCE OF RESONANCE SCATTERING.
KEIPER, R.
PHYS. STATUS SOLIDI
44 B (2), 593-602, 1971.

70653 OPTICAL AND ELECTRICAL PROPERTIES OF CHROMIUM DOPED SODIUM CHLORIDE AND POTASSIUM CHLORIDE CRYSTALS.
RADHAKRISHUA, S. SAI, K. S. K.
PHYS. STATUS SOLIDI
45 B (2), K153-5, 1971.

70661 OPTICAL ABSORPTION OF FREE POLARONS AT WEAK COUPLING.
DEVREESE, J. HUYBRECHTS, W. LEMMENS, L.
PHYS. STATUS SOLIDI
48 B (1), 77-86, 1971.

70662 THEORY OF THE ELECTRICAL CONDUCTIVITY OF SOLIDS IN A STRONG ELECTRIC FIELD.
ENDERLEIN, R. PEUKER, K.
PHYS. STATUS SOLIDI
48 B (1), 231-41, 1971.

70669 EXCITONIC ABSORPTION COEFFICIENT IN SEMICONDUCTORS.
GLINSKI, R. G. SONG, K. S. WOOLLEY, J. C.
PHYS. STATUS SOLIDI
48 B (2), 815-22, 1971.

EPIC Number | Bibliographic Citation

70674 OPTICAL PROPERTIES OF AMORPHOUS III-V COMPOUNDS. II. THEORY.
KRAMER, B. MASCHKE, K. THOMAS, P.
PHYS. STATUS SOLIDI
49 B (2), 525-34, 1972.

70677 PIEZOBIREFRINGENCE IN THE VACUUM ULTRAVIOLET. ALKALI HALIDES AND ALKALINE-EARTH FLUORIDES.
SANCHEZ, C. CARDONA, M.
PHYS. STATUS SOLIDI
50 B (1), 293-304, 1972.

70815 SYNTHESIS AND ELECTRICAL PROPERTIES OF RARE EARTH GERMANATES.
POPOV, V. P. PETROVA, M. A.
IZV. AKAD. NAUK SSSR, NEORG. MATER.
9 (1), 61-63, 1973.
(FOR ENGLISH TRANSLATION SEE E91572)

70817 LIFETIME OF NONEQUILIBRIUM CURRENT CARRIERS IN SINGLE CRYSTALS OF CADMIUM MERCURY TELLURIDE.
VDOVKINA, E. E. BARYSHEV, N. S.
VOLKOVA, F. P. CHERKASOV, A. P.
SHCHETININ, M. P. AVER'YANOV, I. S.
IZV. AKAD. NAUK SSSR, NEORG. MATER.
9 (1), 130-1, 1973.
(FOR ENGLISH TRANSLATION SEE E91573)

70818 PHASE TRANSITIONS IN LEAD ORTHOPHOSPHATE AND IN SOLID SOLUTIONS OF LEAD ORTHOPHOSPHATE AND ORTHOVANADATE.
ISUPOV, V. A. KRAINIK, N. N. KOSENKO, E. L.
IZV. AKAD. NAUK SSSR, NEORG. MATER.
9 (1), 154-5, 1973.
(FOR ENGLISH TRANSLATION SEE E91574)

70819 ELECTRICAL CONDUCTIVITY OF SEMICONDUCTOR GLASS CRYSTALS MADE FROM ARSENIC AND LEAD SELENIDES.
BORISOVA, Z. U. FRISH, G.
SHKOI'NIKOV, E. V.
IZV. AKAD. NAUK SSSR, NEORG. MATER.
9 (2), 213-17, 1973.
(ENGLISH TRANSLATION SEE E91575)

70820 SENSITIZATION OF CADMIUM TELLURIDE CRYSTALS.
ROMANENKO, V. N. RUD, YU. V. SANIN, K. V.
IZV. AKAD. NAUK SSSR, NEORG. MATER.
9 (2), 231-5, 1973.
(FOR ENGLISH TRANSLATION SEE E91576)

70821 ELECTRIC PROPERTIES IN THE SCANDIUM OXIDE - VANADIUM - (III) OXIDE SYSTEM.
BAZUEV, G. V. PERELYAEV, V. A.
SHVEIKIN, G. P.
IZV. AKAD. NAUK SSSR, NEORG. MATER.
9 (2), 257-9, 1973.
(ENGLISH TRANSLATION SEE E 91586)

70822 ELECTRICAL PROPERTIES OF CERIUM SUBGROUP RARE EARTH ELEMENT TITANONIOBATES.
KRYLOV, E. I. BORISOV, A. K.
KAZANTSEV, V. V.
UZV. AKAD. NAUK SSSR, NEORG. MATER.
9 (2), 269-72, 1973.
(FOR ENGLISH TRANSLATION SEE E91587)

70823 SPECTROSCOPIC PROPERTIES OF THEERBIUM (3+) ION IN A GADOLINIUM ALUMINATE LATTICE.
ARSEN'EV, P. A. BIENERT, K. E.
IZV. AKAD. NAUK SSSR, NEORG. MATER.
9 (2), 327-9, 1973.
(FOR ENGLISH TRANSLATION SEE E 91588)

70836 TANTALUM-NIOBIUM-RHENIUM PHASE DIAGRAM.
TYLKINA, M. A. SAVITSKII, E. M.
ALYUSHIN, V. E.
IZV. AKAD. NAUK SSSR, METAL.
(4), 225-9, 1973.
(FOR ENGLISH TRANSLATION SEE E93232)

70905 EMISSION OF FAST ELECTRONS DURING THE DESTRUCTION OF IONIC CRYSTALS.
KROTOVA, N. A. LINKE, E. KHRUSTALEV, YU. A.
VOLLBRANDT, J. SHIPOVSKII, V. I.
DOKL. AKAD. NAUK SSSR
208 (1), 138-41, 1973.
(ENGLISH TRANSLATION SEE E91746)

70911 RADIOTHERMOLUMINESCENCE OF ICE IN THE PRESENCE OF IMPURITIES.
ERSHOV, B. G. PUNTEZHIS, S. A.
PIKAEV, A. K. SPITSYN, V. I.
DOKL. AKAD. NAUK SSSR
209 (1), 889-93, 1973.
(ENGLISH TRANSLATION SEE E 91745)

70946 CONCENTRATION AND TEMPERATURE CHARACTERISTICS OF EU(3+)-ACTIVATED YTTRIUM ORTHOVANDATE LUMINESCENCE.
MOSKVIN, A. S. KHODOS, M. YA.
SHUL'GIN, B. V.
ZH. PRIKL. SPEKTROSK.
18 (1), 54-8, 1973.
(FOR ENGLISH TRANSLATION SEE E 91485)

EPIC Number	Bibliographic Citation

70949 **EFFECT OF THE STRUCTURE ON THE SPECTRAL PROPERTIES OF CRYSTAL PHOSPHORS.**
LAPSHIN, A. I.
ZH. PRIKL. SPEKTROSK.
18 (1), 164, 1973.
(FOR ENGLISH TRANSLATION, SEE E 91481)

70950 **RADICAL RECOMBINATION LUMINESCENCE OF ATOMIC OXYGEN IN CALCIUM ODIDE ACTIVATED BY MERCURY-LIKE IONS.**
STYROV, V. V. POPOV, D. P.
ZH. PROKL. SPEKTROSK.
18 (1), 164–5, 1973.
(FOR ENGLISH TRANSLATION, SEE E 91482)

70952 **PHOTOLUMINESCENCE OF ZINC TELLURIDE DURING LASER EXCITATION.**
YABLONSKII, G. P. GRIBKOVSKII, V. P.
ZH. PRIKL. SPEKTROSK.
18 (2), 313–15, 1973.
(FOR ENGLISH TRANSLATION SEE E91479)

70953 **POLARIZED LUMINESCENCE SPECTRUM OF A RUBIDIUM URANYL NITRATE CRYSTAL AT LIQUID HELIUM TEMPERATURE.**
KOMYAK, A. I. SLEPTSOV, S. E.
VITKOVSKII, G. P.
ZH. PRIKL. SPEKTROSK.
18 (3), 410–15, 1973.
(FOR ENGLISH TRANSLATION SEE E91478)

70954 **EFFECT OF A TRAPEZOIDAL ELECTRICAL FIELD ON CHLORINE-DOPED ZINC SULFIDE PHOTOLUMINESCENCE.**
ANDRIANOV, A. S. BOGACHEVA, L. S.
ZH. PRIKL. SPEKTROSK.
18 (3), 488–90, 1973.
(FOR ENGLISH TRANSLATION SEE E91477)

70971 **INFRARED TRANSMISSION AND REFLECTION SPECTRA OF SILICON NITRIDE GLASSES OBTAINED IN A HIGH-FREQUENCY DISCHARGE PLASMA.**
PROKHOROV, YU. I. SOLOGUB, V. A.
SUKHODAEV, B. A.
ZH. PRIKL. SPEKTROSK. (USSR)
19 (3), 520–3, 1973.
(FOR ENGLISH TRANSLATION SEE E96085)

70985 **DETERMINATION OF THE REFRACTIVE INDEX OF THE SUBSTANCE OF MONODISPERSE PARTICLES ACCORDING TO THE CHARACTERISTICS OF LIGHT SCATTERING.**
DUDO, N. I.
ZH. PRIKL. SPEKTROSK.
19 (5), 904–10, 1973.
(FOR ENGLISH TRANSLATION SEE E96050)

71197 **DIELECTRIC DESPERSION AND THE STRUCTURES OF IONIC LATTICES.**
LOWNDES, R. P. MARTIN, D. H.
PROC. ROY. SOC.
308 A, 473–96, 1969.

71206 **VALIDITY OF URBACH'S RULE FOR THE ABSORPTION EDGE OF VANADIUM PENTOXIDE.**
QUANG, N. T. HEVESI, I.
ACTA PHYS. CHEM.
20 (3), 285–93, 1974.

71344 **TOPOLOGY OF AN INFINITE CLUSTER IN THE THEORY OF PERCOLATION AND ITS RELATIONSHIP TO THE THEORY OF HOPPING CONDUCTION.**
SKAL, A. S. SHKLOVSKII, B. I.
FIZ. TEKH. POLUPROV.
8 (8), 1586–92, 1974.
(FOR ENGLISH TRANSLATION SEE E71345)

71345 **TOPOLOGY OF AN INFINITE CLUSTER IN THE THEORY OF PERCOLATION AND ITS RELATIONSHIP TO THE THEORY OF HOPPING CONDUCTION.**
SKAL, A. S. SHKLOVSKII, B. I.
SOV. PHYS. SEMICOND.
8 (8), 1029–32, 1975.
(ENGLISH TRANSLATION OF FIZ. TEKH. POLUPROV., 8 (8), 1586–92, 1974; FOR ORIGINAL SEE E71344)

71361 **HETEROJUNCTION FORMATION USING AMORPHOUS MATERIALS.**
DUNN, B. MACKENZIE, J. D. CLIFTON, J. K.
MASI, J. V.
APPL. PHYS. LETT. (USA)
26 (3), 85–6, 1975.

71470 **FUNDAMENTAL ABSORPTION EDGE OF HEAVILY DOPED N-TYPE LEAD TELLURIDE.**
DRABKIN, I. A. ELISEEVA, YU. YA.
NEL'SON, I. V.
FIZ. TEKH. POLUPROV.
8 (7), 1382–4, 1974.
(FOR ENGLISH TRANSLATION SEE E71506)

71506 **FUNDAMENTAL ABSORPTION EDGE OF HEAVILY DOPED N-TYPE LEAD TELLURIDE.**
DRABKIN, I. A. ELISEEVA, YU. YA.
NEL'SON, I. V.
SOV. PHYS. SEMICOND.
8 (7), 900, 1975.
(ENGLISH TRANSLATION OF FIZ. TEKH. POLUPROV., 8 (7), 1382–4, 1974; FOR ORIGINAL SEE E71470)

EPIC Number	Bibliographic Citation

71582 **HOW TO MINIMIZE INFRARED ABSORPTION IN SEMICONDUCTING MATERIALS.**
AUTH, J. HERRMANN, K. H.
EXP. TECH. PHYS. (GERMANY)
22 (6), 613–15, 1974.

71644 **EFFECT OF PLASTIC DEFORMATION ON THE OPTICAL PROPERTIES OF POTASSIUM CHLORIDE-EUROPIUM CRYSTAL PHOSPHORS.**
KALABUKHOV, N. P. KOVALEV, V. K.
FIZ. TVERD. TELA (LENINGRAD)
15 (2), 557–8, 1973.
(FOR ENGLISH TRANSLATION SEE E81520)

71653 **EFFECT OF SURFACE STATE ON THE ELECTRICAL CONDUCTIVITY OF CADMIUM TELLURIDE FILMS.**
VINOGRADOV, V. E. BOIKO, B. T.
ZH. FIZ. KHIM.
47 (1), 206–7, 1973.
(FOR ENGLISH TRANSLATION SEE E91466)

71654 **EFFECT OF A GAS MEDIUM ON THE ELECTROLUMINESCENCE OF ALUMINUM OXIDE FILMS.**
FEDCHUK, A. P. MIKHO, V. V.
ZH. FIZ. KHIM.
47 (2), 318–10, 1973.
(FOR ENGLISH TRANSLATION SEE E91465)

71655 **EFFECT OF THE REPLACEMENT OF AMMONIUM ION BY POTASSIUM ION ON THE FERROELECTRIC PROPERTIES OF AMMONIUM SULFATE.**
KOLBENEVA, G. I. LEVINA, M. E.
MAMONTOVA, N. D.
ZH. FIZ. KHIM.
47 (2), 321–3, 1973.
(FOR ENGLISH TRANSLATION SEE E91464)

71659 **KINETICS OF ELEMENTARY PROCESSES IN THE CONDENSED STATE. VIII. IONIC CONDUCTIVITY OF GLASSES AS A PROCESS OCCURRING IN AN ELASTIC MEDIUM.**
NEMILOV, S. V.
ZH. FIZ. KHIM.
47 (6), 1479–85, 1973.
(FOR ENGLISH TRANSLATION SEE E91454)

71670 **ABSORPTION OF SHF POWER IN N-INDIUM ANTIMONIDE AT LOW TEMPERATURES.**
ARENDARCHUK, V. V. GERSHENZON, E. M.
LITVAK-GORSKAYA, L. B.
FIZ. TEKH. POLUPROV.
7 (1), 132–7, 1973.
(FOR ENGLISH TRANSLATION SEE E82405)

71674 **THERMAL CONDUCTIVITY AND THERMOEMF. OF MERCURY CADMIUM TELLURIDE SOLID SOLUTIONS AT LOW TEMPERATURES.**
ALIEV, S. A.
FIZ. TEKH. POLUPROV.
7 (1), 168–70, 1973.
(ENGLISH TRANSLATION SEE E82272)

71681 **EDGE ABSORPTION IN ALUMINUM ANTIMONIDE.**
SIROTA, N. N. LUKOMSKII, A. I.
FIZ. TEKH. POLUPROV.
7 (1), 196–8, 1973.
(FOR ENGLISH TRANSLATION SEE E82265)

71709 **CHANGE IN THE SIZE OF THE ANOMALOUS PHOTOVOLTAIC EFFECT WITH AN INCREASE IN THE THICKNESS OF OBLIQUELY DEPOSITED CADMIUM TELLURIDE LAYERS IN A HIGH VACUUM.**
VYVENKO, O. F. STRAKHOV, L. P.
FIZ. TEKH. POLUPROV.
7 (3), 615–17, 1973.
(FOR ENGLISH TRANSLATION SEE E82121)

71715 **FARADAY EFFECT AND ABSORPTION SPECTRA ON FREE CHARGE CARRIERS IN CADMIUM SELENIDE.**
VOLKOV, V. V. VOLKOVA, L. V. KIREEV, P. S.
FIZ. TEKH. POLUPROV.
7 (4), 685–7, 1973.
(FOR ENGLISH TRANSLATION SEE E81843)

71775 **THERMAL EMISSION PROPERTIES OF RHENIUM ALLOYS WITH ZIRCONIUM CARBIDE.**
MATSKEVICH, T. L. KRACHINO, T. V.
VIL'K, YU. N.
ZH. TEKH. FIZ.
43 (7), 1554–9, 1973.
(FOR ENGLISH TRANSLATION SEE E81483)

71817 **KINETICS OF THE OPTICALLY INDUCED ABSORPTION IN CADMIUM SULFIDE CRYSTALS.**
VANEM, R. A. KIRS, YA. YA. LYUK, P. A.
FIZ. TEKH. POLUPROV.
8 (7), 1349–51, 1974.
(FOR ENGLISH TRANSLATION SEE E71966)

71959 **MECHANISM OF EMISSION OF LANTHANUM HEXABORIDE CATHODES.**
KUZNETSOVA, G. M. KUDINTSEVA, G. A.
IZV. AKAD. NAUK SSSR, SER. FIZ.
37 (12), 2508–12, 1973.
(FOR ENGLISH TRANSLATION SEE E82778)

EPIC Number	Bibliographic Citation
71960	**CARBIDE EMITTERS WITH INCREASED THERMOEMISSION CAPACITY.** KAN, KH. S. KUL'VARSKAYA, B. V. IZV. AKAD. NAUK SSSR, SER. FIZ. 37 (12), 2513–17, 1973. (FOR ENGLISH TRANSLATION SEE E82779)
71966	**KINETICS OF THE OPTICALLY INDUCED ABSORPTION IN CADMIUM SULFIDE CRYSTALS.** VANEM, R. A. KIRS, YA. YA. LYUK, P. A. SOV. PHYS. SEMICOND. 8 (7), 873–4, 1975. (ENGLISH TRANSLATION OF FIZ. TEKH. POLUPROV., 8 (7), 1349–51, 1974; FOR ORIGINAL SEE E71817)
72085	**TEMPERATURE DEPENDENCE OF ENERGY GAPS IN SOME (GROUPS)II–VI COMPOUNDS.** TSAY, Y. F. MITRA, S. S. VETELINO, J. F. J. PHYS. CHEM. SOLIDS 34 (12), 2167–75, 1973. (AD–A012 553, N76–12355)
72152	**ISOTOPE–INDUCED FAR–INFRARED ABSORPTION IN SODIUM CHLORIDE AND POTASSIUM CHLORIDE CRYSTALS.** IKEZAWA, M. NASU, K. J. PHYS. SOC. JAP. 34 (6), 1563–6, 1973.
72313	**THERMOELECTRIC POWER OF LIGHTLY DOPED SEMICONDUCTORS IN THE HOPPING CONDUCTION REGION.** KOSAREV, V. V. FIZ. TEKH. POLUPROV. 8 (7), 1378–82, 1974. (FOR ENGLISH TRANSLATION SEE E72358)
72358	**THERMOELECTRIC POWER OF LIGHTLY DOPED SEMICONDUCTORS IN THE HOPPING CONDUCTION REGION.** KOSAREV, V. V. SOV. PHYS. SEMICOND. 8 (7), 897–9, 1975. (ENGLISH TRANSLATION OF FIZ. TEKH. POLUPROV., 8 (7), 1378–82, 1974; FOR ORIGINAL SEE E72313)
72449	**TRANSITION TO THE NONMETALLIC STATE IN LIQUID CESIUM–GOLD ALLOYS.** HOSHINO, H. SCHMUTZLER, R. W. HENSEL, F. PHYS. LETT. (NETHERLANDS) A, 7–8, 1975.
72525	**ANTIFERROMAGNETISM OF GAMMA–IRON – MANGANESE ALLOYS. III. SPECIFIC HEAT AND THERMOELECTRIC STUDIES.** HASHIMOTO, T. ISHIKAWA, Y. J. PHYS. SOC. JAPAN 23 (2), 213–23, 1967.
72538	**ON THE SPATIAL RESOLVING POWER OF THE TRAP DISTRIBUTION ANALYSIS BY TSEE SPECTROSCOPY.** WILD, W. GLAEFEKE, H. PHYS. STATUS SOLIDI (GERMANY) 27 (2), K93–4, 1975.
72540	**THE INFRARED ATTENUATION IN ALPHA–PARTICLE IRRADIATED GALLIUM ARSENIDE.** BRUDNYI, V. N. BUDNITSKII, D. L. KRIVOV, M. A. REDKO, V. P. PHYS. STATUS SOLIDI (GERMANY) 27 A (2), K95–7, 1975.
72552	**EMISSION AND CRYSTAL SIZE OF OXIDE–COATED CATHODES.** SHIMAZU, J. J. PHYS. SOC. JAPAN 6, 479–85, 1951.
72582	**MICROSCOPIC DEFECTS AND INFRARED ABSORPTION IN CADMIUM TELLURIDE [LASER WINDOW MATERIAL].** MAGEE, T. J. PENG, J. BEAN, J. PHYS. STATUS SOLIDI (GERMANY) 27 A (2), 557–64, 1975.
72651	**ABSORPTION OF LIGHT IN N–TYPE GALLIUM ARSENIDE ASSISTED BY NON–EQUILIBRIUM OPTICAL PHONONS.** VOROB'EV, L. E. OSOKIN, F. I. STAFEEV, V. I. SHTURBIN, A. V. FIZ. TEKH. POLUPROV. 8 (7), 1281–90, 1974. (FOR ENGLISH TRANSLATION SEE E72700)
72658	**MAGNETIC PROPERTIES OF MANGANESE PHOSPHIDE.** IWATA, N. J. SCI. HIROSHIMA UNIV., SER. 33 A–2 (1), 1–21, 1969.
72700	**ABSORPTION OF LIGHT IN N–TYPE GALLIUM ARSENIDE ASSISTED BY NON–EQUILIBRIUM OPTICAL PHONONS.** VOROB'EV, L. E. OSOKIN, F. I. STAFEEV, V. I. SHTURBIN, A. V. SOV. PHYS. SEMICOND. 8 (7), 833–8, 1975. (ENGLISH TRANSLATION OF FIZ. TEKH. POLUPROV., 8 (7), 1281–90, 1974; FOR ORIGINAL SEE E72651)
72727	**THERMAL AND ELECTRICAL CONDUCTIVITIES OF SOME METALLIC COMPOUNDS.** POWELL, R. W. TYE, R. P. THERM. CONDUCTIVITY, PROC. CONF., 8TH 575–83PP., 1969.

EPIC Number	Bibliographic Citation
72756	**PHYSICAL AND MECHANICAL PROPERTIES OF TRANSITION METAL DIBORIDES.** CLOUGHERTY, E. V. POBER, R. L. MET. SOC. AMER. INST. MINING, MET. PETROL. ENGRS, INST. METALS DIV., SPEC. REPT. SER. (13), 423–43, 1964.
72953	**ELECTROPHYSICAL PROPERTIES OF INDIUM BISMUTH COMPOUNDS.** KRIVOV, M. A. MALISOVA, E. V. PRESNOV, V. A. FIZIKA 10 (6), 152–154, 1967.
73152	**A MECHANISM FOR THE ANOMALOUS PHOTOVOLTAIC EFFECT IN CADMIUM TELLURIDE.** WILLIAMS, R. H. JOHNSON, H. R. SOLID STATE COMMUN. 16 (7), 873–5, 1975.
73247	**HYDROSTATIC PRESSURE EFFECT ON SURFACE PHOTOVOLTAGE OF GALLIUM ARSENIC.** LAGOWSKI, J. ILLER, A. SWIATEK, A. SURF. SCI. 49 (1), 1–8, 1975.
73248	**SOME NEW IMMERSION MELTS OF HIGH REFRACTION.** BARTH, T. F. W. AM. MINERALOGIST 14, 358, 1929.
73251	**SOME OPTICAL PROPERTIES OF ZINC SELENIDE.** MARPLE, D. T. F. SEGALL, B. AVEN, M. BULL. AM. PHYS. SOC. 6, 19, 1961.
73252	**THE PREPARATION OF LARGE SINGLE CRYSTALS OF THE ALKALI HALIDES AND THEIR USE FOR OPTICAL INVESTIGATIONS.** KRUGER, E. FYSISK TIDS 40, 17, 1942.
73257	**TRANSMISSION AND REFRACTIOR, DATA ON STANDARD LENS AND PRISM MATERIALS WITH SPECIAL REFERENCE TO INFRARED SPECTRORADIOMETRY.** COBLENTZ, W. W. J. OPT. SOC. AM. 4, 443, 1920.
73259	**REFRACTIVE PROPERTIES OF BARIUM FLUORIDE.** MALITSON, I. H. J. OPT. SOC. AMER. 54 (5), 628–32, 1964.
73260	**TEMPERATURE DEPENDENCE OF THE REFRACTIVE INDEX OF OPTICAL MASER CRYSTALS.** HOUSTON, T. W. JOHNSON, L. F. KISLIUK, P. WALSH, D. J. J. OPT. SOC. AMER. 53 (11), 1286–91, 1963.
73261	**A COMPARISON OF THE PHYSICAL PROPERTIES OF BARIUM FLUORIDE AND CALCIUM FLUORIDE.** BALLARD, S. S. COMBES, L. S. MCCARTHY, K. A. J. OPT. SOC. AMER. 42 (9), 684–5, 1952.
73267	**OPTICAL DISPERSION AND SELECTIVE REFLECTION WITH APPLICATION TO INFRARED NATURAL FREQUENCIES.** HAVELOCK, T. H. PROC. ROY. SOC. (LONDON) 105 A, 488, 1924.
73285	**SOLAR THERMOELECTRIC GENERATOR SYSTEM CONCEPT AND FEASIBILITY STUDY.** KRAUSE, A. J. MCCABRIA, J. L. NAUMER, D. A. FLIGHT ACCESSORIES LAB., WRIGHT PATTERSON AIR FORCE BASE, OHIO 23PP., 1962. (AD–276 092)
73337	**SPACE–CHARGE EFFECT ON ELECTRICAL CONDUCTIVITY IN EXTRINSIC SEMICONDUCTOR FILMS.** COVINGTON, D. W. RAY, D. C. J. APPL. PHYS. 46 (9), 3900–5, 1975.
74174	**MECHANISM OF CHARGE TRANSFER IN AN AMMONIUM PERCHLORATE LATTICE.** KHARIETDINOV, E. F. MISHCHENKO, A. M. BOLDYREV, V. V. ZH. FIZ. KHIM. 49 (1), 211–12, 1975. (FOR ENGLISH TRANSLATION SEE E91460)
74508	**ELECTRON–ELECTRON SCATTERING AND TRANSPORT PHENOMENA IN NONPOLAR SEMICONDUCTORS.** APPEL, J. PHYS. REV. 122 (6), 1760–72, 1961.

EPIC Number	Bibliographic Citation
74575	PHOTOCONDUCTIVITY OF POTASSIUM BROMIDE CONTAINING F CENTERS. CRANDALL, R. S. MIKKOR, M. PHYS. REV. 138 A (4), 1247–9, 1965.
74593	INTERBAND MAGNETO–ABSORPTION AND FARADAY ROTATION IN INDIUM ANTIMONY. PIDGEON, C. R. BROWN, R. N. PHYS. REV. 146 (2), 575–83, 1966.
74594	TEMPERATURE DEPENDENCE OF INFRARED DISPERSION IN IONIC CRYSTALS LITHIUM FLUORIDE AND MAGNESIUM OXIDE. JASPERSE, J. R. KAHAN, A. PLENDL, J. N. MITRA, S. S. PHYS. REV. 146 (2), 526–42, 1966.
74595	ZERO–PHONON LINES AND PHONON COUPLING OF ZINC SELENIDE: MANGANESE AND CADMIUM SULFIDE: MANGANESE. LANGER, D. W. RICHTER, H. J. PHYS. REV. 146 (2), 554–7, 1966.
74596	MAGNETIC PROPERTIES OF SOLID SOLUTIONS OF THE HEAVY RARE EARTHS WITH EACH OTHER. BOZORTH, R. M. GAMBINO, R. J. PHYS. REV. 147 (2), 487–94, 1966.
74601	SELF–CONSISTENT ENERGY BANDS AND COHESIVE ENERGY OF POTASSIUM CHLORIDE. DE CICCO, P. D. PHYS. REV. 153 (3), 931–8, 1967.
74602	ELECTRICAL AND OPTICAL PROPERTIES OF AMORPHOUS GERMANIUM. CLARK, A. H. PHYS. REV. 154 (3), 750–7, 1967.
74607	FAR INFRARED OPTICAL PROPERTIES OF FLUORIDE, STRONTIUM FLUORIDE, BARIUM FLUORIDE, AND CADMIUM FLUORIDE. BOSOMWORTH, D. R. PHYS. REV. 157 (3), 709–15, 1967.
74624	OPTICAL PROPERTIES OF ALKALI HALIDE CRYSTALS. BALDINI, G. BOSACCHI, B. PHYS. REV. 166 (3), 863–70, 1968.
74639	OPTICAL ABSORPTION DUE TO INTER–CONDUCTION–MINIMUM TRANSITIONS IN GALLIUM ARSENIDE. BALSLEV, I. PHYS. REV. 173 (3), 762–6, 1968.
74648	THERMOREFLECTANCE IN SEMICONDUCTORS. MATATAGUI, E. THOMPSON, A. G. CARDONA, M. PHYS. REV. 176 (3), 950–60, 1968.
74658	ELECTRICAL PROPERTIES OF SEMICONDUCTING CADMIUM FLUORIDE: YTTRIUM. KHOSLA, R. P. PHYS. REV. 183 (3), 695–703, 1969.
74971	THE THEORY OF ELECTRONIC SEMI–CONDUCTORS. WILSON, A. H. PROC. ROY. SOC. (LONDON) 133 A, 458–91, 1931.
74974	ON THE ABSORPTION OF LIGHT BY CRYSTALS. MOTT, N. F. PROC. ROY. SOC. (LONDON) 167 A, 384–91, 1938.
75030	AN EXPERIMENTAL INVESTIGATION ON THE REFLEXION OF LIGHT AT CERTAIN METAL LIQUID SURFACES. WHEELER, L. P. PHIL. MAG. 22 (128), 229–45, 1911.
75076	ON THE THEORY OF THE TEMPERATURE DEPENDENCE OF THE REFRACTIVE INDEX OF HOMOPOLAR CRYSTALS. ANTONCIK, E. CZECH. J. PHYS. 6, 209–16, 1956.
75090	LOW TEMPERATURE SPECTRA OF DIVALENT SAMARIUM IN ALKALI–HALIDE SINGLE CRYSTALS. KAPLYANSKII, A. A. FEOFILOV, P. P. OPT. SPECTROS., USSR 16, 144–9, 1964. (ENGLISH TRANSLATION OF OPT. SPEKTROSK., 16, 264–73, 1963; FOR ORIGINAL SEE E91918)
75092	ELECTRIC RESISTANCE AND THERMOELECTROMOTIVE FORCE OF GERMANIUM TELLURIDE IN THE PHASE TRANSITION REGION. KORZHUEV, M. A. ABRIKOSOV, N. KH. SHELIMOVA, L. E. DOKL. AKAD. NAUK SSSR 220 (2), 402–6, 1975. (FOR ENGLISH TRANSLATION SEE E91748)
75114	VARIATION OF THE REFRACTIVE INDICES OF CADMIUM FLUORIDE, BARIUM FLUORIDE AND BETA–LEAD FLUORIDE WITH PRESSURE TO 7 KILOBAR. SCHMIDT, E. D. D. VEDAM, K. J. PHYS. CHEM. SOLIDS 27, 1563–6, 1966.
75135	STRAIN DEPENDENCE OF STATIC AND HIGH FREQUENCY DIELECTRIC CONSTANTS OF SOME ALKALI HALIDES. SRINIVASAN, R. SRINIVASAN, K. J. PHYS. CHEM. SOLIDS 33, 1079–89, 1972.
75146	OPTICAL ABSORPTION IN GALLIUM ARSENIDE WHICH HAS BEEN IRRADIATED BY HIGH INTEGRATED FLUXES OF FAST NEUTRONS. VODOP'YANOV, L. K. KURDIANI, N. I. SOV. PHYS. SOLID STATE 8 (1), 204–5, 1966. (ENGLISH TRANSLATION OF FIZ. TVERD. TELA, 8 (1), 254–6, 1966; FOR ORIGINAL SEE E91926)
75147	NONPARABOLICITY OF THE CONDUCTION BAND OF LEAD TELLURIDE. ZHITINSKAYA, M. K. KAIDANOV, V. I. CHERNIK, I. A. SOV. PHYS. SOLID STATE 8 (1), 246–7, 1966. (ENGLISH TRANSLATION OF FIZ. TVERD. TELA, 8 (1), 295–7, 1966; FOR ORIGINAL SEE E91929)
75166	VITREOUS SEMICONDUCTORS (II). KOLOMIETS, B. T. PHYS. STATUS SOLIDI 7, 713–31, 1964.
75171	SOME OPTICAL PROPERTIES OF THIN EVAPORATED CADMIUM ARSENIDE FILMS. ZDANOWICZ, L. PHYS. STATUS SOLIDI 20, 473–80, 1967.
75175	SOME STRUCTURAL, ELECTRICAL, AND THERMAL PARAMETERS OF VANADIUM CHROMIUM SELENIDE, IRON CHROMIUM SELENIDE, AND NICKEL CHROMIUM SELENIDE TERNARY COMPOUNDS. IVANOVA, V. A. ABDINOV, D. SH. ALIEV, G. M. PHYS. STATUS SOLIDI 24, K23–4, 1967.
75184	INFRARED ABSORPTION IN GALLIUM PHOSPHIDE. PIKHTIN, A. N. YASKOV, D. A. PHYS. STATUS SOLIDI 34, 815–24, 1969.
75188	IONIC CONDUCTIVITY OF SODIUM FLUORIDE. BAUER, C. F. WHITMORE, D. H. PHYS. STATUS SOLIDI 37, 585–98, 1970.
75192	DIELECTRIC PROPERTIES OF THE RUBIDIUM HALIDE CRYSTALS IN THE EXTREME ULTRAVIOLET UP TO 30 ELECTRON VOLTS. PEIMANN, C. J. SKIBOWSKI, M. PHYS. STATUS SOLIDI 46 B, 655–65, 1971.
75197	ELECTROCHEMICAL PHOTO AND SOLAR CELLS. PRINCIPLES AND SOME EXPERIMENTS. GERISCHER, H. J. ELECTROANAL. CHEM. INTERFACIAL ELECTROCHEM. 58 (1), 263–74, 1975.
75203	PIEZO–OPTIC BIREFRINGENCE SIGN REVERSAL AND ISOTROPY IN CUBIC CRYSTALS. RAHMAN, A. IYENGAR, K. S. PHYS. LETT. 25 A (6), 478–9, 1967.
75232	PHOTOINDUCED ADSORPTION LUMINESCENCE ON ALUMINUM OXIDE. ANDREEV, N. S. KOTEL'NIKOV, V. A. KINET. KATAL. 15 (6), 1612–13, 1974. (FOR ENGLISH TRANSLATION SEE E91474)
75247	FAR INFRARED OPTICAL PROPERTIES OF PRESSED CADMIUM TELLURIDE. RANDALL, C. M. RAWCLIFFE, R. D. APPL. OPT. 7 (1), 213, 1968.
75248	FAR INFRARED MEASUREMENT OF THE DIELECTRIC PROPERTIES OF GALLIUM ARSENIDE AND CADMIUM TELLURIDE AT 300 K AND 8 K. JOHNSON, C. J. SHERMAN, G. H. WEIL, R. APPL. OPT. 8 (8), 1667–72, 1969.

EPIC Number	Bibliographic Citation
75288	A GENERAL EXPRESSION FOR THE THERMOELECTRIC POWER. FRITZSCHE, H. SOLID STATE COMMUN. 9 (21), 1813–5, 1971.
75323	THERMIONIC EMISSION PROPERTIES OF REFRACTORY COMPOUNDS AND MATERIALS BASED ON THEM (A REVIEW). SAMSONOV, G. V. FOMENKO, V. S. PODCHERNYAEVA, I. A. OKHREMCHUK, L. N. POROSH. MET. 13 (10), 74–82, 1974. (FOR ENGLISH TRANSLATION SEE E93218)
75337	OPTICAL STUDIES OF METAL SEMICONDUCTOR TRANSMUTATIONS PRODUCED BY INTERCALATION. ACRIVOS, J. V. LIANG, W. Y. WILSON, J. A. YOFFE, A. D. J. PHYS., SOLID STATE PHYS. 4 C, L18–L20, 1971.
75340	THE EFFECT OF MELTING ON THE MULTIPHONON INFRARED ABSORPTION SPECTRA OF POTASSIUM BROMIDE, SODIUM CHLORIDE AND LITHIUM FLUORIDE. BARKER, A. J. J. PHYS., SOLID STATE PHYS. 5 C, 2276–82, 1972.
75362	QUANTUM SIZE EFFECTS IN SEMICONDUCTING AND SEMIMETALLIC FILMS. TAVGER, B. A. DEMIKHOVSKII, V. YA. USP. FIZ. NAUK 96 (1), 61–86, 1968. (FOR ENGLISH TRANSLATION SEE E91450)
75372	ELECTRICAL CONDUCTIVITY AND THERMOELECTRIC POWER OF THE MOLTEN THALLIUM + SELENIUM AND THALLIUM + TELLURIDE SYSTEM. NAKAMURA, Y. SHIMOJI, M. TRANS. FARADAY SOC. 65, 1509–18, 1969.
75374	COLD WORKING AND RECOVERY AT ALLOYS WITH ORDERED ATOM DISTRIBUTION. DAHL, O. Z. METALLK. 28 (5), 133–8, 1936.
75382	STRESS–OPTICAL DISPERSION IN RUBIDIUM BROMIDE, RUBIDIUM IODIDE, CESIUM CHLORIDE, AND CESIUM IODIDE. LAIHO, R. KORPELA, A. ANN. ACAD. SCI. FENN. A (272), 1–10, 1968.
75383	MEASUREMENT OF THE REFRACTIVE INDEX OF DIELECTRICS AND SEMICONDUCTORS WITH A SUBMILLIMETER SPECTROMETER. IGOSHIN, F. F. KIR'YANOV, A. P. MOZHAEV, V. V. TULAIKOVA, M. A. SHERONOV, A. A. PRIB. TEKH. EKSP. 17 (6) (PT. 2), 148–50, 1974. (FOR ENGLISH TRANSLATION SEE E93414)
75395	GALLIUM ARSENIDE TRANSDUCERS. BOHM, J. FARNELL, G. W. IEEE TRANS. SONICS ULTRASON. 13 (4), 125–9, 1966.
75407	CONDUCTION IN AMORPHOUS MAGNESIUM – BISMUTH AND MAGNESIUM – ANTIMONY ALLOYS. FERRIER, R. P. HERRELL, D. J. J. NON–CRYST. SOLIDS 2, 278–83, 1970.
75431	SEEBECK, COEFFICIENT IN AMORPHOUS CHALCOGENIDE FILMS. ROCKSTAD, H. K. FLASCK, R. IWASA, S. J. NON–CRYST. SOLIDS 8–10, 326–30, 1972.
75456	TEMPERATURE DEPENDENCE OF THE ELECTRIC CONDUCTIVITY AND PHOTOSENSITIVITY OF CADMIUM SULFIDE FILM. AKRAMOV, KH. T. TESHABAEV, A. YULDASHEV, B. D. KHUSANOV, M. M. APPL. SOLAR ENERGY, USSR 8 (2), 61–3, 1972. (ENGLISH TRANSLATION OF GELIOTEKHNIKA 8 (2), 9–12, 1972; FOR ORIGINAL SEE E55386)
75534	NONLINEAR VARIATION OF REFRACTIVE INDEX OF VITREOUS SILICA WITH PRESSURE TO 7 KILOBARS. VEDAM, K. SCHMIDT, E. D. D. ROY, R. J. AMER. CERAM. SOC. 49 (10), 531–5, 1966.
75543	ELECTRICAL CONDUCTIVITY OF SILVER MERCURY IODIDE, COPPER MERCURY IODIDE AND THEIR EUTECTOID. SUCHOW, L. POND, G. R. J. AMER. CHEM. SOC. 75, 5242–4, 1953.
75554	INFRARED SPECTRA OF MOLTEN SALTS. WILMSHURST, J. K. J. CHEM. PHYS. 39 (10), 2545–8, 1963.
75570	ALKALI METAL INTERCALATES OF MOLYBDENUM DISULFIDE. SOMOANO, R. B. HADEK, V. REMBAUM, A. J. CHEM. PHYS. 58 (2), 697–701, 1973.
75601	SUPERCONDUCTING MATERIALS UP TO NOW AND INTO THE FUTURE. GEBALLE, T. H. IEEE TRANS. MAGN. MAG–11 (2), 119–24, 1975.
75606	NEW SUPERCONDUCTING CRITICAL TEMPERATURES AND FIELDS. MATTIAS, B. T. IEEE TRANS. MAGN. MAG–11 (2), 154, 1975.
75624	NEUTRON INDUCED IN SUPERCONDUCTING A–15 COMPOUNDS (FUSION REACTOR MAGNET MATERIAL). SWEEDLER, A. R. COX, D. SCHWEITZER, D. G. IEEE TRANS. MAGN. MAG–11 (2), 163–5, 1975.
75629	ELECTROLUMINESCENCE AND PHOTOVOLTAIC DETECTION IN CADMIUM INPLANTED COPPER INDIUM SELENIDE P–N JUNCTION DIODES. PARK, Y. S. YU, P. W. FAILE, S. P. EHRET, J. E. APPL. PHYS. LETT. 26 (12), 717–9, 1975. (AD–A018 814, ARL–75–0253)
75663	THE STRESS BIREFRINGENCE RELATION IN SOME ALKALI HALIDES. BANSIGIR, K. G. IYENGAR, K. S. PROC. PHYS. SOC., (LONDON) 71, 225–30, 1958.
75725	ON THE ELECTRICAL PROPERTIES OF SODIUM NITRATE. FERMOR, J. H. KHEKSHUS, A. ACTA CHEM. SCAND. 22 (5), 1628–36, 1968.
75729	LAVES PHASE COMPOUNDS OF RARE EARTHS AND OF HAFNIUM WITH NOBLE METALS. COMPTON, V. B. MATTHIAS, B. T. ACTA CRYST. 12, 651–4, 1959.
75730	X–RAY AND NEUTRON DIFFRACTION STUDY OF FERROELECTRIC LEAD TITANIUM OXIDE. SHIRANE, G. PEPINSKY, R. FRAZER, B. C. ACTA CRYST. 9, 131–40, 1956.
75731	PIEZO–OPTIC BIREFRINGENCE IN SODIUM CHLORIDE STRUCTURE CRYSTALS. PART II. APPLICATIONS. BANSIGIR, K. G. IYENGAR, K. S. ACTA CRYST. 14, 727–32, 1961.
75744	THE INTER CALARY COMPOUNDS OF SODIUM TITANIUM DISULFIDE. GENERAL STRUCTURAL STUDY OF THE NONSTOICHEMETRIC SODIUM AND POTASSIUM DISULFIDES. ROUXEL, J. DANOT, M. BICHON, J. BULL. SOC. CHIM. FRANCE (11), 3930–5, 1971.
75747	THE DIELECTRICAL BEHAVIOR OF BINARY OXIDE GLASSES IN THE MICROWAVE REGION BETWEEN – 100 AND 900 C. AMRHEIN, E. M. GLASTECH. BER. 36 (11), 425–44, 1963.
75749	MAGNETOCHEMISTRY OF THE HEAVIEST ELEMENTS. PART IV. PLUTONIUM TRIFLUORIDE AND TRICHLORIDE. DAWSON, J. K. MANDLEBERG, C. J. DAVIES, D. J. CHEM. SOC. 2047–50, 1951.
75751	THE MAGNETIC PROPERTIES OF THE QUINPUEVALENT COMPLEX FLUORIDES OF MOLYBDENUM, TUNGSTEN, AND RHENIUM. HARGREAVES, G. B. PEACOCK, R. D. J. CHEM. SOC. (LONDON) 3776–9, 1958.
75759	CRYSTALLOGRAPHIC AND MAGNETIC STUDY OF THE MANGANESE IRON HOLMIUM OXIDE SERIES. APOSTOLOV, A. PATAUD, P. MATER. RES. BULL. 4 (1), 1–6, 1969.
75764	BOROSILICATE GLASSES FOR FIBER OPTICAL WAVEGUIDES. VAN UITERT, L. G. PINNOW, D. A. WILLIAMS, J. C. RICH, T. C. JAEGER, R. E. GRODKIEWICZ, W. H. MATER. RES. BULL. 8 (4), 469–76, 1973.
75767	THE CADMIUM PHOSPHIDE – TIN SYSTEM AND SOME PROPERTIES OF CADMIUM TIN PHOSPHIDE CRYSTALS. BUEHLER, E. WERNICK, J. H. SHAY, J. L. MATER. RES. BULL. 6, 303–9, 1971.

EPIC Number	Bibliographic Citation
75773	**THERMO-OPTIC BEHAVIOUR OF SOLIDS. II. FUSED QUARTZ.** RAMACHANDRAN, G. N. PROC. INDIAN ACAD. SCI. 25 A, 280-5, 1947.
75776	**TEMPERATURE DEPENDENCE OF THE PHOTOELASTIC BEHAVIOUR OF CRYSTALS. PART I.** RAO, K. V. K. MURTY, V. G. K. PROC. INDIAN ACAD. SCI. 64 A, 24-35, 1966.
75780	**STRESS AND WAVELENGTH DEPENDENCE OF BIREFRINGENCE IN CUBIC CRYSTALS IN THE VISIBLE REGION.** PANDYA, N. S. PANDYA, J. R. CURRENT SCI. 27 (11), 436-7, 1958.
75781	**THE NEW BAND SPECTRUM OF HAFNIUM MONOIODIDE.** SAVITHRY, T. RAO, D. V. K. RAO, P. T. CURRENT SCI. 4 (19), 516-8, 1971.
75814	**THE MAGNETIC SUSCEPTIBILITY OF THE ELECTROLYTIC CHARGED PALLADIUM - HYDROGEN ALLOYS.** SVENSSON, B. ANN. PHYSIK 18 (5), 299-304, 1933.
75815	**CALCULATION OF OPTICAL CONSTANTS OF IONIC CRYSTALS IN THE INFRARED BEGINNING WITH THE REFLECTION SPECTRUM.** ABELES, F. MATHIEU, J-P. ANN. PHYS. 3, 5-32, 1958.
75831	**ELECTRICAL PROPERTIES OF ELASTOMERS AND RELATED POLYMERS.** MCPHERSON, A. T. RUBBER CHEM. TECHNOL. 36 (5), 1230-1302, 1963.
75833	**THE METAL-NONMETAL TRANSITION.** MOTT, N. F. ZINAMON, Z. REP. PROGR. PHYS. 33, 881-940, 1970.
75835	**THE ELECTRONIC AND IONIC STRUCTURES OF METAL AMMONIA SOLUTIONS.** COHEN, M. H. ADVAN. PHYS. 17, 857-907, 1968.
75838	**ELECTRONS IN DISORDERED STRUCTURES.** MOTT, N. F. ADVAN. PHYS. 16, 49-144, 1967.
75839	**THE LATTICE DYNAMICS OF AN ANHARMONIC CRYSTAL.** COWLEY, R. A. ADVAN. PHYS. 12, 421-80, 1963.
75842	**SPIN-DISORDER EFFECTS IN THE ELECTRICAL RESISTIVITIES OF METALS AND ALLOYS.** COLES, B. R. ADVAN. PHYS. 1, 40-71, 1958.
75843	**THE TRANSITION METAL DICHALCOGENIDES DISCUSSION AND INTERPRETATION OF THE OBSERVED OPTICAL, ELECTRICAL AND STRUCTURAL PROPERTIES.** WILSON, J. A. YOFFE, A. D. ADVAN. PHYS. 18, 193-335, 1969.
75847	**THE STUDY OF THE FIBRATIONS OF CRYSTAL LATTICES BY FAR INFRARED SPECTROSCOPY.** MARTIN, D. H. ADVAN. PHYS. 14, 39-99, 1965.
75852	**METALLURGICAL CONSIDERATIONS FOR OPTIMIZING THE SUPERCONDUCTING PROPERTIES OF NIOBIUM ALUMINUM.** KOHR, J. G. EAGAR, T. W. ROSE, R. M. MET. TRANS. 3, 1177-82, 1972.
75855	**A PROGRAMMABLE TEMPERATURE CONTROLLER FOR THERMOLUMINESCENCE AND THERMALLY STIMULATED CONDUCTIVITY STUDIES.** NEMETH, K. SVISZT, P. EXP. TECH. PHYS. 21 (5), 443-7, 1973.
75859	**SEMICONDUCTING PROPERTIES OF GRAY TIN.** BUSCH, G. A. KERN, R. SOLID STATE PHYS. 11, 1-40, 1960.
75862	**OPTICAL PROPERTIES OF A CADMIUM SULFIDE SINGLE CRYSTAL WELL INSIDE THE FUNDAMENTAL ABSORPTION REGION AND THE STRUCTURE OF ENERGY BANDS.** BRODIN, M. S. STRASHNIKOVA, M. I. FIZ. TVERDOGO TELA 8 (3), 684-7, 1966. (FOR ENGLISH TRANSLATION SEE E76050)
75866	**THE ABSORPTION SPECTRA OF SOLID CARBON OXIDE AND NITROGEN.** BRITH, M. SCHNEPP, O. MOL. PHYS. 9, 473-89, 1965.
75868	**FAR ULTRAVIOLET ABSORPTION SPECTRA OF ATOMS AND MOLECULES TRAPPED IN RARE GAS MATRICES AT LOW TEMPERATURE.** RONCIN, J. Y. DAMANY, N. ROMAND, J. J. MOL. SPECTROS. 22, 154-64, 1967.
75871	**LOW TEMPERATURE SPECTRA OF THIN POLYCRYSTALLINE COPPER IODIDE LAYERS ON DIFFERENT SUBSTRATES IN THE REGION OF THE FUNDAMENTAL ABSORPTION EDGE.** GHITA, L. TENESCU, E. REV. ROUM. PHYS. 12 (1), 79-85, 1967.
75883	**TEMPERATURE DEPENDENCE OF THE ABSORPTION EDGE OF GALLIUM ARSENIDE.** AFROMOWITZ, M. A. REDFIELD, D. PROC. INT. CONF. PHYS. SEMICOND., 9TH 21, 98-102, 1968.
75884	**ELECTRONIC PROPERTIES OF AMORPHOUS CADIUM GERMANIUM ARSENIDE.** TAUC, J. STOURAC, L. VORLICEK, V. ZAVETOVA, M. PROC. INT. CONF. PHYS. SEMICOND., 9TH 1251-5, 1968.
75887	**ELECTRONIC PROPERTIES OF AMORPHOUS SEMICONDUCTORS.** STUKE, J. PROC. INT. CONF. PHYS. SEMICOND., 10TH 14-22, 1970.
75889	**PIEZOELECTRIC MODULATION OF SURFACE CHARGES.** LOGOWSKI, J. GATOS, H. C. PROC. INT. CONF. SEMICOND. PHYS. 1462-7, 1972.
75890	**ABSORPTION SPECTROSCOPY OF CONDENSED GASES AT LOW TEMPERATURES.** DRESSLER, K. J. QUANT. SPECTROS. RADIAT. TRANSFER 2, 683-8, 1962.
75892	**MIE SCATTERING CALCULATIONS FOR MICRON SIZE ALUMINA AND MAGNESIA SPHERES.** BAUER, E. CARLSON, D. J. J. QUANT. SPECTROS. RADIAT. TRANSFER 4 (3), 363-74, 1964.
75903	**HEUSLER ALLOYS.** WEBSTER, P. J. CONTEMP. PHYS. 10 (6), 559-77, 1969.
75904	**SUPERCONDUCTIVITY AT HIGH PRESSURES.** BRANDT, N. B. GINZBURG, N. I. CONTEMP. PHYS. 10 (4), 355-84, 1969.
75905	**MAGNETIC SEMICONDUCTORS.** AUSTIN, I. G. ELWELL, D. CONTEMP. PHYS. 11 (5), 455-76, 1970.
75911	**TEMPERATURE VARIATION OF THE PHOTOELASTIC CONSTANTS OF AMMONIUM CHLORIDE.** RAO, K. V. K. MURTH, V. G. K. INDIAN J. PHYS. 41, 150-1, 1967.
75921	**THE KNOWLEDGE OF THE SILICON OXIDE PHASE IN THIN LAYERS.** RITTER, E. OPT. ACTA 9, 197-202, 1962.
75928	**THE PROSPECTS FOR ETTINGSHAUSEN AND PELTIER COOLING AT LOW TEMPERATURES.** DELVES, R. T. BRIT. J. APPL. PHYS. 13, 440-5, 1962.
75938	**THE INFRA-RED REFRACTIVE INDEX OF GARNET FERRITES.** JOHNSON, B. WALTON, A. K. BRIT. J. APPL. PHYS. 16, 475-7, 1965.
75941	**QUENCHING OF OSCILLATIONS IN PHOTOCONDUCTIVITY OF CADMIUM SULFIDE.** WEI, T. Y. PENCHINA, C. M. PARK, Y. S. BULL. AMER. PHYS. SOC. 13, 1455, 1968.

EPIC Number | Bibliographic Citation

75942 BAND GAP OF GALLIUM PHOSPHIDE FROM 3 TO 900 K AND HIGH TEMPERATURE DIODE EMISSION.
LORENZ, M. R. PETTIT, G. D. TAYLOR, R. C.
BULL. AMER. PHYS. SOC.
13, 453, 1968.

75947 MAGNETIC SUSCEPTIBILITY OF THE 1-T AND 2-H MODIFICATIONS OF TANTALUM SULFIDE.
MENTH, A. GEBALLE, T. H. GAMBLE, F. R.
BULL. AMER. PHYS. SOC.
16, 403, 1971.

75948 HIGH FIELD MAGNETORESISTANCE OF GOLD GALLIUM AND GOLD LEAD.
BASS, R. SCHROEDER, P. A.
BULL. AMER. PHYS. SOC.
16, 1408, 1971.

75961 A LOW TEMPERATURE RESISTANCE THERMOMETER USING P-TYPE GALLIUM ARSENIDE.
BROOM, R. F.
J. SCI. INSTRUM.
35, 467-8, 1958.

75962 SPECTROPHOTOMETRIC STUDIES OF ULTRA LOW LOSS OPTICAL GLASSES II: DOUBLE BEAM METHOD.
JONES, M. W. KAO, K. C.
J. SCI. INSTRUM.
2 (SER. 2), 331-5, 1969.

75965 SOME PHYSICAL PROPERTIES OF ALKALI GERMANATE GLASSES.
KRISHNA MURTHY, M. IP, J.
NATURE
201 (4916), 285-6, 1964.

75990 RARE EARTH INTERMEDIATE PHASES. V. THE CUBIC LAVES PHASES FORMED BY RARE EARTH METALS WITH IRON AND NICKEL
MANSEY, R. C. RAYNOR, G. V. HARRIS, I. R.
J. LESS-COMMON METALS
14, 329-36, 1968.

75996 PREPARATION, ELECTRICAL AND SUPERCONDUCTING PROPERTIES OF MASSIVE THORIUM HYDRIDE.
SATTERTHWAITE, C. B. PETERSON, D. T.
J. LESS-COMMON METALS
26, 361-8, 1972.

76033 COMPENSATION OF CONDUCTIVITY BY RADIATION DEFECTS IN SEMICONDUCTORS.
VINETSKII, V. L. SMIRNOV, L. S.
SOV. PHYS. SEMICOND.
5 (1), 153-, 1971.
(ENGLISH TRANSLATION OF FIZ. TEKH. POLUPROV., 5 (1), 176-8, 1971; FOR ORIGINAL SEE E77244)

76041 SWITCHING EFFECT IN SELENIUM AND ANTIMONY SESQUISULFIDE MELTS.
ANDREEV, A. A. MAMADALIEV, M. REGEL, A. R.
SOV. PHYS. SEMICOND.
5 (11), 1900-, 1972.
(ENGLISH TRANSLATION OF FIZ. TEKH. POLUPROV., 5 (11), 2187-8, 1971; FOR ORIGINAL SEE E76069)

76043 PHOTOVOLTAIC EFFECT IN THE CADMIUM TELLURIDE - MERCURY TELLURIDE HETEROSTRUCTURE WITH A BUILT-IN HOMOJUNCTION IN CADMIUM TELLURIDE.
KIREEV, P. S. NIKONOVA, T. V.
ARTAMONOV, N. P. KROTOV, I. I.
SOV. PHYS. SEMICOND.
5 (11), 1939-, 1972.
(ENGLISH TRANSLATION OF FIZ. TEKH. POLUPROV., 5 (11), 2222-4, 1971; FOR ORIGINAL SEE E77234)

76050 OPTICAL PROPERTIES OF CADMIUM SULFIDE SINGLE CRYSTAL WELL INSIDE THE FUNDAMENTAL ABSORPTION REGION AND THE STRUCTURE OF ENERGY BANDS.
BRODIN, M. S. STRASHNIKOVA, M. I.
SOV. PHYS. SOLID STATE
8 (3), 549-51, 1966.
(ENGLISH TRANSLATION OF FIZ. TVERD. TELA, 8 (3), 684-7, 1966; FOR ORIGINAL SEE E75862)

76069 SWITCHING EFFECT IN SELENIUM AND ANTIMONY SESQUI-SULFIDE MELTS.
ANDREEV, A. A. MAMADALIEV, M. REGEL, A. R.
FIZ. TEKH. POLUPROV.
5 (11), 2187-8, 1971.
(FOR ENGLISH TRANSLATION SEE E76041)

76160 OPTICAL TRANSITIONS IN THE D(3) ELECTRON SPECTRUM OF A VANADIUM IMPURITY CENTER IN GALLIUM PHOSPHIDE.
ABAGYAN, S. A. IVANOV, G. A.
KUZNETSOV, YU. N. OKUNEV, YU. A.
FIZ. TEKH. POLUPROV.
8 (9), 1691-6, 1974.
(FOR ENGLISH TRANSLATION SEE E76161)

76161 OPTICAL TRANSITIONS IN THE D(3) ELECTRON SPECTRUM OF A VANADIUM IMPURITY CENTER IN GALLIUM PHOSPHIDE.
ABAGYAN, S. A. IVANOV, G. A.
KUZNETSOV, YU. N. OKUNEV, YU. A.
SOV. PHYS. SEMICOND.
8 (9), 1096-9, 1975.
(ENGLISH TRANSLATION OF FIZ. TEKH. POLUPROV., 8 (9), 1691-6, 1974; FOR ORIGINAL SEE E76160)

76189 MAGNETOPHONON OSCILLATIONS OF LONGITUDINAL MAGNETO-RESISTANCE IN SEMICONDUCTORS.
KHARUS, G. I. TSIDIL'KOVSKII, I. M.
SOV. PHYS. SEMICOND.
5 (4), 534-, 1971.
(ENGLISH TRANSLATION OF FIZ. TEKH. POLUPROV. 5 (4), 603-14, 1971; FOR ORIGINAL SEE E77339)

76193 THERMALLY STIMULATED CONDUCTIVITY IN INHOMOGENEOUS SEMICONDUCTORS.
MARKEVICH, I. V. SHEINKMAN, M. K.
SOV. PHYS. SEMICOND.
5 (10), 1723-, 1971.
(ENGLISH TRANSLATION OF FIZ. TEKH. POLUPROV. 5 (10), 1987-8, 1971; FOR ORIGINAL SEE E77301)

76354 CAUSES OF ELECTRON EMISSION INSTABILITY IN THIN DISPERSED FILMS OF GOLD ACTIVATED BY BARIUM OXIDE.
SUKHARIER, A. S. ZAGREBNEVA, S. V.
IZV. AKAD. NAUK SSSR, SER. FIZ.
35 (2), 298-301, 1971.
(FOR ENGLISH TRANSLATION SEE E85675)

76365 THE EFFECT OF ELECTROSTATIC FIELD AND THERMOEMISSION CURRENT ON THE RELEASE OF COMPONENTS AND THE WORK FUNCTION OF BARIUM OXIDE.
PIKUS, G. YA. TETERYA, V. P.
IZV. AKAD. NAUK SSSR SER. FIZ.
35 (5), 1023-30, 1971.
(FOR ENGLISH TRANSLATION SEE E85671)

76387 MEASUREMENT OF CONDUCTIVITY AND HALL COEFFICIENT OF SEMICONDUCTOR SINGLE CRYSTALS BY A FOUR-PROBE METHOD.
KON'KOV, V. L. KUKUI, A. S. POLYAKOV, N. N.
IZV. AKAD. NAUK SSSR, SER. FIZ.
36 (3), 603-6, 1972.
(FOR ENGLISH TRANSLATION SEE E83168)

76400 EFFECTS OF CHEMICAL COMPOSITION ON THE STRUCTURE, ELECTRICAL, AND THERMAL PROPERTIES OF VANADIUM MONOCARBIDE.
NESHPOR, V. S. ORDAN'YAN, S. S.
IZV. AKAD. NAUK SSSR, NEORGAN. MATERIALY
1 (2), 173-80, 1965.
(ENGLISH TRANSLATION SEE E 91743)

76401 SOLID SOLUTIONS IN THE GALLIUM SULFIDE - GALLIUM SELENIDE SYSTEM.
RUSTAMOV, P. G. MELIKOVA, Z. D.
SAFAROV, M. G. ALIDZHANOV, M. A.
IZV. AKAD. NAUK SSSR, NEORG. MATERIALY
1 (3), 419-21, 1965.
(ENGLISH TRANSLATION SEE E 91742)

76422 PHYSICAL PROPERTIES OF CHROMIUM BORIDE PHASES.
SEREBRYAKOVA, T. I. KOVENSKAYA, B. A.
IZV. AKAD. NAUK SSSR, NEORG. MATER.
2 (12), 2134-8, 1966.
(ENGLISH TRANSLATION SEE E 91741)

76453 SUSCEPTIBILITY OF VANADIUM OXIDE BRONZES.
FOTIEV, L. B. VOLKOV, V. L. SURAT, L. L.
IZV. AKAD. NAUK SSSR, NEORG. MATER.
6 (10), 1835-8, 1970.
(FOR ENGLISH TRANSLATION SEE E91544)

76458 FLOURINE-CONTAINING BARIUM TITANATE.
NEKRASOV, M. M. SAVOSHCHENKO, V. S.
SYCH, A. M.
IZV. AKAD, NAUK SSSR, NEORG. MATER.
6 (12), 2175-7, 1970.
(FOR ENGLISH TRANSLATION, SEE E 91515)

76459 NATURE OF BONDING AND ELECTRICAL CONDUCTIVITY OF CUBIC CARBIDES AND OXYCARBIDES OF ZIRCONIUM.
BORUKHOVICH, A. S. MATVEENKO, I. I.
ZAINULIN, YU. G. ALYAMOVSKII, S. I.
GEL'D, P. V.
IZV. AKAD. MAUK SSSR, NEORG. MATER.
6 (12), 2126-31, 1970.
(FOR ENGLISH TRANSLATION, SEE E 91514)

76462 PHYSICOCHEMICAL ANALYSIS OF LIQUID SYSTEMS FORMED BY COPPER AND ANTIMONY CHALCOGENIDES.
GLAZOV, V. M. KULIEV, R. A.
IZV. AKAD. NAUK SSSR, NEORG. MATER.
7 (2), 206-9, 1971.
(ENGLISH TRANSLATION SEE E 91582)

76463 AXIAL HETEROGENEITY OF CADMIUM TELLURIDE RODS.
MATVEEV, O. A. PROKOF'EV, S. V. RUD, YU. V.
SANIN, K. V. SHRETER, YU. G.
IZV. AKAD. NAUK SSSR, NEORG. MATER.
7 (2), 324-5, 1971.
(ENGLISH TRANSLATION SEE E91585)

76465 PREPARATION OF CONDUCTING STANNIC OXIDE FILMS ON GLASS FROM ORGANIC COMPOUNDS.
VOROB'EVA, O. V. POLUROTOVA, T. F.
IZV. AKAD. NAUK SSSR, NEORG. MATER.
7 (2), 266-9, 1971.
(ENGLISH TRANSLATION SEE E91584)

EPIC Number	Bibliographic Citation
76469	**ELECTRICAL PROPERTIES OF MOLYBDENUM-DOPED ZIRCONIUM MONOCARBIDE.** NESHPOR, V. S. NIKITIN, V. P. ORDAN'YAN, S. S. SKALETSKAYA, N. A. IZV. AKAD. NAUK SSSR, NEORG. MATER. 7 (4), 606–9, 1971. (FOR ENGLISH TRANSLATION, SEE E 91495)
76470	**NATURE OF THE DISORDERING SILICON NITRIDE, SI(3)N(4), CRYSTALS.** KAMYSHOV, V. M. GORBATOV, A. G. IZV. AKAD. NAUK SSSR, NEORG. MATER. 7 (4), 601–5, 1971. (FOR ENGLISH TRANSLATION, SEE E 91494)
76472	**GALVANOMAGNETIC PHENOMENA IN P-INDIUM ANTIMONIDE.** ERMOLOVICH, YU. B. IZV. AKAD. NAUK SSSR, NEORG. MATER. 7 (4), 697–8, 1971 (FOR ENGLISH TRANSLATION, SEE E 91496)
76473	**ELECTRICAL CONDUCTIVITY OF MOLTEN ALUMINUM OXIDE.** ELYUTIN, V. P. MITIN, B. S. NAGIBIN, YU. A. IZV. AKAD. NAUK SSSR, NEORG. MATER. 7 (5), 880–1, 1971. (FOR ENGLISH TRANSLATION, SEE E 91499)
76475	**PROCESS THERMODYNAMICS AND ELECTRICAL PROPERTIES OF CADMIUM SULFIDE-CADMIUM OXIDE SINGLE CRYSTALS.** LUTSKAYA, O. F. ORMONT, B. F. KACHALOVA, I. A. IZV. AKAD. NAUK SSSR, NEORG. MATER. 7 (6), 930–3, 1971. (FOR ENGLISH TRANSLATION, SEE E 91501)
76476	**PHYSICAL PROPERTIES OF IRON BORIDES.** KOSTETSKII, I. I. L'VOV, S. N. KUNITSKII, YU. S. IZV. AKAD. NAUK ASSR, NEORG. MATER. 7 (6), 951–5, 1971. (FOR ENGLISH TRANSLATION, SEE E 91521)
76477	**ELECTRICAL RESISTANCE OF LANTHANUM CHROMITE, NEODYMIUM CHROMITE, SAMARIUM CHROMITE, AND YTTRIUM CHROMITE AT HIGH TEMPERATURES.** GORDON, V. G. REKOV, A. I. SPIRIDONOV, E. G. TIMOFEEVA, N. I. IZV. AKAD. NAUK SSSR, NEORG. MATER. 7 (6), 1084–5, 1971. (FOR ENGLISH TRANSLATION SEE E91523)
76478	**PHYSICAL PROPERTIES OF CHROMIUM GERMANIUM SILISIDE SOLID SOLUTIONS.** RYKOVA, M. A. SABIRZYANOV, A. V. ZAGRYAZHSHSKII, V. L. GEL'D, P. V. IZV. AKAD. NAUK SSSR NEORG. MATER. 7 (6), 947–50, 1971. (FOR ENGLISH TRANSLATION SEE E91502)
76480	**MAGNETIC AND ADSORPTION PROPERTIES OF SEMICONDUCTORS OF THE ISOELECTRONIC GERMANIUM SERIES.** KIROVSKAYA, I. A. ZHELTONOZHKO, A. A. IZV. AKAD. NAUK SSSR, NEORG. MATER. 7 (6), 921–4, 1971. (FOR ENGLISH TRANSLATION, SEE E 91500)
76481	**RELAXATION AND FERROELECTRIC PROPERTIES OF SOLID SOLUTIONS IN THE BARIUM TITANATE - STRONTIUM NIOBATE SYSTEM.** GROZNOV, I. N. VISKOV, A. S. PETROV, V. M. IZV. AKAD. NAUK SSSR, NEORG. MATER. 7 (7), 1216–19, 1971. (FOR ENGLISH TRANSLATION, SEE E 91525)
76482	**DIELECTRIC AND STRUCTURAL PROPERTIES OF FERRO-ELECTRICS WITH DIFFUSE PHASE TRANSITIONS.** SAL'NIOV, V. D. KUZ'MINOV, YU. S. VENEVTSEV, YU. N. IZV. AKAD. NAUK SSSR, NEORG. MATER. 7 (7), 1277–8, 1971. (FOR ENGLISH TRANSLATIONS, SEE E 91527)
76484	**ELECTRICAL PROPERTIES AND STRUCTURE OF METANIOBATES AND METATANTALATES OF TRANSITION METALS OF THE SD-SERIES.** BAZUEV, G. V. KRYLOV, E. I. IZV. NAUK SSSR, NEORG. MATER. 7 (7), 1209–12, 1971. (FOR ENGLISH TRANSLATION, SEE E 91524)
76485	**PROPERTIES OF ZIRCONIUM CARBIDE IN THE HOMOGENEITY REGION.** SAMSONOV, G. V. UPADKHAYA, G. SH. IZV. AKAD. NAUK SSSR, NEORG. MATER. 7 (8), 1351–4, 1971. (FOR ENGLISH TRANSLATION, SEE E 91504)
76486	**PROPERTIES OF RHODIUM BORIDES.** KOSENKO, V, A. RUD, B. M. SIDOROVA, V. G. IZV. AKAD. NAUK SSSR, BEORG. MATER. 7 (8), 1455–6, 1971. (FOR ENGLISH TRANSLATION, SEE E 91505)
76488	**ELECTRICAL CONDUCTIVITY IN OXIDE WITH RUTILE STRUCTURE.** KRYLOV, E. I. DVONIN, V. I. ROZDESTVENSKII, F. A. IZV. AKAD. NAUK SSSR, NEORG. MATER. 7 (9), 1636–7, 1972. (FOR ENGLISH TRANSLATION, SEE E 91569)
76489	**ELECTRICAL PROPERTIES OF TRANSITION METAL SELENIDES.** ABDINOV, D. SH. IVANOVA, V. I. ALIEV, G. M. IZV. AKAD. NAUK SSSR, NEORG. MATER. 7 (9), 1622–3, 1971. (FOR ENGLISH TRANSLATION SEE E91568)
76491	**SUPERCONDUCTIVITY AND RESIDUAL RESISTANCE OF TITANIUM CARBIDE.** NESHPOR, V. S. NIKITIN, V. P. NOVIKOV, V. I. IZV. AKAD. NAUK SSSR, NEORG. MATER. 7 (10), 1743–7, 1971. (FOR ENGLISH TRANSLATION SEE E91570)
76493	**VARIABLE RESISTORS OF COMPOSITION TYPE BASED ON REFRACTORY COMPOUNDS.** SAMSONOV, G. V. GREBENKINA, V. G. YUSOV, YU. P. VLASOV, L. G. PEREVEZENTSEV, A. V. IZV. AKAD. NAUK SSSR, NEORG. MATER. 7 (10), 1764–8, 1971. (ENGLISH TRANSLATION SEE E91577)
76494	**PHYSICAL PROPERTIES OF CADMIUM GALLIUM TETRASELENIDE.** TYRZIU, M. P. TYRZIU, V. G. LAZO, K. IZV. AKAD. NAUK SSSR, NEORG. MATER. 7 (10), 1855–6, 1971. (ENGLISH TRANSLATION SEE E91578)
76496	**ELECTRICAL CONDUCTIVITY AND THERMOEMF. OF SINGLE CRYSTALS OF A SERIES OF SILVER - VANADIUM OXYGEN BRONZES.** VINOGRADOV, A. A. ORNATSKAYA, Z. I. IZV. AKAD. NAUK SSSR, NEORG. MATER. 7 (10), 1869–71, 1971. (ENGLISH TRANSLATION SEE E 91580)
76497	**PHASE DIAGRAM AND ELECTRICAL CONDUCTIVITY OF BISMUTH SELENIDE IODIDE - ANTIMONY SELENIDE IODIDE SYSTEM ALLOYS.** BELOTSKII, D. P. LAPSHIN, V. F. IZV. AKAD. NAUK SSSR, NEORG. MATER. 7 (11), 1939–41, 1971. (FOR ENGLISH TRANSLATION SEE E91542)
76498	**PHOTOSENSITIVE CADMIUM SULFIDE FILMS, CHEMICALLY PRECIPITATED FROM AN AQUEOUS SOLUTION.** BOGDANOVICH, V. B. VELIKANOV, A. A. KAGANOVICH, E. B. OSTROVSKAYA, I. K. SVECHNIKOV, S. V. IZV. AKAD. NAUK SSSR, NEORG. MATER. 7 (11), 2075–6, 1971. (ENGLISH TRANSLATION SEE E91581)
76499	**ELECTRICAL CONDUCTIVITY AND THERMO ELECTROMOTIVE FORCE OF SILVER GALLIUM DISELENIDE IN SOLID AND LIQUID STATES.** BALANEVSKAYA, A. E. BERGER, L. I. ISAEV, Z. A. IZV. AKAD. NAUK SSSR, NEORG. MATER. 7 (11), 2084–5, 1971. (FOR ENGLISH TRANSLATION SEE E91563)
76500	**LEAD SELENIDE - TIN DISELENIDE SYSTEM.** LATYPOV, Z. M. SAVEL'EV, V. P. AVER'YANOV, I. S. UL'DANOV, A. S. IZV. AKAD. NAUK SSSR, NEORG. MATER. 7 (11), 2092–3, 1971. (FOR ENGLISH TRANSLATION SEE E91566)
76503	**PHYSICAL PROPERTIES OF BERYLLIUM, CHROMIUM, AND LANTHANUM BOROCARBIDES.** NESHPOR, V. S. VEKSHINA, N. V. NIKITIN, V. P. MARKOVSKII, L. YA. IZV. AKAD. NAUK SSSR, NEORG. MATER. 7 (12), 2170–4, 1971. (FOR ENGLISH TRANSLATION SEE E91564)
76505	**ELECTRICAL AND THERMOGRAPHIC STUDIES OF CADMIUM ANTIMONIDE.** ANATYCHUK, L. I. GNATYUK, A. M. IZV. AKAD. NAUK SSSR, NEORG. MATER. 8 (1), 44–8, 1972. (FOR ENGLISH TRANSLATION, SEE E 91528)
76506	**EFFECT OF THE DOPING ELEMENTS ON THE PHYSICAL PROPERTIES AND NAUURE OF CHEMICAL BONDS IN GALLIUM ANTIMONIDE.** SAFARALIEV, G. I. MURGUZOV, M. I. IZV. AKAD. ANUK SSSR, NEORG. MATER. 8 (1), 53–6, 1972. (FOR ENGLISH TRANSLATION, SEE E 91529)

EPIC Number | Bibliographic Citation

76507 **ELECTRICAL AND PHOTOELECTRIC PROPERTIES OF THALLIUM GALLIUM DISULFIDE, THALLIUM GALLIUM DISELENIDE, AND THALLIUM INDIUM DISULFIDE SINGLE CRYSTALS.**
KARPOVICH, I. A. CHERVOVA, A. A.
DEMIDOVA, L. I. LEONOV, E. I. ORLOV, V. M.
IZV. AKAD. NAUK. SSSR, NEORG. MATER.
8 (1), 70–2, 1972.
(FOR ENGLISH TRANSLATION SEE E91590)

76508 **ELECTRICAL CONDUCTIVITY, THERMOELECTROMOTIVE FORCE AND THERMIONIC EMISSION OF BARIUM OXIDE AND STRONTIUM OXIDE CRYSTALS.**
KOVALEV, N. N. SOROKIN, O. V.
IZV. AKAD. NAUK SSSR, NEORG. MATER.
8 (1), 111–16, 1972.
(FOR ENGLISH TRANSLATION SEE E91530)

76511 **DOPING OF SEMICONDUCTOR LAYERS PRODUCED BY MELT COMPRESSION.**
SANDULOVA, A. V. GONCHAROV, A. D.
RUDOL'F, P.
IZV. AKAD. NAUK SSSR, NEORG. MATER.
8 (2), 224–7, 1972.
(FOR ENGLISH TRANSLATION SEE E91555)

76512 **EFFECT OF DOUBLE DOPING ON THE ELECTRICAL PROPERTIES OF CADMIUM ANTIMONIDE.**
KOSTUR, T. A. KOSTUR, N. L. PSAREV, V. I.
IZV. AKAD. NAUK SSSR, NEORG. MATER.
8 (2), 228–31, 1972.
(FOR ENGLISH TRANSLATION SEE E91556)

76517 **LIGHTLY DOPED INDIUM ANTIMONIDE SINGLE CRYSTALS WITH DIFFERENT DEGREES OF COMPENSATION.**
MIRGALOVSKAYA, M. S. RAUKHMAN, M. R.
SOROKINA, N. G.
IZV. AKAD. NAUK SSSR, NEORG. MATER.
8 (3), 569–70, 1972.
(FOR ENGLISH TRANSLATION SEE E91561)

76518 **EFFECT OF THE VAPORIZATION OF A VOLATILE COMPONENT ON THE ELECTRICAL PROPERTIES OF CADMIUM ANTIMONIDE.**
ANATYCHUK, L. I. KONDRATENKO, V. M.
LUSTE, O. YA. KHAVRUNYAK, P. T.
IZV. AKAD. NAUK SSSR, NEORG. MATER.
8 (4), 653–8, 1972.
(FOR ENGLISH TRANSLATION SEE E91539)

76519 **PHOTOLUMINESCENCE AND PHOTOCONDUCTIVITY OF SINGLE-CRYSTALLINE FILMS OF P-CADMIUM TELLURIDE.**
KORNITSKII, A. G. KROTOV, I. I.
KIREEV, P. S.
IZV. AKAD. NAUK SSSR, NEORG. MATER.
8 (4), 659–64, 1972.
(FOR ENGLISH TRANSLATION SEE E91552)

76520 **ELECTRICAL CONDUCTIVITY OF POLYCRYSTALLINE MAGNESIUM FLUORIDE.**
VOLYNETS, F. K. DRONOVA, G. N.
SMIRNAYA, E. P.
IZV. AKAD. NAUK SSSR, NEORG. MATER.
8 (4), 775–6, 1972.
(FOR ENGLISH TRANSLATION SEE E91553)

76521 **THERMOELECTRIC PROPERTIES OF GALLIUM ANTIMONIDE AT 300 DEGREES K.**
IL'CHENKO, L. N. STREL'NIKOVA, I. A.
MIRGALOVSKAYA, M. S.
IZV. AKAD. NAUK SSSR, NEORG. MATER.
8 (5), 798–801, 1972.
(FOR ENGLISH TRANSLATION, SEE E 91507)

76522 **MAGNETIC PROPERTIES OF CHROMIUM SULFOTELLURIDES.**
IKORSKII, V. N. DORONINA, L. M.
BATSANOV, S. S.
IZV. AKAD. ANUK SSSR, NEORG. MATER.
8 (5), 821–4, 1972.
(FOR ENGLISH TRANSLATION, SEE E 91508)

76523 **ELECTRICAL CONDUCTIVITY OF ALUMINUM OXIDE IN THE MOLTEN STATE.**
ALEKSANDROV, V. I. OSIKO, V. V.
TATARISTSEV, V. M.
IZV. AKAD. NAUK SSSR, NEORG. MATER.
8 (5), 956–7, 1972.
(FOR ENGLISH TRANSLATION SEE E91509)

76524 **TEMPERATURE DEPENDENCE OF THE THERMO ELECTROMOTIVE FORCE OF CUPRIC OXIDE DURING ITS DISSOCIATION.**
ZUEV, K. P. KOLENCHENKO, V. I.
IZV. AKAD. NAUK SSSR, NEORG. MATER.
8 (5), 958–9, 1972.
(FOR ENGLISH TRANSLATION SEE E91510)

76526 **EFFECT OF IMPRUITIES ON THE HIGH-TEMPERATURE ELECTRICAL CONDUCTIVITY OF CADMIUM TELLURIDE CRYSTALS.**
RUD, YU. V. SANIN, K. V.
IZV. AKAD. NAUK SSSR, NEORG. MATER.
8 (6), 1019–24, 1972.
(FOR ENGLISH TRANSLATION, SEE E 91512)

76527 **INTRINSIC CHARGE-CARRIER CONVENTRATION IN MERCURY TELLURIDE.**
KIREEV, P. S. DMITRIEV, V. P.
ZUBAREVA, ZH. M. PTASHINSKII, V. V.
IZV. AKAD. NAUK SSSR, NEORG. MATER.
8 (6), 1025–8, 1972.
(FOR ENGLISH TRANSLATION, SEE E 91532)

76529 **ELECTROPHYSICAL PROPERTIES OF VANADIUM MONOXIDE IN HOMOGENEITY REGION.**
AIVAZOV, M. I. DOMASHNEV, I. A,
SARKISYAN, A. G. GUROV, S. V.
IZV, AKAD. NAUK SSSR, NORRG. MATER.
8 (6), 1069–72, 1972.
(FOR ENGLISH TRANSLATION, SEE E 91534)

76530 **PHOTOELECTRIC PROPERTIES OF CDSI(X)GE(1-X)AS(2) VITREOUS SEMICONDUCTORS.**
AKSENOV, V. V. PETROV, V. M.
KHARAKHORIN, F. F.
IZV. AKAD. ANUK, SSSR, NEORG. MATER.
8 (6), 1152–4, 1972.
(FOR ENGLISH TRANSLATION, SEE E 91535)

76534 **REGION OF A GERMANIUM TELLURIDE SOLID SOLUTION IN BISMUTH SESQUITELLURIDE.**
ABRIKOSOV, N. KH. DANILOVA-DOBRYAKOVA, G. T.
IZV. AKAD. NAUK SSSR, NEORG. MATER.
8 (7), 1221–3, 1972.
(FOR ENGLISH TRANSLATION SEE E91537)

76536 **EFFECT OF GAS-PHASE COMPOSITION ON THE ELECTRICAL PROPERTIES OF GALLIUM ARSENIDE EPITAXIAL FILMS.**
SIDOROV, YU. G. DVORETSKII, S. A.
ALEKSANDROV, L. N. KRAVCHENKO, A. F.
RYNDINA, L. N. LEUTINA, A. P.
IZV. AKAD. NAUK SSSR, NEROG. MATER.
8 (8), 1373–8, 1972.
(FOR ENGLISH TRANSLATION SEE E91519)

76538 **ELECTRIC AND GALVANOMAGNETIC PROPERTIES OF CU(2-X) AG(X)TE SYSTEM.**
RUSTAMOV, A. G. KERIMOV, I. G.
IBRAGIMOVA, P. G.
IZV. AKAD. NAUK SSSR, NEROG. MATER.
8 (8), 1493–4, 1971.
(FOR ENGLISH TRANSLATION, SEE E 91520)

76540 **PHOTOCONDUCTIVITY OF PHOSPHORUS SELENIDES.**
LYUBIN, V. M. FEDOROVA, G. A.
IZV. AKAD. NAUK SSSR, NEORG. MATER.
8 (9), 1559–62, 1972.
(ENGLISH TRANSLATION SEE E 91592)

76545 **MAGNETIC PROPERTIES OF CHROMIUM SULFOSELENOTELLURIDE.**
IKORSKII, V. N. BATSANOV, S. S.
IZV. AKAD. NAUK SSSR, NEORG. MATER.
8 (10), 1858–9, 1972.
(ENGLISH TRANSLATION SEE E 91596)

76546 **THERMOEMF. OF P- AND N-CONDUCTIVITY INDIUM ANTIMONIDE AT ROOM TEMPERATURE.**
MIRGALOVSKAYA, M. S. RAUKHMAN, M. R.
IL'CHENKO, L. N. SOROKINA, N. G.
IZV. AKAD. NAUK SSSR, NEORG. MATER.
8 (10), 1751–4, 1972.
(ENGLISH TRANSLATION SEE E 91593)

76547 **PREPARATION AND PROPERTIES OF BERYLLIUM-DOPED GALLIUM PHOSPHIDE.**
OVCHINNIKOV, S. YU. SOROKIN, V. S.
YAS'KOV, D. A.
IZV. AKAD. NAUK SSSR, NEORG. MATER
8 (11), 1898–904, 1972.
(FOR ENGLISH TRANSLATION SEE E91597)

76548 **CRYSTAL STRUCTURE AND ELECTRICAL PROPERTIES OF INDIUM, SELENIDE - ANTIMONY TELLURIDE ALLOYS.**
BELOTSKII, D. P. LEGETA, L. V.
IZV. AKAD. NAUK SSSR, NEORG. MATER.
8 (11), 1908–12, 1972.
(FOR ENGLISH TRANSLATION SEE E91598)

76549 **MAGNETIC PROPERTIES OF VANADIUM NITRIDE AND VANADIUM DIBORIDE AND THE VANADIUM - BORON - NITROGEN ALLOYS.**
AIVAZOV, M. I. GUROV, S. V.
IZV. AKAD. NAUK SSSR, NEORG. MATER.
8 (11), 1913–16, 1972.
(ENGLISH TRANSLATION SEE E 91599)

76551 **ELECTRICAL CONDUCTIVITY, THERMOELECTROMOTIVE FORCE AND THERMAL CONDUCTIVITY OF COPPER INDIUM TELLURIDE AND COPPER GALLIUM TELLURIDE SEMICONDUCTING COMPOUNDS.**
BERGER, L. I. ISAEV, Z. A.
IZV. AKAD. NAUK SSSR, NEORG. MATER.
8 (11), 2018–20, 1972.
(FOR ENGLISH TRANSLATION SEE E91546)

76553 **WIDTH OF THE FORBIDDEN BAND OF CADMIUM INDIUM SELENIDE - CADMIUM INDIUM TELLURIDE SOLID SOLUTIONS.**
KOVAL, L. S. RADAUTSAN, S. I. SOBOLEV, V. V.
IZV. AKAD. NAUK SSSR, NEORG. MATER.
8 (11), 2021–2, 1972.
(FOR ENGLISH TRANSLATION SEE E91547)

EPIC Number	Bibliographic Citation

76557 **HOMOGENEITY OF SAMARIUM SULFIDE.**
SERGEEVA, V. M. GONCHAROVA, E. V.
KARTENKO, N. F. DEMINA, M. A. SMIRNOV, P. A.
ANDRYUSHIN, A. I. MISYUREV, YU. K.
IZV. AKAD. NAUK SSSR, NEORG. MATER.
8 (12), 2114–19, 1972.
(FOR ENGLISH TRANSLATION SEE E91550)

76600 **CRYSTAL OPTICS OF ALKALINE-EARTH METAVANADATES.**
GLAZYRIN, M. P. IVAKIN, A. A.
GUREVICH, V. A.
SOV. PHYS. CRYSTALLOGR.
18 (5), 685–6, 1974.
(ENGLISH TRANSLATION OF KRISTALLOGRAFIYA, 18 (5),
1088–9, 1973; FOR ORIGINAL SEE E56011)

76649 **EFFECT OF TEMPERATURE AND EXCITATION INTENSITY ON THE EDGE EMISSION OF BETA SILICON CARBIDE (ALUMINUM, NITROGEN) CRYSTALS.**
LONG, N. N. NEDZVETSKII, D. S.
OPT. SPECTROS., USSR
35 (6), 645–7, 1973.
(ENGLISH TRANSLATION OF OPT. SPEKTROSK., 35 (6),
1111–5, 1973; FOR ORIGINAL SEE E56638)

76650 **PHOTOSTIMULATED THERMOLUMINESCENCE OF FLUORITE CRYSTALS DOPED WITH RARE EARTH IONS.**
KORNIENKO, L. S. LOZHNIKOV, A. A.
NAGAROV, V. I. CHERNOV, P. U.
OPT. SPECTROS., USSR
35 (6), 651–3, 1973.
(ENGLISH TRANSLATION OF OPT. SPEKTROSK., 35 (6),
1120–5, 1973; FOR ORIGINAL SEE E56639)

76652 **RADIATION-INDUCED DEFECTS IN FLUORITE UNSTABLE AT 77 K.**
KASK, N. E. KORNIENKO, L. S. CHERNOV, P. U.
OPT. SPECTROS., USSR
35 (6), 683–4, 1973.
(ENGLISH TRANSLATION OF OPT. SPEKTROSK., 35 (6),
1180–1, 1973; FOR ORIGINAL SEE E56640)

76678 **MECHANISM OF THE ELECTRICAL CONDUCTIVITY OF QUASIBINARY MOLYBDENUM SELENIDE - TANTALUM SELENIDE (MOLYBDENUM TANTALUM SELENIDE) ALLOYS.**
KALIKHMAN, V. L. KASIYAN, I. M.
MIKHAILYUK, I. P.
SOV. POWDER MET. METAL CERAM.
12 (11), 922–5, 1973.
(ENGLISH TRANSLATION OF POROSH. MET., 12 (11),
75–9, 1973; FOR ORIGINAL SEE E56469)

76683 **ANOMALOUS SHIFT OF LUMINESCENCE BAND IN CERTAIN SEMICONDUCTORS.**
DAMASKIN, I. A. PYSHKIN, S. L.
RADAUTSAN, S. I. TEZLEVAN, V. E.
JETP LETT.
18 (4), 142–4, 1973.
(ENGLISH TRANSLATION OF ZH. EKSP. TEOR. FIZ.
PIS'MA RED., 18 (4), 239–42, 1973; FOR ORIGINAL
SEE E56678)

76721 **MANUFACTURING METHODS, STRUCTURE AND PHYSICO-CHEMICAL PROPERTIES OF OPTICAL CERAMICS.**
VOLYNETS, F. K.
SOV. J. OPT. TECHNOL.
40 (9), 578–92, 1973.
(ENGLISH TRANSLATION OF OPT. MEKH. PROM., 40 (9),
48–61, 1973; FOR ORIGINAL SEE E56262)

76733 **THERMAL MODELLING OF LASER DAMAGE IN 8–14–MUM MERCURY CADMIUM TELLURIDE PHOTOCONDUCTIVE AND LEAD TIN TELLURIDE PHOTOVOLTAIC DETECTORS.**
BARTOLI, F. ESTEROWITZ, L. KRUER, M.
ALLEN, R.
J. APPL. PHYS.
46 (10), 4519–25, 1975.

76851 **DRAG OF ELECTRONS BY MAGNONS IN FERROMAGNETIC SEMICONDUCTORS.**
NAGAEV, E. L. KOZLOV, V. A.
FIZ. TVERD. TELA
17 (4), 991–8, 1975.
(FOR ENGLISH TRANSLATION SEE E76852)

76852 **DRAG OF ELECTRONS BY MAGNONS IN FERROMAGNETIC SEMICONDUCTORS.**
NAGAEV, E. L. KOZLOV, V. A.
SOV. PHYS. SOLID STATE
17 (4), 635–9, 1975.
(ENGLISH TRANSLATION OF FIZ. TVERD. TELA, 17 (4),
991–8, 1975; FOR ORIGINAL SEE E76851)

77007 **ABSORPTION OF LIGHT IN THIN FILMS ILLUMINATED WITH RESONANCE LASER RADIATION.**
CHAIKOVSKII, I. A.
FIZ. TVERD. TELA
17 (4), 1148–50, 1975.
(FOR ENGLISH TRANSLATION SEE E77008)

77008 **ABSORPTION OF LIGHT IN THIN FILMS ILLUMINATED WITH RESONANCE LASER RADIATION.**
CHAIKOVSKII, I. A.
SOV. PHYS. SOLID STATE
17 (4), 731–2, 1975.
(ENGLISH TRANSLATION OF FIZ. TVERD. TELA, 17 (4),
1148–50, 1975; FOR ORIGINAL SEE E77007)

77041 **ABSORPTION EDGE AND BAND GAP IN CADMIUM TELLURIUM SELENIDE CRYSTALS.**
GAVALESHKO, N. P. KURIK, M. V.
SKITSKO, I. F. OSTAFIICHUK, Z. E.
FIZ. TVERD. TELA
17 (4), 1156–8, 1975.
(FOR ENGLISH TRANSLATION SEE E77042)

77042 **ABSORPTION EDGE AND BAND GAP IN CADMIUM TELLURIUM SELENIDE CRYSTALS.**
GAVALESHKO, N. P. KURIK, M. V.
SKITSKO, I. F. OSTAFIICHUK, Z. E.
SOV. PHYS. SOLID STATE
17 (4), 738–9, 1975.
(ENGLISH TRANSLATION OF FIZ. TVERD. TELA 17 (4),
1156–8, 1975; FOR ORIGINAL SEE E77041)

77075 **SOLID SOLUTIONS OF SULFUR AND SELENIUM IN COPPER TELLURIDE.**
KONEV, V. N. KRUSHATINA, N. A.
KOCHETKOVA, A. A.
INORG. MAT., USSR
10 (1), 113–4, 1974.
(ENGLISH TRANSLATION OF IZV. AKAD. NAUK SSSR, NEORG.
MATER., 10 (1), 140–1, 1974; FOR ORIGINAL SEE
E58280)

77234 **PHOTOVOLTAIC EFFECT IN THE CADMIUM TELLURIDE-MERCURY TELLURIDE HETEROSTRUCTURE WITH A BUILT-IN HOMOJUNCTION IN CADMIUM TELLURIDE.**
KIREEV, P. S. NIKONOVA, T. V.
ARTAMONOV, N. P. KROTOV, I. I.
FIZ. TEKH. POLUPROV.
5 (11), 2222–4, 1971.
(ENGLISH TRANSLATION SEE E 76043)

77244 **COMPENSATION OF CONDUCTIVITY BY RADIATION DEFECTS IN SEMICONDUCTORS.**
VINETSKII, V. L. SMIRNOV, L. S.
FIZ. TEKH. POLUPROV.
5 (1), 176–8, 1971.
(FOR ENGLISH TRANSLATION SEE E76033)

77301 **THERMALLY STIMULATED CONDUCTIVITY IN INHOMOGENEOUS SEMICONDUCTORS.**
MARKEVICH, I. V. SHEINKMAN, M. K.
FIZ. TEKH. POLUPROV.
5 (10), 1987–8, 1971.
(FOR ENGLISH TRANSLATION SEE E76193)

77339 **MAGNETOPHONON OSCILLATIONS OF LONGITUDINAL MAGNETO-RESISTANCE IN SEMICONDUCTORS.**
KHARUS, G. I. TSIDIL'KOVSKII, I. M.
FIZ. TEKH. POLUPROV.
5 (4), 603–14, 1971.
(FOR ENGLISH TRANSLATION SEE E76189)

77830 **INTENSITIES OF IMPURITY VIBRATIONAL SPECTRA WITH VARIOUS CONCENTRATIONS OF NITRITE AND NITRATE IONS IN ALKALI HALIDE MATRIXES.**
GNATVOSKAYA, V. N. OL'KHOVICH, P. F.
KHALIMONOVA, I. N.
ZH. PRIKL. SPEKTROSK.
20 (1), 92–6, 1974.
(FOR ENGLISH TRANSLATION SEE E95926)

77911 **EMISSION OF HOT ELECTRONS FROM AN ALUMINUM-SILICON NITRIDE-ALUMINUM THIN-FILM SYSTEM.**
BARANOV, A. V. BUZNIKOV, YU. N.
VOROB'EV, G. A. GALANSKII, V. L. DREL, N. I.
KRIVOSHCHEKOV, V. P. SMIRNOVA, K. I.
TROYAN, L. A. TROYAN, P. E.
YANKELEVICH, YU. B.
IZV. AKAD. NAUK SSSR, SER. FIZ.
38 (2), 291–5, 1974.
(ENGLISH TRANSLATION SEE E94505)

77912 **FIELD EMISSION IN A SYSTEM WITH ISLET METALLIC FILMS.**
SUKHARIER, A. S. ZAGREBNEVA, S. V.
IVANOV, N. N. TIMOSHINA, L. N.
IZV. AKAD. NAUK SSSR, SER. FIZ.
38 (2), 302–5, 1974.
(FOR ENGLISH TRANSLATION SEE E94503)

77917 **INVESTIGATION OF THE VALENCY BAND OF PHOSPHIDES IN METAL-PHOSPHORUS OF TYPE A–I B–V AND A–II B–V BY AN X-RAY-SPECTRAL METHOD.**
DOMASHEVSKAYA, E. P. TEREKHOV, V. A.
MARSHAKOVA, L. N. UGAI, A.
IZV. AKAD. NAUK SSSR SER. FIZ.,
38 (3), 567–71, 1974.
(FOR ENGLISH TRANSLATION SEE E94485)

EPIC Number	Bibliographic Citation

77919 **PROCESSES IN PHOTOEMISSION UNDER HIGH EXCITATION ENERGIES.**
BLANK, V. A. SOROKIN, O. M.
IZV. AKAD. NAUK SSSR SER. FIZ.
38 (2), 191–4, 1974.
(ENGLISH TRANSLATION SEE E94518)

77920 **PHOTOELECTRON EMISSION FROM F-CENTERS OF ALKALI HALIDE CRYSTALS AND ITS DEPENDENCE ON EXCITATION AND MEASUREMENT CONDITIONS.**
BICHEVIN, V. V.
IZV. AKAD. NAUK SSSR, SER. FIZ.
38 (2), 201–5, 1974.
(ENGLISH TRANSLATION SEE E94516)

77922 **INVESTIGATION OF THE KINETICS OF PHOTOEMISSION OF SOME A(I) - B(V) COMPOUNDS.**
HANEV, K. NIKOLOV, B.
IZV. AKAD. NAUK SSSR SER. FIZ.
38 (2), 212–15, 1974.
(ENGLISH TRANSLATION SEE E94514)

77923 **KINETIC EFFECTS DURING AUTOPHOTOEMISSION OF CADMIUM SULPHIDE.**
SHLYAKHTENKO, P. G. MILESHKINA, N. V.
PREOBRAZHENSKII, R. K. DOROTYNSKII, M. G.
IZV. AKAD. NAUK SSSR SER. FIZ.
38 (2), 216–9, 1974.
(ENGLISH TRANSLATION SEE E94513)

77924 **CALCULATION OF THE ENERGY SPECTRA OF DONOR ELECTRONS OF THERMOCATHODES.**
NAVROZOV, S. V.
IZV. AKAD. NAUK SSSR SER. FIZ.
38 (2), 220–4, 1974.
(ENGLISH TRANSLATION SEE E94512)

77928 **INVESTIGATION OF INTERNAL BREAKDOWN IN STRONG ELECTRICAL FIELDS DURING AUTOEMISSION FROM P-TYPE GERMANIUM.**
IVANOV, V. G. ROZOVA, T. T. FURSEI, G. N.
IZV. AKAD. NAUK SSSR SER. FIZ.
38 (2), 287–90, 1974.
(ENGLISH TRANSLATION SEE E94506)

77932 **ENERGY DISTRIBUTION OF ELECTRONS DURING FIELD EMISSION FROM TUNGSTEN CARBIDE, TANTALUM, AND MOLYBDENUM COATED WITH SILICA AND ALUMINA.**
BOBEV, K. S.
IZV. AKAD. NAUK SSSR SER. FIZ.
38 (2), 338–44, 1974.
(FOR ENGLISH TRANSLATION SEE E94499)

77934 **EXTERNAL PHOTOEFFECT FROM A HIGHLY-ALLOYED SEMICONDUCTOR.**
YUSHINA, M. YA.
IZV. AKAD. NAUK SSSR SER. FIZ.
38 (2), 363–9, 1974.
(FOR ENGLISH TRANSLATION SEE E94494)

77941 **BAND STRUCTURE OF EFFECTIVE PHOTOCATHODES OF A(I) - B(V) COMPOUNDS.**
MOSTOVSKII, A. A. CHALDYSHEV, V. A.
KARAVAEV, G. F. KLIMIN, A. I.
PONOMARENKO, I. N.
IZV. AKAD. NAUK SSSR, SER. FIZ.
38 (2), 195–200, 1974.
(ENGLISH TRANSLATION SEE E94517)

78186 **SPECTRAL DISTRIBUTION OF PHOTOCONDUCTIVITY IN THALLIUM GALLIUM SELENIDE SINGLE CRYSTALS AND FILMS.**
CHERVOVA, A. A.
UCH. ZAP., GOR'K. UNIV., SER. FIZ.
(126), 29–32, 1971.

78213 **INTEGRAL HEMISPHERICAL EMISSIVITY, MONOCHROMATIC EMISSIVITY AT 0.65 MICRON, AND SPECIFIC ELECTRICAL RESISTANCE OF TITANIUM AND TANTALUM CARBIDES.**
PETROV, V. A. CHEKHOVSKOI, V. YA.
SHEINDLIN, A. E.
TR. VSES. NAUCH. - TEKH. KONF. TERMODIN., SB. DOKL.
SEKTS, 'TEPLOFIZ. SVOISTVA VISHCHESTV,' 3RD
237–43, 1969.

78247 **INVESTIGATION OF THE ORDERING OF (INDIUM ARSENIDE) - (CADMIUM TELLURIDE) AND (INDIUM ANTIMONIDE) - (CADMIUM TELLURIDE) SOLID SOLUTIONS ON THE BASIS OF THE OPTICAL INTERBAND ABSORPTION.**
SEMIKOLENOVA, N. A. SKOROBOGATOVA, L. A.
KHABAROV, E. N.
FIZ. TEKH. POLUPROV.
8 (8), 1498–1501, 1974.
(FOR ENGLISH TRANSLATION SEE E78261)

78261 **INVESTIGATION OF THE ORDERING OF (INDIUM ARSENIDE) - (CADMIUM TELLURIDE) AND (INDIUM ANTIMONIDE) - (CADMIUM TELLURIDE) SOLID SOLUTIONS ON THE BASIS OF THE OPTICAL INTERBAND ABSORPTION.**
SEMIKOLENOVA, N. A. SKOROBOGATOVA, L. A.
KHABAROV, E. N.
SOV. PHYS. SEMICOND.
8 (8), 976–7, 1975.
(ENGLISH TRANSLATION OF FIZ. TEKH. POLUPROV., 8 (8), 1498–1501, 1974; FOR ORIGINAL SEE E78247)

EPIC Number	Bibliographic Citation

78324 **THEORY OF OPTICAL ABSORPTION IN DISORDERED SEMICONDUCTORS DESCRIBED BY TWO-BAND MODEL.**
FEDIRKO, V. A.
FIZ. TEKH. POLUPROV.
8 (8), 1528–32, 1974.
(FOR ENGLISH TRANSLATION SEE E78325)

78325 **THEORY OF OPTICAL ABSORPTION IN DISORDERED SEMICONDUCTORS DESCRIBED BY TWO-BAND MODEL.**
FEDIRKO, V. A.
SOV. PHYS. SEMICOND.
8 (8), 995–7, 1975.
(ENGLISH TRANSLATION OF FIZ. TEKH. POLUPROV., 8 (8), 1528–32, 1974; FOR ORIGINAL SEE E78324)

78758 **QUANTUM THEORY OF OHMIC GALVANO- AND THERMAGNETIC EFFECTS IN SEMICONDUCTORS.**
ARORA, V. K. PETERSON, R. L.
PHYS. REV.
12 B (6), 2285–96, 1975.

78759 **ELECTRICAL RESISTANCE OF MOLYBDENUM - TUNGSTEN ALLOYS AT HIGH TEMPERATURES.**
VERTOGRADSKII, V. A.
IZV. AKAD. NAUK SSSR, METAL.
(4), 220–2, 1972.
(FOR ENGLISH TRANSLATION SEE E93228)

78825 **CONDUCTIVITY OF SOLID SODIUM POLYALUMINATE.**
BUKUN, N. G. LANIN, A. A. UKSHE, E. A.
ELEKTROKHIMIYA
8 (8), 1248–51, 1972.
(FOR ENGLISH TRANSLATION SEE E93207)

78826 **ELECTRICAL CONDUCTIVITY AND POLARIZATION OF ARSENIC SESQUISELENIDE - POTASSIUM SELENIDE SYSTEM MELTS.**
VELIKANOV, A. A. MUSTYATSA, O. N.
NOVIK, A. S.
ELEKTROKHIMIYA
7 (6), 827–30, 1971.
(FOR ENGLISH TRANSLATION SEE E93209)

78827 **CONDUCTIVITY OF A SOLID SILVER SULFIDE IODIDE ELECTROLYTE.**
SHIROKOV, YU. V. PUSHKOV, B. I.
BOROVKOV, V. S. LUKOVTSEV, P. D.
ELEKTROKHIMIYA
8 (4), 579–83, 1972.
(FOR ENGLISH TRANSLATION SEE E93210)

78856 **MEASUREMENTS OF THE OPTICAL ABSORPTION EDGE OF AIII-BV SEMICONDUCTORS.**
HORIG, W. FRIESLER, A.
EXP. TECH. PHYS.
19 (5), 337–43, 1971.

78966 **VISCOSITY AND ELECTRICAL RESISTIVITY OF CHROME - NICKEL ALLOYS.**
TYAGUNOV, G. V. BAUM, B. A. KUSHNIR, M. N.
SOV. PHYS. J.
16 (5), 725–7, 1973.
(ENGLISH TRANSLATION OF IZV. VYSSH. UCHEB. ZAVED., FIZ., 16 (5), 149–51, 1973; FOR ORIGINAL SEE E52569)

78977 **BAND STRUCTURE OF SOLID SOLUTIONS OF THE III - V - II - VI TYPE. I. OPTICAL PROPERTIES OF SOLID SOLUTIONS INDIUM ARSENIDE-CADMIUM TELLURIDE, DETERMINED BY THE INTERACTION OF LIGHT WITH FREE CARRIERS OF CURRENT.**
SEMIKOLENOVA, N. A. KHABAROV, E. N.
SOV. PHYS. J.
16 (6), 801–6, 1973.
(ENGLISH TRANSLATION OF IZV. VYSSH. UCHEB. ZAVED., FIZ., 16 (6), 76–82, 1973; FOR ORIGINAL SEE E50744)

78992 **GROWTH RATE AND PARAMETERS OF GALLIUM ARSENIDE AND INDIUM GALLIUM ARSENIDE FILMS IN RELATION TO SUBSTRATE ORIENTATION IN THE (111) - (100) RANGE (LIQUID EPITAXY).**
KULISH, U. M.
SOV. PHYS. J.
16 (6), 841–3, 1973.
(ENGLISH TRANSLATION OF IZV. VYSSH. UCHEB. ZAVED., FIZ., 16 (6), 121–3, 1973; FOR ORIGINAL SEE E51624)

78997 **SHORT TERM ELECTRICAL RELAXATION IN ALKALINE HALIDE CRYSTALS.**
D'YACHENKO, N. G. TYURIN, A. V.
SHEVELEVA, A. S.
SOV. PHYS. J.
16 (6), 824–8, 1973.
(ENGLISH TRANSLATION OF IZV. VYSSH. UCHEB. ZAVED., FIZ., 16 (6), 101–6, 1973; FOR ORIGINAL SEE E51623)

EPIC Number	Bibliographic Citation
79050	**DISPERSION OF THE COMPLEX CONDUCTIVITY IN DOPED POLYCRYSTALLINE BARIUM TITANATE.** BOGATINA, V. N. BOGATIN, A. S. PROKOPALO, O. I. SOV. PHYS. J. 16 (6), 781–4, 1973. (ENGLISH TRANSLATION OF IZV. VYSSH. UCHEB. ZAVED., FIZ., 16 (6), 52–6, 1973; FOR ORIGINAL SEE E 51621)
79073	**GALVANOMAGNETIC PROPERTIES OF MONOCARBIDES OF TRANSITION METALS OF THE IVA–VA SUBGROUPS.** BORUKHOVICH, A. S. GEL'D, P. V. STARTSEV, V. E. SOV. PHYS. J. 16 (5), 716–8, 1973. (ENGLISH TRANSLATION OF IZV. VYSSH. UCHEB. ZAVED., FIZ., 16 (5), 142–5, 1973; FOR ORIGINAL SEE E 50743)
79080	**INVESTIGATION OF ELECTRON CAPTURE PROCESSES IN RECRYSTALLIZED CADMIUM TELLURIDE: SELENIUM LAYERS.** GAVRILENKO, N. V. KATERENYUK, D. M. SOV. PHYS. J. 16 (5), 698–700, 1973. (ENGLISH TRANSLATION OF IZV. VYSSH. UCHEB. ZAVED., FIZ., 16 (5), 126–8, 1973; FOR ORIGINAL SEE E 51625)
79081	**DEPENDENCE OF THE MAGNETIC ANISOTROPY OF LITHIUM–ALUMINUM FERRITES ON DISTORTIONS OF THE CRYSTAL LATTICE.** STEL'MASHENKO, M. A. RUBAL'SKAYA, E. V. PEREVEEVA, A. I. SHLYAKHINA, L. P. NEKHOROSHEV, G. V. SOV. PHYS. J. 16 (5), 685–7, 1973. (ENGLISH TRANSLATION OF IZV. VYSSH. UCHEB. ZAVED., FIZ., 16 (5), 113–6, 1973; FOR ORIGINAL SEE E 50742)
79103	**STRUCTURE AND ELECTRICAL PROPERTIES OF THIN FILMS OF COPPER SELENIDE.** KOGUT, A. N. MEL'NIK, A. I. MIKOLAICHUK, A. G. ROMANISHIN, B. M. SOV. PHYS. J. 16 (8), 1113–6, 1973. (ENGLISH TRANSLATION OF IZV. VYSSH. UCHEB. ZAVED., FIZ., 16 (8), 90–4, 1973; FOR ORIGINAL SEE E 52570)
79136	**PHYSICAL PROPERTIES OF CHROMIUM VANADIUM SILICON SOLID SOLUTIONS AT LOW TEMPERATURES.** RYKOVA, M. A. SABIRZYANOV, A. V. GEL'D, P. V. SOV. PHYS. J. 16 (7), 1005–7, 1973. (ENGLISH TRANSLATION OF IZV. VYSSH. UCHEB. ZAVED., FIZ., 16 (7), 134–6, 1973; FOR ORIGINAL SEE E 51732)
79154	**THE BEHAVIOR OF COPPER IMPURITY IN CADMIUM TIN ARSENIDE.** VOEVODINA, O. V. VYATKIN, A. P. VOEVODIN, V. G. OTMAN, YA. I. OTS, V. L. SOV. PHYS. J. 16 (7), 923–7, 1973. (ENGLISH TRANSLATION OF IZV. VYSSH. UCHEB. ZAVED., FIZ., 16 (7), 39–44, 1973; FOR ORIGINAL SEE E51730)
79184	**RESISTIVITY AND THERMOELECTRIC POWER OF LIQUID ALLOYS CONTAINING TELLURIUM.** VALIANT, J. C. FABER, T. E. PHIL. MAG. 29 (3), 571–83, 1974.
79186	**IMPURITY PHOTOCONDUCTION IN N-TYPE BETA SILICON CARBIDE CRYSTALS.** ALTAISKII, YU. M. KALABUKOV, N. P. KISELEV, V. S. SOV. PHYS. J. 16 (7), 1012–3, 1973. (ENGLISH TRANSLATION OF IZV. VYSSH. UCHEB. ZAVED., FIZ., 16 (7), 139–40, 1973; FOR ORIGINAL SEE E51733)
79190	**SUPERCONDUCTIVITY IN ALKALINE EARTH METAL AND YTTRIUM INTERCALATED GROUP VI LAYERED DICHALCOGENIDES.** RAO, G. V. S. SHAFER, M. W. KAWARAZAKI, S. TOXEN, A. M. J. SOLID STATE CHEM. 9 (4), 323–9, 1974.
79248	**DIELECTRIC PROPERTIES, INFRARED SPECTRA, AND CHARGES ON ATOMS IN CUBIC OXIDES OF RARE EARTH METALS.** DULEPOV, E. V. BATSANOV, S. S. KUSTOVA, G. N. ZH. STRUKT. KHIM. 13 (5), 935–8, 1972. (ENGLISH TRANSLATION SEE E 90275)
79283	**DETERMINATION OF THE OPTICAL CONSTANTS OF GROUP IIA SULFIDES IN THE FAR ULTRAVIOLET REGIONS.** MIKHAILIN, V. V. POPOV, S. P. FEDOROV, G. M. VOP. OBSHCH. PRIKL. FIZ., TR. RESPUB. KONF., 2ND 223–5, 1972.
79418	**ELECTROLUMINESCENCE OF GALLIUM PHOSPHIDE IN THE VISIBLE SPECTRUM REGION.** SAMORUKOV, B. E. SOV. PHYS. J. 16 (4), 451–4, 1973. (ENGLISH TRANSLATION OF IZV. VYSSH. UCHEB. ZAVED., FIZ., 16 (4), 12–6, 1973; FOR ORIGINAL SEE E50115)
79428	**PHOTOCONDUCTIVITY AND PHOTOLUMINESCENCE IN BISMUTH OXYCHLORIDE CRYSTALS.** BLETSKAN, D. I. KOPINETS, I. F. RUBISH, I. D. TURYANITSA, I. I. SHTILIKHA, M. V. SOV. PHYS. J. 16 (5), 646–8, 1973. (ENGLISH TRANSLATION OF IZV. VYSSH. UCHEB. ZAVED., FIZ., 16 (5), 65–8, 1973; FOR ORIGINAL SEE E50741)
79432	**QUESTION OF THE TEMPERATURE DEPENDENCE OF THE STATIONARY INTENSITY OF RADICAL–RECOMBINATION LUMINESCENCE.** KHORUZHII, V. D. SIVOV, YU. A. NASLEDNIKOV, YU. M. SOV. PHYS. J. 16 (4), 587–9, 1973. (ENGLISH TRANSLATION OF IZV. VYSSH. UCHEB. ZAVED., FIZ., 16 (4), 151–4, 1973; FOR ORIGINAL SEE E50122)
79433	**PHOTOLUMINESCENCE OF SODIUM AND POTASSIUM NITRIDES.** GAVRISHCHENKO, YU. V. IVANOV, G. F. SOV. PHYS. J. 16 (4), 585–6, 1973. (ENGLISH TRANSLATION OF IZV. VYSSH. UCHEB. ZAVED., FIZ., 16 (4), 150–1, 1973; FOR ORIGINAL SEE E50121)
79434	**INTERBAND ABSORPTION OF LIGHT IN STRONGLY DOPED SEMICONDUCTORS.** SHKLOVSKII, B. I. EFROS, A. L. SOV. PHYS. JETP 32 (4), 733–8, 1971. (ENGLISH TRANSLATION OF ZH. EKSP. TEOR. FIZ., 59 (4), 1343–52, 1970; FOR ORIGINAL SEE E70339)
80067	**THERMIONIC EMISSION FROM PHOTOCATHODES.** COATES, P. B. J. PHYS. 5 D (8), 1489–98, 1972.
80226	**DIELECTRIC LOSS, OPTICAL ABSORPTION SPECTRA, AND ELECTRICAL CONDUCTIVITY OF LEAD-DOPED ALKALI HALIDES.** JAIN, S. C. SAI, K. S. K. LAL, K. J. PHYS. 4 C (14), 1958–62, 1971.
80277	**ELECTRIC CONDUCTIVITY OF MOLTEN MERCURY (II) IODIDE–MERCURY (II) BROMIDE AND MERCURY (II) IODIDE–ANTIMONY (III) IODIDE.** MENTUS, S. V. SUSIC, M. V. Z. NATURFORSCH., TEIL 30 A (3), 312–15, 1975.
80287	**THERMOELECTRIC POWER OF THE MOLTEN SYSTEMS (COPPER (I), M) CHLORIDE AND (COPPER (I), M) BROMIDE (M = SODIUM, POTASSIUM, RUBIDIUM, AND CESIUM).** PEZZATI, E. MAGISTRIS, A. SCHIRALDI, A. Z. NATURFORSCH., TEIL 30 A (3), 388–90, 1975.
80374	**SCHOTTKY–BARRIER SOLAR–CELL CALCULATIONS.** PULFREY, D. L. MC OUAT, R. F. APPL. PHYS. LETT. 24 (4), 167–9, 1974.
80382	**REFRACTIVE INDEX OF ALUMINUM, GALLIUM ARSENIDE BETWEEN 1.2 AND 1.8 EV.** CASEY, H. C., JR. SELL, D. D. PANISH, M. B. APPL. PHYS. LETT. (USA) 24 (2), 63–5, 1974.
80388	**TEMPERATURE DEPENDENCE OF A STATIC DIELECTRIC CONSTANT AND INFRARED DISPERSION FREQUENCY OF SODIUM AND POTASSIUM HALIDES.** UL'YANOV, V. L. BOTAKI, A. A. IZV. VYSSH. UCHEB. ZAVED., FIZ. 17 (1), 160, 1974. (FOR ENGLISH TRANSLATION SEE E95834)
80405	**EFFECT OF PREEXCITATION ON THE TEMPERATURE DEPENDENCE OF THE ELECTROLUMINESCENCE OF ZINC SULFIDE FILMS.** NUVAR'EVA, V. V. RAMAZANOV, P. E. IZV. VYSSH. UCHEB. ZAVED., FIZ. 17 (2), 131–3, 1974. (FOR ENGLISH TRANSLATION SEE E95258)

EPIC Number	Bibliographic Citation
80406	ACTION OF A WEAK ELECTRICAL FIELD ON THE THERMAL DEEXCITATION OF ZINC SULFIDE FILMS. NUVAR'EVA, V. V. RAMAZANOV, P. E. IZV. VYSSH. UCHEB. ZAVED., FIZ. 17 (2), 133–4, 1974. (FOR ENGLISH TRANSLATION SEE E95257)
80408	THERMOSTIMULATED ELECTRON EMISSION OF BERYLLIUM OXIDE AFTER X-IRRADIATION. KORTOV, V. S. GAPRINDASHVILLE, A. I. PILIPENKO, G. I. LAKHOV, V. M. IZV. VYSSH. UCHEB. ZAVED., FIZ. 17 (2), 154–5, 1974. (FOR ENGLISH TRANSLATION SEE E95255)
80409	X-RAY LUMINESCENCE OF ZINC SULFIDE SINGLE CRYSTALS ACTIVATED BY COPPER, SILVER, MANGANESE, AND THALLIUM. PUTIEV, I. T. CHENETS, V. N. TUKHLIBAEV, A. IZV. VYSSH. UCHEB. ZAVED., FIZ. 17 (2), 155–7, 1974. (FOR ENGLISH TRANSLATION SEE E95254)
80497	MAGNETIC SUSCEPTIBILITY AND ELECTRON PARAMAGNETIC RESONANCE SPECTRA OF TITANIUM OXIDES: CORRELATION OF MAGNETIC PARAMETERS WITH TRANSPORT PROPERTIES AND COMPOSITION. HOULIHAN, J. F. DANLEY, W. J. MULAY, L. N. J. SOLID STATE CHEM. 12 (3–4), 265–9, 1975.
80503	KRAMERS-KRONIG ANALYSIS. REVISED OPTICAL CONSTANTS OF SILVER CHLORIDE. BAUER, R. S. SPICER, W. E. WHITE, J. J., III J. OPT. SOC. AMER. 64 (6), 830–3, 1974.
80552	SILVER NEGATIVE CENTERS IN ALKALI HALIDES. V. SILVER-SODIUM CENTERS. KOJIMA, K. DOI, Y. KOJIMA, T. J. PHYS. SOC. JAP. 37 (1), 122–9, 1974.
80630	RESISTIVITY OF BISMUTH TELLURIDE FROM 1.3 TO 300 K. PAWLEWICZ, W. T. RAYNE, J. A. URE, R. W., JR. PHYS. LETT. 48 A (5), 391–2, 1974.
80748	SENSITIZED PHOTOLUMINESCENCE OF MANGANESE IN CALCIUM SULFATE PHOSPHORS. IVANOV, L. N. KARELIN, V. V. MIKHAILIN, V. V. PETROVA, I. YU. IZV. VYSSH. UCHEB. ZAVED., FIZ. 17 (5), 110–12, 1974. (FOR ENGLISH TRANSLATION SEE E95252)
80749	NEGATIVE RESISTANCE IN LEAD TIN TELLURIDE FILMS. KOVALYUK, Z. D. KONDRATENKO, M. M. MALIK, A. I. ORLETSKII, V. B. IZV. VYSSH. UCHEB. ZAVED., FIZ. 17 (5), 116–17, 1974. (FOR ENGLISH TRANSLATION SEE E95251)
80750	MAGNETIC PROPERTIES OF VANADIUM - SILICON WITH A STRUCTURAL TRANSITION. TTET'YAKOV, B. N. KODESS, B. N. KURITSIN, V. B. IZV. VYSSH. UCHEB. ZAVED., FIZ. 17 (5), 141–3, 1974. (FOR ENGLISH TRANSLATION SEE E95263)
80751	AMPHOTERIC IMPURITIES IN GALLIUM PHOSPHIDE. SAMORUKOV, B. E. IZV. VYSSH. UCHEB. ZAVED., FIZ. 17 (5), 155, 1974. (FOR ENGLISH TRANSLATION SEE E95262)
80752	USE OF THE CONTACT POTENTIAL DIFFERENCES METHOD FOR STUDYING THE MECHANISM OF THE RADICAL RECOMBINATION LUMINESCENCE OF ZINC OXIDE. STYROV, V. V. TOLMACHEV, V. M. IZV. VYSSH. UCHEB. ZAVED., FIZ. 17 (5), 157, 1974. (FOR ENGLISH TRANSLATION SEE E95261)
80753	ELECTRICAL CONDUCTIVITY AND THERMO ELECTROMOTIVE FORCE OF COBALTIC OXIDE AND COBALTOUS OXIDE DOPED WITH CHROMIUM AND SULFUR. SUNTSOV, N. V. SYMBELOV, V. D. IZV. VYSSH. UCHEB. ZAVED., FIZ. 17 (5), 158, 1974. (FOR ENGLISH TRANSLATION SEE E95260)
80756	CALCULATION OF THE PROPERTIES OF GARNETS BY THE CLUSTER COMPONENT METHOD. TALANOV, V. M. VOROB'EV, YU. P. MEN', A. N. LEVCHENKO, V. M. IZV. VUZ FIZ. (USSR) 17 (6), 126–9, 1974. (FOR ENGLISH TRANSLATION SEE E95249)
80826	IONICITY AND ELECTRICAL CONDUCTIVITY IN TRANSITION-METAL OXIDES. HUBNER, K. LEONHARDT, G. PHYS. STATUS SOLIDI 18 B (2), K175–9, 1975.
80889	MEASUREMENT OF THE THERMOELECTRIC PARAMETERS OF SEMICONDUCTORS BY A PULSED PROBE METHOD. BASIN, YU. G. GRITS, YU. A. ISACHENKO, V. I. PRIB. TEKH. EKSP. (6), 199, 1974. (FOR ENGLISH TRANSLATION SEE E94093)
80964	A NOVEL TECHNIQUE FOR MEASURING SMALL ABSORPTION COEFFICIENTS IN SEMICONDUCTOR INFRARED LASER WINDOW MATERIALS. NURMIKKO, A. V. APPL. PHYS. LETT. 26 (4), 175–8, 1975.
80965	OXYGEN SENSORS USING COBALT OXIDE CERAMICS. LOGOTHETIS, E. M. PARK, K. MEITZLER, A. H. LAUD, K. R. APPL. PHYS. LETT. 26 (4), 209–11, 1975.
80980	THE ELECTRIC CONDUCTIVITY OF ALUMINIUM NITRIDE AT TEMPERATURES BETWEEN 1100 AND 1700 C AND DIFFERENT NITROGEN PARTIAL PRESSURES. FISCHER, W. A. SCHUK, B. ARCH. EISENHUETTENWES. (GERMANY) 45 (11), 745–50, 1974.
81026	INDUCED EMISSION IN GALLIUM PHOSPHIDE. PYSHKIN, S. L. DOKL. AKAD. NAUK SSSR 219 (6), 1345–7, 1974. (FOR ENGLISH TRANSLATION SEE TPRC NO. E92633)
81141	THERMOELECTRIC PROPERTIES OF MATERIALS WITH NONSTANDARD MECHANISM OF CONDUCTIVITY. GOLIKOVA, O. A. FIZ. TEKH. POLUPROVODN. 8 (12), 2367–71, 1974. (FOR ENGLISH TRANSLATION SEE E92631)
81166	COMPARISON OF THE RESULTS OF STUDYING ELECTRON PARAMAGNETIC RESONANCE SIGNALS AND HIGH-TEMPERATURE MEASUREMENTS OF THE HALL EFFECT AND SPECIFIC ELECTRIC CONDUCTIVITY OF IRON-DOPED GALLIUM ARSENIDE SAMPLES. SUCHKOVA, N. I. SOLOV'EV, N. N. FIZ. TEKH. POLUPROVODN. 9 (1), 156–8, 1975. (FOR ENGLISH TRANSLATION SEE E94087)
81200	ASYMMETRY OF DOMAIN WALL MOVEMENT IN ORTHOFERRITE CRYSTALS. KANDAUROVA, G. S. VAS'LOVSKII, V. O. DERYAGIN, A. V. RAEV, V. K. PIS'MA ZH. EKSP. TEOR. FIZ. 19 (2), 132–5, 1974. (ENGLISH TRANSLATION SEE E 92399)
81202	DYNAMIC NEGATIVE DIFFERENTIAL CONDUCTIVITY IN HOMOGENEOUS ELECTRICALLY STABLE SEMICONDUCTORS. ZIL'BERMAN, P. E. ZH. ESKP. TEOR. FIZ. PIS'MA 19 (3), 182–5, 1974. (ENGLISH TRANSLATION SEE E 92401)
81213	SUPERCONDUCTIVITY OF BULK NIOBIUM GERMANIDE ABOVE 22 DEGREES K. MIHAILOV, N. N. VORONOVA, I. V. LAVROVA, O. A. MEL'NIKOV, E. V. SMIRNOVA, M. N. PIS'MA ZH. EKSP. TEOR. FIZ. 19 (8), 510–12, 1974. (ENGLISH TRANSLATION SEE E 92395)
81214	INJECTION LIGHT DIODES WITH BLUE AND GREEN GLOW CONSISTING OF LOW-RESISTANCE ZINC SULFIDE. PEKAR, G. S. SUK'YANCHIKOVA, N. B. HOANG, M. S. SHEINKMAN, M. K. PIS'MA ZH. EKSP. TEOR. FIZ. 19 (8), 513–16, 1974. (ENGLISH TRANSLATION SEE E 92373)
81216	ANOMALIES OF THE DISPERSION OF A CADMIUM SULFIDE SINGLE CRYSTAL IN THE EXCITON ABSORPTION REGION. BRODIN, M. S. DAVYDOVA, N. A. STRASHNIKOVA, M. I. PIS'MA ZH. EKSP. TEOR. FIZ. 19 (9), 567–71, 1974. (FOR ENGLISH TRANSLATION SEE E92375)
81218	LIGHT EMISSION BY SEMICONDUCTORS AND DIELECTRICS EXCITED BY AN ELECTRIC FIELD. BASOV, N. G. MOLCHANOV, A. G. NASIBOV, A. S. OBIDIN, A. Z. PECHENOV, A. N. POPOV, YU. M. PIS'MA ZH. EKSP. TEOR. FIZ. 19 (10), 650–4, 1974. (ENGLISH TRANSLATION SEE E 92378)

EPIC Number	Bibliographic Citation

81222 **TRANSTHRESHOLD SUSCEPTIBILITY IN ANTIFERROMAGNETIC MANGANESE CARBONATE AND CESIUM MANGANESE CARBONATE AND CESIUM MANGANESE FLUORIDE DURING PARAMETRIC EXCITATION SPIN WAVES.**
KVEDER, V. V. PROZOROVA, L. A.
PIS'MA ZH. EKSP. TEOR. FIZ.
19 (11), 683-6, 1974.
(FOR ENGLISH TRANSLATION SEE E92382)

81223 **DEFORMATION-STIMULATED LUMINESCENCE OF ZINC SULFIDE CRYSTALS.**
BREDIKHIN, S. I. SHMURAK, S. Z.
PIS'MA ZH. EKSP. TEOR. FIZ.
19 (12), 709-13, 1974.
(FOR ENGLISH TRANSLATION SEE E92383)

81226 **MECHANISM OF RADIATIVE RECOMBINATION IN HEAVILY DOPED P-GALLIUM ARSENIDE.**
ZVEREV, L. P. KRUZHAEV, V. V.
NEGASHEV, S. A.
PIS'MA ZH. EKSP. TEOR. FIZ.
20 (1), 52-6, 1974.
(FOR ENGLISH TRANSLATION SEE E92356)

81227 **MANIFESTATION OF DOMAIN INSTABILITY AND FRANZ-KELDYSH EFFECT IN THE RECOMBINATION RADIATION OF CADMIUM SULFIDE SINGLE CRYSTALS.**
KROLEVETS, N. M. LEPSVERIDZE, D. S.
SAL'KOV, E. A. SHEPEL'SKII, G. A.
PIS'MA ZH. EKSP. TEOR. FIZ.
20 (1), 56-8, 1974.
(FOR ENGLISH TRANSLATION SEE E92357)

81228 **SUPERCONDUCTING AND MAGNETIC PROPERTIES OF TERNARY MOLYBDENUM CHALCOGENIDES.**
ALEKSEEVSKII, N. E. DOBROVOL'SKII, N. M.
TSEBRO, V. I.
PIS'MA ZH. EKSP. TEOR. FIZ.
20 (1), 59-63, 1974.
(FOR ENGLISH TRANSLATION SEE E92358)

81231 **NONCOLLINEARITY OF SUBLATTICES AND EXISTENCE OF DOMAIN STRUCTURE IN HIGH MAGNETIZATION FIELDS IN DYSPROSIUM IRON OXIDE NEAR THE MAGNETIC COMPENSATION POINT.**
LISOVSKII, F. V. SHAPOVALOV, V. I.
PIS'MA ZH. EKSP. TEOR. FIZ.
20 (2), 128-32, 1974.
(FOR ENGLISH TRANSLATION SEE E92361)

81232 **TEMPERATURE HYSTERESIS OF THE MAGNETIZATION IN ORTHOFERRITES AT THE COMPENSATION POINT.**
DERKACHENKO, V. N. KADOMTSEVA, A. M.
TIMOFEEVA, V. A. KHOKHLOV, V. A.
PIS'MA ZH. EKSP. TEOR. FIZ.
20 (4), 236-9, 1974.
(FOR ENGLISH TRANSLATION SEE E92362)

81234 **DETECTION OF THE FERROMAGNETIC STATE IN ANTIFERROMAGNETIC ALLOYS OF THE IRON MANGANESE ARSENIDE SYSTEM.**
GALKIN, A. A. ZAVADSKII, E. A.
SMIRNOV, V. M. VAL'KOV, V. I.
PIS'MA ZH. EKSP. TEOR. FIZ.
20 (4), 253-6, 1974.
(FOR ENGLISH TRANSLATION SEE E92364)

81235 **POSSIBLE FOCUSING AND SELF-FOCUSING OF LIGHT BEAMS IN A SEMICONDUCTOR AS A CONSEQUENCE OF A CHANGE IN THE ELECTRON PART OF ITS DIELECTRIC CONSTANT.**
MAEV, R. G. PADO, G. S. POLUEKTOV, I. A.
PUSTOVOIT, V. I.
PIS'MA ZH. EKSP. TEOR. FIZ.
20 (4), 256-60, 1974.
(FOR ENGLISH TRANSLATION SEE E92365)

81236 **MAGNETIC PROPERTIES OF NICKEL IODIDE BORACITE.**
ZHELUDEV, I. S. PEREKALINA, T. M.
SMIRNOVSKAYA, E. M. FONTON, S. S.
YARMUKHAMEDOV, YU. N.
PIS'MA ZH. EKSP. TEOR. FIZ.
20 (5), 289-92, 1974.
(ENGLISH TRANSLATION SEE E 92366)

81237 **METAMAGNETIC TRANSITION IN IRON (II) CHLORIDE POLARIZED BY NEUTRONS IN A WIDE TEMPERATURE RANGE.**
TRUNOV, V. A. EGOROV, A. I. DMITRIEV, R. P.
UL'YANOV, V. A. KRAVTSOVA, M. E.
KRAVTSOVA, M. E.
PIS'MA ZH. EKSP. TEOR. FIZ.
20 (5), 312-16, 1974.
(ENGLISH TRANSLATION SEE E 92367)

81273 **THERMOELECTRIC POWER AND EFFECTIVE MASS OF ELECTRONS IN GALLIUM ARSENIC PHOSPHIDE SOLID SOLUTIONS.**
GORCHAK, L. V. NEGRESKUL, V. V.
BALEKA, E. S. CHEBAN, A. G.
FIZ. TEKH. POLUPROV.
9 (1), 171-4, 1975.
(FOR ENGLISH TRANSLATION SEE E94088)

81289 **OPTICAL MODE GAMMAS, PRESSURE DERIVATIVES OF ELASTIC AND DIELECTRIC CONSTANTS, AND STABILITY OF RUTILE-STRUCTURE FLUORIDES IN THE RIGID ION APPROXIMATION.**
STRIEFLER, M. E. BARSCH, G. R.
PHYS. STATUS SOLIDI
64 B (2), 613-25, 1974.

81330 **THERMOEMF. OF SILVER CHALCOGENIDE MELTS.**
KUSNITSYNA, T. A. PETRENKO, L. V.
EICHIS, B. A. VELIKANOV, A. A.
IZV. VYSSH. UCHEBN. ZAVED., TSVETN. METALL.
17 (5), 62-4, 1974.

81367 **LOW TEMPERATURE MAGNETIC SUSCEPTIBILITY OF URANIUM TETRACHLORIDE. ERRATUM.**
GRUBER, J. B. HECHT, H. G.
J. CHEM. PHYS.
62 (1), 311-12, 1975.

81407 **OPTICAL PROPERTIES OF ZINC OXIDE SINGLE CRYSTALS GROWN BY A HYDROTHERMAL METHOD.**
NIKITENKO, V. A. KAZANDZHIEV, S. A.
DIMOVA-ALYAKOVA, D. I. KUZ'MINA, I. P.
ZH. PRIKL. SPEKTROSK.
21 (2), 315-19, 1974.
(FOR ENGLISH TRANSLATION SEE E95806)

81418 **THEORETICAL DETERMINATION OF THE OPTICAL CONSTANTS OF WEAKLY ABSORBING THIN FILMS.**
LEDDELL, H. M.
J. PHYS.
7 D (11), 1588-96, 1974.

81475 **PRESSURE AND TEMPERATURE DEPENDENCE OF THE STATIC DIELECTRIC CONSTANT OF POTASSIUM BROMIDE.**
SMITH, P. A. RIEHL, D. H.
J. PHYS. CHEM. SOLIDS
35 (9), 1327-31, 1974.

81483 **THERMAL EMISSION PROPERTIES OF ZIRCONIUM CARBIDE - RHENIUM COMPOSITIONS.**
MATSKEVICH, T. L. KRACHINO, T. V.
VIL'K, YU. N.
SOV. PHYS. TECH. PHYS.
18 (7), 981-4, 1974.
(ENGLISH TRANSLATION OF ZH. TEKH. FIZ., 43 (7), 1554-9, 1973; FOR ORIGINAL SEE E71775)

81520 **EFFECT OF PLASTIC DEFORMATION ON THE OPTICAL PROPERTIES OF POTASSIUM CHLORIDE - EUROPIUM CRYSTAL PHOSPHORS.**
KALABUKHOV, N. P. KOVALEV, V. K.
SOV. PHYS. SOLID STATE
15 (2), 385, 1973.
(ENGLISH TRANSLATION OF FIZ. TVERD. TELA, 15 (2), 557-8, 1973; FOR ORIGINAL SEE E71644)

81547 **REFRACTIVE INDEX OF GALLIUM ALUMINUM ARSENIDE.**
AFROMOWITZ, M. A.
SOLID STATE COMMUN.
15 (1), 59-63, 1974.

81628 **OPTICAL ABSORPTION OF THE MIXED COMPOUND GALLIUM-ALUMINUM ANTIMONY NEAR THE ABSORPTION EDGE.**
ANCE, C. ROBIN, J. NGUYEN VAN MAU, A.
BOUGNOT, G.
SOLID STATE COMMUN.
15 (8), 1295-8, 1974.

81640 **ELECTRICAL RESISTIVITY OF SOME LIQUID CADMIUM-ANTIMONY ALLOYS AS A FUNCTION OF TEMPERATURE.**
GASSER, J. G. KLEIM, R.
J. PHYS. (PARIS), LETT.
36 (4), 93-5, 1975.

81696 **REFRACTIVE INDEX VARIATIONS IN PROTON-BOMBARDED FUSED SILICA.**
PRESBY, W. M. BROWN, W. L.
APPL. PHYS. LETT. (USA)
24 (10), 511-13, 1974.

81762 **ZEEMAN EFFECT OF THE COPPER DIPOSITIVE ION CENTER IN CUBIC ZINC SULFIDE.**
WOEHLECKE, M.
J. PHYS.
7 C (14), 2557-68, 1974.

81763 **LATTICE DYNAMICS OF MAGNESIUM FLUORIDE.**
ALMAIRAC, R. BENOIT, C.
J. PHYS.
7 C (15), 2614-29, 1974.

81843 **FARADAY EFFECT AND ABSORPTION SPECTRA DUE TO FREE CARRIERS IN CADMIUM SELENIDE.**
VOLKOV, V. V. VOLKOVA, L. V. KIREEV, P. S.
SOV. PHYS. SEMICOND.
7 (4), 478-9, 1973.
(ENGLISH TRANSLATION OF FIZ. TEKH. POLUPROV., 7 (4), 685-7, 1973; FOR ORIGINAL SEE E71715)

EPIC Number	Bibliographic Citation

82121 **CHANGES IN THE ANOMALOUS PHOTOVOLTAIC EFFECT WITH INCREASING THICKNESS OF CADMIUM TELLURIDE FILMS EVAPORATED OBLIQUELY IN HIGH VACUUM.**
VYVENKO, O. F. STRAKHOV, L. P.
SOV. PHYS. SEMICOND.
7 (3), 427–8, 1973.
(ENGLISH TRANSLATION OF FIZ. TEKH. POLUPROV., 7 (3), 615–7, 1973; FOR ORIGINAL SEE E71709)

82255 **THERMOEMISSION PROPERTIES OF REFRACTORY METAL BORIDES.**
SAMSONOV, G. V. FOMENKO, V. S.
KUNITSKII, YU. A.
REV. INT. HAUTES TEMP. REFRACT.
10 (1), 11–14, 1973.

82265 **EDGE ADBSORPTION IN ALUMINUM ANTIMONIDE.**
SIROTA, N. N. LUKOMSKII, A. I.
SOV. PHYS. SEMICOND.
7 (1), 140–1, 1973.
(ENGLISH TRANSLATION OF FIZ. TEKH. POLUPROV., 7 (1), 196–8, 1973; FOR ORIGINAL SEE E71681)

82272 **THERMAL CONDUCTIVITY AND THERMOELECTRIC POWER OF MERCURY CADMIUM TELLURIDE SOLID SOLUTIONS AT LOW TEMPERATURES.**
ALIEV, S. A.
SOV. PHYS. SEMICOND.
7 (1), 115–6, 1973.
(ENGLISH TRANSLATION OF FIZ. TEKH. POLUPROV., 7 (1), 168–70, 1973; FOR ORIGINAL SEE E71674)

82405 **ABSORPTION OF MICROWAVE POWER IN N-TYPE INDIUM ANTIMONIDE AT LOW TEMPERATURES.**
ARENDARCHUK, V. V. GERSHENZON, E. M.
LITVAK-GORSKAYA, L. B.
SOV. PHYS. SEMICOND.
7 (1), 89–93, 1973.
(ENGLISH TRANSLATION OF FIZ. TEKH. POLUPROV., 7 (1), 132–7, 1973; FOR ORIGINAL SEE E71670)

82666 **CALCULATION OF HIGH-FREQUENCY DIELECTRIC CONSTANTS OF ALKALI HALIDE CRYSTALS.**
GOYAL, S. C. SHANKER, J.
CURR. SCI.
42 (5), 164, 1973.

82686 **FERROELECTRIC, PIEZOELECTRIC, AND ELECTROOPTIC MATERIALS.**
COOK, W. R., JR.
DIGEST OF LITERATURE ON DIELECTRICS
35, 701PP., 1971.

82778 **EMISSION MECHANISM FOR LANTHANUM HEXABORIDE CATHODES.**
KUZNETSOVA, G. M. KUDINTSEVA, G. A.
BULL. ACAD. SCI. USSR, PHYS. SER.
37 (12), 33–6, 1973.
(ENGLISH TRANSLATION OF IZV. AKAD. NAUK SSSR, SER. FIZ., 37 (12), 2508–12, 1973; FOR ORIGINAL SEE E71959)

82779 **CARBIDE EMITTERS WITH IMPROVED THERMIONIC PROPERTIES.**
KAN, KH. S. KUL'VARSKAYA, B. V.
BULL. ACAD. SCI. USSR, PHYS. SER.
37 (12), 37–41, 1973.
(ENGLISH TRANSLATION OF IZV. AKAD. NAUK SSSR, SER. FIZ., 37 (12), 2513–7, 1973; FOR ORIGINAL SEE E71960)

82820 **DIRECT CONVERSION OF SOLAR LIGHT ENERGY INTO ELECTRICITY.**
GREAVES, C.
PHYS. EDUC.
5 (2), 100–5, 1970.

83168 **ON MEASURING THE CONDUCTIVITY AND HALL COEFFICIENT OF SEMICONDUCTOR SINGLE CRYSTALS BY THE FOUR-POINT PROBE METHOD.**
KON'KOV, V. L. KUKUI, A. S. POLYAKOV, N. N.
BULL. ACAD. SCI. SSSR, PHYS. SER.
36 (3), 545–7, 1972.
(ENGLISH TRANSLATION OF IZV. AKAD. NAUK SSSR, SER. FIZ., 36 (3), 603–6, 1972; FOR ORIGINAL SEE E76387)

83375 **MAGNETIC PROPERTIES OF THE CADMIUM GERMANIUM ARSENIDE PHOSPHIDE SYSTEM.**
BAIDAKOV, L. A. KOUZOVA, N. I.
OSMANOV, E. O.
ZH. PRIKL. KHIM. (LENINGRAD)
46 (1), 28–31, 1973.
(FOR ENGLISH TRANSLATION SEE E90273)

83498 **HIGH FFEQUENCY INSTABILITY OF RECOMBINED RADIATION IN STRONG ELECTRIC FIELDS.**
VRODOVOI, V. A. GOZAK, A. CH. PEKA, G. P.
ZH. ESKP. TEOR. FIZ. PIS'MA
19 (7), 445–7, 1974.
(ENGLISH TRANSLATION SEE E 92391)

83516 **THERMOELECTRIC PROPERTIES OF P-TYPE LEAD TELLURIDE - LEAD SELENIDE ALLOYS.**
KUDMAN, I.
J. MATER. SCI.
7 (9), 1027–9, 1972.

EPIC Number	Bibliographic Citation

83519 **MEASUREMENTS OF THE ABSORPTION OF LIGHT IN LOW-LOSS LIQUIDS.**
STONE, J.
J. OPT. SOC. AMER.
62 (3), 327–33, 1972.

83537 **EXPERIMENTAL VERIFICATION OF THE KRAMERS-KRONIG RELATION BETWEEN INDEXES OF REFRACTION AND ABSORPTION.**
CANIT, J. C. BILLARDON, M. BADOZ, J.
J. PHYS. (PARIS)
32 (8), 691–7, 1971.

83589 **FREQUENCY DEPENDENCE OF CONDUCTIVITY IN HOPPING SYSTEMS.**
JONSCHER, A. K.
J. NON-CRYST. SOLIDS
8–10, 293–315, 1972.

83792 **ENERGY BANDS AND THE OPTICAL PROPERTIES OF LITHIUM CHLORIDE.**
KUNZ, A. B.
PHYS. REV.
[3] 2 B (12), 5015–24, 1970.

83795 **THERMOELECTRIC POWER OF COPPER GOLD AS A FUNCTION OF SHORTRANGE ORDER.**
WANG, K.-P. AMAR, H.
PHYS. REV.
3 (4), 1499–501, 1971.

83801 **ENERGY BANDS AND OPTICAL PROPERTIES OF SODIUM CHLORIDE.**
LIPARI, N. O. KUNZ, A. B.
PHYS. REV.
[3] 3 B (2), 491–7, 1971.

83843 **PHOTO-TRANSMISSION OF POTASSIUM CHLORIDE TABLET.**
NAKATAO, T. SAKATE, K.
FUKUI DAIGAKU KOGAKUBU KENKYU HOKOKU
18 (1), 49–56, 1970.

83872 **WIDE-BAND II-VI SEMICONDUCTORS AND THE PROSPECTS OF THEIR APPLICATION.**
GEORGOBIANI, A. N.
USP. FIZ. NAUK
113 (1–2), 129–55, 1974.
(FOR ENGLISH TRANSLATION SEE E91448)

83952 **TRANSPORT PROPERTIES OF TETRAHEDRALLY BONDED AMORPHOUS SEMICONDUCTORS.**
MELL, H.
AMORPHOUS LIQ. SEMICOND., PROC. INT. CONF., 5TH
1, 203–24, 1974.

83966 **EFFECT OF PREPARATION CONDITIONS AND OF OXYGEN AND HYDROGEN ON THE PROPERTIES OF AMORPHOUS SILICON.**
LE COMBER, P. G. LOVELAND, R. J.
SPEAR, W. E. VAUGHAN, R. A.
AMORPHOUS LIQ. SEMICOND., PROC. INT. CONF., 5TH
1, 245–50, 1974.
(EDITED BY J. STUKE, WILHELM BRENIG; TAYLOR AND FRANCIS: LONDON, ENGLAND)

83981 **AMORPHOUS GROUP III CHALCOGENIDES.**
WOOD, C. GILBERT, L. R. GARNER, C. M.
SHAFFER, J. C.
AMORPHOUS LIQ. SEMICOND., PROC. INT. CONF., 5TH
1, 285–95, 1974.
(EDITED BY J. STUKE, W. BRENIG; TAYLOR AND FRANCIS: LONDON, ENGLAND)

84003 **MAGNETIC TRANSITION AND ANOMALOUS THERMAL EXPANSION IN RARE EARTH - IRON COMPOUNDS.**
GIVORD, D. LEMAIRE, R.
IEEE TRANS. MAGN.
10 (2), 109–13, 1974.

84007 **CONDUCTION IN LOCALIZED BAND-TAIL AND IN EXTENDED STATES. I. TRANSPORT IN AMORPHOUS ARSENIC TELLURIDE.**
GRANT, A. J. MOUSTAKAS, T. D. PENNEY, T.
WEISER, K.
AMORPHOUS LIQ. SEMICOND., PROC. INT. CONF., 5TH
1, 325–33, 1974.

84029 **EVOLUTION OF THE THERMOELECTRIC PROPERTIES OF CUPROUS SELENIDE AS A FUNCTION OF ITS STOICHIOMETRIC INDEX.**
ROUTIE, R. SUDRES, M. MAHENC, J.
REV. CHIM. MINER.
7 (4), 713–21, 1970.

84032 **CONDUCTIVITY OF SOME SIQUID SEMICONDUCTORS AS A FUNCTION OF CURRENT FREQUENCY, TEMPERATURE, AND STRONG ELECTRIC FIELD.**
ANDREEV, A. A.
AMORPHOUS LIQ. SEMICOND., PROC. INT. CONF., 5TH
1, 343–8, 1974.

84126 **ABSORPTION NEAR THE ABSORPTION EDGE OF A THALLIUM ARSENIDE SULFIDE SYSTEM.**
CHLEBNY, J. KOSEK, F.
COLLECT. CZECH. CHEM. COMMUN.
39 (5), 1125–30, 1974.

EPIC Number	Bibliographic Citation
84222	FORMATION OF FERRITES FROM SIMULTANEOUSLY PRECIPITATED HYDROXIDES STUDIED BY NUCLEAR GAMMA-RESONANCE. BELOZERSKII, G. N. BAIKOV, M. V. BOLDYREV, V. V. MURIN, A. N. PAVLYUKHIN, YU. T. SVIRIDOV, V. V. KINET. KATAL. 15 (4), 929–34, 1974. (FOR ENGLISH TRANSLATION SEE E91472)
84223	DETERMINATION OF THE NATURE OF ACTIVE CENTERS IN ALUMINUM OXIDE BY A THERMAL DEEXCITATION METHOD. FEDCHUK, A. P. MIKHO, V. V. KINET. KATAL. 15 (2), 534–5, 1974. (FOR ENGLISH TRANSLATION SEE E91473)
84318	INHOMOGENEOUS MODEL FOR LIQUID SEMICONDUCTORS. HODGKINSON, R. J. AMORPHOUS LIQ. SEMICOND., PROC. INT. CONF., 5TH 2, 841–7, 1974. (EDITED BY J. STUKE, W. BRENIG; TAYLOR AND FRANCIS: LONDON, ENGLAND)
84453	POLARONS IN LIQUID SEMICONDUCTORS. CUTLER, M. AMORPHOUS LIQ. SEMICOND., PROC. INT. CONF., 5TH 2, 1287–93, 1974. (EDITED BY J. STUKE, WILHELM BRENIG; TAYLOR AND FRANCIS: LONDON, ENGLAND)
84454	ELECTRONIC PROPERTIES OF LIQUID SELENIUM-TELLURIUM. MAHDJURI, F. AMORPHOUS LIQ. SEMICOND., PROC. INT. CONF., 5TH 2, 1295–303, 1974.
84459	PHOTOTHERMOPOWER IN AMORPHOUS CHALCOGENIDE ALLOY FILMS. ROCKSTAD, H. K. FLASCK, R. AMORPHOUS LIQ. SEMICOND., PROC. INT. CONF., 5TH 2, 1311–15, 1974.
84584	FAR ULTRAVIOLET ELECTRONIC SPECTRA OF STRONTIUM FLUORIDE AND BARIUM FLUORIDE. NISAR, M. ROBIN, S. PAK, J. SCI. IND. RES. 17 (2–3), 49–54, 1974.
84594	PHYSICAL PROPERTIES OF BORON CARBIDE ALLOYS WITH VANADIUM AND CHROMIUM ADDITIVES. MAREK, E. V. DUDNIK, E. M. MAKARENKO, G. N. REMENYUK, E. A. POROSHK. METALL. (2), 54–6, 1975. (FOR ENGLISH TRANSLATION SEE E93217)
84631	AMORPHOUS SEMICONDUCTORS. ADLER, D. CRIT. REV. SOLID STATE SCI. 2 (3), 317–465, 1971.
84752	SOLUTION OF THE POTENTIAL IN A SEMICONDUCTOR WITH EXPONENTIALLY DEPTH-DEPENDENT CONDUCTIVITY AND APPLICATION TO FOUR-POINT-PROBE MEASUREMENTS. FRANKS, R. F. ROBERTSON, J. B. LANGLEY RES. CENTER, NASA, HAMPTON, VA. 15PP., 1971. (NASA-TN-D-6504)
84840	EFFECT OF DOPING BY TRANSITION METALS ON THE PHYSICAL-CHEMICAL PROPERTIES OF SILVER SELENIDE. KRESTOVNIKOV, A. N. GORBACHEV, V. V. OKHOTIN, A. S. MALYUTINA, G. L. IZV. VYSSH. UCHEB. ZAVED., TSVET. MET. 17 (2), 125–8, 1974.
84846	MAGNETIC SUSCEPTIBILITY MEASUREMENTS. GREGSON, A. K. ELECTRON. STRUCT. MAGN. INORG. COMPOUNDS 3, 153–217, 1974.
85089	MAGNETIZATION OF HEXAGONAL FERROMAGNETS WITH SINGLE-ION ANISOTROPY. PUTIN, N. N. KAZAKOV, A. V. CHISTYAKOV, N. L. TEOR. MAT. FOZ. 20 (1), 126–32, 1974. (FOR ENGLISH TRANSLATION SEE E91490)
85290	ON THE THEORY OF OPTICAL ABSORPTION IN NARROW-GAP DISORDERED SEMICONDUCTORS. FEDIRKO, V. A. PHYS. STATUS SOLIDI (GERMANY) 18 B (2), 775–82, 1975.
85293	POLAR AND IONIC FLUIDS AT HIGH PRESSURES AND TEMPERATURES. FRANCK, E. U. PURE APPL. CHEM. 38 (4), 449–68, 1974.
85322	ELECTRONIC SPECTRUM OF CRYSTALLINE LITHIUM FLUORIDE. ROESSLER, D. M. WALKER, W. C. J. PHYS. CHEM. SOLIDS 28, 1507–15, 1967.
85339	ON THE PREPARATION, OPTICAL PROPERTIES AND ELECTRICAL BEHAVIOUR OF ALUMINIUM NITRIDE. COX, G. A. CUMMINS, D. O. KAWABE, K. TREDGOLD, R. H. J. PHYS. CHEM. SOLIDS 28, 543–8, 1967.
85350	SPIN FLIP TRANSITIONS IN CUBIC MAGNETIC SUBSTANCES. THE MAGNETIC PHASE DIAGRAM OF TERBIUM - YTTRIUM IRON GARNETS. BELOV, K. P. ZVEZDIN, A. K. LEVITIN, R. Z. MARKOSYAN, A. S. MILL', B. V. MUKHIN, A. A. PEROV, A. P. ZH. EKSP. TEOR. FIZ. 68 (3), 1189–202, 1975. (FOR ENGLISH TRANSLATION SEE E94077)
85351	AN INVESTIGATION OF THE PREPARATION AND PROPERTIES OF SOME 111A-VB COMPOUNDS. HISCOCKS, S. E. R. MULLIN, J. B. J. MATER. SCI. 4, 962–73, 1969.
85352	LINE SPECTRA OF THE INFRARED LUMINESCENCE OF CUBIC SILICON CARBIDE CRYSTALS. GORBAN', I. S. SLOBODYANYUK, A. V. ZH. ESKP. TEOR. FIZ. PIS'MA 21 (5), 263–6, 1975. (FOR ENGLISH TRANSLATION SEE E94096)
85354	ELECTRIC FIELD INFLUENCE ON DEFORMATION INDUCED LUMINESCENCE OF ZINC SULFIDE CRYSTALS. BREDIKHIN, S. I. SHMURAK, S. Z. ZH. ESKP. TEOR. FIZ. PIS'MA 21 (6), 342–5, 1975. (ENGLISH TRANSLATION SEE E 92369)
85355	VARIATION IN CONDUCTIVITY OF SEMICONDUCTORS ACCOMPANYING A HIGH FREQUENCY FIELD EFFECT. KALASHNIKOV, S. G. MOROZOV, A. I. FEDOSOV, V. I. ANISIMKIN, V. I. ZH. ESKP. TEOR. FIZ. PIS'MA 21 (6), 349–52, 1975. (FOR ENGLISH TRANSLATION SEE E92370)
85398	ABSORPTION EDGE OF CADMIUM ANTIMONY. ZAVETOVA, M. CZECH. J. PHYS. 14 B 615–21, 1964.
85403	SEMICONDUCTING PROPERTIES OF CADMIUM PHOSPHIDE. ZDANOWICZ, W. WOJAKOWSKI, A. PHYS. STATUS SOLIDI 16, K129–31, 1966.
85417	OPTICAL PROPERTIES OF SODIUM AND LITHIUM HALIDE CRYSTALS AT 55 K. BALDINI, G. BOSACCHI, B. PHYS. STATUS SOLIDI 38, 325–34, 1970.
85421	DIELECTRIC PROPERTIES OF POTASSIUM CHLORIDE, POTASSIUM BROMIDE, AND POTASSIUM IODIDE SINGLE CRYSTALS IN THE EXTREME ULTRAVIOLET UP TO 35 ELECTRON VOLTS. BLECHSCHMIDT, D. KLUCKER, R. SKIBOWSKI, M. PHYS. STATUS SOLIDI 36, 625–34, 1969.
85428	INDIRECT ENERGY GAP IN GALLIUM SELENIDE AND GALLIUM SULFIDE. AULICH, E. BREBNER, J. L. MOOSER, E. PHYS. STATUS SOLIDI 31, 129–31, 1969.
85431	HIGH TEMPERATURE ELECTRICAL CONDUCTIVITY OF CADMIUM TELLURIDE. HOSCHL, P. PHYS. STATUS SOLIDI 13, K101–4, 1966.
85433	THE ELECTRONIC STRUCTURE OF CADMIUM CHALCOGENIDES. II. SPECTRAL DISTRIBUTION OF OPTICAL CONSTANTS. ALTWEIN, M. FINKENRATH, H. KONAK, C. STUKE, J. ZIMMERER, G. PHYS. STATUS SOLIDI 29, 203–9, 1968.
85438	ABSORPTION EDGE OF ZINC ANTIMONIDE. ZAVETOVA, M. PHYS. STATUS SOLIDI 5, K19–21, 1964.
85443	ANISOTROPY OF EDGE ABSORPTION AND PHOTOLUMINESCENCE OF TETRAGONAL ZINC PHOSPHIDE AND CADMIUM PHOSPHIDE SINGLE CRYSTALS. SOBOLEV, V. V. SYRBU, N. N. PHYS. STATUS SOLIDE 43 B K87–91, 1971.
85455	ATOMIC REARRANGEMENT PROCESS IN THE COPPER - GOLD ALLOY COPPER GOLD. II. JONES, F. W. SYKES, C. PROC. ROY. SOC. 166 A, 376–90, 1938.

EPIC Number | Bibliographic Citation

85671 **EFFECT OF AN ELECTRIC FIELD AND THERMIONIC EMISSION CURRENT ON BARIUM OXIDE: EVAPORATION OF THE COMPONENTS AND THE WORK FUNCTION.**
PIKUS, G. YA. TETERYA, V. P.
BULL. ACAD. SCI., USSR, PHYS. SER.
35 (5), 942-9, 1971.
(ENGLISH TRANSLATION OF IZV. AKAD. NAUK SSSR, SER. FIZ., 35 (5), 1023-30, 1971; FOR ORIGINAL SEE E76365)

85675 **REASONS FOR THE UNSTABLE ELECTRON EMISSION FROM THIN DISPERSED FILMS OF BARIUM OXIDE-ACTIVATED GOLD.**
SUKHARIER, A. S. ZAGREBNEVA, S. V.
BULL. ACAD. SCI., USSR, PHYS. SER.
35 (2), 274-7, 1971.
(ENGLISH TRANSLATION OF IZV. AKAD. NAUK SSSR, SER. FIZ., 35 (2), 298-301, 1971; FOR ORIGINAL SEE E76354)

85734 **MEASUREMENT OF 10.6-MU CARBON DIOXIDE LASER TRANSITION PROBABILITY AND OPTICAL BROADENING CROSS SECTIONS.**
GERRY, E. T. LEONARD, D. A.
APPL. PHYS. LETT.
8 (9), 227-9, 1966.

85756 **PLZT(LIGHT VALVE PROJECTOR DISPLAY).**
KHALAFALLA, A. BURBANK, D. ROSE, A.
HONEYWELL, INC., MINNEAPOLIS, MINN.
40PP., 1975.
(N75-25717, AD-A008 281, AFAL-TR-74-344)

85819 **ELECTRICAL AND OPTICAL PROPERTIES OF ZINC SULFIDE CRYSTALS IN POLARIZED LIGHT.**
BEUN, J. A. GOLDSMITH, G. J.
HELV. PHYS. ACTA
33, 508-13, 1960.

85844 **REFLECTION SPECTRA OF ZINC AND CADMIUM ARSENIDES AND PHOSPHIDES IN THE REGION OF INTRINSIC ABSORPTION.**
SOBOLEV, V. V. SYRBU, N. N.
INORG. MAT., USSR
2 (6), 861-5, 1966.
(ENGLISH TRANSLATION OF IZV. AKAD. NAUK SSSR, NEORG. MATER., 2 (6), 1011-15, 1966; FOR ORIGINAL SEE E29425)

85903 **PGL LASER MATERIALS RESEARCH, PHASE III.**
WEBER, M. J.
RAYTHEON RESEARCH DIVISION, WALTHAM, MASS.
47PP., 1972.
(AD-902 708L)

85905 **THE ELECTRICAL, OPTICAL, AND INFRARED PROPERTIES OF VACUUM-DEPOSITED BARIUM TITANATE THIN FILMS.**
BROWN, V. R.
INST. OF SCIENCE AND TECHNOLOGY, MICHIGAN UNIV., ANN ARBOR
94PP., 1967.
(AD-819 559L)

85908 **GROWTH AND PROPERTIES OF MAGNESIUM (TIN, LEAD) SINGLE CRYSTALS.**
GIMPL, M. L. MCMASTER, A. D. FUSCHILLO, N. GIBSON, R.
MELPAR, INC., FALLS CHURCH, VA.
32PP., 1967.
AD-821 564L

85935 **TEMPERATURE DEPENDENCE OF THE ABSORPTION EDGE IN CRYSTALLINE AND VITREOUS ARSENIC (III) SULFIDE.**
ZAKIS, J. R. FRITZSCHE, H.
PHYS. STATUS SOLIDI B
64 (1), 123-30 (ENG.) U.MJ.
(AD-A018 821)

85957 **CALORIMETRIC DETERMINATION OF OPTICAL ABSORPTION IN PROTON BOMBARDED GALLIUM ARSENIDE.**
STEIN, H. J.
ION IMPLANTATION SEMICOND. OTHER MATER., PROC. INT. CONF., 3RD
39-48, 1973.

85970 **DETERMINATION OF THERMOELEMENT QUALITY WITH ACCOUNT FOR COMMUNTATION THERMAL LOSSES.**
MARKMAN, M. A. SIMANOVSKII, L. M. YURKEVICH, I. R.
GELIOTEKHNIKA
8 (5), 21-4, 1972.
(FOR ENGLISH TRANSLATION SEE E85971)

85971 **DETERMINATION OF THERMOELEMENT QUALITY WITH ACCOUNT FOR COMMUTATION THERMAL LOSSES.**
MARKMAN, M. A. SIMANOVSKII, L. M. YURKEVICH, I. R.
APPL. SOLAR ENERGY, USSR
8 (5), 15-7, 1972.
(ENGLISH TRANSLATION OF GELIOTEKHNIKA, 8 (5), 21-4, 1972; FOR ORIGINAL SEE E85970)

86004 **MEASUREMENT OF RESISTIVITIES OF THIN-FILM DIELECTRICS.**
BOITSOV, V. G. DEMIDOV, B. A. TAZENKOV, B. A.
FIZ. POLUPROVODN. ELEKTRON., NAUCHN. DOKL., GERTSENOVSKIE CHTENIYA, 26TH
2, 110-12, 1973.
(EDITED BY I. M. BRONSHTEIN, LENINGR. GOS. PEDAGOG. INST. IM. A. I. GERTSENA: LENINGRAD, USSR)

86009 **PHOTOTHERMOPOWER IN AMORPHOUS CHALCOGENIDE ALLOY FILMS.**
ROCKSTAD, H. K. FLASCK, R.
PROCEEDINGS OF THE 5TH INTERNATIONAL CONFERENCE ON AMORPHOUS AND LIQUID SEMICONDUCTORS. VOL. II, GARMISCH-PARTENKIRCHEN, GERMANY, 3-8 SEPT. 1973
1311-16PP., 1974.

86010 **TRANSPORT PROPERTIES OF A SIMPLE HEAVILY-DOPED MODEL SEMICONDUCTOR.**
FISCHBECK, H. J.
PROCEEDINGS OF THE 5TH INTERNATIONAL CONFERENCE ON AMORPHOUS AND LIQUID SEMICONDUCTORS. VOL. II, GARMISCH-PARTENKIRCHEN, GERMANY, 3-8 SEPT. 1973
849-52PP., 1974.

86019 **PHONON SPECTRA OF AMORPHOUS GALLIUM ARSENIDE AND GERMANIUM.**
STIMETS, R. W. WALDMAN, J. LIN, J. CHANG, T. S. TEMKIN, R. J. CONNELL, G. A. N.
PROCEEDINGS OF THE 5TH INTERNATIONAL CONFERENCE ON AMORPHOUS AND LIQUID SEMICONDUCTORS. VOL. II, GARMISCH-PARTENKIRCHEN, GERMANY, 3-8 SEPT. 1973
1239-44PP., 1974.

86051 **STRUCTURAL AND ELECTRICAL PROPERTIES OF TANTALUM AND TANTALUM NITRIDES DEPOSITED BY CHEMICAL VAPOUR DEPOSITION.**
HIEBER, K.
THIN SOLID FILMS (SWITZERLAND)
24 (1), 157-64, 1974.

86060 **PHOTOCONDUCTION AND PHOTOVOLTAIC EFFECTS IN SPUTTERED THIN FILMS OF ZINC SULFIDE.**
MURRAY, H. TOSSER, A.
THIN SOLID FILMS (SWITZERLAND)
24 (1), 165-80, 1974.

86068 **ELECTRICAL CONDUCTION IN NARROW ENERGY BANDS.**
MARSCH, E. STEEB, W. H.
Z. NATURFORSCH. (GERMANY)
29 A (11), 1655-9, 1974.

86073 **EMISSION IN THE VACUUM ULTRA VIOLET BY A MOLECULAR-GAS PLASMA.**
VARGIN, A. N. GOLUBEV, O. A. MALKIN, O. A.
TEPLOFIZ. VYS. TEMP.
12 (5), 940-6, 1974.
(FOR ENGLISH TRANSLATION SEE E86074)

86074 **EMISSION IN THE VACUUM ULTRA VIOLET BY A MOLECULAR-GAS PLASMA.**
VARGIN, A. N. GOLUBEV, O. A. MALKIN, O. A.
HIGH TEMP.
12 (5), 825-30, 1975.
(ENGLISH TRANSLATION OF TEPLOFIZ. VYS. TEMP., 12 (5), 940-6, 1974; FOR ORIGINAL SEE E86073)

86075 **THE EMISSION INHOMOGENEITY OF MOLYBDENUM.**
GERASHCHENKO, S. S. DOGADAEV, R. V. MARTYNOV, V. L.
TEPLOFIZ. VYS. TEMP.
12 (5), 1019-26, 1974.
(FOR ENGLISH TRANSLATION SEE E86076)

86076 **THE EMISSION INHOMOGENEITY OF MOLYBDENUM.**
GERASHCHENKO, S. S. DOGADAEV, R. V. MARTYNOV, V. L.
HIGH TEMP.
12 (5), 892-8, 1975.
(ENGLISH TRANSLATION OF TEPLOFIZ. VYS. TEMP., 12 (5), 1019-26, 1974; FOR ORIGINAL SEE E86075)

86079 **THERMAL DIFFUSIVITY OF SOLID SOLUTIONS OF ZIRCONIUM AND NIOBIUM MONOCARBIDES AT HIGH TEMPERATURES.**
NESHPOR, V. S. FRIDLENDER, B. A. ORDAN'YAN, S. S. GRISHCHENKO, V. I.
TEPLOFIZ. VYS. TEMP.
12 (5), 1125-8, 1974.
(FOR ENGLISH TRANSLATION SEE E86080)

86080 **THERMAL DIFFUSIVITY OF SOLID SOLUTIONS OF ZIRCONIUM AND NIOBIUM MONOCARBIDES AT HIGH TEMPERATURES.**
NESHPOR, V. S. FRIDLENDER, B. A. ORDAN'YAN, S. S. GRISHCHENKO, V. I.
HIGH TEMP.
12 (5), 992-5, 1975.
(ENGLISH TRANSLATION OF TEPLOFIZ. VYS. TEMP., 12 (5), 1125-8, 1974; FOR ORIGINAL SEE E86079)

86121 **OPTICAL ABSORPTION OF SODIUM FLUORIDE SINGLE CRYSTALS IN THE VUV REGION.**
FOLDVARI, I. VOSZKA, R. RAKSANYI, K.
PHYS. STATUS SOLIDI
26 A (1), K83-5, 1974.

EPIC Number	Bibliographic Citation

86203 **OPTICAL PROPERTIES OF ZONE REFINED LITHIUM IODIDE.**
HASHIMOTO, S. KANZANKI, H.
PHYS. LETT.
49 A (4), 299–300, 1974.

86221 **PROPERTIES OF CADMIUM NERCURY TELLURIDE SEMICONDUCTING SOLID SOLUTIONS UNDER PRESSURE.**
BELOUSOVA, O. N. BOVINA, L. A.
PONOMAREV, YA. G. SAVCHENKO, YU. N.
STAFEEV, V. I.
PIS'MA ZH. EKSP. TEOR. FIZ.
20 (6), 370–4, 1974.
(ENGLISH TRANSLATION SEE E 92626)

86222 **MAGNETIC PROPERTIES OF THE SUPERCONDUCTING COMPOUND MOLYBDENUM TIN GALLIUM SULFIDE.**
ALEKSEEVSKII, N. E. BAZAN, C. Z.
DOBROVOL'SKII, N. M. TSEBRO, V. I.
PIS'MA ZH. EKSP. TEOR. FIZ.
20 (7), 465–8, 1974.
(FOR ENGLISH TRANSLATION SEE E92627)

86318 **THEORETICAL STUDIES OF HIGH POWER INFRARED WINDOW MATERIALS.**
SPARKS, M. AZZARELLI, T.
CONICS, INC., VAN NUYS, CALIF.
86PP., 1972.
(AD–902 441L)

86322 **PROBLEMS WHEN THERMOELECTRIC SEMI–CONDUCTIVE MATERIALS ARE TREATED BY POWDER METALLURGY TECHNOLOGY.**
KULCICKYJ, I.
POKROKY PRASKOVE METALURGIE
(2), 17–33, 1970.
(FOR ENGLISH TRANSLATION SEE E86323)

86323 **PROBLEMS WHEN THERMOELECTRIC SEMI–CONDUCTIVE MATERIALS ARE TREATED BY POWDER METALLURGY TECHNOLOGY.**
KULCICKYJ, I.
FOREIGN SCIENCE AND TECHNOLOGY CENTER, CHARLOTTESVILLE, VA.
18PP., 1973.
(ENGLISH TRANSLATION OF POKROKY PRASKOVE METALURGIE, (2), 17–33, 1970; FOR ORIGINAL SEE E86322)
(AD–911 999L, FSTC–HT–23–1657–72)

86339 **PROPERTIES OF THIN LAYERS OF COPPER AND IRON.**
SEIDL, R.
ACTA PHYS. AUSTR.
10, 402–8, 1957.
(FOR ENGLISH TRANSLATION SEE E 86340)

86340 **PROPERTIES OF THIN LAYERS OF COPPER AND IRON.**
SEIDL, R.
FOREIGN SCIENCE AND TECHNOLOGY CENTER
CHARLOTTESVILLE, VA.
9 PP., 1973.
(ENGLISH TRANSLATION OF ACTA PHYS. AUSTR., 10, 402–8, 1957; FOR ORIGINAL SEE E 86339)
(AD–922 679L, FSTC–HT–23–236–74)

86370 **HIGH ENERGY IR LASER WINDOWS.**
SIEGEL, B. WALD, F. BATES, H. E.
AIR FORCE MATERIALS LAB., WRIGHT PATTERSON AIR FORCE BASE, OHIO
76PP., 1972.
(AD–904 714L, AFML–TR–72–208)

86371 **MODIFIED BRIDGMAN TECHNIQUE GROWTH OF CADMIUM TELLURIDE FOR HIGH POWER INFRARED LASER WINDOWS.**
GENTILE, A. L. KIEFER, J. E. KYLE, N. R.
WINSTON, H. V.
AIR FORCE MATERIALS LAB., WRIGHT PATTERSON AIR FORCE BASE, OHIO
76PP., 1972.
(AD–905 752L, AFML–TR–72–258)

86375 **0.85 MICRON SOLID STATE LASER MATERIAL EVALUATION.**
CHICKLIS, E. P. FOLWEILER, R. C.
NAIMAN, C. S.
AIR FORCE AVIONICS LAB., WRIGHT PATTERSON AIR FORCE BASE, OHIO
76PP., 1973.
(AD–909 527L AFAL–TR–73–94)

86378 **CERMETS AS MATERIAL FOR THERMIONIC EMITTERS WITH SPECIAL REGARD TO BARIUM.**
SCHMIDT, D.
DEUT. LUFT–UND RAUMFAHRT FORSCHUNGS BER.
(69–96), 100PP., 1969.
(FOR ENGLISH TRANSLATION SEE E86379)

86379 **CERMETS AS MATERIAL FOR THERMIONIC EMITTERS WITH SPECIAL REGARD TO BARIUM.**
SCHMIDT, D.
FOREIGN SCIENCE AND TECHNOLOGY CENTER, CHARLOTTESVILLE, VA.
83PP., 1972.
(ENGLISH TRANSLATION OF DEUT. LUFT–UND RAUMFAHRT FORSCHUNGS BER., (69–96), 100PP., 1969; FOR ORIGINAL SEE E86378)
(AD–907 004L, FSTC–HT–23–1201–72)

86380 **GALLIUM ARSENIDE TECHNOLOGY–VOLUME I. CRYSTAL GROWTH AND MATERIAL PROPERTIES.**
HARRISON, J. W.
AIR FORCE AVIONICS LAB., WRIGHT PATTERSON AIR FORCE BASE, OHIO
301PP., 1973.
(AD–908 833L, AFAL–TR–72–312–VOL–1)

86383 **X–RAY AND THERMOLUMINESCENCE IN CRYSTALS OF YTTRIUM ALUMINUM GARNET WITH A CHROMIUM IMPURITY.**
ZAKHARKO, Y. M. ZAKHARKO, M. M.
SEN'KIV, V. A.
UKR. FIZ. ZH.
17 (4), 584–8, 1972.

86425 **KRAMERS–KRONIG ANALYSIS OF REFLECTION DATA.**
KLUCKER, R. NIELSEN, U.
COMPUT. PHYS. COMMUN. (NETHERLANDS)
6 (4), 187–93, 1973.

86428 **SPATIAL CORRELATIONS AND TEMPERATURE DEPENDENCE OF OF THE PHONONASSISTED HOPPING THERMOELECTRIC POWER IN AMORPHOUS SEMICONDUCTORS.**
CAPEK, V.
CZECH. J. PHYS.
24 B (12), 1362–8, 1974.

86432 **INSTALLATION FOR RAPID MEASUREMENT OF ELECTRIC CONDUCTIVITY AND THERMOELECTRIC POWER OF SEMICONDUCTOR MATERIALS.**
JAKLOVSZKY, J. IONESCU, R. NISTOR, N.
ELECTROTEHNICA (RUMANIA)
22 (3), 105–8, 1974.

86433 **PHOTOVOLTAIC EFFECT DUE TO THE DRAG OF FREE CARRIERS BY PHOTONS IN P–N AND P–N–P SEMICONDUCTOR STRUCTURES.**
GRINBERG, A. A. GRINBERG, V. A.
TESHABAEV, A. T.
FIZ. TEKH. POLUPROV.
7 (4), 802–6, 1973.
(FOR ENGLISH TRANSLATION SEE E86434)

86434 **PHOTOVOLTAIC EFFECT DUE TO THE DRAG OF FREE CARRIERS BY PHOTONS IN P–N AND P–N–P SEMICONDUCTOR STRUCTURES.**
GRINBERG, A. A. GRINBERG, V. A.
TESHABAEV, A. T.
SOV. PHYS. SEMICOND.
7 (4), 549–51, 1973.
(ENGLISH TRANSLATION OF FIZ. TEKH. POLUPROV., 7 (4), 802–6, 1973; FOR ORIGINAL SEE E86433)

86448 **MODEL CALCULATIONS FOR D.C. HOPPING CONDUCTION.**
MASCHKE, K. OVERBOF, H. THOMAS, P.
5TH INTERNATIONAL CONFERENCE ON AMORPHOUS AND LIQUID SEMICONDUCTORS, VOL. I, GARMISCH–PARTENKIRCHEN, GERMANY, 3–8 SEPT. 1973
141–6PP., 1974.

86452 **THE CONTINUOUS METAL–NONMETAL TRANSITION IN DISORDERED MATERIALS.**
COHEN, M. H. JORTNER, J.
5TH INTERNATIONAL CONFERENCE ON AMORPHOUS AND LIQUID SEMICONDUCTORS, VOL. I, GARMISCH–PARTENKIRCHEN, GERMANY, 3–8 SEPT. 1973
167–76PP., 1974.

86453 **AMORPHOUS MATERIALS AS 'RELAXATION CASE SEMICONDUCTORS'.**
DOHLER, G. H. HEYSZENAU, H.
5TH INTERNATIONAL CONFERENCE ON AMORPHOUS AND LIQUID SEMICONDUCTORS, VOL. I, GARMISCH–PARTENKIRCHEN, GERMANY, 3–8 SEPT. 1973
177–81PP., 1974.

86454 **HOPPING CONDUCTION: EXPERIMENT VERSUS THEORY.**
KIRKPATRICK, S.
5TH INTERNATIONAL CONFERENCE ON AMORPHOUS AND LIQUID SEMICONDUCTORS, VOL. I, GARMISCH–PARTENKIRCHEN, GERMANY, 3–8 SEPT. 1973
183–7PP., 1974.

86455 **ENERGY SPECTRUM, ELECTRIC PROPERTIES AND STRUCTURE OF CHALCOGENIDE VITREOUS SEMICONDUCTORS.**
KOLOMIETS, B. T.
5TH INTERNATIONAL CONFERENCE ON AMORPHOUS AND LIQUID SEMICONDUCTORS, VOL. I, GARMISCH–PARTENKIRCHEN, GERMANY, 3–8 SEPT. 1973
189–201PP., 1974.

86456 **TRANSPORT PROPERTIES OF TETRAHEDRALLY BONDED AMORPHOUS SEMICONDUCTORS.**
MELL, H.
5TH INTERNATIONAL CONFERENCE ON AMORPHOUS AND LIQUID SEMICONDUCTORS, VOL. I, GARMISCH–PARTENKIRCHEN, GERMANY, 3–8 SEPT. 1973
203–24PP., 1974.

86494 **DETERMINATION OF OPTICAL CONSTANTS OF ANTIMONY SULFIDE ANISOTROPIC CRYSTAL FROM ANALYSIS OF ELLIPTICALLY POLARISED LIGHT REFLECTION.**
AUDZIONI, A. I. KARPUS, A. S.
LITOV, FIZ. SB. (USSR)
14 (1), 129–38, 1974.

EPIC Number	Bibliographic Citation

86505 CHARGE TRANSFER COMPLEXES IN INTERCALATED LAYER COMPOUNDS.
ACRIVOS, J. V. SALEM, J. R.
PHILOS. MAG.
30 (3), 603–19, 1974.

86618 WEAK FERROMAGNETISM ALONG THE TRIGONAL AXIS IN ANTIFERROMAGNETIC COBALT(II) CARBONATE AND NICKEL(II) CARBONATE.
BAZHAN, A. N.
ZH. EKSP. TEOR. FIZ.
67 (4), 1520–6, 1974.
(FOR ENGLISH TRANSLATION SEE E94084)

86642 THE L-ALPHA BAND OF SILICON IN TRANSITION METAL SILICIDES.
BONDARENKO, T. N. ZHURAKOVSKII, E. A.
DOKL. AKAD. NAUK SSSR
218 (1), 84–7, 1974.
(ENGLISH TRANSLATION SEE E 92632)

86647 THERMAL EXPANSION AND NATURE OF INTERATOMIC INTERACTION IN LANTHANIDE SILICIDES.
LAZORENKO, V. I. RUD, B. M. PADERNO, YU. B.
KLOCHKOV, L. A. TIMOFEEVA, I. I.
DOPOV. AKAD. NAUK UKR. RSR, SER.
36 A (9), 850–2, 1974.

86741 MICROSCOPIC ORDER PARAMETERS IN PRASEODYMIUM ALUMINUM OXIDE.
STURGE, M. D. COHEN, E. VANUITERT, L. G.
VAN STAPELE, R. P.
PHYS. REV.
11 B (12), 4768–79, 1975.

86742 ELECTRONIC STRUCTURE OF TIANIUM IRON.
PAPACONSTANTOPOULOS, D. A.
PHYS. REV.
11 (12), 4801–7, 1975.

86744 EXTENDED X-RAY ABSORPTION FINE-STRUCTURE TECHNIQUE. II. EXPERIMENTAL PRACTICE AND SELECTED RESULTS.
LYTLE, F. W. SAYERS, D. E. STERN, E. A.
PHYS. REV.
11 B (12), 4825–35, 1975.

86748 THALLOUS HALIDES PRESSURE DEPENDENCE OF THE ENERGY-BAND STRUCTURE AND THE INSULATOR-METAL TRANSITION.
VAN DYKE, J. P. SAMARA, G. A.
PHYS. REV.
11 B (12), 4935–44, 1975.

86750 STEADY-STATE TRANSPORT IN TRAP-DOMINATED RELAXATION SEMICONDUCTORS.
SCHETZINA, J. F.
PHYS. REV.
11 B (12), 4994–8, 1975.

86751 DETERMINATION OF THE G FACTOR FROM UNSPLIT SHUBNIKOV-DE HAAS OSCILLATIONS IN N-INDIUM ANTIMONIDE.
STEPHENS, A. E. SEILER, D. G. SYBERT, J. R.
MACKEY, H. J.
PHYS. REV.
11 B (12), 4999–5001, 1975.

86752 STRESS EFFECTS ON EXCITONS BOUND TO SHALLOW ACCEPTORS IN GALLIUM ARSENIDE.
SCHMIDT, M. MORGAN, T. N. SCHAIRER, W.
PHYS. REV.
11 B (12), 5002–7, 1975.

86753 CAPTURE AND EMISSION OF ELECTRONS AT 2.4 ELECTRON VOLTS DEEP TRAP LEVEL IN SILICON OXIDE FILMS.
DI MARIA, D. J. FEIGL, F. J. BUTLER, S. R.
PHYS. REV.
11 B (12), 5023–30, 1975.

86754 THEORY OF THE OPTICAL PROPERTIES OF RESONANT STATES IN NITROGEN-DOPED SEMICONDUCTOR ALLOYS.
ALTARELLI, M.
PHYS. REV.
11 B (12), 5031–42, 1975.

86756 FREQUENCY- AND WAVE-NUMBER-DEPENDENT DIELECTRIC FUNCTION OF SEMICONDUCTORS.
CHADI, D. J. WHITE, R. M.
PHYS. REV.
11 B (12), 5077–81, 1975.

86757 UNIVERSAL VALENCE BANDS FOR ROCKSALT-TYPE COMPOUNDS AND THEIR CONNECTION WITH THOSE OF TETRAHEDRAL CRYSTALS.
PANTELIDES, S. T.
PHYS. REV.
11 B (12), 5082–93, 1975.

86758 PHOTOELECTRON SPECTROSCOPY STUDIES OF THE BAND STRUCTURES OF SILVER HALIDES.
MASON, M. G.
PHYS. REV.
11 B (12), 5094–5102, 1975.

86759 ENERGY TRANSFER BETWEEN ERBIUM TRIPOSITIVE IONS IN LANTHANUM FLUORIDE.
OKAMOTO, E. SEKITA, M. MASUI, H.
PHYS. REV.
11 B (12), 5103–11, 1975.

86761 UNIFIED MODEL OF THE INSULATOR-METAL TRANSITION IN TITANIUM OXIDE AND THE HIGH TEMPERATURE TRANSITIONS IN VANADIUM OXIDE.
ZEIGER, H. J.
PHYS. REV.
11 B (12), 5132–44, 1975.

86762 ELECTRONIC BAND STRUCTURE OF THE ALKALI HALIDES. I. EXPERIMENTAL PARAMETERS.
POOLE, R. T. JENKIN, J. G. LIESEGANG, J.
LECKEY, R. C. G.
PHYS. REV.
11 B (12), 5179–89, 1975.

86763 ELECTRONIC BAND STRUCTURE OF THE ALKALI HALIDES. II. CRITICAL SURVEY OF THEORETICAL CALCULATIONS.
POOLE, R. T. LIESEGANG, J. LECKEY, R. C. G.
JENKIN, J. G.
PHYS. REV.
11 B (12), 5190–6, 1975.

86764 ELECTROREFLECTANCE AND BAND STRUCTURE OF ZINC SILICON ARSENIC PHOSPHIDE ALLOYS.
GALLAY, J. DESCHANVRES, A. GAILLARD, S.
ALIBERT, C.
PHYS. REV.
11 B (12), 5199–5202, 1975.

86765 NEUTRAL IMPURITY SCATTERING IN SEMICONDUCTORS.
MC GILL, T. C. BARON, R.
PHYS. REV.
11 B (12), 5208–10, 1975.

86779 KINETIC EFFECTS IN SILVER SELENIDE AND TELLURIDE.
ASTAKHOV, O. P. GOLYSHEV, V. D.
IZV. AKAD. NAUK SSSR, NEORG. MATER.
10 (9), 1614–18, 1974.
(FOR ENGLISH TRANSLATION SEE E90050)

86780 THERMOELECTRIC PROPERTIES OF A TIN TELLURIDE - ZINC TELLURIDE SOLID SOLUTION.
SULTANOVA, N. R. NASIROV, YA. N.
ZARGAROVA, M. I. PIRZADE, M. M.
IZV. AKAD. NAUK SSSR, NEORG. MATER.
10 (8), 1418–20, 1974.
(FOR ENGLISH TRANSLATION SEE E90054)

86817 ANISOTROPY OF THE DIELECTRIC AND PIEZOELECTRIC PROPERTIES OF LEAD TITANATE.
TURIK, A. V. FESENKO, E. G.
GAVRILYACHENKO, V. G. KHASABOVA, G. I.
KRISTALLOGRAFIYA
19 (5), 1095–7, 1974.
(FOR ENGLISH TRANSLATION SEE E92635)

86831 COMPARISON OF INVESTIGATIONS OF THE ENERGY-BAND STRUCTURE OF GALLIUM ARSENIDE AND GALLIUM PHOSPHIDE BY PHOTOELECTRON AND X-RAY SPECTROSCOPY METHODS.
LEONHARDT, G.
FIZ. TVERD. TELA
17 (1), 3–6, 1975.
(FOR ENGLISH TRANSLATION SEE E86832)

86832 COMPARISON OF INVESTIGATIONS OF THE ENERGY-BAND STRUCTURE OF GALLIUM ARSENIDE AND GALLIUM PHOSPHIDE BY PHOTOELECTRON AND X-RAY SPECTROSCOPY METHODS.
LEONHARDT, G.
SOV. PHYS. SOLID STATE
17 (1), 1–2, 1975.
(ENGLISH TRANSLATION OF FIZ. TVERD. TELA, 17 (1), 3–6, 1975; FOR ORIGINAL SEE E86831)

86839 ENHANCEMENT OF THE EXCHANGE INTERACTION IN EUROPIUM SAMARIUM SULFIDE SOLID SOLUTIONS WITH SEMICONDUCTING CONDUCTION.
SAMOKHVALOV, A. A. ARBUZOVA, T. I.
AFANAS'EV, A. YA. BABUSHKIN, V. S.
LOSHKAREVA, N. N. MOROZOV, YU. N.
SIMONOVA, M. I. BAMBUROV, V. G.
LOBACHEVSKAYA, N. I.
FIZ. TVERD. TELA
17 (1), 48–51, 1975.
(FOR ENGLISH TRANSLATION SEE E86840)

86840 ENHANCEMENT OF THE EXCHANGE INTERACTION IN EUROPIUM SAMARIUM SULFIDE SOLID SOLUTIONS WITH SEMICONDUCTING CONDUCTION.
SAMOKHVALOV, A. A. ARBUZOVA, T. I.
AFANAS'EV, A. YA. BABUSHKIN, V. S.
LOSHKAREVA, N. N. MOROZOV, YU. N.
SIMONOVA, M. I. BAMBUROV, V. G.
LOBACHEVSKAYA, N. I.
SOV. PHYS. SOLID STATE
17 (1), 26–8, 1975.
(ENGLISH TRANSLATION OF FIZ. TVERD. TELA, 17 (1), 48–51, 1975; FOR ORIGINAL SEE E86839)

EPIC Number	Bibliographic Citation
86841	**LINEAR BIREFRINGENCE OF LIGHT IN RARE EARTH IRON GARNETS UNDER UNIAXIAL COMPRESSION.** PISAREV, R. V. KOLPAKOVA, N. N. TITOVA, A. G. DASHEVSKAYA, L. M. FIZ. TVERD. TELA 17 (1), 56–63, 1975. (FOR ENGLISH TRANSLATION SEE E86842)
86842	**LINEAR BIREFRINGENCE OF LIGHT IN RARE EARTH IRON GARNETS UNDER UNIAXIAL COMPRESSION.** PISAREV, R. V. KOLPAKOVA, N. N. TITOVA, A. G. DASHEVSKAYA, L. M. SOV. PHYS. SOLID STATE 17 (1), 31–4, 1975. (ENGLISH TRANSLATION OF FIZ. TVERD. TELA, 17 (1), 56–63, 1975; FOR ORIGINAL SEE E86841)
86845	**MANY-PHOTON ABSORPTION OF LIGHT IN CRYSTALS WITH DIAMOND AND ZINC-BLENDE STRUCTURES.** ARIFZHANOV, S. B. IVCHENKO, E. L. FIZ. TVERD. TELA 1M (1), 81–9, 1975. (FOR ENGLISH TRANSLATION SEE E86846)
86846	**MANY-PHOTON ABSORPTION OF LIGHT IN CRYSTALS WITH DIAMOND AND ZINC-BLENDE STRUCTURES.** ARIFZHANOV, S. B. IVCHENKO, E. L. SOV. PHYS. SOLID STATE 17 (1), 46–50, 1975. (ENGLISH TRANSLATION OF FIZ. TVERD. TELA, 17 (1), 81–9, 1975; FOR ORIGINAL SEE E86845)
86849	**SUPERCONDUCTIVITY OF BISMUTH TELLURIDE AT HIGH PRESSURES.** IL'INA, M. A. ITSKEVICH, E. S. FIZ. TVERD. TELA 17 (1), 154–7, 1975. (FOR ENGLISH TRANSLATION SEE E86850)
86850	**SUPERCONDUCTIVITY OF BISMUTH TELLURIDE AT HIGH PRESSURES.** IL'INA, M. A. ITSKEVICH, E. S. SOV. PHYS. SOLID STATE 17 (1), 89–91, 1975. (ENGLISH TRANSLATION OF FIZ. TVERD. TELA, 17 (1), 154–7, 1975; FOR ORIGINAL SEE E86849)
86851	**COMPOSITION DEPENDENCES OF THE PROPERTIES OF SUPERCONDUCTING COMPOUNDS.** SAL'NIKOV, B. V. MEN', A. N. FIZ. TVERD. TELA 17 (1), 158–60, 1975. (FOR ENGLISH TRANSLATION SEE E86852)
86852	**COMPOSITION DEPENDENCES OF THE PROPERTIES OF SUPERCONDUCTING COMPOUNDS.** SAL'NIKOV, B. V. MEN', A. N. SOV. PHYS. SOLID STATE 17 (1), 92–3, 1975. (ENGLISH TRANSLATION OF FIZ. TVERD. TELA, 17 (1), 158–60, 1975; FOR ORIGINAL SEE E86851)
86853	**INFRARED OPTICAL PROPERTIES OF THALLIUM ANTIMONY SULFIDE AND THALLIUM ANTIMONY SELENIDE SINGLE CRYSTALS.** STEPANOV, G. I. BOTGROS, I. V. CHINIK, B. S. KOGALNICHANU, N. F. CHEBAN, A. G. FIZ. TVERD. TELA 17 (1), 166–9, 1975. (FOR ENGLISH TRANSLATION SEE E86854)
86854	**INFRARED OPTICAL PROPERTIES OF THALLIUM ANTIMONY SULFIDE AND THALLIUM ANTIMONY SELENIDE SINGLE CRYSTALS.** STEPANOV, G. I. BOTGROS, I. V. CHINIK, B. S. KOGALNICHANU, N. F. CHEBAN, A. G. SOV. PHYS. SOLID STATE 17 (1), 97–8, 1975. (ENGLISH TRANSLATION OF FIZ. TVERD. TELA, 17 (1), 166–9, 1975; FOR ORIGINAL SEE E86853)
86857	**PROBLEM OF THE SUPERCONDUCTIVITY IN LAYERED SEMICONDUCTOR STRUCTURES.** GABOVICH, A. M. MOISEEV, D. P. FIZ. TVERD. TELA 17 (1), 269–73, 1975. (FOR ENGLISH TRANSLATION SEE E86858)
86858	**PROBLEM OF THE SUPERCONDUCTIVITY IN LAYERED SEMICONDUCTOR STRUCTURES.** GABOVICH, A. M. MOISEEV, D. P. SOV. PHYS. SOLID STATE 17 (1), 160–2, 1975. (ENGLISH TRANSLATION OF FIZ. TVERD. TELA, 17 (1), 269–73, 1975; FOR ORIGINAL SEE E86857)
86859	**INTERACTION OF OXYGEN WITH THE (110) FACE OF A MOLYBDENUM SINGLE CRYSTAL.** ZYKOV, B. M. IKONNIKOV, D. S. TSKHAKAYA, V. K. FIZ. TVERD. TELA 17 (1), 274–9, 1975. (FOR ENGLISH TRANSLATION SEE E86860)
86860	**INTERACTION OF OXYGEN WITH THE (110) FACE OF A MOLYBDENUM SINGLE CRYSTAL.** ZYKOV, B. M. IKONNIKOV, D. S. TSKHAKAYA, V. K. SOV. PHYS. SOLID STATE 17 (1), 163–6, 1975. (ENGLISH TRANSLATION OF FIZ. TVERD. TELA, 17 (1), 274–9, 1975; FOR ORIGINAL SEE E86859)
86863	**PHOTOCONDUCTIVITY IN COMPENSATED N-TYPE INDIUM ANTIMONIDE UNDER CYCLOTRON RESONANCE CONDITIONS.** GULYAEV, YU. V. POPOV, V. A. POTAPOV, V. T. STRAKHOV, V. A. CHUSOV, I. I. YAREMENKO, N. G. FIZ. TVERD. TELA 17 (1), 289–97, 1975. (FOR ENGLISH TRANSLATION SEE E86864)
86864	**PHOTOCONDUCTIVITY IN COMPENSATED N-TYPE INDIUM ANTIMONIDE UNDER CYCLOTRON RESONANCE CONDITIONS.** GULYAEV, YU. V. POPOV, V. A. POTAPOV, V. T. STRAKHOV, V. A. CHUSOV, I. I. YAREMENKO, N. G. SOV. PHYS. SOLID STATE 17 (1), 173–7, 1975. (ENGLISH TRANSLATION OF FIZ. TVERD. TELA, 17 (1), 289–97, 1975; FOR ORIGINAL SEE E86863)
86867	**FERROMAGNETIC PARAMAGNETIC PHASE TRANSITION OF THE FIRST KIND IN COPPER CHROMIUM SELENIDE.** BELOV, K. P. KOROLEVA, L. I. SHALIMOVA, M. A. BATOROVA, S. D. FIZ. TVERD. TELA 17 (1), 322–3, 1975. (FOR ENGLISH TRANSLATION SEE E86868)
86868	**FERROMAGNETIC PARAMAGNETIC PHASE TRANSITION OF THE FIRST KIND IN COPPER CHROMIUM SELENIDE.** BELOV, K. P. KOROLEVA, L. I. SHALIMOVA, M. A. BATOROVA, S. D. SOV. PHYS. SOLID STATE 17 (1), 197, 1975. (ENGLISH TRANSLATION OF FIZ. TVERD. TELA, 17 (1), 322–3, 1975; FOR ORIGINAL SEE E86867)
86869	**MAGNETIC AND ELECTRIC PHASE TRANSITIONS IN VANADIUM OXIDE - TITANIUM OXIDE SOLID SOLUTIONS.** MOTORNYI, A. V. TALLERCHIK, B. A. TESLENKO, S. P. SHUSTROV, B. A. FIZ. TVERD. TELA 17 (1), 324–5, 1975. (FOR ENGLISH TRANSLATION SEE E86870)
86870	**MAGNETIC AND ELECTRIC PHASE TRANSITIONS IN VANADIUM OXIDE - TITANIUM OXIDE SOLID SOLUTIONS.** MOTORNYI, A. V. TALLERCHIK, B. A. TESLENKO, S. P. SHUSTROV, B. A. SOV. PHYS. SOLID STATE 17 (1), 198–9, 1975. (ENGLISH TRANSLATION OF FIZ. TVERD. TELA, 17 (1), 324–5, 1975; FOR ORIGINAL SEE E86869)
86871	**PARAMETERS OF THE CRYSTAL FIELD OF CUBIC PRASEODYMIUM TRIPOSITIVE CENTERS IN FLUORITE-TYPE CRYSTALS.** DAVYDOVA, M. P. STOLOV, A. L. FIZ. TVERD. TELA 17 (1), 329–31, 1975. (FOR ENGLISH TRANSLATION SEE E86872)
86872	**PARAMETERS OF THE CRYSTAL FIELD OF CUBIC PRASEODYMIUM TRIPOSITIVE CENTERS IN FLUORITE-TYPE CRYSTALS.** DAVYDOVA, M. P. STOLOV, A. L. SOV. PHYS. SOLID STATE 17 (1), 203–4, 1975. (ENGLISH TRANSLATION OF FIZ. TVERD. TELA, 17 (1), 329–31, 1975; FOR ORIGINAL SEE E86871)
86873	**INFLUENCE OF ILLUMINATION ON MAGNETIC PROPERTIES OF CADMIUM CHROMIUM SELENIDE.** SALANSKII, N. M. DROKIN, N. A. FIZ. TVERD. TELA 17 (1), 331–3, 1975. (FOR ENGLISH TRANSLATION SEE E86874)
86874	**INFLUENCE OF ILLUMINATION ON MAGNETIC PROPERTIES OF CADMIUM CHROMIUM SELENIDE.** SALANSKII, N. M. DROKIN, N. A. SOV. PHYS. SOLID STATE 17 (1), 205, 1975. (ENGLISH TRANSLATION OF FIZ. TVERD. TELA, 17 (1), 331–3, 1975; FOR ORIGINAL SEE E86873)
86875	**TWO-PARTICLE OPERATORS IN CRYSTAL FIELD THEORY.** EREMIN, M. V. KORNIENKO, A. A. FIZ. TVERD. TELA 17 (1), 333–5, 1975. (FOR ENGLISH TRANSLATION SEE E86876)
86876	**TWOPARTICLE OPERATORS IN CRYSTAL FIELD THEORY.** EREMIN, M. V. KORNIENKO, A. A. SOV. PHYS. SOLID STATE 17 (1), 206–7, 1975. (ENGLISH TRANSLATION OF FIZ. TVERD. TELA, 17 (1), 333–5, 1975; FOR ORIGINAL SEE E86875)

EPIC Number	Bibliographic Citation

86877 **CHARACTERISTICS OF THE SPECTRA OF SLOW ELECTRONS EMITTED FROM P-TYPE GALLIUM ARSENIDE.**
AKHAYAN, A. A. NEMCHENOK, R. L.
PAL'TS, T. N.
FIZ. TVERD. TELA
17 (1), 336-7, 1975.
(FOR ENGLISH TRANSLATION SEE E86878)

86878 **CHARACTERISTICS OF THE SPECTRA OF SLOW ELECTRONS EMITTED FROM P-TYPE GALLIUM ARSENIDE.**
AKHAYAN, A. A. NEMCHENOK, R. L.
PAL'TS, T. N.
SOV. PHYS. SOLID STATE
17 (1), 208-9, 1975.
(ENGLISH TRANSLATION OF FIZ. TVERD. TELA, 17 (1), 336-7, 1975; FOR ORIGINAL SEE E86877)

86881 **RELATIONSHIP BETWEEN THE DOMAIN STRUCTURE OF BARIUM TITANIUM OXIDE CRYSTALS AND THE EMISSION OF LIGHT DURING FAST HEATING ABOVE THE CURIE POINT.**
FLEROVA, S. A. SAMCHENKO, YU. I.
FIZ. TVERD. TELA
17 (1), 347-9, 1975.
(FOR ENGLISH TRANSLATION SEE E86882)

86882 **RELATIONSHIP BETWEEN THE DOMAIN STRUCTURE OF BARIUM TITANIUM OXIDE CRYSTALS AND THE EMISSION OF LIGHT DURING FAST HEATING ABOVE THE CURIE POINT.**
FLEROVA, S. A. SAMCHENKO, YU. I.
SOV. PHYS. SOLID STATE
17 (1), 218-9, 1975.
(ENGLISH TRANSLATION OF FIZ. TVERD. TELA, 17 (1), 347-9, 1975; FOR ORIGINAL SEE E86881)

86883 **MEASUREMENTS OF HIGH TEMPERATURE ABSORPTION COEFFICIENTS OF GLASSES.**
WEDDING, B.
J. AMER. CERAM. SOC.
58 (3-4), 102-5, 1975.

86907 **LIGHT ABSORPTION IN INTRINSIC SEMICONDUCTORS IN THE PRESENCE OF HIGH POWER LASER RADIATION.**
SINYAVSKII, E. P.
OPT. SPECTROS.
37 (3), 281-5, 1974.
(ENGLISH TRANSLATION OF OPT. SPEKTROSK., 37 (3), 495-503, 1974Y FOR ORIGINAL SEE E64576)

86944 **INFRARED TRANSITIONS OF THE TRIVALENT ERBIUM ION IN THE CRYSTAL LATTICE OF CADMIUM FLUORIDE.**
BANCIE-GRILLOT, M. GRILLOT, E.
COMPT. REND.
275 B (2), 109-12, 1972.
(FOR ENGLISH TRANSLATION SEE E86945)

86945 **INFRARED TRANSITIONS OF THE TRIVALENT ERBIUM ION IN THE CRYSTAL LATTICE OF CADMIUM FLUORIDE.**
BANCIE-GRILLOT, M. GRILLOT, E.
LINCOLN LAB., MASS. INST. OF TECH., LEXINGTON
6PP., 1973.
(ENGLISH TRANSLATION OF COMPT. REND., B, 275 (2), 109-12, 1972; FOR ORIGINAL SEE E86944)
(N74-27255, NTC-74-11892)

86959 **ELECTRODES FOR THE THERMIONIC CONVERTERS, PHASE 2-3.**
DE STEESE, J. G.
MC DONNEL-DOUGLAS ASTRONAUTICS CO., RICHLAND, WASH.
51PP., 1972.
(NASA-CR-131838, N73-25723, MDC-G4401)

87019 **INTERFERENCE INSTALLATION FOR INVESTIGATIONS OF THE THERMO- AND ELECTRO-OPTICAL PROPERTIES OF CRYSTALS.**
KOPYLOV, YU. L.
PRIB. TEKH. EKSP.
17 (PT. 2) (1), 202-4, 1974.
(FOR ENGLISH TRANSLATION SEE E87020)

87020 **INTERFERENCE INSTALLATION FOR INVESTIGATIONS OF THE THERMO- AND ELECTRO-OPTICAL PROPERTIES OF CRYSTALS.**
KOPYLOV, YU. L.
INSTRUM. EXP. TECH., USSR
17 (1), (PT. 2), 231-3, 1974.
(ENGLISH TRANSLATION OF PRIB. TEKH. EKSP., 17 (1), (PT. 2), 202-4, 1974; FOR ORIGINAL SEE E87019)

87035 **TWO-PHOTON ABSORPTION AND SPECTROSCOPY.**
BREDIKHIN, V. I. GALANIN, M. D.
GENKIN, V. N.
USP. FIZ. NAUK
110 (1-2), 3-43, 1973.
(FOR ENGLISH TRANSLATION SEE E87036)

87036 **TWO-PHOTON ABSORPTION AND SPECTROSCOPY.**
BREDIKHIN, V. I. GALANIN, M. D.
GENKIN, V. N.
SOV. PHYS. - USP.
16 (3), 299-321, 1973.
(ENGLISH TRANSLATION OF USP. FIZ. NAUK, 110 (1-2), 3-43, 1973; FOR ORIGINAL SEE E87035)

EPIC Number	Bibliographic Citation

87062 **ROLE OF COPPER IN THE FORMATION OF THE FUNDAMENTAL ABSORPTION EDGE OF CADMIUM SELENIDE.**
MOVSESYAN, G. M. MASHCHENKO, V. E.
KIREEV, P. S. VOLKOVA, L. V.
FIZ. TEKH. POLUPROV.
8 (4), 800-3, 1974.
(FOR ENGLISH TRANSLATION SEE E87063)

87063 **ROLE OF COPPER IN THE FORMATION OF THE FUNDAMENTAL ABSORPTION EDGE OF CADMIUM SELENIDE.**
MOVSESYAN, G. M. MASHCHENKO, V. E.
KIREEV, P. S. HOLKOVA, L. V.
SOV. PHYS. SEMICOND.
8 (4), 514-6, 1974.
(ENGLISH TRANSLATION OF FIZ. TEKH. POLUPROV., 8 (4), 800-3, 1974; FOR ORIGINAL SEE E87062)

87069 **CHARACTERISTICS OF SOLID SOLUTIONS OF SUBSTITUTION BASED ON GERMANIUM TELLURIDE.**
BLIZNYUK, G. S. LEV, E. YA. SYSOEVA, L. M.
ZHUKOVA, T. B. KOLOMOETS, N. V.
IZV. AKAD. NAUK SSSR, NEORG. MATER.
10 (2), 213-6, 1974.
(FOR ENGLISH TRANSLATION SEE E87070)

87070 **CHARACTERISTICS OF SOLID SOLUTIONS OF SUBSTITUTION BASED ON GERMANIUM TELLURIDE.**
BLIZNYUK, G. S. LEV, E. YA. SYSOEVA, L. M.
ZHUKOVA, T. B. KOLOMOETS, N. V.
INORG. MAT., USSR
10 (2), 180-3, 1974.
(ENGLISH TRANSLATION OF IZV. AKAD. NAUK SSSR, NEORG. MATER., 10 (2), 213-6, 1974; FOR ORIGINAL SEE E87069)

87071 **THERMIONIC EMISSION BY TRANSITION METAL DODECABORIDES.**
SAMSONOV, G. V. OKHREMCHUK, L. N.
PODCHERNYAEVA, I. A. FOMENKO, V. S.
ODINTSOV, V. V.
IZV. AKAD. NAUK SSSR, NEORG. MATER.
10 (2), 270-2, 1974.
(FOR ENGLISH TRANSLATION SEE E87072)

87072 **THERMIONIC EMISSION BY TRANSITION METAL DODECABORIDES.**
SAMSONOV, G. V. OKHREMCHUK, L. N.
PODCHERNYAEVA, I. A. FOMENKO, V. S.
ODINTSOV, V. V.
INORG. MAT., USSR
10 (2), 231-3, 1974.
(ENGLISH TRANSLATION OF IZV. AKAD. NAUK SSSR, NEORG. MATER., 10 (2), 270-2, 1974; FOR ORIGINAL SEE E87071)

87127 **APPLICATIONS OF ELLIPSOMETRY IN SEMICONDUCTOR TECHNOLOGY.**
ANAND, K. V. MOMODU, S. K.
ELECTRON. ENGINEERING
47 (563), 51-3, 1975.

87145 **EUROPIUM IN THE ULTRAPHOSPHATE LATTICE: POLARIZED SPECTRA AND STRUCTURE OF EUROPIUM ULTRA(PENTA) PHOSPHATE OXIDE.**
BRECHER, C.
J. CHEM. PHYS.
61 (6), 2297-315, 1974.

87146 **INTERBAND TRANSITIONS IN CADMIUM INDIUM SULFIDE.**
ABDULLAEV, G. B. GUSEINOVA, D. A.
KERIMOVA, T. G.
FIZ. TEKH. POLUPROV.
8 (6), 1210-13, 1974.

87147 **INFLUENCE OF SPATIAL DISPERSION ON THE TRANSMISSION SPECTRA OF CADMIUM SULFIDE SINGLE CRYSTALS.**
VOIGT, J.
PHYS. STATUS SOLIDI
64 B (2), 549-56, 1974.

87153 **SUPERCONDUCTIVITY AND ATOMIC ORDERING IN NEUTRON-IRRADIATED NIOBIUM ALUMINUM.**
SWEEDLER, A. R. COX, D. E.
PHYS. REV.
12 B (1), 147-56, 1975.

87154 **SPONTANEOUS MAGNETIZATION IN THE DIPOLAR ISING FERROMAGNET LITHIUM TERBIUM FLUORIDE.**
ALS-NIELSEN, J. HOLMES, L. M. LARSEN, F. K.
GUGGENHEIM, H. J.
PHYS. REV.
12 B (1), 191-7, 1975.

87156 **FLUCTUATIONS AND ORDER IN A ONE-DIMENSIONAL SYSTEM. A SPECTROSCOPICAL STUDY OF THE PEIERLS TRANSITION IN NONSTOICHIOMETRIC POTASSIUM BROMOTETRACYANOPLATINATE TRIHYDRATE.**
BRUESCH, P. STRASSLER, S. ZELLER, H. R.
PHYS. REV.
12 B (1), 219-25, 1975.

87162 **DIELECTRIC AND ULTRASONIC MEASUREMENTS IN CESIUM DIHYDROGEN ARSENATE.**
POLLINA, R. J. GARLAND, C. W.
PHYS. REV.
12 B (1), 362-7, 1975.

EPIC Number	Bibliographic Citation
87171	**PSEUDOPOTENTIAL CALCULATION OF THE SURFACE BAND STRUCTURE OF (111) DIAMOND AND ZINC-BLENDE FACES: GERMANIUM, ALPHA-TIN, GALLIUM ARSENIDE, AND ZINC SULFIDE.** LOUIS, E. ELICES, M. PHYS. REV. 12 B (2), 618-23, 1975.
87172	**SHALLOW IMPURITY STATES IN INDIUM ANTIMONY IN MAGNETIC FIELDS: HIGH FIELD DONOR STATES AND ACCEPTOR STATES.** LIN-CHUNG, P. J. HENVIS, B. W. PHYS. REV. 12 B (2), 630-40, 1975.
87173	**CONDUCTION IN THE RELAXATION REGIME.** DOHLER, G. H. HEYSZENAU, H. PHYS. REV. 12 B (2), 641-9, 1975.
87174	**PRESSURE AND TEMPERATURE DEPENDENCE OF ELECTRONIC ENERGY LEVELS IN LEAD SELENIUM AND LEAD TELLURIDE.** SCHLUTER, M. MARTINEZ, G. COHEN, M. L. PHYS. REV. 12 B (2), 650-8, 1975.
87176	**PIEZOELECTRIC STIFFENING AND ATTENUATION OF ULTRASONIC WAVES IN N-TYPE GALLIUM ANTIMONY DOPED WITH SULFUR.** BOYLE, W. F. SLADEK, R. J. PHYS. REV. 12 B (2), 673-9, 1975.
87179	**DIELECTRIC-BREAKDOWN THRESHOLD AND NONLINEAR-REFRACTIVE-INDEX MEASUREMENTS WITH PICOSECOND LASER PULSES.** SMITH, W. L. BECHTEL, J. H. BLOEMBERGEN, N. PHYS. REV. 12 B (2), 706-17, 1975.
87180	**ELECTRONIC STRUCTURE OF MOLECULAR ARSENIC CHALCOGENIDES.** SALANECK, W. R. LIANG, K. S. PATON, A. LIPARI, N. O. PHYS. REV. 12 B (2), 725-30, 1975.
87185	**SODIUM CHLORIDE SURFACE REACTION IN CHEMICAL-LASER DEVICES.** PETERSEN, A. B. WITTIG, C. IEEE J. QUANTUM ELECTRON. (USA) QE-11 (3), 110-11, 1975.
87197	**STUDIES ON THE SIZE AND THE MISORIENTATION OF THE MOSAIC BLOCKS IN PURE AND DOPED SINGLE CRYSTALS OF POTASSIUM CHLORIDE.** MITRA, G. B. SAMANTARAY, B. K. J. APPL. CRYSTALLOGR. (DENMARK) 8, PT. 1, 15-16, 1975.
87215	**FAR-INFRARED ABSORPTION IN IMPERFECT CRYSTALS: LOW-CONCENTRATION THEORY.** BEHERA, S. N. TRIPATHI, R. S. J. PHYS. (GB) 7 C (24), 4452-69, 1974.
87226	**ABSORPTION SPECTRA OF OPTICALLY PUMPED ZIRCONIUM SULFIDE:MANGANESE.** KUSHIDA, T. TANAKA, Y. OKA, Y. J. PHYS. SOC. JAP. (JAPAN) 37 (5), 1341-8, 1974.
87287	**THE THERMAL CONDUCTIVITY OF A NUMBER OF METALS AT LOW TEMPERATURES.** TYE, R. P. HAYDEN, R. W. SPINNEY, S. C. PROC. INT. CRYOG. ENG. CONF. 14PP., 1975.
87288	**OPTICAL CONSTANTS AND ENERGY-BAND STRUCTURE OF FLUORITE-TYPE CRYSTALS.** GANIN, V. A. KARIN, M. G. SIDORIN, V. K. SIDORIN, K. K. STAROSTIN, N. V. STARTSEV, G. P. SHEPILOV, M. P. FIZ. TVERD. TELA 16 (12), 3554-62, 1974. (FOR ENGLISH TRANSLATION SEE E87289)
87289	**OPTICAL CONSTANTS AND ENERGY-BAND STRUCTURE OF FLUORITE-TYPE CRYSTALS.** GANIN, V. A. KARIN, M. G. SIDORIN, V. K. SIDORIN, K. K. STAROSTIN, N. V. STARTSEV, G. P. SHEPILOV, M. P. SOV. PHYS. SOLID STATE 16 (11), 2313-8, 1975. (ENGLISH TRANSLATION OF FIZ. TVERD. TELA, 16 (12), 3554-62, 1974; FOR ORIGINAL SEE E87288)
87292	**LOW-TEMPERATURE SPECIFIC HEAT OF ANTIFERROMAGNETIC GARNET SODIUM CALCIUM NICKEL VANADIUM OXIDE.** MAMSUROVA, L. G. SPERANSKAYA, E. M. FIZ. TVERD. TELA 16 (12), 3603-5, 1974. (FOR ENGLISH TRANSLATION SEE E87293)
87293	**LOW-TEMPERATURE SPECIFIC HEAT OF ANTIFERROMAGNETIC GARNET SODIUM CALCIUM NICKEL VANADIUM OXIDE.** MAMSUROVA, L. G. SPERANSKAYA, E. M. SOV. PHYS. SOLID STATE 16 (12), 2342-3, 1975. (ENGLISH TRANSLATION OF FIZ. TVERD. TELA, 16 (12), 3603-5, 1974; FOR ORIGINAL SEE E87292)
87294	**DIELECTRIC SPECTRUM OF LEAD GERMANATE CRYSTALS.** DEM'YANOV, V. V. SAL'NIKOV, V. D. FIZ. TVERD. TELA 16 (12), 3623-7, 1974. (FOR ENGLISH TRANSLATION SEE E87295)
87295	**DIELECTRIC SPECTRUM OF LEAD GERMANATE CRYSTALS.** DEM'YANOV, V. V. SAL'NIKOV, V. D. SOV. PHYS. SOLID STATE 16 (12), 2353-5, 1975. (ENGLISH TRANSLATION OF FIZ. TVERD. TELA, 16 (12), 3623-7, 1974; FOR ORIGINAL SEE E87294)
87296	**THEORY OF INTRABAND INFRARED ABSORPTION IN ANISOTROPIC IONIC SEMICONDUCTORS.** GUREVICH, V. L. LANG, I. G. PARSHIN, D. A. FIZ. TVERD. TELA 16 (12), 3628-35, 1974. (FOR ENGLISH TRANSLATION SEE E87297)
87297	**THEORY OF INTRABAND INFRARED ABSORPTION IN ANISOTROPIC IONIC SEMICONDUCTORS.** GUREVICH, V. L. LANG, I. G. PARSHIN, D. A. SOV. PHYS. SOLID STATE 16 (12), 2356-9, 1975. (ENGLISH TRANSLATION OF FIZ. TVERD. TELA, 16 (12), 3628-35, 1974; FOR ORIGINAL SEE E87296)
87298	**SEMICONDUCTOR - METAL TRANSITION IN MOLTEN SEMICONDUCTORS AT HIGH TEMPERATURES.** ANDREEV, A. A. TURGUNOV, T. ALEKSEEV, V. A. FIZ. TVERD. TELA 16 (12), 3660-6, 1974. (FOR ENGLISH TRANSLATION SEE E87299)
87299	**SEMICONDUCTOR - METAL TRANSITION IN MOLTEN SEMICONDUCTORS AT HIGH TEMPERATURES.** ANDREEV, A. A. TURGUNOV, T. ALEKSEEV, V. A. SOV. PHYS. SOLID STATE 16 (12), 2376-9, 1975. (ENGLISH TRANSLATION OF FIZ. TVERD. TELA, 16 (12), 3660-6, 1974; FOR ORIGINAL SEE E87298)
87308	**FUNDAMENTAL LUMINESCENCE OF ALKALI HALIDE CRYSTALS EXCITED BY NANOSECOND HIGH-DENSITY ELECTRON-BEAM PULSES.** SHKATOV, V. T. VAISBURD, D. I. PLOOM, L. A. FIZ. TVERD. TELA 16 (12), 3722-4, 1974. (FOR ENGLISH TRANSLATION SEE E87309)
87309	**FUNDAMENTAL LUMINESCENCE OF ALKALI HALIDE CRYSTALS EXCITED BY NANOSECOND HIGH-DENSITY ELECTRON-BEAM PULSES.** SHKATOV, V. T. VAISBURD, D. I. PLOOM, L. A. SOV. PHYS. SOLID STATE 16 (12), 2420-1, 1975. (ENGLISH TRANSLATION OF FIZ. TVERD. TELA, 16 (12), 3722-4, 1974; FOR ORIGINAL SEE E87308)
87310	**MAGNETIC ANISOTROPY OF INTERMETALLIC RARE EARTH COMPOUNDS.** KAZAKOV, A. A. DERYAGIN, A. V. KUDREVATYKH, N. V. REIMER, V. A. FIZ. TVERD. TELA 16 (12), 3732-4, 1974. (FOR ENGLISH TRANSLATION SEE E87311)
87311	**MAGNETIC ANISOTROPY OF INTERMETALLIC RARE EARTH COMPOUNDS.** KAZAKOV, A. A. DERYAGIN, A. V. KUDREVATYKH, N. V. REIMER, V. A. SOV. PHYS. SOLID STATE 16 (12), 2429-30, 1975. (ENGLISH TRANSLATION OF FIZ. TVERD. TELA, 16 (12), 3732-4, 1974; FOR ORIGINAL SEE E87310)
87312	**PHOTOLUMINESCENCE SPECTRUM OF HOT CARRIERS IN INDIUM PHOSPHIDE CRYSTALS.** ZEMSKII, V. I. KATILYUS, R. MIRLIN, D. N. FIZ. TVERD. TELA 16 (12), 3736-8, 1974. (FOR ENGLISH TRANSLATION SEE E87313)
87313	**PHOTOLUMINESCENCE SPECTRUM OF HOT CARRIERS IN INDIUM PHOSPHIDE CRYSTALS.** ZEMSKII, V. I. KATILYUS, R. MIRLIN, D. N. SOV. PHYS. SOLID STATE 16 (12), 2433-4, 1975. (ENGLISH TRANSLATION OF FIZ. TVERD. TELA, 16 (12), 3736-8, 1974; FOR ORIGINAL SEE E87312)
87314	**IR ABSORPTION COEFFICIENTS AND REFRACTIVE INDICES OF CARBON DIOXIDE AND STEAM.** POPOV, YU. A. SHVARTSBLAT, R. L. TEPLOFIZ. VYS. TEMP. 12 (6), 1188-92, 1974. (FOR ENGLISH TRANSLATION SEE E87315)

EPIC Number	Bibliographic Citation
87315	**IR ABSORPTION COEFFICIENTS AND REFRACTIVE INDICES OF CARBON DIOXIDE AND STEAM.** POPOV, YU. A. SHVARTSBLAT, R. L. HIGH TEMP. 12 (6), 1047–50, 1974. (ENGLISH TRANSLATION OF TEPLOFIZ. VYS. TEMP., 12 (6), 1188–92, 1974; FOR ORIGINAL SEE E87314)
87318	**EFFECT OF ADDITIONS OF VARIOUS ELEMENTS ON THE THERMO–EMF AND HALL EFFECT OF ANTIMONY SELENIDE IN THE LIQUID STATE.** KAZANDZHAN, B. I. MUSHUTKINA, T. I. SELIN, YU. I. TEPLOFIZ. VYS. TEMP. 12 (6), 1312–3, 1974. (FOR ENGLISH TRANSLATION SEE E87319)
87319	**EFFECT OF ADDITIONS OF VARIOUS ELEMENTS ON THE THERMO–EMF AND HALL EFFECT OF ANTIMONY SELENIDE IN THE LIQUID STATE.** KAZANDZHAN, B. I. MUSHUTKINA, T. I. SELIN, YU. I. HIGH TEMP. 12 (6), 1164–5, 1974. (ENGLISH TRANSLATION OF TEPLOFIZ. VYS. TEMP., 12 (6), 1312–3, 1974; FOR ORIGINAL SEE E87318)
87324	**METHODS OF MEASUREMENT FOR SEMICONDUCTOR MATERIALS, PROCESS OONTROL, AND DEVICES.** BULLIS, W. M. NATIONAL BUREAU OF STANDARDS, WASHINGTON, D. C., 41PP., 1969. (AD–692 232 NBS–TN–488)
87361	**THE THERMOELECTRIC EFFECT OF SILVER IODIDE.** HUNGER, H. F. ARMY ELECTRONICS COMMAND, FORT MONMOUTH, N. J. 34PP., 1971. (AD–724 110, ECOM–3418)
87364	**BORON CARBIDE. SURVEY OF SOLID–STATE PROPERTIES.** ALEXANDER, M. N. ARMY MATERUALS AND MECHANICS RESEARCH CENTER, WATERTOWN, MASS, 11PP., 1971. (AD–725 518 AMMRC–TR–71–7)
87384	**THEORY OF TITANIUM ALLOYS FOR HIGH–TEMPERATURE STRENGTH.** COLLINGS, E. W. HO. J. C. JAFFEE, R. I. BATTELLE COLUMBUS LABS., COLUMBUS, OHIO 58PP., 1971. AD–736 053, AFML–TR–71–228
87440	**DETERMINATION OF THE STRESS–OPTIC COEFFICIENTS OF ZINC SELENIDE.** GOLDSTEIN, L. F. THOMPSON, J. S. SCHROEDER, J. B. SLATTERY, J. E. AEROSPACE CORP., EL SEGUNDO, CALIFORNIA 19PP., 1974. (AD–A007 778)
87441	**LASER WINDOW SURFACE FINISHING AND COATING TECHNOLOGY.** BRAUNSTEIN, M. BRAUNSTEIN, A. ALLEN, S. D. GENTILE, A. L. GIULIANO, C. R. HUGHES RESEARCH LABS., MALIBU, CALIF. 103PP., 1975. (N75–24466, AD–A007 791, AFCRL–TR–75–0041)
87444	**THERMOELECTRIC PROPERTIES OF CERAMIC REFRACTORY SEMICONDUCTORS.** GORYACHEV, YU. M. YARMOLA, T. M. CONF. ON CERAMICS FOR ELECTRONICS, 4TH 1–12, 1971. (FOR ENGLISH TRANSLATION SEE E87445)
87445	**THERMOELECTRIC PROPERTIES OF CERAMIC REFRACTORY SEMICONDUCTORS.** GOYACHEV, YU. M. YARMOLA, T. M. ARMY FOREIGN SCIENCE AND TECHNOLOGY CENTER, CHARLOTTESVILLE, VA. 17PP., 1974. (ENGLISH TRANSLATION OF CONF. ON CERAMICS FOR ELECTRONICS, 4TH, 1–12, 1971; FOR ORIGNAL SEE E87444) (AD–A007 862, FSTC–HT–23–0005–75, N75–24519)
87448	**IR WINDOW STUDIES.** KROGER, F. A. MARBURGER, J. H. UNIVERSITY OF SOUTHERN CALIF., LOS ANGELES 111PP., 1974. (N75–25170, AD–A007 975, AFCRL–TR–74–0557)
87482	**LASER DAMAGE IN MATERIALS.** FELDMAN, A. HOROWITZ, D. WAXLER, R. M. NATIONAL BUREAU OF STANDARDS, IST. FOR MATERIALS RESEARCH, WASHINGTON, D. C. 52PP., 1973. (AD–757 789, N73–24554, NBSIR–73–119)

EPIC Number	Bibliographic Citation
87532	**INVESTIGATION OF THE ROLE OF DAMPING IN THE ABSORPTION OF LIGHT BY EXCITONS.** KREINGOL'D, F. I. MAKAROV, V. L. FIZ. TVERD. TELA 17 (2), 472–7, 1975. (FOR ENGLISH TRANSLATION SEE E87533)
87533	**INVESTIGATION OF THE ROLE OF DAMPING IN THE ABSORPTION OF LIGHT BY EXCITONS.** KREINGOL'D, F. I. MAKAROV, V. L. SOV. PHYS. SOLID STATE 17 (2), 297–9, 1975. (ENGLISH TRANSLATION OF FIZ. TVERD. TELA, 17 (2), 472–7, 1975; FOR ORIGINAL SEE E87532)
87534	**ACTIVATION ENERGY OF HOPPING CONDUCTION.** SKAL, A. S. SHKLOVSKII, B. I. EFROS, A. L. FIZ. TVERD. TELA 17 (2), 506–13, 1975. (FOR ENGLISH TRANSLATION SEE E87535)
87535	**ACTIVATION ENERGY OF HOPPING CONDUCTION.** SKAL, A. S. SHKLOVSKII, B. I. EFROS, A. L. SOV. PHYS. SOLID STATE 17 (2), 316–20, 1975. (ENGLISH TRANSLATION OF FIZ. TVERD. TELA, 17 (2), 506–13, 1975; FOR ORIGINAL SEE E87534)
87578	**A SURVEY OF IONIZATION POTENTIALS OF COMBUSTION PRODUCTS.** O'BRYAN, K. K. BROWN, B. PROC. MEETING INTERAGENCY CHEM. ROCKET PROPULSION GROUP THERMOCHEM., 2ND 1, 1–12, 1964. (AD–451 711, N65–14647)
87606	**ELECTRONIC CONDUCTION.** WIMMER, J. M. BRANSKY, I. CERAM. GLASS: SCI. TECHNOL. 4, 269–311, 1974.
87614	**NON–OHMIC TRANSPORT IN SEMICONDUCTORS.** FAWCETT, W. ELECTRONS CRYST. SOLIDS, LECT. INT. COURSE 531–618, 1973.
87615	**BAND STRUCTURE OF SEMICONDUCTORS.** ANTONCIK, E. ELECTRONS CRYST. SOLIDS, LECT. INT. COURSE 461–530, 1973.
87639	**SOLID STATE ASPECTS OF SOLAR ENERGY CONVERSION—AN INTRODUCTION.** SERAPHIN, B. O. PHYS.–GRUNDLAGE TECH., PLENARVORTR. PHYSIKERTAG., 38TH 159–82, 1974.
87656	**THERMIONIC EMISSION AND WORK FUNCTION.** HAAS, G. A. THOMAS, R. E. TECH. MET. RES. 6, (PT. 1), 91–262, 1972.
87659	**CADMIUM TELLURIDE. DATA SHEETS.** NEUBERGER, M. HUGHES AIRCRAFT CO., CULVER CITY, CALIF. 49PP., 1962. (AD–415 331, EPIC–DS–101, N63–21787)
87660	**INDIUM PHOSPHIDE. DATA SHEETS.** NEUBERGER, M. HUGHES AIRCRAFT CO., CULVER CITY, CALIF. 29PP., 1962. (AD–414 847, EPIC–DS–102, N63–21794)
87661	**INDIUM TELLURIDE. DATA SHEETS.** NEUBERGER, M. HUGHES AIRCRAFT CO., CULVER CITY, CALIF. 27PP., 1962. (AD–414 896, EPIC–DS–103, N63–21792)
87662	**MAGNESIUM SILICIDE. DATA SHEETS.** NEUBERGER, M. HUGHES AIRCRAFT CO., CULVER CITY, CALIF. 14PP., 1962. (AD–414 895, EPIC–DS–104, N63–21797)
87666	**ZINC TELLURIDE. DATA SHEETS.** NEUBERGER, M. HUGHES AIRCRAFT CO., CULVER CITY, CALIF. 24PP., 1962. (AD–413 939, EPIC–DS–108, N63–20286)
87667	**INDIUM ARSENIDE. DATA SHEETS.** NEUBERGER, M. HUGHES AIRCRAFT CO., CULVER CITY, CALIF. 57PP., 1962. (AD–413 892, EPIC–DS–109, N63–20380)
87668	**ALUMINUM ANTIMONIDE. DATA SHEETS.** NEUBERGER, M. HUGHES AIRCRAFT CO., CULVER CITY, CALIF. 43PP., 1962. (AD–413 676, EPIC–DS–110, N63–20299)

EPIC Number	Bibliographic Citation
87669	GALLIUM PHOSPHIDE. DATA SHEETS. NEUBERGER, M. HUGHES AIRCRAFT CO., CULVER CITY, CALIF. 23PP., 1962. (AD-413 954, EPIC-DS-111, N63-20296)
87670	GALLIUM ANTIMONIDE. DATA SHEETS. NEUBERGER, M. HUGHES AIRCRAFT CO., CULVER CITY, CALIF. 51PP., 1962. (AD-413 775, EPIC-DS-112, N63-20381)
87671	LEAD TELLURIDE. DATA SHEETS. NEUBERGER, M. HUGHES AIRCRAFT CO., CULVER CITY, CALIF. 35PP., 1962. (AD-437 311, EPIC-DS-113, N63-20297)
87672	MAGNESIUM STANNIDE. DATA SHEETS. NEUBERGER, M. HUGHES AIRCRAFT CO., CULVER CITY, CALIF. 23PP., 1962. (AD-413 825, EPIC-DS-114, N63-20298)
87673	GALLIUM ARSENIDE. DATA SHEETS. NEUBERGER, M. HUGHES AIRCRAFT CO., CULVER CITY, CALIF. 91PP., 1962. (AD-437 310, EPIC-DS-115, N63-20402)
87674	LEAD SELENIDE. DATA SHEETS. NEUBERGER, M. HUGHES AIRCRAFT CO., CULVER CITY, CALIF. 43PP., 1962. (AD-437 309, EPIC-DS-116, N63-20401)
87679	INDIUM ANTIMONIDE, DATA SHEETS. NEUBERGER, M. HUGHES AIRCRAFT CO., CULVER CITY, CALIF. 201PP., 1963. (AD-413 754, EPIC-DS-121, N63-20304)
87681	BERYLLIUM OXIDE. DATA SHEETS. MILEK, J. T. HUGHES AIRCRAFT CO., CULVER CITY, CALIF. 21PP., 1963. (AD-413 831, EPIC-DS-123, N63-20405)
87682	MAGNESIUM OXIDE. DATA SHEETS. MILEK, J. T. HUGHES AIRCRAFT CO., CULVER CITY, CALIF. 45PP., 1963. (AD-413 809, EPIC-DS-125, N63-20306)
87699	SPECTROPHOTOMETRIC STUDY OF TETRAGONAL TUNGSTEN BRONZE CRYSTALS. FUJIEDA, S. NAT. SCI. REP. OCHANOMIZU UNIV. 25 (1), 35-43, 1974.
87701	GALLIUM ARSENIDE. DATA SHEETS. NEUBERGER, M. HUGHES AIRCRAFT CO., CULVER CITY, CALIFORNIA 122PP., 1964. (AD-465 160, EPIC-DS-144)
87702	SILICON CARBIDE. DATA SHEETS. NEUBERGER, M. HUGHES AIRCRAFT CO., CULVER CITY, CALIFORNIA 105PP., 1965. (AD-456 161, EPIC-DS-145)
87703	GALLIUM PHOSPHIDE AND THE GALLIUM ARSENIDE-GALLIUM PHOSPHIDE SYSTEM. DATA SHEETS. NEUBERGER, M. HUGHES AIRCRAFT CO., CULVER CITY, CALIFORNIA 94PP., 1965. (AD-467 537, EPIC-DS-146)
87709	ZINC OXIDE, DATA SHEETS NEUBERGER, M. HUGHES AIRCRAFT CO., CULVER CITY, CALIF. 44PP., 1963. (AD-425 212, EPIC-DS-133, N64-14094)
87710	CADMIUM SELENIDE. DATA SHEETS. NEUBERGER, M. HUGHES AIRCRAFT CO., CULVER CITY, CALIF. 54PP., 1963. (AD-425 216, EPIC-DS-134, N64-14040)
87711	ZINC SULFIDE. DATA SHEETS. NEUBERGER, M. GRIGSBY, D. L. HUGHES AIRCRAFT CO., CULVER CITY, CALIF. 72PP., 1963. (AD-427 288, EPIC-DS-135, N64-13957)
87712	ZINC SULFIDE. DATA SHEETS, 2ND EDITION. NEUBERGER, M. GRIGSBY, D. L. HUGHES AIRCRAFT CO., CULVER CITY, CALIFORNIA 173PP., 1966. (AD-803 885, EPIC-DS-135/2ED.)
87713	ALUMINUM OXIDE. DATA SHEETS. MILEK, J. T. HUGHES AIRCRAFT CO., CULVER CITY, CALIF. 161PP., 1964. (AD-434 173, EPIC-DS-136, N64-18384)
87717	SULFUR HEXAFLUORIDE. DATA SHEETS. MILEK, J. T. HUGHES AIRCRAFT CO., CULVER CITY, CALIF. 68PP., 1964. (AD-607 949, EPIC-DS-140, N65-14093)
87719	FLUOROCARBON GASES. DATA SHEETS. MILEK, J. T. HUGHES AIRCRAFT CO., CULVER CITY, CALIF. 111PP., 1964. (AD-608 897, EPIC-DS-142, N65-15978)
87721	NIOBIUM ALLOYS AND COMPOUNDS. GRIBSBY, D. L. HUGHES AIRCRAFT CO., CULVER CITY, CALIFORNIA 277PP., 1966. (AD-480 000, EPIC-DS-148)
87723	MAGNESIUM OXIDE. NEUBERGER, M. CARTER, D. B. HUGHES AIRCRAFT CO., CULVER CITY, CALIF. 99PP., 1969. (AD-698 343, EPIC-DS-163)
87741	HEAVILY DOPED CRYSTALS OF N-TYPE INDIUM ANTIMONIDE. FILIPCHENKO, A. S. NASLEDOV, D. N. PHYS. STATUS DOLIDI (GERMANY) 27 A (1), 11-26, 1975.
87747	DETERMINATION OF OPTICAL CONSTANTS: DERIVATIVE SPECTRA FROM ELLIPSOMETRIC DATA. JUNGK, G. PHYS. STATUS SOLIDI (GERMANY) 67 B (1), 85-92, 1975.
87755	DETERMINATION OF THE REFRACTIVE INDEX OF PHOTOCONDUCTIVE MATERIALS. KISELEVA, N. K. KOLOMIETS, B. T. PRIB. TEKH. EKSP. 17 (5), (PT. 2), 171-3, 1974. (FOR ENGLISH TRANSLATION SEE E92229)
87759	REVIEW ON HIGH POWER LASER DAMAGE TO MATERIALS 11. GHOSH, A. K. RCA REV. 35 (2), 279-319, 1974.
87770	PRESSURE-INDUCED SEMICONDUCTOR-METAL TRANSITIONS IN AMORPHOUS SILICON, GERMANIUM, AND INDIUM ANTIMONIDE. MINOMURA, S. SHIMOMURA, O. SAKI, N. ASAUMI, K. ENDO, H. TAMURA, K. FUKUSHIMA, J. TSUJI, K. AIP CONF. PROC. 20, 234-40, 1974.
87781	INDIUM ANTIMONIDE. DATA SHEETS. 2ND EDITION. NEUBERGER, M. HUGHES AIRCRAFT CO., CULVER CITY, CALIFORNIA 201PP., 1965. (AD-476 675, EPIC-DS-121/2ED.)
87783	LINEARITY OF CALIBRATION CURVES AND INTENSITY OF SPECTRA IN THE ATTENUATED TOTAL REFLECTION METHOD. MATSUI, T. KURODA, K. TANAKA, S. BUNSEKI KAGAKU 23 (9), 1062-8, 1974.
87791	BEHAVIOUR OF DIELECTRIC MATERIALS AND ELECTRICAL CONDUCTORS AT CRYOGENIC TEMPERATURES. MILEK, J. T. HUGHES AIRCRAFT CO., CULVER CITY, CALIF. 87PP., 1965. (EPIC-IR-5)
87803	A SELECTED BIBLIOGRAPHY AND DATA ON BORON NITRIDE. NEUBERGER, M. HUGHES AIRCRAFT CO., CULVER CITY, CALIF. 58PP., 1966. (EPIC-IR-17)
87805	COLLECTED DATA AND BIBLIOGRAPHY ON SILICON NITRIDE. NEUBERGER, M. HUGHES AIRCRAFT CO., CULVER CITY, CALIF. 45PP., 1968. (EPIC-IR-19)
87819	EPITAXIAL SILICON AND GALLIUM ARSENIDE THIN FILMS ON INSULATING CERAMIC SUBSTRATES. A STATE-OF-THE-ART REPORT. MILEK, J. T. HUGHES AIRCRAFT CO., CULVER CITY, CALIF. 146PP., 1968. (AD-675 578, EPIC-S-9)
87821	BIBLIOGRAPHY OF III-V SEMICONDUCTING FILMS. NEUBERGER, M. HUGHES AIRCRAFT CO., CULVER CITY, CALIF. 92PP., 1969. (AD-701 074, EPIC-S-13)

EPIC Number	Bibliographic Citation
87822	**LINEAR ELECTROOPTIC MODULATOR MATERIALS.** MILEK, J. T. WELLES, S. J. HUGHES AIRCRAFT CO., CULVER CITY, CALIF. 260PP., 1970. (AD-704 556, EPIC-S-14)
87823	**II-VI TERNARY COMPOUNDS DATA TABLES.** NEUBERGER, M. HUGHES AIRCRAFT CO., CULVER CITY, CALIF. 96PP., 1972. (AD-739 359, EPIC-S-15, N72-27799)
87824	**IV-VI TERNARY SEMICONDUCTING COMPOUNDS DATA TABLES.** NEUBERGER, M. HUGHES AIRCRAFT CO., CULVER CITY, CALIF. 80PP., 1972. (AD-740 208, EPIC-S-16, N72-29743)
87828	**SILICON CARBIDE DATA TABLE AND SUPPLEMENTARY BIBLIOGRAPHY.** NEUBERGER, M. HUGHES AIRCRAFT CO., CULVER CITY, CALIF. 44PP., 1968. (EPIC-IR-62, S-1)
87830	**EVALUATED BIBLIOGRAPHY ON ALUMINUM ANTIMONIDE, NITRIDE, PHOSPHIDE, ARSENIDE AND BISMUTHIDE.** NEUBERGER, M. HUGHES AIRCRAFT CO., CULVER CITY, CALIF. 35PP., 1966. (EPIC-IR-23)
87831	**INFRA-RED SENSORS.** NEUBERGER, M. HUGHES AIRCRAFT CO., CULVER CITY, CALIF. 78PP., 1966. (EPIC-IR-24)
87833	**ELECTRICAL PROPERTIES OF THIN FILM TIN OXIDE.** NEUBERGER, M. MILEK, J. T. HUGHES AIRCRAFT CO., CULVER CITY, CALIF. 36PP., 1966. (EPIC-IR-26)
87841	**DATA AND LITERATURE SURVEY ON VARIOUS PROPERTIES OF THALLIUM BROMIDE - IODIDE.** MILEK, J. T. HUGHES AIRCRAFT CO., CULVER CITY, CALIF. 40PP., 1966. (EPIC-IR-34)
87843	**ELECTRICAL RESISTIVITY OF ORDERED COPPER GOLD ALLOYS.** GRIGSBY, D. L. HUGHES AIRCRAFT CO., CULVER CITY, CALIF. 23PP., 1966. (EPIC-IR-36)
87846	**ELECTRICAL RESISTIVITY OF SEVERAL OXIDES AT 20C, 1000C, AND 1500C.** WELLES, S. J. HUGHES AIRCRAFT CO., CULVER CITY, CALIF. 7PP., 1966. (AD-812 497, EPIC-IR-39)
87855	**PHYSICAL AND DIELECTRIC PROPERTY DATA ON GASES.** MILEK, J. T. HUGHES AIRCRAFT CO., CULVER CITY, CALIF. 56PP., 1967. (EPIC-IR-48)
87860	**SOME ELECTRICAL PROPERTIES OF SILVER, SILVER OXIDE AND SILVER SULFIDE.** MILEK, J. T. HUGHES AIRCRAFT CO., CULVER CITY, CALIF. 28PP., 1967. (EPIC-IR-53)
87864	**CABLE AND WIRE INSULATION FOR EXTREME ENVIRONMENTS.** MILEK, J. T. HUGHES AIRCRAFT CO., CULVER CITY, CALIF. 92PP., 1967. (AD-735 626, EPIC-IR-57)
87866	**THIN FILM DIELECTRIC FOR MICROELECTRONICS. A BIBLIOGRAPHY COMPILATION.** MILEK, J. T. HUGHES AIRCRAFT CO., CULVER CITY, CALIF. 34PP., 1968. (AD-689 755, EPIC-IR-63)
87870	**DIELECTRIC CONSTANTS OF RUBBERS, PLASTICS AND CERAMICS. A DESIGN GUIDE.** AKAWIE, R. I. MILEK, J. T. HUGHES AIRCRAFT CO., CULVER CITY, CALIF. 18PP., 1969. (AD-735 628, EPIC-IR-67)
87871	**ANTIFERROELECTRICITY AND ANTIFERROELECTRIC MATERIALS.** MILEK, J. T. HUGHES AIRCRAFT CO., CULVER CITY, CALIF. 8PP., 1970. (AD-735 629, EPIC-IR-68)
87872	**CUPROUS SULFIDE AND CUPROUS SULFIDE - CADMIUM SULFIDE HETEROJUNCTIONS.** NEUBERGER, M. HUGHES AIRCRAFT CO., CULVER CITY, CALIF. 54PP., 1971. (AD-734 536, EPIC-IR-69)
87876	**HEAT TRANSFER AND COOLING OF ELECTRONIC COMPONENTS AND EQUIPMENT.** SMITH, D. C. HUGHES AIRCRAFT CO., CULVER CITY, CALIF. 20PP., 1972. (AD-746 431, EPIC-IR-73)
87879	**THE ELECTRO-OPTIC EFFECT AND PROPERTIES OF GALLIUM ARSENIDE FOR MODULATION APPLICATIONS.** MILEK, J. T. HUGHES AIRCRAFT CO., CULVER CITY, CALIF. 10PP., 1970. (EPIC-IR-77)
87880	**THICK FILM DIELECTRIC FUNCTIONAL INKS AND PASTES.** ELECTRONIC PROPERTIES INFORMATION CENTER. HUGHES AIRCRAFT CO., CULVER CITY, CALIF. 51PP., 1971. (EPIC-IR-78)
87881	**DATA COMPILATION ON VANADIUM OXIDES.** NEUBERGER, M. HUGHES AIRCRAFT CO., CULVER CITY, CALIF. 61PP., 1971. (AD-734 596, EPIC-IR-79)
87883	**OPTICAL MATERIALS PROPERTIES.** MOSES, A. J. HANDBOOK OF ELECTRONIC MATERIALS 1, 104PP., 1971.
87884	**III-V SEMICONDUCTING COMPOUNDS.** NEUBERGER, M. HANDBOOK OF ELECTRONIC MATERIALS 2, 115PP., 1971.
87885	**SILICON NITRIDE FOR MICROELECTRONIC APPLICATIONS. PART 1. PREPARATION AND PROPERTIES.** MILEK, J. T. HANDBOOK OF ELECTRONIC MATERIALS 3, 118PP., 1971.
87886	**NIOBIUM ALLOYS AND COMPOUNDS.** NEUBERGER, M. S. GRIGSBY, D. L. VEAZIE, W. H., JR. HANDBOOK OF ELECTRONIC MATERIALS 4, 70PP., 1972.
87887	**GROUP IV SEMICONDUCTING MATERIALS.** NEUBERGER, M. HANDBOOK OF ELECTRONIC MATERIALS 5, 67PP., 1971.
87888	**SILICON NITRIDE FOR MICROELECTRONIC APPLICATIONS. PART 2. APPLICATIONS AND DEVICES.** MILEK, J. T. HANDBOOK OF ELECTRONIC MATERIALS 6, 117PP., 1972.
87889	**III-V TERNARY SEMICONDUCTING COMPOUNDS-DATA TABLES.** NEUBERGER, M. HANDBOOK OF ELECTRONIC MATERIALS 7, 56PP., 1972.
87890	**LINEAR ELECTROOPTIC MODULAR MATERIALS.** MILEK, J. T. NEUBERGER, M. HANDBOOK OF ELECTRONIC MATERIALS 8, 258PP., 1972.
87891	**ELECTRONIC PROPERTIES OF COMPOSITE MATERIALS.** LEEDS, M. A. HANDBOOK OF ELECTRONIC MATERIALS 9, 103PP., 1972.
87918	**FURTHER REMARKS ON THE IMPROVEMENT OF PELTIER JUNCTIONS FOR THERMOELECTRIC COOLING.** LANDECKER, K. ENERGY CONVERS. 14 (1), 21-33, 1974.
87919	**ELECTRICAL CONDUCTORS AT LOW TEMPERATURE AND SUPERCONDUCTORS IN ELECTROTECHNOLOGY.** CROITORU, Z. ENTROPIE 56, 29-39, 1974.
87930	**OPTICAL PROPERTIES OF HALOGEN ION IMPURITIES IN CADMIUM HALIDES.** KITAMURA, T. NAKAWAWA, H. MATSUMOTO, H. FUKUI DAIGAKU KOGAKUBU KENKYU HOKOKU 22 (2), 217-29, 1974.
87931	**CHANGE IN THE THERMOELECTRIC PROPERTIES OF VACUUM CONDENSATES OF A BISMUTH TELLURIDE SELENIDE SOLID SOLUTION DURING THEIR DEPOSITION.** ARIFOV, U. A. KULAGIN, A. I. ERZIN, N. I. MAKOV, N. V. TURSUNOV, B. SAIDVALIEVA, M. GELIOTEKHNIKA (4), 3-6, 1974.

EPIC Number	Bibliographic Citation

87962 **CADMIUM TELLURIDE FILMS.**
AZIMOV, S. A. AFUZOV, A. YA. ATAKULOV, B.
BILYALOV, E. I. MIRZAAKHMEDOV, A.
IZV. AKAD. NAUK UZB. SSR, SER. FIZ.-MAT. NAUK
18 (5), 61, 1974.

87984 **KRAMERS-KRONIG DISPERSION ANALYSIS OF LITHIUM FLUORINE REFLECTANCE DATA OBTAINED AT AMBIENT AND LOW TEMPERATURES.**
KACHANE, A. SORIAGA, M. P. ANDERMANN, G.
J. OPT. SOC. AM. (USA)
64 (11), 1450-5, 1974.

88040 **SUPERCONDUCTIVITY OF LUTETIUM AT VERY HIGH PRESSURE. IMPLICATIONS WITH RESPECT TO THE SUPERCONDUCTIVITY OF LANTHANUM.**
WITTIG, J. PROBST, C. WIEDEMANN, W.
LOW TEMP. PHYS.-LT 13, PROC. INT. CONF. LOW TEMP. PHYS., 13TH
3, 490-4, 1974.
(EDITED BY KLAUS D. TIMMERHAUS, WILLIAM J. O'SULLIVAN; E. F. HAMMEL, PLENUM: NEW YORK, N.Y.)

88049 **NEUTRON SCATTERING, PHONON SPECTRA, AND SUPERCONDUCTIVITY.**
SMITH, H. G. WAKABAYASHI, N. NICKLOW, R. M.
MIHAILOVICH, S.
LOW TEMP. PHYS.-LT 13, PROC. INT. CONF. LOW TEMP. PHYS., 13TH
3, 615-18, 1974.

88053 **POSSIBILITIES OF RAISING THE CRITICAL TEMPERATURE OF SUPERCONDUCTORS.**
ZHARKOV, G. F.
LOW TEMP. PHYS.-LT 13, PROC. INT. CONF. LOW TEMP. PHYS., 13TH
3, 729-34, 1974.
(EDITED BY KLAUS D. TIMMERHAUS, WILLIAM J. O'SULLIVAN; E. F. HAMMEL, PLENUM: NEW YORK, N.Y.)

88072 **ANOMALOUS PHOTOVOLTAGE IN CADMIUM TELLURIDE FILMS.**
QUARTLY, J. R. ERTL, M. E.
SOLID- STATE ELECTRON.
17 (9), 998-9, 1974.

88134 **THEORY OF THERMIONIC EMISSION. I. CRITICISM OF THE SEMICONDUCTOR MODEL OF THE OXIDE-COATED CATHODE.**
CHANG, E.-C.
WU LI HSUEH PAO
23 (5), 341-50, 1974.

88156 **ANISOTROPIC SYNTHETIC THERMOELEMENTS AND THEIR MAXIMUM CAPABILITIES.**
BABIN, V. P. GUDKIN, T. S. DASHEVSKII, Z. M.
DUDKIN, L. D. IORDANISHVILI, E. K.
KAIDANOV, V. I. KOLOMOETS, N. V.
NARVA, O. M. STIL'BANS, L. S.
FIZ. TEKH. POLUPROV.
8 (4), 748-53, 1974.
(FOR ENGLISH TRANSLATION SEE E88157)

88157 **ANISOTROPIC SYNTHETIC THERMOELEMENTS AND THEIR MAXIMUM CAPABILITIES.**
BABIN, V. P. GUDKIN, T. S. DASHEVSKII, Z. M.
DUDKIN, L. D. IORDANISHVILI, E. K.
KAIDANOV, V. I. KOLOMOETS, N. V.
NARVA, O. M. STIL'BANS, L. S.
SOV. PHYS. SEMICOND.
8 (4), 478-81, 1974.
(ENGLISH TRANSLATION OF FIZ. TEKH. POLUPROV., 8 (4), 748-53, 1974; FOR ORIGINAL SEE E88156)

88174 **II-VI PHOTOVOLTAIC HETEROJUNCTIONS FOR SOLAR ENERGY CONVERSION.**
FAHRENBRUCH, A. L. VASILCHENKO, V. BUCH, F.
MITCHELL, K. BUBE, R. H.
APPL. PHYS. LETT. (USA)
25 (10), 605-8, 1974.

88179 **OPTICAL PROPERTIES OF CADMIUM FLUORIDE SINGLE CRYSTALS IN THE VACUUM ULTRAVIOLET.**
BERGER, J. M. LEVEQUE, G. ROBIN, J.
C. R. HEBD. SEANCES ACAD. SCI (FRANCE)
279 B (20), 509-12, 1974.

88184 **RADIATIVE HEAT TRANSFER IN HIGH TEMPERATURE THERMOELECTRIC MATERIALS.**
DIXON, A. J. ERTL, M. E. GOLDSMID, H. J.
ENERGY CONVERS.
14 (2), 47-8, 1975.

88201 **SINGLE CRYSTAL GROWTH AND OPTICAL ELASTIC, AND PIEZOELECTRIC PROPERTIES OF POLAR MAGNESIUM BARIUM FLUORIDE.**
RECKER, K. WALLRAFEN, F.
J. CRYST. GROWTH
26 (1), 97-100, 1974.

88203 **OPTICAL CHARACTERIZATION OF COMPOUND SEMICONDUCTOR ALLOYS.**
ONTON, A. LORENZ, M. R. WOODALL, J. M.
J. CRYST. GROWTH (NETHERLANDS)
27 (1), 166-76, 1974.

88214 **UNIFIED APPROACH TO THE DC AND AC CONDUCTIVITY AND OPTICAL ABSORPTION OF AMORPHOUS SEMICONDUCTORS BELOW THE FUNDAMENTAL EDGE.**
CAPEK, V.
J. PHYS.
8 C (4), 479-91, 1975.

88215 **SPECTRAL DEPENDENCE OF THE SURFACE PHOTOVOLTAGE IN CADMIUM SULFIDE.**
CHANNON, M. A. MALTBY, J. R. REED, C. E.
SCOTT, C. G.
J. PHYS.
8 D (3), L39-L41, 1975.

88219 **THE ANOMALOUS PHOTOVOLTAIC EFFECT IN ZINC SELENIDE.**
CUTTER, J. R. WOODS, J.
J. PHYS.
8 D (3), 314-21, 1975.

88234 **ELECTRONIC PROPERTIES OF LIQUID INDIUM-BISMUTH ALLOYS.**
OHNO, S. TAMAKI, S.
J. PHYS. SOC. JAP.
38 (2), 538-45, 1975.

88237 **THERMAL EMISSION, ELECTRICAL CONDUCTIVITY, AND HALL EFFECT FOR DEFECTS STUDY AT HIGH TEMPERATURE ($T \geq 1250K$) IN REFRACTORY OXIDES (YTTRIUM OXIDE TITANIUM OXIDE).**
ODIER, PH. BAUMARD, J. F. PANIS, D.
ANTHONY, A. M.
4. SOLID STATE CHEM.
12 (3-4), 324-8, 1975.

88264 **RESISTIVITY OF N-TYPE BISMUTH TELLURIDE FROM 1.3 TO 300 DEGREES K.**
PAWLEWICZ, W. T. RAYNE, J. A.
URE, R. W., JR.
LOW TEMP. PHYS.-LT 13, PROC. INT. CONF. LOW TEMP. PHYS., 13TH
4, 368-72, 1974.

88274 **EFFECTS OF ION BEAM POLISHING ON ALKALI HALIDE LASER WINDOW MATERIALS.**
BRUCE, J. A. COMER, J. J. COLLINS, C. V.
MATER. RES. BULL. (USA)
9 (11), 1531-42, 1974.

88285 **INDEX DISPERSION ABOVE THE FUNDAMENTAL BAND EDGE IN NITROGEN DOPED GALLIUM ARSENIDE PHOSPHIDE.**
COLEMAN, J. J. HOLONYAK, N., JR.
LUDOWISE, M. J. KUNZ, A. B. ALTARELLI, M.
PHYS. REV. LETT. (USA)
33 (26), 1566-9, 1974.

88288 **GRAIN SIZE EFFECT ON THE FIGURE OF MERIT OF SINTERED SOLID SOLUTIONS BASED ON BISMUTH TELLURIDE.**
JAKLOVSZKY, J. IONESCU, R. NISTOR, N.
CHICULITA, A.
PHYS. STATUS DOLIDI (GERMANY)
27 (2), 329-32, 1975.

88316 **TWO-PHOTON ABSORPTION IN CADMIUM SELENIDE.**
BRYUKNER, F. OHEPROVSKII, V. S.
KHATTATOV, V. U.
SOV. J. QUANTUM ELECTRON.
4 (6), 749-51, 1974.
(ENGLISH TRANSLATION OF KVANTOVAYA ELECTRON., 1 (6), 1360-4, 1974; FOR ORIGINAL SEE E64570)

88331 **QUANTUM THEORY OF THE THERMOELECTRIC POWER OF SEMICONDUCTORS WITH NONPARABOLIC BANDS.**
ASKEROV, B. M. EMINOV, R. F.
FIZ. TEKH. POLUPROV.
8 (5), 950-3, 1974.
(FOR ENGLISH TRANSLATION SEE E88332)

88332 **QUANTUM THEORY OF THE THERMOELECTRIC POWER OF SEMICONDUCTORS WITH NONPARABOLIC BANDS.**
ASKEROV, B. M. EMINOV, R. F.
SOV. PHYS. SEMICOND.
8 (5), 611-3, 1974.
(ENGLISH TRANSLATION OF FIZ. TEKH. POLUPROV., 8 (5), 950-3, 1974; FOR ORIGINAL SEE E88331)

88343 **REFRACTIVE INDEX OF LEAD TIN TELLURIDE, LEAD - TIN SELENIDE, AND LEAD SULFUR SELENIDE AND THEORETICAL CALCULATIONS FOR LEAD TIN TELLURIDE AND LEAD TIN SELENIDE 10.6 MICRON HETEROSTRUCTURE INJECTION LASERS.**
OPYD, W. G.
NAVAL POSTGRADUATE SCHOOL, MONTEREY, CALIFORNIA
92PP., 1973.
(AD-767 677, N74-14432)

88429 **THERMOELECTRIC PROPERTIES OF GALLIUM SYSTEM ALLOYS UNDER STANDARD CONDITIONS.**
IORDANISHVILI, E. K. KARTENKO, N. F.
ORLOV, A. G. FINOGENOV, A. D.
ARMY FOREIGN SCIENCE AND TECHNOLOGY CENTER, CHARLOTTESVILLE, VA.
13PP., 1974.
(ENGLISH TRANSLATION OF GELIOTEKHNIKA, (4), 36-42, 1972; FOR ORIGINAL SEE E 55387)
(AD-A331 135, FSTC-HT-23-0015-74)

EPIC Number	Bibliographic Citation

88455 **OPTICAL MATERIALS CHARACTERIZATION.**
FELDMAN, A. HOROWITZ, D. WAXLER, R. M.
MALITSON, I. DODGE, M. J.
INST. OF BASIC STANDARDS, NATIONAL BUREAU OF STANDARDS, WASHINGTON, D. C.
18PP., 1975.
(AD-A005 410, NBSIR-75-639)

88462 **COMBINED ELLIPSOMETRIC AND SOFT X-RAY SPECTROSCOPIC STUDIES OF CORROSION PROCESSES ON TRANSPARENT MATERIALS.**
VEDAM, K. WHITE, E. W.
PENNSYLVANIA STATE UNIV., UNIVERSITY PARK
64PP., 1974.
(AD-A005 656, N75-28232)

88464 **PROTON BOMBARDMENT ON LEAD TIN TELLURIDE AND THEIR ISOCHRONAL ANNEALING.**
TAO, T. F. WANG, C. C. DANDERSON, D.
SIMONS, D. SCHOOLAR, R. B.
NAVAL POSTGRADUATE SCHOOL, MONTEREY, CALIF.
4PP., 1974.
(AD-A005 702, AFML-TR-74-162, NPS-52TV74-1)

88465 **LEAD - TIN CHALCOGENIDE ALLOY THIN FILM PHOTOCONDUCTIVE DETECTORS.**
TAO, T. F. WANG, C. C. HOLMQUIST, K.
MC BRIDE, W.
NAVAL POSTGRADUATE SCHOOL, MONTEREY, CALIF.
23PP., 1974.
(AD-A005 702, AFML-TR-74-162, NPS-52TV74-1, N75-28935)

88485 **SPECTRAL EMITTANCE MEASUREMENTS ON SOME LASER WINDOW MATERIALS.**
SKOLNIK, L. H.
AIR FORCE CAMBRIDGE RESEARCH LABS., HANSCOM AIR FORCE BASE, MASS.
22PP., 1974.
(AD-A006 034, AFCRL-PSRP-615, AFCRL-TR-74-0590 N75-30548)

88488 **INVESTIGATE MATERIAL SYSTEMS FOR MIRRORS USED IN HIGH POWER COBALT AND CARBON DIOXIDE LASERS.**
STEWART, R. W.
BATTELLE PACIFIC NORTHWEST LABS., RICHLAND, WASH.
79PP., 1974.
(AD-A006 101)

88493 **LOW LOSS WINDOW MATERIALS FOR CHEMICAL LASERS.**
HARRINGTON, J. A.
DEPT. OF PHYSICS, ALABAMA UNIV., HUNTSVILLE
30PP., 1975.

88513 **CASTING OF HALIDE AND FLUORIDE ALLOYS FOR LASER WINDOWS.**
NEWBERG, R. T. PAPPIS, J.
RAYTHEON CO., WALTHAM, MASS.
87PP., 1974.
(N75-24468, AD-A007 656, AFCRL-TR-74-0518)

88514 **PIEZOELECTRIC ALUMINUM NITRIDE FILMS.**
DUFFY, M. T. WANG, C. C.
RADIO CORP. OF AMERICA, PRINCETON, N. J.
139PP., 1975.
(N75-24518, AD-A007 657, PRRL-74-CR-65, AFCRL-TR-74-0559)

88516 **DEVELOPMENT OF OPTICAL COATINGS FOR HIGH INTENSITY LASER APPLICATIONS.**
LOOMIS, J. S.
OPTICAL SCIENCES CENTER, ARIZONA UNIV., TUSCON
70PP., 1975.
(N75-24470, AD-A007 692, AFWL-TR-74-117)

88553 **THERMO ELECTROMOTIVE FORCE AND ELECTRIC CONDUCTIVITY OF THE OXIDE FORM OF RADIOACTIVE IRON CATALYSTS FOR AMMONIA SYNTHESIS.**
SPITSYN, V. I. EROFEEV, B. V.
MIKHAILENKO, I. E. CHIKHLADZE, V. V.
DOKL. AKAD. NAUK SSSR
219 (4), 910-13, 1974.
(FOR ENGLISH TRANSLATION SEE E94190)

88597 **FLUCTUATION EFFECTS ON THE MAGNETIC PROPERTIES OF SUPERCONDUCTING LAYERED COMPOUNDS.**
PROBER, D. E. BEASLEY, M. R. SCHWALL, R. E.
LOW TEMP. PHYS.-LT 13, PROC. INT. CONF. LOW TEMP. PHYS., 13TH
3, 428-32, 1974.

88600 **EFFECT OF MECHANICAL TREATMENT ON THE MAGNETIC PROPERTIES OF SOLIDS. I.**
STRAKHOV, L. P.
UCH. ZAP. LENINGR. GOS. UNIV., SER. FIZ. GEOL. NAUK
370, 10-48, 1974.

88610 **INVESTIGATION OF OPTICAL AND ELECTRICAL PROPERTIES OF LIGHT-EMITTING MATERIALS.**
SCHNEIDER, J. YU, P. W.
DEPT. OF PHYSICS, DAYTON UNIV., OHIO
61PP., 1973.
(AD-778 413, ARL-74-0004)

EPIC Number	Bibliographic Citation

88611 **SPECTROSCOPIC CONSTANTS FOR SELECTED HETERONUCLEAR DIATOMIC MOLECULES. VOLUME I. A THROUGH D.**
SUCHARD, S. N.
AEROSPACE CORP., LAB OPERATIONS, EL SEGUNDO, CALIF.
518PP., 1974.
(AD-778 421, SAMSO-TR-74-82-VOL-1)

88612 **SPECTROSCOPIC CONSTANTS FOR SELECTED HETERONUCLEAR DIATOMIC MOLECULES. VOL. II. E THROUGH P.**
SUCHARD, S. N.
AERIOSPACE CORP., LAB OPERATIONS, EL SEGUNDO, CALIF.
539PP., 1974.
(AD-778 422, SAMSO-TR-74-82-VOL-2)

88613 **SPECTROSCOPIC CONSTANTS FOR SELECTED HETERONUCLEAR DIATOMIC MOLECULES. VOLUME III. R THROUGH Z.**
SUCHARD, S. N.
AEROSPACE CORP., LAB. OPERATIONS, EL SEGUNDO, CALIF.
402PP., 1974.
(AD-778 548, SAMSO-TR-82-VOL-3)

88617 **ELECTRON PARAMAGNETIC RESONANCE STUDY OF THE SOLID SOLUTIONS OF NICKEL IRON SULFIDE, COBALT IRON SULFIDE AND COBALT NICKEL YTTRIUM IRON SULFIDE.**
CHANDLER, R. N. BENE, R. W.
PHYS. REV.
8 B (11), 4979-88, 1973.
(AD-778 582, AFOSR-TR-74-0561)

88620 **INFLUENCE OF ELECTRONIC LIFETIME ON THE LATTICE INSTABILITY OF VANADIUM SILICIDES.**
WILLIAMSON, S. J. TING, C. S. FUNG, H. K.
PHYS. REV. LETT.
32 (1), 9-12, 1974.
(AD-779 105)

88681 **SPECIFIC ELECTRICAL RESISTANCE, THERMO-E.M.F. AND HALL EFFECT OF MONO-ALUMINIDES OF IRON, COBALT AND NICKEL.**
SIDORENKO, F. A. BASHKAVTOV, A. N.
ZELENIN, L. P. GELD, P. V.
ARMY FOREIGN SCIENCE AND TECHNOLOGY CENTER, CHARLOTTESVILLE, VA.L
7PP., 1974.
(AD-783-658, FSTC-HT-23-1633-73)

89230 **MATERIAL SCIENCE ASPECTS OF THIN FILM SYSTEMS FOR SOLAR ENERGY CONVERSION.**
SERAPHIN, B. O. MEINEL, A. B.
MATER. RES. COUNCIL SUMMER CONF.
2, 188-224, 1974.

89232 **FABRICATION OF LOW COST THIN-FILM SOLAR CELLS.**
LAEGREID, N. WANG, R. PAWLENWICZ, W. T.
MATER. RES. COUNCIL SUMMER CONF.
2, 279-301, 1974.

89245 **VARIATION IN THE THERMOELECTRIC PROPERTIES OF THE SOLID SOLUTION BISMUTH TELLURIDE SELENIDE IN THE COURSE OF VACUUM DEPOSITION.**
ARIFOV, Y. A. KULAGIN, A. I. ERZIN, N. I.
MAKOV, N. V. TURSUNOV, B. SAIDVALIEVA, M.
GELIOTEKHNIKA
10 (4), 3-6, 1974.
(FOR ENGLISH TRANSLATION SEE E89246)

89246 **VARIATION IN THE THERMOELECTRIC PROPERTIES OF THE SOLID SOLUTION BISMUTH TELLURIDE SELENIDE IN THE COURSE OF VACUUM DEPOSITION.**
ARIFOV, Y. A. KULAGIN, A. I. ERZIN, N. I.
MAKOV, N. V. TURSUNOV, B. SAIDVALIEVA, M.
APPL. SOLAR ENERGY, USSR
10 (4), 63-5, 1974.
(ENGLISH TRANSLATION OF GELIOTEKHNIKA, 10 (4), 3-6, 1974; FOR ORIGINAL SEE E89245)

89251 **INFLUENCE OF THE SCREENED COULOMB INTERACTION ON THE ABSORPTION OF LIGHT IN SEMICONDUCTORS.**
BIR, G. L. PIKUS, G. E. SKAL, A. S.
FIZ. TEKH. POLUPROV.
8 (6), 1096-1100, 1974.
(FOR ENGLISH TRANSLATION SEE E89252)

89252 **INFLUENCE OF THE SCREENED COULOMB INTERACTION ON THE ABSORPTION OF LIGHT IN SEMICONDUCTORS.**
BIR, G. L. PIKUS, G. E. SHAL, A. S.
SOV. PHYS. SEMICOND.
8 (6), 715-7, 1974.
(ENGLISH TRANSLATION OF FIZ. TEKH. POLUPROV., (6), 1096-1100, 1974; FOR ORIGINAL SEE E89251)

89254 **BIREFRINGENCE IN CRYSTALS WITH ISOTROPIC POINTS AND DETERMINATION OF OSCILLATOR STRENGTHS FOR EXCITONS IN CADMIUM SULFIDE BY THE ROZHDESTVENSKII HOOK METHOD.**
BARANETS, I. V. ZILBERSHTEIN, A. KH.
SOLOVEV, L. E.
OPT. SPEKTROSK.
37 (2), 285-7, 1974.
(FOR ENGLISH TRANSLATION SEE E89255)

EPIC Number	Bibliographic Citation
89255	BIREFRINGENCE IN CRYSTALS WITH ISOTROPIC POINTS AND DETERMINATION OF OSCILLATOR STRENGTHS FOR EXCITONS IN CADMIUM SULFIDE BY THE ROZHDESTVENSKII HOOK METHOD. BARANETS, I. V. ZILBERSHTEIN, A. KH. SOLOVEV, L. E. OPT. SPECTROS., USSR 37 (2), 164–5, 1974. (ENGLISH TRANSLATION OF OPT. SPEKTROSK., 37 (2), 285–7, 1974; FOR ORIGINAL SEE E89254)
89256	ELECTRON COLOR CENTERS IN CESIUM BROMIDE. GLADYSHEV, G. E. AVDONIN, V. P. PLACHENOV, B. T. OPT. SPEKTROSK. 37 (2), 364–5, 1974. (FOR ENGLISH TRANSLATION SEE E89257)
89257	ELECTRON COLOR CENTERS IN CESIUM BROMIDE. GLADYSHEV, G. E. AVDONIN, V. P. PLACHENOV, B. T. OPT. SPECTROS., USSR 37 (2), 206–7, 1974. (ENGLISH TRANSLATION OF OPT. SPEKTROSK., 37 (2), 364–5, 1974; FOR ORIGINAL SEE E89256)
89266	THE MEASUREMENT OF ANOMALOUS SCATTERING FACTORS NEAR THE GALLIUM POTASSIUM ABSORPTION EDGE IN GALLIUM PHOSPHIDE. FUKAMACHI, T. HOSOYA, S. ACTA CRYSTALLOGR. (DENMARK) 31 A, PT. 2, 215–20, 1975.
89267	ELLIPSOMETRY APPLIED TO SURFACE PROBLEMS. MEYER, F. LOYEN, F. J. ACTA ELECTRON (FRANCE) 18 (1), 33–8, 1975.
89269	OPTICAL PROPERTIES OF AMORPHOUS GERMANIUM, AMORPHOUS SILICON, AND AMORPHOUS III–V COMPOUNDS. THEYE, M. L. AMORPHOUS LIQ. SEMICOND., PROC. INT. CONF., 5TH 1, 479–98, 1974.
89286	SUPERCONDUCTIVE FIXED POINTS FOR CRYOGENIC THERMOMETRY. SCHOOLEY, J. F. SOULEN, R. J., JR. INSTRUM. TECHNOL. 21 (11), 35–9, 1974.
89292	MOLECULAR–IMPURITY ABSORPTION IN POTASSIUM CHLORIDE FOR INFRARED LASER WINDOWS. LIPSON, H. G. LARKIN, J. J. BENDOW, B. MITRA, S. S. J. ELECTRON. MATER. 4 (1), 1–24, 1975. (AD–A012 553, N76–12355)
89296	THE LOCALIZED VIBRATIONS OF CHARGED AND UNCHARGED IMPURITIES IN GALLIUM ARSENIDE AND GALLIUM PHOSPHIDE. LAITHWAITE, K. NEWMAN, R. C. GREENE, P. D. J. PHYS. 8 C (5), L77–9, 1975.
89309	ABSORPTION, EXCITATION, AND FLUORESCENCE SPECTRA OF LEAD–ACTIVATED RUBIDIUM CHLORIDE SINGLE CRYSTALS. PATHAK, N. K. SEN, S. C. PHYS. STATUS SOLIDI (GERMANY) 26 A (2), 721–7, 1974.
89311	STRESS–INDUCED DICHROISM IN THE ABSORPTION BAND OF COBALT DOPED CADMIUM SULFIDE. RUSZCYNSKI, G. BOYN, R. PHYS. STATUS SOLIDI (GERMANY) 67 B (2), K127–30, 1975.
89371	FREQUENCY DEPENDENCE OF MULTIPHONON INFRA–RED ABSORPTION IN THE TRANSPARENT REGIME OF FLUORITE NAMJOSHI, K. V. MITRA, S. S. BENDOW, B. HARRINGTON, J. A. STIERWALT, D. L. APPL. PHYS. LETT. 26 (2), 41–4, 1975. (AD–A010 079, AD–A012 553, N76–12355)
89390	SYNTHESIS AND PROPERTIES OF SOME NEW ORGANIC INTERCALATION COMPLEXES OF TANTALUM SULFIDE. HARTLESS, R. L. TROZZOLO, A. M. ACS SYMP. SER. 23–33, 1974.
89446	THERMOELECTRIC POWER OF SEMICONDUCTORS IN THE EXTREME QUANTUM LIMIT. II. THE PHONON–DRAG CONTRIBUTION. JAY–GERIN, J. P. PHYS. REV. 12 B (4), 1418–31, 1975.
89451	ANHARMONIC TEMPERATURE DEPENDENCES OF THE RESTSTRAHLEN FREQUENCIES AND THE DIELECTRIC PROPERTIES OF POTASSIUM HALIDES. HAQUE, M. S. PHYS. REV. 12 B (4), 1501–15, 1975.
89452	TEMPERATURE DEPENDENCE OF FRENKEL–PAIR PRODUCTION FROM F–AGGREGATE CENTER DESTRUCTION. SONDER, E. PHYS. REV. 12 B (4), 1516–21, 1975.
89453	PARAELASTIC PROPERTIES AND REORIENTATION BEHAVIOR OF 110 OFF–CENTER SILVER DEFECTS IN RUBIDIUM CHLORIDE AND RUBIDIUM BROMIDE. JIMENEZ, R. V. LUTY, F. PHYS. REV. 12 B (4), 1531–45, 1975.
89483	THE FINE STRUCTURE OF THE IR LIGHT EFFECT ON ELECTROLUMINESCENT MONOCRYSTALS OF ZINC SULPHIDE. USHAKOV, YU. V. ZH. PRIKL. SPEKTROSK. 21 (6), 1015–19, 1974. (FOR ENGLISH TRANSLATION SEE E99259)
89502	REFLECTIVITY MEASUREMENTS NEAR THE L(2,3) EDGE OF P AND N–TYPE SILICON. FUJITA, H. IGUCHI, Y. JAP. J. APPL. PHYS. (JAPAN) 14 (2), 220–7, 1975.
89508	SURFACE CONDITION AND THERMIONIC EMISSION OF LANTHANUM BORIDE. HOSOKI, S. YAMAMOTO, S. HAYAKAWA, K. OKANO, H. JAP. J. APPL. PHYS. (JAPAN) (SUPPL. 2), (PT. 1), 285–8, 1974.
89519	SURFACE STUDIES OF SOME TRANSITION METAL DICHALOCOGENIDES. WILLIAMS, R. H. MC GOVERN, I. T. JAP. J. APPL. PHYS. (JAPAN) (SUPPL. 2), (PT. 2), 413–16, 1974.
89522	THE EFFECT OF THE LIGHT ELEMENTS NITROGEN, CARBON AND OXYGEN ON THE PHYSICAL PROPERTIES OF SPUTTERED TANTALUM FILMS. HUTTEMANN, R. D. MORABITO, J. M. STEIDEL, C. A. GERSTENBERG, D. JAP. J. APPL. PHYS. (JAPAN) (SUPPL. 2) (PT. 1), 513–16, 1974.
89525	RECOVERY PROCESS AND METASTABLE CRYSTALS IN VACUUM CO–DEPOSITED MANGANESE–ALUMINUM FILMS. YOSHIDA, K. KAWAGUCHI, S. NAGATA, S. JAP. J. APPL. PHYS. (JAPAN) (SUPPL. 2) (PT. 1), 645–8, 1974.
89528	VARIABLE AND GRADIENT REFRACTIVE INDEX MULTILAYER FILMS OF DIFFERENT MATERIALS. SHARMA, S. K. YADAVA, V. N. CHOPRA, K. L. JAP. J. APPL. PHYS. (JAPAN) (SUPPL. 2), (PT. 1), 685–8, 1974.
89536	PROPERTIES OF ZINC SULFIDE FILMS EVAPORATED IN HIGH VACUUM. PREISINGER, A. PULKER, H. K. JAP. J. APPL. PHYS. (JAPAN) (SUPPL. 2), (PT. 1), 769–71, 1974.
89571	THE ALKALINE EARTH INTERCALATES OF MOLYBDENUM DISULFIDE. SOMOANO, R. B. HADEK, V. REMBAUM, A. J. CHEM. PHYS. 62 (3), 1068–73, 1975.
89630	FAILURE OF CLASSICAL FRESNEL RELATIONSHIPS IN THE EXCITON ABSORPTION REGION. STRASHNIKOVA, M. I. FIZ. TVERD. TELA 17 (3), 729–34, 1975. (FOR ENGLISH TRANSLATION SEE E89631)
89631	FAILURE OF CLASSICAL FRESNEL RELATIONSHIPS IN THE EXCITON ABSORPTION REGION. STRASHNIKOVA, M. I. SOV. PHYS. SOLID STATE 17 (3), 467–70, 1975. (ENGLISH TRANSLATION OF FIZ. TVERD. TELA, 17 (3), 729–34, 1975; FOR ORIGINAL SEE E89630)
89648	INFRARED ABSORPTION AND LOCAL DYNAMICS OF THE CALCIUM FLUORIDE: YTTERBIUM LATTICE. KAPLYANSKII, A. A. KULAKOV, V. V. LARIONOV, A. L. MALKIN, B. Z. MARKOV, YU. F. FIZ. TVERD. TELA 17 (3), 865–70, 1975. (FOR ENGLISH TRANSLATION SEE E89649)
89649	INFRARED ABSORPTION AND LOCAL DYNAMICS OF THE CALCIUM FLUORIDE: YTTERBIUM LATTICE. KAPLYANSKII, A. A. KULAKOV, V. V. LARIONOV, A. L. MALKIN, B. Z. MARKOV, YU. F. SOV. PHYS. SOLID STATE 17 (3), 549–52, 1975. (ENGLISH TRANSLATION OF FIZ. TVERD. TELA, 17 (3), 865–70, 1975; FOR ORIGINAL SEE E89648)

EPIC Number	Bibliographic Citation
89660	**ESTIMATE OF BAND-BENDING NEAR THE SURFACE OF BERYLLIUM OXIDE FROM MEASUREMENTS OF THERMALLY STIMULATED ELECTRON EMISSION.** KORTOV, V. S. SLESAREV, A. I. FIZ. TVERD. TELA 17 (3), 926-7, 1975. (FOR ENGLISH TRANSLATION SEE E89661)
89661	**ESTIMATE OF BAND-BENDING NEAR THE SURFACE OF BERYLLIUM OXIDE FROM MEASUREMENTS OF THERMALLY STIMULATED ELECTRON EMISSION.** KORTOV, V. S. SLESAREV, A. I. SOV. PHYS. SOLID STATE 17 (3), 591, 1975. (ENGLISH TRANSLATION OF FIZ. TVERD. TELA, 17 (3), 926-7, 1975; FOR ORIGINAL SEE E89660)
89669	**OPTICAL ABSORPTION FROM THE RELAXED EXCITED STATE OF (SILVER) IN POTASSIUM CHLORIDE.** KINNO, S. KUNIEDA, S. TAKEZOE, H. ONAKA, R. J. PHYS. SOC. JAP. (JAPAN) 38 (1), 290, 1975.
89715	**OPTICAL ABSORPTION IN NEUTRON IRRADIATED GALLIUM PHOSPHIDE.** PIVOVAROV, V. YA. TKACHEV, V. D. J. APPL. SPECTROS., USSR 18 (2), 213-6, 1973. (ENGLISH TRANSLATION OF ZH. PRIKL. SPEKTROSK., 18 (2), 283-8, 1973; FOR ORIGINAL SEE E62100)
89717	**CALCULATION OF THE PRINCIPAL VALUE OF THE REFRACTIVE INDEX N(Z) OF AN ALPHA-IODIC ACID CRYSTAL.** POLKOVNIKOV, B. F. J. APPL. SPECTROS., USSR 18 (4), 550-1, 1973. (ENGLISH TRANSLATION OF ZH. PRIKL. SPEKTROSK., 18 (4), 741-2, 1973; FOR ORIGINAL SEE E51319)
89723	**A CADMIUM SULFIDE SOLAR GENERATOR.** HAMMOND, D. A. SHIRLAND, F. A. BAUGHMAN, R. J. WRIGHT AIR DEVELOPMENT CENTER, WRIGHT PATTERSON AFB, OHIO 128PP., 1957. (AD-151 036, WADC-TR-57-770)
89724	**SOLAR CELL ARRAY OPTIMIZATION. VOLUME II.** ASTRO-ELECTRONICS DIVISION OF RCA FLIGHT ACCESORIES LAB., WRIGHT PATTERSON AFB, OHIO 78PP., 1962. (AD-274 841, ASD-TR-61-11-VOL. II)
89778	**LOCAL MODE FREQUENCIES DUE TO SUBSTITUTIONAL IMPURITIES IN ZINC BLENDE TYPE CRYSTALS. II. EFFECT OF FORCE CONSTANT CHANGES.** TALWAR, D. N. AGRAWAL, B. K. PHYS. REV. 12 B (4), 1432-42, 1975.
89783	**STUDY OF THE COPPER - GOLD AND SILVER - GOLD ALLOY SYSTEMS AS A FUNCTION OF COMPOSITION AND ORDER THROUGH THE USE OF THE MOSSBAUER EFFECT FOR GOLD.** HURAY, P. G. ROBERTS, L. D. THOMSON, J. O. PHYS. REV. 4 B (7), 2147-61, 1971.
89787	**ELECTRICAL RESISTANCE AND HALL EFFECT OF GOLD - SILVER ALLOYS.** GRUM-GRZHIMAILO, N. V. ZH. NEORG. KHIM. 1 (9), 2048-51, 1956. (FOR ENGLISH TRANSLATION SEE E89788)
89788	**ELECTRICAL RESISTANCE AND HALL EFFECT OF GOLD - SILVER ALLOYS.** GRUM-GRZHIMAILO, N. V. RUSS. J. INORG. CHEM., USSR 1 (9), 118-22, 1956. (ENGLISH TRANSLATION OF ZH. NEORG. KHIM., 1 (9) 2048-51, 1956; FOR ORIGINAL SEE E89787)
89789	**SOLAR CELL ARRAY OPTIMIZATION.** ASTRO ELECTRONICS DIVISION, RCA AERONAUTICAL SYSTEMS DIVISION, WRIGHT PATTERSON AFB, OHIO 94PP., 1962. (AD-295 558, ASD-TR-61-11, VOL. III)
89950	**N-COLOR (MERCURY, CADMIUM) TELLURIDE PHOTODETECTORS.** HALPERT, H. MUSICANT, B. L. APPL. OPT. 11 (10), 2157-61, 1972.
89951	**THE EMISSIVITY OF HEATED GASES.** PASCHEN, F. ANN. PHYSIK 50, 409-43, 1893.
89952	**THE EMISSIVITY OF GASES.** PASCHEN, F. ANN. PHYSIK 52 (6), 209-37, 1894.
89953	**THE DISPERSION OF ULTRAVIOLET RAYS.** SIMON, H. TH. ANN. PHYSIK 53, 542-58, 1894.
89991	**INTERFERENCE MODULATION OF LIGHT BY HOT ELECTRONS IN N-TYPE INDIUM ANTIMONIDE.** VOROB'EV, L. E. STAFEEV, V. I. USHAKOV, A. YU. FIZ. TEKH. POLUPROV. 8 (9), 1710-3, 1974. (FOR ENGLISH TRANSLATION SEE E89992)
89992	**INTERFERENCE MODULATION OF LIGHT BY HOT ELECTRONS IN N-TYPE INDIUM ANTIMONIDE.** VOROB'EV, L. E. STAFEEV, V. I. USHAKOV, A. YU. SOV. PHYS. SEMICOND. 8 (9), 1108-9, 1975. (ENGLISH TRANSLATION OF FIZ. TEKH. POLUPROV., 8 (9), 1710-3, 1974; FOR ORIGINAL SEE E89991)
89999	**INVESTIGATION OF THE ABSORPTION IN P-TYPE GALLIUM PHOSPHIDE.** AFANAS'EVA, S. S. KAZAKOVA, L. A. SAMORUKOV, B. F. UKHANOV, YU. I. FIZ. TEKH. POLUPROV. 8 (9), 1714-9, 1974. (FSOR ENGLISH TRANSLATION SEE E90000)
90000	**INVESTIGATION OF THE ABSORPTION IN P-TYPE GALLIUM PHOSPHIDE.** AFANAS'EVA, S. S. KAZAKOVA, L. A. SAMORUKOV, B. F. UKHANOV, YU. I. SOV. PHYS. SEMICOND. 8 (9), 1110-3, 1975. (ENGLISH TRANSLATION OF FIZ. TEKH. POLUPROV., 8 (9), 1714-9, 1974; FOR ORIGINAL SEE E89999)
90002	**PHOTOELECTRIC METHOD FOR DETERMINATION OF THE FORBIDDEN BAND WIDTH OF A VARIABLE GAP SEMICONDUCTOR NEAR A P-N JUNCTION.** DANILOVA, T. N. IMENKOV, A. N. TSARENKOV, B. V. YAKOVLEV, YU. P. FIZ. TEKH. POLUPROV. 8 (9), 1725-30, 1974. (FOR ENGLISH TRANSLATION SEE E90004)
90003	**EFFECT OF DEFORMATION ON THE THERMOELECTRIC PROPERTIES OF BISMUTH TELLURIDE - BISMUTH SELENIDE.** KULIEV, A. Z. OKHOTIN, A. S. ASADOV, D. A. KAKHRAMANOV, K. SH. ARMY FOREIGN SCIENCE AND TECHNOLOGY CENTER, CHARLOTTESVILLE, VA. 6PP., 1974. (ENGLISH TRANSLATION OF TEPLOFIZ. SVOISTVA TVERD. TEL., 30-3, 1971; FOR ORIGINAL SEE E58992) (N75-25747, AD-A008 253, FSTC-HT-23-423-74)
90004	**PHOTOELECTRIC METHOD FOR DETERMINATION OF THE FORBIDDEN BAND WIDTH OF A VARIABLE GAP SEMICONDUCTOR NEAR A P-N JUNCTION.** DANILOVA, T. N. IMENKOV, A. N. TSARENKOV, B. V. YAKOVLEV, YU. P. SOV. PHYS. SEMICOND. 8 (9), 1117-20, 1975. (ENGLISH TRANSLATION OF FIZ. TEKH. POLUPROV., 8 (9), 1725-30, 1974; FOR ORIGINAL SEE E90002)
90007	**PHOTOELECTRONIC PROPERTIES OF HIGH RESISTIVITY GALLIUM ARSENIDE: OXYGEN AND GALLIUM ARSENIDE: CHROMIUM SINGLE CRYSTALS.** LIN, A. W.-L. L. STANFORD UNIV., CALIF., PH. D. THESIS 206PP., 1975. (N75-26048, UNIV. MICROFILM NO. 75-13551)
90008	**PHYSICAL PROPERTIES OF VITREOUS ARSENIC(III) SELENIDE DOPED WITH GERMANIUM AND MERCURY.** TRNOVCOVA, V. MARIANI, E. PAVLIKOVA, M. LEZAL, D. PRAC. KONF. CESK. FYZ., [PR.], 3RD 152-4PP., 1974.
90012	**CONDUCTION ELECTRONS IN FERROMAGNETIC SEMICONDUCTORS NEAR THE CURIE POINT.** NAGAEV, E. L. ZIL'BERVARG, V. E. FIZ. TVERD. TELA 17 (5), 1261-9, 1975. (FOR ENGLISH TRANSLATION SEE E90133)
90018	**ELECTRICAL CONDUCTIVITY AND THERMOELECTRIC POWER OF SOME MOLTEN A (I) B (III) C (2) (VI) AND A (I) B (V) C (2) (VI) COMPOUNDS.** NINOMIYA, Y. NAKAMURA, Y. SHIMOJI, M. J. NON-CRYST. SOLIDS 17 (2), 231-40, 1975.
90025	**SURFACE STATES OF THE (110) SURFACE OF GALLIUM ARSENIDE.** CALANDRA, C. SANTORO, G. J. PHYS. 8 C (6), L86-9, 1975.

EPIC Number	Bibliographic Citation
90027	THEORETICAL STUDIES ON THE ULTRAVIOLET PHOTOEMISSION OF CADMIUM SELNIDE. FONG, C. Y. ALWARD, J. F. J. PHYS. 8 C (6), 882–94, 1975.
90031	SPIN-WAVE DISPERSION AND SUBLATTICE MAGNETIZATION IN NICKEL (II) CHLORIDE. ALS-NIELSEN, J. J. PHYS. 8 C (7), 1059–69, 1975.
90032	SELF-CONSISTENT CALCULATIONS FOR SHALLOW DEFECTS IN SEMICONDUCTORS: II. DONOR-ACCEPTOR PAIRS. STONEHAM, A. M. HARKER, A. H. J. PHYS. 8 C (8) 1109–18, 1975.
90033	THE ELECTRONIC BAND STRUCTURE OF TRIVANADIUM GALLIDE. GOLDBERG, I. B. J. PHYS. 8 C (8), 1159–80, 1975.
90034	MODIFIED ATOMIC POTENTIAL WAVEFUNCTIONS BAND-STRUCTURE CALCULATIONS FOR TITANIUM CARBIDE WITH MUFFIN-TIN AND ANGULAR-DEPENDENT POTENTIALS. TREBIN, H. R. BROSS, H. J. PHYS. 8 C (8), 1181–8, 1975.
90035	PHOTOLUMINESCENCE IN CHALCOGENIDE CRYSTALS SHOWING SMALL POLARON CONDUCTION; ORTHORHOMBIC SULPHUR AND ARSENIC SULFIDE. STREET, R. A. AUSTIN, I. G. SEARLE, T. M. J. PHYS. 8 C (8), 1293–300, 1975.
90038	OXIDE FILMS ON ARC CATHODES AND THEIR EMISSION AND EROSION. GUILE, A. E. HITCHCOCK, A. H. J. PHYS. 8 D (6), 663–9, 1975.
90050	KINETIC EFFECTS IN SILVER SELENIDE AND TELLURIDE. ASTAKHOV, O. P. GOLYSHEV, V. D. INORG. MAT., USSR 10 (9), 1391–4, 1974. (ENGLISH TRANSLATION OF IZV. AKAD. NAUK SSSR, NEORG. MATER., 10 (9), 1614–8, 1974; FOR ORIGINAL SEE E86779)
90054	THERMOELECTRIC PROPERTIES OF A SOLID SOLUTION OF THE SYSTEM TIN TELLURIDE – ZINC TELLURIDE. SULTANOVA, N. R. NASIROV, YA. N. ZARGAROVA, M. I. PIRZADE, M. M. INORG. MAT., USSR 10 (8), 1219–21, 1974. (ENGLISH TRANSLATION OF IZV. AKAD. NAUK SSSR, NEORG. MATER., 10 (8), 1418–20, 1974; FOR ORIGINAL SEE E86780)
90059	INTRINSIC LUMINESCENCES OF POTASSIUM IODIDE CRYSTALS. NISHIMURA, H. J. PHYS. SOC. JAP. 38 (2), 450–8, 1975.
90060	CRYSTAL STRUCTURE AND MAGNETIC PROPERTIES OF MANGANESE(II) SELENATE, COBALT(II) SELENATE, NICKEL(II) SELENATE AND COPPER(II) SELENATE. KOHN, K. AKIMOTO, S. INOUE, K. ASAI, K. HORIE, O. J. PHYS. SOC. JAP. 38 (2), 587, 1975.
90062	A NEW PHOTOCONDUCTION BAND IN CADMIUM SULFIDE CRYSTAL PRODUCED BY ELECTRON IRRADIATION. MATSUURA, K. HONJO, T. TSURUMI, I. J. PHYS. SOC. JAP. 38 (2), 591, 1975.
90064	ANTIFERROMAGNETICALLY-COUPLED FERRIMAGNETIC LAYER STRUCTURE IN CESIUM TRIFLUROMANGANATE AND NICKEL DOPED TRIFLUROMANGANATE. YAMAGUCHI, Y. SAKURABA, T. J. PHYS. SOC. JAP. 38 (4), 1011–19, 1975.
90065	CLUSTER APPROACH TO MAGNON RAMAN SCATTERING IN CUBIC ANTIFERROMAGNET. MIYATA, S. MOTIZUKI, K. J. PHYS. SOC. JAP. 38 (4), 1020–6, 1975.
90067	COMPOSITION DEPENDENCE OF THE PHASE TRANSITION TEMPERATURES IN THE MIXED CRYSTAL SYSTEMS NEAR STRONTIUM TITANATE. MIURA, S. MARUTAKE, M. UNOKI, H. UWE, H. SAKUDO, T. J. PHYS. SOC. JAP. 3, (4), 1056–60, 1975.
90068	OPTICAL ABSORPTION AND LUMINESCENCE OF SODIUM CHLORIDE-SODIUM BROMIDE SOLID SOLUTIONS. NAKAGAWA, H. TOYODA, K. NAKAI, Y. J. PHYS. SOC. JAP. (JAPAN) 38 (4), 1067–72, 1975.
90071	CHEMICAL CHANGES IN SECONDARY ELECTRON EMISSION DURING OXIDATION OF NICKEL (100) AND (111) CRYSTAL SURFACES. HOLLOWAY, P. H. HUDSON, J. B. J. VAC. SCI. TECHNOL. 12 (2), 647–9, 1975.
90072	PROPERTIES OF LITHIUM NIOBATE(V) THIN FILMS FABRICATED BY RADIO FREQUENCY SPUTTERING. FUKUNISHI, S. KAWANA, A. UCHIDA, N. NODA, J. PROC. INT. VAC. CONGR., 6TH 749–52, 1974.
90073	ELECTRICAL PROPERTIES OF THE GALLIUM ARSENIDE-INSULATOR INTERFACE. MIYAZAKI, T. NAKAMURA, N. DOI, A. TOKUYAMA, T. PROC. INT. CONF. SOLID SURF., 2ND 441–3, 1974.
90077	PREPARATION OF AND THE ANISOTROPIC DIELECTRIC PROPERTIES OF POTASSIUM TETRACYANOPLATINATE BROMIDE TRIHYDRATE. SAILLANT, R. B. JAKLEVIC, R. C. ACS SYMP. SER. 5, 376–81, 1974.
90079	ELECTRICAL PROPERTIES OF TELLURIUM DIOXIDE. I. DOI, K. SASAKI, T. HIJIKATA, K. BULL. CHEM. SOC. JPN. 48 (1), 144–6, 1975.
90083	SELECTIVE EPITAXIAL GALLIUM ARSENIDE VAPOR GROWTH. ISHIBASHI, Y. YAMAGUCHI, M. UCHIDA, M. REV. ELECTR. COMMUN. LAB. 22 (11–12), 1035–42, 1974.
90087	ENERGY LEVELS OF ELECTRON CENTERS IN POTASSIUM BROMIDE SINGLE CRYSTALS STUDIED BY PHOTOEMISSION METHOD. MATVEEV, M. S. ARSEN'EVA-GEIL, A. N. KAZENNOV, B. A. UCH. ZAP. LENINGR. GOS. UNIV., SER. FIZ. GEOL. NAUK 370, 76–80, 1974.
90089	POSITIVE TEMPERATURE COEFFICIENT OF RESISTIVITY IN THICK FILMS OF SEMICONDUCTING BARIUM TITANATE. KUWABARA, M. YOGYO KYOKAI SHI 83 (4), 198–203, 1975.
90091	PRECISE DETERMINATION OF THE DIELECTRIC PROPERTIES OF ALUMINA. HILL, G. J. IEEE TRANS. INSTRUM. MEAS. IM–23 (4), 443–6, 1974.
90092	HIGH FIELD DIELECTRIC MEASUREMENTS IN WATER. KOLODZIEJ, H. A. JONES, G. P. DAVIES, M. J. CHEM. SOC., FARADAY TRANS. 2 71 (2), 269–74, 1975.
90094	FUNDAMENTAL BAND EDGE ABSORPTION OF THALLOUS SULFATE CRYSTALS. RAMASASTRY, C. SUNANDANA, C. S. ACHARYULU, B. S. V. S. R. J. NONMETALS 1 (4), 283–90, 1973.
90095	INFLUENCE OF GROWTH CONDITIONS ON THE ELECTRICAL PROPERTIES OF PYROLYTICALLY DEPOSITED GALLIUM(III) NITRIDE. NEUMANN, H. PETZKE, W.-H. STAUDTE, M. KRIST. TECH. 10 (1), K9–K11, 1975.
90098	THEORY OF DIELECTRIC RELAXATION. FULTON, R. L. MOL. PHYS. 29 (2), 405–13, 1975.
90101	GROWTH BY CHEMICAL TRANSPORT AND SOME PROPERTIES OF FERROMAGNETIC COPPER TETRASELENODICHROMATE SINGLE CRYSTALS. MASUMOTO, K. NAKATANI, I. J. JAP. INST. MET. 39 (2), 110–17, 1975.
90104	LINEAR AND NONLINEAR OPTICAL PROPERTIES OF FERROELECTRIC BARIUM MAGNESIUM FLUORIDE AND BARIUM ZINC FLUORIDE. BERGMAN, J. G. CRANE, G. R. GUGGENHEIM, H. J. APPL. PHYS. 46 (11), 4645–6, 1975.

EPIC Number	Bibliographic Citation

90105 **PHOTOCONDUCTIVITY OF MICROCRYSTALLINE SILVER BROMIDE: IODINE EMULSIONS.**
BEUTEL, J.
J. APPL. PHYS.
46 (11), 4649–53, 1975.

90109 **PHOTOCONCUCTIVITY OF SCANDIUM-DOPED GALLIUM**
NAKAGAWA, H. ZUKOTYNSKI, S.
J. APPL. PHYS.
46 (11), 4809–11, 1975.

90111 **MICROWAVE MAGNETOCONDUCTIVITY OF POLAR SEMICONDUCTORS.**
NAG, B. R.
J. APPL. PHYS.
46 (11), 4819–22, 1975.

90112 **CATHODOLUMINESCENCE OF GALLIUM ARSENIC PHOSPHIDE ALLOYS.**
MARCINIAK, H. C. WITTRY, D. B.
J. APPL. PHYS.
46 (11), 4823–8, 1975.

90114 **OPTICAL ABSORPTION AND DISPERSION IN RF-SPUTTERED ALPHA-MERCURY SULFIDE FILMS.**
NAKADA, T.
J. APPL. PHYS.
46 (11), 4857–61, 1975.

90115 **COPPER INDIUM SULFIDE THIN FILMS: PREPARATION AND PROPERTIES.**
KAZMERSKI, L. L. AYYAGARI, M. S.
SANBORN, G. A.
J. APPL. PHYS.
46 (11), 4865–9, 1975.

90116 **MAGNETIC PROPERTIES OF RARE EARTH MANGANESE GERMANIUM COMPOUNDS.**
NARASIMHAN, K. S. V. L. RAO, V. U. S.
BERGNER, R. L. WALLACE, W. E.
J. APPL. PHYS.
46 (11), 4957–60, 1975.

90117 **MAGNETIC PROPERTIES OF THE THORIUM COBALT MICKEL SYSTEM.**
NARASIMHAN, K. S. V. L. DO-DINH, C.
WALLACE, W. E. HUTCHENS, R. D.
J. APPL. PHYS.
46 (11), 4961–4, 1975.

90120 **DIRECT MEASUREMENT OF THE ABSORPTION COEFFICIENT FOR THE P (7) TRANSITION IN HYDROGEN FLUORIDE.**
LAGUNA, G. A. STORM, E.
J. APPL. PHYS.
46 (11), 5049–50, 1975.

90133 **CONDUCTION ELECTRONS IN FERROMAGNETIC SEMICONDUCTORS NEAR THE CURIE POINT.**
NAGAEV, E. L. ZIL'BERVARG, V. E.
SOV. PHYS. SOLID STATE
17 (5), 816–20, 1975.
(ENGLISH TRANSLATION OF FIZ. TVERD. TELA, 17 (5), 1261–9, 1975; FOR ORIGINAL SEE E90012)

90134 **INFRARED REFLECTION SPECTRA OF AMMONIUM SULFATE.**
ZHIZHIN, G. N. MYASNIKOVA, T. P.
ROGOVOI, V. N.
FIZ. TVERD. TELA
17 (5), 1270–3, 1975.
(FOR ENGLISH TRANSLATION SEE E90135)

90135 **INFRARED REFLECTION SPECTRA OF AMMONIUM SULFATE.**
ZHIZHIN, G. N. MYASNIKOVA, T. P.
ROGOVOI, V. N.
SOV. PHYS. SOLID STATE
17 (5), 821–2, 1975.
(ENGLISH TRANSLATION OF FIZ. TVERD. TELA 17 (5) 1270–3, 1975; FOR ORIGINAL SEE E90134)

90136 **ENERGY SPECTRUM OF SOLID SOLUTIONS.**
ZAKHAROV, A. YU.
FIZ. TVERD. TELA
17 (5), 1274–9, 1975.
(FOR ENGLISH TRANSLATION SEE E90137)

90137 **ENERGY SPECTRUM OF SOLID SOLUTIONS.**
ZAKHAROV, A. YU.
SOV. PHYS. SOLID STATE
17 (5), 823–6, 1975.
(ENGLISH TRANSLATION OF FIZ. TVERD. TELA 17 (5), 1274–9, 1975; FOR ORIGINAL SEE E90136)

90140 **IMPURITY CONDUCTION IN TRANSITION METAL OXIDES.**
MAKAROV, V. V.
FIZ. TVERD. TELA
17 (5), 1380–3, 1975.
(FOR ENGLISH TRANSLATION SEE E90141)

90141 **IMPURITY CONDUCTION IN TRANSITION METAL OXIDES.**
MAKAROV, V. V.
SOV. PHYS. SOLID STATE
17 (5), 888–90, 1975.
(ENGLISH TRANSLATION OF FIZ. TVERD. TELA 17 (5), 1380–3, 1975; FOR ORIGINAL SEE E90140)

90144 **NONLINEAR PIEZOELECTRIC COEFFICIENTS OF LITHIUM NIOBATE.**
KOROBOV, A. I. LYAMOV, V. E.
FIZ. TVERD. TELA
17 (5), 1448–50, 1975.
(FOR ENGLISH TRANSLATION SEE E90145)

90145 **NONLINEAR PIEZOELECTRIC COEFFICIENTS OF LITHIUM NIOBATE.**
KOROBOV, A. I. LYAMOV, V. E.
SOV. PHYS. SOLID STATE
17 (5), 932–3, 1975.
(ENGLISH TRANSLATION OF FIZ. TVERD. TELA 17 (5), 1448–50, 1975; FOR ORIGINAL SEE E90144)

90146 **ELECTRICAL CONDUCTIVITY OF VANADIUM PENTOXIDE IN STRONG ELECTRIC FIELDS.**
CHERNENKO, I. M. IVON, A. I.
FIZ. TVERD. TELA
17 (5), 1452–4, 1975.
(FOR ENGLISH TRANSLATION SEE E90147)

90147 **ELECTRICAL CONDUCTIVITY OF VANADIUM PENTOXIDE IN STRONG ELECTRIC FIELDS.**
CHERNENKO, I. M. IVON, A. I.
SOV. PHYS. SOLID STATE
17 (5), 935–6, 1975.
(ENGLISH TRANSLATION OF FIZ. TVERD. TELA 17 (5), 1452–4, 1975; FOR ORIGINAL SEE E90146)

90148 **CONTRIBUTION MADE BY TETRAHEDRALLY COORDINATED IRON IONS TO ULTRAVIOLET ABSORPTION OF IRON GARNETS.**
ODARICH, V. A. BABKO, V. A. TARANUKH, YU. G.
FIZ. TVERD. TELA
17 (5), 1468–9, 1975.
(FOR ENGLISH TRANSLATION SEE E90149)

90149 **CONTRIBUTION MADE BY TETRAHEDRALLY COORDINATED IRON IONS TO ULTRAVIOLET ABSORPTION OF IRON GARNETS.**
ODARICH, V. A. BABKO, V. A. TARANUKH, YU. G.
SOV. PHYS. SOLID STATE
17 (5), 949, 1975.
(ENGLISH TRANSLATION OF FIZ. TVERD. TELA 17 (5), 1468–9, 1975; FOR ORIGINAL SEE E90148)

90152 **REVERSIBILITY OF THE PHOTOINDUCED MAGNETIC EFFECT IN YTTRIUM IRON SILICON OXIDE.**
KUTS, P. S. KOVALENKO, V. F.
FIZ. TVERD. TELA
17 (5), 1481–3, 1975.
(FOR ENGLISH TRANSLATION SEE E90153)

90153 **REVERSIBILITY OF THE PHOTOINDUCED MAGNETIC EFFECT IN YTTRIUM IRON SILICON OXIDE.**
KUTS, P. S. KOVALENKO, V. F.
SOV. PHYS. SOLID STATE
17 (5), 960–1, 1975.
(ENGLISH TRANSLATION OF FIZ. TVERD. TELA 17 (5), 1481–3, 1975; FOR ORIGINAL SEE E90152)

90158 **MECHANISM FOR ALKALI HALIDE EMISSION IN STRONG FIELDS.**
VOROB'EV, G. A. EKHANIN, S. G.
LEBEDEVA, N. I. NESMELOV, N. S.
FIZ. TVERD. TELA
17 (5), 1495–6, 1975.
(FOR ENGLISH TRANSLATION SEE E90159)

90159 **MECHANISM FOR ALKALI HALIDE EMISSION IN STRONG FIELDS.**
VOROB'EV, G. A. EKHANIN, S. G.
LEBEDEVA, N. I. NESMELOV, N. S.
SOV. PHYS. SOLID STATE
17 (5), 972–3, 1975
(ENGLISH TRANSLATION OF FIZ. TVERD. TELA 17 (5), 1495–6, 1975; FOR ORIGINAL SEE E 90158)

90164 **DRIFT MOBILITY OF CHARGE CARRIERS IN POLYCRYSTALLINE FILMS OF LEAD OXIDE.**
TIMOFEEV, O. A. LOMASOV, V. N.
FIZ. TVERD. TELA
17 (5), 1505–6, 1975.
(FOR ENGLISH TRANSLATION SEE E90165)

90165 **DRIFT MOBILITY OF CHARGE CARRIERS IN POLYCRYSTALLINE FILMS OF LEAD OXIDE.**
TIMOFEEV, O. A. LOMASOV, V. N.
SOV. PHYS. SOLID STATE
17 (5), 981, 1975.
(ENGLISH TRANSLATION OF FIZ. TVERD. TELA 17 (5) 1505–6, 1975; FOR ORIGINAL SEE E90164)

90172 **DEACTIVATION OF EXCITED STATES OF TERBIUM TRIPOSITIVE IONS IN FLUORITE CRYSTALS.**
ORLOV, M. S. SAITKULOV, I. G. STOLOV, A. L.
FIZ. TVERD. TELA
17 (5), 1539–41, 1975.
(FOR ENGLISH TRANSLATION SEE E90173)

90173 **DEACTIVATION OF EXCITED STATES OF TERBIUM TRIPOSITIVE IONS IN FLUORITE CRYSTALS.**
ORLOV, M. S. SAITKULOV, I. G. STOLOV, A. L.
SOV. PHYS. SOLID STATE
17 (5), 1008–9, 1975.
(ENGLISH TRANSLATION OF FIZ. TVERD. TELA 17 (5), 1539–41, 1975; FOR ORIGINAL SEE E90172)

EPIC Number | Bibliographic Citation

90190 ADSORPTION NATURE OF ASSOCIATIVE LUMINESCENCE CENTRES IN ALUMINIUM OXIDE.
FEDCHUK, A. P. MIKHO, V. V.
OPT. SPEKTROSK.
37 (5), 995–6, 1974.
(FOR ENGLISH TRANSLATION SEE E90191)

90191 ADSORPTION NATURE OF ASSOCIATIVE LUMINESCENCE CENTRES IN ALUMINIUM OXIDE.
FEDCHUK, A. P. MIKHO, V. V.
OPT. SPECTROS., USSR
37 (5), 569–70, 1974.
(ENGLISH TRANSLATION OF OPT. SPEKTROSK., 37 (5), 995–6, 1974; FOR ORIGINAL SEE E90190)

90192 OPTICAL PROPERTIES OF LEAD TITANATE SINGLE CRYSTALS IN THE REGION OF THE INTRINSIC ABSORPTION EDGE.
YAKUBOVSKII, M. A. RABKIN, L. M.
KOHEVSKAYA, D. S. FESENKO, E. G.
KRISTALLOGRAFIYA
19 (4), 873–5, 1974.
(FOR ENGLISH TRANSLATION SEE E 90193)

90193 OPTICAL PROPERTIES OF LEAD TITANATE SINGLE CRYSTALS IN THE REGION OF THE INTRINSIC ABSORPTION EDGE.
YAKUBOVSKII, M. A. RABKIN, L. M.
KOHEVSKAYA, D. S. FESENKO, E. G.
SOV. PHYS. CRYSTALLOGR.
19 (4), 541–2, 1975.
(ENGLISH TRANSLATION OF KRISTALLOGRAFIYA, 19 (4), 873–5, 1974; FOR ORIGINAL SEE E 90192)

90202 CALCULATION OF INTRACRYSTALLINE ELECTRIC FIELDS, THEIR GRADIENTS, AND SPONTANEOUS POLARIZATION IN THE ORTHORHOMBIC PHASE OF FERROELECTRIC NIOBIUM POTASSIUM OXIDE.
VOLKOV, A. F.
KRISTALLOGRAFIYA
19 (4), 781–7, 1974.
(FOR ENGLISH TRANSLATION SEE E90203)

90203 CALCULATION OF INTRACRYSTALLINE ELECTRIC FIELDS, THEIR GRADIENTS, AND SPONTANEOUS POLARIZATION IN THE ORTHORHOMBIC PHASE OF FERROELECTRIC NIOBIUM POTASSIUM OXIDE.
VOLKOV, A. F.
SOV. PHYS. CRYSTALLOGR.
19 (4), 485–8, 1975.
(ENGLISH TRANSLATION OF KRISTALLOGRAFIYA, 19 (4), 781–7, 1974; FOR ORIGINAL SEE E90202)

90204 PHASE COMPOSITION AND FERROELECTRIC PROPERTIES OF CERAMICS AND SINGLE CRYSTALS OF THE SYSTEM LEAD OXIDE - GERMANIUM OXIDE.
PENTEGOVA, N. V. SAL'NIKOV, V. D.
TOMASHPOL'SKII, YU. YA.
KRISTALLOGRAFIYA
19 (4), 820–3, 1974.
(FOR ENGLISH TRANSLATION SEE E90205)

90205 PHASE COMPOSITION AND FERROELECTRIC PROPERTIES OF CERAMICS AND SINGLE CRYSTALS OF THE SYSTEM LEAD OXIDE - GERMANIUM OXIDE.
PENTEGOVA, N. V. SAL'NIKOV, V. D.
TOMASHPOL'SKII, YU. YA.
SOV. PHYS. CRYSTALLOGR.
19 (4), 507–9, 1975.
(ENGLISH TRANSLATION OF KRISTALLOGRAFIYA, 19 (4), 820–3, 1974; FOR ORIGINAL SEE E90204)

90206 ELECTRON-DIFFRACTION ANALYSIS OF THE LATTICE MAGNETIC SUSCEPTIBILITY FOR SEMICONDUCTOR CRYSTALS.
ANDRIANOV, D. B. ZHUKOVA, L. A.
SAVEL'EV, A. FISTUL', V. I.
KRISTALLOGRAFIYA
19 (4), 802–8, 1974.
(FOR ENGLISH TRANSLATION SEE E90207)

90207 ELECTRON-DIFFRACTION ANALYSIS OF THE LATTICE MAGNETIC SUSCEPTIBILITY FOR SEMICONDUCTOR CRYSTALS.
ANDRIZNOV, D. B. ZHUKOVA, L. A.
SAVEL'EV, A. FISTUL', V. I.
SOV. PHYS. CRYSTALLOGR.
19 (4), 497–500, 1975.
(ENGLISH TRANSLATION OF KRISTALLOGRAFIYA, 19 (4), 802–8, 1974; FOR ORIGINAL SEE E90206)

90210 RADIATIVE RECOMBINATION AT SURFACE AND NEAR-SURFACE STRUCTURE DEFECTS IN GALLIUM ARSENIDE.
ZUEV, V. A. KORBUTYAK, D. V.
LITOVCHENKO, V. G.
FIZ. TEKH. POLUPROV.
8 (9), 1651–7, 1974.
(FOR ENGLISH TRANSLATION SEE E90211)

90211 RADIATIVE RECOMBINATION AT SURFACE AND NEAR-SURFACE STRUCTURE DEFECTS IN GALLIUM ARSENIDE.
ZUEV, V. A. KORBUTYAK, D. V.
LITOVCHENKO, V. G.
SOV. PHYS. SEMICOND.
8 (9), 1071–4, 1975.
(ENGLISH TRANSLATION OF FIZ. TEKH. POLUPROV., 8 (9), 1651–7, 1974; FOR ORIGINAL SEE E90210)

90219 INFLUENCE OF NITROGEN ON THE EFFICIENCY OF LUMINESCENCE OF SCANDIUM DOPED SILICON CARBIDE.
TAIROV, YU. M. KHLEBNIKOV, I. I.
TSVETKOV, V. F.
FIZ. TEKH. POLUPROV.
8 (9), 1792–4, 1974.
(FOR ENGLISH TRANSLATION SEE E90220)

90220 INFLUENCE OF NITROGEN ON THE EFFICIENCY OF LUMINESCENCE OF SCANDIUM DOPED SILICON CARBIDE.
TAIROV, YU. M. KHLEBNIKOV, I. I.
TSVETKOV, V. F.
SOV. PHYS. SEMICOND.
8 (9), 1159–60, 1975.
(ENGLISH TRANSLATION OF FIZ. TEKH. POLUPROV., 8 (9), 1792–4, 1974; FOR ORIGINAL SEE E90219)

90221 INDIUM IMPURITY STATES IN LEAD GERMANIUM TELLURIDE SOLID SOLUTIONS.
VEIS, A. N. ERASOVA, N. A.
ZAKHARYUGINA, G. F. KAIDANOV, V. I.
UKHANOV, YU. I.
FIZ. TEKH. POLUPROV.
8 (9), 1798–1800, 1974.
(FOR ENGLISH TRANSLATION SEE E90222)

90222 INDIUM IMPURITY STATES IN LEAD GERMANIUM TELLURIDE SOLID SOLUTIONS.
VEIS, A. N. ERASOVA, N. A.
ZAKHARYUGINA, G. F. KAIDANOV, V. I.
UKHANOV, YU. I.
SOV. PHYS. SEMICOND.
8 (9), 1165–6, 1975.
(ENGLISH TRANSLATION OF FIZ. TEKH. POLUPROV., 8 (9), 1798–1800, 1974; FOR ORIGINAL SEE E90221)

90225 PHOTOMAGNETIC EFFECT IN N-TYPE GALLIUM ARSENIDE IN THE PRESENCE OF OPTICAL ELECTRON HEATING.
IBRAGIMOV, V. YU. KOLCHANOVA, N. M.
NASLEDOV, D. N. SMETANNIKOVA, YU. S.
FIZ. TEKH. POLUPROV.
8 (9), 1808–10, 1974.
(FOR ENGLISH TRANSLATION SEE E90226)

90226 PHOTOMAGNETIC EFFECT IN N-TYPE GALLIUM ARSENIDE IN THE PRESENCE OF OPTICAL ELECTRON HEATING.
IBRAGIMOV, V. YU. KOLCHANOVA, N. M.
NASLEDOV, D. N. SMETANNIKOVA, YU. S.
SOV. PHYS. SEMICOND.
8 (9), 1173–4, 1975.
(ENGLISH TRANSLATION OF FIZ. TEKH. POLUPROV., 8 (9), 1808–10, 1974; FOR ORIGINAL SEE E90225)

90227 STIMULATED EMISSION FROM OPTICALLY EXCITED EPITAXIAL GALLIUM INDIUM PHOSPHIDE SOLID SOLUTIONS.
ALFEROV, ZH. I. ARSENT'EV, I. N.
GARBUZOV, D. Z. MISHURNYI, V. A.
RUMYANTSEV, V. D. FEDORENKO, T. P.
FIZ. TEKH. POLUPROV.
8 (9), 1811–13, 1974.
(FOR ENGLISH TRANSLATION SEE E90228)

90228 STIMULATED EMISSION FROM OPTICALLY EXCITED EPITAXIAL GALLIUM INDIUM PHOSPHIDE SOLID SOLUTIONS.
ALFEROV, ZH. I. ARSENT'EV, I. N.
GARBUZOV, D. Z. MISHURNYI, V. A.
RUMYANTSEV, V. D. FEDORENKO, T. P.
SOV. PHYS. SEMICOND.
8 (9), 1175–6, 1975.
(ENGLISH TRANSLATION OF FIZ. TEKH. POLUPROV., 8 (9), 1811–13, 1974; FOR ORIGINAL SEE E90227)

90233 PHOTOLUMINESCENCE OF GALLIUM NITRIDE SINGLE CRYSTALS.
MARASINA, L. S. PICHUGIN, I. G.
SULEIMANOV, YU. M. TESLENKO, S. I.
FIZ. TEKH. POLUPROV.
8 (9), 1826–8, 1974.
(FOR ENGLISH TRANSLATION SEE E90234)

90234 PHOTOLUMINESCENCE OF GALLIUM NITRIDE SINGLE CRYSTALS.
MARASINA, L. S. PICHUGIN, I. G.
SULEIMANOV, YU. M. TESLENKO, S. I.
SOV. PHYS. SEMICOND.
8 (9), 1187, 1975.
(ENGLISH TRANSLATION OF FIZ. TEKH. POLUPROV., 8 (9), 1826–8, 1974; FOR ORIGINAL SEE E90233)

90235 THERMAL CONDUCTIVITY OF SEMICONDUCTING LIQUIDS WITH A MIXED IONIC-ELECTRONIC CONDUCTION.
MOGILEVSKII, B. M. SOKOLOV, V. N.
FIZ. TEKH. POLUPROV.
8 (9), 1833–5, 1974.
(FOR ENGLISH TRANSLATION SEE E90236)

90236 THERMAL CONDUCTIVITY OF SEMICONDUCTING LIQUIDS WITH A MIXED IONIC-ELECTRONIC CONDUCTION.
MOGILEVSKII, B. M. SOKOLOV, V. N.
SOV. PHYS. SEMICOND.
8 (9), 1192–3, 1975.
(ENGLISH TRANSLATION OF FIZ. TEKH. POLUPROV., 8 (9), 1833–5, 1674; FOR ORIGINAL SEE E90235)

EPIC Number	Bibliographic Citation
90237	**REFRACTIVE INDICES OF CALCIUM FLUORIDE IN THE EXTREME ULTRAVIOLET WAVELENGTH REGION.** SARASIN, E. ARCH. SCI. PHYS. NATUR. 10, 303–4, 1883.
90242	**INFRARED SPECTRA OF SPINEL SOLID SOLUTIONS AND THEIR DESCRIPTION BY THE CLUSTER COMPONENTS METHOD.** TALANOV, V. M. VARSKOI, B. N. VOROBEV, YU. P. IOVLEV, A. A. MEN, A. N. SEREBRYAKOVA, A. V. OPT. SPEKTROSK. 37 (2), 372–4, 1974. (FOR ENGLISH TRANSLATION SEE E90243)
90243	**INFRARED SPECTRA OF SPINEL SOLID SOLUTIONS AND THEIR DESCRIPTION BY THE CLUSTER COMPONENTS METHOD.** TALANOV, V. M. VARSKOI, B. N. VOROBEV, YU. P. IOVLEV, A. A. MEN, A. N. SEREBRYAKOVA, A. V. OPT. SPECTROS., USSR 37 (2), 212–3, 1974. (ENGLISH TRANSLATION OF OPT. SPEKTROSK., 37 (2), 372–4, 1974; FOR ORIGINAL SEE E90242)
90245	**INFLUENCE OF COPPER AND MANGANESE ON ELECTRONIC PROPERTIES OF GLASSY ARSENIC(III) SELENIDE.** MATYAS, M. AMORPHOUS LIQ. SEMICOND., PROC. INT. CONF., 5TH 2, 1061–3, 1974.
90255	**HYSTERESIS CHARACTERISTICS OF FERROELECTRIC CERAMICS.** WERSING, W. BER. DTSCH. CERAM. GES. (GERMANY) 51 (11), 318–23, 1974.
90259	**PREPARATION OF IRON–PALLADIUM ALLOY PARTICLES WITH HIGH–COERCIVITY.** AKIMOTO, Y. HOSHINO, Y. SATO, M. BULL. TOKYO INST. TECHNOL. 120, 93–101, 1974.
90266	**APPLICATION OF THE TRACE OF DIAGRAMS OF COMPLEX IMPEDANCE TO THE DETERMINATION OF THE IONIC CONDUCTIVITY OF LEAD(II) FLUORIDE.** REAU, J. M. CLAVERIE, J. CAMPET, G. DEPORTES, C. RAVAINE, D. SOUQUET, J. L. HAMMOU, A. C. R. HEBD. SEANCES ACAD. SCI., SER. 280 C (6), 325–7, 1975.
90267	**VARIATIONS OF THE IONIC TRANSPORT NUMBER IN SAMARIUM(III) OXIDE, GADOLINIUM(III) OXIDE, AND DYSPROSIUM(III) OXIDE.** WILBERT, Y. BREUIL, H. DHERBOMEZ, N. C. R. HEBD. SEANCES ACAD. SCI., SER. 280 C (6), 373–5, 1975.
90268	**X–RAY, DIELECTRIC, AND RESISTIVITY STUDIES OF BARIUM GERMANATE.** KHER, V. G. PATKI, B. A. DESHPANDE, D. A. CURR. SCI. 44 (2), 46–7, 1975.
90273	**MAGNETIC PROPERTIES OF THE SYSTEM CADMIUM GERMANIUM ARSENIDE PHOSPHIDE SYSTEM.** BAIDAKOV, L. A. KOUZOVA, N. I. OSMANOV, E. O. J. APPL. CHEM., USSR 46 (1), 25–8, 1973. (ENGLISH TRANSLATION OF ZH. PRIKL. KHIM., 46 (1), 28–31, 1973; FOR ORIGINAL SEE E83375)
90275	**DIELECTRIC PROPERTIES, INFRARED SPECTRA, AND CHARGES ON THE ATOMS IN THE CUBIC OXIDES OF THE RARE EARTH METALS.** DULEPOV, E. V. BATSANOV, S. S. KUSTOVA, G. N. J. STRUCT. CHEM., USSR 13 (5), 871–4, 1972. (ENGLISH TRANSLATION OF ZH. STRUKT. KHIM., 13 (5) 935–8, 1972; FOR ORIGINAL SEE E 79248)
90278	**TEMPERATURE DEPENDENCE OF THE COERCIVE FORCE OF MANGANESE BISMUTH FILMS.** DEKKER, P. JEDELOO, P. W. MIDDLEHOEK, S. 1974 DIGESTS OF THE INTERMAG. CONFERENCE, TORONTO, CANADA, 14–17 MAY 1974 7–5/1PP., 1974.
90279	**DOMAIN GROWTH IN THIN MANGANESE BISMUTH FILMS.** DEKKER, P. VAN DEN BERG, H. A. M. DIG. INTERMAG. CONF. (PROC. INT. MAGN. CONF.) 7–6/1PP., 1974.
90280	**THE MICROSTRUCTURE OF SAMARIUM COBALTIDE.** RILEY, A. DIG. INTERMAG. CONF., (PROC. INT. MAGN. CONF.) 20–6/1PP., 1974.
90281	**SPIN POLARIZED ENERGY BAND STRUCTURE OF SAMARIUM COBALTIDE.** ARLINGHAUS, F. J. DIG. INTERMAG. CONF., (PROC. INT. MAGN. CONF.) 20–8/1PP., 1974.
90283	**MAGNETIC PROPERTIES OF SINGLE CRYSTAL YTTRIUM COBALTIDE.** FREDERICK, W. G. D. HOCH, M. DIG. INTERMAG. CONF., (PROC. INT. MAGN. CONF.) 20–11/1PP., 1974.
90284	**EFFECTS OF ANNEALING ON THE COERCIVITY OF AMORPHOUS TERBIUM – IRON.** SAVAGE, H. CLARK, A. PICKART, S. RHYNE, J. ALPERIN, H. DIG. INTERMAG. CONF., (PROC. INT. MAGN. CONF.) 25–5/1PP., 1974.
90295	**ANALYSIS OF METHODS FOR INDICATING ELECTRIC BREAKDOWN FOR ANODIC OXIDATION OF ALUMINUM.** IKONOPISOV, S. M. GIRGINOV, A. A. DOKL. BOLG. AKAD. NAUK 28 (2), 257–60, 1975.
90301	**DYNAMIC MAGNETIC PROPERTIES OF PIEZOMAGNETIC NICKEL – COBALT – COPPER – MANGANESE FERRITES.** KACZKOWSKI, Z. ELECTRON TECHNOL. 7 (1–2), 93–107, 1974.
90306	**ELECTRIC FIELD EFFECT ON THE ELASTIC CONSTANT NEAR THE GADOLINIUM MOLYBDATE PHASE TRANSITION.** COURDILLE, J. M. DUMAS, J. FERROELECTRICS 7 (1–4), 135–7, 1974.
90307	**DIELECTRIC PERMITTIVITY BEHAVIOUR OF NICKEL BORACITE IODIDE AND COBALT BORACITE IODIDE SINGLE CRYSTALS.** SMUTNY, F. FOUSEK, J. KOTRBOVA, M. FERROELECTRICS 7 (1–4), 143, 1974.
90308	**OBSERVATION OF DOUBLE HYSTERESIS LOOPS IN GADOLINIUM MOLYBDATE.** KUMADA, A. FERROELECTRICS 7 (1–4), 145–6, 1974.
90311	**DISPERSION OF OPTICAL AND ELECTRO–OPTIC PROPERTIES OF HOT–PRESSED LEAD LANTHANUM ZIRCONATE TITANATE CERAMIC MATERIALS.** KIRKBY, C. J. FERROELECTRICS 7 (1–4), 157–9, 1974.
90312	**CALCULATION OF THE PHASE SYSTEM OF LEAD ZIRCONIUM TITANATE FROM MEASUREMENTS OF THE DIELECTRIC CONSTANT.** DANIELS, J. FERROELECTRICS 7 (1–4), 161, 1974.
90315	**SIMULTANEOUS PHENOMENON OF FERRO– AND ANTIFERROELECTRICITY IN POTASSIUM DIHYDROGEN PHOSPHATE TYPE CRYSTALS.** LITOV, E. HAVLIN, S. UEHLING, E. A. FERROELECTRICS 7 (1–4), 191–2, 1974.
90316	**EXPERIMENTAL AND THEORETICAL STUDY OF PHASE TRANSITIONS IN POTASSIUM DIHYDROGEN PHOSPHATE–TYPE CRYSTALS.** STRUKOV, B. A. VAKS, V. G. BADDUR, A. KOPTSIK, V. A. ZINENKO, V. I. FERROELECTRICS 7 (1–4), 195–7, 1974.
90322	**LOW LOSS OPTICAL FIBERS WITH PURE SILICON DIOXIDE CORES PRODUCED BY CHEMICAL VAPOR DEPOSITION.** FRENCH, W. G. INT. CONGR. GLASS, (PAP.), 10TH 6, 46–51, 1974.
90337	**THE TEMPERATURE DEPENDENCE OF THE ELASTIC AND DIELECTRIC CONSTANTS OF POTASSIUM DIHYDROGEN PHOSPHATE NEAR THE PHASE TRANSITION.** COOMBS, G. J. FERROELECTRICS 7, (1–4), 201, 1974.
90338	**SPECIFIC HEAT STUDIES OF CESIUM HYDROGEN ARSENIC OXIDE NEAR THE PHASE TRANSITION TEMPERATURE.** DEUTSCH, M. LITOV, E. FERROELECTRICS 7, (1–4), 209–11, 1974.
90339	**GALVANOMAGNETIC PROPERTIES AND BAND STRUCTURE OF STRONTIUM TITANIUM OXIDE BETWEEN 4.2 AND 300 K.** FRANKUS, P. KUCHAR, F. VALENTA, M. W. FERROELECTRICS 7 (1–4), 213–15, 1974.
90340	**VANISHING OF THE FERROELECTRICITY IN DISPLACIVE AND HYDROGEN–BOND FERROELECTRICS AT HIGH PRESSURE.** SAMARA, G. A. FERROELECTRICS 7 (1–4), 221–4, 1974.

EPIC Number	Bibliographic Citation
90342	**ELECTROMECHANICAL PROPERTIES OF KRYPTON NIOBIUM OXIDE SINGLE CRYSTALS IN THE ORTHORHOMBIC PHASE.** HIRANO, H. FUKUDA, T. UEMATSU, Y. FERROELECTRICS 7 (1-4), 235, 1974.
90343	**FIELD-INDUCED SPACE-CHARGE LAYER IN STRONTIUM TITANATE.** HOCHLI, U. T. FERROELECTRICS 7 (1-4), 237-9, 1974.
90344	**TEMPERATURE AND FREQUENCY DEPENDENCE OF PIEZOELECTRIC AND ELECTROSTRICTIVE PROPERTIES OF SILVER SODIUM (NITROGEN OXIDE).** HAMANO, K. YAMAGUCHI, T. FERROELECTRICS 7 (1-4), 241-2, 1974.
90345	**THEORY OF PIEZOELECTRICY AND ELECTROSTRICTION OF BARIUM TITANIUM OXIDE CRYSTAL.** KINASE, W. YOKOYAMA, S. PAK, K. N. FERROELECTRICS 7 (1-4), 243-4, 1974.
90346	**FERROLECTRIC LITHIUM NIOBATE: GROWTH, SURFACE DENDRITE AND DOMAIN STRUCTURE.** DESHMUKH, K. G. SINGH, K. FERROELECTRICS 7 (1-4), 251-2, 1974.
90347	**FERROELECTRIC VACUUM DEPOSITS OF COMPLEX OXIDE TYPE STRUCTURE.** TOMASHPOLSKII, YU. YA. SEVOSTANOV, M. A. PENTEGOVA, M. V. SOROKINA, L. A. VENEVTSEV, YU. N. FERROELECTRICS 7 (1-4), 257-8, 1974.
90349	**FAR-INFRARED REFLECTIVITY SPECTRA OF BISMUTH SULFUR IODIDE.** SIAPKAS, D. FERROELECTRICS 7 (1-4), 295-6, 1974.
90351	**EFFECT OF DOMAIN STRUCTURE ON PHYSICAL PROPERTIES OF FERROELECTRICS.** TURIK, A. V. BONDARENKO, E. I. FERROELECTRICS 7 (1-4), 303-5, 1974.
90352	**STUDY OF THE SURFACE OF FERROELECTRIC CRYSTALS WITH THE SCANNING ELECTRON MICROSCOPE.** BIHAN, R. L. E. MAUSSION, M. FERROELECTRICS 7 (1-4), 307-8, 1974.
90353	**PHASE TRANSITION AND SWITCHING IN LEAD TITANATE CRYSTALS.** FESENKO, E. G. MARTYNENKO, M. A. GAVRILYACHENKO, V. G. SEMENCHEV, A. F. FERROELECTRICS 7 (1-4), 309-10, 1974.
90354	**STRESS RELAXATION STUDY OF FERROELECTRIC DOMAINS.** PRASAD, V. C. S. SUBBARAO, E. C. FERROELECTRICS 7 (1-4), 311, 1974.
90356	**FERROELECTRIC LOSSES IN THE BARIUM TITANIUM OXIDE PRODUCED BY THE 90 DEGREE DOMAIN WALLS.** BENGUIGUI, L. FERROELECTRICS 7 (1-4), 315-17, 1974.
90358	**ON THE DEFECT MODEL AND THE DIELECTRIC PROPERTIES OF LANTHANA SUBSTITUTED LEAD TITANATE CERAMICS.** KEIZER, K. BOUWMA, J. BURGGRAAF, A. J. FERROELECTRICS 7 (1-4), 341-3, 1974.
90359	**FERROELECTRIC AND ANTIFERROELECTRIC PROPERTIES OF (SODIUM BISMUTH) TITANIUM OXIDE - STRONTIUM TITANIUM OXIDE SOLID SOLUTION CERAMICS.** SAKATA, K. MASUDA, Y. FERROELECTRICS 7 (1-4), 347-9, 1974.
90361	**DIELECTRIC LOSS MECHANISMS IN THE PARAELECTRIC REGION FOR CERAMIC BARIUM TITANATE.** PONTON, A. J. HENSON, R. M. FERROELECTRICS 7 (1-4), 359-60, 1974.
90362	**ANOMALOUS TEMPERATURE RESITANCE CHARACTERISTIC OF HIGHLY ACCEPTRO DOPED BARIUM TITANIUM OXIDE PTC RESISTORS.** HEYWANG, W. WERSING, W. FERROELECTRICS 7 (1-4), 361-3, 1974.
90369	**ENERGY BAND STRUCTURE OF CRYSTALS WITH A SPHALERITE TYPE LATTICE.** NEMOSHKALENKO, V. V. ALESHIN, V. G. PANCHENKO, M. T. SENKEVICH, A. I. FIZ. VAK. UL'TRAFIOLET. IZLUCH. 247-52, 1974.
90375	**EFFECT OF SMALL ADDITIONS ON THE MAGNETIC CHARACTERISTICS OF LITHIUM FERRITE FOR MAGNETIC MEMORY.** ILIEV, I. DZHOGLEV, D. GOD. VISSH. KHIMIKOTEKHNOL. INST., SOFIA 18 (2), 217-30, 1972.
90376	**ELECTRIFICATION OF CADMIUM SULFIDE POWDER.** SATO, K. HYOMEN 13 (1), 11-16, 1975.
90378	**SOME MAGNETOOPTICAL AND HF PROPERTIES OF MAGNETIC FILMS.** SALANSKY, N. M. IEEE TRANS. MAGN. MAG 10 (4), 1033, 1974.
90381	**PREPARATION AND PROPERTIES OF MULTIFILAMENT NIOBIUM CARBONITRIDE SUPERCONDUCTOR.** SMITH, W. D. LIN, R. Y. COPPOLA, J. A. ECONOMY, J. IEEE TRANS. MAGN. MAG-11 (2), 182-4, 1975.
90382	**SUPERCONDUCTING PROPERTIES OF THIN FILM NIOBIUM CARBONITRIDES ON CARBON FIBERS.** PIKE, G. E. MULLENDORE, A. W. SCHIRBER, J. E. NAPIER, J. IEEE TRANS. MAGN. MAG-11 (2), 185-8, 1975.
90384	**SUPERCONDUCTIVITY IN TRINIOBIUM GERMANIDE.** GAVALER, J. R. JANOCKO, M. A. BRAGINSKI, A. I. ROLAND, G. W. IEEE TRANS. MAGN. MAG-11 (2), 192-6, 1975.
90387	**BULK SUPERCONDUCTIVITY ABOVE 20 K IN TRINIOBIUM GERMANIDE.** NEWKIRK, L. R. VALENCIA, F. A. GIORGI, A. L. SZKLARZ, E. G. WALLACE, T. C. IEEE TRANS. MAGN. MAG-11 (2), 221-4, 1975.
90393	**DISORDERED SEMICONDUCTORS WITH CONTROLLABLE PROPERTIES.** REDFIELD, D. IEEE TRANS. PARTS, HYBRIDS AND PACKAG. PHP-10 (4), 239-43, 1974.
90396	**ELECTRICAL CONDUCTIVITY AND THERMOELECTRIC POWER OF SILVER IODIDE TUNGSTEN OXIDE SOLID ELECTROLYTE.** SHAHI, K. LAL, H. B. INDIAN J. PURE APPL. PHYS. 13 (1), 1-6, 1975.
90398	**MAGNETOTRANSPORT PROPERTIES OF N-TYPE GALLIUM ARSENIDE IN THE HOPPING RANGE.** KAHLERT, H. INTERN. CONF. APPL. HIGH MAGNET. FIELDS SEMICONDUCTOR PHYS. 470-85, 1974.
90399	**EFFECTS OF UNIAXIAL STRAIN OF THE SHUBNIKOV-DE HAAS AND MAGNETOPHONON EFFECTS IN SEMICONDUCTORS.** SEILER, D. G. INTERN. CONF. APPL. HIGH MAGNET. FIELDS SEMICONDUCTOR PHYS. 492-65, 1974.
90401	**LONGITUDINAL MAGNETORESISTANCE AND HALL EFFECT OF CADMIUM MERCURY TELLURIDE IN STRONG MAGNETIC FIELDS.** TSIDILKOVSKII, I. M. GIRIAT, W. KHARUS, G. I. NEIFELD, E. A. INTERN. CONF. APPL. HIGH MAGNET. FIELDS SEMICONDUCTOR PHYS. 629-57, 1974.
90402	**SUBMILLIMETER-MAGNETO-SPECTROSCOPY OF SEMICONDUCTORS IN INTENSE MAGNETIC FIELDS.** ORTENBERG, M. INTERN. CONF. APPL. HIGH MAGNET. FIELDS SEMICONDUCTOR PHYS. 658-72, 1974.
90403	**THE MAGNETIC ENERGY LEVEL STRUCTURE OF SEMIMETALS IN THE LIMIT OF LOW QUANTUM NUMBER.** DRESSELHAUS, M. S. INTERN. CONF. APPL. HIGH MAGNET. FIELDS SEMICONDUCTOR PHYS. 673-715, 1974.

EPIC Number	Bibliographic Citation
90409	**ABOUT THE BAND OF LIGHT HOLES IN THE CONDUCTIVITY OF MERCURY CADMIUM TELLURIDE.** ALIEV, S. A. GUSEINOVA, S. M. IZV. AKAD. NAUK AZ. SSR SER. FIZ.-TEKH MAT. NAUK (USSR) (4), 37-43, 1974.
90410	**WIDTH OF THE HOMOGENOUS REGION IN ZINC TELLURIDE.** CHESNOKOVA, D. B. MILOSLAVOV, S. L. ORMONT, B. F. MOSHNIKOV, V. A. IZV. LENINGR. ELEKTROTEKH. INST. 116, 30-7, 1972.
90411	**EFFECT OF OXYGEN ON THE IDENTITY PERIOD IN RELATION TO THE TYPE OF POINT DEFECTS IN CADMIUM SULFIDE.** KACHALOVA, I. A. LUTSKAYA, O. F. ORMONT, B. F. IZV. LENINGR. ELEKTROTEKH. INST. 116, 37-40, 1972.
90426	**ANISOTROPY AND DOMAIN STRUCTURE IN MAGNETIC FILMS.** CHUNG, S.-K. WASHINGTON UNIVERSITY, ST. LOUIS, MO., PH.D. THESIS 100PP., 1974. (UNIV. MICROFILM NO. 75-1847)
90433	**MICROHARDNESS OF VANADIUM DIOXIDE IN THE PHASE TRANSITION REGION.** ABLOVA, M. S. GOLUBKOV, A. V. SHELYKH, A. I. NOV. OBL. ISPYT. MIKROTVERDOST, (MATER. SOVESHCH. MIKROTVERDOSTI), 4TH 202-4, 1974.
90437	**PHOTOELECTRIC PARAMETERS OF CADMIUM SULFIDE THIN FILMS.** VLASOV, S. MATER. STUD. NAUCHN. KONF. SAMARK. TASHK. GOS. UNIV. 10-11, 1973.
90442	**HETEROEPITAXY OF ZINC SELENIDE ON GALLIUM ARSENIDE BY OPEN TUBE TRANSPORT.** CHEVRIER, J. GALIBERT, G. ETIENNE, D. BOUGNOT, G. J. CRYST. GROWTH 28 (1), 109-16, 1975.
90443	**GROWTH OF SINGLE CRYSTAL BARIUM STRONTIUM TITANATE BY SOLVENT ZONE MELTING.** HENSON, R. M. POINTON, A. J. J. CRYST. GROWTH 26 (1), 174-6, 1974.
90444	**GROWTH OF SINGLE CRYSTALS OF BARIUM IRON OXIDE, BARIUM NICKEL OXIDE, AND BARIUM COBALT OXIDE UNDER HIGH OXYGEN PRESSURE.** SHIMADA, M. TAKEDA, Y. TAGUCHI, H. KANAMARU, F. KOIZUMI, M. J. CRYST. GROWTH 29 (1), 75-6, 1975.
90460	**ELECTRICAL PROPERTIES AND THE MAGNITUDE OF THE INDIRECT GAP IN THE SEMICONDUCTING TRANSITION METAL DICHALCOGENIDE LAYER CRYSTALS.** GRANT, A. J. GRIFFITHS, T. M. PITT, G. D. YOFFE, A. D. J. PHYS. 8 C (1), L17-23, 1975.
90465	**ON THE ELECTRONIC STRUCTURE AND FERMI SURFACE OF YTTRIUM ZINC ALLOY.** BREEZE, A. PERKINS, P. G. J. PHYS. 5 F (2), 255-60, 1975.
90467	**THE MAGNETIC PROPERTIES OF FERROELCTRIC AND FERROMAGNETIC NICKEL - CHLORIDE BORACITE AT LOW TEMPERATURE.** HAIDA, M. KOHN, K. SCHMID, H. J. PHYS. SOC. JAP. (JAPAN) 37 (5), 1463, 1974.
90468	**RELAXATION TIME OF SPIN SYSTEM IN POTASSIUM COPPER FLUORIDE NEAR T(C) DETERMINED BY MAGNETIC SUSCEPTIBILITY MEASUREMENT IN HIGH FREQUENCY MAGNETIC FIELD.** HASHIMOTO, T. SATO, A. J. PHYS. SOC. JAP. (JAPAN) 38 (2), 345-50, 1975.
90469	**BOUND POLARONS AT FINITE TEMPERATURE.** HATTORI, K. J. PHYS. SOC. JAP. (JAPAN) 38 (2), 356-9, 1975.
90470	**EXPERIMENTAL STUDIES OF RHOMBOHEDRAL CHROMIUM SULFUR SINGLE CRYSTAL. I. MAGNETIC PROPERTIES.** SUGIURA, T. IWAHASHI, K. HORAI, K. MASUDA, Y. J. PHYS. SOC. JAP. (JAPAN) 38 (2), 365-72, 1975.
90471	**CRITICAL MAGNETIZATION NEAR THE CURIE TEMPERATURE IN MAGNANESE PHOSPHIDE.** TERUI, H. KOMATSUBARA, T. HIRAHARA, E. J. PHYS. SOC. JAP. (JAPAN) 38 (2), 383-90, 1975.
90475	**MECHANISM FOR THE POSITIVE TEMPERATURE COEFFICIENT OF RESISTIVITY ANOMALY IN SEMICONDUCTING BARIUM TITANATE.** BRAHMECHA, B. G. J. SHIVAJI UNIV. 6 (12), 153-5, 1973.
90476	**EFFECTS OF GRINDING ON THE PHOTOCONDUCTIVE PROPERTIES OF CADMIUM SULFIDE POWDER.** TAKEUCHI, M. KANEKO, F. NAGASAKA, H. J. SOC. MATER. SCI. JAP. (JAPAN) 23 (250), 536-40, 1974.
90480	**THE NICKEL ARSENIDE - MANGANESE PHOSPHIDE PHASE TRANSITION IN VANADIUM MONOSULFIDE.** FRANZEN, H. F. WIEGERS, G. A. J. SOLID STATE CHEM. (USA) 13 (1-2), 114-17, 1975.
90487	**CHANGE IN REFRACTIVE INDEX OF THE ACTIVE MEDIUM OF A LASER AT ITS EMISSION WAVELENGTH.** ZYKOV, L. I. KIRILLOV, G. A. KORMER, S. B. KULIKOV, S. M. KOMAREVSKII, V. A. SUKHAREV, S. A. KVANTOVAYA ELEKTRON. (MOSCOW) 2 (1), 123-6, 1975.
90493	**ELECTRICAL PROPERTIES OF THE PHASES DICOPPER TRITHIOGERMANATE, DICOPPER TRITHIOSTANNATE, OCTOCOPPER HEXATHIOGERMANATE AND TETRACOPPER TETRATHIOSTANNATE.** KHANAFER, M. GOROCHOV, O. RIVET, J. MATER. RES. BULL. 9 (11), 1543-52, 1974.
90494	**NEW OXYFLUORIDE PHASES DERIVED FROM LEAD NIOBATE: CRYSTALLOGRAPHIC AND DIELECTRIC STUDIES.** CAMPET, G. CLAVERIE, J. PERIGORD, M. RAVEZ, J. PORTIER, J. HAGENMULLER, P. MATER. RES. BULL. 9 (12), 1589-95, 1974.
90495	**EFFECT OF IMPURITY AND RADIATION DEFECTS ON LUMINESCENCE AND ELECTRICAL EFFECTS DURING FRACTURE OF LITHIUM FLUORIDE CRYSTALS.** BELYAEV, L. M. DOBRZHANSKII, G. F. MARTYSHEV, YU. N. MEKHANOEMISSIYA MEKHANOKHIM. TVERD. TEL., (DOKL. VSES. SIMP.), 2ND 128-32, 1974.
90496	**KINETIC ANALYSIS OF GAS DISCHARGE PHENOMENA IN FRESHLY FORMED SODIUM SULFATE CRYSTALS.** MAMBETOV, D. M. GUBAIDULLIN, Z. KH. MEKHANOEMISSIYA MEKHANOKHIM. TVERD. TEL., (DOKL. VSES. SIMP.), 2ND 138-40, 1974.
90504	**FERROELECTRIC PROPERTIES OF LANTHANUM TITANATE SINGLE CRYSTAL.** NANAMATSU, S. KIMURA, M. YAMADA, N. NEC RES. DEV. (34), 39-42, 1974.
90506	**ELECTRIC CONDUCTIVITY OF POWDERED MATERIALS UNDER PRESSURE.** ERNST, J. D. NATURWISSENSCHAFTEN 62 (1), 35, 1975.
90511	**BEHAVIOR OF RESIDUAL CONDUCTIVITY IN CADMIUM SELENIDE.** CARINI, G., JR. GALLI, G. WANDERLINGH, F. NUOVO CIMENTO SOC. ITAL. FIS. 27 B (1), 65-78, 1975.
90517	**PHYSICAL PROPERTIES AND CRYSTAL CHEMISTRY OF SOLID SOLUTIONS BASED ON NEODYMIUM AND SAMARIUM SELENIDES.** GORELIK, S. S. MALOVETSKAYA, V. M. BUZANOV, V. I. LETYUK, L. M. THERMOELEK. MATER. 72-83, 1971.
90522	**PHOSPHORS FOR SOLID-STATE INFRARED-TO-VISIBLE IMAGE CONVERSION.** ALLEN, J. W. ISELER, G. W. REMOTE SENSING EARTH RESOUR., TECH. PAP. CONF. EARTH RESOUR. OBS. INF. ANAL. SYST., 2ND 473-89, 1973.
90524	**TEMPERATURE DEPENDENCE OF MAGNETIC ANISOTROPY OF ERBIUM - COBALT, THULIUM - COBALT, AND SAMARIUM - COBALT.** NARASIMHAN, K. S. V. L. WALLACE, W. E. HUTCHENS, R. D. GREEDAN, J. E. PROC. RARE EARTH RES. CONF., 11TH 1, 449-50, 1974.

EPIC Number	Bibliographic Citation
90527	REFRACTIVE INDEX OF GLASSY ARSENIC(III) TELLURIDE. ZAVETOVA, M. HORVATH, J. PRAC. KONF. CESK. FYZ., [PR.], 3RD 282–3PP., 1974.
90530	ELECTRICAL AND ELECTROLUMINESCENT PROPERTIES OF ALUMINUM NITRIDE. PASTRNAK, J. JASTRABIK, L. KUBATOVA, J. PRAC. KONF. CESK. FYZ., [PR.], 3RD 230–1PP., 1974.
90531	TERNARY 4A–5A TELLURIDES. FRUMAR, M. HORAK, J. TICHY, L. VASKO, A. PRAC. KONF. CESK. FYZ., [PR.], 3RD 226–7PP., 1974.
90535	DEFECT EQUILIBRIA AND CONDUCTION MECHANISMS IN ICE. BILGRAM, J. H. GRANICHER, H. PHYS. CONDENS. MATTER 18 (4), 275–91, 1974.
90538	MAGNETIC ORDERING OF CRYSTALLINE AND VITREOUS GADOLINIUM PHOSPHITE. AMBLER, E. MANGUM, B. W. PFEIFFER, E. R. UTTON, D. B. PHYS. LETT. 50 A (4), 249–50, 1974.
90540	THE DIELECTRIC BREAKDOWN OF ANODIC ALUMINIUM OXIDE. DE WIT, H. J. CREVECOEUR, C. PHYS. LETT. 50 A (5), 365–6, 1974.
90545	DIAMAGNETIC SUSCEPTIBILITY OF TETRAHEDRAL SEMICONDUCTORS [RELATION TO CHEMICAL BONDING]. HUDGENS, S. KASTNER, M. FRITZSCHE, H. PHYS. REV. LETT. 33 (26), 1552–5, 1974.
90552	RECHARGING PROCESSES OF CHROMIUM IONS IN ZINC SELENIDE SINGLE CRYSTALS. ROPPISCHER, H. ELSSNER, W. BOTTNER, H. PHYS. STATUS SOLIDI 27 A (2), 375–82, 1975.
90553	MAGNETIC DOMAINS IN THIN SPUTTERED IRON MONOSILICIDE FILMS. I. EDGE EFFECTS AND INFLUENCE OF THE SUBSTRATE TEMPERATURE AND THE ARGON PRESSURE DURING SPUTTERING. POCKRAND, I. VERWEEL, J. PHYS. STATUS SOLIDI 27 A (2), 413–27, 1975.
90554	ON THE STATISTICAL CHARACTER OF MAGNETIC PROPERTIES OF SINGLE–CRYSTAL PARTICLES IN HIGHLY ANISOTROPIC FERROMAGNETICS. KANDAUROVA, G. S. DERYAGIN, A. V. LAGUTIN, A. E. PHYS. STATUS SOLIDI 27 A (2), 429–40, 1975.
90555	GALVANOTHERMOMAGNETIC EFFECTS IN ANISOTROPIC MEDIA. BARANSKII, P. I. BUDA, I. S. DAKHOVSKII, I. V. SAMOILOVICH, A. G. PHYS. STATUS SOLIDI 67 B (1), 291–9, 1975.
90563	OPTICAL PROPERTIES OF THE SUBGROUP III B NITRIDES. MALAKHOV, V. YA. SHAGINYAN, L. R. POLUCH. SVOISTVA TONKIKH PLENOK 1, 88–92, 1973.
90572	STABILISATION OF RESONANCE FREQUENCIES IN PIEZOELECTRIC CERAMIC RESONATORS AGAINST SUDDEN TEMPERATURE CHANGE. TAKAHASHI, M. YAMAUCHI, F. TAKAHASHI, S. PROCEEDINGS OF THE 28TH ANNUAL FREQUENCY CONTROL SYMPOSIUM 1974 109–16PP., 1974.
90575	COMPARATIVE STUDY OF SILICON AND GALLIUM ARSENIDE PHOSPHIDE [METAL–INSULATOR–SEMICONDUCTOR] CAPACITORS FABRICATED BY USING ELECTRON–BEAM–EVAPORATED ALUMINUM OXIDE. GRANNEMANN, W. W. KIM, T. W. DEOKAR, V. D. CHENG, C. C. PROC. – ELECTRON. COMPONENTS CONF. 23, 273–6, 1973.
90579	MOLECULAR OXYGEN ON LEAD(II) SULFIDE. NEW SURFACE MECHANISM AFFECTING SEMICONDUCTOR ELECTRICAL PROPERTIES. LEE, R. N. PROC. INT. CONF. SOLID SURF., 2ND 311–14, 1974.
90583	THIN FILM CATHODES OF LANTHANUM HEXABORIDE. OSHIMA, C. HORIUCHI, S. KAWAI, S. PROC. INT. VAC. CONGR., 6TH 281–4, 1974.
90590	POLYCRYSTALLINE CADMIUM SULFIDE FILMS. KASSING, R. BAX, W. PROC. INT. VAC. CONGR., 6TH 801–4, 1974.

EPIC Number	Bibliographic Citation
90612	DEBYE WALLER FACTORS AND TEMPERATURE DEPENDENCE OF BAND GAPS OF ZINCBLENDE TYPE SEMICONDUCTORS. MITRA, S. S. TSAY, Y. F. VETELINO, J. F. PROC. INT. CONF. PHYS. SEMICOND., 11TH 776–82, 1972. (AD–A012 553, AFCRL–TR–75–0283, N76–12355)
90613	SEMIMETAL–METAL AND METAL–METAL PHASE TRANSITIONS IN 1T– AND 2H–TANTALUM(IV) SULFIDE. RELATION TO SUPERLATTICE STRUCTURES. GRANT, A. J. GRIFFITHS, T. M. PITT, G. D. YOFFE, A. D. PROC. INT. CONF. PHYS. SEMICOND., 12TH 592–6, 1974.
90615	VARIATION OF THE ABSORPTION COEFFICIENT AFTER OPTICAL EXCITATION IN ARSENIC(III) SELENIDE AT 1.6 K. CERNOGORA, J. MOLLOT, F. BENOIT, C. BENOIT A LA GUILLAUME, C. PROC. INT. CONF. PHYS. SEMICOND., 12TH 1027–31, 1974.
90631	PHOTOELECTRIC PROPERTIES OF ALKALI METAL DOPE: CADMIUM SULFIDE SINGLE CRYSTALS. KAERIYAMA, T. WATANABE, H. WAVA, M. REC. ELECTR. COMMUN. ENG. CONVERSAZIONE TOHOKU UNIV. 43 (3), 102–9, 1974.
90637	ACCURATE DETERMINATION OF THE ELECTRICAL RESISTIVITY FROM MUTUAL INDUCTANCE MEASUREMENTS. ROSENTHAL, M. D. MAXFIELD, B. W. REV. SCI. INSTRUM. 46 (4), 398–408, 1975.
90647	PHOTOELECTRICAL PROPERTIES OF POLYCRYSTALLINE SILICON CARBIDE LAYERS ON SPINEL AT HIGH TEMPERATURES. WAGNER, E. GRAUL, J. SILICON CARBIDE, PROC. INT. CONF., 3RD 458–63, 1974.
90649	FERROMAGNETIC PROPERTIES OF PALLADIUM NICKEL ALUMINIDE. SATO, M. SOLID STATE COMMUN. 15 (11–12), 1863–5, 1974.
90651	SPATIAL FLUCTUATIONS OF CARRIER DENSITY IN N TYPE INDIUM GALLIUM ANTIMONIDE DETERMINED BY SHUBNIKOV–DE HAAS EFFECT. PISTOULET, B. ROBERT, J. L. BARJON, D. RAYMOND, A. JOULIE, A. SOLID STATE COMMUN. 16 (3), 289–92, 1975.
90653	HIGH–FREQUENCY 1/F NOISE OF PHOTOCURRENT AND RESIDUAL CONDUCTIVITY IN CADMIUM SULFIDE. LUKYANCHIKOVA, N. B. KONOVAL, A. A. SHEINKMAN, M. K. SOLID–STATE ELECTRON. 18 (1), 65–70, 1975.
90658	OPTICAL PROPERTIES OF PRASEODYMIUM OXIDE FILMS. GOSWAMI, A. GOSWAMI, A. P. THIN SOLID FILMS 27 (1), 123–8, 1975.
90666	ANISOTROPY OF SINGLE–CRYSTAL FILMS OF LITHIUM FERRITE. GAVRILIN, V. P. UCH. ZAP., KUIBYSHEV, GOS. PEDAGOG. INST. 125, 3–17, 1973.
90667	MAGNETIC ANISOTROPY AND DOMAIN STRUCTURE OF SINGLE–CRYSTAL FILMS OF NICKEL FERRITE. GUSEVA, E. F. KOSHKIN, L. I. BUDRINA, G. V. UCH. ZAP., KUIBYSHEV. GOS. PEDAGOG. INST. 125, 34–45, 1973.
90669	INDUCED MAGNETIC ANISOTROPY IN SINGLE–CRYSTAL FERRITE FILMS OF THE MAGNESIUM–MANGANESE SYSTEM. STRYGIN, YU. F. BORODINOVA, R. V. BORODINOV, M. V. UCH. ZAP., KUIBYSHEV. GOS. PEDAGOG. INST. 125, 53–9, 1973.
90672	ANOMALIES OF MAGNETOSTRICTION TEMPERATURE–DEPENDENCE IN ALUMINIUM–SUBSTITUTED MAGNETITE. KOVTUN, E. F. KUSHNIR, A. K. SIZOVA, A. I. UKR. FIZ. ZH. 19 (11), 1919–21, 1974.
90673	THE ETTINGSHAUSEN EFFECT IN SEMICONDUCTORS WITH MIXED CONDUCTIVITY IN QUANTIZING MAGNETIC FIELDS. KOROLYUK, S. L. CHERNYSH, V. V. UKR. FIZ. ZH. 20 (1), 89–94, 1975.
90674	A SIMPLE MODEL OF ELECTRICAL AND MAGNETIC PROPERTIES OF MAGNETIC SEMICONDUCTORS. DIDUKH, V. D. DIDUKH, L. D. STASYUK, I. V. UKR. FIZ. ZH. 20 (1), 95–100, 1975.

EPIC Number	Bibliographic Citation
90680	MODIFICATION OF THE REFRACTIVE INDEX OF FLUORITE BY HEAVY ION BOMBARDMENT [OF THIN FILMS. OPTICAL WAVEGUIDE REALISATION]. CAPURON, J. P. AMALRIC, J. L. LEFEUVRE, S. VIDE 29 (171-172), 337-40, 1974.
90682	EFFECTS OF MAGNESIUM FLUORIDE ADDITION ON THE FORMATION OF SINTERED MAGNESIUM FERRITE COMPACTS AND ITS MAGNETIC PROPERTIES. AMEMIYA, M. YOGYO KYOKAI SHI 83 (4), 164-9, 1975.
90683	CRYSTAL GROWTH AND SOME FERROELECTRIC PROPERTIES OF TUNGSTEN-BRONZE TYPE NIOBATES BARIUM SODIUM LITHIUM NIOBATE. MASUDA, Y. WADA, M. YOGYO KYOKAI SHI 83 (5), 209-13, 1975.
90686	HALL EFFECT AND CONDUCTIVITY MEASUREMENTS OF ZINC OXIDE SINGLE CRYSTALS WITH OXYGEN VACANCIES AS DONORS. UTSCH, B. HAUSMANN, A. Z. PHYS. 21 B (1), 27-31, 1975.
90692	PHYSICAL PROPERTIES AND PHASE TRANSITIONS IN TUNGSTEN TRIOXIDE. SALJE, E. VISWANATHAN, K. ACTA CRYSTALLOGR. 31 A (3), 356-9, 1975.
90703	ABSORPTION COEFFICIENT MEASUREMENTS OF NITROUS OXIDE AND METHANE AT DEUTERIUM FLUORIDE LASER WAVELENGTHS. [APPARATUS SUITABLE FOR POLLUTION DETECTION]. DEATON, T. F. DEPATIE, D. A. WALKER, T. W. APPL. PHYS. LETT. 26 (6), 300-3, 1975.
90711	ESCA APPLIED TO SOLID-STATE PHYSICS. HEDMAN, J. AT. ENERGY REV. 12 (4), 763-85, 1974.
90718	TRENDS IN ATOMIC SPIN-ORBIT SPLITTINGS, ENERGY GAPS AND IONICITIES OF I I I - V INTERMETALLIC SEMICONDUCTORS. SAXENA, K. N. SAXENA, N. N. ANIKHINDI, R. G. CHEM. PHYS. LETT. 31 (3), 563-5, 1975.
90739	ABSORPTION OF LIGHT AND LUMINESENCE DUE TO IMPURITIES IN SILVER HALIDE CRYSTALS. BARSHCHEVSKII, B. U. SAFRONOV, G. M. DOKL. AKAD. NAUK SSSR 218 (5), 1124-7, 1974. (FOR ENGLISH TRANSLATION SEE E95949)
90770	ELECTRICAL CONDUCTIVITY OF AMORPHOUS ARSENCI (III) SELENIDE AT HIGH ELECTRIC FIELDS. DAS, A. R. KAR, R. K. MIKHERJEE, M. N. INDIAN J. PHYS. 48 (12), 1124-8, 1975.
90777	ELECTRONIC EXCITATION OF HC1 TRAPPED IN INERT MATRICES. BOURSEY, E. J. CHEM. PHYS. 62 (8), 3353-4, 1975.
90787	A STUDY OF CONDUCTIVITY OF MOLTEN VANADIC ANHYDRIDE. DESAGHER, S. YU, L. T. BUVET, R. J. CHIM. PHYS. PHYS.-CHIM. BIOL. 72 (3), 397-404, 1975.
90801	CRYSTALLOGRAPHIC AND MAGNETIC INVESTIGATIONS OF GADOLINIUM IRON NICKEL ALLOYS. STEINER, W. HRUBEC, J. J. LESS-COMMON MET. 41 (1), 165-74, 1975.
90805	INTRINSIC AND IMPURITY INFRARED ABSORPTION IN DIARSENIC TRISELENIDE GLASS. MOYNIHAN, C. T. MACEDO, P. B. MAKLAD, M. S. MOHR, R. K. HOWARD, R. E. J. NON-CRYST. SOLIDS 17 (3), 369-85, 1975.
90806	PROPERTIES OF AMORPHOUS SILICON FILMS DEPENDENCE ON DEPOSITION CONDITIONS. BAHL, S. K. BHAGAT, S. M. J. NON-CRYST. SOLIDS 17 (3), 409-27, 1975.
90807	THE MAGNETIC SUSCEPTIBILITIES OF SELENIUM-RICH ARSENIC-SELENIUM GLASSES. BAGLEY, B. G. DISALVO, F. J. WASZCZAK, J. V. J. NON-CRYST. SOLIDS 17 (3), 433-5, 1975.
90821	CALORIMETRIC MEASUREMENTS OF THE EMISSION PROPERTIES OF OXIDE CATHODES IN A LOW-PRESSURE GAS DISCHARGE. BOUWKNEGT, A. VAN DER KOOI, A. G. J. PHYS. 8 D (8), 952-63, 1975.
90838	EFFECTIVE CHARGE IN THE II - VI AND III - V COMPOUNDS WITH ZINCBLENDE OR WURTZITE TYPE STRUCTURE. SAKAMOTO, A. OGAWA, T. J. PHYS. CHEM. SOLIDS 36 (6), 583-9, 1975.
90841	ELECTRICAL PROPERTIES OF HIGH DIGENITE ALPHA COPPER SULFIDE. GUASTAVINO, F. LUQUET, H. BOUGNOT, J. SAVELLI, M. J. PHYS. CHEM. SOLIDS 36 (6), 621-2, 1975.
90844	MAGNETIZATION PROCESS IN ANTIFERROMAGNETIC ISING SYSTEM DYSPROSIUM CHROMATE. YAMAGUCHI, T. J. PHYS. SOC. JAP. 38 (5), 1270-8, 1975.
90846	DOMAIN GROWTH IN GOLD COPPER INTERMETALLIC. BRONSVELD, P. M. RADELAAR, S. J. PHYS. SOC. JAP. 38 (5), 1336-8, 1975.
90856	DIELECTRIC INSTABILITY AND BREAKDOWN IN WIDE BANDGAP INSULATORS. DI STEFANO, T. H. J. VAC. SCI. TECHNOL. 12 (1), 37-46, 1975. (AD-BO13 807L)
90858	ELECTRICAL CONDUCTION THROUGH THERMAL AND ANODIC OXIDES IN INDIUM ANTIMONIDE. WILMSEN, C. W. VASBINDER, G. C. CHAN, Y. K. J. VAC. SCI. TECHNOL. 12 (1), 56-9, 1975.
90859	THE OPTICAL PROPERTIES AND STOICHIOMETRY OF EVAPORATED BISMUTH OXIDE THIN FILMS. MEDERNACH, J. W. MARTIN, R. C. J. VAC. SCI. TECHNOL. 12 (1), 63-6, 1975.
90860	CHARACTIZATION OF TRANSPORT CONDUCTIVE THIN FILMS OF INDIUM OXIDE. MOLZEN, W. W. J. VAC. SCI. TECHNOL. 12 (1), 99-102, 1975.
90863	EMISSION OF POLARIZED ELECTRONS FROM MAGNETIC MATERIALS. SIEGMANN, H. C. PHYS. REP. PHYS. LETT. 17 C (2), 37-76, 1975.
90866	MAGNETIC INVESTIGATIONS ON DYSPTOSIUM - IRON - ALUMINUM LAVES PHASE COMPOUNDS. GROSSINGER, R. STEINER, W. PHYS. STATUS SOLIDI 28 A (2), K135-8, 1975.
90868	THERMOMAGNETIC PROPERTIES OF INDIUM ANTIMONIDE - INDIUM FILMS. KAILA, M. M. GOLDSMID, H. J. PHYS. STATUS SOLIDI 28 A (2), K167-70, 1975.
90870	AN ANNEALING STAGE OF ELECTRON RADIATION DAMAGES IN INDIUM - DOPED N-TYPE CADMIUM TELLURIDE CRYSTALS. MATSUURA, K. TSURUMI, I. PHYS. STATUS SOLIDI 28 A (2), K175-8, 1975.
90871	A HIGH PRESSURE SEARCH FOR K-PRIME BANDS IN POTASSIUM BROMIDE AND POTASSIUM IODIDE. MAMOLA, K. C. PHYS. STATUS SOLIDI 68 B (1), 337-40, 1975.
90874	TIGHT-BINDING CALCULATIONS OF THE VALENCE BANDS OF DIAMOND AND ZINCBLENDE CRYSTALS. CHADI, D. J. COHEN, M. L. PHYS. STATUS SOLIDI 68 B (1), 405-19, 1975.
90876	HOPPING CONDUCTION IN SEMICONDUCTOR FILMS. SHKLOVSKII, B. I. PHYS. LETT. 51 A (5), 289-90, 1975.
90889	MEASUREMENT OF THE REFRACTIVE INDEX OF SOLID AND LIQUID DIELECTRICS AT SUBMILLIMETER WAVELENGTHS. CHIGRYAI, E. E. PRIB. TEKH. EKSP. 17 (PT. 2) (6), 146-8, 1974. (FOR ENGLISH TRANSLATION SEE E93413)

EPIC Number	Bibliographic Citation
90911	OPTICAL ABSORPTION EDGE AND LUMINESCENCE OF LEAD (II) IODIDE. LEVY, F. DEPEURSINGE, C. LE CHI THANH MERCIER, A. MOOSER, E. VOITCHOVSKY, J. P. PROC. INT. CONF. PHYS. SEMICOND., 12TH 1237-41, 1974.
90915	PHOTOEMISSION AND OPTICAL PROPERTIES OF GALLIUM SELENIDE. THIRY, P. PINCHEAUX, R. DAGNEAUX, D. PETROFF, Y. PROC. INT. CONF. PHYS. SEMICOND., 12TH 1324-8, 1974.
90967	THE STRUCTURE OF THE EXCITON AND THE BIEXCITON IN COPPER (I) BROMIDE. COMTE, C. OPT. COMMUN. 14 (1), 79-84, 1975.
90976	THE ABSORPTION BAND EDGE OF LEAD TELLURIDE FILMS UNDER QUANTUM SIZE EFFECT. ABOU EL ELA, A. H. REV. PHYS. APPL. 10 (3), 105-8, 1975.
90985	ELECTRICAL CONDUCTIVITY OF CERTAIN CHARGE-UNSYMMETRICAL FUSED CHLORIDE SYSTEMS POTASSIUM CHLORIDE-CALCIUM CHLORIDE, POTASSIUM CHLORIDE-STRONTIUM CHLORIDE, POTASSIUM CHLORIDE-BARIUM CHLORIDE. ZUCA, S. OLTEANU, M. REV. ROUM. CHIM. 20 (4), 449-58, 1975.
90990	ANOMALOUS THERMOELECTRIC POWER OF SOME LIQUID CHALCOGENIDE SYSTEMS. MOUSTAKAS, T. D. WEISER, K. GRANT, A. J. SOLID STATE COMMUN. 16 (5), 575-9, 1975.
91000	THERMOELECTRIC EFFECT IN A LIQUID. KOROTAEV, S. K. KRIVTSOV, V. A. TEPLOENERGETIKA (4), 66-8, 1975. (ENGLISH TRANSLATION SEE E 97077)
91012	VACUUM-DEPOSITED CADMIUM SELENIDE FILMS GROWN UNDER EXCESS SELENIUM FLUX. MOORE, R. M. FISCHER, J. T. KOZIELEC, F., JR. THIN SOLID FILMS 26 (2), 363-70, 1975.
91134	DYNAMIC SEEBECK COEFFICIENT MEASURING DEVICE FOR HIGH RESISTIVITY MATERIALS. KEEM, J. CHEM. INSTRUM. 6 (2), 133-41, 1975.
91146	ROLE OF ATOMIC NUMBER OF ELEMENTS, BAND GAP, AND REFRACTIVE INDEX ON THE ELECTRICAL SUSCEPTIBILITIES OF A-II - B-VI COMPOUNDS. SINGH, V. P. SINGH, S. CZECH. J. PHYS. 25 B (3), 357-8, 1975.
91201	THERMOELECTRIC PROPERTIES OF SILICON TELLURIDE - GALLIUM TELLURIDE ALLOYS. ALIDZHANOV, M. A. ORUDZHEV, N. M. NASIROV, YA. N. IZV. AKAD. NAUK SSSR, NEORG. MATER. 11 (4), 762-3, 1975. (FOR ENGLISH TRANSLATION SEE E94197)
91206	MARTENSITE DECOMPOSITION IN NICKEL - ALUMINUM ALLOYS. PANTSYREVA, E. G. BOGACHEV, I. N. LITVINOV, V. S. IZV. VYSSH. UCHEBN. ZAVED., TSVETN. METALL. (1), 95-100, 1975. (FOR ENGLISH TRANSLATION SEE E103292)
91217	FUNDAMENTAL ANALOGIES BETWEEN SOLID, MOLTEN, AND AQUEOUS MATERIALS. APPLICATION OF THE CONCEPTS OF ENERGY LEVELS AND THE BAND THEORY OF SOLIDS. VIJH, A. K. J. MATER. SCI. 10 (1), 123-35, 1975.
91218	REVIEW. PROBLEMS IN OPTOELECTRONIC SEMICONDUCTORS. WHITE, A. M. J. MATER. SCI. 10 (4), 714-26, 1975.
91219	SPECTROMETER FOR SEMIAUTOMATIC TWO PHOTON FLUORESCENCE SPECTROSCOPY. FRITZLER, U. KELLER, PH. SCHAACK, G. J. PHYS. 8 E (6), 530-2, 1975.
91272	ELECTRICAL PROPERTIES OF SAMPLES AT UP TO 300 KILOBARS AND IN THE 0.1-200 K RANGE. BRANDT, N. B. BERMAN, I. V. KURKIN, YU. P. SIDOROV, V. I. PRIB. TEKH. EKSP. (1), 204-6, 1975. (FOR ENGLISH TRANSLATION SEE E95909)
91273	PRECISION MEASUREMENT OF DIFFERENTIAL THERMO ELECTROMOTIVE FORCE OF SEMICONDUCTORS. KIRSONS, J. KLOTINS, E. FELITINS, I. PRIB. TEKH. EKSP. (1), 224-5, 1975. (FOR ENGLISH TRANSLATION SEE E95910)
91288	OPTICAL PROPERTIES OF STRONTIUM TITANATE AND LITHIUM NIOBATE. WEAKLIEM, H. A. BURKE, W. J. REDFIELD, D. KORSUN, V. RCA REV. 36 (1), 149-62, 1975.
91289	OPTICAL PROPERTIES OF LAYER STRUCTURE COMPOUNDS. HARBEKE, G. TOSATTI, E. RCA REV. 36 (1), 40-69, 1975.
91290	OPTICAL PROPERTIES OF GALLIUM NITRIDE. PANKOVE, J. I. BLOOM, S. HARBEKE, G. RCA REV. 36 (1), 163-76, 1975.
91295	ELECTRICAL CONDUCTIVITY OF MOLTEN ALKALI HALIDES. VASU, L. REV. ROUM. CHIM. 20 (2), 169-75, 1975.
91299	CHEMICAL BONDIN INTERMETALLIC COMPOUNDS AND ITS INFLUENCE ON ELECTRICAL PROPERTIES. VELJKOVIC, V. TOSIC, B. JANJIC, J. SCR. METALL. 9 (5), 459-66, 1975.
91346	THERMO ELECTROMOTIVE FORCE OF COPPER - SULFUR, COPPER - SELENIUM, AND COPPER - TELLURIUM SYSTEM MELTS. KUSNITSYNA, T. A. APANOVICH, V. N. EICHIS, B. A. VELIKANOV, A. A. UKR. KHIM. ZH. (RUSS. ED.) 41 (4), 382-4, 1975.
91366	THERMIONIC EMISSION OF ALUMINUM OXIDE THIN FILMS. BAZANOV, V. G. BAN'KOVSKII, N. G. CHADAEVA, I. A. ZH. TEKH. FIZ. 45 (3), 676-8, 1975. (FOR ENGLISH TRANSLATION SEE E95225)
91401	BONDING AND SUPERCONDUCTIVITY IN THE PLUTONIUM SESQUICARBIDE STRUCTURE TYPE. CARTER, F. L. FRANCAVILLA, T. L. HEIN, R. A. PROC. RARE EARTH RES. CONF., 11TH 1, 36-45, 1974.
91407	MAGNETIC PROPERTIES OF THE SYSTEM THORIUM-YTTRIUM-COBALT-IRON. GANAPATHY, E. V. WALLACE, W. E. CRAIG, R. S. PROC. RARE EARTH RES. CCONF., 11TH 1, 430-8, 1974.
91408	MAGNETOCRYSTALLINE ANISOTROPY IN RARE EARTH-COBALT COMPOUNDS. MILLER, A. E. IGARASHI, H. PROC. RARE EARTH RES. CONF., 11TH 1, 439-48, 1974.
91409	MAGNETIC PROPERTIES OF THORIUM-COBALT-NICKEL COMPOUNDS. NARASIMHAN, K. S. V. L. DO, D. C. WALLACE, W. E. HUTCHENS, R. D. PROC. RARE EARTH RES. CONF., 11TH 1, 451-9, 1674.
91410	NEUTRON DIFFRACTION AND MAGNETIZATION STUDIES OF PRASEODYMIUM-THORIUM-COBALT AND THORIUM-IRON-COBALT. DO, D. C. JOHNSON, P. SPARLIN, D. JAMES, W. J. PROC. RARE EARTH RES. CONF., 11TH 1, 460, 1974.
91411	MAGNETIZATION AND MAGNETOSTRICTION IN LUTETIUM-COBALT, THULIUM-COBALT, AND LUTETIUM-THULIUM-COBALT INTERMETALLICS. MILLER, A. E. D'SILVA, T. MIURA, K. PROC. RARE EARTH RES. CONF., 11TH 1, 461-8, 1974.
91412	MAGNETIZATION AND MAGNETIC ANISOTROPY IN YTTRIUM-DYSPROSIUM-COBALT INTERMETALLICS. MILLER, A. E. SHANLEY, J. F., III D'SILVA, T. PROC. RARE EARTH RES. CONF., 11TH 1, 469-76, 1974.

EPIC Number	Bibliographic Citation

91413 **MAGNETOCRYSTALLINE ANISOTROPY MEASURED ON SINGLE CRYSTAL YTTRIUM–COBALT–ALUMINUM INTERMETALLICS.**
HAMANO, M. YAJIMA, S. UMEBAYASHI, H.
PROC. RARE EARTH RES. CONF., 11TH
1, 477–86, 1974.

91414 **EFFECT OF THULIUM AND ERBIUM SUBSTITUTION ON THE MAGNETIC ANISOTROPY OF NEODYMIUM–COBALT AND PRASEODYMIUM–COBALT.**
NARASIMHAN, K. S. V. L. WALLACE, W. E.
HUTCHENS, R. D.
PROC. RARE EARTH RES. CONF., 11TH
1, 487–94, 1974.

91448 **WIDE BAND II–VI SEMICONDUCTORS AND THE PROSPECTS OF THEIR APPLICATION.**
GEORGOBIANI, A. N.
SOV. PHYS. USP.
17 (3), 424–37, 1974.
(ENGLISH TRANSLATION OF USP. FIZ. NAUK, 113 (1), 129–55, 1974; FOR ORIGINAL SEE E83872)

91450 **QUANTUM SIZE EFFECTS IN SEMICONDUCTING AND SEMIMETALLIC FILMS.**
TAVGER, B. A. DEMIKHOVSKII, V. YA.
SOV. PHYS. USP.
11 (5), 644–58, 1969.
(ENGLISH TRANSLATION OF USP. FIZ. NAUK, 96 (1), 61–86, 1968; FOR ORIGINAL SEE E75362)

91454 **KINETICS OF ELEMENTARY PROCESSES IN THE CONDENSED STATE. VIII. IONIC CONDUCTION OF GLASSES AS A PROCESS IN AN ELASTIC MEDIUM.**
NEMILOV, S. V.
RUSS. J. PHYS. CHEM.
47 (6), 831–5, 1973.
(ENGLISH TRANSLATION OF ZH. FIZ. KHIM., 47 (6), 1479–85, 1973; FOR ORIGINAL SEE E71659)

91460 **THE MECHANISM OF CHARGE TRANSFER IN THE AMMONIUM PERCHLORATE LATTICE.**
KHAIRETDINOV, E. F. MISHCHENKO, A. M.
BOLDYREV, V. V.
RUSS. J. PHYS. CHEM.
49 (1), 117–9, 1975.
(ENGLISH TRANSLATION OF ZH. FIZ. KHIM., 49 (1), 211–2, 1975; FOR ORIGINAL SEE E74174)

91464 **EFFECT OF THE REPLACEMENT OF THE AMMONIUM ION BY THE POTASSIUM ION ON THE FERROELECTRIC PROPERTIES OF AMMONIUM SULPHATE.**
KOLBENEVA, G. I. LEVINA, M. E.
MAMONTOVA, N. D.
RUSS. J. PHYS. CHEM.
47 (2), 182–4, 1973.
(ENGLISH TRANSLATION OF ZH. FIZ. KHIM., 47 (2), 321–3, 1973; FOR ORIGINAL SEE E71655)

91465 **EFFECT OF THE GASEOUS MEDIUM ON THE ELECTROLUMINESCENCE OF ALUMINIUM OXIDE FILMS.**
FEDCHUK, A. P. MIKHO, V. V.
RUSS. J. PHYS. CHEM.
47 (2), 181–2, 1973.
(ENGLISH TRANSLATION OF ZH. FIZ. KHIM., 47 (2), 318–20, 1973; FOR ORIGINAL SEE E71654)

91466 **INFLUENCE OF THE STATE OF THE SURFACE ON THE ELECTRICAL CONDUCTIVITY OF CADMIUM TELLURIDE FILMS.**
VINOGRADOV, V. E. BOIKO, B. T.
RUSS. J. PHYS. CHEM.
47 (11), 112–3, 1973.
(ENGLISH TRANSLATION OF ZH. FIZ. KHIM., 47 (11), 206–7, 1973; FOR ORIGINAL SEE E71653)

91472 **NGR INVESTIGATION OF THE FORMATION OF FERRITES FROM COPRECIPITATED HYDROXIDES.**
BELOZERSKII, G. N. BAIKOV, M. V.
BOLDYREV, V. V. MURIN, A. N.
PAVLYUKHIN, YU. T. SVIRIDOV, V. V.
KINET. CATAL., USSR
15 (4), 829–33, 1974.
(ENGLISH TRANSLATION OF KINET. KATAL., 15 (4), 929–34, 1974; FOR ORIGINAL SEE E84222)

91473 **DETERMINATION OF THE CHARACTER OF THE ACTIVE CENTERS IN ALUMINUM OXIDE BY THE METHOD OF THERMOLUMINESCENCE.**
FEDCHUK, A. P. MIKHO, V. V.
KINET. CATAL., USSR
15 (2), 478–9, 1974.
(ENGLISH TRANSLATION OF KINET. KATAL., 15 (2), 534–5, 1974; FOR ORIGINAL SEE E84223)

91474 **PHOTO–INDUCED ADSORBOLUMINESCENCE ON ALUMINA.**
ANDREEV, N. S. KOTEL'NIKOV, V. A.
KINET. CATAL., USSR
15 (6), 1431–2, 1974.
(ENGLISH TRANSLATION OF KINET. KATAL., 15 (6), 1612–3, 1974; FOR ORIGINAL SEE E75232)

91477 **EFFECT OF A TRAPEZIFORM ELECTRIC FIELD ON THE PHOTOLUMINESCENCE OF ZINC SULFIDE(CHLORINE).**
ANDRIANOV, A. S. BOGACHEVA, L. S.
J. APPL. SPECTROSC., USSR
18 (3), 362–3, 1973.
(ENGLISH TRANSLATION OF ZH. PRIKL. SPEKTROSK., 18 (3), 488–90, 1973; FOR ORIGINAL SEE E70954)

91478 **POLARIZED LUMINESCENCE SPECTRUM OF A RUBIDIUM URANYL NITRATE CRYSTAL AT LIQUID – HELIUM TEMPERATURE.**
KOMYAK, A. I. SLEPTSOV, S. E.
VITKOVSKII, G. P.
J. APPL. SPECTROSC., USSR
18 (3), 301–5, 1973.
(ENGLISH TRANSLATION OF ZH. PRIKL. SPEKTROSK., 18 (3), 410–5, 1973; FOR ORIGINAL SEE E70953)

91479 **PHOTOLUMINESCENCE OF ZINC TELLURIDE WITH LASER EXCITATION.**
YABLONSKII, G. P. GRIBKOVSKII, V. P.
J. APPL. SPECTROSC., USSR
18 (2), 234–6, 1973.
(ENGLISH TRANSLATION OF ZH. PRIKL. SPEKTROSC., 18 (2), 313–5, 1973; FOR ORIGINAL SEE E70952)

91481 **MATRIZ EFFECTS IN THE SPECTRA OF CRYSTAL PHOSPHORS.**
LAPSHIN, A. I.
J. APPL. SPECTROSC., USSR
18 (1), 127, 1973.
(ENGLISH TRANSLATION OF ZH. PRIKL. SPEKTROSK., 18 (1), 164, 1973; FOR ORIGINAL, SEE E 70949)

91482 **RADICAL–RECOMBINATION LUMINESCENCE IN ATOMIC AXYGEN OF CALCIUM OXIDE ACTIVATED BY MERCURY–LIKE IONS.**
STYROV, V. V. POPOV, D. P.
J. APPL SPECTROSC., USSR
18 (1), 127, 1973.
(ENGLISH TRANSLATION OF ZH. PRIKL. SPEKTROSK., 18 (1), 164–5, 1973; FOR ORIGINAL, SEE E 70950)

91485 **CONCENTRATION AND TEMPERATURE CHARACTERISTICS OF THE LUMINESCENCE OF YTTRIUM ORTHOVANADATE–EUROPIUM.**
MOSKVIN, A. S. KHODOS, M. YA.
SHU'GIN, B. V.
J. APPL. SPECTROSC., USSR.
18 (1), 39–42, 1973.
(ENGLISH TRANSLATION OF ZH. PRIKL. SPEKTROSK., 18 (1), 54–8, 1973; FOR ORIGINAL, SEE E 70946)

91486 **PROPERTIES OF ALUMINUM NITRIDE FILMS OBTAINED BY REACTIVE EVAPORATION.**
SLAVNIKOV, V. S. USYNINA, N. A.
SLAVNIKOVA, M. M. TRUBITSYN, A. M.
SOV. PHYS.
16 (6), 877–9, 1973.
(ENGLISH TRANSLATION OF IZV. VYSSH. UCHEB. ZAVED. FIZ., 16 (6), 149–51, 1973; FOR ORIGINAL SEE E51626)

91490 **MAGNETIZATION OF HEXAGONAL FERROMAGNETS WITH A SINGLE–ION ANISOTROPY.**
IUTIN, N. N. KAZAKOV, A. A.
CHISTYAKOV, N. L.
THEOR. MATH. PHYS.
20 (1), 714–8, 1974.
(ENGLISH TRANSLATION OF THEOR. MAT. FIZ., 20 (1), 126–32, 1974; FOR ORIGINAL, SEE E 85089)

91494 **THE CHARACTER OF DISORDER IN SILICON NITRIDE CRYSTALS.**
KAMYSHOV, V. M. GORBATOV, A. G.
INORG. MAT., USSR
7 (4), 524–8, 1971.
(ENGLISH TRANSLATION OF IZV. AKAD. NAUK SSSR, NEORG. MATER., 7 (J), 601–5, 1971; FOR ORIGINAL SEE E 76470)

91495 **ELECTRICAL PROPERTIES OF MOLYBDENUM–DOPED ZIRCONIUM MONOCARBIDE.**
NESHPOR, V. S. NIKITIN, V. P.
ORDAN'YAN, S. S. SKALETSKAYA, N. A.
INORG. MAT., USSR
7 (4), 529–31, 1971.
(ENGLISH TRANSLATION OF IZV. AKAD. NAUK SSSR, NEORG. MATER., 7 (4), 606–9, 1971; FOR ORIGINAL, SEE E 76469)

91496 **GLAVANOMAGNETIC PHENOMENA IN P–INDIUM ANTIMONIDE.**
ERMOLOVICH, YU. B.
INORG. MAT., USSR
7 (4), 604–5, 1971.
(ENGLISH TRANSLATION OF IZV. AKAD. NAUK SSSR, NEORG. MATER., 7 (4), 697–8, 1971; FOR ORIGINAL, SEE E 76472)

91499 **ELECTRICAL CONDUCTIVITY OF LIQUID ALUMINUM.**
ELYTIN, V. P. MITIN, B. S. NAGIBIN, YU. A.
INORG. MAT. USSR
7 (5), 775–6, 1971.
(ENGLISH TRANSLATION OF IZV. AKAD. NAUK SSSR, NEORG. MATER., 7 (5), 880–1, 1971; FOR ORIGINAL SEE E 76473)

EPIC Number	Bibliographic Citation
91500	**MAGNETIC AND ADSORPTION PROPERTIES OF SEMICONDUCTORS OF THE GERMANIUM ISOELECTRIC SERIES.** KIROVSKAYA, I. A. ZHELTONOZHKO, A. A. INORG. MAT., USSR 7 (6), 813–5, 1971. (ENGLISH TRANSLATION OF IZV. AKAD. NAUK SSSR, NEORG. MATER., 7 (6), 921–4, 1971; FOR ORIGINAL, SEE E 76480)
91501	**PROCESS THERMODYNAMICS AND ELECTRICAL PROPERTIES OF CADMIUM SULFIDE-CADMIUM OXIDE SINGLE CRYSTALS.** LUTSKAYA, O. F. ORMONT, B F. KACHALOVA, I. A. INORG. MAT., USSR. 7 (5), 820–3, 1671. (ENGLISH TRANSLATION OF IZV. AKAD. NAUK SSSR, NEORG. LMATER. 7 (5), 930–3, 1971; FOR ORIGINAL, SEE E 76475)
91502	**PHYSICAL PROPERTIES OF THE SOLID SOLUTIONS CHROMIUM GERMANIUM SILICON.** RYKOVA, M. A. SABIRZYANOV, A. V. ZAGRYAZHSKII, V. L. GEL'D, P. V. INORG. MAT., USSR 7 (6), 835–8, 1971. (ENGLISH TRANSLATION OF IZV. AKAD. NAUK SSR, NEORG. MATER. 7 (6), 947–50, 1971; FOR ORIGINAL, SEE E 76478)
91504	**PROPERTIES OF ZIRCONIUM MONOCARBIDE IN ITS REGION OF HOMOGENEITY.** SAMSONOV, G. V. UPADKHAYA, G. SH. INORG. MAT., USSR, 7 (8), 1203–5, 1971. (ENGLISH TRANSLATION OF IZV. AKAD. NAUK SSSR, NEORG. MATER., 7 (8), 1351–4, 1971; FOR ORIGINAL, SEE E 76485)
91505	**PROPERTIES OF THE BORIDES OF RHODIUM.** KOSENKO, V. A. RUD', B. M. SIDOROVA, V. G. INORG. MAT., USSR 7 (8), 1294–5, 1971. (ENGLISH TRANSLATION OF IZV. AKAD. NAUK SSSR, NEORG. MATER., 7 (8), 1455–6, 1971; FOR ORIGINAL, SEE E 76486)
91507	**THERMOELECTRICAL PROPERTIES OF GALLIUM ANTIMONIDE AT 300 K.** IL'CHENKO, L. N. STREL'NIKOVA, I. A. MIRGALOVSKAYA, M. S. INORG. MAT., USSR 8 (5), 693–6, 1972. (ENGLISH TRANSLATION OF IZV. AKAD. NAUK SSSR, NEORG. MATER., 8 (5), 798–801, 1972; FOR ORIGINAL, SEE E76521)
91508	**MAGNETIC PROPERTIES OF CHROMIUM SULFOTELLURIDES.** IKORSKII, V. N. DORONINA, L. M. BATSANOV, S. S. I ORG. MAT., USSR 8 (5), 713–6, 1972. (ENGLISH TRANSLATION OF IZV. AKAD. NAUK SSSR, NEORG. MATER., 8 (5), 821–4, 1972; FOR ORIGINAL, SEE E 76522)
91509	**ELECTRICAL CONDUCTIVITY OF FUSED ALUMINUM OXIDE.** ALEKSANDROV, V. I. OSIKO, V. V. TATARISTSEV, V. M. INORG. MAT., USSR 8 (5), 835–6, 1972. (ENGLISH TRANSLATION OF IZV. NAUK SSSR, NEORG. MATER., 8 (5), 956–7, 1972; FOR ORIGINAL SEE E 76523)
91510	**TEMPERATURE DEPENDENCE OF THE THERMO-EMF OF CUPRIC OXIDE DURING ITS DISSOCIATION.** ZUEV, K. P. KOLENCHENKO, V. I. INORG. MAT., USSR 8 (5), 837–8, 1972. (ENGLISH TRANSLATION OF IZV. AKAD. NAUK SSSR, NEORG. MATER., 8 (5), 958–9, 1972; FOR ORIGINAL, SEE E 76524)
91512	**EFFECT OF IMPURITIES ON THE HIGH TEMPERATURE ELECTRICAL CONDUCTIBITY OF CADMIUM TELLURIDE CRYSTALS.** RUD', YU. V. SANIN, K. S. INORG. MAT., USSR, 8 (6), 892–6, 1972. (ENGLISH TRANSLATION OF IZV. AKAD. NAUK SSSR, NEORG. MATER., 8 (6), 1019–24, 1972; FOR ORIGINAL, SEE E 76526)
91514	**THE NATURE OF THE BOND AND ELECTRICAL CONDUCTIVITY OF CUBIC ZIRCONIUM CARBIDES AND OXYCARBIDES.** BORUKHOVICH, A. S. MATVEENKO, I. I. ZAINULIN, YU. G. ALYAMOVSKII, S. I. GEL'D, P. V. INORG. MAT., USSR 6 (12), 1866–70, 1970. (ENGLISH TRANSLATION OF IZV. AKAD. NAUK SSSR, NEORG. MATER., 6 (12), 2126–31, 1970; FOR ORIGINAL, SEE E 76459)
91515	**BARIUM TITANATE CONTAINING FLOURINE.** NAKRASOV, M. M. DAVOSHCHENKO, V. S. SYCH, A. M. INORG. MAT., USSR 6 (12), 1907–9, 1970. (ENGLISH TRANSLATION OF IZV. AKAD. NAUK SSSR, NEORG. MATER., 6 (12), 2175–7, 1973; FOR ORIGINAL, SEE E 76458)
91519	**EFFECT OF THE GAS PHASE COMPOSITION ON THE ELECTRICAL PROPERTIES OF EPITAXIAL LAYERS OF GALLIUM ARSENIDE.** SIDOROV, YU. G. DVORTESKII, S. A. ALEKSANDROV, L. N. KRAVCHENKO, A. F. RYNDINA, L. N. LEUTINA, A. P. INORG. MAT., USSR 8 (8), 1213–7, 19729 (ENGLISH TRANSLATION OF IZV, AKAD. NAUK SSSR, NEORG. MATER., 8 (8), 1373–8, 1972; FOR ORIGINAL, SEE E 76536)
91520	**ELECTRICAL AND GALVANOMAGNETIC PROPERTIES OF ALLOYS OF THE SYSTEM COPPER SILVER TELLURIDE.** RUSTAMOV, A. G. KERIMOV, I. G. IBRAGIMOVA, P. G. INORG. MAT., USSR 8 (8), 1315–6, 1972. (ENGLISH TRANSLATION OF IZV. NAUK SSSR, NEORG. MATER 8 (8), 1493–4, 1972; FOR ORIGINAL, SEE E 76538)
91521	**PHYSICAL PROPERTIES OF ORIN BORIDES.** KOSTETSKII, I. I. L'VOV, S. N. KUNITSKII, YU. A. INORG. MAT., USSR. 7 (6), 839–43, 1971. (ENGLISH TRANSLATION OF IZV. AKAD. NAUK SSSR, NEORG. MATER., 7 (6), 951–8, 1971; FOR ORIGINAL, SEE E 76476)
91523	**ELECTRICAL RESISTANCES OF LANTHANUM CHROMITE, NEODYMIUM CHROMITE, SAMARIUM CHROMITE, AND YTTRIUM CHROMITE AT HIGH TEMPERATURES.** GORDON, V. G. REKOV, A. I. SPIRIDONOV, E. G. TIMOFEEVA, N. I. INORG. MAT., USSR 7 (6), 965–6, 1971. (ENGLISH TRANSLATION OF IZV. AKAD. NAUK SSSR, NEORG. MATER., 7 (6), 1084–5, 1971; FOR ORIGINAL, SEE E 76477)
91524	**ELECTRICAL PROPERTIES AND STRUCTURES OF METANIOBATES AND METATANTALATES OF TRANSITION METALS OF THE 3D SERIES.** BAZUEV, G. V. KRYLOV, E. I. INORG. MAT., USSR 7 (7), 1072–4, 1971. (ENGLISH TRANSLATION OF IZV. AKAD. NAUK SSSR, NEORG. MATER., 7 (7), 1209–12, 1971; FOR ORIGINAL, SEE E 76484)
91525	**RELAXATION AND FERROELECTRIC PROPERTIES OF SOLID SOLUTIONS IN THE SYSTEM BARIUM TITANIUM OXIDE - STRONTIUM NIOBIUM OXIDE.** GROZNOV, I. N. VISKOV, A. S. PETROV, V. M. INORG. MAT., USSR 7 (7), 1078–81M 1971. (ENGLISH TRANSLATION OF IZV. AKAD. NAUK SSSR, NEORG. MATER., 7 (7), 1216–9, 1971; FOR ORIGINAL, SEE E 76481)
91527	**DIELECTRIC AND STRUCTURAL PROPERTIES OF FERRO-ELECTRICS WITH DIFFUSE PHASE TRANSITIONS.** SAL' IKOV, V. D. KUZ'MINOV, YU. S. VENEVTSEV, YU. N. INORG. MAT., USSR 7 (7), 1138–9, 1971. (ENGLISH TRANSLATION OF IZV. AKAD. NAUK SSSR, NEORG. MATER., 7 (7), 1277–8, 1971; FOR ORIGINAL, SEE E 76482)
91528	**ELECTRICAL AND THERMOGRAPHIC INVESTIGATION OF CADMIUM ANTIMONIDE.** ANATYCHUK, L. I. GNATYUK, A. M. INORG. MAT., USSR 8 (1), 37–40, 1972. (ENGLISH TRANSLATION OF IZV. AKAD. NAUK SSSR, NEORG. MATER., 8 (1), 44–8, 1972; FOR ORIGINAL, SEE E 76505)
91529	**EFFECT OF DOPANTS ON THE PHYSICAL PROPERTIES AND CHARACTER OF THE CHEMICAL BONDS IN GALLIUM ANTIMONIDE.** SAFARALIEV, G. I. MURGUZOV, M. I. INORG. MAT., USSR 8 (1), 44–6, 1972. (ENGLISH TRANSLATION OF IZV. AKAD. NAUK SSSR, NEORG. MATER., 8 (1), 53–6, 1972; FOR ORIGINAL, SEE E 76506)

EPIC Number	Bibliographic Citation

91530 **ELECTRICAL CONDUCTIVITY, THERMOELECTROMOTIVE FORCE, AND THERMIONIC EMISSION OF BARIUM OXIDE AND STRONTIUM OXIDE CRYSTALS.**
KOVALEV, N. N. SOROKIN, O. V.
INORG. MAT., USSR
8 (1), 94-9, 1972.
(ENGLISH TRANSLATION OF IZV. AKAD. NAUK SSSR, NEORG. MATER., 8 (1), 111-6, 1972; FOR ORIGINAL SEE E76508)

91532 **INTRINSIC CARRIER CONCENTRATION IN MERCURY TELLURIDE.**
KIREEV, P. S. DMITRIEV, V. P.
ZUBAREVA, ZH. M. PTASHINSKII, V. V.
INORG. MAT., USSR
8 (6), 987-900, 1972.
(ENGLISH TRANSLATION OF IZV. AKAD. NAUK USSR, NEORG. MATER., 8 (6), 1025-8, 1972; FOR ORIGINAL, SEE E 76527)

91534 **ELECTROPHYSICAL PROPERTIES OF VANADIUM MONOXIDE IN THE HOMOGENEOUS REGION.**
AIVAZOV, M. I. DOMASHNEV, I. A.
SARKISYAN, A. G. GUROV, S. V.
INORG. MAT., USSR
8 (6), 937-40, 1972.
(ENGLISH TRANSLATION OF IZV. AKAD. NAUK SSSR, NEORG. MATER., 8 (6), 1069-72, 1972; FOR ORIHIANL, SEE E 76529)

91535 **PHOTOELECTRIC PROPERTIES OF THE VITREOUS SEMICONDUCTORS CADMIUM SILICON GEMANIUM ARSENIDE.**
AKSENOV, V. V. PETROV, V. M.
KHARAKHORIN, F. F.
INORG. MAT., USSR
8 (6), 1010-12, 1972.
(ENGLISH TRANSLATION OF IZV. AKAD. NAUK SSSR, NOERG. MATER., 8 (6), 1152-4, 1972; FOR ORIGINAL, SEE E 76530)

91537 **REGION OF THE SOLID SOLUTION OF GERMANIUM TELLURIDE IN BISMUTH SESQUITELLURIDE.**
ABRIKOSOV, N. KH. DANILOVA-DOBRYAKOVA, G. T.
INORG. MAT., USSR
8 (7), 1075-7, 1972.
(ENGLISH TRANSLATION OF IZV. AKAD. NAUK SSSR, NEORG. MATER., 8 (7), 1221-3, 1972; FOR ORIGINAL SEE E76534)

91539 **EFFECT OF EVAPORATION OF THE VOLATILE COMPONENT ON THE ELECTRICAL PROPERTIES OF CADMIUM ANTIMONIDE.**
ANATYCHUK, L. I. KONDRATENKO, V. M.
LUSTE, O. YA. KHAVRUNYAK, P. T.
INORG. MAT., USSR
8 (4), 570-4, 1972.
(ENGLISH TRANSLATION OF IZV. AKAD. NAUK SSSR, NEORG. MATER., 8 (4), 653-8, 1972; FOR ORIGINAL SEE E76518)

91542 **PHASE DIAGRAM AND ELECTRICAL CONDUCTIVITY OF ALLOYS OF THE SYSTEM BISMUTH SELENIDE IODIDE - ANTIMONY SELENIDE IODIDE.**
BELOTSKII, D. I. LAPSHIN, V. F.
INORG. MAT., USSR
7 (11), 1727-9, 1971.
(ENGLISH TRANSLATION OF IZV. AKAD. NAUK SSSR, NEORG. MATER., 7 (11), 1939-41, 1971; FOR ORIGINAL SEE E76497)

91544 **MAGNETIC SUSCEPTIBILITY OF OXYGEN VANADIUM BRONZES.**
DUBROVSKAYA, L. B. FOTIEV, A. A.
VOLKOV, V. L. SURAT, L. L.
INORG. MAT., USSR
6 (10), 1616-8, 1970.
(ENGLISH TRANSLATION OF IZV. AKAD. NAUK SSSR, NEORG. MATER., 6 (10), 1835-8, 1970; FOR ORIGINAL SEE E76453)

91546 **ELECTRICAL CONDUCTIVITY, THERMO ELECTROMOTIVE FORCE, AND THERMAL CONDUCTIVITY OF SEMICONDUCTIVE COPPER INDIUM TELLURIDE AND COPPER GALLIUM TELLURIDE.**
BERGER, L. I. ISAEV, Z. A.
INORG. MAT., USSR
8 (11), 1773-5, 1972.
(ENGLISH TRANSLATION OF IZV. AKAD. NAUK SSSR, NEORG. MATER., 8 (11), 2018-20, 1972; FOR ORIGINAL SEE E76551)

91547 **FORBIDDEN-ZONE WIDTHS OF SOLID SOLUTIONS CADMIUM INDIUM SELENIDE - CADMIUM INDIUM TELLURIDE.**
KOVAL', L. S. RADAUTSAN, S. I.
SOBOLEV, V. V.
INORG. MAT., USSR
8 (11), 1776-7, 1972.
(ENGLISH TRANSLATION OF IZV. AKAD. NAUK SSSR, NEORG. MATER., 8 (11), 2021-2, 1972; FOR ORIGINAL SEE E76553)

91550 **REGION OF HOMOGENEITY OF SAMARIUM SULFIDE.**
SERGEEVA, V. M. GONCHAROVA, E. V.
KARTENKO, N. F. DEMINA, M. A. SMIRNOV, P. A.
ANDRYUSHIN, A. I. MISYUREV, YU. K.
INORG. MAT., USSR
8 (12), 1859-63, 1972.
(ENGLISH TRANSLATION OF IZV. AKAD. NAUK SSSR, NEORG. MATER., 8 (12), 2114-9, 1972; FOR ORIGINAL SEE E76557)

91552 **PHOTOLUMINESCENCE AND PHOTOCONDUCTIVITY OF P-TYPE MONOCRYSTALLINE CADMIUM TELLURIDE FILMS.**
KORNITSKII, A. G. KROTOV, I. I.
KIREEV, P. S.
INORG. MAT., USSR
8 (4), 575-8, 1972.
(ENGLISH TRANSLATION OF IZV. AKAD. NAUK SSSR, NEORG. MATER., 8 (4), 659-64, 1972; FOR ORIGINAL SEE E76519)

91553 **ELECTRICAL CONDUCTIVITY OF POLYCRYSTALLINE MAGNESIUM FLUORIDE.**
VOLYNETS, F. K. DRONOVA, G. N.
SMIRNAYA, E. P.
INORG. MAT., USSR
8 (4), 675-6, 1972.
(ENGLISH TRANSLATION OF IZV. AKAD. NAUK SSSR, NEORG. MATER., 8 (4), 775-6, 1972; FOR ORIGINAL SEE E76520)

91555 **DOPING OF SEMICONDUCTIVE LAYERS OBTAINED BY COMPRESSING A MELT.**
SANDULOVA, A. V. GONCHAROV, A. G.
RUDOL'F, P.
INORG. MAT., USSR
8 (2), 202-4, 1972.
(ENGLISH TRANSLATION OF IZV. AKAD. NAUK SSSR, NEORG. MATER., 8 (2), 224-7, 1972; FOR ORIGINAL SEE E76511)

91556 **EFFECT OF DOUBLE DOPING ON THE ELECTRICAL PROPERTIES OF CADMIUM ANTIMONIDE.**
KOSTUR, T. A. KOSTUR, N. L. PSAREV, V. I.
INORG. MAT., USSR
8 (2), 205-7, 1972.
(ENGLISH TRANSLATION OF IZV. AKAD. NAUK SSSR, NEORG. MATER., 8 (2), 228-31, 1972; FOR ORIGINAL SEE E76512)

91561 **SLIGHTLY DOPED INDIUM ANTIMONIDE CRYSTALS WITH VARYING DEGREES OF COMPENSATION.**
MIRGALOVSKAYA, M. S. RAUKHMAN, M. R.
SOROKINA, N. G.
INORG. MAT., USSR
8 (3), 495-6, 1972.
(ENGLISH TRANSLATION OF IZV. AKAD. NAUK SSSR, NEORG. MATER., 8 (3), 569-70, 1972; FOR ORIGINAL SEE E76517)

91563 **ELECTRICAL CONDUCTIVITY AND THERMO ELECTROMOTIVE FORCE OF SILVER GALLIUM DISELENIDE IN THE SOLID AND LIQUID STATES.**
BALANEVSKAYA, A. E. BERGER, L. I.
ISAEV, Z. A.
INORG. MAT., USSR
7 (11), 1857-8, 1971.
(ENGLISH TRANSLATION OF IZV. AKAD. NAUK SSSR, NEORG. MATER., 7 (11), 2084-5, 1971; FOR ORIGINAL SEE E76499)

91564 **SOME PHYSICAL PROPERTIES OF BERYLLIUM, CHROMIUM, AND LANTHANUM BOROCARBIDES.**
NESHPOR, V. S. VEKSHINA, N. V.
NIKITIN, V. P. MARKOVSKII, L. YA.
INORG. MAT., USSR
7 (12), 1931-4, 1971.
(ENGLISH TRANSLATION OF IZV. AKAD. NAUK SSSR, NEORG. MATER., 7 (12), 2170-4, 1971; FOR ORIGINAL SEE E76503)

91566 **THE SYSTEM LEAD SELENIDE - TIN DISELENIDE.**
LATYPOV, Z. M. SAVEL'EV, V. P.
AVER'YANOV, I. S. UL'DANOV, A. S.
INORG. MAT., USSR
7 (11), 1865-6, 1971.
(ENGLISH TRANSLATION OF IZV. AKAD. NAUK SSSR, NEORG. MATER., 7 (11), 2092-3, 1971; FOR ORIGINAL SEE E76500)

91568 **ELECTRICAL PROPERTIES OF TRANSITION METAL SELENIDES.**
ABDINOV, D. SH. IVANOVA, V. I. ALIEV, G. M.
INORG. MAT., USSR
7 (9), 1438-9, 1971.
(ENGLISH TRANSLATION IZV. AKAD. NAUK SSSR, NEORG. MATER., 7 (9), 1622-3, 1971; FOR ORIGINAL SEE E76489)

91569 **ELECTRICAL CONDUCTIVITY IN OXIDE SYSTEMS WITH THE RUTILE STRUCTURE.**
KRYLOV, E. I. DVOININ, V. I.
ROZHDESTVENSKII, F. A.
INORG. MAT., USSR
7 (9), 1454-5, 1971.
(ENGLISH TRANSLATION OF IZV. AKAD. NAUK SSSR, NEORG. MATER., 7 (9), 1636-7, 1971; FOR ORIGINAL, SEE E 76488)

91570 **SUPERCONDUCTIVITY AND RESIDUAL RESISTANCE OF TITANIUM CARBIDE.**
NESHPOR, V. S. NIKITIN, V. P. NOVIKOV, V. I.
INORG. MAT., USSR
7 (10), 1557-60, 1971.
(ENGLISH TRANSLATION OF IZV. AKAD. NAUK SSSR, NEORG. MATER. 7 (10), 1743-7, 1971; FOR ORIGINAL SEE E76491)

EPIC Number	Bibliographic Citation

91572 SYNTHESIS AND ELECTRICAL PROPERTIES OF RARE EARTH GERMANATES.
POPOV, V. P. PETROVA, M. A.
INORG. MAT., USSR
9 (1), 54–6, 1973.
(ENGLISH TRANSLATION OF IZV. AKAD. NAUK SSSR, NEORG. MATER. 9 (1), 61–3, 1973; FOR ORIGINAL SEE E70815)

91573 LIFETIME OF NONEQUILIBRIUM CARRIERS IN SINGLE CRYSTALS OF CADMIUM MERCURY TELLURIDE.
VDOVKINA, E. E. BARYSHEV, N. S.
VOLKOVA, F. P. CHERKASOV, A. P.
SHCHETININ, M. P. AVER'YANOV, I. S.
INORG. MAT., USSR
9 (1), 115–6, 1973.
(ENGLISH TRANSLATION OF IZV. AKAD. NAUK SSSR, NEORG. MATER. 9 (1), 130–1, 1973; FOR ORIGINAL SEE E70817)

91574 PHASE TRANSITIONS IN LEAD ORTHOPHOSPHATE AND SOLID SOLUTIONS OF LEAD ORTHOPHOSPHATE AND ORTHOVANADATE.
ISUPOV, V. A. KRAINIK, N. N. KOSENKO, E. L.
INORG. MAT., USSR
9 (1), 139–40, 1973.
(ENGLISH TRANSLATION OF IZV. AKAD. NAUK SSSR, NEORG. MATER. 9 (1), 154–5, 1973; FOR ORIGINAL SEE E70818)

91575 ELECTRICAL CONDUCTIVITY OF SEMICONDUCTIVE GLASS CRYSTALS BASED ON ARSENIC AND LEAD SELENIDES.
BORISOVA, Z. U. FRISH, G. SHKOL'NIKOV, E. V.
INORG. MAT., USSR
9 (2), 194–7, 1973.
(ENGLISH TRANSLATION OF IZV. AKAD. NAUK SSSR, NEORG. MATER. 9 (2), 213–7, 1973; FOR ORIGINAL SEE E70819)

91576 SENSITIZATION OF CADMIUM TELLURIDE CRYSTALS.
ROMANENKO, V. N. RUD', YU. V. SANIN, K. V.
INORG. MAT., USSR
9 (2), 208–11, 1973.
(ENGLISH TRANSLATION OF IZV. AKAD. NAUK SSSR, NEORG. MATER. 9 (2), 231–5, 1973; FOR ORIGINAL SEE E 70820)

91577 VARIABLE RESISTORS OF THE BULK TYPE BASED ON REFRACTORY COMPOUNDS.
SAMSONOV, G. V. GREBENKINA, V. G.
YASOV, YU. P. VLASOV, L. G.
PEREVEZENTSEV, A. V.
INORG. MAT., USSR
7 (10), 1575–8, 1971.
(ENGLISH TRANSLATION OF IZV. AKAD. NAUK SSSR, NEORG. MATER. 7 (10), 1764–8, 1971; FOR ORIGINAL SEE E 76493)

91578 PHYSICAL PROPERTIES OF CADMIUM GALLIUM TETRASELENIDE.
TYRZIU, M. P. TYRZIU, V. G.
INORG. MAT., USSR
7 (10), 1655–6, 1971.
(ENGLISH TRANSLATION OF IZV. AKAD. NAUK SSSR, NEORG. MATER. 7 (10), 1855–6, 1971; FOR ORIGINAL SEE E 76494)

91580 ELECTRICAL CONDUCTIVITY AND THERMO–EMF OF SINGLE CRYSTALS OF A SERIES OF SILVER – VANADIUM OXYGEN BRONZES.
VINOGRADOV, A. A. ORNATSKAYA, Z. I.
INORG. MAT., USSR
7 (10), 1669–71, 1971.
(ENGLISH TRANSLATION OF IZV. AKAD. NAUK SSSR, NEORG. MATER. 7 (10), 1869–71, 1971; FOR ORIGINAL SEE E 76496)

91581 PHOTOSENSITIVITY OF CADMIUM SULFIDE FILMS DEPOSITED CHEMICALLY FROM AQUEOUS SOLUTIONS.
BOGDANOVICH, V. B. VELIKANOV, A. A.
KAGANOVICH, E. B. OSTROVSKAYA, I. K.
SVECHNIKOV, S. V.
INORG. MAT., USSR
7 (11), 1847–8, 1971.
(ENGLISH TRANSLATION OF IZV. AKAD. NAUK SSSR, NEORG. MATER. 7 (11), 2075–6, 1971; FOR ORIGINAL SEE E 76498)

91582 PHYSICOCHEMICAL ANALYSIS OF LIQUID SYSTEMS FORMED BY COPPER AND ANTIMONY CHALCOGENIDES.
GLAZOV, V. M. KULIEV, R. A.
INORG. MAT., USSR
7 (2), 181–4, 1971.
(ENGLISH TRANSLATION OF IZV. AKAD. NAUK SSSR, NEORG. MATER. 7 (2), 206–9, 1971; FOR ORIGINAL SEE E 76462)

91584 PREPARATION OF CONDUCTING STANNIC OXIDE FILMS, OBTAINED FROM ORGANIC COMPOUNDS, ON GLASS.
VOROB'EVA, O. V. POLUROTOVA, T. F.
INORG. MAT., USSR
7 (2), 235–7, 1971.
(ENGLISH TRANSLATION OF IZV. AKAD. NAUK SSSR, NEORG. MATER. 7 (2), 266–9, 1971; FOR ORIGINAL SEE E 76465)

91585 AXIAL INHOMOGENEITY OF CADMIUM TELLURIDE BARS.
MATVEEV, O. A. PROKOF'EV, S. V. RUD', YU. V.
SANIN, K. V. SHRETER, YU. G.
INORG. MAT., USSR
7 (2), 286–7, 1971.
(ENGLISH TRANSLATION OF IZV. AKAD. NAUK SSSR, NEORG. MATER. 7 (2), 324–5, 1971; FOR ORIGINAL SEE E 76463)

91586 ELECTRICAL PROPERTIES IN THE SYSTEM SCANDIUM OXIDE – VANADIUM (III) OXIDE.
BAZUEV, G. V. PERELYAEV, V. A.
SHVEIKIN, G. P.
INORG. MAT., USSR
9 (2), 229–31, 1973.
(ENGLISH TRANSLATION OF IZV. AKAD. NAUK SSSR, NEORG. MATER. 9 (2), 257–9, 1975; FOR ORIGINAL SEE E 70821)

91587 ELECTRICAL PROPERTIES OF TITANONIOBATES OF RARE EARTHS OF THE CERIUM SUBGROUP.
KRYLOV, E. I. BORISOV, A. K.
KAZANTSEV, V. V.
INORG. MAT., USSR
9 (2), 240–3, 1973.
(ENGLISH TRANSLATION OF IZV. AKAD. NAUK SSSR, NEORG. MATER. 9 (2), 269–72, 1973; FOR ORIGINAL SEE E 70822)

91588 SPECTROSCOPIC PROPERTIES OF THE ERBIUM (3+) ION IN THE GADOLINIUM ALUMINATE LATTICE.
ARSEN'EV, P. A. BINERT, K. E.
INORG. MAT., USSR
9 (2), 298–9, 1973.
(ENGLISH TRANSLATION OF IZV. AKAD. NAUK SSSR, NEORG. MATER. 9 (2), 327–9, 1973; FOR ORIGINAL SEE E 70823)

91590 ELECTRIC AND PHOTOELECTRIC PROPERTIES OF SINGLE CRYSTALS OF THALLIUM GALLIUM DISULFIDE, THALLIUM GALLIUM DISELENIDE, AND THALLIUM INDIUM DISULFIDE.
KARPOVICH, I. A. CHERVOVA, A. A.
DEMIDOVA, L. I. LEONOV, E. I. ORLOV, V. M.
INORG. MAT., USSR
8 (1), 58–9, 1972.
(ENGLISH TRANSLATION OF IZV. AKAD. NAUK SSSR, NEORG. MATER. 8 (1), 70–2, 1972; FOR ORIGINAL SEE E 76507)

91592 PHOTOCONDUCTIVITY OF PHOSPHORUS SELENIDES.
LYUBIN, V. M. FEDOROVA, G. A.
INORG. MAT., USSR
8 (9), 1368–71, 1972.
(ENGLISH TRANSLATION OF IZV. AKAD. NAUK SSSR, NEORG. MATER. 8 (9), 1559–62, 1972; FOR ORIGINAL SEE E 76540)

91593 THERMO–EMF OF P– AND N–TYPE INDIUM ANTIMONIDE AT ROOM TEMPERATURE.
MIRGALOVSKAYA, M. S. RAUKHMAN, M. R.
IL'CHENKO, L. N. SOROKINA, N. G.
INORG. MAT., USSR
8 (10), 1539–42, 1972.
(ENGLSIH TRANSLATION OF IZV. AKAD. NAUK SSSR, NEORG. MATER. 8 (10), 1751–4, 1972; FOR ORIGINAL SEE E 76546)

91596 MAGNETIC PROPERTIES OF CHROMIUM SULFOSELENOTELLURIDE.
IKORSKII, V. N. BATSANOV, S. S.
INORG. MAT., USSR
8 (10), 1633–4, 1972.
(ENGLISH TRANSLATION OF IZV. AKAD. NAUK SSSR, NEORG. MATER. 8 (10), 1858–9, 1972; FOR ORIGINAL SEE E 76545)

91597 PREPARATION AND PROPERTIES OF BERYLLIUM – DOPED GALLIUM PHOSPHIDE.
OVCHINNIKOV, S. YU. SOROKIN, V. S.
YAS'KOV, D. A.
INORG. MAT., USSR
8 (11), 1669–73, 1972.
(ENGLISH TRANSLATION OF IZV. AKAD. NAUK SSSR, NEORG. MATER. 8 (11), 1898–1904, 1972; FOR ORIGINAL SEE E 76547)

91598 CRYSTAL STRUCTURE AND ELECTRICAL PROPERTIES OF ALLOYS OF THE SYSTEM INDIUM SELENIDE – ANTIMONY TELLURIDE.
BELOTSKII, D. P. LEGETA, L. V.
INORG. MAT., USSR
8 (11), 1677–81, 1972.
(ENGLISH TRANSLATION OF IZV. AKAD. NAUK SSSR, NEORG. MATER., 8 (11), 1908–12, 1972; FOR ORIGINAL SEE E76548)

91599 MAGNETIC PROPERTIES OF VANADIUM NITRIDE AND DIBORIDE AND ALLOYS IN THE SYSTEM VANADIUM – BORON – NITROGEN.
AIVAZOV, M. I. GUROV, S. V.
INORG. MAT., USSR
8 (11), 1682–5, 1972.
(ENGLISH TRANSLATION OF IZV. AKAD. NAUK SSSR, NEORG. MATER., 8 (11), 1913–6, 1972; FOR ORIGINAL SEE E76549)

EPIC Number	Bibliographic Citation
91600	**VALENCE ELECTRON TRANSITION IN RARE-EARTH MONOCHALCOGENIDES INDUCED BY PRESSURE, ALLOYING, AND TEMPERATURE.** JAYARAMAN, A. DERNIER, P. D. LONGINOTTI, L. D. HIGH TEMP. HIGH PRESSURES 7 (1), 1-28, 1975.
91605	**ELECTRIC FIELD ENHANCES CONDUCTIVITY SOLIDS.** PAI, D. M. J. APPL. PHYS. 46 (12), 5122-6, 19 75.
91619	**OPTICAL PROPERTIES OF RUBIDIUM GOLD AND CESIUM GOLD.** LIU, T. L. PHYS. REV. 12 B (8), 3008-12, 1975.
91631	**PHOTOVOLTAIC PROPERTIES OF ANISOTROPIC RELAXATION SEMICONDUCTORS.** SCHETZINA, J. F. PHYS. REV. 12 B (8), 3339-52, 1975.
91637	**PHONON-GENERATED MOCROFIELDS AND THE HIGH-TEMPERATURE SHIFT OF THE ABSORPTION EDGE IN CUBIC ZINC SULFIDE.** BRADA, Y. YACOBI, B. G. PELED, A. PHYS. REV. 12 B (8), 3494-6, 1975.
91671	**RESONANT EXCITON NONLINEARITIES WITH SPATIAL DISPERSION.** LEVINE, B. F. MILLER, R. C. NORDLAND, W. A. PHYS. REV.P 12 B (10), 4512-21, 1975.
91718	**DEPENDENCE OF THE DIRECT ENERGY GAP OF GALLIUM ARSENIDE ON HYDROSTATIC PRESSURE.** WELBER, B. CARDONA, M. KIM, C. K. RODRIQUEZ, S. PHYS. REV. 12 (12), 5729-38, 1975.
91725	**PHOTOVOLTAIC EFFECT AND INTERBAND MAGNETO-OPTICAL TRANSITIONS IN INDIUM PHOSPHIDE.** ROCHON, P. FORTIN, E. PHYS. REV. 12 B (12), 5 803-10, 1975.
91730	**OPTICAL ABSORPTION AND PHOTO EMISSION EDGES IN INSULATING SOLIDS.** KUNZ, A. B. PHYS. REV. 12 B (12), 5890-5906, 1975.
91733	**VACUUM ULTRAVIOLET REFLECTIVITIES OF LITHIUM FLUORIDE, SODIUM FLOURIDE, AND POTASSIUM FLUORIDE.** RAO, K. K. MORAVEC, T. J. RIFE, J. S. DEXTER, R. N. PHYS. REV. 12 B (12), 5937-50, 1975.
91741	**PHYSICAL PROPERTIES OF BORIDE PHASES OF CHROMIUM.** SEREBRYAKOVA, T. I. KOVENSKAYA, B. A. INORG. MAT., USSR 2 (12), 1846-9, 1966. (ENGLISH TRANSLATION OF IZV. AKAD. NAUK SSSR, NEORG. MATER. 2 (12), 2134-8, 1966; FOR ORIGINAL SEE E 76422)
91742	**SOLID SOLUTIONS IN THE SYSTEM GALLIUM SUFLIDE - GALLIUM SELENIDE.** RUSTAMOV, P. G. MELIKOVA, Z. D. SAFAROV, M. G. ALIDZHANOV, M. A. INORG. MAT., USSR 1 (3), 387-9, 1965. (ENGLISH TRANSLATION OF IZV. AKAD. NAUK SSSR, NEORG. MATER. 1 (3), 419-21, 1965; FOR ORIGINAL SEE E 76401)
91743	**EFFECT OF CHEMICAL COMPOSITION ON THE STRUCTURE AND ELECTRO- AND THERMOPHYSICAL PROPERTIES OF VANADIUM MONOCARBIDE IN THE REGION OF HOMOGENEITY.** NESHPOR, V. S. ORDAN'YAN, S. S. INORG. MAT., USSR 1 (2), 173-80, 1965. (ENGLISH TRANSLATION OF IZV. AKAD. NAUK SSSR, NEORG. MATER. 1 (2), 173-80, 1965; FOR ORIGINAL SEE E 76400)
91745	**RADIOTHERMOLUMINESCENCE OF ICE IN THE PRESENCE OF ADDITIVES.** ERSHOV, B. G. PUNTEZHIS, S. A. PIKAEV, A. K. SPITSYN, A. V. I. PROC. ACAD. SCI., USSR, PHYS. CHEM. SECT. 209 (4), 297-300, 1973. (ENGLISH TRANSLATION OF DOKL. AKAD. NAUK SSSR 209 (4), 889-92, 1973; FOR ORIGINAL SEE E 70911)
91746	**EMISSION OF FAST ELECTRONS DURING THE BREAKING OF IONIC CRYSTALS.** KROTOVA, N. A. LINKE, E. KHRUSTALEV, YU. A. VOLLBRANDT, I. SHIPOVSKII, V. I. PROC. ACAD. SCI. USSR, PHYS. CHEM. SECT. 208 (1), 138-41, 1973. (ENGLISH TRANSLATION OF DOKL. AKAD. NAUK SSR 208 (1), 138-41, 1973; FOR ORIGINAL SEE E 70905)
91748	**ELECTRICAL RESISTANCE AND THERMAL EMF OF GERMANIUM TELLURIDE IN THE REGION OF PHASE TRANSITION.** KORZHUEV, M. A. ABRIKOSOV, N. KH. SHELIMOVA, L. E. PROC. ACAD. SCI. USSR, CHEM. SECT. 220 (2), 21-4, 1975. (ENGLISH TRANSLATION OF DOKL. AKAD. NAUK SSSR, 220 (2), 402-6, 1975; FOR ORIGINAL, SEE E 75092)
91759	**KUBELKA-MUNK OPTICAL COEFFICIENTS FOR A BARIUM SULFATE WHITE REFLECTANCE STANDARD.** GILLESPIE, J. B. LINDBERG, J. D. LAUDE, L. S. APPL. OPT. 14 (4), 807-9, 1975.
91762	**TWO WAVELENGTH MEASUREMENTS OF OPTICAL WAVEGUIDE PARAMETERS.** BRANDT, G. B. APPL. OPT. 14 (4), 946-9, 1975.
91765	**PLEXIGLAS: A CONVENIENT TRANSMISSION FILTER FOR THE FIR SPECTRAL REGION.** MOH, K. K. SIEVERS, A. J. APPL. OPT. 14 (5), 1054-5, 1975.
91781	**CONSTRUCTION OF A REFLECTO-POLARIMETER-ELLIPSOMETER FOR FREQUENCY OF 16 GIGAHERTZ. APPLICATION TO THE DETERMINATION OF THE TERMS OF MAGNETO-CONDUCTIVITY TENSOR OF A SEMI-CONDUCTOR CRYSTAL.** HAYE, K. C. R. HEBD. SEANCES ACAD. SCI. 280 B (18), 567-70, 1975.
91784	**PHYSICAL CHARACTERISTICS OF SOLID SOLUTIONS IN THE VICINITY OF DIFFUSE PHASE TRANSITION WITH RESPECT TO FLUCTUATIONS OF COMPOSITION.** YURKEVICH, V. E. ROLOV, B. N. CZECH. J. PHYS. 25 B (6), 701-11, 1975.
91840	**CHEMILUMINESCENCE AND PHOTOLUMINESCENCE OF DIATOMIC IRON OXIDE.** WEST, J. B. BROIDA, H. P. J. CHEM. PHYS. 62 (7), 2566-74, 1975.
91863	**ABSORPTION OF INFRARED RADIATION BY IONIZED DONOR PAIRS IN GALLIUM ARSENIDE, INDIUM PHOSPHIDE AND CADMIUM TELLURIDE.** GOLKA, J. J. PHYS. 8 C (9), 1443-9, 1975.
91864	**MANY-BODY EFFECTS IN THE TEMPERATURE DEPENDENCE OF SUSCEPTIBILITY OF NORMAL PARAMAGNETIC METALS AND FERMI LIQUIDS.** BARNEA, G. J. PHYS. 8 C (10), L216-21, 1975.
91874	**SOME ELECTRICAL AND OPTICAL EFFECTS OF IMPURITY ASSOCIATIONS IN CRYSTALS OF SODIUM CHLORIDE.** WHITHAM, W. CALDERWOOD, J. H. J. PHYS. 8 D (9), 1133-9, 1975.
91879	**OPTICAL PROPERTIES OF AMORPHOUS SILICON CARBIDE FILMS.** FAGEN, E. A. SILICON CARBIDE, PROC. CONF., 3RD 542-9, 1974.
91887	**THERMOLUMINESCENCE OF YTTRIUM ALUMINUM GARNET ACTIVATED BY RARE EARTH IONS.** BAGDASAROV, KH. S. VAKHIDOV, S. A. YUSUPOV, A. A. METOD. RADIATS. VOZDEISTV. ISSLED. STRUKT. SVOISTV TVERD. TEL 96-8, 1971.
91888	**PROBLEM OF THE ALPHA SILICON CARBIDE ENERGY STRUCTURE.** ORLOVA, N. I. SHISHKIN, P. T. IZV. AKAD. NAUK UZ. SSR, SER. FIZ. MAT. NAUK 8 (4), 53-61, 1964.
91890	**OPTICAL CONSTANTS AND BAND WIDTH OF AMORPHOUS SILICON NITRIDE LAYERS IN THE UV AND NEAR VACUUM UV REGIONS.** BAUER, J. RIEMANN, M. WISS. Z. TECH. HOCHSCH. 20 (4-5), 181-9, 1974.

EPIC Number	Bibliographic Citation
91893	ELECTRICAL CONDUCTIVITY OF COPPER ALLOYS WITH ARSENIC. PUSHINA, N. A. DISHLERA, E. G. J. RUSS. PHYS. CHEM. SOC. 44 (1), 125–32, 1912.
91913	EFFECT OF NON-STOICHIOMETRY IN NICKEL-FERRITES ON ELECTRICAL CONDUCTION. YAMADA, T. J. PHYS. SOC. JAP. 38 (5), 1378–82, 1975.
91918	LOW TEMPERATURE SPECTRA OF DIVALENT SAMARIUM IN KAPLYANSKII, A. A. FEOFILOV, P. P. OPT. SPEKTROSK. 16, 264–73, 1963. (FOR ENGLISH TRANSLATION, SEE E 75090)
91926	OPTICAL ABSORPTION IN GALLIUM ARSENIDE WHICH HAS BEEN IRRADIATED BY HIGH INTEGRATED FLUXES OF FAST NEUTRONS. VODOP'YANOV, L. K. KURDIANI, N. I. FIZ. TVERD. TELA 8 (1), 254–6, 1966. (FOR ENGLISH TRANSLATION, SEE E 75146)
91929	NONPARABOLICITY OF THE CONDUCTION BAND OF LEAS TELLURIDE. ZHITINSKAYA, M. K. KAIDANOV, V. I. CHERNIK, I. A. FIZ. TVERD. TELA 8 (1), 295–7, 19669 (FOR ENGLISH TRANSLATION, SEE E 75147)
91930	FIELD EMISSION FROM LEAD TELLURIDE. SYKES, D. E. BRAUN, E. PHYS. STATUS SOLIDI 69 B (2), K137–40, 1975.
91944	FERROELECTRIC PHASE TRANSITION IN AMMONIUM SULFATE - POTASSIUM SULFATE MIXED CRYSTALS. SAWADA, A. OHYA, S. ISHIBASHI, Y. TAKAGI, Y. J. PHYS. SOC. JAP. 38 (5), 1408–14, 1975.
91953	PROPERTIES OF SPUTTERED HIGH SUPERCONDUCTING TRANSITION TEMPERATURE THIN FILMS. GAVALER, J. R. J. VAC. SCI. AND TECHNOL. 12 (1), 103–6, 1975.
91954	SUPERCONDUCTING TRANSITION TEMPERATURES OF REACTIVELY SPUTTERED FILMS OF TANTALUM NITRIDE AND TUNGSTEN NITRIDE. KILBANE, F. M. HABIG, P. S. J. VAC. SCI. AND TECHNOL. 12 (1), 107–9, 1975.
91956	ION BACKSCATTERING STUDY OF TANTALUM NITRIDE THIN FILM RESISTORS. LANGLEY, R. A. SHARP, D. J. J. VAC. SCI. AND TECHNOL. 12 (1), 155–9, 1975.
91963	ON ACTIVATED SINTERING AND ELECTRICAL PROPERTIES OF SODIUM POTASSIUM NIOBATE. KOSEC, M. KOLAR, D. MATER. RES. BULL. 10 (5), 335–40, 1975.
91965	THE EFFECT OF COMPOSITION ON THE SUPERCONDUCTING TRANSITION TEMPERATURE IN NIOBIUM OXYNITRIDE. ROY, R. CARCIA, P. F. MESSIER, R. ROGOWSKI, D. MATER. RES. BULL. 10 (5), 379–82, 1975.
91972	THE CONDUCTIVITY OF MAGNETICALLY-ORDERED MANGANESE ARSENIDE PHOSPHIDE COMPOUNDS. BERG, H. BARNER, K. SCHROTER, W. PHILOS. MAG. 31 (5), 1049–62, 1975.
91987	ELECTRON EMISSION OF METALS INTO INSULATORS. VODENICHAROV, C. M. PHYS. STATUS SOLIDI 29 A (1), 223–9, 1975.
91991	FREE CARRIER ABSORPTION IN SEMICONDUCTORS WITH NON-PARABOLIC AND ELLIPSOIDAL ENERGY BAND STRUCTURES. DAS, A. K. NAG, B. R. PHYS. STATUS SOLIDI 69, B (2), 329–38, 1975.
91993	NONPARABOLICITY OF THE VALENCE BANDS OF BISMUTH TELLURIDE DEDUCED FROM TRANSPORT EQUATIONS. STORDEUR, M. KUHNBERGER, W. PHYS. STATUS SOLIDI 69 B (2), 377–87, 1975.
92020	MAGNETIC PROPERTIES OF IRON IMPURITIES IN A HOST OF METALLIC NICKEL SULPHIDE. ROUX-BUISSON, H. COEY, J. M. D. AIP CONF. PROC. (24), 57–8, 1974.
92022	THE X-AXIS METAMAGNETIC TRANSITIONS OF THE TERBIUM ORTHOFERRITE. BIDAUX, R. BOUREE, J. E. HAMMANN, J. AIP CONF. PROC. (24), 67–8, 1974.
92033	MEASUREMENT OF VERY LOW ABSORPTION COEFFICIENTS BY LASER CALORIMETRY. HASS, M. DAVISSON, J. W. ROSENSTOCK, H. B. BABISKIN, J. APPL. OPT. 14 (5), 1128–30, 1975.
92037	THE FUNDAMENTAL RESEARCH OF THERMOELECTRIC EFFECTS. I. TWO-DIMENSIONAL SEEBECK EFFECT. UMEMIYA, H. ITOO, M. KIKUCHI, T. BULL. JSME 28 (115), 25–32, 1975.
92059	IONIZATION AND BREAKDOWN IN SULFUR HEXA-FLUORIDE-AIR AND FREON-NITROGEN MIXTURES. MALLER, V. N. NAIDU, M. S. IEEE TRANS. PLASMA SCI. PS-3 (2), 49–54, 1975.
92079	DEGRADATION OF GALLIUM ARSENIDE CRYSTALS BY THE COLD-WORKING TREATMENT (ABRASION). OTSUBO, M. MIKI, H. SHIRAHATA, K. FUJIBAYASHI, K. JAP. J. APPL. PHYS. 14 (6), 849–54, 1975.
92112	MELTING PRESSURE CURVES AND HIGH TEMPERATURE SOLID - SOLID TRANSITIONS OF MERCURY II HALIDES UP TO KBAR AND A NEW HIGHLY CONDUCTING POLYMORPH OF MERCURY II IODIDE. BARDOLL, B. TODHEIDE, K. HIGH TEMP. HIGH PRESSURES 7 (3), 341–9, 1975.
92132	OPTICAL AND ELECTRICAL PROPERTIES OF DOPED INDIUM SESQUIOXIDE FILMS. KOSTIN, H. JOST, R. LEMS, W. PHYS. STATUS SOLIDI 29 A (1), 87–93, 1975.
92137	ON THE CORRELATION BETWEEN THE ELECTRICAL RESISTIVITY AND MAGNETIC MOMENTS. IKEDA, K. NAKAMICHI, T. SHIMIZU, M. ONO, S. PHYS. STATUS SOLIDI 29 A (1), K89–91, 1975.
92149	OPTICAL INVESTIGATION OF THE SILICON - SILICON DIOXIDE SYSTEM. HOFFMANN, G. NEMETH-SALLAY, M. SCHANDA, J. ACTA PHYS. ACAD. SCI. HUNG. 36 (4), 349–64, 1974.
92154	POSSIBLY MIXED VALENCY OF URANIUM IN URANIUM - NICKEL - COPPER. VAN DAAL, H. J. BUSCHOW, K. H. J. VAN AKEN, P. B. VAN MAAREN, M. H. PHYS. REV. LETT. 34 (23), 1457–60, 1975.
92166	A NEW METHOD OF MEASURING THE THERMOELECTRIC FIGURE OF MERIT [EMPLOYING CRYOSTAT]. PEGNA, G. CONGIU, A. REV. PHYS. APPL. 10 (3), 177–8, 1975.
92178	DIELECTRIC PROPERTIES OF CESIUM DIHYDROGEN PHOSPHATE AND CESIUM DIDEUTERIUM PHOSPHATE. LEVSTIK, A. BLINC, R. KABADA, P. CIZIKOV, S. LEVSTIK, I. FILIPIC, C. SOLID STATE COMMUN. 16 (12), 1339–41, 1975.
92200	EFFECT OF THERMOELASTIC STRESSES ON THE OPTICAL INDICATRIX OF A UNIAXIAL CRYSTAL. VIGASIN, A. A. GOROKHOV, YU. A. KRINDACH, D. P. SUKHORUKOV, A. P. OPT. SPEKTROSK. 37 (6), 1139–42, 1974. (FOR ENGLISH TRANSLATION SEE E92201)
92201	EFFECT OF THERMOELASTIC STRESSES ON THE OPTICAL INDICATRIX OF A UNIAXIAL CRYSTAL. VIGASIN, A. A. GOROKHOV, YU. A. KRINDACH, D. P. SUKHORUKOV, A. P. OPT. SPECTROS., USSR 37 (6), 654–5, 1974. (ENGLISH TRANSLATION OF OPT. SPEKTROSK., 37 (6), 1139–42, 1974; FOR ORIGINAL SEE E92200)
92220	BAND STRUCTURE AND OPTICAL PROPERTIES OF FLUORITE TYPE CRYSTALS. III. STAROSTIN, N. V. GANIN, V. A. OPT. SPEKTROSK 37 (6), 1109–15, 1974. (FOR ENGLISH TRANSLATION, SEE E 92221)

EPIC Number | Bibliographic Citation

92221 **BAND STRUCTURE AND OPTICAL PROPERTIES OF FLUORITE TYPE CRYSTALS. III.**
STAROSTIN, N. V. GANIN, V. A.
OPT. SPECTROS, USSR.
37 (6), 635–8, 1974.
(ENGLISH TRANSLATION OF OPT. SPEKTROSK., 37 (6), 1109–15, 1974; FOR ORIGINAL, SEE E 92220)

92229 **DETERMINATION OF THE REFRACTIVE INDEX OF PHOTOCONDUCTIVE MATERIALS.**
KISELEVA, N. K. KOLOMIETS, B. T.
INSTRUM. EXP. TECH.
17 (5), (PT. 2), 1452–4, 1974.
(ENGLISH TRANSLATION OF PRIB. TEKH. EKSP., 17 (5), (PT. 2), 171–3, 1974; FOR ORIGINAL SEE E87755)

92259 **OPTICAL INVESTIGATION OF THE INDIUM IMPURITY LEVEL IN LEAD TELLURIDE AND ITS SOLID SOLUTIONS.**
DRABKIN, I. A. ELISEEVA, YU. YA.
ZAKHARYUGINA, G. F. RAVICH, YU. I.
NEL'SON, I. V.
FIZ. TEKH. POLUPROV.
8 (10), 1947–51, 1974.
(FOR ENGLISH TRANSLATION, SEE E 92260)

92260 **OPTICAL INVESTIGATION OF THE INDIUM IMPURITY LEVEL IN LEAS TELLURIDE AND ITS SOLID SOLUTIONS.**
DRABKIN, I. A. ELISEEVA, YU. YA.
ZAKHARYUGINA, G. F. RAVICH, YU. I.
NEL'SON, I. V.
SOV. PHYS. SEMICOND.
8 (10), 1261–3, 1975.
(ENGLISH TRANSLATION OF FIZ. TEKH. POLUPROV., 8 (10), 1974–51, 1974; FOR ORIGINAL, SEE E 92259)

92266 **METHOD OF REFRACTIVE INDEX MEASUREMENT FOR TRANSPARENT SUBSTANCES.**
ODARICH, V. A.
OPT. SPEKTROSK.
37 (4), 761–4, 1974.
(FOR ENGLISH TRANSLATION SEE E92267)

92267 **METHOD OF REFRACTIVE INDEX MEASUREMENT FOR TRANSPARENT SUBSTANCES.**
ODARICH, V. A.
OPT. SPECTROS., USSR
37 (4), 431–3, 1974.
(ENGLISH TRANSLATION OF OPT. SPEKTROSK., 37 (4), 761–4, 1974; FOR ORIGINAL SEE E92266)

92274 **SPECTROSCOPY OF SAMARIUM IN LANTHANIDE AND YTTRIUM OXYSULFIDES.**
BABKINA, T. V. GAIDUK, M. I. ZORINA, L. N.
SOSHCHIN, N. P.
OPT. SPEKTROSK
37 (4), 706–10, 1974.
(FOR ENGLISH TRANSLATION SEE E92275)

92275 **SPECTROSCOPY OF SAMARIUM IN LANTHANIDE AND YTTRIUM OXYSULFIDES.**
BABKINA, T. V. GAIDUK, M. I. ZORINA, L. N.
SOSHCHIN, N. P.
OPT. SPECTROS., USSR
37 (4), 401–3, 1974.
(ENGLISH TRANSLATION OF OPT. SPEKTROSK. 37 (4), 706–10, 1974; FOR ORIGINAL SEE E 92274)

92292 **METHOD FOR CERTIFYING STANDARD SPECIMENS OF PERMITTIVITY AT ULTRAHIGH FREQUENCIES.**
BEL'SKAYA, L. P. IVOLOV, L. I.
YATSYNINA, N. L.
IZMER. TEKH.
17 (8), 52–4, 1974.
(FOR ENGLISH TRANSLATION SEE E92293)

92293 **METHOD FOR CERTIFYING STANDARD SPECIMENS OF PERMITTIVITY AT ULTRAHIGH FREQUENCIES.**
BEL'SKAYA, L. P. IVOLOV, L. I.
YATSYNINA, N. L.
MEAS. TECH., USSR
17 (8), 1226–8, 1974.
(ENGLISH TRANSLATION OF IZMER. TEKH., 17 (8), 52–4, 1974; FOR ORIGINAL SEE E92292)

92299 **ANALYSIS OF THE FREQUENCY DEPENDENCE OF THE HOT CARRIER THERMOELECTRIC POWER OF SEMICONDUCTORS.**
PITANOV, V. S.
FIZ. TEKH. POLUPROV.
8 (10), 1980–3, 1974.
(ENGLISH TRANSLATION, SEE E 92300)

92300 **ANALYSIS OF THE FREQUENCY DEPENDENCE OF THE HOT CARRIER THERMOELECTRIC POWER OF SEMICONDUCTORS.**
PITANOV, V. S.
SOV. PHYS. SEMICOND.
8 (10), 1283–4, 1975.
(ENGLISH TRANSLATION OF FIZ. TEKH. POLUPROV. 8 (10), 1980–3, 1974; FOR ORIGINAL, SEE E 92299)

92307 **CHANGES IN THE SHORT RANGE ORDER IN SEMICONDUCTOR METAL TRANSITIONS.**
POLTAVTSEV, YU. G.
FIZ. TEKH. POLUPROV.
8 (10), 2022–4, 1974.
(FOR ENGLISH TRANSLATION SEE E 92308)

92308 **CHANGES IN THE SHORT RANGE ORDER IN SEMICONDUCTOR METAL TRANSITIONS.**
POLTAVTSEV, YU. G.
SOV. PHYS. SEMICOND.
8 (10), 1315–6, 1975.
(ENGLISH TRANSLATION OF FIZ. TEKH. POLUPROV., 8 (10), 2022–4, 1974; FOR ORIGINAL SEE E 92307)

92311 **DETERMINATION OF THE CARRIER DENSITY PROFILE IN GALLIUM ARSENIDE STRUCTURES BY THE PHOTOLUMINESCENCE METHOD.**
KESAMANLY, F. P. KOVALENKO, V. F.
MARONCHUK, I. E.
FIZ. TEKH. POLUPROV.,
8 (10), 2017–9, 1974.
(FOR ENGLISH TRANSLATION SEE 92312)

92312 **DETERMINATION OF THE CARRIER DENSITY PROFILE IN FALLIUM ARSENIDE STRUCTURES BY THE PHOTOLUMINESCENCE METHOD.**
KESAMANLY, F. P. KOVALENKO, V. F.
MARONCHUK, I. E.
SOV. PHYS. SEMICOND.
8 (10), 1311–2, 1975.
(ENGLISH TRANSLATION OF FIZ. TEKH. POLUPROV., 8 (10), 2017–9, 1974; FOR ORIGINAL SEE E 92311)

92325 **POSSIBLE ORIGIN OF THE COMPLEX STRUCTURE OF THE ENERGY BANDS OF SOME SEMICONDUCTORS AND THEIR SOLID SOLUTIONS.**
KUDINOV, V. A.
FIZ. TEKH. POLUPROV.,
8 (10), 2057–8, 1974.
(FOR ENGLISH TRANSLATION SEE E 92326)

92326 **POSSIBLE ORIGIN OF THE COMPLEX STRUCTURE OF THE ENERGY BANDS OF SOME SEMICONDUCTORS AND THEIR SOLID SOLUTIONS.**
KUDINOV, A. V.
SOV. PHYS. SEMICOND.,
8 (10), 1340, 1975.
(ENGLISH TRANSLATION OF FIZ. TEKH. POLUPROV., 8 (10), 2057–8, 1974; FOR ORIGINAL SEE E 92325)

92329 **PHOTOCONDUCTIVITY OF ZINC CADMIUM SULFIDE SINGLE CRYSTALS IRRADIATED WITH FAST NEUTRONS.**
ADRIANOV, A. A. KODZHESPIROV, F. F.
FIZ. TEKH. POLUPROV.
8 (10), 2043–6, 1974.
(FOR ENGLISH TRANSLATION SEE E92330)

92330 **PHOTOCONDUCTIVITY OF ZINC CADMIUM SULFIDE SINGLE CRYSTALS IRRADIATED WITH FAST NEUTRONS.**
ADRIANOV, A. A. KODZHESPIROV, F. F.
SOV. PHYS. SEMICOND.
8 (10), 1330–1, 1975.
(ENGLISH TRANSLATION OF FIZ. TEKH. POLUPROV., 8 (10), 2043–6, 1974; FOR ORIGINAL SEE E92329)

92356 **MECHANISM OF RADIATIVE RECOMBINATION IN STRONGLY DOPED P–GALLIUM ARSENIDE.**
ZVEREV, L. P. KRUZHAEV, V. V.
NEGASHEV, S. A.
JETP LETT.
20 (1), 22–4, 1974.
(ENGLISH TRANSLATION OF ZH. EKSP. TEOR. FIZ., PIS'MA RED., 20 (1), 52–6, 1974; FOR ORIGINAL SEE E81226)

92357 **MANIFESTATION OF DOMAIN INSTABILITY AND THE FRANZ–KELDYSH EFFECT IN THE RECOMBINATION RADIATION OF CADMIUM SULFIDE SINGLE CRYSTALS.**
KROLEVETS, N. M. LEPSVERIDZE, D. S.
SAL'KOV, E. A. SHEPEL'SKII, G. A.
JETP LETT.
20 (1), 24–5, 1974.
(ENGLISH TRANSLATION OF ZH. EKSP. TEOR. FIZ., PIS'MA RED., 20 (1), 56–8, 1974; FOR ORIGINAL SEE E81227)

92358 **SUPERCONDUCTING AND MAGNETIC PROPERTIES OF TERNARY CHALCOGENIDES OF MOLYBDENUM.**
ALEKSEEVSKII, N. E. DOBROVOL'SKII, N. M.
TSEBRO, V. I.
JETP LETT.
20 (1), 25–7, 1974.
(ENGLISH TRANSLATION OF ZH. EKSP. TEOR. FIZ., PIS'MA RED., 20 (1), 59–63, 1974; FOR ORIGINAL SEE E81228)

92361 **NONCOLLINEARITY OF SUBLATTICES AND EXISTENCE OF A DOMAIN STRUCTURE IN DYSPROSIUM IRON OXIDE NEAR THE MAGNETIC COMPENSATION POINT IN STRONG MAGNETIZATION FIELDS.**
LISOVSKII, F. V. SHAPOVALOV, V. I.
JETP LETT.
20 (2), 55–6, 1974.
(ENGLISH TRANSLATION OF ZH. EKSP. TEOR. FIZ., PIS'MA RED., 20 (2), 128–32, 1974; FOR ORIGINAL SEE E81231)

EPIC Number	Bibliographic Citation

92362 **TEMPERATURE HYSTERESIS OF THE MAGNETIZATION IN ORTHOFERRITES AT THE COMPENSATION POINT.**
KERKACHENKO, V. N. KADOMTSEVA, A. M.
TIMOFEEVA, V. A. KHOKHLOV, V. A.
JETP LETT.
20 (4), 104–5, 1974.
(ENGLISH TRANSLATION OF ZH. EKSP. TEOR. FIZ., PIS'MA RED., 20 (4), 236–9, 1974; FOR ORIGINAL SEE E81232)

92364 **OBSERVATION OF FERROMAGNETIC STATE IN ANTIFERROMAGNETIC ALLOYS OF THE IRON MANGANESE ARSENIDE SYSTEM.**
GALKIN, A. A. ZAVADSKII, E. A.
SMIRNOV, V. M. VAL'KOV, V. I.
JETP LETT.
20 (4), 111–2, 1974.
(ENGLISH TRANSLATION OF ZH. EKSP. TEOR. FIZ., PIS'MA RED., 20 (4), 253–6, 1974; FOR ORIGINAL SEE E81234)

92365 **POSSIBILITY OF FOCUSING AND SELF-FOCUSING OF LIGHT BEAMS IN A SEMICONDUCTOR BY VARYING THE ELECTRON COMPONENT OF ITS DIELECTRIC CONSTANT.**
MAEV, R. G. PADO, G. S. POLUEKTOV, I. A.
PUSTOVOIT, V. I.
JETP LETT.
20 (4), 113–4, 1974.
(ENGLISH TRANSLATION OF ZH. EKSP. TEOR. FIZ., PIS'MA RED., 20 (4), 256–60, 1974; FOR ORIGINAL SEE E81235)

92366 **MAGNETIC PROPERTIES OF NICKEL IODINE BORACITE.**
ZHELUDEV, I. S. PEREKALINA, T. M.
SMIRNOVSKAYA, E. M. FONTON, S. S.
YARMUKHAMEDOV, YU. N.
JETP LETT.
20 (5), 129–30, 1974.
(ENGLISH TRANSLATION OF ZH. EKSP. TEOR. FIZ., PIS'MA RED., 20 (5), 289–92, 1974; FOR ORIGINAL SEE E 81236)

92367 **INVESTIGATION OF METAMAGNETIC TRANSITION IN IRON CHLORIDE WITH POLARIZED NEWUTRONS IN A WIDE TEMPERATURE RANGE.**
TRUNOV, V. A. EGOROV, A. I. DMITRIEV, R. P.
UL'YANOV, V. A. KRAVTSOVA, M. E.
JETP LETT.
20 (5), 139–40, 1974.
(ENGLISH TRANSLATION OF ZH. EKSP. TEOR. FIZ., PIS'MA RED., 20 (5), 312–6, 1974; FOR ORIGINAL SEE E 81237)

92369 **EFFECT OF ELECTRIC FIELD ON DEFORMATION INDUCED LIGHT EMISSION OF ZINC SULFIDE CRYSTALS.**
BREDIKHIN, S. I. SHMURAK, S. Z.
JETP LETT.
21 (6), 156–7, 1975.
(ENGLISH TRANSLATION OF ZH. EKSP. TEOR. FIZ., PIS'MA RED., 21 (6), 342–5, 1975; FOR ORIGINAL SEE E 85354)

92370 **MEASUREMENT OF THE CONDUCTIVITY OF SEMICONDUCTORS IN THE HIGH FREQUENCY FIELD EFFECT.**
KALASHNIKOV, S. G. MOROZOV, A. I.
FEDOSOV, V. I. ANISIMKIN, V. I.
JETP LETT.
21 (6), 159–61, 1975.
(ENGLISH TRANSLATION OF ZH. SKEP. TEOR. FIZ., PIS'MA RED., 21 (6), 349–52, 1975; FOR ORIGINAL SEE E85355)

92373 **INJECTION LIGHT EMITTING DIODES BASED ON LOW RESISTANCE ZINC SULFIDE WITH BLUE AND GREEN EMISSION.**
PEKAR', G. S. LUK'YANCHIKOVA, N. B.
SHIN, H. M. SHEINKMAN, M. K.
JETP LETT.
19 (8), 272–3, 1974.
(ENGLISH TRANSLATION OF ZH. EKSP. TEOR. FIZ., PIS'MA RED., 19 (8), 513–6, 1974; FOR ORIGINAL SEE E 81214)

92375 **ANOMALIES OF THE DISPERSION OF SINGLE CRYSTAL CADMIUM SULFIDE IN THE REGION OF EXCITON ABSORPTION.**
BRODIN, M. S. DAVYDOVA, N. A.
STRASHNIKOVA, M. I.
JETP LETT.
19 (9), 297–8, 1974.
(ENGLISH TRANSLATION OF ZH. EKSP. TEOR. FIZ., PIS'MA RED., 19 (9), 567–71, 1974; FOR ORIGINAL SEE E81216)

92378 **GENERATION OF LIGHT IN SEMICONDUCTORS AND DIELECTRICS EXCITED BY AN ELECTRIC FIELD.**
BASOV, N. G. MOLCHANOV, A. G. NASIBOV, A. S.
OBIDIN, A. Z. PECHENOV, A. N. POPOV, YU. M.
JETP LETT.
19 (10), 336–7, 1974.
(ENGLISH TRANSLATION OF ZH. EKSP. TEOR. FIZ., PIS'MA RED., 19 (10), 650–4, 1974; FOR ORIGINAL SEE E 81218)

92382 **INVESTIGATION OF THE BEYOND THRESHOLD SUSCEPTIBILITY IN ANTIFERROMAGNETIC MANGANESE CARBONATE AND CESIUM MANGANESE FLUORIDE IN PARAMETRIC EXCITATION OF SPIN WAVES.**
KVEDER, V. V. PROZOROVA, L. A.
JETP LETT.
19 (11), 353–4, 1974.
(ENGLISH TRANSLATION OF ZH. EKSP. TEOR. FIZ., PIS'MA RED., 19 (11), 683–6, 1974; FOR ORIGINAL SEE E81222)

92383 **DEFORMATION-STIMULATED EMISSION OF ZINC SULFIDE CRYSTALS.**
BREDIKHIN, S. I. SHMURAK, S. Z.
JETP LETT.
19 (12), 367–8, 1974.
(ENGLISH TRANSLATION OF ZH. EKSP. TEOR. FIZ., PIS'MA RED., 19 (12), 709–13, 1974; FOR ORIGINAL SEE E81223)

92391 **HIGH FREQUENCY INSTABILITY OF RECOMBINATION RADIATION IN STRONG ELECTRIC FIELDS.**
BRODOVOI, V. A. GOZAK, A. CH. PEKA, G. P.
JETP LETT.
19 (7), 240–1, 1974.
(ENGLISH TRANSLATION OF ZH. EKSP. TEOR. FIZ., PIS'MA RED., 19 (7), 445–7, 1974; FOR ORIGINAL SEE E83498)

92395 **SUPERCONDUCTIVITY OF BULKY NIOBIUM GERMANIUM ABOVE 22 DEGREES K.**
MIKHAILOV, N. N. VORONOVA, I. V.
LAVROVA, O. A. MEL'NIKOV, E. V.
SMIRNOVA, M. N.
JETP LETT.
19 (8), 271–2, 1974.
(ENGLISH TRANSLATION OF ZH. EKSP. TEOR. FIZ., PIS'MA RED., 19 (8), 510–2, 1974; FOR ORIGINAL SEE E 81213)

92399 **ASYMMETRY OF MOTION OF DOMAIN WALL IN AN ORTHOFERRITE CRYSTAL.**
KANDAUROVA, G. S. VAS'KOVSKII, V. O.
DERYAGIN, A. V. RAEV, V. K.
JETP LETT.
19 (2), 80–2, 1974.
(ENGLISH TRANSLATION OF ZH. EKSP. TEOR. FIZ., PIS'MA RED., 19 (2), 132–5, 1974; FOR ORIGINAL SEE E 81200)

92401 **DYNAMIC NEGATIVE DIFFERENTIAL CONDUCTIVITY IN HOMOGENEOUS AND ELECTRICALLY-STABLE SEMICONDUCTORS.**
ZIL'BERMAN, P. E.
JETP LETT.
19 (3), 114–6, 1974.
(ENGLISH TRANSLATION OF ZH. EKSP. TEOR. FIZ., PIS'MA RED., 19 (3), 182–5, 1974; FOR ORIGINAL SEE E 81202)

92408 **GLASS FORMATION AND PROPERTIES OF CALCIUM MAGNESIUM SILICON 206-SAMARIUM MAGNESIUM ALUMINUM SILICON SYSTEM.**
ISMATOV, A. A. GULYAMOV, B. M.
UZB. KHIM. ZH.
(2), 69–71, 1972.

92409 **DISLOCATIONS AND PHYSICAL PROPERTIES OF SOLIDS.**
OSIPYAN, YU. A.
VEST. AKAD. NAUK SSSR
(4), 32–42, 1972.

92433 **LOW FREQUENCY MODES IN AMORPHOUS SEMICONDUCTORS.**
TAYLOR, P. C. STROM, U. HENDRICKSON, J. R.
RUBINSTEIN, M.
PROC. INT. CONF. PHYS. SEMICOND., 12TH
1071–5, 1974.

92436 **MAGNETIC AND ELECTRICAL PROPERTIES OF RARE EARTH-MANGANESE-GERMANIUM COMPOUNDS.**
RAO, V. U. S. NARASIMHAN, K. S. V. L.
BERGNER, R. L. WALLACE, W. E.
RARE EARTH RES. CONF., 11TH
1, 90–6, 1974.

92437 **MAGNETISM OF EUROPIUM PHOSPHIDES.**
BRYGALINA, G. P. IKORSKII, V. N.
PROC. RARE EARTH RES. CONF., 11TH
1, 105–14, 1974.

92621 **CADMIUM TELLURIDE AS A MATERIAL FOR INFRARED OPTICS.**
SHILLIDAY, T. S. DAVIS, P. W.
J. OPT. SOC. AMER.
49 (5), 497, 1959.

92626 **PROPERTIES OF SEMICONDUCTING CADMIUM MERCURY TELLURIDE SOLID SOLUTIONS UNDER PRESSURE.**
BELOUSOVA, O. N. BOVINA, L. A.
PONOMAREV, YA. G. SAVCHENKO, YU. N.
STAFEEV, V. I.
JETP LETT.
20 (6), 166–8, 1974.
(ENGLISH TRANSLATION OF ZH. EKSP. TEOR. FIZ., PIS'MA RED., 20 (6), 370–4, 1974; FOR ORIGINAL SEE E 86221)

EPIC Number	Bibliographic Citation
92627	**MAGNETIC PROPERTIES OF THE SUPERCONDUCTING COMPOUND MOLYBDENUM TIN GALLIUM DULFIDE.** ALEKSEEVSKII, N. E. BAZAN, CH. DOBROVOL'SKII, N. M. TSEBRO, V. I. JETP LETT. 20 (7), 211-2, 1974. (ENGLISH TRANSLATION OF ZH. EKSP. TEOR. FIZ., PIS'MA RED., 20 (7), 465-8, 1974; FOR ORIGINAL SEE E 86222)
92631	**THERMOELECTRIC PROPERTIES OF MATERIALS WITH NONSTANDARD CONDUCTION MECHANISMS.** GOLIKOVA, O. A. SOV. PHYS. SEMICOND. 8 (12), 1543-5, 1975. (ENGLISH TRANSLATION OF FIZ. TEKH. POLUPROV., 8 (12), 2367-71, 1974; FOR ORIGINAL SEE E81141)
92632	**THE L-ALPHA BAND OF SILICON IN TRANSITION METAL SILICIDES.** BONDARENKO, T. N. ZHURAKOVSKII, E. A. SOV. PHYS. DOKL. 19 (9), 595-7, 1975. (ENGLISH TRANSLATION OF DOKL. AKAD. NAUK SSSR, 218 (1), 84-7, 1974; FOR ORIGINAL SEE E 86642)
92633	**STIMULATED EMISSION IN GALLIUM PHOSPHIDE.** PYSHKIN, S. L. SOV. PHYS. DOKL. 19 (12), 845-6, 1975. (ENGLISH TRANSLATION OF DOKL. AKAD. NAUK SSSR, 219 (6), 1345-7, 1974; FOR ORIGINAL SEE E81026)
92635	**ANISOTROPY OF THE DIELECTRIC AND PIEZOELECTRIC PROPERTIES OF LEAD TITANATE.** TURIK, A. V. FESENKO, E. G. GAVRILYACHENKO, V. G. KHASABOVA, G. I. SOV. PHYS. CRYSTALLOGR. 19 (5), 677-8, 1975. (ENGLISH TRANSLATION OF KRISTALLOGRAFIYA, 19 (5), 1095-7, 1974; FOR ORIGINAL SEE E86817)
92648	**CAPACITIVE ALTERNATING CURRENT METHOD FOR MEASURING RESISTIVITY OF SEMICONDUCTORS AT LOW TEMPERATURES (2.3 TO 300 K).** HOYER, W. ARCH. ELEKTROTECH. 57 (2), 93-101, 1975.
92664	**SUPERCONDUCTIVITY IN THE PALLADIUM - HYDROGEN SYSTEM.** PAPACONSTANTOPOULOS, D. A. KLEIN, B. M. PHYS. REV. LETT. 35 (2), 110-13, 1975.
92665	**SUPERCONDUCTIVE FIXED POINTS FOR THERMOMETRY IN CRYOGENICS.** SCHOOLEY, J. F. SOULEN, R. J., JR. ADVANCES IN INSTRUMENTATION 29 (PT. II), 28-31, 1974.
92666	**MAGNETIC PROPERTIES OF ELECTROPLATED FILMS.** ROMANKIW, L. T. THOMPSON, D. A. PROPERTIES OF ELECTRODEPOSITS: THEIR MEASUREMENT AND SIGNIFICANCE 389-426, 1974.
92677	**ANISOTROPIC MAGNETORESISTANCE IN FERROMAGNETIC 3D ALLOYS.** MC GUIRE, T. R. IEEE TRANS. MAGN. 11 (4), 1018-38, 1975.
92725	**SURFACE PHOTOVOLTAGE AND AUGER SPECTROSCOPY STUDIES OF (1120) CADMIUM SULFIDE SURFACE.** BRILLSON, L. J. J. VAC. SCI. TECHNOL. 12 (1), 249-52, 1975.
92754	**ENERGY DISTRIBUTION OF THERMALLY STIMULATED EXOCELECTRONS FROM LITHIUM FLUORIDE POWDER.** HAYAKAWA, Y. ODA, N. PHYS. STATUS SOLIDI 29 A (2), K117-19, 1975.
92755	**EXOELECTRON EMISSION OF ZINC OXIDE.** KRIEGSEIS, W. SCHARMANN, A. PHYS. STATUS SOLIDI 29 A (2), 407-14, 1975.
92802	**KRAMERS-KRONIG ANALYSIS FOR THE DETERMINATION OF THE OPTICAL CONSTANTS OF THIN SURFACE FILMS.** NAEGELE, K. PLIETH, W. J. SURF. SCI. 50 (1), 64-76, 1975.
92822	**ELECTRICAL CONDUCTION IN FERROMAGNETIC METALS.** MIEDEMA, A. R. DORLEIJN, J. W. F. PHILLIPS TECH. REV. 35 (2-3), 29-40, 1975.
92849	**CHARACTERIZATION OF ZINC OXYGEN EPTIAXIAL FILMS BY THEIR OPTICAL PROPERTIES IN THE EXCITON REGION.** SCHNECK, H. HELBIG, R. THIN SOLID FILMS 27 (1), 101-9, 19 .
92860	**SPATIAL DISPERSION AND ADDITIONAL LIGHT WAVES IN THE REGION OF EXCITON ABSORPTION IN CADMIUM-SULFIDE.** PEKAR, S. I. STRASHNIKOVA, M. I. ZH. EKSP. TEOR. FIZ. 68 (6), 2047-54, 1975. (ENGLISH TRANSLATION SEE E 96883)
92867	**INFRARED REFLECTANCE OF SILICON OXIDE AND MAGNESIUM FLUORIDE PROTECTED ALUMINIUM MIRRORS AT VARIOUS ANGLES OF INCIDENCE FROM 8 TO 12.** COX, J. H. HASS, G. HUNTER, W. R. APPL. OPT. 14 (6), 1247-50, 1975.
92880	**NEW MICROWAVE SYSTEM TO DETERMINE THE COMPLEX PERMITTIVITY OF SMALL DIELECTRIC AND SEMICONDUCTING SAMPLES.** MUSIL, J. ZACEK, F. BURGER, A. KARLOVSKY CZECH. J. PHYS. 25 B (8), 916-26, 1975.
92915	**LOW TEMPERATURE RESISTANCE ANOMALIES IN SINGLE CRYSTALS OF TERBIUM AND DYSPROSIUM.** TINDALL, D. A. JERICHO, M. H. J. PHYS. 5 (7), 1359-64, 1975.
92943	**MAGNETORESISTANCE DUE TO CONDUCTION BAND SPLITTING IN MAGNETIC SEMICONDUCTORS.** KAUTZ, R. L. SHAPIRA, Y. AIP CONF. PROC. (24), 42-3, 1974.
92949	**REFRACTICE INDICES OF POWDERED MATERIALS AND MATERIALS WITH NONSPECULARLY REFLECTING SURFACE: A SIMPLE METHOD OF DETERMINATION.** SPITZER, D. APPL. OPT. 14 (7), 1489-91, 1975.
93012	**THERMIONIC EMISSION OF REFRACTORY COMPOUNDS AND MATERIALS.** SAMSONOV, G. V. FOMENKO, W. S. PODCHERNYAEVA, I. A. OCHREMTSCHUK, L. N. REV. INT. HAUTES TEMP. AND REFRACT. 11 (4), 269-76, 1975.
93037	**THERMIONIC EMISSION PROPERTIES OF ZIRCONIUM, HAFNIUM AND TITANIUM NITRIDES IN CAESIUM VAPOUR.** EREMAEV, M. A. NESHPOR, V. S. NOVIKOV, A. B. STEFANOVSKAYA, B. M. FEDORINOV, V. P. ZH. TEKH. FIZ. 44 (10), 2159-67, 1974. (FOR ENGLISH TRANSLATION SEE E93038)
93038	**THERMIONIC EMISSION PROPERTIES OF ZIRCONIUM, HAFNIUM AND TITANIUM NITRIDES IN CAESIUM VAPOUR.** EREMAEV, M. A. NESHPOR, V. S. NOVIKOV, A. B. STEFANOVSKAYA, B. M. FEDORINOV, V. P. SOV. PHYS. TECH. PHYS. 19 (10), 1337-41, 1975. (ENGLISH TRANSLATION OF ZH. TEKH. FIZ., 44 (10), 2159-67, 1974; FOR ORIGINAL SEE E93037)
93080	**ELECTRON-ELECTRON COLLISIONS IN SEMICONDUCTORS UNDER INTERMEDIATE DEGENERACY CONDITIONS.** GRYAZNOV, O. S. TAMARCHENKO, V. I. FIZ. TEKH. POLUPROV. 8 (11), 2131-7, 1974. (FOR ENGLISH TRANSLATION SEE E93081)
93081	**ELECTRON-ELECTRON COLLISIONS IN SEMICONDUCTORS UNDER INTERMEDIATE DEGENERACY CONDITIONS.** GRYAZNOV, O. S. TAMARCHENKO, V. I. SOV. PHYS. SEMICOND. 8 (11), 1383-6, 1975. (ENGLISH TRANSLATION OF FIZ. TEKH. POLUPROV., 8 (11), 2131-7, 1974; FOR ORIGINAL SEE E93080)
93120	**CHARACTERISTICS OF ELECTRON SCATTERING IN THIN LEAD TELLURIDE FILMS.** GUDKIN, T. S. DRABKIN, I. A. KAIDANOV, V. I. STERLYADKINA, O. G. FIZ. TEKH. POLUPROV. 8 (11), 2233-5, 1974. (FOR ENGLISH TRANSLATION SEE E93121)
93121	**CHARACTERISTICS OF ELECTRON SCATTERING IN THIN LEAD TELLURIDE FILMS.** GUDKIN, T. S. DRABKIN, I. A. KAIDANOV, V. I. STERLYADKINA, O. G. SOV. PHYS. SEMICOND. 8 (11), 1453-4, 1975. (ENGLISH TRANSLATION OF FIZ. TEKH. POLUPROV., 8 (11), 2233-5, 1974; FOR ORIGINAL SEE E93120)
93147	**CHEMICALLY STRENGTHENED POLYCRYSTALLINE POTASSIUM CHLORIDE FOR HIGH POWER, INFRARED LASER WINDOWS.** SHRADER, E. F. HARSHAW CHEMICAL COMP., SOLON, OHIO 88PP., 1974. (AD-B002 046L, AFML-TR-74-165)

EPIC Number	Bibliographic Citation
93160	**SPECTRAL EMITTANCE MEASUREMENTS WITH A CRYOGENICALLY COOLED INSTRUMENT.** STIERWALT, D. L. NAVAL RESEARCH LAB., WASHINGTON, D. C. 41–50, 1975. (AD–B008 044L)
93161	**POLISHING AND COATING FOR LARGE DIAMETER (15 CM) HIGH ENERGY ZINC SELENIDE LASER WINDOWS AND COATINGS FOR ALKALI HALIDE WINDOWS.** BRAUNSTEIN, M. RUDISILL, J. E. PROC. ANN. CONF. INFRARED LASER WINDOW MATERIALS, 4TH 23–39, 1975. (AD–B008 167L, AFML–TR–75–79)
93162	**HIGH THERMAL CONDUCTIVITY MICROWAVE SUBSTRATES.** POPE, B. J. HORTON, M. D. BOWMAN, L. S. HALL, H. T. ADANIYA, H. N. BRIGHAM YOUNG UNIV., PROVO, UTAH 56 PP., 1975. (AD–B003 038L)
93167	**THERMAL ELECTRICAL, AND PHYSICAL MEASUREMENTS OF LASER WINDOW MATERIALS.** WURST, J. C. GRAHAM, T. P. RESEARCH INST., DAYTON UNIVERSITY, OHIO 191PP., 1975. (AD–B004 548L, AFML–TR–75–28)
93177	**OPTICAL PROCESSING OF ALKALI HALIDES AND POLYCRYSTALLINE ZINC SELENIDE FOR HIGH POWER LASER APPLICATIONS.** KURDOCK, J. R. STROUSE, E. A. PERKIN–ELMER CORP., NORWALK, CONN. 76PP., 1975. (AD–B007 691L, AFML–TR–74–166–PT. 2)
93181	**HANDBOOK OF THE INFRARED OPTICAL PROPERTIES OF ALUMINUM OXIDE, CARBON, MAGNESIUM OXIDE, AND ZIRCONIUM OXIDE. VOLUME I.** WHITSON, M. E., JR. AEROSPACE CORP., EL SEGUNDO, CALIF. 1, 469PP., 1975. (AD–A013 722, SAMSO–TR–75–131, N76–14274)
93182	**HANDBOOK OF THE INFRARED OPTICAL PROPERTIES OF ALUMINUM OXIDE, CARBON MAGNESIUM OXIDE, AND ZIRCONIUM OXIDE.** WHITSON, M. E., JR. AEROSPACE CORP., EL SEGUNDO, CALIF. 2, 479PP., 1975. (AD–A013 723, SAMSO–TR–75–131–VOL–2, N76–14275)
93187	**ADVANCED TECHNIQUES FOR IMPROVING LASER OPTICAL SURFACES.** WILLINGHAM, C. B. COSGRO, R. H. BAU, D. P. SCHAPIRA, M. R. RAYTHEON, CO., WALTHAM, MASS 152PP., 1975. (AD–A012 289, AFCRL–TR–75–0225, N76–11429)
93191	**ABSORPTION IN MATERIALS FOR OPTICAL FIBRES.** ZAGANIARIS, A. BOUVY, G. BRITISH LIBRARY, LENDING DIV., BOSTON SPA. ENGL. 15PP., 1974. (ENGLISH TRANSLATION OF ANN. TELECOMMUN. 29 (5), 189–94, 1974; FOR ORIGINAL SEE E63406) N75–28224, BLL–TRANS–3187 (9022.81)
93207	**CONDUCTIVITY OF SOLID SODIUM POLYALUMINATE.** BUKUN, N. G. LANIN, A. A. UKSHE, E. A. SOV. ELECTROCHEM. 8 (8), 1222–4, 1972. (ENGLISH TRANSLATION OF ELEKTROKHIMIYA, 8 (8), 1248–51, 1972; FOR ORIGINAL SEE E78825)
93209	**ELECTRICAL CONDUCTIVITY AND POLARIZATION OF MELTS OF THE SYSTEM ARSENIC SESQUISELENIDE POTASSIUM SELENIDE.** VELIKANOV, A. A. MUSTYATSA, O. N. NOVIK, A. S. SOV. ELECTROCHEM. 7 (6), 796–8, 1971. (ENGLISH TRANSLATION OF ELEKTROKHIMIYA, 7 (6), 827–30, 1971; FOR ORIGINAL SEE E78826)
93210	**CONDUCTIVITY OF THE SOLID ELECTROLYTE SILVER SULFIDE IODIDE.** SHIROKOV, YU. V. PUSHKOV, B. I. BOROVKOV, V. S. LUKOVTSEV, P. D. SOV. ELECTROCHEM. 8 (4), 561–4, 1972. (ENGLISH TRANSLATION OF ELEKTROKHIMIYA, 8 (4), 579–83, 1972; FOR ORIGINAL SEE E78827)
93217	**SOME PHYSICAL PROPERTIES OF BORON CARBIDE WITH VANADIUM AND CHROMIUM ADDITIONS.** MAREK, E. V. DUDNIK, E. M. MAKARENKO, G. N. REMENYUK, E. A. SOV. POWDER MET. METAL CERAM. (2), 130–1, 1975. (ENGLISH TRANSLATION OF POROSH. MET., (2), 54–6, 1975; FOR ORIGINAL SEE E84594)
93218	**THERMIONIC EMISSION PROPERTIES OF REFRACTORY COMPOUNDS AND MATERIALS BASED ON THEM.** SAMSONOV, G. V. FOMENKO, V. S. PODCHERNYAEVA, I. A. OKHREMCHUK, L. N. SOV. POWDER MET. METAL CERAM. (10), 836–42, 1974. (ENGLISH TRANSLATION OF POROSH. MET., (10), 74–82, 1974; FOR ORIGINAL SEE E75323)
93221	**LOW RESISTANCE CARBIDE RESISTORS.** GREBENKINA, V. G. YUSOV, YU. P. SOROKIN, V. N. PEREVEZENTSEV, A. V. SOV. POWDER MET. METAL CERAM. (4), 345–7, 1973. (ENGLISH TRANSLATION OF POROSH. MET., (4), 97–1008 1973; FOR ORIGINAL SEE E70259)
93225	**SOME PROPERTIES OF ALLOYS OF ZIRCONIUM AND NIOBIUM CARBIDES IN THEIR HOMOGENEITY RANGE.** SAMSONOV, G. V. NAUMENKO, V. YA. RYABOKON, L. P. VERKHOTUROV, A. D. SOV. POWDER MET. METAL CERAM. (1), 44–6, 1975. (ENGLISH TRANSLATION OF POROSH. MET., (1), 54–8, 1975; FOR ORIGINAL SEE E70607)
93228	**RESISTIVITY OF MOLYBDENUM – TUNGSTEN ALLOYS AT ELEVATED TEMPERATURES.** VERTOGRADSKII, V. A. RUSS. MET., (METALLY) (4), 147–9, 1972. (ENGLISH TRANSLATION OF IZV. AKAD. NAUK SSSR, METAL., (4), 220–2, 1972; FOR ORIGINAL SEE E78759)
93232	**THE TANTALUM – NIOBIUM – RHENIUM PHASE DIAGRAM** TYLKINA, M. A. SAVITSKII, E. M. ALYUSHIN, V. E. RUSS. MET., (METALLY) (4), 159–62, 1973. (ENGLISH TRANSLATION OF IZV. AKAD. NAUK SSSR, METAL., (4), 225–9, 1973; FOR ORIGINAL SEE E70836)
93257	**TWO–PHOTON ABSORPTION AND SECOND HARMONIC GENERATION IN SEMICONDUCTORS.** LEE, C. C.–C. PURDUE UNIV., LAFAYETTE, IND., PH. D. THESIS 178PP., 1974. (UNIV. MICROFILM NO. 74–26740, N75–20113)
93277	**EXPERIMENTAL INVESTIGATION OF TRANSPORT PROPERTIES OF LOW–TEMPERATURE PLASMA BY MEANS OF ELECTRIC ARC.** ASINOVSKII, E. I. KIRILLIN, A. V. PAKHOMOV, E. P. SHABASHOV, V. I. PROC. IEEE 59 (4), 592–601, 1971.
93279	**EXPERIMENTAL DETERMINATION OF THE ELECTRIC RESISTANCE AND THE TOTAL HEMISPHERIC AND MONOCHROMATIC RADIATION CAPACITY OF NIOBIUM AND ZIRCONIUM CARBIDES AT TEMPERATURES 1200 AND 3500 K.** PETROV, V. A. CHEKHOVSKOI, V. YA. SHEINDLIN, A. E. ELEC. MHD, PROC. SYMP., (SALZBURG) 3, 429–37, 1966.
93280	**INFRARED ABSORPTION SPECTRA OF P–CADMIUM GERMANIUM ARSENIDE CRYSTALS.** BOLTOVETS, N. S. MAMEDOV, B. KH. OSMANOV, E. O. TROINYE. POLUPROV. 143–5, 1972.
93283	**OPTICAL ABSORPTION OF SILVER COLLOIDS IN POTASSIUM CHLORIDE CRYSTALS AT LOW TEMPERATURE.** JAIN, S. C. ARORA, N. D. SOLID STATE COMMUN. 16 (4), 421–3, 1975.
93286	**THE PHYSICAL AND MECHANICAL PROPERTIES OF BERYLLIDES.** STONEHOUSE, A. J. PAINE, R. M. BEAVER, W. W. MET. SOC., AMER. INST. MINING, MET. PETROL. ENGRS., INST. METALS DIV., SPEC. REPT. SER. (13), 445–55, 1964.
93287	**PROPERTIES OF THE CARBIDES OF THE TRANSITION METALS.** COSTA, P. CONTE, R. R. MET. SOC. AMER. INST. MINING, MET. PETROL. ENGRS. INST. METALS DIV., SPEC. REPT. SER. (13), 3–27, 1964.
93290	**ACOUSTIC AND ACOUSTO–OPTICAL PROPERTIES OF TELLURIUM OXIDE SINGLE CRYSTAL.** OHMACHI, Y. UCHIDA, N. REV. ELECT. COMMUN. LAB. 20 (5–6), 529–41, 1972.
93293	**PIEZOELECTRIC, ELASTIC AND DIELECTRIC PROPERTIES OF LITHIUM GALLIUM OXIDE.** NANAMATSU, S. DOI, K. TAKAHASHI, M. JAP. J. APPL. PHYS. 11 (6), 816–22, 1972.

EPIC Number	Bibliographic Citation
93295	**OPTICAL REFLECTION OF VANADIUM OXIDE SINGLE CRYSTALS.** HEVESI, I. KARVALY, B. ACTA PHYS. ACAD. SCI. HUNG. 29 (2-3), 182-92, 1970.
93296	**EXCITON EXCITON TRANSITIONS IN MANGANESE FLUORIDE.** STOKOWSKI, S. E. SELL, D. D. PHYS. REV. 3 B (1), 208-14, 1971.
93309	**OPTICAL MATERIALS CHARACTERIZATION.** FELDMAN, A. HOROWITZ, D. WAXLER, R, M. MALITSON, I. H. DODGE, M. J. NATIONAL BUREAU OF STANDARDS, WASHINGTON, D. C. 24PP., 1975. (AD-A015 636, BBSIR-75-781) (N76-16929, COM-75-11375)
93312	**DETERMINATION OF CHANGE IN REFRACTIVE INDEX WITH TEMPERATURE FOR ZINC SELENIDE AND POTASSIUM CHLORIDE USING PHOTOMETRIC TECHNIQUES.** KROK, P. C. AIR FORCE INST. OF TECHNOLOGY, OHIO, M. S. THESIS 58PP., 1975. (AD-A012 743, N76-12351, GEP/PH/75-7)
93315	**LASER WINDOW STUDIES.** WILLINGHAM, C. B. STATZ, H. BUA, D. HORRIGAN, F. RAYTHEON CO., WALTHAM, MASS. 117PP., 1975. AD-A015 567
93316	**LOW LOSS WINDOW MATERIALS FOR CHEMICAL LASERS.** HARRINGTON, J. A. DEPT. OF PHYSICS, ALABAMA UNIV., HUNTSVILLE 56PP., 1975. (AD-A015 587, N76-18451, UAH-RR-177)
93318	**EFFECTS OF ION BEAM POLISHING ON ALKALI HALIDE LASER WINDOW MATERIALS.** BRUCE, J. A. COMER, J. J. COLLINS, C. V. LIPSON, H. G. AIRFORCE CAMBRIDGE RES. LABS., HANSCOM AFB, MASS. 15PP., 1975. AD-A010 459, AFCRL-TR-75-0257
93319	**STRESS-OPTIC COEFFICIENTS OF POTASSIUM CHLORIDE, BARIUM FLUORIDE, CADMIUM FLUORIDE, CADMIUM TELLURIDE, THALLIUM-1120, AND THALLIUM-1173.** PITHA, C. A. FRIEDMAN, J. D. AIR FORCE CAMBRIDGE RES. LABS., HANSCOM AFB, MASS. 11PP., 1975. (AD-A017 173, AFCRL-TR-75-0407, AFCRL-PSRP-639) (N76-19949)
93320	**CHEMICAL VAPOR DEPOSITION OF CHALCOGENIDE SEMICONDUCTORS.** BOWEN, H. K. VANDER SANDE, J. MASSACHUSETTS INST. OF TECHNOLOGY, CAMBRIDGE 110PP., 1975. (AD-A017 524, N76-20000, AFML-TR-75-91)
93322	**DEVELOPMENT OF GALLIUM ARSENIDE FOR INFRARED WINDOWS.** HAFNER, H. C. CRONIN, G. R TEXAS INSTRUMENTS INC., DALLAS TEXAS 71PP., 1975. (AD-A014 809, AFML-TR-75-49, TI-UI-862001-F) (N76-16927)
93323	**THIN FILM OPTICAL WAVEGUIDES IN III-V SEMICONDUCTORS.** KEUNE, D. L. CRAFORD, M. G. FINN, D. CHANG, W. S. C. SOPORI, B. L. MONSANTO CO., ST. LOUIS, MO. 164PP., 1975. (AD-A014 863, N76-16964, AFCRL-TR-75-0279)
93324	**CASTING OF HALIDE FLUORIDE ALLOYS.** NEWBERG, R. T. PAPPIS, J. RAYTHEON CO., WALTHAM, MASS., 68PP., 1975. (AD-014 864, N76-16924, AFCRL-TR-75-0289)
93325	**GROWTH AND HARDENING OF ALKALI HALIDES FOR USE IN INFRARED LASER WINDOWS.** SIBLEY, W. A. BUTLER, C. T. MARTIN, J. J. DEPT. OF PHYSICS, OKLAHOMA STATE UNIV., STILLWATER 22PP., 1975. (AD-A015 073, N76-16437, AFCRL-TR-74-0567)
93326	**CUMULANT METHODS IN THE THEORY OF MULTIPHONON ABSORPTION.** YUKON, S. P. BENDOW, B. PARKE MATHEMATICAL LABS., INC., CARLISLE, MASS. 12PP., 1975. AD-A010 465, AFCRL-TR-75-0278
93327	**THEORY OF MULTIPHONON ABSORPTION IN THE TRANSPARENT REGIME OF AMORPHOUS SOLIDS.** YUKON, S. P. TSAY, Y-P. BENDOW, B. PARKE MATHEMATICAL LABS., INC., CARLISLE, MASS 11PP., 1974. AD-A010 464, AFCRL-TR-75-0277
93328	**LOW LOSS WINDOW MATERIALS FOR CHEMICAL AND CARBON OXIDE LASERS.** HARRINGTON, J. A. BENDOW, B. NAMJOSHI, K. V. MITRA, S. S. STIERWALT, D. L. AIR FORCE CAMBRIDGE RES. LAB., HANSCOM AFB, MASS. 26PP., 1975. (AD-A010 462, AFCRL-TR-75-0275)
93330	**THEORY OF MULTIPHONON ABSORPTION IN SEMICONDUCTING CRYSTALS.** YING, S-C. BENDOW, B. YUKON, S. P. BROWN UNIVERSITY, PROVIDENCE, R. I. 7PP., 1975. AD-A010 460, AFCRL-TR-75-0272
93334	**TEMPERATURE DEPENDENCE OF MULTIPHONON ABSORPTION IN FLUORITE CRYSTALS.** MITRE, S. S. LIPSON, H. G. BENDOW, B. RHODE ISLAND UNIV., KINGSTONL 15PP., 1975. AD-A010 466, AFCRL-TR-75-0281
93335	**INFRARED OPTICAL PROPERTIES OF GALLIUM ARSENIDE AFTER NITROGEN ION IMPLANTATION.** EULER, F. COMER, J. J. BERGERON, C. A. J. ELECTRON. MATER. 4 (3), 481-95, 1975. (AD-A010 080, AFCRL-TR-75-0256)
93338	**SYNTHESIS AND CRYSTAL CHEMISTRY OF SULFIDES AND TELLURIDES WITH THE TH3P4 STRUCTURE.** PROVENZANO, P. L. WHITE, W. B. PENNSYLVANIA STATE UNIV., UNIVERSITY PARK, PA. 31PP., 1974. AD-A008 490, AFCRL-TR-74-0560
93339	**THE EFFECT OF REACTIVE PROCESSING ON WINDOW PROPERTIES OF SODIUM CHLORIDE.** ARMINGTON, A. POSEN, H. BRUCE, J. LIPSON, H. PROC. ANNUAL CONF. INFRARED LASER WINDOW MATERIALS, 4TH 559-71, 1974. AD-A008 478, AFCRL-TR-75-0171, N75-24886
93340	**SYNTHESIS OF SULFIDES WITH THE CALCIUM FERRITE STRUCTURE.** DRAFALL, L. E. WHITE, W. B. PENNSYLVANIA STATE UNIV., UNIVERSITY PARK, PA. 35PP., 1974. AD-A008 492, AFCRL-TR-74-0459
93341	**SELECTION, SYNTHEISI, GROWTH AND CHARACTERIXATION OF POTENTIAL 10.6 MICRON WINDOW MATERIALS.** WHITE, W. B. ROY, R. PENNSYLVANIA STATE UNIV., UNIVERSITY PARK, PA. 24PP., 1974. AD-A/08-495, AFCRL-TR-74-0618
93343	**10.6 MICROMETER PULSED LASER DAMAGE IN ZINC SELENIDE.** POSEN, H. BRUCE, J. MILAM, D. AIR FORCE CAMBRIDGE RES, LABS., HANSCON AFB, MASS. 13PP., 1975. AD-A011 609, AFCRL-TR-75-0336 (N76-10463)
93344	**COATING SCIENCE AND TECHNOLOGY.** KNOX, B. E. VEDAM, K. PENNSYLVANIA STATE UNIV., UNIVERSITY PARK, PA. 56PP., 1975. AD-A010 457, AFCRL-TR-75-1152
93346	**THEORITICAL STUDIES OF HIGH POWER ULTRAVIOLET AND INFRARED MATERIALS.** SPARKS, M. S. DUTHLER, C. J. ZONICS INC., VAN NUYS, CALIF. 224PP., 1674. AD-A009 256
93349	**ELECTRONIC EXCITION PROCESSES IN SEMICONDUCTORS** SEGALL, B. HOSTRIA, E. D. CASE WESTREN RESERVE UNIV., CLEVELAND, OHIO 35PP., 1975. (AD-A011 996, N76-12859, ARL-75-0111)
93350	**COMPARISION OF PHOTOVOLATIC AND PHOTOCONDUCTIVE EFFECTS IN INSULATING CADMIUM SULFIDE CRYSTALS.** KRAMER, B. WALLMARK, J. T. MARK, P. J. VAC. SCI. TECHNOL., 12 (3), 713-20, 1975. AD-A012 069
93351	**THIN FILM IOTICAL WAVEGUIDES IN III-V SEMOCONDUCTORS.** CRAFORD, M. G. MONSANTO CO., ST. LOUIS, MO. 34PP., 1974. AD-A011 716, AFCRL-TR-74-0554
93352	**CHEMICAL VAPOR DEPOSITION OF CADMIUM TELLURIDE.** SEANSON, A. W. REAGAN, P. RAYTHEON CO., WALTHAM, MASS. 66PP., 1975.J (AD-A011 723, N76-11864, AFML-TR-75-68)

EPIC Number	Bibliographic Citation

93354 **INFRARED MODULATED LIGHT ELLIPSOMETER.**
ALLEN., S. D. BRAUNSTEIN, A. I.
HUGHES RESEARCH LABS., MALIBU CALIF.
28-69, 1975.
(AD-017 605, N76-19948, AFCRL-TR-75-0429)

93355 **STUDY OF DEFECTS IN II-VI COMPOUNDS.**
KROGER, F. A. SELIM, F. A.
UNIVERSITY OF SOUTHERN CALIFORNIA, LOS ANGELES
16-23, U975.
(AD-A014 867, N76-16928, AFCRL-TR-75-0236)

93356 **ABSORPTION STUDIES OF CADMIUM TELLURIDE AND ZINC SELENIDE.**
SPITZER, W. G. DUTT, B. V.
UNIVERSITY OF SOUTHERN CALIFORNIA, LOS ANGELES
53-60, 1975.
(AD-A014 867, N76-16928, AFCRL-TR-75-0236)

93357 **THERMAL LENSING IN IMPERFECT WINDOWS.**
MARBURGER, J. FLANNERY, M.
UNIVERSITY OF SOUTHERN CALIFORNIA, LOS ANGELES
68-88, 1975.
(AD-A014 867, N76-16928, AFCRL-TR-75-0236)

93358 **SCANNING ELECTRON BEAM STUDIES OF LASER WINDOW MATERIALS.**
WITTRY, D. B.
UNIVERSITY OF SOUTHERN CALIFORNIA, LOS ANGELES
92-8, 1975.
(AD-A014 867, N76-16928, AFCRL-TR-75-0236)

93373 **PULSED CARBON DIOXIDE LASER DAMAGE IN WINDOWS, REFLECTORS, AND COATINGS.**
WANG, V. RUDISILL, J. E. GIULIANO, C. R.
BRAUNSTEIN, M. BRAUNSTEIN, A.
NATIONAL BUREAU OF STANDARDS, WASHINGTON, D. C.
59-65, 1974.
(AD-A012 377, N76-12347, NBS-SP-414)

93374 **PULSED CARBON DIOXIDE LASER DAMAGE STUDIES OF REACTIVE ATMOSPHERE PROCESSING GROWN POTASSIUM CHLORIDE.**
ALLEN, S. D. BRAUNSTEIN, M. GIULIANO, C.
WANG, V.
NATIONAL BUREAU OF STANDARDS, WASHINGTON, D. C.
66-75, 1974.
(AD-A012 377, N76-12347, NBS-SP-414)

93375 **CHARACTERIZATION OF INFRARED LASER WINDOW MATERIALS AT THE NATIONAL BUREAU OF STANDARDS.**
FELDMAN, A. MALITSON, I. HOROWITZ, D.
WAXLER, R. M. DODGE, M.
NATIONAL BUREAU OF STANDARDS, WASHINGTON, D. C.
141-8, 1974.
(AD-A012 377, N76-12347, NBS-SP-414)

93376 **EXTRINSIC ABSORPTION IN LASER WINDOW MATERIALS.**
DUTHLER, C. J. SPARKS, M.
NATIONAL BUREAU OF STANDARDS, WASHINGTON, D. C.
219-26, 1974.
(AD-A012 377, N76-12347, NBS-SP-414)

93378 **TEMPERATURE DEPENDENCE OF MULTIPHONON ABSORPTION IN FLUORITE CRYSTALS.**
LIPSON, H. G. BENDOW, B. MITRA, S. S.
DEPT. OF ELECTRICAL ENGR., RHODE ISLAND, UNIV.
24-35, 1975.
(AD-A012 553, N76-12355, AFCRL-TR-75-0283)

93379 **THE HIGH FREQUENCY TAIL OF THE LATTICE ABSORPTION SPECTRA OF SIMPLE CRYSTALS.**
BARKER, A. J. WILKINSON, G. R. MASSA, N. E.
MITRA, S. S.
DEPT. OF ELECTRICAL ENGR., RHODE ISLAND UNIV.
36-49, 1975.
(AD-A012 553, N76-12355, AFCRL-TR-75-0283)

93380 **OPTICAL PROPERTIES OF AMORPHOUS MATERIALS FOR LASER WINDOWS.**
MITRA, S. S. NAMJOSHI, K. V. PAUL, D. K.
TSAY, Y. F. BENDOW, B.
PROC. CONF. HIGH POWER LASER WINDOW MATERIALS
797-839, 1974.
(AD-A012 553, N76-12355, AFCRL-TR-75-0283)

93381 **AN INTERPRETATION OF THE FIRST ORDER RAMAN AND INFRARED SPECTRA OF TETRAHEDRALLY BONDED AMORPHOUS SEMICONDUCTORS.**
MITRA, S. S. PAUL, D. K. TSAY, Y. P.
BENDOW, B.
AIP (AMER. INST. PHYS.) CONF. PROC., 20TH
284-9, 1974.
(AD-A012 553, N76-12355, AFCRL-TR-75-0283)

93382 **STATISTICAL INTERPRETATION OF LATTICE RESPONSE IN AMORPHOUS SEMICONDUCTORS.**
MITRA, S. S. TSAY, Y. F. PAUL, D. K.
BENDOW, B.
DEPT. OF ELECTRICAL ENGR., RHODE ISLAND UNIV.
125-49, 1975.
(AD-A012 553, N76-12355, AFCRL-TR-75-0283)

93384 **BAND STRUCTURE AND OPTICAL SPECTRUM OF A AND P.**
TSAY, Y. F. COROY, A. J. MITRA, S. S.
DEPT. OF ELECTRICAL ENGR., RHODE ISLAND UNIV.
197-215, 1975.
(AD-A012 553, N76-12355, AFCRL-TR-75-0283)

93385 **THEORY OF PHOTOELESTICITY OF SEMICONDUCTING CRYSTALS.**
BENDOW, B. GIANINO, P. D. TSAY, Y. F.
MITRA, S. S.
PROC. INT. CONF. PHYS. SEMICOND., 12TH
1247-51, 1974.
(AD-A012 553, N76-12355, AFCRL-TR-75-0283)

93386 **GROWTH AND HARDENING OF ALKALI HALIDES FOR USE IN INFRARED LASER WINDOWS.**
MARTIN, J. J. BUTLER, C. T. SIBLEY, W. A.
DEPT. OF PHYSICS, OKLAHOMA STATE UNIV.
58PP., 1975.
(AD-A017 960, N76-21541, AFCRL-TR-75-0432)

93387 **ELECTRON EMISSION FROM MAGNETOHYDRODYNAMIC ELECTRODE MATERIALS.**
PETERSEN, C. K. CUTLER, I. B. URE, R. W.
MICROWAVE DEVICE AND PHYS. LAB, UTAH UNIV.
59-65, 1974.
(AD-A012 539, N76-13382)

93400 **STRESS OPTICAL PROPERTIES OF SOLIDS IN THE 1 TO 20 MICRON WAVELENGTH REGION.**
SZCZESNIAK, J. P. CORELLI , J. C.
RENNSSELAER POLYTECHNIC INST., TROY, N. Y.
22PP., 1975.
(AD-A018 871, N76-23990, AFCRL-TR-75-0476)

93405 **EFFECT OF ANNEALING AND TEMPERATURE ON THE KINETIC COEFFICIENTS OF BISMUTH TELLURIDE SELENIDE SOLID SOLUTION FILMS.**
ARIFOV, U. A. ERZIN, N. I. KULAGIN, A. I.
MAKOV, N. V. DASHEVSKII, Z. M. TURSUNOV, B.
GELIOTEKHNIKA
11 (1), 3-4, 1975.
(FOR ENGLISH TRANSLATION SEE E93406)

93406 **EFFECT OF ANNEALING AND TEMPERATURE ON THE KINETIC COEFFICIENTS OF BISMUTH TELLURIDE SELENIDE SOLID SOLUTION FILMS.**
ARIFOV, U. A. ERZIN, N. I. KULAGIN, A. I.
MAKOV, N. V. DASHEVSKII, Z. M. TURSUNOV, B.
APPL. SOLAR ENERGY, USSR
11 (1), 1-2, 1975.
(ENGLISH TRANSLATION OF GELIOTEKHNIKA, 11 (1), 3-4, 1975; FOR ORIGINAL SEE E93405)

93407 **STRUCTURE AND PROPERTIES OF FILMS BASED ON BISMUTH TELLURIDE AND SELENIDE.**
ARIFOV, U. A. ERZIN, N. I. KULAGIN, A. I.
MAKOV, N. V. DASHEVSKII, Z. M.
LUKASHEVICH, L. L. KHAFIZOV, KH. KH.
GELIOTEKHNIKA
11 (1), 5-8, 1975.
(FOR ENGLISH TRANSLATION SEE E93408)

93408 **STRUCTURE AND PROPERTIES OF FILMS BASED ON BISMUTH TELLURIDE AND SELENIDE.**
ARIFOV, U. A. ERZIN, N. I. KULAGIN, A. I.
MAKOV, N. V. DASHEVSKII, Z. M.
LUKASHEVICH, L. L. KHAFIZOV, KH. KH.
APPL. SOLAR ENERGY, USSR
11 (1), 3-5, 1975.
(ENGLISH TRANSLATION OF GELIOTEKHNIKA, 11 (1), 5-8, 1975; FOR ORIGINAL SEE E93407)

93413 **MEASUREMENT OF THE REFRACTIVE INDEX OF SOLID AND LIQUID DIELECTRICS AT SUBMILLIMETER WAVELENGTHS.**
CHIGRYAI, E. E.
INSTRUM. EXP. TECH.
17 (PT. 2) (6), 1724-6, 1974.
(ENGLISH TRANSLATION OF PRIB. TEKH. EKSP., 17 (PT. 2) (6), 146-8, 1974; FOR ORIGINAL SEE E90889)

93414 **MEASUREMENT OF THE REFRACTIVE INDEX OF DIELECTRICS AND SEMICONDUCTORS WITH A SUBMILLIMETER SPECTROMETER.**
IGOSHIN, F. F. KIR'YANOV, A. P. MOZHAEV, V.
TULAIKOVA, M. A. SHERONOV, A. A.
INSTRUM. EXP. TECH.
17 (6), (PT. 2), 1727-9, 1974.
(ENGLISH TRANSLATION OF PRIB. TEKH. EKSP. 17 (6), (PT. 2), 148-50, 1974; FOR ORIGINAL SEE E75383)

93417 **MINIATURE HOLDER FOR MEASURING THE HALL EFFECT AND ELECTRICAL CONDUCTIVITY.**
GLAZOV, V. I. ZHUKOV, V. F.
PRIB. TEKH. EKSP.
17 (6), (PT. 2), 186-7, 1974.
(FOR ENGLISH TRANSLATION SEE E93418)

93418 **MINIATURE HOLDER FOR MEASURING THE HALL EFFECT AND ELECTRICAL CONDUCTIVITY.**
GLAZOV, V. I. ZHUKOV, V. F.
INSTRUM. EXP. TECH.
17 (PT. 2) (6), 1776-7, 1974.
(ENGLISH TRANSLATION OF PRIB. TEKH. EKSP., 17 (PT. 2) (6), 186-7, 1974; FOR ORIGINAL SEE E93417)

EPIC Number	Bibliographic Citation
93419	**INFLUENCE OF THE TEMPERATURE OF THE GROWTH OF FILAMENTARY CRYSTALS OF POTASSIUM CHLORIDE ON THE CONCENTRATION OF POINT DEFECTS IN THE CRYSTALS.** MELIK-GAIKAZYAN, I. YA. DERYABIN, P. E. TURGUMBAEV, K. T. LAVRYASHINA, T. V. KRISTALLOGRAFIYA 19 (5), 1121-2, 1974. (FOR ENGLISH TRANSLATION SEE E93420)
93420	**INFLUENCE OF THE TEMPERATURE OF THE GROWTH OF FILAMENTARY CRYSTALS OF POTASSIUM CHLORIDE ON THE CONCENTRATION OF POINT DEFECTS IN THE CRYSTALS.** MELIK-GAIKAZYAN, I. YA. DERYABIN, P. E. TURGUMBAEV, K. T. LAVRYASHINA, T. V. SOV. PHYS. CRYSTALLOGR. 19 (5), 696-7, 1975. (ENGLISH TRANSLATION OF KRISTALLOGRAFIYA, 19 (5), 1121-2, 1974; FOR ORIGINAL SEE E93419)
93434	**SOME PROPERTIES OF HYDRATED ALUMINUM ORTHO- AND PYROVANADATE.** CHERNYSH, L. F. NAKHODNOVA, A. P. MOKHOSOEV, M. V. IZV. AKAD. NAUK SSSR, NEORG. MATER., 10 (4), 640-4, 1974. (FOR ENGLISH TRANSLATION SEE E93435)
93435	**SOME PROPERTIES OF HYDRATED ALUMINUM ORTHO- AND PYROVANADATE.** CHERNYSH, L. F. NAKHODNOVA, A. P. MOKHOSOEV, M. V. INORG. MAT., USSR 10 (4), 546-9, 1974. (ENGLISH TRANSLATION OF IZV. AKAD. NAUK SSSR, NEORG. MATER., 10 (4), 640-4, 1974; FOR ORIGINAL SEE E93434)
93436	**MAGNETIC SUSCEPTIBILITY OF DIBORIDES OF TRANSITION METALS OF GROUPS IV-VI.** L'VOV, S. N. LESNAYA, M. I. VINITSKII, I. M. KOVENSKAYA, B. A. MAKOSEVSKII, B. G. IZV. AKAD. NAUK SSSR, NEORG. MATER. 10 (4), 600-3, 1974. (FOR ENGLISH TRANSLATION, SEE E93437)
93437	**MAGNETIC SUSCEPTIBILITY OF DIBORIDES OF TRANSITION METALS OF GROUPS IV-VI.** L'VOV, S. N. LESNAYA, M. I. VINITSKII, I. M. KOVENSKAYA, B. A. MAKOSEVSKII, B. G INORG. MAT., USSR 10 (4), 512-4, 1974. (ENGLISH TRANSLATION OF IZV. AKAD. NAUK SSSR, NEORG. MATER., 10 (4), 600-3, 1974; FOR ORIGINAL SEE E93436)
93444	**PROPERTIES OF CERTAIN OXYGEN COMPOUNDS OF GROUP IV ELEMENTS.** SUKHANOV, N. M. KRIKOROV, V. S. SHEVCHENKO, B. I. TVERSKOVA, V. A. STRIZHKOV, B. V. IZV. AKAD. NAUK SSSR, NEORG. MATER. 10 (7), 1356-8, 1974. (FOR ENGLISH TRANSLATION SEE E93445)
93445	**PROPERTIES OF CERTAIN OXYGEN COMPOUNDS OF GROUP IV ELEMENTS.** SUKHANOV, N. M. KRIKOROV, V. S. SHEVCHENKO, B. I. TVERSKOVA, V. A. STRIZHKOV, B. V. INORG. MAT., USSR 10 (7), 1163-5, 1974. (ENGLISH TRANSLATION OF IZV. AKAD. ANUK SSSR, NEORG. MATER., 10 (7), 1356-8, 1974; FOR ORIGINAL SEE E93444)
93451	**NATURE OF THE CONDUCTIVITY OF GERMANIUM TELLURIDE AT HIGH TEMPERATURES.** GRUZINOV, B. F. ZHUKOVA, T. B. KOLOMOETS, N. V. KONSTANTINOV, P. P. LEV, E. YA. SYSOEVA, L. M. IZV. AKAD. NAUK SSSR, NEORG. MATER. 10 (7) 1219-25, 1974. (FOR ENGLISH TRANSLATION SEE E93452)
93452	**NATURE OF THE CONDUCTIVITY OF GERMANIUM TELLURIDE AT HIGH TEMPERATURES.** GRUZINOV, B. F. ZHUKOVA, T. B. KOLOMOETS, N. V. KONSTANTINOV, P. P. LEV, E. YA. SYSOEVA, L. M. INORG. MAT., USSR 10 (7), 1044-9, 1974. (ENGLISH TRANSLATION OF IZV. AKAD. NAUK SSSR, NEORG. MATER., 10 (7), 1219-25, 1974; FOR ORIGINAL SEE E93451)
93453	**ELECTRICAL PROPERTIES OF THE ALLOYS MOLYBDENUM SELENIDE - NIOBIUM SELENIDE AND MOLYBDENUM SELENIDE - TANTALUM SELENIDE.** KALIKHMAN, V. L. PRAVOVEROVA, L. L. IZV. AKAD. NAUK SSSR, NEORG. MATER. 10 (7), 1190-4, 1974. (FOR ENGLISH TRANSLATION SEE E93454)
93454	**ELECTRICAL PROPERTIES OF THE ALLOYS MOLYBDENUM SELENIDE - NIOBIUM SELENIDE AND MOLYBDENUM SELENIDE - TANTALUM SELENIDE.** KALIKHMAN, V. L. PRAVOVEROVA, L. L. INORG. MAT., USSR 10 (7), 1021-4, 1974. (ENGLISH TRANSLATION OF IZV. AKAD. NAUK SSSR, NEORG. MATER., 10 (7), 1190-4, 1974; FOR ORIGINAL SEE E93453)
93455	**PHYSICAL PROPERTIES OF INDOCHALCOGENIDES OF RARE EARTHS OF THE CERIUM GROUP.** REDORCHENKO, V. P. LASHKAREV, G. V. IZV. AKAD. NAUK SSSR, NEORG. MATER. 10 (7), 1177-83, 1974. (FOR ENGLISH TRANSLATION SEE E93456)
93456	**PHYSICAL PROPERTIES OF INDOCHALCOGENIDES OF RARE EARTHS OF THE CERIUM GROUP.** FEDORCHENKO, V. P. LASHKAREV, G. V. INORG. MAT., USSR 10 (7), 1009-14Y 1974. (ENGLISH TRANSLATION OF IZV. AKAD. NAUK SSSR, NEORG. MATER., 10 (7), 1177-83, 1974; FOR ORIGINAL SEE E93455)
93457	**CHARACTERISTICS OF HIGH TEMPERATURE ELECTRICAL CONDUCTIVITY OF CADMIUM TELLURIDE CRYSTALS DOPED WITH INDIUM.** RUD', YU. V. SANIN, K. V. IZV. AKAD. NAUK SSSR, NEORG. MATER. 10 (6), 975-9, 1974. (FOR ENGLISH TRANSLATION SEE E93458)
93458	**CHARACTERISTICS OF HIGH TEMPERATURE ELECTRICAL CONDUCTIVITY OF CADMIUM TELLURIDE CYRSTALS DOPED WITH INDIUM.** RUD', YU. V. SANIN, K. V. INORG. MAT., USSR 10 (6), 839-42, 1974. (ENGLISH TRANSLATION OF IZV. AKAD. NAUK SSSR, NEORG. MATER., 10 (6), 975-9, 1974; FOR ORIGINAL SEE E93457)
93465	**SOME PROPERTIES OF COPPER - SELENIDE.** SOROKIN, G. P. IDRICHAN, G. Z. DERGACH, L. V. KOVTUN, E. V. SOROKINA, Z. M. IZV. AKAD. NAUK SSSR, NEORG. MATER. 10 (6), 969-74, 1974. (FOR ENGLISH TRANSLATION SEE E93466)
93466	**SOME PROPERTIES OF COPPER - SELENIDE.** SOROKIN, G. P. IDRICHAN, G. Z. DERGACH, L. V. KOVTUN, E. V. SOROKINA, Z. M. INORG. MAT., USSR 10 (6), 834-8, 1974. (ENGLISH TRANSLATION OF IZV. AKAD. NAUK SSSR, NEORG. MATER., 10 (6), 969-74, 1974; FOR ORIGINAL SEE E93465)
93485	**MEASUREMENT OF THE TEMPORAL CHANGE IN THE REFRACTIVE INDEX OF ZINC SULFIDE THIN FILMS.** AOYAGI, T. TOYODA, K. NAMBA, S. JAP. J. APPL. PHYS. 14 (7), 1095-6, 1975.
93512	**BONDING AND ANTIBONDING POTENTIALS IN GROUP-IV SEMICONDUCTORS.** KEYES, R. W. PHYS. REV. LETT. 34 (21), 1334-7, 1975.
93520	**THE SPATIAL DISPERSION EFFECTS IN CADMIUM SULFIDE CRYSTALS AND THEIR TEMPERATURE DEPENDENCE.** BRODIN, M. S. DAVYDOVA, N. A. STRASHNIKOVA, M. I. PHYS. STATUS SOLIDI 70 B (1), 365-71, 1975.
93527	**ULTRAVIOLET ABSORPTION AND EMISSION OF CYANIDE CENTRES IN ALKALI HALIDES.** VON DER HEYDEN, E. FISCHER, F. PHYS. STATUS SOLIDI 69 B (1), 63-9, 1975.
93528	**OPTICAL ABSORPTION OF MANGANESE IODIDE.** VAN ERK, W. HAAS, C. PHYS. STATUS SOLIDI 70 B (2), 517-24, 1975.
93531	**TOWARD A THEORY OF ABSORPTION EDGES IN AMORPHOUS SOLIDS.** MAJERNIKOVA, E. PHYS. STATUS SOLIDI 70 B (1), K47-50, 1975.
93537	**ELECTRICAL RESISTIVITY OF LEAD-HYDRIDE. I. RESIDUAL RESISTIVITY.** BURGER, J. P. MAILFERT, R. SOUFFACHE, B. SOLID STATE COMMUN. 17 (3), 277-80, 1975.

EPIC Number	Bibliographic Citation
93559	**INFLUENCE OF HIGH ALTERNATING ELECTRIC-FIELD TREATMENT ON X-RAY-INDUCED COLORATION IN POTASSIUM - BROMIDE SINGLE CRYSTALS.** GOVINDA, S. PHYSICA 79 B+C (2), 192-204, 1975.
93561	**THE ALTERNATING CURRENT CONDUCTIVITY OF DISORDERED AND DIELECTRIC SOLIDS. II. DISTRIBUTIONS OF RELAXATION TIMES FOR CLUSTERS.** HALPERN, V. PHYSICA 79 B+C (4), 336-49, 1975.
93580	**REVERSAL OF PHOTOVOLTAIC PHENOMENA IN SPUTTERED ZINC SULPHIDE.** ARSALANE, M. TOSSER, A. THIN SOLID FILMS 28 (2), L31-3, 1975.
93621	**OPTICAL ABSORPTION IN A HEAVILY-DOPED SEMICONDUCTOR WITH A NARROW FORBIDDEN BAND.** FEDIRKO, V. A. IZV. VYSSH. UCHEBN. ZAVED., FIZ. (7), 65-70, 1975. (FOR ENGLISH TRANSLATION SEE E102035)
93622	**RADIATION-INDUCED CONVERSION OF F- AND M-CENTRES IN CALCIUM FLUORIDE CRYSTALS.** KOREPANOV, V. M. LISITSYN, V. M. BARANOV, A. I. STEPANOV, V. G. ZHAPAROVA, S. IZV. VYSSH. UCHEBN. ZAVED., FIZ. (5), 118-20, 1975. (FOR ENGLISH TRANSLATION SEE E102033)
93623	**TEMPERATURE DEPENDENCE OF THE ACCUMULATION OF RADIATIONAL DEFECTS IN DOPED CALCIUM FLUORIDE CRYSTALS.** LISITSYN, V. M. SHTAN'KO, V. F. IZV. VYSSH. UCHEBN. ZAVED., FIZ. (5), 116-18, 1975. (FOR ENGLISH TRANSLATION SEE E102032)
93628	**OBSERVATIONS AND ANALYSIS OF THE OPTICAL ABSORPTION AND FLUORESCENCE SPECTRA OF GREEN-COLOURED NEPTUNIUM:CALCIUM FLUORIDE.** NATARAJAN, A. WANG, S. D. ARTMAN, J. O. J. CHEM. PHYS. 62 (7), 2707-19, 1975.
93630	**THE PREPARATION AND PROPERTIES OF ALUMINUM NITRIDE FILMS.** CHU, T. L. KELM, R. W., JR. J. ELECTROCHEM. SOC. 122 (7), 995-1000, 1975.
93698	**DETERMINATION OF THE ABSORPTION COEFFICIENTS OF DIELECTRIC EVAPORATED LAYERS AS FUNCTIONS OF DIFFERENT PREPARATION PARAMETERS.** AHRENS, H. VAK.-TECH. 24 (2), 33-7, 1975.
93997	**OPTICAL STORAGE EFFECTS IN ARSENIC TRISULFIDE AND RELATED MATERIALS.** KENEMAN, S. A. UNIV. OF PENNSYLVANIA, PHILADELPHIA, PH. D. THESIS 268PP., 1975. (UNIV. MICROFILM NO. 75-2745)
93998	**ELECTRON-NONHOMOGENEOUS MAGNETIZATION INTERACTION IN THIN FILMS OF CADMIUM CHROMIUM SELENIDE.** SYLLAIOS, A. J. UNIVERSITY OF TEXAS, AUSTIN, PH. D. THESIS 83PP., 1974. (UNIV. MICROFILM NO. 75-4461)
94018	**AN APPARATUS FOR DETERMINING THE ELECTRICAL AND THERMOPHYSICAL PARAMETERS OF THERMOELECTRIC MATERIALS BY KOHLRAUSH'S METHOD.** SKLOKIN, F. N. KORNILOV, V. P. ZAVOD. LAB. 41 (1), 56-7, 1975. (FOR ENGLISH TRANSLATION SEE E 94019)
94019	**AN APPARATUS FOR DETERMINING THE ELECTRICAL AND THERMOPHYSICAL PARAMETERS OF THERMOELECTRIC MATERIALS BY KOHLRAUSH'S METHOD.** SKLOKIN, F. N. KORNILOV, V. P. IND. LAB., USSR 41 (1), 77-8, 1975. (ENGLISH TRANSLATION OF ZAVOD. LAB., 41 (1), 56-7, 1975; FOR ORIGINAL SEE E 94018)
94022	**FORMATION AND PILE-UP OF EXCESS HOLE CONCENTRATION ON IRRADIATION WITH POSITRONS AND SOME RESULTING PHENOMENA IN DIELECTRICS.** VOROB'EV, A. A. AREF'EV, K. P. VOROB'EV, S. A. DOKL. AKAD. NAUK SSSR 219 (5), 1092-5, 1974. (FOR ENGLISH TRANSLATION SEE E94023)
94023	**FORMATION AND PILE-UP OF EXCESS HOLE CONCENTRATION ON IRRADIATION WITH POSITRONS AND SOME RESULTING PHENOMENA IN DIELECTRICS.** VOROB'EV, A. A. AREF'EV, K. P. VOROB'EV, S. A. SOV. PHYS. DOKL. 19 (12), 836-7, 1975. (ENGLISH TRANSLATION OF DOKL. AKAD9 NAUK SSSR, 219 (5), 1092-5, 1974; FOR ORIGINAL SEE E94022)
94024	**ANOMALOUS PHOTOELECTRIC EFFECT.** LIDOVENKO, N. S. STREBKOV, D. S. DOKL. AKAD. NAUK SSSR 219 (2), 325-8, 1974. (FOR ENGLISH TRANSLATION SEE E94025)
94025	**ANOMALOUS PHOTOELECTRIC EFFECT.** LIDOVENKO, N. S. STREBKOV, D. S. SOV. PHYS. DOKL. 19 (11), 789-90, 1975. (ENGLISH TRANSLATION OF DOKL. AKAD. NAUK SSSR, 219 (2), 325-8, 1974; FOR ORIGINAL SEE E94024)
94028	**PHOTOVOLTAIC EFFECT IN BISMUTH TELLURIDE FILMS BOMBARDED WITH CESIUM IONS.** ARIFOV, U. A. AYUKHANOV, A. KH. GARAFUTDINOVA, I. A. ABDULLAEV, N. A. DOKL. AKAD. NAUK SSSR 219 (2), 315-7, 1974. (FOR ENGLISH TRANSLATION SEE E94029)
94029	**PHOTOVOLTAIC EFFECT IN BISMUTH TELLURIDE FILMS BOMBARDED WITH CESIUM IONS.** ARIFOV, U. A. AYUKHANOV, A. KH. GARAFUTDINOVA, I. A. ABDULLAEV, N. A. SOV. PHYS. DOKL. 19 (11), 781-2, 1975. (ENGLISH TRANSLATION OF DOKL. AKAD. NAUK SSSR, 219 (2), 315-7, 1974; FOR ORIGINAL SEE E94028)
94077	**SPIN FLIP TRANSITIONS IN CUBIC MAGNETS. MAGNETIC PHASE DIAGRAM OF TERBIUM - YTTERIUM IRON GARNETS.** BELOV, K. P. ZVEZDIN, A. K. LEVITIN, R. Z. MARKOSYAN, A. S. MILL, B. V. MUKHIN, A. A. PEROV, A. P. SOV. PHYS. JETP 41 (3), 590-6, 1976. (ENGLISH TRANSLATION OF ZH. EKSP. TEOR. FIZ., 68 (3), 1189-1202, 1975; FOR ORIGINAL SEE E85350)
94084	**WEAK FERROMAGNETISM ALONG THE TRIGONAL AXIS IN ANTIFERROMAGNETIC COBALT(II) CARBONATE AND NICKEL(II) CARBONATE.** BAZHAN, A. N. SOV. PHYS. JETP 40 (4), 757-9, 1975. (ENGLISH TRANSLATION OF ZH. EKSP. TEOR. FIZ., 67 (4), 1520-6, 1974; FOR ORIGINAL SEE E86618)
94087	**COMPARISON OF THE RESULTS OF AN INVESTIGATION OF ELECTRON SPIN RESONANCE SIGNALS AND HIGH TEMPERATURE MEASUREMENTS OF THE HALL EFFECT AND ELECTRICAL CONDUCTIVITY OF IRON DOPED GALLIUM ARSENIDE SAMPLES.** SUCHKOVA, N. I. SOLOV'EV, N. N. SOV. PHYS. SEMICOND. 9 (1), 104-5, 1975. (ENGLISH TRANSLATION OF FIZ. TEKH. POLUPROV., 9 (1), 156-8, 1975; FOR ORIGINAL SEE E81166)
94088	**THERMOELECTRIC POWER AND EFFECTIVE MASS OF ELECTRONS IN GALLIUM ARSENIDE PHOSPHIDE SOLID SOLUTIONS.** GORCHAK, L. V. NEGRESKUL, V. V. BALEKA, E. S. CHEBAN, A. G. SOV. PHYS. SEMICOND. 9 (1), 117-8, 1975. (ENGLISH TRANSLATION OF FIZ. TEKH. POLUPROV., 9 (1), 171-4, 1975; FOR ORIGINAL SEE E81273)
94093	**A PULSE PROBE METHOD OF THERMOELECTRIC PARAMETER MEASUREMENT ON SEMICONDUCTORS.** BASIN, YU. G. GRITS, YU. A. ISACHENKO, V. I. INSTRUM. EXP. TECH. (6), 1791, 1974. (ENGLISH TRANSLATION OF PRIB. TEKH. EKSP., (6), 199, 1974; FOR ORIGINAL SEE E80889)
94096	**LINE SPECTRA OF INFRARED LUMINESCENCE OF CUBIC SILICON CARBIDE CRYSTALS.** GORBAN', I. S. SLOBODYANYUK, A. V. JETP LETT. 21 (5), 120-1, 1975. (ENGLISH TRANSLATION OF ZH. EKSP. TEOR. FIZ., PIS'MA RED., 21 (5), 263-6, 1975; FOR ORIGINAL SEE E85352)
94099	**PHYSICAL CHARACTERIZATION OF ELECTRONIC MATERIALS.** KULIN, S. A. KREDER, K. NESHE, P. MANLABS INC., CAMBRIDGE, MASS. 43-114, 1975. (AD-A018 661, N76-24471, AFCRL-TR-75-0480)

EPIC Number	Bibliographic Citation

94145 **OPTICAL ABSORPTION SPECTRUM OF CHROMIUM TRIPOSITIVE ION IN UVAROVITE GARNET.**
LAKSHMAN, S. V. J. REDDY, B. J.
PHYSICA (UTRECHT)
71 (1), 197–203, 1974.

94147 **ULTRAVIOLET ABSORPTION SPECTRUM OF THE CALCIUM HYDRIDE MOLECULE. I. ROTATIONAL ANALYSIS OF THE 3060 ANGSTROM BAND SYSTEM.**
KAVNG, B. LINDGREN, B. RAMSAY, D. A.
PHYS. SCR.
10 (1–2), 73–9, 1974.

94148 **VIBRATIONAL SPECTRUM OF SODIUM BROMATE.**
BERENBLUT, B. J. DAWSON, P. MORSE, P.
WILKINSON, G. R.
J. RAMAN SPECTROSE.
1 (6), 523–32, 1973.

94149 **LIQUID SEMICONDUCTORS.**
GLAZOV, V. M. CHIZHEVSKAYA, S. N.
GLAGOLEVA, N. N.
PLENUM PRESS, NEW YORK
362PP., 1969.

94150 **CHARACTERIZATION OF THIN FILM ZINC SELENIDE COATINGS USING INFRARED ELLIPSOMETRY.**
FRANKLIN, A. L. JR.
AIR FORCE INST. OF TECHNOLOGY, M. S. THESIS
59PP., 1975.
(AD–A019 497, N76–25554, GEP/PH/75–16)

94151 **THERMAL COEFFICIENT OF REFRACTIVE INDEX OF POLYCRYSTALLINE ZINC SELENIDE, BARIUM FLUORIDE AND CADMIUM FLUORIDE IN THE VISIBLE AND NEAR INFRARED.**
MUKAI, H.
AIR FORCE INST, OF TECGNOLOGY, M. S. THESIS
93PP., 1975.
(AD–A019 526, GE/PH/75–2)
(N76–24570)

94190 **INVESTIGATION OF THE THERMO ELECTROMOTIVE FORCE AND ELECTRICAL CONDUCTIVITY OF THE OXIDE FORMS OF RADIOACTIVE IRON CATALYSTS IN AMMONIA SYNTHESIS.**
SPITSYN, V. I. EROFEEV, B. V.
MIKHAILENKO, I. E. CHIKHLADZE, V. V.
PROC. ACAD. SCI., USSR, PHYS. CHEM. SECT.
219 (4), 1149–52, 1974.
(ENGLISH TRANSLATION OF DOKL. AKAD. NAUK SSSR, 219 (4), 910–3, 1974; FOR ORIGINAL SEE E88553)

94197 **THERMOELECTRIC PROPERTIES OF ALLOYS SILICON TELLURIDE - GALLIUM TELLURIDE.**
ALIDZHANOV, M. A. ORUDZHEV, N. M.
NASIROV, YA. N.
INORG. MAT., USSR
11 (4), 657–8, 1975.
(ENGLISH TRANSLATION OF IZV. AKAD. NAUK SSSR, NEORG. MATER., 11 (4), 762–3, 1975; FOR ORIGINAL SEE E91201)

94215 **A PAIR MODE IN THE FAR INFRARED ABSORPTION SPECTRUM OF POTASSIUM IODIDE: CHLORIDE.**
WARD, R. W. CLAYMAN, B. P. JASWAL, S. S.
SOLID STATE COMMUN.
14, 1335–7, 1974.

94479 **LOW LOSS WINDOW MATERIALS FOR CHEMICAL LASERS.**
HARRINGTON, J. A.
DEPT OF PHYSICS, ALABAMA UNIV., HUNTSVILLE
15PP., 1975.
(AD–A–19 774)

94480 **THE ELECTRONIC BAND STRUCTURE OF VANADIUM OXIDE.**
KRAAN, D. J.
IMPRIMERIE DEROUAUX - LIEGE
93PP., 1974.

94481 **GROWTH AND OPTICAL ABSORPTION SPECTRA OF THE LAYER-TYPE TRICHALCOGENIDES ZIRCONIUM TRISULFIDE AND HAFNIUM TRISULFIDE.**
SCHAIRER, W. SHAFER, M. W.
PHYS. STATUS SOLIDI
17 A (1), 181–4, 1973.

94485 **INVESTIGATION OF VALENCE BANDS OF PHOSPHIDES IN METAL-PHOSPHORUS SYSTEMS OF THE A–I B–V AND A–II B–V TYPE BY THE X-RAY SPECTRAL METHOD.**
DOMASHEVSKAYA, E. P. TEREKHOV, V. A.
MARSHAKOVA, L. N. UGAI, YA. A.
BULL. ACAD. SCI., USSR, PHYS. SER.
38 (3), 119–23, 1974.
(ENGLISH TRANSLATION OF IZV. AKAD. NAUK SSSR, SER. FIZ., 38 (3), 567–71, 1974; FOR ORIGINAL SEE E77917)

94494 **EXTERNAL PHOTOELECTRIC EFFECT OF A HEAVILY DOPED SEMICONDUCTOR.**
YUSHINA, M. YA.
BULL. ACAD. SCI., USSR, PHYS. SER.
38 (2), 166–71, 1974.
(ENGLISH TRANSLATION OF IZV. AKAD. NAUK SSSR, SER. FIZ. 38 (2), 363–9, 1974; FOR ORIGINAL SEE E77934)

94499 **ELECTRON ENERGY DISTRIBUTION IN FIELD EMISSION FROM TANTALUM, MOLYBDENUM, AND TUNGSTEN CARBIDE COVERED BY SILICON AND ALUMINUM OXIDE.**
BOBEV, K. S.
BULL. ACAD. SCI., USSR, PHYS. SER.
38 (2), 145–50, 1974.
(ENGLISH TRANSLATION OF IZV. AKAD. NAUK SSSR, SER. FIZ., 38 (2), 338–44, 1974; FOR ORIGINAL SEE E77932)

94503 **FIELD EMISSION IN SYSTEMS WITH ISLAND METAL FILMS.**
SUKHARIER, A. S. ZAGREBNEVA, S. V.
IVANOV, N. N. TIMONINA, L. N.
BULL. ACAD. SCI., USSR, PHYS. SER.
38 (2), 111–4, 1974.
(ENGLISH TRANSLATION OF IZV. AKAD. NAUK SSSR, SER. FIZ., 38 (2), 302–5, 1974; FOR ORIGINAL SEE E77912)

94505 **HOT ELECTRON EMISSION FROM THE ALUMINUM-SILICON NITRIDE-ALUMINUM THIN FILM SYSTEM.**
BARANOV, A. V. BUZNIKOV, YU. N.
BOROB'EV, G. A. GALANSKII, V. L. DREL, N. I.
KRIVOSHCHEKOV, V. P. SMIRNOVA, K. I.
TROYAN, L. A. TROYAN, P. E.
YANKELEVICH, YU. B.
BULL. ACAD. SCI., USSR, PHYS. SER.
38 (2), 100–3, 1974.
(ENGLISH TRANSLATION OF IZV. AKAD. NAUK SSSR, SER. FIZ., 38 (2), 291–5, 1974; FOR ORIGINAL SEE E77911)

94506 **INTERNAL BREAKDOWN IN STRONG ELECTRIC FIELDS DURING FIELD EMISSION FROM P-TYPE GERMANIUM.**
IVANOV, V. G. ROZOVA, T. T. FURSEI, G. N.
BULL. ACAD. SCI., USSR, PHYS. SER.
38 (2), 96–9, 1974.
(ENGLISH TRANSLATION OF IZV. AKAD. NAUK SSSR, SER FIZ., 38 (2), 287–90, 1974; FOR ORIGINAL SEE E77928)

94512 **CALCULATION OF THE ENERGY SPECTRA OF DONOR ELECTRONS OF THERMIONIC CATHODES.**
NAVROZOV, S. V.
BULL. ACAD. SCI., USSR, PHYS. SER.
38 (2), 33–7, 1974.
(ENGLISH TRANSLATION OF IZV. AKAD. NAUK SSSR, SER. FIZ., 38 (2), 220–4, 1974; FOR ORIGINAL SEE E77924)

94513 **KINETIC PHENOMENA IN THE PHOTOFIELD EMISSION OF CADMIUM SULFIDE.**
SHLYAKHTENKO, P. G. MILESHKINA, N. V.
PREOBRAZHENSKII, R. K. DOROTYNSKII, M. G.
BULL. ACAD. SCI., USSR, PHYS. SER.
38 (2), 29–32, 1974.
(ENGLISH TRANSLATION OF IZV. AKAD. NAUK SSSR, SER. FIZ., 38 (2), 216–9, 1974; FOR ORIGINAL SEE E77923)

94514 **KINETICS OF THE PHOTOEMISSION OF CERTAIN A–I B–V COMPOUNDS.**
NANEV, K. NIKOLOV, B.
BULL. ACAD. SCI., USSR, PHYS. SER.
38 (2), 26–8, 1974.
(ENGLISH TRANSLATION OF IZV. AKAD. NAUK SSSR, SER. FIZ., 38 (2), 212–5, 1974; FOR ORIGINAL SEE E77922)

94516 **PHOTOELECTRIC EMISSION FROM F CENTERS OF ALKALI HALIDE CRYSTALS AND ITS DEPENDENCE ON THE EXCITATION AND MEASUREMENT CONDITIONS.**
BICHEVIN, V. V.
BULL. ACAD. SCI., USSR, PHYS. SER.
38 (2), 15–9, 1974.
(ENGLISH TRANSLATION OF IZV. AKAD. NAUK SSSR, SER FIZ., 38 (2), 201–5, 1974; FOR ORIGINAL SEE E77920)

94517 **BAND STRUCTURE OF THE A(I) B(V) EFFICIENT PHOTOCATHODES.**
MOSTOVSKII, A. A. CHALDYSHEV, V. A.
KARAVAEV, G. F. KLIMIN, A. I.
PONOMARENKO, I. N.
BULL. ACAD. SCI., USSR, PHYS. SER.
38 (2), 10–4, 1974.
(ENGLISH TRANSLATION OF IZV. AKAD. NAUK SSSR, SER. FIZ., 38 (2), 195–200, 1974; FOR ORIGINAL SEE E77941)

94518 **PROCESSES INVOLVED IN PHOTOEMISSION AT HIGH EXCITATION ENERGIES.**
BLANK, V. A. SOROKIN, O. M.
BULL. ACAD. SCI., USSR, PHYS. SER.
38 (2), 6–9, 1974.
(ENGLISH TRANSLATION OF IZV. AKAD. NAUK SSSR, SER. FIZ., 38 (2), 191–4, 1974; FOR ORIGINAL SEE E77919)

94546 **CONVERSION OF A MONOCHROMATOR FOR ABSORPTION COEFFICIENT MEASUREMENT.**
VARMA, S. P.
REV. SCI. INSTRUM.
46 (10), 1424–5, 1975.

EPIC Number	Bibliographic Citation
94550	ELECTRONIC PROPERTIES OF II–IV–V(2) TYPE AND II(3)–V(2) TYPE SEMICONDUCTING COMPOUNDS. ISOMURA, S. TRANS. NATL. RES. INST. MET. 17 (2), 98–109, 1975.
94551	EXACTLY SOLVABLE MODEL OF THE PHONON–ASSISTED HOPPING DIRECT CURRENT CONDUCTIVITY. CAPEK, V. CZECH. J. PHYS. 25 B (9), 1020–7, 1975.
94567	ACTION OF LOW–ENERGY ELECTRONS ON THE PHOTOELECTRIC PROPERTIES OF CADMIUM TELLURIDE FILMS HAVING ANOMALOUS PHOTOVOLTAGE. ARIFOV, U. A. AYUKHANOV, A. KH. ABDULLAEV, N. A. ARIFDZHANOVA, M. S. DOKL. AKAD. NAUK SSSR 223 (5), 1102–5, 1975. (FOR ENGLISH TRANSLATION SEE E95912)
94569	PHOTOCONDUCTIVE EFFECTS IN CADMIUM SULFIDE – COPPER(I) SULFIDE PHOTOVOLTAIC CELLS. CASWELL, B. G. RUSSELL, G. J. WOODS, J. J. PHYS. 8 D (15), 1889–900, 1975.
94581	CHARACTERIZATION OF INFRARED LASER WINDOW MATERIALS AT THE NATIONAL BUREAU OF STANDARDS. FELDMAN, A. MALITSON, I. HOROWITZ, D. WAXLER, R. M. DODGE, M. NATIONAL BUREAU STANDARDS, WASHINGTON, D. C. 141–8, 1974. (NBS–SP–414 AD–A012 377)
94588	ELECTRONIC TRANSPORT IN POLYCRYSTALLINE FILMS. BUBE, R. H. ANNU. REV. MATER. SCI. 5, 201–24, 1975.
94595	NEW MICROWAVE SYSTEM TO DETERMINE THE COMPLEX PERMITTIVITY OF SMALL DIELECTRIC AND SEMICONDUCTING SAMPLES. MUSIL, J. ZACEK, F. BURGER, A. KARLOVSKY, J. CZECH. J. PHYS. 25 B (8), 916–26, 1975.
94599	DISPERSION OF THE TEMPERATURE COEFFICIENT OF BIREFRINGENCE IN CADMIUM SULFIDE AND CADMIUM SELENIDE. REZA, A. A. BABONAS, G. SILEIKA, A. FIZ. TEKH. POLUPROVODN. 9 (8), 1494–8, 1975. (FOR ENGLISH TRANSLATION SEE E95900)
94600	THERMOEMF. IN PSEUDOBINARY LEAD SULFIDE SOLID SOLUTIONS. KULIEV, A. Z. KAKHRAMANOV, K. SH. SAGATOV, E. S. TUKHTASINOV, I. GELIOTEKHNIKA (3–4), 12–14, 1975. (FOR ENGLISH TRANSLATION SEE E100283)
94613	ANOMALOUS PHOTOVOLTAIC EFFECT IN CADMIUM TELLURIDE. JOHNSON, H. R. WILLIAMS, R. H. MEE, C. H. B. J. PHYS. 8 D (13), 1530–41, 1975.
94627	ELECTRICAL AND OPTICAL PROPERTIES OF TELLURIUM–DOPED GALLIUM ANTIMONIDE. OSAMURA, K. NAKAJIMA, K. MURAKAMI, Y. MEM. FAC. ENG., KYOTO UNIV. 37, PT. 1, 47–61, 1975.
94636	CHEMICAL VAPOR DEPOSITION OF OPTICAL MATERIALS. MILES, P. PROC. SYMP. MATER. SCI. ASPECTS THIN FILM SYST. SOL. ENERGY CONVERS. (PB–239 270), 402–18, 1974.
94637	PRESENTATION AND OPTICAL PROPERTIES OF AMORPHOUS SEMICONDUCTING FILMS. DE NEUFVILLE, J. P. PROC. SYMP. MATER. SCI. ASPECTS THIN FILM SYST. SOL. ENERGY CONVERS. (PB–239 270), 356–81, 1974.
94639	RECOMMENDED REFERENCE MATERIALS FOR REALIZATION OF PHYSICOCHEMICAL PROPERTIES. OPTICAL REFRACTION (REFRACTIVE INDEX). IUPAC PHYSICAL CHEMISTRY DIVISION PURE APPL. CHEM. 40 (3), 463–72, 1974.
94644	ANALYSIS OF THE SURFACE PHOTOVOLTAIC EFFECT IN PHOTOCONDUCTORS. CADMIUM SULFIDE. MALTBY, J. R. REED, C. E. SCOTT, C. G. SURF. SCI. 51 (1), 89–108, 1975.
94661	ORDER DEPENDENCE OF THE THERMOELECTRIC POWER OF BINARY ALLOYS. WANG, K. P. CAN. J. PHYS. 53 (11), 1115–16, 1975.
94894	DIMENSIONAL ANISOTROPY OF TRANSVERSE MAGNETORESISTANCE IN SEMICONDUCTOR FILMS IN A STRONG MAGNETIC FIELD. ZOT'EV, B. P. KRAVCHENKO, A. F. SKOK, E. M. YUDAEV, V. I. FIZ. TEKH. POLUPROV. 6 (6), 1072–6, 1972. (FOR ENGLISH TRANSLATION SEE E95899)
94899	THERMOELECTRIC PROPERTIES OF SEMICONDUCTING MATERIALS WITH A NONSTANDARD CONDUCTION MECHANISM. GOLIKOVA, O. A. ZAITSEV, V. K. PETROV, A. V. STIL'BANS, L. S. TKALENKO, E. N. FIZ. TEKH. POLUPROV. 6 (9), 1724–8, 1972. (FOR ENGLISH TRANSLATION SEE E95896)
94907	REFLECTION SPECTRA FOR BISMUTH AND BISMUTH – ANTIMONY ALLOYS IN THE FAR–INFRARED REGION. KULAKOVSKII, V. D. ROZHDESTVENSKAYA, V. V. BELOV, A. G. VAVILOV, V. S. GIPPIUS, A. A. EGOROV, V. D. ZEMSKOV, V. S. FIZ. TEKH. POLUPROV. 6 (11), 2268–70, 1972. (FOR ENGLISH TRANSLATION SEE E95897)
94941	THERMOELECTRIC EFFECTS IN SEMICONDUCTORS IN THE DRAG EFFECT REGION. APPLICATION OF THE THEORY TO N–GERMANIUM. PINCHUK, I. I. KOGUTYUK, I. P. FIZ. TEKH. POLUPROVODN. 9 (6), 1198–201, 1975. (ENGLISH TRANSLATION SEE E96880)
94942	THERMOELECTRIC EFFICIENCY OF LEAD TELLURIDE – TIN TELLURIDE ALLOYS. GURIEVA, E. A. PROKOF'EVA, L. V. STIL'BANS, L. S. TAMARCHENKO, V. I. FIZ. TEKH. POLUPROVODN. 9 (6), 1213–16, 1975. (FOR ENGLISH TRANSLATION SEE E95895)
95056	ELECTRICAL RESISTIVITY OF IRON – ALUMINUM MOLTEN ALLOYS. LEVIN, E. S. GEL'D, P. V. AYUSHINA, G. D. IZV. VYSSH. UCHEB. ZAVED., FIZ. 15 (10), 135–8, 1972. (FOR ENGLISH TRANSLATION SEE E95814)
95124	THERMIONIC EMISSION OF ALUMINUM OXIDE IN A BARIUM ATOM FLOW. BAZANOV, V. G. BAN'KOVSKII, N. G. CHADAEVA, I. A. ZH. TEKH. FIZ. 45 (7), 1524–6, 1975. (FOR ENGLISH TRANSLATION SEE E95907)
95126	THERMOEMF. AND ELECTRIC CONDUCTIVITY OF METALS IN DIRECT AND ALTERNATING CURRENT. GLAZOV, V. M. AIVAZOV, A. A. KARAGODIN, YU. A. ARSLANOV, D. E. ZAVOD. LAB. 41 (6), 701–4, 1975 (ENGLISH TRANSLATION SEE E97093)
95131	METHODS FOR DETERMINATION OF THERMOELECTRIC PROPERTIES OF SEMICONDUCTORS IN A LIQUID STATE. GLAZOV, V. M. EVSEEV, V. A. PAVLOV, V. G. ZAVODSK. LAB. 32 (3), 290–300, 1966. (FOR ENGLISH TRANSLATION SEE E96497)
95225	THERMIONIC EMISSION FROM THIN FILMS OF ALUMINUM OXIDE. BAZANOV, V. G. BAN'KOVSKII, N. G. CHADAEVA, I. A. SOV. PHYS. TECH. PHYS. 20 (3), 422–3, 1975. (ENGLISH TRANSLATION OF ZH. TEKH. FIZ., 45 (3), 676–8, 1975; FOR ORIGINAL SEE E91366)
95249	CLUSTER COMPONENT CALCULATION OF THE PROPERTIES OF GARNETS. TALANOV, V. M. VOROB'EV, YU. P. MEN', A. N. LEVCHENKO, V. M. SOV. PHYS. 17 J (6), 860–3, 1974. (ENGLISH TRANSLATION OF IZV. VYSSH. UCHEB. ZAVED., FIZ., 17 (6), 126–9, 1974; FOR ORIGINAL SEE E80756)
95251	NEGATIVE RESISTANCE IN LEAD TIN TELLURIDE FILMS. KOVALYUK, Z. D. KONDRATENKO, M. M. MALIK, A. I. ORLETSKII, V. B. SOV. PHYS. J. 17 (5), 693–4, 1974. (ENGLISH TRANSLATION OF IZV. VYSSH. UCHEB. ZAVED., FIZ., 17 (5), 116–7, 1974; FOR ORIGINAL SEE E80749)

EPIC Number	Bibliographic Citation
95252	**SENSITIVIZED PHOTOLUMINESCENCE OF MANGANESE IN CALCIUM SULFATE PHOSPHORS.** IVANOV, L. N. KARELIN, V. V. MIKHAILIN, V. V. PETROVA, I. YU. SOV. PHYS. 17 J (5), 686–8, 1974. (ENGLISH TRANSLATION OF IZV. VYSSH. UCHEB. ZAVED., FIZ., 17 (5), 110–2, 1974; FOR ORIGINAL SEE E80748)
95254	**X-RAY LUMINESCENCE OF ZINC SULFIDE SINGLE CRYSTALS ACTIVATED WITH COPPER, SILVER, MANGANESE, AND THALLIUM.** PUTIEV, I. T. CHENETS, V. N. TUKHLIBAEV, A. SOV. PHYS. 17 J (2), 290–1, 1974. (ENGLISH TRANSLATION OF IZV. VYSSH. UCHEB. ZAVED., FIZ., 17 (2), 155–7, 1974; FOR ORIGINAL SEE E80409)
95255	**THERMOSTIMULATED ELECTRON EMISSION OF BERYLLIUM OXIDE AFTER X-IRRADIATION.** KORTOV, V. S. GAPRINDASHVILI, A. I. PILIPENKO, G. I. LAKHOV, V. M. SOV. PHYS. 17 J (2), 288–9, 1974. (ENGLISH TRANSLATION OF IZV. VYSSH. UCHEB. ZAVED., FIZ., 17 (2), 154–5, 1974; FOR ORIGINAL SEE E80408)
95257	**ACTION OF WEAK ELECTRIC FIELD ON THERMOLUMINESCENCE OF ZINC SULFIDE FILMS.** NUVAR'EVA, V. V. RAMAZANOV, P. E. SOV. PHYS. 17 J (2), 263–4, 1974. (ENGLISH TRANSLATION OF IZV. VYSSH. UCHEB. ZAVED., FIZ., 17 (2), 133–4, 1974; FOR ORIGINAL SEE E80406)
95258	**INFLUENCE OF PRELIMINARY EXCITATION ON THE TEMPERATURE DEPENDENCE OF ELECTROLUMINESCENCE OF ZINC SULFIDE FILMS.** NUVAR'EVA, V. V. RAMAZANOV, P. E. SOV. PHYS. 17 J (2), 260–2, 1974. (ENGLISH TRANSLATION OF IZV. VYSSH. UCHEB. ZAVED., FIZ., 17 (2), 131–3, 1974; FOR ORIGINAL SEE E80405)
95260	**EFFECTS OF COMPLEXING ON THE ABSORPTION SPECTRA OF P-BENZOQUINONE AND CHLORANIL.** KUZNETSOVA, R. T. FOFONOVA, R. M. DANILOVA, V. I. SOV. PHYS. 17 J (5), 747, 1974. (ENGLISH TRANSLATION OF IZV. VYSSH. UCHEB. ZAVED., FIZ., 17 (5), 158, 1974; FOR ORIGINAL SEE E80753)
95261	**CONTACT POTENTIAL DIFFERENCE AND THE RADICAL-RECOMBINATION LUMINESCENCE FOR ZINC OXIDE.** STYROV, V. V. TOLMACHEV, V. M. SOV. PHYS. 17 J (5), 746, 1974. (ENGLISH TRANSLATION OF IZV. VYSSH. UCHEB. ZAVED., FIZ., 17 (5), 157, 1974; FOR ORIGINAL SEE E80752)
95262	**AMPHOTERIC DOPES IN GALLIUM PHOSPHIDE.** SAMORUKOV, B. E. SOV. PHYS. 17 J (5), 744, 1974. (ENGLISH TRANSLATION OF IZV. VYSSH. UCHEB. ZAVED., FIZ., 17 (5), 155, 1974; FOR ORIGINAL SEE E80751)
95263	**MAGNETIC PARAMETERS OF VANADIUM SILICON AND STRUCTURAL TRANSITION.** TRET'YAKOV, B. N. KODESS, B. N. KURITSIN, V. B. SOV. PHYS. 17 J (5), 727–8, 1974. (ENGLISH TRANSLATION OF IZV. VYSSH. UCHEB. ZAVED., FIZ., 17 (5), 141–3, 1974; FOR ORIGINAL SEE E80750)
95265	**OPTICAL ABSORPTION IN UNORDERED SYSTEMS.** FEDIRKO, V. A. SOV. PHYS. 17 J (2), 163–7, 1974. (ENGLISH TRANSLATION OF IZV. VYSSH. UCHEB. ZAVED., FIZ., 17 (2), 21–6, 1974; FOR ORIGINAL SEE E61409)
95324	**ELECTRICAL CONDUCTION IN DISORDERED NONMETALLIC FILMS.** JONSCHER, A. K. HILL, R. M. PHYS. THIN FILMS 8, 169–249, 1975.
95369	**RADIATION EFFECTS ON BETA 10.6 OF PURE AND EUROPIUM DOPED POTASSIUM CHLORIDE.** GRIMES, H. MAISEL, J. HARTFORD, R. H. PROC. CONF. INFRARED LASER WINDOW MATERIALS, 5TH 279–90, 1976. (AFML-TR-76-83, AD-B014 718, UDRI-TR-76-35, N76-13296, NASA-TM-X-71847)
95378	**MEASUREMENT OF ELECTRICAL CONDUCTIVITY OF OXIDES AT HIGH TEMPERATURE BY MICROWAVE ELLIPSOMETRY.** SAKURAI, T. MOCHIZUKI, S. ISHIGAME, M. HIGH TEMP. HIGH PRESSURES 7 (4), 411–7, 1975.
95407	**THE USE OF X-RAY INTERFEROMETRY TO MEASURE X-RAY REFRACTIVE INDICES.** CREAGH, D. C. AUST. J. PHYS. 28 (5), 543–55, 1975.
95469	**DIRECT CONVERSION OF SOLAR ENERGY THROUGH PHOTOVOLTAIC CELLS.** ROTHWARF, A. BOER, K. W. PROG. SOLID STATE CHEM. 10, (PT. 2), 71–102, 1975.
95509	**INFLUENCE OF THE ELECTRON-ELECTRON SCATTERING ON THE KINETIC EFFECTS IN MANY-VALLEY SEMICONDUCTORS.** MITIN, V. V. TOLPYGO, E. I. PHYS. STATUS SOLIDI 72 B (1), 51–8, 1975.
95524	**PHOTOVOLTAIC EFFECTS ON OXYGEN ION IMPLANTED GALLIUM ARSENIDE.** DEVEAUD, B. PALMIER, J. F. FAVENNEC, P. N. KAR, R. K. SOLID STATE COMMUN. 17 (10), 1253–5, 1975.
95534	**OPTICAL PROPERTIES OF BETA-SILICON CARBIDE CRYSTALS PREPARED BY CHEMICAL VAPOR DEPOSITION.** NISHINO, S. MATSUNAMI, H. TANAKA, T. JAP. J. APPL. PHYS. 14 (11), 1833–4, 1975.
95560	**ANTIFERROMAGNETIC-TYPE SPIN FLUCTUATIONS IN ACTINIDE SYSTEMS: RESISTIVITY AND MAGNETIC SUSCEPTIBILITY AT HIGH TEMPERATURES.** JULLIEN, R. COQBLIN, B. J. LOW TEMP. PHYS. 22 (3–4), 437–53, 1976.
95569	**TEMPERATURE DEPENDENCE OF THE FAR-INFRARED ABSORPTION SPECTRUM IN AMORPHOUS DIELECTRICS.** MON, K. K. CHABAL, Y. J. SIEVERS, A. J. PHYS. REV. LETT. 35 (20), 1352–5, 1975.
95584	**QUASICUBIC STATE AND PIEZOBIREFRINGENCE OF CADMIUM SULFIDE AND CADMIUM SELENIDE.** REZA, A. BABONAS, G. SILEIKA, A. PHYS. STATUS SOLIDI 72 B (1), 421–9, 1975.
95668	**FUNDAMENTAL ABSORPTION EDGE IN LASER WINDOW CADMIUM TELLURIDE.** NURMIKKO, A. V. APPL. OPT. 14 (11), 2662–4, 1975.
95705	**VACUUM DEPOSITION OF DIELECTRIC AND SEMICONDUCTOR FILMS BY A CARBON DIOXIDE LASER.** HASS, G. RAMSEY, J. B. APPL. OPT. 8 (6), 1115–8, 1969.
95706	**AN EXPERIMENTAL STUDY OF THE CHANGE IN PHASE ACCOMPANYING REFLECTION OF LIGHT FROM THIN EVAPORATED FILMS.** SCHULZ, L. G. SCHEIBNER, E. J. J. OPT. SOC. AMER. 40 (11), 761–5, 1950.
95707	**DIELECTRIC THIN FILMS.** HEAVENS, O. S. SMITH, S. D. J. OPT. SOC. AMER. 47 (6), 469–72, 1957.
95776	**OPTICAL ABSORPTION IN A HEAVILY-DOPED SEMICONDUCTOR WITH A NARROW FORBIDDEN BAND.** FEDIRKO, V. A. FIZ. TEKH. POLUPROV. 9 (5), 1009–11, 1975. (FOR ENGLISH TRANSLATION SEE E95777)
95777	**OPTICAL ABSORPTION IN A HEAVILY-DOPED SEMI-CONDUCTOR WITH A NARROW FORBIDDEN BAND.** FEDIRKO, V. A. SOV. PHYS. SEMICOND. 9 (5), 664–5, 1975. (ENGLISH TRANSLATION OF FIZ. TEKH. POLUPROV., 9 (5), 1009–11, 1975; FOR ORIGINAL, SEE E95776)
95806	**THE OPTICAL PROPERTIES OF SINGLE CRYSTALS OF ZINC OXIDE GROWN BY THE HYDROTHERMAL METHOD.** NIKITENKO, V. A. KAZANDZHIEV, S. A. MALOV, M. M. DIMOVA-ALYAKOVA, D. I. KUZ'MINA, I. P. J. APPL. SPECTROSC., USSR 21 (2), 1084–7, 1974. (ENGLISH TRANSLATION OF ZH. PRIKL. SPEKTROSK., 21 (2), 315–9, 1974; FOR ORIGINAL, SEE E81407)

EPIC Number	Bibliographic Citation
95814	**RESISTIVITY OF LIQUID IRON - ALUMINUM ALLOYS.** LEVIN, E. S. GEL'D, P. B. AYUSHINA, G. D. SOV. PHYS. J. 15 (10), 1505–7, 1972. (ENGLISH TRANSLATION OF IZV. VYSSH. UCHEB. ZAVED., FIZ., 15 (10), 135–8, 1972; FOR ORIGINAL SEE E95056)
95834	**TEMPERATURE DEPENDENCE OF THE STATIC DIELECTRIC CONSTANT AND OF THE INFRARED DISPERSION FREQUENCY FOR SODIUM AND POTASSIUM HALIDES.** UL'YANOV, V. L. BOTAKI, A. A. SOV. PHYS. J. 17 (1), 149, 1974. (ENGLISH TRANSLATION OF IZV. VYSSH. UCHEB. ZAVED., FIZ., 17 (1), 160, 1974; FOR ORIGINAL SEE E80388) (PAPER DEPOSITID AT VINITI, REGISTRATION NO. 6471–73 DEP.)
95874	**PHOTOELASTIC PROPERTIES AND RESIDUAL STRESSES IN MAGNESIUM FLUORIDE CRYSTALS.** AFANAS'EV, I. I. ANDRIANOVA, L. K. MAMONTOV, I. YA. REITEROV, V. M. SOV. PHYS. SOLID STATE 17 (10), 2006–7, 1976. (ENGLISH TRANSLATION OF FIZ. TVERD. TELA, 17 (10), 3025–7, 1975; FOR ORIGINAL SEE E97090)
95895	**THERMOELECTRIC FIGURE OF MERIT OF LEAD TELLURIDE - TIN TELLURIDE ALLOYS.** GURIEVA, E. A. PROKOF'EVA, L. V. STIL'BANS, L. S. TAMARCHENKO, V. I. SOV. PHYS. SEMICOND. 9 (6), 809–10, 1975. (ENGLISH TRANSLATION OF FIZ. TEKH. POLUPROV., 9 (6), 1213–6, 1975; FOR ORIGINAL SEE E94942)
95896	**THERMOELECTRIC PROPERTIES OF SEMICONDUCTING MATERIALS WITH A NONSTANDARD CONDUCTION MECHANISM.** GOLIKOVA, O. A. ZAITSEV, V. K. PETROV, A. V. STIL'BANS, L. S. TKALENKO, E. N. SOV. PHYS. SEMICOND. 6 (9), 1488–91, 1973. (ENGLISH TRANSLATION OF FIZ. TEKH. POLUPROV., 6 (9), 1724–8, 1972; FOR ORIGINAL SEE E94899)
95897	**FAR-INFRARED REFLECTION SPECTRA OF BISMUTH AND BISMUTH - ANTIMONY ALLOYS.** KULAKOVSKII, V. D. ROZHDESTVENSKAYA, V. V. BELOV, A. G. VAVILOV, V. S. GIPPIUS, A. A. EGOROV, V. D. ZEMSKOV, V. S. SOV. PHYS. SEMICOND. 6 (11), 1912–3, 1973. (ENGLISH TRANSLATION OF FIZ. TEKH. POLUPROV., 6 (11), 2268–70, 1972; FOR ORIGINAL SEE E94907)
95899	**SIZE ANISOTROPY OF THE TRANSVERSE MAGNETORESISTANCE OF SEMICONDUCTOR FILMS SUBJECTED TO STRONG MAGNETIC FIELDS.** ZOT'EV, B. P. KRAVCHENKO, A. F. SKOK, E. M. YUDAEV, V. I. SOV. PHYS. SEMICOND. 6 (6), 933–6, 1972. (ENGLISH TRANSLATION OF FIZ. TEKH. POLUPROV., 6 (6), 1072–6, 1972; FOR ORIGINAL SEE E94894)
95900	**DISPERSION OF THE TEMPERATURE COEFFICIENTS OF THE BIREFRINGENCE OF CADMIUM SULFIDE AND CADMIUM SELENIDE.** REZA, A. A. BABONAS, G. A. SHILEIKA, A. YU. SOV. PHYS. SEMICOND. 9 (8), 986–8, 1976. (ENGLISH TRANSLATION OF FIZ. TEKH. POLUPROV., 9 (8), 1494–8, 1975; FOR ORIGINAL SEE E94599)
95907	**THERMIONIC EMISSION OF ALUMINUM OXIDE IN A BARIUM FLUX.** BAZANOV, V. G. BAN'KOVSKII, N. G. CHADAEVA, I. A. SOV. PHYS. TECH. PHYS. 20 (7), 967–8, 1976. (ENGLISH TRANSLATION OF ZH. TEKH. FIZ., 45 (7), 1524–6, 1975; FOR ORIGINAL SEE E95124)
95909	**A METHOD OF EXAMINING ELECTRICAL PARAMETERS AT 0.1-200 K AND PRESSURES UP TO 300 KILOBAR.** BRANDT, N. B. BERMAN, I. V. KURKIN, YU. P. SIDOROV, V. I. INSTRUM. EXP. TECH., USSR (1), 237–9, 1975. (ENGLISH TRANSLATION OF PRIB. TEKH. EKSP., (1), 204–6, 1975; FOR ORIGINAL SEE E91272)
95910	**PRECISION MEASUREMENT OF DIFFERENTIAL THERMO-ELECTROMOTIVE FORCE IN SEMECONDUCTORS.** KIRSON, YA. E. KLOTYN'SH, E. E. FELTYN', I. A. INSTRUM. EXP. TECH., USSR (1), 261–2, 1975. (ENGLISH TRANSLATION OF PRIB. TEKH. EKSP., (1), 224–5, 1975; FOR ORIGINAL SEE E91273)

EPIC Number	Bibliographic Citation
95912	**SOME SPECIAL FEATURES OF THE ACTION OF LOW-ENERGY ELECTRONS ON THE PHOTOELECTRIC PROPERTIES OF ANOMALOUS PHOTOVOLTAIC FILMS OF CADMIUM TELLURIDE.** ARIFOV, U. A. AYUKHANOV, A. KH. ABDULLAEV, N. A. ARIFDZHANOVA, M. S. SOV. PHYS. DOKL. 20 (8), 570–2, 1976. (ENGLISH TRANSLATION OF DOKL. AKAD. NAUK SSSR, 223 (5), 1102–5, 1975; FOR ORIGINAL SEE E94567)
95926	**A STUDY OF THE INTENSITIES OF THE IMPURITY VIBRATIONAL SPECTRA AT DIFFERENT CONCENTRATIONS OF NITRITE AND NITRATE IONS IN ALKALI HALIDE MATRICES.** GNATVOSKAYA, V. N. OL'KHOVICH, P. F. KHALIMONOVA, I. N. J. APPL. SPECTROSC., USSR 20 (1), 71–4, 1974. (ENGLISH TRANSLATION OF ZH. PRIKL. SPEKTROSK., 20 (1), 92–6, 1974; FOR ORIGINAL SEE E77830)
95949	**LIGHT ABSORPTION AND LUMINESCENCE CAUSED BY IMPURITIES IN SILVER HALIDE CRYSTALS.** BARSHCHEVSKII, B. U. SAFRONOV, G. M. PROC. ACAD. SCI., USSR, PHYS. CHEM. SECT. 218 (5), 964–7, 1974. (ENGLISH TRANSLATION OF DOKL. AKAD. NAUK, SSSR, 218 (5), 1124–7, 1974; FOR ORIGINAL SEE E90739)
96044	**COLOR CENTERS IN ANNEALED BARIUM CHLORIDE FLUORIDE SINGLE CRYSTALS PRODUCED BY IRRADIATION WITH X-RAYS AT LIQUID NITROGEN TEMPERATURE.** RAHMANI, M. Q. BULL. FAC. SCI., TEHRAN UNIV. 6 (3–4), 148–63, 1975.
96050	**DETERMINATION OF THE REFRACTIVE INDEX OF THE SUBSTANCE OF MONIDISPERSIVE PARTICLES FROM THE CHARACTERISTICS OF SCATTERED LIGHT.** DUDO, N. I. J. APPL. SPECTROSC., USSR 19 (5), 1492–6, 1973. (ENGLISH TRANSLATION OF ZH. PRIKL. SPEKTROSK., 19 (5), 904–10, 1973; FOR ORIGINAL SEE E70985)
96085	**THE INFRARED TRANSMISSION AND REFLECTANCE SPECTRA OF SILICON NITRIDE FILMS OBTAINED IN A HIGH-FREQUENCY DISCHARGE PLASMA.** PROKHOROV, YU. I. SOLOGUB, V. A. SUKHODAEV, B. A. J. APPL. SPECTROSC., USSR 19 (3), 1211–3, 1973. (ENGLISH TRANSLATION OF ZH. PRIKL. SPEKTROSK., 19 (3), 520–3, 1973; FOR ORIGINAL SEE E70971)
96118	**SOME PROPERTIES OF THIN EVAPORATED FILMS ON GLASS.** ROOD, J. L. J. OPT. SOC. AMER. 39 (10), 854–9, 1949.
96122	**X-RAY INVESTIGATION AND ENTROPIE RELATIONSHIPS OF THE EARTH ALKALI FLUORIDES.** THILO, F. Z. KRISTALLOGR. 65, 720–2, 1927.
96126	**POLLE-FRENKEL PHOTOVOLTAIC EFFECTS IN SPUTTERED ZINC SULFIDE.** MURRAY, G. H. TOSSER, A. J. APPL. PHYS. 8 (3), 277–9, 1975,
96147	**DIRECT AND WAVELENGTH MODULATED PHOTOCONDUCTIVITY AND PHOTOVOLTAIC EXCITATION SPECTRA OF COPPER GALLIUM DISULFIDE.** ROCHON, P. FORTIN, E. J. PHYS. COLLOQ. (3), 67–71, 1975.
96148	**P-COPPER INDIUM SELENIDE/N-CADMIUM SULDIDE HETERODIODE. PHOTOVOLTAIC DETECTOR, SOLAR CELL, AND LIGHT EMITTING DIODE.** WAGNER, S. SHAY, J. L. KASPER, H. M. J. PHYS. COLLOQ. (8), 101–4, 1975.
96170	**BULK PHOTOVOLTAIC EFFECT IN BARIUM TITANATE (IV).** KOCH, W. T. H. MUNSER, R. RUPPEL, W. WUERFEL, P. SOLID STATE COMMUN. 17(7), 847–50, 1975.
96222	**HIGH TEMPERATURE REFRACTIVE INDEX MEASUREMENT BY LASER-BEAM FOR MOLTEN SALTS IN A PRISMATIC QUARTZ CELL.** NAKAMURA, T. TANEMOTO, K. JAP. J. APPL. PHYS. 14 (12), 2089–90, 1975.
96224	**EXCITED STATE POLARIZATION, BULK PHOTOVOLTAIC EFFECT AND THE PHOTOREFRACTIVE EFFECT IN ELECTRICALLY POLARIZED MEDIA.** GLASS, A. M. VON DER LINDE, D. AUSTON, D. H. NEGRAM, T. J. J. ELECTRON. MATER. 4 (5), 915–43, 1975.

EPIC Number	Bibliographic Citation
96226	**MECHANISM FOR THE HIGH VOLTAGE PHOTOVOLTAIC EFFECT IN CERAMIC FERROELECTRICS.** BRODY, P. S. CROWNE, F. J. ELECTRON. MATER. 4 (5), 955–71, 1975.
96242	**MODULATED SPECTROSCOPY OF ZINCBLENDE SEMICONDUCTORS. CALCULATION OF PIEZOMODULATION PARAMETERS FOR INDIRECT SEMICONDUCTORS.** MATHIEU, H. AUVERGNE, D. MERLE, P. PHYS. STATUS SOLIDI 72 B (2), 609–19, 1975.
96245	**THEORY OF FREE-CARRIER ABSORPTION IN N-LEAD SELENIDE.** SZYMANSKI, J. PHYS. STATUS SOLIDI 72 B (2), 667–74, 1975.
96246	**ON EXCITON ABSORPTION, BAND STRUCTURE, AND PHASE TRANSFORMATION OF GALLIUM SELENIDE UNDER PRESSURE.** PANFILOV, V. V. SUBBOTIN, S. I. VERESHCHAGIN, L. F. IVANOV, I. I. MOLCHANOVA, R. T. PHYS. STATUS DOLIDI 72 B (2), 823–31, 1975.
96258	**CALCULATIONS OF THE ELECTRON-PHONON INTERACTION AND SUPERCONDUCTIVITY IN THE PALLADIUM - HYDROGEN SYSTEM.** KLEIN, B. M. PAPACONSTANTOPOULOS, D. A. PROC. INT. CONF. LOW TEMP. PHYS., 14TH 399–402PP., 1975.
96306	**CHANGES IN THE TRANSMISSION OF ZINC SELENIDE NEAR THE ABSORPTION EDGE UNDER THE INFLUENCE OF GAMMA = 10.6 MICRONS RADIATION PULSES.** BONCH-BRUEVICH, A. M. DOGADOV, V. V. RAIKHMAN, B. A. SMIRNOV, V. N. FIZ. TEKH. POLUPROV. 9 (2), 403–4, 1975. (FOR ENGLISH TRANSLATION SEE E96307)
96307	**CHANGES IN THE TRANSMISSION OF ZINC SELENIDE NEAR THE ABSORPTION EDGE UNDER THE INFLUENCE OF GAMMA = 10.6 MICRONS RADIATION PULSES.** BONCH-BRUEVICH, A. M. DOGADOV, V. V. RAIKHMAN, B. A. SMIRNOV, V. N. SOV. PHYS. SEMICOND. 9 (2), 269–70, 1975. (ENGLISH TRANSLATION OF FIZ. TEKH. POLUPROV., 9 (2), 403–4, 1975; FOR ORIGINAL SEE E96306)
96340	**TRANSVERSE MAGNETORESISTANCE OF THIN SEMICONDUCTOR FILMS IN HEATING ELECTRIC FIELDS.** PRIMA, N. A. FIZ. TEKH. POLUPROV. 9 (3), 543–8, 1975. (FOR ENGLISH TRANSLATION SEE E96341)
96341	**TRANSVERSE MAGNETORESISTANCE OF THIN SEMICONDUCTOR FILMS IN HEATING ELECTRIC FIELDS.** PRIMA, N. A. SOV. PHYS. SEMICOND. 9 (3), 356–8, 1975. (ENGLISH TRANSLATION OF FIZ. TEKH. POLUPROV., 9 (3), 543–8, 1975; FOR ORIGINAL SEE E96340)
96398	**ADVANCES IN BLEACHING METHODS FOR PHOTOGRAPHICALLY RECORDED HOLOGRAMS: COMMENTS.** VAN RENESSE, R. L. APPL. OPT. 14 (8), 1763–4, 1975.
96400	**ELLIPSOMETRIC METHOD FOR SEPARATE MEASUREMENTS OF N AND D OF A TRANSPARENT FILM.** YAMAGUCHI, T. TAKAHASHI, H. APPL. OPT. 14 (8), 2010–15, 1975.
96448	**PHASE-TRANSITION-LIKE ANNEALLING BEHAVIOUR OF HEAVILY IMPLANTED GALLIUM PHOSPHIDE.** SHIMADA, T. SHIRAKI, Y. KATO, Y. KOMATSUBARA, K. F. LATTICE DEFECTS IN SEMICONDUCTORS 446–52PP., 1975.
96477	**ELECTRONIC PROCESSES ON OXIDE CATHODES.** CHIN, T. N. COHEN, R. W. COUTTS, M. P. RCA REV. 35 (4), 520–38, 1974.
96486	**OPTICAL LOSSES OF EVAPORATION-DEPOSITED DIELECTRIC WAVEGUIDES.** KERSTEN, R. T. MAHLEIN, H. F. RAUSCHER, W. THIN SOLID FILMS 28 (2), 369–74, 1975.
96497	**METHODS FOR INVESTIGATING THE THERMOELECTRIC PROPERTIES OF LIQUID SEMICONDUCTORS.** GLAZOV, V. M. EVSEEV, V. A. PAVLOV, V. G. IND. LAB., USSR 32 (3), 355–67, 1966. (ENGLISH TRANSLATION OF ZAVOD. LAB., 32 (3), 290–300, 1966; FOR ORIGINAL SEE E95131)
96599	**SPECTRAL SENSITIVITY OF THE PHOTOVOLTAIC EFFECT IN CADMIUM - MERCURY - TELLURIUM P-N JUNCTIONS.** BECIA, P. DUDZIAK, E. PAWLIKOWSKI, J. M. OPT. APPL. 4 (4), 3–6, 1974.
96613	**REFRACTIVE INDICES OF CADMIUM SULPHIDE - TELLURIDE ALLOYS.** HILL, R. CASPERD, A. N. SOLID STATE COMMUN. 17 (6), 735–7, 1975.
96639	**PHOTOVOLTAGE CALCULATIONS IN SEMICONDUCTORS.** BODO, Z. TUY, T. Q. ACTA TECH. ACAD. SCI. HUNG. 80 (1–2), 205–30, 1975.
96659	**EFFECT OF HEAT TREATMENT ON THE IONIC CONDUCTION AND THE OPTICAL ABSORPTION IN SULFUR-DOPED SODIUM CHLORIDE.** BABA, M. IKEDA, T. YOSHIDA, S. JAP. J. APPL. PHYS. 14 (9), 1273–81, 1975.
96664	**PHOTOVOLTAIC EFFECT IN CADIUM SULFIDE - CADMIUM TELLURIDE JUNCTIONS.** YAMAGUCHI, K. NAKAYAMA, N. MATSUMOTO, H. HIOKI, Y. IKEGAMI, S. JAP. J. APPL. PHYS. 14 (9), 1397–8, 1975.
96691	**SUPERCONDUCTIVITY OF TANTALUM SULFIDE SELENIDE LAYER COMPOUNDS AT HIGH PRESSURE.** SMITH, T. F. SHELTON, R. N. J. PHYS. 5 F (9), 1913–25, 1975.
96701	**THE URBACH TAIL IN CUPROUS HALIDES.** TAKUBO, Y. KODA, T. J. PHYS. SOC. JAP. 39 (3), 715–19, 1975.
96710	**EXTRINSIC ABSORPTION IN LASER WINDOW MATERIALS.** DUTHLER, C. J. SPARKS, M. LASER INDUCED DAMAGE IN OPTICAL MATERIALS 219–26PP., 1974.
96723	**STRUCTURAL, ELECTRICAL, AND OPTICAL PROPERTIES OF THERMALLY EVAPORATED AMORPHOUS GERMANIUM - TELLURIUM FILMS.** NATH, P. SURI, S. K. CHOPRA, K. L. PHYS. STATUS SOLIDI 30 A (2), 771–80, 1975.
96735	**TENSOR COMPONENTS OF THE LINEAR MAGNETOCONDUCTIVITY OF WARM ELECTRONS IN MANY-VALLEY SEMICONDUCTORS.** ASCHE, M. SARBEI, O. G. PHYS. STATUS SOLIDI 71 B (1), 191–6, 1975.
96737	**LINEAR MAGNETORESISTANCE IN PARABOLIC SEMICONDUCTORS.** ARORA, V. K. PHYS. STATUS SOLIDI 71 B (1), 293–303, 1975.
96738	**ON THE THEORY OF CONDUCTIVITY OF AN ELECTRONIC GAS WITH ANISOTROPIC EFFECTIVE MASS IN QUANTIZING MAGNETIC FIELDS.** BARANSKII, P. I. DEMIDENKO, L. S. KOROLYUK, S. L. SAMOILOVICH, A. G. PHYS. STATUS SOLIDI 71 B (1), 359–67, 1975.
96773	**CRYSTAL STRUCTURE AND ELECTRICAL PROPERTIES OF THIN LAYERS OF MERCURY TELLURIDE.** SHALIMOVA, K. S. DMITRIEV, V. A. SHNITNIKOV, A. S. GULYAEV, A. M. KRISTALLOGRAFIYA 19 (6), 1239–43, 1974. (FOR ENGLISH TRANSLATION SEE E96774)
96774	**CRYSTAL STRUCTURE AND ELECTRICAL PROPERTIES OF THIN LAYERS OF MERCURY TELLURIDE.** SHALIMOVA, K. S. DMITRIEV, V. A. SHNITNIKOV, A. S. GULYAEV, A. M. SOV. PHYS. CRYSTALLOGR. 19 (6), 769–71, 1975. (ENGLISH TRANSLATION OF KRISTALLOGRAFIYA, 19 (6), 1239–43, 1974; FOR ORIGINAL SEE E96773)
96810	**ELECTRONIC SPECTRUM AND INTRINSIC ABSORPTION OF HEAVILY DOPED N-GALLIUM ARSENIDE.** LEVKOV, A. N. LOMAKIN, G. G. IZV. VYSSH. UCHEBN. ZAVED., FIZ. 18 (8), 30–5, 1975. (FOR ENGLISH TRANSLATION SEE E103608)
96816	**AN AUTOMATIC SYSTEM FOR LOW TEMPERATURE ELECTRICAL MEASUREMENTS ON SEMICONDUCTORS.** BLOOD, P. HEADON, R. F. J. PHYS. 8 E (11), 958–63, 1975.

EPIC Number	Bibliographic Citation

96822 **TEMPERATURE DEPENDENCE OF THE ELASTOOPTICAL EFFECT IN CERTAIN ALKALI HALIDE CRYSTALS.**
PAKHNEV, A. V. SHASKOL'SKAYA, M. P.
GORBACH, S. S.
KRISTALLOGRAFIYA
20 (5), 1059–61, 1975.
(FOR ENGLISH TRANSLATION SEE E99237)

96857 **EFFECTS OF HEAT TREATMENT ON THE SEEBECK COEFFICIENT OF BISMUTH(III) TELLURIDE, BISMUTH(III) SELENIDE, AND ANTIMONY(III) TELLURIDE COMPOUNDS.**
YOKOTA, K. KATAYAMA, S.
TECHNOL. REP. KANSAI UNIV.
16, 65–73, 1975.

96880 **THERMOELECTRIC EFFECTS IN SEMICONDUCTORS IN THE DRAG EFFECT RANGE. APPLICATION OF THE THEORY TO N-TYPE GERMANIUM.**
PINCHUK, I. I. KOGUTYUK, I. P.
SOV. PHYS. SEMICOND.
9 (6), 798–9, 1975.
(ENGLISH TRANSLATION OF FIZ. TEKH. POLUPROV., 9 (6), 1198–1201, 1975; FOR ORIGINAL SEE E94941)

96883 **SPATIAL DISPERSION AND ADDITIONAL LIGHT WAVES IN THE REGION OF EXCITON ABSORPTION IN CADMIUM SULFIDE.**
PEKAR, S. I. STRASHNIKOVA, M. I.
SOV. PHYS. JETP
41 (6), 1024–7, 1976.
(ENGLISH TRANSLATION OF ZH. EKSP. TEOR. FIZ., 68 (6), 2047–54, 1975; FOR ORIGINAL SEE E92860)

96888 **THE ELECTRICAL RESISTIVITY AND THERMOPOWER OF PURE AND OF HYDROGEN-CHARGED BARIUM.**
COOK, J. G. LAUBITZ, M. J.
CAN. J. PHYS.
54 (9), 928–37, 1976.

96894 **METHOD FOR CALCULATING THE INDEX OF REFRACTION OF THIN FILMS.**
WOHLGEMUTH, J. H. BRODIE, D. E.
CAN. J. PHYS.
53 (18), 1737–42, 1975.

96972 **ENERGY DISTRIBUTION OF THERMALLY STIMULATED EXOELECTRONS FROM LITHIUM FLUORIDE UNDER ULTRAHIGH VACUUM CONDITIONS.**
SAMUELSSON, L. I.
PHYS. STATUS SOLIDI
32 A (2), K155–K159, 1975.

96982 **LOW-TEMPERATURE OPTICAL PROPERTIES OF X-IRRADIATED RUBIDIUM CHLORIDE AND RUBIDIUM BROMIDE CRYSTALS.**
RIGGIN, M. RADHAKRISHNA, S. WHIPPEY, P. W.
PHYS. STATUS SOLIDI
32 A (2), 711–16, 1975.

97023 **THE ELECTRIC RESISTANCE OF COBALT AT HIGH TEMPERATURES.**
KNOTT, C. G.
PROC. ROY. SOC. EDINBURGH
18, 303–19, 1891.

97056 **OBSERVATION OF THE EXCITON STRUCTURE OF THE FUNDAMENTAL ABSORPTION EDGE OF INDIUM ARSENIDE CRYSTALS.**
VARFOLOMEEV, A. V. SEISYAN, R. P.
YAKIMOVA, R. N.
FIZ. TEKH. POLUPROV.
9 (4), 804–5, 1975.
(FOR ENGLISH TRANSLATION SEE E97057)

97057 **OBSERVATION OF THE EXCITON STRUCTURE OF THE FUNDAMENTAL ABSORPTION EDGE OF INDIUM ARSENIDE CRYSTALS.**
VARFOLOMEEV, A. V. SEISYAN, R. P.
YAKIMOVA, R. N.
SOV. PHYS. SEMICOND.
9 (4), 530, 1975.
(ENGLISH TRANSLATION OF FIZ. TEKH. POLUPROV., 9 (4), 804–5, 1975; FOR ORIGINAL SEE E97056)

97077 **THERMOELECTRIC EFFECT IN LIQUID.**
KOROTAEV, S. K. KRIVTSOV, V. A.
THERM. ENG., USSR
(4), 87–9, 1975.
(ENGLISH TRANSLATION OF TEPLOENERGETIKA, (4), 66–8, 1975; FOR ORIGINAL SEE E91000)

97090 **PHOTOELASTIC PROPERTIES AND RESIDUAL STRESSES IN MAGNESIUM FLUORIDE CRYSTALS.**
AFANAS'EV, I. I. ANDRIANOVA, L. K.
MAMONTOV, I. YA. REITEROV, V. M.
FIZ. TVERD. TELA
17 (10), 3025–7, 1975.
(FOR ENGLISH TRANSLATION SEE E95874)

97093 **METHOD OF STUDYING THE THERMO-ELECTROMOTIVE FORCE AND ELECTRICAL CONDUCTIVITY OF MELTS FOR DIRECT CURRENT AND ALTERNATING CURRENT.**
GLAZOV, V. M. AIVAZOV, A. A.
KARAGODIN, YU. A. ARSLANOV, D. E.
IND. LAB., USSR
41 (6), 867–70, 1975.
(ENGLISH TRANSLATION OF ZAVOD. LAB., 41 (6), 701–4, 1975; FOR ORIGINAL SEE E95126)

97147 **REFRACTIVE INDEX OF IRTRAN 6 (HOT-PRESSED CADMIUM TELLURIDE) AS A FUNCTION OF WAVELENGTH AND TEMPERATURE.**
HARVEY, J. E. WOLFE, W. L.
J. OPT. SOC. AM.
65 (11), 1267–8, 1975.

97173 **EFFECT OF ILLUMINATION INTENSITY ON THE REFRACTIVE INDEX IN GALLIUM SELENIDE AND GALLIUM SULFIDE.**
AKHUNDOV, G. A. MUSAEVA, L. G.
KHOMUTOVA, M. D.
OPT. SPEKTROSK.
39 (4), 700–2, 1975.
(FOR ENGLISH TRANSLATION SEE E98000)

97183 **TEMPERATURE DEPENDENCE OF PHOTEL ASTIC CONSTANTS OF CESIUM IODIDE CRYSTALS.**
KAPLAN, M. S. NAGORNAYA, L. L.
STUSHKOV, I. V. STROILOVA, D. L.
SUMIN, V. I.
FIZ. TVERD. TELA
17 (10), 3014–5, 1975.
(FOR ENGLISH TRANSLATION SEE E97184)

97184 **TEMPERATURE DEPENDENCE OF PHOTEL ASTIC CONSTANTS OF CESIUM IODIDE CRYSTALS.**
KAPLAN, M. S. NAGORNAYA, L. L.
STUSHKOV, I. V. STROILOVA, D. L.
SUMIN, V. I.
SOV. PHYS. SOLID STATE
17 (10), 19999, 1976.
(ENGLISH TRANSLATION OF FIZ. TVERD. TELA, 17 (10), 3014–5, 1975; FOR ORIGINAL SEE E97183)

97217 **SCANNING ELECTRON BEAM STUDIES OF LASER WINDOW MATERIALS.**
WITTRY, D. B.
UNIVERSITY OF SOUTHERN CALIFORNIA, LOS ANGELES
2–8, 1975.
(AD–A022 828, AFCRL–TR–75–0623)

97218 **ABSORPTION STUDIES OF CADMIUM TELLURIDE AND ZINC SELENIDE.**
SPITZER, W. G. DUTT, B. V.
UNIVERSITY OF SOUTHERN CALIFORNIA, LOS ANGELES
15–29, 1975.
(AD–A022 828, AFCRL–TR–75–0623)

97219 **STUDY OF DEFECTS IN II–VI COMPOUNDS.**
KROGER, F. A. SELIM, F. A. RAY, A.
UNIVERSITY OF SOUTHERN CALIFORNIA, LOS ANGELES
30–6, 1975.
(AD–A022 828, AFCRL–TR–75–0623)

97220 **OPTIMIZATION OF ALKALI HALIDE WINDOW MATERIALS.**
SHLICHTA, P. J. YEE, J. F. MILLER, E. A.
UNIVERSITY OF SOUTHERN CALIFORNIA, LOS ANGELES
37–54, 1975.
(AD–A022 828, AFCRL–TR–75–0623)

97221 **STRAIN OPTICAL COEFFICIENTS.**
STEIER, W. JOINER, R. CHRISTENSEN, C. P.
UNIVERSITY OF SOUTHERN CALIFORNIA, LOS ANGELES
55–7, 1975.
(AD–A022 828, AFCRL–TR–0623)

97222 **SURFACE STUDIES WITH ACOUSTIC PROBE TECHNIQUES.**
PARKS, J. H. ROCKWELL, D. A.
UNIVERSITY OF SOUTHERN CALIFORNIA, LOS ANGELES
60–9, 1975.
(AD–A022 828, AFCRL–TR–0623)

97223 **STRAIN OPTIC TENSORS FOR POLYCRYSTALLINE AGGREGATE MATERIALS.**
MARBURGER, J. FLANNERY, M.
UNIVERSITY OF SOUTHERN CALIFORNIA, LOS ANGELES
113–24, 1975.
(AD–A022 828, AFCRL–TR–0623)

97225 **CASTING OF HALIDE AND FLUORIDE ALLOYS FOR LASER WINDOWS.**
NEWBERG, R. T. PAPPIS, J.
RAYTHEON COMP., WALTHAM, MASS.
133PP., 1976.
(AD–A023 460, AFCRL–TR–76–0011)

97227 **STUDIES OF LASER DAMAGE PHENOMENA IN MATERIALS.**
MAGEE, T. J.
STANFORD RESEARCH INST., MENLO PARK, CALIF.
72PP., 1976.
(AD–A023 269, AFOSR–TR–76–0157)

97230 **LASER WINDOW SURFACE FINISHING AND COATING SCIENCE.**
BRAUNNSTEIN, M. ALLEN, S. D.
BRAUNSTEIN, A. I. GIULIANO, C. R.
RUDISILL, J. E.
HUGHES RESEARCH LABS., MALIBU, CALIF.
41PP., 1976.
(AD–A022 684, AFCRL–TR–76–0048)

97231 **OPTICAL MATERIALS CHARACTERIZATION.**
FELDMAN, A. HOROWITZ, D. WAXLER, R. M.
NATIONAL BUREAU OF STANDARDS, WASHINGTON, D. C.
27PP., 1976.
(NBSIR–76–1010, AD–A022 027, N76–30065)

EPIC Number	Bibliographic Citation

97244 **THERMOELECTRIC GENERATOR EFFICIENCY.**
SAMPSON, R. L.
INTERN. HEAT TRANSFER CONF.
86–92, 1961.

97245 **AN EXACT METHOD FOR DETERMINING THE THEORETICAL PERFORMANCE OF A THERMOELECTRIC GENERATOR WHEN MATERIAL PROPERTIES ARE ARBITRARY FUNCTIONS OF TEMPERATURE.**
KERR, D. L.
INTERN. HEAT TRANSFER CONF.
93–103, 1961.

97249 **OPTICAL PROPERTIES AND BAND STRUCTURE OF GERMANIUM AND ZINC BLENDE-TYPE SEMICONDUCTORS.**
CARDONA, M.
PROC. INT. SCH. PHYS. 'ENRICO FERMI'
52, 514–80, 1972.

97255 **II–VI MATERIALS IN SOLAR ENERGY CONVERSION.**
FAHRENBRUCH, A. L.
PROC. SYMP. MATER. SCI. ASPECTS THIN FILM SYST. SOL. ENERGY CONVERS.
384–401, 1974.
(PB–239 270)

97296 **GROWTH OF LOW LOSS POTASSIUM BROMIDE IN HALIDE ATMOSPHERES.**
KLEIN, P. H.
NAVAL RESEARCH LABS., WASHINGTON, D. C.
3–10, 1976.
(AD–A024 018, NRL–MR–3266)

97297 **CHEMICAL POLISHING OF POTASSIUM BROMIDE AND ABSORPTION MEASUREMENTS AT 1.06 MICRONS.**
DAVISSON, J. W.
NAVAL RESEARCH LABS., WASHINGTON, D. C.
11–8, 1976.
(AD–A024 018, NRL–MR–3266)

97298 **INFRARED BULK AND SURFACE ABSORPTION BY NEARLY TRANSPARENT CRYSTALS.**
ROSENSTOCK, H. B. GREGORY, D. A.
HARRINGTON, J. A.
NAVAL RESEARCH LABS., WASHINGTON, D. C.
19–32, 1976.
(AD–A–24 018, NRL–MR–3266)

97311 **STORAGE CAMERA TUBE WITH NON-DESTRUCTIVE READOUT.**
YAGGY, L. S.
HUGHES AIRCRAFT CO., CARLSBAD, CALIF.
14PP., 1976.
(AD–A024 280, ECOM–75–1305–2)

97315 **APPLIED RESEARCH ON II–VI COMPOUND MATERIALS FOR HETEROJUNCTION SOLAR CELLS.**
BUBE, R. H. FAHRENBRUCH, A. ARANOVICH, J.
BUCH, F. CHU, M. MITCHELL, K.
STANFORD UNIVERSITY, CALIFORNIA
60PP., 1976.
(N76–32687, PB–252893)

97322 **TERNARY COMPOUND THIN FILM SOLAR CELLS.**
KAZMERSKI, L. L.
DEPT. OF ELECTRICAL ENGR., MAINE UNIV., ORONO
62PP., 1975.
(N76–32689, PB–252 923/8, NSF/RA/N–75–232, NSF/RANN/SE/AER75–19576/PR–75)

97348 **LASER WINDOW MATERIALS – AN OVERVIEW.**
DEUTSCH, T. F.
J. ELECTRON. MATER.
4 (4), 663–719, 1975.

97414 **TWO-PHOTON ABSORPTION IN THE VICINITY OF THE EXCITON ABSORPTION IN CADMIUM SULFIDE.**
SVOREC, R. W. CHASE, L. L.
SOLID STATE COMMUN.
17 (7), 803–6, 1975.

97464 **PROFILES OF ABSORPTION AND LUMINESCENCE SPECTRA OF DEEP CENTERS IN SEMICONDUCTORS (OXYGEN IN GALLIUM PHOSPHIDE).**
KOPYLOV, A. A. PIKHTIN, A. N.
FIZ. TEKH. POLUPROV.
8 (12), 2398–2404, 1974.
(FOR ENGLISH TRANSLATION SEE E97465)

97465 **PROFILES OF ABSORPTION AND LUMINESCENCE SPECTRA OF DEEP CENTERS IN SEMICONDUCTORS (OXYGEN IN GALLIUM PHOSPHIDE).**
KOPYLOV, A. A. PIKHTIN, A. N.
SOV. PHYS. SEMICOND.
8 (12), 1563–6, 1975.
(ENGLISH TRANSLATION OF FIZ. TEKH. POLUPROV., 8 (12), 2398–2404, 1974; FOR ORIGINAL SEE E97464)

97468 **STRUCTURE OF THE VALENCE BAND OF P-TYPE LEAD TIN SELENIDE.**
VOLKOV, B. A. KUCHERENKO, I. V.
TAKTAKISHVILI, M. S. SHOTOV, A. P.
FIZ. TEKH. POLUPROV.
8 (12), 2346–9, 1974.
(FOR ENGLISH TRANSLATION SEE E97469)

97469 **STRUCTURE OF THE VALENCE BAND OF P-TYPE LEAD TIN SELENIDE.**
VOLKOV, B. A. KUCHERENKO, I. V.
TAKTAKISHVILI, M. S. SHOTOV, A. P.
SOV. PHYS. SEMICOND.
8 (12), 1530–1, 1975.
(ENGLISH TRANSLATION OF FIZ. TEKH. POLUPROV., 8 (12), 2346–9, 1974; FOR ORIGINAL SEE E97468)

97477 **PREPARATION AND INVESTIGATION OF THE EMISSION PROPERTIES OF MATERIAL BASED ON CESIUM ALUMINOSILICATE.**
SHKUL'TETSKAYA, D. V. DANILKAN, V. I.
IZV. AKAD. NAUK SSSR, NEORG. MATER.
10 (8), 1515–7, 1974.
(FOR ENGLISH TRANSLATION SEE E97478)

97478 **PREPARATION AND INVESTIGATION OF THE EMISSION PROPERTIES OF MATERIAL BASED ON CESIUM ALUMINOSILICATE.**
SKKUL'TETSKAYA, L. V. DANILKIN, V. I.
INORG. MAT., USSR
10 (8), 1305–7, 1974.
(ENGLISH TRANSLATION OF IZV. AKAD. NAUK SSSR, NEORG. MATER., 10 (8), 1515–7, 1974; FOR ORIGINAL SEE E97477)

97481 **PHASE DIAGRAM OF THE SYSTEM LEAD SELENIDE – TIN TELLURIDE.**
ABRIKOSOV, N. KH. GONCHAROVA, L. S.
IZV. AKAD. NAUK SSSR, NEORG. MATER.
10 (8), 1533–4, 1974.
(FOR ENGLISH TRANSLATION SEE E97482)

97482 **PHASE DIAGRAM OF THE SYSTEM LEAD SELENIDE – TIN TELLURIDE.**
ABRIKOSOV, N. KH. GONCHAROVA, L. S.
INORG. MAT., USSR
10 (8), 1321–2, 1974.
(ENGLISH TRANSLATION OF IZV. AKAD. NAUK SSSR, NEORG. MATER., 10 (8), 1533–4, 1974; FOR ORIGINAL SEE E97481)

97511 **STRESS-OPTIC COEFFICIENTS OF ZINC SELENIDE.**
GOLDSTEIN, L. F. THOMPSON, J. S.
SCHROEDER, J. B. SLATTERY, J. E.
APPL. OPT.
14 (10), 2432–4, 1975.

97520 **ON AN INCORRECT FORM OF HIGHER-ORDER CORRECTIONS TO THE LOWEST-ORDER THEORY OF THE DIRECT CURRENT HOPPING CONDUCTIVITY.**
CAPEK, V.
CZECH. J. PHYS.
25 B (6), 715–17, 1975.

97574 **LOCAL AND BAND CHARACTERS OF STRONGLY CORRELATED ELECTRONS.**
KAWABATA, A.
PROG. THEOR. PHYS.
54 (1), 45–59, 1975.

97579 **A NEW INTERPRETATION OF THE FUNDAMENTAL EXCITON REGION IN LITHIUM FLUORIDE.**
PIACENTINI, M.
SOLID STATE COMMUN.
17 (6), 697–700, 1975.

97638 **APPLICATION OF DISPERSION RELATIONS FOR THE DETERMINATION OF OPTICAL CONSTANTS OF SEMICONDUCTING LAYERS USING TRANSMISSION.**
MILOSLAVSKII, V. K. NABOIKINA, E. N.
OPT. SPEKTROSK.
38 (5), 983–7, 1975.
(FOR ENGLISH TRANSLATION SEE E97639)

97639 **APPLICATION OF DISPERSION RELATIONS FOR THE DETERMINATION OF OPTICAL CONSTANTS OF SEMICONDUCTING LAYERS USING TRANSMISSION.**
MILOSLAVSKII, V. K. NABOIKINA, E. N.
OPT. SPECTROS., USSR
38 (5), 565–7, 1975.
(ENGLISH TRANSLATION OF OPT. SPEKTROSK., 38 (5), 983–7, 1975; FOR ORIGINAL SEE E97638)

97658 **THERMAL CONDUCTIVITY (80–300K) OF PSUDOBINARY SOLID SOLUTIONS BASED ON N-TYPE LEAD TELLURIDE.**
ALEKSEEVA, G. T. EFIMOVA, B. A.
LOGACHEV, YU. A.
FIZ. TEKH. POLUPROV.
9 (1), 128–30, 1975.
(FOR ENGLISH TRANSLATION SEE E97659)

97659 **THERMAL CONDUCTIVITY (80–300K) OF PSUDOBINARY SOLID SOLUTIONS BASED ON N-TYPE LEAD TELLURIDE.**
ALEKSEEVA, G. T. EFIMOVA, B. A.
LOGACHEV, YU. A.
SOV. PHYS. SEMICOND.
9 (1), 83–4, 1975.
(ENGLISH TRANSLATION OF FIZ. TEKH. POLUPROV., 9 (1), 128–30, 1975; FOR ORIGINAL SEE E97658)

EPIC Number	Bibliographic Citation

97671 **PROPERTIES OF P–N JUNCTION FORMED IN N–TYPE CADMIUM SULFIDE BY IMPLANTATION OF ANTIMONY IONS.**
AKIMCHENKO, I. P. VAVILOV, V. S.
KRASNOPEVTSEV, V. V. MILYUTIN, YU. V.
HARSY, M. LOI, C. K.
FIZ. TEKH. POLUPROV.
9 (1), 32–5, 1975.
(FOR ENGLISH TRANSLATION SEE E97672)

97672 **PROPERTIES OF P–N JUNCTION FORMED IN N–TYPE CADMIUM SULFIDE BY IMPLANTATION OF ANTIMONY IONS.**
AKIMCHENKO, I. P. VAVILOV, V. S.
KRASNOPEVTSEV, V. V. MILYUTIN, YU. V.
HARSEY, M. LOI, C. K.
SOV. PHYS. SEMICOND.
9 (1), 19–21, 1975.
(ENGLISH TRANSLATION OF FIZ. TEKH. POLUPROV., 9 (1), 32–5, 1975; FOR ORIGINAL SEE E97671)

97730 **THE OPTICAL AND ELECTRICAL EFFECTS OF HIGH CONCENTRATIONS OF DEFECTS IN IRRADIATED CRYSTALLINE GALLIUM ARSENIDE.**
COATES, R. MITCHELL, E. W. J.
ADV. PHYS.
24 (5), 593–644, 1975.

97743 **PIEZO–OPTICAL CONSTANTS IN THE INFRARED.**
FELDMAN, A. HOROWITZ, D. WAXLER, R.
PROC. CONF. INFRARED LASER WINDOW MATERIALS, 5TH
943–51, 1976.
(AFML–TR–76–83, AD–B014 718, UDRI–76–35, PB–253540, N76–33981)

97799 **NATURAL BIREFRINGENCE IN CRYSTALS.**
SWAMIMUTHU, T. RAO, K. V. RAMANAIAH, K. V.
TECHNOLOGY (COIMBATORE, INDIA)
23, 78–81, 1975.

97860 **ELECTRONIC PROPERTIES OF CLEAVED GALLIUM ARSENIDE (110) SURFACES COVERED WITH CESIUM.**
CLEMENS, H. MOENCH, W.
CRC CRIT. REV. SOLID STATE SCI.
5 (3), 273–80, 1975.

97891 **PREPARATION AND PROPERTIES OF FUSED SILICA CONTAINING ALUMINA.**
NASSAU, K. SHIEVER, J. W. KRAUSE, J. T.
J. AM. CERAM. SOC.
58 (9–10), 461, 1975.

97924 **THE NIOBIUM – ALUMINUM – IRIDIUM TENARY SYSTEM. I. PHASE EQUILIBRIA AT 1100 C AND SUPERCONDUCTIVITY OF ALLOYS.**
HORYN, R.
J. LESS–COMMON MET.
44, 221–7PP., 1976.

97925 **THE NIBIUM – ALUMINIUM – GALLIUM SYSTEM. II. SUPERCONDUCTING TRANSITION TEMPERATURES.**
DRYS, M. ILIEW, N.
J. LESS–COMMON MET.
44, 235–8, 1976.

97963 **MODEL CALCULATIONS ON THE INFLUENCE OF DANGLING BONDS ON THE OPTICAL PROPERTIES OF AMORPHOUS SILICON FILMS.**
SCHWIDEFSKY, F.
THIN SOLID FILMS
30 (2), 233–44, 1975.

97977 **INFORMATION RETRIEVAL PROGRAM ELECTRONIC/ELECTRICAL PROPERTIES OF MATERIALS.**
HUGHES AIRCRAFT COMPANY
HUGHES AIRCRAFT COMPANY, CULVER CITY, CA.
97PP., 1962.
(AD–275 439)

97982 **THERMOPHYSICAL PROPERTIES OF HIGH TEMPERATURE SOLID MATERIALS. VOLUME 4: OXIDES AND THEIR SOLUTIONS AND MIXTURES. PART I: SIMPLE OXYGEN COMPOUNDS AND THEIR MIXTURES.**
TOULOUKIAN, Y. S.
THERMOPHYSICAL PROPERTIES RESEARCH CENTER, PURDUE UNIVERSITY
4 (PT. I), 973PP., 1967.

97983 **THERMOPHYSICAL PROPERTIES OF HIGH TEMPERATURE SOLID MATERIALS. VOLUME 4: OXIDES AND THEIR SOLUTIONS AND MIXTURES. PART II: SOLUTIONS AND THEIR MIXTURES OF SIMPLE OXYGEN COMPOUNDS, INCLUDING GLASSES AND CERAMIC GLASSES.**
TOULOUKIAN, Y. S.
THERMOPHYSICAL PROPERTIES RESEARCH CENTER, PURDUE UNIVERSITY
4 (PT. II), 1877PP., 1967.

97984 **THERMOPHYSICAL PROPERTIES OF HIGH TEMPERATURE SOLID MATERIALS. VOLUME 5: NONOXIDES AND THEIR SOLUTIONS AND MIXTURES, INCLUDING MISCELLANEOUS CERAMIC MATERIALS.**
TOULOUKIAN, Y. S.
THERMOPHYSICAL PROPERTIES RESEARCH CENTER, PURDUE UNIVERSITY
5, 1060PP., 1967.

97985 **THERMOPHYSICAL PROPERTIES OF HIGH TEMPERATURE SOLID MATERIALS. VOLUME 6: INTERMETALLICS, CERMETS, POLYMERS, AND COMPOSITE SYSTEMS. PART I: INTERMETALLICS.**
TOULOUKIAN, Y. S.
THERMOPHYSICAL PROPERTIES RESEARCH CENTER, PURDUE UNIVERSITY
6 (PT. I), 726PP., 1967.

98000 **DEPENDENCE OF THE REFRACTIVE INDEX OF GALLIUM SELENIDE AND GALLIUM SULFIDE ON THE ILLUMINATION INTENSITY.**
AKHUNDOV, G. A. MUSAEVA, L. G.
KHOMUTOVA, M. D.
OPT. SPECTROS., USSR
39 (4), 395–6, 1975.
(ENGLISH TRANSLATION OF OPT. SPEKTROSK., 39 (4), 700–2, 1975; FOR ORIGINAL SEE E97173)

98002 **ELECTRICAL AND ELECTRONIC PROPERTIES OF MATERIALS INFORMATION RETRIEVAL PROGRAM.**
JOHNSON, H. T. SCHAFER, E. WALLACE, E. M.
AIR FORCE SYSTEMS COMMAND, WPAFB, OHIO
219PP., 1963.
(ASD–TDR–62–539)

98023 **PROPERTIES OF SILICON NITRIDE FILMS.**
VOROB'EV, G. A. DANILINA, T. I.
KRIVOSHCHEKOV, V. P. SMIRNOVA, K. I.
SHANDRA, Z. A.
IZV. AKAD. NAUK SSSR, NEORG. MATER.
10 (11), 1972–5, 1974.
(FOR ENGLISH TRANSLATION SEE E98024)

98024 **PROPERTIES OF SILICON NITRIDE FILMS.**
VOROB'EV, G. A. DANILINA, T. I.
KRIVOSHCHEKOV, V. P. SMIRNOVA, K. I.
SHANDRA, Z. A.
INORG. MAT., USSR
10 (11), 1690–3, 1974.
(ENGLISH TRANSLATION OF IZV. AKAD. NAUK SSSR, NEORG. MATER., 10 (11), 1972–5, 1974; FOR ORIGINAL SEE E98023)

98033 **METHOD OF DETERMINATION OF THE DISPERSION OF THE WAVE PATH DIFFERENCE OF DOUBLE–BEAM–REFRACTING CRYSTALS FOR INTERFERENCE–POLARIZATION FILTERS.**
IOFFE, S. B. VINOGRADOVA, T. A.
OPT. MEKH. PROM.
42 (3), 52–4, 1975.
(FOR ENGLISH TRANSLATION SEE E98034)

98034 **METHOD OF DETERMINATION OF THE DISPERSION OF THE WAVE PATH DIFFERENCE OF DOUBLE–BEAM–REFRACTING CRYSTALS FOR INTERFERENCE–POLARIZATION FILTERS.**
IOFFE, S. B. VINOGRADOVA, T. A.
SOV. J. OPT. TECHNOL.
42 (3), 167–9, 1975.
(ENGLISH TRANSLATION OF OPT MEKH. PROM., 42 (3), 52–4, 1975; FOR ORIGINAL SEE E98033)

98067 **ABSORPTION OF THIN FILM MATERIALS AT 10.6 MICROMETER.**
GIBBS, W. E. K. BUTTERFIELD, A. W.
APPL. OPT.
14 (12), 3043–6, 1975.

98079 **DETERMINATION OF THE THERMOELECTRIC POWER COEFFICIENT AT CONSTANT CHEMICAL COMPOSITION IN NONSTOICHLOMETRIC OXIDES.**
CARPENTIER, J. L. OEHLIG, J. J.
DUQUESNOY, A.
C. R. HEBD. SEANCES ACAD. SCI.
281 C (10), 287–90, 1975.

98084 **FIGURE OF MERIT DETERMINATION OF THERMO–ELECTRIC MODULES.**
HEYLEN, A. E. D.
ENERGY CONVERS.
15 (1–2), 65–70, 1975.

98087 **AN ALTERNATING CURRENT DIVICE WITH HIGH ACCURACY FOR THE MEASUREMENT OF LOW ELECTRICAL RESISTANCES.**
GRUN, R.
EXP. TECH. PHYS.
23 (5), 539–41, 1975.

98108 **PHOTOVOLTAIC EFFECT OF GALLIUM SELENIDE – SELENIUM – TIN (IV) OXIDE HETEROSTRUCTURE.**
NANG, T. T. MATSUSHITA, T.
YOKOTA, S. SUZUKI, A.
JAP. J. APPL. PHYS.
15 (2), 383–4, 1976.

98151 **PHYSICAL PROPERTIES OF METALS AND ALLOYS.**
LIVSHITS, B. G.
FIZICHESKIYE SVOISTVA METALLOV I SPLAVOV
368PP., 1959.

98207 **ELECTRICAL TRANSPORT IN THE SPACE–CHARGE REGION.**
MANY, A.
SURFACE SCIENCE
447–500, 1974.

EPIC Number | Bibliographic Citation

98250 **EXPERIMENTAL APPARATUS FOR DETERMINATION OF REFRACTION INDEX IN GASEOUS AND LIQUID PHASES.**
TIMOSHENKO, N. I. KOBELEV, V. P.
KHOLODOV, E. P.
DOKL. NAUCH. TEKH. KONF. PO ITOGAM NAUCHN. ISSLED. RABOT ZA.
102–7, 1969.

98278 **DETERMINATION OF REFRACTIVE INDEX BY DISPERSION STAINING.**
MCCRONE, W. C.
MICROSCOPE
23 (4), 213–20, 1975.

98283 **PHOTOELASTIC BEHAVIOR OF ALKALI HALIDES AND GLASSES.**
KRISHNAN, R. S. VASUDEVAN, T. N.
NARAYANAN, P. S.
PROC. NUCL. PHYS. SOLID STATE PHYS. SYMP.
17 C, 198–200, 1974.

98289 **INFLUENCE OF FREE CARRIERS ON THE EXCITON ABSORPTION OF LIGHT IN SEMICONDUCTORS.**
KHADZHI, P. I.
FIZ. TEKH. POLUPROV.
9 (11), 2156–60, 1975.
(FOR ENGLISH TRANSLATION SEE E99570)

98390 **SOLUTIONS OF METALS IN MOLTEN SALTS.**
NACHTRIEB, N. H.
NON-SIMPLE LIQUIDS
31, 465–80PP., 1975.

98408 **THE EFFECT OF ILLUMINATION ON THE 10.6 MICROMETERS ABSORPTION COEFFICIENT OF ELECTRON-IRRADIATED SINGLE CRYSTAL POTASSIUM CHLORIDE.**
MAGEE, T. J. JOHNSON, N. M. PENG, J.
PHYS. STATUS SOLIDI
33 A (1), 415–19, 1976.
(AD-A037 163)

98423 **THE LONGITUDINAL MAGNETOPHONON EFFECT IN SEMICONDUCTORS CONTAINING MAGNETIC IMPURITIES.**
HOSSUT, J. WALUKIEWICZ, W.
SOLID STATE COMMUN.
18 (3), 343–5, 1976.

98555 **INFORMAL PROGRESS REPORT. GENERAL ELECTRIC COMPANY, HANFORD LABORATORIES.**
BATES, J. L. BAKER, D. E. HINMAN, C. A.
THERMAL CONDUCTIVITY CONFERENCE, 4TH
VIII-G-1–VIII-G-4, 1964.

98632 **MOLTEN SALTS: VOLUME 1, ELECTRICAL CONDUCTANCE, DENSITY, AND VISCOSITY DATA.**
JANZ, G. J. DAMPIER, F. W.
LAKSHMINARAYANAN, G. R. LORENZ, P. K.
TOMKINS, R. P. T.
NATIONAL STANDARD REFERENCE DATA SERIES
139 PP., 1968.
(NSRDS-NBS-15)

98639 **HIGH POWER INFRARED LASER WINDOWS.**
AD HOC COMMITTEE
NATIONAL MATERIALS ADVISORY BOARD, NATIONAL RESEARCH COUNCIL
168PP., 1972.
(NMAB-292)

98644 **THERMAL CONDUCTIVITY OF URANIUM DIOXIDE AT HIGH TEMPERATURES.**
BATES, J. L.
THERMAL CONDUCTIVITY CONFERENCE, 2ND
189–200, 1962.

98647 **SOME 'STANDARD' SPECIMENS FOR HIGH TEMPERATURE THERMAL CONDUCTIVITY APPARATUSES.**
PEAR, C. D.
THERMAL CONDUCTIVITY CONFERENCE, 2ND
342–76, 1962.

98648 **THERMAL CONDUCTIVITY OF III–V COMPOUNDS AT HIGH TEMPERATURES.**
STEIGMEIER, E. F. KUDMAN, I.
THERMAL CONDUCTIVITY CONFERENCE, 3RD
1,44–56, 1963.

98655 **EXPERIMENTS ON THE THERMAL CONDUCTIVITY OF URANIUM DIOXIDE AT HANFORD LABORATORIES.**
BATES, J. L. DE HALAS, D. R.
MCPARTLAND, J. O. MONTGOMERY, M. H.
CHRISTENSEN, J. A.
THERMAL CONDUCTIVITY CONFERENCE, 3RD
1, 410–22, 1963.

98656 **PROGRESS REPORT ON THERMAL CONDUCTIVITY AT ARGONNE NATIONAL LABORATORY.**
DUNWORTH, R. J.
THERMAL CONDUCTIVITY CONFERENCE, 3RD
1, 480–2, 1963.

98662 **THE METALLURGY OF ZIRCONIUM.**
LUSTMAN, B. KERZE, F., JR.
MCGRAW HILL BOOK COMPANY
776PP., 1955.

98663 **PHYSICAL PROPERTIES AND ANALYSIS OF HEAVY WATER.**
KIRSHENBAUM, I.
MCGRAW HILL BOOK COMPANY
(1ST EDITION), 438PP., 1951.

98664 **HANDBOOK OF CHEMISTRY.**
LANGE, N. A.
MCGRAW HILL BOOK COMPANY
(10TH EDITION), 2001PP., 1967.

98671 **FAR INFRARED ABSORPTION IN HYDROXIDE DOPED SODIUM CHLORIDE: BELOW 1 K.**
KIRBY, R. D. HUGHES, A. E. SIEVERS, A. J.
PROC. INT. CONF. LOW TEMP. PHYS., 11TH
1, 558–62, 1968.

98747 **ATLAS OF THE ABSORPTION SPECTRUM OF NITRIC OXIDE BETWEEN 1420 AND 1250 A.**
MIESCHER, E. ALBERTI, F.
J. PHYS. CHEM. REF. DATA
5 (2), 309–17, 1976.

98762 **THE LATTICE THERMAL CONDUCTIVITY OF BISMUTH TELLURIDE AND SOME BISMUTH TELLURIDE - BISMUTH SELENIDE ALLOYS.**
DAMON, D. H. URE, R. W., JR. GERSI, J.
THERMAL CONDUCTIVITY CONFERENCE, 7TH
111–22, 1968.
(NBS-SP-302)

98783 **PRESSURE DEPENDENCE OF THE CURIE TEMPERATURE IN TRANSITION METAL COMPOUNDS AND ALLOYS.**
BARTEL, L. C. EDWARDS, L. R. SAMARA, G. A.
AIP (AMER. INST. PHYS.) CONF. PROC.
(5) (PT. 1), 482–6, 1972.

98834 **ELECTRONIC PROPERTIES.**
HODBY, J. W.
CRYST. FLUORITE STRUCT.
1–42, 1974.

98850 **DIELECTRIC FOR AEROSPACE APPLICATIONS.**
WITTEBORT, J. I.
AIR FORCE MATERIALS SYMPOSIUM
585–98, 1965.
(AFML-TR-65-29)

98851 **SUPERCONDUCTING MATERIALS.**
EVANS, D. J.
AIR FORCE MATERIALS SYMPOSIUM
599–610, 1965.
(AFML-TR-65-29)

98852 **SEMICONDUCTOR MATERIALS.**
CORNELISSEN, R.
AIR FORCE MATERIALS SYMPOSIUM
611–34, 1965.
(AFML-TR-65-29)

98858 **DEVELOPMENT OF HIGH TEMPERATURE THERMAL CONDUCTIVITY STANDARDS.**
WECHSLER, A. E.
AIR FORCE MATERIALS LABORATORY, WPAFB, OHIO
186PP., 1969.
(AFML-TR-69-2)

98864 **PRELIMINARY STUDIES TOWARD THE DETERMINATION OF SPECTRAL ABSORPTION COEFFICIENTS OF HOMOGENEOUS DIELECTRIC MATERIALS IN THE INFRARED AT ELEVATED TEMPERATURES.**
FUSSELL, W. STAIR, R.
SYMPOSIUM ON THERMAL RADIATION OF SOLIDS
287–92, 1964.
(AD-629 980)

98865 **API TABLES.**
THERMODYNAMIC RESEARCH CENTER.
TEXAS A AND M UNIVERSITY, COLLEGE STATION, TEXAS
1-PP., 1973.

98883 **THE STATIC DIELECTRIC CONSTANT OF ALKALI HALIDES AT LOW TEMPERATURES.**
ROBINSON, M. C. HOLLIS HALLETT, A. C.
PROC. INT. CONF. LOW TEMP. PHYS., 9TH
(PART B), 1162–4, 1965.

98888 **SELECTION OF MATERIALS.**
SMITH, J. M.
HIGH TEMPERATURE MATERIALS AND TECHNOLOGY
131–51, 1967.

98889 **OXIDE CERAMICS.**
BRADSTREET, S. W.
HIGH TEMPERATURE MATERIALS AND TECHNOLOGY
235-303, 1967.

98890 **COMMERCIAL OXIDE REFRACTORIES.**
SHEETS, H. D. SULLIVAN, J. D.
HIGH TEMPERATURE MATERIALS AND TECHNOLOGY
304–11, 1967.

98891 **CARBIDES FOR HIGH TEMPERATURE APPLICATIONS.**
WESTBROOK, J. H. STOVER, E. R.
HIGH TEMPERATURE MATERIALS AND TECHNOLOGY
312–48, 1967.

EPIC Number	Bibliographic Citation

98892 **BORIDES.**
POWELL, C. F.
HIGH TEMPERATURE MATERIALS AND TECHNOLOGY
349–78, 1967.

98893 **NITRIDES.**
BLOCHER, J. M., JR.
HIGH TEMPERATURE MATERIALS AND TECHNOLOGY
379–98, 1967.

98894 **SILICIDES.**
WEHRMANN, R.
HIGH TEMPERATURE MATERIALS AND TECHNOLOGY
399–430, 1967.

98895 **SULFIDES.**
LITZ, L. M. BLOCHER, J. M., JR.
HIGH TEMPERATURE MATERIALS AND TECHNOLOGY
431–54, 1967.

98897 **REFRACTORY COATINGS.**
BRADSTREET, S. W.
HIGH TEMPERATURE MATERIALS AND TECHNOLOGY
512–25, 1967.

98900 **BERYLLIA.**
LONG, R. E. SCHOFIELD, H. Z.
REACTOR HANDBOOK: MATERIALS
4, 41–53, 1955.

98902 **BERYLLIUM CARBIDE.**
QUIRK, J. F.
REACTOR HANDBOOK: MATERIALS
4, 95–106, 1955.

98904 **CARBIDES.**
MALLETT, M. W. SHEIPLINE, V. M.
REACTOR HANDBOOK: MATERIALS
4, 113–22, 1955.

98912 **SILICON CARBIDES.**
HARMAN, C. G.
REACTOR HANDBOOK: MATERIALS
4, 255–62, 1955.

99011 **OPTICAL PARAMETERS OF PARTIALLY TRANSMITTING THIN FILMS. 2: EXPERIMENT AND FURTHER ANALYSIS OF A NOVEL METHOD FOR THEIR DETERMINATION.**
SHAMIR, J.
APPL. OPT.
15 (1), 120–6, 1976.

99063 **MAGNETORESISTANCE OF INHOMOGENEOUS SEMICONDUCTORS. II.**
SHIK, A. YA.
FIZ. TEKH. POLUPROV.
9 (6), 1152–4, 1975.
(FOR ENGLISH TRANSLATION SEE E99064)

99064 **MAGNETORESISTANCE OF INHOMOGENEOUS SEMICONDUCTORS. II.**
SHIK, A. YA.
SOV. PHYS. SEMICOND.
9 (6), 761–2, 1975.
(ENGLISH TRANSLATION OF FIZ. TEKH. POLUPROV., 9 (6), 1152–4, 1975; FOR ORIGINAL SEE E99063)

99100 **AERODYNAMICALLY HEATED THERMOELECTRIC CONVERTORS FOR POWERING PROXIMITY FUZES IN 20–MILLIMETER AND 30–MILLIMETER PROJECTILES.**
EGGERS, P. E. GAWTHROP, W. E. HOWARD, J. M.
REC. INTERSOC. ENERGY CONVERS. ENG. CONF., 10TH
736–49, 1975.

99118 **MULTIPHONON INFRARED ABSORPTION IN THE TRANSPARENT REGIME OF ALKALINE–EARTH FLUORIDES.**
LIPSON, H. G. BENDOW, B. MASSA, N. E.
MITRA, S. S.
PHYS. REV.
13 B (6), 2614–9, 1976.
(AD–B013 807L)

99119 **OPTICAL ABSORPTION OF SODIUM FLUORIDE SINGLE CRYSTALS IN THE VUV REGION.**
FOLDVARI, I. VOSZKA, R. RAKSANYI, K.
PHYS. STATUS SOLIDI
26 A, K83–K85, 1974.

99127 **STUDY OF THE FUNDAMENTAL ABSORPTION EDGE OF A SEMICONDUCTOR USING A PHOTOCAPACITY CURRENT.**
MISHCHENKO, A. M. NEIZVESTNYI, I. G.
OVSYUK, V. N. SINYUKOV, M. P.
FIZ. TEKH. POLUPROVODN.
10 (1), 10–14, 1976.
(FOR ENGLISH TRANSLATION SEE E99855)

99137 **THE INFLUENCE OF HIGH ENERGY ELECTRON IRRADIATION ON THE 10.5 MICRON ABSORPTION OF MIXED POTASSIUM CHLORIDE CRYSTALS.**
MAGEE, T. J. JOHNSON, N. PENG, J.
PHYSICA STATUS SOLIDI
30 A, 81–, 1975.
(AD–A023 269, AFSOR–TR–76–0157, AD–A037 163)

99140 **THE QUANTUM MECHANICAL EXTENSION OF THE BOLTZMANN TRANSPORT EQUATION AND OPTICAL ABSORPTION IN SEMICONDUCTORS.**
JENSEN, B.
ANN. PHYS.
95 (2), 229–66, 1975.

99141 **REFRACTIVE INDEX INTERPOLATION IN PHASE–MATCHING.**
BHAR, G. C.
APPL. OPT.
15 (2), 305–7, 1976.

99154 **OPTICAL AND ELECTRICAL PROPERTIES OF SELENIUM.**
STUKE, J.
SELENIUM
174–297, 1974.

99156 **REVIEW OF ELECTRICAL AND THERMAL PROPERTIES OF CARBON AND GRAPHITE.**
WOOLLAM, J. A.
ACS SYMP SER.
21, 378–410, 1975.

99169 **APPARATUS FOR THE MEASUREMENT OF OPTICAL ABSORPTION AT 10.6 MICROMETERS.**
BOIS, D.
REV. PHYS. APPL.
11 (2), 293–8, 1976.

99175 **POINT DEFECTS, LOCALIZED VIBRATIONAL MODES, AND FREE–CARRIER ABSORPTION OF ALUMINUM–DOPED CADMIUM TELLURIDE.**
DUTT, B. V. AL–DELAIMI, M. SPITZER, W. G.
J. APPL. PHYS.
47 (2), 565–72, 1976.

99177 **EFFECTS OF ENERGY–BAND NONPARABOLICITY ON THE FREE–CARRIER ABSORPTION IN N–TYPE GALLIUM PHOSPHIDE.**
DAS, A. K. NAG, B. R.
PHYS. REV.
13 B (4), 1857–60, 1976.

99185 **FREE CARRIER PLASMA IN GRAPHITE COMPOUNDS.**
FISCHER, J. E. THOMPSON, T. E. VOGEL, F. L.
ACS SYMP. SER.
21, 418–34, 1976.

99215 **SURFACE PROPERTIES OF ZINC OXIDE.**
HEILAND, G.
ELECTROPHOTOGR., INT. CONF., 2ND
117–23, 1974.

99234 **EFFECTS OF THE SODIUM ION IMPURITY ON THE RELAXATION OF AN EXCITON IN POTASSIUM BROMIDE AT LOW TEMPERATURES.**
TANIMURA, K. OKADA, T.
PHYS. REV.
13 B (4), 1811–16, 1976.

99237 **ON THE TEMPERATURE DEPENDENCE OF THE ELASTO–OPTIC EFFECT IN SOME ALKALI HALIDE CRYSTALS.**
PAKHNEV, A. V. SHASKOL'SKAYA, M. P.
GORBACH, S. S.
SOV. PHYS. CRYSTALLOGR.
20 (5), 648–9, 1976.
(ENGLISH TRANSLATION OF KRISTALLOGRAFIYA, 20 (5), 1059–61, 1975; FOR ORIGINAL SEE E96822)

99243 **FREE CARRIER OPTICAL ABSORPTION AT 10.6 MICROMETERS IN GALLIUM ARSENIDE.**
BOIS, D. LEYRAL, P. SCHILLER, C.
J. ELECTRON. MATER.
5 (2), 275–86, 1976.

99245 **MEASUREMENT OF HIGH NEAR–EDGE ABSORPTION COEFFICIENTS IN SURFACE LAYERS OF INDIUM PHOSPHIDE.**
LOESCH, K. FISCHBACH, J. U.
PHYS. STATUS SOLIDI
33 A (2), 473–8, 1976.

99259 **FINE STRUCTURE AND ACTION OF INFRARED RADIATION ON ELECTROLUMINESCENCE OF MONOCRYSTALS OF ZINC SULFIDE.**
USHAKOV, YU. V.
J. APPL. SPECTROSC., USSR
21 (6), 1626–8, 1974.
(ENGLISH TRANSLATION OF ZH. PRIKL. SPEKTROSK., 21 (6), 1015–9, 1974; FOR ORIGINAL SEE E89483)

99263 **IMPURITY INDUCED ABSORPTION IN TRANSPARENT CRYSTALS.**
MARADUDIN, A. A.
OPT. PROPERTIES OF HIGHLY TRANSPARENT SOLIDS
191–219, 1975.
(AD–A027 795, AFOSR–TR–76–0792)

99319 **THE OPTICAL CONSTANTS OF QUARTZ, VITREOUS SILICA AND NEUTRON–IRRADIATED VITREOUS SILICA. (I).**
GASKELL, P. H. JOHNSON, D. W.
J. NON–CRYST. SOLIDS
20 (2), 153–69, 1976.

99351 **BEHAVIOUR OF ELECTRICAL RESISTIVITY AND ELASTIC CONSTANTS AT THE PHASE TRANSITION IN GERMANIUM TIN TELLURIDE.**
SEDDON, T. GUPTA, S. C. SAUNDERS, G. A.
PHYS. LETT.
56 A (1), 45–7, 1976.

EPIC Number	Bibliographic Citation
99364	**INDIRECT ABSORPTION EDGE OF GALLIUM PHOSPHIDE - INDIUM ARSENIDE MIXED CRYSTALS.** SIROTA, N. N. BODNAR, I. V. LUKOMSKII, A. I. SMIRNOVA, G. F. FINKELSTEIN, L. M. PHYS. STATUS SOLIDI 73 B (2), K135–6, 1976.
99454	**INTERCOMPARISON OF TEMPERATURE SCALES USING LOW TRANSITION - TEMPERATURE SUPERCONDUCTORS.** UTTON, D. B. SOULEN, R. J., JR. MARSHAK, H. PROC. INT. CONF. LOW TEMP. PHYS., 14TH 4, 76–9, 1975.
99463	**OPTICAL PROPERTIES OF CRYSTALLINE COPPER AND COPPER - ALUMINUM ALLOYS.** REA, R. S. UNIVERSITY OF VIRGINIA, PH. D. THESIS 124PP., 1972. (UNIV. MICROFILM NO. 72–22, 644)
99492	**DISPERSION OF N–INDIUM ANTIMONIDE IN THE SUBMILLIMETER RANGE.** LISTVIN, V. N. POTAPOV, V. T. SOKOLOVSKII, A. A. STRAKHOV, V. A. TREGUB, D. P. FIZ. TVERD. TELA 17 (6), 1580–3, 1975. (FOR ENGLISH TRANSLATION SEE E99493)
99493	**DISPERSION OF N–INDIUM ANTIMONIDE IN THE SUBMILLIMETER RANGE.** LISTVIN, V. N. POTAPOV, V. T. SOKOLOVSKII, A. A. STRAKHOV, V. A. TREGUB, D. P. SOV. PHYS. SOLID STATE 17 (6), 1034–6, 1975. (ENGLISH TRANSLATION OF FIZ. TVERD. TELA, 17 (6), 1580–3, 1975; FOR ORIGINAL SEE E99492)
99536	**LASER ANNEALING OF THE DEFECTS RESPONSIBLE FOR ADDITIONAL OPTICAL ABSORPTION IN ION–IRRADIATED GALLIUM ARSENIDE.** BOLOTOV, V. V. PRIDACHIN, N. B. SMIRNOV, L. S. FIZ. TEKH. POLUPROVODN. 10 (3), 566–7, 1976. (FOR ENGLISH TRANSLATION SEE E99856)
99549	**COMPACT CALORIMETER FOR MEASURING LASER ABSORPTION COEFFICIENTS OF SMALL SAMPLES.** MAGEE, T. J. JOHNSON, N. M. LEHMANN, M. PENG, J. HANNIGAN, J. REV. SCI. INSTRUM. 47 (3), 301–2, 1976.
99553	**GROWTH AND PROPERTIES OF VACUUM–DEPOSITED FILMS OF ALUMINUM ANTIMONIDE, ALUMINUM ARSENIDE, AND ALUMINUM PHOSPHIDE.** FRANCOMBE, M. H. NOREIKA, A. J. ZEITMAN, S. A. JOHNSON, J. E. THIN SOLID FILMS 32 (2), 259–62, 1976.
99561	**PROPERTIES OF MATERIALS.** WESTMAM, H. P. SCHLAIKJER, J. E. REFERENCE DATA FOR RADIO ENGINEERS (4TH ED), 41–75, 1956.
99570	**INFLUENCE OF FREE CARRIERS ON THE EXCITON ABSORPTION OF LIGHT IN SEMICONDUCTORS.** KHADZHI, P. I. SOV. PHYS. SEMICOND. 9 (11), 1402–4, 1976. (ENGLISH TRANSLATION OF FIZ. TEKH. POLUPROV., 9 (11), 2156–60, 1975; FOR ORIGINAL SEE E98289)
99618	**ACTION OF LASER RADIATION ON THE OPTICAL SPECTRA OF CADMIUM SULFIDE SINGLE CRYSTALS.** BRODIN, M. S. DAVYDOVA, N. A. SHABLII, I. YU. FIZ. TEKH. POLUPROVODN. 10 (4), 625–30, 1976. (FOR ENGLISH TRANSLATION SEE E99857)
99625	**THE OPTICAL CONSTANTS OF QUARTZ, VITREOUS SILICA AND NEUTRON–IRRADIATED VITREOUS SILICA. (II). ANALYSIS OF THE INFRARED SPECTRUM OF VITREOUS SILICA.** GASKELL, P. H. JOHNSON, D. W. J. NON–CRYST. SOLIDS 20 (2), 171–91, 1976.
99646	**PRODUCING THE OPTIMUM CONCENTRATION OF CURRENT CARRIERS IN THERMOELEMENTS WITH A NEGATIVE SIDE OF LEAD TELLURIDE.** KULIEV, A. Z. KAKHRAMANOV, K. SH. TUKHTASINOV, I. GELIOTEKHNIKA (6), 77–8, 1975. (FOR ENGLISH TRANSLATION SEE E103293)
99658	**LASER DAMAGE OF CADMIUM SULFIDE AND ZINC SULFIDE THIN FILMS.** LEUNG, K. M. TANG, C. C. DESHAZER, L. G. THIN SOLID FILMS 34 (1), 119–23, 1976.
99665	**HIGH TEMPERATURE PROPERTIES OF INFRARED OPTICAL MATERIALS.** MCALISTER, E. D. PROC. IRIS 4 (4), 139–45, 1959.
99666	**OPTICAL PROPERTIES OF INFRARED–TRANSPARENT SOLIDS AT ELEVATED TEMPERATURES.** MERGERIAN, D. PROC. IRIS 4 (4), 146–54, 1959.
99712	**INVESTIGATION OF THE STRUCTURE OF THE EDGE ABSORPTION IN GALLIUM SULFIDE AND GALLIUM SELENIDE CRYSTALS.** KARAMAN, M. I. MUSHINSKII, V. P. FIZ. TEKH. POLUPROV. 9 (7), 1415–18, 1975. (FOR ENGLISH TRANSLATION SEE E99713)
99713	**INVESTIGATION OF THE STRUCTURE OF THE EDGE ABSORPTION IN GALLIUM SULFIDE AND GALLIUM SELENIDE CRYSTALS.** KARAMAN, M. I. MUSHINSKII, V. P. SOV. PHYS. SEMICOND. 9 (7), 934–6, 1975. (ENGLISH TRANSLATION OF FIZ. TEKH. POLUPROV., 9 (7), 1415–18, 1975; FOR ORIGINAL SEE E99712)
99741	**METHOD AND SPECTROMETER FOR MEASURING OPTICAL ABSORPTION IN THIN EPITAXIAL LAYERS.** GAL, M. NEMETH, K. EPPELDAUER, G. J. PHYS. 9 E (6), 484–7, 1976.
99748	**SILICON CARBIDE DOPED WITH GALLIUM.** VODAKOV, YU. A. LOMAKINA, G. A. MOKHOV, E. N. RADOVANOVA, E. I. SOKOLOV, V. I. USMANOVA, M. M. YULDASHEV, G. F. MAKHMUDOV, B. S. PHYS. STATUS SOLIDI 35 A (1), 37–42, 1976.
99749	**INTRABAND CONDUCTIVITY AND THERMOPOWER OF SEMICONDUCTORS WITH SLOWLY VARYING GAUSSIAN RANDOM FIELD.** ZHUMATII, P. G. PHYS. STATUS SOLIDI 75 B (1), 61–72, 1976.
99754	**ANOMALOUS PHOTOVOLTAGE IN ANTIMONY ORTHONIOBATE.** VERKHOVSKAYA, K. A. LOBACHEV, A. N. POPOV, B. N. POPOLITOV, V. I. PESKIN, V. F. FRIDKIN, V. M. PIS'MA ZH. EKSP. TEOR. FIZ. 23 (9), 522–3, 1976. (FOR ENGLISH TRANSLATION SEE E101631)
99762	**CONCENTRATION DEPENDENCE OF THE EMISSION PROPERTIES OF ZIRCONIUM CARBIDE + TUNGSTEN ALLOYS.** KOMOZYNSKII, P. A. OSTROVSKII, E. K. KALININA, N. G. NESHPOR, V. S. BEDNYAK, L. G. ZH. TEKH. FIZ. 43 (3), 552–7, 1976. (FOR ENGLISH TRANSLATION SEE E101355)
99775	**A PRODUCTION REACTOR FOR LOW TEMPERATURE PLASMA–ENCHANCE SILICON NITRIDE DEPOSITION.** ROSLER, R. S. BENZING, W. C. BALDO, J. SOLID STATE TECHNOL., 19 (6), 45–50, 1976.
99786	**EFFECT OF TEMPERATURE AND STRESS ON THE REFRACTIVE INDEX OF WINDOW MATERIALS.** FELDMAN, A. HOROWITZ, D. WAXLER, R. M. NATIONAL BUREAU OF STANDARDS, WASHINGTON, D. C. 9–15, 1976. (NBSIR–76–1115, PB–257 196, AD–A029 059)
99794	**PRINCIPAL LATTICE FREQUENCY OF MAGNESIUM OXIDE.** SAKSENA, B. D. VISWANATHAN, S. PROC. PHYS. SOC. 69, 129–38, 1955.
99798	**EXPERIMENTAL INVESTIGATION OF THE SPECIFIC ELECTRICAL CONDUCTIVITY OF ALUMINUM OXIDES NEAR THE MELTING POINT.** SHPIL'RAYN, E. E. KAGAN, D. N. BARKHATOV, L. S. ZHMAKIN, L. I. EUROPEAN CONF. ON THERMOPHYSICAL PROPERTIES OF SOLIDS AT HIGH TEMP., 5TH 10PP., 1976.
99799	**ELECTRONIC CONDUCTIVITY AND OXYDO–REDUCTION IN ZIRCONIA BASED CERAMICS.** GOUET, M. CHAPPEY, B. AUCLAIR, B. GUILLOU, M. EUROPEAN CONF. ON THERMOPHYSICAL PROPERTIES OF SOLIDS AT HIGH TEMP., 5TH 14PP., 1976.

EPIC Number	Bibliographic Citation
99855	**PHOTOCAPACITANCE-CURRENT INVESTIGATION OF THE FUNDAMENTAL ABSORPTION EDGE OF A SEMICONDUCTOR.** MISCHENKO, A. M. NEIZVESTNYI, I. G. OVSYUK, V. N. SINYUKOV, M. P. SOV. PHYS. SEMICOND. 10 (1), 5–7, 1976. (ENGLISH TRANSLATION OF FIZ. TEKH. POLUPROV., 10 (1), 10–14, 1976; FOR ORIGINAL SEE E99127)
99856	**LASER ANNEALING OF DEFECTS RESPONSIBLE FOR ADDITIONAL OPTICAL ABSORPTION IN ION-IRRADIATED GALLIUM ARSENIDE.** BOLOTOV, V. V. PRIDACHIN, N. B. SMIRNOV, L. S. SOV. PHYS. SEMICOND. 10 (3), 338–9, 1976. (ENGLISH TRANSLATION OF FIZ. TEKH. POLUPROV., 10 (3), 566–7, 1976; FOR ORIGINAL SEE E99536)
99857	**EFFECT OF LASER RADIATION ON OPTICAL SPECTRA OF CADMIUM SULFIDE SINGLE CRYSTALS.** BRODIN, M. S. DAVYDOVA, N. A. SHABLII, I. YU. SOV. PHYS. SEMICOND. 10 (4), 375–8, 1976. (ENGLISH TRANSLATION OF FIZ. TEKH. POLUPROV., 10 (4), 625–30, 1976; FOR ORIGINAL SEE E99618)
99870	**INFRARED ABSORPTION LIMITS OF HYDROGEN FLUORIDE AND DEUTERIUM FLUORIDE LASER WINDOWS.** HASS, M. HARRINGTON, J. A. GREGORY, D. A. DAVISSON, J. W. APPL. PHYS. LETT. 28 (10), 610–11, 1976.
99871	**OPTICAL BIREFRINGENCE OF THIN GALLIUM ARSENIDE - ALUMINUM ARSENIDE MULTILAYER FILMS.** VAN DER ZIEL, J. P. ILEGEMS, M. MIKULYAK, R. M. APPL. PHYS. LETT. 28 (12), 735–7, 1976.
99875	**FAR-INFRARED ABSORPTION IN CUBIC ZINC SULFIDE.** KWASNIEWSKI, E. A. KOTELES, E. S. DATARS, W. R. CAN. J. PHYS. 54 (10), 1053–60, 1976.
99882	**CHANGE OF THE REFRACTIVE INDEX IN ION IMPLANTED QUARTZ AND FUSED SILICA.** KARGE, H. PRAGER, R. EXP. TECH. PHYS. 24 (1), 87–94, 1976.
99883	**THE MEASUREMENT OF THE THERMOPOWER OF LIQUID METALS AND SEMICONDUCTORS.** POPP, K. TSCHIRNER, H. U. WOBST, M. EXP. TECH. PHYS. 24 (1), 115–21, 1976.
99887	**ANISOTROPY OF EFFECTIVE MASSES IN CONDUCTION BAND MINIMUMS OF A GALLIUM PHOSPHIDE CONDUCTION BAND.** KOPYLOV, A. A. FIZ. TEKH. POLUPROVODN. 10 (5), 833–5, 1976. (FOR ENGLISH TRANSLATION SEE E101356)
99905	**CALCULATIONS OF THE FAR-INFRARED ANHARMONIC OPTICAL PROPERTIES OF CESIUM CHLORIDE AT 300 AND 80 K.** SHIMIZU, H. OHBAYASHI, Y. YAMAMOTO, K. ABE, K. ISHIBASHI, Y. J. PHYS. SOC. JPN. 40 (6), 1684–9, 1976.
99911	**PHYSICAL PROPERTIES OF THORIUM FLUORIDE.** VAN UITERT, L. G. GUGGENHEIM, H. J. O'BRYAN, H. M. WARNER, A. W., JR. BROWNLOW, D. BERNSTEIN, J. L. PASTEUR, G. A. JOHNSON, L. F. MATER. RES. BULL. 11 (6), 669–71, 1976.
99913	**EFFECT OF UNIAXIAL STRESS AND HYDROSTATIC PRESSURE ON THE OPTICAL PROPERTIES OF IONIC CRYSTALS.** ISHIGURO, M. MEM. INST. SCI. IND. RES., OSAKA UNIV. 33, 1–16, 1976.
99920	**THE USE OF LATERAL WAVES FOR THE EXAMINATION OF WEAKLY ABSORBING SURFACE FILMS.** HEAVENS, O. S. SHARMA, S. K. OPT. COMMUN. 17 (3), 339–41, 1976.
99923	**ON THE LUMINESCENCE EXCITATION AND UV-ABSORPTION SPECTRA OF CESIUM IODIDE ACTIVATED WITH SODIUM.** STEVELS, A. L. N. SCHRAMA DE PAUW, A. D. M. PHILIPS RES. REP. 31 (1), 1–22, 1976.
99925	**STRUCTURAL SENSITIVITY OF TRANSPORT AND OPTICAL PROPERTIES OF AMORPHOUS GERMANIUM TELLURIDE.** CHOPRA, K. L. BARTHWAL, S. K. PANDYA, D. K. PHYS. STATUS SOLIDI 35 A (2), 761–8, 1976.

EPIC Number	Bibliographic Citation
99966	**OPTICAL PROPERTIES OF PERIODICALLY INHOMOGENEOUS SILICON OXIDE FILMS.** LUTTER, A. RONAKY, J. THIN SOLID FILMS 34 (2), 411–15, 1976.
99984	**POLISHING STUDIES AND BACKSCATTER MEASUREMENTS ON ALKALI-HALIDE WINDOWS.** SOILEAU, M. J. BENNETT, H. E. BETHKE, J. M. SHAFFER, J. LASER INDUCED DAMAGE IN OPTICAL MATERIALS: 1975 20–8, 1976. (NBS-SP-435, PB-252 186)
99986	**ARSENIC TRISULFIDE COATINGS ON POTASSIUM CHLORIDE.** BAER, A. D. DONOVAN, T. M. SOILEAU, M. J. LASER INDUCED DAMAGE IN OPTICAL MATERIALS: 1975 244–7, 1976. (NBS-SP-435, PB-252 186)
99987	**PICOSECOND BREAKDOWN STUDIES: THRESHOLD AND NONLINEAR REFRACTIVE INDEX MEASUREMENTS AND DAMAGE MORPHOLOGY.** SMITH, W. L. BECHTEL, J. H. BLOEMBERGEN, N. LASER INDUCED DAMAGE IN OPTICAL MATERIALS: 1975 321–30, 1976. (NBS-SP-435, PB-252 186)
99989	**REFRACTIVE INDEX AND TEMPERATURE COEFFICIENT OF INDEX OF CVD ZINC SELENIDE.** DODGE, M. J. MALITSON, I. H. LASER INDUCED DAMAGE IN OPTICAL MATERIALS: 1975 170–4, 1976. (NBS-SP-435, PB-252 186)
100000	**R F SPUTTERED ALUMINUM OXIDE FILMS ON SILICON.** SALAMA, C. A. T. J. ELECTROCHEM. SOC. 117 (7), 913–17, 1970.
100007	**OPTICAL PROPERTIES OF HEXAGONAL BORON NITRIDE.** ZUNGER, A. KATZIR, A. HALPERIN, A. PHYS. REV. 13 B (12), 5560–73, 1976.
100013	**OPTICAL TRANSMISSION OF GRAPHITE COMPOUNDS.** HENNIG, G. R. J. CHEM. PHYS. 43 (4), 1201–6, 1965.
100019	**SPECTRAL EMITTANCE MEASUREMENTS WITH A CRYOGENICALLY COOLED INSTRUMENT.** STIERWALT, D. L. LASER INDUCED DAMAGE IN OPTICAL MATERIALS: 1975. 148–56, 1976. (NBS-SP-435, PB-252 186)
100026	**LOW TEMPERATURE PROPERTIES OF SOME INTERMETALLIC COMPOUNDS.** OUYANG, G. B. CARNEGIE-MELLON UNIVERSITY, PH.D. THESIS 164PP., 1975. (UNIV. MICROFILMS NO. 75-19859)
100030	**DEVELOPMENT OF COMPUTER CONTROLLED VACUUM ULTRAVIOLET REFLECTOMETER AND STUDY OF OPTICAL PROPERTIES OF LITHIUM FLUORIDE, SODIUM FLUORIDE AND POTASSIUM FLUORIDE.** RAO, K. K. UMIVERSITY OF WISCONSIN, MADISON; PH.D. THESIS 176PP., 1975. (UNIV. MICROFILM NO. 75-18190)
100033	**MOSSBAUER STUDY OF COBALT - AND IRON - VANADIUM SPINELS.** LEE, J. D. UNIVERSITY OF NORTH CAROLINA, CHAPEL HILL, PH. D. THESIS 125PP., 1975. (UNIV. MICROFILM NO. 75-29044)
100034	**MAGNETO-PLASMA STUDIES OF THE LATTICE AND ELECTRONIC PROPERTIES OF LEAD TELLURIDE.** FOLEY, G. M. T. UNIVERSITY OF PENNSYLVANIA, PH. D. THESIS 326PP., 1975. (UNIV. MICROFILM NO. 75-24067)
100036	**REFLECTION MEASUREMENTS OF THE FAR INFRARED VIBRATIONAL SPECTRA OF AMORPHOUS SEMICONDUCTORS.** LIN, J. T.-C. LOWELL TECHNOLOGICAL UNIVERSITY, MASS., PH. D. THESIS 104PP., 1975. (N76-13931, UNIV. MICROFILM NO. 75-26384)
100047	**ATTENUATION MEASUREMENT IN GLASSES FOR OPTICAL COMMUNICATIONS: AN IMMERSION METHOD.** HEITMANN, W. APPL. OPT. 15 (1), 256–60, 1976.
100152	**PHOTOCONDUCTION AND PHOTOVOLTAIC EFFECTS IN SPUTTERED CADMIUM SULFIDE FILMS.** TAKEUCHI, M. SAKAGAWA, Y. NAGASAKA, H. THIN SOLID FILMS 33 (1), 89–98, 1976.

EPIC Number	Bibliographic Citation
100173	**THIN FILM INFRARED DETECTOR ARRAYS FOR INTEGRATED ELECTRONIC STRUCTURES.** CORSI, C. CAPPUCCIO, G. D'AMICO, A. PETROCCO, G. VITALI, G. INFRARED PHYS. 16 (1–2), 37–45, 1976.
100174	**NEW TECHNIQUES FOR DISPERSIVE FOURIER TRANSFORM SPECTROMETRY OF LIQUIDS.** AFSAR, M. N. HASTED, J. B. CHAMBERLAIN, J. INFRARED PHYS. 16 (1–2), 301–10, 1976.
100222	**ELECTRICAL PROPERTIES OF VACUUM DEPOSTED BISMUTH FILMS.** GOSWAMI, A. OJHA, S. M. INDIAN J. PHYS. 49 (11), 847–55, 1975.
100267	**THE PRECIPITATION OF DIINDIUM BISMUTHIDE FROM SUPERSATURATED INDIUM.** OTTO, G. H. SCR. METALL. 10 (2), 139–42, 1976.
100283	**THERMOELECTRIC EFFECT IN PSEUDOBINARY SOLUTIONS BASED ON LEAD SULFIDES.** KULIEV, A. Z. KAKHRAMANOV, K. SH. SAGATOV, E. S. TUKHTASINOV, I. APPL. SOLAR ENERGY, USSR 11 (3–4), 8–9, 1975. (ENGLISH TRANSLATION OF GELIOTEKHNIKA, 11 (3–4), 12–14, 1975; FOR ORIGINAL SEE E94600)
100287	**SOME SPECIAL FEATURES OF THE ACTION OF LOW ENERGY ELECTRONS ON THE PHOTOELECTRIC PROPERTIES OF ANOMALOUS PHOTOVOLTAIC FILMS OF CADMIUM TELLURIDE.** ARIFOV, U. A. AYUKHANOV, A. KH. ABDULLAEV, N. A. ARIFDZHANOVA, M. S. DOKL. AKAD. NAUK SSSR 223 (4–6), 1102–5, 1975. (FOR ENGLISH TRANSLATION SEE E100288)
100288	**SOME SPECIAL FEATURES OF THE ACTION OF LOW ENERGY ELECTRONS ON THE PHOTOELECTRIC PROPERTIES OF ANOMALOUS PHOTOVOLTAIC FILMS OF CADMIUM TELLURIDE.** ARIFOV, U. A. AYUKHANOV, A. KH. ABDULLAEV, N. A. ARIFDZHANOVA, M. S. SOV. PHYS. DOKL. 20 (8), 570–2, 1975. (ENGLISH TRANSLATION OF DOKL. AKAD. NAUK SSSR, 223 (4–6), 1102–5, 1975; FOR ORIGINAL SEE E100287)
100322	**ABSORPTION EDGE AND STRUCTURE OF ABSORPTION SPECTRUM OF HYPERBOLIC EXCITONS IN A THALLIUM SCANDIUM CRYSTAL.** ABUTALYBOV, G. I. BELLE, M. L. FIZ. TEKH. POLUPROV. 9 (7), 1330–4, 1975. (FOR ENGLISH TRANSLATION SEE E100323)
100323	**ABSORPTION EDGE AND STRUCTURE OF ABSORPTION SPECTRUM OF HYPERBOLIC EXCITONS IN A THALLIUM SCANDIUM CRYSTAL.** ABUTALYBOV, G. I. BELLE, M. L. SOV. PHYS. SEMICOND. 9 (7), 878–80, 1975. (ENGLISH TRANSLATION OF FIZ. TEKH. POLUPROV., 9 (7), 1330–4, 1975; FOR ORIGINAL SEE E100322)
100328	**THEORY OF THE DRAG OF ELECTRONS BY PHONONS.** SAMOILOVICH, A. G. BUDA, I. S. FIZ. TEKH. POLUPROV. 9 (8), 1478–84, 1975. (FOR ENGLISH TRANSLATION SEE E100329)
100329	**THEORY OF THE DRAG OF ELECTRONS BY PHONONS.** SAMOILOVICH, A. G. BUDA, I. S. SOV. PHYS. SEMICOND. 9 (8), 977–80, 1975. (ENGLISH TRANSLATION OF FIZ. TEKH. POLUPROV., 9 (8), 1478–84, 1975; FOR ORIGINAL SEE E100328)
100407	**MAGNON-DRAG THERMOELECTRIC POWER OF A NARROW-BAND ANTIFERROMAGNETIC SEMICONDUCTOR.** IGNACIUK, J. ADAMOWICZ, L. ZAGORSKI, A. ACTA PHYS. POL. 49 A (4), 495–501, 1976.
100412	**DIELECTRIC CONSTANT AND ITS TEMPERATURE DEPENDENCE FOR GALLIUM ARSENIDE, CADMIUM TELLURIUM AND ZINC SELENIUM.** STRZALKOWSKI, I. JOSHI, S. CROWELL, C. R. APPL. PHYS. LETT. 2, (6), 350–2, 1976.
100416	**A COMPARISON OF THE OPTICAL PROPERTIES OF CRYSTALLINE AND AMORPHOUS CADMIUM SULFIDE.** WOHLGEMUTH, J. H. BRODIE, D. E. EASTMAN, P. C. CAN. J. PHYS. 54 (7), 785–93, 1976.
100436	**LUMINESCENCE AND ABSORPTION OF ELECTRON-IRRADIATED COMMON OPTICAL GLASSES, SAPPHIRE, AND QUARTZ.** TREADAWAY, M. J. PASSENHEIM, B. C. KITTERER, B. D. IEEE TRANS. NUCL. SCI. 22 (6), 2253–8, 1975.
100572	**RESISTIVITY AND LATTICE PARAMETER VARIATIONS IN DINIOBIUM ALUMINIDE TYPE SIGMA PHASES.** BROWN, P. W. WORZALA, F. J. J. MATER. SCI. 11 (4), 760–6, 1976.
100580	**THERMIONIC EMISSION OF AN OXIDE CATHODE IN A LOW-PRESSURE GAS DISCHARGE.** BOUWKNEGT, A. VAN DER KOOI, A. G. J. PHYS. 9 D (7), 111–21, 1976.
100607	**PROPERTIES OF THE NATIVE OXIDE ON GALLIUM ANTIMONIDE.** FISCHER, C. W. LESLIE, N. ETCHELLS, A. J. VAC. SCI. TECHNOL. 13 (1), 59–63, 1976.
100620	**ION IMPLANTATION INTO FUSED QUARTZ FOR INTEGRATED OPTICAL CIRCUITS.** KERSTEN, R. TH. BOROFFKA, H. OPT. COMMUN. 17 (1), 119–23, 1976.
100631	**POLARITON EFFECTS IN THE EXCITON ABSORPTION OF GALLIUM SELENIDE.** BOSACCHI, A. BOSACCHI, B. FRANCHI, S. PHYS. REV. LETT. 36 (18) 1086–9, 1976.
100646	**THE USE OF MODIFIED RELAXATION TIME IN THE TRANSPORT THEORY OF NON-CRYSTALLINE SEMICONDUCTORS.** KREMPASKY, J. BARANCOK, D. PHYS. STATUS SOLIDI 74 B (2), 741–51, 1976.
100720	**STUDIES OF SUPERCONDUCTING A-15 VANADIUM-BASED ALLOYS.** PENDRYS, L. A. DOUGLASS, D. H. J. LOW TEMP. PHYS. 23 (3–4), 367–91, 1976.
100761	**OPTICAL TRANSMISSION MEASUREMENTS AND ELECTRON MICROPROBE ANALYSIS OF A BULK INDIUM ARSENIDE PHOSPHIDE ALLOY SYSTEM.** LI, S. S. SCHOENFELD, D. W. OWEN, R. T. PHYS. STATUS SOLIDI 34 A (1), 255–61, 1976.
100785	**ONE-DIMENSIONAL EFFECTS IN THE INTERMETALLIC COMPOUND ALUMINUM MANGANESE.** DUNLOP, J. B. GRUNER, G. SOLID STATE COMMUN. 18 (7), 827–9, 1976.
100786	**INFRARED ABSORPTION OF HYDROGEN - DETERIUM ION PAIRS IMPURITY IN POTASSIUM CHLORIDE.** GUPTA, R. K. MATHUR, P. SOLID STATE COMMUN. 18 (7), 835–6, 1976.
100825	**PHYSICO-CHEMICAL CONSIDERATIONS IN THE PREPARATION OF NEW COMPOUND SEMICONDUCTOR SOLAR CELLS.** BACHMANN, K. J. BUEHLER, E. SHAY, J. L. WAGNER, S. Z. PHYS. CHEM., FRANKFURT 98 (1–6), 365–76, 1975.
100839	**PHASE TRANSITION IN NONSTOICHIOMETRIC GERMANIUM TELLURIDE.** NOVIKOVA, S. I. SHELIMOVA, L. E. AVILOV, E. S. KORZHUEV, M. A. FIZ. TVERD. TELA 17 (8), 2379–81, 1975. (FOR ENGLISH TRANSLATION SEE E100840)
100840	**PHASE TRANSITION IN NONSTOICHIOMETRIC GERMANIUM TELLURIDE.** NOVIKOVA, S. I. SHELIMOVA, L. E. AVILOV, E. S. KORZHUEV, M. A. SOV. PHYS. SOLID STATE 17 (8), 1570–1, 1976. (ENGLISH TRANSLATION OF FIZ. TVERD. TELA, 17 (8), 2379–81, 1975; FOR ORIGINAL SEE E100839)
100849	**LUMINESCENCE AND THE OFF-CENTER POSITION OF COPPER ATOMS IN POTASSIUM CHLORIDE, POTASSIUM BROMIDE AND RUBIDIUM CHLORIDE CRYSTALS.** VARANOV, P. G. VESHCHUNOV, YU. P. ZHITNIKOV, R. A. ROMANOV, N. G. FIZ. TVERD. TELA 17 (8), 2459–62, 1975. (FOR ENGLISH TRANSLATION SEE E100850)

EPIC Number	Bibliographic Citation
100850	**LUMINESCENCE AND THE OFF-CENTER POSITION OF COPPER ATOMS IN POTASSIUM CHLORIDE, POTASSIUM BROMIDE AND RUBIDIUM CHLORIDE CRYSTALS.** VARANOV, P. G. VESHCHUNOV, YU. P. ZHITNIKOV, R. A. ROMANOV, N. G. SOV. PHYS. SOLID STATE 17 (8), 1633–4, 1976. (ENGLISH TRANSLATION OF FIZ. TVERD. TELA, 17 (8), 2459–62, 1975; FOR ORIGINAL SEE E100849)
100869	**CONCENTRATION-DEPENDENT ABSORPTION AND SPONTANEOUS EMISSION OF HEAVILY DOPED GALLIUM ARSENIDE.** CASEY, H. C., JR. STERN, F. J. APPL. PHYS. 47 (2), 631–43, 1976.
100892	**THE ELECTRICAL CONDUCTIVITY OF ALLOYS IN THE LIQUID STATE.** BORNEMANN, K. WAGENMANN, K. FERRUM (Z. THEORETISCHE EISENHUTTENKUNDE ALLGEMEINE MATERIALKUNDE) 11 (10), 289–314, 1914.
100960	**CEROUS MAGNESIUM NITRATE: A MAGNETIC TEMPERATURE SCALE 0.002–2 K.** HUDSON, R. P. KAESER, R. S. PHYSICS 3 (2), 95–113, 1967.
100961	**SINGLE-CRYSTAL RAMAN AND INFRARED SPECTRA OF VANADIUM PENTOXIDE.** GILSON, T. R. BIZRI, O. F. CHEETHAM, N. J. CHEM. SOC., DALTON TRANS. (3), 291–4, 1973.
100962	**OPTICAL PROPERTIES OF TIN SELENIDE AND TIN SULFIDE.** TAKAHASHI, K. ARAI, T. KUDO, K. SCI. LIGHT (TOKYO) 21 (2), 131–44, 1972.
100963	**AMMONIA ABSORPTION RELEVANT TO THE ALBEDO OF JUPITER. I. EXPERIMENTAL RESULTS.** DICK, K. A. ZIKO, A. O. ASTROPHYS. J. 182 (2), (PT. 1), 609–13, 1973.
100965	**FAR INFRARED PROPERTIES OF THE PSEUDOPROPER FERROELECTRIC AMMONIUM SULFATE.** PETZELT, J. GRIGAS, J. MAYEROVA, I. FERROELECTRICS 6 (3–4), 225–34, 1974.
100970	**REFLECTIVITY OF IODINE-DOPED ANTIMONY TELLURIDE CRYSTALS.** HORAK, J. TICHY, L. VASKO, A. FRUMAR, M. PHYS. STATUS SOLIDI 14 A (1), 289–98, 1972.
100974	**PHYSICAL PROPERTIES OF NEODYMIUM - ANTIMONY ALLOYS AND THEIR CORRELATION WITH THE PHASE DIAGRAM.** KUNGUROV, I. M. L'VOV, S. N. CHERNOGORENKO, V. B. KOBZENKO, G. F. UKR. FIZ. ZH. 17 (11), 1787–90, 1972.
100982	**PROPERTIES OF INFRARED SENSOR MATERIALS.** CAREN, R. P. FUANI, A. I. FRYE, W. E. SKLENSKY, A. F. MATER. RES. STAND. 11 (6), 10–15, 51, 1971.
101002	**EXCITONS AND POLARONS. EXPERIMENT WITH THALLIUM HALIDES.** KOBAYASHI, K. KURITA, S. BUSSCI 11 (9), 483–94, 1970.
101010	**THEORY OF MULTIPHONON ABSORPTION: A REVIEW.** MCGILL, T. C. OPT. PROP. HIGHLY TRANSPARENT SOLIDS 3–19, 1975.
101011	**MULTIPHONON ABSORPTION FOR VARIOUS FORMS OF THE ANHARMONIC POTENTIAL.** NEDOLUHA, A. OPT. PROP. HIGHLY TRANSPARENT SOLIDS 21–33, 1975.
101012	**CUMULANT METHODS IN THE THEORY OF MULTIPHONON ABSORPTION.** BENDOW, B. YUKON, S. P. OPT. PROP. HIGHLY TRANSPARENT SOLIDS 35–43, 1975.
101013	**THE HIGH FREQUENCY TAIL OF THE LATTICE ABSORPTION SPECTRA OF SIMPLE CRYSTALS.** BARKER, A. J. WILKINSON, G. R. MASSA, N. E. MITRA, S. S. OPT. PROP. HIGHLY TRANSPARENT SOLIDS 45–58, 1975.
101014	**OPTICAL ABSORPTION BY ALKALI HALIDES: POSSIBLE STRUCTURE IN THE MULTIPHONON REGION.** BOYER, L. L. HARRINGTON, J. A. HASS, M. ROSENSTOCK, H. B. OPT. PROP. HIGHLY TRANSPARENT SOLIDS 59–69, 1975.
101015	**EXPERIMENTAL STUDIES OF MULTIPHONON IR ABSORPTION.** POHL, D. W. OPT. PROP. HIGHLY TRANSPARENT SOLIDS 71–85, 1975.
101016	**TEMPERATURE DEPENDENCE OF MULTIPHONON ABSORPTION IN FLUORITE CRYSTALS.** LIPSON, H. G. BENDOW, B. MITRA, S. S. OPT. PROP. HIGHLY TRANSPARENT SOLIDS 87–98, 1975.
101017	**MULTIPHONON ABSORPTION IN THE ALKALINE EARTH FLUORIDES.** CHEN, M. HASS, M. MCGILL, T. C. OPT. PROP. HIGHLY TRANSPARENT SOLIDS 99–107, 1975.
101018	**MULTIPHONON ABSORPTION IN POTASSIUM CHLORIDE, SODIUM CHLORIDE AND ZINC SELENIDE.** ROWE, J. M. HARRINGTON, J. A. OPT. PROP. HIGHLY TRANSPARENT SOLIDS 109–18, 1975.
101019	**TWO-PHONON ABSORPTION SPECTRA OF III-V COMPOUND SEMICONDUCTORS.** KOTELES, E. S. DATARS, W. R. OPT. PROP. HIGHLY TRANSPARENT SOLIDS 119–27, 1975.
101020	**URBACH'S RULE.** DOW, J. D. OPT. PROP. HIGHLY TRANSPARENT SOLIDS 131–43, 1975.
101021	**MAGNETIC CIRCULAR DICHROISM OF THE URBACH EDGE IN POTASSIUM IODIDE, CADMIUM TELLURIDE AND THALLIUM CHLORIDE.** WILLIAMS, R. T. SCHNATTERLY, S. E. OPT. PROP. HIGHLY TRANSPARENT SOLIDS 145–60, 1975.
101022	**DISPERSION OF THE ELASTO-OPTIC CONSTANTS OF POTASSIUM HALIDES.** VEDAM, K. SCHMIDT, E. D. D. SCHNEIDER, W. C. OPT. PROP. HIGHLY TRANSPARENT SOLIDS 169–77, 1975.
101023	**OPTICAL TRANSMISSION IN IODINE TRANSPORTED ALPHA - MERCURY SULFIDE.** KREITMAN, M. M. FAILE, S. P. LITTON, C. W. REYNOLDS, D. C. OPT. PROP. HIGHLY TRANSPARENT SOLIDS 179–88, 1975.
101024	**RAMAN, PHOTOCONDUCTIVE AND ACOUSTOELECTRIC PROBES OF RESIDUAL DEEP IMPURITIES AND ABSORPTION IN GALLIUM ARSENIDE.** ABRAMSCHN, D. A. CELLER, G. K. BRAY, R. OPT. PROP. HIGHLY TRANSPARENT SOLIDS 221–30, 1975.
101026	**PICOSECOND SPECTROSCOPY OF TRANSIENT ABSORPTION IN PURE POTASSIUM CHLORIDE.** WILLIAMS, R. T. BRADFORD, J. N. FAUST, W. L. OPT. PROP. HIGHLY TRANSPARENT SOLIDS 233–41, 1975.
101027	**HIGHLY TRANSPARENT GLASSES.** TAUC, J. OPT. PROP. HIGHLY TRANSPARENT SOLIDS 245–60, 1975.
101028	**MULTIPHONON ABSORPTION IN THE CHALCOGENIDE GLASSES ARSENIC SULFIDE AND GERMANIUM SULFIDE.** TREACY, D. TAYLOR, P. C. OPT. PROP. HIGHLY TRANSPARENT SOLIDS 261–9, 1975.
101029	**MULTIPHONON ABSORPTION IN CHALCOGENIDE GLASSES.** HOWARD, R. E. DANIELSON, P. S. MAKLAD, M. S. MOHR, R. K. MACEDO, P. B. MOYNIHAN, C. T. OPT. PROP. HIGHLY TRANSPARENT SOLIDS 271–85, 1975.
101030	**THEORY OF MULTIPHONON ABSORPTION IN THE TRANSPARENT REGIME OF AMORPHOUS SOLIDS.** TSAY, Y.-F. BENDOW, B. YUKON, S. P. OPT. PROP. HIGHLY TRANSPARENT SOLIDS 287–96, 1975.
101031	**OPTICALLY INDUCED EFFECTS IN PHOTOLUMINESCENCE STUDIES OF CHALCOGENIDE GLASSES.** BISHOP, S. G. STROM, U. OPT. PROP. HIGHLY TRANSPARENT SOLIDS 317–35, 1975.

EPIC Number	Bibliographic Citation
101032	**HYDROGEN FLUORIDE AND CARBON DIOXIDE LASER MEASUREMENTS OF DISPERSION OF THE NONLINEAR SUSCEPTIBILITY IN ZINC-BLENDE CRYSTALS.** WEISS, J. A. OPT. PROP. HIGHLY TRANSPARENT SOLIDS 339-51, 1975.
101033	**MULTIPHOTON IONIZATION PROBABILITY AND NONLINEAR ABSORPTION OF LIGHT BY TRANSPARENT SOLIDS.** MITRA, S. S. NARDUCCI, L. M. SHATAS, R. A. TSAY, V. F. VAIDYANATHAN, A. OPT. PROP. HIGHLY TRANSPARENT SOLIDS 353-64, 1975.
101034	**A REVIEW OF TECHNIQUES FOR MEASURING SMALL OPTICAL LOSSES IN INFRARED TRANSMITTING MATERIAL.** SKOLNIK, L. H. OPT. PROP. HIGHLY TRANSPARENT SOLIDS 405-33, 1975.
101035	**IMPROVED LASER CALORIMETRIC TECHNIQUES.** HASS, M. DAVISSON, J. W. ROSENSTOCK, H. B. SLINKMAN, J. A. BABISKIN, J. OPT. PROP. HIGHLY TRANSPARENT SOLIDS 435-42, 1975.
101036	**MEASUREMENT OF SMALL ABSORPTION COEFFICIENTS FROM THERMALLY INDUCED SHIFTS AT THE FUNDAMENTAL EDGE.** NURMIKKO, A. V. EPSTEIN, D. J. LINZ, A. OPT. PROP. HIGHLY TRANSPARENT SOLIDS 443-49, 1975.
101038	**A CALORIMETRIC TECHNIQUE FOR THE MEASUREMENT OF LOW OPTICAL ABSORPTION LOSSES IN BULK GLASS AND OPTICAL COMMUNICATION FIBRES.** WHITE, K. I. MIDWINTER, J. E. OPT. PROP. HIGHLY TRANSPARENT SOLIDS 461-71, 1975.
101039	**RAMAN SCATTERING TECHNIQUE TO EVALUATE LOSSES IN GALLIUM ARSENIDE DIELECTRIC WAVEGUIDES.** MERZ, J. L. LOGAN, R. A. SERGENT, A. M. OPT. PROP. HIGHLY TRANSPARENT SOLIDS 473-82, 1975.
101040	**ACCURATE SPECTROPHOTOMETER FOR THE ATTENUATION MEASUREMENT OF LOW LOSS OPTICAL MATERIALS.** KRAUSE, D. OPT. PROP. HIGHLY TRANSPARENT SOLIDS 483-92, 1975.
101041	**SURFACE STUDIES WITH ACOUSTIC PROBE TECHNIQUES.** ROCKWELL, D. A. COLBERT, T. S. PARKS, J. H. OPT. PROP. HIGHLY TRANSPARENT SOLIDS 493-502, 1975.
101042	**A 10.6 MICRON MODULATED LIGHT ELLIPSOMETER.** ALLEN, S. D. BRAUNSTEIN, A. I. BRAUNSTEIN, M. CHENG, J. C. NAFIE, L. A. OPT. PROP. HIGHLY TRANSPARENT SOLIDS 503-14, 1975.
101043	**MEASURING PHOTOELASTIC AND ELASTIC CONSTANTS OF TRANSPARENT MATERIALS BY APPLICATION OF STATIC STRESS.** FELDMAN, A. WAXLER, R. M. HOROWITZ, D. OPT. PROP. HIGHLY TRANSPARENT SOLIDS 517-25, 1975.
101124	**LINEAR STARK EFFECT IN F-F SPECTRA OF TRIPLY CHARGED RARE-EARTH IONS IN FLUORITE CRYSTALS.** KAPLYANSKII, A. A. MEDVEDEV, V. N. SKVORTSOV, A. P. OPT. SPEKTROSK. 39 (4), 775-6, 1975. (FOR ENGLISH TRANSLATION SEE E101125)
101125	**LINEAR STARK EFFECT IN F-F SPECTRA OF TRIPLY CHARGED RARE-EARTH IONS IN FLUORITE CRYSTALS.** KAPLYANSKII, A. A. MEDVEDEV, V. N. SKVORTSOV, A. P. OPT. SPECTROS., USSR 39 (4), 437-8, 1975. (ENGLISH TRANSLATION OF OPT. SPEKTROSK., 39 (4), 775-6, 1975; FOR ORIGINAL SEE E101124)
101158	**MERCUROUS CHLORIDE—A NEW POLARIZER MATERIAL.** FORMAN, R. A. BROWER, W. S. PARKER, H. S. DIG. TECH. PAP. - INT. QUANTUM ELECTRON. CONF., 8TH 9, 1974.
101176	**ELECTRICAL PROPERTIES OF GERMANIUM TELLURIDE FILMS.** VASIL'KOVA, O. G. LEBEDEVA, V. E. KONSTANTINOV, P. P. LEV, E. YA. SYSOEVA, L. M. IZV. AKAD. NAUK SSSR, NEORG. MATER. 12 (6), 1000-3, 1976. (ENGLISH TRANSLATION SEE E101886)
101192	**BAND STRUCTURE AND OPTICAL PROPERTIES OF MAGNESIUM FLUORIDE.** JOUANIN, C. ALBERT, J. P. GOUT, C. J. PHYS. 37 (5), 595-602, 1976.
101193	**INTERPRETATION OF THE ELECTRICAL PROPERTIES OF LIQUID SEMICONDUCTORS.** HODGKINSON, R. J. J. PHYS. 9 C (8), 1467-82, 1976.
101201	**A SIMPLE TECHNIQUE FOR MEASURING NONLINEAR ALTERNATING CURRENT PROPERTIES OF MATERIALS AT FREQUENCIES BELOW 1 HERTZ.** BAKER, A. J. PIERCY, A. R. J. PHYS. 9 E (6), 475-7, 1976.
101211	**EXCITON ABSORPTION, PHOTOLUMINESCENCE AND BAND STRUCTURE OF N-FREE AND N-DOPED INDIUM GALLIUM PHSOPHIDE.** NELSON, R. J. HOLONYAK, N., JR. J. PHYS. CHEM. SOLIDS 37 (6), 629-37, 1976. (AD-A034 255, AFOSR-TR-76-1280)
101287	**MULTIPHONON ABSORPTION OF ALKALI HALIDES AND QUASISELECTION RULES.** HARRINGTON, J. A. SOLID STATE COMMUN. 18 (8), 1043-6, 1976.
101295	**SOME CONSIDERATIONS ON THE DETERMINATION OF OPTICAL PROPERTIES OF ADSORBED FILMS.** GULTEPE, M. A. B. SURF. SCI. 56 (1), 76-86, 1976.
101298	**THE PREPARATION AND OPTICAL PROPERTIES OF THIN FILMS OF SEMICONDUCTOR ALLOYS.** HILL, R. THIN SOLID FILMS 34 (2), 395-8, 1976.
101304	**TOTAL ABSORPTANCE CORRELATIONS FOR SEMITRANSPARENT SOLIDS.** ANDERSON, E. E. OSNES, J. D. SOUTH DAKOTA SCHOOL OF MINES AND TECHNOLOGY 49PP., 1976. (PB-258 089, SDSMT-MNSF-7601)
101320	**ELECTRO- OPTIC PROPERTIES OF POTASSIUM DIHYDROGEN PHOSPHATE AND ISOMORPHS.** AUTHOR ANON. CLEVELAND CRYSTALS, INC., CLEVELAND, OHIO 12PP., 1976.
101321	**TRANSMISSION SPECTRA OF SOME TRANSITION METAL DICHALCOGENIDES: II. GROUP VIA: TRIGONAL PRISMATIC COORDINATION.** BEAL, A. R. KNIGHTS, J. C. LIANG, W. Y. J. PHYS. SOLID STATE PHYS. 5 C, 3540-51, 1972.
101327	**NEUTRON DISPLACEMENT DAMAGE IN HEAVILY DOPED GALLIUM ARSENIDE.** EULER, F. BOUTHILLETTE, L. KAHAN, A. STEIN, H. J. RADIAT. DAMAGE DEFECTS SEMICOND., PROC. INT. CONF. 113-20PP., 1973.
101330	**REFLECTIVITY MEASUREMENTS OF SINGLE CRYSTAL CADMIUM INDIUM SULFIDE AT ROOM TEMPERATURE.** FUJITA, H. OKADA, Y. JAP. J. APPL. PHYS. 13 (11), 1823-7, 1974.
101344	**DIELECTRIC AND THERMAL PROPERTIES OF LEAD NIOBIUM OXIDE AT LOW TEMPERATURE.** SIEGWARTH, J. D. LAWLESS, W. N. MORROW, A. J. J. APPL. PHYS. 47 (9), 3789-91, 1976.
101355	**VARIATION OF EMISSION PROPERTIES WITH COMPOSITION OF ZIRCONIUM CARBON + TUNGSTEN ALLOYS.** KOMOZYNSKII, P. A. OSTROVSKII, E. K. KALININA, N. G. NESHPOR, V. S. BEDNYAK, L. G. SOV. PHYS. TECH. PHYS. 21 (3), 316-19, 1976. (ENGLISH TRANSLATION OF ZH. TEKH. FIZ., 46 (3), 552-7, 1976; FOR ORIGINAL SEE E99762)
101356	**EFFECTIVE MASS ANISOTROPY AT THE X (IC) AND X (3C) MINIMA OF THE GALLIUM PHOSPHIDE COMDUCTION BAND.** KOPYLOV, A. A. SOV. PHYS. SEMICOND. 10 (5), 494-5, 1976. (ENGLISH TRANSLATION OF FIZ. TEKH. POLUPROV., 10 (5), 833-5, 1976; FOR ORIGINAL SEE E99887)
101374	**OPTICAL PHENOMENA, MATERIALS AND TECHNIQUES.** BENDOW, B. GIANINO, P. D. SOLID STATE SCIENCES DIVISION, HANSCOM AFB, MASS. 125PP., 1976. (AD-B013 807L)

EPIC Number	Bibliographic Citation

101375 **STRESS INDUCED BIREFRINGENCE OF INFRARED TRANSMITTING MATERIALS.**
PITHA, C. A. FRIEDMAN, J. D.
SZCZESNIAK, J. P. CUTTEBACK, D.
CORELLI, J. C.
SOLID STATE SCIENCES DIVISION, HANSCOM AFB, MASS.
199–206, 1976.
(AD–B013 807L)

101377 **EFFECT OF IONIZING RADIATION ON THE 10.6 MICRON ABSORPTION OF POTASSIUM CHLORIDE.**
LIPSON, H. G. KAHAN, A. LIGOR, P.
MARTIN, J. J.
SOLID STATE SCIENCES DIVISION, HANSCOM AFB, MASS.
233–40, 1976.
(AD–B013 807L)

101379 **HYDROCHLORIC ACID.**
KLECKNER, W. R. SUTTER, R. C.
ENCYCL. CHEM. TECHNOL.
11, 307–37, 1966.

101390 **BERYLLIUM COMPOUNDS.**
SCHWENZFEIER, C. W., JR.
ENCYCL. CHEM. TECHNOL.
3, 474–80, 1964.

101393 **BORON COMPOUNDS.**
NIES, N. P.
ENCYCL. CHEM. TECHNOL.
3, 608–52, 1964.

101404 **GLASS.**
HUTCHINS, J. R., III HARRINGTON, R. V.
ENCYCL. CHEM. TECHNOL.
10, 533–604, 1966.

101407 **INDIUM AND INDIUM COMPOUNDS.**
SMITH, A. A., JR.
ENCYCL. CHEM. TECHNOL.
11, 581–4, 1966.

101416 **RUBIDIUM AND RUBIDIUM COMPOUNDS.**
DAVIS, R. E.
ENCYCL. CHEM. TECHNOL.
17, 684–93, 1968.

101441 **INFRARED ABSORPTION IN CHEMICAL LASER WINDOW MATERIALS.**
HARRINGTON, J. A. GREGORY, D. A.
OTTO, W. F., JR.
APPL. OPT.
15 (8), 1953–9, 1976.

101442 **PHOTOELASTIC CONSTANTS OF INFRARED MATERIALS [LASER WINDOWS].**
FELDMAN, A. HOROWITZ, D. WAXLER, R. M.
LASER INDUCED DAMAGE IN OPTICAL MATERIALS: 1975.
164–9PP., 1976.
(NBS–SP–435, PB 252 186)

101446 **INADEQUACY OF THE STATISTICAL MANY–BODY MODEL FOR MOLECULAR INFRARED ABSORPTION IN THE FAR WINGS.**
FOWLER, B. W. SUNG, C. C.
PHYS. REV.
13 A (6), 2318–21, 1976.

101450 **THERMOMAGNETIC PROPERTIES OF N–TYPE AND P–TYPE MERCURY TELLURIDE.**
JEDRZEJCZAK, A. DIETL, T.
PHYS. STATUS SOLIDI
76 B (2), 737–51, 1976.

101451 **DOPING PROPERTIES OF LEAD IN ANTIMONY (III) TELLURIDE.**
SUESSMANN, H. RAU, H.
PHYS. STATUS SOLIDI
36 A (1), K55–K58, 1976.

101465 **TEMPERATURE SCALING OF ABSORPTION COEFFICIENTS.**
HEATON, H. I.
J. QUANT. SPECTROSC. RADIAT. TRANSFER
16 (9), 801–4, 1976.

101470 **MULTIPHOTON ABSORPTION COEFFICIENTS IN COMPOUND SEMICONDUCTORS FROM RUBY TO CARBON DIOXIDE LASER WAVELENGTHS.**
SHATAS, R. A. MITRA, S. S. NARDUCCI, L. M.
LASER INDUCED DAMAGE IN OPTICAL MATERIALS
369–88, 1976.
(NBS–SP–435, PB–252 186)

101471 **LIGHT ABSORPTION BY TWO–LAYER COLLOIDAL POTASSIUM AND COPPER COLOR CENTERS IN A POTASSIUM CHLORIDE CRYSTAL.**
RADCHENKO, I. S. PETRENKO, I. V.
OPT. SPEKTROSK.
40 (6), 1019–23, 1976.
(ENGLISH TRANSLATION SEE E102037)

101494 **ULTIMATES, PRAGMATISM AND NEW MATERIALS.**
MILES, P.
PROC. CONF. INFRARED LASER WINDOW MATERIALS, 5TH
7–15, 1976.
(AFML–TR–76–83, AD–B014 718L, UDRI–TR–76–35)

101501 **TEMPERATURE AND PRESSURE DEPENDENCES OF THE DIELECTRIC PROPERTIES OF LEAD(II) FLUORIDE AND THE ALKALINE–EARTH FLUORIDES.**
SAMARA, G. A.
PHYS. REV.
13 B (10), 4529–44, 1976.

101515 **HYDROSTATIC PRESSURE COEFFICIENTS OF ENERGY GAPS AND REFRACTIVE INDICES OF III–V CRYSTALS.**
BAZHENOV, V. K. MUTAL', A. M.
SOLOSHENKO, V. I.
FIZ. TEKH. POLUPROV.
9 (10), 1893–6, 1975.
(FOR ENGLISH TRANSLATION SEE E101516)

101516 **HYDROSTATIC PRESSURE COEFFICIENTS OF ENERGY GAPS AND REFRACTIVE INDICES OF III–V CRYSTALS.**
BAZHENOV, V. K. MUTAL', A. M.
SOLOSHENKO, V. I.
SOV. PHYS. SEMICOND.
9 (10), 1247–8, 1975.
(ENGLISH TRANSLATION OF FIZ. TEKH. POLUPROV., 9 (10), 1893–6, 1975; FOR ORIGINAL SEE E101515)

101526 **REFRACTIVE INDEX PROFILES INDUCED BY ION IMPLANTATION INTO SILICA.**
WEBB, A. P. TOWNSEND, P. D.
J. PHYS.
9 D (9), 1343–54, 1976.

101534 **GLASS IN A DIRECT ELECTRIC FIELD.**
MAZURIN, O. V.
ELECTRICAL PROPERTIES AND STRUCTURE OF GLASS
4, 5–55, 1965.

101536 **VARIATIONS OF ACTIVATION ENERGY AND VOLUME CONDUCTIVITY OF SOLID GLASSES IN RELATION TO THE CONDUCTION MECHANISM.**
ZERTSALOVA, I. N. FAINBERG, E. A.
GRECHANIK, L. A.
ELECTRICAL PROPERTIES AND STRUCTURE OF GLASS
4, 74–7, 1965.

101557 **BAND STRUCTURE OF MONOCRYSTALLINE FILMS OF SOLID SOLUTIONS BISMUTH ANTIMONY TELLURIDE.**
LIDORENKO, N. S. GALEV, V. N.
DASHEVSKII, Z. M. KOLOMOETS, N. V.
DOKL. AKAD. NAUK SSSR
224 (4–6), 1059–62, 1975.
(FOR ENGLISH TRANSLATION SEE E101558)

101558 **BAND STRUCTURE OF MONOCRYSTALLINE FILMS OF SOLID SOLUTIONS BISMUTH ANTIMONY TELLURIDE.**
LIDORENKO, N. S. GALEV, V. N.
DASHEVSKII, Z. M. KOLOMOETS, N. V.
SOV. PHYS. DOKL.
20 (10), 699–701, 1975.
(ENGLISH TRANSLATION OF DOKL. AKAD. NAUK SSSR, 224 (4–6), 1059–62, 1975; FOR ORIGINAL SEE E101557)

101559 **FAR–INFRARED ABSORPTION DUE TO IMPURITIES IN CESIUM BROMIDE AND CESIUM IODIDE.**
PRETTL, W. SIEP, E.
INT. CONF.
415–19, 1971.

101562 **EXPOSURE DAMAGE MECHANISMS FOR POTASSIUM CHLORIDE WINDOWS IN HIGH POWER LASER SYSTEMS.**
BLASZUK, P. R. WOODY, B. A. HUSLE, C. O.
DAVIS, J. W.
UNITED TECHNOLOGIES RES. CENTER, EAST HARTFORD, CONN.
144PP., 1976.
(N76–28544, NASA–CR–134982)

101579 **THERMOELECTRIC MATERIALS FOR DEVICES.**
GOFF, J. F. LOWNEY, J. R.
TRANS. AMER. NUCL. SOC.
23, 121, 1976.

101592 **EFFECTS OF PRESSURE OF OPTICAL F–BANDS IN RUBIDIUM HALIDES.**
MAMOLA, K. WU, R.
J. PHYS. CHEM. SOLIDS
37 (7), 383–8, 1976.

101595 **TEMPERATURE DEPENDENCE OF THE HALF–WIDTH OF THE 2.3 ELECTRON VOLTS OPTICAL ABSORPTION BAND IN NEUTRON–IRRADIATED ZINC SELENIDE.**
MATSUURA, K. TERATANI, S. KISHIDA, S.
TSURUMI, I.
PHYS. STATUS SOLIDI
35 A (1), K57–60, 1976.

101596 **ON THE ROLE OF Z CENTERS IN THE TRAPPING MECHANISM OF THERMOLUMINESCENT LITHIUM FLUORIDE.**
NINK, R. KOS, H.–J.
PHYS. STATUS SOLIDI
35 A (1), 121–9, 1976.

EPIC Number	Bibliographic Citation
101610	**FREQUENCY DEPENDENCE OF THE COEFFICIENT OF TWO-PHOTON ABSORPTION IN ZINC SELENIDE.** VALTRAMEYUNAS, R. GAURYUSHIN, V. VAITKUS, YU. FIZ. TVERD. TELA 17 (10), 3047–9, 1975. (FOR ENGLISH TRANSLATION SEE E101611)
101611	**FREQUENCY DEPENDENCE OF THE COEFFICIENT OF TWO-PHOTON ABSORPTION IN ZINC SELENIDE.** VALTRAMEYUNAS, R. GAURYUSHIN, V. VAITKUS, YU. SOV. PHYS. SOLID STATE 17 (10), 2020–1, 1976. (ENGLISH TRANSLATION OF FIZ. TVERD. TELA, 17 (10), 3047–9, 1975; FOR ORIGINAL SEE E101610)
101612	**ANISOTROPY OF ALKALI-HALIDE CRYSTALS CONTAINING QUASI-METALLIC AND COLLOIDAL CENTERS.** GOLUBTSOV, V. V. GLAUBERMAN, A. E. GOL'DENBERG, A. B. LUKASHUK, S. B. FIZ. TVERD. TELA 17 (10), 3053–5, 1975. (FOR ENGLISH TRANSLATION SEE E101613)
101613	**ANISOTROPY OF ALKALI-HALIDE CRYSTALS CONTAINING QUASI-METALLIC AND COLLOIDAL CENTERS.** GOLBUTSOV, V. V. GLAUBERMAN, A. E. GOL'DENBERG, A. B. LUKASHUK, S. B. SOV. PHYS. SOLID STATE 17 (10), 2024–5, 1976. (ENGLISH TRANSLATION OF FIZ. TVERD. TELA, 17 (10), 3053–5, 1975; FOR ORIGINAL SEE E101612)
101623	**EXCITON ABSORPTION IN CADMIUM SULFIDE FILMS WITH GRAIN BOUNDARY BARRIERS.** ARKHIPOV, A. N. ZHDAN, A. G. FIZ. TEKH. POLUPROV. 9 (11), 2181–3, 1975. (FOR ENGLISH TRANSLATION SEE E101624)
101624	**EXCITON ABSORPTION IN CADMIUM SULFIDE FILMS WITH GRAIN BOUNDARY BARRIERS.** ARKHIPOV, A. N. ZHDAN, A. G. SOV. PHYS. SEMICOND. 9 (11), 1417–18, 1975. (ENGLISH TRANSLATION OF FIZ. TEKH. POLUPROV., 9 (11), 2181–3, 1975; FOR ORIGINAL SEE E101623)
101629	**MECHANISMS OF CHARGES IN THE STATIC RESISTIVITY OF N-TYPE GERMANIUM AND N-TYPE INDIUM ANTIMONY UNDER ELECTRON SPIN RESONANCE CONDITIONS.** GERSHENZON, E. M. SEMENOV, I. T. FOGEL'SON, M. S. FIZ. TEKH. POLUPROV. 9 (11), 2150–5, 1975. (FOR ENGLISH TRANSLATION SEE E101630)
101630	**MECHANISMS OF CHARGES IN THE STATIC RESISTIVITY OF N-TYPE GERMANIUM AND N-TYPE INDIUM ANTIMONY UNDER ELECTRON SPIN RESONANCE CONDITIONS.** GERSHENZON, E. M. SEMENOV, I. T. FOGEL'SON, M. S. SOV. PHYS. SEMICOND. 9 (11), 1399–1402, 1975. (ENGLISH TRANSLATION OF FIZ. TEKH. POLUPROV., 9 (11), 2150–5, 1975; FOR ORIGINAL SEE E101629)
101631	**THE ANOMALOUSLY LARGE PHOTOVOLTAGE EFFECT IN ANTIMONY ORTHONIOBATE.** VERKHOVSKAYA, K. A. LOBACHEV, A. N. POPOV, B. N. POPOLITOV, V. I. PESKIN, V. F. FRIDKIN, V. M. JETP LETT. 23 (9), 476–8, 1976. (ENGLISH TRANSLATION OF ZH. EKSP. TEOR. FIZ., PIS'MA RED., 23 (9), 522–3, 1976; FOR ORIGINAL SEE E99754)
101641	**HEAT CAPACITY OF NICKEL - IRON. EXPERIMENTAL DATA FROM 300 TO 1670 K.** KOLLIE, T. G. BROOKS, C. R. PHYS. STATUS SO: IDI 19 A (2), 545–54, 1973.
101642	**THERMAL CONDUCTIVITY OF BORON AND OF ITS CRYSTAL STRUCTURE ANALOGS.** GOLIKOVA, O. A. ZAITSEV, V. K. ORLOV, V. M. PETROV, A. V. STIL'BANS, L. S. TKALENKO, E. N. PHYS. STATUS SOLIDI 21 A (2), 405–12, 1974.
101643	**RESONANCE RAMAN EFFECT AND FAR-INFRARED SPECTRA OF RHODIUM-DOPED SILVER BROMIDE CRYSTALS.** KUAN, T. S. INORG. CHEM. 13 (5), 1256–8, 1974.
101646	**MEASUREMENT OF OPTICAL ABSORPTION IN DIELECTRIC REFLECTORS.** AHRENS, H. WELLING, H. SCHEEL, H. E. APPL. PHYS. 1 (1), 69–71, 1973.
101649	**ADVANCED THERMIONIC TECHNOLOGY PROGRAM PROGRESS REPORT NO. 3.** THERMO ELECTRON CORPORATION THERMO ELECTRON CORP., WALTHAM, MASS. 17PP., 1975. (TE-4202/4203-32-76)
101650	**REFRACTIVE INDEX AND ITS TEMPERATURE COEFFICIENT FOR HOT-FORGED CALCIUM FLUORIDE.** DODGE, M. J. NATIONAL BUREAU OF STANDARDS, WASHINGTON, D. C. 3–8, 1976. (NBSIR-76-1115, PB-257 196, AD-A029 059)
101652	**GROWTH OF LOWLOSS POTASSIUM BROMIDE IN HOLOGENATING ATMOSPHERES.** KLEIN, P. H. NAVAL RESEARCH LAB., WASHINGTON, D. C. 1–14, 1975. (AD-B008 044L)
101655	**THALLIUM IODIDE PROTECTIVE COATINGS FOR ALKALI HALIDE OPTICAL COMPONENTS.** CHAFFIN, J. H. SKOGMAN, R. A. PROC. ANN. CONF. INFRARED LASER WINDOW MATERIALS, 4TH 13–22, 1975. (AD-B008 167L, AFML-TR-75-79)
101656	**GERMANIUM AND THORIUM FLUORIDE FILMS FOR HIGH ENERGY LASER COMPONENTS.** BRAUNSTEIN, M. BRAUNSTEIN, A. I. ZUCCARO, D. HART, R. R. PROC. ANN. CONF. INFRARED LASER WINDOW MATERIALS, 4TH 63–5, 1975. (AD-B008 167L, AFML-TR-75-79)
101657	**OPTICAL PROPERTIES OF POLYCRYSTALLINE ZINC SELENIDE.** FELDMAN, A. MALITSON, I. H. HOROWITZ, D. WAXLER, R. M. DODGE, M. J. PROC. ANN. CONF. INFRARED LASER WINDOW MATERIALS, 4TH 117–29, 1975. (AD-B008 167L AFML-TR-75-79 PB-253541)
101658	**STRESS BIREFRINGENCE IN POTASSIUM BROMIDE, POTASSIUM CHLORIDE, LITHIUM FLUORIDE AND ZINC SELENIDE IN THE 4 TO 11.6 MICRON WAVELENGTH REGION.** CORELLI, J. C. SZCZESNIAK, J. P. PROC. ANN. CONF. INFRARED LASER WINDOW MATERIALS, 4TH 131–48, 1975. (AD-B008 167L, AFML-TR-75-79)
101659	**STRESS-OPTIC COEFFICIENTS OF POTASSIUM CHLORIDE, BARIUM FLUORIDE, CALCIUM FLUORIDE, CADMIUM TELLURIDE, TI-1120 AND TI-1173.** PITHA, C. A. FRIEDMAN, J. D. PROC. ANN. CONF. INFRARED LASER WINDOW MATERIALS, 4TH 149–57, 1975. (AD-B008 167L, AFML-TR-75-79)
101660	**IMPURITY ABSORPTION IN HALIDE WINDOW MATERIALS.** DUTHLER, C. J. PROC. ANN. CONF. INFRARED LASER WINDOW MATERIALS, 4TH 165–72, 1975. (AD-B008 167L, AFML-TR-75-79)
101661	**IDENTIFICATION AND ELIMINATION OF IMPURITY-INDUCED 10.6 MU ABSORPTION IN POTASSIUM BROMIDE.** SHLICHTA, P. J. YEE, J. CHANEY, R. E PROC. ANN. CONF. INFRARED LASER WINDOW MATERIALS, 4TH 173–83, 1975. (AD-B008 167L, AFML-TR-75-79)
101662	**DETERMINATION OF MULTI-PHONON ABSORPTION MECHANISM BY REFRACTIVE INDEX MEASUREMENTS.** MANGIR, M. HELLWARTH, R. PROC. ANN. CONF. INFRARED LASER WINDOW MATERIALS, 4TH 185–91, 1975. (AD-B008 167L, AFML-TR-75-79)
101663	**A CRYOGENIC EMITTANCE SPECTROMETER FOR MEASURING ABSORPTION LOSSES IN LASER WINDOW MATERIALS.** MCCANN, W. SHIELDS, W. MC CANN, W. SHIELDS, W. PROC. ANN. CONF. INFRARED LASER WINDOW MATERIALS, 4TH 197–212, 1975. (AD-B008 167L, AFML-TR-75-79)
101664	**CARBON OXIDE LASER CALORIMETRY FOR SURFACE AND COATING EVALUATION.** KRAATZ, P. MENDOZA, P. J. PROC. ANN. CONF. INFRARED LASER WINDOW MATERIALS, 4TH 213–30, 1975. (AD-B008 167L, AFML-TR-75-79)
101665	**IMPROVED LASER CALORIMETRIC TECHNIQUES.** HASS, M. DAVISSON, J. W. ROSENSTOCK, H. B. BABISKIN, J. PROC. ANN. CONF. INFRARED LASER WINDOW MATERIALS, 4TH 231–9, 1975. (AD-B008 167L, AFML-TR-75-79)

EPIC Number	Bibliographic Citation

101666 **EFFECTS OF ENVIRONMENTAL FACTORS ON THE OPTICAL PROPERTIES OF HIGH POWER INFRARED LASER WINDOW COATINGS.**
JOHNSTON, G. T. WALSH, D. A. HARRIS, R. J.
DETRIO, J. A.
PROC. ANN. CONF. INFRARED LASER WINDOW MATERIALS, 4TH
369–85, 1975.
(AD–B008 167L, AFML–TR–75–79)

101667 **CURRENT STATUS OF HIGH INTENSITY VACUUM ULTRAVIOLET MATERIALS.**
SPARKS, M. DUTHLER, C. J.
PROC. ANN. CONF. INFRARED LASER WINDOW MATERIALS, 4TH
389–400, 1975.
(AD–B008 167L, AFML–TR–75–79)

101668 **LOW LOSS WINDOW MATERIALS FOR CHEMICAL AND CARBON OXIDE LASER.**
HARRINGTON, J. A. BENDOW, B. NAMJOSHI, K. V.
MITRA, S. S. STIERWALT, D. L.
PROC. ANN. CONF. INFRARED LASER WINDOW MATERIALS, 4TH
401–21, 1975.
(AD–B008 167L, AFML–TR–75–79)

101669 **FLUORIDE WINDOW MATERIALS FOR THE 2–6 MICRON REGION.**
WINSTON, H. V. TURK, R. R. PASTOR, R. C.
SHCOLL, R. F.
PROC. ANN. CONF. INFRARED LASER WINDOW MATERIALS, 4TH
437–43, 1975.
(AD–B008 167L, AFML–TR–75–79)

101670 **FUSION CASTING OF ALKALINE EARTH FLUORIDE LASER OPTICS.**
NEWBERG, R. T. READEY, D. W. NEWBORN, H. A.
MILES, P. A.
PROC. ANN. CONF. INFRARED LASER WINDOW MATERIALS, 4TH
445–63, 1975.
(AD–B008 167L, AFML–TR–75–79)

101671 **GROWTH, SURFACE FINISHING, AND OPTICAL CHARACTERIZATION OF SODIUM FLUORIDE AND OTHER FLUORIDE LASER WINDOW CRYSTALS.**
KLEIN, P. H. DAVISSON, J. W.
PROC. ANN. CONF. INFRARED LASER WINDOW MATERIALS, 4TH
465–74, 1975.
(AD–B008 167L, AFML–TR–75–79)

101672 **CHEMICAL VAPOR DEPOSITION OF CADMIUM TELLURIDE AND LARGE PLATE FABRICATION OF CHEMICAL VAPOR DEPOSITION ZINC SELENIDE FOR LASER WINDOWS.**
DONADIO, R. N. SWANSON, A. W. PAPPIS, J.
PROC. ANN. CONF. INFRARED LASER WINDOW MATERIALS, 4TH
493–509, 1975.
(AD–B0008 167L, AFML–TR–75–79)

101673 **SINGLE CRYSTAL GROWTH OF ZINC SELENIDE FROM THE VAPOR PHASE.**
REYNOLDS, D. C. LITTON, C. W. NAAS, D. W.
JOHNSON, D. E.
PROC. ANN. CONF. INFRARED LASER WINDOW MATERIALS, 4TH
519–30, 1975.
(AD–B008 1676, AFML–TR–75–79)

101674 **VAPOR DEPOSITION AND TRANSMISSION ELECTRON MICROSCOPY OF CADMIUM TELLURIDE.**
HALL, E. L. VANDER SANDE, J. B.
LEMAIRE, P. J. BOWEN, H. K.
PROC. ANN. CONF. INFRARED LASER WINDOW MATERIALS, 4TH
531–56, 1975.
(AD–B008 167L, AFML–TR–75–79)

101675 **EFFECT OF IONIZING RADIATION ON THE 10.6 MICRON ABSORPTION OF POTASSIUM CHLORIDE.**
LIPSON, H. G. KAHAN, A. LIGOR, P.
MARTIN, J. J.
PROC. ANN. CONF. INFRARED LASER WINDOW MATERIALS, 4TH
589–97, 1975.
(AD–B008 167L, AFML–TR–75–79)

101676 **THE GROWTH, CHARACTERIZATION AND RECRYSTALLIZATION OF ALKALI HALIDE ALLOYED AND DOPED POTASSIUM CHLORIDE.**
HARRISON, V. B. HENDRICKSON, G. O.
HEINISCH, R. P. STARLING, J. E.
PROC. ANN. CONF. INFRARED LASER WINDOW MATERIALS, 4TH
599–610, 1975.
(AD–B008 167L, AFML–TR–75–79)

101677 **HYDROSTATIC PRESS FORGING OF ALKALI HALIDE CRYSTALS FOR LASER WINDOW APPLICATIONS.**
KOEPKE, B. G. ANDERSON, R. H. BERNAL G. E.
STOKES, R. J.
PROC. ANN. CONF. INFRARED LASER WINDOW MATERIALS, 4TH
621–67, 1975.
(AD–B008 167L, AFML–TR–75–79)

101678 **OVERVIEW OF THE LOW–POWER WINDOW FOR THE AIRBORNE LASER LABORATORY.**
LOOMIS, J. BLACKBURN, A. ALPERT, T.
PROC. ANN. CONF. INFRARED LASER WINDOW MATERIALS, 4TH
751–9, 1975.
(AD–B008 167L, AFML–TR–75–79)

101679 **OPTICAL CHARACTERIZATION OF WINDOWS FOR THE AIRBORNE LASER LABORATORY.**
DUEWEKE, P. W. KESTER, J. M. MCBROOM, R. J.
PREONAS, D. D.
PROC. ANN. CONF. INFRARED LASER WINDOW MATERIALS, 4TH
789–802, 1975.
(AD–B008 167L, AFML–TR–75–79)

101680 **PROPERTIES OF NEODYMIUM LASER MATERIALS.**
THORNTON, J. R. FOUNTAIN, W. D. FLINT, G. W.
CROW, T. G.
APPL. OPT.
8 (6), 1087–1102, 1969.

101691 **THE DETERMINATION OF THE REFRACTIVE INDEX AND THICKNESS OF A TRANSPARENT FILM.**
KHAWAJA, E. E.
J. PHYS.
9 D (14), 1939–43, 1976

101704 **THE DIRECT DETERMINATION OF THE TEMPERATURE DEPENDENCE OF THE REFRACTIVE INDEX OF LIQUIDS AND SOLIDS.**
ABBATE, G. ATTANASIO, A. BERNINI, U.
RAGOZZINO, E. SOMMA, F.
J. PHYS.
9 D (14), 1945–51, 1976.

101714 **INFRARED BULK AND SURFACE ABSORPTION BY NEARLY TRANSPARENT CRYSTALS.**
ROSENSTOCK, H. B. GREGORY, D. A.
HARRINGTON, J. A.
APPL. OPT.
15 (9), 2075–9, 1976.

101723 **ELECTRONIC CONTRIBUTIONS TO THE ELASTIC CONSTANTS OF P–TYPE DIAMOND AND ZINC–BLENDE–TYPE SEMICONDUCTORS AND DEPENDENCE OF THE ENERGY GAPS OF DIAMOND AND ZINC–BLENDE–TYPE SEMICONDUCTORS ON HYDROSTATIC PRESSURE.**
KIM, C. K.
PURDUE UNIVERSITY, W. LAFAYETTE, IND., PH. D. THESIS
114PP., 1975.

101746 **EXPLICIT SOLUTION FOR THE OPTICAL PROPERTIES OF A UNIAXIAL CRYSTAL IN GENERALIZED ELLIPSOMETRY.**
ELSHAZLY–ZAGHLOUL, M. AZZAM, R. M. A.
BASHARA, N. M.
SURF. SCI.
56 (1), 281–92, 1976.

101754 **BEHAVIOR OF THE ELECTRICAL RESISTIVITY AT PHASE TRANSITIONS IN BINARY ALLOYS.**
BINDER, K. STAUFFER, D.
Z. PHYS.
24 B (4), 407–15, 1976.

101768 **INSTRUMENT FOR MEASURING THE INDEX OF REFRACTION OF THIN DIELECTRIC FILMS (THICKNESS MONITORING).**
CHERNYAEV, V. N. OBICHKIN, YU. G.
SEMENOV, E. I.
SOV. J. OPT. TECHNOL.
42 (12), 730–2, 1975.
(ENGLISH TRANSLATION OF OPT. MEKH. PROM., 42, 38–40, 1975; FOR ORIGINAL SEE E101769)

101769 **INSTRUMENT FOR MEASURING THE INDEX OF REFRACTION OF OF THIN DIELECTRIC FILMS (THICKNESS MONITORING).**
CHERNYAEV, V. N. OBICHKIN, YU. G.
SEMENOV, E. I.
OPT. MEKH. PROM.
42, 38–40, 1975.
(FOR ENGLISH TRANSLATION SEE E101768)

101796 **LASER WINDOW MATERIALS CHARACTERIZATION.**
DETRIO, J. A. HARRIS, R. J.
JOHNSTON, G. T. WALSH, D. A.
AIR FORCE MATERIALS LAB., WPAFB, OHIO
97PP., 1976.
(AFML–TR–76–96, AD–B014 990L, UDRI–TR–76–15)

101804 **TEMPERATURE COEFFICIENT OF THE REFRACTIVE INDEX OF SOME ALKALI HALIDE CRYSTALS.**
VISHNEVSKII, V. N. KUZYK, M. P.
STEFANSKII, I. V.
FIZ. TVERD. TELA
17 (11), 3201–4, 1975.
(FOR ENGLISH TRANSLATION SEE E101805)

101805 **TEMPERATURE COEFFICIENT OF THE REFRACTIVE INDEX OF SOME ALKALI HALIDE CRYSTALS.**
VISHNEVSKII, V. N. KUZYK, M. P.
STEFANSKII, I. V.
SOV. PHYS. SOLID STATE
17 (11), 2110–12, 1976.
(ENGLISH TRANSLATION OF FIZ. TVERD. TELA, 17 (11), 3201–4, 1975; FOR ORIGINAL SEE E101804)

101808 **OPTICAL FABRICATION—STATE–OF–THE–ART WITH MATERIALS, ISSUES, AND PROSPECTS.**
BENNETT, H.
PROC. CONF. INFRARED LASER WINDOW MATERIALS, 5TH
19–42, 1976.
(AFML–TR–76–83, AD–B014 718L, UDRI–TR–76–35)

EPIC Number	Bibliographic Citation

101810 **OPTICAL FINISHING OF POTASSIUM CHLORIDE WINDOWS TO MINIMIZE ABSORPTION IN THE INFRARED.**
TURK, R. PASTOR, R. TIMPER, A.
BRAUNSTEIN, M. HEUSSNER, G.
PROC. CONF. INFRARED LASER WINDOW MATERIALS, 5TH
103–12, 1976.
(AFML–TR–76–83, AD–B014 718, UDRI–TR–76–35)

101811 **CHEMICAL POLISHING OF POTASSIUM BROMIDE AND ABSORPTION MEASUREMENTS AT 1.06 MU M.**
DAVISSON, J.
PROC. CONF. INFRARED LASER WINDOW MATERIALS, 5TH
113–21, 1976.
(AFML–TR–76–83, AD–B014 718L, UDRI–TR–76–35)

101812 **LOW ABSORPTION ANTIREFLECTION COATINGS FOR POTASSIUM CHLORIDE.**
BRAUNSTEIN, M. ZUCCARO, D. RUDISILL, J.
BRAUNSTEIN, A.
PROC. CONF. INFRARED LASER WINDOW MATERIALS, 5TH
135–42, 1976.
(AFML–TR–76–83, AD–B014 718L, UDRI–TR–76–35)

101813 **THE DEVELOPMENT OF ANTIREFLECTIVE THIN FILMS FOR POLYCRYSTALLINE ALKALI HALIDE LASER WINDOW MATERIALS.**
STARLING, J. HARRISON, W. BOORD, W.
MAR, H.
PROC. CONF. INFRARED LASER WINDOW MATERIALS, 5TH
143–54, 1976.
(AFML–TR–76–83, AD–B014 718L, UDRI–TR–76–35)

101814 **THICK COATINGS OF THALLIUM IODIDE ON POTASSIUM CHLORIDE SUBSTRATES FOR AR APPLICATIONS.**
CHAFFIN, J. SKOGMAN, R.
PROC. CONF. INFRARED LASER WINDOW MATERIALS, 5TH
155–65, 1976.
(AFML–TR–76–83, AD–B014 718L, UDRI–TR–76–35)

101815 **A STUDY OF SELECTED FLUORIDES OF THE LATHANIDE SERIES AS POTENTIAL OPTICAL COATING MATERIALS FOR 10.6 MICRON OPTICS.**
GOLUBOVIC, A. BERMAN, I. COMER, J.
POSEN, H.
PROC. CONF. INFRARED LASER WINDOW MATERIALS, 5TH
167–79, 1976.
(AFML–TR–76–83, AD–B014 718, UDRI–TR–76–35)

101816 **THE ROLE OF INTERFACE TOPOLOGY ON ANTIREFLECTIVE COATING PERFORMANCE AS ILLUSTRATED BY ZINC SULFUR/CERIUM FLUORIDE ON POTASSIUM CHLORIDE.**
EWING, W. GOLUBOVIC, A. BERMAN, I.
BRADBURY, R. FITZGERALD, J. BRUCE, J.
COMER, J.
PROC. CONF. INFRARED LASER WINDOW MATERIALS, 5TH
181–92, 1976.
(AFML–TR–76–83, AD–B014 718L, UDRI–TR–76–35)

101817 **SPUTTER-DEPOSITED ZINC SELENIDE FILMS ON POTASSIUM CHLORIDE.**
WALSH, D. BERTKE, R.
PROC. CONF. INFRARED LASER WINDOW MATERIALS, 5TH
193–203, 1976.
(AFML–TR–76–83, AD–B014 718L, UDRI–TR–76–35)

101819 **REFRACTIVE INDEX OF HIGH PURITY POTASSIUM CHLORIDE AND POTASSIUM IODIDE DOPED POTASSIUM CHLORIDE.**
DODGE, M. MALITSON, I.
PROC. CONF. INFRARED LASER WINDOW MATERIALS, 5TH
215–23, 1976.
(AFML–TR–76–83, AD–B014 718L, UDRI–TR–76–35,
PB–263–151)

101820 **COMPARISON OF THERMAL COEFFICIENT OF REFRACTIVE INDEX OF VARIOUS LASER WINDOW MATERIALS.**
MUKAI, H. KROK, P. KEPPLE, G.
HARRIS, R. JOHNSTON, G.
PROC. CONF. INFRARED LASER WINDOW MATERIALS, 5TH
225–32, 1976.
(AFML–TR–76–83, AD–B014 718, UDRI–TR–76–35)

101821 **OPTICAL PROPERTIES OF EUOPIUM-DOPED POTASSIUM CHLORIDE LASER WINDOWS MATERIALS.**
STOEBE, T. SPRY, R. LEWIS, J.
PROC. CONF. INFRARED LASER WINDOW MATERIALS, 5TH
265–77, 1976.
(AFML–TR–76–83, AD–B014 718L, UDRI–TR–76–35)

101822 **ARSENIC SULFIDE AND THORIUM FLUORIDE COATINGS ON POTASSIUM CHLORIDE AND SODIUM CHLORIDE WINDOWS.**
DONOVAN, T. BAER, A.
PROC. CONF. INFRARED LASER WINDOW MATERIALS, 5TH
291–300, 1976.
(AFML–TR–76–83, AD–B014 718L, UDRI–76–35)

101823 **MULTIPHOTON ABSORPTION IN OPTICAL MATERIALS FROM RUBY TO CARBON DIOXIDE LASER WAVELENGTHS.**
SHATAS, R. MITRA, S.
PROC. CONF. INFRARED LASER WINDOW MATERIALS, 5TH
301–12, 1976.
(AFML–TR–76–83, AD–B014 718L, UDRI–76–35)

101824 **ABSORPTANCE OF COATED ALKALINE EARTH FLUORIDE WINDOWS AT CARBON OXIDE LASER WAVELENGTHS.**
KRAATZ, P. HOLMES, S. KLUGMAN, A.
PROC. CONF. INFRARED LASER WINDOW MATERIALS, 5TH
315–28, 1976.
(AFML–TR–76–83, AD–B014 718L, UDRI–76–35)

101825 **ANTIREFLECTION COATINGS FOR CALCIUM FLUORIDE LASER WINDOWS OPERATING AT 5.3 MICROMETERS.**
RUDISILL, J. BRAUNSTEIN, M. BOWERS, J.
PROC. CONF. INFRARED LASER WINDOW MATERIALS, 5TH
329–35, 1976.
(AFML–TR–76–83, AD–B014 718L, UDRI–76–35)

101826 **COMPARISON OF THE 5.3 MICROMETERS ABSORPTION IN VARIOUS ANTIREFLECTION COATINGS.**
GREASON, P. JOHNSTON, G. OHMER, M.
PROC. CONF. INFRARED LASER WINDOW MATERIALS, 5TH
337–46, 1976.
(AFML–TR–76–83, AD–B014 718L, UDRI–76–35)

101827 **COATING MATERIALS FOR CHEMICAL LASER WINDOWS.**
BRAUNSTEIN, A. BRAUNSTEIN, M. RUDISILL, J.
HARRINGTON, J. GREGORY, D.
PROC. CONF. INFRARED LASER WINDOW MATERIALS, 5TH
347–54, 1976.
(AFML–TR–76–83, AD–B014 718L, UDRI–76–35)

101828 **LASER CALORIMETRY OF INFRARED OPTICAL THIN FILMS.**
WILLINGHAM, C. BUA, D. VARITIMOS, T.
SCHAPIRA, M. STATZ, H. HORRIGAN, F.
PROC. CONF. INFRARED LASER WINDOW MATERIALS, 5TH
355–69, 1976.
(AFML–TR–76–83, AD–B014 718L, UDRI–76–35)

101829 **CONTINUOUS WAVE LASER-INDUCED DAMAGE IN POTASSIUM CHLORIDE.**
DETRIO, J. PETTY, R. FOX, J. LARGER, P.
FENTER, J.
PROC. CONF. INFRARED LASER WINDOW MATERIALS, 5TH
381–9, 1976.
(AFML–TR–76–83, AD–B014 718L, UDRI–76–35)

101830 **LASER DAMAGE TO HIGH ENERGY LASER WINDOW MATERIALS AS RELATED TO SURFACE DAMAGE.**
SOILEAU, M. BENNETT, H. PORTEUS, J.
TEMPLE, P. BASS, M.
PROC. CONF. INFRARED LASER WINDOW MATERIALS, 5TH
391–417, 1976.
(AFML–TR–76–83, AD–B014 718L, UDRI–76–35)

101833 **HIGH-POWER TESTING OF INTERMEDIATE SIZE 10.6 MICRON WINDOWS.**
BLACKBURN, A. HUGULEY, C.
PROC. CONF. INFRARED LASER WINDOW MATERIALS, 5TH
505–16, 1976.
(AFML–TR–76–83, AD–B014 718L, UDRI–76–35)

101834 **INTERFEROMETRY OF LASER HEATED WINDOWS.**
BERNAL, G. E. LOOMIS, J.
PROC. CONF. INFRARED LASER WINDOW MATERIALS, 5TH
587–609, 1976.
(AFML–TR–76–83, AD–B014 718L, UDRI–76–35)

101835 **ROUND ROBIN ON CALORIMETRIC MEASUREMENT OF 10.6 MICROMETER ABSORPTION IN POTASSIUM CHLORIDE.**
LIPSON, H. LIGOR, P.
PROC. CONF. INFRARED LASER WINDOW MATERIALS, 5TH
613–26, 1976.
(AFML–TR–76–83, AD–B014 718L, UDRI–76–35)

101837 **AN OPTOACOUSTIC TECHNIQUE FOR MEASURING THE OPTICAL ABSORPTION COEFFICIENT IN SOLIDS.**
HORDVIK, A. SCHLOSSBERG, H.
PROC. CONF. INFRARED LASER WINDOW MATERIALS, 5TH
639–50, 1976.
(AFML–TR–76–83, AD–B014 718L, UDRI–76–35)

101838 **THERMAL DISTORTION CALCULATIONS FOR COOLED ZINC SELENIDE LASER WINDOWS.**
GIANINO, P. BENDOW, B.
PROC. CONF. INFRARED LASER WINDOW MATERIALS, 5TH
663–77, 1976.
(AFML–TR–76–83, AD–B014 718L, UDRI–76–35)

101839 **TEMPERATURE DEPENDENCE OF THE REFRACTIVE INDEX OF ALKALINE EARTH FLUORIDES.**
LIPSON, H. YSAY, Y. LIGOR, P.
BENDOW, B. MITRA, S.
PROC. CONF. INFRARED LASER WINDOW MATERIALS, 5TH
679–88, 1976.
(AFML–TR–76–83, AD–B014 718L, UDRI–76–35)

101840 **OPTICAL, MECHANICAL AND MICROSTRUCTURAL INVESTIGATIONS IN CADMIUM TELLURIDE.**
HALL, E. NURMIKKO, A. VANDER SANDE, J.
BOWEN, H.
PROC. CONF. INFRARED LASER WINDOW MATERIALS, 5TH
715–28, 1976.
(AFML–TR–76–83, AD–B014 718L, UDRI–76–35)

EPIC Number	Bibliographic Citation
101841	**CADMIUM TELLURIDE AS A CARBON DIOXIDE LASER WINDOW MATERIAL.** KROGER, F. SELIM, F. PROC. CONF. INFRARED LASER WINDOW MATERIALS, 5TH 729–37, 1976. (AFML–TR–76–83, AD–B014 718L, UDRI–76–35)
101842	**IMPURITY INDUCED ABSORPTION IN PHOSPHORUS DOPED CADMIUM TELLURIDE.** DUTT, B. SPITZER, W. PROC. CONF. INFRARED LASER WINDOW MATERIALS, 5TH 739–57, 1976. (AFML–TR–76–83, AD–B014 718L, UDRI–76–35)
101843	**MULTIPHONON ABSORPTION OF ALKALI HALIDES AND QUASISELECTION RULES.** DUTHLER, C. HARRINGTON, J. PATTEN, F. HASS, M. PROC. CONF. INFRARED LASER WINDOW MATERIALS, 5TH 759–69, 1976. (AFML–TR–76–83, AD–B014 718L, UDRI–76–35)
101844	**TEMPERATURE DEPENDENCE OF THE ABSORPTION COEFFICIENT OF LASER WINDOW MATERIALS.** STIERWALT, D. PROC. CONF. INFRARED LASER WINDOW MATERIALS, 5TH 771–7, 1976. (AFML–TR–76–83, AD–B014 718L, UDRI–76–35)
101845	**THEORY OF ELASTO-OPTIC COEFFICIENTS IN POLYCRYSTALLINE MATERIALS.** FLANNERY, M. MARBURGER, J. PROC. CONF. INFRARED LASER WINDOW MATERIALS, 5TH 781–9, 1976. (AFML–TR–76–83, AD–B014 718L, UDRI–76–35)
101846	**EMITTANCE STUDIES ON COATED LASER WINDOW MATERIALS.** SKOLNIK, L. KAHAN, A. BROWN, R. GOLUBOVIC, A. ENGEL, J. PROC. CONF. INFRARED LASER WINDOW MATERIALS, 5TH 805–23, 1976. (AFML–TR–76–83, AD–B014 718L, UDRI–76–35)
101847	**SURFACE AND BULK ABSORPTION IN POTASSIUM CHLORIDE, POTASSIUM BROMIDE, AND SODIUM CHLORIDE AS A FUNCTION OF TEMPERATURE AND CARBON DIOXIDE LASER FREQUENCIES.** ROWE, J. HARRINGTON, J. PROC. CONF. INFRARED LASER WINDOW MATERIALS, 5TH 825–37, 1976. (AFML–TR–76–83, AD–B014 718L, UDRI–76–35)
101848	**EXPERIMENTAL DETERMINATION OF MULTIPHONON ABSORPTION MECHANISM AND PARAMETERS IN COLD VAPOUR DEPOSITE ZINC SELENIDE.** MAGNIR, M. HELLWARTH, R. PROC. CONF. INFRARED LASER WINDOW MATERIALS, 5TH 839–48, 1976. (AFML–TR–76–83, AD–B014 718L, UDRI–76–35)
101849	**ORIGIN OF ABSORPTION IN HIGHLY TRANSPARENT INFRARED LASER WINDOWS.** HASS, M. PROC. CONF. INFRARED LASER WINDOW MATERIALS, 5TH 849–58, 1976. (AFML–TR–76–83, AD–B014 718L, UDRI–76–35)
101850	**INFRARED BULK AND SURFACE ABSORPTION BY NEARLY TRANSPARENT CRYSTALS.** ROSENSTOCK, H. GREGORY, D. HARRINGTON, J. PROC. CONF. INFRARED LASER WINDOW MATERIALS, 5TH 859–70, 1976. (AFML–TR–76–83, AD–B014 718L, UDRI–76–35)
101851	**OPTICAL ABSORPTION IN CHEMICAL LASER WINDOW MATERIALS.** HARRINGTON, J. GREGORY, D. OTTO, W. PROC. CONF. INFRARED LASER WINDOW MATERIALS, 5TH 871–86, 1976. (AFML–TR–76–83, AD–B014 718L, UDRI–76–35)
101852	**FREQUENCY AND TEMPERATURE DEPENDENCE OF THE ABSORPTION COEFFICIENT OF ALKALINE EARTH FLUORIDES.** LIPSON, H. BENDOW, B. SKOLNIK, L. MITRA, S. MASSA, N. PROC. CONF. INFRARED LASER WINDOW MATERIALS, 5TH 889–907, 1976. (AFML–TR–76–83, AD–B014 718L, UDRI–76–35)
101853	**STRESS INDUCED BIREFRINGENCE OF INFRARED TRANSMITTING MATERIALS.** PITHA, C. FRIEDMAN, J. SZCZESNIAK, J. CUTTEBACK, D. CORELLI, J. PROC. CONF. INFRARED LASER WINDOW MATERIALS, 5TH 927–35, 1976. (AFML–TR–76–83, AD–B014 718L, UDRI–76–35)
101854	**MEASUREMENT OF STRAIN-OPTIC COEFFICIENTS BY ACOUSTO-OPTIC INTERACTIONS IN WINDOW MATERIALS.** JOINER, R. STEIER, W. CHRISTENSEN, C. PROC. CONF. INFRARED LASER WINDOW MATERIALS, 5TH 937–42, 1976. (AFML–TR–76–83, AD–B014 718L, UDRI–76–35)
101857	**GROWTH OF LOWLOSS POTASSIUM BROMIDE IN HALIDE ATMOSPHERES.** KLEIN, P. PROC. CONF. INFRARED LASER WINDOW MATERIALS, 5TH 983–91, 1976. (AFML–TR–76–83, AD–B014 718L, UDRI–76–35)
101858	**RECRYSTALLIZATION OF PREFORGED ALKALI HALIDE MATERIALS.** HARRISON, W. HENDRICKSON, G. STARLING, J. PROC. CONF. INFRARED LASER WINDOW MATERIALS, 5TH 1013–25, 1976. (AFML–TR–76–83, AD–B014 718L, UDRI–76–35)
101859	**HIGH STRENGTH FORGINGS OF RUBIDIUM CHLORIDE DOPED POTASSIUM CHLORIDE.** KLAUSUTIS, N. ADAMSKI, J. SAMPSON, J. NIKULA, J. O'CONNOR, J. PROC. CONF. INFRARED LASER WINDOW MATERIALS, 5TH 1037–50, 1976. (AFML–TR–76–83, AD–B014 718L, UDRI–76–35)
101860	**LARGE WINDOW FABRICATION AND LOW-COST ZINC SELENIDE.** SWANSON, A. DONADIO, R. GENTILMAN, R. PAPPIS, J. CONNOLLY, J. REAGAN, P. PROC. CONF. INFRARED LASER WINDOW MATERIALS, 5TH 1051–63, 1976. (AFML–TR–76–83, AD–B014 718L, UDRI–76–35)
101861	**FABRICATION OF FLUORIDE LASER WINDOWS BY FUSION CASTING.** NEWBERG, R. PAPPIS, J. PROC. CONF. INFRARED LASER WINDOW MATERIALS, 5TH 1065–78, 1976. (AFML–TR–76–83, AD–B014 718L, UDRI–76–35)
101862	**EVALUATION OF GROWTH AND FORGING TECHNIQUES FOR ALKALINE EARTH FLUORIDES.** LARKIN, J. KLAUSUTIS, N. HILTON, R. ADAMSKI, J. PROC. CONF. INFRARED LASER WINDOW MATERIALS, 5TH 1079–85, 1976. (AFML–TR–76–83, AD–B014 718L, UDRI–76–35)
101886	**ELECTRICAL PROPERTIES OF GERMANIUM TELLURIDE FILMS.** VASIL'KOVA, O. G. LEBEDEVA, V. E. KONSTANTINOV, P. P. LEV, E. YA. SYSOEVA, L. M. INORG. MAT., USSR 12 (6), 838–41, 1976. (ENGLISH TRANSLATION OF IZV. AKAD. NAUK, SSSR, NEORG. MATER., 12 (6), 1000–3, 1976; FOR ORIGINAL SEE E101176)
101890	**LIGHT DEFLECTION BY INDEX CHANGES.** PANKOVE, J. I. PHOTONICS 87–122, 1974.
101894	**OUTLOOKS FOR GALLIUM ARSENIDE TERRESTRIAL PHOTOVOLTAICS.** WOODALL, J. M. HOVEL, H. J. J. VAC. SCI. TECHNOL. 12 (5), 1000–9, 1975.
101913	**DETERMINATION OF THE THICKNESS AND REFRACTIVE INDEX OF NONADSORBING FILMS ON ABSORBING SUBSTRATES. SILICON DIOXIDE - SILICON SYSTEM.** POLI, G. GIRONDI, F. Z. PALOMBARINI, G. MET. ITAL. 65 (7–8), 414–20, 1973.
101914	**THE INFRA-RED ABSORPTION SPECTRA OF QUARTZ AND FUSED SILICA FROM 1 TO 7.5 MU. I. EXPERIMENTAL METHOD.** DRUMMOND, D. G. PROC. ROY. SOC. 153 A (879), 318–27, 1936.
101917	**EFFECT OF CHANGES IN BAND STRUCTURE PARAMETERS ON THE FUNDAMENTAL ABSORPTION SPECTRUM OF SEMICONDUCTORS (FUNDAMENTAL ABSORPTION EDGE OF GALLIUM ARSENIC PHOSPHIDE).** PIKHTIN, A. N. RAZBEGAEV, V. N. YAS'KOV, D. A. FIZ. TEKH. POLUPROV. 7 (3), 471–9, 1973. (FOR ENGLISH TRANSLATION SEE E101918)
101918	**EFFECT OF CHANGES IN BAND STRUCTURE PARAMETERS ON THE FUNDAMENTAL ABSORPTION SPECTRUM OF SEMICONDUCTORS (FUNDAMENTAL ABSORPTION EDGE OF GALLIUM ARSENIC PHOSPHIDE).** PIKHTIN, A. N. RAZBEGAEV, V. N. YAS'KOV, D. A. SOV. PHYS. SEMICOND. 7 (3), 337–41, 1973. (ENGLISH TRANSLATION OF FIZ. TEKH. POLUPROV., 7 (3), 471–9, 1973; FOR ORIGINAL SEE E101917)
101924	**INVESTIGATION OF THERMAL CONDUCTIVITY, THERMAL DIFFUSIVITY, AND EMITTANCE OF SEMITRANSPARENT MATERIALS AT HIGH TEMPERATURES.** MEN', A. A. SERGEEV, O. A. HIGH TEMP. HIGH PRESSURES 5, 19–28, 1973.

EPIC Number | Bibliographic Citation

101925 **ON THE EFFECT OF IRRADIATION INTENSITY ON DEFECT PRODUCTION IN PURE AND IODINE DOPED POTASSIUM CHLORIDE AT ROOM TEMPERATURE.**
GOLDSTEIN, F. T.
PHYS. STATUS SOLIDI
49 B (2), 711–19, 1972.

101939 **ELECTROPHYSICAL PROPERTIES OF LIQUID SEMICONDUCTORS.**
MAVLONOV, S.
SOV. SCI. REV.
3, 99–101, 1972.

101946 **OPTICAL CONSTANTS OF LEAD HALIDES.**
PLEKHANOV, V. G.
PHYS. STATUS SOLIDI
57 B (1), K55–K59, 1973.

101947 **INFRARED ABSORPTION AND THERMAL CONDUCTIVITY OF CALCIUM FLUORIDE CONTAINING HEAVY METAL IMPURITIES.**
HAYES, W. WILTSHIRE, M. C. K. BERMAN, R.
HUDSON, P. R. W.
J. PHYS., SOLID STATE PHYS.
6 C (7), 1157–65, 1973.

101949 **DETERMINATION OF THE OPTICAL PROPERTIES OF THIN FILMS FROM SINGLE ANGLE REFLECTANCE MEASUREMENTS.**
PULFREY, D. L. RECHE, J. J. H.
APPL. OPT.
12 (7), 1577–80, 1973.

102007 **ELECTRICAL AND THERMAL TRANSPORT PROPERTIES OF URANIUM AND PLUTONIUM CARBIDES.**
LEWIS, H. D. KERRISK, J. F.
LOS ALAMOS SCIENTIFIC LAB., UNIVERSITY OF CALIFORNIA, LOS ALAMOS, NEW MEXICO
33PP., 1976.
(LA-6096)

102012 **MAGNETIC AND ELECTRICAL PROPERTIES OF INTERNALLY OXIDIZED COPPER IRON ALLOYS.**
FICKETT, F. R.
AIP CONF. PROC.
(34), 25–6, 1976.
(PB-262 289/2)

102015 **MULTILAYER ENHANCED DIELECTRIC MIRRORS FOR 10.6 MICRONS.**
BRAUNSTEIN, M. BRAUNSTEIN, A. GARCIA, B.
PROC. ANN. CONF. INFRARED LASER WINDOW MATERIALS, 5TH
433–41, 1976.
(AD-B014 718L, AFML-TR-76-83, UDRI-TR-76-35)

102032 **TEMPERATURE DEPENDENCE OF RADIATION DEFECT BUILDUP IN DOPED CALCIUM FLUORIDE CRYSTALS.**
LISITSYN, V. M. SHTAN'KO, V. F.
SOV. PHYS. J., USSR
18 (5), 695–7, 1975.
(ENGLISH TRANSLATION OF IZV. VYSSH. UCHEB. ZAVED. FIZ., 18 (5), 116–18, 1975; FOR ORIGINAL SEE E93623)

102033 **RADIATION STIMULATED TRANSFORMATION OF F- AND M-CENTERS IN CALCIUM FLUORIDE CRYSTALS.**
KOREPANOV, V. I. LISITSYN, V. M.
BARANOV, A. I. STEPANOV, V. G.
ZHAPAROVA, S.
SOV. PHYS. J., USSR
18 (5), 698–700, 1975.
(ENGLISH TRANSLATION OF IZV. VYSSH. UCHEB. ZAVED., FIZ., 18 (5), 118–20, 1975; FOR ORIGINAL SEE E93622)

102035 **OPTICAL ABSORPTION IN A HEAVILY DOPED SEMICONDUCTOR WITH A NARROW FORBIDDEN BAND.**
FEDIRKO, V. A.
SOV. PHYS. J., USSR
18 (7), 960–5, 1975.
(ENGLISH TRANSLATION OF IZV. VYSSH. UCHEB. ZAVED., FIZ., 18 (7), 65–70, 1975; FOR ORIGINAL SEE E93621)

102037 **LIGHT ABSORPTION IN TWO LAYER COLLOIDAL POTASSIUM AND COPPER COLOR CENTERS IN A POTASSIUM CHLORIDE CRYSTAL.**
RADCHENKO, I. S. PETRENKO, I. V.
OPT. SPECTROS., USSR
40 (6), 586–8, 1976.
(ENGLISH TRANSLATION OF OPT. SPEKTROSK., 40 (6), 1019–23, 1976; FOR ORIGINAL SEE E101471)

102038 **OPTICAL PROPERTIES OF INDIUM SELENIDE SINGLE CRYSTALS NEAR THE FUNDAMENTAL ABSORPTION EDGE. I.**
BAKUMENKO, V. L. KOVALYUK, Z. D.
KURBATOV, L. N. CHISHKO, V. F.
FIZ. TEKH. POLUPROV.
10 (6), 1045–51, 1976.
(FOR ENGLISH TRANSLATION SEE E102039)

102039 **OPTICAL PROPERTIES OF INDIUM SELENIDE SINGLE CRYSTALS NEAR THE FUNDAMENTAL ABSORPTION EDGE. I.**
BAKUMENKO, V. L. KOVALYUK, Z. D.
KURBATOV, L. N. CHISHKO, V. F.
SOV. PHYS. SEMICOND.
10 (6), 621–5, 1976.
(ENGLISH TRANSLATION OF FIZ. TEKH. POLUPROV., 10 (6), 1045–51, 1976; FOR ORIGINAL SEE E102038)

EPIC Number | Bibliographic Citation

102041 **ABSORPTION SPECTRA OF LEAD DIPOSITIVE ION DOPED SODIUM CHLORIDE AT THE A-BAND REGION.**
PASCUAL, J. L. CABRERA, J. M.
AGULLO-LOPEZ, F.
SOLID STATE COMMUN.
19 (9), 917–20, 1976.

102042 **INFRARED ABSORPTION IN CHEMICAL LASER WINDOW MATERIALS.**
HARRINGTON, J. A. GREGORY, D. A.
OTTO, W. F., JR.
APPL. OPT.
15 (8), 1953–9, 1976.

102056 **MULTIPHONON INFRARED ABSORPTION IN THE HIGHLY TRANSPARENT FREQUENCY REGIME OF SOLIDS: A REVIEW.**
BENDOW, B.
AIR FORCE CAMBRIDGE RESEARCH LAB., BEDFORD, MA.
116PP., 1975.
(AFCRL-TM-29)

102094 **CUBIC BORON NITRIDE: HANDBOOK OF PROPERTIES.**
DE VRIES, R. C.
GENERAL ELECTRIC COMPANY, SCHENECTADY, N. Y.
17PP., 1972.
(72-CRD-178)

102095 **INFRARED REFRACTIVE INDICES OF LEAD TIN TELLURIDE ALLOYS AT ROOM TEMPERATURE.**
JAGER, H. SCHUBERT, G.
INFRARED PHYS.
13 (1), 29–36, 1973.

102101 **DISPERSIVE REFLECTION SPECTROSCOPY IN THE FAR INFRARED BY DIVISION OF THE FIELD OF VIEW IN A NICHELSON INTERFEROMETER.**
PARKER, T. J. CHAMBERS, W. G. ANGRESS, J. F.
INFRARED PHYS.
14 (3), 207–15, 1974.

102104 **INTERBAND SCATTERING CONTRIBUTIONS TO THE RESISTIVITY OF A-15 METALS.**
BADER, S. D. FRADIN, F. Y.
SUPERCONDUCTIVITY IN D- AND F- BAND METALS
567–81, 1976.
(CONF-760464-2)

102146 **ELECTRON HOLE RECOMBINATION.**
PILKUHN, M. H.
PROC. INT. CONF. PHYS. SEMICOND., 13TH
61–70, 1976.

102151 **FREQUENCY AND TEMPERATURE DEPENDENCE STUDIES OF RESIDUAL INFRARED ABSORPTION IN THE HIGHLY TRANSPARENT FREQUENCY REGIME OF TETRAHEDRAL SEMICONDUCTORS.**
BENDOW, B. SKOLNIK, L. H. LIPSON, H. G.
YUKON, S. P. MITRA, S. S.
PROC. IN, CONF. PHYS. SEMICOND., 13TH
192–5, 1976.

102163 **OBSERVATION OF THE INDIRECT EXCITONIC TRANSITION IN GALLIUM SELENIDE.**
DEPEURSINGE, C. THANH, L. C.
PROC. INT. CONF. PHYS. SEMICOND., 13TH
388–91, 1976.

102168 **ENERGY BAND OF LEAD TIN SELENIDE CRYSTALS FROM MEASUREMENTS OF OPTICAL REFLECTION AND THERMOELECTRIC POWER IN MAGNETIC FIELD.**
VODOPYANOV, L. K. KUTCHERENKO, I. V.
MITJAGIN, A. TAKTAKISHVILY, M. C.
SHOTOV, A. P.
PROC. INT. CONF. PHYS. SEMICOND., 13TH
463–6, 1976.

102173 **INFLUENCE OF LATTICE DEFECTS ON THE PARAELECTRIC BEHAVIOUR OF LEAD TELLURIDE.**
JANTSCH, W. LOPEZ-OTERO, A.
PROC, INT. CONF. PHYS. SEMICOND., 13TH
487–90, 1976.

102175 **HIGH TEMPERATURE MATERIALS WITH SPECIFIC CONDUCTION MECHANISM.**
GOLIKOVA, O. A. KAZANIN, M. M.
LUTSENKO, E. L. ORLOV, V. M. TKALENKO, E. N.
ZAITSEV, V. K.
PROC. INT. CONF. PHYS. SEMICOND., 13TH
497–500, 1976.

102229 **OPTICAL FREQUENCY DEPENDENCE OF THE PHOTOELASTIC COEFFICIENTS OF FUSED SILICA.**
BIEGELSEN, D. K. ZESCH, J. C.
J. APPL. PHYS.
47 (9), 4024–5, 1976.

102245 **10.6 MICROMETERS PULSED LASER DAMAGE IN ZINC SELENIDE.**
POSEN, H. BRUCE, J. MILAM, D.
LASER INDUCED DAMAGE IN OPTICAL MATERIALS
85–92, 1974.
(NBS-SP-414, AD-A012 377)

EPIC Number	Bibliographic Citation
102278	**REFRACTIVE INDEX OF ION-IMPLANTED GALLIUM ARSENIDE.** KACHARE, A. H. SPITZER, W. G. FREDRICKSON, J. E. J. APPL. PHYS. 47 (9), 4209–12, 1976.
102375	**INVESTIGATION OF THE DEPENDANCE OF MAGNETIC PARAMETERS OF FERRITES FROM COMPOSITION AND CONDITION AT HEAT TREATMENT IN THE SYSTEM LITHIUM - SODIUM - IRON - OXIDE.** LIPATOV, P. V. ORLOV, G. N. OLEINIKOV, N. N. POPOV, G. P. TRUSHKINA, N. A. SHREIBERT, YA. YA. KHIM. KHIM. TEKHNOL. 468–73, 1968.
102400	**THERMOREFLECTANCE OF LITHIUM FLUORIDE BETWEEN 12 AND 30 ELECTRON VOLTS.** PIACENTINI, M. LYNCH, D. W. OLSON, C. G. PHYS. REV. 13 B (12), 5530–43, 1976.
102402	**MEASUREMENT OF NONLINEAR REFRACTIVE-INDEX COEFFICIENTS USING TIME-RESOLVED INTERFEROMETRY: APPLICATION TO OPTICAL MATERIALS FOR HIGH-POWER NEODYMIUM LASERS.** MILAM, D. WEBER, M. J. J. APPL. PHYS. 47 (6), 2497–501, 1976.
102403	**TEMPERATURE CHANGES OF THE PHOTOELASTIC EFFECT OF SODIUM CHLORIDE, POTASSIUM CHLORIDE, AND POTASSIUM BROMIDE.** KATO, E. SAJI, Y. J. APPL. PHYS. 47 (6), 2751–3, 1976.
102567	**THE DEVELOPMENT OF ANTIREFLECTIVE THIN FILMS FOR POLYCRYSTALLINE ALKALI HALIDE LASER WINDOW MATERIALS.** HARRISON, W. B. MAR, H. Y. B. BOORD, W. T. STARLING, J. E. AIR FORCE MATERIALS LAB., WPAFB, OHIO 91PP., 1976. (AD–B016 873L, AFML–TR–76–160)
102978	**CADMIUM STANNATE SELECTIVE OPTICAL FILMS FOR SOLAR ENERGY APPLICATIONS.** HAACKE, G. BURTON, L. C. AMERICAN CYANAMID CO., STAMFORD, CONN. 32PP., 1976. (PB–254 879)
103142	**THEORETICAL STUDIES OF MATERIALS FOR HIGH POWER INFRARED COATINGS.** SPARKS, M. XONICS INC., VAN NUYS, CALIF. 345PP., 1975. (AD–A031 948)
103149	**OPTICAL ABSORPTION BY FREE POLARONS IN ZINC OXIDE.** FINKENRATH, H. KRUG, K. UHLE, N. PHYS. STATUS SOLIDI 78 B (1), K27–K30, 1976.
103154	**EXTRINSIC ABSORPTION IN POTASSIUM CHLORIDE AND POTASSIUM BROMIDE AT CARBON DIOXIDE LASER FREQUENCIES.** ROWE, J. M. HARRINGTON, J. A. J. APPL. PHYS. 47 (11), 4926–8, 1976.
103155	**ONE-PHOTON KELDYSH ABSORPTION IN DIRECT-GAP SEMICONDUCTORS.** NARDUCCI, L. M. MITRA, S. S. SHATAS, R. A. PFEIFFER, P. A. VAIDYANATHAN, A. PHYS. REV. 14 B (6), 2508–13, 1976.
103162	**PHOTOELASTICITY OF THE CUPROUS HALIDES.** BIEGELSEN, D. K. ZESCH, J. C. SCHWAB, C. PHYS. REV. 14 B (8), 3578–82, 1976.
103163	**IONIZATION AND DECAY OF EXCITONS IN SODIUM BROMIDE CRYSTALS.** DENKS, V. P. LUSHCHIK, N. E. LUSHCHIK, CH. B. SOOVIK, T. A. FIZ. TVERD. TELA 18 (8), 2151–7, 1976. (FOR ENGLISH TRANSLATION SEE E103164)
103164	**IONIZATION AND DECAY OF EXCITONS IN SODIUM BROMIDE CRYSTALS.** DENKS, B. P. LUSHCHIK, N. E. LUSHCHIK, CH. B. SOOVIK, T. A. SOV. PHYS. SOLID STATE 18 (8), 1254–7, 1976. (ENGLISH TRANSLATION OF FIZ. TVERD. TELA, 18 (8), 2151–7, 1976; FOR ORIGINAL SEE E103163)
103167	**MAGNETOPHONON RESONANCE AND QUANTUM OSCILLATIONS IN N-TYPE CADMIUM MERCURY TELLURIDE.** AMIRKHANOV, KH. I. BASHIROV, R. I. GADZHIEVA, R. M. ELIZAROV, V. A. FIZ. TVERD. TELA 18 (8), 2331–3, 1976. (FOR ENGLISH TRANSLATION SEE E103168)
103168	**MAGNETOPHONON RESONANCE AND QUANTUM OSCILLATIONS IN N-TYPE CADMIUM MERCURY TELLURIDE.** AMIRKHANOV, KH. I. BASHIROV, R. I. GADZHIEVA, R. M. ELIZAROV, V. A. SOV. PHYS. SOLID STATE 18 (8), 1360–1, 1976. (ENGLISH TRANSLATION OF FIZ. TVERD. TELA, 18 (8), 2331–3, 1976; FOR ORIGINAL SEE E103167)
103177	**BIREFRINGENCE IN SILICON CARBIDE POLYTYPES.** MAKHALOV, YU. A. MOKHOV, E. N. FIZ. TVERD. TELA 18 (8), 2482–4, 1976. (FOR ENGLISH TRANSLATION SEE E103178)
103178	**BIREFRINGENCE IN SILICON CARBIDE POLYTYPES.** MAKHALOV, YU. A. MOKHOV, E. N. SOV. PHYS. SOLID STATE 18 (8), 1451–2, 1976. (ENGLISH TRANSLATION OF FIZ. TVERD. TELA, 18 (8), 2482–4, 1976; FOR ORIGINAL SEE E103177)
103180	**SOME SUPERIONIC CONDUCTORS AND THEIR APPLICATIONS.** TAKAHASHI, T. SUPERIONIC CONDUCTORS 379–94, 1976.
103193	**UTILIZATION OF THERMOELECTRONIC EMISSION TO STUDY POINT DEFECTS: CASE OF YTTRIUM OXIDE.** LOUP, O. J.-P. ANTHONY, A. M. REV. INT. HAUTES TEMP. REFRACT. 8 (3–4), 243–52, 1971.
103208	**DEVELOPMENT OF INFRARED ANTIREFLECTION COATING FOR GERMANIUM SELENIUM ARSENIDE GLASS.** MAR, H. Y. B. HONEYWELL INC., ST. PAUL MINN. 51PP., 1971. (AD–882 268, AFAL–TR–71–16)
103259	**GROWTH AND THE CRYSTAL CHARACTERISTICS OF DICHALCOGENIDES HAVING LAYER STRUCTURES.** BALCHIN, A. A. CRYSTALLOGRAPHY AND CRYSTAL CHEMISTRY OF MATERIALS WITH LAYERED STRUCTURES 1–50PP., 1976.
103263	**STRUCTURAL INSTABILITY AND ELECTRONIC PROPERTIES OF THE LAYERED COMPOUNDS.** THOMPSON, A. H. COMMENTS SOLID STATE PHYS. 7 (5), 125–33, 1976.
103292	**MARTENSITE DECOMPOSITION IN NICKEL - ALUMINUM ALLOYS.** PANTSYREVA, E. G. BOGACHEV, I. N. LITVINOV, V. S. SOV. NON-FERROUS METALS RESEARCH 3 (1), 24–5, 1975. (ENGLISH TRANSLATION OF IZV. VYSSH. UCHEB. ZAVED., TSVETN. METALL., (1), 95–100, 1975; FOR ORIGINAL SEE E91206)
103293	**PRODUCTION OF OPTIMUM CARRIER DENSITY IN THERMOCOUPLES USING LEAD TELLURIDE IN THE NEGATIVE BRANCH.** KULIEV, A. E. KAKHRAMANOV, K. SH. TUKHTASINOV, I. APPLIED SOLAR ENERGY 11 (6), 129–30, 1975. (ENGLISH TRANSLATION OF GELIOTEKHNIKA, (6), 77–8, 1975; FOR ORIGINAL SEE E99646)
103336	**BISMUTH CENTRES IN ALKALI HALIDES.** RADHAKRISHNA, S. SRINIVASA, R. S. S. PHYS. REV. 14 B (3), 969–76, 1976.
103350	**QUASISELECTION RULES FOR MULTIPHONON ABSORPTION IN ALKALI HALIDES.** DUTHLER, C. J. PHYS. REV. 14 B (10), 4606–15, 1976.
103351	**PRESSURE DEPENDENCE AND THEORIES OF ELECTRONIC DIELECTRIC CONSTANT OF BINARY CRYSTALS.** SHANKER, J. GOYAL, S. C. VERMA, M. P. PHYS. REV. 14 B (10), 4699–701, 1976.
103366	**DETERMINATION OF THE ANHARMONICITY PARAMETERS AND OPTICAL CONSTANTS OF CRYSTALS FROM SURFACE POLARITION SPECTRA.** RESHINA, I. I. MIRLIN, D. N. BANSHCHIKOV, A. G. FIZ. TVERD. TELA 18 (2), 506–10, 1976. (FOR ENGLISH TRANSLATION SEE E103367)

EPIC Number	Bibliographic Citation
103367	**DETERMINATION OF THE ANHARMONICITY PARAMETERS AND OPTICAL CONSTANTS OF CRYSTALS FROM SURFACE POLARITION SPECTRA.** RESHINA, I. I. MIRLIN, D. N. BANSHCHIKOV, A. G. SOV. PHYS. SOLID STATE 18 (2), 292–4, 1976. (ENGLISH TRANSLATION OF FIZ. TVERD. TELA, 18 (2), 506–10, 1976; FOR ORIGINAL SEE E103366)
103384	**ELECTRICAL CONDUCTIVITY OF MOLTEN SEMICONDUCTORS IN A WIDE TEMPERATURE RANGE.** ANDREEV, A. A. MELEKH, B. T TURGUNOV, T. FIZ. TVERD. TELA 18 (1), 244–7, 1976. (FOR ENGLISH TRANSLATION SEE E103385)
103385	**ELECTRICAL CONDUCTIVITY OF MOLTEN SEMICONDUCTORS IN A WIDE TEMPERATURE RANGE.** ANDREEV, A. A. MELEKH, B. T. TURGUNOV, T. SOV. PHYS. SOLID STATE 18 (1), 141–2, 1976. (ENGLISH TRANSLATION OF FIZ. TVERD. TELA, 18 (1), 244–7, 1976; FOR ORIGINAL SEE E103384)
103396	**TEMPERATURE DEPENDENCE OF THE ABSORPTION EDGE OF ARSENIC SELENIDE IN THE SOLID AND LIQUID STATES.** ANDREEV, A. A. KOLOMIETS, B. T. MAZETS, T. F. MANUKYAN, A. L. PAVLOV, S. K. FIZ. TVERD. TELA 18 (1), 53–7, 1976. (FOR ENGLISH TRANSLATION SEE E103397)
103397	**TEMPERATURE DEPENDENCE OF THE ABSORPTION EDGE OF ARSENIC SELENIDE IN THE SOLID AND LIQUID STATES.** ANDREEV, A. A. KOLOMIETS, B. T. MAZETS, T. F. MANUKYAN, A. L. PAVLOV, S. K. SOV. PHYS. SOLID STATE 18 (1), 29–31, 1976. (ENGLISH TRANSLATION OF FIZ. TVERD. TELA, 18 (1), 53–7, 1976; FOR ORIGINAL SEE E103396)
103402	**LASER WINDOW SURFACE FINISHING AND COATING SCIENCE.** BRAUNSTEIN, M. ALLEN, S. D. PEDINOFF, M. E. BRAUNSTEIN, A. I. RUDISILL, J. E. TURK, R. R. WANG, V. ZUCCARO, D. ROME AIR DEVELOPMENT CENTER, GRIFFISS AFB, N. Y. 33PP., 1976. (AD–B016 536L, RADC–TR–76–368)
103404	**SUPERCONDUCTIVITY, ENERGY STORAGE AND SWITCHING.** LAQUER, H. L. ENERGY STORAGE, COMPRESSION, SWITCHING 279–305, 1976.
103586	**ELECTRIC FIELD INDUCED CHANGES OF THE FUNDAMENTAL ABSORPTION AND LOW–TEMPERATURE ENERGY RELAXATION IN N–TYPE GALLIUM ANTIMONIDE.** OBIDITSCH, M. KAHLERT, H. PHYS. STATUS SOLIDI 77 B (2), 677–84, 1976.
103588	**CADMIUM STANNATE SELECTIVE OPTICAL FILMS FOR SOLAR ENERGY APPLICATIONS.** HAACKE, G. BURTON, L. C. AMERICAN CYANAMID COMP., STAMFORD, CONN. 25PP., 1976. (PB–261 850)
103589	**ELECTROCALORIC REFRIGERATION FOR SUPERCONDUCTORS.** RADEBAUGH, R. SIEGWARTH, J. D. LAWLESS, W. N. MORROW, A. J. NATIONAL BUREAU OF STANDARDS, BOULDER, COLO. 194PP., 1977. (NBSIR–76–847)
103590	**OPTICAL DISTORTION BY LASER HEATED WINDOWS.** LOOMIS, J. S. BERNAL, G. LASER INDUCED DAMAGE IN OPTICAL MATERIALS: 1975 126–41, 1976. (NBS–SP–435, PB–252 186)
103591	**SURFACE STUDIES WITH ACOUSTIC PROBE TECHNIQUES.** PARKS, J. H. ROCKWELL, D. A. LASER INDUCED DAMAGE IN OPTICAL MATERIALS: 1975 157–63, 1976. (NBS–SP–435, PB–252 186)
103592	**SINGLE AND MULTILONGITUDINAL MODE DAMAGE IN MULTILAYER REFLECTORS AT 10.6 MICROMETERS AS A FUNCTION OF SPOT SIZE AND PULSE DURATION.** WANG, V. GIULIANO, C. R. GARCIA, B. LASER INDUCED DAMAGE IN OPTICAL MATERIALS: 1975 216–29, 1976. (NBS–SP–435, PB–252 186)
103593	**IRRADIANCE LIMITS FOR VACUUM ULTRAVIOLET MATERIAL FAILURE.** DUTHLER, C. J. SPARKS, M. LASER INDUCED DAMAGE IN OPTICAL MATERIALS: 1975. 395–405, 1976. (NBS–SP–435, PB–252 186)
103608	**ELECTRON SPECTRUM AND INTRINSIC ABSORPTION OF HEAVILY DOPED N–GALLIUM ARSENIDE.** LEVKOV, A. N. LOMAKIN, G. G. SOV. PHYS. J. 18 (8), 1084–8, 1975. (ENGLISH TRANSLATION OF IZV. VYSSH. UCHEB. ZAVED., FIZ., 18 (8), 30–5, 1975; FOR ORIGINAL SEE E96810)

Part D
AUTHOR INDEX

PART D

USE OF AUTHOR INDEX

The *Author Index* is given in two parts, namely, personal authors and coauthors followed by corporate authors. The numbers shown along with the name of each author refer to the EPIC numbers of the references cited in the *Bibliography* (Part C).

For simplification in the automated production of the *Author Index* it was decided to use only author's last name and his initials. Naturally, in the case of some of the more popular last names having the same initials, this practice is likely to lead to the unfortunate result of improperly crediting papers to similarly named different authors. In such instances, the users of this *Author Index* should inspect the titles of the documents cited in the *Bibliography* to properly identify those technical papers which may have been improperly credited.

The term "corporate author" applies to industrial organizations, government agencies, colleges, universities, etc. In alphabetizing corporate names, the main listing is made under the key word of the parent company or organization's name, and names of divisions, laboratories, departments, etc., are cross-referenced under the key words of their names.

In the case of universities, the word "university" always appears second in abbreviated form. In identification of corporate names, information is listed in the following sequence: name of organization, city, state, division, laboratory, etc.

PERSONAL AUTHOR INDEX

ASO T 57997
ASPNES D E 61382
ASSAADI K 65242
ASTAFEVA L V 58314
ASTAKHOV O P 50095 50724 53025 53312 53313 55711 55758 56861 57295 57781 59068 59069 68005 68006 86779 90050
ASTAPCHIKA S A 57030
ASTELS M G 57738
ASTLES M G 57739 57740
ASTOPIEVA A M 50950
ASTY M 59386
ATABAEVA E YA 57802 57803 67802
ATABEK B A 58292
ATABEKOV B A 67982 67983
ATAEV K 49578
ATAKOVA M M 56315
ATAKULOV B 87962
ATALLA M M 68792
ATO Y 51989
ATROSHCHENKO L V 51987
ATTANASIO A 101704
ATZMONY U 53594 60348 61161
AU COIN T R 62037
AUBIN M J 53622
AUCLAIR B 99799
AUDZIONI A I 86494
AUDZIONIS A I 50838 51973
AUKER B H 65199
AULICH E 85428
AULICH H 49600
AUSLOOS P 63677
AUSTIN A E 51173 52964 53116
AUSTIN I G 75905 90035
AUSTIN R R 63255
AUSTON D H 96224
AUTH J 71582
AUTHOR ANON 66038 101320
AUVERGNE D 51216 57322 65494 68602 96242
AV-RON M 54552
AVAKYANTS G M 66976
AVDEEV A L 55066 55067
AVDEEV B V 55056 55057
AVDONIN V P 54472 54473 61944 61945 66778 66779 89256 89257
AVEN M 50774 57325 73251
AVERKIEVA G K 49811 51051 55338 58866 59276 66570 66571 67749 67759 68034 68035
AVERKIN A A 52541 53676
AVEROUS M 57941
AVERYANOV E E 51628
AVERYANOV I S 70817 76500 91566 91573
AVGUSTINIK A I 50707
AVILOV A S 55199 55200
AVILOV E S 100839 100840
AWAZU K 49895
AXE J D 56767 60341
AYER J W JR 55126
AYER W J JR 57438
AYUKHANOV A KH 94028 94029 94567 95912 100287 100288
AYUSHINA G D 95056 95814
AYYAGARI M S 90115
AZAROV V V 49896 50948
AZER A A 55522
AZIKOV B S 66450 66451
AZIMOV S A 51618 87962
AZZAM R M A 101746
AZZARELLI T 68907 86318
BABA M 96659
BABA N 51918
BABAEV S KH 67414
BABEL D 51146
BABERSCHKE K 55121
BABICH YA I 51329
BABICH YA M 52331
BABIN V P 88156 88157
BABISKIN J 62317 92033 101035 101665
BABKINA T V 52331 92274 92275
BABKO V A 90148 90149
BABONAS G 58597 94599 95584
BABONAS G A 61986 61987 95900
BABOT D 55965 55966
BABUSHKIN V S 86839 86840
BABUSIAUX A 59303
BACCI M 66687
BACHERIKOV V V 51084 65916
BACHININ YU G 57800 57801
BACHMAN K J 53915
BACHMANN K 51137
BACHMANN K J 57905 100825
BACHRACH R Z 52468 52772 54558 57726 61181 61186
BACON D D 66720
BACON J 65974
BADDUR A 51358 51359 52876 52877 90316
BADER S D 68710 102104
BADOZ J 83537
BAER A 101822
BAER A D 51032 55249 57646 99986
BAER W 57538
BAEUERLE D 57471
BAFICO M A 50906 53238
BAGCHI A 54061
BAGDASAROV KH S 51047 51949 54432 55828 56014 91887
BAGINSKII V M 50966
BAGLEY B G 90807
BAGUS P S 52408 53585
BAHL S K 90806
BAHRAMAN A 53259
BAIDAKOV L A 49763 50173 83375 90273
BAIKOV M V 84222 91472
BAIKOVA N D 55465
BAILYN M 58042
BAIRAMOV B KH 52852 52853
BAJ M 60534
BAJAJ K K 63847
BAKER A J 101201
BAKER A T J 50845
BAKER D E 98555
BAKER E H 53715 67201
BAKER G L 60297
BAKER R T 63510
BAKHSHIEVA G F 52216 61830
BAKHTEUZOV V E 56696 66752 66753
BAKIROV M YA 53223 53224
BAKUMENKO V L 102038 102039
BAKUTIS I P 61039
BAKUTIS J 61035
BALA W 53844
BALAKRISHNA S 50714
BALANEVSKAYA A E 76499 91563
BALBAKOV D ZH 66138
BALBASHOV A M 55068 55069 56696 66752 66753
BALBERG I 50516 53113 66711
BALCHIN A A 103259
BALDERESCHI A 50925 54081 59831
BALDINI G 50142 74624 85417
BALDO J 99775
BALDWIN J A JR 59403 60385
BALEKA E S 81273 94088
BALESHTA T M 59164
BALESTRA C L 61758 61760
BALETSKII D YU 53673 53674 58120 58121
BALEVA M I 50638
BALEVICIUS L 56044
BALKANSKI M 50777 51642 53356 53574 53599 59867
BALLARD R E 51467
BALLARD S S 63242 73261
BALLEGEER D J 63955
BALLESTRACCI R 59041
BALLINGER R A 51791
BALLOMAL L S 64538
BALMER B 50496
BALSLEV I 55728 74639
BALTATEANU N 59520
BALTOG I 60963
BALTOV I 56818
BALTRAMEYUNAS R A 50217

DESAGHER S 90787
DESAI V P 51863 58058
DESBLANCS R G 53801
DESCHANVRES A 86764
DESCOUTS P 50953
DESHAZER L G 62276 99658
DESHMUKH K G 90346
DESHPANDE D A 90268
DESNICA U V 60042
DESTRY J 65497
DESYATKOVA S M 52904 52905
DESYATNIK V N 67558
DETRIO J 101829
DETRIO J A 59602 101666 101796
DEULING H 60338
DEUTSCH M 90338
DEUTSCH T F 58212 62525 68832 68841 97348
DEVEAUD B 95524
DEVINE J Z 50774
DEVORE R 62277
DEVREESE J 53573 70661
DEVREESE J T 62384 63978
DEVYATOVA T A 60489 60490
DEVYATYKH E V 55337 59275
DEWITT D P 53512
DEXTER R N 91733
DHERBOMEZ N 50619 54836 90267
DI BARTOLO B 52957 57524
DI DOMENICO M JR 64544 70519
DI MARIA D J 86753
DI SALVO F J 49917 53051 55229 57600 61379 63276 70494
DI STEFANO T H 90856
DIAKONOVA N P 54683
DICK K A 54727 100963
DICKEINSON T 55967
DICKEY D H 65962
DIDOSYAN YU S 50349 50350
DIDUKH L D 90674
DIDUKH V D 90674
DIEDERIX K M 53701
DIEFENDORF R J 60165
DIEHL R 51742 55786 68705
DIELEMAN J 62480 63763
DIESEL J 68792
DIESEL T J 60796
DIESELMAN H D 62186
DIETL T 101450
DIETRICH H B 53581
DIETRICH K 52195
DILLON J F JR 51198 57169 68546
DILLON R O 52184
DIMITRASHCHUK V T 53071 60141 60142
DIMITRENKO K A 58210
DIMITRIJEVIC Z 52689
DIMITROVA S K 51522 59951
DIMOVA-ALYAKOVA D I 81407 95806
DINAN J H 59711
DINGLE R 50904 52644
DIONNE G 65985
DIONNE G F 52794
DIORDANO R F 62272
DIREL A 60095
DIRKSEN G J 51882
DISALVO F J 60573 90807
DISHLERA E G 91893
DISHMAN J M 54026 60392 70519
DISLAVO F J 52748
DISTEFANO T H 60584 60585
DITE A F 56697
DITTMANN R 50854
DITZENBERGER J A 55242
DIVECHA A P 66313
DIVRECHY A 63636
DIXON A J 88184
DIXON G D 65762
DIXON R W 52772 54558
DIXON S JR 62272
DJERASSI H 59552
DMITRENKO K A 59206
DMITRIEV M V 62710 65306
DMITRIEV R P 81237 92367
DMITRIEV V A 96773 96774
DMITRIEV V P 76527 91532
DMITRIEVA A M 57235
DMITRIEVSKII A S 54274 54275
DMITRUK N L 56372 62691
DMYTRIV A YU 52528 55298 57769 59283
DNEPROVSKAYA T S 66484
DNEPROVSKII V S 64570
DO D C 91409 91410
DO-DINH C 90117
DOBBYN R C 65062
DOBIERZEWSKA-MOZRZYMAS E 59438
DOBROVINSKII R YU 67359
DOBROVOLSKII N M 81228 86222 92358 92627
DOBROWOLSKI W 57587
DOBRYNINA N A 61824 61825
DOBRYNINA T A 66990
DOBRZHANSKII G F 62099 64715 67086 90495
DODD C V 64269
DODGE M 93375 94581 101819
DODGE M J 65967 88455 93309 99989 101650 101657
DOERFEL H 66105
DOGADAEV R V 86075 86076
DOGADOV V V 96306 96307
DOHLER G 59721
DOHLER G H 86453 87173
DOI A 90073
DOI K 53958 90079 93293
DOI Y 49481 80552
DOKOUPIL S 63823
DOLBINOVA E A 58865
DOLEJSI J 50633
DOLGINTSEV V D 60135 60136
DOLIDZE G M 67821
DOLLING G 53606
DOLNE CAMPOS M 54661
DOMANEVSKII D S 58700 66268
DOMASHEVSKAYA E P 62436 67079 77917 94485
DOMASHNEV I A 53995 53996 65450 65451 76529 91534
DOMBROVSKII L A 53997 53998
DONADIO R 101860
DONADIO R N 101672
DONALLY J M 49460
DONATO E 49665
DONG D 54774
DONIKA F G 52206 56997
DONIKA T V 67048
DONLAN V L 49856
DONNELLY J P 62195
DONOHUE P C 57750 65212
DONOVAN T 101822
DONOVAN T M 99986
DORAIN P B 53439
DORDA G 67175
DORLEIJN J W F 50386 92822
DORN R 62055
DORNHOUS R 61351
DOROFEEV YU A 51540
DOROFEYEV YU A 63179
DORONINA L M 76522 91508
DOROTYNSKII M G 52537 77923 94513
DOROUDIAN M 59977
DOSER M 55525 55529
DOSKOCH V P 55493
DOSYAGAEV A V 50704
DOUCAS G 51284
DOUCET Y 51497 61324 62084
DOUGAROVA L D 66778 66779
DOUGHERTY F C 62550
DOUGHTY J R 52636
DOUGLAS R W 64850
DOUGLASS D H 100720
DOUGLASS D L 53403 58340
DOVLETMURADOV CH 50105
DOVLETOV K 49578 53312 53313 55711 62447
DOVTONYUK N F 58678

GUSEINOV R E	63090	63091	
GUSEINOVA D A	50068	51422	87146
GUSEINOVA S M	90409		
GUSEVA E F	90667		
GUSEVA E G	58193		
GUSEVA I N	58949	65919	
GUSEVA L M	58074	58075	66788
66789			
GUSEVA M I	52357	66562	66563
GUSEVA M U	68396		
GUSLIKOV V M	55305		
GUSTAFSON J	50957		
GUTAN V B	51306	54149	54150
GUTKIN A A	62710	65306	
GUTOROVA E V	58542		
GUYOT M	52706		
GUZHAVINA T I	51330	64877	
GUZHOV A A	52318		
GUZZI M	50142		
GUZZI R	55796		
GYLYAEV I B	52929		
GYORGY E M	49998	51198	57169
GYUNSBURG K E	50213	50214	62006
62007			
HAACKE G	102978	103588	
HAAS C	51883	58565	93528
HAAS G A	56720	87656	
HAAS K J	61764		
HABBAL F	58633		
HABER J	65641		
HABERER J P	58242		
HABERLAND D H	56617		
HABIG P S	91954		
HABOVCIK P	59998		
HACKER K	70646		
HACKETT W H JR		57726	61181
HADEK V	57666	75570	89571
HADLEY H C	53177		
HADLEY L N JR	64344		
HADNI A	64247		
HAERTLING G H	66864		
HAFNER H C	93322		
HAGEDORN F B	52641	53733	57999
60299			
HAGEMARK K I	64818		
HAGEN S H	57522		
HAGENMULLER P	49777	50942	55973
57939 58551	60325	90494	
HAGGERTY J S	52988	53274	
HAGIWARA H	50034		
HAGSTON W E	56545	65217	
HAGSTROM S B M		56375	
HAHN D	50854		
HAHN H	66313		
HAHN J R	56718		
HAHN W C JR	52640		

HAIDA M	90467		
HAIRIE A	52778		
HAISMA J	56652		
HAISTY R W	62127		
HALASA N A	58007		
HALDRE T	53804		
HALDRE U	58763	58764	
HALES M C	50148	55380	70600
HALFF A F	57633		
HALL D B	62201		
HALL E	101840		
HALL E L	101674		
HALL H T	56077	93162	
HALLETT A C H	61683		
HALLIBURTON L E		52696	
HALPERIN A	50143	50849	51878
65492 65499	100007		
HALPERIN B I	53448		
HALPERN V	93561		
HALPERT H	89950		
HAMAGUCHI C	49739	52628	
HAMAKAWA Y	49585	55876	55881
55944			
HAMANAKA K	51984		
HAMANO K	62833	90344	
HAMANO M	70390	91413	
HAMBOURGER P D		66703	
HAMBURGER A I	56428		
HAMEKA H F	50968		
HAMES M D	54890		
HAMM R N	60354		
HAMMANN J	92022		
HAMMER R	54774		
HAMMOND C R	50509		
HAMMOND D A	68871	89723	
HAMMOU A	55972	90266	
HAMPLE E F JR	53500		
HAMPSHIRE M J	50581		
HAMPSON R F	51441		
HANAK J J	52965	52990	
HANAMURA E	49956	50822	
HANDEL P H	63321		
HANDLER P	54595	57610	
HANDWERK J H	60530		
HANEDA K	51655	53860	58059
65663			
HANEMAN D	51220		
HANEV K	77922		
HANG K W	57797		
HANKE I	54629	54630	
HANLON J E	57750		
HANLON L R	66884		
HANNIGAN J	99549		
HANSEN P	49592	50528	51658
52438 57974	60302	68615	
HANSON R C	54346	61365	

HANSON W F	64338		
HANZEL D	51761	55422	56162
HAQUE M S	89451		
HARA K	56541		
HARA Y	50023		
HARADA Y	60530		
HARARI E	53262		
HARASYN D E	66719		
HARBEKE G	91289	91290	
HARDIMAN B	52756		
HARDING W	53471		
HARDY J R	53169		
HARGREAVES G B		75751	
HARGREAVES W A		49687	50890
HARJULIN C	50584		
HARKER A H	90032		
HARMAN C G	98912		
HARMAN T C	53852	54772	62195
65962 66865			
HARMER A L	51464		
HARMS H	50716		
HARPER H W	53423		
HARPSTER J W	53427	62277	
HARRINGTON J	101827	101843	101847
101850 101851			
HARRINGTON J A		62305	63327
68850 88493	89371	93316	93328
94479 97298	99870	101014	101018
101287 101441	101668	101714	102042
103154			
HARRINGTON R V		101404	
HARRIS D H	51121		
HARRIS F M	51589	56514	
HARRIS I R	57503	75990	
HARRIS J J	52233	59070	61768
HARRIS R	101820		
HARRIS R J	101666	101796	
HARRISON D A	52637		
HARRISON J W	86380		
HARRISON V B	101676		
HARRISON W	101813	101858	
HARRISON W A	52449	58043	58810
66684			
HARRISON W B	68870	102567	
HARRISON W J	65974		
HARROWER I T	57298		
HARSEY M	97672		
HARSY M	97671		
HART R R	101656		
HART R W	62303		
HARTFORD R H	95369		
HARTLESS R L	89390		
HARTMAN N F	53924		
HARTMANN S R	55120		
HARTMANN U	62372		
HARTMANOVA M	49545	54820	
HARTSTEIN A	53159	54596	
HARTWICK T S	52291		

Name	Numbers
MC CARTHY S L	61179
MC CARTY R D	62376
MC CAULEY J W	53073
MC CLURE D S	57306 68675
MC CULLOCH J C	49793
MC CULLOH K E	52480
MC CURRIE R A	49540 52681
MC DERMOTT I T	55135 57266
MC DEVITT N T	64255
MC DONALD J R	53874
MC DONIE A F	53644
MC DOWELL C A	52491
MC FEELY F R	53607 54604 58030
MC GEOCH M W	52583
MC GEVNA V	53292
MC GILL T C	86765
MC GOVERN I T	57480 89519
MC GROODY J C	65439
MC GUIRE T R	52969 53010 53158 57153 92677
MC HUGH J P	55151
MC KINZIE H	51890 56164
MC LANE G F	57986 61199
MC LENNAN J C	67892
MC LINTOCK I S	54768
MC NALLY P J	53406
MC NEILLY J	53292
MC NICOL B D	50144
MC NIFF E J JR	53075
MC OUAT R F	80374
MC PHERSON G L	53989
MC WHAN D B	57195 60600
MC WHORTER A L	52970 52995 53184 53357 53358
MCALISTER E D	99665
MCBROOM R J	101679
MCCABRIA J L	73285
MCCALL W M	50404
MCCANN W	101663
MCCARTHY D E	65533
MCCARTHY K A	73261
MCCLURE D S	50492
MCCOLL M	52973
MCCOLLUM B C	57902
MCCOY E F	58999
MCCRONE W C	98278
MCCUBBIN T K JR	58426
MCCURRIE R A	51140
MCELROY D L	64268
MCFEE J H	55511
MCFEELY F R	60648 63331
MCGILL T C	59611 101010 101017
MCGLYNN S P	50479 51636
MCGUIRE T R	50000 50608
MCKINLEY J D	51441
MCMANAMAN V L	65811
MCMASTER A D	85908
MCNICOL B D	55962
MCPARTLAND J O	98655
MCPHERSON A T	75831
MCSHEEHY C J	58630
MCWHORTER A L	53271
MEAD C A	52973
MEAD D G	58441
MEAUDRE M	52306
MEAUDRE R	52306
MEBED M M	52724 52725
MEDEISIS A	61029
MEDERNACH J W	90859
MEDIS P M	65179
MEDNIKOVA V N	52340 54373 54374
MEDNIS P M	62853
MEDVEDEV B A	58125
MEDVEDEV K S	56943
MEDVEDEV M N	56509 67914 67915
MEDVEDEV V N	60399 60400 101124 101125
MEE C H B	57480 94613
MEEK R L	68709
MEEKS T	70530
MEERSON E E	52386 58579
MEESE J M	52152
MEGAW H D	53796
MEGSON B	65732
MEHANDJIEV D R	65676
MEHMEL M	65983 65984
MEHRKAM L	50859
MEHROTRA A K	51939
MEHTEIEV A SH	57568
MEIER G H	67432
MEIER H	55832
MEIER P F	57861
MEIJER H C	50996
MEIKLYAR P V	49672 62856 65177
MEILIKHOV E Z	52702
MEILIKOV E Z	66580 66581
MEINCKE P P M	57154
MEINEL A B	89230
MEISSNER H E	50874 52435 60609
MEITZLER A H	80965
MEIXNER A E	55242
MEIZER K I	55078 55079
MEJIA C R	54605
MEKHTIEV A SH	60023
MEKHTIEV N M	55322 59258
MEKHTIEV T E	65723 65724
MELAMED SH G	67668
MELEKH B T	103384 103385
MELESHINA V A	56014
MELEV V G	50803 56328 66659 66660
MELIK-GAIKAZYAN I YA	56306 93419 93420
MELIKHOVA A N	51609
MELIKOVA Z D	67054 76401 91742
MELKOV G A	50275 50276
MELL H	83952 86456
MELNGAILIS I	66865
MELNGAILIS J	53852
MELNIK A I	52570 79103
MELNIK A P	60141 60142
MELNIK G I	57025
MELNIK R B	50672 52418 62719 65315
MELNIK V M	49562
MELNIKOV E V	81213 92395
MELNIKOV M M	51556 53687
MELNIKOVA L L	55710
MELNIKOVA S V	62863 65166
MELTON L A	51738
MEN A A	54984 54985 57334 59347 59413 61433 64885 65922 101924
MEN A N	51710 63060 63061 80756 86851 86852 90242 90243 95249
MENANT M	57454
MENDEZ E	66874
MENDOZA P J	101664
MENES M	61390
MENESES E A	65490
MENEZES C A	54594
MENKE H	60155
MENTH A	49917 51137 57195 57198 60573 60600 75947
MENTSER A N	62718 65314
MENTUS S V	80277
MENYUK N	51187 60284
MENZEL W P	50545
MERCIER A	50776 52057 65493 90911
MERCURID J P	58551
MERCURIO J P	50942 55973 57939
MERGERIAN D	99666
MERIAKRI V V	51366 51367 55064 55065 61548 61555 65901 65906
MERIEL P	57149
MERILOO I	49754
MERKAM L	54522
MERKLE L D	62309
MERKULOV I A	51557 53688
MERLE P	96242
MERZ J L	51020 52774 55257 101039
MERZLYAKOV A T	58714
MERZLYAKOV V P	50082 51428
MESHKAUSKAS I	63032 63033
MESNARD G	50150 63848
MESSERER M A	51696 52304 52929

MOROZOVA N K 56938 56942 56948
MORRIS W G 50747
MORRISON A D 53093
MORRISON C A 53430 55156 62977
MORRISON G I 60932
MORRISSY J H 58432
MORROW A J 101344 103589
MORSE C T 67476
MORSE P 94148
MORSE P L R 50155
MORUZZI V L 54587 62044
MORZENTI P T 57831
MOSER F 50574 51151
MOSES A J 65877 87883
MOSHNIKOV V A 90410
MOSKALENKO S A 65250
MOSKOWITZ H 52014
MOSKVIN A S 67371 70946 91485
MOSS R H 68871
MOSS T S 53782
MOSSER I 51458
MOSTOVSKII A A 77941 94517
MOTA A C 53355
MOTEGI N 57521
MOTIZUKI K 90065
MOTORNYI A V 52898 52899 86869 86870
MOTSCHMANN H 59223
MOTSNYI F V 63054 63055 63141 63142
MOTT N F 53775 59800 74974 75833 75838
MOTULEVICH G P 55213 55214 60465 60466 63076 63077
MOTZ H 59036 61325
MOURIKIS S 62066
MOUSTAKAS T D 67289 84007 90990
MOUTONNET D 65442
MOVSESYAN G M 87062 87063
MOYNIHAN C T 68845 90805 101029
MOZGOVAYA L A 57354
MOZHAEV V 93414
MOZHAEV V V 75383
MOZHAROVSKII L A 56217
MOZOL P E 66448 66449
MOZRZYMAS J 59438
MROWEC S 52827 66845
MUCHA B 52214
MUEHLE P 52006
MUELLER G 57678
MUELLER J J 60173
MUELLER K H 56342
MUELLER M H 49502 54055 54963 57180 60334 60340 63278
MUELLER R 49467 51901
MUELLER W H G 67506
MUKAI H 94151 101820
MUKATOV T 61851 61852 61853 62287 62288
MUKHACHEV V A 66036 66037
MUKHERJEE M K 63515
MUKHERJEE M L 51581
MUKHERJEE P K 57962
MUKHIN A A 85350 94077
MUKHIN YU A 49816
MUKHINA O B 56941
MUKHORTOV YU P 51390 51391
MULA G 57392 57398
MULAK J 50437
MULAY L N 53050 80497
MULDAWER L 54059
MULDER B J 52061 59903
MULIKOVA G M 56966
MULLEN M E 50921 58010
MULLENDORE A W 90382
MULLER G 65617
MULLER J 66369
MULLER K H 61351
MULLIN J B 50089 50154 57738 85351
MUNCRO I H 58436
MUNK NIELSEN T 51594
MUNOX E 57426
MUNOZ E 66874
MUNRO P 62293
MUNSER R 96170
MUNTONI C 50506 67430
MURAHASHI T 57142
MURAKAMI K 56856
MURAKAMI T 50125 50126 60363
MURAKAMI Y 94627
MURAKHTANOV V V 51330 64877
MURANAKA S 52621 57129
MURANEVICH A KH 53995 53996
MURANOVA G A 65446 65447
MURASE K 64851
MURASHIMA S 55859 59479
MURASHKO N I 58519
MURASHKO N V 52567 57792
MURASIK A 56347 56390
MURAVEV E N 52560 57785
MURAVEV L N 56939
MURAVEV Z N 52331
MURAVEVA K K 51616
MURAVLEV YU B 54955
MURCRAY D G 54312
MUREL A V 51983
MURGATROYD P N 64085
MURGIA M 50506 50836 67430
MURGUZOV M I 76506 91529
MURIN A N 50189 50190 52898 52899 84222 91472
MURIN I V 50189 50190 57238
MUROYA M 65652
MURPHY C 52085
MURPHY J A 51131 51197
MURRAY G H 96126
MURRAY H 86060
MURRAY R B 53581 57405 57406 67264
MURRI R 56398 61354
MURTAZIN A M 55323 59259
MURTH V G K 75911
MURTHY M K 57297 57298 63252
MURTUZOV M I 56998
MURTY D S 50381
MURTY V G K 54230 75776
MURYGIN V I 50071 62726 65322
MUSAEV A M 49759 60544 60545
MUSAEVA L G 97173 98000
MUSATOV A L 56581
MUSHINSKII V P 50679 52205 52425 62689 63472 64417 65150 99712 99713
MUSHINSKIY V P 53201 53202
MUSHUTKINA T I 87318 87319
MUSICANT B L 89950
MUSIL J 92880 94595
MUST M 58768
MUSTAFINA R KH 50950
MUSTYA I G 56997
MUSTYATSA O N 78826 93209
MUTAL A M 101515 101516
MUTLIN V M 55897
MUTO R 57908
MYASNIKOV E N 51278 54646 55190 61952 61953
MYASNIKOV I A 51345 53848
MYASNIKOVA T P 52914 52915 90134 90135
MYCIELSKI A 51870 57454
MYCIELSKI J 66686
MYDLARZ T 56352 67854
MYERS B E 53127
MYERS F 58426
MYKITYUK V I 50229 50230 50247 50248
MYKOLAJEWYCZ R 53212
MYRON H W 50898 53598 66668 66701
MYSYROWICZ A 59694
MYTILINEOU E 67288
NAAS D W 68854 101673
NABER J A 53423 55149 58248 60690 66893
NABER J E 53401
NABITOVICH I D 49571
NABOIKINA E N 97638 97639
NACHSHON Y 51253
NACHTRIEB N H 65109 98390
NADLER C 52064

ZAKS E 50143
ZALESSKII A V 52908 52909
ZALIVA V I 52562 57787
ZALLEN R 55244
ZALUCHA D J 51737 65758
ZAMEROWSKI T 58345
ZAMFIR E 61670 64583
ZANCHETTA J V 51740
ZANDBERGEN H W 65471
ZANETIC J 68082
ZANZUCCHI P J 53638
ZAPASSKII V S 57807 57808
ZAPOROZHETS V M 58084 58085
ZARABI M J 53752
ZARE R N 54306
ZAREMBOVITCH A 57149
ZARGAROVA M I 86780 90054
ZARIFYANTS YU A 55323 59259
ZARIPOV M M 50343 50344
ZAUTKIN V V 60467 60468
ZAVADOVSKAYA E K 49455 64286 67726 68416
ZAVADSKII E A 81234 92364
ZAVARITSKAYA E I 54950 55290 55303 59228 59249
ZAVERTANNAYA L S 55289 59248
ZAVETOVA M 63884 75884 85398 85438 90527
ZAWADZKI W 57687 64457 65942
ZAYACHKOVSKII M P 53673 53674
ZAYTSEV G S 66134
ZAZUBOVICH S G 49846 54518
ZBASNIK J 50999
ZDANOWICZ L 75171
ZDANOWICZ W 49646 51526 53799 56364 85403
ZDUKOS A T 50954 57016
ZEHE A 62913
ZEHE M J 53706
ZEIDLER J R 50958 53240
ZEIGER H J 86761
ZEINALLY A K 66587
ZEINALLY A KH 51714 62845 65172 66586
ZEINALOV A A 67166
ZEINALOV S A 67413
ZEITMAN S A 99553
ZELENIN L I 57791
ZELENIN L P 52566 88681
ZELEVINSKAYA V M 52561 57786 66450 66451
ZELLER H R 87156
ZEMBUTSU S 52650
ZEMEL J N 53416
ZEMLICKA J 61011
ZEMSKII V I 87312 87313
ZEMSKOV V S 94907 95897
ZENAIDI N 49544
ZENCHENKO V P 50309 50310
ZERTSALOVA I N 101536
ZESCH J C 102229 103162
ZEVIN L S 49958
ZEYFANG R 52756
ZEYHER R 51860
ZHAATA L 56028
ZHABITENKO N K 51280
ZHABOTINSKII V A 58713
ZHADKO I P 50075 51426 51453 66555 66556
ZHANG H I 60633
ZHANG H J M 56074
ZHANG H L 56074
ZHAPAROV ZH ZH 52541 53676
ZHAPAROVA S 93622 102033
ZHARIKOV E V 58082 58083
ZHARKOV G F 88053
ZHARKOV I P 52916 52917
ZHDAN A G 51696 52304 52929 60739 60740 101623 101624
ZHDANOV G S 56878
ZHELTONOZHKO A A 76480 91500
ZHELTOVSKII G A 61564 65915
ZHELUDEV I S 58096 58097 81236 92366
ZHEMCHUZHINA E A 52541 62320 62321
ZHEMOHUZHINA E A 53676
ZHEREBETSKII S K 50045
ZHEREBTSOVA L I 55020 55021
ZHILICH A G 50682 52428
ZHILYAEVA V A 51520
ZHITAR V F 67048
ZHITINSKAYA M K 75147 91929
ZHITNIKOV R A 100849 100850
ZHIZHIN G N 90134 90135
ZHMAKIN L I 99798
ZHMOIDIN G I 61774
ZHUKOV V F 93417 93418
ZHUKOVA L A 58130 58131 90206 90207
ZHUKOVA T B 87069 87070 93451 93452
ZHUKOVA V M 50645
ZHUKOVSKII A N 67315
ZHUKOVSKII V M 67359
ZHUMATII P G 99749
ZHURAKOVSKII E A 52275 86642 92632
ZHURAVLEVA V M 67320
ZHUSUPOV T 54640
ZHUZE V P 55479
ZIEGLER E 51683 52054
ZIEMER P L 55500 65811
ZIJLSTRA H 57194 63748
ZIKO A O 54727 100963
ZILBERMAN P E 81202 92401
ZILBERSHTEIN A KH 89254 89255
ZILBERVARG V E 66726 66727 90012 90133
ZIMICHEVA G M 49727
ZIMKINA T M 60409 60410 65883 65884
ZIMMERER G 85433
ZIMMERMANN P H 51875
ZIMNAL M 66692
ZINAMON Z 75833
ZINENKO V I 52876 52877 90316
ZINENKO V N 51358 51359
ZINOVEV V B 66572 66573
ZINOVEVA I G 51518 53242
ZINOVYEVA I G 50650
ZIOLKOWSKI J 53046
ZITTER R N 65242 65477
ZIVITZ M 60664
ZLENKO V YA 58487
ZLOBIN V N 51938
ZLOMANOV V P 58895 64884
ZOLIN V F 51326 51329 54464 54465
ZOLLWEG R J 54330
ZOLNIKOV P P 66104
ZOLOTAREV V M 54377 54378 65446 65447
ZOLOTKOVSKII B S 50662
ZOLOVKINA I S 58532
ZOLYAN T S 60193
ZONN Z N 52330 62658
ZORIC I 65773
ZORIN E I 51983
ZORINA E L 63697 65339
ZORINA L N 52331 92274 92275
ZOROOFCHI J 51650 60692
ZOTEV B P 94894 95899
ZOTOV V V 66798
ZOTOVA N V 62428 65331 66562 66563
ZOZULYA L P 56300 64236 64237
ZSINDELY S 66801
ZSOLDOS E 51199
ZUBAREV I G 54204
ZUBAREVA ZH M 76527 91532
ZUBENKO V V 63165 63166
ZUBENKO YU W 53183
ZUBKOV V G 51394 51395 55026 55027
ZUBKOVA S M 51376
ZUBKOVA T I 52531 57772
ZUBOV V G 67370
ZUCA S 90985
ZUCCA R 61188 65475
ZUCCARO D 101656 101812 103402
ZUCKERMANN M J 63810

CORPORATE AUTHOR INDEX

CONDENSED MATERIALS GROUP INDEX TO FOUR-VOLUME RETRIEVAL GUIDE*

Volume 1: Elements
Volume 2: Inorganic and Intermetallic Compounds
Volume 3: Alloys and Cermets
Volume 4: Mixtures, Rocks and Minerals, Composites and Systems, Polymers

*Material classes such as nonspecific (very general) substances or references concerning major compendia are not reported in this four-volume Retrieval Guide. Special bibliographic searches on these may be requested from CINDAS directly.